Calculus
Third Edition
Concepts & Computation

early transcendentals

David Betounes | Mylan Redfern

University of Texas of the Permian Basin

Kendall Hunt
publishing company

Cover image: © Shutterstock.com

www.kendallhunt.com
Send all inquiries to:
4050 Westmark Drive
Dubuque, IA 52004-1840

Published in the United States of America

CONTENTS  Calculus
Concepts & Computation

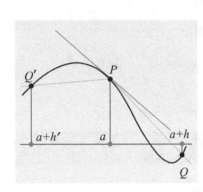
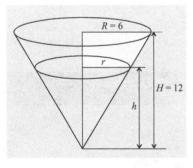

Chapter 3  Applications of Derivatives

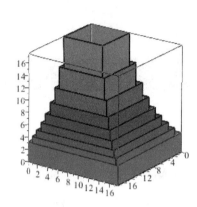

Chapter 4  Integrals

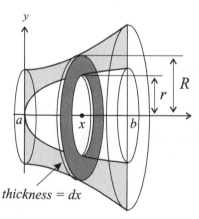

rectangular approximation

Chapter 5  Applications of Integrals

thickness = dx

Chapter 6   Techniques of Integration

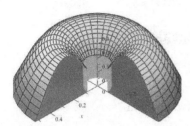

Chapter 7   Differential Equations

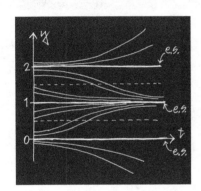

Chapter 8   Sequences and Series

Chapter 9 — Plane Curves and Polar Coordinates

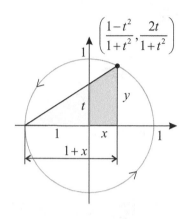

Chapter 10 — Vectors and Geometry

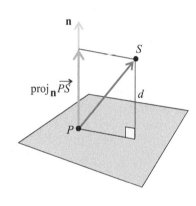

Chapter 11 — Partial Derivatives

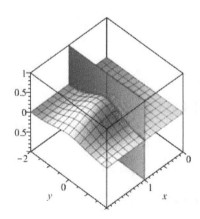

Chapter 12 Multiple Integrals

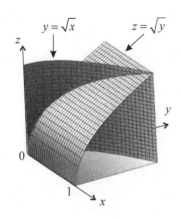

Chapter 13 Geometry of Curves and Surfaces

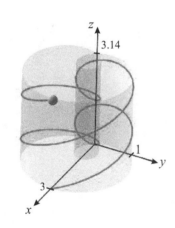

Chapter 14 Vector Analysis

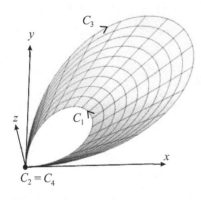

Preface

This edition of **Calculus**: *Concepts & Computation* contains all the material needed a complete course in calculus. It provides an "early transcendentals" version of calculus, with derivatives of trigonometric, exponential, and logarithmic functions covered in Chapter 2. Our book follows the tradition of most calculus books, which have become fairly uniform and standard in their approach and organization. We have tried to achieve a clarity of style and presentation that will provide a gentle introduction to what are complicated and powerful concepts.

Concepts: The basic concepts in calculus are limits, derivatives, and integrals. Mastery of these concepts will lead to success in everything else. Understanding the sophisticated concepts involved in applications, such as velocity, acceleration, laws of motion, chemical reaction rates, tangent lines, length, area, and volume, relies on a firm grasp of the basic concepts. So, basic concepts are essential. No concept in calculus can be fully appreciated without foundational skills in algebra and geometry.

Computation: Our book provides a predominant emphasis on traditional *by hand* computations and graphing. But, it also employs Maple, a computer algebra system (or CAS), as an auxiliary tool, appearing throughout the reading material and exercises. This tool, as we have designed it, affords a dynamical, visual illustration of the concepts, fostering a deeper understanding of these concepts.

The use of computers in calculus needs to be focused and flexible in order to be beneficial to instructors and students. Otherwise it can become a distraction and take much time away from learning the concepts. Our book was written with this in mind.

Many of the computational aspects in the book, whether done by hand or by computer, are intended to reinforce the maxim that approximate quantities lead to, in the limit, exact, ideal quantities. That is the basis for calculus.

Interactive Figures (Use of Maple): In the reading material and the exercises, there are Maple commands (or input) which can be recognized by the color and font. They are in red typewriter font with a prompt sign **>**, such as `> polygonlimit;`. The Maple output in this case is a movie showing a circle being filled with polygons. Other Maple output, which is numerical or algebraic, is shown in blue right after the input command.

Those parts of the book where the Maple input and output occur are available to instructors and students in electronic form (Maple worksheets) for use in classroom lectures, demonstrations, working of exercises, and studying of concepts. These worksheets are excerpts from the book and contain not only the Maple input/output, but also the reading material and figures that accompany it in the book. This ancillary consists of: (1) *Maple Movies* and *Maple Figures*, which, using either Maple or the free Maple Player, gives the reader the ability to interact with the Maple figures in the book by viewing a movie or rotating and changing 3-D figures, and (2) The Maple code that generates the the graphics, animations, and calculations, which, if one has Maple, can be changed to produce alternative output.

Some code in the reading and exercises requires special-purpose Maple procedures that we have written. These are *only* available in your school's computer lab (stored in the Maple's library folder on each computer).

Some instructors may choose not to use Maple and teach the course traditionally (as we have done with this book several times). In this case, just ignore the Maple input and output. However, students, if they wish, can learn Maple on their own and try using the code in the reading and exercises.

Exercises: Working exercises is essential to understanding of concepts and de-

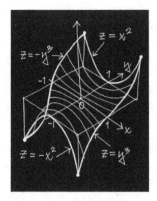

Figure 11.1.4: *x-traces*
for $z = x^2 y^3$.

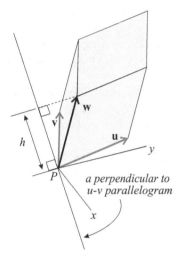

Figure 10.4.10: *The u-v*
parallelepiped determined
by vectors $\mathbf{u}, \mathbf{v}, \mathbf{w}$.

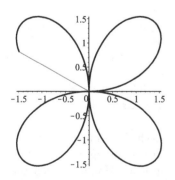

Figure 9.4.18: *A dynamic*
plot of $r = 2 \sin 2\theta$.

veloping calculus skills. For this, our book contains thoughtfully designed exercise sets, with exercises ranging from basic to hard, both computational and theoretical. Exercises that use Maple are labeled with the acronym CAS (Computer Algebra System).

Solutions Manual: There is a complete and extensive electronic solutions manual for the odd-numbered exercises in Chapters 1–8. We have written this with students in mind—it contains most all of the steps in the progression toward the answer and many comments on the underlying algebra (and calculus). Our Solutions Manual is more detailed and elaborate than other solutions manuals that typcally are seen or used. We think it can serve as a valuable tool in the learning of calculus. We suggest students use it as follows:

(1) Work each assigned exercise with pencil and paper.

(2) Check all the steps, especially the algebra, leading to the answer carefully with those given in the Solutions Manual.

(3) If necessary, ask an instructor, tutor, or success center worker to clarify and explain the steps.

(4) Keep a notebook of all the work done on the exercises.

(5) Study the notebook carefully before each exam. This refreshes the memory of how to approach a problem and all the steps to take toward its solution.

Graphics: The figures are an important feature of our book. (See the examples in the margin.) They were carefully created to convey concepts and information in the most direct and clear way. Specially featured are the blackboard drawings (sketches) which we think appeal to students and encourage them to produce such figures on their own. For example, we have had good success getting students, after proper instruction, to sketch planar regions and the solids of revolution generated by such regions. The Solutions Manual provides an abundance of such sketches for students to study and practice on. The other static figures in the book were created by Maple and Corel Draw.

The dynamic figures (animations/movies) in the book constitute a valuable learning and instructional tool, one which is physically part of the reading and exercise material. As mentioned, these animations are produced by special-purpose Maple procedures which we have written to convey the dynamic (moving) aspects of calculus. The electronic files containing these procedures must be copied to Maple's library file (`lib`) before they can be used in a Maple worksheet (after loading them using a `with` command).

Lecture Videos: There are lecture videos, tailored specifically to this book, for most of the sections. These videos, created by the authors, were produced using SmartBoard Recorder. Each video alternates between (1) views of the text material, displayed in DrawPDF, being annotated and explained, (2) examples being worked by hand in OneNote, and (3) the animations and figures being exhibited in the Maple worksheets. There are also book-orientation videos to ease the students' progress through the material.

The videos are forty to fifty-five minutes in length, much like classroom lectures, and have been used successfully by the authors in online classes for Calculus I, II, and III.

ADDITIONAL FEATURES: The book has innovative material and new techniques. These are:

- **An Alternative to Trig Substitutions:** Chapter 6 introduces a technique called u^2-*substitutions*.

u^2- substitutions			
n odd	$u^2 = a^2 - x^2$	$u^2 = a^2 + x^2$	$u^2 = x^2 - a^2$
n even	$u^2 = \dfrac{a^2 - x^2}{x^2}$	$u^2 = \dfrac{a^2 + x^2}{x^2}$	$u^2 = \dfrac{x^2 - a^2}{x^2}$

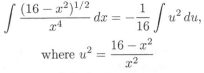

$$\int \frac{(16 - x^2)^{1/2}}{x^4}\, dx = -\frac{1}{16} \int u^2\, du,$$

where $u^2 = \dfrac{16 - x^2}{x^2}$

A u^2-Substitution.

This technique can be used effectively on any trig substitution problem and in some cases is quicker and easier for students.

- **A New Class of Arc Length Problems:** For a suitable function g, let $f(x) = g(x) + h(x)$, where

$$h(x) = -\frac{1}{4} \int \frac{1}{g'(x)}\, dx.$$

Then $1 + [f'(x)]^2$ is a perfect square. This construction extends to parametrically defined curves: for suitable functions f, G, the parametric equations $x = f(t)$, $y = G(t) + H(t)$, where

$$H(t) = -\frac{1}{4} \int \frac{[f'(t)]^2}{G'(t)}\, dt,$$

lead to $[x'(t)]^2 + [y'(t)]^2$ being a perfect square. There is also a similar setup for polar curves $r = f(\theta)$ which gives $[r(\theta)]^2 + [r'(\theta)]^2$ as a perfect square.

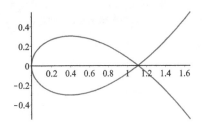

Figure 9.3.4: *The curve*
$$x = 4\sqrt{1 + t^2} - 4,$$
$$y = {}^4 t^3 - \tan^{-1} t.$$

The technique also extends to curves in $\mathbb{R}^3$. Section 13.1 contains numerous exercises with new types of curves which have lengths that are computable exactly (in closed form).

- **A New Class of Surface Area Problems:** Section 13.2 contains numerous exercises with new types of surfaces which have areas that are computable exactly (in closed form).

- **An Overlooked Class of Solids of Revolution:** In spherical coordinates the the equation $\rho = g(\phi)$ is a surface of revolution obtained by revolving the polar curve $\rho = g(\phi)$ in the x-z plane about the z-axis. We call these *polar surfaces of revolution*. A solid bounded by two of these: $\rho = g(\phi)$, $\rho = h(\phi)$ and the planes $\phi = \alpha$, $\phi = \beta$, is called a *polar solid of revolution*. It has volume:

$$V = \frac{2\pi}{3} \int_{\phi=\alpha}^{\phi=\beta} \left([h(\phi)]^3 - [g(\phi)]^3 \right) \sin\phi\, d\phi \qquad (12.6.11)$$

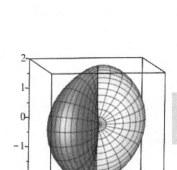

The surface $\rho = 2\sin 2\theta$ in spherical coordinates, for θ in $[0, \frac{\pi}{2}]$.

Additionally, in spherical coordinates, the equation $\rho = g(\theta)$ is a surface obtained by revolving each point P on the polar curve $\rho = g(\theta)$ in the x-y plane on a circular arc in the plane containing $\overrightarrow{OP}$ and the z-axis. We call these *polar surfaces of radial revolution*. The solid bounded by the surfaces $\rho = g(\theta)$, $\rho = h(\theta)$, $\theta = \alpha$, $\theta = \beta$, is called a *polar solid of radial revolution*. It has volume:

$$V = \frac{4}{3} \int_{\theta=\alpha}^{\theta=\beta} \left([h(\theta)]^3 - [g(\theta)]^3 \right) d\theta \qquad (12.6.12)$$

- **A Modified Approach to Vector Analysis:** The presentation of Stokes' Theorem, Green's Theorem, and Gauss' Divergence Theorem is along traditional lines, but uses the more modern approach of having the "boundaries" of surfaces and solids defined in terms of parameter maps. Thus, the boundary of a surface consists of four "curves" (some which may be degenerate or coincide) and the boundary of a solid consists of six "surfaces" (some which may be degenerate or coincide). This allows for a simple and easy discussion of these theorems without the burden of including difficult topological concepts, such as orientability and simply connected regions.

This parametric approach also enables us to give complete and easy proofs of Stokes' Theorem, Green's Theorem, and the Divergence Theorem.

Unlike most calculus books, we define surface integrals and state Stokes' Theorem without the need for orientability of the surface. Thus, rather than disparaging the Möbius strip for its non-orientibilty, we can apply Stokes' theorem to it in some interesting examples. See Example 14.5.3, where the boundary of the Möbius strip consists of the four curves shown in Figure 14.5.7.

The parametric version of Green's Theorem is particularly simple because it views regions in the plane as parametrized regions. In essence, this more clearly demonstrates that Green's Theorem is a special case of Stokes' Theorem:

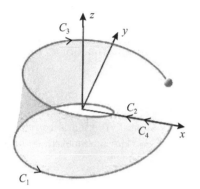

Figure 14.5.7

THEOREM 14.5.2 (Green's Theorem - Parametric Version)

Suppose $\mathbf{F}: U \to \mathbb{R}^3$ *is a vector field in the plane and S is a parametrized region in the plane with parametrization* $\mathbf{r}: [a,b] \times [c,d] \to \mathbb{R}^3$. *Let* $C = \partial S$ *be the boundary of S. Then*

$$\int_S \operatorname{curl} \mathbf{F} \cdot d\mathbf{A} = \int_C \mathbf{F} \cdot d\mathbf{r} \qquad (14.5.6)$$

In a similar fashion, the parametric version of the Divergence Theorem involves solids that are given parametically. This allows us to work problems that are either difficult or impossible to do using the traditional version of the Divergence Theorem. See the solid torus or the Möbius slab in Example 14.6.4.

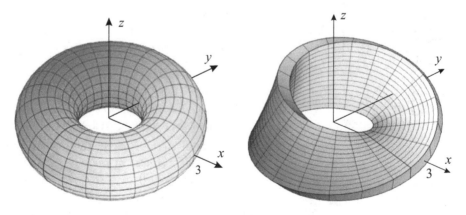

A solid torus (left) *and Möbius slab* (right).

Limits

Calculus *Concepts & Computation*

1.1 Limits: An Informal View

```
> with(code_ch1sec1);
```
$$[polygonlimit, secantlimit]$$

The concept of a *limit* is fundamental to all aspects of calculus. It is the very essence of what we mean by an *ideal* quantity which arises from a sequence of *approximating* quantities. The process of passing from the approximate quantities to the ideal quantity is known as *taking limits*, or more precisely, as finding the limit of the sequence of approximate quantities.

For example, to define *ideal* objects and notions such as the tangent line to a curve, the length of a curve, the area of a planar region, or the volume of a solid, we devise various ways of obtaining a sequence of approximating lines, lengths, areas, or volumes, and then take limits. This you will see when these topics are discussed later in the book and you will come to appreciate how important limits are in calculus.

Two Motivating Examples

Two examples will help motivate what we have just said. These examples will also lead us toward a more formal definition of the limit concept.

Example 1.1.1 (The Area of a Circle)

One of the oldest limits in mathematics is the area of the region inside a circle (often just referred to as the area of a circle). This area was determined by the ancient Greek mathematicians using the *method of exhaustion*, which turned out to be the precursor of the modern method of limits. Figure 1.1.1 indicates how the method of exhaustion is applied to finding the area enclosed by a circle.

The idea is to try to fill up (or exhaust) the region inside the circle with some simple geometric figures whose areas are known, or easily calculated. One choice would be to use triangles for this.

As shown in Figure 1.1.1, we can start the process of filling up the circle by placing 2 isosceles triangles on the diameter. These are shown in red and constitute the first stage of the process. At the second stage of the process, add 4 more isosceles triangles to each of the exposed sides of the triangles from the first stage. These are shown in maroon.

You could continue like this for as long as you wish. For example, at the third stage you could add 8 more isosceles triangles to each of the exposed sides of the triangles from the second stage. At the fourth stage you could add 16 triangles, to each of the exposed sides of the triangles from the third stage. And so on.

The triangles become smaller and smaller as you continue the process, and if you continue forever you will, theoretically, fill up the entire circular region and thereby obtain its area as a limit. The following command produces an animation which shows this process. Click on the graphic produced by it and run the movie several times to obtain an intuitive feel for this limiting process.

```
> polygonlimit;
```

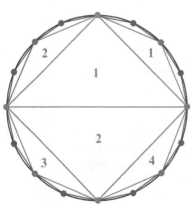

Figure 1.1.1: *Filling a circle with isosceles triangles.*

Figure 1.1.2 shows the last frame in the animation. It illustrates all the isosceles triangles added out to the fourth stage in the process described above. The first stage is 2 red triangles. The second stage is 4 maroon triangles. The third stage is 8 purple triangles. The fourth stage is 16 blue triangles (which are barely discernible).

The animation in truth doesn't show the limit, but rather only indicates the areas of all the accumulated triangles at to the point where adding additional ones would not be discernible. You will see this sort of thing many times in this book. An ideal quantity, in this case the area of the circle, is measured with fair exactitude by an approximate quantity.

In order to add more concreteness to the above example of a limit, we introduce some notation. We let

$A(1)$ = the area of the 2 red triangles,

$A(2)$ = the area of the 2 red and 4 maroon triangles,

$A(3)$ = area of the 2 red, 4 maroon, and 8 purple triangles,

$A(4)$ = area of the 2 red, 4 maroon, 8 purple, and 16 blue triangles,

In general let $A(n)$ denote the total area of all the triangles added by the nth stage of the process. Otherwise said, $A(n)$ denotes the nth approximation to the exact, or ideal, area of the circle, which we will denote by A_{circle}. Thus, the process yields a sequence

$$A(1), A(2), A(3), A(4), \ldots$$

of approximations to the area of the circle. Continuing the process forever amounts to letting the variable n get larger and larger, and we will denote this by

$$n \to \infty$$

Read this as: "n tends to infinity." While the variable n is thus tending to infinity, the approximate area "area $A(n)$ is tending to A_{circle}," and we denote this by

$$A(n) \to A_{circle}$$

These are two of our standard notations, and they will be very useful in our discussions of limits. Since we have to take n to infinity in order to get $A(n)$ to go toward A_{circle}, we will often abbreviate this as

$$A(n) \to A_{circle} \quad \text{as} \quad n \to \infty$$

This last bit of notation will also be written in the following more compact, standard form

$$\lim_{n \to \infty} A(n) = A_{circle}.$$

In this last form, the notation suggests some sort of operation that is to be applied to $A(n)$. The result of the operation is the number A_{circle}, which is called the *limit*. In this example the limit is the area of the circle. This is what we mean by *taking limits*, and the primary aim of this chapter is to teach you how to do this.

The concept of a limit is central to calculus and, while it is a new and different thing for you in your math experience, understanding it will be key to your success in this subject.

The next example is slightly different, but has all the same ingredients. There will be an expression, or function, such as $A(n)$, that depends on some variable, such as n, and we will want to determine how the expression behaves as the variable n approaches something, such as ∞ in this example.

Example 1.1.2 (The Tangent to a Curve at a Given Point)

The Greeks also handed down to us the problem of determining the *tangent line* to a curve at a given point on the curve. They solved this problem for some

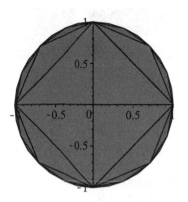

Figure 1.1.2: *The last frame in the animation* `polygonlimit`.

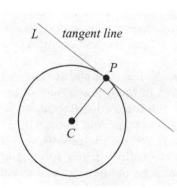

Figure 1.1.3

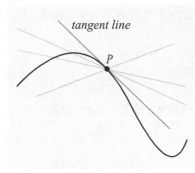

Figure 1.1.4: *Lines through a point P on a curve.*

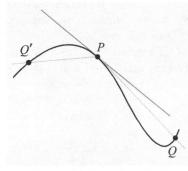

Figure 1.1.5: *Two secant lines and a hypothetical tangent line (in red).*

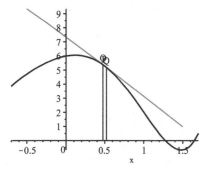

Figure 1.1.6: *The two secant lines PQ, PQ' almost line up to define the tangent line at P.*

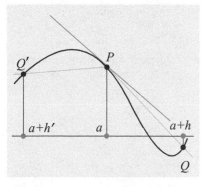

Figure 1.1.7: *The slopes of the secant lines PQ, PQ' depend on the quantities h, h'.*

standard curves, such as the circle and other conic sections (parabolas, ellipses, and hyperbolas). However, they did not use limits to determine these tangent lines. Rather, they gave a geometric method of constructing these lines and then provided proof of the fact these lines were indeed tangent to the respective curves.

For example, the tangent line to a circle at a point P is constructed by joining P to the center C of the circle and then drawing a line L which is perpendicular to the line PC and passes through P. See Figure 1.1.3.

Having made this construction, one can prove that the line L touches the circle at point P, but does not intersect it at any other point. Thus, the line L is the desired tangent line.

It was only in later times that Newton and Leibniz (following initial work by Descartes and Fermat) developed the notion of limits and showed how to use it in an intuitive way to determine tangent lines to curves in general (not just for circles, ellipses, hyperbolas, and parabolas). Their method will be discussed in greater detail in Chapter 2, but here, we consider it briefly as a motivation for the concept of the limit.

Figure 1.1.4 shows a curve, a selected point P on that curve, and numerous lines that pass through P and have various slopes.

The tangent line at P is intuitively the one shown in red in the figure. It has just the right slope so that, *near P*, it touches the curve in *only* one point, namely P. Note the key phase is "near P," because, as you can see, if the red line is extended, then it appears that it will intersect the curve in a second point distinct from P.

Compare this with the situation for the circle where every line through P intersects the circle in either two points or only one point. A tangent line for a circle is one that intersects it in only one point. All the other lines are called secant lines. (In Latin, *tangent* means "touching" and *secant* means "cutting.")

Thus, for curves other than the circle, we need a definition of what we mean by a tangent line at a given point on the curve. That's where the calculus is needed (in particular the idea of limits). We will end up defining the tangent line as a line arising from the limit of a sequence of secant lines. The full details of this will be given in Chapter 2. Here we are just trying to motivate the limit concept, so we won't worry too much about the details for now.

The intuitive idea is this. Take two points Q, Q' on the curve on opposite sides of P, and draw the secant lines PQ and PQ' as indicated in Figure 1.1.5

Now visualize the process of sliding Q and Q' along the curve toward P. As you do so, the lines PQ, PQ' will change in slope and perhaps you can see that these moving secant lines will eventually (in the limit) coincide with a line that you would want to call the tangent line (indicated by the red line in the figure).

To visualize this better, execute the following Maple command and view the resulting animation.

```
>   secantlimit;
```

Figure 1.1.6 shows the last frame in this movie.

As a means of comparing the limiting process here with that in Example 1.1.1, we introduce some notation. Our aim is to abstract the limit idea and make it more general than the ones in these examples.

In realizing the tangent line as the limit of a sequence of secant lines, it is important to focus on how the *slopes* of the secant lines change as the points Q and Q' slide toward the point P. These slopes naturally depend on the horizontal distance from Q and Q' to P as indicated in the Figure 1.1.7.

The figure shows perpendiculars dropped on the x-axis from P, Q, and Q', giving for x coordinates of these points a, $a + h$, and $a + h'$. The slopes of lines PQ and PQ' depend on the quantities h and h' (the quantity a is fixed throughout the discussion). We denote these slopes by $m(h)$ and $m(h')$. You should note that h is a positive quantity while h' is negative, and as Q and Q' slide along the curve toward P, both h and h' tend toward 0. Thus, in the limit we get the slope of the tangent line, which we denote by $m_{tangent}$. The limiting process here is written as:

$$\lim_{h \to 0} m(h) = m_{tangent}$$

The Limit of a Function

The two examples above give very concrete situations in which limits naturally arise and should motivate the intuitive meaning of those particular limits:

$$\lim_{n \to \infty} A(n) = A_{circle} \quad \text{and} \quad \lim_{h \to 0} m(h) = m_{tangent}$$

We would now like to abstract this so that we can talk about limits in a very general way. Then once we understand limits in this general way, we can come back and apply that knowledge to particular situations like measuring areas and finding slopes of tangent lines. These types of applications will keep us busy throughout the book. As we have said, limits are fundamental to all aspects of calculus.

So how do we talk about limits in general? For starters, note that the examples above involve functions $A(n)$ and $m(h)$ which depend on variables n and h. While we did not show you formulas for these functions (we'll do that later), we interpreted $A(n)$ as the nth approximation to the area of the circle and $m(h)$ as the approximate slope of the tangent line. The approximation $A(n)$ is good if n is large (n is near ∞) and the approximation $m(h)$ is good if h is small (h is near 0).

From this it seems like the general situation should involve a function $y=f(x)$, which depends on a variable x, and a particular value a that we want x to tend toward, $x \to a$ (such as ∞ and 0 in the examples). Then an intuitive definition of the limit is:

DEFINITION 1.1.1 (Limits)

The function $y = f(x)$ is said to have limiting value L *as x tends to* a*, if the y-values can be made as close to L as we wish by restricting x to being sufficiently close to a. When this is the case we use the notation*

$$\lim_{x \to a} f(x) = L$$

We say "L is the limit of $f(x)$ as x tends to a." Alternatively, we say that $f(x)$ approaches L as x approaches a and write

$$f(x) \to L \quad as \quad x \to a$$

In the definition, it is understood that L is a real number. (Later we will extend the definition to allow for the possibility that L is an extended real number, such as $\pm\infty$). In the particular case $x \to \infty$, the phrase: "being sufficiently close to ∞" means "being sufficiently large."

This definition is rather imprecise and is meant only as an intuitive description of what a limit is. After building upon this intuition in the next few sections, we will give a mathematically precise definition of what a limit is. The precise definition is called the ε-δ definition of the limit.

1.2   Limits Tools: The Graphical Method

Calculus *Concepts & Computation*

1.2 Limit Tools: The Graphical Method

> `with(limit_tools,twosidelimit,printtwosidelimit);`
$$[\textit{twosidelimit}, \textit{printtwosidelimit}]$$

Section 1.1 gave you an intuitive introduction to the concept of a limit. This section continues to develop your understanding of this important concept and introduces you to the first of three tools (or methods) for evaluating limits.

We need to emphasize from the start that the first two methods, for the most part, are only a means to make an educated *guess* as to what the limit is. These two methods could lead, especially if improperly applied, to an incorrect value for the limit, and even if the tools allow you to guess correctly what the limit should be, that is not the same thing as *knowing* or *proving* that your guess is correct. (Proving that a limit is what you think it is will be discussed later, in Section 1.9, where we give a rigorous definition of limits).

So what are these three methods for analyzing limits? They are: (1) the graphical method, (2) the numerical method, and (3) the algebraic method. We begin with the graphical method here, and discuss the other two methods in Sections 1.3 and 1.4.

The graphical method for analyzing the limit

$$\lim_{x \to a} f(x)$$

uses the graph of the function f either to guess at the approximate/exact value of the limit, or to determine that the limit does not exist. There are several different ways in which you will do this, depending on how you get a graph of the function in the first place. These ways are:

(A) Use a special-purpose Maple command to create a dynamic animation of the graph.

(B) Use the Maple `plot` command to create the graph.

(C) Use pencil and paper to create the graph by hand.

(D) Use a given picture of the graph.

In each case you will have to analyze and look carefully at the graph in order to obtain a good guess for the correct limit. We discuss each of the cases, (A)–(D), in the subsections below:

Using the Animation Generated by `twosidelimit`

We think that you will like this method best, since it is as easy as watching a movie. All you have to do is plug in the appropriate parameters to the command `twosidelimit`. (The reason for the strange name for this command will become apparent when you learn about one-sided limits in Section 1.6.) Of course you will have to study the movie (maybe run it several times) and understand the concept before you can guess the limit correctly. Here is the first example.

Example 1.2.1 (A Famous Limit)

The limit

$$\lim_{x \to 0} \frac{\sin x}{x}$$

is a famous limit because it occurs in a variety of important situations. Suppose we let f denote the corresponding function:

$$f(x) = \frac{\sin x}{x},$$

so that the limit is asking about the behavior of this function as x gets close to 0. Note in this case

$$f(0) = \frac{\sin(0)}{0}$$

is undefined, i.e., 0 is not in the domain of f. This often occurs when studying limits: the function is not defined at the place where the limit is being taken and so evaluating the function there makes no sense.

To study what is happening to $f(x)$ as x goes to 0, we use the command `twosidelimit` as follows. First define the function f as usual in Maple,

```
> f:=x->sin(x)/x;
```

$$f := x \mapsto \frac{\sin(x)}{x}$$

Next decide how close to $x = 0$ you want to be in the investigation of the limit. In this case let's choose the interval $[-16, 16]$, so that we will have a viewing window of 16 units on each side of 0. (That is not very close to 0, but will suffice in this example.) Finally, choose how many frames you want in the animation. Let's use 30 in this case. (Be careful about using too many frames if your computing power is limited). Having made these decisions, we can use the following command to produce the desired animation.

```
> twosidelimit(f,0,-16,16,30);
```

Compare the animation you get with the following static plot in Figure 1.2.1, which shows the next to last frame in the movie. Then read the analysis below.

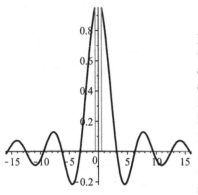

Figure 1.2.1: *The 29th frame in the movie* `twoside(f,0,-16,16,30).`

Notice the red lines in the movie (and in Figure 1.2.1). They are the y-values corresponding to the x-values, $x_1, -x_1, x_2, -x_2, \ldots, x_{30}, -x_{30}$. These y-values oscillate around, taking on positive and negative values, but eventually get close to the value 1 in the 30th frame when $x_{30}, -x_{30}$ are both close to zero. Thus, 1 is a good guess for the limiting value, and we write this as

$$\lim_{x \to 0} \frac{\sin x}{x} = 1$$

There is a way to prove that this is the exact value for the limit, and perhaps you will study this later in the book. For now we just concentrate on guessing the values for limits from appropriate graphs.

Example 1.2.2 (A Limit Involving a Rational Function)

From your previous study of rational functions $f(x) = \frac{p(x)}{q(x)}$, you know that they are not defined at points x_0 where the denominator is zero: $q(x_0) = 0$. Otherwise said, x_0 is not in the domain of f. It turns out that such points are important in understanding the nature of the rational function f, and so it is natural to consider limits at such points:

$$\lim_{x \to x_0} \frac{p(x)}{q(x)}$$

You should recall from algebra that if $q(x_0) = 0$, and in addition the numerator is not zero, $p(x_0) \neq 0$, then f has a vertical asymptote at x_0. We will look at this type of behavior in Section 1.8, but here we consider the other possibility. Namely, suppose *both* numerator and denominator are zero at x_0:

$$p(x_0) = 0, \quad \text{and} \quad q(x_0) = 0.$$

What then is the limit as $x \to x_0$? A good particular example to look at first is the following function:

```
> f:=x->(x^4-16)/(x-2);
```

$$f := x \mapsto \frac{x^4 - 16}{x - 2}.$$

Clearly the denominator is zero only for $x = 2$. But this value also makes the numerator zero. Thus, there is *not* a vertical asymptote at $x = 2$. So what happens as $x \to 2$? Namely, does the limit

$$\lim_{x \to 2} \frac{x^4 - 16}{x - 2}$$

exist, and if so what is its value? Note that substituting $x = 2$ directly in the expression for f gives

$$\frac{2^4 - 16}{2 - 2} = \frac{0}{0}$$

and this gives no information about the behavior of the function near $x = 2$. So we use the graphical method to make a guess as to the limit.

```
> twosidelimit(f,2,0,4,20);
```

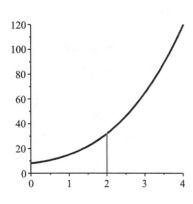

Figure 1.2.2: *The 20th frame in the animation created by* `twosidelimit(f,2,0,4,20)`.

The animation and Figure 1.2.2 seem to indicate that the limit exists and has a value between 20 and 40. To get a better estimate of the limiting value, use the cursor probe on the last frame in the animation, and place it on the y-value where the two red lines appear to be coming together (i.e., place it on the tops of the red lines). When we did this, we found 32.19. Trying several more times gave us other values (like 32.65 and 31.83), so we are not precisely sure of what the limit is using the graphical method. A basic guess would be 32 point something. Let's just use 32.19 as the our guess for the value of the limit. That is the best we can do with the graphical method, however we can get the *exact* value using the algebraic method in Section 1.4 later. We will find that

$$\lim_{x \to 2} \frac{x^4 - 16}{x - 2} = 32.$$

You might have used that as your guess here.

Example 1.2.3 (A Nonexistent Limit)

It is often the case that piecewise-defined functions do not have limits at the points where the "piecing together" occurs. For example consider the function

$$g(x) = \begin{cases} -x & x < 0 \\ 1 - x^2 & 0 \le x \end{cases}.$$

This formula creates the function g by piecing together the two functions $y = -x$ and $y = 1 - x^2$ at the point $x = 0$. So let's consider the limit:

$$\lim_{x \to 0} g(x).$$

Before using the animation command, we define the function g in Maple as follows. (See the Appendix A.10 for a discussion of how to handle piecewise-defined functions in Maple.)

```
> g:=proc(x)
> if x<0 then -x else 1-x^2 end if
> end proc:
```

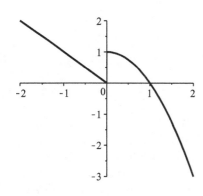

Figure 1.2.3: *The 20th frame in the animation created by* `twosidelimit(g,0,-2,2,20)`.

We view the limit on the interval $[-2, 2]$, letting $x \to 0$ and choose twenty frames for the animation.

```
> twosidelimit(g,0,-2,2,20);
```

The animation clearly indicates that the limit *does not exist* in this case. This is so because there is no *single* y-value that $g(x)$ approaches as x approaches zero from *both* sides. In fact, as x approaches 0 from the left side $g(x)$ tends to 0, while as x approaches 0 from the right side $g(x)$ approaches 1. Since $0 \neq 1$, the limit does not exist.

This example illustrates the two-sided nature of the limit

$$\lim_{x \to a} f(x)$$

The variable x has to approach a from *both* sides, and the limit exists only if there is a *single* number that $f(x)$ approaches as x gets close to a.

Example 1.2.4 (Another Famous Limit)

Consider the function

$$f(x) = (1 + x)^{1/x},$$

which is defined for all x, *except* $x = 0$. Indeed trying to evaluate the formula for f at $x = 0$ gives

$$f(0) = (1 + 0)^{1/0} = 1^{1/0}$$

and the problem with this is that $1/0$ is not defined. So f is not defined for $x = 0$. However, we can investigate what happens when x gets close to 0, i.e., find the limit

$$\lim_{x \to 0} (1 + x)^{1/x},$$

if it exists. Using the `twosidelimit` command below indicates that there does indeed appear to be a limit.

```
> f:=x->(1+x)^(1/x);
```
$$f := x \mapsto (1 + x)^{1/x}$$
```
> twosidelimit(f,0,-0.5,0.5,30);
```

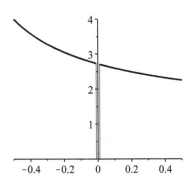

Figure 1.2.4: *The last frame in a movie for investigating the limit* $\lim\limits_{x \to 0} (1 + x)^{1/x}$.

By using the cursor probe on the graphic in Figure 1.2.4, you can get an approximation to the limiting value. When we did this we found it was approximately 2.72. So we write

$$\lim_{x \to 0} (1 + x)^{1/x} \approx 2.72.$$

Later we will see that the exact value for this limit is e (Euler's number), and this limit is one of the possible ways that this number can be defined:

$$e \equiv \lim_{x \to 0} (1 + x)^{1/x}.$$

To ten decimal places, the approximate value of e is
```
> exp(1.0);
```
$$2.718281828$$
So we see that our guess above of 2.72 is fairly accurate.

Using Maple's `plot` Command

Now that you have experience using `twosidelimit` to guess at the limiting values for certain limits, you should easily be able to use Maple's ordinary `plot` command to do the same thing. In essence the `plot` command gives a static picture which can be considered as the last frame in a `twosidelimit` animation (it just doesn't show the movement toward the limiting value). Here is an example to illustrate what we mean.

Example 1.2.5 (The `plot` Command)

Consider the function

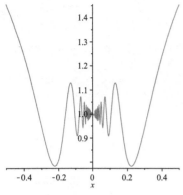

Figure 1.2.5: *A graph of* $f(x) = 1 + x\sin(1/x)$ *on the interval* $[-0.5, 0.5]$.

```
> f:=x->1+x*sin(1/x);
```
$$f := x \mapsto 1 + x\sin(1/x)$$

This function is defined for all values of x except $x = 0$. But this is where the function has interesting behavior. So even though $f(0)$ is not defined, it may be possible that the limit

$$\lim_{x \to 0} f(x)$$

exists. To investigate this, we use Maple's `plot` command to graph the function on an interval about the point $x = 0$. The size of this interval depends on the function and you will usually have to experiment with several sizes before getting a suitable picture. Here we use the interval $[-0.5, 0.5]$.

```
> plot(f(x),x=-0.5..0.5);
```

This gives Figure 1.2.5. In looking at and analyzing the figure, try to imagine two vertical ordinate lines starting at $x = -0.5$ and $x = 0.5$ respectively and sliding toward the origin from each side (just like in the movies you viewed above). You might even want to print out the graph and mark a sequence of these ordinate lines on the graph with a pencil, indicating their direction of motion with an arrow.

These ordinate lines begin with heights about 1.48, decrease to heights about 0.75, increase to heights about 1.14, etc. So there's a lot of oscillation in the heights as the x-values approach the origin, but the heights appear to oscillate more closely about the value 1, the closer x is to zero. Hence, our guess for the limit is

$$\lim_{x \to 0} \left[1 + x\sin\left(\frac{1}{x}\right) \right] = 1.$$

Using Pencil and Paper

This method for analyzing limits is essentially the same as the one above that uses Maple's plot command. The only difference is that *you* have to do all the work. The functions in the limits here will usually be simple, and so you should be able to sketch them by hand fairly quickly. Having done this, draw, directly on the graph, a sequence of vertical lines approaching the $x = a$ value, and try to discern what value the y-values are approaching. That value will be your guess for the limit.

Example 1.2.6 (Graphing By Hand)

Problem: Consider the function defined by

$$f(x) = 1 + \frac{x^3}{|x|},$$

for all $x \neq 0$. Since this function is not defined at 0, that will be the interesting place to investigate it's behavior. So we find

$$\lim_{x \to 0} \left[1 + \frac{x^3}{|x|} \right].$$

using a by-hand sketch of the function.

Solution: A sketch is easy enough to do by hand using the formula for f to calculate numerous points on the graph and then plotting these. When doing this we observe that for x positive

$$\frac{x^3}{|x|} = \frac{x^3}{x} = x^2,$$

while for x negative

$$\frac{x^3}{|x|} = \frac{x^3}{-x} = -x^2,$$

Thus, the function f is the piecewise-defined function

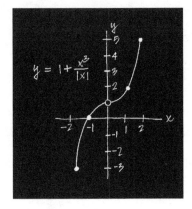

Figure 1.2.6: *A hand-drawn sketch of $f(x) = 1 + \dfrac{x^3}{|x|}$*

$$f(x) = \begin{cases} 1 - x^2 & x < 0 \\ 1 + x^2 & 0 < x \end{cases}.$$

So we could also sketch the graph by piecing together these two parts of parabolas. A hand-drawn sketch of this function is shown in Figure 1.2.6

Note that the open circle on the graph indicates that point is *not* part of the graph. From the graph, and all your previous experience, it is easy to see that the limit is

$$\lim_{x \to 0} 1 + \frac{x^3}{|x|} = 1.$$

Using a Given Graph

This method for analyzing limits is essentially the same as methods (2) and (3) above, and, luckily for you, requires the least amount of work. All you have to do is look at the given graph and think about what you have learned above. Then guess the value of the limit. Here is an example for you to consider.

Example 1.2.7 (Analyzing A Graph)

Problem: Consider the function f whose graph on the interval $[-2, 4]$ is shown in Figure 1.2.7.

Use your understanding of the limit concept to find the following limits by reading values off the graph.

$$\text{(a) } \lim_{x \to 2} f(x) \quad \text{(b) } \lim_{x \to -1} f(x) \quad \text{(c) } \lim_{x \to 3} f(x).$$

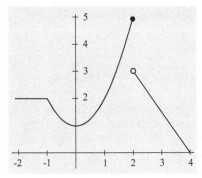

Figure 1.2.7: *The graph of a function f.*

Solution: The limit in Part (a) does not exist since as x approaches 2 from the left side, the y-values approach $5 = f(2)$, while as x approaches 2 from the right side, the y-values approach 3. Since $3 \neq 5$, the limit does not exist.

The limit in Part (b) exists and is equal to 2 since that is the y-value the function approaches as x approaches -1 from either side. The limit is $2 = f(-1)$, and, in this case, 2 is the value of the function -1.

The limit in Part (c) exists since the y-values appear to be approaching $f(3)$ as x approaches 3 from either side. It is hard to say exactly from the figure, but a good guess for the function's value at 3 is $f(3) = 1.5$. So 1.5 is the limiting value.

A Sequence of Ordinates

When analyzing a graph to determine a limit $\lim_{x \to a} f(x)$, it is often useful to sketch a sequence of ordinates corresponding to a sequence of x-values approaching a from each side. The *ordinate*, for a given x is the line segment drawn from the point $(x, 0)$ on the x-axis to the point $(x, f(x))$ on the graph. These are shown in the movies for the dynamic plots produced by the `dplot` command. Figure 1.2.8 shows a sketch of three ordinates on each side of $a = 2$ for the function in this example. These help us visualize that the limit does not exist since the y-values approach different limiting values.

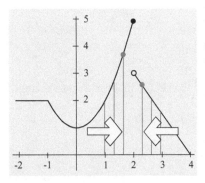

Figure 1.2.8: *Ordinates (in red) to the graph of a function f.*

Exercises: 1.2 (Limit Tools: The Graphical Method)

```
>with(limit_tools, twosidelimit,printtwosidelimit);
```
$$[\textit{twosidelimit, printtwosidelimit}]$$

Using `twosidelimit`

Use the special purpose Maple routine: `twosidelimit` to create a dynamic plot of the graph of $y = f(x)$ as x approaches a. After viewing the animation several times use it to make an informed guess about the values of the limits (when they exist). If the limit does not exist, write DNE.

1. $\lim\limits_{x \to 1} \dfrac{x^3 - 1}{x - 1}$

2. $\lim\limits_{x \to 1} \dfrac{x - 1}{x^3 - 1}$

3. $\lim\limits_{x \to 1} \dfrac{x^2 + 2x - 3}{x^3 - 1}$

4. $\lim\limits_{x \to 2} \dfrac{x^2 - 5x + 6}{x - 2}$

5. $\lim\limits_{x \to 0} \dfrac{1 - \cos x}{x}$

6. $\lim\limits_{x \to 0} \dfrac{\tan x}{x}$

7. $\lim\limits_{x \to 0} \dfrac{e^{-x} - 1}{x}$

8. $\lim\limits_{x \to 1} \dfrac{\ln x}{x^2 - 1}$

9. $\lim\limits_{x \to 4} \dfrac{\sqrt{x} - 2}{x - 4}$

10. $\lim\limits_{x \to 9} \dfrac{x - 9}{\sqrt{x} - 3}$

11. $\lim\limits_{x \to 0} [1 + x \sin(1/x^2)]$

12. $\lim\limits_{x \to 0} \sqrt{|x|} \cos(1/x)$

13. $\lim\limits_{x \to 0} \left[1 + x \sin\left([\ln|x|]^2\right)\right]$

14. $\lim\limits_{x \to 0} \sin(\csc x)$

15. $\lim\limits_{x \to 0} |\sin x|^{\sin x}$

16. $\lim\limits_{x \to 0} |\sin x|^{1 - \cos x}$

17. $\lim\limits_{x \to 2} f(x)$, where $f(x) = \begin{cases} 4 - x^2 & \text{if } x \le 2 \\ x - 2 & \text{if } x > 2 \end{cases}$.

18. $\lim\limits_{x \to 1} f(x)$, where $f(x) = \begin{cases} 1 - x^2 & \text{if } x \le 1 \\ x - 2 & \text{if } x > 1 \end{cases}$.

Using Maple's `Plot` Command

Use the Maple command: `plot` to plot the functions f involved in the following limits: $\lim\limits_{x \to a} f(x)$. Choose an appropriate interval for the x-values about the value a where the limit is being taken. Use the graph to make an informed guess about the values of the limits (when they exist). If the limit does not exist, write DNE.

19. $\lim\limits_{x \to 3} \dfrac{x^2 - 9}{x - 3}$

20. $\lim\limits_{x \to 4} \dfrac{x^2 - 16}{x - 4}$

21. $\lim\limits_{x \to 5} \dfrac{x - 5}{x^2 - 25}$

22. $\lim\limits_{x \to -1} \dfrac{x + 1}{x^2 - 1}$

23. $\lim\limits_{x \to 0} \sin\left(\dfrac{x}{\sin x}\right)$

24. $\lim\limits_{x \to 0} e^{-\left[\sin^2\left(\frac{x}{\sin x}\right)\right]}$

25. $\lim\limits_{x \to 0} (x + 1)^{1/x}$

26. $\lim\limits_{x \to 0} (x + 1)^{-1/x}$

27. $\lim\limits_{x \to -1} \dfrac{x + 1}{x^5 + 1}$

28. $\lim\limits_{x \to -1} \dfrac{x + 1}{x^9 + 1}$

29. $\lim\limits_{x \to 0} (1 - \cos x)^x$

30. $\lim\limits_{x \to 0} |\sin|^x$

31. $\lim\limits_{x \to 0} (1 - \cos x)^{\sin x}$

32. $\lim\limits_{x \to 0} |\cos x|^{\sin x}$

33. $\lim\limits_{x \to 0} (1 - \cos x)^{1 - \cos x}$

34. $\lim\limits_{x \to 0} (1 - \sin x)^{1 - \cos x}$

35. $\lim\limits_{x \to 0} (1 - \cos(1/x))^x$

36. $\lim\limits_{x \to 0} (1 - \sin(1/x))^x$

Using Pencil and Paper

Sketch, by hand, a plot of the graph of $y = f(x)$ on the specified interval about a and use this to make an informed guess about the values of the limits $\lim\limits_{x \to a} f(x)$ (when they exist). If the limit does not exist, write DNE.

37. $\lim\limits_{x \to 1} (4 - x^2)$

38. $\lim\limits_{x \to 1} \left(1 - (x - 2)^2\right)$

39. $\lim\limits_{x \to 0} |x|$

40. $\lim\limits_{x \to 1} |x - 1|$

41. $\lim\limits_{x \to 0} \dfrac{x}{|x|}$

42. $\lim\limits_{x \to 0} \dfrac{x^2}{|x|}$

43. $\lim\limits_{x \to 0} 1 + \dfrac{x^4}{|x|}$

44. $\lim\limits_{x \to 0} \dfrac{|x|}{x^2}$

45. $\lim\limits_{x \to 0} x|x|$

46. $\lim\limits_{x \to 0} -x|x|$

47. $\lim\limits_{x \to 0} |x|(|x| - 1)$

48. $\lim\limits_{x \to 0} |x|(1 - |x|)$

49. $\lim\limits_{x \to 0} |x||x - 2|$

50. $\lim\limits_{x \to 0} -|x||x - 2|)$

51. $\lim\limits_{x \to 1} \dfrac{|x| - 1}{|x|}$

52. $\lim\limits_{x \to 2} \dfrac{|x| - 2}{|x|}$

53. $\lim\limits_{x \to 0} \dfrac{|x - 1|}{|x|}$

54. $\lim\limits_{x \to 0} \dfrac{|x - 2|}{|x|}$

55. $\lim\limits_{x \to 1} f(x)$, where $f(xt) = \begin{cases} x & \text{if } x \le 1 \\ 3 - x & \text{if } x > 1 \end{cases}$

56. $\lim\limits_{x \to 0} f(x)$, where $f(x) = \begin{cases} -x & \text{if } x \le 0 \\ 1 + x^2 & \text{if } x > 0 \end{cases}$

57. $\lim\limits_{x \to 1} f(x)$, where $f(x) = \begin{cases} 2x & \text{if } x \le 1 \\ (x - 2)^2 + 1 & \text{if } x > 1 \end{cases}$

58. $\lim\limits_{x \to 1} f(x)$, where $f(x) = \begin{cases} 1 - x & \text{if } x \le 1 \\ -(x - 2)^2 + 1 & \text{if } x > 1 \end{cases}$

59. $\lim\limits_{x \to 1} f(x)$, where $f(x) = \begin{cases} x^2 & \text{if } x \le 1 \\ \frac{1}{x} & \text{if } x > 1 \end{cases}$

60. $\lim\limits_{x \to 1} f(x)$, where $f(x) = \begin{cases} 2 - x^2 & \text{if } x \le 1 \\ \frac{1}{x} & \text{if } x > 1 \end{cases}$

61. $\lim\limits_{x\to 0}\ |\sin x|$

62. $\lim\limits_{x\to \pi/2}\ |\cos x|$

63. $\lim\limits_{x\to 0}\ \sin(|x|)$

64. $\lim\limits_{x\to \pi/2}\ \cos(|x|)$

65. $\lim\limits_{x\to 0}\ e^{|x|}$

66. $\lim\limits_{x\to 0} -e^{|x|}$

67. $\lim\limits_{x\to 0}\ \ln(1+|x|)$

68. $\lim\limits_{x\to 0} \ln(1-|x|)$

69. $\lim\limits_{x\to 0} f(x)$, where $f(x) = \begin{cases} -x & \text{if } x \le 0 \\ 1+\sin x & \text{if } x > 0 \end{cases}$

70. $\lim\limits_{x\to 0} f(x)$, where $f(x) = \begin{cases} -x & \text{if } x \le 0 \\ 1+\cos x & \text{if } x > 0 \end{cases}$

71. $\lim\limits_{x\to 0}\ \tan x$

72. $\lim\limits_{x\to \pi/2}\ \cot x$

73. $\lim\limits_{x\to 0}\ \sec x$

74. $\lim\limits_{x\to \pi/2}\ \csc x$

Using a Given Graph

For the functions f whose graphs are shown below, use your understanding of the limit concept to determine the limits.

75. (a) $\lim\limits_{x\to 1} f(x)$ (b) $\lim\limits_{x\to 2} f(x)$ (c) $\lim\limits_{x\to 4.5} f(x)$

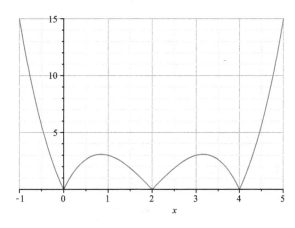

76. (a) $\lim\limits_{x\to 1} f(x)$ (b) $\lim\limits_{x\to 2} f(x)$ (c) $\lim\limits_{x\to 3} f(x)$

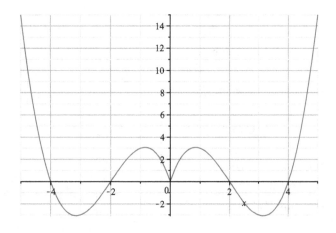

77. (a) $\lim\limits_{x\to 1} f(x)$ (b) $\lim\limits_{x\to 2} f(x)$ (c) $\lim\limits_{x\to 3} f(x)$

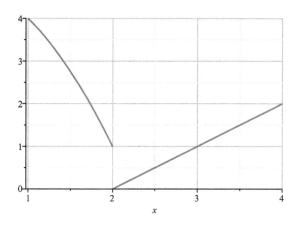

78. (a) $\lim\limits_{x\to -0.5} f(x)$ (b) $\lim\limits_{x\to 0} f(x)$ (c) $\lim\limits_{x\to 0.5} f(x)$

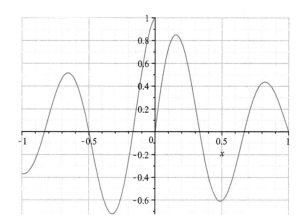

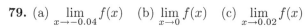

79. (a) $\lim\limits_{x\to -0.04} f(x)$ (b) $\lim\limits_{x\to 0} f(x)$ (c) $\lim\limits_{x\to 0.02} f(x)$

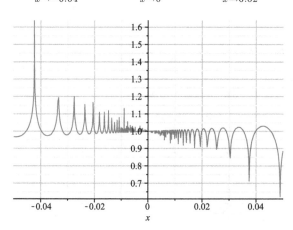

Calculus *Concepts & Computation*

1.3 Limit Tools: The Numerical Method

```
>  with(limit_tools,twosidelimit,printtwosidelimit);
```
$$[twosidelimit, printtwosidelimit]$$

To further your understanding of the limit concept, we discuss in this section a method for evaluating limits numerically. As with the graphical method, this will only allow you to make an educated guess about the value of the limit.

The numerical method for analyzing the limit

$$\lim_{x \to a} f(x)$$

amounts to choosing a sequence of x-values, $x_1, x_2, x_3, \ldots$ that approach a, from either side of a, and computing (either by hand, by calculator, or by computer) the corresponding $f(x_1), f(x_2), f(x_3), \ldots$ To be effective you must choose the x-values very close to a, but distinct from it. Remember that in many limits the function f is not defined at a, so computing $f(a)$ is not possible.

Example 1.3.1 (A Limit of a Rational Function)

Consider the function defined by

$$f(x) = \frac{x^3 - 1}{x - 1}$$

for any real number x other than 1. To study the behavior of f near $x = 1$, we look at the limit

$$\lim_{x \to 1} \frac{x^3 - 1}{x - 1},$$

and analyze it numerically. For this, choose some numbers x greater than 1, but near 1, such as

$$1.1, 1.01, 1.001, 1.0001, \ldots$$

and calculate the corresponding y-values $f(x)$:

$$f(1,1), f(1.01), f(1.001), f(1.0001), \ldots$$

This gives:

$$3.310000000, 3.030100000, 3.003001000, 3.000300000, \ldots$$

Thus, it looks like the y-values are going toward 3 as x approaches 1 from the right-side. We must also check what happens as x approaches 1 from the left-side. So we choose some numbers x less than 1, but near 1, such as

$$0.9, 0.99, 0.999, 0.9999, \ldots$$

The corresponding y-values

$$f(0.9), f(0.99), f(0.999), f(0.9999), \ldots$$

are

$$2.710000000, 2.970100000, 2.997001000, 2.999700000, \ldots$$

This gives us evidence to substantiate a guess that the limit is actually equal to 3:

$$\lim_{x \to 1} \frac{x^3 - 1}{x - 1} = 3.$$

You should record your calculations in the form of a table in order to fully justify your guess. Guesses with no justifications are not acceptable. For this example, the table of the calculations could be written something like that shown in Table 1.3.1.

NOTE: When using the numerical method, some students have the tendency to only calculate one value of $f(x)$. After all, as the table indicates, the y-values are closer to the limit for $x = 1.0001$ than for $x = 1.1$. So why not just plug in $x = 1.0001$ to begin with and be done with it? Or better yet, why not use 1.00000001, which is even closer to where the limit is taking place? There are several reasons not to do this:

(1) While this "one-calculation" guess will give you the right answer for some limits (such as this one), it will give you the wrong answer for many other limits (see the next example).

(2) Your guess for the limit is suppose to be an *educated* guess. This means that on homework and tests you must show at least *eight* calculations of $f(x)$ (or whatever number your instructor requests). Four with x less than but near a and four for x greater than but near a. There are no standard values to choose for x, so different students may get different values in their tables.

x	f(x)
1.1	3.31
1.01	3.0301
1.001	3.003001
1.0001	3.000300
0.9	2.71
0.99	2.9701
0.999	2.997001
0.9999	2.999700

Table 1.3.1: *Values of* $f(x) = \frac{x^3-1}{x-1}$ *(for x near 1).*

Example 1.3.2 (Another (In)famous Trig Limit)

To illustrate some drawbacks with the numerical method, we consider the following interesting limit:

$$\lim_{x \to 0} \sin\left(\frac{1}{x}\right).$$

If we take the sequence of x-values $x = 0.1, 0.01, 0.001, 0.0001$ greater than zero and then the sequence of x-values $x = -0.1, -0.01, -0.001, -0.0001$ less than zero, we get the corresponding y-values $f(x)$ shown in Table 1.3.2. Note that in the table, the values $f(x)$ for $x = 0.1$ and $x = -0.1$ are the same in magnitude but opposite in sign. You should have expected this since the sine function is an *odd* function, i.e.,

$$\sin(-\theta) = -\sin(\theta),$$

for all θ. You can take advantage of this in the future and cut your work in half. (Similarly when the function is an *even* function.)

After further study of the table, can you discern a reasonable guess for the limit? Maybe a few more calculations will help. For example, let's try:

$$f(0.00001) = 0.03574879797$$
$$f(0.000001) = -0.3499935022.$$

If you continue on like this, you may soon reach the conclusion that there no single y-value that $f(x)$ is approaching as x gets closer and closer to zero. Thus, you may suspect that the limit does not exist, and in fact that is the case:

$$\lim_{x \to 0} \sin\left(\frac{1}{x}\right) = \text{does not exist.}$$

x	f(x)
0.1	-0.54402
0.01	0.50637
0.001	0.82688
0.0001	-0.30561
-0.1	0.54402
-0.01	-0.50637
-0.001	-0.82688
-0.0001	0.30561

Table 1.3.2: *Values of* $f(x) = \sin(1/x)$ *(for x near 0).*

But how do we know this? Later, in Section 1.9, after you have some more experience, you can trying proving that the limit does not exist using the hints in exercises there. But for now, you might try using the graphical method to add more credence to a guess of "does not exist."

Let's do this, using the animation created by `twosidelimit`.

```
> f:=x->sin(1/x);
```
$$f := x \mapsto \sin(1/x)$$
```
> twosidelimit(f,0,-1,1,30);
```

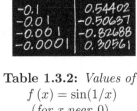

Figure 1.3.1: *The 30th frame of* `twosidelimit(f,0,-1,1,30)`.

As you can see from the animation and Figure 1.3.1, showing of the last frame of the animation, the y-values oscillate continuously through all values between -1 and 1 as $x \to 0$. Furthermore this oscillation between the minimum and maximum y-values of -1 and 1 becomes more frequent (or rapid) as x gets closer to 0. In summary, no matter how close x is to 0, we can always get a little closer and find a y-value of -1 and a y-value of 1. Hence, the limit cannot exist.

When you use the numerical method to analyze a limit

$$\lim_{x \to a} f(x).$$

you will have to make calculations, and these calculations are usually done with (1) pencil and paper, (2) a calculator, or (3) a computer. You would only use pencil and paper, or by-hand calculations, if the $f(x)$ were particularly simple, such as

$$\lim_{x \to -2} \frac{x^2 - 3}{x + 2}.$$

If the function f is more complicated, then a calculator or computer is almost a necessity.

Example 1.3.3 (The Numerical Method with a Calculator)

The following limit is easy to study using a calculator.

$$\lim_{x \to 1} \frac{\ln x}{x^3 - 1}.$$

Taking values $x = 1.1, 1.01, 1.001, 1.0001$ and $x = 0.9, 0.99, 0.999, 0.9999$, we get the values shown in Table 1.3.3. From this we would guess that the limit is

$$\lim_{x \to 1} \frac{\ln x}{x^3 - 1} = \frac{1}{3}.$$

Example 1.3.4 (The Numerical Method in Maple)

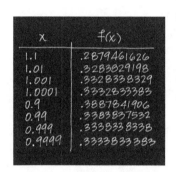

x	f(x)
1.1	.2879461626
1.01	.3283829198
1.001	.3328338329
1.0001	.3332833383
0.9	.3887841906
0.99	.3383837532
0.999	.3338338338
0.9999	.3333833383

Table 1.3.3: *Values of* $f(x) = \frac{\ln x}{x^3 - 1}$ *(for x near 1).*

Let's consider the following limit

$$\lim_{x \to 2} \frac{1 - \cos(x - 2)}{(x - 2)^2}.$$

It would be somewhat tedious and time consuming to do this by hand or by using a scientific calculator which doesn't have the facility to define functions. So we discuss here how to do this with Maple handling the calculations. First define the function whose limit is being taken:

```
> f:=x->(1-cos(x-2))/(x-2)^2;
```

$$f := x \mapsto \frac{1 - \cos(x - 2)}{(x - 2)^2}$$

Now just evaluate this at $x = 2.1, 2.01, 2.001, 2.00001$, using the following format to create a table-like output:

```
> 2.1,f(2.1); 2.01,f(2.01); 2.001,f(2.001); 2.0001,f(2.0001);
```

$$2.1, 0.4995834700$$
$$2.01, 0.4999960000$$
$$2.001, 0.5000000000$$
$$2.0001, 0.5000000000$$

Note carefully the distinction between the commas and semi-colons in the above Maple command. Next we must check out what happens as x approaches 2 from below (i.e., for values of x less than 2):

```
> 1.9,f(1.9);1.99,f(1.99);1.99,f(1.99);1.999,f(1.999);
```

1.9, 0.4995834700

1.99, 0.4999960000

1.99, 0.4999960000

1.999, 0.5000000000

That is simple enough to enter, and you might guess (correctly) that the limit is 0.5:

$$\lim_{x \to 2} \frac{1 - \cos(x - 2)}{(x - 2)^2} = \frac{1}{2}.$$

Warning: *Numerical Problems Can Occur*

When working with a computer or calculator you should be aware of the inaccuracies and errors that can occur in numerical calculations. The above example is perfect for illustrating numerical errors. To see this, compute a larger table of values:

```
>  2.1,f(2.1); 2.01,f(2.01); 2.001,f(2.001); 2.0001,f(2.0001);
   2.00001,f(2.00001); 2.000001,f(2.000001); 2.0000001,f(2.0000001);
   2.00000001,f(2.00000001);
```

2.1, 0.4995834700

2.01, 0.4999960000

2.001, 0.5000000000

2.0001, 0.5000000000

2.00001, 0.0

2.000001, 0.0

2.0000001, 0.0

2.00000001, 0.0

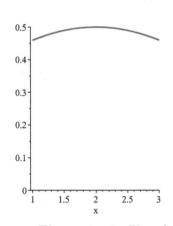

Figure 1.3.2: *Plot of* $f(x) = \frac{1 - \cos(x - 2)}{(x - 2)^2}$ *near* 2

Well, those last four calculations seem to invalidate our guess of 0.5 for the limit. Were we wrong? Maybe the limit should be 0? It turns out that we can *prove* by other means that the limit *is* 0.5. Or we could try the graphical method to try to give a little more credence to the value 0.5. Here is the result of that:

```
>  plot([0,f(x)],x=1..3,color=[black,blue],thickness=[1,2]);
```

See Figure 1.3.2. But changing methods doesn't do away with the annoying numerical results we got in the above do loop. So how do we fix that?

One thing you can always try when attempting to eliminate numerical inaccuracies is to increase the number of digits that Maple uses in its calculations. By default, Maple uses ten decimal digits in calculation. If you want to change this, say increase it to 20, use the following command:

```
>  Digits:=20;
```

$$digits = 20$$

Note the use of an upper case D in Digits. Now we can try the above calculations again and get the following:

```
>  2.1,f(2.1); 2.01,f(2.01); 2.001,f(2.001); 2.0001,f(2.0001);
   2.00001,f(2.00001); 2.000001,f(2.000001); 2.0000001,f(2.0000001);
   2.00000001,f(2.00000001);
```

2.1, 0.49958347219742339000

2.01, 0.49999583334722220000

2.001, 0.49999995833333000000

2.0001, 0.49999999958300000000

2.00001, 0.50000000000000000000

2.000001, 0.50000000000000000000

2.0000001, 0.50000000000000000000

2.00000001, 0.50000000000000000000

That is much better. Fewer than twenty digits may give good results too.

Exercises: 1.3 (Limit Tools: The Numerical Method)

Evaluate the following limits $\lim_{x \to a} f(x)$ numerically. For this, choose four values of x on each side of a (eight values total) and calculate the corresponding y-values: $y = f(x)$. You may use a calculator or Maple to do the calculations. Arrange the results of your calculations in a table.

1. $\lim_{x \to 3} \dfrac{x^2 - 9}{x - 3}$

2. $\lim_{x \to -1} \dfrac{x^3 + 1}{x + 1}$

3. $\lim_{x \to 0} \dfrac{e^x - 1}{x}$

4. $\lim_{x \to 1} \dfrac{2^x - 2}{x - 1}$

5. $\lim_{x \to 0} (x + 1)^{1/x}$

6. $\lim_{x \to 0} (1 + 2x)^{1/x}$

7. $\lim_{x \to 1} \dfrac{\ln x}{x - 1}$

8. $\lim_{x \to 1} \dfrac{(\ln x)^2}{x - 1}$

9. $\lim_{x \to 0} \dfrac{\tan x}{x}$

10. $\lim_{x \to 0} \dfrac{\tan x - x}{x^3}$

11. $\lim_{x \to 0} \dfrac{\tan x}{x^2}$

12. $\lim_{x \to 0} \dfrac{x}{\tan x}$

13. $\lim_{x \to 1} \dfrac{\ln x}{x^2 - 1}$

14. $\lim_{x \to 1} \dfrac{(\ln x)^2}{x^2 - 1}$

15. $\lim_{x \to 0} \dfrac{\cos x - 1}{\sin x}$

16. $\lim_{x \to 0} \dfrac{1 - \sec x}{\tan x}$

17. $\lim_{x \to 0} \dfrac{\cos 3x - 1}{x^2}$

18. $\lim_{x \to 0} \dfrac{\sin x - x}{x^2}$

19. $\lim_{x \to 0} \dfrac{\sin(x^2.}{3x^2}$

20. $\lim_{x \to 0} \dfrac{\cos(x^2) - 1}{3x^2}$

21. $\lim_{x \to 0} \dfrac{\tan x - x}{x^3}$

22. $\lim_{x \to 0} \dfrac{\tan x - x}{x^2}$

23. $\lim_{x \to 0} x \ln(x^2)$

24. $\lim_{x \to 0} x^2 \ln(x^2)$

25. $\lim_{x \to 0} (1 + 2x)^{1/x}$

26. $\lim_{x \to 0} (1 + 3x)^{1/x}$

27. $\lim_{x \to 0} x^{2 \sin x}$

28. $\lim_{x \to 0} x^{3 \sin x}$

Do-Loops in Maple

When estimating a limit numerically, if you want to create a large table of values, then you probably want to automate the calculations by using a "do-loop." A do-loop is a programming structure that allows you to execute a command (or several commands) repetitively, over an over again, a specified number of times. All programming languages have do-loop structures although they may not be called do-loops.

In Maple, do-loops work like this. Suppose we want to calculate the values of $2^n, 3^n, 4^n, 5^n$, for $n = 1, 2, 3, 4, 5, 6$. We can do this simply with the following do-loop:

```
>    for n from 1 to 6 do
>    2^n, 3^n,4^n,5^n
>    end do;
```

2,3,4,5
4,9,16,25
8,27,64,125
16,81,256,625
32,243,1024,3125
64,729,4096,15625

Notice the special structure of the code in these commands: The first line is the "header" for the loop and gives the range for the parameter n that controls the do-loop. The last line signals the end of the do-loop. The commands between the header and the last line of code are what get executed as n ranges from 1 to 6.

A more pertinent example is a do-loop to automate the numerical calculations of the limit

$$\lim_{x \to 2} \frac{1 - \cos(x - 2)}{(x - 2)^2} = \frac{1}{2}.$$

For this, we need to express the x-values 2.1, 2.01, 2.001, 2.0001, etc. in a form that can be used in a do-loop. But this clearly is

$$2 + (.1)^1, \ 2 + (.1)^2, \ 2 + (.1)^3, \ 2 + (.1)^4$$

So we use $2 + (0.1)^n$, for the general nth term in the sequence of x values and write the following code for the do-loop: `> for n from 1 to 4 do`
```
>  2+(.1)^n, f(2+(.1)^n);
> end do
```
2.1, 0.4995834700
2.01, 0.4999960000
2.001, 0.5000000000
2.0001, 0.5000000000

If we want to approach 2 with values less than 2, we alter the above do loop as follows:
```
> for n from 1 to 4 do
> 2-(.1)^n, f(2-(.1)^n);
> end do;
```
1.9, 0.4995834700
1.99, 0.4999960000
1.999, 0.5000000000
1.9999, 0.5000000000

Use a do-loop to numerically estimate the values of the following limits.

29. $\lim_{x \to 3} \dfrac{x^2 - 9}{x - 3}$

30. $\lim_{x \to -1} \dfrac{x^3 + 1}{x + 1}$

31. $\lim_{x \to 0} \dfrac{e^x - 1}{x}$

32. $\lim_{x \to 1} \dfrac{2^x - 2}{x - 1}$

33. $\lim_{x \to 0} (x + 1)^{1/x}$

34. $\lim_{x \to 0} (1 + 2x)^{1/x}$

35. $\lim_{x \to 1} \dfrac{\ln x}{x - 1}$

36. $\lim_{x \to 1} \dfrac{(\ln x)^2}{x - 1}$

Calculus Concepts & Computation

1.4 Limit Tools: The Algebraic Method

```
> with(limit_tools,twosidelimit,printtwosidelimit);
```
$$[twosidelimit, printtwosidelimit]$$

The algebraic method for evaluating limits is different from the graphical and numerical methods is several respects:

(1) It does not require a computer or a calculator, only pencil, paper, and some good skill at algebra on your part (that's why it is called the algebraic method).

(2) It generally will lead you to the *exact* value for the limit, rather than an educated guess for the exact value, as the graphical and numerical methods do.

Because of these two reasons, the algebraic method is a preferred method to use when possible. Of course, you can also check your work with either of the other two methods if you wish.

Regrettably, the algebraic method can not be used on *all* limit problems, but rather only on limits

$$\lim_{x \to a} f(x)$$

where the function f can be simplified using algebra (and where limit laws can be applied to the simplified expression). By studying the following examples you will learn the types of limits that can be handled with the algebraic method, and you will also see the type of algebra needed.

Example 1.4.1 (Factoring and Reducing)

Here we consider the rational function

$$f(x) = \frac{x^2 - 4}{2x - 4}.$$

which is undefined at $x = 2$, and that's where we want to investigate the limit:

$$\lim_{x \to 2} \frac{x^2 - 4}{2x - 4}$$

Substituting $x = 2$ into this is not possible, as we have seem many times before. It gives $f(2) = 0/0$, which is undefined. However, note that we can factor and reduce the rational function f as follows:

$$\frac{x^2 - 4}{2x - 4} = \frac{(x - 2)(x + 2)}{2(x - 2)} = \frac{x + 2}{2}.$$

The last expression is defined at $x = 2$, and we can just substitute in 2 and get the correct limiting value:

$$\lim_{x \to 2} \frac{x^2 - 4}{2x - 4} = \lim_{x \to 2} \frac{x + 2}{2} = \frac{2 + 2}{2} = 2.$$

A quick check of this by the graphical method gives the following information that also suggests that the limit is 2.

```
> f:=x->(x^2-4)/(2*x-4);
```
$$f := x \mapsto \frac{x^2 - 4}{2x - 4}$$

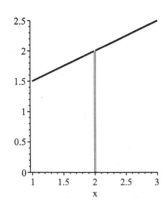

Figure 1.4.1: *The* 30*th frame in the movie*
`twosidelimit(f,2,1,3,30)`

```
> twosidelimit(f,2,1,3,30);
```
In the movie and Figure 1.4.1, the graph of f appears to be a straight line. The reason for this, is that the above algebra shows that the formula for f reduces to the formula for the following function

$$g(x) = \frac{x+2}{2} = \frac{1}{2}x + 1$$

whose graph is a line with slope $1/2$ and y-intercept $(0, 1)$. Note that g is defined for all x, but f is not, so technically f and g are different functions.

The example above involves factoring the difference of two squares: $x^2 - 4 = (x-2)(x+2)$ and this occurs frequently, along with similar techniques for factoring the difference of two cubes, the difference of two fourth powers, and so forth. For your convenience, we include a table of a few of these formulas in a margin box.

You should be able to see the pattern in the formulas and inductively determine how $a^n - b^n$ factors for any positive integer n. It is important to note that the sum of two powers $a^n + b^n$ factors only for *odd* powers n. The box in the margin shows the first two of these.

Factoring Differences of Powers
$a^2 - b^2 = (a-b)(a+b)$
$a^3 - b^3 = (a-b)(a^2 + ab + b^2)$
$a^4 - b^4 = (a-b)(a^3 + a^2b + ab^2 + b^3)$

Factoring Sums of Odd Powers
$a^3 + b^3 = (a+b)(a^2 - ab + b^2)$
$a^5 + b^5 = (a+b)(a^4 - a^3b + a^2b^2 - ab^3 + b^4)$

Example 1.4.2 (Factoring and Reducing)

This example uses factoring of sums of odd powers, as well as trial-and-error factoring of a quadratic polynomial. The function is

$$f(x) = \frac{x^3 + 27}{x^2 + 4x + 3}$$

and we investigate the limit as $x \to -3$. Note that f is not defined at $x = -3$, since it's denominator is zero for this value of x. The numerator is also zero for $x = -3$, so possibly there's a limit. Factoring the numerator gives

$$x^3 + 27 = x^3 + 3^3 = (x+3)\left(x^2 - 3x + 9\right).$$

Factoring the denominator gives

$$x^2 + 4x + 3 = (x+3)(x+1)$$

Thus, $x + 3$ is a common a factor, so we can reduce f and find the limit as follows

$$\lim_{x \to -3} \frac{x^3 + 27}{x^2 + 4x + 3} = \lim_{x \to -3} \frac{(x+3)\left(x^2 - 3x + 9\right)}{(x+3)(x+1)}.$$

$$= \lim_{x \to -3} \frac{x^2 - 3x + 9}{x+1} = \frac{(-3)^2 - 3(-3) + 9}{-3 + 1} = -\frac{27}{2} = -13.5$$

Note that after factoring and reducing, the limit can be evaluated by just substituting $x = -3$ into the numerator and denominator. This is generally the last step in the algebraic method. The fact that you can get the correct limit by substituting in $x = -3$, comes from one of the limit laws in Section 1.5.

We can check our work by using the graphical method, say with `twosidelimit`. Figure 1.4.2 shows the last frame in this movie.

```
> f:=x->(x^3+27)/(x^2+4*x+3);
```

$$f := x \mapsto \frac{x^3 + 27}{x^2 + 4x + 3}$$

```
> twosidelimit(f,-3,-4,-2,20);
```

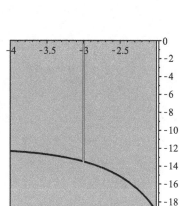

Figure 1.4.2: *The* 20*th frame in the movie* `twosidelimit(f,-3,-4,-2,20).`

Example 1.4.3 (Rationalizing a Numerator)

The rationalization technique (applied to either the numerator or denominator) allows us to evaluate certain limits involving radicals. The technique comes from the factoring techniques above and uses the identity shown in the margin box.

We use this to evaluate the following limit

$$\lim_{x \to 4} \frac{\sqrt{x} - 2}{x - 4}.$$

A Rationalizing Identity

$$(\sqrt{a} - \sqrt{b})(\sqrt{a} + \sqrt{b}) = a - b$$

View the numerator as $\sqrt{x} - 2 = \sqrt{x} - \sqrt{4}$, then multiply the numerator and denominator by $\sqrt{x} + 2$, and simplify the numerator:

$$\frac{\sqrt{x} - 2}{x - 4} = \frac{\sqrt{x} - 2}{x - 4} \cdot \frac{\sqrt{x} + 2}{\sqrt{x} + 2} = \frac{x - 4}{(x - 4)(\sqrt{x} + 2)} = \frac{1}{\sqrt{x} + 2}.$$

Note that we do NOT multiply out the denominator. We leave it in factored form so that we can cancel common factors at the last step of the simplification.

We can now find the limit by evaluating at $x = 4$:

$$\lim_{x \to 4} \frac{\sqrt{x} - 2}{x - 4} = \lim_{x \to 4} \frac{1}{\sqrt{x} + 2} = \frac{1}{\sqrt{4} + 2} = \frac{1}{4}.$$

Example 1.4.4 (Simplifying and Factoring)

Find the limit: $\lim\limits_{x \to 1} \dfrac{\frac{1}{x} - 1}{1 - \frac{1}{x^2}}.$

We simplify first and then factor an reduce.

$$\frac{\frac{1}{x} - 1}{1 - \frac{1}{x^2}} = \frac{\frac{1-x}{x}}{\frac{x^2-1}{x^2}} = \frac{x(1 - x)}{x^2 - 1} = \frac{x(1 - x)}{(x - 1)(x + 1)} = \frac{-x}{x + 1}$$

Then

$$\lim_{x \to 1} \frac{\frac{1}{x} - 1}{1 - \frac{1}{x^2}} = \lim_{x \to 1} \frac{-x}{x + 1} = \frac{-1}{1 + 1} = -\frac{1}{2}.$$

Example 1.4.5 (Simplifying and Reducing)

Some limits can be evaluated by simplifying and reducing either the numerator or the denominator. For instance, consider

$$\lim_{x \to 0} \frac{4 - (x - 2)^2}{4x(x - 2)^2}.$$

Plugging in $x = 0$, gives $0/0$, which is meaningless. But if we simplify the numerator first, we get

$$\frac{4 - (x - 2)^2}{4x(x - 2)^2} = \frac{4 - (x^2 - 4x + 4)}{4x(x - 2)^2} = \frac{x(4 - x)}{4x(x - 2)^2} = \frac{4 - x}{4(x - 2)^2}$$

Thus

$$\lim_{x \to 0} \frac{4 - (x - 2)^2}{4x(x - 2)^2} = \lim_{x \to 0} \frac{4 - x}{4(x - 2)^2} = \frac{4 - 0}{4(0 - 2)^2} = \frac{1}{4}.$$

Example 1.4.6 (Trig Identity and Factoring)

The standard trig identity $\sin^2 x + \cos^2 x = 1$, or equivalently $\cos^2 x = 1 - \sin^2 x$, is often useful, as the following limit shows.

$$\lim_{x \to \pi/2} \frac{\cos^2 x}{1 - \sin x} = \lim_{x \to \pi/2} \frac{1 - \sin^2 x}{1 - \sin x} = \lim_{x \to \pi/2} \frac{(1 - \sin x)(1 + \sin x)}{1 - \sin x}$$

$$= \lim_{x \to \pi/2} (1 + \sin x) = 1 + 1 = 2$$

Exercises: 1.4 (Limit Tools: The Algebraic Method)

Use the algebraic method to evaluate the following limits. Show all your steps.

1. $\lim\limits_{x \to 5} \dfrac{x-5}{x^2-25}$

2. $\lim\limits_{x \to 4} \dfrac{x^2-16}{x-4}$

3. $\lim\limits_{x \to -3} \dfrac{x^3+27}{x+3}$

4. $\lim\limits_{x \to -2} \dfrac{x+2}{x^5+32}$

5. $\lim\limits_{x \to 2} \dfrac{x^2-4}{x^3-8}$

6. $\lim\limits_{x \to 3} \dfrac{x^3-27}{x^2-9}$

7. $\lim\limits_{x \to 1} \dfrac{\sqrt{x}-1}{x-1}$

8. $\lim\limits_{x \to 16} \dfrac{\sqrt{x}-4}{x-16}$

9. $\lim\limits_{x \to 25} \dfrac{x-25}{\sqrt{x}-5}$

10. $\lim\limits_{x \to 9} \dfrac{x-9}{3-\sqrt{x}}$

11. $\lim\limits_{x \to 8} \dfrac{x-8}{x^{1/3}-2}$

12. $\lim\limits_{x \to 27} \dfrac{x-27}{x^{1/3}-3}$

13. $\lim\limits_{h \to 0} \dfrac{1}{h}\left(\dfrac{1}{2+h}-\dfrac{1}{2}\right)$

14. $\lim\limits_{h \to 0} \dfrac{1}{h}\left(\dfrac{1}{\sqrt{4+h}}-\dfrac{1}{2}\right)$

15. $\lim\limits_{x \to 0} \dfrac{(x+1)^2-1}{x}$

16. $\lim\limits_{x \to 0} \dfrac{27-(x+3)^3}{x}$

17. $\lim\limits_{x \to 0} \dfrac{1-\sqrt{x+1}}{x\sqrt{x+1}}$

18. $\lim\limits_{x \to 0} \dfrac{x^2\sqrt{x+4}}{4-\sqrt{x^2+16}}$

19. $\lim\limits_{x \to 0} \dfrac{(x+2)^3-8}{x}$

20. $\lim\limits_{x \to 0} \dfrac{(x+2)^4-16}{x}$

21. $\lim\limits_{x \to -2} \dfrac{x^2-4}{x^2+5x+6}$

22. $\lim\limits_{x \to -1} \dfrac{x^2-1}{x^2+4x+3}$

23. $\lim\limits_{x \to 3} \dfrac{x^2-2x-3}{2x^2-5x-3}$

24. $\lim\limits_{x \to 5} \dfrac{x^2-3x-10}{3x^2-16x+5}$

25. $\lim\limits_{x \to \pi/2} \dfrac{1-\sin^2 x}{\cos x}$

26. $\lim\limits_{x \to 0} \dfrac{\cos^2 x-1}{\sin x}$

27. $\lim\limits_{x \to 0} \dfrac{\sin^2 x}{1-\cos x}$

28. $\lim\limits_{x \to \pi/2} \dfrac{\cos^2 x}{1-\sin x}$

29. $\lim\limits_{x \to 0} \dfrac{\sin 2x}{\sin x}$

30. $\lim\limits_{x \to \pi/4} \dfrac{\cos 2x}{\cos^2 x-\sin^2 x}$

31. $\lim\limits_{x \to 0} \dfrac{\sin x-x}{\sin(-x)+x}$

32. $\lim\limits_{x \to 0} \dfrac{\cos x-1}{\cos(-x)-1}$

33. $\lim\limits_{x \to 0} \dfrac{\sec^2 x-1}{\tan x}$

34. $\lim\limits_{x \to 0} \dfrac{\tan^2 x}{\sec^2 x-1}$

35. $\lim\limits_{x \to 0} \dfrac{\tan^2 x}{\sec x-1}$

36. $\lim\limits_{x \to 0} \dfrac{\sec x-1}{\tan^2 x}$

37. $\lim\limits_{x \to 0} \dfrac{e^{2x}-1}{e^x-1}$

38. $\lim\limits_{x \to 0} \dfrac{e^{6x}-1}{e^{2x}-1}$

39. $\lim\limits_{x \to 0} \dfrac{4^x-1}{2^x-1}$

40. $\lim\limits_{x \to 0} \dfrac{9^x-25}{3^x-5}$

41. $\lim\limits_{x \to 0} \dfrac{1-e^{-x}}{e^x-1}$

42. $\lim\limits_{x \to 0} \dfrac{1-2^{-x}}{2^x-1}$

43. $\lim\limits_{x \to 0} \dfrac{e^{2x}-1}{e^{-x}-1}$

44. $\lim\limits_{x \to 0} \dfrac{2^{2x}-1}{2^{-x}-1}$

45. $\lim\limits_{x \to 0} \dfrac{e^x=\frac{1}{e^x}}{1-\frac{1}{e^x}}$

46. $\lim\limits_{x \to 0} \dfrac{1-2^{-x}}{2^x-1}$

47. $\lim\limits_{x \to 0} \dfrac{1-e^{-x}}{e^x-1}$

48. $\lim\limits_{x \to 0} \dfrac{1-2^{-x}}{2^x-1}$

49. $\lim\limits_{x \to 1} \dfrac{1-\frac{1}{x}}{x-1}$

50. $\lim\limits_{x \to 2} \dfrac{1-\frac{2}{x}}{x-2}$

51. $\lim\limits_{x \to 4} \dfrac{1-\frac{2}{\sqrt{x}}}{x-4}$

52. $\lim\limits_{x \to 0} \dfrac{1-\frac{1}{\sqrt{x}}}{x-1}$

53. $\lim\limits_{x \to 1} \dfrac{\sqrt{x}-\frac{1}{\sqrt{x}}}{x-1}$

54. $\lim\limits_{x \to 9} \dfrac{\sqrt{x}-\frac{9}{\sqrt{x}}}{x-9}$

Limits of Difference Quotients

Many of the limits that we have encounter so far are of the form

$$\lim_{x \to a} \frac{f(x)-f(a.}{x-a},$$

where f is a function defined on an interval about the number a (but not necessarily at a. These are known as limits of difference quotients and many of these limits can be evaluated by the algebraic method. You will see how this type of limit arises in Chapter 2.

For each of the following, form the difference quotient and take its limit using the algebraic method.

55. $f(x)=x^2$, $a=2$

56. $f(x)=x^2$, $a=4$

57. $f(x)=x^3$, $a=2$

58. $f(x)=x^3$, $a=4$

59. $f(x)=x^4$, $a=2$

60. $f(x)=x^4$, $a=4$

61. $f(x)=\sqrt{x}$, $a=4$

62. $f(x)=\sqrt{x}$, $a=9$

63. $f(x)=x^2-3x$, $a=1$

64. $f(x)=x^2-5x$, $a=1$

65. $f(x)=x^3+2x^2$, $a=2$

66. $f(x)=x^3+3x^2$, $a=1$

66. $f(x)=x^3-4x$, $a=2$

68. $f(x)=x^3-16x$, $a=2$

69. $f(x)=x^4-x$, $a=1$

70. $f(x)=x^4-8x$, $a=2$

71. $f(x)=\dfrac{1}{x}$, $a=2$

72. $f(x)=\dfrac{1}{x}$, $a=-2$

73. $f(x)=\dfrac{1}{x^2}$, $a=2$

74. $f(x)=\dfrac{1}{x^2}$, $a=-2$

75. $f(x)=\dfrac{1}{x-1}$, $a=2$

76. $f(x)=\dfrac{1}{x-1}$, $a=-1$

77. $f(x)=\dfrac{x}{1+x}$, $a=1$

78. $f(x)=\dfrac{x}{1+x}$, $a=-2$

79. $f(x)=\dfrac{x^2}{1+x^2}$, $a=1$

80. $f(x)=\dfrac{x^2}{1+x^2}$, $a=-1$

81. $f(x)=\dfrac{1}{\sqrt{x}}$, $a=1$

82. $f(x)=\dfrac{1}{\sqrt{x}}$, $a=4$

Calculus Concepts & Computation

1.5 Limit Laws

So far we have learned three ways of calculating limits. Numerical and graphical methods lead to answers which are actually educated guesses. The algebraic method gives exact answers when it can be applied. In this section we will state some theorems, called **Limit Laws**, which will allow us to calculate many limits exactly.

We will not prove these theorems because we have not yet given a rigorous definition of the limit concept (See Section 1.9). Rather, we have been working intuitively and considering the limit:

$$\lim_{x \to a} f(x) = L,$$

as meaning: *there exists a number L that the values $f(x)$ of f get close to as x gets close to a.* So, within this context, we present the limit laws and argue that they are intuitively reasonable.

For instance, consider

$$\lim_{x \to a} c$$

where c is a constant. Here, we want to find the limit of a constant function $f(x) = c$, as x approaches some value a. Is there a value that the function values are close to, if we choose values of x close to a? Since the function values are *always* equal to c, it must be that c is the limit. Thus, $\lim_{x \to a} c = c$. Next look at

$$\lim_{x \to a} x$$

Here we are interested in the behavior of the function $f(x) = x$ as x approaches a. To rephrase this problem, we ask: What is x getting close to x gets close to a? Of course, the answer is a. Thus,

$$\lim_{x \to a} x = a.$$

These observations make up the content of the following theorem. We have a good many of these limit laws and so we number them.

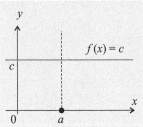

Table 1.5.1

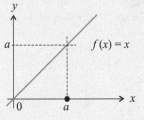

Table 1.5.2

THEOREM 1.5.1 (Limit Laws 1 & 2)

(1) $\lim_{x \to a} c = c$, *for any constant c.*   (Constant Law)

(2) $\lim_{x \to a} x = a$ (Identity Law)

The next theorem summarizes the rules for taking limits of the standard algebraic combinations of functions. These limit laws are the real work horses for all of our efforts in evaluating limits.

THEOREM 1.5.2 (Limit Laws 3 - 7)

Suppose that c is a constant and that the limits $\lim_{x\to a} f(x)$ *and* $\lim_{x\to a} g(x)$ *exist. Then*

(3) $\lim_{x\to a}[f(x)+g(x)] = \lim_{x\to a} f(x) + \lim_{x\to a} g(x)$ (Sum Law)

(4) $\lim_{x\to a}[f(x)-g(x)] = \lim_{x\to a} f(x) - \lim_{x\to a} g(x)$ (Difference Law)

(5) $\lim_{x\to a}[cf(x)] = c\lim_{x\to a} f(x)$ (Constant Multiple Law)

(6) $\lim_{x\to a}[f(x)g(x)] = \lim_{x\to a} f(x) \cdot \lim_{x\to a} g(x)$ (Product Law)

(7) $\lim_{x\to a}\dfrac{f(x)}{g(x)} = \dfrac{\lim_{x\to a} f(x)}{\lim_{x\to a} g(x)}$ if $\lim_{x\to a} g(x) \neq 0$ (Quotient Law)

It helps sometimes to think of these rules in words:

(3) *The limit of a sum is the sum of the limits.*

(4) *The limit of a difference is the difference of the limits.*

(5) *Constants multiplying functions can be factored out of the limiting process.*

(6) *The limit of the product is the product of the limits.*

(7) *The limit of a quotient is the quotient of the limits, if the limit in the denominator is not 0.*

Example 1.5.1 (Using the Limit Laws)

Problem: Evaluate the following limits using the limit laws. Explicitly state which of the limit laws are being used.

(a) $\lim_{x\to 2} 7x^2$ (b) $\lim_{x\to a} x^n$, where n is a positive integer.

(c) $\lim_{x\to -2} \left(4x^3 + 8x^2 - 3x - 9\right)$ (d) $\lim_{x\to 1} \dfrac{2x^2 - 3}{x^3 + 5x + 4}$

Solution:

(a) By the Constant Multiple Law, $\lim_{x\to 2} 7x^2 = 7\lim_{x\to 2} x^2$. Also, by the Product Law $\lim_{x\to 2} x^2 = \lim_{x\to 2} x \cdot \lim_{x\to 2} x$. We know that $\lim_{x\to 2} x = 2$, by the Identity Law. Thus, $\lim_{x\to 2} 7x^2 = 7(2)(2) = 28$.

(b) We can evaluate this limit by repeatedly applying the Product Law and then applying the Identity Law. Thus,

$$\lim_{x\to a} x^n = \lim_{x\to a}(x \cdot x \cdots x) = \lim_{x\to a} x \cdot \lim_{x\to a} x \cdots \lim_{x\to a} x = \left(\lim_{x\to a} x\right)^n = a^n .$$

(c) First we apply the Sum and Difference Laws for limits. Then we can factor out the constants by the Constant Multiple Law. Finally, we use the result in Part (b) and Constant Law.

$$\lim_{x\to -2}\left(4x^3 + 8x^2 - 3x - 9\right) = \lim_{x\to -2} 4x^3 + \lim_{x\to -2} 8x^2 - \lim_{x\to -2} 3x - \lim_{x\to -2} 9$$

$$= 4\lim_{x\to -2} x^3 + 8\lim_{x\to -2} x^2 - 3\lim_{x\to -2} x - \lim_{x\to -2} 9$$

$$= 4(-2)^3 + 8(-2)^2 - 3(-2) - 9 = -32 + 32 + 6 - 9 = -3$$

(d) Using the Quotient Law, the limit of a quotient is the quotient of the limits unless the limit of the denominator is 0. Since the numerator and denominator are polynomials, their limits are found as we did in Part (c) above: Just substitute 1 in for x. Thus,

$$\lim_{x \to 1} \frac{2\,x^2 - 3}{x^3 + 5\,x + 4} = \frac{\lim_{x \to 1}(2x^2 - 3)}{\lim_{x \to 1}(x^3 + 5\,x + 4)} = \frac{2(1)^2 - 3}{(1)^3 + 5(1) + 4} = -\frac{1}{10}$$

We see in parts (c) and (d) of Example 1.5.1, that computing the limit of polynomials or rational functions amounts to substituting the limiting value a in for x. This is our next limit law.

THEOREM 1.5.3 (Polynomial & Rational Function Limits)

(8) *If f is a polynomial or a rational function and a is in the domain of f, then*

$$\lim_{x \to a} f(x) = f(a)$$

NOTE: An important part of the hypotheses of the theorem is that number a be in the domain of f. For many limits, this is *not* the case, and so the theorem does not apply. The following example illustrates this.

Example 1.5.2 (Limit of a Rational Function)

Problem: Evaluate $\lim\limits_{x \to 5} \dfrac{3\,x - 2}{x - 5}$.

Solution: We cannot apply Law 8 in the above theorem for rational functions since 5 is not in the domain of the function

$$f(x) = \frac{3\,x - 2}{x - 5}.$$

Also, since $x - 5$ is not a factor of the numerator, we cannot calculate this limit algebraically by reduction. Informally, however, we can tell what is happening here. As x approaches 5, the denominator approaches 0 and the numerator approaches 13. The quotient is negative for x less than 5 (and close to 5) and positive for x greater than 5 (and close to 5). Also the magnitude of the quotient becomes larger and larger as x approaches 5. Thus, the quotient is not approaching any number and this limit does not exist. We will discuss this type of limit in Section 1.8.

The next theorem contains the Limit Laws concerning powers and roots of functions.

THEOREM 1.5.4 (Limit Laws 9 & 10)

Assume that $\lim\limits_{x \to a} f(x)$ *exists. Then for a positive integer n,*

(9) $\lim\limits_{x \to a}[f(x)]^n = \left[\lim\limits_{x \to a} f(x)\right]^n$ \hfill (Power Law)

(10) $\lim\limits_{x \to a} \sqrt[n]{f(x)} = \sqrt[n]{\lim\limits_{x \to a} f(x)}$ \quad (*If n is even, assume* $\lim\limits_{x \to a} f(x) \geq 0$) \hfill (Root Law)

These laws say that the limit can be carried inside nth powers and nth roots.

Example 1.5.3

Problem: Evaluate the following limits using the Power and Root Laws, as well as previous limit laws.

(a) $\lim\limits_{x \to 6} \sqrt{x^2 - 4}.$ (b) $\lim\limits_{x \to -3} \left(\dfrac{2}{x} - 4 \right)^4.$

Solution (a): This is a straight-forward application of the Root Law. This amounts to substituting in the limiting value 6 for x. So,

$$\lim_{x \to 6} \sqrt{x^2 - 4} = \sqrt{\lim_{x \to 6} (x^2 - 4)} = \sqrt{36 - 4} = \sqrt{32} = 4\sqrt{2}.$$

Solution(b): Using several limit laws, we get

$$\lim_{x \to -3} \left(\frac{2}{x} - 4 \right)^4 = \left(\lim_{x \to -3} \left(\frac{2}{x} - 4 \right) \right)^4 \qquad \text{Power Law}$$

$$= \left(\lim_{x \to -3} \frac{2}{x} - \lim_{x \to -3} 4 \right)^4 \qquad \text{Limit Law 4}$$

$$= \left(\frac{2}{-3} - 4 \right)^4 = \left(-\frac{14}{3} \right)^4 \qquad \text{Thm 1.5.3 and Constant Law}$$

$$= \frac{38416}{81}.$$

The next example illustrates the need for yet another limit law, different from those discussed above.

Example 1.5.4 (Squeezing a Limit)

Problem: Evaluate $\lim\limits_{x \to 0} \left| e^{-x} - 1 \right| \cos \left(\dfrac{1}{x} \right).$

Solution: Since this is the limit of the product of two functions, we would naturally think of evaluating this as the product of the limits:

$$\lim_{x \to 0} \left| e^{-x} - 1 \right| \cdot \lim_{x \to 0} \cos \left(\frac{1}{x} \right).$$

This would work if both the limits: $\lim\limits_{x \to 0} \left| e^{-x} - 1 \right|$ and $\lim\limits_{x \to 0} \cos (1/x)$ existed, and we could find their values. Let's begin our investigation by plotting the graphs of $g(x) = \cos (1/x)$ and $h(x) = \left| e^{-x} - 1 \right|$ on an interval about 0. We begin with the graph of $g(x)$ which is obtained by entering the following code. (Figure 1.5.1 displays the graph.)

```
> g:=x->cos(1/x);
```
$$g := x \mapsto \cos \left(\frac{1}{x} \right)$$
```
> plot(g(x),x=-1..1);
```

From this graph, we can tell that the function $g(x) = \cos (1/x)$ oscillates between -1 and 1 as x approaches 0 and thus $\lim\limits_{x \to 0} \cos (1/x)$ does not exist. Next we graph $h(x) = \left| e^{-x} - 1 \right|$ by executing the following two commands. The graph is in Figure 1.5.2.

```
> h:=x->abs(exp(-x)-1);
```
$$h := x \mapsto \left| e^{-x} - 1 \right|$$
```
> plot(h(x),x=-1..1,color=black);
```

From this graph we see that $\lim\limits_{x \to 0} \left| e^{-x} - 1 \right| = 0$. However, since $\lim\limits_{x \to 0} \cos (1/x)$ does not exist, we *cannot* use the product law for limits (Limit Law 6) to evaluate $\lim\limits_{x \to 0} \left| e^{-x} - 1 \right| \cos (1/x)$. However, it is still possible that this limit exists.

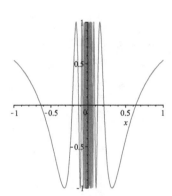

Figure 1.5.1: *Graph of* $g(x) = \cos (1/x).$

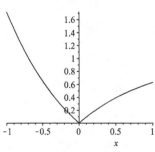

Figure 1.5.2: *Graph of* $h(x) = \left| e^{-x} - 1 \right|.$

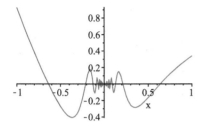

Figure 1.5.3: *Graph of*
$f(x) = \left|e^{-x} - 1\right| \cos\left(x^{-1}\right)$.

To investigate, we use the graphical method and plot the graph of $f(x) = \left|e^{-x} - 1\right| \cos(1/x)$. We execute the following code to get the graph shown in Figure 1.5.3.

```
> f:=x->abs(exp(-x)-1)*cos(1/x);
```
$$f := x \mapsto \left|e^{-x} - 1\right| \cos\left(x^{-1}\right)$$
```
plot(f(x),x=-1..1);
```

It certainly looks as if $\lim_{x \to 0} \left|e^{-x} - 1\right| \cos(1/x) = 0$. Adding a little theory will show us that this is definitely the limit.

The main idea behind the theory is that the graph of $f(x) = \left|e^{-x} - 1\right| \cos(1/x)$ is *squeezed* between the functions $h(x) = \left|e^{-x} - 1\right|$ and $-h(x) = -\left|e^{-x} - 1\right|$. To see this we graph f, h, and $-h$ in the same picture using the following code.

```
> plot([f(x),h(x),-h(x)],x=-1..1,y=-1..1,color=[red,black,blue]);
```

This gives Figure 1.54 showing the graph of f being squeezed by the black and blue graphs.

Now to prove what Figure 1.5.4 suggests, we need some inequlities, First, for any $x \neq 0$, the expression $\cos(1/x)$ is always between -1 and 1. Writing this observation as an inequality:

$$-1 \leq \cos\left(\frac{1}{x}\right) \leq 1$$

and multiplying through by $\left|e^{-x} - 1\right|$ gives us

$$-\left|e^{-x} - 1\right| \leq \left|e^{-x} - 1\right| \cos\left(\frac{1}{x}\right) \leq \left|e^{-x} - 1\right|.$$

This tells us that the function $f(x) = \left|e^{-x} - 1\right| \cos(1/x)$ is *squeezed* between the functions $h(x) = \left|e^{-x} - 1\right|$ and $-h(x) = -\left|e^{-x} - 1\right|$. We know that $\lim_{x \to 0} h(x) = 0$ and so also $\lim_{x \to 0} -h(x) = 0$. Since $-h(x) \leq f(x) \leq h(x)$, it must also be that $\lim_{x \to 0} f(x) = 0$.

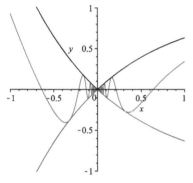

Figure 1.5.4: *Graphs of*
$f(x) = \left|e^{-x} - 1\right| \cos(1/x)$
$h(x) = \left|e^{-x} - 1\right|$ *and* $-h(x)$.

This last example is an application of the next theorem, which is appropriately called the *squeeze theorem*.

THEOREM 1.5.5 (The Squeeze Theorem)

Suppose that
$$k(x) \leq f(x) \leq h(x)$$

for all x in some interval containing a except possibly at a, and that

$$\lim_{x \to a} k(x) = \lim_{x \to a} h(x) = L$$

for some number L. Then, also

$$\lim_{x \to a} f(x) = L$$

Exercises: 1.5 (Limit Laws)

Applying the Limit Laws - Part 1

In problems 1–14, $\lim\limits_{x\to 0} f(x) = 3$, $\lim\limits_{x\to 0} g(x) = -8$.

1. $\lim\limits_{x\to 0}[3\,f(x) + 2\,g(x)]$

2. $\lim\limits_{x\to 0}[4\,f(x) + 7\,g(x)]$

3. $\lim\limits_{x\to 0}[f(x)\,g(x) - 4]$

4. $\lim\limits_{x\to 0}[3\,f(x)\,g(x) - 2]$

5. $\lim\limits_{x\to 0}\dfrac{[f(x)]^2}{x - 3g(x.}$

6. $\lim\limits_{x\to 0}\dfrac{]f(x)]^3}{2x + 5g(x}$

7. $\lim\limits_{x\to 0}\left(4[f(x)]^3 - 3[f(x)]^2\right)$

8. $\lim\limits_{x\to 0}\left(2[f(x)]^4 - 5[f(x)]^3\right)$

9. $\lim\limits_{x\to 0} 4\,\dfrac{[g(x)]^3}{g(x) + 2}$

10. $\lim\limits_{x\to 0} 4\,\dfrac{[f(x)]^3}{f(x) + 2}$

11. $\lim\limits_{x\to 0} \sqrt[3]{g(x)}$

12. $\lim\limits_{x\to 0} \sqrt[3]{g(x) - 19}$

13. $\lim\limits_{x\to 0} 4\,\dfrac{\sqrt{f(x) + 6}}{\sqrt[5]{g(x) + 7}}$

14. $\lim\limits_{x\to 0} 4\,\dfrac{\sqrt{f(x) + 61}}{\sqrt[5]{g(x) + 16}}$

Applying the Limit Laws - Part 2

In Exercises 15–34, use the limit laws and other results to find the limits. NOTE: In some of the expressions, the limit laws do not apply, so (1) try using the algebraic method to simplify to an expression where the laws do apply, or (2) try using the numerical or graphical methods to determine a value for the limit (if one exists).

15. $\lim\limits_{x\to 5} \left(x^2 - 4x + 5\right)$

16. $\lim\limits_{x\to -1} \left(x^6 - 12x + 1\right)$

17. $\lim\limits_{x\to 1} \left(x^4 - 5x^3 + 3\right)\left(x^4 - 2x^3 - 6\right)$

18. $\lim\limits_{x\to -1} \left(x^4 - x^3 + 3\right)\left(x^4 - x^3 + 5\right)$

19. $\lim\limits_{x\to 2} \dfrac{x^3 - 4}{x^2 + 1}$

20. $\lim\limits_{x\to -2} \dfrac{8 + x}{4 - x}$

21. $\lim\limits_{x\to -2} \dfrac{2 + x}{4 - x^2}$

22. $\lim\limits_{x\to -2} \dfrac{3 + x}{9 - x^2}$

23. $\lim\limits_{x\to 4} \dfrac{x - 4}{64 - x^3}$

24. $\lim\limits_{x\to -2} \dfrac{x - 3}{27 - x^3}$

23. $\lim\limits_{x\to 5} \sqrt{x^3 - 3x - 1}$

24. $\lim\limits_{x\to 2} \sqrt[3]{8 - x^4}$

25. $\lim\limits_{x\to 3} \dfrac{x}{x - 3}$

26. $\lim\limits_{t\to -2} \dfrac{x^3 + 8}{2 + x}$

27. $\lim\limits_{x\to 2} x^2\sqrt{8 - x^2}$

28. $\lim\limits_{x\to 2} x^3\sqrt{12 - x^3}$

29. $\lim\limits_{x\to 2} \sqrt{8 - x^2}\,\sqrt[3]{4 + 2x}$

30. $\lim\limits_{x\to 3} \sqrt{18 - x^2}\,\sqrt[3]{18 + 3x}$

31. $\lim\limits_{x\to 4} \sqrt{\dfrac{x + 23}{\sqrt{x} + 1}}$

32. $\lim\limits_{x\to 9} \sqrt{\dfrac{x + 55}{\sqrt{x} + 1}}$

33. $\lim\limits_{x\to 4} \dfrac{x - 4}{\sqrt{x} - 2}$

34. $\lim\limits_{x\to 9} \dfrac{x - 9}{\sqrt{x} - 3}$

Applying the Squeeze Theorem

In Exercises 35–44, find the limit by applying the squeeze theorem. Illustrate the result by plotting, in Maple, the function you are taking the limit of together with the two functions that are squeezing it toward its limit.

35. $\lim\limits_{x\to 0} x^2 \sin(1/x)$

36. $\lim\limits_{x\to 0} x^3 \sin(1/x)$

37. $\lim\limits_{x\to 0} x^2 \arctan(1/x)$

38. $\lim\limits_{x\to 0} x^3 \arctan(1/x)$

39. $\lim\limits_{x\to 0} \ln(1 + x) \sin(1/x)$

40. $\lim\limits_{x\to 0} \ln(1 + x) \cos(1/x)$

41. $\lim\limits_{x\to 0} \tan(\sin(1/x))(1 - \cos x)$

42. $\lim\limits_{x\to 0} \tan(\cos(1/x)) \sin x$

43. $\lim\limits_{x\to 0} \ln\left(1 + \cos^2(1/x)\right)|\sin x|$

44. $\lim\limits_{x\to 0} \ln\left(1 + \sin^2(1/x)\right)|1 - \cos, x|$

Using Limit Laws and Given Graphs

45. If the graphs of f and g are,

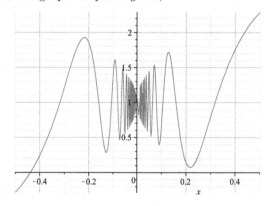

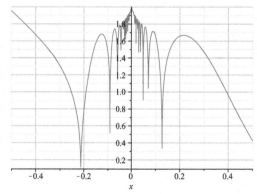

respectively, find the following limits (approximately).

(a) $\lim\limits_{x\to 0}[f(x) + g(x)]$ **(b)** $\lim\limits_{x\to 0} f(x)g(x)$

(c) $\lim\limits_{x\to -0.4}[f(x)/g(x)]$ **(d)** $\lim\limits_{x\to -0.4} \sqrt{g(x) - f(x)}$

1.6 One-Sided Limits

> `with(limit_tools,leftlimit,rightlimit,twosidelimit);`

$$[leftlimit, rightlimit, twosidelimit]$$

We have seen that $\lim_{x \to a} f(x) = L$ intuitively means that the values of $f(x)$ can be made arbitrarily close to L by choosing values of x sufficiently close to a. The values of x can be chosen to the left or to the right of a, and so this limit is called a *two-sided limit*. Pictorially, we visualize x approaching a from both sides simultaneously and the corresponding y-values approaching L (if the limit exists and is equal to L). Figure 1.6.1 illustrates this two-sided approach to the limiting value L.

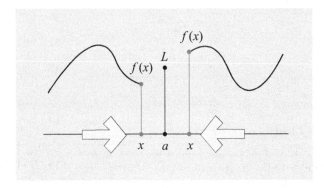

Figure 1.6.1: *The limit:* $\lim_{x \to a} f(x) = L$, *is a called a two-sided limit.*

You have also seen this two-sided limiting process illustrated in a dynamic way whenever you used the `twosidelimit` command. If the y-values on both sides approach the same value L then the limit exists and is equal to L. Otherwise the limit does not exist.

But often when the limit does not exist, it is because the limiting behavior is different on the left-side of a as opposed to the right-side of a. This suggests that we need additional notions of the limit to describe the limiting behavior of functions $y = f(x)$ to the right and left of the limiting value a. These notions are called *one-sided limits* and are discussed in the first part of this section. We will then use all these limit concepts (two-sided limits and one-sided limits) to define continuous functions in the next section.

One-Sided Limits

As we have seen before, piecewise-defined functions often fail to have limits at the point a where they are pieced together. These types of functions serve to motivate the introduction of one-sided limits, as the following example illustrates.

Example 1.6.1 (Limits of Piecewise-Defined Functions)

Consider the following piecewise-defined function

$$f(x) = \begin{cases} 3 - x^2 & x \le 1 \\ (x-1)^2 + 1 & x > 1 \end{cases}.$$

Suppose we want to evaluate $\lim_{x \to 1} f(x)$. Since the function is defined by one formula for $x \le 1$, and by a different formula for $x > 1$, we must analyze the behavior of

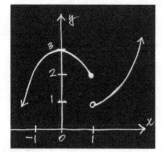

Figure 1.6.2: *Graph of*
$$f(x) = \begin{cases} 3 - x^2 & x \le 1 \\ (x-1)^2 + 1 & x > 1 \end{cases}.$$

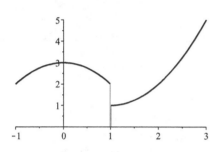

Figure 1.6.3: *Last frame of*
`twosidelimit(f,1,-1,3,15)`.

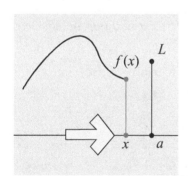

Figure 1.6.4: *A one-sided limit as x approaches a from the left.*

the function to the left of 1 and to the right of 1 separately. Sketching the graph provides a good bit of information.

A by-hand sketch is easily done by first drawing the standard parabola $y = x^2$ and then transforming it. Specifically, flip it over and translate it vertically upward 3 units to get the graph of $y = 3 - x^2$. Next, translating $y = x^2$ horizontally rightward and vertically upward 1 unit gives the graph of $y = (x-1)^2 + 1$. Then piecing these two parabolas together at $x = 1$ gives the graph of f shown Figure 1.6.2.

For further information, let's look at a dynamic plot of f in Figure 1.6.2 showing the curve being drawn from both sides as x approaches 1. For this we can use the `twosidelimit` command. Before using this command we must define the piecewise function in Maple. Recall how this is done using code such as the following.

```
>  f:=proc(x)
>  if x<=1 then 3-x^2 else (x-1)^2+1 end if;
>  end proc:
```

Now we can use the `twosidelimit` command to produce the animation.

```
>  twosidelimit(f,1,-1,3,15);
```

The last frame of this animation is shown in Figure 1.6.3.

Run the animation a few times and maybe slow it down to see that there is no real number L that the function values $f(x)$ approach as x gets close to 1. If we choose values of x arbitrarily close to 1 but less than 1 then the function values approach 2. If we choose values of x close to 1 but larger than 1 the values of $f(x)$ approach 1. We conclude that the two-sided limit $\lim_{x \to 1} f(x)$ does not exist. Summarizing our observations:

(1) If we choose values of x arbitrarily close to 1 but less that 1, the function values approach 2. The mathematical notation for this behavior is

$$\lim_{x \to 1^-} f(x) = 2.$$

This is called a *one-sided limit* or more specifically a *left-hand limit*. NOTE: the minus sign (-) that is superscripted on the 1 indicates that x approaches 1 from the left side (that's the negative side of 1).

(2) If we choose values of x arbitrarily close to 1 but greater than 1, the function values approach 1 and we denote this by

$$\lim_{x \to 1^+} f(x) = 1.$$

This is called a *right-hand limit* or a *limit from the right*. NOTE: the plus sign (+) that is superscripted on the 1 indicates that x approaches 1 from the right side (that's the positive side of 1).

We can investigate left-hand and right-hand limits for functions other than the one in Example 1.6.1. The general notion of a left-hand limit is illustrated in Figure 1.6.4, while the general notion of a right-hand limit is illustrated in Figure 1.6.5.

The following is an informal definition of these types of one-sided limits.

DEFINITION 1.6.1 (One-Sided Limits)

The limit

$$\lim_{x \to a^-} f(x) = L$$

means that the function values $f(x)$ approach L as x approaches a from the left-side of a.

The limit

$$\lim_{x \to a^+} f(x) = L$$

means that the function values $f(x)$ approach L as a approaches a from the right-side of a.

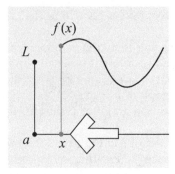

Figure 1.6.5: *A one-sided limit as x approaches a from the right.*

As with two-sided limits, there are some special-purpose Maple commands that we have written to display the behavior of a function f as x approaches a from either the left or the right. These commands have the form

```
leftlimit(f,a,c,N)        rightlimit(f,a,c,N)
```

These work much like the command `twosidelimit`, except in the first one, the movie displays the behavior of f on the interval (c,a) with x approaching a from the left, and in the second one the movie displays the behavior of f on the interval(a,c) with x approaching a from the right. You will see how to use these new commands in the following examples.

NOTE:

(1) One-sided limits do not require that the function f be defined on an interval containing a. It is only required that f be defined on an open interval with a as an endpoint.

(2) It is always possible that one, or both, of the one-sided limits do not exist.

These observations are illustrated in the some of the examples below.

Example 1.6.2 (The Square Root Function)

Consider the function $f(x) = \sqrt{x}$. The domain for this function is $\{x \mid x \geq 0\}$, and so we cannot evaluate the function values as x approaches 0 through negative numbers. Thus, there is no two-sided limit and there is no left-hand limit for f as $x \to 0^-$. We can, however, evaluate the one-sided limit from the right: $\lim_{x \to 0^+} \sqrt{x}$.

You can easily convince yourself, using a quick sketch or a basic knowledge of how the square root function behaves, that this one-sided limit is 0:

$$\lim_{x \to 0^+} \sqrt{x} = 0.$$

The other one-sided limit and the two-sided limit do not exist in this example solely because $\sqrt{x}$ is not defined for negative numbers x.

Example 1.6.3 (An Exponential Function with Variable Base)

An interesting real-valued function with domain $(0, \infty)$ is $f(x) = x^x$.

Problem: Determine the behavior of $f(x) = x^x$ near $x = 0$.

Solution: First note that we only consider $f(x) = x^x$ for positive x. While x^x is defined for negative real numbers, the resulting value of x^x is often a non-real complex number. So we look at the one-sided limit of f as x approaches 0 through positive values:

$$\lim_{x \to 0^+} x^x.$$

It is tempting to say that the limit is 1, but how do we interpret this? Should we say that $0^0 = 1$, using the dictum that anything raised to the zero-th power is 1? Or does this dictum only apply when the base is a positive number? Later, in Chapter 3, we will discuss a convenient tool known as L' Hospital's rule which will enable us to find this one-sided limit exactly. We will see that indeed

$$\lim_{x \to 0^+} x^x = 1.$$

For now, however, we can use graphical methods to estimate experimentally the value of this one-sided limit. We employ the command `rightlimit` as follows:

```
> f:=x->x^x;
```

$$f := x \mapsto x^x$$

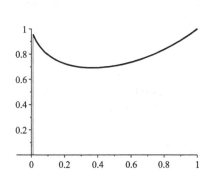

Figure 1.6.6: *The last frame in the movie* `rightlimit(f,0,15)`.

```
> rightlimit(f,0,1,15);
```

This last frame in the movie (see Figure 1.6.6) suggests that $\lim_{x \to 0^+} x^x = 1$ is indeed true.

Example 1.6.4 (An Oscillatory Sine Wave)

Problem: Examine the behavior of the function $f(x) = \sin\left(\dfrac{1}{\ln x}\right)$ near $x = 1$.

Solution: Since $\ln x$ is defined only for positive numbers x, the same is true for the function f. Additionally, f is not defined for $x = 1$, since

$$f(1) = \sin\left(\frac{1}{\ln 1}\right) = \sin\left(\frac{1}{0}\right) = ?$$

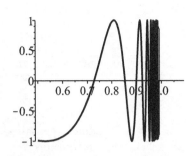

Figure 1.6.7: *The last frame in* `leftlimit(f,1,.5,15)`.

As in the last example, we use one-sided limits to analyze the behavior of f as x approaches the number 1, where f is not defined. We do this experimentally with the `leftlimit` and `rightlimit` commands, employing intervals and containing 1 as an endpoint and producing movies with 15 frames in them.

```
> f:=x->sin(1/ln(x));
```
$$f := x \mapsto \sin\left((\ln(x))^{-1}\right)$$
```
> leftlimit(f,1,.5,15);
> rightlimit(f,1,1.5,15);
```

Figures 1.6.7-1.6.8 show the last frame (the 15th frame) in each of these movies. Viewing each movie several times reveals that the values of the function oscillate between 1 and -1 as x approaches 1 from either side. Furthermore, the oscillation becomes faster the closer x gets to 1.

Indeed, observe that going from the next-to-the-last frame to the last frame (the 14th to the 15th frame) the portion of the graph that appears is a black smear of closely packed sine waves. Thus, the experimental evidence suggests that *neither* of the one-sided limits:

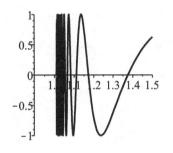

Figure 1.6.8: *The last frame in* `rightlimit(f,1,.5,15)`.

$$\lim_{x \to 0^-} \sin\left(\frac{1}{\ln x}\right), \qquad \lim_{x \to 0^+} \sin\left(\frac{1}{\ln x}\right),$$

exists.

Example 1.6.5 (Limits of Piecewise-Defined Functions)

Problem: Evaluate the one-sided and two-sided limits at $x = 1$ for the following functions. Compare and contrast the results.

(a) $f(x) = \begin{cases} 4x & x < 1 \\ (x-3)^2 & 1 \le x \end{cases}$,   (b) $g(x) = \begin{cases} 2x & x < 1 \\ (x-3)^2 & 1 \le x \end{cases}$.

Solution: These are each piecewise-defined functions that are pieced together at the point $x = 1$, where we are taking limits. Generally one-sided limits are well suited for this situation, since you can just use the appropriate formula, depending on whether x is less than or greater than 1. Thus, for part (a)

$$\lim_{x \to 1^-} f(x) = \lim_{x \to 1^-} 4x = 4,$$

since $f(x) = 4x$, when $x < 1$, as it certainly is when x approaches 1 from the left. Similarly, when x approaches 1 from the right, $f(x) = (x-3)^2$, and so

$$\lim_{x \to 1^+} f(x) = \lim_{x \to 1^+} (x-3)^2 = 4$$

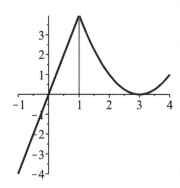

Figure 1.6.9: *Last frame in*
`twosidelimit(f,1,-1,4,15)`

The results indicate that the two pieces of the graph join together at the y-value 4. This is exhibited by looking at the movie produced by the `twosidelimit` command, using a viewing interval about $x = 1$ and 15 frames in the movie.

```
>  f:=proc(x)
>  if x<1 then 4*x
>  else (x-3)^2
>  end if
>  end proc:

>  twosidelimit(f,1,-1,4,15);
```

Figure 1.6.9 displays the last frame in this movie. The movie suggests that the two-sided limit is 4:

$$\lim_{x \to 1} f(x) = 4.$$

It is important to note that the movie produced by twosidelimit actually contains the movies produced by `leftlimit` and `rightlimit`. This is not unexpected, since from your experience you know that the two-sided limit $\lim_{x \to 1} f(x)$ involves approaching 1 from both sides. Hence, if the one-sided limits both give 4, it is clear that the two-sided limit should be 4 also.

Let's see what happens in part (b), where the formula for g is very similar to that for f.

$$\lim_{x \to 1^-} g(x) = \lim_{x \to 1^-} 2x = 2,$$

$$\lim_{x \to 1^+} g(x) = \lim_{x \to 1^+} (x-3)^2 = 4.$$

Now the left and right limits are different, 2 and 4 respectively. So, the two pieces of the graph of g do not match up at $x = 1$. This can be seen in the movie produced by the following code.

```
>  g:=proc(x)
>  if x<1 then 2*x
>  else (x-3)^2
>  end if
>  end proc:

>  twosidelimit(g,1,-1,4,15);
```

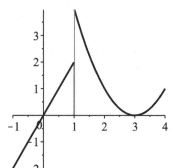

Figure 1.6.10: *Last frame in*
`twosidelimit(g,1,-1,4,15)`

The last frame in this movie is displayed in the Figure 1.6.10. From this figure, we conclude that the two-sided limit does not exist:

$$\lim_{x \to 1} g(x) = \text{ does not exist.}$$

This is due to the fact that while the one-sided limits exist, their limiting values 2 and 4 are different. Again we see that the movie of the two-sided limit contains the movies of the one-sided limits.

From the above examples we see how one-sided and two-sided limits are related. We state this formally in the following theorem.

THEOREM 1.6.1 (One-Sided Limits)

If the function f is defined on an interval containing a, except possibly at a, then

$$\lim_{x \to a} f(x) = L \quad \textit{if and only if} \quad \lim_{x \to a^-} f(x) = L \ \textit{ and } \ \lim_{x \to a^+} f(x) = L$$

In words: *The limit (two-sided limit) exists if and only if both of the one-sided limits exist and are the same number. This number is the value of the limit.*

Exercises: 1.6 (One-sided Limits)

```
> with(limit_tools,rightlimit,twosidelimit);
        [rightlimit, twosidelimit]
```

Finding One-sided Limits from a Given Graph

1. For the function f graphed below, find the following values (if they exist.

(a) $\lim\limits_{x \to 4^-} f(x)$ (b) $\lim\limits_{x \to 4^+} f(x)$ (c) $\lim\limits_{x \to 4} f(x)$ (d) $f(4)$

(e) $\lim\limits_{x \to 8^-} f(x)$ (f) $\lim\limits_{x \to 8^+} f(x)$ (g) $\lim\limits_{x \to 8} f(x)$ (h) $f(8)$

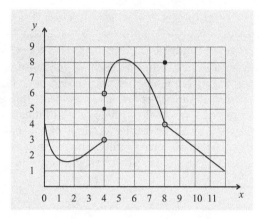

2. For the function g graphed below, find the following values (if they exist)

(a) $\lim\limits_{x \to 3^-} g(x)$ (b) $\lim\limits_{x \to 3^+} g(x)$ (c) $\lim\limits_{x \to 3} g(x)$ (d) $g(3)$

(e) $\lim\limits_{x \to 7^-} f(x)$ (f) $\lim\limits_{x \to 7^+} f(x)$ (g) $\lim\limits_{x \to 7} f(x)$ (h) $f(7)$

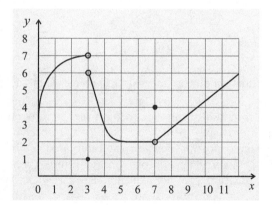

Using twosidelimit to Find One-sided Limits

In Exercises 3–8, investigate whether the one-sided limits, $\lim\limits_{x \to a^-} f(x)$, $\lim\limits_{x \to a^+} f(x)$ of the given function f exist or not, and if both do, whether the two-sided limit exists. Do this by analyzing the movie produced by the command twosidelimit. Print out the last frame of the movie and record your assessments of the limits.

3. $f(x) = \begin{cases} 5 - x^2 & \text{if } x < 2 \\ 1 + x & \text{if } x \geq 2 \end{cases}$, at $a = 2$.

4. $f(x) = \begin{cases} 5 - x^2 & \text{if } x < 2 \\ -1 + x & \text{if } x \geq 2 \end{cases}$, at $a = 2$

5. $f(x) = \begin{cases} \sin(\pi x/2) & \text{if } x < 1 \\ 2 - x & \text{if } x \geq 1 \end{cases}$, at $a = 1$

6. $f(x) = \begin{cases} \sin(\pi x/2) & \text{if } x < 1 \\ \cos(\pi x/2) & \text{if } x \geq 1 \end{cases}$, at $a = 1$

7. $f(x) = \begin{cases} \tan(\pi x/2) & \text{if } x < 1 \\ 1 + x & \text{if } x \geq 1 \end{cases}$, at $a = 1$

8. $f(x) = \begin{cases} 1/x & \text{if } x < 0 \\ x & \text{if } x \geq 0 \end{cases}$, at $a = 0$

Using rightlimit to Find One-sided Limits

The functions in this set of exercises are not defined for $x \leq 0$. For each of these, investigate whether the one-sided limit $\lim\limits_{x \to 0^+} f(x)$ exists or not. Do this by analyzing the movie produced by the command rightlimit. Print out the last frame of the movie and record your assessments of the limits.

9. $\lim\limits_{x \to 0^+} x^{\sin x}$

10. $\lim\limits_{x \to 0^+} x^{1 - \cos x}$

11. $\lim\limits_{x \to 0^+} (\sin 3x)^{\sin 2x}$

12. $\lim\limits_{x \to 0^+} (\sin 3x)^{1 - \cos 4x}$

13. $\lim\limits_{x \to 0^+} x^{x \sin(x^{-1})}$

14. $\lim\limits_{x \to 0^+} x^{x \cos(x^{-1})}$

15. $\lim\limits_{x \to 0^+} [x - x \cos(x^{-1})]^x$

16. $\lim\limits_{x \to 0^+} [x - x \sin(x^{-1})]^x$

In Exercises 17–27 find the one-sided and two sided limits of the function at the specified value a. Sketch, by hand, the graph of the function on an interval about a.

17. $f(x) = \begin{cases} x^2 & \text{if } x < 1 \\ 2 - x & \text{if } x \geq 1 \end{cases}$, at $a = 1$

18. $f(x) = \begin{cases} 1/x & \text{if } x < 1 \\ x & \text{if } x \geq 1 \end{cases}$, at $a = 1$

19. $f(x) = \begin{cases} 2 - x^2 & \text{if } x < 1 \\ x - 2 & \text{if } x \geq 1 \end{cases}$, at $a = 1$

20. $f(x) = \begin{cases} 1/x & \text{if } x < 1 \\ x - 1 & \text{if } x \geq 1 \end{cases}$, at $a = 1$

21. $f(x) = \begin{cases} (x + 1)^2 + 1 & \text{if } x < 0 \\ 4 - x^2 & \text{if } x \geq 0 \end{cases}$, at $a = 1$

22. $f(x) = \begin{cases} 1 + x^3 & \text{if } x < 1 \\ 3 - \sqrt{x} & \text{if } x \geq 1 \end{cases}$, at $a = 1$

23. $f(x) = \begin{cases} x^3 & \text{if } x < 1 \\ 2 - \sqrt{x} & \text{if } x \geq 1 \end{cases}$, at $a = 1$

24. $f(x) = \begin{cases} 1 + x^3 & \text{if } x < 1 \\ 2 - x^3 & \text{if } x \geq 1 \end{cases}$, at $a = 1$

25. $f(x) = \begin{cases} x^3 & \text{if } x < 1 \\ 1 - x^3 & \text{if } x \geq 1 \end{cases}$, at $a = 1$

26. $g(x) = |x - 2| + 1$, at $a = 2$

27. $g(x) = |4 - x^2|$, at $a = 2$

Calculus Concepts & Computation

1.7 Continuous Functions

```
> with(dplot_tools,dplot);
```
$$[dplot]$$

In our study of calculus we will encounter a great variety functions with many different and important properties that make them useful in science, engineering, and just about every field of human endeavor. One distinguished property that a function can have is *continuity*, which roughly means that the functional values $y=f(x)$ of the function flow continuously from one value to the next without any abrupt changes, or breaks. In terms of graphs, a *continuous* function is one whose graph, on any interval in its domain, consists of one piece. If there is a break in the graph, the function is *discontinuous*. Figure 1.7.1 illustrates this concept.

Many of the functions we work with in mathematics, such as polynomial, rational, trigonometric, exponential, and logarithmic functions, are continuous function on their domains. However, discontinuous functions are also prevalent, important, and occur in diverse fields, such as physics, medical technology, and financial analysis. So, it is essential that we develop a better understanding of the notion of continuity. In this section we will use what we have learned about limits to *define* what is meant by a continuous function, and then study this concept in greater detail.

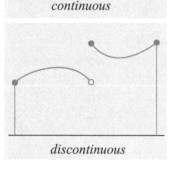

Figure 1.7.1: *A continuous function has no breaks in its graph on its domain.*

Motivating Examples

Before defining what is meant by continuity of a function, we first look at some examples that will help motivate the definition.

Example 1.7.1 (A Piecewise-Defined Function)

Consider the piecewise-defined function

$$f(x) = \begin{cases} 2x & x < 3 \\ -(x-3)^2 - 1 & x \geq 3 \end{cases}$$

A quick sketch, by hand, of this function on the interval $[0,6]$ reveals that the graph has a break in it at $x = 3$.

If you were drawing this graph by hand from left to right on the interval $[0,6]$, tracing it out as you go, you would have to pick up your pencil at $x = 3$ and move it down to trace out the curved portion beneath the interval $[3,6]$. In other words, you could not continuously draw the graph of f on any interval containing 3. So, you might say that the function f is not continuous at $x = 3$. We are going to make this informal notion of continuity more precise below, and in order to do this we use limits. If we think about the behavior of this function near the value 3 in terms of limits, we notice that there is a break in the graph because $\lim_{x \to 3^-} f(x) \neq \lim_{x \to 3^+} f(x)$. Thus, the two-sided limit does not exist at $x = 3$.

Whenever the one-sided limits exist and are different, there is a break in the graph, and the function has a discontinuity at the point. In this example, there is a discontinuity at $x = 3$. This is often called a *jump discontinuity*, since as you trace the graph from left to right, you must jump from the y-value 6 down to the y-value -1 as you pass through $x = 3$. If you do a dynamic plot of this function using the dplot command you will see this very clearly. Here is the code for this:

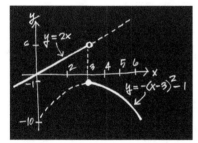

Figure 1.7.2: *A sketch of*
$$f(x) = \begin{cases} 2x & x < 3 \\ -(x-3)^2 - 1 & x \geq 3 \end{cases}$$
on the interval $[0,6]$

```
> with(dplot_tools);
```
$$[dplot, dplot2, dplotinverse, plotinverse, runrise, tanplot]$$

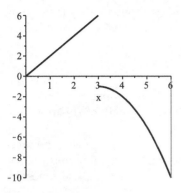

Figure 1.7.3: *The last frame in the dynamic plot.*

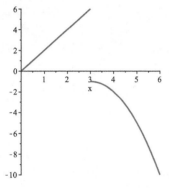

Figure: *A true graph of f.*

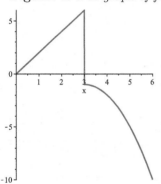

Figure: *The graph of f without* `discont=true`.

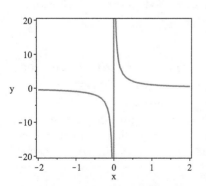

Figure 1.7.4: *The last frame in the dynamic plot of* $f(x) = \frac{1}{x}$

```
>  f:=proc(x)
>  if x<3 then 2*x else -(x-3)^2-1 end if
>  end proc:

>  dplot(f,0,6,25,1);
```

Figure 1.7.3 displays the last frame in the animation created by `dplot`. The animation clearly shows the jump in the y-values that occurs at $x = 3$.

NOTE: The `dplot` command can have a 5th argument,

$$\text{dplot(f,a,b,N,discont)}$$

which we've set to 1 here. This is so the breaks in the graph will show during the animation.

Generally when plotting, Maple just connects the points it calculates with straight lines. So any break in the graph gets filled in with a vertical line. In mathematics, this is *not* actually part of the graph. So the graph has a break in it, even though Maple does not show it.

To have Maple take account of the discontinuities (breaks in the graph) and not put in vertical lines, just use the option: `discont=true` (the default value is `false`) in its `plot` command. That's what our `dplot` procedure does when the 5th argument is 1 (instead of 0).

Thus, to have Maple plot the (mathematical) graph of this function f we can use the following command:.

```
>  plot('f(x)',x=0..6,discont=true,color=blue,thickness=2);
```

On the other-hand if we do not ask Maple to look for discontinuities, we will get the picture shown in the 3rd margin picture.

```
plot('f(x)',x=0..6,color=blue,thickness=2);
```

Note here that Maple's plotting routine, in this case, will put in the vertical line segment connecting the point $(3, 6)$ to the point $(3, -1)$ in the figure. You know this can't be part of the graph of the function, since by the *vertical line test*, each vertical line intersects the graph in at most one point. You can think of the vertical line as indicating that a jump discontinuity occurs at $x = 3$.

Example 1.7.2 (Discontinuities at Vertical Asymptotes)

The function $f(x) = \frac{1}{x}$, is a standard example of a function with a vertical asymptote, in this case at $x = 0$. The domain D for f is all real numbers other than 0 (which is where the expression $1/x$ is not defined). How then could we think of continuity or discontinuity of this function on an interval such as $[-2, 2]$, which contains 0? Suppose we do a dynamic plot of f on this interval as follows.

```
>f:=x->1/x;
```

$$f := x \mapsto \frac{1}{x}$$

```
>  dplot(f,-2,2,25,0,-20,20);
```

This produces a movie with 25 frames in it and the 5th argument to `dplot` is set to 0 so that Maple will not search for discontinuities. Note that because of the vertical asymptote at $x = 0$, we have included $-20, 20$ as the last two arguments in the `dplot` command. This restricts the y-values to the range $y = -20$ to $y = 20$.

In the above animation you should change the axis style to boxed, since the y-axis obscures what is going on at $x = 0$. Then when viewing the movie you will see the graph coming in from the left and appearing to go down to $-\infty$ as x approaches 0. Then the graph appears to jump up to ∞ as x passes through 0, before coming back down asymptotically toward the x-axis. See Figure 1.7.4.

Again, as you can see from Figure 1.7.4, Maple attempts to connect the two portions of the graph by a vertical line.

A more precise description of the behavior of the function near $x = 0$ is accomplished by taking one-sided limits. In the next section we will extend the notion of limits to allow for y-values increasing or decreasing without bounds (i.e., going toward $-\infty$ and ∞), and so in this case we will express this behavior by writing

$$\lim_{x \to 0^-} \frac{1}{x} = -\infty, \qquad \lim_{x \to 0^+} \frac{1}{x} = \infty.$$

Figuratively speaking, we say that the function has an *infinite jump discontinuity* at $x = 0$. Of course, the point $x = 0$ is not in the domain of this function, and that is the principal reason it is not continuous there.

This phenomenon of infinite jump discontinuities is synonymous with the presence of vertical asymptotes. For example, the well-known tangent function $f(x) = \tan x$, has 2 infinite jump discontinuities in the interval $[0, 2\pi]$, as the following dynamic plot clearly shows.

```
> f:=x->tan(x);
                                  f := tan
> dplot(f,0,2*Pi,25,0,-20,20);
```

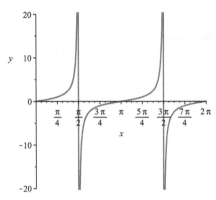

Figure 1.7.5: *The tangent function and 2 of its infinite jump discontinuities.*

The last frame of this movie is displayed in Figure 1.7.5.

The definition of continuity below will be such that $f(x) = \tan x$ is *continuous on its domain*, but is *discontinuous* on intervals such as $[0, 3\pi]$ which contains values of x where $\tan x$ is not defined.

Example 1.7.3 (A Piecewise-Defined Function)

Problem: Sketch, by hand, the graph of

$$f(x) = \begin{cases} -1 & x < -1 \\ (x+1)^2 - 2 & -1 \le x < 2 \\ 3 & x = 2 \\ 9 - x & x > 2 \end{cases}$$

on the interval $[-2, 3]$ and identify the points of discontinuity in the graph of f.

Solution: This is just another piecewise-defined function, and we can easily sketch it to get Figure 1.7.6.

We see that this function is not continuous at $x = -1$ nor $x = 2$. But this is so for different reasons.

At $x = -1$, we see from the graph that

$$\lim_{x \to -1^-} f(x) = -1 \quad \text{and} \quad \lim_{x \to -1^+} f(x) = -2$$

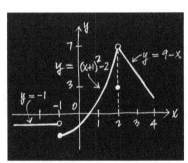

Figure 1.7.6: *A piecewise-defined function with four pieces to its graph.*

and so $\lim_{x \to -1^-} f(x) \neq \lim_{x \to -1^+} f(x)$, indicating the break in the graph (i.e., the jump discontinuity) However, at $x = 2$ we see that the one-sided limits have the same value

$$\lim_{x \to -2^-} f(x) = 7 = \lim_{x \to -2^-} f(x)$$

and so the two-sided limit at $x = 2$ exists with $\lim_{x \to 2} f(x) = 7$. However, the function *value* at $x = 2$ is not equal to 7. Indeed, $f(2) = 3$, from the very definition of f. As you can see from the figure, this creates a *hole* in the graph at $x = 2$, and this is another type of discontinuity. Thinking dynamically, as x approaches 2 from the left the y-values approach 7, but just as x reaches 2 the y-value jumps down to value 3, before immediately jumping back to value 7 and continuing continuously thereafter on its way.

Continuity and Its Consequences

With the motivating examples above as a guide, we now put forth an exact definition of continuity. It appears that for a function to be continuous at $x = a$, it must be defined at a, the two-sided limit at a must exist, and this limit must be equal to the function value at a.

DEFINITION 1.7.1 (Continuity at a Point)

A function f is called continuous at $x=a$ when

      (i) $f(a)$ is defined, and

      (ii) $\lim\limits_{x \to a} f(x)$ exists, and

      (iii) $\lim\limits_{x \to a} f(x) = f(a)$

If either (i), (ii), or (iii) is not true, then f is said to be discontinuous at $x=a$

The definition gives us three parts to check when verifying continuity of a function *at a point*. Note that parts (*i*) and (*ii*) are implicit in part (*iii*), so the crux of the matter is contained in part (*iii*), properly interpreted.

We need to broaden this definition to include continuity of a function *on an interval* and *on more general sets*.

First, we will say that a function f is continuous on an open interval if it is continuous at each point in that interval. Further, we will say that f is continuous on the non-open intervals (*i*) $[c, d)$, or (*ii*) $(c, d]$, or (*iii*) $[c, d]$, if it is continuous on the open interval (c, d), it is defined at the endpoint c, or d, or both c and d, and

Basic Continuous Functions
Polynomial Functions
$p(x) = a_0 + a_1 x + a_2 x + \cdots + a_n x^n$
Rational Functions
$r(x) = \dfrac{p(x)}{q(x)}$
Power Functions
$f(x) = x^r$
Trig Functions
$\sin x \quad \cos x \quad \tan x$
$\cot x \quad \sec x \quad \csc x$
Exponential and Log Functions
$e^x, \ a^x, \ \ln x, \ \log_a x$

Table 1.7.1

(i) For $[c, d)$: $\lim\limits_{x \to c^+} f(x) = f(c)$

(ii) For $(c, d]$: $\lim\limits_{x \to d^-} f(x) = f(d)$

(iii) For $[c, d]$: $\lim\limits_{x \to c^+} f(x) = f(c)$ and $\lim\limits_{x \to d^-} f(x) = f(d)$

Finally, we will say f is continuous on a set D, if it is continuous on each subinterval contained in D. (It is assumed that D is such that each of its points is contained in a nondegenerate interval which itself is contained in D.)

Usually the functions that we encounter are continuous at most of the points in the intervals under consideration and have only a few points of discontinuity. This is the case for the piecewise-defined functions that we have discussed.

Additionally, all the basic functions in mathematics that we have been dealing with are continuous *on their domains D*. Table 1.7.1 gives a list of some of these basic functions.

It actually takes some work to *prove* that these basic functions are continuous on their domains, but here we will take this as a given.

Note that a function f that is continuous on its domain D may not be continuous on some intervals we may wish to consider. We saw this in Example 1.7.2: The function $f(x) = \tan x$ is continuous on its domain D (which consists of all real numbers except $\pm (2k - 1)(\pi/2)$, $k = 1, 2, 3, \dots$). However, $\tan x$ is not continuous on, say, the interval $[0, 2\pi]$. This is because the interval $[0, 2\pi]$ contains 2 numbers, $\pi/2, 3\pi/2$, not in the domain of $\tan x$, and so, by definition it can not be continuous there.

Given that the basic functions in Table 1.7.1 are continuous on their domains, we can extend our list of continuous functions by combining the basic ones in various ways. Specifically the sum, difference, and product of continuous functions, defined on the same interval I, gives a new continuous function on I. Likewise the quotient of continuous functions is continuous on the subset of I obtained by excluding the points where the denominator is zero. For suitably more general sets D than intervals I, these results are also true, as the following theorem records.

THEOREM 1.7.1 (Algebraic Combinations of Continuous Functions)

Suppose that f and g are continuous on a set D. Then,

    (i) $(f \pm g)$ *is continuous on D*

    (ii) $(f \cdot g)$ *is continuous on D*

    (iii) $\dfrac{f}{g}$ *is continuous on $D' = \{x \in D \mid g(x) \neq 0\}$*

We will not prove this result, but rather just use it where needed. You should realize that Theorem 1.7.1 is actually employed to prove that many of the basic functions in Table 1.7.1 are continuous on their domains. Once we know the basic functions are continuous on their domains, then we can use Theorem 1.7.1 to show that more complicated functions are continuous. The following example illustrates what we mean.

Example 1.7.4 (Continuity and Evaluation of Limits)

Problem: Show that the function $h(x) = e^x \cos x$ is continuous and then evaluate $\lim_{x \to 2} e^x \cos x$.

Solution: The function h is the product of two continuous functions: $f(x) = e^x$, $g(x) = \cos x$, and so is continuous. It is continuous everywhere since f and g are. Limits of continuous functions at points where they are continuous are easy to compute. Just evaluate the function at the point. In this case, h is continuous everywhere, so in particular $x = 2$. Hence:

$$\lim_{x \to 2} e^x \cos x = e^2 \cos 2 \approx 3.075.$$

Another fundamental consequence of continuity is the preservation of limits, i.e., a continuous function transforms limits into new limits. The following theorem states this more specifically.

THEOREM 1.7.2

Suppose that $\lim_{x \to a} g(x) = L$ *and that f is continuous at L. Then,*

$$\lim_{x \to a} (f(g(x)) = f(\lim_{x \to a} g(x)) = f(L)$$

Note that the function g need *not* be continuous at a. Also, with similar hypotheses the theorem holds for one-sided limits $x \to a^+$ and $x \to a^-$, as well.

Example 1.7.5 (Using Continuity to Evaluate a Limit)

Problem: Evaluate $\lim_{x \to 0^+} \cos(x \ln x)$.

Solution: Here $f(x) = \cos x$ and $g(x) = x \ln x$. The cosine function is continuous everywhere (its domain is all real numbers), but g is not continuous at $x = 0$, since it is not defined there. However, by graphical or numerical methods, you can readily discern that

$$\lim_{x \to 0^+} x \ln x = 0.$$

Hence, by Theorem 1.7.2, we can say

$$\lim_{x \to 0^+} \cos(x \ln x) = \cos\left(\lim_{x \to 0^+} x \ln x\right) = \cos(0) = 1.$$

A direct consequence of Theorem 1.7.2, is that the composition of continuous functions is continuous, as the following corollary states.

COROLLARY 1.7.1 (Composition of Continuous Functions)

If f is continuous on D and g is continuous on E, with $g(E) \subseteq D$, then the composite

$$f \circ g$$

is continuous on E

This corollary is most useful in extending the basic collection of continuous functions to a much wider collection of continuous functions and in evaluating limits of these more complicated functions.

Example 1.7.6

Problem: Calculate the values of: (a) $\lim_{x \to 1} \cos(x^2)$ (b) $\lim_{x \to \pi} e^{\tan x}$.

Solution: The functions $f(x) = \cos x$ and $g(x) = x^2$ are continuous everywhere $(D = \mathbb{R})$ and so $(f \circ g)(x) = \cos(x^2)$ is continuous everywhere. Thus,

$$\lim_{x \to 1} \cos(x^2) = \cos(1) \approx 0.54$$

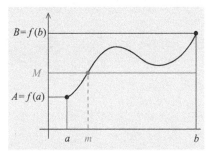

Figure 1.7.7: *Illustration of the intermediate-value theorem.*

In Part (b): $f(x) = e^x$ is continuous everywhere $(D = \mathbb{R})$, but $g(x) = \tan x$ is continuous only where $\cos x \neq 0$, namely

$$E = \{x \mid \cos x \neq 0\}.$$

So the tangent function is continuous at $x = \pi$ and we have that $\lim_{x \to \pi} \tan x = \tan(\pi) = 0$. By the corollary, $(f \circ g)(x) = e^{\tan x}$ is continuous at $x = \pi$ and we get

$$\lim_{x \to \pi} e^{\tan x} = e^{\tan(\pi)} = e^0 = 1.$$

One further consequence of continuity, one that is essential in advanced mathematics, is the intermediate-value theorem.

THEOREM 1.7.3 (The Intermediate Value Theorem)

Suppose that f is a continuous function on a closed interval [a,b] and that M is a number between f(a) and f(b). Then there exists at least one number m in the open interval (a,b) such that

$$f(m) = M$$

An analytic proof of this theorem is too advanced to present here, but the validity of the theorem is easily motivated geometrically. In terms of graphs, the theorem says that the graph of the curve $y = f(x)$ and the graph of the horizontal line $y = M$ must intersect (at least once, maybe more). See Figure 1.7.7 above.

Observe that the intuitive notion of f being continuous (*there are no breaks in the graph of f*), makes this result very plausible. You cannot move along the graph from point to point without crossing the horizontal line through M. With breaks in the graph, there could be many horizontal lines that do not intersect it. Another way to interpret the content of the intermediate-value theorem is algebraically. It guarantees, under the stated hypotheses, that there exists at least one solution of the equation

$$f(x) = M,$$

in the interval (a, b). This is intuitively reasoned by saying that you cannot go *continuously* from A to B along the graph of f without assuming the intermediate-value M at some point x between a and b. Note that the theorem is existential, only stating the existence of a solution, but not giving any method for finding one.

Example 1.7.7 (Illustration of The Intermediate-Value Theorem)

Problem: Apply the intermediate-value theorem to the function

$$f(x) = 2 + 3x^2 - x^3,$$

on the intervals $[0, 2]$ and $[-1, 3]$ with $M = 4$ as the intermediate-value. In each case:

(a) Illustrate the result geometrically by plotting the function f on the respective intervals along with the horizontal line through the intermediate value 4, and

(b) Use `dplot` to find, by using with the cursor probe, the approximate solutions $f(x) = 4$, and then use algebra to find the exact solutions.

Solution: First for the interval $[0, 2]$, we use the `dplot` command to plot f dynamically. Then we can combine the output of this command with a plot of the horizontal line through 4 as follows.

```
> f:=x->2+3*x^2-x^3;
```
$$f := x \mapsto 2 + 3x^2 - x^3$$
```
> p1:=dplot(f,0,2,25):
> p2:=plot(4,x=0..2):
> display({p1,p2});
```

The last frame of this movie is shown in the following Figure 1.7.8.

From the movie it appears that f achieves the intermediate-value $M = 4$ at $x = 1$. That is, $f(1) = 4$. This is readily verified from looking at the formula for f:

$$f(x) = 2 + 3x^2 - x^3$$

Next, we consider the same problem with intermediate value $M = 4$, but with a larger interval $[-1, 3]$. The following code produces a movie of this situation

```
> p1:=dplot(f,-1,3,25):
> p2:=plot(4,x=-1..3):
> display({p1,p2});
```

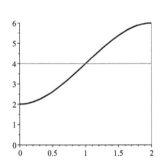

Figure 1.7.8: *The last frame in a movie illustrating the intermediate-value theorem.*

Now we see that the intermediate-value 4 is assumed at three places in the interval: at $x = 1$, as before, at $x = -0.74$, and at $x = 2.73$. These latter two values were obtained by using the cursor probe on the figure in the last frame of the movie. They are only approximate, since if we check them in Maple, we get:

```
> f(-.74),f(2.73);
```
$$4.048024, \ 4.012283$$

These are close to 4, but not exactly 4. To find the exact values of x for which $f(x) = 4$, we need to solve the cubic equation

$$2 + 3x^2 - x^3 = 4.$$

Rearranging gives

$$x^3 - 3x^2 + 2 = 0,$$

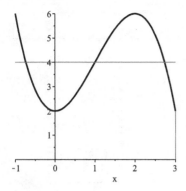

Figure 1.7.9: *The last frame in a movie illustrating IVT .*

and we already know that $x = 1$ is one root of this. To find the other root, use long division to divide $x^3 - 3x^2 + 2$ by $x - 1$ to get a quotient of $x^2 - 2x - 2$. Thus, the above equation factors as

$$x^3 - 3x^2 + 2 = (x - 1)\left(x^2 - 2x - 2\right).$$

The roots of the quadratic part, $x^2 - 2x - 2 = 0$, are $x = 1 \pm \sqrt{3}$. These, then, are the exact values for the other two places where $f(x) = 4$. The decimal approximations to these exact values are

```
> evalf(1-sqrt(3)),evalf(1+sqrt(3));
```
$$-0.732050808, 2.732050808$$

and these are seen to be better than the approximate values we found above by using the cursor probe on the graph.

Example 1.7.8 (Population Models) Many populations of fish, such as halibut in the Northern Pacific or catfish in a Mississippi pond have their growth modeled by what is called a *logistic curve*. Suppose, for example, a certain commercial catfish pond has has its fish population modeled by

$$p(t) = \frac{4000}{1 + 3e^{-.71t}},$$

where $p(t)$ is he population at time t (measured in in months). Figure 1.7.10 shows a plot of how the number of catfish in the pond grows over the year (12 months) assuming the pond was initially stocked with 1000 catfish. As you can see, there appears to be a limiting number of 4000 catfish in the pond as the year draws to an end (a horizontal asymptote in the graph).

At some point during the 12 months, the growers wish to harvest the catfish, say at the time when there are 3000 catfish. At this time they remove 2000 catfish to take to market and leave 1000 in the pond to resume the same growth shown in the logistic curve. To determine the time when the harvesting should occur the growers must find the time t when the function p assumes the intermediate value 3000. (Note that the function p is continuous on the interval $[0, 12]$.) Thus, they must solve $p(t) = 3000$ for t, This equation is

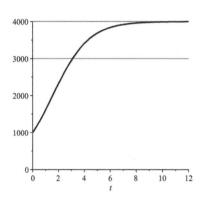

Figure 1.7.9: *The graph of* $p(t) = \frac{4000}{1+3e^{-.71t}}$.

$$\frac{4000}{1 + 3e^{-.71t}} = 3000$$

Equivalently

$$4000 = 3000 + 9000e^{-0.71t}.$$

which gives

$$e^{-0.71t} = \frac{4000 - 3000}{9000} = \frac{1}{9}.$$

Taking the logarithm of both sides and using $\ln(e^A) = A$ yields

$$-0.71t = \ln\left(\frac{1}{9}\right) = \ln 1 - \ln 9 = -\ln 9.$$

Thus,

$$t = \frac{\ln 9}{0.71} \approx 3.095 \text{ months}$$

This gives the growers a schedule to harvest 2000 catfish from the pond every 3 months.

Exercises: 1.7 (Continuous Functions)

```
> with(dplot_tools,dplot);
                    [dplot]
```

Determining Points of Discontinuity from a Given Graph

The figures below show a plots of functions f on the certain intervals. Determine all points of discontinuity of f and state which of the three criteria (i), (ii), (iii) in Definition 1.7.1 fail.

1.

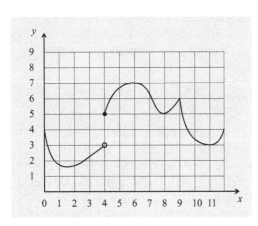

2.

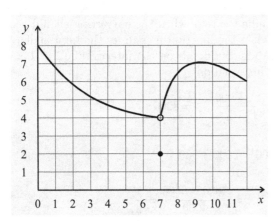

3.

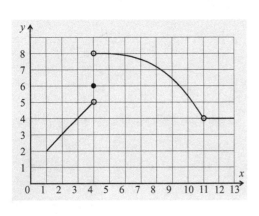

4.

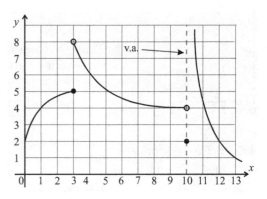

Using `dplot` to Identify Points of Discontinuity

In Exercises 5–12 use `dplot` to create a dynamic plot of the function and use this to identify the points of discontinuity of the function. For each point of discontinuity say which of the criteria (i), (ii), (iii) of Definition 1.7.1 fail. Print out the last frame in the movie and annotate it, labeling the points of discontinuity.

5. $f(x) = \begin{cases} 1 - x & \text{if } x \le 1 \\ 1 + \sqrt{x - 1} & \text{if } 1 < x \le 5 \\ 1 & \text{if } x > 5 \end{cases}$

CODE for 5 (Revise and use for 6–10)
```
> f:=proc(x)
> if x<=1 then 1-x
> elif x<=5 then 1+sqrt(x-1)
> else 1  end if;
> end proc:
> dplot(f,-1,7,40,1);
```

6. $f(x) = \begin{cases} x & \text{if } x \le 1 \\ 2 + \sqrt{x - 1} & \text{if } 1 < x \le 5 \\ -2x + 14 & \text{if } x > 5 \end{cases}$

7. $f(x) = \begin{cases} 4\cos x & \text{if } x \le 0 \\ 4\sin(1/x) & \text{if } 0 < x \le 2/\pi \\ 4 & \text{if } x > 2/\pi \end{cases}$

8. $f(x) = \begin{cases} 4 + \sin x & \text{if } x \le 0 \\ -4\cos(1/x) & \text{if } 0 < x \le 1/\pi \\ 4 & \text{if } x > 1/\pi \end{cases}$

9. $f(x) = \begin{cases} -3x & \text{if } x \le 0 \\ 1/x & \text{if } 0 < x \le 2 \\ 4 & \text{if } x > 2/\pi \end{cases}$

10. $f(x) = \begin{cases} 2x & \text{if } x \le 0 \\ -1/x & \text{if } 0 < x \le 2 \\ 1 & \text{if } x > 2 \end{cases}$

11. $f(x) = \begin{cases} 1 + x & \text{if } x < 0 \\ 2 - x^2 & \text{if } 0 \le x < 1 \\ 0 & \text{if } x = 1 \\ x & \text{if } x > 1 \end{cases}$

CODE for 11 (Revise and use for 12)

```
> f:=proc(x)
> if x<=0 then 1+x
> elif x<1 then 2-x^2
> elif x=1 then 0
> else x  end if;
> end proc:
> dplot(f,-2,2,40,1);
```

12. $f(x) = \begin{cases} 1-x & \text{if } x < 0 \\ x^2 & \text{if } 0 \le x < 1 \\ 0 & \text{if } x = 1 \\ 2-x & \text{if } x > 1 \end{cases}$

Determining Discontinuities by Sketching

In problems 13–26 determine all discontinuities of the function and say why the discontinuity occurs. Sketch, by hand, a graph of the function.

13. $g(x) = \dfrac{x - x^2}{|x|}$

14. $g(x) = \begin{cases} \frac{x^2 - x^3}{|x|} & \text{if } x \ne 0 \\ 0 & \text{if } x = 0 \end{cases}$

15. $g(x) = \dfrac{|x-1|}{|x|}$

16. $g(x) = \dfrac{|x-2|}{|x|}$

17. $f(x) = \begin{cases} x & \text{if } x \le 1 \\ 3-x & \text{if } 1 < x < 2 \\ \sqrt{x-2} & \text{if } x \ge 2 \end{cases}$

18. $f(x) = \begin{cases} -x & \text{if } x \le 0 \\ 1+x^2 & \text{if } 0 < x \le 1 \\ 2-x & \text{if } x \ge 1 \end{cases}$

19. $f(x) = \begin{cases} 2x & \text{if } x \le 1 \\ (x-2)^2 + 1 & \text{if } 1 < x < 3 \\ x-3 & \text{if } x \ge 3 \end{cases}$

20. $f(x) = \begin{cases} 1-x & \text{if } x \le 1 \\ -(x-2)^2 + 1 & \text{if } 1 < x < 3 \\ x-4 & \text{if } x \ge 3 \end{cases}$

21. $f(x) = \begin{cases} x^2 & \text{if } x < 1 \\ 2 & \text{if } x = 1 \\ 1/x & \text{if } 1 < x < 2 \\ x-3 & \text{if } x \ge 2 \end{cases}$

22. $f(x) = \begin{cases} 4-x^2 & \text{if } x < 1 \\ 2 & \text{if } x = 1 \\ 3/x & \text{if } 1 < x < 2 \\ x-4 & \text{if } x \ge 2 \end{cases}$

23. $f(x) = \begin{cases} -x & \text{if } x \le 0 \\ 1+\sin x & \text{if } 0 < x < 3\pi/2 \\ 0 & \text{if } x \ge 3\pi/2 \end{cases}$

24. $f(x) = \begin{cases} -x & \text{if } x \le 0 \\ 1+\cos x & \text{if } 0 < x < \pi \\ 0 & \text{if } x \ge \pi \end{cases}$

25. $f(x) = \begin{cases} 4-x^2 & \text{if } x < 2 \\ 2 & \text{if } x = 2 \\ -x+4 & \text{if } 2 < x < 4 \\ 2 & \text{if } x = 4 \\ \sqrt{x-4} & \text{if } x > 4 \end{cases}$

26. $f(x) = \begin{cases} x^2 & \text{if } x < 2 \\ 2 & \text{if } x = 2 \\ x-4 & \text{if } 2 < x < 4 \\ 3 & \text{if } x = 4 \\ -\sqrt{x-4} & \text{if } x > 4 \end{cases}$

In Exercises 27–44 for the given limit: $\lim\limits_{x \to a} f(x)$, use the Table of Basic Continuous Functions, the theorems in this sections and the limit laws to find the following limits.

27. $\lim\limits_{x \to 1} (x^2 + 1) \ln x$

28. $\lim\limits_{x \to 1} (x^2 + 1) \ln(x+2)$

29. $\lim\limits_{x \to 0} \ln(x^2 + 1)$

30. $\lim\limits_{x \to 0} \ln(x^4 + 2)$

31. $\lim\limits_{x \to \pi} x^2 \cos x)$

32. $\lim\limits_{x \to 3\pi/2} x^2 \sin x$

33. $\lim\limits_{x \to 0} \dfrac{\cos x}{e^x}$

34. $\lim\limits_{x \to \pi/2} \dfrac{\sin x}{e^{2x}}$

35. $\lim\limits_{x \to 0} \dfrac{e^x - e^{-x}}{e^x + e^{-x}}$

36. $\lim\limits_{x \to 0} \dfrac{2^x - 2^{-x}}{2^x + 2^{-x}}$

37. $\lim\limits_{x \to 0} \sin\left(\dfrac{\sin x}{x}\right)$

38. $\lim\limits_{x \to 0} \cos\left(\dfrac{\sin x}{x}\right)$

39. $\lim\limits_{x \to \pi} e^{\cos x}$

40. $\lim\limits_{x \to 3\pi/2} e^{-\sin x)}$

41. $\lim\limits_{x \to 0} e^{(x^x)}$

42. $\lim\limits_{x \to 0} e^{-(x^x)}$

43. $\lim\limits_{x \to 1} \cos(x^2 + pix - 1)$

44. $\lim\limits_{x \to 1} \sin(x^2 + 3\pi x/2 - 1)$

Illustrations of the Intermediate-Value Theorem

In Exercises 45–50, for the given continuous function f on the closed interval $[a, b]$, find all values x for which f assumes the given intermediate value M. Do this two ways: (1) First do a dynamic plot of the function on the interval, including the horizontal line $y = M$. Use the cursor probe to locate the approximate values x in the interval where $f(x) = M$. (2) Then use algebra to solve the equation $f(x) = M$ exactly.

45. $f(x) = x^3 + 4x^2 + 2x$ on the interval $[-4, 1]$. Intermediate value $M = 3$.

46. $f(x) = x^4 - x^3 - 6x + 4$ on the interval $[-2.5, 3.5]$. Intermediate value $M = -2$.

47. $f(x) = e^{2-x-x^2}$ on the interval $[-3, 2]$. Intermediate value $M = 1$.

48. $f(x) = e^{2+x-x^2}$ on the interval $[-2, 3]$. Intermediate value $M = 1$.

49. $f(x) = \ln(x^2 + 1)$ on the interval $[-2, 2]$. Intermediate value $M = 1$.

50. $f(x) = \ln(x^2 + 1)$ on the interval $[-2, 2]$. Intermediate value $M = 1$.

Calculus Concepts & Computation

1.8 Limits Involving Infinity

```
> with(dplot_tools,dplot);
```
$$[dplot]$$

In the previous sections we have learned what it means to say that for a given function f and a given number a, the limit

$$\lim_{x \to a} f(x) = L.$$

exists and has value L. Intuitively this means that there is real number L which the values $f(x)$ of the function approach as x approaches a. Similar meaning was given to one-sided limits

$$\lim_{x \to a^-} f(x) = L \qquad \lim_{x \to a^+} f(x) = L.$$

The existence of such limiting values tells us something about the behavior of f near a (where it may not even be defined) and conveys both numerical and geometrical information about the function f.

In this section, we will extend the limit concept in two ways. First, we will relax the requirement that the limiting value L be a real number, allowing for the situation where the values $f(x)$ increase or decrease without bound (i.e., become infinite) as x approaches a. This significant behavior of f near a indicates the presence of a vertical asymptote (or an infinite jump discontinuity) at $x = a$, and occurs in many physical phenomena.

Secondly, we extend the limit concept to study the "far off" behavior of a function f. Namely, how does f behave far from the origin. For example, if the independent variable x represents the time, then we are asking about the variation of either very long ago in the past or very far in the future. These are limits as $x \to past$ or as $x \to future$.

To handle these two extended notions of limits, we use the symbols $-\infty$ and ∞, which are considered as *extended real numbers*. They are viewed as (non-real) numbers at the extreme ends of the number axes, with $-\infty$ being less than every real number (i.e., $-\infty < x, y$, for every real x, y) and ∞ being greater than every real number (i.e., $\infty > x, y$, for every real x, y). See the margin figure.

Often the extended real number ∞ is denoted by $+\infty$. Based on this notation, the two types of extended limits are expressed as follows. The first type occurs when the values $f(x)$ approach either $+\infty$ or $-\infty$:

$$\lim_{x \to a} f(x) = \pm\infty,$$

and are called *infinite limits*. Note that this type also includes the one-sided limits: $x \to a^-$ and $x \to a^+$.

The second type of extended limit occurs when we allow x to approach either $+\infty$ or $-\infty$:

$$\lim_{x \to \pm\infty} f(x) = L,$$

and are called *limits at infinity*. Note that the limiting "value" L in this second type of limit could possibly be infinite as well: $L = \pm\infty$.

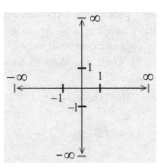

The extended real axes.

Infinite Limits (Vertical Asymptotes)

To help you understand the meaning of the two-sided infinite limits $\lim\limits_{x \to a} f(x) = \pm\infty$ and the one-sided infinite limits $\lim\limits_{x \to a^\pm} f(x) = \pm\infty$, we look an a number of motivating examples. If you know about vertical asymptotes for functions, then you understand that having an infinite limit at a means $x = a$ is a vertical asymptote.

Example 1.8.1 (The Reciprocal Function)

The simplest and most canonical example of a function that becomes infinite, or unbounded, near a point is $f(x) = \frac{1}{x}$. This is called the *reciprocal function*, for the obvious reason that its action on numbers is to take their reciprocals

$$f\left(\frac{3}{2}\right) = \frac{2}{3}, \ f(1) = 1, \ f\left(\frac{1}{2}\right) = 2$$

and so forth. Of course, this function is not defined at $x = 0$ (i.e., there is no reciprocal for 0), but the function's behavior near 0 is easily understood. We saw this behavior when discussing infinite jump discontinuities in Section 1.7. However, in very simple terms, you know from your work with numbers that reciprocals of small positive numbers are large positive numbers—the smaller the number, the larger the reciprocal. Similarly, small negative numbers have reciprocals that are negative, but large in magnitude. See Figure 1.8.1.

We express the behavior in terms of *extended* limits, by writing

$$\lim_{x \to 0^+} \frac{1}{x} = \infty \quad \text{and} \quad \lim_{x \to 0^-} \frac{1}{x} = -\infty$$

Since these one-sided limits are about as far apart as one could imagine, it seems reasonable to say that the two-sided limit does not exist:

$$\lim_{x \to 0} \frac{1}{x} = \text{ does not exist.}$$

So you see that even with an extend notion of the limit, there will still be some limits that do not exist.

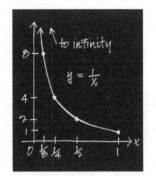

Figure 1.8.1: *Graph of the reciprocal function* $f(x) = \frac{1}{x}$ *on* $[0, 1]$.

Example 1.8.2 (The Inverse Square Law)

Many physical systems involve quantities that become infinite at certain points. One of the most famous examples is the inverse square law of repulsion between two electrons. If the electrons have charges q_1, q_2 respectively, and one charge is located at the origin while the other is located at the point x on the x-axis, then the magnitude f of the force that they exert on each other is given by

$$f(x) = \frac{k}{x^2}.$$

Here $k = q_1 q_2 > 0$ is the product of the charge strengths. This inverse square law has been measured and verified with great exactitude by many different types of experiments.

What happens as the electron located at position x moves toward the electron fixed in place at the origin? The magnitude of their repulsion increases without bound. It can be made as large as we please by taking x to be close to 0, and this is so for x on either side of 0. So we write this as

$$\lim_{x \to 0^+} \frac{k}{x^2} = \infty \quad \text{and} \quad \lim_{x \to 0^-} \frac{k}{x^2} = \infty.$$

Since these one-sided limits exist in the extended sense and have the same value, we say that the two-sided limit exists and has this common value

$$\lim_{x \to 0} \frac{k}{x^2} = \infty.$$

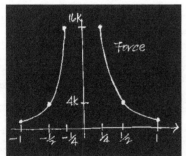

Figure 1.8.2: *The force becomes infinite at the origin.*

See Figure 1.8.2.

The above examples, motivate the following informal definition of infinite limits.

DEFINITION 1.8.1 (Infinite Limits)

If the function values $f(x)$ increase without bound as x approaches a from either side, then we write
$$\lim_{x \to a} f(x) = \infty$$

and say the limit exists in the extended sense and has value ∞.

If the function values $f(x)$ decrease without bound as x approaches a from either side, then we write
$$\lim_{x \to a} f(x) = -\infty$$

and say the limit exists in the extended sense and has value $-\infty$.

Canonical Infinite Limits

For positive numbers p and k:
$$\lim_{x \to 0+} \frac{k}{x^p} = \infty$$

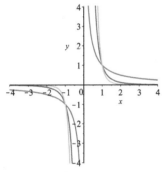

Figure 1.8.3: $f(x) = k/x^p$ *for $p = 1, 3, 5$ (red, blue, green).*

NOTE 1: The definition also applies to one-sided limits, where $x \to a$ is replaced by either $x \to a^+$ or $x \to a^-$, with x approaching a from one-side only. In all cases, left-sided, right-sided, or two-sided, when the limit is either ∞ or $-\infty$, we call the limit an *infinite limit*.

NOTE 2: The existence of a one-sided infinite limit at $x = a$ indicates, by definition, that the line $x = a$ is a *vertical asymptote* (v.a.) for the function.

Reciprocal (Positive) Power Functions

It is easy to see, based on Examples 1.8.1–1.8.2 above for $f(x) = \frac{1}{x}$ and $f(x) = \frac{k}{x^2}$, that reciprocal power functions have infinite limits at $x = 0$ (i.e., the y-axis is a vertical asymptote) for *positive* powers p. See the margin box and Figures 1.8.3 below it.

Note the result is for right-sided limits. Left-sided limits at 0 may not exist for some powers p, because x^p is not defined for negative numbers. For instance, if $p = 1/2$, then $\lim_{x \to 0^-} \frac{1}{\sqrt{x}}$ does not exist, because we cannot take square roots of negative numbers. However, it is easy to see that

$$\lim_{x \to 0^-} \frac{1}{x^{1/3}} = -\infty \quad \text{and} \quad \lim_{x \to 0^-} x^{-6} = \infty \qquad (1.8.1)$$

exist in the extended sense. In general, the left-side limits like this will exist whenever the reciprocal power function is defined for negative numbers. The result will be either ∞ or $-\infty$, and you will have to reason through which of these is the case. For this, note in limits (1.8.1), the denominators both go to zero, but the first one does so through *negative* values and the latter one through *positive* values. You can use the rule of thumb in the margin box to remember this.

In the box the $+0$ indicates that you have a limit where the denominator is going to 0 through positive values, while the -0 indicates an approach to 0 through negative values. All that we have said here about reciprocal positive power functions $f(x) = \frac{k}{x^p}$ applies to their translates: $f(x) = \frac{k}{(x-a)^p}$. Thinking geometrically, you should see that translating the graph also translates the vertical asymptote from $x = 0$ to $x = a$. Thus,

$$\lim_{x \to a^{\pm}} \frac{1}{(x-a)^p} = \pm\infty$$

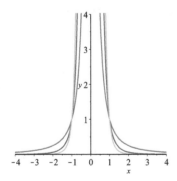

Figure 1.8.4: $f(x) = k/x^p$ *for $p = 2, 4, 6$ (red, blue, green).*

Extended Arithmetic

For any positive real number k:
$$\frac{k}{+0} = +\infty \qquad \frac{k}{-0} = -\infty$$

assuming that $(x-a)^p$ is defined for x near a. Here you always get ∞ when $x \to a^+$, but for the left-sided limit $x \to a^-$, the extended limit can be $\pm\infty$, and so you'll have to figure out which it is.

Example 1.8.3 (Shifted Vertical Asymptotes)

Problem: Evaluate $\lim\limits_{x\to 2^-} \dfrac{x^3}{x-2}$, $\lim\limits_{x\to 2^+} \dfrac{x^3}{x-2}$, $\lim\limits_{x\to 2^-} \dfrac{x^3}{\sqrt{x-2}}$, and $\lim\limits_{x\to 2^+} \dfrac{x^3}{\sqrt{x-2}}$.

Solution: We use the reasoning in the extended real number arithmetic as follows

$$\lim_{x\to 2^-} \frac{x^3}{x-2} = \frac{8}{-0} = -\infty, \qquad \lim_{x\to 2^+} \frac{x^3}{x-2} = \frac{8}{+0} = +\infty$$

$$\lim_{x\to 2^-} \frac{x^3}{\sqrt{x-2}} = \text{ does not exist}, \qquad \lim_{x\to 2^+} \frac{x^3}{\sqrt{x-2}} = \frac{8}{\sqrt{+0}} = \frac{8}{+0} = +\infty$$

The third of these does not exist because $\sqrt{x-2}$ is not defined for $x < 2$. Of course you can always check your work by using the graphical or numerical methods. However, you will generally find the above method quicker, but you must understand it well in order to use it to get correct answers. Figures 1.8.5–1.8.6 are rough sketches showing the behavior of each of these functions near its asymptote $x = 2$;

Example 1.8.4 (Vertical Asymptotes of a Rational Function)

Problem: Find the vertical asymptotes of $f(x) = \dfrac{x^2 + x + 5}{x^2 - x - 2}$ and describe the behavior of f near each asymptote.

Solution: Since this is a rational function we first see if it can be simplified by factoring.

$$f(x) = \frac{x^2 + x + 5}{x^2 - x - 2} = \frac{x^2 + x + 5}{(x-2)(x+1)}.$$

The numerator has no factors in common with the denominator. We see that neither $x = 2$ nor $x = -1$ is in the domain of this function since they make the denominator 0. An evaluation of the one-sided limits of f at each of these values will tell us if there are vertical asymptotes. First, we examine what happens near 2:

$$\lim_{x\to 2^+} \frac{x^2 + x + 5}{(x-2)(x+1)} = \frac{2^2 + 2 + 5}{(+0)(3)} = \frac{11}{+0} = +\infty$$

The reasoning here is that for $x > 2$ the quantity $x - 2$ is positive and goes to 0 through positive values as x approaches 2 from above. This gives an asymptote at $x = 2$, and the function increases without bound as x approaches 2 from the right. It is easy to see that as $x \to 2^-$, we get $f(x) \to \dfrac{11}{-0} = -\infty$, and so the function decreases without bound as x approaches 2 from the left. Similarly we can analyze the behavior of f near -1:

$$\lim_{x\to -1^+} \frac{x^2 + x + 5}{(x-2)(x+1)} = \frac{(-1)^2 + (-1) + 5}{(-3)(+0)} = \frac{5}{-0} = -\infty$$

In a like manner we get, as $x \to -1^-$, that $f(x) \to \dfrac{5}{+0} = +\infty$. Thus, the behavior near this asymptote is the reverse of what it was near the other one. In summary, a quick sketch of the vertical asymptotes and the function's behavior near them is shown in Figure 1.8.7.

Example 1.8.5 (Vertical Asymptotes of Non Rational Functions)

Problem: For the function $f(x) = \dfrac{x^2}{1 - \sin x}$, on the interval $[-2\pi, 2\pi]$, determine all the vertical asymptotes and the function's behavior near each asymptote.

Solution: Generally, a function which is a quotient of two functions will have vertical asymptotes where its denominator is zero and its numerator is nonzero. In this

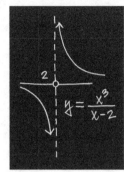

Figure 1.8.5:
The behavior of
$f(x) = \frac{x^3}{x-2}$ *near its vertical asymptote.*

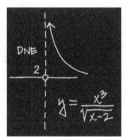

Figure 1.8.6:
The behavior of
$f(x) = \frac{x^3}{\sqrt{x-2}}$ *near its vertical asymptote.*

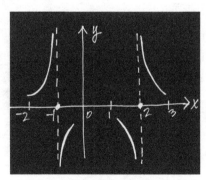

Figure 1.8.7: *The behavior of* $f(x) = \frac{x^2 + x + 5}{x^2 - x - 2}$ *near its two vertical asymptotes.*

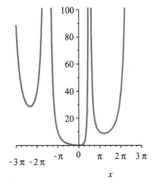

Figure 1.8.8: *Plot of*
$f(x) = \frac{x^2}{1-\sin x}$.

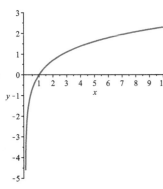

Figure 1.8.9: *Plot of*
$f(x) = \ln x$.

example, $1 - \sin x = 0$ for infinitely many values of x, but the only such values in the interval $[-2\pi, 2\pi]$ are $x = -3\pi/2,\ \pi/2$. The numerator x^2 is not zero for these values of x and so f has vertical asymptotes at these points. If we take limits from each side and use the fact that $1 - \sin x \geq 0$, for all x, we get

$$\lim_{x \to \frac{\pi}{2}\pm} \frac{x^2}{1-\sin x} = \frac{\frac{\pi^2}{4}}{+0} = +\infty, \qquad \lim_{x \to \frac{3\pi}{2}\pm} \frac{x^2}{1-\sin x} = \frac{\frac{9\pi^2}{4}}{+0} = +\infty.$$

Thus, $f(x)$ tends to ∞ from each side of $\frac{\pi}{2}$ and $\frac{3\pi}{2}$. Consequently, the two-sided limits exist at each point and are both ∞. See Figure 1.8.8.

Example 1.8.6 (Vertical Asymptotes in Log-Related Functions) Vertical asymptotes can occur in other types of functions, ones that are *not* quotients of two functions. Here are two examples involving $\ln x$.

Problem: Find the vertical asymptotes for

(a) $f(x) = \ln(x+2)$ (b) $g(x) = \ln(x^2 - 4)$,

and determine the behavior of each function near its asymptotes.

Solution: We must use our basic understanding of $\ln x$ and its graph. The natural logarithmic function is defined only for $x > 0$ and

$$\lim_{x \to 0^+} \ln x = -\infty,$$

which indicates a vertical asymptote at $x = 0$. We write this heuristically as

$$\ln(+0) - -\infty.$$

Part(a): The function $f(x) = \ln(x+2)$, being a shift of $\ln x$ two units to the left, is defined only for $x > -2$, has a vertical asymptote at $x = -2$, and has limit

$$\lim_{x \to -2^+} \ln(x+2) = \ln(+0) = -\infty,$$

Part (b): The function $g(x) = \ln(x^2 - 4)$ is a more complicated composition of the log function and $x^2 - 4$. So it is only defined for $x^2 - 4 > 0$, i.e., for either $x < -2$ or $x > 2$. A little thought gives

$$\lim_{x \to -2^-} \ln(x^2 - 4) = \ln(+0) = -\infty \qquad \text{and } \lim_{x \to 2^+} \ln(x^2 - 4) = \ln(+0) = -\infty.$$

We will study this function graphically in the exercises.

Limits at Infinity (Looking for Horizontal Asymptotes)

We have introduced the symbols ∞ and $-\infty$, thought of as extended real numbers, and have used them to define infinite limits. We will now use them to define *limits at infinity*, which express the behavior of functions far from the origin, that is, behavior near ∞ or $-\infty$. We assume the functions we deal with are defined on intervals of the form $(c, \infty) = \{x \mid x > c\}$, $(-\infty, d) = \{x \mid x < d\}$. These assumptions are necessary so that the discussion of behavior "near ∞" or "near $-\infty$" makes sense. To motivate the definition of limits at infinity, we look at a motivating example.

Example 1.8.7 (Horizontal Asymptotes)

Problem: Investigate the behavior of $f(x) = \dfrac{x}{x+1}$ for x far from the origin.

Solution: First we look at the limiting behavior of f as x increases, becoming ever larger and larger. As with all limiting processes, we can do the investigation numerically, taking a sequence of values of x, say

$$x = 10, 100, 1000, 10000, \dots$$

and computing the corresponding y-values

$$y = \frac{10}{11}, \frac{100}{101}, \frac{1000}{1001}, \frac{10000}{10001}, \ldots$$

Even without converting the y-values to decimal form, it is clear that they are getting closer and closer to 1. We record our observations in terms of limit notation by writing

$$\lim_{x \to \infty} \frac{x}{x+1} = 1.$$

Next, we go the other way with x, letting x decrease through negative values toward $-\infty$. Say,

$$x = -10, -100, -1000, -10000, \ldots$$

Now the corresponding y-values are

$$y = \frac{10}{9}, \frac{100}{99}, \frac{1000}{999}, \frac{10000}{9999}, \ldots$$

Again, it is easy to see that these numbers are getting closer and closer to 1, and we record this observation by writing

$$\lim_{x \to -\infty} \frac{x}{x+1} = 1.$$

This limiting behavior as $x \to \infty$ and as $x \to -\infty$ indicates the values of the function eventually become 1, or more precisely, as close to 1 as we please, as x goes far from the origin in either direction. This signals the presence of a *horizontal asymptote* for the function, namely the line $y = 1$. Figure 1.8.10 shows this asymptotic behavior clearly, even though the x-values are only 20 units from the origin.

With the above example as a motivation, we next give an informal definition of limits at infinity.

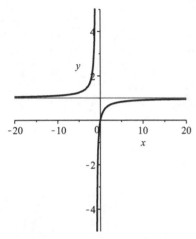

Figure 1.8.10: *A graph of* $f(x) = \frac{x}{x+1}$ *and its horizontal asymptote.*

DEFINITION 1.8.2 (Limits at Infinity)

Suppose the function values $f(x)$ get arbitrarily close to the number L as x increases without bound. Then we write

$$\lim_{x \to \infty} f(x) = L$$

and say that f has limit L as x tends to ∞.

Suppose the function values $f(x)$ get arbitrarily close to the number L as x decreases without bound. Then we write

$$\lim_{x \to -\infty} f(x) = L$$

and say that f has limit L as x tends to $-\infty$.

The existence of *either* one of the two limits at infinity $\lim\limits_{x \to \infty} f(x) = L$, $\lim\limits_{x \to -\infty} f(x) = L$ indicates (by definition) that the line $y = L$ is a *horizontal asymptote* for the function f. Note that we do not require that *both* of these limits at infinity exist for there to be an horizontal asymptote. Also, if both of these limits exist, the limiting values L need *not* be the same. Thus, some functions could have two horizontal asymptotes (but never more than two). Finally, some examples below show that a great many functions have no horizontal asymptotes whatsoever.

As an historical note, you should be aware that asymptotes for curves first arose in studying certain conic sections called hyperbolas. Indeed, in Example 1.8.1 the graph is a hyperbola. You will study conic sections later in this book.

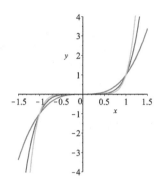

Figure 1.8.11: $f(x) = x^p$ *for* $p = 3, 5, 7$ *(red, blue, green).*

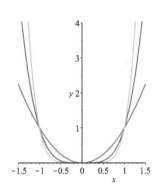

Figure 1.8.12: $f(x) = x^p$ *for* $p = 2, 4, 6$ *(red, blue, green).*

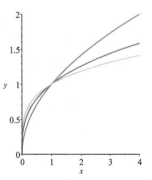

Figure 1.8.13: $f(x) = x^{1/n}$ *for* $n = 2, 3, 4$ *(red, blue, green).*

Canonical Limits @ Infinity
For positive numbers p *and* k:
$\lim\limits_{x \to \infty} \dfrac{k}{x^p} = 0$
$\lim\limits_{x \to \infty} kx^p = \infty$

Example 1.8.8 (Power Functions)

Problem: Determine the distant behavior, far from the origin, of the following functions. Indicate horizontal asymptotes, if any.

(a) $f(x) = \dfrac{1}{x}$, $g(x) = \dfrac{1}{x^3}$, $h(x) = \dfrac{1}{\sqrt{x}}$,   (b) $F(x) = x$, $G(x) = x^3$, $H(x) = \sqrt{x}$.

Solution:

Part (a): Here f, g, h are reciprocal positive power functions. Basically, the larger x gets the smaller the reciprocal power becomes. For example, if

$$x = 10, 100, 1000, 10000, \ldots$$

then

$$\frac{1}{x} = 0.1, 0.01, 0.001, 0.0001 \ldots$$

$$\frac{1}{x^3} = 0.001, 0.00001, 0.000000001, 0.0000000000001, \ldots$$

and

```
> 1/sqrt(x)=seq(1/sqrt(10.^n),n=1..4);
```

$$\frac{1}{\sqrt{x}} = 0.3162277660, 0.1000000000, 0.03162277660, 0.01000000000$$

So it is pretty easy to see that

$$\lim_{x \to \infty} \frac{1}{x} = 0, \qquad \lim_{x \to \infty} \frac{1}{x^3} = 0, \qquad \text{and } \lim_{x \to \infty} \frac{1}{\sqrt{x}} = 0.$$

Thus all three function have $y = 0$ as a horizontal asymptote. See Figures 1.8.3–1.8.4. Taking limits in the other direction it is easy to see that

$$\lim_{x \to -\infty} \frac{1}{x} = 0, \; \lim_{x \to -\infty} \frac{1}{x^3} = 0, \qquad \text{and } \lim_{x \to -\infty} \frac{1}{\sqrt{x}} = \text{does not exist.}$$

Of course the third limit does not exist because $\sqrt{x}$ is not defined for x negative.

Part (b): These functions do not have limits at infinity in the sense of Definition 1.8.2, but it seems natural to extend the definition to allow the limiting value L to be either ∞ or $-\infty$. Then, it is clear, even without numerical calculations, that

$$\lim_{x \to \infty} x = \infty \qquad \lim_{x \to \infty} x^3 = \infty, \qquad \text{and} \qquad \lim_{x \to \infty} \sqrt{x} = \infty.$$

The concept here is that all of these functions increase without bound as x does. Similarly, it is easy to see, that as x tends to $-\infty$, we get

$$\lim_{x \to -\infty} x = -\infty, \qquad \lim_{x \to -\infty} x^3 = -\infty, \qquad \text{and} \qquad \lim_{x \to \infty} \sqrt{x} = \text{does not exist.}$$

While none of these functions, F, G, H, has horizontal asymptotes in its graph, the limits given above indicate important aspects of their behavior far from the origin. The first two limits just indicate that x and x^3 decrease without bound as $x \to -\infty$. See Figures 1.8.11–1.8.13.

The limit results in the last example clearly generalize to positive power functions and reciprocal positive power functions. These are *canonical limits at infinity* and can be used to determine limits at infinity for more complicated functions. We record this in the margin box.

There are similar canonical limits for $x \to -\infty$, but the limiting value depends on the power p:

$$\lim_{x \to -\infty} \frac{k}{x^p} = 0, \quad \text{or does not exist.}$$

$$\lim_{x \to -\infty} kx^p = \pm\infty, \quad \text{or does not exist.}$$

Extended Arithmetic

For any positive real number k:

$$\frac{k}{\pm\infty} = 0 \qquad \pm\infty \cdot k = \pm\infty$$

The case "does not exist" occurs when x^p is not defined for negative numbers x, and so the limit at $-\infty$ cannot even be considered. When using these canonical limits at infinity to find more complicated limits, it is often convenient to use the rules shown in the margin box for working with the extended real numbers $\infty, -\infty$.

Example 1.8.9 (Rational Functions)

Problem: Evaluate $\displaystyle\lim_{x \to \infty} \frac{2x^2 - 3x + 1}{x^2 + 5x - 3}$.

Solution: We use the algebraic method to analyze this limit. If we divide both numerator and denominator by x^2, we get

$$\lim_{x \to \infty} \frac{2x^2 - 3x + 1}{x^2 + 5x - 3} = \lim_{x \to \infty} \frac{2 - \frac{3}{x} + \frac{1}{x^2}}{1 + \frac{5}{x} - \frac{3}{x^2}}$$

and the limit on the right side is easy to evaluate using the canonical limits at infinity. Namely, each of the reciprocal power functions tend to 0 as $x \to \infty$, and so

$$\lim_{x \to \infty} \frac{2 - \frac{3}{x} + \frac{1}{x^2}}{1 + \frac{5}{x} - \frac{3}{x^2}} = \frac{2 - 0 + 0}{1 + 0 - 0} = 2.$$

This means that the graph of $f(x) = \dfrac{2x^2 - 3x + 1}{x^2 + 5x - 3}$ has a horizontal asymptote at $y = 2$.

Example 1.8.10 (Rational Functions)

Problem: Evaluate $\displaystyle\lim_{x \to \pm\infty} \frac{2x^3 - 30x^2 - 5x + 89}{x^5 - 4x^4 + 6x^3 - x^2 + 55x - 1}$.

Interpret the behavior of this rational function far from the origin.

Solution: In the previous example we divided both numerator and denominator by x^m, where m is the degree of the denominator. So in this case we divide x^5. Thus,

$$\lim_{x \to \pm\infty} \frac{2x^3 - 30x^2 - 5x + 89}{x^5 - 4x^4 + 6x^3 - x^2 + 55x - 1}$$

$$= \lim_{x \to \pm\infty} \frac{\frac{2}{x^2} - \frac{30}{x^3} - \frac{5}{x^4} + \frac{89}{x^5}}{1 - \frac{4}{x} + \frac{6}{x^2} - \frac{1}{x^3} + \frac{55}{x^4} - \frac{1}{x^5}} = \frac{0}{1} = 0$$

Note that we have evaluated limits at ∞ and $-\infty$ simultaneously since it was easy to see that we get 0 in both cases. For other types of expressions we might need to do the two limits separately. See the examples below.

We conclude that the rational function $r(x) = \frac{2x^3 - 30x^2 - 5x + 89}{x^5 - 4x^4 + 6x^3 - x^2 + 55x - 1}$ has $y = 0$ as a horizontal asymptote and approaches this asymptote in both directions.

Example 1.8.11 (Rational Functions)

Problem: Evaluate $\displaystyle\lim_{x \to -\infty} \frac{3x^5 - 6x^2 - x - 9}{2x^2 - 4x + 1}$.

Solution: In the previous two examples, we saw that dividing numerator and denominator by the highest power in the denominator will help clarify the nature of limits at infinity for rational functions. Following that pattern in this example, we divide the numerator and the denominator x^2 and then use the canonical infinite limits together with the extended real number arithmetic:

$$\lim_{x \to -\infty} \frac{3\,x^5 - 6\,x^2 - x - 9}{2\,x^2 - 4\,x + 1} = \lim_{x \to -\infty} \frac{3x^3 - 6 - \frac{1}{x} - \frac{9}{x^2}}{2 - \frac{4}{x} + \frac{1}{x^2}} = \frac{-\infty - 6}{2} = \frac{-\infty}{2} = -\infty$$

This indicates that the rational function we are dealing with decreases without bound as $x \to -\infty$. Also, using the above work, it is easy to see that as $x \to \infty$ this rational function tends to ∞. This means that the function grows without bound as x gets large.

The previous example involved the $\lim_{x \to -\infty}(3x^3 - 6) = -\infty - 6 = -\infty$ of a polynomial, which is a shift of the basic power function $3\,x^3$. It seems like a reasonable conclusion to have gotten $-\infty$ from $-\infty - 6$. But what about general polynomial functions? Can we say they always have limits at infinity that are $\pm\infty$? The next example will illustrate what we can expect for the general result.

Example 1.8.12 (Polynomials)

Problem: Determine the behavior of the polynomial $p\,(x) = 2\,x^4 - 4\,x - 10$ far from the origin.

Solution: We look at the limits $\lim_{x \to \pm\infty}\left(2x^4 - 4x - 10\right)$, both at the same time. At first glance it is hard to tell how $2\,x^4 - 4\,x - 10$ is behaving as x gets large. The terms $2\,x^4$ and $4\,x$ tend to ∞ and $\pm\infty$, respectively, by the result on canonical limits at infinity. But it is unclear how the difference $2x^4 - 4x$ is behaving. For instance, as $x \to \infty$, we might want to write that this difference tends to $\infty - \infty$. But how do we interpret that? As zero? Using a little algebra will make clear what is happening in this limit. We factor out the first term to get

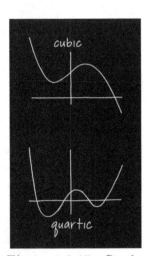

cubic

quartic

Figure 1.8.15: *Graphs of 3rd and 4th degree polynomials.*

$$\lim_{x \to \pm\infty}\left(2x^4 - 4x - 10\right) = \lim_{x \to \pm\infty} 2x^4\left(1 - \frac{2}{x^3} - \frac{5}{x^4}\right) = \infty \cdot (1) = \infty$$

The argument in the above example generalizes to taking limits of any polynomial. NOTE: For any polynomial function $p\,(x) = a_n x^n + a_{n-1} x^{n-1} + \cdots + a_1 x + a_0$, where $a_n \neq 0$, we have that

$$p\,(x) = a_n x^n \left(1 + \frac{a_{n-1}}{a_n x} + \frac{a_{n-2}}{a_n x^2} + \cdots + \frac{a_1}{a_n x^{n-1}} + \frac{a_0}{a_n x^n}\right).$$

Also, by the limit theorems

$$\lim_{x \to \pm\infty}\left(1 + \frac{a_{n-1}}{a_n x} + \frac{a_{n-2}}{a_n x^2} + \cdots + \frac{a_1}{a_n x^{n-1}} + \frac{a_0}{a_n x^n}\right) = 1$$

What this means is that the behavior of $p(x)$ as $x \to \pm\infty$ is determined by the leading term $a_n x^n$. In other words,

$$\lim_{x \to \pm\infty} p\,(x) = \lim_{x \to \pm\infty} a_n x^n = \pm\infty.$$

Whether you get ∞ or $-\infty$, depends on whether a_n is positive or negative, whether n is even or odd, and whether the limit is at ∞ or $-\infty$. In any particular example, what answer you get should be easy to discern.

We can summarize what we have learned from Examples 1.8.7–1.8.12 in the following theorem.

> ## THEOREM 1.8.1 (Rational Function Asymptotics)
>
> *Suppose p(x) and q(x) are polynomials of degree n and k respectively*
>
> If $n < k$, then $\qquad \lim\limits_{x \to \pm\infty} \dfrac{p(x)}{q(x)} = 0$
>
> If $n = k$, then $\qquad \lim\limits_{x \to \pm\infty} \dfrac{p(x)}{q(x)} = L \qquad$ *where L is a nonzero real number*
>
> If $n > k$, then $\qquad \lim\limits_{x \to \pm\infty} \dfrac{p(x)}{q(x)} = \pm\infty$

We can be more specific about the third case $(n > k)$ in the Theorem. The exercises will show you how to determine a polynomial $s(x)$ that the rational function $\frac{p(x)}{q(x)}$ approaches asymptotically at infinity.

We next look at the behavior of a few other types of functions (not rational functions) as $x \to \pm\infty$.

Example 1.8.13 (Algebraic Functions)

Problem: (a) Evaluate $\lim\limits_{x \to \infty} \dfrac{\sqrt{x^2 + 2}}{3x - 6}$ (b) Evaluate $\lim\limits_{x \to -\infty} \dfrac{\sqrt{x^2 + 2}}{3x - 6}$

Solution:

Part (a): The function in this limit is not the quotient of polynomials but we can evaluate this limit by algebraically rewriting this quotient so that we can use Theorem 1.8.1. We will divide the numerator and the denominator by x. In the numerator this amounts to dividing by $x = |x| = \sqrt{x^2}$ since we can assume that x is positive. Thus,

$$\lim\limits_{x \to \infty} \frac{\sqrt{x^2 + 2}}{3x - 6} = \lim\limits_{x \to \infty} \frac{\sqrt{x^2 + 2} \cdot \left(\frac{1}{\sqrt{x^2}}\right)}{(3x - 6) \cdot \left(\frac{1}{x}\right)} = \lim\limits_{x \to \infty} \frac{\sqrt{1 + \frac{2}{x^2}}}{3 - \frac{6}{x}} = \frac{\sqrt{1 + 0}}{3} = \frac{1}{3}$$

Part (b): The function here is the same as in Part (a). However, here we want to evaluate the limit as $x \to -\infty$. For this problem, we also divide the numerator and denominator by x, but in the numerator we write x as $x = -|x| = -\sqrt{x^2}$. The reason for this is that we want to know what happens to the function values for x-values which are large negative, so we assume that x is negative. Thus,

$$\lim\limits_{x \to -\infty} \frac{\sqrt{x^2 + 2}}{3x - 6} = \lim\limits_{x \to -\infty} \frac{\sqrt{x^2 + 2} \cdot \left(\frac{1}{-\sqrt{x^2}}\right)}{(3x - 6) \cdot \left(\frac{1}{x}\right)} = \lim\limits_{x \to -\infty} \frac{-\sqrt{1 + \frac{2}{x^2}}}{3 - \frac{6}{x}} = \frac{-\sqrt{1 + 0}}{3} = -\frac{1}{3}$$

Exponential & Logartihmic Limits

$\lim\limits_{x \to \infty} e^x = \infty \quad \lim\limits_{x \to -\infty} e^x = 0$

$\lim\limits_{x \to \infty} e^{-x} = 0 \quad \lim\limits_{x \to -\infty} e^{-x} = \infty$

$\lim\limits_{x \to \infty} \ln x = \infty \quad \lim\limits_{x \to 0+} \ln x = -\infty$

The natural exponential and logarithmic functions have important limits at infinity. The basic results shown in the margin box are essential for your understanding of more complicated limits involving these functions. See also Figure 1.8.15.

Example 1.8.14 (Exponential Expressions)

Problem:

(a) Determine the long range behavior of the function $f(t) = \dfrac{e^t}{e^t + 1}$.

(b) Determine the behavior of the function $f(x) = e^{1/x}$ near the origin.

Solution:

Part (a): The function f occurs in certain population models from biology and ecology. One considers $f(t)$ as the population (in, say, millions) of the species at time t. The population at time 0 is $1/2$ million, and it seems natural to ask if there will be a limiting value of the population in the future. Thus, we look at the limit as $t \to \infty$. Using the result in the above margin box (and the limit theorems) we get

$$\lim_{t \to \infty} \frac{e^t}{e^t + 1} = \lim_{t \to \infty} \frac{e^t}{e^t + 1} \cdot \frac{e^{-t}}{e^{-t}} = \lim_{t \to \infty} \frac{1}{1 + e^{-t}} = \frac{1}{1 + e^{-\infty}} = \frac{1}{1 + 0} = 1$$

Thus, there is a limiting population of 1 million of the species.

Part (b): The function g is not defined at 0, but it has the following one-sided limits there:

$$\lim_{x \to 0^-} e^{1/x} = e^{1/-0} = e^{-\infty} = 0$$

$$\lim_{x \to 0^+} e^{1/x} = e^{1/+0} = e^{+\infty} = +\infty$$

Thus, the function tends to zero from the left and to infinity from the right. There is a vertical asymptote at the origin.

SUMMARY: In this section we have seen three types of limits involving $\pm\infty$. They are

(1) $\displaystyle\lim_{x \to a} = \pm\infty$ Vertical Asymptote (a is a real number).

(2) $\displaystyle\lim_{x \to \pm\infty} = L$ Horizontal Asymptote (L is a real number).

(3) $\displaystyle\lim_{x \to \pm\infty} = \pm\infty$ Unbounded Graph.

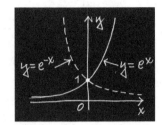

Figure 1.8.16: *Graphs of the exponential function and its reciprocal.*

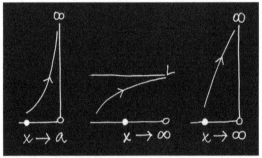

Figure 1.8.16: *Limits involving ∞: (1) Vertical Asymptote, (2) Horizontal Asymptote, (3) Unbounded.*

Exercises: 1.8 (Limits Involving Infinity)

```
> with(dplot_tools,dplot);
                    [dplot]
```

Finding Vertical Asymptotes

In Exercises 1–20 find the vertical asymptotes of the function, i.e., determine the places $x = a$ for which $\lim_{x \to a} f(x) = \pm\infty$. Do a sketch that indicates the behavior of the graph as x approaches a from each side. NOTE: In the problems where an interval is given, just find the vertical asymptotes in that interval.

1. $f(x) = \dfrac{x}{x-3}$ **2.** $f(x) = \dfrac{x}{x-6}$

3. $f(x) = \dfrac{x+1}{x^2+x-6}$ **4.** $f(x) = \dfrac{x+2}{x^2+3x-10}$

5. $f(x) = \dfrac{x+5}{x^2-2x+1}$ **6.** $f(x) = \dfrac{x+5}{x^2-6x+9}$

7. $f(x) = \dfrac{x+6}{x(x+2)(x-4)}$ **8.** $f(x) = \dfrac{x+8}{x(x+3)(x-5)}$

9. $f(x) = \dfrac{x+1}{\cos x - 1}$ on $[-\pi, \pi]$

10. $f(x) = \dfrac{x+2}{\sin x - 1}$ on $[0, \pi]$

11. $f(x) = \dfrac{1}{\sin x \cos x}$ on $[-\pi/4, 3\pi/4]$

12. $f(x) = \dfrac{1}{\sin 2x \cos x}$ on $[-\pi/4, 3\pi/4]$

13. $f(x) = \dfrac{1}{\sin x - \cos x}$ on $[0, 2\pi]$

14. $f(x) = \dfrac{1}{\sin x + \cos x}$ on $[0, 2\pi]$

15. $f(x) = \ln|x|$ **16)** $f(x) = \ln|x-1|$

17. $f(x) = \dfrac{e^x + e^{-x}}{e^x - e^{-x}}$ **18.** $\dfrac{2^x + 2^{-x}}{2^x - 2^{-x}}$

19. $f(x) = \dfrac{3e^x + e^{-x}}{e^x - 2e^{-x}}$ **20.** $\dfrac{2^x + 2^{-x}}{2^x - 2 \cdot 2^{-x}}$

Limits at Infinity & Horizontal Asymptotes

In Exercises 21–54 find the limits and identify horizontal asymptotes, if any.

21. $\lim\limits_{x \to \pm\infty} \dfrac{1}{x-12}$ **22.** $\lim\limits_{x \to \pm\infty} \dfrac{2}{x-7}$

23. $\lim\limits_{x \to \pm\infty} \dfrac{1-2x}{x-12}$ **24.** $\lim\limits_{x \to \pm\infty} \dfrac{2x-3}{12-7x}$

25. $\lim\limits_{x \to \pm\infty} \dfrac{5x^2+7}{3x^2-x}$ **26.** $\lim\limits_{x \to \pm\infty} \dfrac{5x^2+7}{3x^2-x}$

27. $\lim\limits_{x \to \pm\infty} \dfrac{x-2}{x^2+2x+1}$ **28.** $\lim\limits_{x \to \pm\infty} \dfrac{4x-2}{x^2-2x+1}$

29. $\lim\limits_{x \to \pm\infty} \dfrac{x^4+4x-2}{x^2+2x+1}$ **30.** $\lim\limits_{x \to \pm\infty} \dfrac{x^5+5x-2}{x^3+3x+1}$

31. $\lim\limits_{x \to \pm\infty} \dfrac{3x-2}{\sqrt{x^2+1}}$ **32.** $\lim\limits_{x \to \pm\infty} \dfrac{5x+1}{\sqrt{2x^2+1}}$

33. $\lim\limits_{x \to \pm\infty} \dfrac{5\sqrt{x^4-x^2+1}}{2x^2}$ **34.** $\lim\limits_{x \to \pm\infty} \dfrac{3\sqrt{2x^4-x^2+6}}{5x^2}$

35. $\lim\limits_{x \to \infty} \sqrt{x}$ **36.** $\lim\limits_{x \to \infty} \sqrt{x+1}$

37. $\lim\limits_{x \to \infty} \dfrac{\sqrt{x}+\frac{1}{\sqrt{x}}}{2\sqrt{x}+\frac{1}{x}}$ **38.** $\lim\limits_{x \to \infty} \dfrac{\sqrt{x}-\frac{1}{\sqrt{x}}}{3\sqrt{x}-\frac{1}{x}}$

39. $\lim\limits_{x \to \infty} \dfrac{e^x - e^{-x}}{e^x + e^{-x}}$ **40.** $\lim\limits_{x \to \infty} \dfrac{2^x - 2^{-x}}{2^x + 2^{-x}}$

41. $\lim\limits_{x \to \pm\infty} \tan^{-1} x$ **42.** $\lim\limits_{x \to \pm\infty} \cot^{-1} x$

43. $\lim\limits_{x \to \pm\infty} \tan^{-1}(1+1/x)$ **44.** $\lim\limits_{x \to \pm\infty} \cot^{-1}(1+1/x)$

45. $\lim\limits_{x \to \pm\infty} (x^4 - 2x^3 + 5)$ **46.** $\lim\limits_{x \to \pm\infty} (2x^6 - 5x^2 + 3)$

46. $\lim\limits_{x \to \pm\infty} (x^2 - x^4)$ **47.** $\lim\limits_{x \to \pm\infty} (x^4 - x^6)$

49. $\lim\limits_{x \to \pm\infty} (3 - 5x - 2x^3)$ **50.** $\lim\limits_{x \to \pm\infty} (2 - x^2 - 4x^3)$

51. $\lim\limits_{x \to \infty} \ln x$ **52.** $\lim\limits_{x \to \infty} \ln(x+1)$

53. $\lim\limits_{x \to \infty} \dfrac{\ln x}{1+2\ln x}$ **54.** $\lim\limits_{x \to \infty} \dfrac{\ln x}{1+3\ln x}$

Finding Asymptotes and Graphing

In Exercises 55–67, find all the vertical and horizontal asymptotes of the given function. Do a by-hand sketch of the graphs of the function and its asymptotes. EXTRA CREDIT: Use Maple to graph the function. Choose ranges so that all the asymptotes are shown. Remember to use cutoffs on the y-ranges so that all features of the graph are discernible.

55. $f(x) = \dfrac{x-1}{x-2}$ **56.** $f(x) = \dfrac{x-2}{x-1}$

57. $f(x) = \dfrac{x^2-4}{x^2-4x+3}$ **58.** $f(x) = \dfrac{9-x^2}{x^2+3x-4}$

59. $f(x) = \dfrac{x^2-9}{x^3-2x^2-x+2}$ **60.** $f(x) = \dfrac{x^5-1}{e^x-e^{-x}}$

61. $f(x) = \dfrac{x}{e^x-e^{-x}}$ **62.** $f(x) = \dfrac{x^2}{e^x-e^{-x}}$

63. $f(x) = \dfrac{e^{2x}}{e^{2x}-1}$ **64.** $f(x) = 2\dfrac{e^{2x}}{e^{2x}-1}$

65. $g(x) = \dfrac{e^x}{3e^{2x}-7e^x+2}$

66. $g(x) = \dfrac{e^x}{4e^{2x}-9e^x+2}$

67. $f(x) = \dfrac{\ln x}{1+2\ln x}$ for x in $(0, \infty)$

68. Asymptotic Functions: $\lim\limits_{x \to \pm\infty} \dfrac{p(x)}{q(x)} = h(x)$

Theorem 1.8.1 gives the basic information about the limits at infinity for rational functions. In this exercise you will explore the third case:

$$\lim_{x \to \pm\infty} \frac{p(x)}{q(x)} = \pm\infty, \quad \text{when} \quad \deg(p(x)) > \deg(q(x))$$

It turns out that we can be a lot more specific about the limit at infinity being $\pm\infty$

From basic algebra, we know that when $\frac{p(x)}{q(x)}$ is not a proper fraction (i.e. when $\deg(p(x)) > \deg(q(x))$), then we can divide (using long-division) and express it as a sum of a polynomial $h(x)$ plus a proper fraction:

$$\frac{p(x)}{q(x)} = h(x) + \frac{k(x)}{q(x)}$$

(a) Show that $\lim\limits_{x \to \pm\infty} \dfrac{p(x)}{q(x)} = h(x)$, or equivalently that $\lim\limits_{x \to \pm\infty} \left(\dfrac{p(x.}{q(x.} - h(x) \right) = 0$. This says that $\dfrac{p(x)}{q(x)}$ approaches $h(x)$ asymptotically as x approaches $\pm\infty$. For this reason, h is called the *asymptotic function* for the rational function.

(b) What is the degree of the asymptotic function h?

(c) The discussion above is for the case $\deg(p(x)) > \deg(q(x))$, but is this really necessary? Explain how the other two cases in Theorem 1.8.1 are covered by the above discussion.

In Exercises 67–72 use the results of Exercise 66 to analyze the asymptotic behavior of the function at infinity. In particular, find the asymptotic function h for f. EXTRA CREDIT: Use Maple to plot h and f in the same figure. Choose your ranges and other parameters to produce a good picture showing all the features in the graphs.

67. $f(x) = \dfrac{x^2 + x + 1}{x - 1}$ **68.** $f(x) = \dfrac{x^2 + x}{x - 1}$

69. $f(x) = \dfrac{x^4 - x^3 - 3x^2 + 6x - 4}{x^2 + x - 2}$

70. $f(x) = \dfrac{x^5 - 3x^4 + 2x^3 + 2x^2 - 3x + 2}{x^2 - 1}$

71. $f(x) = \dfrac{x^3 - 3x^2 + 2x + 2}{x^2 - 3x + 2}$

72. $f(x) = \dfrac{-2x^3 - 4x^2 + 6x + 4}{x^2 + 2x - 3}$

In Exercises 73–94, use Maple's `plot` command and/or the special-purpose Maple procedure `dplot` to find vertical and horizontal asymptotes of the function. Remember to use cut-offs in the y-ranges so that the large y-values, near the vertical asymptotes do not distort the graph. Also use a large enough x-range so that the approach of the function toward its horizontal asymptotes is clear.

Recall that `dplot` command has the form

$$\texttt{dplot(f,a,b,N,discont,c,d.}$$

where `f` is the name of the function, `[a,b]` is interval for the x-values, `[c,d]` is the interval for the y–values, `N` is the number of frames in the movie, and `discont = 0` means ignore discontinuities, while `discont = 1` means lookout for discontinuities. Use `discont = 0`.

73. $f(x) = \dfrac{1}{x - 2}$ **74.** $f(x) = \dfrac{2}{x - 3}$

75. $\lim\limits_{x \to \pm\infty} \dfrac{x}{x + 1}$ **76.** $\lim\limits_{x \to \pm\infty} \dfrac{2x}{x + 1}$

77. $f(x) = \dfrac{x^2 + 1}{x^2 + x - 6}$ **78.** $f(x) = \dfrac{2x - 3}{12 - 7x}$

79. $f(x) = \dfrac{5x^2 + 7}{3x^2 - x}$ **80.** $f(x) = \dfrac{5x^2 + 7}{3x^2 - x}$

81. $f(x) = \dfrac{1}{\sin x \cos x}$ on $[-\pi/4, 3\pi/4]$

82. $f(x) = \dfrac{1}{\sin 2x \cos x}$ on $[-\pi/4, 3\pi/4]$

83. $f(x) = \dfrac{1}{\sin x - \cos x}$ on $[0, 2\pi]$

84. $f(x) = \dfrac{1}{\sin x + \cos x}$ on $[0, 2\pi]$

85. $f(x) = \dfrac{e^x + e^{-x}}{e^x - e^{-x}}$ **86.** $f(x) = \dfrac{2^x + 2^{-x}}{2^x - 2^{-x}}$

87. $f(x) = \dfrac{e^x + e^{-x}}{e^x - 2e^{-x}}$ **88.** $f(x) = \dfrac{2^x + 2^{-x}}{2^x - 2 \cdot 2^{-x}}$

89. $f(x) = \tan^{-1}(1 + 1/x)$ **90.** $f(x) = \cot^{-1}(1 + 1/x)$

91. $f(x) = (1 + 1/x)^x$ on $(0, \infty)$

92. $f(x) = (1 + 3/x)^x$ on $(0, \infty)$

93. $f(x) = |1 + 1/x|^x$ **94.** $f(x) = |1 + 3/x|^x$

95. For the function f graphed below, find the following limts (if they exist, in thr extended sense.

(a) $\lim\limits_{x \to -1^-} f(x)$ (b) $\lim\limits_{x \to -1^+} f(x)$ (c) $\lim\limits_{x \to -1} f(x)$

(d) $\lim\limits_{x \to 3^-} f(x)$ (e) $\lim\limits_{x \to 3^+} f(x)$ (f) $\lim\limits_{x \to 3} f(x)$

(g) $\lim\limits_{x \to -\infty} f(x)$ (h) $\lim\limits_{x \to \infty} f(x)$

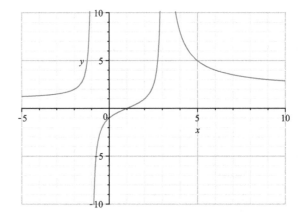

Calculus *Concepts & Computation*

1.9 The Definition of a Limit

So far we have taken an informal and intuitive approach to the limit concept. In this section we will give the precise mathematical definition of $\lim_{x \to a} f(x) = L$, called the ε -δ definition.

Our work with limits in Sections 1.2–1.8 was based on the following definition from Section 1.1. Recall that, with a and L being real numbers, the informal definition of the limit is:

DEFINITION 1.1.1 (Limits)

The function $y = f(x)$ is said to have limiting value L as x tends to a, *if the y-values can be made as close to L as we wish by restricting x to being sufficiently close to a. When this is the case we use the notation*

$$\lim_{x \to a} f(x) = L$$

We say "L is the limit of $f(x)$ as x tends to a." Alternatively, we say that $f(x)$ approaches L as x approaches a and write

$$f(x) \to L \quad as \quad x \to a$$

Initially our approach was to guess what number L, if any, the y-values $y = f(x)$ get close to as x gets close to a, with our guess supported by graphical, numerical, or algebraic evidence. Applying the Limit Laws in section 1.5 allowed us to find limits without guessing. These are in fact theorems whose proofs require a precise definition of $\lim_{x \to a} f(x) = L$. Such a definition will clarify what exactly it means to say

"The y-values an be made as close to L as we wish
by restricting x to being sufficiently close to a"

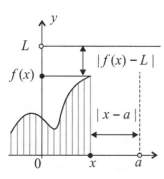

Figure 1.9.1: *Distance from $f(x)$ to L and from x to a.*

Since the distance between two real numbers is the absolute value of their difference, this means that

$$|f(x) - L|$$

measures how close $f(x)$ is to L and

$$|x - a|$$

measures how close x is to a. See Figure 1.9.1. Let's use this notation to develop a rigorous concept of the limit.

To do this look at, for example, the behavior of the function $f(x) = 5x - 2$ near $x = a = 1$. As x gets close to 1, $f(x)$ gets close to 3. Suppose we want $f(x)$ to be less that 0.2 units from 3, that is, we want $|f(x) - 3| < 0.2$. How close to 1 should x be? Consider the following equivalent inequalities:

$$
\begin{aligned}
|f(x) - 3| &< 0.2 \\
|5x - 2 - 3| &< 0.2 \\
|5x - 5| &< 0.2
\end{aligned}
$$

The last inequality can be rewritten without the absolute value as

$$-0.2 < 5x - 5 < 0.2$$

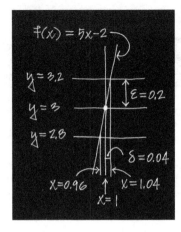

Figure 1.9.2: *Choosing
δ for a given ε.*

which is

$$-0.2 < 5(x-1) < 0.2.$$

Dividing through the compound inequality by 5 gives an inequalities involving $x-1$.

$$0.04 < x - 1 < 0.04$$

which is equivalent to

$$|\,x-1\,| < 0.04.$$

Thus, if x differs from 1 by less than 0.04, then $f(x)$ will differ from 3 by less than 0.2. Symbolically, if $|x-1| < 0.04$, then $|f(x) - 3| < 0.2$. Figure 1.9.1 gives the graphical illustration of this.

Let's do a similar analysis, requiring $|f(x) - 3| < 0.1$, for x sufficiently close to 1. For this case we would need $|x-1| < 0.02$. In fact, we can generalize and derive a formula for the restriction on $|x - 1|$ required to get $|f(x) - 3|$ as small as we wish. Let ε (a positive number) represent this smallness and suppose we want to have $|\,f(x) - 3\,| < \varepsilon$ What restriction on $|x - 1|$ would be needed? We have the following string of equivalent inequalities, analogous to the ones above for $\varepsilon = 0.2$.

$$|f(x) - 3| < \varepsilon$$

$$|5x - 2 - 3| < \varepsilon$$

$$|5x - 5| < \varepsilon$$

$$-\varepsilon < 5x - 5 < \varepsilon$$

$$-\varepsilon < 5(x - 1) < \varepsilon$$

$$-\frac{\varepsilon}{5} < x - 1 < \frac{\varepsilon}{5}$$

$$|x - 1| < \frac{\varepsilon}{5}$$

This shows that for any $\varepsilon > 0$, if $|x - 1| < \varepsilon/5$, then $|\,f(x) - 3\,| < \varepsilon$. For the function $f(x) = 5x - 2$ this makes it very precise what it means to say "the y-values can be made as close to 3 as we wish by restricting x to being sufficiently close to 1." This also constitutes a mathematical proof that

$$\lim_{x \to 1}(5x - 2) = 3,$$

according to the following formal (rigorous) definition.

DEFINITION 1.9.1 (The $\varepsilon - \delta$ Definition of a Limit)

*Let $f(x)$ be defined for all x in an open interval containing the number a, except
possibly at a. For a real number L, we say*

$$\lim_{x \to a} f(x) = L$$

if for any number $\varepsilon > 0$, there exists a number $\delta > 0$, so that

$$\left| f(x) - L \right| < \varepsilon$$

whenever $x \neq a$ satisfies

$$\left| x - a \right| < \delta.$$

<u>CONVENTION</u>: When dealing with limits and making a statement like $|x - a| < \delta$, we will tacitly assume that $x \neq a$. The inequality is sometimes read as saying that

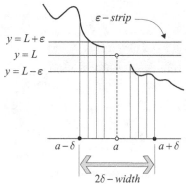

Figure 1.9.2: *The chosen δ is not small enough for the graph on* $[a-\delta, a), (a, a+\delta]$ *to lie within the ε-strip.*

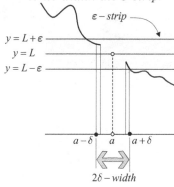

Figure 1.9.3: *A smaller δ that works.*

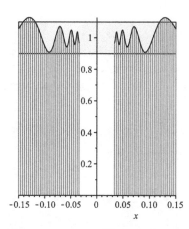

Figure 1.9.4: *The 32nd frame of the movie produced by* epsilon_delta_limit *with δ = 0.15.*

"*x is within δ of a,*" that is, the distance from x to a is less than δ (and x is not equal to a).

Generally, the problem of finding a δ that works for a given ε can be difficult. There are some algebraic techniques (see the examples below) and limit laws that one can use. Graphically, you can always experiment with choosing a δ. The requirement that $|f(x) - L| < \varepsilon$ for all $x \neq a$ satisfying $|x - a| < \delta$ is equivalent to

$$L - \varepsilon < f(x) < L + \varepsilon \text{ for all } x \neq a \text{ such that } a - \delta < x < a + \delta.$$

Geometrically, this means that graph of f on the intervals $(a - \delta, a), (a, a + \delta)$ lies between the graphs of the two lines $y = L - \varepsilon, y = L + \varepsilon$. We call this an ε-strip. Figure 1.9.2 shows a hypothetical graph of a function, an ε-strip (in yellow), a choice for δ that is not small enough. (Part of the graph of f lies outside the ε-strip.) Choosing a smaller δ, as shown in Figure 1.9.3, can make the entire graph lie within the strip (which is fixed in the process of choosing a δ that works).

Example 1.9.1 (Using epsilon_delta_limit **To Find δ)**

Problem: Use the special-purpose Maple procedure epsilon_delta_limit to illustrate the ε–δ for the limit $\lim_{x \to 0}(1 + \sin(1/x)) = 1$. Specifically, for the function $f(x) = 1 + \sin(1/x)$, the numbers $a = 0, L = 1$, and the given $\varepsilon = 0.1$, find a $\delta > 0$ so that the graph of f on the intervals $(-\delta, 0), (0, \delta)$ lies within the ε-strip.

Solution: The procedure epsilon_delta_limit makes a movie like dplot does except it also shows the ε-strip. Its are arguments are:

```
epsilon_delta_limit(f,a,L,e,d,N)
```

where e is ε, d is δ, N is the number of frames in the movie. So with $\varepsilon = 0.1$, we first try $\delta = 0.15$ for delta. The movie is produced by the following commands.

```
> f:=x->1+sin(1/x);
```

$$f :\to 1 + \sin\left(\frac{1}{x}\right)$$

```
> epsilon_delta_limit(f,0,1,.1,.15,40);
```

Figure 1.9.4 shows the 32nd frame in this movie and indicates that $\delta = 0.15$ is not small enough since the initial part of the graph of f is not inside the the ε-strip. So we try a smaller value $\delta = 0.1$, which we chose after studying Figure 1.9.4:

```
> epsilon_delta_limit(f,0,1,.1,.15,40);
```

Figure 1.9.5 indicates that for this δ, the entire graph is within the ε-strip. **Example**

1.9.2 (Using the $\varepsilon - \delta$ **Definition)**

Problem: Prove each of the following limits using Definition 1.9.1.

(a) $\lim_{x \to 1}(5x - 2) = 3$ (b) $\lim_{x \to -2}(7 - 2x) = 11$

(c) $\lim_{x \to 3} f(x) = 7$, where $f(x) = \begin{cases} 2x - 1 & \text{if } x \neq 2 \\ 5 & \text{if } x = 2 \end{cases}$

Solution:

Part (a): Given a number $\varepsilon > 0$, we must find a number $\delta > 0$ so that if $|5x - 5| < \varepsilon$. From our work above we take $\delta = \varepsilon/5$ and show that it works by tracing back the steps above. If $|x - 1| < \varepsilon/5$, then rewriting this without the absolute value gives $-\varepsilon/5 < x - 1 < \varepsilon/5$, which is equivalent to $-\varepsilon < 5x - 5 \wedge 5x - 5 < \varepsilon$. This says that $|5x - 5| < \varepsilon$ which can be rewritten as $|5x - 2 - 3| < \varepsilon$. Thus, for any $\varepsilon > 0$, there is a $\delta > 0$, namely, $\delta = \varepsilon/5$, such that if $|x - 1| < \delta$, then $|5x - 5| < \varepsilon$

Part (b): Given any $\varepsilon > 0$, we need a choice of $\delta > 0$, so that if $|x - (-2)| = |x + 2| < \delta$, then $|(7 - 2x) - 11| < \varepsilon$. We see that

$$|(7 - 2x) - 11| = |-4 - 2x| = |(-2)(x + 2)| = |-2| \cdot |x + 2| = 2|x + 2|$$

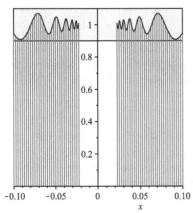

Figure 1.9.5: *The 32nd frame of the movie produced by* `epsilon_delta_limit` *with $\delta = 0.15$.*

So to get $\mid (7-2x) - 11 \mid < \varepsilon$, we need $2\,|x+2| < \varepsilon$, or equivalently, we need $|x+2| < \varepsilon/2$. We take $= \varepsilon/2$. Thus, for any $\varepsilon > 0$ there is a δ, namely, $\delta = \varepsilon/2$, such that whenever $|x-(-2)| = |x+2| < \delta$, then $|(7-2x) - 11| < \varepsilon$.

Part (c): In this problem the function f is not continuous at $x = 2$, see the graph in Figure 1.9.6. However, the two sided limit $\lim_{x\to 2} f(x)$ does exist and we will use the ε-δ definition to prove that it is equal to 3. For any $\varepsilon > 0$, let $\delta = \varepsilon/2$. If $|x-2| < \delta$ and $x \neq 1$, then we have $f(x) = 2x - 1$, so $|f(x) - 3| = |2x - 1 - 3| = |2x - 4| = 2\,|x-2|$. Since $|x-2| < \varepsilon/2$ we see that $2\,|x-2| < \varepsilon$. Thus, $\lim_{x\to 2} f(x) = 3$

In using Definition 1.9.1, the key is to find the relationship between the expressions $|f(x) - L|$ and $|x - a|$ and use this to find a formula for δ in terms of ε. In the above example the relationship turned out to be $|f(x) - L| = C\,|x-a|$ where C is a positive constant. Since $C\,|x-a| < \varepsilon$ is equivalent to $|x-a| < \varepsilon/C$ the choice for

δ is $\delta = \varepsilon/C$. Also note that for any ε, once a δ has been found then any positive number smaller than the chosen δ will also work.

Example 1.9.3 (Using the ε - δ Definition with a Quadratic Function)

Problem: Prove that $\lim_{x\to 2}(x^2 + 1) = 5$.

Solution: Given any $0 < \varepsilon$, we want to find a number $0 < \delta$, so that whenever $|x-2| < \delta$ then $|x^2 + 1 - 5| = |x^2 - 4| < \varepsilon$. We see that

$$|x^2 - 4| = |(x-2)(x+2)| = \mid x-2 \mid \cdot \mid x + 2 \mid$$

We want this to be less than ε, that is, make $|x-2|\,|x+2| < \varepsilon$. If we can find a constant C such that $|x+2| < C$, then $|x-2|\,|x+2| < |x-2|\,C$ and the choice for δ would be $\delta = \varepsilon/C$. We can find such a C by restricting $|x-2|$ to be less than some fixed number, say $|x-2| < 1$. Then,

$$-1 < x - 2 \ \text{ and } \ x - 2 < 1$$

Adding 4 on both sides of each of these inequality gives

$$3 < x + 2 \ \text{ and } \ x + 2 < 4$$

Since $x+2$ is between 3 and 4 we see that $x+2\,|x+2| < 4$. So if $|x-2| < 1$ then $|x^2 - 4| = |x-2|\,|x+2| < 4\,|x-2|$ and $4\,|x-2| < \varepsilon$ when when $|x-2| < \varepsilon/4$. Since we need both $|x-2| < 1$ and $|x-2| < \varepsilon/4$, we choose δ to be the smaller of the numbers 1 and $\varepsilon/4$, denoted $\delta = \min\{1, \varepsilon\}$. In summary, for $\varepsilon > 0$, let $\delta = \min\{1, \varepsilon\}$. If $|x-2| < \delta$ then

$$|x^2 + 1 - 5| = |x^2 - 4| = |x-2|\,|x+2| < 4\,|x-2| < 4 \cdot \frac{\varepsilon}{4} = \varepsilon$$

Example 1.9.4 (Using the ε - δ Definition with a Rational Function)

Problem: Prove that $\lim_{x\to 3} \dfrac{1}{x+1} = \dfrac{1}{4}$

Solution: We need to relate the expressions $\left|\frac{1}{x+1} - \frac{1}{4}\right|$ and $|x-3|$. We see that

$$
\begin{aligned}
\left|\frac{1}{x+1} - \frac{1}{4}\right| &= \left|\frac{4-(x+1)}{4(x+1)}\right| = \left|\frac{3-x}{4(x+1)}\right| \\
&= \frac{\mid 3-x \mid}{4\mid x+1 \mid} = \frac{\mid x-3 \mid}{4\mid x+1 \mid} = |x-3| \cdot \frac{1}{|x+1|}
\end{aligned}
$$

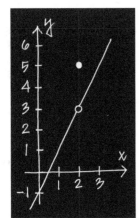

Figure 1.9.6: *Graph of*
$f(x) = \begin{cases} 2x - 1 & \text{if } x \neq 2 \\ 5 & \text{if } x = 2 \end{cases}$

We will make the restriction $|x - 3| < 1$. Then $-1 < x - 3 < 1$,, or equivalently, $3 < x + 1 < 5$. Since $x + 1 > 3$, we have that $4|x + 1| > 12$. Thus, when $|x - 3| < 1$, we get

$$\frac{1}{4|x + 1|} < \frac{1}{12} \quad \text{which gives} \quad |x - 3| \cdot \frac{1}{4|x + 1|} < \frac{1}{12} \cdot |x - 3|$$

Therefore when $|x - 3| < 1$ and $|x - 3| < 12\,\varepsilon$ it follows that

$$\left| \frac{1}{x + 1} - \frac{1}{4} \right| = |x - 3| \cdot \frac{1}{4|x + 1|} < \frac{1}{12}|x - 3| < \frac{1}{12}(12\varepsilon = \varepsilon$$

Thus, for any given $0 < \varepsilon$, we let $\delta = \min\{12, 1\}$. Then if $|x - 3| < \delta$, we have $|\frac{1}{x+1} - \frac{1}{4}| < \varepsilon$.

The formal definition of a limit provides the theoretical foundation for the limit laws in Section 1.5 which are used in evaluating limits. In this next example we prove several of these.

Example 1.9.5 (Proving Limit Laws)

Problem: Prove the following limit theorems:

(a) For c any constant: $\lim_{x \to a} c = c$ (b) $\lim_{x \to a} x = a$

(c) If $\lim_{x \to a} f(x) = L$ and $\lim_{x \to a} g(x) = M$, then $\lim_{x \to a} f(x) + g(x) = L + M$

Solution:

Part (a): Here let $f(x) = c$ be the constant function. Let $\varepsilon > 0$ be given. then $|f(x) - c| = |c - c| = 0 < \varepsilon$, so any δ will work.

Part (b): Here let $f(x) = x$. For any $\varepsilon > 0$, let $\delta = \varepsilon$. Then if $|x - a| < \delta$, we have that $|f(x) - a| = |x - a| < \varepsilon$.

Part(c): Let $\varepsilon > 0$ be given. We need to find a δ such that if $|x - a| < \delta$, then $|f(x) + g(x) - L - M| < \varepsilon$. Since $\lim_{x \to a} f(x) = L$ and $\lim_{x \to a} g(x) = M$, we can choose a $\delta_1 > 0$ such that if $|x - a| < \delta_1$ then $|f(x) - L| < \varepsilon/2$. Also, we can choose a $\delta_2 > 0$ so that if $|x - a| < \delta_2$, then $|g(x) - M| < \varepsilon/2$. Let $\delta = \min\{\delta_1, \delta_2\}$. If $|x - a| < \delta$, then we have both $|x - a| < \delta_1$ and $|x - a| < \delta_2$. We see that

$$| (f(x) + g(x)) - (L + M) | = | f(x) + g(x) - L - M |$$
$$= | (f(x) - L) + (g(x) - M) | \le | f(x) - L | + | g(x) - M | < \frac{\varepsilon}{2} + \frac{\varepsilon}{2} = \varepsilon.$$

Here we used an important tool for working with inequalities:

The Triangle Inequality: For any real numbers A and B: $|A + B| \le |A| + |B|$.

Exercises: 1.9 (The Definition of a Limit)

Finding δ for a given ε

In exercises 1–12 for the limit, find a δ that works for the given ε.

1. $\lim\limits_{x \to 3} 2x = 6$, $\varepsilon = 0.02$

2. $\lim\limits_{x \to 1} 5x = 5$, $\varepsilon = 0.001$

3. $\lim\limits_{x \to 1} (3x + 2) = 5$, $\varepsilon = 0.12$

4. $\lim\limits_{x \to 2} (4x - 3) = 5$, $\varepsilon = 0.002$

5. $\lim\limits_{x \to -1} (5 - 3x) = 8$, $\varepsilon = 0.072$

6. $\lim\limits_{x \to -2} (2 - 7x) = 16$, $\varepsilon = 0.014$

7. $\lim\limits_{x \to 4} (\frac{1}{2}x + 3) = 5$, $\varepsilon = 0.08$

8. $\lim\limits_{x \to 12} (\frac{1}{4}x - 1) = 2$, $\varepsilon = 0.001$

9. $\lim\limits_{x \to 2} (x^2 - 1) = 3$, $\varepsilon = 0.20$

10. $\lim\limits_{x \to 1} (x^2 + 5) = 6$, $\varepsilon = 0.02$

11. $\lim\limits_{x \to 5} \dfrac{1}{x + 3} = \dfrac{1}{8}$, $\varepsilon = 0.012$

12. $\lim\limits_{x \to 1} \dfrac{1}{3x - 1} = \dfrac{1}{2}$, $\varepsilon = 0.001$

Finding δ for an arbitrary ε

For each limit $\lim\limits_{x \to a} f(x) = L$ and for an arbitrary $\varepsilon > 0$, find a $\delta > 0$ such that whenever $0 < |x - a| < \delta$ then $|f(x) - L| < \varepsilon$. In other words, prove the limit statement.

13. $\lim\limits_{x \to 3} 2x = 6$

14 $\lim\limits_{x \to 1} 5x = 5$

15. $\lim\limits_{x \to 1} (3x + 2) = 80$

16 $\lim\limits_{x \to 2} (4x - 3) = 5$

17. $\lim\limits_{x \to -1} (5 - 3x) = 8$

18. $\lim\limits_{x \to -2} (2 - 7x) = 16$

19. $\lim\limits_{x \to 4} (\frac{1}{2}x + 3) = 5$

20 $\lim\limits_{x \to 12} (\frac{1}{4}x - 1) = 2$

21. $\lim\limits_{x \to 2} (1 - 6x) = -11$

22. $\lim\limits_{x \to -2} (4 - 3x) = 10$

23. $\lim\limits_{x \to 2} (x^2 - 1) = 2$

24. $\lim\limits_{x \to 1} (3x^2 + 1) = 4$

25. $\lim\limits_{x \to 3} (x^2 - 5) = 4$

26. $\lim\limits_{x \to -1} (2x^2 - 3) = -1$

27. $\lim\limits_{x \to 5} \dfrac{1}{x + 3} = \dfrac{1}{8}$

28. $\lim\limits_{x \to 1} \dfrac{1}{3x - 1} = \dfrac{1}{2}$

29. $\lim\limits_{x \to 2} \dfrac{x^2 - 4}{x - 2} = 4$

30. $\lim\limits_{x \to -3} \dfrac{x^2 - 9}{x + 3} = -6$

31. $\lim\limits_{x \to 9} \sqrt{x - 5} = 2$

32. $\lim\limits_{x \to 10} \sqrt{x - 1} = 9$

33. $\lim\limits_{x \to 0} \left(1 + \dfrac{x^3}{|x|}\right) = 1$

34. $\lim\limits_{x \to 0} \left(1 - \dfrac{x^3}{|x|}\right) = 1$

35. $\lim\limits_{x \to 1} f(x) = 2$, $f(x) = \begin{cases} 2x & \text{if } x < 1 \\ -\frac{1}{2}x + \frac{5}{2} & \text{if } x \geq 1 \end{cases}$

36. $\lim\limits_{x \to 0} f(x) = 1$, $f(x) = \begin{cases} x + 1 & \text{if } x < 0 \\ 1 - x & \text{if } x \geq 0 \end{cases}$

Using a Graph to Find δ for a Given ε

The graphs below show functions with $\lim\limits_{x \to 1} f(x) = 1$. For $\varepsilon = 0.5$, use the graphs to find a δ (as large as possible) such that $|f(x) - 1| < \varepsilon$ for all x such that $|x - 1| < \delta$.

37. $f(x) = \dfrac{1}{x}$

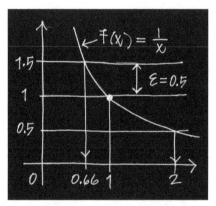

38. $f(x) = x^2$

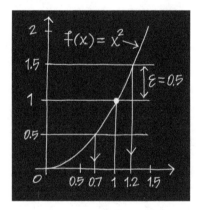

Using `epsilon_delta_limit`

In exercises 39–42 for the limit, find a δ that works for the given ε.

39. $\lim\limits_{x \to o} (1 - \sin(1/x))^x = 1$, $\varepsilon = 0.5$

40. $\lim\limits_{x \to 1} (1 - \cos(1/x))^x = 1$, $\varepsilon = 0.5$

41. $\lim\limits_{x \to 0} 2\sqrt{|x|} \sin(1/x) = 0$, $\varepsilon = 0.2$

42. $\lim\limits_{x \to 0} \sqrt[10]{|x|} \sin(1/x) = 0$, $\varepsilon = 0.2$

Derivatives

Calculus *Concepts & Computation*

2.1 The Tangent Line Problem

```
> with(code_ch2sec1);with(limit_tools,twosidelimit);
```
[diff_triangles, lim_triangles, limitsecants, limsec2, tanplot]

[twosidelimit]

One of the principal achievements of the calculus developed by Newton and Leibniz was the solution of the tangent line problem:

Through a given point on a curve, construct a tangent line to the curve.

As mentioned in Section 1.1 (which you should read now if you have not done so already), this problem was solved by ancient Greek mathematicians for conic sections, but they were unable to extend their methods to more general curves. To construct tangent lines in the general case requires the notion of limits, and, indeed, the very definition of what is meant by a tangent line arises by taking limits of secant lines.

In this section we give all the details and notation for the solution of the tangent line problem in the case that the curve is the graph of a function f. We denote the given point by $P = (x_0, y_0)$, and of course $y_0 = f(x_0)$, since P is on the graph of f. Now any line through P has an equation of the form

$$y = y_0 + m(x - x_0).$$

where m is the slope of the line. Our strategy is to pick a special value for m, so that the above equation represents, and indeed defines, the tangent line at P.

To get m, take a point Q on the graph (and on either side of P) and consider the line determined by P and Q, as shown in Figure 2.1.1. This is a typical *secant* line.

Now let Q slide along the graph toward P and consider what happens to the corresponding secant lines through P, Q. This is illustrated in the movie produced by the following Maple command. Execute this command and view this movie several times.

```
> limsec2();
```

The next to the last frame in this movie is shown in Figure 2.1.2.

This certainly suggests that the tangent line can be obtained as the limit of these secant lines. In fact, the two secant lines in the next to the last frame appear to be lined up on the tangent line and seem to give a good approximation to it. Now the question is, how do we handle this mathematically? We start with some notation.

Let m_{PQ} denote the slope of the secant line through point P and Q. Since we are denoting the coordinates of P by $P = (x_0, y_0)$, we let $Q = (x_1, y_1)$ denote the coordinates of Q. Also, we let the differences in the y-coordinates and the differences in the x-coordinates be denoted by

$$\Delta y = y_1 - y_0 \qquad \Delta x = x_1 - x_0,$$

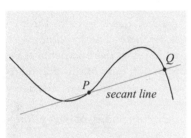

Figure 2.1.1: *A typical secant line at P determined by choosing a point Q on the graph.*

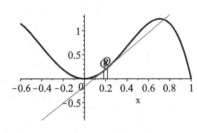

Figure 2.1.2: *The next to last frame in the movie* `limsec2()` *showing two secant lines PQ just before Q coincides with P.*

respectively. Then the slope of the secant line is

$$m_{PQ} = \frac{\Delta y}{\Delta x}.$$

This is shown in Figure 2.1.3.

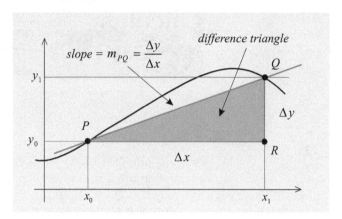

Figure 2.1.3: *The secant line $\overline{PQ}$ with slope m_{PQ} and difference triangle ΔPQR.*

Note that the differences Δx and Δy are (for this picture) the lengths of the two sides of the right triangle, which is called a *difference triangle*. The hypotenuse of this difference triangle has slope m_{PQ}, and this is what we want to calculate for various choices of Q. As Q approaches P, the sides and hypotenuse of this difference triangle continually change and, as the movie `limsec2()` above indicates, the slope m_{PQ} should approach the tangent-line slope.

To get some experience with this, we do some computations of m_{PQ} for a particular function in the following example.

Example 2.1.1 (Difference Triangles and Slopes of Secant Lines)

Problem: Consider the simple polynomial function

$$f(x) = 2x^2 - x^3$$

of degree three (a cubic polynomial) and the point $P = (1, 1)$ on its graph. Use a movie showing a sequence of difference triangles ΔPQR, with $Q \to P$, to estimate the slope of the tangent line at P.

Solution: The following command produces the movie.

```
> lim_triangles();
```

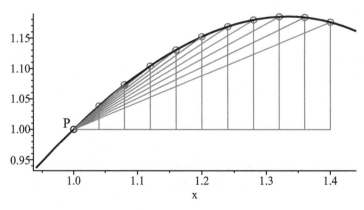

Figure 2.1.4: *A sequence of 10 difference triangles.*

The movie shows a portion of the graph near P and 10 points Q on the right side of P and on the graph of f. The movie also displays a sequence of 10 difference triangles, which get smaller and smaller as $Q \to P$. Note that in each frame of the movie, the slope m_{PQ} of the hypotenuse of the difference triangle gives an approximation to the slope of the tangent line. The initial approximations are not so good, but observe how good the approximation in the last frame is. In fact, the hypotenuse of the triangle in the last frame is indistinguishable from the part of the curve near the right side of P.

To compute some of these approximations m_{PQ} to the tangent line-slope m we use the Maple plot in Figure 2.1.4, which is a composite of all the frames in the movie. We just employ the mouse to cursor probe on the centers $Q = (x_1, y_1)$ of each of the circles and this will give the approximate coordinates, (x_1, y_1), of the point. These numbers are rounded to three digits and also depend on the accuracy of your screen resolution, so they won't be very accurate. Note the coordinates of P are exactly $P = (1, 1)$.

The point Q farthest from P has approximate coordinates $Q = (1.4, 1.17)$ and so the secant-line slope is

$$m_{PQ} = \frac{1.17 - 1}{1.4 - 1} = \frac{0.17}{0.4} = 0.425$$

Similarly the point Q next farthest from P has approximate coordinates $Q = (1.35, 1.18)$ and so the secant line slope is

$$m_{PQ} = \frac{1.18 - 1}{1.35 - 1} = \frac{0.18}{0.35} = 0.514$$

Continuing like this, we get the following table of values.

x_0	x_1	Δx	y_0	y_1	Δy	$\dfrac{\Delta y}{\Delta x}$
1	1.40	.40	1	1.17	.17	.425
1	1.35	.35	1	1.18	.18	.514
1	1.32	.32	1	1.18	.18	.562
1	1.28	.28	1	1.18	.18	.643
1	1.24	.24	1	1.17	.17	.708
1	1.20	.20	1	1.15	.15	.750
1	1.16	.16	1	1.13	.13	.812
1	1.12	.12	1	1.10	.10	.833
1	1.08	.08	1	1.07	.07	.875
1	1.04	.04	1	1.04	.04	1.00

Table 2.1.1: *Ten secant-line slopes.*

Based on these calculations, we estimate the slope of the tangent line to be $m = 1$.

Table 2.1.1 together with the graphical evidence in the above example suggests that we define the slope m of the tangent line at P to be the limit of the slopes m_{PQ} of the secant lines. That is, define

$$m = \lim_{Q \to P} m_{PQ}.$$

Applying this to Example 2.1.1, the table and graphs in that example lead us to guess that the limiting value is 1

$$m = \lim_{Q \to P} m_{PQ} = 1.$$

In the above limiting process, it is understood that Q is on the graph of f and approaches P from either side (a two-sided limit). So, technically, to be sure that the limit is 1 in this example, we need to choose a sequence of points Q on the graph that approach P from the left side.

Analytic Expressions for the Secant-Line Slopes

The definition of the slope of the tangent line involves a limiting process that looks somewhat different than the limits we discussed in the previous chapter. In order to rephrase the limit here so that it is the same as the one there, we need to rewrite m_{PQ} making it a function of a single variable. There are two ways to do this depending on what we choose for this variable:

First Way (x variable): Here we choose the variable to be the x-coordinate of the variable point Q. It will help simplify the notation if we change the designations for the coordinates of Q and P, so that there are no subscripts. So suppose $a = x_0, x = x_1$, then

$$P = (x_0, y_0) \;=\; (a, f(a))$$
$$Q = (x_1, y_1) \;=\; (x, f(x))$$

with a standing for the fixed x-coordinate of P and x standing for the variable x-coordinate of Q. With this change of notation, the differences of the x-coordinates and the differences of the y-coordinates are

$$\Delta y \;=\; y_1 - y_0 = f(x) - f(a)$$
$$\Delta x \;=\; x_1 - x_0 = x - a$$

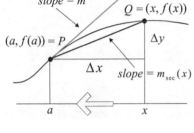

Figure 2.1.5: *The secant-slope-tion $m_{sec}(x)$ as a function of x.*

Consequently,

$$m_{PQ} = \frac{\Delta y}{\Delta x} = \frac{f(x) - f(a)}{x - a}.$$

Since a is fixed, the latter expression is a function of the single variable x only. Hence, we change the notation for m_{PQ} to $m_{sec}(x)$ in order to emphasize that it is a function of x. Now this is an ordinary function of x, and so we can take limits of $m_{sec}(x)$ just like we did in Chapter 1. We summarize this in the following definition:

DEFINITION 2.1.1 (Slope of the Tangent Line)

The secant-slope function (x variable version) is the function :

$$m_{sec}(x) = \frac{f(x) - f(a)}{x - a}$$

This expression is also called the Newton quotient. The slope of the tangent line at x = a is defined by the limit:

$$m \equiv \lim_{x \to a} \frac{f(x) - f(a)}{x - a}$$

provided this limit exists.

Note that in the definition, the limit is taken of the function $m_{sec}(x)$, which traditionally called the *Newton quotient*. So we are not taking limits of f, but rather of the Newton quotient function that is built from f. (The Newton quotient is also called the *difference quotient*.)

Figure 2.1.5 illustrates the geometry of the quantities in the definition. Also note, that in order for the slope of the tangent line to be defined like this, the (two-sided) limit of the Newton quotient must exist. When this limit does not exist, then there is no tangent line at the point P.

Example 2.1.2 (Limits of Difference Quotients)

Problem: Find the slopes of the tangent lines to the graphs of the following functions at the specified points $x = a$. Also, find an equation for each tangent line.

(a) $f(x) = \dfrac{4x}{1+x}$, $a = 2$ (b) $f(x) = \dfrac{1}{1+x^2}$, $a = 1$ (c) $f(x) = \sqrt{4 + x^2}$, $a = 2$

Solution: In each part we form the difference quotient $\dfrac{\Delta y}{\Delta x} = \dfrac{f(x) - f(a)}{x - a}$ and take the limit.

Part (a): First compute

$$f(x) - f(2) = \frac{4x}{1+x} - \frac{8}{3} = \frac{12x - 8(1+x)}{(1+x)3} = \frac{4x - 8}{3(1+x)} = \frac{4(x - 2)}{3(1+x)}$$

Then

$$\frac{f(x) - f(2)}{x - 2} = \frac{1}{x - 2} \cdot \frac{4(x - 2)}{3(1+x)} = \frac{4}{3(1+x)}$$

So the slope of the tangent line at $(2, 8/3)$ is

$$m = \lim_{x \to 2} \frac{f(x) - f(2)}{x - 2} = \lim_{x \to 2} \frac{4}{3(1+x)} = \frac{4}{3(3)} = \frac{4}{9}$$

An equation for the tangent line is $y - \dfrac{8}{3} = \dfrac{4}{9}(x - 2)$, i.e., $y = \dfrac{4}{9}x + \dfrac{16}{9}$. Figure 2.1.6 shows a graph of the function and this tangent line.

Part (b): First compute

$$f(x) - f(1) = \frac{1}{1+x^2} - \frac{1}{2} = \frac{2 - (1+x^2)}{(1+x^2)2} = \frac{1 - x^2}{2(1+x^2)} = \frac{(1 - x)(1 + x)}{2(1+x^2)}$$

Then

$$\frac{f(x) - f(1)}{x - 1} = \frac{1}{x - 1} \cdot \frac{(1 - x)(1 + x)}{2(1+x^2)} = \frac{-(1 + x)}{2(1+x^2)}$$

So the slope of the tangent line at $(1, 1/2)$ is

$$m = \lim_{x \to 1} \frac{f(x) - f(1)}{x - 1} = \lim_{x \to 1} \frac{-(1 + x)}{2(1+x^2)} = \frac{-2}{2(2)} = -\frac{1}{2}$$

An equation for the tangent line is $y - \dfrac{1}{2} = -\dfrac{1}{2}(x - 1)$, i.e., $y = -\dfrac{1}{2}x + 1$.

Part (c): For $f(x) = \sqrt{4 + x^2}$, we have $f(2) = \sqrt{8}$, and

$$
\begin{aligned}
\frac{f(x) - f(2)}{x - 2} &= \frac{\sqrt{4 + x^2} - \sqrt{8}}{x - 2} = \frac{\sqrt{4 + x^2} - \sqrt{8}}{x - 2} \cdot \frac{\sqrt{4 + x^2} + \sqrt{8}}{\sqrt{4 + x^2} + \sqrt{8}} \\
&= \frac{4 + x^2 - 8}{(x - 2)(\sqrt{4 + x^2} + \sqrt{8})} = \frac{x^2 - 4}{(x - 2)(\sqrt{4 + x^2} + \sqrt{8})} \\
&= \frac{(x - 2)(x + 2)}{(x - 2)(\sqrt{4 + x^2} + \sqrt{8})} = \frac{x + 2}{\sqrt{4 + x^2} + \sqrt{8}}
\end{aligned}
$$

So the slope of the tangent line at $(2, \sqrt{8})$ is

$$m = \lim_{x \to 2} \frac{f(x) - f(2)}{x - 2} = \lim_{x \to 2} \frac{x + 2}{\sqrt{4 + x^2} + \sqrt{8}} = \frac{4}{\sqrt{8} + \sqrt{8}} = \frac{2}{\sqrt{8}} = \frac{\sqrt{8}}{4}$$

An equation for the tangent line is $y - \sqrt{8} = \dfrac{\sqrt{8}}{4}(x - 2)$, i.e., $y = \dfrac{\sqrt{8}}{4}x + \dfrac{\sqrt{8}}{2}$.

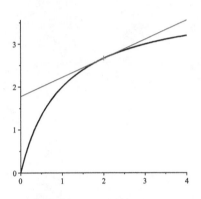

Figure 2.1.6: *The graph of* $f(x) = \frac{4x}{1+x}$ *and its tangent line at* $(2, 8/3)$.

Second Way (h variable): There is a second way to express the secant line slope

$$m_{PQ} = \frac{\Delta y}{\Delta x}$$

as a function. We choose the variable, which we call h, to be the *difference* between the x-coordinates of Q and P. As above in the x-variable way, we relabel things so that there are no subscripts in coordinates for P and Q

$$\begin{aligned} P &= (x_0, y_0) = (a, f(a)) \\ Q &= (x_1, y_1) = (x, f(x)). \end{aligned}$$

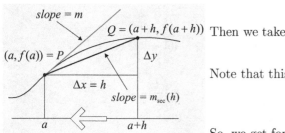

Figure 2.1.7: *The secant-slope function $m_{\text{sec}}(h)$ depends on h.*

Then we take

$$h = x - a.$$

Note that this means, upon rearranging, that

$$x = a + h.$$

So, we get for the differences

$$\begin{aligned} \Delta y &= y_1 - y_0 = f(x) - f(a) = f(a + h) - f(a) \\ \Delta x &= x_1 - x_0 = x - a = h. \end{aligned}$$

Consequently,

$$m_{PQ} = \frac{\Delta y}{\Delta x} = \frac{f(x) - f(a)}{x - a} = \frac{f(a + h) - f(a)}{h}.$$

The last expression gives us m_{PQ} as a function of h, which as before we denote by $m_{sec}(h)$, even though it is a different function. We summarize this in the following definition.

DEFINITION 2.1.2 (Slope of the Tangent Line)

The secant-slope function (h variable version) is the function :

$$m_{\text{sec}}(h) = \frac{f(a + h) - f(a)}{h}$$

This expression is also called the Newton quotient. The slope of the tangent line at x = a is the defined by the limit :

$$m \equiv \lim_{h \to 0} \frac{f(a + h) - f(a)}{h}$$

provided this limit exists.

The geometry of the quantities in this definition are illustrated in Figure 2.1.7

NOTE: The two expressions for the secant-slope function (a.k.a., the Newton quotient and the difference quotient) are similar but distinct. The limit notations are slightly different too. In the x-variable limit notation, $x \to a$, while in the h-variable limit notation, $h \to 0$. So you need to focus on which of these two ways (x-variable way or h-variable way) you are using to find the tangent-line slope.

YOUR CHOICE: The choice of which way you write the Newton/Difference quotient (x-variable way or h-variable way) depends on the nature of the function. Sometimes one way may seem easier to you than the other.

Example 2.1.3 (Using the h Variable Way)

Problem: Reconsider the function

$$f(x) = 2x^2 - x^3$$

from a previous example. Use the h-variable expression for the Newton quotient to find the slope m of the tangent line to the graph of f at $x = 1$. For this, employ the algebraic method of evaluating limits.

Solution: First we compute $f(1 + h)$ using the binomial formula:

$$\begin{aligned} f(1+h) &= 2(1+h)^2 - (1+h)^3 = 2(1 + 2h + h^2) - (1 + 3h + 3h^2 + h^3) \\ &= 2 + 4h + 2h^2 - 1 - 3h - 3h^2 - h^3 \\ &= 1 + h - h^2 - h^3 \end{aligned}$$

Since $f(1) = 1$, we get the following simple expression for the Newton quotient

$$m_{\text{sec}}(h) = \frac{f(1+h) - f(1)}{h} = \frac{1 + h - h^2 - h^3 - 1}{h} = \frac{h - h^2 - h^3}{h} = 1 - h - h^2$$

We can take limits of this as $h \to 0$ by using the last expression $1 - h - h^2$ and plugging in $h = 0$:

$$m = \lim_{h \to 0} m_{\text{sec}}(h) = \lim_{h \to 0}(1 - h - h^2) = 1 - 0 - 0 = 1.$$

You should compare the expression for $m_{sec}(h)$ with $m_{sec}(x) = \frac{2x^2 - x^3 - 1}{x - 1}$, which is the x-variable version. This seems a little harder to factor and reduce before taking the limit.

Here are some additional examples to illustrate the process of forming the Newton quotient and taking limits to get the tangent-line slope (when one exists).

Example 2.1.4 (Using the h Variable Way)

Problem: For the function

$$f(x) = \frac{1}{x},$$

find the tangent-line slope at $x = 2$.

Solution: First we form the Newton quotient and simplify it:

$$\begin{aligned} \frac{f(2+h) - f(2)}{h} &= \frac{\frac{1}{2+h} - \frac{1}{2}}{h} \\ &= \frac{1}{h}\left(\frac{1}{2+h} - \frac{1}{2}\right) = \frac{1}{h}\left(\frac{2 - (2+h)}{(2+h)2}\right) \\ &= \frac{1}{h}\left(\frac{-h}{(2+h)2}\right) = \frac{-1}{(2+h)2} \end{aligned}$$

Thus, the slope of the tangent line at $x = 2$ is easily computed to be

$$m = \lim_{h \to 0} \frac{f(2+h) - f(2)}{h} = \lim_{h \to 0} \frac{-1}{(2+h)2} = \frac{-1}{(2+0)2} = -\frac{1}{4}.$$

Example 2.1.5 (Switch Back to the x Variable Way)

Problem: For the function

$$f(x) = \frac{\sqrt{x}}{1 + \sqrt{x}},$$

find an equation for the tangent line at $a = 4$.

Solution: Here is a problem that easier to do using the x-variable difference quotient. So we look at $\Delta y = f(x) - f(4)$, simplify it, and rationalize the numerator:

$$
\begin{aligned}
f(x) - f(4) &= \frac{\sqrt{x}}{1 + \sqrt{x}} - \frac{2}{3} = \frac{3\sqrt{x} - 2(1 + \sqrt{x})}{(1 + \sqrt{x}) \cdot 3} \\
&= \frac{\sqrt{x} - 2}{3(1 + \sqrt{x})} = \frac{\sqrt{x} - 2}{3(1 + \sqrt{x})} \cdot \frac{\sqrt{x} + 2}{\sqrt{x} + 2} \\
&= \frac{x - 4}{3(1 + \sqrt{x})(\sqrt{x} + 2)}
\end{aligned}
$$

Dividing this result by $x - 4$ and taking the limit gives the slope

$$
m = \lim_{x \to 4} \frac{f(x) - f(4)}{x - 4} = \lim_{x \to 4} \frac{1}{3(1 + \sqrt{x})(\sqrt{x} + 2)} = \frac{1}{3(3)(4)} = \frac{1}{36}
$$

Having this, we can write an equation for the tangent line at $(4, 2/3)$:

$$
y - \frac{2}{3} = \frac{1}{36}(x - 4), \text{ i.e., } y = \frac{1}{36}x + \frac{5}{9}
$$

EXERCISE: Try this problem using the h-variable way. Is it harder?

Example 2.1.6 (The Graphical Method)

Problem: Here is a problem where the algebraic method cannot be used to evaluate the limit of the Newton quotient. So, we use the graphical method to approximate this limit.

The function is

```
> f:=x->x*exp(-2*x);
```

$$
f := x \to xe^{-2x}
$$

and we want the slope of the tangent line at $x = 1$.

Solution: The Newton quotient is

$$
\frac{f(1 + h) - f(1)}{h} = \frac{(1 + h)e^{-2(1+h)} - e^{-2}}{h}.
$$

The only obvious algebraic simplification of this is to factor out e^{-2} from the numerator. But this does not help us see what the limit is as $h \to 0$, so we leave the Newton quotient as it is and use, say, the graphical method to approximate the limit of the secant-slope function:

$$
\lim_{h \to 0} \frac{(1 + h)e^{-2(1+h)} - e^{-2}}{h}
$$

First we define the function that we are taking the limit of:

```
> msec:=h->(f(1+h)-f(1))/h;
```

$$
msec := h \to \frac{f(1+h) - f(1)}{h}
$$

Then we plot it on an interval about $h = 0$:

```
> plot(msec(h),h=-1..1);
```

This gives Figure 2.1.8. By using the cursor probe on the point in the figure where the graph crosses the y-axis, we discern that the limit of $m_{sec}(h)$ as $h \to 0$ is approximately $m = -0.14$, i.e.,

$$
m = \lim_{h \to 0} \frac{f(1 + h) - f(1)}{h} = \lim_{h \to 0} \frac{(1 + h)e^{-2(1+h)} - e^{-2}}{h} \approx -0.14.
$$

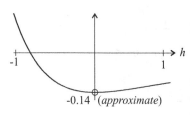

Figure 2.1.8: *Plot of the secant slope function* $m_{\text{sec}}(h) = \frac{(1+h)e^{-2(1+h)} - e^{-2}}{h}.$

This is supposed to be the approximate slope of the tangent line. To check this, we plot the original function and the line with this slope passing through the point $(1, f(1))$. First, let's compute the approximate y-value of this point:

> evalf(f(1));

$$0.1353352832$$

Then the approximate tangent-line equation should be

$$y = 0.135 - 0.14(x - 1)$$

So we define this as a function, called g, and plot it along with the function f.

> g:=x->.135-0.14*(x-1);

$$g := x \to 0.275 - 0.14x$$

> plot([f(x),g(x)],x=0..2,color=[black,red],thickness=2);

Since the line in Figure 2.1.9 appears to be tangent to the graph at $(1, f(1))$, we conclude that the approximation to m is pretty good. Later in this chapter we will be able to find the exact value of m using other methods.

The next example illustrates that some functions may fail to have a tangent line at certain points on their graphs.

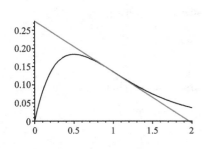

Figure 2.1.9: *Plot of and the approximate tangent line $y = .135 - .14(x - 1)$ at the point $(1, f(1))$ on the graph.*

Example 2.1.7 (A Piecewise-Defined Function)

Problem: Many piecewise-defined functions fail to have tangent lines at the points where the "piecing" occurs. The reason this can happen is that on the left side of such a point, one formula is used, while on the right side another formula is used. These separate formulas represent the different functions being pieced together at the point, and these functions may have tangent lines that are different.

Here is an example where this occurs:

$$f(x) = \begin{cases} \frac{3}{4} x^2 & \text{if } x < 2 \\ 4 - \frac{1}{4} x^2 & \text{if } x \geq 2 \end{cases}.$$

Use the limit definition to find, if possible, the slope of the tangent line at $x = 2$. If there is no tangent line use some Maple plots to illustrate why this is so.

Solution: As usual, just form the Newton quotient and take limits. However, the Newton quotient

$$\frac{f(2 + h) - f(2)}{h}$$

is a little bit trickier to express and simplify here than it is for a function given by a single formula. It is easy enough to compute

$$f(2) = 4 - \frac{2^2}{4} = 4 - 1 = 3.$$

But how do we compute $f(2 + h)$? To do this we have to split into cases according to whether $h < 0$ or $h \geq 0$.

If $h < 0$, then $2 + h < 2$ and so

$$f(2 + h) = \frac{3}{4}(2 + h)^2 = \frac{3}{4}(4 + 4h + h^2) = 3 + 3h + \frac{3}{4}h^2$$

While if $h \geq 0$, then $2 + h \geq 2$, and so

$$f(2 + h) = 4 - \frac{1}{4}(2 + h)^2 = 4 - \frac{1}{4}(4 + 4h + h^2) = 3 - h - \frac{1}{4}h^2$$

Thus, in the first case (i.e., $h < 0$)

$$\frac{f(2 + h) - f(2)}{h} = \frac{3h + \frac{3}{4}h^2}{h} = 3 + \frac{3}{4}h$$

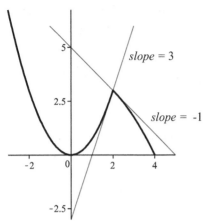

Figure 2.1.10: *Plot of f (in black) and the two lines through (2, 3) with slopes 3 (in red) and −1 (in blue), respectively.*

while in the second case (i.e., $h \geq 0$)

$$\frac{f(2+h) - f(2)}{h} = \frac{-h - \frac{1}{4}h^2}{h} = -1 - \frac{1}{4}h$$

Consequently the secant-slope function is the piecewise-defined function:

$$m_{\text{sec}}(h) = \begin{cases} 3 + \frac{3}{4}h & \text{if } h < 0 \\ -1 - \frac{1}{4}h & \text{if } h \geq 0 \end{cases}$$

From your work in Chapter 1 with one-sided limits, you see that each one-sided limit exists at $h = 0$:

$$\lim_{h \to 0-} m_{\text{sec}}(h) = 3$$

$$\lim_{h \to 0+} m_{\text{sec}}(h) = -1$$

However, since these one-sided limits have different values, the two sided limit

$$\lim_{h \to 0} m_{\text{sec}}(h) = \textit{does not exist}$$

Hence, by definition, there is no tangent line to the graph of f at $x = 2$. To examine more closely why this is so, we plot the function f and the two lines through the point $(2, 3)$ with slopes 3 and −1, respectively. Figure 2.1.10 shows this.

The figure shows that the left-sided and right-sided limits 3 and −1 are the slopes of tangent lines to the left side and right side of the graph of f. There is, however, no tangent line to the graph of f at $x = 1$ because of this jump from slope 3 to slope −1 as x moves from left to right past $x = 2$. The graph changes abruptly from increasing to decreasing and a jagged edge is created at the point $(2, 3)$ on the graph. We say that the graph is not smooth there because of the abrupt (noncontinuous) change in the tangent-line slopes.

Figure 2.1.10 was produced with the following, standard, Maple code. Note several things about the code:

(1) We plot the function f with constrained scaling. This is so the slopes of lines in the figure will appear correctly.

(2) We create separate plots and then combine them with the display command. This is so we can adjust the lengths of the two lines and achieve a nice looking figure. (Using the range x = -3..4 in the plots of the lines makes them too long.)

```
> f:=proc(x)
>     if x<2 then 3*x^2/4
>        else 4-x^2/4
>      end if;
>   end proc:
>
> line1:=x->3+3*(x-2);}
```

$$\textit{line1} := x \to -3 + 3x$$

```
line2:=x->3-1*(x-2);
```

$$\textit{line2} := x \to 5 - x$$

```
> pf:=plot('f(x)',x=-3..4,color=black,thickness=2,scaling=constrained):
> pline1:=plot(line1(x),x=0..3):
> pline2:=plot(line2(x),x=-1..5,color=blue):
> with(plots,display):
> display({pf,pline1,pline2});
```

Exercises: 2.1 (The Tangent Line Problem)

```
> with(code_ch2sec1);
> with(limit_tools,twosidelimit);
> with(plots,display);
```
[diff_triangles,lim_triangles,limitsecants ,limsec2,tanplot]
[twosidelimit]
[display]

CAS: **Graphically Estimating Slopes of Tangent Lines–Part 1 (Limits of Secant Lines)**

In each of Exercises 1–10, watch the movie generated by `limitsecants` showing the secant lines approaching the tangent line at the point $P = (x_0, f(x_0))$ on the graph of a function f. Use the last frame in the movie to estimate the slope m of the tangent line. You can do this by using the cursor probe on a point $R = (x_1, y_1)$ on the approximate tangent line (R must be different that P). Then compute $\dfrac{y_1 - y_0}{x_1 - x_0} \approx m$. NOTE: The last argument of `limitsecants` determines whether you get a movie or a static plot of the last frame of the movie. Use 1 for a movie and use 0 for the a plot of the last frame.

1. $f(x) = 4x^2 - x^4 + 1$, at $x_0 = 1$
2. $f(x) = 4x^3 - x^5 + 1$, at $x_0 = 1$
3. $f(x) = x^{\sin x}$, at $x_0 = 1$
4. $f(x) = x^{\cos(x/2)}$, at $x_0 = 1$
5. $f(x) = \ln(x - 1)$, at $x_0 = 2$
6. $f(x) = \sqrt{\ln x}$, at $x_0 = 2$
7. $f(x) = \frac{1}{2}x^2 \ln x$, at $x_0 = 1$
8. $f(x) = \frac{1}{3}x \ln x$, at $x_0 = 1$
9. $f(x) = \sqrt{|x|}$, at $x_0 = 0$
10. $f(x) = x^{1/3}$ at $x_0 = 0$

CAS: **Graphically Estimating Slopes of Tangent Lines–Part 2 (Limits Difference Triangles)**

In Exercises 11–20 estimate the slope of the tangent line to the graph of $y = f(x)$ at the point $P = (x_0, f(x_0))$. Do this as we did in Example 2.1.1. Specifically:

(a) Watch the movie of the ten difference triangles.

(b) Use the cursor probe on the last frame of the movie to obtain data to compute the lengths Δx and Δy of the sides of each difference triangle.

(c) Compute the slope $m_{PQ} = \dfrac{\Delta y}{\Delta x}$ of each hypotenuse. Use the data from these ten slopes to estimate the slope of the tangent line at P.

(d) Compare the the tangent-line slope you got here with the one in the corresponding exercise above (assuming you did that one).

Record your data and calculations in a table like Table 2.1.1.

NOTE: The data you collect from the movie (and therefore your estimate of the tangent-line slope) are approximate and can vary from person-to-person. Even clicking very carefully can give results different from the ones we give below in the answers.

11. $f(x) = 4x^2 - x^4 + 1$, at $x_0 = 1$
12. $f(x) = 4x^3 - x^5 + 1$, at $x_0 = 1$
13. $f(x) = x^{\sin x}$, at $x_0 = 1$
14. $f(x) = x^{\cos(x/2)}$, at $x_0 = 1$
15. $f(x) = \ln(x - 1)$, at $x_0 = 2$
16. $f(x) = \sqrt{\ln x}$, at $x_0 = 2$
17. $f(x) = \frac{1}{2}x^2 \ln x$, at $x_0 = 1$
18. $f(x) = \frac{1}{3}x \ln x$, at $x_0 = 1$
19. $f(x) = \sqrt{|x|}$, at $x_0 = 0$
20. $f(x) = x^{1/3}$, at $x_0 = 0$

CAS: **Numerically Estimating Slopes of Tangent Lines–(Newton Quotients $m_{sec}(x)$)**

In Exercises 21–30, for the given function f and the given point a, do the following:

(a) Write the expression for the Newton quotient $m_{sec}(x)$ (a.k.a, the secant-slope function) in the x-variable form:

$$m_{\sec}(x) = \frac{f(x) - f(a)}{x - a}$$

Simplify where possible.

(b) Use Maple or a calculator to compute the ten values of $m_{\sec}(x)$ for the ten x-values you found for this function in Exercises 11–20 above (just the ones you worked out of that group).

(c) Use this information to guess the value $m = \displaystyle\lim_{x \to a} \dfrac{f(x) - f(a)}{x - a}$ for the slope of the tangent line (provided the limit exists).

21. $f(x) = 4x^2 - x^4 + 1$, at $a = 1$
22. $f(x) = 4x^3 - x^5 + 1$, at $a = 1$
23. $f(x) = x^{\sin x}$, at $a = 1$
24. $f(x) = x^{\cos(x/2)}$, at $a = 1$
25. $f(x) = \ln(x - 1)$, at $a = 2$
26. $f(x) = \sqrt{\ln x}$, at $a = 2$
27. $f(x) = \frac{1}{2}x^2 \ln x$, at $a = 1$
28. $f(x) = \frac{1}{3}x \ln x$, at $a = 1$
29. $f(x) = \sqrt{|x|}$, at $a = 0$
30. $f(x) = x^{1/3}$, at $a = 0$

Algebraically Calculating Slopes of Tangent Lines–(Newton Quotients, x Variable Version)

In Exercises 31–68 , for the given function f and the given point a, do the following:

(a) Write the expression for the secant-slope function in the x-variable form:

$$m_{\sec}(x) = \frac{f(x) - f(a)}{x - a},$$

and simplify as much as possible.

(b) Find the slope of the tangent line $m = \lim_{x \to a} m_{\sec}(x)$ by evaluating the limit. Find this limit exactly using the algebraic method,

(c) Write an equation for the tangent line to f at $(a, f(a))$. Optional: Check your work by graphing the function f and the tangent line at the given point.

31. $f(x) = 4 - x^2, a = 1$ **32.** $f(x) = 9 - x^2, a = 2$
33. $f(x) = 1 - x^3, a = 2$ **34.** $f(x) = 2 - x^3, a = 1$
35. $f(x) = 1/x, a = 2$ **36.** $f(x) = 2/x, a = 1$
37. $f(x) = 1/x^2, a = 3$ **38.** $f(x) = 1/x^2, a = 2$
39. $f(x) = 1/x^3, a = 2$ **40.** $f(x) = 1/x^3, a = 1$
41. $f(x) = 1/\sqrt{x}, a = 4$ **42.** $f(x) = -1/\sqrt{x}, a = 9$
43. $f(x) = \dfrac{6}{x + 2}, a = 2$ **44.** $f(x) = \dfrac{5}{x + 3}, a = 2$
45. $f(x) = \dfrac{x}{1 + x}, a = 2$ **46.** $f(x) = \dfrac{x}{2 + x}, a = 1$
47. $f(x) = \dfrac{x + 1}{x + 3}, a = 2$ **48.** $f(x) = \dfrac{x + 2}{x + 5}, a = 1$
49. $f(x) = \sqrt{5 + x^2}, a = 1$ **50.** $f(x) = \sqrt{3 + x^2}, a = 2$
51. $f(x) = \dfrac{1}{1 + x^2}, a = 2$ **52.** $f(x) = \dfrac{2}{2 + x^2}, a = 1$
53. $f(x) = \dfrac{1}{1 + x^3}, a = 2$ **54.** $f(x) = \dfrac{2}{2 + x^3}, a = 1$
55. $f(x) = \dfrac{x^2}{1 + x^2}, a = 2$ **56.** $f(x) = \dfrac{x^2}{2 + x^2}, a = 1$
57. $f(x) = \dfrac{x}{1 + x^2}, a = 2$ **58.** $f(x) = \dfrac{x}{2 + x^2}, a = 1$
59. $f(x) = \sqrt{x^2 + 3x}, a = 1$ **60.** $f(x) = \sqrt{x^2 + 5x}, a = 1$
61. $f(x) = \sqrt{x^3 + 1}, a = 1$ **62.** $f(x) = \sqrt{x^3 + 2}, a = 1$
63. $f(x) = \dfrac{1}{\sqrt{4 - x^2}}, a = 1$ **64.** $f(x) = \dfrac{1}{\sqrt{9 - x^2}}, a = 2$
65. $f(x) = \dfrac{1}{\sqrt{1 + x^2}}, a = 2$ **66.** $f(x) = \dfrac{1}{\sqrt{4 + x^2}}, a = 1$
67. $f(x) = \sqrt{1 + \sqrt{x}}, a = 1$ **68.** $f(x) = \sqrt{2 + \sqrt{x}}, a = 1$

Algebraically Calculating Slopes of Tangent Lines–(Newton Quotients h Variable Version)

In Exercises 69–106 , for the given function f and the given point a, do the following:

(a) Write the expression for the secant-slope function in the h-variable form:

$$m_{\sec}(h) = \frac{f(a + h) - f(a)}{h},$$

and simplify as much as possible.

(b) Find the slope of the tangent line $\lim_{h \to 0} m_{\sec}(h)$ by evaluating the limit. NOTE: In Exercises 69–100, find this limit exactly using the algebraic method, but in Exercises 101–104, you will have to guess the value of the limit using Maple and the graphical method (See Example 2.1.6).

(c) Write an equation for the tangent line to f at $(a, f(a))$. Optional: Check your work by graphing the function f and the tangent line at the given point.

NOTE: In 105–106, the function f is piecewise-defined, so in evaluating the limit, you will have to use one-sided limits. (See Example 2.1.7.) Also in this situation the tangent line may fail to exist, but tangent lines on each side of where the graph is pieced together may exist. If so, for part (c) write equations for these two lines and check your work by graphing them and along with f.

69. $f(x) = x^2 - 3x, a = 2$ **70.** $f(x) = x^2 - 4x, a = 1$
71. $f(x) = x^3 - 4x^2 + 12, a = 1$
72. $f(x) = x^3 - 3x^2 + 2, a = 0$
73. $f(x) = \sqrt{x + 1}, a = 1$ **74.** $f(x) = \sqrt{x - 2}, a = 5$
75. $f(x) = 1/x, a = 2$ **76.** $f(x) = 3/x, a = 1$
77. $f(x) = 2/(x + 3), a = 2$ **78.** $f(x) = 3/(x + 2), a = 3$
79. $f(x) = 1/x^2, a = 2$ **80.** $f(x) = 3/x^2, a = 1$
81. $f(x) = 1/x^3, a = 2$ **82.** $f(x) = 1/x^3, a = 1$
83. $f(x) = 1/\sqrt{x}, a = 4$ **84.** $f(x) = -1/\sqrt{x}, a = 9$
85. $f(x) = \dfrac{6}{x + 2}, a = 2$ **86.** $f(x) = \dfrac{5}{x + 3}, a = 2$
87. $f(x) = \dfrac{x}{1 + x}, a = 2$ **88.** $f(x) = \dfrac{x}{x - 1}, a = 3$
89. $f(x) = \dfrac{1 + x}{2 + x}, a = 2$ **90.** $f(x) = \dfrac{1 - x}{2 + x}, a = 3$
91. $f(x) = \dfrac{1}{1 + x^2}, a = 2$ **92.** $f(x) = \dfrac{2}{2 + x^2}, a = 1$
93. $f(x) = \dfrac{1}{1 + x^3}, a = 2$ **94.** $f(x) = \dfrac{2}{2 + x^3}, a = 1$
95. $f(x) = \dfrac{x^2}{1 + x^2}, a = 2$ **96.** $f(x) = \dfrac{x^2}{2 + x^2}, a = 1$
97. $f(x) = \dfrac{10}{1 + \sqrt{x}}, a = 1$ **98.** $f(x) = \dfrac{20}{2 + \sqrt{x}}, a = 1$
99. $f(x) = \sqrt{1 + \sqrt{x}}, a = 1$ **100.** $f(x) = \sqrt{2 + \sqrt{x}}, a = 1$
101. $f(x) = (10 \ln x)/x, a = 2$ **102.** $f(x) = \ln(x + 2), a = 1$
103. $f(x) = x^2 e^{-x}, a = 1$ **104.** $f(x) = x^3 e^{-x}, a = 1$
105. $f(x) = \begin{cases} 4 - x^2 & \text{if } x < -1 \\ x^2 + 2 & \text{if } x \geq -1 \end{cases}, a = -1$
106. $f(x) = \begin{cases} -x^3 & \text{if } x \leq 0 \\ x^3 + 1 & \text{if } x > 0 \end{cases}, a = 0$

Calculus Concepts & Computation
2.2 The Derivative Function

In Section 2.1 we solved the tangent line problem by using limits to define and calculate the slope of the tangent line at a given point. Specifically, for a function f and a given point $P = (a, f(a))$ on the graph of f, we formed the Newton quotient

$$m_{\text{sec}}(h) = \frac{f(a+h) - f(a)}{h},$$

and then took the limit of this function of h, as $h \to 0$, to get the slope m of the tangent line at $x = a$:

$$m = \lim_{h \to 0} m_{\text{sec}}(h) = \lim_{h \to 0} \frac{f(a+h) - f(a)}{h}$$

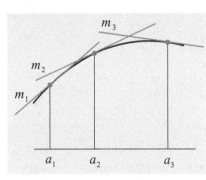

(assuming this limit exists). In the limiting process h goes to zero and a remains fixed. The end result, namely m, depends on the fixed value of a that is chosen. A different choice of a will, generally lead to a different value of m. So the whole process is:

(1) Choose a.

(2) Form the Newton quotient: $\dfrac{f(a+h) - f(a)}{h}$.

(3) Take the limit as $h \to 0$ to get m.

This can be thought of as defining m as a function of a. Figure 2.2.1 shows three choices a_1, a_2, a_3 for a and the corresponding values m_1, m_2, m_3 for m.

Figure 2.2.1: *Tangent line slopes* m_1, m_2, m_3 *for three choices of* a.

We need to introduce a notation for this functional dependence of m on a. One common notation is to use the function's name f with a prime mark on it for the name of the new function that expresses the functional dependence of m on a. That is, use f' for the new function (read this as eff prime). Then the functional dependence is written as

$$m = f'(a).$$

This notation is natural, because the process of getting m from a involves doing something to the function f to get a new, or derived function f'.

Example 2.2.1 (The Derivative of the Squaring Function)

Problem: As a simple example to illustrate this new concept, consider the function $f(x) = x^2$. Calculate $f'(a)$ for an unspecified value of a.

Solution: This is very similar to what you did in the previous section. Let's do a few calculations for particular values of a first, and then we will do it for a general, or unspecified, value of a.

For $a = 1$, the slope of the tangent line at 1 is $m = f'(1)$ and is calculated as follows:

$$
\begin{aligned}
f'(1) &= \lim_{h \to 0} \frac{f(1+h) - f(1)}{h} = \lim_{h \to 0} \frac{(1+h)^2 - 1}{h} \\
&= \lim_{h \to 0} \frac{1 + 2h + h^2 - 1}{h} = \lim_{h \to 0} \frac{2h + h^2}{h} = \lim_{h \to 0}(2 + h) = 2
\end{aligned}
$$

For $a = 2$, the slope of the tangent line at 2 is calculated as follows:

$$
\begin{aligned}
f'(2) &= \lim_{h \to 0} \frac{f(2+h) - f(2)}{h} = \lim_{h \to 0} \frac{(2+h)^2 - 4}{h} \\
&= \lim_{h \to 0} \frac{4 + 4h + h^2 - 4}{h} = \lim_{h \to 0} \frac{4h + h^2}{h} = \lim_{h \to 0}(4 + h) = 4
\end{aligned}
$$

Maybe you can guess from these two particular calculations what the formula for $f'(a)$ is in general. If not, just do the general calculation as follows.

$$f'(a) = \lim_{h\to 0}\frac{f(a+h)-f(a)}{h} = \lim_{h\to 0}\frac{(a+h)^2 - a^2}{h}$$

$$= \lim_{h\to 0}\frac{a^2 + 2ah + h^2 - a^2}{h} = \lim_{h\to 0}\frac{2ah + h^2}{h} = \lim_{h\to 0}(2a+h) = 2a$$

The algebra involved in the general calculation here is only slightly more complicated than in the two particular calculations for $a = 1$ and $a = 2$. The motive for doing the general calculation should be clear. Namely, now we have a formula for the slope of the tangent line at a:

$$f'(a) = 2a,$$

which is valid for any a. So now we do not have to use limits to calculate $f'(0)$ or $f'(-5)$. We just use the formula to get

$$f'(0) = 0 \qquad \text{and} \qquad f'(-5) = -10,$$

respectively.

The above example motivates the differentiation process: Start with a given function f and derive a new function f' called the derivative function. The example shows that if we start with the simple second-power function

$$f(x) = x^2,$$

then the limit definition (either the h variable or the x variable version) gives the formula

$$f'(a) = 2a,$$

which we can rewrite in terms of the traditional independent variable x:

$$f'(x) = 2x.$$

We formally record all of this in the next definition.

DEFINITION 2.2.1 (The Derivative Function)

Suppose f is a given function. Then for any a in the domain of f, we let

$$f'(a) \equiv \lim_{h\to 0}\frac{f(a+h)-f(a)}{h} = \lim_{x\to a}\frac{f(x)-f(a)}{x-a} \qquad (2.2.1)$$

provided this limit exists. The number $f'(a)$ is called the derivative of f at a, and f is said to be differentiable at a. This defines a function f' called the derivative function, with domain consisting of those a for which the limit (2.2.1) exists.

One of our primary tasks from now on will be to take a function f and differentiate it to determine the derivative function f', i.e., determine the expression for $f'(a)$ (for an arbitrary a). You will see plenty of applications and uses of the derivative function. The principal application (and motivation) so far is: $f'(a)$ is the slope of the tangent line at a. Thus, it is important for you to become skilled at calculating the expression $f'(a)$ for the derivative. In this section you will use Equation (2.2.1) for this, which is called *finding the derivative using the limit definition*.

NOTE: Equation (2.2.1) gives two ways (h-variable and x-variable) for calculating $f'(a)$. As you saw in Section 2.1, depending on the function, one way is sometimes easier than the other.

Later, we will discuss theorems and short-cut formulas that will be quicker than using the limit definition. They will also allow you to tackle more complicated functions.

Example 2.2.2 (The Derivative of a Polynomial Function)

Problem: One of the primary examples from the previous section involved the function
$$f(x) = 2x^2 - x^3.$$
So it seems appropriate to calculate the derivative of this function.

Solution: Rather than plugging everything directly into the limit definition (2.2.1), you may find it easier to calculate the Newton quotient separately and simplify it. Then take limits of the result. That's what we do here, using the h-variable way.

First use the binomial theorem to calculate
$$\begin{aligned} f(a+h) &= 2(a+h)^2 - (a+h)^3 \\ &= 2(a^2 + 2ah + h^2) - (a^3 + 3a^2h + 3ah^2 + h^3) \\ &= 2a^2 + 4ah + 2h^2 - a^3 - 3a^2h - 3ah^2 - h^3 \end{aligned}$$

Note that we have not combined any terms in the final line. That's because if we now subtract $f(a) = 2a^2 - a^3$, then the first and fourth terms will be cancelled. Thus
$$\begin{aligned} f(a+h) - f(a) &= (2a^2 + 4ah + 2h^2 - a^3 - 3a^2h - 3ah^2 - h^3) - (2a^2 - a^3) \\ &= 4ah + 2h^2 - 3a^2h - 3ah^2 - h^3 \end{aligned}$$

and so the Newton quotient is
$$\frac{f(a+h) - f(a)}{h} = \frac{4ah + 2h^2 - 3a^2h - 3ah^2 - h^3}{h} = 4a + 2h - 3a^2 - 3ah - h^2$$

Now it's easy to take the limit of this to get the derivative of f:
$$f'(a) = \lim_{h \to 0} \frac{f(a+h) - f(a)}{h} = \lim_{h \to 0} (4a + 2h - 3a^2 - 3ah - h^2) = 4a - 3a^2$$

In summary, the limit definition gives us that derivative of the function
$$f(x) = 2x^2 - x^3$$
is the function
$$f'(a) = 4a - 3a^2, \text{ that is, } f'(x) = 4x - 3x^2.$$

Example 2.2.3 (The Derivative of the Square Root Function)

Problem: A simple, but important function is the square root function $f(x) = \sqrt{x}$. Find its derivative and an equation for the tangent line to its graph at $a = 1$.

Solution: Finding the derivative function can be easily done by rationalizing the numerator of the x-variable version of Newton quotient as follows;
$$\begin{aligned} \frac{f(x) - f(a)}{x - a} &= \frac{\sqrt{x} - \sqrt{a}}{x - a} = \frac{\sqrt{x} - \sqrt{a}}{x - a} \cdot \frac{\sqrt{x} + \sqrt{a}}{\sqrt{x} + \sqrt{a}} \\ &= \frac{x - a}{(x - a)(\sqrt{x} + \sqrt{a})} = \frac{1}{\sqrt{x} + \sqrt{a}} \end{aligned}$$

Notice that in going from the second to the third line, we multiplied out the numerator, but not the denominator. Usually this is the rule: *keep the denominator in factored form when rationalizing the numerator (and vice versa when rationalizing the denominator)*

Now with the Newton quotient in the above form, we can easily take its limit as follows:

$$f'(a) \;=\; \lim_{x \to a} \frac{f(x) - f(a)}{x - a} = \lim_{x \to a} \frac{1}{\sqrt{x} + \sqrt{a}}$$

$$=\; \frac{1}{\sqrt{a} + \sqrt{a}} = \frac{1}{2\sqrt{a}}$$

This is a result that we will use many times, so, we record it in the margin box.

The derivative of $\quad f(x) = \sqrt{x}$

is $\quad f'(x) = \dfrac{1}{2\sqrt{x}}$

This formula for the derivative is easily remembered. It says that the *derivative of the square root function is one over two times the square root function*. Alternatively, if you wish to express the result in terms of power functions, you can say that the derivative of

$$f(x) = x^{1/2},$$

is given by

$$f'(x) = \frac{1}{2} x^{-1/2}.$$

Doing this allows you to perhaps see what the derivative of a general power function $f(x) = x^r$ should be. (See the next section). Finally, the tangent line at the point $(1,1)$ has slope $f'(1) = 1/2$. So, an equation for it is

$$y - 1 = \frac{1}{2}(x - 1), \quad \text{equivalently,} \quad y = \frac{1}{2} x + \frac{1}{2}$$

The sketch in Figure 2.2.2 suggests that our calculations are correct.

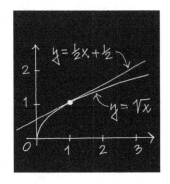

Figure 2.2.2: *The graph of* $f(x) = \sqrt{x}$ *and its tangent line at* $(1,1)$.

Example 2.2.4 (The Derivative of a Rational Function)

Problem: For the function $f(x) = \dfrac{1}{1 + x^2}$, find $f'(x)$.

Solution: The x-variable version of the Newton quotient for f is

$$\frac{f(x) - f(a)}{x - a} \;=\; \frac{1}{x - a}\,(f(x) - f(a)) = \frac{1}{x - a}\left(\frac{1}{1 + x^2} - \frac{1}{1 + a^2}\right)$$

$$=\; \frac{1}{x - a} \cdot \frac{1 + a^2 - (1 + x^2)}{(1 + x^2)(1 + a^2)} = \frac{1}{x - a} \cdot \frac{a^2 - x^2}{(1 + x^2)(1 + a^2)}$$

$$=\; \frac{1}{x - a} \cdot \frac{(a - x)(a + x)}{(1 + x^2)(1 + a^2)} = \frac{-(a + x)}{(1 + x^2)(1 + a^2)}$$

Hence,

$$f'(a) = \lim_{x \to a} \frac{f(x) - f(a)}{x - a} = \lim_{x \to a} \frac{-(a + x)}{(1 + x^2)(1 + a^2)} = \frac{-2a}{(1 + a^2)^2}$$

Thus,

$$f'(x) = \frac{-2x}{(1 + x^2)^2}$$

NOTE (Switching a and x): In all the examples so far, whether we used the x-variable or the h-variable way, the a was fixed in the limiting process and the formula for f' was expressed in terms of a. We then rewrote $f'(a)$ as $f'(x)$, since x is the traditional independent variable. Observe, however, if we replace a by x in the h-variable version of the Newton quotient, then the limit will involve x instead of a and no rewriting is required.

ALTERNATIVE FORMULA for the DERIVATIVE FUNCTION

The formula for the derivative function can also be calculated by

$$f'(x) \equiv \lim_{h \to 0} \frac{f(x+h) - f(x)}{h} \qquad (2.2.2)$$

for any x in its domain

The next example shows how this works

Example 2.2.5 (The Derivative of the Inverse Square Function)

Problem: As an example that uses fractional algebra to simplify the Newton quotient, consider the function $f(x) = 1/x^2$. Find $f'(x)$ for this function.

Solution: The Newton quotient for f is

$$\begin{aligned}
\frac{f(x+h) - f(x)}{h} &= \frac{\frac{1}{(x+h)^2} - \frac{1}{x^2}}{h} = \frac{1}{h} \cdot \left(\frac{1}{(x+h)^2} - \frac{1}{x^2} \right) \\
&= \frac{1}{h} \cdot \left(\frac{x^2 - (x+h)^2}{(x+h)^2 x^2} \right) = \frac{1}{h} \cdot \left(\frac{x^2 - x^2 - 2xh - h^2}{(x+h)^2 x^2} \right) \\
&= \frac{1}{h} \cdot \left(\frac{-2xh - h^2}{(x+h)^2 x^2} \right) = \frac{-2x - h}{(x+h)^2 x^2}
\end{aligned}$$

In this simplified form, we can now easily take the limit:

$$f'(x) = \lim_{h \to 0} \frac{f(x+h) - f(x)}{h} = \lim_{h \to 0} \frac{-2x - h}{(x+h)^2 x^2} = \frac{-2x - 0}{(x+0)^2 x^2} = \frac{-2x}{x^2 x^2} = -\frac{2}{x^3}$$

In summary, we have found (using the power function notation) that the derivative of the function:

$$f(x) = x^{-2},$$

is given by

$$f'(x) = -2\, x^{-3}.$$

Example 2.2.6 (The Derivative of the Natural Exponential Function)

Problem: Derive the famous result about the derivative of the exponential function $f(x) = e^x$, where e is the natural base (Euler's number).

Solution: The Newton quotient is

$$\frac{f(x+h) - f(x)}{h} = \frac{e^{x+h} - e^x}{h} = \frac{e^x e^h - e^x}{h} = e^x \left(\frac{e^h - 1}{h} \right).$$

Now taking limits gives

$$f'(x) = \lim_{h \to 0} \frac{f(x+h) - f(x)}{h} = \lim_{h \to 0} e^x \left(\frac{e^h - 1}{h} \right) = e^x \cdot \lim_{h \to 0} \frac{e^h - 1}{h}.$$

Here we have used one of the limit laws. The limit of the expression involving h is a famous limit. We investigate this limit graphically by plotting the function involved.

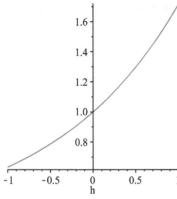

Figure 2.2.3: *A plot of $\frac{e^h - 1}{h}$.*

The derivative of $f(x) = e^x$

is $f'(x) = e^x$

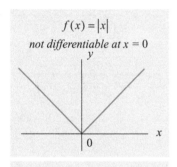

Figure 2.2.4: *Derivative of the absolute value function.*

```
>  N:=h->(exp(h)-1)/h;
```

$$N := h \rightarrow \frac{e^h - 1}{h}$$

```
>  plot(N(h),h=-1..1);
```

Figure 2.2.3 gives strong evidence for the guess that this limit is 1:

$$\lim_{h \to 0} \frac{e^h - 1}{h} = 1.$$

Later we will look at a rigorous proof of this famous result. Taking this for granted and using the above work, we get the important formula for the derivative of the natural exponential function. See the margin box.

This is an amazing result. Its says that $f(x) = e^x$ is a function that is equal to its own derivative

$$f' = f.$$

More generally, functions of the form $f(x) = ae^x$, with a any constant, are the only functions in all of mathematics that are equal to their own derivatives: $f' = f$. This is why the base e is called the natural base.

Example 2.2.7 (The Derivative of the Absolute Value Function)

The absolute value function $f(x) = |x|$ is an important function for us, even though you may think of it as being rather simple. This function is a piecewise-defined function given by

$$f(x) = \begin{cases} -x & \text{for } x \leq 0 \\ x & \text{for } x > 0 \end{cases}$$

and so the graph is obtained by piecing the two functions $y = -x$ and $y = x$. See Figure 2.2.4.

Just as in Example 2.1.6, we see that the derivative does not exist at $x = 0$. (A quick look at the graph of f convinces us that there is no tangent line at $x = 0$.) But this is the only x-value for which the function is not differentiable, and in fact for any x other than zero, the tangent line at x coincides with the graph of f. Thus, the slope is either -1 or 1. Otherwise said, the derivative function is

$$f'(x) = \begin{cases} -1 & \text{for } x < 0 \\ 1 & \text{for } x > 0 \end{cases}$$

Note (again) that $f'(x)$ is not defined for $x = 0$. The derivative function in this example is called the Heaviside function after the British mathematician/engineer who found it convenient in the study of differential equations. See Figure 2.2.4.

This last example above is an example of a continuous function which is not differentiable at a point in its domain. So continuity is not enough to ensure differentiability. Differentiable functions are often called smooth functions because in order to have a tangent line at each point their graphs must flow "smoothly" from point-to-point. There cannot be any sharp bends in the graphs, such as in the last example for the graph of the absolute function $f(x) = |x|$.

So a continuous function need not be differentiable. What about the converse? Is a differentiable function necessarily continuous? Seems like this should be true since if there were breaks in its graph, then how could there be tangent lines at the breaks? The following theorem tells us that our intuition on this is correct.

THEOREM 2.2.1 (Differentiability Implies Continuity)

If f is defined and differentiable on an interval (a, b), then f is continuous on (a, b).

Exercises: 2.2 (The Derivative Function)

Computing the Derivative Function

In Exercises 1–40 use the limit definition (Equation 2.2.1 in Definition 2.2.1) to find the the derivative functions for the following functions. *Hint:* It's easier to use the x-variable version of the Newton Quotient for 7–40.

1. $f(x) = 3x - 1$
2. $f(x) = -5x + 2$

3. $f(x) = x^2 - 3x + 5$
4. $f(x) = x^2 + 4x - 6$

5. $f(x) = 2x^3 - x^4$
6. $f(x) = 4x^3 - 2x^5$

7. $f(x) = (x + 3)^2$
8. $f(x) = (x + 5)^2$

9. $f(x) = 1/x$
10. $f(x) = 2/x$

11. $f(x) = 1/x^3$
12. $f(x) = 1/x^3$

13. $f(x) = 1/\sqrt{x}$
14. $f(x) = -1/\sqrt{x}$

15. $f(x) = \dfrac{6}{x + 2}$
16. $f(x) = \dfrac{5}{x + 3}$

17. $f(x) = \dfrac{x}{1 + x}$
18. $f(x) = \dfrac{x}{2 + x}$

19. $f(x) = \dfrac{x + 1}{x + 3}$
20. $f(x) = \dfrac{x + 2}{x + 5}$

21. $f(x) = \sqrt{5 + x^2}$
22. $f(x) = \sqrt{3 + x^2}$

23. $f(x) = \dfrac{1}{1 + x^2}$
24. $f(x) = \dfrac{2}{2 + x^2}$

25. $f(x) = \dfrac{1}{1 + x^3}$
26. $f(x) = \dfrac{2}{2 + x^3}$

27. $f(x) = \dfrac{x^2}{1 + x^2}$
28. $f(x) = \dfrac{x^2}{2 + x^2}$

29. $f(x) = \dfrac{x}{1 + x^2}$
30. $f(x) = \dfrac{x}{2 + x^2}$

31. $f(x) = \sqrt{x^2 + 3x}$
32. $f(x) = \sqrt{x^2 + 5x}$

33. $f(x) = \sqrt{x^3 + 1}$
34. $f(x) = \sqrt{x^3 + 2}$

35. $f(x) = \dfrac{1}{\sqrt{4 - x^2}}$
36. $f(x) = \dfrac{1}{\sqrt{9 - x^2}}$

37. $f(x) = \dfrac{1}{\sqrt{1 + x^2}}$
38. $f(x) = \dfrac{1}{\sqrt{4 + x^2}}$

39. $f(x) = \sqrt{1 + \sqrt{x}}$
40. $f(x) = \sqrt{2 + \sqrt{x}}$

Derivatives of Exponential Functions

In Exercises 41–44 find the derivative f' of the function f by using the limit definition. NOTE: Work these like we did in Example 2.2.6. Namely factor out the part that depends on h.

41. $f(x) = 2^x$
42. $f(x) = 10^x$

43. $f(x) = e^{-2x}$
44. $f(x) = e^{-3x - 2}$

Finding Tangent Lines

In Exercises 45–54, (a) Compute the derivative of the function, by the limit definition, and use this to find equations for the tangent lines at the two given points $x = a$.

(b) Sketch a graph of the function and the two tangent lines as a check on your calculations.

45. $f(x) = x^3 + 1$, $a = \pm 1$
46. $f(x) = x^3 - 1$, $a = \pm 1$

47. $f(x) = 4 - x^2$, $a = \pm 1$
48. $f(x) = x^2 - 4$, $a = \pm 1$

49. $f(x) = 4x - x^2$, $a = 1, 2$
50. $f(x) = 6x - x^2$, $a = 2, 4$

51. $y = \sqrt{4 - x^2}$, $a = \pm 1$
52. $y = \sqrt{9 - x^2}$, $a = \pm 2$

53. $f(x) = \dfrac{1}{1 + x^2}$, $a = \pm 1$
54. $y = \dfrac{4}{1 + x^2}$, $a = \pm 1$

Horizontal Tangent Lines

In Exercises 55–68, Compute the derivative of the function, by the limit definition, and use this to find all places x where the tangent line to the graph is horizontal.

55. $f(x) = 4 - x^2$
56. $f(x) = x^2 - 4$

57. $f(x) = x(4 - x)$
58. $f(x) = x(6 - x)$

59. $f(x) = 3x - x^3$
60. $f(x) = 6x - 2x^3$

61. $f(x) = 3x^2 - x^3$
62. $f(x) = x^3 - x^2$

63. $f(x) = x^2 - x^4$
64. $f(x) = x^4 = x^2$

65. $f(x) = x + \dfrac{1}{x}$
66. $f(x) = -x - \dfrac{1}{x}$

67. $f(x) = x + \dfrac{1}{x^2}$
68. $f(x) = -x - \dfrac{1}{x^2}$

Differentiability and Continuity

In Exercises 69–82 sketch, by hand, the graph of the function. Then determine the points x where (a) the function is not differentiable and (b) the function is discontinuous. At all other points x, find the formula for the derivative function. You may use any prior results.

69. $f(x) = \begin{cases} x^2 & \text{if } x \le 1 \\ 1/x & \text{if } x > 1 \end{cases}$

70. $f(x) = \begin{cases} -x & \text{if } x \le 0 \\ 1 + x^2 & \text{if } x > 0 \end{cases}$

71. $f(x) = \begin{cases} 0 & \text{if } x \le 0 \\ \sqrt{x} & \text{if } 0 < x \le 1 \\ 3 - x & \text{if } x > 1 \end{cases}$

72. $f(x) = \begin{cases} -x^3 & \text{if } x \le 0 \\ x^2 & \text{if } x > 0 \end{cases}$

73. $f(x) = x|x|$
74. $f(x) = -x|x|$

75. $f(x) = |x|(|x| - 2)$
76. $f(x) = |x|(2 - |x|)$

77. $f(x) = \dfrac{|x| - 1}{|x|}$
78. $f(x) = \dfrac{|x| - 2}{|x|}$

79. $f(x) = \dfrac{|x - 1|}{|x|}$
80. $f(x) = \dfrac{|x - 2|}{|x|}$

81. $f(x) = \dfrac{x + x^2}{|x|}$
82. $f(x) = \dfrac{x^3 - x}{|x|}$

Calculus *Concepts & Computation*

2.3 Derivatives of Power Functions

```
> with(dplot_tools,tanplot);
```

$$[tanplot]$$

This section begins the process of discussing various theorems (a.k.a. differentiation rules) that will allow us to more quickly and easily compute the derivatives of functions. In theory we could use the limit definition to calculate the derivative of any (differentiable) function, but for complicated functions this can be a lot of work. For example, we could find the derivative of the function

$$f(x) = 3\sqrt{x} + 5x^2 + \frac{2}{x^2},$$

by using the limit definition, but this would take awhile to do. However, since we know the derivatives of the functions,

$$\sqrt{x}, x^2, \text{ and } \frac{1}{x^2}$$

from previous examples, it would be nice to have a theorem that would tell us how to use these known derivatives to find the derivative of f. This is what Theorem 2.3.3 below will do for us.

The other purpose of the section is to give the general power-rule formula for differentiating any power function. For example, each of the three functions above is a power function, which we write in the standard power-function form as

$$x^{1/2}, x^2, x^{-2}.$$

Then Formula (2.3.2) in Theorem 2.3.2 below will allow us to easily differentiate these functions without using the limit definition.

So generally as we proceed from this point our interest will be to move away from using the limit definition to differentiate functions. Rather, we will develop formulas for all the basic types of functions (such as polynomial, rational, trigonometric, exponential, and logarithmic functions), and derive differentiation rules that show us how to differentiate combinations of these functions. For example, finding the derivatives of the functions

$$f(x) = x^{\sin(3x)}, \ g(x) = \frac{e^{2x}}{1 + x^2},$$

by the limit definition would be totally impractical. So we will use the chain rule, discussed in Section 2.8, and the quotient rule, discussed in Section 2.6, along with formulas for the derivatives of the sine and exponential functions, to make the calculation of $f'(x)$ and $g'(x)$ quite a bit easier.

The Power Function Rule

Power functions are the most basic of all the types of functions that we deal with, so it is important to determine their derivatives. We have done this for a few powers r in previous examples. We found for

$$f(x) = x^2$$

that

$$f'(x) = 2x,$$

and for

$$f(x) = x^3$$

that

$$f'(x) = 3x^2.$$

Each of these derivatives is easily found using the limit definition. We can extend these results to a general positive integer power $f(x) = x^n$ by using the x-vaiable version of the Newton quotient and the identity for factoring the difference of two powers. For example, consider $f(x) = x^7$ Since

$$x^7 - a^7 = (x - a)(x^6 + x^5 a + x^4 a^2 + x^3 a^3 + x^2 a^4 + xa^5 + a^6)$$

we get that

$$
\begin{aligned}
f'(a) = \lim_{x \to a} \frac{x^7 - a^7}{x - a} &= \lim_{x \to a} (x^6 + x^5 a + x^4 a^2 + x^3 a^3 + x^2 a^4 + xa^5 + a^6) \\
&= a^6 + a^5 a + a^4 a^2 + a^3 a^3 + a^2 a^4 + aa^5 + a^6 \\
&= 7a^6
\end{aligned}
$$

The above work for the power $n = 7$, will be much the same for any positive integer n, so in essence we have motivated the proof of the following theorem.

THEOREM 2.3.1 (The Derivative of a Power Function)

Suppose n is any nonnegative integer. Then the power function

$$f(x) = x^n$$

has derivative

$$f'(x) = nx^{n-1} \qquad (2.3.1)$$

Proof: The general factorization formula (with $n \geq 2$ an integer) is

$$x^n - a^n = (x - a)(x^{n-1} + x^{n-2} a + x^{n-3} a^2 + x^{n-4} a^3 + \cdots + xa^{n-2} + a^{n-1})$$

we get that

$$
\begin{aligned}
f'(a) &= \lim_{x \to a} \frac{x^n - a^n}{x - a} \\
&= \lim_{x \to a} (x^{n-1} + x^{n-2} a + x^{n-3} a^2 + x^{n-4} a^3 + \cdots + xa^{n-2} + a^{n-1}) \\
&= a^{n-1} + a^{n-2} a + a^{n-3} a^2 + a^{n-4} a^3 + \cdots + aa^{n-2} + a^{n-1} \\
&= na^{n-1}
\end{aligned}
$$

The remaining cases are for $n = 0, 1$. These are easy. First, for $n = 0$, we have $f(x) = x^0 = 1$ is a constant function and so the Newton quotient is zero for every value of x. Consequently $f'(x) = 0 = 0 \cdot x^{0-1}$, for all x. Next, for $n = 1$, we have $f(x) = x^1 = x$ and so

$$f'(a) = \lim_{x \to a} \frac{x - a}{x - a} = \lim_{x \to a} 1 = 1 = 1 \cdot x^0 = 1 \cdot x^{1-1},$$

for every a.

Note that using the power-rule formula for the cases $n = 0$ and $n = 1$ can be a little confusing (unless you read the proof above) so let's discuss these cases explicitly.

For $n = 0$, the function f is (by definition) $f(x) = x^0 = 1$. Also, the right side of (2.3.1) is $0 \cdot x^{0-1} = 0$, and so the power-rule formula in this case is shown in Box 2.3.1.

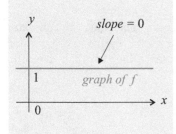

$$\text{If } f(x) = 1$$

$$\text{then } f'(x) = 0$$

Box 2.3.1: *A special case of the power rule.*

The function f here is the constant 1 function and its graph, as shown, is a horizontal line through $y = 1$. Clearly the graph of the function and the tangent line at any point are one and the same. All horizontal lines have slope 0, so that is why the derivative function here is identically zero.

For $n = 1$, the function f is $f(x) = x^1 = x$ and the right side of (2.3.1) is $1 \cdot x^{1-1} = x^0 = 1$, and so the power-rule formula in this case is shown in Box 2.3.2. Here, as in the special case above, the graph of f is a straight line, and so it coincides with its tangent line at each point. Thus, its derivative function is constant, the constant being the slope of the line $y = x$.

Our next task is to show that the power-rule formula holds not only for nonnegative integer powers n, but indeed for any real number power r. It is not hard to do this for positive rational numbers $r = n/k$ (where n and k are positive integers). See the proof at the end of this section. The case for r an irrational number is harder, so we defer that until later.

For the record, the general power rule formula is

THEOREM 2.3.2 (The General Power Rule)

Suppose r is any real number. Then the power function

$$f(x) = x^r$$

has derivative

$$f'(x) = rx^{r-1} \qquad (2.3.2)$$

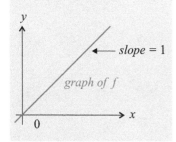

$$\text{If } f(x) = x$$

$$\text{then } f'(x) = 1$$

Box 2.3.2: *A special case of the power rule.*

As you see the general power-rule Formula (2.3.2) is identical to Formula (2.3.1) for nonnegative integer powers, so there is only one formula to memorize. However, you may have some trouble using the formula for powers r which are not positive integers. The reason for this is that mathematical notation evolved and developed with many alternative notations for the same thing. For example:

Example 2.3.1 (Using the Power Rule)

Problem: Use the power rule to find the derivatives of the functions:

$$f(x) = \sqrt[3]{x^2} \qquad \text{and} \qquad g(x) = \frac{1}{\sqrt{x}}.$$

Also find the equations for the tangent lines at $x = 1$ and use the `tanplot` command to check your answers.

Solution: First we rewrite the two functions f and g using the following notation:

$$f(x) = \sqrt[3]{x^2} = x^{2/3}$$

and

$$g(x) = \frac{1}{\sqrt{x}} = \frac{1}{x^{1/2}} = x^{-1/2}.$$

NOTE: Only the last two notations for f and g can be used in applying the power-rule formula. In these cases we get

$$f'(x) = \frac{2}{3}x^{2/3-1} = \frac{2}{3}x^{-1/3}$$

and

$$g'(x) = -\frac{1}{2}x^{-1/2-1} = -\frac{1}{2}x^{-3/2}.$$

These examples illustrate the following general recommendation:

RECOMMENDATION: *Convert all expressions involving radicals to exponent notation and rewrite denominators using negative exponents.*

Let's use the calculations above to find tangent-line equation for each function at the point $x = 1$ and then plot these along with the graphs of the functions. For this, note that $f(1) = 1$ and $g(1) = 1$, while the slopes are

$$f'(1) = \frac{2}{3}, \ g'(1) = -\frac{1}{2},$$

respectively. Thus the tangent-line equations are

$$y = 1 + \frac{2}{3}(x - 1), \ \ y = 1 - \frac{1}{2}(x - 1).$$

For plotting we use the special-purpose command `tanplot`. First we define the functions f and g as usual:

```
f:=x->x^(2/3);g:=x->x^(-1/2);
```

$$f := x \to x^{2/3}$$

$$g := x \to \frac{1}{\sqrt{x}}$$

Note how Maple prefers to use the radical notation for g, even though we input g using the exponent notation. We now use `tanplot` to plot f, g on the intervals $[0, 2], [0.2, 2]$ respectively (note g is not defined at $x = 0$), and plot the lines through $(1, 1)$ with slopes $m = 2/3$, $m = -1/2$. This gives the Figures 2.3.1–2.3.2 below.

```
> tanplot(f,1,0,2,2/3);
> tanplot(g,1,0.2,2,-1/2);
```

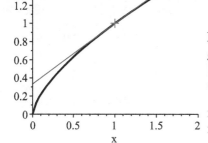

Figure 2.3.1: *Tangent line to* $f(x) = x^{2/3}$ *at* $x = 1$.

The blue line in the figure appears to go through the point $(1, 1)$ and to be tangent to the graph. While this is not an absolute guarantee that our work is correct, it is helpful, as well as quick and easy. Similarly the next figure seems to indicate that our calculation for the tangent line to g are correct.

The Sum Rule, Multiple Rule, and Linear Combination Rule

Two natural and easy-to-use differentiation rules are the sum rule and constant multiple rule. The sum rule allows us to easily differentiate a function s, if we recognize it as the sum of two functions, each of whose derivatives we know. For example,

$$s(x) = x^2 + x^3$$

is the sum of two power functions $f(x) = x^2, g(x) = x^3$ whose derivatives are $f'(x) = 2x, \ g'(x) = 3x^2$, respectively. The sum rule given below simply says that the derivative of h is the sum of the derivatives of f and g. In this case this gives

$$s'(x) = 2x + 3x^2.$$

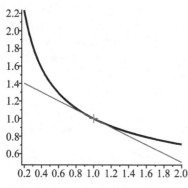

Figure 2.3.2: *Tangent line to* $f(x) = 1/\sqrt{x}$ *at* $x = 1$.

The constant multiple rule says that if a function s is a multiple of a function f, then the derivative of s is the same multiple of the derivative of f. For example, if

$$s(x) = 6x^2,$$

then

$$s'(x) = 6(2x) = 12x.$$

These two differentiation rules are the simplest to use and apply of all the differentiation rules, and with a small amount of practice you will soon forget that you are automatically using them when differentiating functions. We record these two rules, formally in terms of symbols, in the following theorem.

THEOREM 2.3.3 (Sum Rule and Constant Rule)

The sum $f + g$ of two differentiable functions f, g is differentiable and

$$(f + g)' = f' + g'$$

A constant multiple cf of a differentiable function f is differentiable and

$$(cf)' = cf'$$

Proof: To prove the sum rule, let $s = f + g$. For x in the domains of both f and g, we have to show that s is differentiable at x and that $s'(x) = f'(x) + g'(x)$. To do this we use the limit definition of the derivative and the sum rule for limits:

$$
\begin{aligned}
\lim_{h \to 0} \frac{s(x+h) - s(x)}{h} &= \lim_{h \to 0} \left[\frac{f(x+h) + g(x+h) - (f(x) + g(x))}{h} \right] \\
&= \lim_{h \to 0} \left[\frac{f(x+h) - f(x)}{h} + \frac{g(x+h) - g(x)}{h} \right] \\
&= \lim_{h \to 0} \left[\frac{f(x+h) - f(x)}{h} \right] + \lim_{h \to 0} \left[\frac{g(x+h) - g(x)}{h} \right] \\
&= f'(x) + g'(x)
\end{aligned}
$$

Similarly to prove the constant multiple rule, we let $s = cf$, and look at the limit definition of the derivative. For x in the domain of f, we have:

$$\lim_{h \to 0} \frac{s(x+h) - s(x)}{h} = \lim_{h \to 0} \frac{cf(x+h) - cf(x)}{h} = c \lim_{h \to 0} \frac{f(x+h) - f(x)}{h} = cf'(x).$$

An important corollary to the constant multiple rule is the case when $f(x) = 1$, for all x (i.e., f is the constant 1 function). Then $f' = 1' = 0$. More generally, for any constant function $f(x) = c$ and so $f' = c' = (c \cdot 1)' = c \cdot 1' = c \cdot 0 = 0$. Hence the corollary is that the derivative of any constant function is 0:

Corollary: $c' = 0$, for any constant c.

Before we look at more examples of applying these rules, let's consider the situation where we can combine the use of both rules, and perhaps do so many times. For instance, if we take a multiple of f and add g to it, then a use of both rules gives

$$(cf + g)' = cf' + g'.$$

This uses the sum rule first and then the constant multiple rule. Next, if we take multiples of both f and g and add them together, then it's easy to see that the derivative of the combined function is

$$(cf + bg)' = cf' + bg'.$$

Here c and b are constants. For example, if

$$s(x) = 6x^2 - 5x^3$$

then
$$s'(x) = 6(2x) - 5(3x^2) = 12x - 15x^2.$$

Note here $b = -5$, so the sum becomes a difference. There is special name for combining two functions f and g as we did above.

Definition (Linear Combinations): Suppose f and g are functions with a common domain. If c and b are any two real numbers, then the function $s = cf + bg$ is called a linear combination of f and g. Specifically, for x in the domain of f and g, the function s is defined by

$$s(x) = cf(x) + bg(x).$$

This concept of linear combinations is important and you may see it a lot if you take a course in linear algebra. The concept extends to combining functions $f_1, f_2, \ldots, f_k$ with constants $c_1, c_2, \ldots, c_k$ to get a function s defined by

$$s(x) = c_1 f_1(x) + c_2 f_2(x) + \cdots + c_k f_k(x),$$

for x in the common domain of all these functions. By applying the sum and constant multiple rule many times, we get the following corollary, which is a generalization of the sum and constant multiple rules.

COROLLARY 2.3.1 (Linear Combination Rule)

A linear combination $c_1 f_1 + c_2 f_2 + \cdots + c_k f_k$ *of differentiable functions* $f_1, f_2, \ldots, f_k$, *where* $c_1, c_2, \ldots, c_k$ *are constants, is differentiable and*

$$(c_1 f_1 + c_2 f_2 + \cdots + c_k f_k)' = c_1 f_1' + c_2 f_2' + \cdots + c_k f_k'$$

Example 2.3.2 (Polynomials)

The corollary above allows us to easily differentiate any polynomial function.

(1) *Problem*: Find the derivative of the fourth degree polynomial:

$$s(x) = 5 + 3x - 4x^2 + 6x^3 - x^4.$$

Solution: Since $5' = 0$ and $x' = 1$, the linear combination rule gives

$$s'(x) = 0 + 3(1) - 4(2x) + 6(3x^2) - 4x^3 = 3 - 8x + 18x^2 - 4x^3.$$

(2) *Problem*: Find the derivative of the general nth degree polynomial

$$f(x) = a_0 + a_1 x + a_2 x^2 + \cdots + a_n x^n.$$

Solution: As with the above particular case, we easily get

$$f'(x) = a_1 + 2a_2 x + 3a_3 x^2 + \cdots + na_n x^{n-1}.$$

The derivative of an nth degree polynomial is a polynomial of degree $n - 1$.

Example 2.3.3 (Linear Combinations of Power Functions)

(1) *Problem*: Find the derivative of the following function, which is a simple linear combination of three power functions, two with non-integer exponents:

$$s(x) = 5x^{4/3} - 3x^{1/2} + 6x^{-4}.$$

Solution:

$$s'(x) = 5\left(\frac{4}{3}x^{4/3-1}\right) - 3\left(\frac{1}{2}x^{1/2-1}\right) + 6\left(-4x^{-4-1}\right) = \frac{20}{3}x^{1/3} - \frac{3}{2}x^{-1/2} - 24x^{-5}$$

(2) *Problem:* Find the derivative of the function:

$$f(x) = 3\sqrt{x} + 5x^2 + \frac{2}{x^2}.$$

Solution: Sometimes you will have to convert the power functions to exponent notation, and you see that is the case here. So we first rewrite f as:

$$f(x) = 3x^{1/2} + 5x^2 + 2x^{-2}.$$

Then we take derivatives:

$$f'(x) = \frac{3}{2}x^{-1/2} + 10x - 4x^{-3}.$$

Notice that we have skipped putting in the arithmetical steps in calculating the derivative. With some practice you should be able to do this arithmetic in your head and quickly compute the derivative of any linear combination of power functions (when they are in standard exponential form).

(3) *Problem:* Differentiate the function

$$g(x) = \frac{3\sqrt[7]{x^5} - 4x + 2x^{-1}}{x^2}$$

Solution: This problem involves a little more work than the last one since we have to put the given function in standard form before differentiating. Basic algebra allows us to convert g to a linear combination of three power functions. Here's how the work goes:

$$\begin{aligned}
g(x) &= \frac{3x^{5/7} - 4x + 2x^{-1}}{x^2} = 3\frac{x^{5/7}}{x^2} - 4\frac{x}{x^2} + 2\frac{x^{-1}}{x^2} \\
&= 3x^{5/7-2} - 4x^{1-2} + 2x^{-1-2} = 3x^{-9/7} - 4x^{-1} + 2x^{-3}
\end{aligned}$$

Thus,

$$g'(x) = -\frac{27}{7}x^{-16/7} + 4x^{-2} - 6x^{-4}.$$

(4) *Problem:* Here is another example that involves doing some algebra before differentiating. Differentiate the function:

$$f(x) = \sqrt{x}(x-3)^2$$

Solution: Convert this to a linear combination of power functions as follows:

$$f(x) = x^{1/2}(x-3)^2 = x^{1/2}(x^2 - 6x + 9) = x^{5/2} - 6x^{3/2} + 9x^{1/2}.$$

Now we easily get the derivative:

$$f'(x) = \frac{5}{2}x^{3/2} - 9x^{1/2} + \frac{9}{2}x^{-1/2}.$$

Proof of the Power Rule for Rational Powers n/k: In the factorization identity:

$$y^n - b^n = (y-b)(y^{n-1} + y^{n-2}b + y^{n-3}b^2 + y^{n-4}b^3 + \cdots + yb^{n-2} + b^{n-1})$$

take $y = x^{1/k}$ and $b = a^{1/k}$ to get

$$x^{\frac{n}{k}} - a^{\frac{n}{k}} = (x^{\frac{1}{k}} - a^{\frac{1}{k}})(x^{\frac{n-1}{k}} + x^{\frac{n-2}{k}}a^{\frac{1}{k}} + x^{\frac{n-3}{k}}a^{\frac{2}{k}} + x^{\frac{n-4}{k}}a^{\frac{3}{k}} + \cdots + x^{\frac{1}{k}}a^{\frac{n-2}{k}} + a^{\frac{n-1}{k}})$$

Take $n = k$ in this to get

$$x - a = (x^{\frac{1}{k}} - a^{\frac{1}{k}})(x^{\frac{k-1}{k}} + x^{\frac{k-2}{k}}a^{\frac{1}{k}} + x^{\frac{k-3}{k}}a^{\frac{2}{k}} + x^{\frac{k-4}{k}}a^{\frac{3}{k}} + \cdots + x^{\frac{1}{k}}a^{\frac{k-2}{k}} + a^{\frac{k-1}{k}})$$

Now use these to compute $\lim\limits_{x\to a} \dfrac{x^{1/k} - a^{1/k}}{x - a}$ and then $\lim\limits_{x\to a} \dfrac{x^{n/k} - a^{n/k}}{x - a}$.

Exercises: 2.3 (Derivatives of Power Functions)

```
> with(dplot_tools,tanplot);
```
$$[tanplot]$$

The Power Function & Linear Combination Rules

In Exercises 1–54 use the power rule and the linear combination rule to find the derivative of each function. DO NOT use the limit definition to find the derivative.

1. $f(x) = 10\,x^{8/5}$ **2.** $f(x) = 8\,x^{7/4}$

3. $f(x) = 4\,x^{-3/5}$ **4.** $f(x) = 2\,x^{-2/7}$

5. $f(x) = 9\sqrt[3]{x^{-5}}$ **6.** $f(x) = 10\sqrt[5]{x^{-6}}$

7. $y = \dfrac{-3}{\sqrt[17]{x^6}}$ **8.** $y = \dfrac{-4}{\sqrt[15]{x^{20}}}$

9. $f(x) = 4\,x^7 - 5\,x^5 + 2\,x^3 - 8$

10. $f(x) = 2\,x^9 - 4\,x^7 + 8\,x^3 - 7\,x + 2$

11. $f(x) = 3\,x^{4/3} - x^{2/3}$ **12.** $f(x) = 7\,x^{4/5} - 3\,x^{-2/3}$

13. $y = 2\sqrt{x} + \dfrac{7}{x}$ **14.** $y = 4\sqrt{x} - \dfrac{5}{x}$

15. $y = 2\sqrt[5]{x^3} + \dfrac{7}{x^4}$ **16.** $y = 4\sqrt[5]{x^3} - \dfrac{5}{x^3}$

17. $y = 5\sqrt[3]{x} + 2\sqrt{x} - 3\sqrt{x^{-5}}$

18. $y = -4\sqrt[5]{x} + \sqrt{x^3} - 10\sqrt{x^{-3/5}}$

19. $R(x) = \dfrac{x^2 + 1}{3}$ **20.** $S(x) = \dfrac{4x^2 - 5x}{2}$

21. $y = \dfrac{2\sqrt[3]{x} + 4}{x^2}$ **22.** $y = \dfrac{5\sqrt[5]{x} - 3}{x^4}$

23. $y = \dfrac{5\,x^{-2/3} - 3\,x^4}{\sqrt{x}}$ **24.** $y = \dfrac{5\,x^{-3/5} - 6\,x^2}{\sqrt[3]{x}}$

25. $f(x) = x^2\left(5\sqrt{x} - 6x^3 + 4\right)$

26. $f(x) = x^3\left(2\sqrt{x} - 5x^2 + 4\right)$

27. $f(x) = \sqrt{x}\left(3x^{5/2} + 6x^{2/3} + 4x^{-1/2}\right)$

28. $f(x) = \sqrt[3]{x}\left(4x^{5/3} + 5x^{5/2} + 2x^{-1/3}\right)$

29. $f(x) = (x^2 - 3)^2$ **30.** $f(x) = (x^2 - 4)^2$

31. $f(x) = (x + 2)^3$ **32.** $f(x) = (x + 3)^3$

33. $f(x) = (\sqrt{x} + 5)^2$ **34.** $f(x) = (\sqrt{x} + 3)^2$

35. $f(x) = \left(x - \dfrac{1}{x}\right)^2$ **36.** $f(x) = \left(x + \dfrac{1}{x}\right)^2$

37. $f(x) = \left(\sqrt{x} - \dfrac{1}{\sqrt{x}}\right)^2$ **38.** $f(x) = \left(\sqrt{x} + \dfrac{1}{\sqrt{x}}\right)^2$

39. $f(x) = \left(\sqrt{x} - \dfrac{1}{\sqrt{x}}\right)^3$ **40.** $f(x) = \left(\sqrt{x} + \dfrac{1}{\sqrt{x}}\right)^3$

41. $f(x) = \dfrac{x^2 + \frac{1}{x^2}}{x^3}$ **42.** $f(x) = \dfrac{x^3 + \frac{1}{x^3}}{x^4}$

43. $f(x) = \left(\dfrac{x^3 - 2}{x^5}\right)^2$ **44.** $f(x) = \left(\dfrac{x^4 - 5}{x^6}\right)^2$

45. $f(x) = \left(\sqrt{x + \sqrt{x}}\right)^2$ **46.** $f(x) = \left(\sqrt{x - \sqrt{x}}\right)^2$

47. $f(x) = \left(\sqrt{x + \sqrt{x}}\right)^4$ **48.** $f(x) = \left(\sqrt{x - \sqrt{x}}\right)^4$

49. $f(x) = \dfrac{\sqrt{x} + 1/\sqrt{x}}{x^2}$ **50.** $f(x) = \dfrac{\sqrt{x} - 1/\sqrt{x}}{x^3}$

51. $f(x) = \dfrac{\sqrt[3]{x} + 1/\sqrt[3]{x^2}}{x^2}$ **52.** $f(x) = \dfrac{\sqrt[3]{x} - 1/\sqrt{x^2}}{x^3}$

53. $f(x) = \dfrac{\sqrt{x} + 1/\sqrt{x}}{x^2 + x}$ **54.** $f(x) = \dfrac{\sqrt{x} - 1/\sqrt{x}}{x^2 - x}$

Equations of Tangent Lines

Find equations for the tangent lines to the graph of f at the two specified points $x = a_1, a_2$. Do this by finding $f'(x)$ and then using it to find the two slopes.

55. $f(x) = \frac{1}{10}(x^3 - 4x^2 + x + 10),\ 2, 4$

56. $f(x) = \frac{1}{10}(-x^3 + 6x^2 - 10),\ 2, 4$

57. $f(x) = 4x - x^2,\ 1, 4$ **58.** $f(x) = 6x - x^2,\ -1, 1$

59. $f(x) = x + \dfrac{1}{x},\ -2, 2$ **60.** $f(x) = x + \dfrac{2}{x},\ -1, 1$

61. $f(x) = \sqrt{x} - \dfrac{2}{\sqrt{x}},\ 2, 4$

62. $f(x) = \sqrt{x} - \dfrac{3}{\sqrt{x}},\ 2, 4$

63. $f(x) = 2\sqrt[3]{x} - \dfrac{4}{\sqrt[3]{x^2}},\ 2, 6$

64. $f(x) = 3\sqrt[4]{x} - \dfrac{6}{\sqrt[4]{x^2}},\ 2, 6$

Horizontal Tangent Lines

In Exercises 65–74 find all places x where the tangent line is horizontal.

65. $f(x) = 2x^3 - 3x^2 - 12x - 3$

66. $f(x) = 2x^3 - 3x^2 - 36x + 2$

67. $f(x) = x + 1/x$ **68.** $f(x) = 4x + 1/x$

69. $f(x) = x^2 + 1/x^2$ **70.** $f(x) = x^2 + 8/x^2$

71. $f(x) = \sqrt{x} + 1/\sqrt{x}$ **72.** $f(x) = \sqrt{x} + 2/\sqrt{x}$

73. $f(x) = x^{1/3} + x^{-2/3}$ **74.** $f(x) = x^{1/4} + x^{-3/4}$

Using `tanplot` to Check Your Calculations

75. CAS: Check the result of your work in Exercises 55–64 above (or at least the ones of these you were assigned) by using the special purpose Maple routine `tanplot`. See Example 2.3.1. REMEMBER to execute the `with` command at the beginning of this exercise set.

Calculus Concepts & Computation

2.4 Velocity

> with(code_ch2sec4);with(dplot_tools,dplot,dplot2);

$$[average\_velocity, stepplot, ymotion]$$

$$[dplot, dplot2]$$

In addition to the tangent line problem, another major problem that motivated the development of calculus in the 17th century was the formulation of the laws of motion. Galileo initiated the understanding and clarification of the concepts connected with motion of a body near the earth's surface, but it was left to Newton, using the newly invented calculus, to define in mathematical terms the notions of velocity and acceleration, and to formulate his second law, connecting mass and acceleration to the forces acting on a body.

This section examines how the more common notion of *average velocity* helps motivate the definition of *velocity* (also called *instantaneous velocity*). The definition of velocity involves taking limits of average velocities, and thus you will see how the derivative concept from the previous sections is connected to the velocity concept here.

Average velocity is an easy concept to define. Suppose the motion of the body is along a straight line, say the y-axis, and the body moves from point P at time $t = a$ to point Q at time $t = b$ (with $a < b$). See Figure 2.4.1.

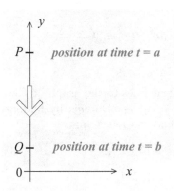

Figure 2.4.1: *A body moves from P to Q.*

Then the change in position is $\Delta y = Q - P$, the amount of time elapsed is $\Delta t = b - a$, and the *average velocity* of the body over the time interval $[a,b]$ is

$$v_{ave} = \frac{\Delta y}{\Delta t}$$

Note that for the situation depicted in Figure 2.4.1, the average velocity is negative since the change in position Δy is negative. Thus, the average velocity is a *signed quantity*. The negative value here indicates (relative to the standard choice of coordinate system) that the body is falling during the time interval $[a,b]$. (We are assuming the body does not change its direction of motion in going from P to Q.) A positive value of the average velocity would indicate that the body is rising.

The magnitude of the average velocity is called the *average speed*:

$$speed_{ave} = |v_{ave}| = \left| \frac{\Delta y}{\Delta t} \right|$$

Otherwise said, *the average speed is the distance traveled divided by the time elapsed*. This quantity is a relative measure of the quickness of the motion. You should note the distinction between speed and velocity. Velocity not only indicates the quickness of the motion but also the direction in which it takes place (the body is either rising or falling). The reason that the quantity v_{ave} is called the average velocity will be explained in Chapter 4. It is only an approximate indication of the speed and direction for the body's motion during the time interval $[a,b]$. Closer observation of the motion may reveal a variability in the speed (and the direction) of the motion.

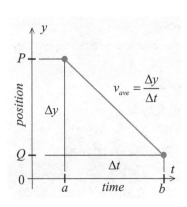

Figure 2.4.1x: v_{ave} *is the difference in position divided the difference in time.*

For example, suppose between the times a and b, when the body is at positions P and Q, three intermediate positions are measured. Say, the body has positions $y_0 = P, y_1, y_2, y_3, y_4 = Q$ at times $t_0 = a, t_1, t_2, t_3, t_4 = b$. Figure 2.4.2 below shows the positions plotted along the y-axis and also a plot of the positions versus the times (with the time axis taken horizontally). Based on this figure, we develop some notation to handle the computations of the average velocities on the separate intervals shown.

For simplicity we assume, as shown, that the four time intervals have the same duration T:

$$\Delta t = t_i - t_{i-1} = T$$

for $i = 1, 2, 3, 4$. Then, qualitatively, we see that the body is moving most rapidly

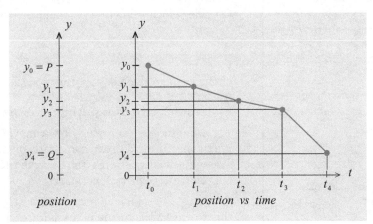

position   *position vs time*

Figure 2.4.2: *Intermediate positions of a body as it moves from P to Q.*

in going from position y_3 to position y_4, since the distance between these points is the greatest of those shown. On the other hand the motion is the slowest in going from y_2 to position y_3, since the distance between these points is the least of those shown.

In the graph of the position versus time (right side of Figure 2.4.2), the successive time-position points (t_i, y_i) have been connected by straight line segments to form a polygonal function. This function is an approximation to the "actual" position function: $y = f(t)$.

The function f that gives the actual position y at each time t is often predicted by some physical theory and therefore has a known formula. However, sometimes it is only "known" from physical experiments and collected data. Hypothetically the actual position function f could be determined by recording each of the infinitely many positions $f(t)$ as t varies through the continuum of times in $[a,b]$. While this would be a physically impossible experiment, you know from your prior work with polygonal functions that observations of the positions at a large number of, but finitely many, times $t_0, t_1, \ldots, t_N$, will give a good polygonal approximation to $f(t)$.

The polygonal position function shown above in Figure 2.4.2, also reveals, qualitatively, the variation in the quickness of the body's motion. The steepest slope occurs on the interval $[t_3, t_4]$, indicating that this is where the body is moving most quickly. On the other hand the polygonal side with the least slope is on the interval $[t_2, t_3]$, and this is when the quickness is the least. The four slopes shown in Figure 2.4.2 are the four average velocities for the motion during the respective time intervals: $[t_0, t_1], [t_1, t_2], [t_2, t_3]$ and $[t_3, t_4]$.

These qualitative assertions can be made quantitative by computing the average velocities

$$v_i = \frac{y_i - y_{i-1}}{t_t - t_{i-1}} = \frac{\Delta y_i}{\Delta x_i},$$

$i = 1, 2, 3, 4$, on each of the individual time intervals. Then a plot of these average velocities, as shown in Figure 2.4.3, gives a step-function exhibiting the variability of the body's quickness on each of the time intervals.

This discussion of the polygonal position function and corresponding average velocity function is intended to establish the following ideas, which this section will analyze more closely:

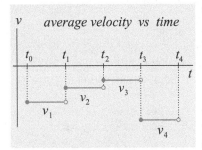

Figure 2.4.3: *Plot of an average velocity function.*

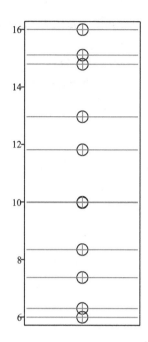

Figure 2.4.4: *A composite picture showing all 11 frames in the animation. The body starts at a height of 16 feet, comes as close as 6 feet to the ground, and normals direction twice during the motion.*

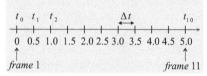

Figure 2.4.5: *The times and intervals between the frames of the movie.*

i	t_i	y_i	Δt_i	Δy_i	$\dfrac{\Delta y_i}{\Delta t_i}$
0	0.0	16.00	*	*	*
1	0.5	11.85	0.5	-4.15	-8.30
2	1.0	8.37	0.5	-3.48	-6.96
3	1.5	6.29	0.5	-2.08	-4.16
4	2.0	5.97	0.5	-0.32	-0.64
5	2.5	7.37	0.5	1.40	2.80
6	3.0	10.00	0.5	2.63	5.26
7	3.5	12.93	0.5	2.93	5.86
8	4.0	15.10	0.5	2.17	4.34
9	4.5	14.80	0.5	-0.30	-0.60
10	5.0	10.00	0.5	-4.80	-9.60

Table 2.4.1: *Observed positions and calculated average velocities.*

(1) If the actual position function $f(t)$ is approximated by a polygonal position-function, then the corresponding step-function v_{ave} of average velocities should be an approximation to what we would call the velocity (or instantaneous velocity) function v.

(2) The velocity function v should be defined as the limit,

$$v = \lim_{\Delta t \to 0} v_{ave} = \lim_{\Delta t \to 0} \frac{\Delta y}{\Delta t},$$

of the average velocity step-functions.

Example 2.4.1 (Computing Average Velocities from a Movie)

Problem: In this example, view a movie showing the motion of a body along the y-axis and use this to record data on the body's positions. Then compute the average velocities during the observed time intervals and construct a plot of the approximate velocity function.

Solution: The movie is generated by the following Maple command. We execute this to create the movie in a separate viewing window, and we also look at Figure 2.4.4.

> `ymotion(1,10);` The figure is a record of each of the frames in the animation, all shown in the same picture. We could use this figure to record the positions of the body, but we need to know which times go with which positions. So we must use the animation to collect the data.

You should view the movie several times to get a feel for the motion. Also, slow the frame rate down to 2 frames per second. This, as we will explain below, gives the actual speed of the motion.

Now the main question is: *How do we use the movie to compute the average velocities?*

When we step through the movie one frame at a time, we find that there are 11 frames. We will set the times as follows. Take the initial frame to be time zero, $a = t_0 = 0$. (This is standard procedure.) The experimentalist who shot the movie needs to provide us with some information so that we can match the other frames with times. Suppose she tells us that the frames are equally spaced and that the whole movie takes 5 seconds in real time (not slow motion, fast motion, etc., but actual time). Then we know that $b = t_{10} = 5$ is the time corresponding to the last frame in the movie. Now the movie begins (at time 0) with the first frame already showing and ends with the last frame appearing five seconds later. So that is

$$10 \text{ frames in 5 seconds,}$$

or a frame rate of 2 frames per second (which is a pretty slow motion). On the other hand, one frame appears every $5/10 = 0.5$ seconds, which means the interval of time between frames is

$$\Delta t = 1/2 = 0.5 \text{ seconds}$$

Using this we get the times corresponding to the 11 frames are

$$t_i = i \Delta t = 0.5 \, i$$

for $i = 0, 1, 2, \ldots, 10$. Figure 2.4.5 shows a diagram of this.

Now we make a table of the these times and collect the data on the positions by viewing the movie one frame at a time, using the cursor probe on the center of the body to get its y-coordinate. Table 2.4.1 records our observations along with calculation of the ten average velocities.

The column labeled y_i contains the positions we found by using the cursor on the graph, and differences Δy_i in positions are calculated from these by subtracting adjacent entries in the y_i column.

Note: The observed positions recorded in the table are approximate and depend on our measuring instrument (the mouse) and our ability to use it (positioning the

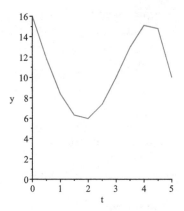

Figure 2.4.6: *A polygonal approximation to the position function.*

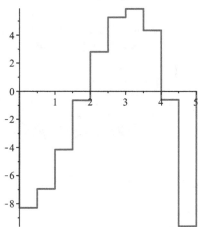

Figure 2.4.7: *Plot of the average velocity function v_{ave} using* `stepplot`.

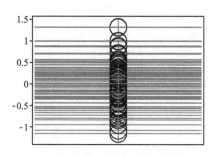

Figure 2.4.8: *A composite of all the frames in the movie* `ymotion(0,80)`.

cursor probe on the exact center of the body). So if you follow this process you may get different numbers. Don't worry about exact answers (there are none) in this experimental work. Just be as careful and exact as possible.

Next we construct some plots of the observed and calculated data.

First, for the approximate position function we plot the time-position points (t_i, y_i), $i = 0, 1, \ldots, 10$ from the table (See Section A.0 and Section A.11 in the Appendix)

>   `datapoints:=[0,16],[.5,11.85],[1,8.37],[1.5,6.29],[2,5.97],`
       `[2.5,7.37], [3,10],[3.5,12.93],[4,15.1],[4.5,14.8],[5,10];`

$$datapoints := [0,16],[\,0.5, 11.85],[1, 8.37],[\,1.5, 6.29],[2, 5.97],$$
$$[\,2.5, 7.37],[3,10],[\,3.5, 12.93],[4, 15.1],[\,4.5, 14.8],[5,10]$$

> `plot([datapoints],t=0..5,y=0..16);`

Figure 2.4.6 shows the polygonal approximation f_{approx} to the actual position function f, which in this example in is not known, nor is it given by some formula. However, the figure gives a fairly good idea of what this actual position function f looks like. If you click on the figure and use the tool bar to change the plotting style to point, you will see the 11 data points (t_i, y_i), $i = 0, 1, \ldots, 10$, from Table 2.4.1.

Next we plot the ten average velocities from the table, making a step-function v_{ave} out of the data. This function is called the *average velocity function*, and is the piecewise-defined function that has constant value v_1 on the first time interval $[t_0, t_1] = [0, 0.5]$, constant value v_2 on the second time interval $[t_1, t_2] = [0.5, 1.0]$, . . . , etc., until the last value of v_{10} on $[t_9, t_{10}] = [4.5, 5]$.

To get the plot we use the special-purpose command called `stepplot`. First we make a list of the 11 time values:

> `T:=[0,.5,1,1.5,2,2.5,3,3.5,4,4.5,5];`
$$T := [0, 0.5, 1, 1.5, 2, 2.5, 3, 3.5, 4, 4.5, 5]$$

Then we make a list of the 10 average velocities:

> `V:=[-8.3,-6.96,-4.16,-.64,2.8,5.26,5.86,4.34,-.6,-9.6];`
$$V := [-8.3, -6.96, -4.16, -0.64, 2.8, 5.26, 5.86, 4.34, -0.6, -9.6]$$

Finally, we use the command `stepplot` to create the plot of the step function:

> `stepplot(T,V);`

It is important to note that each of the 10 average velocities shown in Figure 2.4.7 and in Table 2.4.1 is the slope of one of the 10 polygonal sides of f_{approx}.

Example 2.4.2 (Damped Harmonic Motion)

Problem: Consider a particular motion of a mass on a spring, vibrating about equilibrium with the motion shown in the following movie. Execute the command and view the motion.

> `ymotion(0,80);`

The movie has 81 frames in it and represents 4 seconds of real time, so the frame-rate is $80/4 = 20$ frames per second. The mass has its motion damped by resistance, so that the motion back and forth across equilibrium (at position $y = 0$) becomes less and less over time, as you can see from the movie. Figure 2.4.8 shows a composite of all the frames in the movie.

Theory predicts the position function f is given by the formula:

$$f(t) = e^{-t/2}\left(\sin 10t + \cos 10t\right),$$

for all $t \geq 0$. Take this as given and do not worry about where this formula comes from. Now we have the *exact* position function, not an approximation to it that was constructed from data. So we do not have to compute average velocities, but rather we can determine actual velocities at any point in time. The problem here

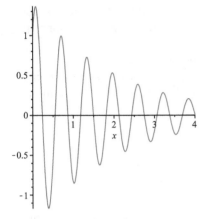

Figure 2.4.9: *A plot of*
$f(t) = e^{-t/2}(\sin 10t + \cos 10t)$.

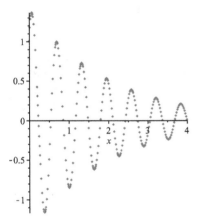

Figure 2.4.10: *A point plot of*
$f(t) = e^{-t/2}(\sin 10t + \cos 10t)$.

is to (1) plot the position versus time graph and (2) interpret how the velocity is exhibited in the graph.

Solution: We define the function as usual and then use the `plot` command to produce the position versus time plot on the time interval $[0, 4]$:

```
> f:=t->exp(-t/2)*(sin(10*t)+cos(10*t));
```
$$f := t \mapsto e^{-t/2}(\cos(10\,t) + \sin(10\,t))$$
```
> plot(f(t),t=0..4,color=red);
```

Figure 2.4.9 shows the graph of the position function. This graph can be used to interpret the nature of the spring-mass motion as follows. The actual motion takes place along the y-axis, so you have to mentally project the y-values at points on the graph onto the y-axis to get the positions at the various times.

You see that there are 12 times when the vibrating mass passes through equilibrium position ($y = 0$) and at time $t = 4$ the mass is at $y = 0$ again (that's when the movie `ymotion(0,80)` ends). As time goes on the maximum displacements of the mass from equilibrium get less and less (i.e., the vibration gets damped out).

The plot in Figure 2.4.9 can also be used to determine the velocity of the mass at each time, but this takes a little thought. For this we change the style of the plot in Figure 2.4.9 to "points," which gives the plot in Figure 4.2.10. This shows the actual points Maple used the create Figure 2.4.9, which is what results when it connects these points with straight line segments. Thus, the plot in Figure 2.4.9, is actually the graph of a polygonal function, even though it looks "smooth" at this scale because the are a great many points. On the polygonal function graph, each line segment has a slope which is an average velocity. This slope turns into a slope of a tangent line to the graph of the position function as the number of points in the plot goes (theoretically) to infinity. Thus

The slope of the tangent line at a point $(t, f(t))$ on the

position versus time graph is the velocity $v = \dfrac{dy}{dt}$ at that time.

Figure 2.4.11 illustrates this. The tangent lines have slopes which are negative,

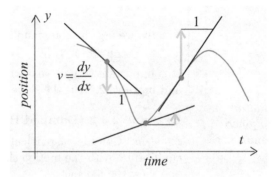

Figure 2.4.11: *Velocity is the the slope of the tangent line.*

positive, and positive, respectively from left to right. The magnitudes of the slopes are the respective speeds, with the last one shown appearing to be the greatest. Velocity is a *vector* quantity: it has both a direction and a magnitude. Three velocity vectors are indicated by the green arrows in the figure. These velocity vectors have directions that are either up or down and the magnitudes (speeds) are represented by the length of the arrows. *Note:* The slope of a tangent line (which is velocity for the position versus time graph) is the ratio of the rise (drop) to the run. In the figure, the runs are all 1 unit and so the yellow arrows indicate the slope (or velocity) at the point.

SUMMARY: You should understand now that velocity is a very practical application of the abstract geometrical process of finding slopes of tangent lines to curves. In this case the curve is the graph of the position function.

DEFINITION 2.4.1 (The Velocity Function)

Suppose f is the position function for an object moving along a straight line. For any time t in the domain of f, the velocity at time t is defined by

$$v(t) = \lim_{\Delta t \to 0} \frac{\Delta y}{\Delta t} = \lim_{h \to 0} \frac{f(t+h) - f(t)}{h} = f'(t) \qquad (2.4.1)$$

provided this limit exists. The velocity function is the derivative of the position function.

Having this definition of the velocity of an object, we can now dispense with the concept of average velocity, which was only used to motivate it. Velocity is the more important concept and is used to answer many questions about a body's motion. The following example shows what we mean by this.

Example 2.4.3 (Tossing a Ball Vertically)

Problem: From Newton's second law of motion (see Section 2.5), one can deduce that a body moving in a vertical line, near the earth's surface, has position function given by

$$y = -\frac{1}{2}gt^2 + v_0 t + y_0,$$

where g is the acceleration of gravity (near the earth's surface), v_0 is the initial velocity of the object, and y_0 is the initial position of the object on the y-axis. In the English system $g = 32\,\text{ft/s}^2$. We will discuss acceleration later.

For example, a ball thrown directly upward with velocity 64 ft/s from the top of a 48-foot tall building has position function given by

$$y = -16\,t^2 + 64\,t + 48.$$

With this as given, compute the corresponding velocity function and use this to determine how high above the ground the ball will travel before turning around and falling back to earth. Also determine the velocity of the ball when it hits the ground.

Solution: Since the position function is a simple quadratic polynomial in t:

$$f(t) = -16\,t^2 + 64\,t + 48,$$

it is a simple matter to compute its derivative to get the velocity function for the motion:

$$v(t) = f'(t) = -32t + 64.$$

This gives the velocity of the ball at any time t. To determine how high the ball goes, we need to find the time at which it turns around and begins its descent back to earth. We use the fact that this time occurs when the velocity is 0, that is, $v(t) = 0$. This makes sense. The ball with positive initial velocity travels upward and continuously slows down as gravity keeps tugging on it. At some point the ball loses all of its velocity and then begins to fall with its velocity being negative and increasing in magnitude continually until its hits the ground. From our work above, the equation $v(t) = 0$, in this example, is

$$-32t + 64 = 0,$$

and this says that $t = 2$. So the velocity vanishes and the ball turns around 2 seconds after it was thrown upward. Its position at this time is

$$f(2) = -16(2)^2 + 64(2) + 48 = 112 \text{ feet}$$

That is as high as the ball gets. Next, to determine the velocity with which it hits the ground, we first determine the time at which it hits the ground. By the way the coordinate system was chosen in this example, the ground is position $y = 0$. So we set the position function equal to zero, $f(t) = 0$, and solve the resulting equation for t. This equation is

$$-16\,t^2 + 64\,t + 48 = 0,$$

or, dividing by -16,

$$t^2 - 4t - 3 = 0.$$

This does not factor readily, so we use the quadratic formula to find the roots

$$t = \frac{4 \pm \sqrt{16 + 12}}{2} = 2 \pm \sqrt{7}.$$

There are two times here, but we use the positive one $t = 2 + \sqrt{7}$, since the ball was launched at time 0, and so it will hit the ground at a positive time. The velocity of the ball at this time is

$$v\left(2 + \sqrt{7}\right) = -32(2 + \sqrt{7}) + 64 = -32\sqrt{7} \approx -84.664\,\text{feet/sec}$$

Example 2.4.4 (A Hypothetical Motion)

Problem: Suppose a particle moves along the y-axis with known position function given by

$$f(t) = 4 - 7t + 5t^2 - t^3.$$

Study the motion on the time interval using the `dplot2` command. Then find the velocity function and plot the velocity and position functions in the same figure. Determine all times t when the particle changes its direction.

Solution: The `dplot2` command works like the `dplot` command, but its output is different as you will see by executing the following code:

```
> f:=t->4-7*t+5*t^2-t^3;
            f := t ↦ 4 - 7t + 5 t^2 - t^3
> dplot2(f,0,3,40);
```

When you view the movie, try to concentrate on the ends of the horizontal red lines at the y-axis. These track along with the moving particle. Note also the spacing between the horizontal lines from one time to the next (one frame to the next). The greater the spacing, the greater the average velocity over that time interval. Observe that the particle begins by falling, slowing down before turning around and rising. After briefly rising it slows down, turns around and begins falling again.

The motion is easy to analyze exactly using the derivative. Thus, we compute the velocity function v by

$$v\,(t) = f'\,(t) = \frac{d}{dt}\left(4 - 7t + 5t^2 - t^3\right) = -7 + 10t - 3t^2\,.$$

The velocity varies in a quadratic fashion with t, as the Figure 2.4.13 shows.

To determine the times t when the particle changes its direction, we note that to change direction, the particle must slow down and come to a stop in order to turn around. Stopping occurs when the velocity vanishes $v = 0$. Thus, the stopping times are the roots of the equation

$$v\,(t) = -7 + 10t - 3t^2 = 0.$$

This quadratic equation factors as $-(3t - 7)(t - 1) = 0$. Thus, the times when the velocity is zero are $t = 1, 7/3$. You can perhaps discern these two times in Figure 2.4.13 or from the movie of the motion.

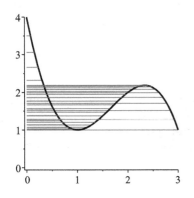

Figure 2.4.12: *The last frame in the dynamic plot of* $f(t) = 4 - 7t + 5t^2 - t^3$ *on* $[0, 3]$.

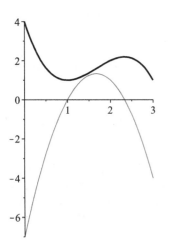

Figure 2.4.13: *Plot of the velocity function* v *(red curve) for a particle with position function* $f(t) = 4 - 7t + 5t^2 - t^3$.

Exercises: 2.4 (Velocity)

```
> with(code_ch2sec4);with(dplot_tools);
>with(plots,display);
        [average_velocity,stepplot,ymotion]
        [dplot,dplot2,dplotinverse,plotinverse]
            [printdplot,printdplot2,runrise]
                    [tanplot]]
```

CAS: **Studying Average Velocity with** ymotion

In Exercises 1–4 you will study the concept of average velocity by measuring the positions of a moving body, as in Example 2.4.1. Specifically, do the following:

(a) For your assigned value of n ($n = 2, 3, 4, 5$), execute the Maple command ymotion(n,10) to create an animation of the motion for your study. NOTE: Be sure to execute the with command at the top of this worksheet before using the the ymotion command. Run the animation several times and then discuss how the ball moves.

(b) Step through the 10-frame movie one frame at a time and measure the approximate y-coordinate of the body's position by using the cursor probe on the graphic.

(c) Given that the whole movie takes 5 seconds of real time, compile a table like Table 2.4.1, showing the times and positions t_i, y_i and their differences Δt_i, Δy_i and the resulting average velocities $\dfrac{\Delta y_i}{\Delta t_i}$.

(d) Use the data in your table to plot the approximate polygonal position function f_{approx}, as in Figure 2.4.6, and the corresponding average velocity function v_{ave}, as in Figure 2.4.7. Print out the plot of the average velocity. Mark, by hand on the printout, the average velocity values above each step in the plot of v_{ave}.

(e) On the printout of the average velocity plot, sketch a smooth curve which you think best approximates the graph of velocity function. Use this to determine the approximate times when the ball changes direction of motion.

1. ymotion(2,50)   **2.** ymotion(3,50)

3. ymotion(4,50)   **4.** ymotion(5,50)

Projectile Motion with $y_0 = 0$

A ball is projected vertically upward from ground level with an initial velocity of v_0 ft/s and is acted upon by the force of gravity. For the initial velocities v_0 and heights y_1 given in Exercises 5–10, answer the following questions:

(a) What is the position function of the ball as a function of time t?

(b) What is the velocity function of the ball as a function of time?

(c) What is the maximum height reached by the ball?

(d) What is the velocity of the ball when it is y_1 ft above the ground on its way up? On its way down?

5. $v_0 = 48$, $y_1 = 32$ **6.** $v_0 = 96$, $y_1 = 128$
7. $v_0 = 64$, $y_1 = 48$ **8.** $v_0 = 80$, $y_1 = 64$
9. $v_0 = 80$, $y_1 = 96$ **10.** $v_0 = 112$, $y_1 = 192$

Projectile Motion with $v_0 = 0$

A rock is dropped from the top of tower which is y_0 ft high. For the heights y_0 given in Exercises 11–14, answer the following questions:

(a) What is the position function of the rock as a function of time t?

(b) What is the velocity function of the rock as a function of time?

(c) How long will it take for the rock to hit the ground?

(d) What will be its speed at impact?

11. $y_0 = 64$ **12.** $y_0 = 144$
13. $y_0 = 256$ **14.** $y_0 = 400$

Projectile Motion (General)

A ball thrown vertically from the top of building which is y_0 ft high. For the initial velocities v_0 and heights y_0 given in Exercises 15–20, answer the following questions:

(a) What is the position function of the ball as a function of time t?

(b) What is the velocity function of the ball as a function of time?

(c) What is the maximum height of the ball above ground?

(d) How long will it take for the ball to hit the ground?

(e) What will be its speed at impact?

15. $v_0 = 16$, $y_0 = 32$ **16.** $v_0 = 16$, $y_0 = 96$
17. $v_0 = -16$, $y_0 = 192$ **18.** $v_0 = -16$, $y_0 = 96$
19. $v_0 = 48$, $y_0 = 64$ **20.** $v_0 = 112$, $y_0 = 192$

In Exercises 21–22, the function given is the actual position function for the motion studied in Exercises 1–2. Use derivatives to find the velocity function $v = f'$. CAS: plot v and f in the same figure and compare with the plots in Exercises 1–2 (if you did these exercises).

21. $f(t) = -t^3 + 7t^2 - 14t + 20$, for t in $[0, 5]$.

22. $f(t) = \frac{1}{2}t^4 - 3t^3 + \frac{5}{2}t^2 + 6t + 10$, for t in $[-1, 4.5]$.

Calculus *Concepts & Computation*

2.5 Differentials and Higher Derivatives

> with(code_ch2sec5); with(dplot_tools,runrise);

$$[berkeleylimit,\ newtonleibnizlimit\,]$$

$$[runrise\,]$$

There are some alternative notations for the derivative function of a given function f that you need to see which are convenient to use in working problems. To this point in the book we have been denoting the derivative of f by f', and will continue to use this notation quite a bit. The prime denotes that we derived a new function f' from the given function f by the differentiation process. We view this as "operating" on f to get f', i.e., symbolically $f \mapsto f'$.

In addition to the alternative notation for the derivative, in this section we will look at (1) the concepts of differentials and rates of change, (2) the repeated application the differentiation process to a function to get its higher-order derivatives, and (3) the concepts of acceleration and laws of motion.

The Leibniz Notation

Leibniz used a particularly handy alternative notation for the differentiation process. He introduced the symbol $\frac{d}{dx}$ to stand for an operator, which when applied to f gives its derivative:

$$f \mapsto \frac{df}{dx}.$$

(Why he chose this notation will become more clear in a minute.) In modern terms, we think of Leibniz's operator as an elementary type of differential operator, and often use the symbol D for such operators:

$$D = \frac{d}{dx}.$$

Notationally, when we apply this operator $\frac{d}{dx}$ to a function f, we put f in the numerator, by convention

$$\frac{d}{dx} f = \frac{df}{dx}.$$

This is just as if we were multiplying a fraction and a whole number (which is really not the case here, but that is how Leibniz handled his notation). Additionally, if we denote the dependent and independent variables by y and x, then the equation gives the functional dependence of y on x. Thus, it is natural to view y as a function of x and to use $\frac{dy}{dx}$ as the notation for the derivative function.

Hence, at the risk of confusing you, we now have introduced six different notations for the derivative function, namely:

Six Notations for the Derivative of f: $Df = \dfrac{df}{dx} = f' = y' = \dfrac{dy}{dx} = Dy.$

The above notation is for the derivative function. Leibniz's notation for the value of the derivative function at a particular number x is

$$f'(x) = \frac{dy}{dx}(x) = \left.\frac{dy}{dx}\right|_x.$$

It is important for you to learn all these alternative notations because you will see and use them elsewhere in your education. Leibniz's notation is convenient and easy to use as the following examples illustrate.

Example 2.5.1 (Using the Leibniz Notation)

(1) *Problem*: Suppose y is the following function of x

$$y = 3x^5 + 4x^{-2} + 2x^{1/2}.$$

Compute the derivative using the Leibniz notation.

Solution: We just apply Leibniz's operator $\frac{d}{dx}$ to both sides of the equation to get:

$$\begin{aligned}
\frac{dy}{dx} &= \frac{d}{dx}(3x^5 + 4x^{-2} + 2x^{1/2}) = \frac{d}{dx}(3x^5) + \frac{d}{dx}(4x^{-2}) + \frac{d}{dx}(2x^{1/2}) \\
&= 15x^4 - 8x^{-3} + x^{-1/2}
\end{aligned}$$

Of course with all of your practice in the previous section, you should be able to quickly compute this derivative without the Leibniz notation. However, later you will see some situations where the Leibniz notation is more useful.

(2) *Problem*: You have learned by now the derivative of the function $y = x$ is the constant 1 function. Look at this result in the Leibniz notation:

Solution: Again we apply $\frac{d}{dx}$ to both sides of the equation $y = x$ to get:

$$\frac{dy}{dx} = \frac{d}{dx}x = \frac{dx}{dx} = 1.$$

Thus, the Leibniz notation is very suggestive. It enabled Leibniz to derive many of the correct differentiation rules without much rigorous justification.

The differentiation rules and formulas from the Section 2.3 can be written as follows in the Leibniz notation:

General Power Rule:

$$\frac{d}{dx}(x^r) = rx^{r-1},$$

Sum and Constant Rules:

$$\frac{d}{dx}(f+g) = \frac{df}{dx} + \frac{dg}{dx}$$

$$\frac{d}{dx}(cf) = c\frac{df}{dx}$$

Linear Combination Rule:

$$\frac{d}{dx}(c_1 f_1 + c_2 f_2 + \cdots + c_k f_k) = c_1\frac{df_1}{dx} + c_2\frac{df_2}{dx} + \cdots + c_k\frac{df_k}{dx}.$$

Where Leibniz's Notation Came From

At the inception, when calculus was invented, the ideas and concepts were totally new and radical, and they were not well understood by many people outside of Newton and Leibniz. Even Newton and Leibniz, judged by today's mathematical standards, did not have a rigorous understanding of the limit concept they had invented. They thought of things intuitively and geometrically in terms of the difference triangle shown in Figure 2.5.1.

The ratio $\frac{\Delta y}{\Delta x}$ of the sides about the right angle made perfect sense, but the idea of letting Δx tend to 0 and getting something out of this ratio was rather vaguely explained by Newton and Leibniz. Newton spoke of the limiting ratio as the "ultimate and evanescent ratio," and argued that while the difference triangle vanished in the limit, something definite came out of the ratio of its sides.

Leibniz thought of Δx turning in an ideal quantity, called an infinitesimal, and he denoted it by dx. He regarded dx as an infinitely small quantity, one of

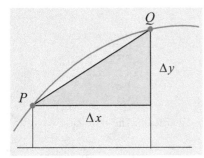

Figure 2.5.1: *A difference triangle at P with sides Δx and Δy about the right angle.*

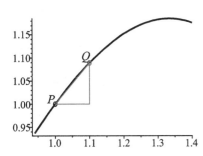

Figure 2.5.2: *The 10th frame of the movie showing Berkeley's vanishing triangle.*

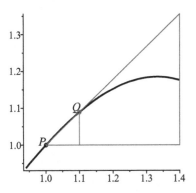

Figure 2.5.3: *The 10th frame of the movie showing Newton's and Leibniz's nonvanishing triangle (in blue).*

no magnitude, but definitely not 0. Likewise in the limit, Δy also turns into an infinitesimal denoted by dy. Then the ratio $\frac{\Delta y}{\Delta x}$ itself, in the limit, turns into the ratio of the infinitesimals:

$$\lim_{\Delta x \to 0} \frac{\Delta y}{\Delta x} = \frac{dy}{dx}.$$

This is essentially Leibniz's thinking behind his notation. The infinitesimals dx and dy are called differentials. Even though it is difficult to think of these as quantities which are infinitesimally small, but not zero, $dx \neq 0$, $dy \neq 0$, that was what Leibniz asked us to do. He also asked that we believe that the ratio of these differentials was something meaningful

$$\frac{dy}{dx} \neq \frac{0}{0}.$$

All of this intuitive thinking by Leibniz and Newton was vigorously criticized by one of their contemporaries, Bishop Berkeley. (Perhaps rightly so, because the precise definition of limits took about a hundred more years to develop). Berkeley didn't see how one could obtain a definite ratio in the limit, if the difference triangle vanished. If you run the following animation you might tend to agree with him. (Slow the animation down to 2 frames per second.)

```
> berkeleylimit;
```

But Newton and Leibniz knew what they were doing and could calculate these limiting ratios (much as you have been doing in this chapter). Perhaps they were thinking (we can't be sure) that while the difference triangle does vanish at our human eyesight scale, nevertheless if you could look at it down at the atomic scale, its proportions are fairly constant. Try visualizing this in your mind. The following animation may help you with this. It shows the difference triangle (in red) at each step is similar (has proportional sides) to a right triangle whose horizontal side is fixed in length (shown in blue). (Slow the animation down to 2 frames per second.)

```
> newtonleibnizlimit;
```

Well, the animation is much more convincing than vague talk about differentials being infinitesimally small quantities. But then, recall that in the 1600s, movies and computers were some 300 years in the future, not to mention electron-scanning microscopes.

Rates of Change and Differentials

The Leibniz notation is very useful when discussing the concept of the rate of change of some quantity with respect to another. Typically one quantity, say y, is a function of another quantity, say x, and this functional dependence is given by a function f:

$$y = f(x).$$

In particular examples, the x and y represent various real and measurable quantities and are often denoted by other symbols suggested by the physical situation. For example, in studying motion, the position s is a function of the time t, or in chemistry, the pressure P is a function of the volume V. In tracking rockets at launching, one might observe the angle θ of elevation as function of the time t.

In all of these situations, we are interested in studying what kind of changes in the dependent variable y result from corresponding changes in the independent variable x. To be specific, we fix x and consider moving from x to a new value x_1. Then the change in x-values is

$$\Delta x = x_1 - x,$$

and the corresponding change in the y-values, $y = f(x)$ and $y_1 = f(x_1)$, is

$$\Delta y = f(x_1) - f(x).$$

To further quantify how y changes with respect to x, we can introduce the ratio of these changes

$$\frac{\Delta y}{\Delta x} = \text{average rate of change of } y \text{ with respect to } x$$

Where this ratio is large, the change in y is large relative to the change in x, and where this ratio is small the change in y is small relative to the change in x. As a measure of how fast y is changing with respect to x, this average rate is a better approximation when Δx is small. This is similar to the discussion of average velocity in the previous section, and indeed, average velocity is one of the prime examples of an average rate of change. It is an average rate of change of position with respect to time.

Example 2.5.2 (Visualizing Average Rates of Changes)

As an abstract example, one not pertaining to any particular physical situation, suppose the relation between the variables x and y is

$$y = 2\sqrt{x} - \sqrt[3]{x^2}.$$

We can use the Maple command `runrise` to get an intuitive feel for this notion of the average rate of change of x with respect to y. First define the function

```
> f:=x->2*sqrt(x)-x^(2/3);
```
$$f := x \to 2\sqrt{x} - x^{2/3}$$

The following command generates a movie showing a run-rise diagram (stair-steps) on the interval $[0, 2]$, with the changes in x all equal to $\Delta x = 2/10 = 0.2$.

```
> runrise(f,0,2,10);
```

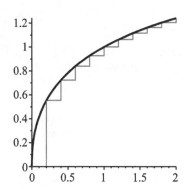

Figure 2.5.4: *The last frame in the movie* `runrise(f,0,2,10)`.

As you can see from Figure 2.5.4, the changes Δy in y for each change Δx in x are greatest at the beginning, near 0, and gradually decrease. Since the changes Δx are all the same ($\Delta x = 0.2$), the average rates of change $\Delta y/\Delta x$ get smaller as we move from left-to-right along the graph.

Next view the movie generated by the following command. It consists of 50 steps with each change in x much smaller than above, i.e., now $\Delta x = 2/50 = 0.04$.

```
> runrise(f,0,2,50);
```

The above example illustrates the average rate of change concept and suggests taking ever smaller steps in the x direction to arrive at the concept of the rate of change of y with respect to x. Technically this requires letting Δx tend to 0.

DEFINITION 2.5.1 (Rates of Change)

Suppose $y = f(x)$ is a given function relating the variables x and y. Then the rate of change of y with respect to x at $x = a$ is

$$\left.\frac{dy}{dx}\right|_{x=a} = \lim_{\Delta x \to 0} \left.\frac{\Delta y}{\Delta x}\right|_{x=a} = f'(a)$$

As with the velocity concept, this generalization to the rate of change of one variable with respect to another is more important than the average rate of change concept that we used to motivate it.

Example 2.5.3 (Boyle's Law)

Problem: Boyle's law from chemistry relates the pressure P and the volume V of a gas in a container. Specifically, this law simply says that

$$P = \frac{k}{V},$$

for some positive constant k. Thus, the pressure increases as the volume of the container is decreased. On the other hand the pressure will decrease if the volume of the container is increased. Find the rate of change of pressure with respect to volume and interpret the result.

Solution: Write P in the power function notation: $P = kV^{-1}$. Then we use the Leibniz notation to find the derivative of P with respect to V:

$$\frac{dP}{dV} = \frac{d}{dV}\left(kV^{-1}\right) = -kV^{-2} = -\frac{k}{V^2}.$$

The negative values for the rates of change indicate that P decreases as V increases. The rates of change go as the reciprocal of the square in V, and so are much smaller for larger V.

Example 2.5.4 (Reaction Rates in Chemistry)

Problem: Hydrogen Iodide (HI) is known to decompose into hydrogen (H_2) and iodide (I_2). This is called a chemical reaction and is written as a diagram

$$2HI \longrightarrow H_2 + I_2$$

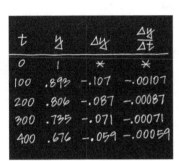

Because of this reaction, the concentration y of hydrogen iodide in a container will decrease over time. Starting at time $t = 0$ with a concentration of $y(0) = 1$ M/L, measurements, in the lab, of the concentration every 100 seconds give the data shown in the margin table. Also shown are the *average rates of reaction* $\Delta y / \Delta t$ for each of the 100 second time intervals. From chemical theory, one can determine that the concentration y as a function of t is

$$y = f(t) = \frac{1}{kt + 1},$$

Table 2.5.1: *Hydrogen iodide concentration data.*

where k, found from the lab data, is $k = 0.0012$. Use this to plot the concentration of Hydrogen Iodide on the time interval $0, 400]$ and include a `runrise` plot of the four average rates of reaction on the four intervals. Also compute the (instantaneous) rate of reaction dy/dt at any time t. From this show that the hydrogen iodide reaction is a *second-order reaction*, i.e., show that

$$\frac{dy}{dt} = -ky^2$$

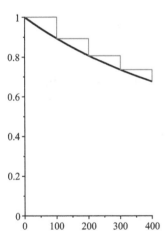

Figure 2.5.5: *Hydrogen Iodide concentration decrease and four average rates of reaction.*

Solution: We define the hydrogen iodide concentration and do a `runrise` plot as follows.

```
> k:=0.0012; f:=t->1/(k*t+1);
```

$$k := 0.0012$$

$$f := t \to \frac{1}{kt + 1}$$

```
> runrise(f,0,400,2);
```

The last frame in the movie is shown in Figure 2.5.5. Note that the plot of the concentration data from Table 2.5.1 gives a polygonal function that approximates the plot of the theoretical concentration y. These plots are indistinguishable at this scale. Also note that the average reaction rates shown are decreasing with time.

To calculate the reaction rate dy/dt, we need to use the limit definition. The change in time is $\Delta t = (t+h) - t = h$ and the corresponding change in concentration is

$$\Delta y = f(t+h) - f(t) = \frac{1}{k(t+h)+1} - \frac{1}{kt+1} = \frac{kt + 1 - (kt + kh + 1)}{(kt + kh + 1)(kt + 1)}$$

$$= \frac{-kh}{(kt + kh + 1)(kt + 1)}$$

Thus,

$$\frac{dy}{dt} = \lim_{\Delta t \to 0} \frac{\Delta y}{\Delta t} = \lim_{h \to 0} \frac{f(t+h) - f(t)}{h} = \lim_{h \to 0} \frac{1}{h} \cdot \frac{-kh}{(kt + kh + 1)(kt + 1)}$$

$$= \lim_{h \to 0} \frac{-k}{(kt + kh + 1)(kt + 1)} = \frac{-k}{(kt + 1)^2}.$$

From this we clearly get, by substitution,

$$-ky^2 = -k\left(\frac{1}{kt+1}\right)^2 = \frac{-k}{(kt+1)^2} = \frac{dy}{dt},$$

which shows, by definition, that this is a second-order reaction rate.

Differentials: The Leibniz notation dx and dy for the infinitesimals, or differentials of x and y, is meant to suggest infinitesimal changes in x and y, while the differences Δx and Δy give the discrete changes in x and y respectively. The former are not rigorous, while the latter are. Even though we are not attaching here a rigorous meaning to the notion of differentials, we will find it helpful heuristically to use differentials in motivating other concepts and constructions. One such concept is the u-substitution method (or change of variables formula) that you will study in Chapter 5. For this we need to know how the differentials dx and dy are related if the variables x and y are related by $y = f(x)$. A motivational derivation of this relation is as follows. See Figure 2.5.6.

Fix x, let $y = f(x)$. Then for a discrete change Δx in x, the corresponding discrete change in y is $\Delta y = f(x + \Delta x) - f(x)$. The average rate of change is then expressed by

$$\frac{\Delta y}{\Delta x} = \frac{f(x + \Delta x) - f(x)}{\Delta x}.$$

The rate of change of y with respect to x comes from taking the limit of this as $\Delta x \to 0$. In the limit, Δx turns into the differential dx and Δy turns into dy:

$$f'(x) = \frac{dy}{dx} = \frac{f(x + dx) - f(x)}{dx}.$$

Multiplying all sides of the above equation by dx gives: $dy = f'(x)dx$ This is a heuristic derivation of the following:

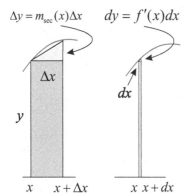

$\Delta y = m_{\sec}(x)\Delta x \qquad dy = f'(x)dx$

Figure 2.5.6: *The differences Δx, Δy become infinitesimals dx, dy.*

CHANGE OF DIFFERENTIALS FORMULA

If the variables x and y are related by

$$y = f(x) \qquad (2.5.1)$$

then their differentials are related by

$$dy = f'(x)dx \qquad (2.5.2)$$

Example 2.5.5

Problem: If y is related to x by

$$y = 5x^3 + 4x^2 - 6x + 2,$$

find the relation between the differentials.

Solution: In the Leibniz notation, we have

$$dy = \frac{dy}{dx} \cdot dx = \frac{d}{dx}\left(5x^3 + 4x^2 - 6x + 2\right) \cdot dx = \left(15x^2 + 8x - 6\right)dx.$$

Higher Derivatives

Since the process of differentiating a function f gives a new function f' (the derivative function), we can apply the differentiation process to f' to get another new function $(f')'$, which is called the *second derivative* of the original function f. The second derivative of f is denoted by using two primes without the parentheses:

$$f'' \quad \text{(The second derivative of } f\text{)}$$

Differentiating f'' gives another new function, called the *third derivative* of f, which is denoted by three primes:

$$f''' \quad \text{(The third derivative of } f\text{)}$$

Continuing like this we get the fourth, fifth, sixth, ..., etc., derivatives of f. These are called the higher derivatives (or higher-order derivatives) of the original function f. Once we get past the fourth or fifth derivative, the prime notation for the higher derivatives becomes somewhat cumbersome, and so we will often use either (1) the parentheses notation or (2) the Leibniz notation. These alternative notations are:

$$f' \;=\; f^{(1)} = \frac{dy}{dx}$$

$$f'' \;=\; f^{(2)} = \frac{d^2y}{dx^2}$$

$$f''' \;=\; f^{(3)} = \frac{d^3y}{dx^3}$$

$$\vdots$$

$$f''^{\cdots\prime} \;=\; f^{(n)} = \frac{d^ny}{dx^n}$$

You may wonder why the Leibniz notation for the higher derivatives is the way it is. To explain this, think of $\frac{d}{dx}$ in terms of the D operator

$$D = \frac{d}{dx}.$$

Applying this operator to a function gives its 1st derivative. Applying it twice gives its 2nd derivative, and it is natural to write

$$D^2 = DD = \frac{d}{dx}\frac{d}{dx} = \frac{d^2}{dx^2},$$

for the 2nd derivative operator. Notice that the differential dx is treated as one quantity, and so its square is written as shown in the denominator above. Similarly applying D three times to a function gives its 3rd derivative, and the 3rd derivative operator is written as

$$D^3 = DDD = \frac{d}{dx}\frac{d}{dx}\frac{d}{dx} = \frac{d^3}{dx^3}.$$

Now that we have all this notation, we will look at a few examples of how to apply it to compute higher derivatives. The usefulness of the higher derivative concept will be discussed in the next subsection, and at other places throughout the book.

Example 2.5.6

(1) *Problem*: Find the 3rd derivative of the polynomial $f(x) = 2-3x+8x^2-x^3+4x^4$.

Solution: To find the 3rd derivative, we have to find the 1st and 2nd derivatives. We get

$$
\begin{aligned}
f'(x) &= -3 + 16x - 3x^2 + 16x^3 \\
f''(x) &= 16 - 6x + 48x^2 \\
f'''(x) &= -6 + 96x
\end{aligned}
$$

(2) *Problem*: Find the 5th derivative of $f(x) = x^{-1}$. Use the work to conjecture what the nth derivative is.

Solution: The successive derivatives are:

$$
\begin{aligned}
f'(x) &= -x^{-2} \\
f''(x) &= 2x^{-3} \\
f'''(x) &= -3 \cdot 2x^{-4} \\
f^{(4)}(x) &= 4 \cdot 3 \cdot 2x^{-5} \\
f^{(5)}(x) &= -5 \cdot 4 \cdot 3 \cdot 2x^{-6}
\end{aligned}
$$

From these we can deduce a pattern that allows us to determine what the nth derivative will be. It should involve x raised to the power $-(n+1)$, a plus or minus sign depending on whether n is even or odd, respectively, and a product of all the integers between n and 2. This latter number is called the *factorial* of n, and is denoted by

$$
n! = n(n-1)(n-2)\cdots 3 \cdot 2 \cdot 1
$$

Thus we can write the nth derivative as

$$
f^{(n)}(x) = (-1)^n n!\, x^{-(n+1)}.
$$

Newton's Notation and Acceleration

Newton's notation for the derivatives of a function uses dots instead of a primes. While this notation is not as discernible as the prime notation (dots are smaller than primes) and not as handy as the Leibniz notation (operators are basic to mathematics), it is a notation that you will see in discussions of motions of objects, where the independent variable is the time t.

Thus, if $y = f(t)$ is the given function, then use one dot to denote the 1st derivative, two dots for the 2nd derivative, and so on:

$$
\dot{y} = \frac{dy}{dt}, \quad \ddot{y} = \frac{d^2y}{dt^2}, \quad \dddot{y} = \frac{d^3y}{dt^3}
$$

Newton's dot notation is primarily restricted to situations involving time varying quantities, and even in these situations the other notation is often used interchangeably.

Much more important than the dot notation are all the concepts and laws that Newton introduced to describe the motion of an object. It was indeed the very calculus, which he co-invented with Leibniz, that enabled Newton to clarify and make precise the notions of velocity and acceleration of a moving body and to formulate the relation of these to the forces acting on that body. Acceleration is defined as the rate of change of velocity with respect to time. Specifically:

DEFINITION 2.5.2 (Velocity and Acceleration)

Suppose $y = f(t)$ is the position function for a body moving along the y-axis. If v is the
the velocity function

$$v = \dot{y} = \frac{dy}{dt}$$

then the acceleration function a is derivative of the velocity function, or equivalently,
the second derivative of the position function:

$$a = \dot{v} = \frac{dv}{dt} = \frac{d^2 y}{dt^2} = \ddot{y}$$

Example 2.5.7 (Acceleration Near the Earth's Surface)

Problem: As discussed in Example 2.4.3, a ball thrown directly upward from the top of a 48 foot high building and released with an initial velocity of 64 feet per second has position function given by

$$s = -16t^2 + 64t + 48.$$

Given this, find the acceleration of the ball at any time t.

Solution: We differentiate s once with respect to t to get the velocity function:

$$v = \dot{s} = \frac{ds}{dt} = \frac{d}{dt}\left(-16t^2 + 64t + 48\right) = -32t + 64.$$

Then we differentiate again to get the acceleration function:

$$a = \dot{v} = \frac{dv}{dt} = \frac{d}{dt}\left(-32t + 64\right) = -32.$$

The result is that the acceleration of the ball is constant during its entire motion, -32 feet per second per second. (The negative sign is because the position axis is directed upward.) This is a well-known phenomenon. All bodies, regardless of their mass, experience the same constant acceleration near the earth's surface. This is called the acceleration of gravity.

Using the concept of acceleration, Newton formulated his famous 2nd Law of motion as follows. We assume that the mass of the body is constant and that the force F acting on the body is the net force (sum of all the forces acting on the body).

NEWTON'S SECOND LAW

Suppose $y = f(t)$ is the position function for a body moving along the y-axis. Then the
mass m of the body times the acceleration a is equal to the force acting on the body:

$$ma = F \qquad (2.5.4)$$

or equivalently,

$$m\ddot{y} = F \qquad (2.5.5)$$

There are several ways in which this law can be used. If the position function is known, then we can differentiate twice with respect to t to determine the force F acting on the body at each time. This is a direct use of the law. More commonly the law is used indirectly: the force F is given (and may depend on the body's position and velocity, as well as the time) and we have to determine the position function $y = f(x)$ from this. This is often not so easy, because we have to take the equation

$$m\ddot{y} = F,$$

and solve it for y. The above equation is known as a differential equation, and solving this equation amounts to finding a function y which when differentiated twice gives F/m. You may have the chance to study this topic in one or more of your future courses. The following examples give several easy situations where this differential equation is easy to solve.

Example 2.5.8 (Linear Motion with Constant Force)

Problem: Suppose a body moves along the y-axis with constant force F acting on it. Assuming y_0, v_0 are the body's position and velocity at time zero, find the position function for the body's motion.

Solution: Newton's 2nd Law gives the equation

$$m\ddot{y} = F,$$

or equivalently

$$\ddot{y} = \frac{F}{m},$$

for the position function y. How do we find y from this? It might help to interpret the equation as saying that the acceleration is constant. But the acceleration is also the rate of change of velocity, $\ddot{y} = \dot{v}$, and so the above equation can be written as

$$\dot{v} = \frac{F}{m}.$$

What functions have derivative equal to a constant? Recall from your work with the differentiation formulas, that

$$\frac{d}{dt}(kt) = k,$$

where k is any constant and so in particular

$$\frac{d}{dt}\left(\frac{F}{m}t\right) = \frac{F}{m},$$

But also, since the derivative of any constant c is 0, we have, more generally,

$$\frac{d}{dt}\left(\frac{F}{m}t + c\right) = \frac{F}{m},$$

Thus, we see that v must have the form

$$v = \frac{F}{m}t + c,$$

where c is an arbitrary constant. But since $v = v_0$, when $t = 0$, we get from the above that the constant c must be $c = v_0$. Next, since $v = \dot{y}$, we can determine y by solving the differential equation

$$\dot{y} = v = \frac{F}{m}t + v_0.$$

To ease the process of determining y from this, we divide it into parts. First we ask what function of t when differentiated gives t? We know that $\frac{d}{dt}\left(t^2\right) = 2t$, which is close, except for the factor of 2. In order to correct for this we multiply t^2 by $\frac{1}{2}$. Then $\frac{d}{dt}\left(\frac{1}{2}t^2\right) = t$. So also

$$\frac{d}{dt}\left(\frac{F}{2m}t^2\right) = \frac{F}{m}t.$$

This is part of what we need. The other part is a function whose derivative is v_0. But from our work above we know that

$$\frac{d}{dt}\left(v_0 t + k\right) = v_0,$$

for any constant k. Putting both of these parts together, we get that the position function y is

$$y = \frac{F}{2m}t^2 + v_0 t + k.$$

The constant k here is determined by the initial condition that $y = y_0$, when $t = 0$. Thus, $k = y_0$.

Summary: The y that satisfies the differential equation $\ddot{y} = F/m$, with F a constant, and has initial position y_0 and velocity v_0 is given by

$$y = \frac{F}{2m}t^2 + v_0 t + y_0.$$

Special Case 1 (Zero Force): The the absence of any force acting on it ($F = 0$), the position of the body varies linearly with time:

$$y = v_0 t + y_0,$$

which means the velocity is constant: $v = v_0$ for all times t.

Special Case 2 (Motion Near a Planet's Surface): An important extension of Case 1 is the situation where $F = -mg$. Here g is a positive constant and the minus sign indicates that the force is directed downward (in the negative y-direction). This is a realistic physical situation that models, to a very good approximation, the motion of a body near a planet's surface when it is projected vertically upward or downward. For the earth, $g = 32$ ft/s^2, and for the moon $g = 4$ ft/s^2. In this case the position function is

$$y = -\frac{1}{2}gt^2 + v_0 t + y_0.$$

Note that the mass m does not enter into the above formula for the position. Thus, all bodies, released from the same height with the same initial velocity, will have the same motion regardless of their masses. This motion is a quadratic function of the time, the velocity is a linear function of the time,

$$v = -gt + v_0,$$

and the acceleration is the constant $-g$

$$a = -g.$$

Exercises: 2.5 (Differentials and Higher Derivatives)

Practice using the Leibniz notation by finding the 1st and 2nd derivatives, $\dfrac{dy}{dx}$, $\dfrac{d^2y}{dx^2}$, of the functions $y = f(x)$ in Exercises 1–20.

1. $y = 3x^4 - 6x^3 + \frac{2}{3}x^2 + x - 7$

2. $y = 5x^4 + 12x^3 + \frac{3}{7}x^2 + 2x - 9$

3. $3y = 3x^{5/2} - 5x^{4/3} + \dfrac{2}{\sqrt{x}}$

4. $y = 2x^{7/2} - 6x^{5/3} + 5x^{-3/2}$

5. $y = x + \sqrt{x} + \dfrac{1}{\sqrt{x}}$ **6.** $y = x + \sqrt[3]{x} + \dfrac{1}{\sqrt[3]{x}}$

7. $y = \sqrt{x}\left(5x^3 + 2\sqrt{x}\right)$ **8.** $\sqrt[3]{x}\left(5x^3 + 2\sqrt{x}\right)$

9. $y = \dfrac{2x^4 - \sqrt[3]{x^2}}{x}$ **10.** $y = \dfrac{2x^4 - \sqrt[3]{x}}{x}$

11. $f(x) = x^{-3} + \dfrac{3}{x^2} + \dfrac{4}{x}$

12. $f(x) = x^{-5/2} + \dfrac{2}{\sqrt{x^3}} + \dfrac{4}{\sqrt{x}}$

13. $f(x) = \left(3x^2 + 2\right)^2$ **14.** $f(x) = \left(2x^3 - 1\right)^3$

15. $y = \left(x + \sqrt{x}\right)^2$ **16.** $y = \left(x - \sqrt{x}\right)^3$

17. $y = \left(\sqrt{x} + \dfrac{1}{\sqrt{x}}\right)^2$ **18.** $y = \left(\sqrt[3]{x} - \dfrac{1}{\sqrt[3]{x}}\right)^2$

19. $f(x) = \left(2 - 3x + x^2\right)^2$ **20.** $f(x) = \left(3 - x + 2x^2\right)^2$

Rates of Change (Applications)

21. Gas is confined in a container whose volume is increasing. Find the rate of change of the pressure (in pounds/cubic foot) that the gas exerts on the container when the volume is 3 cubic feet. Assume the constant in Boyle's Law is $k = 5$.

22. In thermodynamics the study of gases leads to the quantity known as the compressibility of a gas. This quantity is the negative of the rate of change of volume *per unit volume*, i.e.

$$\beta = -\frac{1}{V}\frac{dP}{dV} \qquad \text{(compressibility)}$$

The negative sign is there by convention. (We want β to be positive when the pressure decreases with increasing volume.) Using this definition, find the compressibility of a gas that obeys Boyle's Law.

23. Consider a growing, single-celled organism of spherical shape. Let r denote the radius of the cell. The volume V of the cell is given by the formula $V = \frac{4}{3}\pi r^3$. As the cell grows the radius increases. Find a formula for the rate of increase of the volume with respect to the radius. At what rate is the volume increasing when the radius is 10 nanometers? Find the relation between the differentials dV and dr and interpret this geometrically.

24. The volume of a right circle cylinder of radius r and height h is $V = \pi r^2 h$. Find the rate of change of volume with respect to the radius (height held constant) and the rate of change of volume with respect to height (radius held constant). Interpret each of these geometrically.

25. The area of a square is increasing. Find a formula for the rate of change of the area A with respect to the square's side x. Find the relation between the differentials dA, dx and interpret this geometrically.

26. Some sodium chlorate crystals are grown in the shape of cubes. If V denotes the volume of such a cube with side length x, find the rate of change of volume with respect to the side length when $x = 2.5$. Find the relation between the differentials of V and x and interpret this relation geometrically.

Reaction Rates

The following data give the concentrations y of a certain reactant at five specified times. (a) Compute the corresponding four average rates of reaction. (b) If the concentration is given by

$$y = f(t) = \frac{y_0}{kt + 1},$$

find the (instantaneous) rate of reaction and show the this reaction is a second-order reaction.

27. $t = 0, 40, 83, 129, 179$ $(k = 0.00097)$
$y = 0.800, 0.775, 0.750, 0.725, 0.700$

28. $t = 0, 250, 750, 1750, 3750$ $(k = 0.0013)$
$y = 0.0500, 0.0250, 0.0125, 0.00625, 0.00312$

Higher Derivatives

For the following functions $f(x)$, find the derivatives $f'(x), f''(x), f'''(x), f^{(4)}(x)$.

29. $f(x) = 2 + 3x - 5x^2 + 4x^3$
30. $f(x) = 5 - 2x + 6x^2 - 4x^3$
31. $f(x) = x^{3/2} + 4x^{5/2}$ **32.** $f(x) = x^{5/3} + 9x^{7/3}$
33. $f(x) = x^3 + 1/x$ **34.** $f(x) = x^4 + 1/x^2$
35. $f(x) = \sqrt{x}$ **36.** $f(x) = \sqrt[3]{x}$
37. $f(x) = e^x$ **38.** $f(x) = x + 3e^x$

Velocity and Acceleration

In Exercises 39–48, you are given the position function $y = s(t)$ of a particle moving along the y-axis. Find the velocity function v and the acceleration function a. **CAS:** Use Maple's plot command to graph the position function and then comment on the nature of the motion.

39. $s(t) = -3t + 2$ **40.** $s(t) = -5t + 3$
41. $s(t) = 25 + 6t - 16t^2$ **42.** $s(t) = 12 + 5t - 8t^2$
43. $s(t) = t^3 - 3t + 1$ **44.** $s(t) = 2t^3 - 3t + 1$
45. $s(t) = t + 1/t$ **46.** $s(t) = \sqrt{t} + 1/\sqrt{t}$
47. $s(t) = t^2 + t^{-2}$ **48.** $s(t) = t^3 + t^{-3}$

Calculus Concepts & Computation

2.6 The Product and Quotient Rules

The sum rule, constant multiple rule, and linear combination rule are all very natural and easy to use. They essentially express the idea that $D = \frac{d}{dx}$ is a linear differential operator. In contrast to this, the product and quotient rules discussed in this section, as well as the chain rule in Section 2.8, are somewhat unexpectedly complicated and you may find them more difficult to use correctly until you have practiced on a few exercises.

We begin with the product rule. It tells us that the product fg of two differentiable functions f and g has a derivative $(fg)'$ which is not as simple as you might expect. In fact, many students would like for the easy formula $(fg)' = f'g'$ to be true. *But this is an incorrect formula.* The reason why things don't work out this simply is inherently due to the rules of algebra. The correct formula $(fg)' = f'g + fg'$ is given in the following theorem, and you can study the proof to understand why it must have this more complicated form.

THEOREM 2.6.1 (Product Rule)

The product fg of two differentiable functions f and g is differentiable and

$$(fg)' = f'g + fg'$$

In the Leibniz notation:

$$\frac{d}{dx}(fg) = \frac{df}{dx}g + f\frac{dg}{dx}$$

Proof: We look at the Newton quotient for the product function $p(x) = f(x)g(x)$ and see if the limit exists. We fix x, increment by h, and get that $p(x + h) = f(x + h)g(x + h)$. So the Newton quotient for p is

$$\frac{p(x + h) - p(x)}{h} = \frac{f(x + h)g(x + h) - f(x)g(x)}{h} \tag{2.1}$$

Now the question is: how do we do we use some basic algebra on the latter expression in Equation (2.1) so that the Newton quotients

$$\frac{f(x + h) - f(x)}{h} \quad \text{and} \quad \frac{g(x + h) - g(x)}{h}$$

for f and g appear? A little bit of fiddling suggests that we add and subtract $f(x)g(x + h)$ in the numerator of the expression on the right side of Equation (2.1) to get

$$\frac{f(x + h)g(x + h) - f(x)g(x + h) + f(x)g(x + h) - f(x)g(x)}{h}.$$

Now, in the numerator of this, group the first two terms together and factor out $g(x + h)$. Then group the last two terms together and factor out $f(x)$. From this we get

$$\frac{p(x + h) - p(x)}{h} = \frac{[f(x + h) - f(x)]g(x + h) + f(x)[g(x + h) - g(x)]}{h}$$

$$= \left[\frac{f(x + h) - f(x)}{h}\right] \cdot g(x + h) + f(x) \cdot \left[\frac{g(x + h) - g(x)}{h}\right]$$

This is what we need. The terms in the square brackets are the Newton quotients for f and g, and they tend to $f'(x)$ and $g'(x)$ respectively as $h \to 0$. The factor

$g(x + h)$ tends to $g(x)$, since g, being differentiable at x, is therefore continuous at x (See Theorem 2.2.1). Hence, by the limit theorems, the limit of the Newton quotient for p exists and

$$
\begin{aligned}
p'(x) &= \lim_{h \to 0} \frac{p(x + h) - p(x)}{h} \\
&= \lim_{h \to 0} \left[\frac{f(x + h) - f(x)}{h} \right] \cdot \lim_{h \to 0} g(x + h) + f(x) \cdot \lim_{h \to 0} \left[\frac{g(x + h) - g(x)}{h} \right] \\
&= f'(x)g(x) + f(x)g'(x)
\end{aligned}
$$

This completes the proof.

The following examples should help you understand how to apply the product rule correctly.

Example 2.6.1 (Applying the Product Rule)

Problem: Differentiate the function:
$$p(x) = x^3 e^x.$$

Solution: We recognize this as being the product of two functions:

$$f(x) = x^3, \ g(x) = e^x,$$

which have derivatives

$$f'(x) = 3x^2, \ g'(x) = e^x.$$

Hence by the product rule

$$
\begin{aligned}
p'(x) &= f'(x)g(x) + f(x)g'(x) = 3x^2 e^x + x^3 e^x \\
&= (3x^2 + x^3)e^x.
\end{aligned}
$$

Note that the initial result $3x^2 e^x + x^3 e^x$, before we factored it, involves the sum of two terms with each term being a product. Look for this when applying the product rule. As we mentioned, there is a tendency for students to apply the product rule incorrectly and just write $f'(x)g'(x)$ for the result. Here this gives $f'(x)g'(x) = 3x^2 e^x$, which is definitely different than the correct answer $(3x^2 + x^3)e^x$. So beware of this common mistake.

Let's see how the Leibniz notation works in this example. The way we compute the derivative is slightly different than above. Instead of computing the derivatives separately and then plugging them into the formula, we start with the equation

$$p(x) = x^3 e^x,$$

apply the derivative operator to both sides, and then use the product rule formula:

$$
\begin{aligned}
p'(x) &= \frac{d}{dx}(x^3 e^x) = \frac{d}{dx}(x^3) \cdot e^x + x^3 \cdot \frac{d}{dx}(e^x) \\
\\
&= (3x^2)e^x + x^3(e^x) = 3x^2 e^x + x^3 e^x
\end{aligned}
$$

We will use both approaches through out the book. Some students may find the Leibniz approach easier to comprehend.

A Caution About Notation: In using the Leibniz notation for the product rule:

$$\frac{d}{dx}(fg) = \frac{df}{dx}g + f\frac{dg}{dx},$$

the first term $\frac{df}{dx}g$ the sum can be confusing in particular examples. For instance, in the last example

$$\frac{d}{dx}(x^3 e^x) = \frac{d}{dx}(x^3) \cdot e^x + x^3 \cdot \frac{d}{dx}(e^x),$$

the first term is $\frac{d}{dx}(x^3) \cdot e^x$, and it is important to note that the $\frac{d}{dx}$ only applies to x^3. (So e^x does not get differentiated in this term.)

Example 2.6.2 (A Product of Polynomials)

Here is a simple example which we could do without the product rule (see the next example), but it serves to illustrate the procedure of applying the product rule. The function is the product of two polynomials:

$$p(x) = (3x^2 - 5x + 1)(x^5 + 2).$$

The two polynomials in the product are

$$f(x) = 3x^2 - 5x + 1, \quad g(x) = x^5 + 2,$$

and they have derivatives

$$f'(x) = 6x - 5, \quad g'(x) = 5x^4.$$

Plugging these four things into the product rule gives

$$\begin{aligned} p'(x) &= f'(x)g(x) + f(x)g'(x) = (6x - 5)(x^5 + 2) + (3x^2 - 5x + 1)(5x^4) \\ &= 6x^6 + 12x - 5x^5 - 10 + 15x^6 - 25x^5 + 5x^4 \\ &= 21x^6 - 30x^5 + 5x^4 + 12x - 10 \end{aligned}$$

Let's redo the calculation, but this time use the Leibniz notation. We start with the original function:
$$p(x) = (3x^2 - 5x + 1)(x^5 + 2),$$

apply $\frac{d}{dx}$ to both sides and use the product rule

$$\begin{aligned} p'(x) &= \frac{d}{dx}(3x^2 - 5x + 1) \cdot (x^5 + 2) + (3x^2 - 5x + 1) \cdot \frac{d}{dx}(x^5 + 2) \\ &= (6x - 5)(x^5 + 2) + (3x^2 - 5x + 1)(5x^4) \end{aligned}$$

From this point on the work is the same as above (i.e., multiply out and combine like terms).

NOTE: As we mentioned before this example, the first term

$$\frac{d}{dx}(3x^2 - 5x + 1) \cdot (x^5 + 2)$$

in the above calculation can be confusing at first. If we include an extra bracket and write

$$\left[\frac{d}{dx}(3x^2 - 5x + 1) \right] (x^5 + 2),$$

then it is clear that the $\frac{d}{dx}$ only applies to $(3x^2 - 5x + 1)$. (So $(x^5 + 2)$ does not get differentiated in this term.) Usually we will not include this extra bracket.

You see that this method with the Leibniz notion is a little bit quicker than the one with the prime notation, mainly because you don't calculate the derivatives separately before plugging them into the product rule formula. In fact, we want you to become skilled enough at using the product rule so that, for simple problems, you can take derivatives in your head as you are writing out the work. For instance, with practice you should be able to go from

$$p(x) = (3x^2 - 5x + 1)(x^5 + 2)$$

directly to

$$p'(x) = (6x - 5)(x^5 + 2) + (3x^2 - 5x + 1)(5x^4),$$

which is the correct answer (before simplification).

Example 2.6.3 (An Alternative for the Previous Example)

The previous example can be easily worked *without* the product rule. First multiply out to get a single polynomial and then differentiate that. Here's what we mean. Multiply out the product first:

$$
\begin{aligned}
p(x) &= (3x^2 - 5x + 1)(x^5 + 2) = 3x^7 + 6x^2 - 5x^6 - 10x + x^5 + 2 \\
&= 3x^7 - 5x^6 + x^5 + 6x^2 - 10x + 2
\end{aligned}
$$

Now differentiate to get

$$
p'(x) = 21x^6 - 30x^5 + 5x^4 + 12x - 10;
$$

This is what we got using the product rule above. Clearly not every product of functions can be simplified like this. So the product rule is a very necessary tool for calculating derivatives. The next example exhibits this.

Example 2.6.4 (A Product Involving a Square Root Function)

Suppose we want to compute the derivative of

$$
p(x) = x^4\sqrt{x^2 + 3x}
$$

which is the product of the two functions

$$
f(x) = x^4, \ \ g(x) = \sqrt{x^2 + 3x}
$$

To use the product rule we need to know the derivatives of both f and g. Generally, you would use the chain rule in Section 2.8 to differentiate g, but we will use the result from Exercise 31, Section 2.2 (which uses the limit definition). Then we have

$$
f'(x) = 4x^3, \ g'(x) = \frac{2x + 3}{2\sqrt{x^2 + 3x}}.
$$

Then

$$
\begin{aligned}
p'(x) &= 4x^3\sqrt{x^2 + 3x} + x^4\left(\frac{2x + 3}{2\sqrt{x^2 + 3x}}\right) = \frac{8x^3(x^2 + 3x) + x^4(2x + 3)}{2\sqrt{x^2 + 3x}} \\
&= \frac{10x^5 + 27x^4}{2\sqrt{x^2 + 3x}}
\end{aligned}
$$

NOTE: In using the product rule formula

$$
(fg)' = f'g + fg',
$$

It my help you to think of the result as

derivative of the 1st function times the 2nd function
plus
1st function times the derivative of the 2nd function

Example 2.6.5 (Another Product Involving a Square Root Function)

Problem: Differentiate $p(x) = (x^3 + 1)\sqrt{x + 1}$

Solution: The second function here is $g(x) = \sqrt{x + 1}$ which has derivative that is easy to calculate using the chain rule (Section 2.8), but here we do a quick calculation of it by the limit definition

$$
\begin{aligned}
\frac{g(x) - g(a)}{x - a} &= \frac{\sqrt{x + 1} - \sqrt{a + 1}}{x - a} = \frac{\sqrt{x + 1} - \sqrt{a + 1}}{x - a} \cdot \frac{\sqrt{x + 1} + \sqrt{a + 1}}{\sqrt{x + 1} + \sqrt{a + 1}} \\
&= \frac{x + 1 - (a + 1)}{(x - a)\sqrt{x + 1} + \sqrt{a + 1}} = \frac{1}{\sqrt{x + 1} + \sqrt{a + 1}}
\end{aligned}
$$

Letting $x \to a$ gives $g'(a) = 1/2\sqrt{a+1}$. Using this in the product rule gives

$$
\begin{aligned}
p'(x) &= 3x^2\sqrt{x+1} + (x^3+1)\left(\frac{1}{2\sqrt{x+1}}\right) = 3x^2\sqrt{x+1} + \frac{x^3+1}{2\sqrt{x+1}} \\
&= \frac{6x^2(x+1) + x^3 + 1}{2\sqrt{x+1}} = \frac{7x^3 + 6x^2 + 1}{2\sqrt{x+1}}
\end{aligned}
$$

Next we discuss the quotient rule. This rule extends the set of rules for differentiating to functions that are quotients f/g. If you found that the product rule was unexpected in form, then you will probably be surprised with the form of the quotient rule. The derivative of a quotient is NOT the quotient of the derivatives, i.e., $(f/g)'$ is not f'/g'. This is a common mistake, so we warn you about it up front.

The correct quotient rule formula is given in the following theorem. Its form comes from the algebra shown in the proof.

THEOREM 2.6.2 (Quotient Rule)

The quotient $\dfrac{f}{g}$ of two differentiable functions f, g is differentiable and

$$
\left(\frac{f}{g}\right)' = \frac{f'g - fg'}{g^2}
$$

In the Leibniz notation:

$$
\frac{d}{dx}\left(\frac{f}{g}\right) = \frac{\dfrac{df}{dx}g - f\dfrac{dg}{dx}}{g^2}
$$

Proof: We first prove the special case when $f = 1$ is the constant 1 function. Then we will use the product rule to get the general case. So suppose

$$
Q(x) = \frac{1}{g(x)}.
$$

Then

$$
Q(x+h) - Q(x) = \frac{1}{g(x+h)} - \frac{1}{g(x)} = \frac{g(x) - g(x+h)}{g(x+h)g(x)} = \frac{-[g(x+h) - g(x)]}{g(x+h)g(x)}.
$$

Hence the Newton quotient for Q is

$$
\frac{Q(x+h) - Q(x)}{h} = \frac{-[g(x+h) - g(x)]}{hg(x+h)g(x)} = -\left[\frac{g(x+h) - g(x)}{h}\right]\frac{1}{g(x+h)g(x)}
$$

The expression in the square brackets is the Newton quotient for g and it tends to $g'(x)$ as $h \to 0$. Also $\lim_{h\to 0} g(x+h) = g(x)$, since differentiability of g implies continuity of g. Consequently

$$
\begin{aligned}
Q'(x) &= \lim_{h\to 0}\frac{Q(x+h) - Q(x)}{h} = -\lim_{h\to 0}\left[\frac{g(x+h) - g(x)}{h}\right] \cdot \lim_{h\to 0}\frac{1}{g(x+h)g(x)} \\
&= -g'(x) \cdot \frac{1}{g(x)^2} = \frac{-g'(x)}{g(x)^2}
\end{aligned}
$$

Now that this special case is proved, we get the general case using the product rule as follows:

$$
\left(\frac{f}{g}\right)' = \left(f \cdot \frac{1}{g}\right)' = f' \cdot \frac{1}{g} + f \cdot \frac{-g'}{g^2} = \frac{f'}{g} + \frac{-fg'}{g^2} = \frac{f'g - fg'}{g^2}
$$

A Special Case of the Quotient Rule

$$\left(\frac{1}{g}\right)' = \frac{-g'}{g^2}$$

This completes the proof.

An important corollary of the theorem is the special case that we used in the proof. This is shown in the margin box.

Example 2.6.6 (Using the Special Case of the Quotient Rule)

A good use of the special case of the quotient rule is in determining the derivative of the exponential decay function:

$$Q(x) = e^{-x} = \frac{1}{e^x}.$$

We easily get

$$Q'(x) = \frac{d}{dx}\left(\frac{1}{e^x}\right) = \frac{-\frac{d}{dx}(e^x)}{(e^x)^2} = \frac{-e^x}{e^{2x}} = -e^{-x}.$$

Example 2.6.7 (Using the Quotient Rule)

A standard use of the quotient rule is to differentiate rational functions. For example,

$$R(x) = \frac{x^2}{5x-2}.$$

The quotient rule, with the Leibniz notation, gives

$$R'(x) = \frac{\frac{d}{dx}(x^2)\cdot(5x-2) - x^2\cdot\frac{d}{dx}(5x-2)}{(5x-2)^2} = \frac{2x(5x-2) - x^2(5)}{(5x-2)^2}$$

$$= \frac{10x^2 - 4x - 5x^2}{(5x-2)^2} = \frac{5x^2 - 4x}{(5x-2)^2}.$$

Note: You should simplify the numerator in your answers, but *do not multiply out the denominator*. Leave it in factored form.

Also note that the derivative of a rational function is another rational function, as this example indicates.

Example 2.6.8 (An Algebraic Function)

Here's a function which is not a rational function because its numerator is not a polynomial:

$$Q(x) = \frac{\sqrt{x}}{x+1}.$$

It's derivative is easily found using the quotient rule

$$Q'(x) = \frac{\frac{d}{dx}(\sqrt{x})\cdot(x+1) - \sqrt{x}\cdot\frac{d}{dx}(x+1)}{(x+1)^2} = \frac{\frac{1}{2\sqrt{x}}(x+1) - \sqrt{x}\,(1)}{(x+1)^2}$$

$$= \frac{\frac{x+1}{2\sqrt{x}} - \sqrt{x}}{(x+1)^2} = \frac{\frac{x+1-2x}{2\sqrt{x}}}{(x+1)^2} = \frac{1-x}{2\sqrt{x}(x+1)^2}.$$

Example 2.6.9 (An Exponential Expression)

This example uses the result

$$\frac{d}{dx}\left(e^{-x}\right) = -e^{-x},$$

which we derived in Example 2.6.6 above. We apply this and the quotient rule to differentiate the function:

$$Q(x) = \frac{e^{-x}}{e^{-x}+x}.$$

The computation is

$$Q'(x) = \frac{\frac{d}{dx}(e^{-x}) \cdot (e^{-x} + x) - e^{-x} \cdot \frac{d}{dx}(e^{-x} + x)}{(e^{-x} + x)^2}$$

$$= \frac{-e^{-x}(e^{-x} + x) - e^{-x}(-e^{-x} + 1)}{(e^{-x} + x)^2}$$

$$= \frac{-e^{-2x} - e^{-x}x + e^{-2x} - e^{-x}}{(e^{-x} + x)^2} = \frac{-(x+1)e^{-x}}{(e^{-x} + x)^2}$$

Example 2.6.10 (Another Exponential Expression)

The function

$$f(x) = \frac{e^x - e^{-x}}{e^x + e^{-x}}$$

is an important function known as the hyperbolic tangent function. (See Section 2.12 for a discussion of hyperbolic functions). Its derivative is easy to compute using the quotient rule. We use the prime notation, which you may find a little bit less complicated looking.

$$f'(x) = \frac{(e^x - e^{-x})' \cdot (e^x + e^{-x}) - (e^x - e^{-x}) \cdot (e^x + e^{-x})'}{(e^x + e^{-x})^2}$$

$$= \frac{(e^x + e^{-x}) \cdot (e^x + e^{-x}) - (e^x - e^{-x}) \cdot (e^x - e^{-x})}{(e^x + e^{-x})^2}$$

$$= \frac{(e^x + e^{-x})^2 - (e^x - e^{-x})^2}{(e^x + e^{-x})^2}$$

$$= \frac{e^{2x} + 2 + e^{-2x} - (e^{2x} - 2 + e^{-2x})}{(e^x + e^{-x})^2}$$

$$= \frac{4}{(e^x + e^{-x})^2}$$

Example 2.6.11 (Use Algebra Before Differentiating)

Problem: Differentiate

(a) $f(x) = \dfrac{x + e^{2x}}{e^x}$ (b) $f(x) = \dfrac{2 - \frac{1}{x}}{3 + \frac{1}{x}}$

Solution (a): While you could use the quotient rule here, we think you will find it easier to write this not as a quotient before differentiating:

$$f'(x) = \frac{d}{dx}\left(\frac{x + e^{2x}}{e^x}\right) = \frac{d}{dx}\left(xe^{-x} + e^x\right) = e^{-x} - xe^{-x} + e^x$$

Solution (b): While we do have to use the quotient rule here, it will be best, again, to simplify before differentiating:

$$f'(x) = \frac{d}{dx}\left(\frac{2 - \frac{1}{x}}{3 + \frac{1}{x}}\right) = \frac{d}{dx}\left(\frac{\frac{2x-1}{x}}{\frac{3x+1}{x}}\right) = \frac{d}{dx}\left(\frac{2x - 1}{3x + 1}\right)$$

$$= \frac{2(3x + 1) - (2x - 1)3}{(3x + 1)^2} = \frac{5}{(3x + 1)^2}$$

Exercises: 2.6 (The Product and Quotient Rules)

In Exercises 1–60, find the derivative of each function using the product rule or the quotient rule. To get accustomed to the notation, try using both the differential dy/dx and the prime y' forms for the derivatives. NOTE: Derivatives of some of the quotients can be done without the quotient rule. Look out for this! Where possible simplify the expression using algebra before you differentiate.

1. $y = (x^2 + 3)e^x$ **2.** $y = (x^3 - 3x)e^x$

3. $y = (7x^4 + 2x^3)(x^2 - 5x - 10)$

4. $y = (5x^5 - 3x^2)(x^3 - 3x + 8)$

5. $f(x) = x^2 e^{-x}$ **6.** $g(x) = x^3 e^{-x}$

7. $y = e^{-x}\sqrt{x}$ **8.** $y = e^x\sqrt{2x+5}$

9. $f(x) = \sqrt[3]{x}\sqrt{x}$ **10.** $f(x) = x^{2/3}\sqrt{x}$

11. $f(x) = \sqrt{x}\left(5x^2 - 5x + 2\right)$

12. $f(x) = \sqrt{x}\left(3x^3 - 2x^2 + 1\right)$

13. $f(x) = x^2\sqrt{3x-4}$ **14.** $y = (x^2-1)\sqrt{3x-4}$

15. $y = e^{2x}$ **16.** $y = e^{kx}$, $k > 0$ an integer

17. $y = \dfrac{e^{2x}+1}{e^x}$ **18.** $y = \dfrac{2e^{2x}+3}{e^x}$

19. $y = \dfrac{xe^{2x}+x^2}{e^x}$ **20.** $y = \dfrac{x^3e^{2x}+x^2}{e^x}$

21. $y = \dfrac{xe^{2x}+x^2}{\sqrt{x}}$ **22.** $y = \dfrac{x^3e^{2x}+x^2}{\sqrt{x}}$

23. $y = \dfrac{3x}{2x-5}$ **24.** $y = \dfrac{cx}{ax+b}$

25. $y = \dfrac{3x^2}{2x^2+1}$ **26.** $y = \dfrac{cx^2+d}{ax^2+b}$

27. $f(x) = \dfrac{2x-3}{x^2+6x+1}$ **28.** $f(x) = \dfrac{x^2-x-3}{2x^2-3x+5}$

29. $y = \dfrac{3}{1+x^2}$ **30.** $y = \dfrac{5}{x+x^3}$

31. $y = \dfrac{3/x}{1+x^2}$ **32.** $y = \dfrac{5/x}{x+x^3}$

33. $f(x) = \dfrac{4x^2-3x+2}{x^2+x+1}$ **34.** $y = \dfrac{ex^2+fx+g}{ax^2+bx}$

35. $y = \dfrac{1}{1+\dfrac{1}{x}}$ **36.** $y = \dfrac{1}{1-\dfrac{1}{x}}$

37. $y = \dfrac{x}{x+\dfrac{1}{x^2}}$ **38.** $y = \dfrac{x}{x-\dfrac{1}{x^2}}$

39. $y = \dfrac{1-\dfrac{1}{x}}{2+\dfrac{1}{x}}$ **40.** $y = \dfrac{1+\dfrac{1}{x}}{3+\dfrac{1}{x}}$

41. $y = \dfrac{x}{1+\sqrt{x}}$ **42.** $y = \dfrac{\sqrt{x}}{1+\sqrt{x}}$

43. $f(x) = \dfrac{\sqrt{x}}{1+\sqrt{x}}$ **44.** $f(x) = \dfrac{\sqrt{x}}{1-\sqrt{x}}$

45. $f(x) = \dfrac{1-\sqrt{x}}{1+\sqrt{x}}$ **46.** $f(x) = \dfrac{1+\sqrt{x}}{1-\sqrt{x}}$

47. $f(x) = \dfrac{1-\dfrac{1}{\sqrt{x}}}{1+\dfrac{1}{\sqrt{x}}}$ **48.** $f(x) = \dfrac{1+\dfrac{1}{\sqrt{x}}}{1-\dfrac{1}{\sqrt{x}}}$

49. $y = \dfrac{1-\dfrac{1}{\sqrt{x}}}{1+\sqrt{x}}$ **50.** $y = \dfrac{1-\dfrac{1}{\sqrt{x}}}{1+\sqrt{x}}$

51. $y = \dfrac{e^x}{e^x+e^{-x}}$ **52.** $y = \dfrac{e^x}{e^x-e^{-x}}$

53. $y = \dfrac{\dfrac{1}{e^x}}{1+\dfrac{1}{e^x}}$ **54.** $y = y = \dfrac{\dfrac{1}{e^x}}{1-\dfrac{1}{e^x}}$

55. $y = -\dfrac{3e^x-4e^{-x}}{e^x+2e^{-x}}$ **56.** $y = \dfrac{ae^x+be^{-x}}{ce^x+de^{-x}}$

57. $y = \dfrac{e^x}{2+x}$ **58.** $y = \dfrac{e^{-x}}{1-x^2}$

59. $f(x) = \dfrac{e^x}{2+\dfrac{1}{x}}$ **60.** $f(x) = \dfrac{e^x}{2+\dfrac{1}{x^2}}$

In Exercises 61–66, find the 2nd derivative $y'' = \dfrac{d^2y}{dx^2}$ of y.

61. $y = x^2 e^{-x}$ **62.** $y = x^3 e^{-x}$

63. $y = \dfrac{1}{1+x^2}$ **64.** $y = \dfrac{1}{1-x^2}$

65. $y = \dfrac{x}{1+x^2}$ **66.** $y = \dfrac{x}{1-x^2}$

In Exercises 67–72, find an equation for the tangent line to $y = f(x)$. CAS: Use Maple to graph the function and the tangent line in the same picture.

67. $y = 3x^4 e^{-x}$ at the point $(1, 3e^{-1})$.

68. $y = 2x^3 e^{-x}$ at the point $(1, 2e^{-1})$

69. $y = \dfrac{\sqrt{x}}{x+1}$ at the point $(1, 0.5)$

70. $y = \dfrac{\sqrt{x}}{\sqrt{x}+1}$ at the point $(1, 0.5)$

71. $y = \dfrac{3}{1+x^2}$ at the point $(1, 3/2)$

72. $y = \dfrac{5}{x+x^2}$ at the point $(1, 5/2)$

Calculus Concepts & Computation

2.7 Derivatives of Trig Functions

In this section we determine the derivative functions for the six trigonometric functions and examine how to differentiate expressions involving these functions using the product, quotient, and linear combination rules.

After you understand how the derivatives of sin, cos, tan, cot, sec, and csc are determined, you should add these derivatives to your list of basic derivatives to memorize. These functions are important and occur so often in what we do that a good facility at differentiating expressions involving them is essential. We begin with a proof of the facts that:

(a) The derivative of the sine is the cosine: $\dfrac{d}{dx}(\sin x) = \cos x$.

(b) The derivative of the cosine is minus the sine: $\dfrac{d}{dx}(\cos x) = -\sin x$.

Remembering which one the minus sign goes with may cause you trouble initially.

THEOREM 2.7.1

The sine and cosine functions are differentiable and

$$\frac{d}{dx}(\sin x) = \cos x$$

$$\frac{d}{dx}(\cos x) = -\sin x$$

Proof: As usual, when we do not know a basic derivative, we fall back on the limit definition of the derivative. So we look at the Newton quotient for sin and use the standard angle-addition identity

$$\sin(A + B) = \sin A \cos B + \sin B \cos A$$

to expand the expression we get. Namely:

$$\frac{\sin(x+h) - \sin x}{h} = \frac{\sin x \cos h + \sin h \cos x - \sin x}{h}$$

$$= \frac{\sin x \cdot [\cos h - 1]}{h} + \frac{\sin h \cos x}{h}$$

Now take the limit

$$\lim_{h \to 0} \frac{\sin(x+h) - \sin x}{h} = \sin x \cdot \lim_{h \to 0}\left[\frac{\cos h - 1}{h}\right] + \lim_{h \to 0}\left[\frac{\sin h}{h}\right] \cdot \cos x$$

$$= \sin x \cdot [0] + [1] \cdot \cos x = \cos x.$$

Here we have used the limit theorems and the two standard limits

$$\lim_{h \to 0} \frac{\cos h - 1}{h} = 0, \quad \lim_{h \to 0} \frac{\sin h}{h} = 1.$$

Next, we leave it as an exercise for you to follow a similar procedure to prove that $\frac{d}{dx}(\cos x) = -\sin x$.

With these two basic results and the quotient rule, we can easily derive the derivatives for the other four trig functions: tan, cot, sec, csc. These derivations are easy because these functions are defined as quotients involving sines and cosines and so we can use the quotient rule to determine their derivatives. We look at how this goes for the derivative of the tangent function and leave the other three functions for the exercises.

$$\frac{d}{dx}(\tan x) \;=\; \frac{d}{dx}\left(\frac{\sin x}{\cos x}\right) \;=\; \frac{\frac{d}{dx}(\sin x)\cdot \cos x - \sin x \frac{d}{dx}(\cos x)}{\cos^2 x}$$

$$=\; \frac{\cos x \cdot \cos x - \sin x \cdot (-\sin x)}{\cos^2 x} \;=\; \frac{\cos^2 x + \sin^2 x}{\cos^2 x}$$

$$=\; \frac{1}{\cos^2 x} \;=\; \sec^2 x.$$

For convenience, we have summarized the derivatives of all six trig functions in Table 2.7.1.

Basic Trigonometric Derivatives	
$\dfrac{d}{dx}(\sin x) = \cos x$	$\dfrac{d}{dx}(\cos x) = -\sin x$
$\dfrac{d}{dx}(\tan x) = \sec^2 x$	$\dfrac{d}{dx}(\cot x) = -\csc^2 x$
$\dfrac{d}{dx}(\sec x) = \sec x \tan x$	$\dfrac{d}{dx}(\csc x) = -\csc x \cot x$

Table 2.7.1

Now that we know how to differentiate the basic trig functions, we can differentiate many interesting and important functions which involve trig function as sums, products, and quotients.

Example 2.7.1 (The Product Rule and Trig Functions)

Problem: Use the product rule to find the derivatives of the following functions:
(a) $f(x) = x^3 \cos x$,   (b) $g(x) = \sec x \csc x$

Solution:

(a) $f'(x) = (x^3)' \cos x + x^3 (\cos x)' = 3x^2 \cos x - x^3 \sin x.$

(b) $g'(x) \;=\; (\sec x)' \csc x + \sec x (\csc x)' = \sec x \tan x \csc x - \sec x \csc x \cot x$
$\;=\; \sec x \csc x (\tan x - \cot x)$

Example 2.7.2 (The Quotient Rule and Trig Functions)

Problem: Consider finding the derivative of the function

$$f(x) = \frac{\cos x}{x + \sin x}.$$

Solution: Using the basic derivatives and the quotient rule gives

$$f'(x) \;=\; \frac{\frac{d}{dx}(\cos x)\cdot(x+\sin x) - \cos x \cdot \frac{d}{dx}(x+\sin x)}{(x+\sin x)^2}$$

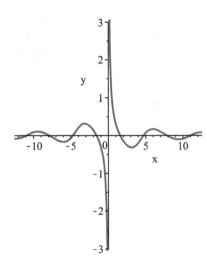

Figure 2.7.1: *Plot of $f(x) = \frac{\cos x}{x + \sin x}$ on the interval $[-4\pi, 4\pi]$.*

$$= \frac{-\sin x \cdot (x + \sin x) - \cos x \cdot (1 + \cos x)}{(x + \sin x)^2}$$

$$= \frac{-x \sin x - \sin^2 x - \cos x - \cos^2 x)}{(x + \sin x)^2}$$

$$= \frac{-(x \sin x + \cos x + 1)}{(x + \sin x)^2}$$

Note in the last step we used the trig identity $\sin^2 x + \cos^2 x = 1$. This function has an interesting graph, as shown in Figure 2.7.1.

Also note the vertical asymptote at the origin. Also the x-axis is a horizontal asymptote with the y-values oscillating from positive to negative as they tend to 0 in the limit.

Example 2.7.3 (A Damped Sine Wave)

Problem: Example 2.4.2 in the velocity section discussed damped oscillatory motion of a mass on a spring. A somewhat simpler example of such a motion is where the position function is given by

$$f(t) = e^{-t} \sin t$$

Here $y = f(t)$ gives the position of the mass relative to the equilibrium position $y = 0$. Discuss the nature of the motion and find the velocity of the mass at the first time it passes through equilibrium. Plot the graph of f and the tangent line at this time. Also find the first turn-around time and the mass's position at this time

Solution: A straight-forward use of the product rule gives

$$v = f'(t) = \frac{d}{dt}(e^{-t}) \cdot \sin t + e^{-t} \frac{d}{dt}(\sin t) = -e^{-t} \sin t + e^{-t} \cos t$$

$$= e^{-t}(\cos t - \sin t)$$

The motion starts at time $t = 0$ with the mass at equilibrium and the mass returns to equilibrium at those times t when $f(t) = e^{-t} \sin t = 0$, i.e., when $\sin t = 0$ (since e^{-t} is never zero). Thus, $t = \pi$ is the next time the mass is at equilibrium. The velocity (slope of the tangent line to the position graph) at $t = \pi$ is

$$v = m = e^{-\pi}(\cos \pi - \sin \pi) = -e^{-\pi} \approx -0.0432.$$

So the approximate tangent-line equation is

$$y = -0.0432(t - \pi).$$

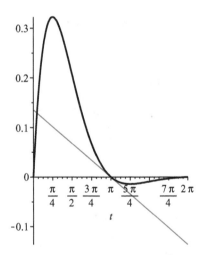

Figure 2.7.2: *Plot of $f(x) = e^{-t} \sin t$ and its tangent line at $t = \pi$.*

To check our work, we plot this line along with the graph of f as follows.

```
> f:=t->exp(-t)*sin(t);
                    f := t → e^{-t} sin(t)
> m:=-evalf(exp(-Pi));
                    m := -0.04321391825
> line:=t->m*(t-Pi);
                    line := t → m(t − Pi)
> pf:=plot(f(t),t=0..2*Pi,color=black,thickness=2):
> pt:=plot(line(t),t=0..2*Pi):
> with(plots,display);
                    [display]
> display({pf,pt});
```

This gives the result in Figure 2.7.2 and appears to be approximately correct. The turn-around times are when the velocity is zero, which in this example are the times t when

$$v = e^{-t}(\cos t - \sin t) = 0,$$

equivalently the times t when $\cos t = \sin t$. The first such time is $t = \pi/4$ and the displacement from equilibrium at this time is

$$f\left(\frac{\pi}{4}\right) = e^{-\pi/4}\sin\left(\frac{\pi}{4}\right) = \frac{\sqrt{2}e^{-\pi/4}}{2} \approx 0.322 \text{ ft}$$

Example 2.7.4

This example gives several alternative ways of computing the derivative, depending on how the function is represented. You will see when working with trig functions that there are many identities that allow you to write expressions in different forms. This will make checking answers more challenging.

Consider the function:

$$f(x) = \frac{\tan x}{1 + \tan x}.$$

A straight-forward calculation of the derivative using the quotient rule gives:

$$
\begin{aligned}
f'(x) &= \frac{\frac{d}{dx}(\tan x)\cdot(1+\tan x) - \tan x \cdot \frac{d}{dx}(1+\tan x)}{(1+\tan x)^2} \\[2mm]
&= \frac{\sec^2 x \cdot (1+\tan x) - \tan x \cdot \sec^2 x}{(1+\tan x)^2} \\[2mm]
&= \frac{\sec^2 x}{(1+\tan x)^2}.
\end{aligned}
$$

That is simple enough. An alternative way to work the problem (which is not necessarily simpler) is to rewrite the original function in terms of sines and cosines, simplify and then differentiate. Here is how the work goes:

$$f(x) = \frac{\tan x}{1 + \tan x} = \frac{\frac{\sin x}{\cos x}}{1 + \frac{\sin x}{\cos x}} = \frac{\sin x}{\cos x + \sin x}.$$

Now we differentiate

$$
\begin{aligned}
f'(x) &= \frac{d}{dx}\left(\frac{\sin x}{\cos x + \sin x}\right) = \frac{\cos x(\cos x + \sin x) - \sin x(-\sin x + \cos x)}{(\cos x + \sin x)^2} \\[2mm]
&= \frac{1}{(\cos x + \sin x)^2}.
\end{aligned}
$$

This looks different than our previous answer, but if you convert the previous answer to sines and cosines and simplify, you will get the above expression.

Example 2.7.5 (Higher Derivatives of Trig Functions)

Finding higher derivatives for the sine and cosine functions is easy, but becomes increasingly difficult for the other four trigonometric functions.

Problem:

(a) For $y = \sin x$, find the higher order derivatives $y', y'', y'', y^{(4)}$.

(b) For $y = \tan x$, find y' and y''.

Solution:

(a) These higher derivatives are easy to calculate because the sine and cosine functions are, up to a sign, derivatives of each other. Thus,

$$y' = \cos x, \ y'' = -\sin x, \ y''' = -\cos x, \ y^{(4)} = \sin x.$$

You can see that after the fourth derivative, the higher derivatives repeat with this same pattern.

(b) The first derivative of $y = \tan x$ is by Table 2.7.1,

$$y' = \sec^2 x.$$

To find the 2nd derivative, we use the product rule

$$
\begin{aligned}
y'' &= \frac{d}{dx}(y') = \frac{d}{dx}\left(\sec^2 x\right) = \frac{d}{dx}\left(\sec x \cdot \sec x\right) \\
&= \frac{d}{dx}(\sec x) \cdot \sec x + \sec x \cdot \frac{d}{dx}(\sec x) \\
&= \sec x \tan x \sec x + \sec x \sec x \tan x \\
&= 2\sec^2 x \tan x
\end{aligned}
$$

As an exercise, you should now try continuing this to get $y''', y^{(4)}$.

Example 2.7.6 (A Tuning Fork)

Problem: A tuning fork is often used to tune a piano. When the fork is struck it vibrates periodically, as does a piano string when plucked. Theory tells us that when the tuning fork and the piano string are "in tune" the combined sound we hear exhibits the phenomenon of "beats." An example of such is the motion with displacement function:

$$f(t) = \sin t \sin 10t,$$

Calculate the velocity of this vibration.

Solution: We use the product rule, together with the general formula

$$\frac{d}{dt}\left(\sin kt\right) = k \cos kt,$$

from the next section. Then

$$
\begin{aligned}
v &= f'(t) = \frac{d}{dt}\left(\sin t \sin 10t\right) = \cos t \sin 10t + \sin t (10 \cos 10t) \\
&= \cos t \sin 10t + 10 \sin t \cos 10t
\end{aligned}
$$

Figure 2.7.3 shows the plot of f (one beat) as well as the plots of $\pm \sin t$ which serve as enveloping curves for the motion.

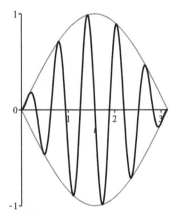

Figure 2.7.3: *Plot of* $f(x) = \sin t \sin 10t$ *(black) and* $\pm \sin t$ *(red).*

Exercises: 2.7 (Derivatives of Trig Functions)

Differentiating Functions Involving Trig Functions

In Exercises 1–40, differentiate the function.

1. $f(x) = 3\sin x - 6\cos x$ **2.** $f(x) = 2\sec x - \cot x$

3. $f(x) = x^3 \sin x$ **4.** $f(x) = x^4 \cos x$

5. $y = \sqrt{x}\cos x$ **6.** $y = \sqrt{x}\sin x$

7. $f(x) = e^x \cos x$ **8.** $f(x) = e^x \sin x$

9. $y = x^2 \sec x$ **10.** $y = x^3 \csc x$

11. $y = x^3 \tan x$ **12.** $y = x^4 \cot x$

13. $f(x) = \dfrac{\sin x}{x}$ **14.** $f(x) = \dfrac{1 - \cos x}{x}$

15. $y = \dfrac{\sin x}{\sqrt{x}}$ **16.** $y = \dfrac{\cos x}{\sqrt{x}}$

17. $f(x) = \dfrac{\sin x}{1 + \sin x}$ **18.** $f(x) = \dfrac{\cos x}{1 + \cos x}$

19. $f(x) = \dfrac{1 - \cos x}{1 + \sin x}$ **20.** $f(x) = \dfrac{1 - \cos x}{1 - \sin x}$

21. $y = \dfrac{e^x}{\sin x + \cos x}$ **22.** $y = \dfrac{e^{-x}}{\sin x + \cos x}$

23. $y = \dfrac{\sin x}{1 + e^x}$ **24.** $y = \dfrac{\cos x}{1 + e^x}$

25. $f(x) = \dfrac{x + \cos x}{x + 1}$ **26.** $f(x) = \dfrac{1 + \sin x}{x + 1}$

27. $f(x) = \dfrac{\sin x}{x(2 + \cos x)}$ **28.** $f(x) = \dfrac{1 - \cos x}{x(2 + \sin x)}$

29. $f(x) = \dfrac{\sec x}{1 + \tan x}$ **30.** $f(x) = \dfrac{\csc x}{1 + \cot x}$

31. $y = \dfrac{\tan x}{1 + \sec x}$ **32.** $y = \dfrac{\cot x}{1 + \csc x}$

33. $f(x) = \sec x \tan x$ **34.** $f(x) = \csc x \cot x$

35. $f(x) = \dfrac{1}{\sec x}$ **36.** $f(x) = \dfrac{1}{\cot x}$

37. $f(x) = \sin^2 x$ **38.** $f(x) = \sec^2 x$

39. $f(x) = \sin 2x$ **40.** $f(x) = \cos 2x$

Tangent Lines

In Exercises 41–50, find an equation for the tangent line to the function f at the point $(a, f(a))$. Extra Credit: Use Maple to graph, in the same picture, the function and the tangent line on the given interval. NOTE: You can use the derivative you found in working a corresponding problem above. For example, Exercise 45 involves the function whose derivative was calculated in Exercise 3 above.

41. $f(x) = x + 2\sin x$, $a = \pi$, on $[0, 7]$

42. $f(x) = x - 2\sin x$, $a = \pi$, on $[0, 7]$

43. $f(x) = x + 2\cos x$, $a = \pi/2$, on $[0, 7]$

44. $f(x) = x - 2\cos x$, $a = \pi/2$, on $[0, 7]$

45. $f(x) = x^3 \sin x$, $a = \pi/2$, on $[0, 3]$

46. $f(x) = \sqrt{x}\cos x\, a = \pi/4$, on $[0, 2]$

47. $f(x) = \dfrac{x + \cos x}{x + 1}$, $a = \pi$, on $[0, 4]$

48. $f(x) = \dfrac{1 + \sin x}{x + 1}$, $a = \pi$, on $[0, 8]$

49. $f(x) = \dfrac{\sin x}{x(2 + \cos x)}$, $a = 3\pi/2$, on $[0, 8]$

50. $f(x) = \dfrac{1 - \cos x}{x(2 + \sin x)}$, $a = 3\pi/2$, on $[0, 8]$

2nd Derivatives

In Exercises 51–60, find the 2nd derivative $y'' = \dfrac{d^2 y}{dx^2}$.

51. $y = x\cos x$ **52.** $y = x^2 \cos x$

53. $y = e^{-x}\sin x$ **54.** $y = e^{-x}\cos x$

55. $y = \sec x$ **56.** $y = \sec^2 x$

57. $y = \tan x$ **58.** $y = \tan^2 x$

59. $y = \sin 2x$ **60.** $y = \cos 2x$

Horizontal Tangent Lines

In Exercises 61–72, find the places, in the given interval, where the graph of the function has horizontal tangent lines. **CAS**: Use Maple to plot the function and check your answers with the cursor probe.

61. $f(x) = x + \sin x$, $[0, 11]$ **62.** $f(x) = x + \cos x$, $[0, 10]$

63. $f(x) = x + 2\cos x$, $[0, 2\pi]$

64. $f(x) = x - 2\cos x$, $[0, 2\pi]$

65. $f(x) = x + 2\sin x$ $[0, 2\pi]$

66. $f(x) = x - 2\sin x$, $[0, 2\pi]$

67. $f(x) = x - \tan x$, $(\pi/2, 3\pi/2)$

68. $f(x) = x - \cot x$, $[0, \pi]$

69. $f(x) = \dfrac{\sin x}{1 + \sin x}$, $[0, 4\pi/3]$

70. $f(x) = \dfrac{\sin x}{1 - \sin x}$, $[\pi, 2\pi]$

71. $f(x) = \dfrac{\cos x}{1 + \cos x}$, $[-\pi/2, \pi/2]$

72. $f(x) = \dfrac{\cos x}{1 - \cos x}$, $[\pi/2, 3\pi/2]$

Derivation of Derivative Formulas

73. Use the limit definition of the derivative to derive the formula: $\frac{d}{dx}(\cos x) = -\sin x$

74. Use the quotient rule to show: $\frac{d}{dx}(\cot x) = -\csc^2 x$.

75. Use the quotient rule to show:
$$\frac{d}{dx}(\sec x) = \sec x \tan x.$$

76. Use the quotient rule to show:
$$\frac{d}{dx}(\csc x) = -\csc x \cot x.$$

2.8 The Chain Rule

> with(code_ch2sec8);

[*runner_arm, sandpile*]

In the previous sections we learned that, from the known derivatives of two functions f and g, we could calculate the derivatives of the more complicated functions, such as $f + g$, $f - g$, fg, and f/g. This we did using the linear combination rule, the product rule, and the quotient rule. These more complicated functions arise by combining f and g using the four standard arithmetic operations from algebra. In this section we will consider a fifth, non-algebraic, way of combining f and g, namely the composition $f \circ g$ of f and g. The formula for computing the derivative $(f \circ g)'$ of the composite function is called the *chain rule*. Before stating this rule formally, we look at two motivating examples.

Example 2.8.1 (Differentiating a Composite Function)

Problem: Find the derivative of the function $y = (x^2 + 1)^4$.

Solution: We could compute y' by first using the binomial theorem to expand out and get an expression for y as an eighth degree polynomial. But this approach will not work so well for larger powers (much larger than 4) and will not work at all for fractional powers (such as $\frac{1}{2}$). So we try another approach.

We note that y is the composition of two functions whose derivatives we can calculate. If we let

$$f(x) = x^4$$

and

$$g(x) = x^2 + 1,$$

then

$$y = (x^2 + 1)^4 = f(g(x)) = (f \circ g)(x)$$

Thus, the function we are trying to differentiate is a composite function. We can easily differentiate f and g separately:

$$f'(x) = \frac{d}{dx}(x^4) = 4x^3,$$

$$g'(x) = \frac{d}{dx}(x^2 + 1) = 2x.$$

But how do we put these derivatives together to get the derivative y' of the composite function y? Let's change notation in order to clarify things. Introduce a variable u and write y as

$$y = f(u) = u^4,$$

where

$$u = g(x) = x^2 + 1.$$

Then, Instead of writing y', we will use the Leibniz notation and think of the derivative $\frac{dy}{dx}$ as a rate of change. We know that

$$\frac{dy}{du} = 4u^3.$$

and

$$\frac{du}{dx} = 2x.$$

So, y changes (with respect to u) at the rate of $4u^3$, and u changes (with respect to x) at the rate of $2x$. Then our intuition suggests (and the chain rule tells us) that y changes with respect to x at a rate which is the product of these two rates: $(4u^3)(2x)$. That is to say

$$\frac{dy}{dx} = \frac{dy}{du} \cdot \frac{du}{dx}.$$

In words: The rate of change of y with respect to x is the product of the rate of change of y with respect to u and the rate of change of u with respect to x. In this example, we get

$$\frac{dy}{dx} = \frac{dy}{du} \cdot \frac{du}{dx} = (4u^3)(2x) = 4(x^2+1)^3(2x) = 8x(x^2+1)^3.$$

That is the correct answer and is a typical use of the chain rule.

Example 2.8.2 (Dredging Sand from a River)

The solution of the following applied problem illustrates how the chain rule arises as a product of two rates of change.

Problem: A dredging company is discharging sand from a river bed onto an adjacent piece of land. Their pump discharges the sand at a rate of 24 cubic feet per minute, and the laws of physics dictate the resulting pile of sand takes a conical shape as shown in Figure 2.8.1.

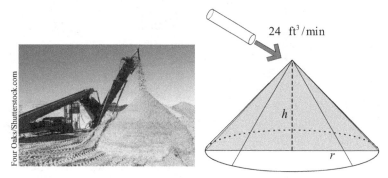

Figure 2.8.1: *A sandpile takes a conical shape.*

Physics also forces the conical sand pile to have proportions so that its height h is equal to the radius r of its circular base. As the pile grows ever higher, the proportions remain the same: $h = r$. Given this, find the rate $\frac{dh}{dt}$ at which the height h is increasing at the particular moment when $h = 8$ feet.

Solution: While the volume V of the sand pile changes at a constant rate, namely $\frac{dV}{dt} = 24$ ft^3/min, the same is not true for the height h. This can be easily seen from the animation created by the following command. (Figure 2.8.2 shows the last frame in this animation.)

```
> sandpile;
```

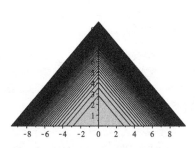

Figure 2.8.2: *The 40th frame in the sandpile movie.*

As you can see from the animation, the height is changing less rapidly in the later stages of the growth of the sandpile. This seems reasonable since, in the later stages, the surface area of the cone is larger, and so each new layer of sand gets distributed in a thinner layer. Hence less is added to the height of the pile.

   Now how can we tackle this problem mathematically?

We are asked to find $\frac{dh}{dt}\big|_{h=8}$ (this stands for the time rate of change of h at the time when $h = 8$), and we know that $\frac{dV}{dt} = 24$ ft^3/min. Recalling the formula for the volume of a cone, we see that V and h are related by

$$V = \frac{1}{3}\pi r^2 h,$$

where r is the radius of the cone. For this cone $r = h$, for all times t. Thus, we can eliminate the r in the above equation and get the following

$$V = \frac{1}{3}\pi h^2 h = \frac{1}{3}\pi h^3.$$

This gives V as a function of h, but it will be more convenient to express h as a function of V. So, we solve the last equation for h:

$$h = \sqrt[3]{\frac{3}{\pi}V} = \sqrt[3]{\frac{3}{\pi}} \cdot V^{\frac{1}{3}}.$$

Using the differentiation rules we have already learned, we calculate the rate of change of the height with respect to the volume:

$$\frac{dh}{dV} = \sqrt[3]{\frac{3}{\pi}}\left(\frac{1}{3}V^{-\frac{2}{3}}\right) \text{ft/ft}^3.$$

However, this is not the derivative we need. So, how do we find $\frac{dh}{dt}$? Examining the units gives us a clue to the answer. The above gives rate $\frac{dh}{dV}$ at which height changes with respect to the volume (units: $\frac{\text{ft}}{\text{ft}^3}$), and we know the rate $\frac{dV}{dt}$ at which the volume changes with respect to time (units: $\frac{\text{ft}^3}{\text{min}}$). We might guess that we multiply these two rates to get the rate $\frac{dh}{dt}$ at which the height changes with respect to time (units: $\frac{\text{ft}}{\text{min}}$). Thus, our guess is

$$\frac{dh}{dt} = \frac{dh}{dV} \cdot \frac{dV}{dt},$$

which gives the correct units:

$$\frac{\text{ft}}{\text{min}} = \frac{\text{ft}}{\text{ft}^3} \cdot \frac{\text{ft}^3}{\text{min}}.$$

The chain rule tells us that this is exactly right. Thus,

$$\frac{dh}{dt} = \sqrt[3]{\frac{3}{\pi}}\left(\frac{1}{3}V^{-\frac{2}{3}}\right)(24).$$

Now when $h = 8$, we calculate that $V = \frac{1}{3}\pi(8)^3 = \frac{512}{3}\pi$. Hence,

$$\frac{dh}{dt}\bigg|_{h=8} = \sqrt[3]{\frac{3}{\pi}}\left(\frac{1}{3}\left(\frac{512}{3}\pi\right)^{-\frac{2}{3}}\right)(24) = \frac{3}{8\pi} \approx 0.12\,\text{ft/min}$$

So the height of the pile is increasing at the rate of 0.12 ft/min when the pile is 8 ft high.

Based on the two examples above, we see that the derivative $(f \circ g)'$ of the composition of f and g should involve the product of their respective derivatives: f' and g'. The following theorem, called the *chain rule*, makes this more precise. The theorem gives two versions of the chain rule: one using the prime notation and the other using the rate of change notation (or the differential notation of Leibniz). Both versions are important and should be learned. The proof of a special case of the chain rule appears at the end of the section.

THEOREM 2.8.1 (The Chain Rule)

Suppose that f and g are differentiable functions, with the range of g contained in the the domain of f. Then the composite function f ∘ g is also differentiable and the derivative is given by

$$(f \circ g)'(x) = f'(g(x))g'(x)$$

for each x in the domain of g. In Leibniz notation, if y = f(u) and u = g(x), then

$$\frac{dy}{dx} = \frac{dy}{du}\frac{du}{dx}$$

It is important to note that, in the prime notation, the derivative of $f \circ g$ is NOT the product of the derivatives of f and g. That is,

$$(f \circ g)'(x) \quad \text{is NOT equal to} \quad f'(x)g'(x).$$

but rather

$$(f \circ g)'(x) = f'(g(x))g'(x).$$

Thus, to calculate the derivative of the composite function $f \circ g$, you should (1) take the derivatives of f and g separately, (2) evaluate f' at $g(x)$, and (3) then take the product $f'(g(x))g'(x)$.

Using the chain rule correctly takes some practice. First you must realize that the derivative to be calculated is the derivative of a composition of two functions. Then you must figure out what the two functions are and find their derivatives. We will do several examples. In some of these we use the prime notation for the derivative and in others we use the differential or Leibniz notation.

Example 2.8.3

Problem: Find $h'(x)$ if $h(x) = \sqrt{3x^2 + 2}$.

Solution: In this example we will use the Leibniz form of the chain rule. To use the chain rule we must first recognize the function h, whose derivative we seek, as the composition of two functions. Remember, a composition is a sequence of two functions, one applied first and then the other. If we look at $\sqrt{3x^2 + 2}$ in terms of order of operations, we see that the operation $3x^2 + 2$ must be done first. Secondly, the square root is taken. Thus,

$$y = \sqrt{u}$$

where

$$u = 3x^2 + 2,$$

is the first operation to be performed. Now,

$$\frac{dy}{du} = \frac{1}{2\sqrt{u}}$$

and

$$\frac{du}{dx} = 6x.$$

Thus,

$$h'(x) = \frac{dy}{dx} = \frac{dy}{du}\frac{du}{dx} = \frac{1}{2\sqrt{u}}(6x) = \frac{3x}{\sqrt{u}} = \frac{3x}{\sqrt{3x^2 + 2}}.$$

SUGGESTION:(1): To use the Leibniz or rate of change version of the chain rule, rewrite the composite function $h = f \circ g$ by introducing a dependent variable u for the first function g to be performed:

$$y = h(x) = f(g(x)) = f(u),$$

where $u = g(x)$. The variable u is called the *auxiliary variable*. Of course, another letter besides u could be used.

Example 2.8.4

Problem: Find $h'(x)$, if $h(x) = \sin(x + \sqrt{x})$.

Solution: In this example we will use the prime notation form of the chain rule. To think of h as a composition, again notice that in the expression $\sin(x + \sqrt{x})$, the operation $x + \sqrt{x}$ is done first and then the sine of $x + \sqrt{x}$ is calculated. Thus, $h = f \circ g$ where $g(x) = x + \sqrt{x}$ is the first function performed and $f(u) = \sin u$ is the second. The chain rule tells us that $h'(x) = f'(g(x))g'(x)$. Now,

$$f'(x) = \cos x \quad \text{and} \quad g'(x) = 1 + \frac{1}{2\sqrt{x}}$$

By substitution then,

$$h'(x) = f'(x + \sqrt{x}) \cdot g'(x) = \cos(x + \sqrt{x}) \cdot \left(1 + \frac{1}{2\sqrt{x}}\right)$$

Note that the parentheses in the above expression have different interpretations. The first set in $\cos(x + \sqrt{x})$ is part of the function notation: cosine is evaluated at $x + \sqrt{x}$. The second set of parentheses is for grouping the two terms to be multiplied by $\cos(x + \sqrt{x})$.

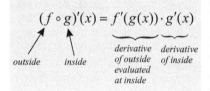

RECOMMENDATION (2): To use the prime notation version of the chain rule, write the function to be differentiated, say h, as a composition $h = f \circ g$. The derivative of h is then the derivative of the *outside* function evaluated at the *inside* function times the derivative of the *inside* function. See the margin box.

Example 2.8.5

Problem: Differentiate the function $h(x) = \sin^5 x$.

Solution: In this problem we will use the prime notation. In the formula for h,

$$h(x) = \sin^5 x = (\sin x)^5,$$

the order of operations is: $\sin x$ is evaluated first and then the 5th power of $\sin x$ is performed. Here, $u = g(x) = \sin x$ is the inside function and $f(u) = u^5$ is the outside function. The derivative of the composition, $h = f \circ g$, is then the derivative $f'(u) = 5u^4$ of the outside function evaluated at the inside function $u = g(x) = \sin x$ times the derivative $g'(x) = \cos x$ of the inside function evaluated at the independent variable x. Thus,

$$h'(x) = 5u^4 \cdot \cos x = 5\sin^4 x \cdot \cos x.$$

It does not matter which version of the chain rule you use. If you use the Leibniz form, however, you must remember to give your answer in terms of the independent variable x, not in terms of the auxiliary variable u. One advantage of the prime notation form is that it does not involve an auxiliary variable.

Often derivatives are found by applying several differentiation rules.

Example 2.8.6

Problem: Differentiate $h(x) = \left(\dfrac{2x}{3x+1}\right)^8$.

Solution: This example involves applying both the chain rule and the quotient rule. The function h is a composition of functions and the inside function is $u = g(x) = \frac{2x}{3x+1}$. So we let

$$u = \frac{2x}{3x+1}.$$

The outside function is $y = f(u) = u^8$. We calculate the two derivatives

$$\frac{dy}{du} = 8u^7,$$

and, using the quotient rule

$$\frac{du}{dx} = \frac{2(3x+1) - (2x)(3)}{(3x+1)^2} = \frac{2}{(3x+1)^2}.$$

Thus, by the chain rule,

$$\begin{aligned}
\frac{dy}{dx} &= \frac{dy}{du} \cdot \frac{du}{dx} = 8u^7 \left(\frac{2}{(3x+1)^2} \right) \\
&= 8 \left(\frac{2x}{3x+1} \right)^7 \left(\frac{2}{(3x+1)^2} \right) \\
&= \frac{16(2^7)x^7}{(3x+1)^9} = \frac{2048x^7}{(3x+1)^9}
\end{aligned}$$

It is sometimes quicker, and easier, to NOT break the composite function apart and differentiate separately its two functions (inside and outside). For example, we could have worked this problem as follows. For

$$h(t) = \left(\frac{2x}{3x+1} \right)^8,$$

we get

$$h'(x) = 8 \left(\frac{2x}{3x+1} \right)^7 \cdot \frac{d}{dx} \left(\frac{2x}{3x+1} \right) = 8 \left(\frac{2x}{3x+1} \right)^7 \cdot \frac{2(3x+1) - (2x)(3)}{(3x+1)^2}.$$

Simplifying this gives the result we found above.

Example 2.8.7

Problem: Find the derivative of $f(x) = x^3 \cos(3x+2)$.

Solution: This problem involves both the product rule and the chain rule. Since f is the product of two functions we apply the product rule first.

$$f'(x) = 3x^2 \cos(3x+2) + x^3 \frac{d}{dx} \cos(3x+2).$$

Next we apply the chain rule to compute $\frac{d}{dx} \cos(3x+2)$. The inside function here is $3x+2$ and the outside function is $\cos x$. Thus,

$$\frac{d}{dx} \cos(3x+2) = -\sin(3x+2)(3).$$

Substituting this in gives

$$\begin{aligned}
f'(x) &= 3x^2 \cos(3x+2) + x^3(-3\sin(3x+2)) \\
&= 3x^2 \cos(3x+2) - 3x^3 \sin(3x+2)
\end{aligned}$$

New Basic Derivatives

$$\frac{d}{dx}(e^{kx}) = ke^{kx}$$

$$\frac{d}{dx}(\sin kx) = k \cos kx$$

$$\frac{d}{dx}(\cos kx) = -k \sin kx$$

$$\frac{d}{dx}(\tan kx) = k \sec^2 kx$$

$$\frac{d}{dx}(\sec kx) = k \sec kx \tan kx$$

Table 2.8.1

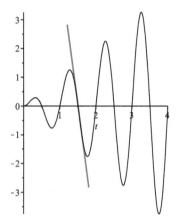

Figure 2.8.3: *Resonant vibrations in a bridge and the velocity (tangent slope) at time $t = 3/2$.*

Example 2.8.8 (Basic Derivatives)

Problem: Find the derivatives of the following functions:
  (a) $y = e^{-3x/5}$ (b) $y = \sin \pi x$ (c) $y = \tan \sqrt{2}x$

Solution: These three functions all are basic composite functions with the inside functions of the form $u = kx$, where $k = -3/5$, π, $\sqrt{2}$, respectively. So the derivative of the inside function is just a constant $\frac{du}{dx} = \frac{d}{dx}(kx) = k$. Then the derivatives of these basic functions are

$$\frac{dy}{dx} = \frac{d}{dx}\left(e^{-3x/5}\right) = e^{-3x/5} \cdot \left(-\frac{3}{5}\right) = -\frac{3}{5}e^{-3x/5}$$

$$\frac{dy}{dx} = \frac{d}{dx}(\sin \pi x) = (\cos \pi x) \cdot \pi = \pi \cos \pi x$$

$$\frac{dy}{dx} = \frac{d}{dx}\left(\tan \sqrt{2}x\right) = \left(\sec^2 \sqrt{2}x\right)\sqrt{2} = \sqrt{2}\sec^2 \sqrt{2}x$$

You can easily see how to generalize the work here involving the constants $k = -3/5$, π, $\sqrt{2}$ to any constant a. Table 2.8.1 lists these general results.

Example 2.8.9 (Resonance in Vibrations)

Problem: A platoon of soldiers marching across a bridge will sometimes have a cadence that matches (resonates with) the natural frequency of the bridge. When this happens the vibrations in the bridge due to their steps will be amplified, causing a possible collapse of the bridge. This phenomenon is called *resonance* and one model for it involves the function

$$y = f(t) = t \sin 2\pi t.$$

Here y is the displacement (in centimeters) of the center of the bridge from it natural position (when it's not vibrating). Find the velocity at which the center of the bridge is moving at time $t = 3/2$ and write an equation for the tangent line to the position graph at this time.

Solution: The velocity function v is the derivative of the position function. So, using the product rule and one of the basic derivatives from Table 2.8.1 gives

$$v = \frac{dy}{dt} = f'(t) = \sin 2\pi t + 2\pi t \cos 2\pi t$$

Thus, the velocity at time $t = 3/2$ is

$$v = f'\left(\frac{3}{2}\right) = \sin\left(2\pi \cdot \frac{3}{2}\right) + \left(2\pi \cdot \frac{3}{2}\right)\cos\left(2\pi \cdot \frac{3}{2}\right) = \sin(3\pi) + 3\pi \cos(3\pi) = -3\pi$$

Note that the position at time $t = 3/2$ is $f(3/2) = 0$ (one of the many times the center of the bridge is passing through its equilibrium position). Thus, an equation for the tangent line to the position graph at $(3/2, 0$ is

$$y = -3\pi\left(t - \frac{3}{2}\right)$$

To get plot of the bridge displacement during the first four seconds and and also a plot of the tangent line at $(3/2, 0)$ we use the following Maple code. See Figure 2.8.3.

```
> with(plots):
> f:=t->t*sin(2*Pi*t);
```
$$f := t \rightarrow t \sin(2\pi t)$$

```
> p:=plot(f(t),x=0..4,color=black):
> q:=plot(-3*Pi*(t-3/2),x=1.2..1.8,color=red,thickness=2):
> display({p,q});
```

Example 2.8.10 (Application: A Runner's Upper Arm Movement)

When people run they tend to swing their arms rhythmically, at a rate that more or less matches the pace of their legs. The faster they run, the more rapid the swinging motion of their arms. We present several models for the arm movement of a runner.

Consider tracking just the upper arm movement over time t. Suppose that a runner swings her arms rhythmically such that each upper arm PQ rotates back and forth about the point P. The position of the upper arm is measured by the angle y between the actual position and the downward vertical position, as shown in the Figure 2.8.4. When the angle $y = 0$, her upper arm is vertical, while $y > 0$ or $y < 0$ indicates that her arm is forward or backward of vertical. We consider several possible mathematical models for the movement of her upper arm, and this amounts to specifying y as a function of t. One possible model is called simple harmonic motion, and arises when y is given by something like the following:

$$y = \frac{2}{3}\sin 8t,$$

The function y is periodic, with period $2\pi/8 = \pi/4 \approx 0.75$ s, and this means that one full swing of her upper arm, back and forth, is completed in about 0.75 second. The amplitude 2/3 of the motion is in radians and so the maximum angular deviation from vertical is $2(180/\pi)3 = 120/\pi \approx 38$ degrees. Note that y is a simple composite function:

$$y = \frac{2}{3}\sin u,$$

where

$$u = g(t) = 8t$$

Figure 2.8.4: *Rhythmic arm movement while running.*

is a simple linear function of t. A simulation of her arm movement is given in the following animation.

```
> g:=t->8*t;
```
$$g := t \to 4t$$
```
> runner_arm(g,0,2*Pi,32);
```

Figure 2.8.5 is a static picture of the movement, with all the frames in the movie displayed in the same frame.

The movie consists of 33 frames (remember the initial frame is frame 0) and shows the motion of the runner's arm during the time interval $[0, 1.5]$. Note: When viewing the above animation, put it in the 'cycle' mode using the button on the animation tool bar. Then the movie repeatedly plays the 32 frames over and over and this gives a better feel for the periodic nature of the swinging arm. Also note from the movie that the arm appears to be moving faster, as measured by the change in the angle y, when it is near the vertical position and slower when it is farther away from vertical. This is also apparent from Figure 2.8.5, since each of the 32 arm positions shown there are separated in time by $2\pi/32 = 0.196$ s, and the successive angle changes are smaller, the further they are from the vertical position. Also note that there are only 8 positions on each side of the vertical position. But this is clear, because in moving forward and backward, the arm takes up the same 8 positions.

The derivative function dy/dt measures the rate of change of the angle y with respect to time. This is called the *angular velocity* function, and we can easily

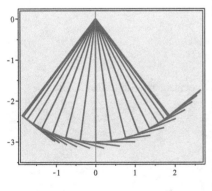

Figure 2.8.5: *Position of the runner's arm at 32 equally spaced times.*

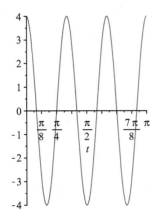

Figure 2.8.6: *Periodic angular velocity.*

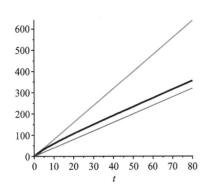

Figure 2.8.7: *Plot of* $h(t) = \frac{80t+4t^2}{10+t}$ *between the graphs of the two linear functions* $y = 8t$ *and* $y = 4t$.

calculate it using the chain rule.

$$v = \frac{dy}{dt} = \frac{d}{dt}\left[\frac{2}{3}\sin 8t\right] = \frac{2}{3}\cos 8t \cdot 8 = \frac{16}{3}\cos 8t.$$

Thus, the angular velocity v varies over time much as the angle y itself does, except the variation is phase shifted (it is a cosine wave, not a sine wave) and the amplitude has been magnified by the factor 4 (which came from the chain rule). See Figure 2.8.6. Next, we want to consider a more sophisticated model of the runner's arm, one that takes into account that her pace will slow soon after beginning the race. The angular velocity is influenced by

$$g(t) = 8t$$

Suppose that after her start, running at this pace for a while, she settles down into a slower pace, one that is half this initial pace, and continues to the end with this pace. Thus, her initial pace is governed by the above function g, and her eventual pace is governed by

$$g(t) = 4t.$$

Since we want to have a continuous change from one pace to the other, a suitable function h that will replace g is

$$h(t) = \frac{80t + 4t^2}{10 + t} = 4\left[\frac{1}{1 + t/10} + 1\right]t.$$

Then $h(t) \approx 8t$, for t close to zero, and $h(t) \approx 4t$, for t very large. This is approximate behavior of h is shown in Figure 2.8.7.

Also the computation of the derivative of h is

$$\begin{aligned}
h'(t) &= \frac{d}{dt}\left[\frac{80t + 4t^2}{10 + t}\right] = \frac{(80 + 8t)(10 + t) - (80t + 4t^2)}{(10 + t)^2} \\
&= \frac{800 + 80t + 80t + 8t^2 - 80t - 4t^2}{(10 + t)^2} = \frac{800 + 80t + 4t^2}{(10 + t)^2} \\
&= \frac{800 + 80t + 4t^2}{100 + 20t + t^2}
\end{aligned}$$

From this we see that

$$h'(0) = 8 \quad \text{and} \quad \lim_{t \to \infty} h'(t) = 4$$

With this choice of h, the model for the angle y governing the arm's motion is

$$y = \frac{2}{3}\sin(h(t)),$$

and so the angular velocity is (using the chain rule)

$$v = \frac{dy}{dt} = \frac{2}{3}\cos(h(t)) \cdot h'(t)$$

The following commands will create an animation of this more complicated motion.

```
> h:=t->(80*t+4*t^2)/(10+t):
> runner_arm(h,0,4*Pi,96):
>
```

You should run the movie several times and observe how the frequency of the arm's motion changes from rapid at first to slower later on. It's hard to discern this transition to a slower pace, but by the end of the movie the arm swinging motion appears to be periodic. So while y and v are not periodic, they are *eventually periodic.* This assertion is easily discerned by graphing the angular velocity, as Figure 2.8.8 exhibits.

```
> h:=t->(80*t+4*t^2)/(10+t):
```
$$h := t \to \tfrac{80t+4t^2}{10+t}$$
```
> h1:=t->(800+80*t+4*t^2)/(100+20*t+t^2);
```
$$h1 := t \to \tfrac{800+80t+4t^2}{100+20t+t^2}$$
```
> v:=t->2*cos(h(t))*h1(t)/3
```
$$v := t \to \tfrac{2}{3}\cos(h(t))h1(t)$$
```
> plot(v(t),t=0..40,color=blue,thickness=2);

>
```

As you can see, the graph is not periodic, but sometime after $t = 30$ seconds it appears to settle into a periodic mode. If you use the mouse to probe the first two peaks after this time in the figure, you should get, approximately, $t_1 = 31.6$ and $t_2 = 33.1$. Thus, the approximate period is $t_2 - t_1 = 1.5$. In theory the period should eventually be (for t very large) $2\pi/4 = \pi/2 \approx 1.5$.

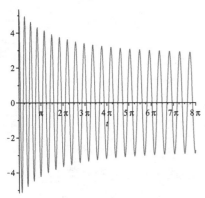

Figure 2.8.8: *Plot of the angular velocity function for the runner's arm in the 2nd model.*

Proof of Chain Rule: Special Case

Even though the chain rule seems correct intuitively, mathematical verification requires a proof. While the total proof is beyond the scope of this book, we will prove a special case.

In the composition $f \circ g$, fix a particular x in the domain of g and assume the special case that $g'(x) \neq 0$. Then g is either strictly increasing or decreasing on a neighborhood $O = (x - c, x + c)$ of x. By the definition of the derivative,

$$
\begin{aligned}
(f \circ g)'(x) &= \lim_{h \to 0} \frac{(f \circ g)(x+h) - (f \circ g)(x)}{h} \\
&= \lim_{h \to 0} \frac{f(g(x+h)) - f(g(x))}{h}
\end{aligned}
$$

In the limit we restrict h so that $x + h \in O$. Then, in the limiting expression above, we can multiply the numerator and denominator by $g(x + h) - g(x) \neq 0$ (so we are not dividing by 0):

$$
\begin{aligned}
(f \circ g)'(x) &= \lim_{h \to 0} \frac{f(g(x+h)) - f(g(x))}{h} \cdot \frac{g(x+h) - g(x)}{g(x+h) - g(x)} \\
&= \lim_{h \to 0} \frac{f(g(x+h)) - f(g(x))}{g(x+h) - g(x)} \lim_{h \to 0} \frac{g(x+h) - g(x)}{h}
\end{aligned}
$$

The second equality comes from rearranging the terms and applying the product rule for limits. Since g is continuous at x, we know that $h \to 0$ implies that $g(x + h) \to g(x)$. Thus, we can rewrite the above limits to get

$$
(f \circ g)'(x) = \lim_{g(x+h) \to g(x)} \frac{f(g(x+h)) - f(g(x))}{g(x+h) - g(x)} \lim_{h \to 0} \frac{g(x+h) - g(x)}{h}
$$

The first limit on the right-hand side is $f'(g(x))$ and the second factor is $g'(x)$ and therefore we have shown that

$$
(f \circ g)'(x) = f'(g(x))g'(x).
$$

Exercises: 2.8 (The Chain Rule)

```
> with(code_ch2sec8);
```
$$[runner\_arm, sandpile]$$

Applying the Chain Rule

In Exercises 1–70 use the chain rule to differentiate the function. Do this in one of two ways:

(1) Use the Leibniz notation: $\dfrac{dy}{dx} = \dfrac{dy}{du}\dfrac{du}{dx}$ and specifically identify $y = f(u)$ and $u = g(x)$.

(2) Use the formula $(f \circ g)'(x) = f'(g(x))g'(x)$ and the "inside-outside" function routine.

1. $y = \left(x^3 + 2x + 3\right)^{17}$ **2.** $y = \left(x^2 + 4\right)^{-25}$

3. $y = (x + \sin x)^8$ **4.** $y = (x + \cos x)^8$

5. $y = (\cos x + x \sin x)^{5/2}$

6. $y = (\sin x + x \cos x)^{5/2}$

7. $y = \sqrt{3x^2 + \cos x}$ **8.** $y = \sqrt{2x^3 + \sin x}$

9. $y = \sqrt[3]{\dfrac{3x - 5}{2x + 7}}$ **10.** $y = \left(\dfrac{x^2 - 1}{3x^2 + 2}\right)^{5/2}$

11. $y = \left(\dfrac{t^2}{1 + t^2}\right)^{5/2}$ **12.** $y = \left(\dfrac{t^3}{1 + t^3}\right)^{7/5}$

13. $y = \left(\dfrac{\sin x}{1 + \sin x}\right)^{10}$ **14.** $y = \left(\dfrac{\cos x}{1 + \cos x}\right)^{10}$

15. $y = \sqrt{\dfrac{\tan x}{1 + \tan x}}$ **16.** $y = \sqrt{\dfrac{\cot x}{1 + \cot x}}$

17. $f(x) = \left(\dfrac{\sec x}{1 + \sec x}\right)^{8/5}$

18. $f(x) = \left(\dfrac{\csc x}{1 + \csc x}\right)^{7/6}$

19. $f(x) = \sin^2 5x \cos^4 3x$

20. $f(x) = \sin^3 6x \cos^5 7x$

21. $y = e^{\sin x}$ **22.** $y = e^{(x - \cos x)}$

23. $y = e^{\sqrt{x}}$ **24.** $y = e^{1/x}$

25. $y = e^{\sin^2 x}$ **26.** $y = e^{\cos^2 x}$

27. $y = e^{x \sin 6x}$ **28.** $y = e^{x \cos 3x}$

29. $f(x) = e^{\tan^2 x}$ **30.** $f(x) = e^{\cot^2 x}$

31. $f(x) = \dfrac{e^{\sin x}}{1 + e^{\sin x}}$ **32.** $f(x) = \dfrac{e^{\cos, x}}{1 + e^{\cos xx}}$

33. $y = \dfrac{\sin(e^x)}{1 + \sin(e^x)}$ **34.** $y = \dfrac{\cos(e^x)}{1 + \cos(e^x)}$

35. $y = \sin\left(x^2 - 5x + 7\right)$

36. $y = \cos\left(3x^2 - 4x + 1\right)$

37. $f(x) = 5 + 2\sin x + 3\sin^2 x - 6\sin^3 x$

38. $f(x) = 2 - 3\cos x + 7\cos^2 x + 5\cos^3 x$

39. $y = \cos(\sqrt{x})$ **40.** $y = \sin(x^{5/3})$

41. $y = \sin\left(1/x^2\right)$ **42.** $y = \sqrt{\cos x}$

43. $y = \sin^2 x \cos^3 x$ **44.** $y = \sin^{7/3} x \cos^{5/3} x$

45. $y = \sin 2x \cos 3x$ **46.** $y = \sec 3x \tan 5x$

47. $y = \sec^2 x \tan^3 x$ **48.** $y = \csc^4 x \cot^7 x$

49. $y = \sec 2x \tan 3x$ **50.** $y = \csc 3x \cot 5x$

51. $f(x) = \sin^2 4x$ **52.** $f(x) = \cos^2 6x$

53. $f(x) = \sin^2 5x \cos^4 3x$ **54.** $f(x) = \sin^3 5x \cos^5 6x$

55. $y = \sec^2 5x \tan^3 4x$ **56.** $y = \csc^2 3x \cot^2 4x$

57. $f(x) = x^3 \sin 5x$ **58.** $f(x) = \sqrt{x} \cos 3x$

59. $f(x) = \sin\left(\dfrac{2x}{x + 4}\right)$ **60.** $f(x) = \cos\left(\dfrac{3x}{x + 4}\right)$

61. $y = \sin(1 + \cos x)$ **62.** $y = \cos(1 - \sin x)$

63. $y = \sin\left(\dfrac{e^{2x}}{1 + e^{3x}}\right)$ **64.** $y = \cos\left(\dfrac{e^{4x}}{1 + e^{5x}}\right)$

65. $f(x) = \sin\left(7x^2\right)\cos^3 x$ **66.** $f(x) = \sin^2 x \cos 5x$

67. $y = \sqrt{1 + \sqrt{x}}$ **68.** $y = \sqrt{1 - \sqrt{x}}$

69. $y = \sqrt{1 + \sqrt{1 + \sqrt{x}}}$ **70.** $y = \sqrt{1 - \sqrt{1 - \sqrt{x}}}$

Velocity and Tangent Lines

In Exercises 71–74: A position function $y = f(t)$ is given. (a) Find the velocity function function, (b) find equations for the tangent lines at the given times t, and (c) **CAS:** use Maple to graph, on the interval $[0, 4]$, the function and the tangent lines in the same figure.

71. $y = t \sin 4\pi t$, $t = 0.5, 1.25$

72. $y = t \sin 6\pi t$, $t = 0.5, 1.5$

73. $y = \sin \pi t \sin 8\pi t$, $t = 0.5, 1.25$

74. $y = \sin 2\pi t \sin 12\pi t$, $t = 0.5, 1.5$

A Runner's Arm Motion

The next group of exercises pertain to Example 2.8.10 about a runner's arm motion. In each case

$$y = \frac{2}{3}\sin(h(t)),$$

is the angular deviation of the runner's arm from vertical. (a) For t near 0 and very large, determine the approximations $h(t) \approx r_1 t$ and $h(t) \approx r_2 t$. (b) Calculate $h'(0)$ and $\lim_{t \to \infty} h'(t)$ (c) Calculate the angular velocity v. (d) **CAS:** Do a complete study, with graphics, of the runner's arm motion as was done in Example 2.8.10.

75. $h(t) = \dfrac{120t + 5t^2}{12 + t}$ **76.** $h(t) = \dfrac{54t + 3t^2}{9 + t}$

77. $h(t) = 2(t + te^{-t/10})$ **78.** $h(t) = 2(t + te^{-t/10}\cos t)$

Calculus *Concepts & Computation*

2.9 Derivatives of Exponential and Logarithmic Functions

```
> with(code_ch2sec9);with(limit_tools,twosidelimit);
```

$$[\textit{expo\_growth}\,]$$
$$[\textit{twosidelimit}\,]$$

Two Important Limits

$$\lim_{h\to0}\frac{e^{h}-1}{h}=1 \quad (2.9.1)$$

$$\lim_{h\to0}\frac{\ln(1+h)}{h}=1 \quad (2.9.2)$$

Back in Section 2.2, Example 2.2.5, we found the formula for the derivative of the natural exponential function. We did this using the limit definition of derivative and the first of the two limits shown in the margin.

Here we again use this approach, and the second of the limits shown in the margin box, to derive the formula for the derivative of the natural logarithmic function $y=\ln x$. Then we use these results and the chain rule to obtain the derivative formulas for exponential and logarithmic functions with any base. In essence the limits in (2.9.1) and (2.9.2), each being 1, are what makes Euler's number e the 'natural' (or simplest) base to use for exponential and logarithmic.

Derivatives of Exponential and Logarithmic Functions

We can motivate the validity of the limits in (2.9.1)–(2.9.2) by using graphical methods, in particular the `twosidelimit` command. We do this for (2.9.2):

$$\lim_{h\to0}\frac{\ln(1+h)}{h}=1,$$

and leave it to you to alter the code below to view the movie for limit (2.9.1). The last frame of the movie is shown in Figure 2.9.1.

```
> f:=h->ln(1+h)/h;
```

$$f:=h\to\frac{\ln(1+h)}{h}$$

```
> twosidelimit(f,0,-.5,.5,20);
```

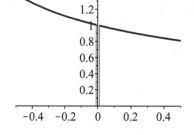

Figure 2.9.1: *Illustration of the limit* $\lim\limits_{h\to0}\frac{\ln(1+h)}{h}=1$.

We can now use these famous limits to prove the main theorem on derivatives of the natural exponential and logarithmic functions.

THEOREM 2.9.1

For the natural base $e=2.71828...$

$$\frac{d}{dx}\left(e^{x}\right)=e^{x} \qquad \frac{d}{dx}(\ln x)=\frac{1}{x}$$

Proof: In each case, we apply the limit definition of the derivative and use one of the famous limits.

(a) In the case of $f(x)=e^{x}$, we repeat here the work we did on this in Example 2.2.6

$$\begin{aligned}
f'(x) &= \lim_{h\to0}\frac{f(x+h)-f(x)}{h}=\lim_{h\to0}\frac{e^{x+h}-e^{x}}{h} \\
&= \lim_{h\to0}\frac{e^{x}\left(e^{h}-1\right)}{h}=e^{x}\cdot\lim_{h\to0}\frac{e^{h}-1}{h}=e^{x}\cdot1=e^{x}
\end{aligned}$$

(b) In the case of $y=\ln x$, we use the law of logarithms $\ln\left(\frac{a}{b}\right)=\ln a-\ln b$, to simplify first. Then a little algebraic manipulation and the introduction of

$k = h/x$, with $k \to 0$, gives the result. Specifically:

$$
\begin{aligned}
f'(x) &= \lim_{h \to 0} \frac{f(x+h) - f(x)}{h} = \lim_{h \to 0} \frac{\ln(x+h) - \ln x}{h} \\[2mm]
&= \lim_{h \to 0} \frac{\ln\left(\frac{x+h}{x}\right)}{h} = \lim_{h \to 0} \frac{1}{h} \ln\left(1 + \frac{h}{x}\right) \\[2mm]
&= \lim_{h \to 0} \frac{1}{x} \cdot \frac{x}{h} \cdot \ln\left(1 + \frac{h}{x}\right) = \frac{1}{x} \cdot \lim_{h \to 0} \frac{x}{h} \cdot \ln\left(1 + \frac{h}{x}\right) \\[2mm]
&= \frac{1}{x} \cdot \lim_{k \to 0} \frac{1}{k} \cdot \ln\left(1 + k\right) = \frac{1}{x} \cdot 1 = \frac{1}{x}
\end{aligned}
$$

By combining the basic derivatives in Theorem 2.9.1 with the chain rule, linear combination rule, and the product and quotient rules, we can differentiate more complicated types of functions. The following examples illustrate this.

Example 2.9.1

Problem: Find the derivatives of the following functions.

(a) $f(x) = e^{6x}$ (b) $f(x) = e^{\tan x}$ (c) $f(x) = \dfrac{\sin x}{e^{2x}}$.

Solution:

(a) We first note that f is the composition of two functions and let $y = e^u$ with $u = 6x$. Thus, by the chain rule,

$$
f'(x) = \frac{dy}{dx} = \frac{dy}{du}\frac{du}{dx} = e^u \cdot 6 = 6e^{6x}.
$$

(b) Here we apply the chain rule with outside-inside function routine, rather than using the auxiliary variable u. Thus,

$$
\frac{d}{dx}\left(e^{\tan x}\right) = e^{\tan x} \cdot \frac{d}{dx}(\tan x) = e^{\tan x} \cdot \sec^2 x.
$$

At first you may find that differentiating a composite function involving the natural exponential a little strange. That is because e^x is its own derivative. In the example here, e^x is the function on the outside and $\tan x$ is the function on the inside. So in differentiating the function on the outside, it may seem like nothing changes. The general formula is

$$
\frac{d}{dx}\left(e^u\right) = e^u \frac{du}{dx}
$$

(c) In this part it is best to rewrite f first, before differentiating, and then use the product rule instead of the quotient rule.

$$
\begin{aligned}
f'(x) &= \frac{d}{dx}\left(\frac{\sin x}{e^{2x}}\right) = \frac{d}{dx}\left(e^{-2x}\sin x\right) = \frac{d}{dx}\left(e^{-2x}\right) \cdot \sin x + e^{-2x} \cdot \frac{d}{dx}(\sin x) \\[2mm]
&= -2e^{-2x}\sin x + e^{-2x}\cos x = e^{-2x}(\cos x - 2\sin x)
\end{aligned}
$$

Example 2.9.2

Problem: Differentiate the following functions.

(a) $y = x \ln x$ (b) $f(x) = \ln\left(x^3\right)$ (c) $y = \sqrt{\ln x}$.

Solution:

(a) First apply the product rule and then the formula $\frac{d}{dx}(\ln x) = \frac{1}{x}$ to get

$$\frac{dy}{dx} = \frac{d}{dx}(x) \cdot \ln x + x\frac{d}{dx}(\ln x) = 1 \cdot \ln x + x \cdot \frac{1}{x} = \ln x + 1.$$

(b) There are two ways to do this problem. One is to apply the chain rule and the other is to simplify the function first using the properties of logarithms.

Method 1: This function is the composition of two functions with x^3 the inside function and $\ln x$ the outside function. Thus, by the chain rule,

$$f'(x) = \left(\ln(x^3)\right)' = \frac{1}{x^3}(3x^2) = \frac{3}{x}.$$

Method 2: Using the properties of logarithms we can rewrite f as

$$f(x) = \ln(x^3) = 3\ln x$$

Then

$$f'(x) = 3\left(\frac{1}{x}\right) = \frac{3}{x}.$$

(c) This function $y = \sqrt{\ln x}$ is a composite function with the inside function being $\ln x$. So we write $y = \sqrt{u}$, where $u = \ln x$. Thus, by the chain rule

$$y' = \frac{1}{2\sqrt{u}} \cdot \frac{1}{x} = \frac{1}{2x\sqrt{\ln x}}.$$

Example 2.9.3

Problem: Differentiate $f(x) = \ln|x|$.

Solution: The function f here is an important extension of the natural log function to allow for negative values of x. It may surprise you that this extended function has the same derivative as (i.e., including the absolute bars does not change the derivative).

Notice that the domain of f function is $\{\, x \mid x \neq 0 \,\}$, and that f is the composition of the natural logarithm with the absolute value function. To differentiate this function, we break it into the two cases determined by $|x|$.

$$f(x) = \begin{cases} \ln x & \text{if } x > 0 \\ \ln(-x) & \text{if } x < 0 \end{cases}.$$

This helps us analyze the function and graph it. For instance note that since $\lim_{x \to 0^+} \ln x = -\infty$ and $\lim_{x \to 0^-} \ln(-x) = -\infty$, there is a vertical asymptote at $x = 0$. The graph of f is shown in Figure 2.9.2.

Now, we differentiate f (using the chain rule on the part where $x < 0$).

$$f'(x) = \begin{cases} \dfrac{1}{x} & \text{if } x > 0 \\ \dfrac{1}{-x} \cdot (-1) & \text{if } x < 0 \end{cases}$$

So, in either case, we get that

$$f'(x) = \frac{1}{x}.$$

and f has a well-defined tangent line for all $x \neq 0$. You should think about why the formula $f'(x) = \frac{1}{x}$ is the same regardless of whether x is positive or negative and interpret this geometrically. See Figure 2.9.2 above.

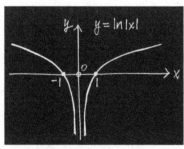

Figure 2.9.2: *Graph of* $f(x) = \ln|x|$.

Identities

$$a^x = e^{x \ln a} \qquad (2.9.3)$$

$$\log_a x = \frac{\ln x}{\ln a} \qquad (2.9.4)$$

For the most part in calculus we will restrict ourselves to working with exponential and logarithmic functions to the base e. This greatly simplifies the calculus, and it is important to know that there is no loss of generality in working with base e. Even though many applications arise naturally with other bases, such as base 2 or base 10, we can always rewrite expressions involving base a in terms of base e. For this we use the identities relating base a to base e shown in the margin.

For example,

$$2^x = e^{x \ln 2} \qquad \text{and} \qquad 10^x = e^{x \ln 10},$$

while

$$\log_2 x = \frac{\ln x}{\ln 2} \qquad \text{and} \qquad \log_{10} x = \frac{\ln x}{\ln 10}.$$

In terms of functions, these identities say that the exponential and logarithmic functions to the base a are simple alterations of the natural exponential and logarithmic functions. Specifically

$$f(x) = a^x$$

is the same as the composite function

$$f(x) = e^{x \ln a} = \exp(x \ln a),$$

and

$$g(x) = \log_a x$$

is just a constant times the natural logarithmic function

$$g(x) = \frac{\ln x}{\ln a} = \frac{1}{\ln a} \cdot \ln x.$$

Because of this, we easily get the following corollary (and generalization) of Theorem 2.9.1.

COROLLARY 2.9.1

For any real number base $a > 0$

$$\frac{d}{dx}\left(a^x\right) = (\ln a) \cdot a^x \qquad\qquad \frac{d}{dx}\left(\log_a x\right) = \frac{1}{\ln a} \cdot \frac{1}{x}$$

Proof: For the exponential function, we rewrite in terms of base e and then use the chain rule:

$$\frac{d}{dx}\left(a^x\right) = \frac{d}{dx}\left(e^{x \ln a}\right) = e^{x \ln a} \cdot \frac{d}{dx}(x \ln a) = e^{x \ln a} \cdot \ln a = a^x \cdot \ln a.$$

For the logarithmic function there is even less to do

$$\frac{d}{dx}\left(\log_a x\right) = \frac{d}{dx}\left(\frac{\ln x}{\ln a}\right) = \frac{d}{dx}\left(\frac{1}{\ln a} \cdot \ln x\right) = \frac{1}{\ln a} \cdot \frac{d}{dx}(\ln x) = \frac{1}{\ln a} \cdot \frac{1}{x}.$$

Example 2.9.4

Problem: Use the new differentiation formulas from Corollary 2.91. (along with the various differentiation rules) to differentiate the following functions

(a) $f(x) = 5^{-2x}$ (b) $g(x) = 2^{\sqrt{x}}$ (c) $h(x) = \log\left(\sqrt{x}\right)$.

(d) $F(x) = x^x$ (e) $G(x) = \left(1 + x^2\right)^{\sin x}$

Solution: In (a) and (b) we use the chain rule. In (c) it is simpler to use a law of logarithms before differentiating.

$$\text{(a)} \quad f'(x) \;=\; \frac{d}{dx}\left(5^{-2x}\right) = (\ln 5)5^{-2x}\cdot\frac{d}{dx}(-2x) = (\ln 5)5^{-2x}\cdot(-2)$$

$$=\; (-2\ln 5)5^{-2x} \approx -(3.22)5^{-2x}$$

$$\text{(b)} \quad g'(x) = (\ln 2)2^{\sqrt{x}}\cdot\frac{d}{dx}\left(\sqrt{x}\right) = (\ln 2)2^{\sqrt{x}}\cdot\frac{1}{2\sqrt{x}} = \left(\frac{\ln 2}{2}\right)\frac{2^{\sqrt{x}}}{\sqrt{x}} \approx .34657\frac{2^{\sqrt{x}}}{\sqrt{x}}$$

$$\text{(c)} \quad h'(x) = \frac{d}{dx}\left(\log\left(\sqrt{x}\right)\right) = \frac{d}{dx}\left(\log\left(x^{1/2}\right)\right) = \frac{d}{dx}\left(\frac{1}{2}\log x\right) = \frac{1}{2\ln 10}\cdot\frac{1}{x}$$

$$\text{(d)} \quad F'(x) \;=\; \frac{d}{dx}\left(x^x\right) = \frac{d}{dx}\left(e^{x\ln x}\right) = e^{x\ln x}\cdot\frac{d}{dx}\left(x\ln x\right)$$

$$=\; e^{x\ln x}\cdot\left(\ln x + x\cdot\left(\frac{1}{x}\right)\right) = e^{x\ln x}\left(\ln x + 1\right)$$

$$=\; x^x\left(\ln x + 1\right)$$

$$\text{(e)} \quad G'(x) \;=\; \frac{d}{dx}\left[(1+x^2)^{\sin x}\right] = \frac{d}{dx}\left[e^{\sin x\cdot\ln\left(1+x^2\right)}\right]$$

$$=\; e^{\sin x\ln\left(1+x^2\right)}\cdot\frac{d}{dx}\left(\sin x\ln\left(1+x^2\right)\right)$$

$$=\; (1+x^2)^{\sin x}\left(\cos x\ln\left(1+x^2\right) + \sin x\cdot\frac{2x}{1+x^2}\right)$$

Exponential Growth and Decay

In modeling the growth and decay of populations and substances, exponential functions are often used as elementary, first approximations to the real-life dynamics. Assuming that $a > 1$ is the base, and $N_0 > 0$ is a positive constant, a function of the form

$$N(t) = N_0 a^t$$

models exponential growth, while one of the form

$$N(t) = N_0 a^{-t}$$

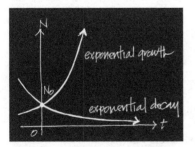

Figure 2.9.3: *Graphs of exponential growth and decay.*

models exponential decay. Figure 2.9.3 shows the typical graphs of these types of functions.

In these models t represents the time, and $N(t)$ is the population size (or the amount of substance) present at time t. Note that N_0 represents the initial $(t = 0)$ population size: $N(0) = N_0$. Also as $t \to \infty$, one has that $N(t) \to \infty$ (for exponential growth), and $N(t) \to 0$ (for exponential decay). Additionally, from Corollary 2.9.1, we see that the rate of change of population with respect to time is

$$\frac{dN}{dt} = (\ln a)N_0 a^t = (\ln a)N \qquad \text{(for exponential growth)}$$

$$\frac{dN}{dt} = -(\ln a)N_0 a^{-t} = -(\ln a)N \qquad \text{(for exponential decay)}$$

Letting $k = \ln a$, we see that characteristic feature for exponential growth or decay is that the population size N satisfies an equation of the form

$$\frac{dN}{dt} = \pm kN.$$

This says that at each instant, the time rate of change of the population is proportional to the population size. (k is the proportionality constant, and the sign indicates growth or decay.)

Let's look at a particular example of exponential growth, one that comes from biology. Biologists know that growth takes place at the cellular level by the process of each cell dividing into two, with the division occurring at equal intervals of time. Suppose, to give a particular example, a culture of the bacteria *E. coli* is growing in a medium and each cell divides into 2 cells every 50 minutes. Thus, every 50 minutes the number N of cells present doubles, as indicated by Figure 2.9.4.

So, starting with an initial number N_0 of *E. coli* cells, there are $2N_0$, $4N_0$, and $8N_0$ present after 50, 100, and 150 minutes respectively. A model for the continuous growth of the number of *E. coli* naturally involves a base 2 exponential function of the form

$$N(t) = N_0 2^{t/50}.$$

To get a feel for the explosive nature of this growth, you should view the movie created by the following command:

```
> expo_growth(12);
```

The movie has 13 frames and depicts the number of cells present at times $t = 50i$ for $i = 0, 1, 2, \ldots, 12$. The number of cells is represented by the area of total figure (composed of rectangles) shown in each frame. Thus, in frame 0, if the single square represents one cell (1 square unit of area), then frame 1 shows 2 cells, frame 2 shows $2^2 = 4$ cells, and so on, out to frame 12 which shows $2^{12} = 4096$ cells (a total area of 64 x 64 = 4096 square units).

You can run the movie for longer or shorter periods of time by changing $n = 12$ to something larger or smaller ($50n$ is the simulated duration of the movie in minutes, but the movie itself runs much quicker than this in real time). These movies will tend to look the same because the small-sized initial areas are barely, if at all, visible, and exponential growth is similar at any scale. You should readily discern from the movie that growth rate speeds up considerably, from a very slow rate at first to a rapid one at the end. We can determine the growth rate exactly, using the differentiation rules we have learned, and use this calculation to quantify the speed-up in the growth rate.

$$\frac{dN}{dt} = N_0 \frac{d}{dt}\left(2^{t/50}\right) = N_0 (\ln 2) 2^{t/50} \frac{d}{dt}\left(\frac{t}{50}\right) = \frac{N_0}{50}(\ln 2) 2^{t/50}$$

$$\approx (0.01386 N_0)\, 2^{t/50} \quad \text{cells/min}$$

Thus, the growth rate itself is exponential, doubling every 50 minutes.

Note: It is interesting to run the movie backwards. Then the movie depicts exponential decay.

Euler's Number e as a Limit

In the Appendix, Section A.9 we discussed Euler's number e informally and gave 2.718 as an approximation. We are now in the position to give limit expression for e, from which we can calculate very good approximate values for e. This limit expression for e comes easily from the limit

$$\lim_{h \to 0} \frac{\ln(1 + h)}{h} = 1,$$

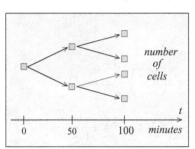

Figure 2.9.4: *Each cell divides in two every 50 minutes.*

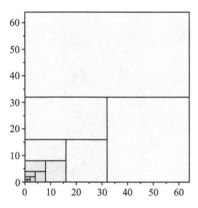

Figure 2.9.5: *The last frame in the movie* expo_growth(12).

which we used to prove that $\frac{d}{dx}\ln x = 1/x$. We also will need to use the facts that $\ln x$ and e^x are continuous functions and are inverse functions to each other, so that $\exp(\ln A) = A$. Additionally we need the law of logarithms: $p\ln A = \ln(A^p)$. Finally we will need the limit law

$$\lim_{h\to a} f(g(h)) = f\left(\lim_{h\to a} g(h)\right).$$

Now consider

$$1 = \lim_{h\to 0} \frac{\ln(1+h)}{h} = \lim_{h\to 0} \frac{1}{h}\cdot\ln(1+h) = \lim_{h\to 0}\left[\ln(1+h)^{\frac{1}{h}}\right] = \ln\left(\lim_{h\to 0}(1+h)^{\frac{1}{h}}\right)$$

Thus,

$$e = \exp(1) = \exp\left(\ln\left(\lim_{h\to 0}(1+h)^{\frac{1}{h}}\right)\right) = \lim_{h\to 0}(1+h)^{\frac{1}{h}}$$

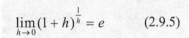

$$\lim_{h\to 0}(1+h)^{\frac{1}{h}} = e \qquad (2.9.5)$$

This is the expression we were seeking. Because of its importance, we record this result in Formula (2.9.5) in the margin.

An equivalent, and often more useful, limit expression for e comes from the above by letting $h = 1/n$, and taking $n\to\infty$, so that $h\to 0$. Then we get Formula (2.9.6) in the margin.

$$e = \lim_{n\to\infty}\left(1+\frac{1}{n}\right)^n \qquad (2.9.6)$$

It is fairly easy to use this result to calculate, by hand, the first five approximations to the value of e. Namely, compute $(1+1/n)^n$, for $n = 1,2,3,4,5$.

$$\left(1+\frac{1}{1}\right)^1 = 2^1 = 2$$

$$\left(1+\frac{1}{2}\right)^2 = \left(\frac{3}{2}\right)^2 = \frac{9}{4} = 2.25$$

$$\left(1+\frac{1}{3}\right)^3 = \left(\frac{4}{3}\right)^3 = \frac{64}{27} = 2.37\overline{037}$$

$$\left(1+\frac{1}{4}\right)^4 = \left(\frac{5}{4}\right)^4 = \frac{625}{256} = 2.44140625$$

$$\left(1+\frac{1}{5}\right)^5 = \left(\frac{6}{5}\right)^5 = \frac{7776}{3125} = 2.48832$$

The decimal expressions for the above rational numbers were produced by computer calculation. We can also illustrate the limit $\lim_{n\to\infty}(1+1/n)^n$ in the animation created by the following commands.

```
> with(dplot_tools,dplot);
```
$$[dplot]$$
```
> f:=n->(1+1/n)^n;
```
$$f := n \to \left(1+\frac{1}{n}\right)^n$$
```
> p1:=dplot(f,0,50,20):
> p2:=plot(exp(1),x=0..50,color=blue):
> display({p1,p2});
```

The last frame in the animation is shown in Figure 2.9.6.

You should note that the limit expression converges rather slowly to e. An approximate value of e, as produced by Maple, is

```
> evalf(exp(1));
```
$$2.718281828$$

Using the limit expression, the approximation does not reach three-digit accuracy until $n = 164$:

```
> for n from 160 to 165 do evalf((1+1/n)^n);end do;
```

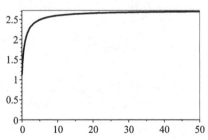

Figure 2.9.6: *Plot of* $f(n) = \left(1+\frac{1}{n}\right)^n$ *(in black) and the horizontal line (in blue)* $y = 2.718281828$.

$$2.709835576$$
$$2.709887741$$
$$2.709939265$$
$$2.709990160$$
$$2.710040438$$
$$2.710090110$$

Continuously Compounded Interest

Different banks offer varying interest policies such as interest being compounded monthly, weekly, daily, and in some cases, even continuously. Of course, the more frequently a given interest rate is compounded the larger will be the accumulated total. Thus, for a given principal, 6% per year compounded continuously will be worth more that 6% compounded quarterly. Suppose that $10000 is deposited in a savings account at 6% per year.

Problem: Find the value of the account at the end of 1 year if (a) interest is compounded quarterly and (b) if interest is compounded continuously.

Solution (a): Let A be the value of the account. The interest rate per quarter is $0.06/4$, so, after 1 quarter the value of the account is

$$A = 10000 + (10000)\frac{0.06}{4} = 10000\left(1 + \frac{0.06}{4}\right).$$

After 2 quarters the value is

$$A = 10000\left(1 + \frac{0.06}{4}\right) + 10000\left(1 + \frac{0.06}{4}\right)\left(\frac{0.06}{4}\right) = 10000\left(1 + \frac{0.06}{4}\right)^2$$

After 3 quarters the value is

$$A = 10000\left(1 + \frac{0.06}{4}\right)^2 + 10000\left(1 + \frac{0.06}{4}\right)^2\left(\frac{0.06}{4}\right) = 10000\left(1 + \frac{0.06}{4}\right)^3$$

After 1 year

$$\begin{aligned}A &= 10000\left(1 + \frac{0.06}{4}\right)^3 + 10000\left(1 + \frac{0.06}{4}\right)^3\left(\frac{0.06}{4}\right) = 10000\left(1 + \frac{0.06}{4}\right)^4\\&= 10000(1.06136) = \$10613.60\end{aligned}$$

Solution (b): Generalizing the procedure in part (a) we see that the value of the account after 1 year if interest is compounded n times a year is

$$A_n = 10000\left(1 + \frac{0.06}{n}\right)^n.$$

To compute the value of the account if interest is compounded continuously we take the limit of A_n as the number of interest periods n goes to ∞, i.e. we take the limit:

$$A = \lim_{n\to\infty} A_n = 10000 \lim_{n\to\infty}\left(1 + \frac{0.06}{n}\right)^n = 10000e^{0.06} \approx \$10,618.37$$

We see that the account earns $4.77 more if interest is compounded continuously rather than quarterly.

Exercises: 2.9 (Derivatives of Exponential & Logarithmic Functions)

Calculating Derivatives

Find the derivatives of the following functions

1. $f(x) = \ln(x^3 + 4x + 2)$

2. $f(x) = \ln(x^3 + 3x + 1)$

3. $f(x) = \ln(\sin x)$ **4.** $f(x) = \ln(\cos x)$

5. $f(x) = \log_2(5x^2 + 3x + 1)$

6. $f(x) = \log_{10}(8x^2 + 5x + 2)$

7. $f(x) = 2^{-5x}$ **8.** $f(x) = 10^{-2x}$

9. $y = 10^{-x}\sin 5x$ **10.** $y = 9^{-x}5^x$

11. $y = e^{x^2 + 3x}$ **12.** $y = e^{x^3 + 4x}$

13. $y = \ln(\ln x)$ **14.** $y = \log_2(\log_2 x)$

15. $s = (\ln t)^2$ **16.** $s = (\ln t)^3$

17. $s = (\ln(\ln t))^2$ **18.** $s = (\ln(\ln t))^3$

19. $f(z) = \dfrac{\ln z}{1 + 2\ln z}$ **20.** $f(z) = \dfrac{\ln z}{1 + 3\ln z}$

21. $V = \dfrac{1 + \ln x}{1 - \ln x}$ **22.** $V = \dfrac{1 + 2\ln x}{1 - 2\ln x}$

23. $y = \sin(\ln x)$ **24.** $y = \cos(\ln x)$

25. $y = \sin x \ln x$ **26.** $y = \cos x \ln x$

27. $y = e^{-x}\ln x$ **28.** $y = e^{-2x}\ln x$

29. $f(x) = x \ln x - x$ **30.** $f(x) = x^3 \ln x - x^3$

31. $y = e^{-x^2}\ln(1 + x^2)$ **32.** $y = e^{-x^3}\ln(1 + x^2)$

33. $f(x) = e^{-2x}\sin 3x$ **34.** $f(x) = e^{-5x}\sin 4x$

35. $f(x) = e^{\cos 6x}$ **36.** $f(x) = e^{\sin 3x}$

37. $y = \dfrac{x^2}{e^x}$ **38.** $f(x) = \dfrac{x^3}{e^x}$

39. $f(x) = \sqrt{e^{2x} + 1}$ **40.** $f(x) = \sqrt{e^{3x} + 1}$

41. $f(x) = (2e^{-x/2} + 5)^{-6}$

42. $f(x) = (3e^{-x/3} + 5)^{-5}$

43. $y = \sin(e^{-x})$ **44.** $y = \cos(e^{-x})$

45. $y = e^{1/x}$ **46.** $y = e^{1/x^2}$

47. $y = \sqrt{\ln(1 + x^2)}$ **48.** $y = (\ln 4x)^2$

49. $f(x) = x^3 e^{-2x}$ **50.** $f(x) = x^4 e^{-3x}$

51. $f(x) = \dfrac{e^x}{\ln x}$ **52.** $f(x) = \dfrac{e^{-x}}{\ln x}$

53. $f(x) = \dfrac{e^x}{1 + e^x}$ **54.** $f(x) = \dfrac{e^x}{1 - e^x}$

55. $f(x) = \dfrac{e^x - e^{-x}}{e^x + e^{-x}}$ **56.** $f(x) = \dfrac{e^x + e^{-x}}{e^x - e^{-x}}$

Some Special Derivative Formulas

57. Show that if $f(x) = \ln(g(x))$, then $f'(x) = \dfrac{g'(x)}{g(x)}$. Here g is a differentiable, positive function. This is not a difficult thing to show, but the formula provides a useful way of viewing the derivative of a composition with the log function. It says the the derivative of the $\ln(g)$ is g divided into the derivative of g.

58. Derive a formula for the derivative of $y = (g(x))^{f(x)}$, the general exponential function with variable base and variable exponent.

Using The Formulas in Exercises 59–60

Find the derivatives of the following functions.

59. $f(x) = \ln(\tan x)$ **60.** $f(x) = \ln(\cot x)$

61. $f(x) = \ln(\ln(\ln x))$ **62.** $f(x) = \log_2(\log_5(\ln x))$

63. $f(x) = \ln(1 + \sin^2 5x)$

64. $f(x) = \ln(e^{-3x} + x^2 \sin 4x)$

65. $f(x) = \ln\sqrt{\dfrac{3x + 5}{1 + x^2}}$ **66.** $f(x) = \ln\sqrt{\dfrac{2x - 5}{1 + x^2}}$

67. $y = x^{\sin x}$ **68.** $y = x^{\cos x}$

69. $y = x^{(x^2 + 3x)}$ **70.** $y = x^{(x^3 + 2x)}$

Limits Involving e

In Exercises 71–74 evaluate the limit.

71. $\lim\limits_{n \to \infty}(1 + 1/n)^{100n}$ **72.** $\lim\limits_{n \to \infty}(1 + 1/n)^{2n}$

73. $\lim\limits_{n \to \infty}\left(1 + \dfrac{1}{3n}\right)^n$ **74.** $\lim\limits_{n \to \infty}\left(1 + \dfrac{2}{n}\right)^n$

Applications

75. The element polonium (Po, atomic number 84, mass number 210) undergoes radioactive decay. If N_0 is the number of atoms in a given sample of Po, then when t days have elapsed the number N of atoms left in the sample is $N = N_0 2^{-t/140}$. How long does it take for a sample to be reduced to one-half of its original size? Calculate its rate of decomposition at this time.

76. A drug is administered intravenously to a subject. The blood carries the drug to the proper cells, and any excess drug is removed by the liver. Let a denote the concentration, in units per liter, of the drug in the blood immediately after the injection. The relation between the concentration C of the drug in the blood after t minutes have elapsed is given by the equation $C = a2^{-kt}$ (units/liter) for some constant k. For penicillin injected into a particular patient assume that $k = 1/25$. If 10 milliliters of penicillin are injected in the patient, find: (a) the concentration of penicillin in the blood after 25 minutes, and (b) the rate at which the drug is being eliminated from the blood 25 minutes after the drug was administered.

77. Suppose that $15,000 is deposited in a savings account which earns 7% annually. What is the amount that will be in the account in 10 years if (a) interest is compounded quarterly? (b) interest is compounded continuously?

78. Parents decide to place $P in a savings account today so that in 15 years they will have $20,000 for educational expenses. Find P if the interest rate is 6% per year compounded continuously.

Calculus Concepts & Computation

2.10 Implicit Differentiation

The technique of implicit differentiation allows us to solve the tangent line problem for a general (smooth) curve C in $\mathbb{R}$. For us, a curve in $\mathbb{R}^2$ is defined to be the set of points in the x-y plane that satisfy an equation $H(x,y) = 0$. Specifically, the curve C given by the equation is the set of points

$$C = \left\{ (x,y) \in \mathbb{R}^2 \mid H(x,y) = 0 \right\}$$

For example, the curve given by the equation $x^2 - y + 1 = 0$ has $H(x,y) = x^2 - y + 1$ as its defining function. If you rewrite the equation $x^2 - y + 1 = 0$ as $y = x^2 + 1$, then you recognize the curve in this case is a parabola (and is the graph of the function $f(x) = x^2 + 1$).

Generally, curves are not graphs of functions. Rather, the graph C_f of a function f is a rather special type of curve in the plane, i.e., it is the set of points given by

$$C_f = \left\{ (x,y) \in \mathbb{R}^2 \mid y = f(x) \right\}$$

A defining function H for this type of curve is $H(x,y) = y - f(x)$.

In this section, we will see that the equation $H(x,y) = 0$ for a general curve C implicitly defines one or more functions and that the graphs of these functions are pieced together to give the curve. The implicit differentiation technique allows us to find the derivatives of these functions, even though they are not given explicitly as functions $y = f(x)$ of x. Using this, we can find an equation for the tangent line at a given point on the curve.

Example 2.10.1

Problem: Describe the curve defined by the equation $(x-1)^2 + y^2 = 4$.

Solution: We recall that the graph of this equation is a circle with center $(1,0)$ and radius 2. Thus, if we let $H(x,y) = (x-1)^2 + y^2 - 4$ we see that H defines this curve:

$$C = \left\{ (x,y) \in \mathbb{R}^2 \mid (x-1)^2 + y^2 - 4 = 0 \right\}.$$

This is not the graph of a function, but notice that if we restrict y to being non-negative, $y \geq 0$, so that we only have the upper semicircle, then we do get the graph of a function. Similarly, $y \leq 0$ determines a function, whose graph is the lower semicircle. The formulas for these two functions are

$$y = \sqrt{4 - (x-1)^2}$$

and

$$y = -\sqrt{4 - (x-1)^2}$$

These formulas, naturally, are found by solving the equation $(x-1)^2 + y^2 = 4$ for y. We say that these functions are *implicitly-defined* by the equation $(x-1)^2 + y^2 = 4$.

Even though the curve in Example 2.10.1 is not the graph of a function it has a well defined tangent line at each point. Except for the horizontal and vertical tangent lines it is not so clear what the equations of the other tangent lines are. We need to find their slopes and for this we use implicit differentiation.

Example 2.10.2 (A Tangent Line to a Circle Via Implicit Differentiation)

Problem: Find the equation of the tangent line to the curve $(x-1)^2 + y^2 = 4$ at the point $(2, \sqrt{3})$.

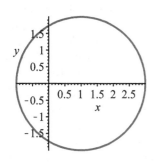

Figure 2.10.1: *The curve defined by* $(x-1)^2 + y^2 - 4 = 0$.

Solution: To write the equation of the line we need its slope m which is y' evaluated at $x = 2$. But this computation would require having y given explicitly as a function of x. Then, using the differentiation rules, we could find y' explicitly as a function of x. Instead of doing this, we use the technique of *implicit differentiation* to compute m as follows. We begin by finding y' implicitly by differentiating the equation $(x-1)^2 + y^2 = 4$ with respect to x.

$$\frac{d}{dx}\left((x-1)^2\right) + \frac{d}{dx}\left(y^2\right) = \frac{d}{dx}(4)$$

Using the chain rule we calculate that

$$\frac{d}{dx}\left((x-1)^2\right) = 2(x-1)(1) = 2x - 2.$$

Also, $\frac{d}{dx}(4) = 0$. The derivative $\frac{d}{dx}\left(y^2\right)$ must be calculated using the chain rule since y is an implicit function of x. Thus,

$$\frac{d}{dx}\left(y^2\right) = 2y\frac{dy}{dx} = 2yy'$$

Making these substitutions then gives us the following equation involving x, y, and y'.

$$2x - 2 + 2yy' = 0$$

Solving this equation for y' we see that

$$y' = \frac{2 - 2x}{2y} = \frac{1 - x}{y}.$$

Thus, the slope m of the tangent line at the point $(x, y) = (2, \sqrt{3})$ is

$$m = y'(2) = y'\big|_{(2,\sqrt{3})} = \frac{1-2}{\sqrt{3}} = \frac{-1}{\sqrt{3}}$$

Note the interpretation of $y'(2)$ here. The expression we have for y' doesn't give it explicitly as a function of x, but only in terms of x and y. In summary, the equation of the tangent line, see Figure 2.10.2, is

$$y - \sqrt{3} = -\frac{1}{\sqrt{3}}(x - 2)$$

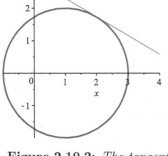

Figure 2.10.2: *The tangent to the circle at* $P = (2, \sqrt{3})$.

As we mentioned, we could have computed the slope m directly using one of the two functions defined implicitly by the equation $(x-1)^2 + y^2 = 4$. The functions are $y = \pm\sqrt{4 - (x-1)^2}$. (See Example 1 above.) Since the point $(2, \sqrt{3})$ lies on the graph of $y = \sqrt{4 - (x-1)^2}$, we use it and the differentiation rules to find

$$y' = \frac{-(x-1)}{\sqrt{4 - (x-1)^2}}.$$

Evaluating this at $x = 2$ gives the same slope m we found above. However, with a little practice, implicit differentiation will be easier than this method. In addition to being easier, implicit differentiation is the only method available when the equation $H(x, y) = 0$ defining the curve cannot be solved to give y explicitly as a function of x.

Example 2.10.3

Problem (a): Determine two functions implicitly defined by the equation

$$xy^2 + x - 1 = 0.$$

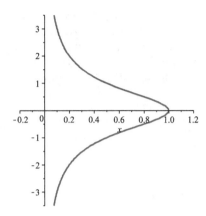

Figure 2.10.3: *The curve defined by* $xy^2 + x - 1 = 0$.

Solution (a): We need to solve the equation for y. We do this in the following sequence of steps.

$$xy^2 = 1 - x$$

$$y^2 = \frac{1-x}{x}$$

$$y = \sqrt{\frac{1-x}{x}} \quad \text{or} \quad y = -\sqrt{\frac{1-x}{x}}$$

The graph of the curve defined by $xy^2 + x - 1 = 0$ is shown in Figure 2.10.3. We see that the part of the curve which lies above the x-axis gives the graph of the function $y = \sqrt{\dfrac{1-x}{x}}$ (since all the y-values are positive) and that the part of the curve below the x-axis should be the graph of the function $y = -\sqrt{\dfrac{1-x}{x}}$ (since all the y-values are negative).

Problem (b): find an equation for the tangent line to the curve $xy^2 + x - 1 = 0$ at the point $(\frac{1}{2}, 1)$.

Solution (b): You should verify that this point is indeed on the curve (i.e., substitute $x = \frac{1}{2}$, $y = 1$ into the equation for the curve and see that the equation is satisfied.) First we find the slope of the tangent line by implicit differentiation. Differentiating (with respect to x) the equation for the curve gives

$$\frac{d}{dx}\left(xy^2 + x - 1\right) = \frac{d}{dx}(0),$$

or

$$x' \cdot y^2 + x \cdot \left(y^2\right)' + x' - 1' = 0,$$

or

$$1 \cdot y^2 + x \cdot 2yy' + 1 = 0$$

and finally

$$y^2 + 2xyy' + 1 = 0.$$

Substituting $x = \frac{1}{2}$, $y = 1$ into this gives

$$1 + y' + 1 = 0.$$

So

$$y' = -2$$

is the slope of the tangent line.

We could also find this same slope by differentiating explicitly one of the two explicit functions $y = \pm\sqrt{\frac{1-x}{x}}$ we found above. We use the one with the $+$ sign since the graph of passes through our chosen point $(\frac{1}{2}, 1)$ (the one with the $-$ sign does not). We write the function as

$$y = \sqrt{\frac{1-x}{x}} = \left(\frac{1-x}{x}\right)^{1/2} = \left(x^{-1} - 1\right)^{1/2},$$

and then differentiate using the chain rule. We get

$$\frac{dy}{dx} = \frac{d}{dx}\left[\left(x^{-1} - 1\right)^{1/2}\right] = \frac{1}{2}\left(x^{-1} - 1\right)^{-1/2} \cdot \frac{d}{dx}\left(x^{-1} - 1\right)$$

$$= -\frac{1}{2}\left(x^{-1} - 1\right)^{-1/2} \cdot \frac{1}{x^2}$$

Evaluating this at $x = \frac{1}{2}$ gives

$$\left.\frac{dy}{dx}\right|_{x=1/2} = -\frac{1}{2}((2-1)^{-1/2} \cdot 4 = -2.$$

With either calculation, an equation for the tangent line $y - 1 = -2(x - \frac{1}{2})$.

Example 2.10.4

Problem: Find the equation of the tangent line to the curve $xy^3 - x^3y + x - 1 = 0$ at the point $(1,1)$.

Solution: First, we need to find $y'(1)$, where y is a function implicitly defined by this equation. We will use implicit differentiation. Thus, we differentiate both sides of the equation with respect to x.

$$\frac{d}{dx}(xy^3 - x^3y + x - 1) = 0.$$

We calculate the derivatives on the left-hand side term by term. The first two terms involve the function $y = y(x)$ and we are differentiating with respect to x, so we must be careful. Since xy^3 and x^3y are each the product of two functions of x, we must use the product rule to differentiate them.

$$\frac{d}{dx}(xy^3) = (1)y^3 + x(3y^2y') = y^3 + 3xy^2y'$$

$$\frac{d}{dx}(x^3y) = 3x^2y + x^3y'$$

Now, substituting these into the equation and using $\frac{d}{dx}(x-1) = 1$, we get the equation.

$$y^3 + 3xy^2y' - 3x^2y - x^3y' + 1 = 0. \qquad (2.10.1) \qquad\qquad (2.2)$$

Taking $x = 1$ and $y = 1$ in this equation gives

$$1 + 3y' - 3 - y' + 1 = 0$$

and so $y' = 1/2$ is the slope of the tangent line at the point $(1, 1)$. Thus, an equation for the tangent line at $(1, 1)$ is

$$y - 1 = \frac{1}{2}(x - 1) \quad \text{or simply} \quad y = \frac{1}{2}x + \frac{1}{2}$$

While we did not need it for the stated problem, we could find a general formula for y' by solving Equation (2.10.1) for y'. Here are the steps: Start with

$$3xy^2y' - x^3y' = 3x^2y - y^3 - 1$$

$$(3xy^2 - x^3)y' = 3x^2y - y^3 - 1$$

$$y' = \frac{3x^2y - y^3 - 1}{3xy^2 - x^3}$$

This, then, gives the slope of the tangent line to the curve at any point (x, y) on the curve. For example, at $(1, 1)$.

$$y'|_{(1,1)} = \frac{3(1)^2(1) - (1)^3 - 1}{3(1)(1)^2 - (1)^3} = \frac{1}{2}.$$

This is what we found above.

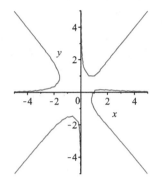

Figure 2.10.4: *Maple's graph of $xy^3 - x^3y + x - 1 = 0$.*

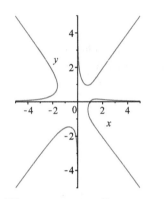

Figure 2.10.5: *Better graph of $xy^3 - x^3y + x - 1 = 0$.*

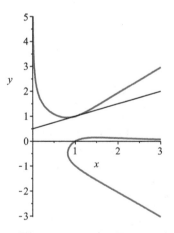

Figure 2.10.6: *Tangent line to $xy^3 - x^3y + x - 1 = 0$ at the point $(1, 1)$.*

As another example, consider the point $(1, 0)$, which is also on the curve (i.e., $x = 1$, $y = 0$ satisfy the equation $xy^3 - x^3y + x - 1 = 0$.) Using the above formula for y' we find that the slope of the tangent line at $(1, 0)$ is

$$y'|_{(1,0)} = \frac{3(1)^2(0) - (0)^3 - 1}{\left(3(1)(0)^2 - (1)^3\right)} = 1.$$

Graphing Curves in Maple

A curve defined by an equation can be graphed in Maple using the `implicitplot` command. This command is not automatically loaded when you open a Maple worksheet. It is part of the plots package and can be loaded with the command

```
with(plots,implicitplot);
```
$$[implicitplot]$$

Let's see what the curve in Example 2.10.4 looks like.

```
> H:=(x,y)->x*y^3-x^3*y+x-1;
```
$$H := (x, y) \rightarrow xy^3 - x^3y + x - 1$$
```
> implicitplot(H(x,y)=0,x=-5..5,y=-5..5,color=blue);
```

See Figure 2.10.4. We see that the curve is not very smooth. This means that Maple needs to use more points in drawing the graph. We can include the `grid` option to increase the number of points Maple uses to draw the graph.

```
> implicitplot(H(x,y)=0,x=-5..5,y=-5..5,color=blue,grid=[150,150]);
```

This gives a better graph as shown Figure 2.10.5. We could increase the grid size even more. The default grid size is [25,25]. Let's use the display command to include the graph of the tangent line at the point $(1,1)$ in the picture. From Example 2.10.4, we calculated the equation of this tangent line to be $y = \frac{1}{2}x + \frac{1}{2}$. So, we need to store the plots of the curve and the tangent line in plot structures and then display them. The code for doing this follows. Remember to load the display command.

```
> with(plots,display);
```
$$[display]$$
```
> p:=implicitplot(x*y^3-x^3*y+x-1=0,x=-5..5,grid=[100,100]):
> q:=plot(x/2+1/2,x=0..2,color=black):
> display({p,q});
```

The result is shown in Figure 2.10.6.

Implicit differentiation can also be used to find the second derivative y'' of an implicitly-defined function y.

Example 2.10.5 (Finding 2nd Derivatives Implicitly)

Problem: Use implicit differentiation to find y'' where y is defined implicitly by: $4x^2 - 2y^2 = 9$.

Solution: Using the prime notation, we need to find y''. Thus, we will differentiate twice implicitly. Differentiating both sides of $4x^2 - 2y^2 = 9$ gives

$$8x - 4yy' = 0.$$

Now, solving for y' we obtain

$$y' = \frac{2x}{y}.$$

We differentiate again to find y'.

$$y'' = \frac{2y - 2xy'}{y^2}.$$

We can substitute $y' = \frac{2x}{y}$ into this to get

$$y'' = \frac{2y - 2x\left(\frac{2x}{y}\right)}{y^2} = \frac{2y^2 - 4x^2}{y^3} = \frac{-9}{y^3},$$

where in the last equation, we have use the fact that points (x, y) on the curve satisfy $4x^2 - 2y^2 = 9$ (which is the equation defining the curve).

Example 2.10.6 (A Sinsoidal Oval)

Problem: Find an equation for the tangent line to the curve

$$\sin(x + y) = y^2,$$

at the point $(0, 0)$ and use Maple to plot the curve and the tangent line.

Solution: Differentiating implicitly and using the chain rule gives

$$\frac{d}{dx}[\sin(x + y)] = \frac{d}{dx}[y^2], \quad \text{i.e.,} \quad \cos(x + y) \cdot \frac{d}{dx}(x + y) = 2yy'$$

So

$$\cos(x + y)(1 + y') = 2yy'$$

Substituting in $x = 0, y = 0$ gives

$$1(1 + y') = 0, \quad \text{and so} \quad y' = -1$$

for the slope of the tangent line at $(0, 0)$. Thus, an equation for the tangent line is simply $y = -x$. We can plot the curve and its tangent using commands like those prior to the last example.

```
> with(plots,display);
                          [display]
> p:=implicitplot(sin(x+y)=y^2,x=-0.5..5,y=-2..2,grid=[50,50]):
> q:=plot(-x,x==0.5..1,color=red):
> display({p,q});
```

These give

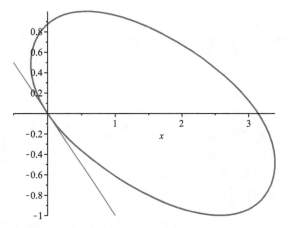

Figure 2.10.7: *Plot of the curve* $\sin(x + y) = y^2$ *and its tangent line at* $(0, 0)$

Exercises: 2.10 (Implicit Differentiation)

```
> with(plots,display,implicitplot);
```
$$[display, implicitplot]$$

Using Implicit Differentiation

In Exercises 1–34 find $y' = \dfrac{dy}{dx}$ by implicit differentiation.

1. $x^2 + y^2 = 9$ 2. $x^2 - y^2 = 9$

3. $x^2 y + 3xy^3 - x = 3$ 4. $x^3 y^2 - 5x^2 y + x = 1$

5. $x^3 y^4 - 2x^4 y^3 + 5xy + 1 = 0$

6. $x^5 y^2 - 2x^2 y^5 + 2xy + 1 = 0$

7. $x^{-1} + y^{-1} = 1$ 8. $x^{-1} - y^{-1} = 1$

9. $x^4 + y^4 = 1$ 10. $x^6 + y^6 = 1$

11. $x^3 + y^3 = 1$ 12. $x^5 + y^5 = 1$

13. $\sqrt{x} + \sqrt{y} = 1$ 14. $\sqrt[4]{x} + \sqrt[4]{y} = 1$

15. $\sqrt{x} + \sqrt{y} + x = 1$ 16. $2\sqrt{x} - \sqrt{y} + x = 1$

17. $\sqrt{xy} + 1 = y$ 18. $\sqrt{xy} + x = y$

19. $\sqrt{xy} + \sqrt{x} = y\sqrt{y}$ 20. $\sqrt{xy} + \sqrt{x} = x\sqrt{y}$

21. $\dfrac{x}{y} + \dfrac{y}{x} = 1$ 22. $\dfrac{x}{y} - \dfrac{y}{x} = 1$

23. $\left(x^2 + 3y^2\right)^9 = x$ 24. $\left(x^2 - 5y^3\right)^7 = x$

25. $\sin x + \cos y = 1$ 26. $\cos x + \sin y = 1$

27. $\sin x \cos y = xy$ 28. $\cos x \sin y = xy$

29. $\sin\left(x^2 y^2\right) = x$ 30. $\cos\left(x^3 y^5\right) = x^3$

31. $e^{-xy} + 10x^2 + 10y^2 = 20$

32. $e^{-xy} + 10x^4 + 10y^4 = 20$

33. $10x^2 e^{-x^2 - y^2} = 1$ 34. $10x^3 e^{-x^2 - y^2} = 1$

Tangent Lines to Curves

In Exercises 35–46, use implicit differentiation to find the slope of the tangent line and the equation of the tangent line to the given curve at the specified point.

35. $x^2 y - 5xy^2 + 6 = 0$, $(3, 1)$

36. $xy^2 = 1 - x$, $(1/2, 1)$

37. $x^3 y^2 - x^2 y^3 - 2x + 2y = 0$, $(1, 1)$

38. $x^2 y^3 - x^3 y^2 - 2x + 2y = 0$, $(1, 1)$

39. $x^2 y^3 - x^4 y - 6x = 0$, $(1, 2)$

40. $x^3 y^3 - x^2 y - 6x = 0$, $(1, 2)$

41. $ye^{-x} + xe^{-y} = 1$, $(1, 0)$ 42. $xe^{-y} - ye^{-x} = 1$, $(1, 0)$

43. $\sin(xy) = y - 1$, $(\pi, 1)$ 44. $\cos(xy) = y - 1$, $(\pi/2, 1)$

45. $\sin(x - y) = y - x$, $(1, 1)$

46. $\cos(x - y) = y$, $(1, 1)$

2nd Derivatives Found Implicitly

In Exercises 47–58 find y'' by implicit differentiation.

47. $x^{-1} + y^{-1} = 1$ 48. $x^{-1} - y^{-1} = 1$

49. $x^4 + y^4 = 1$ 50. $x^6 + y^6 = 1$

51. $x^3 + y^3 = 1$ 52. $x^5 + y^5 = 1$

53. $\sqrt{x} + \sqrt{y} = 1$ 54. $\sqrt[4]{x} + \sqrt[4]{y} = 1$

55. $x^2 - 4y^2 = 4$ 56. $x^3 + y^3 = 1$

57. $2xy - y^2 = 3$ 58. $xy - y^3 = 1$

Functions Implicitly Defined by an Equation

59. Determine two functions that are implicitly defined by the equation $x^2 + (y - 1)^2 = 25$. Find equations for the tangent lines to the curve at the two points $(4, 4), (4, -2)$. Sketch (by hand) the curve, the two tangent lines, and label the two functions you found.

60. Determine two functions that are implicitly defined by the equation $x - x^2 y^2 = 1$. Find equations for the tangent lines to the curve at the two points $(2, \pm 1/2)$. CAS: Use Maple to plot the curve on the range x=1..10, y=-1..1, print it out, and sketch in the two tangent lines.

Plotting Curves and Tangent Lines

In Exercises 61–64, for the given equation $H(x, y) = 0$, do the following. (a) Use implicit differentiation to find the value of y' at the given points on the curve and write equations for the two tangent lines at these points. Where possible also find y' explicitly by first solving the equation for y and then differentiating as usual. (b) CAS: Graph the curve and the tangent lines in the same figure. Use the implicitplot command, choosing a grid size so the curve looks smooth. Print out the figure and annotate it.

61. $y^2 - x^3 + x - 1 = 0$, points: $(1, \pm 1)$

62. $y^2 - xy + x^3 - 1 = 0$, points: $(1, 0), (0, 1)$

63. $x^2 y^3 - xy + x^3 - 1 = 0$, points: $(1, \pm 1)$

64. $x^2 y^2 + y^2 - x^3 y + x - 2 = 0$, points: $(1, -1), (1, -1/2)$

Implicitly Defined Functions and Their Graphs

In Exercises 65–68 do the following: (a) Solve the equation explicitly for y, finding all possible explicit functions that satisfy the equation. CAS: (b) Plot the curve defined by the original equation, and plot (in the same figure, using different color for each) the graphs of all the explicit functions you found in Part (a).

65. $x^3 - xy^2 + 1 = 0$ 66. $x^3 + y^2 - 2xy - 1 = 0$

67. $y^4 - xy^2 + x^2 - 1 = 0$ 68. $x^2 y^4 - xy^2 + x - 1 = 0$

Generalized Circles

69. Use implicit differentiation to find y' and y'', where y is defined implicitly by

$$x^p + y^p = a^p.$$

Here p is any real number. Use this to check the answers in Exercises 47–54.

Calculus *Concepts & Computation*

2.11 Derivatives of Inverse Functions

```
> with(dplot_tools,plotinverse,dplotinverse);
```
$$[plotinverse, \; dplotinverse]$$

In this section we derive the inverse function derivative formula:

$$\left(f^{-1}\right)'(x) = \frac{1}{f'(f^{-1}(x))}.$$

This gives the derivative of the inverse function f^{-1} at x. Of course the validity of this formula requires that $f'(f^{-1}(x)) \neq 0$. While the formula may look complicated, you will see that, geometrically, it really is a very simple and easily understood result.

We then apply this inverse function derivative formula to the trigonometric functions and derive the formulas for the derivatives of the inverse trigonometric functions.

Finally, we summarize and extend the differentiation formulas for all the basic functions, i.e., power functions, exponential functions, logarithmic functions, trigonometric functions, and inverse trigonometric functions.

Derivatives of Inverse Functions

One of the simplest things about the topic of inverse functions is the underlying geometry. If we know what the graph of the function looks like, then the graph of the inverse function (when it exists) is easily obtained by reflecting it about the line $y = x$. More generally, the same thing is true for relations. Recall that a relation R is any set of ordered pairs, and the inverse relation is defined by

$$R^{-1} = \{(a,b) | (b,a) \in R\}.$$

When R is a subset of $\mathbb{R}^2$, this says that the graph of R^{-1} is obtained by reflecting the points in R about the line $y = x$. See Figure 2.11.1.

In particular, any curve C, being a subset of $\mathbb{R}^2$, has a corresponding inverse curve C^{-1} associated with it. Even more particular, and germane to our discussion here, is the case when the curve is the graph C_f of a function f. Note: Mathematically, a function is really the same as its graph, $f = C_f$, although we often think of them as being different objects. Thus, the corresponding inverse curve for a function f is

$$f^{-1} = \{(a,b) | (b,a) \in f\}.$$

This broad definition of the inverse function gives us a curve, but not necessarily a function. However, if f is one-to-one (or suitably restricted so that it is one-to-one) then f^{-1} is a function.

For example, the function $f(x) = -x^3 + 6x^2 - 9x + 6$, has an inverse curve, but the inverse curve is not the graph of a function unless we restrict the original domain of f. To see this, use the standard plot command to plot the graph of f on, say, the interval $[0,4]$, and then use the special-purpose plot command `plotinverse` to plot the inverse f^{-1}. Note that f restricted to $[0,4]$ has range $[2,6]$. You can determine this from a plot of f. Then, the inverse curve f^{-1} has domain $[2,6]$ and range $[0,4]$. You will need this information as input to the special-purpose Maple command:

$$\text{plotinverse(f,0,4,2,6)}$$

The plots are done as follows.

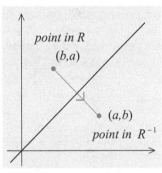

Figure 2.11.1: *Points (a,b) in R^{-1} come from points (b,a) in R.*

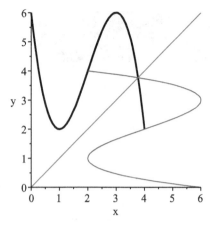

Figure 2.11.2: *Plot of $f(x) = -x^3 + 6x^2 - 9x + 6$ (in black) and its inverse curve (in blue).*

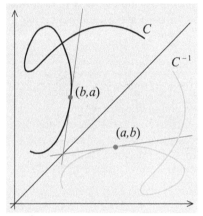

Figure 2.11.3: *A tangent line on the inverse curve C^{-1} comes from a tangent line the curve C.*

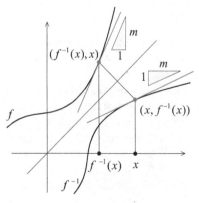

Figure 2.11.4: *Finding the slope of the tangent line to f^{-1} at x.*

```
> f:=x->-x^3+6*x^2-9*x+6;
```
$$f := x \to -x^3 + 6x^2 - 9x + 6$$
```
> with(dplot_tools,plotinverse):
> p2:=plotinverse(f,0,4,2,6):
> p3:=plot(x,x=0..6):
> display({p1,p2,p3},scaling=constrained);
```

Note that if we restrict f to the interval $[1, 3]$, then f is one-to-one and the inverse curve is the graph of the corresponding inverse function. The following command generates an animation of this function and its inverse being drawn dynamically from left-to-right.

```
> dplotinverse(f,1,3,20,0,6);
```

Note that we used 0, 6 instead of 2, 6 as the last arguments to the `dplotinverse` command. This was to achieve a better picture. Try 2, 6 instead and see what you get.

When you view the above movie you should note how the ordinates to the graphs of f and f^{-1} correspond at each instant. If x denotes the point on the x-axis at the foot of the ordinate to the graph of f^{-1}, then $f^{-1}(x)$ is the corresponding point at the foot of the ordinate to the graph of f. In this particular example, the ordinate at $f^{-1}(x)$ always lags behind the ordinate at x.

So, how can we do the calculus for inverse functions? The derivative is easy if we think geometrically. Suppose C is a curve and we want to construct a tangent line at a point (a, b) on the inverse curve C^{-1}. Figure 2.11.3 indicates how this is done.

We simply take the corresponding point (b, a) on the curve C, construct the tangent line to C at that point, and then reflect this line about the line $y = x$ to get the tangent line to C^{-1} at (a, b). A little thought, and some elementary geometry, will convince you that if m is the slope of the tangent line to C at (b, a), then $\frac{1}{m}$ is the slope of the tangent line to C^{-1} at (a, b). Otherwise said, the slopes on the inverse curve are the inverses, $m^{-1} = \frac{1}{m}$, of the slopes m on the original curve. This seems like a reasonable result.

How does all of this apply to the case of a function f which has an inverse function f^{-1} on a certain interval? Figure 2.11.4 shows all the particular notation we need.

To get the slope of the tangent line to the graph of f^{-1} at x (more specifically at the point $(x, f^{-1}(x))$ on the graph), we take the corresponding point $(f^{-1}(x), x)$ on the graph of f, and let m be the slope of the tangent line at this point. Thus,

$$m = f'(f^{-1}(x)).$$

Then

$$\frac{1}{m} = \frac{1}{f'(f^{-1}(x))},$$

is the slope of the tangent line to the graph of f^{-1} at x. In our derivative notation, this slope is denoted by

$$\left(f^{-1}\right)'(x) = \frac{df^{-1}}{dx}(x).$$

Thus, we have given a geometrical proof of the following theorem.

THEOREM 2.11.1 (Inverse Function Derivatives)

Suppose f is differentiable on an interval I and that f' is never zero in I. Then f⁻¹ exists on f(I) and for each x in f(I)

$$\left(f^{-1}\right)'(x) = \frac{1}{f'(f^{-1}(x))} \qquad (2.11.5)$$

Proof: We give here an analytic proof of the theorem using the chain rule. Since f' is never zero in I, it follows that f is one-to-one on I (we do not prove this), and thus has an inverse f^{-1} on I. We can get formula (2.11.5) by noting that

$$f(f^{-1}(x)) = x,$$

for all x in $f(I)$. Differentiating both sides of this equation with respect to x and using the chain rule on the left-side gives

$$f'(f^{-1}(x)) \cdot (f^{-1})'(x) = 1,$$

for all x in $f(I)$. Rearranging this gives Formula (2.11.5).

In practice, the difficult part about using Formula (2.11.5) is finding the expression for $f^{-1}(x)$. While for any particular x this is easy, finding an explicit formula for $f^{-1}(x)$, one that holds for all x in an interval, is difficult in most cases. Of course, if we had an explicit formula giving f^{-1} in terms of x, then we could just differentiate it directly without using Formula 2.11.5.

Example 2.11.1 (Using the Inverse Function Derivative Formula)

Problem: Suppose $f(x) = x^2$. Restrict x to being positive and use the Formula (2.11.5) for derivatives of inverse functions to find the derivative of f^{-1}.

Solution: First we calculate the derivative of f, which is easy enough

$$f'(x) = 2x.$$

Thus,

$$f'(f^{-1}(x)) = 2f^{-1}(x),$$

so that

$$\left(f^{-1}\right)'(x) = \frac{1}{2f^{-1}(x)}.$$

Normally this would be as far as we could go, but since $f(x) = x^2$, it is easy to see that for $x > 0$,

$$f^{-1}(x) = \sqrt{x}.$$

Using this gives

$$\left(f^{-1}\right)'(x) = \frac{1}{2\sqrt{x}},$$

which of course is the well-known result that comes easily and directly from the power rule.

Example 2.11.2 (The Derivative of the Natural Log Function)

Problem: Use the derivative formula for inverse functions to derive the formula for the derivative of the natural log function from the derivative formula for the exponential function.

Solution: If we let $f(x) = e^x$, then $f^{-1}(x) = \ln x$. The derivative formula for f is

$$f'(x) = e^x,$$

and so by the inverse function derivative formula:

$$\frac{d}{dx}(\ln x) = \left(f^{-1}\right)'(x) = \frac{1}{f'(f^{-1}(x))} = \frac{1}{e^{f^{-1}(x)}} = \frac{1}{e^{\ln x}} = \frac{1}{x}.$$

Example 2.11.3

Problem: Suppose $f(x) = -x^3 + 6x^2 - 9x + 6$ (the function discussed at the beginning of this section).

(a) Find, if possible, an explicit formula for the derivative of the inverse function f^{-1}.

(b) Consider the point $(2, 4)$ on the graph of f. (See Figure 2.11.2.) Find an equation for the tangent line to f^{-1} at the point $(4, 2)$.

Solution: We have that $f'(x) = -3x^2 + 12x - 9$, and so by the inverse function derivative formula

$$\left(f^{-1}\right)'(x) = \frac{1}{-3(f^{-1}(x))^2 + 12f^{-1}(x) - 9}.$$

This is the best we can do, since we cannot find an explicit formula for $f^{-1}(x)$ to use in this equation. To get such a formula, we would have to solve the cubic equation

$$x = -y^3 + 6y^2 - 9y + 6,$$

for $y = f^{-1}(x)$. However, we can always compute the slope of the tangent line to f^{-1} at a specific point like $(4, 2)$. For this note, that saying the point $(4, 2)$ is on the graph of f^{-1} means that $f^{-1}(4) = 2$. Then the slope of f^{-1} at this point is

$$\left(f^{-1}\right)'(4) = \frac{1}{-3(2)^2 + 12(2) - 9} = \frac{1}{3}$$

So an equation for the tangent line is

$$y - 2 = \frac{1}{3}(x - 4).$$

Example 2.11.4

Problem: Suppose $f(x) = \dfrac{e^x}{e^x + 1}$.

(a) Consider the point $(1/2, 0)$ on the graph of f^{-1}. Find an equation for the tangent line to f^{-1} at the point $(1/2, 0)$.

(b) Find, if possible, an explicit formula for the derivative $\left(f^{-1}\right)'$ of the inverse function f^{-1}. Use this to check your work in part (a).

Solution: Note that f is defined for all x, and has horizontal asymptotes $y = 1$ and $y = 0$. More specifically

$$\lim_{x \to \infty} \frac{e^x}{e^x + 1} = 1, \qquad \lim_{x \to -\infty} \frac{e^x}{e^x + 1} = 0.$$

Further, the derivative of f is

$$f'(x) = \frac{d}{dx}\left(\frac{e^x}{e^x + 1}\right) = \frac{e^x(e^x + 1) - e^x(e^x)}{(e^x + 1)^2} = \frac{e^x}{(e^x + 1)^2}.$$

Since this is always positive, f is an increasing function and thus has an inverse function f^{-1}, defined on its range, which is the interval $(0, 1)$. The graphs of f

and f^{-1} are generated by the following commands and the results are displayed in Figure 2.11.5.

```
> f:=x->exp(x)/(exp(x)+1);
```
$$f := x \to \frac{e^x}{e^x + 1}$$
```
> p1:=plot(f(x),x=-4..4,y=0..1,color=black,thickness=2):
> p2:=plotinverse(f,-4,4,0,1):
> p3:=plot(x,x=-4..4):
> display({p1,p2,p3},scaling=constrained);
>
```

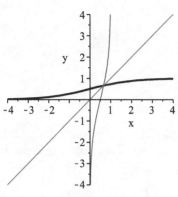

Figure 2.11.5: *Plot of* $f(x) = \frac{e^x}{e^x+1}$ *(in black) and its inverse* f^{-1} *(in blue).*

As you can see f^{-1} is defined only on the interval $(0, 1)$, and has vertical asymptotes at the endpoints of this interval.

To compute the slope of the tangent line to f^{-1} at the point $(1/2, 0)$, we note that $(0, 1/2)$ is the corresponding point on the graph of f. The slope of the tangent line to f at this point is

$$m = f'(0) = \frac{e^0}{(e^0 + 1)^2} = \frac{1}{4},$$

and hence is the slope we need is

$$\frac{1}{m} = 4.$$

The equation of the tangent line to f^{-1} at $(1/2, 0)$ is then

$$y = 4\left(x - \frac{1}{2}\right), \quad \text{i.e.} \quad y = 4x - 2.$$

Next we seek an explicit formula for the derivative $(f^{-1})'$ at any point x in the interval $(0, 1)$. We found that

$$f'(x) = \frac{e^x}{(e^x + 1)^2},$$

and so by the inverse function derivative formula

$$\left(f^{-1}\right)'(x) = \frac{1}{f'(f^{-1}(x))} = \frac{\left(e^{f^{-1}(x)} + 1\right)^2}{e^{f^{-1}(x)}}. \tag{2.11.6}$$

Now all we need is an explicit formula for $f^{-1}(x)$. To get this, let $y = f^{-1}(x)$. Then $f(y) = x$, that is,

$$\frac{e^y}{e^y + 1} = x.$$

Solving this equation for y in terms of x will give us what we need. First, multiply both sides by $e^y + 1$ to get

$$e^y = xe^y + x.$$

Then

$$(1 - x)e^y = x,$$

and so

$$e^y = \frac{x}{1 - x}.$$

Taking the natural logarithm of each side gives

$$f^{-1}(x) = y = \ln\left(\frac{x}{1 - x}\right) \tag{2.11.7},$$

for x in $(0,1)$. Now we can use this in Equation (2.11.6). For this note that

$$e^{f^{-1}(x)} = \frac{x}{1-x},$$

and so Equation (2.11.6) simplifies to

$$\left(f^{-1}\right)'(x) = \frac{\left(\frac{x}{1-x}+1\right)^2}{\frac{x}{1-x}} = \frac{\frac{1}{(1-x)^2}}{\frac{x}{1-x}} = \frac{1}{x(1-x)}.$$

This is an explicit formula for the derivative of this inverse function. It is left as an exercise to show that you can get the same thing by differentiating Equation (2.11.7) directly.

Example 2.11.5 (The Derivative of the Inverse Secant)

Problem: Find an explicit formula for the derivative of the inverse secant function.

Solution: Here $f(x) = \sec x$, but unlike the previous example there is no simple, explicit formula for the inverse function $f^{-1}(x) = \sec^{-1} x$. (There is an integral formula for $\sec^{-1} x$, but that will come much later.) So how can we expect to find an explicit formula for $(f^{-1})'$? The key is the use of the standard trigonometric identities (and the fact that derivatives of trig functions are also trig functions).

Additionally, this problem suggests the use of an alternative technique in calculating the derivatives of inverse functions, a technique that does not involve the inverse function derivative formula (2.11.5). This alternative technique is just a special case of implicit differentiation. Here is how it works for the secant function.

First let $y = \sec^{-1} x$. Then

$$\sec y = x.$$

We view this equation as an equation that implicitly defines y (i.e., the inverse secant function) as a function of x. Using implicit differentiation gives

$$\sec y \tan y \cdot \frac{dy}{dx} = 1,$$

and so

$$\frac{dy}{dx} = \frac{1}{\sec y \tan y} \qquad (2.11.8).$$

As in Section 2.10 on implicit differentiation, we can easily use this formula for $\frac{dy}{dx}$ to compute the slope of the tangent line at any given point on the curve $\sec y = x$. This viewpoint disregards the fact that the equation $\sec y = x$ is not the graph of a function, but rather is just the graph of the inverse curve to $y = \sec x$. See Figure 2.11.6.

If we want to go from implicit to explicit, then we rewrite Formula (2.11.8) using $\sec y = x$ and the trig identity

$$\tan^2 y = \sec^2 y - 1 = x^2 - 1,$$

or

$$\tan y = \pm\sqrt{x^2 - 1}.$$

Now Formula (2.11.8) becomes

$$\frac{d}{dx}\left(\sec^{-1} x\right) = \frac{1}{\pm x\sqrt{x^2 - 1}}.$$

To be more specific, we must determine what to do with the $\pm$ signs. This depends on how one defines $\sec^{-1} x$. Be cautioned that some books do this differently, and

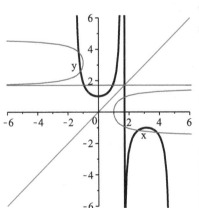

Figure 2.11.6: *Graph of the curve $y = \sec x$ (in black), which is a function, and its inverse curve $x = \sec y$ (in blue) which is not a function.*

so the formula we get will be different from theirs. Here we chose to define $\sec^{-1} x$ by restricting $\sec x$ to the interval $[0, \pi]$, where it is one-to-one. Then $\sec^{-1} x$ has graph as shown in Figure 2.11.7. Note that Maple has the same definition of $\sec^{-1} x$ as we do.

From the plot in the figure it is clear that for any x, either positive of negative, in the domain of $\sec^{-1} x$, the tangent line at x has positive slope. Consequently the interpretation of $\pm x$ is as x, when x is positive, and as $-x$ when x is negative. Otherwise said, $\pm x = |x|$. In summary then, we have found the following explicit formula for the derivative of the inverse secant function.

$$\frac{d}{dx}\left(\sec^{-1}x\right) = \frac{1}{|x|\sqrt{x^2-1}}.$$

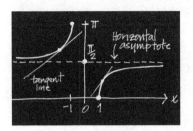

Figure 2.11.7: *Plot of* $\sec^{-1} x$.

Derivatives of the Inverse Trigonometric Functions

One of the main applications of the inverse function derivative formula is in obtaining the derivatives of the inverse trigonometric functions:

$$\sin^{-1} x, \ \tan^{-1} x, \ \sec^{-1} x,$$

and the corresponding inverse cofunctions

$$\cos^{-1} x, \ \cot^{-1} x, \ \csc^{-1} x.$$

It turns out that each inverse function and its inverse cofunction have derivatives that are the negatives of each other, and, perhaps more surprisingly, that the derivatives are algebraic functions. This we saw in Example 2.11.5 above. The exact results are presented in the following theorem.

THEOREM 2.11.2 (Derivatives of the Inverse Trig Functions)

On their domains, the inverse trigonometric functions have derivatives given by

$$\frac{d}{dx}\sin^{-1}x = \frac{1}{\sqrt{1-x^2}} \qquad \frac{d}{dx}\cos^{-1}x = \frac{-1}{\sqrt{1-x^2}}$$

$$\frac{d}{dx}\tan^{-1}x = \frac{1}{1+x^2} \qquad \frac{d}{dx}\cot^{-1}x = \frac{-1}{1+x^2}$$

$$\frac{d}{dx}\sec^{-1}x = \frac{1}{|x|\sqrt{x^2-1}} \qquad \frac{d}{dx}\csc^{-1}x = \frac{-1}{|x|\sqrt{x^2-1}}$$

Proof: The proof uses the alternative method discussed in Example 2.11.5, where we derived the formula for the derivative of the inverse secant function. In general, to find the derivative of $y = f^{-1}(x)$, write this as $f(y) = x$, and use implicit differentiation to find dy/dx. Then use appropriate trigonometric identities to write everything in terms of x. We show how this method works for the inverse sine and inverse tangent, leaving the other inverse trigonometric functions for an exercise.

For $y = \sin^{-1} x$, we have $\sin y = x$, and differentiating implicitly gives

$$\cos y \cdot \frac{dy}{dx} = 1,$$

or

$$\frac{dy}{dx} = \frac{1}{\cos y}.$$

Next rewrite $\cos y$ in terms of x. We have $\cos^2 y = 1 - \sin^2 y = 1 = x^2$, and so $\cos y = \pm\sqrt{1 - x^2}$. But since $-\frac{\pi}{2} \leq y \leq \frac{\pi}{2}$, it follows that $\cos y$ is nonnegative. So we use the positive sign $+$. Hence we have

$$\frac{d}{dx}\left(\sin^{-1}x\right) = \frac{dy}{dx} = \frac{1}{\sqrt{1 - x^2}}.$$

For the inverse tangent function $y = \tan^{-1} x$, we have $\tan y = x$. So by implicit differentiation:

$$\sec^2 y \cdot \frac{dy}{dx} = 1,$$

or

$$\frac{dy}{dx} = \frac{1}{\sec^2 y}.$$

But $\sec^2 y = 1 + \tan^2 y = 1 + x^2$, and consequently

$$\frac{d}{dx}\left(\tan^{-1}x\right) = \frac{dy}{dx} = \frac{1}{1 + x^2}.$$

In the next subsection, we will look at some examples involving derivatives of these inverse trigonometric functions.

Extended Derivative Formulas for all the Basic Functions

At this point in the chapter, we have derived the derivative formulas for all of the basic functions—power functions, the six trigonometric functions, the six inverse trigonometric functions, and exponential and logarithmic functions. (In truth, some people consider the hyperbolic functions as basic functions also, and thus we discuss them in the next section).

Knowing the basic derivatives along with the various differentiation rules (the sum and difference rules, the product rule, the quotient rule, and the chain rule) enables us to differentiate some truly complicated functions. You probably will need more practice before you get really good at differentiating such functions, and so we give a few more examples here and provide plenty of them for you to work on in the exercises.

The following examples use the results in Table 2.11.1 (see the end of this section) which gives the extended differentiation rules for all the basic functions. The results consider composite functions of the form $y = f(u)$, where $u = g(x)$ is a function of x. The chain rule then readily yields the formulas listed in the table.

Example 2.11.6

Problem: Find the derivatives of the following functions

(a) $f(x) = \sin^{-1}5x$ (b) $g(x) = \sin^{-1}\left(\dfrac{1}{x}\right).$

Solution: In both cases we use the basic formula that

$$\frac{d}{dx}\left(\sin^{-1}(u)\right) = \frac{1}{\sqrt{1 - u^2}} \cdot \frac{du}{dx}.$$

(a) Here $u = 5x$, so

$$\frac{d}{dx}\left(\sin^{-1}(5x)\right) = \frac{1}{\sqrt{1 - (5x)^2}} \cdot \frac{d}{dx}(5x) = \frac{1}{\sqrt{1 - 25x^2}} \cdot 5 = \frac{5}{\sqrt{1 - 25x^2}}.$$

(b) Here $u = \frac{1}{x}$, and so

$$\frac{d}{dx}\left(\sin^{-1}\left(\frac{1}{x}\right)\right) = \frac{1}{\sqrt{1 - \left(\frac{1}{x}\right)^2}} \cdot \frac{d}{dx}\left(\frac{1}{x}\right) = \frac{1}{\sqrt{1 - \frac{1}{x^2}}} \cdot \left(-\frac{1}{x^2}\right)$$

$$= \frac{1}{\sqrt{\frac{x^2-1}{x^2}}} \cdot \left(-\frac{1}{x^2}\right) = \frac{1}{\frac{\sqrt{x^2-1}}{|x|}} \cdot \left(-\frac{1}{x^2}\right)$$

$$= \frac{-|x|}{x^2\sqrt{x^2-1}} = -\frac{1}{|x|\sqrt{x^2-1}} = \frac{d}{dx}\left(\csc^{-1}x\right)$$

This gives us the interesting result that $g(x) = \sin^{-1}(1/x)$ has the same derivative as the inverse cosecant function. Note that these functions have the same domain:

$$S = (-\infty, -1) \cup [1, \infty).$$

In Chapter 3 we will prove a theorem (Theorem 3.5.3) which says that if two functions have the same derivative, then they differ by a constant. Here, this means that there exists a constant C such that

$$\sin^{-1}\left(\frac{1}{x}\right) = \csc^{-1}(x) + C,$$

for all x in S. We can determine the constant C by taking $x = 1$ in the above equation and using $\sin^{-1}(1) = \pi/2$ and $\csc^{-1}(1) = \pi/2$. Thus, $C = 0$. This gives us the identity

$$\sin^{-1}\left(\frac{1}{x}\right) = \csc^{-1}(x).$$

for all x in S.

Example 2.11.7

Problem: Find the derivatives of the following functions

(a) $g(x) = \sec^{-1}(x^2)$ (b) $f(x) = \tan^{-1}\left(\frac{1}{\sqrt{x}}\right).$

Solution:
(a)

$$g'(x) = \frac{d}{dx}\left(\sec^{-1}(x^2)\right) = \frac{1}{|x^2|\sqrt{(x^2)^2 - 1}} \cdot \frac{d}{dx}\left(x^2\right)$$

$$= \frac{1}{x^2\sqrt{x^4 - 1}} \cdot 2x = \frac{2}{x\sqrt{x^4 - 1}}.$$

(b)

$$f'(x) = \frac{d}{dx}\left(\tan^{-1}\left(\frac{1}{\sqrt{x}}\right)\right) = \frac{1}{1 + \left(\frac{1}{\sqrt{x}}\right)^2} \cdot \frac{d}{dx}\left(\frac{1}{\sqrt{x}}\right)$$

$$= \frac{1}{1 + \frac{1}{x}} \cdot \frac{d}{dx}\left(x^{-1/2}\right) = \frac{1}{\frac{x+1}{x}} \cdot \left(-\frac{1}{2}x^{-3/2}\right)$$

$$= \frac{x}{x + 1} \cdot \left(\frac{-1}{2x^{3/2}}\right) = \frac{-1}{2\sqrt{x}(x + 1)}$$

Summary of the Basic Derivatives

As this section ends, we note that you now have derivative formulas for all the "basic" functions in mathematics. (The hyperbolic functions in the next section are important but are not considered basic by many instructors.) These formulas together with all the differentiation rules will allow you to differentiate just about every function that you will encounter in your studies. In particular, it is important to also note that by composing a basic function with another (differentiable) function $u = g(x)$, the result can be differentiated using the chain rule. The following table gives the formulas for the derivatives of such "basic composite functions."

Derivative Rules for the Basic Composite Functions

Suppose $u = g(x)$ is a differentiable function of x. Then, with the domain of u suitably restricted, we have

$$\frac{d}{dx}\left(u^r\right) = r\,u^{r-1}\frac{du}{dx} \qquad \text{for any constant power } r$$

$$\frac{d}{dx}\left(e^u\right) = e^u\frac{du}{dx} \qquad\qquad \frac{d}{dx}\left(\ln u\right) = \frac{1}{u}\frac{du}{dx}$$

$$\frac{d}{dx}\left(\sin u\right) = \cos u \cdot \frac{du}{dx} \qquad\qquad \frac{d}{dx}\left(\cos u\right) = -\sin u \cdot \frac{du}{dx}$$

$$\frac{d}{dx}\left(\tan u\right) = \sec^2 u \cdot \frac{du}{dx} \qquad\qquad \frac{d}{dx}\left(\cot u\right) = -\csc^2 u \cdot \frac{du}{dx}$$

$$\frac{d}{dx}\left(\sec u\right) = \sec u \tan u \cdot \frac{du}{dx} \qquad\qquad \frac{d}{dx}\left(\csc u\right) = -\csc u \cot u \cdot \frac{du}{dx}$$

$$\frac{d}{dx}\left(\sin^{-1}(u)\right) = \frac{1}{\sqrt{1-u^2}} \cdot \frac{du}{dx} \qquad\qquad \frac{d}{dx}\left(\tan^{-1}(u)\right) = \frac{1}{1+u^2} \cdot \frac{du}{dx}$$

$$\frac{d}{dx}\left(\sec^{-1}(u)\right) = \frac{1}{|u|\sqrt{u^2-1}} \cdot \frac{du}{dx}$$

Table 2.11.1

Exercises: 2.11 (Derivatives of Inverse Functions)

```
> with(dplot_tools,plotinverse,dplotinverse);
> with(plots,display);
        [plotinverse,dplotinverse]
                [display]
```

Using `plotinverse` and `dplotinverse`

CAS: In Exercises 1–4, plot the graph of the function f on the given interval. Use this to determine the range $[c,d]$ of f. (a) Then use the command `plotinverse(f,a,b,c,d)` to plot the inverse curve on the interval. Determine a subinterval $[a',b']$ on which f is 1-1. For this you can either use the Horizontal Line Test or determine where the the derivative f' is never zero and use Theorem 2.11.1, Then plot f on this interval and the inverse function f^{-1} on its corresponding interval. Display these in the same figure. Use the dynamic plot command `plotinverse(f,a',b',N,c'd')` to create a movie with N frames showing the function and its inverse being plotting simultaneously.

1. $f(x) = \frac{1}{3}(x^3 - 3x), [-3,3]$
2. $f(x) = x^3 - x, [-1,2]$
3. $f(x) = \frac{1}{5}x^5 - x^3 + 1, [-2,2]$
4. $f(x) = \frac{1}{10}x^6 - x^3, [-1,2]$

Tangent Lines to an Inverse Function

In Exercises 5–18, a function f and a point (x_0, y_0) on its graph are given. (a) Use the Inverse Function Derivative Formula 2.11.5 to find the slope of the tangent line at the point (y_0, x_0) on the graph of the inverse function. Then find an equation for this tangent line. (b) If possible find an explicit formula for the inverse function f^{-1} and use it to (i) compute $(f^{-1})'$ directly, and (ii) compute $(f^{-1})'$ using the Inverse Function Derivative Formula 2.11.5.

5. $f(x) = x^3 + 1, (-1, 0)$ 6. $f(x) = x^5 + 1, (1, 2)$
7. $f(x) = x^3 - x^2 - 4x + 1, (1, -3)$
8. $f(x) = \frac{1}{10}x^6 - x^3, (1, -\frac{9}{10})$
9. $f(x) = \frac{2x}{x-1}, (2, 4)$ 10. $f(x) = \frac{x+2}{x-1}, (0, -2)$
11. $f(x) = \frac{1}{1+x^2}, (1, \frac{1}{2})$ 12. $f(x) = \frac{1}{1+x^3}, (1, \frac{1}{2})$
13. $f(x) = x + \frac{1}{x}, (2, \frac{5}{2})$
14. $f(x) = x - \frac{2}{x}, (1, -1)$
15. $f(x) = 2\ln x + (\ln x)^5, (1, 0)$
16. $f(x) = \ln x - (\ln x)^3, (1, 0)$
17. $f(x) = \frac{1}{1+e^x}, (0, \frac{1}{2})$ 18. $f(x) = \frac{e^{-x}}{1+e^x}, (0, \frac{1}{2})$

Derivatives Involving Inverse Functions

In Exercises 19–66, find the derivative of the function.

19. $y = \sin^{-1}(5x^2)$ 20. $y = \sin^{-1}(3x^4)$
21. $y = \sin^{-1}(x^{-2})$ 22. $y = \sin^{-1}(x^{-3})$
23. $y = \sin^{-1}(\sqrt{x})$ 24. $y = \sin^{-1}(\sqrt{x^3})$
25. $y = \sin^{-1}(\ln x)$ 26. $y = \sin^{-1}(2\ln x)$
27. $y = \tan^{-1}\left(\frac{1}{x}\right)$ 28. $y = \tan^{-1}\left(\frac{2}{x}\right)$
29. $y = \tan^{-1}\left(\frac{1}{x^2}\right)$ 30. $y = \tan^{-1}\left(\frac{2}{x^3}\right)$
31. $y = \tan^{-1}\left(\frac{1}{\sqrt{x}}\right)$ 32. $y = \tan^{-1}\left(\frac{1}{\sqrt{x^3}}\right)$
33. $y = \sec^{-1}(\sqrt{x})$ 34. $y = \sec^{-1}(2\sqrt{x})$
35. $y = \sec^{-1}\left(\frac{1}{\sqrt{x}}\right)$ 36. $y = \sec^{-1}\left(\frac{1}{2\sqrt{x}}\right)$
37. $y = x^2\sin^{-1}(5x)$ 38. $y = x^3\sin^{-1}(5x - 2)$
39. $y = x^{-1}\arctan(2x)$ 40. $y = x^{-2}\arctan(3x)$
41. $y = \arctan^2(2x)$ 42. $y = \arctan^3(3x)$
43. $y = \frac{1}{2}\sin^{-1}x + \frac{1}{2}x\sqrt{1-x^2}$
44. $y = \frac{1}{2}\sin^{-1}x - \frac{1}{2}x\sqrt{1-x^2}$
45. $y = \tan^{-1}(5e^{2x})$ 46. $y = \tan^{-1}(4e^{3x})$
47. $y = \sin^{-1}(2e^{5x})$ 48. $y = \sin^{-1}(3e^{4x})$
49. $y = \sin^{-1}\left(\frac{x}{4}\right)$ 50. $y = \sin^{-1}\left(\frac{x}{3}\right)$
51. $y = \frac{1}{5}\tan^{-1}\left(\frac{x}{5}\right)$ 52. $y = \frac{1}{2}\tan^{-1}\left(\frac{x}{2}\right)$
53. $y = \frac{1}{7}\sec^{-1}\left(\frac{x}{7}\right)$ 54. $y = \frac{1}{4}\sec^{-1}\left(\frac{x}{4}\right)$
55. $y = \sin^{-1}\left(\frac{4}{x}\right)$ 56. $y = \sin^{-1}\left(\frac{3}{x}\right)$
57. $y = \frac{1}{5}\tan^{-1}\left(\frac{5}{x}\right)$ 58. $y = \frac{1}{2}\tan^{-1}\left(\frac{2}{x}\right)$
59. $y = \frac{1}{7}\sec^{-1}\left(\frac{7}{x}\right)$ 60. $y = \frac{1}{4}\sec^{-1}\left(\frac{4}{x}\right)$
61. $y = \sin^{-1}\left(\frac{x}{a}\right)$ 62. $y = \sin^{-1}\left(\frac{x+1}{2}\right)$
63. $y = \frac{1}{a}\tan^{-1}\left(\frac{x}{a}\right)$ 64. $y = \frac{1}{3}\tan^{-1}\left(\frac{x+2}{3}\right)$
65. $y = \frac{1}{a}\sec^{-1}\left(\frac{x}{a}\right)$ 66. $y = \frac{1}{4}\sec^{-1}\left(\frac{x+3}{4}\right)$

Calculus Concepts & Computation

2.12 Hyperbolic Functions

This section is devoted to the study of the hyperbolic functions. These six functions are analogous to the six trigonometric functions: sine, cosine, tangent, cotangent, secant and cosecant. They are named accordingly: *hyperbolic sine, hyperbolic cosine, hyperbolic tangent, hyperbolic cotangent, hyperbolic secant,* and *hyperbolic cosecant.* As could be expected, these new functions are related to the geometry of the hyperbolas, much like the trigonometric functions are connected to the geometry of circles.

The analogies between the hyperbolic and trigonometric functions extend beyond their names. Corresponding to the trig identities that you have learned in trigonometry, you will now encounter hyperbolic identities, which are similar but slightly different than the trig identities. And you will see that the derivatives of the six hyperbolic functions are very similar to the corresponding derivatives of the six trigonometric functions.

Definition of the Hyperbolic Functions

The functional names for the hyperbolic functions are
$$\sinh,\ \cosh,\ \tanh,\ \coth,\ \operatorname{sech},\ \operatorname{csch}$$
and are obtained by appending an h (for hyperbolic) to the name for the corresponding trig function.

The two basic hyperbolic functions, sinh and cosh, are defined, perhaps surprisingly, in terms of the natural exponential function as follows:

DEFINITION 2.12.1 (The Hyperbolic Sine and Cosine)

The hyperbolic sine and cosine functions are defined by

$$\sinh x = \frac{1}{2}\left(e^x - e^{-x}\right) \qquad\qquad (2.12.1)$$

$$\cosh x = \frac{1}{2}\left(e^x + e^{-x}\right) \qquad\qquad (2.12.2)$$

You can view sinh and cosh as an average of the exponential growth/decay functions: $y = e^x$ and $y = e^{-x}$. Knowing the graphs of these latter functions, allows us to use superposition to construct, by hand, the graphs of the sinh and cosh. This is shown in Figure 2.12.1.

From the graphs you can see that the graph of $\sinh x$ asymptotically approaches the graph of $e^x/2$ as $x \to \infty$ and also asymptotically approaches $-e^{-x}/2$ as $x \to -\infty$. For instance, the first assertion is shown by the limit:

$$\lim_{x \to \infty}\left(\frac{1}{2}e^x - \sinh x\right) = \lim_{x \to \infty}\frac{1}{2}e^{-x} = 0.$$

Similar asymptotics apply to the hyperbolic cosine function.

For clarity, we plot the graphs of sinh and cosh without the exponential functions from which they are constructed. This is shown in the Maple plot below.

```
> with(plots,display):
> p1:=plot(sinh(x),x=-2..2,color=blue,thickness=2):
> p2:=plot(cosh(x),x=-2..2,color=green,thickness=2):
> display({p1,p2},scaling=constrained);
```

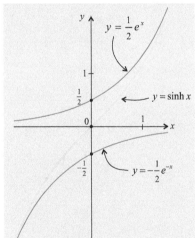

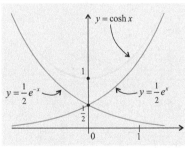

Figure 2.12.1: *Graphs of* sinh *and* cosh *(in blue) constructed from the graphs of* $y = \frac{1}{2}e^x$ *and* $y = \frac{1}{2}e^{-x}$ *(in red).*

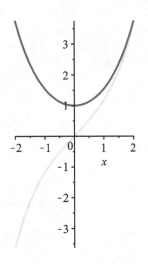

Figure 2.12.2: *Graphs of* sinh *(in turquoise) and* cosh *(in blue).*

Note that the graph of $y = \cosh x$ is very similar to the graph of the parabola $y = x^2 + 1$. Historically, it has been said that Galileo thought the shape of a hanging chain (or necklace) to be that of a parabola, when in fact the shape is that of a hyperbolic cosine. (This was shown to be the case after the invention of the calculus.)

Also note that the graphs of $y = \cosh x$ and $y = \sinh x$ approach each other asymptotically as $x \to \infty$. This is so because $\cosh x - \sinh x = e^{-x}$ and $\lim_{x \to \infty} e^{-x} = 0$.

Having the hyperbolic sine and cosine thus defined, we can now define the other four hyperbolic functions:

$$\tanh, \coth, \operatorname{sech}, \operatorname{csch}$$

in a manner entirely similar to what is done for the trigonometric functions tan, cot, sec, and csc. That is, they are defined in terms of ratios of sinh and cosh.

DEFINITION 2.12.2 (The Other Hyperbolic Functions)

The hyperbolic tangent, cotangent, secant, and cosecant functions are defined by

$$\tanh x = \frac{\sinh x}{\cosh x} = \frac{e^x - e^{-x}}{e^x + e^{-x}} = \frac{e^{2x} - 1}{e^{2x} + 1} \qquad (2.12.3)$$

$$\coth x = \frac{\cosh x}{\sinh x} = \frac{e^x + e^{-x}}{e^x - e^{-x}} = \frac{e^{2x} + 1}{e^{2x} - 1} \qquad (2.12.4)$$

$$\operatorname{sech} x = \frac{1}{\cosh x} = \frac{2}{e^x + e^{-x}} = \frac{2e^x}{e^{2x} + 1} \qquad (2.12.5)$$

$$\operatorname{csch} x = \frac{1}{\sinh x} = \frac{2}{e^x - e^{-x}} = \frac{2e^x}{e^{2x} - 1} \qquad (2.12.6)$$

As you can see, these four hyperbolic functions can also be expressed solely in terms of the natural exponential function. Use of one expression over the other depends on the application you have in mind.

The hyperbolic tangent function is fundamental. It has $\cosh x$ in its denominator, and since this is never zero, $\tanh x$ has no vertical asymptotes (unlike the tangent function $\tan x$. However, $\tanh x$ does have horizontal asymptotes. To find them, take limits at $\pm\infty$:

$$\lim_{x \to \infty} \tanh x = \lim_{x \to \infty} \frac{e^{2x} - 1}{e^{2x} + 1} = \lim_{x \to \infty} \frac{e^{2x} - 1}{e^{2x} + 1} \cdot \frac{e^{-2x}}{e^{-2x}} = \lim_{x \to \infty} \frac{1 - e^{-2x}}{1 + e^{-2x}} = \frac{1 - 0}{1 + 0} = 1$$

and

$$\lim_{x \to -\infty} \tanh x = \lim_{x \to -\infty} \frac{e^{2x} - 1}{e^{2x} + 1} = \frac{0 - 1}{0 + 1} = -1.$$

This shows that $\tanh x$ has two horizontal asymptotes: $y = 1$ and $y = -1$. The graph of tanh is shown in Figure 2.12.3.

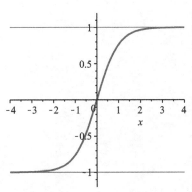

Figure 2.12.3: *Plot of* $y = \tanh x$ *and its asymptotes* $y = \pm 1$.

```
> with(plots,display):
> p1:=plot(tanh(x),x=-5..5,y=-1.2..1.2,color=blue,thickness=2):
> p2:=plot([-1,1],x=-5..5,color=[red,red]):
> display({p1,p2});
>
```

In the exercises you can study the graphs of the other hyperbolic functions and their asymptotics.

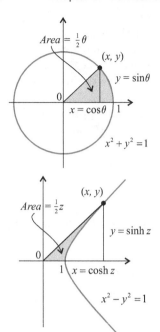

Figure 2.12.4: *The sine and cosine functions are related to the geometry of the unit circle $x^2 + y^2 = 1$. The corresponding hyperbolic functions are related to the geometry of the the unit hyperbola $x^2 - y^2 = 1$.*

Hyperbolic Identities

For every trig identity there is a corresponding hyperbolic identity and, as you will see, the hyperbolic identity is very similar, but slightly different due to the hyperbolic geometry on which it is based. For example, the trig identity

$$\cos^2\theta + \sin^2\theta = 1,$$

for every θ, comes from the geometry of the unit circle $x^2 + y^2 = 1$. This is shown in Figure 2.12.4.

The corresponding hyperbolic identity is

$$\cosh^2 z - \sinh^2 z = 1,$$

for every z. Notice the minus sign in the identity which makes it decidedly different from the related trig identity. This hyperbolic identity follows easily from the definitions of the cosh and sinh and properties of exponential functions. Namely,

$$
\begin{aligned}
\cosh^2 z - \sinh^2 z &= \left[\frac{1}{2}\left(e^z + e^{-z}\right)\right]^2 - \left[\frac{1}{2}\left(e^z - e^{-z}\right)\right]^2 \\
&= \frac{1}{4}\left(e^{2z} + 2 + e^{-2z}\right) - \frac{1}{4}\left(e^{2z} - 2 + e^{-2z}\right) = 1
\end{aligned}
$$

Because of this identity, for each value of z, the point $P = (\cosh z, \sinh z)$ lies on the unit hyperbola: $x^2 - y^2 = 1$, as shown in Figure 2.12.4.

The geometric meaning of the quantity z is that it is twice the area A of the curvilinear segment shown in orange in Figure 2.12.4 (bottom). That is, $z = 2A$. To prove this assertion requires the integral calculus that you will study later. Compare this with the quantity θ which can be interpreted as twice the area A of the circular sector shown in orange in Figure 2.12.4 (top). That is, $\theta = 2A$. To see this note that θ is the length of the arc that bounds the circular sector (since the circle has radius $r = 1$). But the length of the whole circumference is 2π (remember the radius is 1) and the area of the whole circle is π (again the radius is 1). Proportionality gives

$$\frac{A}{\pi} = \frac{\theta}{2\pi} \qquad \text{and so} \qquad 2A = \theta.$$

A few of the other hyperbolic identities are shown in the following table:

Hyperbolic Identities	
(1) $\cosh^2 x - \sinh^2 x = 1$	(2) $1 - \tanh^2 x = \operatorname{sech}^2 x$
(3) $\sinh(x+y) = \sinh x \cosh y + \sinh y \cosh x$	
(4) $\cosh(x+y) = \cosh x \cosh y + \sinh x \sinh y$	
(5) $\sinh 2x = 2 \sinh x \cosh x$	(6) $\cosh 2x = \cosh^2 x + \sinh^2 x$
(7) $\sinh^2 x = -\dfrac{1}{2} + \dfrac{1}{2}\cosh 2x$	(8) $\cosh^2 x = \dfrac{1}{2} + \dfrac{1}{2}\cosh 2x$
(9) $\sinh(-x) = -\sinh x$	(10) $\cosh(-x) = \cosh x$

Table 2.12.1:

You can easily prove these identities using techniques such as those used above in proving Identity (1). The exercises deal with some of these. Note that the Addition Formulas (3)-(4) directly give Formulas (5)-(6) as special cases. Formula (9) says that sinh is an odd function and Formula (10) says that cosh is an even function (as can be discerned from their graphs).

Example 2.12.1 (Proof of a Hyperbolic Identity)

We can prove Formula (3) from Table 2.12.1 by writing out the right-side of the identity in terms of exponential functions and then simplifying to get the left-side of the identity. Here's how the work goes:

$$
\begin{aligned}
\sinh x \cosh y &= \frac{1}{2}\left(e^x - e^{-x}\right) \cdot \frac{1}{2}\left(e^y + e^{-y}\right) \\
&= \frac{1}{4}\left(e^x e^y + e^x e^{-y} - e^{-x} e^y - e^{-x} e^{-y}\right) \\
&= \frac{1}{4}\left(e^{x+y} + e^{x-y} - e^{-x+y} - e^{-(x+y)}\right)
\end{aligned}
$$

and

$$
\begin{aligned}
\sinh y \cosh x &= \frac{1}{2}\left(e^y - e^{-y}\right) \cdot \frac{1}{2}\left(e^x + e^{-x}\right) \\
&= \frac{1}{4}\left(e^y e^x + e^y e^{-x} - e^{-y} e^x - e^{-y} e^{-x}\right) \\
&= \frac{1}{4}\left(e^{x+y} + e^{y-x} - e^{-y+x} - e^{-(x+y)}\right)
\end{aligned}
$$

Thus, adding these gives

$$
\sinh x \cosh y + \sinh y \cos x = \frac{1}{4}\left(2e^{x+y} - 2e^{-(x+y)}\right) = \sinh(x+y).
$$

This proves the identity.

Derivatives of the Hyperbolic Functions

The derivatives of the six hyperbolic functions are easy to calculate using what we know about derivatives of exponential functions and the quotient rule. The following table gives these derivatives, which you should add to your vocabulary of basic derivatives.

Basic Hyperbolic Derivatives	
$\dfrac{d}{dx}\left(\sinh x\right) = \cosh x$	$\dfrac{d}{dx}\left(\cosh x\right) = \sinh x$
$\dfrac{d}{dx}\left(\tanh x\right) = \operatorname{sech}^2 x$	$\dfrac{d}{dx}\left(\coth x\right) = -\operatorname{csch}^2 x$
$\dfrac{d}{dx}\left(\operatorname{sech} x\right) = -\operatorname{sech} x \tanh x$	$\dfrac{d}{dx}\left(\operatorname{csch} x\right) = -\operatorname{csch} x \coth x$

Table 2.12.2: *Hyperbolic Derivatives*

Notice that the derivative of the hyperbolic cosine is the hyperbolic sine (there's no minus sign as with the trigonometric cosine). Likewise, the other hyperbolic derivatives have the same forms (except for the signs) as the corresponding trig derivatives.

Example 2.12.2 (The Derivative of $\sinh x$)

Problem: Verify the formula for the derivative of the hyperbolic sine function.

Solution: We simply write it in terms of exponential functions. That is,

$$
\sinh x = \frac{1}{2}\left(e^x - e^{-x}\right)
$$

and so

$$\frac{d}{dx}\left(\sinh x\right) = \frac{1}{2}\frac{d}{dx}\left(e^x - e^{-x}\right) = \frac{1}{2}\left(e^x - \left(-e^{-x}\right)\right) = \frac{1}{2}\left(e^x + e^{-x}\right) = \cosh x.$$

Example 2.12.3 (The Derivative of $\tanh x$)

Problem: Verify the formula for the derivative of the hyperbolic tangent.

Problem: We use the quotient rule and the formulas for the derivatives of sinh and cosh. We will also need the hyperbolic identity $\cosh^2 x - \sinh^2 x = 1$. The calculation is

$$
\begin{aligned}
\frac{d}{dx}\left(\tanh x\right) &= \frac{d}{dx}\left(\frac{\sinh x}{\cosh x}\right) = \frac{\frac{d}{dx}\left(\sinh x\right)\cdot \cosh x - \sinh x \cdot \frac{d}{dx}\left(\cosh x\right)}{\cosh^2 x} \\[2mm]
&= \frac{\cosh x \cdot \cosh x - \sinh x \cdot \sinh x}{\cosh^2 x} = \frac{\cosh^2 x - \sinh^2 x}{\cosh^2 x} \\[2mm]
&= \frac{1}{\cosh^2 x} = \operatorname{sech}^2 x.
\end{aligned}
$$

Once you learn the basic derivatives, you can differentiate more complicated functions involving the hyperbolic functions, as the following example illustrates.

Example 2.12.4 (Derivatives of Expressions with Hyperbolic Functions)

Problem: Find the derivative of the function $y = \sinh 5x\sqrt{\cosh x}$.

Solution: Use the product rule first and then the chain rule on each part.

$$
\begin{aligned}
\frac{dy}{dx} &= \frac{d}{dx}\left(\sinh 5x\sqrt{\cosh x}\right) \\[2mm]
&= \frac{d}{dx}\left(\sinh 5x\right)\cdot \sqrt{\cosh x} + \sinh 5x \cdot \frac{d}{dx}\left(\sqrt{\cosh x}\right) \\[2mm]
&= 5\cosh 5x \cdot \sqrt{\cosh x} + \sinh 5x \cdot \frac{\sinh x}{2\sqrt{\cosh x}} \\[2mm]
&= \frac{10\cosh 5x\cosh x + \sinh 5x\sinh x}{2\sqrt{\cosh x}}
\end{aligned}
$$

Example 2.12.5 (2nd Derivatives)

Problem: Find the second derivatives of sinh and cosh. Comment on the results

Solution: If $y = \sinh x$, then $y' = \cosh x$. Differentiating this gives $y'' = \sinh x$. This says that the sinh is equal to its second derivative:

$$y'' = y.$$

Similarly, you can see that cosh is also equal to its second derivative, i.e., $y = \cosh x$ satisfies the differential equation $y'' = y$. There are other functions that have this property of having its second derivative equal to itself, but sinh and cosh are two of the basic ones. Indeed, using these two basic ones, we see that for any two constants A, B, the function

$$y = A\sinh x + B\cosh x$$

satisfies the differential equation $y'' = y$. Conversely, one can show that any function y that satisfies $y'' = y$, is expressible in the above form for some choice of constants A, B. For example, it's easy to see that the natural exponential function $y = e^x$ satisfies $y'' = y$. In this case the constants are $A = 1, B = 1$.

Inverse Hyperbolic Functions

All six hyperbolic functions have inverse functions (with appropriate restrictions on their domains). We limit the discussion here to just the three: sinh, cosh, and tanh. Both sinh and tanh are 1-1 functions on their entire domains (which is $(-\infty, \infty)$ in each case). On the otherhand, cosh is 1-1 if we restrict it to the interval $[0, \infty)$ (which is the convention). The inverse functions are typically denoted by

$$y = \sinh^{-1} x, \ y = \cosh^{-1} x, \ y = \tanh^{-1} x$$

Maple uses

$$\texttt{arcsinh, arccosh, arctanh}$$

for these functions, even though the prefix "arc" only makes sense for inverse trig functions.

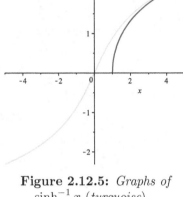

Figure 2.12.5: *Graphs of* $\sinh^{-1} x$ *(turquoise) and* $\cosh^{-1} x$ *(blue).*

The graphs of these three inverse hyperbolic functions can easily be sketched from the graphs shown above for the respective function (flip it about the 45 degree line). Alternatively you can use Maple as follows:

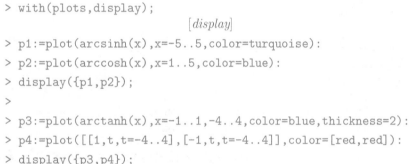

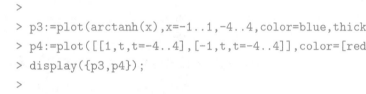

This gives the results shown in Figures 2.12.5–2.12.6.

To find the derivative function for one of the inverse hyperbolic functions, we can either use the general Formula (2.11.5) from Section 2.11, or implicit differentiation. The latter approach, applied to $\sinh^{-1}$, goes as follows. Let $y = \sinh^{-1} x$. Then $\sinh y = x$. To find dy/dx, we differentiate $\sinh y = x$ implicitly:

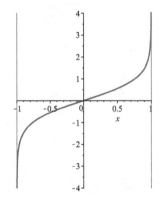

Figure 2.12.6: *Graph of* $\tanh^{-1} x$ *and its asymptotes.*

$$\frac{d}{dx}(\sinh y) = \frac{d}{dx}(x),$$

or

$$\cosh y \cdot \frac{dy}{dx} = 1.$$

So

$$\frac{dy}{dx} = \frac{1}{\cosh y}.$$

Now rewrite $\cosh y$ in terms of x. We have $\sinh y = x$, and from one of the hyperbolic identities

$$\cosh^2 y = 1 + \sinh^2 y = 1 + x^2.$$

Thus, $\cosh y = \sqrt{1 + x^2}$ and this then gives

$$\frac{dy}{dx} = \frac{1}{\sqrt{1 + x^2}}.$$

Inverse Hyperbolic Derivatives

$$\frac{d}{dx}\left(\sinh^{-1}x\right) = \frac{1}{\sqrt{x^2+1}}$$

$$\frac{d}{dx}\left(\cosh^{-1}x\right) = \frac{1}{\sqrt{x^2-1}}$$

$$\frac{d}{dx}\left(\tanh^{-1}x\right) = \frac{1}{1-x^2}$$

Table 2.12.3: *Derivatives of the inverse hyperbolic functions.*

Inverse Hyperbolic Identities

(1) $\sinh^{-1}x = \ln\left(x+\sqrt{x^2+1}\right)$

(2) $\cosh^{-1}x = \ln\left(x+\sqrt{x^2-1}\right)$

(3) $\tanh^{-1}x = \frac{1}{2}\ln\left(\frac{1+x}{1-x}\right)$

Table 2.12.4: *Inverse hyperbolic identities.*

The other derivatives can be found in a similar fashion. The results are recorded in Table 2.12.3.

One other interesting aspect of the inverse hyperbolic functions is that each of them can be expressed in terms of the natural log function. This should not be too surprising since each hyperbolic function can be expressed in terms of the natural exponential function, the inverse of which is the natural log function. Using basic algebra (and the quadratic formula) one can find the expressions for $\sinh^{-1}$, $\cosh^{-1}x$, and $\tanh^{-1}x$. These are shown in Table 2.12.4. Note: In the table, (1) is for any x, (2) is only for $x \geq 1$, and (3) is for $-1 < x < 1$.

To verify expression (3), we proceed as follows. First, if $y = \tanh^{-1}x$, then $\tanh y = x$. Then write this latter equation in terms of natural exponentials:

$$\frac{e^{2y}-1}{e^{2y}+1} = x.$$

Next, solve for y:

$$e^{2y}-1 = xe^{2y}+x,$$

or

$$e^{2y}(1-x) = 1+x.$$

So

$$e^{2y} = \frac{1+x}{1-x}.$$

Taking the natural log of each side, using $\ln(e^y) = y$, and dividing the result by 2, gives

$$y = \frac{1}{2}\ln\left(\frac{1+x}{1-x}\right).$$

This is the expression in the table for $y = \tanh^{-1}x$. It is left to the exercises to verify expressions (1)-(2).

Example 2.12.6 (Derivatives of Inverse Hyperbolic Functions)

Problem: Find the derivative of $y = \tanh^{-1}(\sin x)$.

Solution: Using the chain rule we get

$$\begin{aligned}
\frac{dy}{dx} &= \frac{d}{dx}\left(\tanh^{-1}(\sin x)\right) = \frac{1}{1-\sin^2 x} \cdot \frac{d}{dx}(\sin x) \\[2mm]
&= \frac{1}{1-\sin^2 x} \cdot \cos x = \frac{\cos x}{1-\sin^2 x} = \frac{\cos x}{\cos^2 x} \\[2mm]
&= \sec x
\end{aligned}$$

This is an interesting result. It gives us a function whose derivative is the secant function. Previously we found the function $y = \ln(\sec x + \tan x)$ also has its derivative equal to the secant function. It is an exercise to show that these two function are the same.

Exercises: 2.12 (Hyperbolic Functions)

Derivatives Involving Hyperbolic Functions

In Exercises 1–56, find the derivative of the function.

1. $f(x) = \sinh(\sqrt{x})$ **2.** $f(x) = \cosh(x^2 - x)$

3. $f(x) = \sinh 5x \cos 3x$ **4.** $f(x) = \cosh 2x \sin 4x$

5. $f(x) = \cosh^2 x \sin^3 5x$ **6.** $f(x) = \sinh^2 x \cos^3 4x$

7. $f(x) = e^x \sinh(e^{-x})$ **8.** $f(x) = e^{-5x} \cosh(e^{5x})$

9. $f(x) = e^{2x} \operatorname{sech}(e^{-2x})$ **10.** $f(x) = e^{3x} \operatorname{sech}(e^{-3x})$

11. $f(x) = x^2 e^{\sinh 5x}$ **12.** $f(x) = x^2 e^{\cosh 5x}$

13. $f(x) = x^2 \sinh(3x)$ **14.** $f(x) = x^2 \cosh(3x)$

15. $f(x) = \operatorname{sech}2x \sec 2x$ **16.** $f(x) = \operatorname{sech}5x \sec 2x$

17. $f(x) = \operatorname{sech}(\sec 2x)$ **18.** $f(x) = \operatorname{sech}(\sec 5x)$

19. $f(x) = \tanh^2(x^3)$ **20.** $f(x) = \tanh^3(x^2)$

21. $f(x) = \operatorname{sech}^2 x \tanh^2 x$ **22.** $f(x) = \operatorname{sech}^3 x \tanh^3 x$

23. $f(x) = \ln(\operatorname{sech}x + \tanh x)$

24. $f(x) = \ln(\operatorname{sech}x - \tanh x)$

25. $f(x) = \ln(\cosh x)$ **26.** $f(x) = \ln(\cosh 2x)$

27. $f(x) = \ln(\sinh x)$ **28.** $f(x) = \ln(\sinh 2x)$

29. $f(x) = \ln(\operatorname{sech}x)$ **30.** $f(x) = \ln(\operatorname{sech}2x)$

31. $f(x) = \ln(\operatorname{csch}x)$ **32.** $f(x) = \ln(\operatorname{csch}2x)$

33. $f(x) = \ln(\tanh x)$ **34.** $f(x) = \ln(\coth x)$

35. $f(x) = \sinh(\ln x)$ **36.** $f(x) = \cosh(\ln x)$

37. $f(x) = \dfrac{\sinh x}{\sinh x + 1}$ **38.** $f(x) = \dfrac{\cosh x}{\cosh x + 1}$

39. $f(x) = \dfrac{\sinh x}{\cosh x + 1}$ **40.** $f(x) = \dfrac{\cosh x}{\sinh x + 1}$

41. $f(x) = \dfrac{\tanh x}{\tanh x + 1}$ **42.** $f(x) = \dfrac{\tanh x}{\tanh x - 1}$

43. $f(x) = \dfrac{\operatorname{sech}x}{\operatorname{sech}x + 1}$ **44.** $f(x) = \dfrac{\operatorname{csch}x}{\operatorname{csch}x - 1}$

45. $f(x) = \sinh^{-1}(\sqrt{x})$ **46.** $f(x) = \sinh^{-1}(2\sqrt{x})$

47. $f(x) = \cosh^{-1}(x^{-1})$ **48.** $f(x) = \cosh^{-1}(3x^{-1})$

49. $f(x) = \cosh^{-1}(x + 6)$ **50.** $f(x) = \cosh^{-1}(x - 5)$

51. $f(x) = \tanh^{-1}(\sqrt{x})$ **52.** $f(x) = \tanh^{-1}(3\sqrt{x})$

53. $f(x) = \tanh^{-1}(x^{-1})$ **54.** $f(x) = \tanh^{-1}(2x^{-1})$

55. $f(x) = \tanh^{-1}(x - 2)$ **56.** $f(x) = \tanh^{-1}(x + 3)$

Asymptotes of Hyperbolic Functions

In Exercises 57–60, do the following: (a) Find all vertical and horizontal asymptotes of the given hyperbolic function. (b) Determine if the hyperbolic function is even, odd, or neither. **CAS:** (c) Use Maple to plot the given hyperbolic function along with the given function g and comment on the similarities in the two graphs.

57. $f(x) = \operatorname{sech}x$, $g(x) = \dfrac{1}{x^2 + 1}$

58. $f(x) = \operatorname{csch}x$, $g(x) = \dfrac{1}{x}$

59. $f(x) = \coth x$, $g(x) = \dfrac{|x|}{x} + \dfrac{1}{x}$

60. $f(x) = e^{-x}\operatorname{sech}x$, $g(x) = 1 - \dfrac{x}{|x| + 1}$

Proving Hyperbolic Identities

In Exercises 61–70, prove the hyperbolic identity.

61. $\sinh(-x) = \sinh x$ **62.** $\cosh(-x) = \cosh x$

63. $\sinh 2x = 2\sinh x \cosh x$

64. $\cosh(x + y) = \cosh x \cosh y + \sinh x \sinh y$

65. $\sinh^2 x = -\frac{1}{2} + \frac{1}{2}\cosh 2x$

66. $\cosh^2 x = \frac{1}{2} + \frac{1}{2}\cosh 2x$

67. $1 - \tanh^2 x = \operatorname{sech}^2 x$ **68.** $\coth^2 x - 1 = \operatorname{csch}^2 x$

69. $\sinh(\ln x) = \dfrac{x^2 - 1}{2x}$ **70.** $\tanh(\ln x) = \dfrac{x^2 - 1}{x^2 + 1}$

Catenaries

The shape assumed by vertically hanging cables and chains (suspended from their endpoints held at equal heights) is called a *catenary*. The word comes from the latin word for chain. From the laws of physics one can show that a catenary's shape coincides with the graph of a hyperbolic cosine function:

$$y = f(x) = a\cosh\left(\frac{x}{a}\right) + c,$$

for x in $[-b, b]$, the constants a, c depending on the setup of the catenary and $2b$ is the distance between its endpoints.

71. A power line is to be suspended between two towers space 200 ft apart with the low point of the cable 30 ft above the ground.

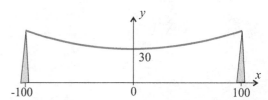

Figure 2.12.1x: *An electric power cable.*

Assuming the cable's shape is the graph of

$$y = f(x) = 300\cosh\left(\frac{x}{300}\right) - 270,$$

find (a) The height of the towers, (b) the amount of sag in the cable, and (c) the slope of the cable where it meets the right tower.

Calculus Concepts & Computation

2.13 Related Rates

```
> with(code_ch2sec13)
```

[cone, conical_tank, conical_tank2, disk, display, display3d, ellipticArc,
paintspill, polygon, rising_balloon, separating_cars, sliding_ladder]

In just about every quantitative field of study, such as the sciences, engineering, business, medicine, and economics, to name a few, there are quantities of interest that change over time. Often two (or more) of these quantities, call them A and B, are related to each other by some equation, and in this case their time rates of change $\frac{dA}{dt}$, $\frac{dB}{dt}$ are connected with each other through a derived equation. So changes in A are related to changes in B, and this gives rise to a relation between their rates.

In this section we study some simple situations of this. The quantities A and B that are changing with time t are usually not given explicitly as functions of t. However, by analyzing the situation and using a little geometry, we can find an equation involving A and B. Then differentiating this equation with respect to t (using the chain rule or implicit differentiation) gives an equation relating their rates. With the given information about one of the rates and values of the quantities, we can determine the other rate.

Before formulating a general strategy for solving related rates problems, we look at a particular example to see what's involved.

Example 2.13.1 (A Circular Paint Spill)

Paint is spilling from an over-turned five gallon bucket onto your concrete driveway and forming an expanding circular puddle with thickness of 1/10 th of an inch at all times. See Figure 2.13.1.

Suppose the paint is flowing from bucket at the rate of 27 cubic inches per second. Study the following animation which shows the expanding circular puddle. Then find the rate at which the radius of the circular puddle is changing when the radius is 40 inches. Comment on whether this rate is increasing or decreasing and give reasons why this is so.

Execute the next command to generate the animation of the paint spill. (It starts at time $t = 1$ second and has 20 frames spaced 1 second apart. So you may want to view the animation at a frame rate of 1 fps.)

```
> paintspill(27,.1,20);
```

We see that the radius is changing more slowly as the spill expands. We will comment on this further below. Figure 2.13.2 shows the circular spill at about the time when the radius is about 41.5 inches

Now let's analyze the situation and set up some notation. First observe that the puddle at all times forms the shape of a cylinder with constant height $h = 1/10$ and circular base with increasing radius r. If we let V denote the volume of this cylinder (i.e., the paint spill), then r and V are the two quantities that are changing with time. The problem then is

GIVEN: $\dfrac{dV}{dt} = 27\,\mathrm{in}^3/\mathrm{s}$ (a constant rate). FIND: $\dfrac{dr}{dt}$, when $r = 40$ in.

To solve the problem, we need an equation relating r and V. A standard result from geometry is that the volume of a cylinder is equal to the area of the base times the height: $V = \pi r^2 h$. So in our case, the relation (or equation) between V and r

Figure 2.13.1: *A paint spill with expanding radius r and constant thickness h.*

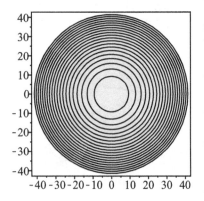

Figure 2.13.2: *The last frame in the paint spill movie.*

is
$$V = \frac{\pi}{10}r^2.$$

Remember that both r and V are functions of t, but neither is given explicitly as a function of t. However, we can still differentiate both sides of the above equation with respect to t. Using the chain rule on $\frac{d}{dt}\left(r^2\right) = 2r\frac{dr}{dt}$, this gives

$$\frac{dV}{dt} = \frac{\pi}{5} \cdot r\frac{dr}{dt}.$$

Now, the rate of change of volume is constant, so the above specializes to

$$27 = \frac{\pi}{5} \cdot r\frac{dr}{dt}. \qquad (2.13.1) \qquad\qquad (2.3)$$

This simple relation between the two rates holds for all times, and in particular at the time when $r = 40$, we get

$$27 = \frac{\pi}{5} \cdot 40 \cdot \left.\frac{dr}{dt}\right|_{r=40}.$$

Thus

$$\left.\frac{dr}{dt}\right|_{r=40} = \frac{27}{8\pi} \approx 1.074 \text{ in/s}.$$

For comparison, let's compute the rate of change of r when $r = 9$ (that's when the spill is about the size shown in the first frame of the movie). Substituting $r = 9$ into Eq. (2.13.1) and rearranging gives

$$\left.\frac{dr}{dt}\right|_{r=9} = \frac{15}{\pi} \approx 4.775 \text{ in/s}.$$

So, as we found in viewing the movie, the rate of change of the radius is larger at the beginning and lesser as time goes on. We can make this more precise by rearranging Eq. (2.13.1) as follows:

$$\frac{dr}{dt} = \frac{135}{\pi} \cdot \frac{1}{r}.$$

This says $\frac{dr}{dt}$ decreases in proportion to $\frac{1}{r}$. One qualitative way to explain why the rate $\frac{dr}{dt}$ decreases over time is as follows. Note that the rate of change of volume is constant and so, since the thickness of the spill is constant, the rate of change of the area covered by the spill is constant. In going from any moment to the next the same amount of new area is added to the spill, like a new ring in its growth. (See Figure 2.13.2.)

There are a few general steps that can help you tackle related rates problems and solve them. These are shown in the table below. By following this format and by gaining experience from working a lot of exercises, you should be successful in mastering this aspect of calculus.

Guidelines for Related Rates

1. Identify and assign letters to the quantities that vary with time, such as V for volume, A for area, h for height, and r for radius. Draw a figure showing the quantities at one instant in time.

2. Write down the given rate (or rates) and the given value (or values) of the quantities at the time of interest. Identify which rate you are looking for.

3. Find (usually using elementary geometry) an equation that relates the quantity whose rate you are seeking to the other quantities. In this equation eliminate (using algebra or geometry) any quantities not directly involved

4. Find an equation that relates the rates by differentiating, with respect to time, the equation you found in Step 3. For this use implicit differentiation and the chain rule.

5. Substitute the given rate (or rates) and values in the related rates equation you found in Step 4. Solve the resulting equation for the unknown rate. Discuss, if instructed to, how the unknown rate varies with time (increases/decreases).

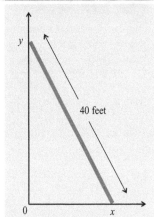

Figure 2.13.3: *A ladder leaning against a wall.*

Example 2.13.2 (A Sliding Ladder)

A forty foot ladder leans against the wall at an angle and begins slipping, with its bottom end sliding across the ground, away from the wall, at 2 ft/s. See Figure 2.13.3. Determine how fast the top of the ladder is sliding down the wall when the top is 10 feet from the ground. Also, comment on whether this speed is greater or lesser, the closer the ladder gets to the ground and give reasons why this is so.

Execute the following command to see a movie of the sliding ladder:

```
> sliding_ladder(40,2,30,0);
```

The movie has 30 frames and the ladder hits the ground in the last frame. The following command gives a movie with each frame showing all the preceding positions of the ladder (its tracks).

```
> sliding_ladder(40,2,30,1);
```

Figure 2.13.4 shows the 29th frame of the above movie (right before it his the ground).

Note: If you look closely at the movie, you can determine that the frames are 1/2 second apart (based on the fact that the bottom end of the ladder moves 2 feet every second. So there's 1 frame every 1/2 second, or 2 frames per second (fps). You should view the movie at that frame rate.

The movie clearly shows that the speed of the top of the ladder is small at the beginning and becomes quite large right before it hits the ground. Figure 2.13.4 also shows this—look at the distance the top end moves between one position and the next. We will see why the speed of the top of the ladder increases, after we answer the basic question.

To answer the basic question, we set up some notation. We position a coordinate system with the x-axis along the ground and y-axis along the wall, placing the origin at the corner. Let x denote the position of the bottom end of the ladder at time t and y the position of the top end at time t. Then the velocities of the two ends of the latter are $\frac{dx}{dt}$ and $\frac{dy}{dt}$. In terms of this notation, the problem is phrased like this:

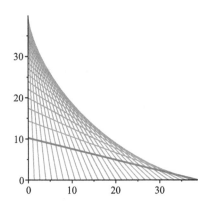

Figure 2.13.4: *The successive positions of the ladder as it slides toward the floor.*

GIVEN: $\frac{dx}{dt} = 2$ ft/s. FIND: $\frac{dy}{dt}$, when $y = 10$ ft.

To get an equation that relates x and y, note that at each time during its fall, the 40 foot ladder forms the hypotenuse of a right triangle with x and y being the lengths of the sides about the right angle. Thus, by the Pythagorean theorem:

$$x^2 + y^2 = 1600. \qquad (2.13.2) \qquad\qquad (2.4)$$

This is the equation relating the quantities x and y. To get an equation relating their rates, we differentiate both sides with respect to t:

$$2x\frac{dx}{dt} + 2y\frac{dy}{dt} = 0,$$

or, dividing the 2 out and substituting in the constant $\frac{dx}{dt} = 2$ ft/s rate,

$$2x + y\frac{dy}{dt} = 0. \qquad (2.13.3) \qquad\qquad (2.5)$$

Now at the time when $y = 10$, the x position is

$$x = \sqrt{1600 - 100} = \sqrt{1500} = 10\sqrt{15} \approx 38.7.$$

(Use Eq. (2.13.2) to get this.) Substituting these values for x and y into Eq. (2.13.3) gives

$$20\sqrt{15} + 10\frac{dy}{dt} = 0.$$

So when $y = 10$,

$$\frac{dy}{dt} = -2\sqrt{15} \approx -7.75 \text{ ft/s}.$$

This answers the basic question. To get a precise statement about the speed of the top end of the ladder as it approaches the ground, we rearrange Eq. (2.13.3):

$$\frac{dy}{dt} = -\frac{2x}{y}.$$

This clearly shows that the speed: $\left|\frac{dy}{dt}\right| = \frac{2x}{y}$ is increasing since, as time goes on, x increases (toward position 40) and y decreases (toward position 0) and so $\frac{1}{y}$ goes to infinity. Note that the top end hits the ground with infinite speed at time $t = 20$.

Example 2.13.3 (Filling A Tank)

An inverted conical tank is being filled with water at the rate of 8 m^3/s. The tank has a height of 12 meters and the radius of its circular base is 6 meters. Find the rate at which the water level is rising when the water level is 7 meters high (measured from the vertex). Discuss how the rate of change of the water level slows down over time and why. Figure 2.13.5 shows the basic geometry for the problem.

View a movie of the tank being filled by executing the following command:

```
> conical_tank(6,12,8,50,25);
```

See Figure 2.13.6. You should slow the frame rate down to 2 fpm and watch the movie several times. Note how, as time goes on, the water level rises more slowly in the tank. We will quantify this below.

To get a better view of how the water level changes over time, view the following movie which shows a planar cross-section through the tank.

```
> conical_tank2(6,12,8,50,25);
```

Figure 2.13.7 shows the last frame in the above movie.

To analyze the problem, we let h denote the height of the water in the tank at time t, and r the radius of the circular water surface at that time. Also let V designate the volume of the water in the tank at time t. Then, we are

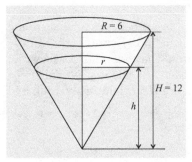

Figure 2.13.5: *Filling an inverted conical tank of height 12 m and base radius 6 m.*

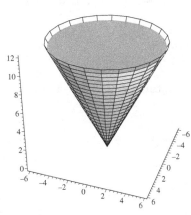

Figure 2.13.6: *The last frame in the conical tank movie*

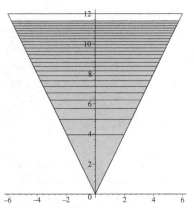

Figure 2.13.7: *The water levels in the conical tank.*

GIVEN: $\dfrac{dV}{dt} = 8$, and we must FIND: $\dfrac{dh}{dt}$, when $h = 7$.

To get a relation between the quantities V, r, and h, we use the well-known formula for the volume of a cone:

$$V = \frac{1}{3}\pi r^2 h. \qquad (2.13.4) \qquad\qquad (2.6)$$

Note that this problem is slightly different than the two others, because there are three quantities that vary with time in the above equation. However, we can use elementary geometry to eliminate the quantity r from the equation. As shown in the Figure 2.13.5 above, the h and r are sides of a right triangle that is similar the right triangle with sides $H = 12$ and $R = 6$, which are the height of the tank and the radius of its base. By similar triangles

$$\frac{r}{h} = \frac{6}{12}, \quad \text{or} \quad r = \frac{1}{2}h.$$

Substituting this for r in Eq. (2.13.4) gives

$$V = \frac{\pi}{12}h^3.$$

Now we differentiate both sides of this equation with respect to t and get the following relation between the rates:

$$\frac{dV}{dt} = \frac{\pi}{12} \cdot 3h^2 \frac{dh}{dt} = \frac{\pi h^2}{4}\frac{dh}{dt}.$$

Since the water flows in at the constant rate of 8 m^3/s, this equation specializes to

$$8 = \frac{\pi h^2}{4}\frac{dh}{dt}. \qquad (2.13.5) \qquad\qquad (2.7)$$

At the time when $h = 7$, this equation gives

$$8 = \frac{\pi(7)^2}{4}\frac{dh}{dt}$$

or

$$\frac{dh}{dt} = \frac{32}{49\pi} \approx 0.208 \text{ m/s}.$$

More generally, from Eq. (2.13.5) we get

$$\frac{dh}{dt} = \frac{32}{\pi h^2},$$

which says the rate of change of water level goes as the inverse square of the water level. Thus, the higher the water level, the slower its rate of change. This makes sense if we consider that each second, 8 cubic meters of water volume is added to the tank. But for large h, most of this volume is spread out over a large circular area. The above movies show this clearly.

Example 2.13.4 (A Rising Balloon)

Your friend, standing 40 meters away in the gondelier of a hot-air balloon launches the balloon and it proceeds to rise vertically at a constant rate of 3 meters per second. You track your friend using binoculars, which are initially horizontal since you are both the same height. How fast is the angle between the binoculars and the horizontal changing when the balloon is 30 meters above your eye-level. Discuss how the rate of change of the angle changes over time.

EPG EuroPhotoGraphics/Shutterstock.com

Figure 2.13.8: *tracking a rising balloon.*

Figure 2.13.8 shows the situation at one instant in time. Notice that we have chosen a coordinate system with origin at the binoculars and x-axis horizontal. A movie of the rising balloon is created by the following command:

```
> rising_balloon(40,3,20,10,lastframe);
```

The movie consists of 10 frames shot over a 20 second time interval. Figure 2.13.9 shows the last frame in the movie.

Viewing the movie and studying the composite figure above shows that the angle is changing more slowly as time goes on. If we let θ denote the angle (in radians) the binoculars make with the horizontal, then $s = 20\theta$ is the length of the arc of the circle shown in red in the movie. By viewing the movie, you will see that the increments $\Delta s = 20\Delta\theta$ to the arcs get smaller and smaller, and thus, so do the corresponding changes $\Delta\theta$ in the angle. By comparison, the increments Δy in the height are all the same: $\Delta y = 3\Delta t = 3(2) = 6$ meters, in going from one frame to the next. (The balloon rises 6 meters every 2 seconds.) To start the analysis, let y denote the height of the balloon above eye-level. Then the problem is:

GIVEN: $\dfrac{dy}{dt} = 3$ m/s. FIND: $\dfrac{d\theta}{dt}$, when $y = 30$ m.

To find an equation connecting y and θ we note that, at each time, the line of sight is the hypotenuse of a right triangle with legs 40 and y. Thus, by trigonometry

$$\tan\theta = \frac{y}{40}.$$

Differentiating both sides with respect to t gives:

$$\sec^2\theta \cdot \frac{d\theta}{dt} = \frac{1}{40}\frac{dy}{dt} = \frac{3}{40},$$

Solving for the angle rate gives

$$\frac{d\theta}{dt} = \frac{3}{40}\cos^2\theta.$$

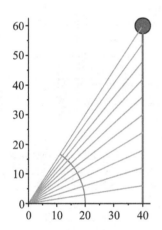

Figure 2.13.9: *Ten lines of sight from the binoculars to balloon over a 20 second interval as the balloon rises.*

To determine the value of this rate when $y = 30$, we need the value of $\cos\theta$. But $x = 40$ (in all the triangles) and when $y = 30$, the triangle has hypotenuse $\sqrt{x^2 + y^2} = \sqrt{(40)^2 + (30)^2} = \sqrt{2500} = 50$. (The triangle is similar to a 3-4-5 right triangle.) Thus, we have $\cos\theta = 40/50 = 4/5$, and so

$$\frac{d\theta}{dt}\bigg|_{y=30} = \frac{3}{40}\cos^2\theta = \frac{3}{40}\left(\frac{4}{5}\right)^2 = \frac{6}{125} \text{ rad/s}$$

This answers the basic question. A discussion of how $d\theta/dt$ varies as time goes on is easy using the equation we found:

$$\frac{d\theta}{dt} = \frac{3}{40}\cos^2\theta.$$

As time goes by, the angle θ increases from 0 initially, going toward $\pi/2$ as the balloon rises to infinity. But, by the above equation, the rate of change of the angle $d\theta/dt$ decreases as θ increases (since $\cos\theta$ decreases as the balloon rises and, of course, $\cos^2\theta$ decreases even more rapidly). A plot of $f(\theta) = 3(\cos^2\theta)/40$, exhibits this more precisely. Use the following code to get Figure 2.13.10.

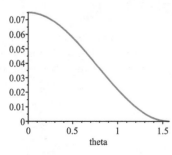

Figure 2.13.10: *Plot of the angular rate of change $\frac{d\theta}{dt}$.*

```
> f:=theta->3*(cos(theta))^2/40
```

$$f := x \rightarrow \frac{3}{40}\cos(\theta)^2$$

```
> plot(f(theta),theta=0..Pi/2,thickness=2);
```

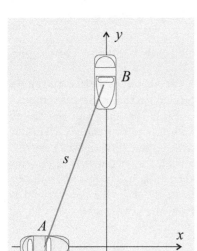

Figure 2.13.11: *Two cars headed for the same intersection.*

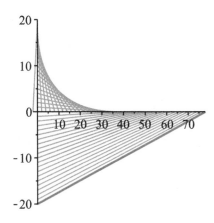

Figure 2.13.12: *The brown lines connect the positions of cars A and B at successive times during their trips.*

xx

Example 2.13.5 (Separating Cars)

Two cars, A and B, are approaching an intersection, car A traveling east at 80 miles per hour and car B traveling south at 40 miles per hour. Initially the car A is 2 miles west of the intersection and car B is 20 miles north of the intersection. They each pass through the intersection and continue on their way. Their separation at any time is the (straight line) distance $s = \overline{AB}$ between them.

Figure 2.13.11 shows the situation at one instant in time. Notice that we have chosen a coordinate system with origin at the intersection, so x will represent the position of car A and y the position of car B.

The related rates problem is this: Find the rate at which the cars are separating when car A is 18 miles east of the intersection and car B is 10 miles north of the intersection.

A movie of the cars approaching an passing through the intersection is created by the following command. Study it to get a feel for how the separation s changes over time.

```
> separating_cars(-2,20,80,-40,1,40);
```

The movie represents a real-time duration of one hour and consists of 41 frames, the first is time zero and the rest are spaced at 40 equal time intervals apart (so there is 1.5 minutes between frames). Of course you cannot slow the animation down to this rate (and would not want to spend an hour watching it if you could). If you click through it frame-by-frame, the 10th click shows car A at $x = 18$ and car B at $y = 10$.

Execute the following command to get a movie where each frame shows the separation line (in red) and all the previous separation lines (in brown).

```
> separating_cars(-2,20,80,-40,1,40,lastframe);
```

Figure 2.13.12 shows the last frame in the above movie.

In studying the movie and the above figure, you should note that the positions x and y can have positive and negative values, depending upon the time. The rates, or velocities are constant, but the velocity of car A is positive (80 mph), while the velocity of car B is negative (-40 mph). CAUTION: In these types of problems it is important to get the sign of the rates right. The stated 40 mph for car B is the speed of the car, not its velocity. In summary, the problem is

GIVEN: $\dfrac{dx}{dt} = 80,\quad \dfrac{dy}{dt} = -40$. FIND: $\dfrac{ds}{dt}$, when $x = 18$ and $y = 10$.

To solve the problem, note that in this problem we have three quantities that vary with time: the positions x, y of cars A, B, and their distance s apart. The positions are more precisely specified as being at points $(x, 0)$ and $(0, y)$ respectively. So, by the distance formula, the distance apart is

$$s = \sqrt{(x-0)^2 + (0-y)^2} = \sqrt{x^2 + y^2}.$$

(Alternatively, you could use the Pythagorean theorem to get the same thing.) While the above equation does give a relation among the variables, x, y, and s, it will not be a convenient equation to differentiate. However, squaring both sides of the equation gives

$$s^2 = x^2 + y^2,$$

which is easy to differentiate. Doing so, gives

$$2s\frac{ds}{dt} = 2x\frac{dx}{dt} + 2y\frac{dy}{dt}.$$

Dividing the $2s$ out, gives the related rate equation

$$s\frac{ds}{dt} = x\frac{dx}{dt} + y\frac{dy}{dt}.$$

At the time when $x = 18$ and $y = 10$, we calculate that $s = \sqrt{(18)^2 + (10)^2} = \sqrt{324 + 100} = \sqrt{424} = 2\sqrt{106}$. Substituting these values for x, y, s, along with the given rates into the above equation gives

$$2\sqrt{106} \cdot \frac{ds}{dt} = 18(80) + 10(-40) = 1040$$

or

$$\frac{ds}{dt} = \frac{520}{\sqrt{106}} \approx 50.5 \quad \text{miles/hour.}$$

This solves the problem.

Exercises: 2.13 (Related Rates)

1. (Paint Spills) Paint is spilling from a bucket at the rate of 125 cubic centimeters per second and forming a circular puddle with expanding radius r and constant thickness $h = 2$ millimeters. Find the rate at which the radius r is changing when $r = 30$ centimeters.

2. (Paint Spills) In the situation described in Exercise (1), determine the the rate at which the circumference is changing when $r = 30$ cm.

3. (Paint Spills) In Squaresville, paint spills form puddles that are always square in shape. See Figure 2.13.1x below. A certain paint spill, flowing out of a can at 64 cubic inches per second, expands with changing side-length x and with constant thickness $h = 1/8$ inch. Find the rate at which the side length x is changing when $x = 30$ inches. Does the side rate increase or decrease over time? Why? What is the side length when the rate of side length change is 2 inch per second?

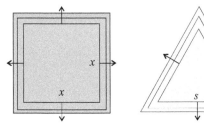

Figure 2.13.1x: *Squaresville (left) and Equilateral Land (right).*

4. (Paint Spills) In the situation described in Exercise (3), determine the rate at which the *diagonal* of the square paint spill is changing when the side-length is $x = 20$ inches.

5. (Paint Spills) In Equilateral Land, paint spills form puddles in the shape of an equilateral triangle. See Figure 2.13.1x above. A certain paint spill of 729 cubic centimeters per second expands with changing side length s and with constant thickness $h = 4$ millimeters. Find the rate at which the side length s is changing when $s = 80$ centimeters. Does the side rate increase or decrease over time. Why? What is the side length when the rate of side length change is 2 centimeters per second?

6. (Paint Spills) In the situation described in Exercise (5), determine the rate at which an *altitude* of the equilateral paint spill is changing when the side-length is $s = 80$ centimeters. (Recall: an altitude is a perpendicular from a vertex to an opposite side.) *Hint*: Write the volume relation in terms of the altitude a rather than the side s.

7. (Sliding Ladder) A 100 foot ladder, inclined against an exterior wall of a building, is being lowered by a rope attached to its top end and controlled by a workman on the roof. If he lowers the ladder at a constant rate of 3

feet per second, find the rate at which the bottom end of the ladder is sliding away from the building when the bottom end is 30 feet from the building. Is this rate increasing or decreasing? Explain why.

8. (Sliding Ladder) Work the general sliding ladder problems (generalizations of Example 2.13.2 and Exercise 7 above). That is, suppose a ladder of length L is leaning against a wall. Its top end slides down the wall while its bottom end slides along the floor away from the wall. Given that one of the ends moves with constant velocity v, find the velocity of the other end in terms of $v, x,$ and y. Discuss what happens at the time when $x = L$ and $y = 0$.

9. (Sliding Ladder) As in Example 2.13.2, a forty foot ladder falls toward the floor with its top end sliding along the wall and its bottom end sliding along the floor. The bottom end slides away from the wall at a rate of 2 feet per second. Suppose a workman's glove is caught on the ladder 10 feet from its top end.

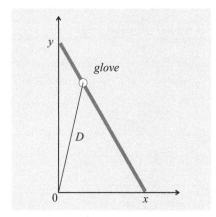

Figure 2.13.2x: *A sliding ladder with a glove.*

Find the rate at which the distance between the glove and the corner of the wall and floor is changing when the top end is 10 feet from the floor.

10. (Sliding Ladder) Work the generalization of Exercise 9 above. That is, suppose a ladder of length L is leaning against a wall. Its top end slides down the wall while its bottom end slides along the floor away from the wall with constant velocity v. A workman's glove is caught at a distance cL from the top of the ladder, where c is a number between 0 and 1. (Note: $c = 1/4$ in Exercise 9.) Let D denote the distance between the glove and the corner where the wall meets the floor. Show that $dD/dt = (2c - 1)xv/D$. Discuss the cases $c = 0$ and $c = 1$. What happens in the case $c = 1/2$? Explain. What about the other cases? Is the rate of change of the distance to the corner increasing or decreasing?

11. (Draining a Tank) An inverted conical tank is being drained by letting the water flow out of the bottom at the rate of 27 m^3/s. The tank has a height of 24 meters and the radius of its circular base is 8 meters. Find the rate at which the water level is falling when the water level is 12 meters high (measured from the vertex). Discuss how the rate of change of the water level varies over time and why.

12. (Filling a Tank) For the conical tank in Example 2.13.3, being filled at the same rate, find the rate at which the radius of the circular water surface is changing when the water level is $h = 9$ meters. Discuss how the rate of change of the water level varies over time and why.

13. (Filling a Tank) The inverted pyramidal tank shown on the left in the Figure 2.13.3x below has height 20 feet and a square top of side 12 feet. It is being filled with water at the rate of 8 cubic feet per minute. Find the rate of change of the water level when it is 14 feet high (measured from the vertex). NOTE: A pyramid's volume is one third the area of the base times the height.

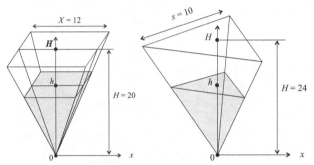

Figure 2.13.3x: *Two pyramidal tanks.*

14. (Filling a Tank) The tank shown on the right in the Figure 2.13.3x above has height 24 feet and a top which is an equilateral triangle of side 10 feet. Each horizontal section through the tank is an equilateral triangle similar to the top. NOTE: The volume of such a pyramid is one third the area of the base times the height. If the tank is being filled with water at the rate of 10 cubic feet per minute, find the rate of change of the water level when it is 12 feet high (measured from the vertex).

15. (A Rising Helicopter) A helicopter lifts off the ground 100 meters from you, rising vertically at a rate of 30 meters per second. You are filming the takeoff with a tripod-mounted camera and rotate the camera to track the helicopter as it rises. How fast is the angle between the camera's direction and the horizontal changing when the helicopter is 120 meters off the ground.

16. (A Falling Rock) A rock dropped off the top of a 200 foot building has a height $y = 200 - 16t^2$ feet above the ground at time t after it is released. You track its descent with a laser device mounted on the ground 100 feet from the base of the building. How fast is the angle of elevation of the laser changing when the rock is 136 feet from the ground?

17. (Distance of Separation) An airplane flying at 400 miles per hour at an altitude of 6 miles passes directly over a radar tower. How fast is the distance between the plane and the bottom of the tower changing when the plane is 50 miles past the point right over the tower.

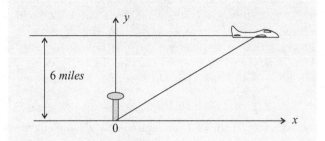

Figure 2.13.4x: *Rate of Separation.*

18. (Distance of Separation) Do a general analysis of the situation described in Exercise 17. That is, assume the plane is flying at v miles per hour at an altitude of y miles. Let x denote the plane's position relative to the point right over the tower. Letting s denote the distance between the plane and the bottom of the tower, find a formula for $\frac{ds}{st}$. For what positions x is this rate negative, positive, or zero? What is the limiting rate $\frac{ds}{dt}$ as $x \to \pm\infty$ for s? Explain why this makes sense.

19. (Separating Cars) Car A is 15 miles east of an intersection, traveling west toward it at 60 miles per hour. Car B is 25 miles north of the same intersection traveling south at 75 miles per hour. Find the rate at which the distance between them is changing when Car A is 7 miles east of the intersection and car B is 5 miles north of the intersection.

20. (Angle of Elevation) In the situation described in Exercise 17, find the rate at which the angle between the line of separation and the horizontal is changing when the plane is 50 miles past the point right over the tower. (The line of separation is the line from the bottom of the tower to the center of the plane.)

Filling Troughs

Exercises 21–26 are related rates problems about filling a trough with water. A trough is a vessel that has a horizontal axis such that all sections perpendicular to this axis have the same shape S. The trough has a fixed length L measured along this axis. See the figure below.

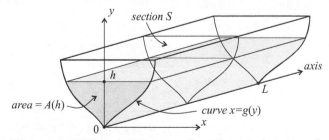

Figure 2.13.5x: *A water trough with typical section S.*

When filling such a tank with water, the water level h rises as the volume of water in the tank increases. When the water level is h, the volume of water in the tank is $V = A(h)L$, where $A(h)$ is the area of the section through the water perpendicular to the axis.

The most typical sectional shapes are triangles and trapezoids, but one could generally have a sectional S formed by some curve as shown in the figure. It is assumed that g is positive and continuous for $y > 0$. After studying the integral calculus in Chapter 4, you will be able to show that the sectional area is given by $A(h) = 2 \int_0^h g(y)\,dy$. In the problems below, $A(h)$ will be given to you (or you can figure it out from elementary geometry) and so you need not worry about the integral calculus for now.

21. (Filling a Trough) Suppose each sectional shape S is an inverted isosceles triangle with base $B = 3$ meters, a height $H = 2$ meters, and the length $L = 10$ meters. See Figure 2.13.6x, left side. Use similar triangles to find the area function $A(h)$ for the sections through the water. If water is pouring into the tank at 0.25 cubic meters per second, find the rate at which the water is rising when the water level is 1.2 meters.

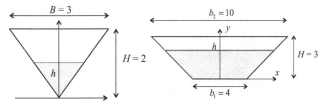

Figure 2.13.6x: *Sectional shapes which are an isosceles triangle (left) and a trapezoid (right).*

22. (Filling a Trough) Suppose the sectional shape S is a trapezoid with bases $b_1 = 4$, $b_2 = 10$ feet, height $H = 3$ feet, and length $L = 12$ feet. If water is pouring into the tank at 3 cubic feet per minute, find the rate at which the water is rising when the water level is 2 feet.

23. (Filling a Trough) Suppose the sectional shape S of the trough is the parabolic segment shown on the left in the Figure 2.13.7x below. The length of the trough is $L = 12$ feet and, for a section through the water when it is at height h, the area function is $A(h) = 4h^{3/2}/3$ square feet. If water is flowing into the tank at the rate of 2 cubic feet per second, find the rate at which the water level is changing when h is 16 feet.

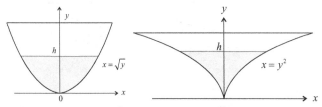

Figure 2.13.7x: *Sectional shapes which are parabolic (left) and cuspsoidal (right).*

24. (Filling a Trough) Suppose the sectional shape S of the trough is cuspsoidal as shown on the right in the

Figure 2.13.7x above. The length of the tank is $L = 10$ feet and, for a section through the water when it is at height h, the area function is $A(h) = 2h^3/3$. If water is flowing into the tank at the rate of 1.2 cubic feet per second, find the rate at which the water level is changing when h is 4 feet.

25. (Filling a Trough) Suppose the sectional shape S of the trough is the exponential segment shown on the top in the Figure 2.13.8x below. The length of the tank is $L = 10$ meters, and for a section through the water when it is at height h, the area function is $A(h) = 2e^h - 2h - 2$ square meters. If water is flowing into the tank at the rate of 2 cubic meters per second, find the rate at which the water level is changing when h is 1 meter.

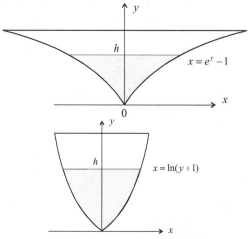

Figure 2.13.8x: *Sectional shapes which are exponential (top) and logarithmic (bottom).*

26. (Filling a Trough) Suppose the sectional shape S of the trough is the logarithmic shape as shown on the bottom in Figure 2.13.8x above. The length of the tank is $L = 15$ feet and, for a section through the water when it is at height h, $A(h) = (2h+1)[\ln(h+1) - 1] + 2$ is the area function (in square feet). If water is flowing into the tank at the rate of 1.5 cubic feet per second, find the rate at which the water level is changing when h is 3 feet.

3

Applications of Derivatives

Calculus *Concepts & Computation*

3.1 Curve Sketching: 1st Derivatives

```
> with(dplot_tools,dplot);
```
$$[dplot\,]$$
```
> with(code_ch3,tanlines,tanlines2);
```
$$[tanlines,\ tanlines2]$$

In the previous sections we have seen many applications and uses for derivatives of functions. The first derivative gives us the slope of the tangent line to the function at points along its graph. The first and second derivatives of a position function are the velocity and acceleration of the moving object. The first derivative describes the rate of change of some quantity with respect to an underlying variable.

An additional important application of derivatives is in analyzing the geometrical properties of functions. These properties are reflected in the graph of the function—(1) the way it rises and falls, and (2) the way it bends one way and then the other. In this section we will see how the 1st derivative is used to determine where the graph of a function $y = f(x)$ is rising and where it is falling (as x moves from left to right). In the next section we will see how the bending (or curving) in the graph is determined by the 2nd derivative.

Intervals of Increase and Decrease

One of the most distinguishing properties of a function $y = f(x)$ is the nature of the variation in its y-values—specifically how the y-values change, as the independent variable x varies, moving from left to right. The y-values can increase or decrease as x varies (unless we are dealing with a constant function, whose y-values never change), and the pattern of fluctuation (increasing-decreasing, decreasing-increasing) is something that is important to know about a function. You have seen this increasing/decreasing behavior illustrated many times now whenever you execute a dynamic plot (dplot) of the graph of a function. For instance, consider the polynomial function defined by

```
> f:=x->2+2*x+5*x^2-x^4;
```
$$f := x \rightarrow 2 + 2x + 5x^2 - x^4$$

A dynamic plot of this function, created by the following command, illustrates how the y-values change as x moves from -2 to 2.

```
> dplot(f,-2,2,40);
```

Study the animation of this dynamic plot and observe the variation in the y-values, represented by the red vertical line segments (or ordinates). Starting on the left, these ordinates first increase, but then begin to decrease at $x = -1.5$. Then, at $x = -0.2$ (approximately), the ordinates start to increase again, before changing back to decreasing at approximately $x = 1.7$.

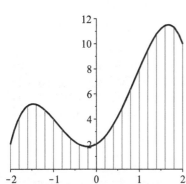

Figure 3.1.1: *Plot of the function* $f(x) = 2 + 2x + 5x^2 - x^4$ *showing the variation of the y-values on the interval* $[-2, 2]$.

Nelson Sirlin/Shutterstock.com

Mountain Range Analogy: In thinking about the way the graph of a function rises and falls, it is often helpful to view the graph as a mountain range—consisting of a succession of *peaks* and *valleys*. As you move from left to right, mountain peaks occur where the function changes from increasing to decreasing. On the other hand, the valleys occur where the function changes from decreasing to increasing.

You can use the cursor probe on the plot in Figure 3.1.1 to determine the *approximate* places where the function changes from increasing to decreasing, or vice-versa, and thus determine the approximate places of the peaks and valleys. Below we will show how to use the first derivative to determine these places *ex-actly*. But first we need mathematical definitions of the concepts: *increasing* and *decreasing*.

DEFINITION 3.1.1 (Increasing/Decreasing on an Interval)

Suppose I is any interval and f is a function defined on I.

(1) *We say f is* increasing *on the interval I if for all* x_1, x_2 *in I*

$$x_1 < x_2 \Rightarrow f(x_1) \leq f(x_2)$$

(2) *We say f is* decreasing *on the interval I if for all* x_1, x_2 *in I*

$$x_1 < x_2 \Rightarrow f(x_1) \geq f(x_2)$$

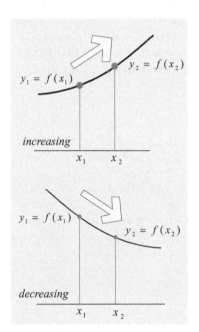

Figure 3.1.2: *Illustration of the increasing/decreasing properties of a function.*

We will also use the word *monotonic*, and the phrase: *f is monotonic on the interval I*, to mean that f is either increasing on I or f is decreasing on I. Figure 3.1.2 illustrates the geometry in the above definition.

NOTE: According to our definition, a function f can be increasing on an interval I and yet there can be places in I where the values of f are the same. In fact an increasing function, as we have defined it, can be constant on a whole subinterval of I. For this reason many people use the word *non-decreasing* for what we are what we are calling *increasing*.

The 1st Derivative and Monotonicity

In this section we discuss how the 1st derivative of a function determines where the function is increasing and where it is decreasing. Knowing this information about a function enables us to construct a relatively good graph of the function by plotting only a small number of points.

We should expect that the first derivative tells us something about the increasing/decreasing properties, since geometrically it gives us the slope of the tangent line at each point on the graph. See Figure 3.1.3.

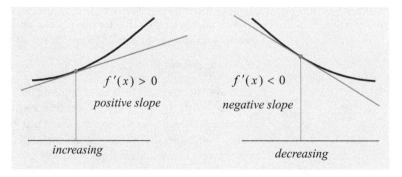

Figure 3.1.3: *The slope of the tangent line indicates where a function is increasing or decreasing.*

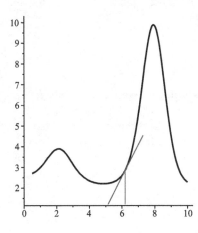

And indeed, the tangent line approximates the graph of the function near that point. So, we expect the function will be increasing on a neighborhood of any point where the tangent line has *positive* slope. Likewise, as shown in Figure 3.1.3, we expect the function will be decreasing on a neighborhood of any point where the tangent line has *negative* slope.

We can view all of this dynamically by using the special-purpose Maple command `tanlines` to show the tangent lines for a point moving along the graph of a function.

```
>  f:=x->x^sin(x)+2;
```
$$f := x \to x^{\sin x} + 2$$
```
> tanlines(f,.5,10,60,4);
```

If you study the above animation you will easily see the tangent lines have positive, but varying, slopes on intervals where the function is increasing, while the tangent lines have negative, but varying, slopes on intervals where the function is decreasing. It is important to note, for later use, how the slope of the tangent line goes to zero as the tangent lines change from positive to negative slopes, or vica-versa. The following theorem makes these observations precise.

THEOREM 3.1.1 (The 1st Derivative and Monotonicity)

Suppose f is a function which is defined and differentiable on an interval I. Then

(1) *f is increasing on I if and only if $f' \geq 0$ on I*

(2) *f is decreasing on I if and only if $f' \leq 0$ on I*

Proof: We prove statement (1) and leave the proof of statement (2) as an exercise. Suppose first that f is increasing on I and x is any point in I (other than an endpoint). We have to show that $f'(x) \geq 0$. For this we resort to the limit definition of the derivative. Suppose that h is a positive number, small enough so that $x+h$ is in I. Then since $x < x+h$ and f is increasing, we have $f(x) \leq f(x+h)$, and so $0 \leq f(x + h) - f(x)$. Dividing both sides of this inequality by h, which is positive, gives

$$0 \leq \frac{f(x + h) - f(x)}{h}. \qquad (3.1.1) \qquad (3.1)$$

This holds for all small positive h. On the other hand if h is small and negative then $x+h < x$, and so $f(x+h) \leq f(x)$, since f is increasing. Thus, $f(x+h) - f(x) \leq 0$, and if we divide this by h, which is negative, we get the same inequality as in (3.1.1). Hence, inequality (3.1.1) holds for all small h (whether positive or negative). Taking limits gives

$$0 \leq \lim_{h \to 0} \frac{f(x + h) - f(x)}{h} = f'(x).$$

This proves the "only if" part of the theorem.

To prove the "if" part of the theorem, suppose that $f' \geq 0$ on I. This means that $f'(x) \geq 0$ at each point x in I. We now must use this to show that f is increasing on I. So suppose x_1, x_2 are in I with $x_1 < x_2$. We have to show that $f(x_1) \leq f(x_2)$. For this, we use the Mean Value Theorem (see the Section 3.5). This theorem guarantees that there is a number c between x_1 and x_2, such that

$$f'(c) = \frac{f(x_2) - f(x_1)}{x_2 - x_1}.$$

But since c is in I, we have by assumption that $f'(c) \geq 0$. From this and the last equation we get

$$\frac{f(x_2) - f(x_1)}{x_2 - x_1} \geq 0.$$

Since $x_2 - x_1 > 0$, this last inequality implies that $f(x_2) - f(x_1) \geq 0$. Hence, $f(x_2) \geq f(x_1)$, and that is what we wanted to show.

Increasing/Decreasing Diagrams

We will apply Theorem 3.1.1 to curve sketching as follows. We assume that f is a given function which is differentiable on an interval (a, b) and that its derivative is continuous on this interval. (This will be the case if the 2nd derivative of f exists, as it will be in most examples we consider.) We calculate the formula for the derivative $f'(x)$ and ask where this expression is positive and where this expression is negative. These questions are easier to answer if we first determine where this expression is 0, that is, if we first solve the equation

$$f'(x) = 0.$$

Assume this equation has only finitely many solutions $x = c_1, c_2, \ldots, c_k$ in the interval (a, b). These numbers are called critical numbers of f. (You will see why in the discussion below). Assuming these numbers are labeled in order, we see that they divide the interval (a, b) into subintervals

$$(a, c_1), (c_1, c_2), \ldots, (c_{k-1}, c_k), (c_k, b).$$

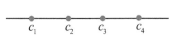

$$c_1 \quad c_2 \quad c_3 \quad c_4$$

Figure 3.1.4: *The critical numbers divide the interval into subintervals.*

This is illustrated in Figure 3.1.4 ,where there are four critical numbers and $a = -\infty$, $b = \infty$.

Then we *claim* that on each subinterval f is either increasing or f is decreasing. To see this, note that if there is a subinterval (c_{i-1}, c_i) on which this is not the case, then f must be increasing on part of (c_{i-1}, c_i) and decreasing on another part of (c_{i-1}, c_i). By Theorem 3.1.1 this means that $f' \geq 0$ on part of (c_{i-1}, c_i) and $f' \leq 0$ on another part of (c_{i-1}, c_i). But by the intermediate value theorem (See Section 1.7) this means that $f'(x) = 0$ for some x in the interval (c_{i-1}, c_i). But this contradicts that $c_1, c_2, \ldots, c_k$ is a complete list of all the places in (a, b) where the 1st derivative is 0. Thus, our original claim must be true.

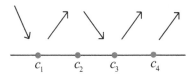

$$c_1 \quad c_2 \quad c_3 \quad c_4$$

Figure 3.1.5: *An increasing-decreasing diagram.*

Now that we know that f must be increasing or decreasing on each subinterval (c_{i-1}, c_i), how do we determine which type it is? To answer this, just pick any test point t in the interval and evaluate the 1st derivative at t. If $f'(t) > 0$, then f is increasing on (c_{i-1}, c_i), while if $f'(t) < 0$, then f is decreasing on (c_{i-1}, c_i).

We can record our work in a diagram, called an increasing/decreasing diagram for the function. This is shown schematically in Figure 3.1.5.

Once we have the increasing/decreasing diagram for the function, we can sketch in a rough curve on the diagram that follows the rising and falling pattern indicated by the diagram. See Figure 3.1.6. This will give a fair indication of what the actual graph will look like.

To get the actual graph of the function, we plot a number of points on the graph. We always plot the points corresponding to the critical numbers $c_1, c_2, \ldots, c_k$ and the end points a, b, of the interval under consideration (unless of course $a = -\infty$ or $b = \infty$). Thus, we make a table of x and y values and find the coordinates of the points

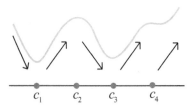

$$c_1 \quad c_2 \quad c_3 \quad c_4$$

Figure 3.1.6: *A rough sketch of a function's increasing-decreasing properties.*

$$(a, f(a)), (c_1, f(c_1)), (c_2, f(c_2)), \ldots, (c_k, f(c_k)), (b, f(b))$$

on the graph of f. Then use the increasing/decreasing diagram to connect the points. This will give a fairly accurate graph of the function. The following two examples illustrate this curve sketching technique.

Example 3.1.1 Consider the polynomial function

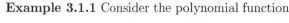

$$f(x) = \frac{1}{10}(3x^4 - 4x^3 - 12x^2 + 5),$$

on the interval $(-\infty, \infty)$. (The factor $1/10$ is just for scaling purposes and does not affect the other features of the function.) The 1st derivative of this function is easily calculated to be

$$f'(x) = \frac{1}{10}(12x^3 - 12x^2 - 24x) = \frac{12}{10}x(x^2 - x - 2) = \frac{6}{5}x(x-2)(x+1).$$

We have factored the above expression for the derivative because it will be easier to find the critical numbers if $f'(x)$ is in factored form. The critical numbers here are the solutions of the equation $f'(x) = 0$, i.e., the roots of

$$\frac{6}{5}x(x-2)(x+1) = 0.$$

Thus, the critical numbers are easily seen to be

$$x = 0, 2, -1.$$

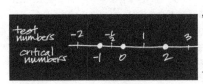

Figure 3.1.7: *A plot of the three critical numbers and a choice of four test points.*

We plot these on the number line is shown in Figure 3.1.7..

The critical numbers $-1, 0, 2$ divide the given interval $(-\infty, \infty)$ into four subintervals. Now we have to evaluate f' at test points t in each of these subintervals. The selected test points $t = -2, -1/2, 1, 3$ are shown in the figure.

(1) Subinterval $(-\infty, -1)$: Choose test point $t = -2$, and calculate

$$f'(-2) = \frac{6}{5}(-2)(-2-2)(-2+1) = \frac{6}{5}(-2)(-4)(-1) < 0.$$

Thus, the function is decreasing on this interval. Note: We do not need to determine the actual value of $f'(-2)$, only whether this value is positive or negative. Also, the factored form of $f'(x)$ is easiest to use in this determination.

(2) Subinterval $(-1, 0)$: Choose test point $t = -1/2$, and calculate

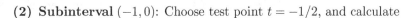
$$f'(-\frac{1}{2}) = \frac{6}{5}(-\frac{1}{2})(-\frac{1}{2} - 2)(-\frac{1}{2} + 1) = \frac{6}{5}(-\frac{1}{2})(-\frac{5}{2})(\frac{1}{2}) > 0$$

Thus, the function is increasing on this interval.

(3) Subinterval $(0, 2)$: Choose a test point $t = 1$, and calculate

$$f'(1) = \frac{6}{5}(1)(1-2)(1+1) = \frac{6}{5}(1)(-1)(2) < 0.$$

Thus, the function is decreasing on this interval.

(4) Subinterval $(2, \infty)$: Choose a test point $t = 3$, and calculate

$$f'(3) = \frac{6}{5}(3)(3-2)(3+1) = \frac{6}{5}(3)(1)(4) > 0.$$

Thus, the function is increasing on this interval.

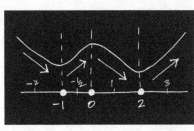

Figure 3.1.8: *The increasing/ decreasing diagram for* $f(x) = (3x^4 - 4x^3 - 12x^2 + 5)/10$.

We now record all this work in an increasing/decreasing diagram. See Figure 3.1.8. This figure also shows a sketch of a curve that fits the increasing/decreasing pattern.

Now we are ready to plot the curve. We make a table of values, which includes the values $f(-1), f(0), f(2)$ of f at all the critical numbers as well as its values at $x = -2, 1, 3$. This gives a six points on graph as shown in Figure 3.1.9.

CAUTION: When making the table of values for the plot be sure to use the formula $f(x)$ for the given function and NOT the formula $f'(x)$ that you computed for its derivative.

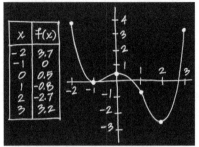

Figure 3.1.9: *The graph of* $f(x) = \frac{1}{10}(3x^4 - 4x^3 - 12x^2 + 5)$.

Plotting six points is usually not sufficient to draw a good graph of a function, unless we know some other things about the function. In this example, we know the increasing/decreasing properties, so these six points can give a good graph as shown in Figure 3.1.9.

Using the mountain range analogy in discussing the above graph, we would say that there are two *valleys* on the graph, at $x = -1$ and $x = 2$, and there is one *peak* on the graph, at $x = 0$. The mathematical terms for peak and valley are *local maximum* and *local minimum*. Thus, we would say that the graph has a local maximum value at $x = 0$ and local minimum values at $x = -1$ and $x = 2$. We will discuss the concept of local maxima and minima more in Section 3.2. The reason for the term "local" in the designation of local maximum value is that "near" $x = 0$ the function's values $f(x)$ are less than it's value $0.5 = f(0)$ at $x = 0$. As you can see from the graph, further away from 0 the function has values greater than 0.5. In the mountain slope analogy, if you are standing on a peak it appears to be highest point until you gaze off into the distance and spot a higher peak. Likewise, when standing in a valley, you might judge it to be the lowest point in the mountain range, but you could only be sure of that locally.

Example 3.1.2

Problem: For the function
$$f(x) = x^2 e^{-x}$$
defined on the whole real line, draw an increasing decreasing diagram, identify the local maxima and minima (peaks and valleys), and sketch the graph of the function.

Solution: The 1st derivative of this function is easily calculated using the product rule:
$$f'(x) = 2xe^{-x} + x^2(-e^{-x}) = (2x - x^2)e^{-x} = x(2 - x)e^{-x}.$$

Note that we have factored this expression for the 1st derivative. Setting this expression equal to zero gives the equation for the critical numbers:
$$x(2 - x)e^{-x} = 0.$$

The exponential function is positive for all x, so the only critical numbers are $x = 0, 2$. We get three subintervals in the increasing/decreasing diagram to analyze.

(1) Subinterval $(-\infty, 0)$: Choose test point $t = -1$, and calculate
$$f'(-1) = (-1)(2 - (-1))e^{-(-1)} = (-1)(3)e^1 < 0.$$

Thus, the function is decreasing on this interval.

(2) Subinterval $(0, 2)$: Choose test point $t = 1$, and calculate
$$f'(1) = 1(2 - 1)e^{-1} = e^{-1} > 0$$

Thus, the function is increasing on this interval.

(3) Subinterval $(2, \infty)$: Choose test point $t = 3$, and calculate
$$f'(3) = 3(2 - 3)e^{-3} = 2(-1)e^{-3} < 0.$$

Thus, the function is decreasing on this interval.

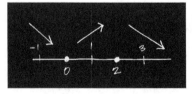

Figure 3.1.10: *The increasing/decreasing diagram for* $f(x) = x^2 e^{-x}$.

With the analysis complete, we can now draw the increasing/decreasing diagram for the function. This is shown in Figure 3.1.10.

We can identify the peaks and valleys directly from this diagram. Thus, the graph will have a local minimum (a valley) at $x = 0$ and will have a local maximum (a peak) at $x = 2$.

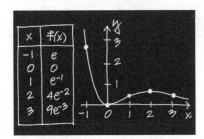

Figure 3.1.11: *Sketch of the graph of* $f(x) = x^2 e^{-x}$.

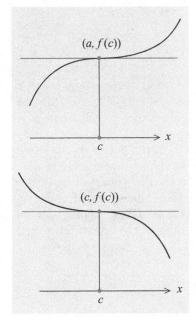

Figure 3.1.12

We now plot points, calculating the y-values corresponding to the two critical numbers $x = 0, 2$ and, say, the two test points $t = -1, 3$. This only gives us four points on the graph, but with the above diagram we can get a fairly good graph of the function. This sketch is shown in Figure 3.1.11.

In doing the plot, you will have to use a calculator or computer to find approximate values for the exponential function. We used the approximations: $e \approx 2.7$, $e^{-1} \approx 0.37$, $4e^{-2} \approx 0.54$, and $9e^{-3} \approx 0.45$.

Critical Numbers

The curve sketching technique discussed in the previous section relies on finding the x-values at which the first derivative vanishes: $f'(x) = 0$. These x-values: $c = c_1, c_2, \ldots, c_k$ are called *critical numbers* (or *critical points*) for f and give points $(c_i, f(c_i))$ on the graph where the tangent line is horizontal. These numbers are called critical numbers since we can expect (but not always get) a change in the behavior of the function at these points: the function changes from increasing to decreasing, or changes from decreasing to increasing, as x moves from left to right across the critical number. We say "expect a change" because sometimes the monotonicity does not change at a critical point. This situation is illustrated by Figure 3.1.12.

Thus, at the critical numbers c in Figure 3.1.12, the tangent line at the point $(c, f(c))$ is horizontal, but the function continues to increase or to decrease as x moves past c. Such points are often called *stationary points* on the graph. In terms of the mountain slope analogy, a stationary point on the mountain is a place where a climber can momentarily pause before she either continues her ascent of the mountain or continues her descent of the mountain. You can use the increasing/decreasing diagram for the function to easily determine which critical numbers correspond to stationary points and to distinguish these points from the peaks and valleys (local max's and min's).

In order to make the notion of a critical number more useful, we need to extend its scope to include those numbers for which the 1st derivative does not exist. This may seem strange at first, but the examples below and the exercise problems will show you the utility of this broader definition. The formal definition is as follows:

DEFINITION 3.1.2 (Critical Numbers)

A number c in the domain of a function f is called a critical number for f if either

(1) *f is differentiable at c and $f'(c) = 0$ or*

(2) *f is not differentiable at c (i.e., $f'(c)$ does not exist)*

Thus, there are two types of critical numbers: ones where the tangent line is horizontal and ones where the tangent line does not exist (because the derivative does not exist there). The following examples illustrate how this latter type of critical number arises.

Example 3.1.3

Problem: Find all the critical numbers of the power function

$$f(x) = x^{2/3},$$

and determine the behavior of the function at each critical number.

Solution: The derivative is easy enough to calculate:

$$f'(x) = \frac{2}{3} x^{-1/3} = \frac{2}{3x^{1/3}}.$$

To determine the critical numbers we first look for the ones that make $f'(x)$ zero. These are the solutions of

$$\frac{2}{3x^{1/3}} = 0.$$

But there are no numbers x that make the left side zero, and so there are no critical numbers of this type. The other type of critical number is an x for which $f'(x)$ is undefined, and we see that this happens only for $x = 0$. So 0 is the only critical number.

Next we determine what happens on the graph of f at this critical number. For this, we determine the monotonicity on each side of $x = 0$ using test points $t = -1$ and $t = 1$:

$$f'(-1) = \frac{2}{3(-1)^{1/3}} = -\frac{2}{3} < 0$$

$$f'(1) = \frac{2}{3(1)^{1/3}} = \frac{2}{3} > 0.$$

Thus, the function is decreasing on the left side of $x = 0$ and increasing on the right side. Since f is defined at $x = 0$, it has a local minimum (valley) there. However, this is a rather "tight" valley because the 'tangent line" at $t = 0$ is vertical, as shown in Figure 3.1.13.

The point $(0,0)$ on the graph here is known as a cusp. The graph in Figure 3.1.13 shows only three plotted points, which generally is not enough information to construct an accurate plot. However, knowing that the tangent line is vertical at the origin and that the curve decreases to the origin before increasing after passing it, helps us draw the picture. In the next section we will discuss concavity, which will tell us that the graph is curved down on both sides of the origin. Then with just three plotted points, and all this other information, we can be sure that the graph is fairly accurate.

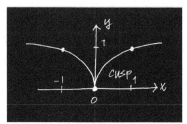

Figure 3.1.13: *Graph of* $f(x) = x^{2/3}$.

Example 3.1.4

Problem: For the rational function

$$f(x) = x + \frac{1}{x},$$

find all the critical numbers and determine the behavior of the function at these numbers. Sketch a graph of the function.

Solution: The derivative is

$$f'(x) = 1 - \frac{1}{x^2},$$

and setting this equal to zero gives

$$1 - \frac{1}{x^2} = 0,$$

or equivalently (for $x \neq 0$)

$$x^2 = 1.$$

So $x = -1, 1$ are the two critical numbers. But note that even though $f'(x)$ does not exist at $x = 0$, there is not a critical number there. This is because $x = 0$ is not in the domain of f. A quick sketch of the increasing/decreasing diagram is shown in Figure 3.1.14.

We conclude that there is a local max (a peak) on the graph at $x = -1$ and a local min (a valley) on the graph at $x = 1$. However, what is the behavior of the graph near $x = 0$? The function is not defined there, and in fact has a vertical asymptote at $x = 0$. Note: If f were defined at $x = 0$, then the above

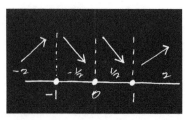

Figure 3.1.14: *The increasing-decreasing diagram for* $f(x) = x + \frac{1}{x}$.

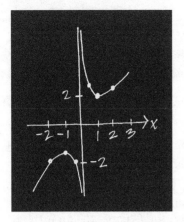

Figure 3.1.15: *A sketch of the graph of $f(x) = x + \frac{1}{x}$.*

increasing/decreasing diagram would indicate that there is a stationary point on the graph. But that is not the case here. Figure 3.1.15 shows a plot of this function.

Example 3.1.5

Problem: This problem shows that some functions can have the same increasing/decreasing diagram and yet be quite different in their behavior. For example, consider the quintic polynomial

$$g(x) = 3x^5 - 5x^3.$$

Find all the critical points of g and draw an increasing/decreasing diagram. Check your work by graphing g in Maple.

Solution: The derivative of g is easily computed as

$$g'(x) = 15x^4 - 15x^2 = 15x^2(x^2 - 1).$$

So clearly the critical points are $x = -1, 0, 1$. Using the usual procedure to construct the increasing/decreasing diagram, we get the same diagram as in Figure 3.1.14 for the function $f(x) = x + 1/x$. However, the function g is defined at $x = 0$, and so the increasing/decreasing diagram now indicates that $x = 0$ is a stationary point. This is shown clearly by graphing g in Maple.

```
> f:=x->x+1/x;
```

$$f := x \to x + \frac{1}{x}$$

```
> g:=x->3*x^5-5*x^3;
```

$$g := x \to 3x^5 - 5x^3$$

```
> p1:=plot(f(x),x=-1.5..1.5,y=-6..6,color=blue):
> p2:=plot(g(x),x=-1.5..1.5,color=black,thickness=2):
> with(plots,display):
> display({p1,p2});
```

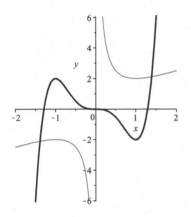

Figure 3.1.16: *Plot of the function $g(x) = 3x^5 - 5x^3$ (in black) and the function $f(x) = x + 1/x$ (in blue) which have the same increasing/decreasing diagrams.*

As you can see from the figure, the appearance of f and g is different at each of the points $x = -1, 0, 1$. At $x = -1, 1$ the local maximum and minimum are barely discernible for f, but are quite pronounced for g. Of course, at $x = 0$, the function f has a vertical asymptote, making it not continuous there.

Note: You may find it helpful to check your work by plotting, in Maple, the function you are investigating. However, you are expected to know how to find critical points, draw in increasing/decreasing diagrams, and sketch the graph by hand.

Exercises: 3.1 (Curve Sketching: 1st Derivatives)

```
> with(dplot_tools,dplot);
```
$$[dplot]$$

Using the Command dplot

In Exercises 1–6, use dplot(f,a,b,40) to plot the graph of the function f on the given interval $[a,b]$. After viewing the animation determine, by viewing the graph, the largest subintervals on which f is increasing and the largest subintervals on which it is decreasing.

1. $f(x) = 3x^4 - 16x^3 + 18x^2$, $[-1,4]$
2. $f(x) = x^3 - 3x^2 + 1$, $[-2,4]$
3. $f(x) = 4x^3 - x^4$, $[-2,4.5]$
4. $f(x) = 4x^3 + x^4 - x^5$, $[-2,2.5]$
5. $f(x) = x + \sin x$, $[0,20]$ 6. $f(x) = x\sin x$, $[0,15]$

Finding Critical Numbers

In Exercises 7–46 , find all the critical numbers of the function. NOTE: For the ones that involve trig functions there will be infinitely many critical numbers, so just find those in the interval $[0,2\pi]$. Optional CAS: Check your work by graphing the function in Maple, using the cursor probe on the peaks and valleys to approximate the x-coordinates of the peaks/valleys.

7. $f(x) = 18x^2 - x^4$ 8. $f(x) = x^6 - 3x^4$
9. $f(x) = x^3 - 6x^2 - 9x$ 10. $f(x) = x^3 - 3x^2 - 3x$
11. $f(x) = x + \dfrac{1}{x}$ 12. $f(x) = 4x + \dfrac{1}{x}$
13. $f(x) = x^2 + \dfrac{16}{x^2}$ 14. $f(x) = x^3 + \dfrac{64}{x^3}$
15. $f(x) = 2\sqrt[3]{x} - x^{2/3}$ 16. $f(x) = 2x^{1/5} - x^{4/5}$
17. $f(x) = 2x^{1/5} - x^{6/5}$ 18. $f(x) = 2x^{1/3} - x^{4/3}$
19. $f(x) = \dfrac{x^3}{x-1}$ 20. $f(x) = \dfrac{x^4}{x-1}$
21. $f(x) = \dfrac{4x}{x^2+1}$ 22. $f(x) = \dfrac{4x-4}{x^2+1}$
23. $f(x) = x\ln x - x$ 24. $f(x) = 2x\ln x - x$
25. $f(x) = x^2\ln x - x^2$ 26. $f(x) = 3x^2\ln x - x^2$
27. $f(x) = x^4 e^{-2x}$ 28. $f(x) = x^6 e^{-3x}$
29. $f(x) = \sqrt{x}e^{-x/2}$ 30. $f(x) = \sqrt{x}e^{-x/4}$
31. $f(x) = 10(x-1)e^{-x}$ 32. $f(x) = 2(x^2-1)e^{-x}$
33. $f(x) = x^2 e^{-x^2/2}$ 34. $f(x) = x^3 e^{-x^2/2}$
35. $f(x) = 2\cos x + x$ 36. $f(x) = 2\sin x - x$
37. $f(x) = \sin x + \cos x$ 38. $f(x) = \sin \pi x + \cos \pi x$
39. $f(x) = \cos^2 x - \cos x$ 40. $f(x) = \sin x - \sin^2 x$
41. $f(x) = \frac{1}{2}\cos 2x + \sin x$ 42. $f(x) = \cos x - \frac{1}{2}\cos 2x$
43. $f(x) = \tan x - 4x$ 44. $f(x) = \cot x + 4x$
45. $f(x) = \ln|\sec x + \tan x| - 2x$
46. $f(x) = \ln|\csc x + \cot x| + 2x$

Increasing/Decreasing Diagrams and Sketching

In Exercises 47–72 do the following:

(a) Find all the critical numbers of the function f in the given interval $[a,b]$.

(b) Use the critical numbers to draw an Increasing/Decreasing Diagram for f.

(c) From the Increasing/Decreasing Diagram determine the local maxima/minima (peaks/valleys) and stationary points (if any) for f. Label them on the Diagram. (d) Sketch, *by hand*, the graph of f. (Be honest. DO NOT use Maple as a guide. Chances are your instructor will want you to sketch graphs by hand on the tests.)

47. $f(x) = x^3 - 3x + 1$, $[-3,3]$
48. $f(x) = 2x^3 + 3x^2 - 12x + 2$, $[-3,2]$
49. $f(x) = 3x^4 - 4x^3 - 12x^2$, $[-2,3]$
50. $f(x) = 3x^4 - 20x^2 - 48x$, $[-3,3]$
51. $f(x) = x^4 - 4x$, $[-2,2]$
52. $f(x) = 2x^3 - x^4$, $[-1,2]$
53. $f(x) = x^4 - 2x^2$, $[-2,2]$
54. $f(x) = 3x^2 - x^4$, $[-2,2]$
55. $f(x) = \frac{1}{5}x^5 - 3x^3$, $[-4,4]$
56. $f(x) = \frac{1}{5}x^5 - \frac{5}{3}x^3$, $[-3,3]$
57. $f(x) = 2xe^{-x^2/2}$, $[-4,4]$
58. $f(x) = 2x^2 e^{-x}$, $[-4,4]$
59. $f(x) = (x^2-1)e^{-x}$, $[-1.5,4]$
60. $f(x) = (x^2-1)e^{-x/2}$, $[-1.5,7]$
61. $f(x) = x\ln x$, $(0,3]$
62. $f(x) = 2\ln x - (\ln x)^2$, $[0.5,6]$
63. $f(x) = \ln(x^4 - 2x^2 + 2)$, $[-3,3]$
64. $f(x) = \ln(-3x^2 + 5)$, $[-4,4]$
65. $f(x) = x^2 + \dfrac{1}{x^2}$, $[-3,3]$
66. $f(x) = x^2 + \dfrac{1}{x^3}$, $[-3,3]$
67. $f(x) = \dfrac{8x^2}{x^3-1}$, $[-4,4]$
68. $f(x) = \dfrac{8x^3}{x^5-1}$, $[-4,4]$
69. $f(x) = 3\sqrt[5]{x} - x^{3/5}$, $[-6,6]$
70. $f(x) = 3\sqrt[7]{x} - x^{3/7}$, $[-7,7]$
71. $f(x) = \dfrac{1}{2+\cos x}$, $[1,12]$
72. $f(x) = \dfrac{1}{3+\sin x}$, $[0,10]$

Calculus *Concepts & Computation*

3.2 Curve Sketching: 2nd Derivatives

```
> with(code ch3,tanlines,tanlines2);
```
$$[tanlines, \ tanlines2]$$

In this section we discuss the *concavity* property of the graph of a function f and how this property is related to the 2nd derivative f''. You should find this discussion entirely analogous to the discussion of the monotonicity (increasing/decreasing) property and its relation to the 1st derivative f'.

Intervals of Concavity

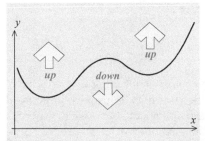

Figure 3.2.1: *Portions of a graph are concave up or concave down.*

In analyzing the graph of any function f, it is important to know not only where it is increasing and decreasing but also where it is curving upward and where it is curving downward. This "curving" property is called *concavity* and the portions of the graph will be either *concave up* or *concave down* (unless a portion is a straight line). This is illustrated in Figure 3.2.1.

The points on the graph where the concavity changes from up to down, or from down to up, are called *inflection points*. There are two inflection points in the graph shown in Figure 3.2.1 since the concavity changes twice. Perhaps you can locate these points approximately. Figure 3.2.2 illustrates this.

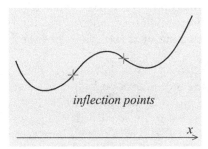

Figure 3.2.2: *Inflection points are where the concavity changes.*

Knowing where the graph is concave up and where it is concave down is information that supplements the information we get from analyzing the monotonicity of the graph. For example, if we know that a function f increases on an interval (a, b) from point $A = (a, f(a))$ to point $B = (b, f(b))$, then it can do this many ways. Its graph can be concave up or concave down as it goes from A to B, or the concavity can change one or more times. This is illustrated in Figure 3.2.3.

Similar comments apply if the function is decreasing on the interval (a, b). Thus, you can see that knowing something about the concavity of a function will be valuable in understanding its behavior.

So how do we analyze the concavity of a function? To do this, we first need a precise mathematical definition of concavity. To discover the appropriate definition, we look at a few pictures and make the following observations. See Figure 3.2.4.

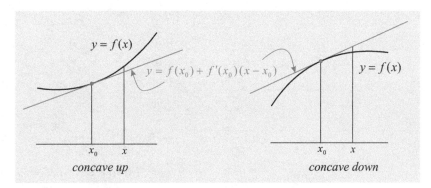

Figure 3.2.4: *Concavity is determined by whether the graph is above or below the tangent line.*

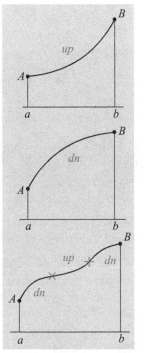

Figure 3.2.3: *Possibilities the concavity as f increases.*

We see from Figure 3.2.4, that if the graph of f is "curved up" on an interval, then the graph lies above the tangent line at each point. This means that for each x_0 in the interval, the equation $y = f(x_0) + f'(x_0)(x - x_0)$ for the tangent line gives y-values that are less than or equal to the corresponding y-values given by $y = f(x)$. The opposite is true if the graph is "curved down." Thus, with these observations as a guide, we define concave up and concave down as follows.

DEFINITION 3.2.1 (Concavity)

Suppose I is any interval and f is a differentiable function defined on I.

(1) *We say f is* concave up *on the interval I if for all* x_0 *in I*

$$f(x) \geq f(x_0) + f'(x_0)(x - x_0) \quad \text{for all } x \text{ in } I$$

(2) *We say f is* concave down *on the interval I if for all* x_0 *in I*

$$f(x) \leq f(x_0) + f'(x_0)(x - x_0) \quad \text{for all } x \text{ in } I$$

This is a nice precise definition which captures the geometric meaning of concavity. However, using the definition directly to determine concavity is usually impossible. Thus, we will need a theorem that gives us an equivalent, but easier, way of determining concavity. This is Theorem 3.2.1 in the next section.

The 2nd Derivative and Concavity

The original motivation for the derivative function f' is that it gives the slope of the tangent line at each point on the graph of f. This captures the basic geometric meaning of the 1st derivative. When f represents the position function for a moving object, we have seen that f' also has a dynamic meaning, it is the velocity of the object – the rate of change of position.

So far in the discussion, the second derivative function f'' has only been given a dynamic meaning – it is the acceleration of a moving object with position function f. But what geometric meaning does the 2nd derivative have? There are several answers to this, but we will learn here that f'' is naturally identified with the concavity of the graph of f.

To see this, think of f'' as the derivative, or rate of change, of f'. Since f' gives the slope of the tangent line, f'' gives the rate of change of the slope of the tangent line. Figure 3.2.5 should help you visualize how the slope of the tangent line changes as we take successive points along the graph.

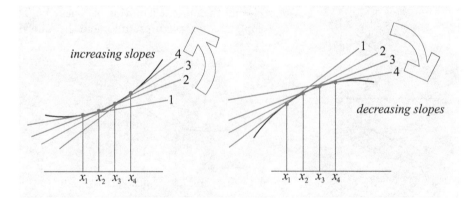

Figure 3.2.5: *The changes in slope as the tangent line moves along the curve.*

The picture on the left shows a graph where the slopes *increase* as the tangent line moves from left-to-right along the curve. Note also how the tangent lines are turning in a *counter-clockwise* direction. Thus, where the slopes are increasing the graph is concave up. But increasing slopes means the function f' is increasing, and so its derivative must be nonnegative, i.e., $f'' \geq 0$.

The picture on the right shows a graph where the slopes *decrease* as the tangent line moves from left-to-right along the curve. Note also how the tangent lines are turning in a *clockwise* direction. Thus, where the slopes are decreasing the graph is concave down. But decreasing slopes means the function f' is decreasing, and so its derivative must be nonpositive, i.e., $f'' \leq 0$.

These ideas can be illustrated better by using a dynamic plot of the tangent line moving along the graph. You can use the command `tanlines` as you did in Section 3.1 for this, or you can use the command `tanlines2`. This latter command works the same way, but its output also includes a "turning diagram." This turning diagram is just a plot of each tangent line segment with one endpoint at the origin. For example, suppose we want to study the concavity of the function:

$$f(x) = x^{\sin x} + 2,$$

on the interval $[0.5, 10]$. First we define this function in Maple as usual and then use `tanlines2` as follows:

```
> f:=x->x^sin(x)+2;
```

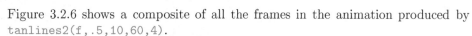
$$f := x \to x^{\sin(x)} + 2$$

```
> tanlines2(f,.5,10,60,4);
```

Figure 3.2.6 shows a composite of all the frames in the animation produced by `tanlines2(f,.5,10,60,4)`.

Study the animation produced by the above code and observe how the turning diagram works somewhat like a clock – except that it can run backward as well as forward. Where the graph is concave up, the clock is turning counter-clockwise (running backward). Where the graph is concave down, the clock is turning clockwise (running forward).

Having made all of the above observations about the connection of the second derivative with the concavity of the graph, we can now make them into a precise statement in the following theorem.

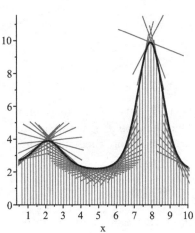

Figure 3.2.6: *A composite picture of all the frames in the animation.*

THEOREM 3.2.1 (2nd Derivative and Concavity)

Suppose f is a function which is defined and twice differentiable on an interval I. Then

    (1) *f is concave up on I if and only if $f'' \geq 0$ on I*

    (2) *f is concave down on I if and only if $f'' \leq 0$ on I*

Proof: We prove statement (1) and leave the proof of statement (2) to the exercises. Suppose first that f is concave up on I. We have to show that $f'' \geq 0$ on I. But by Theorem 3.1.1 this is equivalent to showing that the function f' is increasing on I. Thus, what we need to show is that if $x_1 < x_2$ are any two points in I, then $f'(x_1) \leq f'(x_2)$. Now if we use the definition of concave up with x_2 in place of x and x_1 in place of x_0, then we get the inequality:

$$f(x_2) \geq f(x_1) + f'(x_1)(x_2 - x_1) \qquad (1)$$

On the other hand, we can apply the definition of concave up with x_1 in place of x and x_2 in place of x_0, then we get the inequality:

$$f(x_1) \geq f(x_2) + f'(x_2)(x_1 - x_2) \qquad (2)$$

Now rearrange Inequality (2) to get

$$f(x_1) - f'(x_2)(x_1 - x_2) \geq f(x_2).$$

Combine this with Inequality (1) to get

$$f(x_1) - f'(x_2)(x_1 - x_2) \geq f(x_2) \geq f(x_1) + f'(x_1)(x_2 - x_1) \qquad (3).$$

Disregarding the middle inequality in (3) and subtracting $f(x_1)$ from both sides of this gives

$$-f'(x_2)(x_1 - x_2) \geq f'(x_1)(x_2 - x_1).$$

Hence (since $x_2 - x_1 > 0$),

$$f'(x_2) \geq f'(x_1),$$

and this is what we needed to show.

To prove the "if" part of statement (1), assume that $f'' \geq 0$ on I. As mentioned in the proof above, this is equivalent to saying that the function f' is increasing on I. From this it follows that f is concave up on I because if not, then there must exist some x_0 in I such that

$$f(x) < f(x_0) + f'(x_0)(x - x_0), \qquad (4)$$

for some x in I. To get a contradiction out of this, note that $x \neq x_0$, and so either $x > x_0$ or $x < x_0$.

Suppose first that $x > x_0$. Then we can rearrange Inequality (4) to get

$$\frac{f(x) - f(x_0)}{x - x_0} < f'(x_0) \qquad (5)$$

We apply the Mean Value Theorem (see Section 3.5 later in this chapter). This theorem guarantees that there exists a number c, between x_0 and x such that

$$f'(c) = \frac{f(x) - f(x_0)}{x - x_0}.$$

Putting this together with Inequality (5) gives

$$f'(c) < f'(x_0).$$

But this contradicts the assumption that f' is increasing on I. (Note that $c > x_0$ since c is between x_0 and x.)

Similarly if it happens that $x < x_0$, then rearranging Inequality (4) gives

$$f'(x_0) < \frac{f(x) - f(x_0)}{x - x_0} \qquad (6)$$

Now apply the Mean Value Theorem to get a number c between x and x_0 such that

$$f'(c) = \frac{f(x) - f(x_0)}{x - x_0}.$$

Thus $f'(x_0) < f'(c)$. But $c < x_0$, since c is between x and x_0. This contradicts the assumption that f' is increasing on I.

Concavity Diagrams

We apply the above theorem to curve sketching much like we did with Theorem 3.1.1. Here however, our intent to produce a concavity diagram, which shows where the graph is concave up and where it is concave down. By Theorem 3.2.1 this is equivalent to determining where $f'' \geq 0$ and where $f'' \leq 0$. For this, we first determine where the 2nd derivative is zero, i.e., find all the solutions x of the equation

$$f''(x) = 0.$$

This will typically give finitely many solutions $x = p_1, p_2, \ldots, p_r$, on the interval (a, b) where f is defined. Thus, as before with critical numbers, these numbers will divide the interval into finitely many subintervals. Then choosing test numbers t in each of these subintervals, we evaluate $f''(t)$, and, if it is positive, the graph is concave up on the entire subinterval, while if it is negative, the graph is concave down. From this analysis we then produce a concavity diagram, as for example, the hypothetical one shown in Figure 3.2.7.

The following examples illustrate the technique of constructing concavity diagrams and using these diagrams for sketching graphs of functions.

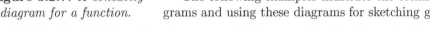

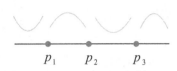

Figure 3.2.7: *A concavity diagram for a function.*

Example 3.2.1 (Concavity for a Polynomial)

Problem: For the function

$$f(x) = \tfrac{1}{10} \left(x^3 - 6x^2 - 15x + 40 \right),$$

draw a concavity diagram, find all the inflection points, and sketch a graph of the function.

Solution: The 1st and 2nd derivatives are readily calculated to be

$$
\begin{aligned}
f'(x) &= \tfrac{1}{10} \left(3x^2 - 12x - 15 \right) \\
f''(x) &= \tfrac{1}{10} \left(6x - 12 \right) = \tfrac{6}{10}(x - 2).
\end{aligned}
$$

We set the 2nd derivative equal to zero, $f''(x) = 0$, and get the equation $\tfrac{6}{10}(x-2) = 0$, which has a single solution $x = 2$. This divides the whole real line into two subintervals, which we now test for concavity.

Subinterval $(-\infty, 2)$: Choose test point $t = 0$ and calculate

$$f''(0) = \tfrac{6}{10}(0 - 2) < 0$$

Thus the graph is concave down on this interval.

Subinterval $(2, \infty)$: Choose test point $t = 3$ and calculate

$$f''(3) = \tfrac{6}{10}(3 - 2) > 0$$

Thus, the function is concave up on this interval. We can now draw the concavity diagram as shown in Figure 3.2.8.

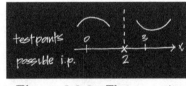

Figure 3.2.8: *The concavity diagram for* $f(x) = \tfrac{1}{10} \left(x^3 - 6x^2 - 15x + 40 \right)$.

From the concavity diagram, we see that the concavity is different on each side of $x = 2$, and so by definition the graph has an inflection point there. Computing the y-value at $x = 2$ gives

$$f(2) = \tfrac{1}{10} \left((2)^3 - 6(2)^2 - 15(2) + 40 \right) = \tfrac{1}{10}(-6) = -0.6$$

Thus, the inflection point is $(2, -0.6)$. We will need more points on the graph in order to get a good sketch, so we use the 1st derivative to locate the critical numbers and then plot the corresponding points. The 1st derivative in factored form is

$$f'(x) = \tfrac{1}{10} \left(3x^2 - 12x - 15 \right) = \tfrac{3}{10} \left(x^2 - 4x - 5 \right) = \tfrac{3}{10}(x + 1)(x - 5).$$

The critical numbers are the solutions of

$$\tfrac{3}{10}(x + 1)(x - 5) = 0,$$

which gives $x = -1, 5$. If you construct an increasing/decreasing diagram, you will find that f is increasing to the left of -1, decreasing between -1 and 5, and increasing to the right of 5. Thus, there is a local max at $x = -1$ and a local min at $x = 5$. We now can plot the graph by plotting the inflection point and points corresponding to the local max and min, as well as two others corresponding to $x = -5, 8$. The resulting graph is shown in Figure 3.2.9.

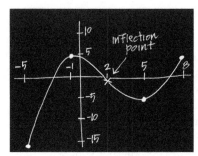

Figure 3.2.9: *The graph of* $f(x) = \frac{1}{10}(x^3 - 6x^2 - 15x + 40)$

Example 3.2.2

Problem: For the function

$$f(x) = x^2 e^{-x},$$

which was studied and graphed in Example 3.1.2, draw a concavity diagram, find all the inflection points, and draw another graph showing all the inflection points.

Solution: The 1st derivative was found to be

$$f'(x) = (2x - x^2)\,e^{-x},$$

and so the 2nd derivative is

$$f''(x) = (2 - 2x)\,e^{-x} + (2x - x^2)(-e^{-x}) = (2 - 4x + x^2)\,e^{-x}.$$

Then the equation $f''(x) = 0$ is

$$(2 - 4x + x^2)\,e^{-x} = 0$$

or equivalently (since the exponential function is never zero)

$$x^2 - 4x + 2 = 0$$

Trial-and-error factoring of this does not lead to any success, so we find the roots using the quadratic formula:

$$x = \frac{4 \pm \sqrt{16 - 8}}{2} = 2 \pm \sqrt{2} \approx 0.586, 3.42$$

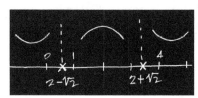

Figure 3.2.10: *The concavity diagram for* $f(x) = x^2 e^{-x}$.

Thus, we get three intervals on which to test the concavity.

Subinterval $(-\infty, 0.586)$: Choose test point $t = 0$ and calculate

$$f''(0) = \left(2 - 4(0) + (0)^2\right) e^0 = 2 > 0$$

Thus, the graph is concave up on this interval.

Subinterval $(0.586, 3.41)$: Choose test point $t = 1$ and calculate

$$f''(1) = \left(2 - 4(1) + (1)^2\right) e^{-1} = -e^{-1} < 0$$

Thus, the graph is concave down on this interval.

Subinterval $(3.42, \infty)$: Choose test point $t = 4$ and calculate

$$f''(4) = \left(2 - 4(4) + (4)^2\right) e^{-4} = 2e^{-4} > 0$$

Thus, the graph is concave up on this interval.

With the analysis complete, we can now draw the concavity diagram as shown in Figure 3.2.10.

As you can see from the diagram, the concavity changes at $2 - \sqrt{2}$ and at $2 + \sqrt{2}$, and thus the graph has inflection points at these places. When we plotted this function before in Figure 3.1.11, we did not include the inflection point analysis, so we re-plot the graph showing these points. See Figure 3.2.11.

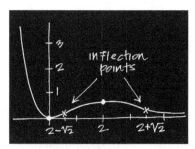

Figure 3.2.11: *Graph of* $f(x) = x^2 e^{-x}$ *showing inflection points.*

Exercises: 3.2 (Curve Sketching: 2nd Derivatives)

> with(code_ch3,tanlines,tanlines2);
[*tanlines,tanlines2*]

CAS: Using tanline2 to Find Inflection Points

In Exercises 1–6, (a) Use tanlines2(f,a,b,N,h) to create an animation of tangent lines moving along the graph of f on the interval $[a, b]$, Use N=40 frames. *Recall*: The value of h determines how long the tangent lines are. Experiment with this until you get tangent lines that are neither too small or too large. (b) View the animation several times, step through it frame-by-frame, and then use the cursor probe on the graph to locate, approximately, the inflection points on the graph. NOTE: The answers given in the solutions manual may be different than your answers. This is because results using the cursor probe can vary and positioning the probe over what is judged to be an inflection point can vary.

1. $f(x) = x + x \cos x,\ [0, 8]$
2. $f(x) = x - x \sin x,\ [0, 10]$
3. $f(x) = \frac{1}{10}x^5 - \frac{1}{2}x^3,\ (-2, 2)$
4. $f(x) = \frac{1}{20}x^5 - \frac{1}{4}x^2,\ [-2, 2]$
5. $f(x) = e^{-2x} \sin 10x,\ [0, 1.1]$
6. $f(x) = x^{\cos x},\ [0.5, 7]$

Using a Concavity Diagram to Find Inflection Points

In Exercises 7–24 find all the inflection points of the function f on the given interval $[a, b]$. Do this by constructing a Concavity Diagram and locating the points where the concavity changes. Optional CAS: Check your work with a Maple graph.

7. $f(x) = x^3 - 3x^2 + 2,\ [-2, 3]$
8. $f(x) = 2x^3 + 3x^2 - x,\ [-2, 1]$
9. $f(x) = x^4 - 4x^3,\ [-2, 4]$
10. $f(x) = \frac{1}{10}x^5 - \frac{1}{6}x^4 - \frac{2}{3}x^3,\ [-2, 3]$
11. $f(x) = 3x^5 - 10x^4 + 15x,\ [-2, 4]$
12. $f(x) = \frac{1}{30}x^6 - \frac{5}{12}x^4 - 2x^2,\ [-3, 3]$
13. $f(x) = x^2 + \cos 2x,\ [-2, 3]$
14. $f(x) = x^2 - \sin 2x,\ [-3, 3]$
15. $f(x) = \frac{1}{2}\cos 2x - 2\cos x,\ [-2, 3]$
16. $f(x) = \frac{1}{2}\cos 2x + 2\sin x,\ [-3, 3]$
17. $f(x) = \tan x - 4x,\ [-1.5, 1.5]$
18. $f(x) = \cot x + 4x,\ [0.1, 3]$
19. $f(x) = 2xe^{-x^3/3},\ [-1.1, 3]$
20. $f(x) = 2xe^{-\sqrt{x}},\ [-3, 3]$
21. $f(x) = x^4 e^{-2x},\ [0, 7]$
22. $f(x) = x^4 e^{-4x},\ [0, 4]$
23. $f(x) = 2x^2 \ln x,\ (0, 1.5]$
24. $f(x) = 2x^3 \ln x,\ (0, 1.5]$

Sketches Using Increasing/Decreasing and Concavity Diagrams

In Exercises 25–50, sketch the graph of the function f on the given interval $[a, b]$. For this do the following:

(a) Find all the critical numbers, draw an Increasing/Decreasing Diagram, and determine the local maxima and minima.

(b) Draw a Concavity Diagram and determine all the inflection points.

(c) Determine vertical asymptotes, if any. Also if the function extends beyond the given interval $[a, b]$ to $\pm\infty$, determine if its graph has any horizontal asymptotes.

(d) Make a table of function values $y = f(x)$, for x-values: the critical numbers, possible places where inflection points occur, endpoints a, b, and any other values you find pertinent. Plot these points and use all the information in (a)-(c) to sketch an accurate graph of f. Label local maxima/minima and inflection points. Do not use Maple.

25. $f(x) = x^3 - 3x^2 + 2,\ [-1, 3]$
26. $f(x) = \frac{1}{4}x^3 - \frac{3}{4}x^2 + 1/2,\ [-3, 2]$
27. $f(x) = x^4 - 4x^3 + 10,\ [-2, 4]$
28. $f(x) = 3x^4 - 16x^3 + 18x^2,\ [-1, 4]$
29. $f(x) = 3x^5 - 25x^3 + 60x,\ [-2.5, 2.5]$
30. $f(x) = 3x^5 - 5x^3,\ [-1.5, 1.5]$
31. $f(x) = x - 2\sqrt{x},\ [0, 5]$
32. $f(x) = 6x^2 - 8x^{3/2},\ [0, 2]$
33. $f(x) = \dfrac{1}{2x^2 - x},\ [-1, 2]$
34. $f(x) = \dfrac{x^3}{x^2 + x - 2},\ [-5, 3]$
35. $f(x) = \dfrac{4x}{x^2 + 1},\ [-4, 4]$ 36. $f(x) = \dfrac{4x - 4}{x^2 + 1},\ [-4, 4]$
37. $f(x) = 10(x - 1)e^{-x},\ (0.5, 5)$
38. $f(x) = 2(x^2 - 1)e^{-x},\ [-1, 5]$
39. $f(x) = 2e^{-x^2/2},\ [-4, 4]$ 40. $f(x) = e^{-\sqrt{x}},\ [-1, 5]$
41. $f(x) = \ln(x^2 + 1),\ [-4, 4]$
42. $f(x) = \ln(x^3 + 1),\ [-0.9, 3]$
43. $f(x) = x \ln x - x + 2,\ (0, 4]$
44. $f(x) = 2\sqrt{x} \ln x,\ (0, 2]$
45. $f(x) = \sin x + \cos x,\ [0, 2\pi]$
46. $f(x) = \sin x - \cos x,\ [0, 2\pi]$
47. $f(x) = \sin^2 x,\ [0, \pi]$ 48. $f(x) = \cos^2 x,\ [0, 2\pi]$
49. $f(x) = \ln(2 + \sin x),\ [0, 2\pi]$
50. $f(x) = \ln(2 + \cos x),\ [\pi/, 9\pi/4]$

Calculus Concepts & Computation

3.3 Maximum and Minimum Values

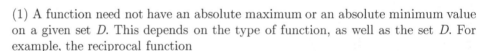

```
> with(dplot_tools,dplot2);
```
$$[dplot2]$$

In this section we consider techniques for determining the largest and smallest values of a function f on some set D, which is usually an interval contained in the domain of f. The largest value of f is called its *maximum value* (or *absolute maximum value*) and the smallest value is called its *minimum value* (or *absolute minimum value*). It is entirely possible that f has neither a maximum value nor a minimum value on D, but when it does these must occur at critical points of f. You have already learned how critical points are instrumental in determining the behavior of the graph of f and have encountered *local* maximum and minimum values in the construction of the graph. Now we look at more details, and a few theorems, connected with this.

After learning these techniques and theorems in this section, you will see some concrete applications in the next section where the determination of maximum and minimum values for functions is important and useful in real-life applications.

Absolute Extrema

For a real-valued function f defined on a set D, the set of *values* of f on D is

$$R = \{f(x) \mid x \varepsilon D\}.$$

R is just the range of the function if D is its domain. The largest value in R (if there is one) is called the *absolute maximum value* of f, and the smallest value in R (if there is one) is called the *absolute minimum value* of f. The term "absolute" is used to distinguish this type of maximum or minimum from the "local" maxima and minima which were discussed in Section 3.1 (and will be further discussed here). Often the absolute maximum value of f is merely called the maximum value of f. Similarly, the absolute minimum value is often referred to as the minimum value. Collectively, the absolute maximum and minimum are called the *absolute extrema* of the function.

There are two things to note about the above definition:

(1) A function need not have an absolute maximum or an absolute minimum value on a given set D. This depends on the type of function, as well as the set D. For example, the reciprocal function

$$f(x) = \frac{1}{x},$$

has neither a maximum nor a minimum value on the set $(0, \infty)$. However, on the interval $[1/2, 3]$ the same function has a maximum value 2 and a minimum value $1/3$. See Figure 3.3.1.

(2) If a function has an absolute maximum or an absolute minimum, then these can occur at more than one point in the set D. For example, the sine function $f(x) = \sin x$ has maximum value 1 and minimum value -1 on the interval $D = [0, \infty]$. The maximum value occurs at the points

$$x = \frac{\pi}{2} + 2\pi n, n = 0, 1, 2, \ldots$$

while the minimum value occurs at the points

$$x = \frac{3\pi}{2} + 2\pi n, n = 0, 1, 2, \ldots$$

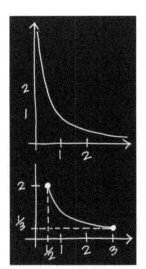

Figure 3.3.1: *The function $f(x) = \frac{1}{x}$ on two intervals.*

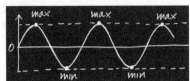

Figure 3.3.2: *The sine wave achieves it maximum and minimum values infinitely often.*

Figure 3.3.2 shows the well-known graph of a sine wave.

Thus, as you may surmise from these simple examples, the problem of determining whether a function f has absolute extrema in D, and if so where these extrema occur, can be a complicated problem to solve. There are a few theorems that will help us solve this problem in certain cases. One basic theorem, called the *extreme value theorem*, guarantees the existence of absolute extrema under fairly general conditions: the function f only needs to be continuous (not necessarily differentiable) and the set D is any closed interval.

THEOREM 3.3.1 (The Extreme Value Theorem)

Suppose f is a continuous function on the a closed interval $[a,b]$. Then f has an absolute maximum value $f(c)$ at some point c in $[a,b]$, and f has an absolute minimum value $f(d)$ at some point d in $[a,b]$

The proof of the theorem is fairly complicated, requiring some advanced techniques, and so is not presented here. (Consult an advanced calculus book if you are interested.)

Example 3.3.1

Finding the absolute maximum and minimum values for a function can be difficult. However, from computer plots of the function's graph, we can always obtain *approximate* information about the absolute extrema and where they occur.

Problem: Use computer plots to determine, approximately, the absolute maximum and minimum values of the following functions on the given intervals:

(a) $f(x) = x^6 - 2x^4 - 6x^2 + 5x$, $[-2, 2]$. (b) $f(x) = \sin 3x \sin 20x$, $[0, \pi]$.

Solution:

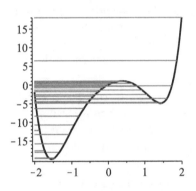

Figure 3.3.3: *The last frame in the movie produced by* `dplot2(f,-2,2,30)`.

Part (a): We could do a standard plot of this polynomial function on the interval $[-2, 2]$, but to help you visualize and understand the concept of absolute extrema, we use a dynamic plot of the graph which shows the y-values projected from the graph to the y-axis. The special-purpose Maple procedure for this is a variation of `dplot`. It is called `dplot2`, and has the same input as `dplot`. We use this to produce a movie of the dynamic plot with frames. You should slow the movie down to run at, say, 3 frames per second.

```
> f:=x->x^6-2x^4-6x^2+5*x;
```
$$f := x \mapsto x^6 - 2x^4 - 6x^2 + 5x$$
```
> dplot2(f,-2,2,30);
```

The horizontal red lines in the animation show how the values of this function vary on the interval $[-2, 2]$. Inspecting the graph in the final frame of the movie, we see that all the horizontal lines appear to lie between $y = -20$ and $y = 18$. Thus, the absolute minimum value of the function is approximately $y = -20$ and occurs at approximately $x = -1.5$. The absolute maximum appears to be 18 and occurs at the right endpoint $x = 2$ of the interval.

Part (b): We use `dplot2` again to examine the variation of the values of this function on the given interval.

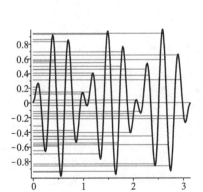

Figure 3.3.4: *Variation of the values of* $f(x) = \sin 3x \sin 20x$

```
> f:=x->sin(3*x)*sin(20*x);
```
$$f := x \mapsto \sin(3x)\sin(20x)$$
```
> dplot2(f,0,Pi,50);
```

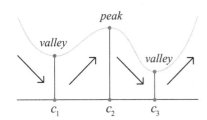

Examining the last frame in the animation (Figure 3.3.4 above), you see that three of the peaks in the graph appear to be candidates for the maximum value of the function. Likewise, three valleys in the graph are candidates for the minimum. The horizontal red lines help us see that the peak at $x \approx 2.6$ gives an absolute maximum value of 1 (approximately). You can get these approximate values by using the cursor probe on the highest peak in Figure 3.3.4. Similarly, the absolute minimum value appears to be -1 and occurs at approximately $x \approx 0.55$.

Note that Theorem 3.3.1 is only an existential theorem, and so gives us no information about how to find the extreme values or where they occur. However, if we restrict to functions that are differentiable, then we can use the first and second derivatives to help locate the absolute extrema. The key to this is to look at the more general concept of *local extrema* (there are more of these and the absolute extrema occur among the local extrema). The local extrema are the local maxima and local minima that we discussed informally in Section 3.1. We return now to this topic and give a more detailed analysis of local extrema.

Local Extrema

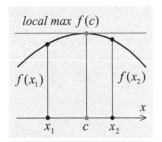

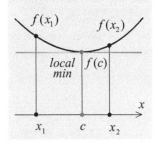

Figure 3.3.5: *Near c a local max or min looks like an absolute max or min.*

As you have seen many times in the previous sections, the behavior of the graph of a function f is best captured in an increasing/decreasing diagram. For example, suppose the increasing/decreasing diagram for f looks like the one in the margin above and, with further analysis, the actual graph of f looks like that shown in the diagram.

From the mountain-slope analogy, we see that the peaks in the graph occur where the function f changes from increasing to decreasing (as x moves from left to right), while the valleys occur where f changes from decreasing to increasing. Technically, each peak is a *local maximum* for f and each valley is a *local minimum* for f. Collectively these are known as *local extrema*.

The question now is: How do we express this idea of local maximum or minimum, which is visually apparent in the figures, in more precise mathematical terms involving analytic properties of the function f? This is easy. Take any local extrema in the above figures and focus on just the graph of the function on a small enough interval I about the point c where the local extrema occurs. Then we get that the graph looks like one of the two pictures shown in Figure 3.3.5. The figure is the basis for the following definition of local extrema.

DEFINITION 3.3.1 (Local Extrema)

(1) *f* has a *local maximum* **value at** *c* *if there is an interval I containing c such that*

$$f(c) \geq f(x) \qquad \text{for all } x \text{ in } I$$

(2) *f* has a *local minimum* **value at** *c* *if there is an interval I containing c such that*

$$f(c) \leq f(x) \qquad \text{for all } x \text{ in } I$$

Now that we have a precise definition of local extrema, we turn to the task of determining where these local extrema occur. From your previous work with graphing functions by hand, using increasing/decreasing diagrams, it should now seem obvious that these diagrams can be used to determine the local extrema and the points where they occur. This is recorded in the following theorem.

THEOREM 3.3.2 (The 1st Derivative Test)

Suppose c is a critical point of f

(1) *If the first derivative $f'(x)$ changes from positive to negative as x passes through c, then f has a local maximum at c*

(2) *If the first derivative $f'(x)$ changes from negative to positive as x passes through c, then f has a local minimum at c*

This theorem is called the *first derivative test* because the nature of the critical point c, whether is a local max or a local min, is determined solely by looking at the first derivative of the function. In order to use the 1st derivative test, you must construct the increasing/decreasing diagram for the function, just like you do when attempting to graph the function by hand.

If you are not interested in graphing the function, but rather only interested in classifying the critical points of f as being a local maxima or minima, then there is a more convenient, often more efficient, way of doing the classification. The method uses the second derivative of f, and so is called the *second derivative test* (for classifying critical points).

THEOREM 3.3.3 (The 2nd Derivative Test)

Suppose c is a critical point of f and f'' is continuous on an interval containing c.

(1) *If $f''(c) < 0$, then $f(c)$ is a local maximum value.*

(2) *If $f''(c) > 0$, then $f(c)$ is a local minimum value.*

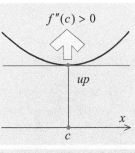

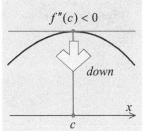

Figure 3.3.6: *Concavity can be used to classify local extrema.*

Proof: To prove (1), note that since $f''(c) < 0$ and f'' is continuous on an interval containing c, we can find a smaller interval I containing c, such that $f''(x) < 0$, for any x in I. By Theorem 3.2.1, this says that f is concave down on I, and this means, by Definition 3.2.1, that for all x_0 in I,

$$f(x) \leq f(x_0) + f'(x_0)(x - x_0),$$

for all x in I. In particular, for $x_0 = c$

$$f(x) \leq f(c) + f'(c)(x - c),$$

for all x in I. But c is a critical number of f and so $f'(c) = 0$. Thus, the last inequality reduces to

$$f(x) \leq f(c),$$

for all x in I. This says that f has a local maximum at c. The proof of (2) is entirely similar.

Geometrically, the content of Theorem 3.3.3 is clear: If the graph is concave down (the negative direction) at c, then the critical point is a local maximum, and if the graph is concave up (the positive direction) at c, then the critical point is local minimum. Figure 3.3.6 indicates this.

The 2nd derivate test is easy to apply, provided the calculation of the second derivative is not too difficult, as the following example shows.

Example 3.3.2 (Using the 2nd Derivative Test)

Problem: Without graphing the functions, find the critical points of the following functions and use the 2nd derivative test to classify them as local maxima or local minima.

(a) $f(x) = 6x^5 - 15x^4 - 10x^3 + 30x^2$, for x in $(-\infty, \infty)$.

(b) $f(x) = \dfrac{x^2 + 1}{x}$, for $x \neq 0$.

(c) $f(t) = e^{-t} \sin t$, for t in $[0, \infty)$.

Solution:

Part(a): The first derivative is

$$f'(x) = 30x^4 - 60x^3 - 30x^2 + 60x = 30x\left(x^3 - 2x^2 - x + 2\right),$$

and so the critical points are the roots of the equation

$$30x\left(x^3 - 2x^2 - x + 2\right) = 0$$

The roots are $x = 0$ and the roots of the cubic equation $x^3 - 2x^2 - x + 2 = 0$. By guess-work, an obvious root of this cubic equation is $x = 1$. Then dividing by $x - 1$ gives the factorization

$$x^3 - 2x^2 - x + 2 = (x - 1)\left(x^2 - x - 2\right)$$

The quadratic part of this factors as

$$x^2 - x - 2 = (x - 2)(x + 1).$$

Thus, there are four critical numbers $-1, 0, 1, 2$. To classify these as local maxima or minima, look at the 2nd derivative

$$f''(x) = 120x^3 - 180x^2 - 60x + 60.$$

Then, just evaluate this function at the four critical numbers

(1) $f''(-1) = -120 - 180 + 60 + 60 = -180 < 0$, so there is a local maximum at $x = -1$.

(2) $f''(0) = 60 > 0$, so there is a local minimum at $x = 0$.

(3) $f''(1) = 120 - 180 - 60 + 60 = -60 < 0$, so there is a local maximum at $x = 1$.

(4) $f''(2) = 960 - 720 - 120 + 60 = 180 > 0$, so there is a local minimum at $x = 2$.

Note that the actual local extreme values of $f(x) = 6x^5 - 15x^4 - 10x^3 + 30x^2$ are

$$f(-1) = 19, \ f(0) = 0, \ f(1) = 11, \ f(2) = -8$$

Since the local extreme values are easily determined once we know *where* they occur (the critical points), we will usually just concentrate on determining the locations rather than the actual values.

Part(b): We first write the function f as

$$f(x) = \frac{x^2 + 1}{x} = x + \frac{1}{x},$$

since it is easier to differentiate when in this form:

$$f'(x) = 1 - \frac{1}{x^2}.$$

Thus, the critical numbers are $x = \pm 1$. These are easily classified by looking at the second derivative

$$f''(x) = \frac{2}{x^3}.$$

Then

(1) $f''(-1) = -2 < 0$, so there is a local maximum at $x = -1$.

(2) $f''(1) = 2$, so there is a local minimum at $x = 1$.

Part(c): Finally we look at the function $f(t) = e^{-t} \sin t$, for t nonnegative.

$$f'(t) = -e^{-t} \sin t + e^{-t} \cos t = e^{-t} (\cos t - \sin t).$$

Thus, the critical numbers occur where the sine and cosine are equal $\cos t = \sin t$. Two basic times when this occurs are $t = \pi/4$ and $t = 5\pi/4$. All the other positive times come from adding a multiple of 2π to these:

$$t = \frac{\pi}{4} + 2n\pi \quad \text{and} \quad t = \frac{5\pi}{4} + 2n\pi.$$

$n = 0, 1, 2, \ldots$ Thus, this function has infinitely many critical points. To classify them, look at the 2nd derivative.

$$\begin{aligned} f''(t) &= \frac{d}{dt} \left[e^{-t} (\cos t - \sin t) \right] = -e^{-t} (\cos t - \sin t) + e^{-t} (-\sin t - \cos t) \\ &= -2e^{-t} \cos t. \end{aligned}$$

At the two basic critical points, we have

(1) $f''\left(\frac{\pi}{4}\right) = -2e^{-\pi/4} \cos\left(\frac{\pi}{4}\right) = -\sqrt{2}e^{-\pi/4} < 0$, so there is a local maximum value at $t = \pi/4$.

(2) $f''\left(\frac{5\pi}{4}\right) = -2e^{-5\pi/4} \cos\left(\frac{5\pi}{4}\right) = \sqrt{2}e^{-5\pi/4} > 0$, so there is a local minimum value at $t = 5\pi/4$.

Adding a multiple of 2π to $t = \pi/4, 5\pi/4$ does not change the value of the cosine. Since the exponential function is always positive, we see that the function f has

$$\text{local maxima at} \quad t = \frac{\pi}{4} + 2n\pi \quad \text{and} \quad \text{local minima at} \quad t = \frac{5\pi}{4} + 2n\pi,$$

for $n = 0, 1, 2, 3, \ldots$

The function $f(t) = e^{-t} \sin t$ in this example is called a "damped" sine wave and represents an oscillatory motion about an equilibrium point $(y = 0)$ which gradually dies out. During oscillation, each change in direction (where the velocity $v = f'(t)$ is zero) introduces a local maximum or minimum in the graph of f. Since it takes infinitely long for the motion to die off ($\lim_{t \to \infty} f(t) = 0$), we expect to have infinitely many local maxima and minima. However, it only takes a short while before the displacement from equilibrium is essentially zero: $f(t) \approx 0$, for t large. This is apparent from a dynamic plot of this function on, say, the interval $[0, 15]$. See Figure 3.3.7.

Thus, while the calculations show that there are infinitely many local extrema for this function, the graph above shows that only two of these extrema are readily apparent at the scale used. Plotting the function on other intervals will reveal the other extrema. There is one in the interval $[6, 8]$, one in the interval $8, 12]$, etc.

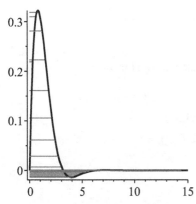

Figure 3.3.7: *Damped harmonic motion about equilibrium.*

Optimizing a Function

An important application of the derivative calculus, one which will be studied in great detail in the next section, involves finding the optimum, or best, value for a variable quantity. Typically one wants to maximize profit, minimize cost, minimize the distance, maximize the container size, minimize the material used, and so on.

If the quantity being optimized (i.e., maximized or minimized) is expressed as a function f defined on an interval I, then optimization amounts to finding the absolute maximum value or the absolute minimum value for f on I.

So how do we optimize f on I? We studied how to find *local* extrema in the previous subsection, and in the section before that we defined what *absolute* extrema are and had a theorem (the extreme-value theorem) that guarantees their existence in certain cases. Now we need a method for finding these absolute extrema.

In the case when the interval I is a closed interval, $I = [a, b]$, we can give a straight-forward procedure, or method, for finding the absolute maximum and absolute minimum. Assuming f is differentiable, the extreme value theorem guarantees that f has an absolute maximum and minimum somewhere, say at c and d, respectively, in $[a, b]$. Now it is possible that c or d coincides with one of the end points, but if neither does, then each lies in the open interval (a, b). Since $f(c)$ and $f(d)$ are absolute extrema, they are also local extrema. Hence, in this case c and d are critical points of f. The reasoning is that c and d are either end points of the interval $[a, b]$ or critical points in the open interval (a, b). This is summarized in the following box.

THE CLOSED INTERVAL METHOD (for Absolute Extrema)

Suppose f is continuous on a closed interval $I = [a, b]$ and differentiable on (a, b).

To find the absolute extrema of f on I do the following.

(1) Find all the critical points $c_1, c_2, \ldots, c_k$ of f in the interval (a, b).

(2) Compute the values of f at the endpoints and the critical points
$$f(a), f(c_1), f(c_2), \ldots, f(c_k), f(b)$$

Then the largest of these values is the absolute maximum value of f and the smallest of these values is the absolute minimum value of f.

This is a particularly simple method to apply. The only difficult part can be finding the critical points of f, that is, solving the equation $f'(x) = 0$, for x. But, once we have these, we simply evaluate the *original* function f at these critical points and the endpoints, and look for the largest and smallest values that occur.

Example 3.3.3 (Optimizing a Function)

Problem: Find the absolute extrema for the following functions

(a) $f(x) = 3x^4 + 4x^3 - 12x^2$, for x in $[-3, 2]$. (b) $f(x) = x + \frac{1}{x}$, for x in $[1/2, 3]$.

Solution:

Part(a): The 1st derivative is

$$f'(x) = 12x^3 + 12x^2 - 24x = 12x\left(x^2 + x - 2\right) = 12x(x+2)(x-1).$$

Thus, the critical points are $x = -2, 0, 1$. Evaluating f at these points and at the end points $x = -3, 2$ of the interval gives

$$
\begin{aligned}
f(-3) &= 3(-3)^4 + 4(-3)^3 - 12(-3)^2 = 243 - 108 - 108 = 27 \\
f(-2) &= 3(-2)^4 + 4(-2)^3 - 12(-2)^2 = 48 - 32 - 48 = -32 \\
f(0) &= 0 \\
f(1) &= 3(1)^4 + 4(1)^3 - 12(1)^2 = 3 + 4 - 12 = -5 \\
f(2) &= 3(2)^4 + 4(2)^3 - 12(2)^2 = 48 + 32 - 48 = 32
\end{aligned}
$$

Hence the absolute minimum value is -32 and occurs at the critical point $x = -2$, while the absolute maximum value is 32 and occurs at the right endpoint $x = 2$ of the interval.

Part(b): The 1st derivative of the function $f(x) = x + \dfrac{1}{x}$ is

$$f'(x) = 1 - \frac{1}{x^2}.$$

Thus, the critical points are $x = \pm 1$, but only $x = 1$ is in the interval $[1/2, 3]$ under consideration. Evaluating f at $x = 1$ and at the endpoints $x = 1/2, 3$ gives

$$
\begin{aligned}
f\left(\frac{1}{2}\right) &= \frac{1}{2} + 2 = \frac{5}{2} \\
f(1) &= 1 + 1 = 2 \\
f(3) &= 3 + \frac{1}{3} = \frac{10}{3}
\end{aligned}
$$

Hence, the absolute minimum value of f on the interval $[1/2, 3]$ is 2 and occurs at the critical point $x = 1$. The absolute maximum value is $10/3$ and occurs at the endpoint $x = 3$.

Exercises: 3.3 (Maximum and Minimum Values)

```
> with(dplot_tools,dplot2);
              [dplot2]
```

CAS: **Using** `dplot2` **to Find Approximate Maximum and Minimum Values**

In Exercises 1–6, use `dplot2(f,a,b,N)` to create a dynamic plot of the function f on the interval $[a, b]$. After viewing it several times, use the last frame of the movie to find, approximately, the (absolute) maximum and minimum values of f and where these values occur.

1. $f(x) = x^2 \sin 20x$, $[1, 2]$ **2.** $f(x) = x^{(\cos x)/x}$, $[0.5, 7]$
3. $f(x) = \cos x \sin 15x$, $[0, \pi]$
4. $f(x) = 5 + xe^{-x} - xe^{-x/10} \sin x$, $[0, 40]$
5. $f(x) = x^{\sin 15x}$, $[0, 4]$
6. $f(x) = 1 + xe^{-x} - \sin x$, $[0, 10]$

Using the 2nd Derivative Test

In Exercises 7–42 do the following: Without graphing, find (by hand) the critical numbers of the function and use the 2nd derivative test to classify them as local maxima or local minima. If the 2nd derivative test does not work, use the 1st derivative test.

7. $f(x) = x^3 + x^2 - x$ **8.** $f(x) = \frac{1}{20}x^5 - \frac{1}{4}x^2$
9. $f(x) = 2x^2 - x^4$ **10.** $f(x) = \frac{1}{10}x^5 - \frac{1}{6}x^4 - \frac{2}{3}x^3$
11. $f(x) = x^6 - 6x^4$ **12.** $f(x) = \frac{1}{30}x^6 - \frac{5}{12}x^4 - 2x^2$
13. $f(x) = 5x^3 - 3x^5$ **14.** $f(x) = x^4 - 4x^3$
15. $f(x) = x^5 - 5x^4 + 5x^3$
16. $f(x) = 3x^4 + 4x^3 - 24x^2 - 48x$
17. $f(x) = (3 - x^2)e^{-x}$ **18.** $f(x) = (1 - x^2)e^{-2x}$
19. $f(x) = \sqrt{x} + \dfrac{1}{\sqrt{x}}$ **20.** $f(x) = x^{1/3} + x^{-1/3}$
21. $f(x) = 2x^2 \ln x$, $(0, 1.5]$
22. $f(x) = 2x^3 \ln x$, $(0, 1.5]$
23. $f(x) = \sqrt{x} \ln x$ **24.** $f(x) = \ln(x^3 + 1)$
25. $f(x) = \ln(x^2 + 1)$ **26.** $f(x) = \ln(3x^2 + 2)$
27. $f(x) = e^{-x^2}$ **28.** $f(x) = 2xe^{-x}$
29. $f(x) = 2xe^{-x^3/3}$, $[-1.1, 3]$
30. $f(x) = 2xe^{-\sqrt{x}}$, $[-3, 3]$
31. $f(x) = x^4 e^{-2x}$, $[0, 7]$
32. $f(x) = x^4 e^{-4x}$, $[0, 4]$
33. $f(x) = e^{-x} \sin x$, just on $[0, 2\pi]$
34. $f(x) = e^{-2x} \sin x$, just on $[0, 2\pi]$
35. $f(x) = x + \cos 2x$, $[0, \pi]$
36. $f(x) = x - \sin 2x$, $[0, \pi]$
37. $f(x) = \frac{1}{2} \cos 2x - 2 \cos x$, $[-2, 3]$
38. $f(x) = \frac{1}{2} \cos 2x + 2 \sin x$, $[-3, 3]$

39. $f(x) = \tan x - 4x$, $[-1.5, 1.5]$
40. $f(x) = \cot x + 4x$, $[0.1, 3]$
41. $f(x) = x^x$ **42.** $f(x) = x^{x^2}$

Using the Closed Interval Method

In Exercises 43–64, find the absolute extrema for the function f on the closed interval $[a, b]$. Use the Closed Interval Method.

43. $f(x) = 36x - x^2$, $[0, 36]$
44. $f(x) = (a - x)x$, $[-a, a]$
45. $f(x) = x^2 + 16x^{-2}$, $[1, 3]$
46. $f(x) = x^4 + x^{-4}$, $[0.5, 2]$
47. $f(x) = x^3 - 27x$, $[-4, 5]$
48. $f(x) = 5x^3 - x^5$, $[-1, 2]$
49. $f(x) = x^5 - 5x^3$, $[-1, 2]$
50. $f(x) = 8x^2 - x^4$, $[-1, 3]$
51. $f(x) = x^4 - 8x^2$, $[-1, 3]$
52. $f(x) = x^3 - 3a^2x$, $[-\sqrt{3}a, \sqrt{3}a]$
53. $f(x) = 3x^4 + 4x^3 - 12x^2$, $[-3, 2]$
54. $f(x) = 3x^4 + 4x^3 - 24x^2 - 48x$, $[-3, 3]$
55. $f(x) = x^4 e^{-2x}$, $[0, 4]$
56. $f(x) = x^4 e^{-4x}$, $[0, 4]$
57. $f(x) = 2\sqrt{x} e^{-x/2}$, $[0, 4]$
58. $f(x) = 2\sqrt[3]{x} e^{-x/3}$, $[0, 8]$
59. $f(x) = \sin x + \cos x$, $[0, \pi]$
60. $f(x) = \sin x - \cos x$, $[0, \pi]$
61. $f(x) = x^2 - x^2 \ln x$, $[0.5, 3]$
62. $f(x) = x^3 - x^3 \ln x$, $[0.5, 3]$
63. $f(x) = e^{\sin x}$, $[0, 2\pi]$ **64.** $f(x) = e^{\cos x}$, $[0, 2\pi]$

Approximate and Exact Extreme Values

CAS: In Exercises 65–68, find all the absolute extrema (maxima/minima), local extrema (maxima/minima), and inflection points by doing the following:

(a) Use Maple to graph the function and then use the cursor probe on the graph to find, approximately, the required values.

(b) Compute $f'(x), f''(x)$ (by hand) and use these to find more exact values for those you found in Part (a). In the cases where you cannot solve the equations $f'(x) = 0, f''(x) = 0$, exactly, use Maple to approximate the solutions by either (i) graphing , or (ii) using using `fsolve`.

65. $f(x) = x^{-\ln x}$, $(0, 4]$
66. $f(x) = x^{-(\ln x)^2}$, $(0.5, 3]$
67. The odds 7–41 you were assigned.
68. The evens 8–42 you were assigned.

Calculus *Concepts & Computation*

3.4 Optimization

```
> with(code_ch3_new);
```

$[PrintmaxAfences,\ PrintmaxVbox,\ PrintminPfences,\ PrintminSbox,$
$\quad hallway,\ isosceles,\ maxAfences,\ maxVbox,\ meanvalue,$
$\quad minPfences,\ minSbox,\ paths,\ printmeanvalue\,]$

An important use of the derivative calculus is the determination of the optimum value of a function in various applied settings. Corporations may want to maximize their profit or minimize their cost in making a certain type of product. The profit functions for corporations can be very complicated functions, depending an many independent variables, and typically there will be additional constraints in the manufacturing process which connect the independent variables to each other. So, such profit functions are typically too difficult to analyze using the techniques we have learned for finding the absolute maximum value of a function. However, by abstracting and simplifying such real-life situations, we can present here some interesting functions, which measure the profit, cost, or other quantities, and depend on only two variables. After eliminating one of these variables using what's known as a *constraint equation*, we arrive at a function of one variable that we can optimize using the methods from Section 3.3.

One of the big challenges in this section will be writing down the explicit form for the function to be maximized or minimized. As you will see, the problems presented will give you basic information about the quantity to be maximized or minimized, and from this you are to determine, usually using elementary geometry, a functional expression for this quantity. The problems fall into several different categories, and there are no specific rules, other than first-hand experience, for how to go about tackling these problems.

Area and Perimeter

The applied problems in this subsection deal with simple planar regions (rectangles, triangles, etc.), where we wish to maximize the area of the region given a constraint on its perimeter or, dually, minimize the perimeter given a constraint on the area.

Example 3.4.1 (Fencing a Corral)

Problem: A cattle rancher wants to construct a rectangular corral for her cattle using 1600 yards of barbed-wire fencing which she has on hand. The corral is a temporary holding area for her cattle before she takes them to market, but needs to be as large as possible to afford temporary grazing for her herd.

The rancher wants to take advantage of the fact that one side of her property borders on a river and that she will not need fencing along the river-side of the corral since cattle will not generally attempt to swim the river. So, only three sides of the rectangular corral need fencing as shown in Figure 3.4.1.

How should she construct her corral so that it encloses the greatest amount of area, and thus allows the largest amount of grazing area for her herd?

Solution: For a typical rectangular corral as shown in Figure 3.4.1, we label the base and height of the rectangle by b and h respectively. Then the area enclosed by the fencing is

$$A = bh \qquad (3.4.1)$$

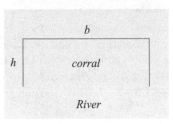

Figure 3.4.1

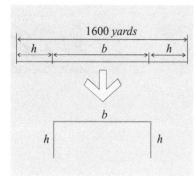

Figure 3.4.2: *Each corral is constrained by the* 1600 *yards of fencing available.*

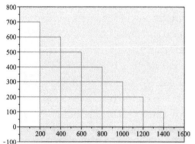

Figure 3.4.3: *Some corrals possible using* 1600 *yards of fencing.*

b	h	A
1400	100	140,000
1200	200	240,000
1000	300	300,000
800	400	320,000
600	500	300,000
400	600	240,000
200	700	140,000

Table 3.4.1: *The dimensions and areas of* 7 *possible corrals.*

The area A is what we want to maximize, but as it stands A is a function of two variables b and h. To make A large we could simply take b and h large. If there were no constraints on b and h, then there would be no limit as to how large we could make the enclosed area. However, b and h are constrained by the fact that the rancher has only 1600 yards of fencing. It is clear that the rancher will need to use all of this fencing to achieve the maximum enclosed area, and that to enclose an area such as that in Figure 3.4.1, she has to divide the fencing into three pieces as shown in Figure 3.4.2.

As you can see from the figure, the constraint on the choices of b and h is that they satisfy the equation:

$$b + 2h = 1600 \qquad (3.4.2)$$

To get a feel for what this constraint says, we choose a few values for b and h that satisfy it, and look at the corresponding enclosed corrals that result. The following command generates an animation showing 7 possible corrals that could be constructed using values of b and h that satisfy the constraint equation (3.4.2).

```
> maxAfences(1600,7,river,0);
```

Slow the frame rate down to 1 frame per second and view the animation several times. Figure 3.4.3 shows a composite of all the frames in this animation.

This gives us a visual understanding of the possible corrals that can be constructed out of the available 1600 yards of fencing. The figure only shows 7 of the infinitely many possible corrals. Our job now is to find which one of these infinitely many has the maximum area.

Before we use calculus to solve this problem, we look at the experimental evidence afforded us in the 7 possibilities shown in Figure 3.4.3. We analyze the figure carefully, reading off the dimensions for b and h in each of the 7 corrals, record these in Table 3.4.1, and then compute the corresponding areas.

You should also check the b and h values in the table to verify that they satisfy $b + 2h = 1600$. For example,

$$1400 + 2(100) = 1600$$
$$1200 + 2(200) = 1600$$

and so forth. Of the seven corrals shown in Table 3.4.1, the one with the largest area is the one with dimensions 800 yards by 400 yards. But the table does not include all possible corrals. Is there possibly one with larger area? To answer this definitely, we rewrite the area function

$$A = bh$$

as a function of a single variable. For this we take the constraint equation:

$$b + 2h = 1600,$$

and solve it for one of the variables, say b,

$$b = 1600 - 2h,$$

and then substitute this for b in the area function, giving

$$A = (1600 - 2h)\, h = 1600h - 2h^2$$

Now we have a function of a single variable only and we can maximize A on an appropriate interval. The appropriate interval is found from the observation that $b = 1600 - 2\,h$ must be positive, since b represents one side of the corral. Thus, h must be less than 800. So we take the interval $[0, 800]$ for h and maximize A on this interval. First we find the critical points of A by setting its derivative equal to zero

$$\frac{dA}{dh} = 1600 - 2h = 0$$

This gives $h = 400$ as the only critical point. Now we evaluate A at the critical point and the two endpoints of the interval.

$$A(400) = 320,000, \quad A(0) = 0,\ A(800) = 0$$

Thus, the maximum value of A is 320,000 and the corresponding dimensions of the corral with the largest enclosed area are

$$h \;=\; 400$$
$$b \;=\; 1600 - 2h = 800$$

This, coincidentally, is what we found from the above experimental work, recorded in Table 3.4.1. But this is just a lucky happenstance. Experimenting with a few configurations for the corrals is *not* a guaranteed way to find the one with maximum area. You must use the calculus!

Note that $b = 2h$. This is a general result, not connected to the particular numbers used in this example. (See the exercises.)

Also note that the values, reflect the fact that there is no enclosed area if none of the fencing is used for h or if all of the fencing is used for h. It is a general rule that in the applied problems for this section, the maximum or minimum value always occurs at a critical point, and so there is no need to check the endpoints in using the closed interval method.

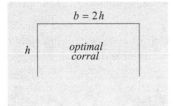

Figure 3.4.4: *The optimal corral has base that is twice its height.*

Example 3.4.2 (Largest Rectangle)

The problem in the previous Example 3.4.1 is related to the classical *isoperimetrical* problem:

Isoperimetrical Problem: *Out of all rectangles with the same perimeter, which one has the greatest area?*

Note that "iso" means "same" in Greek. So the problem is the "same-perimeter" problem in English. To connect this problem with the previous one above, we consider a specific version of the problem:

Out of all rectangles with perimeter $= 1600$, which one has the largest area?

Solution: If you wish you can consider this as a fencing problem where the rancher has no river to act as the fourth side of the rectangular corral, but rather must use some of her fencing for the fourth side as well. Using b and h for the base and height of a typical rectangle, we again have

$$A = bh,$$

and $P = 2b + 2h = 1600$, or

$$b + h = 800.$$

As before we solve the constraint equation for b, giving $b = 800 - h$, and then substitute this into the area function to obtain

$$A = (800 - h)\,h = 800h - h^2.$$

Now the critical point equation is

$$\frac{dA}{dh} = 800 - 2h = 0,$$

which gives $h = 400$, as the only critical point. This is where A achieves its maximum value, and so the rectangle with largest area has dimensions

$$h = 400, \qquad b = 800 - h = 400$$

This rectangle is thus a square: $b = h$, and this holds in general: Out of all rectangles with a given perimeter, the square has the largest area. You should compare this result with that in the previous Example 3.4.1 where $b = 2h$. Including the fourth side in the perimeter makes a big difference!

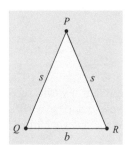

Figure 3.4.5: *A typical isosceles triangle.*

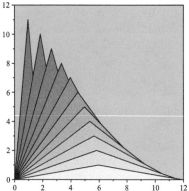

Figure 3.4.6: *Eleven isosceles triangles with perimeter $P = 24$.*

b	h	$A = \dfrac{1}{2}bh$
11.8	1	5.6
11.6	2	11.6
11.2	3	16.8
10.6	4	21.2
9.9	5	24.75
9.0	6	27.0
7.9	7	27.65
6.6	8	26.4
5.2	9	23.4
3.6	10	18.0
1.9	11	10.45

Table 3.4.2

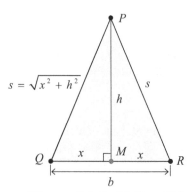

Figure 3.4.7: *Median PM.*

Example 3.4.3 (Largest Isosceles Triangle)

Here is an isoperimetrical problem which is a little more challenging than the one in the previous example.

Problem: *Out of all isosceles triangles with perimeter 24, which one has the greatest area?*

Solution: Recall that an isosceles triangle is one with two sides of equal lengths. The third side can be of any length b and is typically taken as the base of the triangle. See Figure 3.4.5.

To get a feel for the variety of different isosceles triangles with perimeter 24, view the animation produced by the following command.

```
> isosceles();
```

The last frame of this animation is shown in Figure 3.4.6. As you can see from the figure, the heights vary from $h = 1$ to $h = 11$. The bases b are more difficult to discern, but by using the cursor probe, we found the values shown in Table 3.4.2.

You should check the values for the bases b by examining Figure 3.4.6. Note that using the cursor probe on the figure only gives approximate values, and your values for the bases may be slightly different from those in table. As an exercise, you can use the data in the table to check that each of these eleven isosceles triangles has perimeter 24, approximately. Out of these eleven, the one with the largest area is the one having base $b = 7.9$ and height $h = 7$. Its area is $A = 27.65$. But what about the infinitely many others? Could we have overlooked one with larger area?

Having done this experimental work on the problem, we now solve it exactly with calculus. For this, we take a typical isosceles triangle, bisect the base at the point M and join M to the opposite vertex P, as shown in Figure 3.4.7.

By elementary geometry, we get two similar triangles $\triangle PMQ$, $\triangle PMR$, which therefore are right triangles with the right angle at M. Thus, PM is an altitude of the triangle. If we label the bases in the right triangles $\triangle PMQ$, $\triangle PMR$ by x and their common height by h as shown, then the two equal sides of the original isosceles triangle have length,

$$s = \sqrt{x^2 + h^2}$$

and the base has length

$$b = 2x.$$

Thus, the perimeter of this isosceles triangle is

$$P = 2x + 2\sqrt{x^2 + h^2},$$

while its area is

$$A = \tfrac{1}{2}bh = xh \qquad (3.4.3)$$

The variables x and h are constrained by the condition that the perimeter must be 24. Thus, the constraint equation is

$$2x + 2\sqrt{x^2 + h^2} = 24,$$

or equivalently

$$x + \sqrt{x^2 + h^2} = 12 \qquad (3.4.4)$$

The problem now is to maximize the area A in (3.4.3) subject to the constraint (3.4.4). For this, we solve the constraint equation (3.4.4) for one of the variables and use this to express the area function as a function of a single variable. We can solve equation (3.4.4) for either x or h, so we choose to solve for x. (As an exercise you can solve it for h and see how this affects the calculus.) First, we rearrange

$$\sqrt{x^2 + h^2} = 12 - x,$$

and square both sides

$$x^2 + h^2 = 144 - 24\,x + x^2.$$

So

$$h^2 = 144 - 24\,x,$$

and thus

$$x = \frac{1}{24}\left(144 - h^2\right) \qquad (3.4.5)$$

Now we can express the area function as a function of h only:

$$A = \frac{1}{24}\left(144 - h^2\right)h = \frac{1}{24}\left(144h - h^3\right) \qquad (3.4.6)$$

We consider maximizing this function on an appropriate interval. We see from Equation (3.4.5) that $x = 0$ when $h = 12$, and thus the interval for h that we need is $[0, 12]$. As before $A = 0$ at endpoints $0, 12$, and so the critical points in $[0, 12]$ are the only candidates for the absolute maximum area. The critical point equation is

$$\frac{dA}{dh} = \frac{1}{24}\left(144 - 3h^2\right) = 0.$$

Thus, the critical points are

$$h = \pm\sqrt{\frac{144}{3}} = \pm\sqrt{48} = \pm 4\sqrt{3}.$$

The positive value $4\sqrt{3}$ is the one we need. The corresponding value of x (given by Equation (3.4.5)) is

$$x = \frac{1}{24}\left(144 - \left(4\sqrt{3}\right)^2\right) = 4$$

Thus, the length of the base is $b = 2\,x = 8$. However, the length of the two equal sides in the isosceles triangle is

$$s = \sqrt{x^2 + h^2} = \sqrt{16 + 48} = \sqrt{64} = 8.$$

Hence, this shows that the maximum area isosceles triangle is an *equilateral* triangle (all three sides have the same length 8). Note that this is approximately what we found from our experimental work. The maximum area is

$$A = xh = 4(4\sqrt{3}) = 16\sqrt{3} \approx 27.7128$$

Volume and Surface Area

The volume-surface area problems in this subsection are similar to the area-perimeter problems in the previous subsection. There is just an extra dimension involved. Typically the problems either maximize volume with a constraint on the surface area or minimize surface area with a constraint on the volume. The maximization problems are dual to the minimization problems (see the exercises).

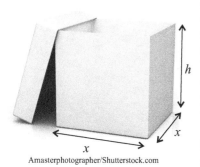

Figure 3.4.8: *A box with square base.*

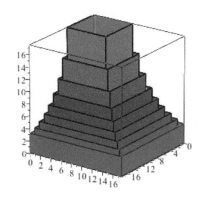

Figure 3.4.9: *Nine boxes with volume* 1000 *cubic inches.*

x	h	$V = x^2h$	$S = x^2 + 4xh$
7.6	17.5	1010.800	589.76
8.8	13.0	1064.700	535.04
10.1	9.8	999.698	497.93
11.4	7.8	1013.698	485.64
12.6	6.4	1016.064	481.32
13.9	5.2	1004.692	482.33
15.1	4.4	1003.244	493.77
16.4	3.7	995.152	511.68
17.7	3.2	1002.528	539.85

Table 3.4.3: *The data* x *and* h *collected from Figure* 3.4.9.

Example 3.4.4 (Pecan Boxes)

Problem: A pecan company has for years sold its special baked pecans in cubical boxes measuring 10 inches on a side. The box has aluminum sides and bottom, with a special plastic top. Recently the company's costs for aluminum have risen to 0.1 cents per square inch, and the company wishes to determine if it will be cheaper to make the aluminum part of the box in some other configuration besides cubical. For aesthetic reasons, the company wishes to keep the bottom of the box as a square. What dimensions should the company make the boxes in order to minimize the cost for the aluminum used, assuming that the boxes contain the same volume of pecans as before? How much money per box will this save over the previous cubical version of the box?

Solution: Consider the possible boxes one could have with square base, say x inches on a side, height h inches, and subject only to the constraint that it contain a given volume. Figure 3.4.8 shows such a typical box.

Such a box has volume

$$V = x^2h,$$

and aluminum surface area (the bottom and four sides)

$$S = x^2 + 4\,xh,$$

Remember that there is no top to the box (it does not count in computing the surface area). The original box had dimensions $x = 10$, $h = 10$ inches, volume $V = x^2h = 1000$ cubic inches, and aluminum surface area $S = x^2 + 4\,xh = 500$ square inches. Since the cost per box is $C = 0.1\,S$ cents, in order to reduce costs, the company needs to reduce the surface area S to the least possible while maintaining the same volume of 1000 cubic inches.

To get a feel for the problem, consider a variety of the different types of boxes that can be made, all with volume 1000. The animation created by the following command shows 9 different boxes with volume 1000.

```
> minSbox(1000,9,notop);
```

Figure 3.4.9 shows the last frame in this animation.

To compute the surface areas (approximately) for these 9 boxes, we change the above figure to a wireframe style, with no perspective, and rotate to an orientation of $\theta = -90$, $\phi = 90$, $\psi = -90$.

While we cannot use the cursor probe on this figure to get coordinates (since it is a 3-D graphic), careful examination of the figure gives us the data for the base lengths x and heights h shown in Table 3.4.3.

Using this data, which arguably is not very accurate, we compute the surface area of the nine boxes as shown in Table 3.4.3. Note that as a check, we also computed the volumes of the 9 boxes. Each volume should be 1000, but, as the numbers in the table show, inaccuracies in our measurements give values that differ slightly from this.

In summary, the experimental data from the table indicates that a box of dimensions $x = 12.6$, $h = 6.4$ inches will give the minimum surface area $S = 481.32\,\text{in}^2$ (at least of out of these 9 boxes). This costs about 48 cents for the aluminum, while the originally cubical box had a cost of 50 cents for the aluminum. There is a savings of 2 cents per box.

Having explored the problem experimentally, we now look at its exact solution using calculus. The problem is to minimize

$$S = x^2 + 4xh \qquad (3.4.7)$$

subject to the constraint

$$x^2h = 1000 \qquad (3.4.8)$$

If we solve the constraint equation (3.4.8) for one of the variables and then use the result to rewrite the surface area function S as a function of a single variable, then we can minimize S using previous techniques. It is easiest to solve equation (3.4.8) for h:

$$h = \frac{1000}{x^2} = 1000\,x^{-2}.$$

Substituting this into equation (3.4.7) gives

$$S = x^2 + 4\,x\left(1000\,x^{-2}\right) = x^2 + 4000\,x^{-1}.$$

This gives S as a function of x only. Now this problem is slightly different from the ones we previously encountered, since the interval for the independent variable x is $(0, \infty)$. Thus, we have no endpoints to test in checking for the minimum value of S on $(0, \infty)$. So we just check the critical points. The critical point equation is

$$\frac{dS}{dx} = 2\,x - 4000\,x^{-2} = \frac{2\,x^3 - 4000}{x^2} = 0$$

So

$$2x^3 = 4000, \quad \text{or} \quad x = 10 \cdot 2^{1/3}.$$

This is the only critical point. The function S has a minimum at this value of x. To see this note that

$$\frac{d^2 S}{dx^2} = 2 + 8000\,x^{-3},$$

and this is positive at the critical point (and for all positive values of x). The 2nd derivative test then says that S has a local minimum at $x = 10 \cdot 2^{1/3}$. But this is also an absolute minimum. The height of the box corresponding to $x = 10 \cdot 2^{1/3}$ is

$$h = \frac{1000}{x^2} = \frac{1000}{100 \cdot 2^{2/3}} = \frac{10}{2^{2/3}} = \frac{10 \cdot 2^{1/3}}{2^{2/3} \cdot 2^{1/3}} = 5 \cdot 2^{1/3}.$$

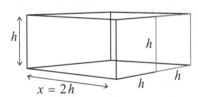

Figure 3.4.10: *The optimal box has $x = 2h$.*

It is important to note that the optimal solution is the one where the side of the base x is twice the height h:

$$x = 2\,h.$$

This gives a box with the proportions shown in Figure 3.4.10. This is a general result for this type of problem (independent of the particular numbers used) and you can study this more in the exercises.

Also note that $x = 10 \cdot 2^{1/3} \approx 12.59921050$, and so our experimental work shown in Table 3.4.3 gives us approximately the "right" answer for the box with minimum area. Using the precise value of x and h, we find the optimal surface area is

$$S = x^2 + 4xh = (2h)^2 + 4\,(2h)\,h = 12h^2 = 12\left(5 \cdot 2^{1/3}\right)^2 = 300 \cdot 2^{2/3} \approx 476.22\ \text{in}^2.$$

The surface area of the original cubical box was 500 square inches and at 0.1 cents per square inch, the original cost was fifty cents for each box. Using the optimal configuration gives a box with surface area of approximately 476 square inches and the cost is about $0.476 per box. That is a saving of 2.4 cents per box, which would be a savings of 24 thousand dollars if the company ships one million boxes each year.

Example 3.4.5 (Cylindrical Storage Tanks)

The previous example involved minimizing surface area while maintaining a given volume. This example will deal with maximizing volume while maintaining a given surface area.

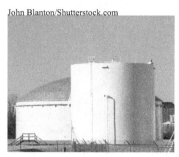

John Blanton/Shutterstock.com

Figure 3.4.11: *The optimal storage tank has* $h = 2r$.

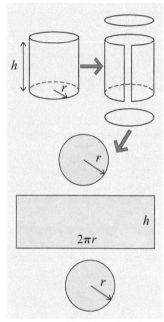

Figure 3.4.12: *Explode, cut and unroll to get the surface area of the tank.*

Problem: A storage-tank company donates 400 square meters of scrap steel to the city for a cylindrical storage tank. What is the maximum volume that can be contained by such a tank, assuming the cylinder has a top and bottom?

Solution: This is similar to the last example, except now we are maximizing volume, the geometry is cylindrical, and the container has a top as well as a bottom. We denote the height of the cylinder by h and the radius of the circular base by r. See Figure 3.4.12.

The volume of such a cylinder is

$$V = \pi r^2 h \qquad (3.4.9)$$

and we want to maximize V, subject to the constraint that the surface area of the cylindrical container is $S = 400 \, \text{m}^2$. But how does S involve the two variables h and r? The surface area of the container consists of the top and bottom, each with area πr^2, together with the area of the lateral surface of the cylinder. As indicated in Figure 3.4.12, the area of the lateral surface can be determined by cutting the side of the cylinder and rolling it out. This gives an area of $2\pi rh$ for the lateral surface of the cylinder. Hence, the total surface area of the cylindrical container is

$$S = 2\pi r^2 + 2\pi rh.$$

Thus, the constraint equation is

$$S = 2\pi r^2 + 2\pi rh = 400, \qquad (3.4.10)$$

and we want to maximize V subject to this constraint on the variables r and h. You should realize that each choice of r and h that satisfy the constraint equations gives a different cylinder, with different volume, but the same surface area. We use the calculus directly to find, from these infinitely many different cylinders, the one with the maximum volume.

As before, we can rewrite V as a function of a single variable if we solve equation (3.4.10) for one of the variables and substitute the result in equation (3.4.9). Since it is easier to solve equation (3.4.10) for h, we do that to get

$$h = \frac{200 - \pi r^2}{\pi r} = \frac{1}{\pi} \left(200 \, r^{-1} - \pi \, r \right) \qquad (3.4.11)$$

Substituting this into equation (3.4.9) gives

$$V = r^2 \left(200 \, r^{-1} - \pi \, r \right) = 200 \, r - \pi \, r^3 \qquad (3.4.12)$$

This gives V as a function of r only. The interval for r is determined as follows. First r must be positive, since it represents a radius. Also r cannot be too large, otherwise the height h given by Formula (3.4.11) will be negative. Specifically, we must have

$$0 < \frac{200 - \pi r^2}{\pi r},$$

or

$$r < \sqrt{\frac{200}{\pi}} \approx 7.98 \, \text{m}.$$

Thus, we take the interval for r to be $[0, \sqrt{200/\pi}]$, recognizing that there is no cylinder for the endpoint values $r = 0$ and $r = \sqrt{200/\pi}$, and indeed, $V = 0$ for either of these values of r. Thus, the maximum value of V will occur at a critical point in the interval $[0, \sqrt{200/\pi}]$. The critical point equation is

$$\frac{dV}{dr} = 200 - 3 \, \pi \, r^2 = 0,$$

and so the only *positive* critical point is

$$r = \sqrt{\frac{200}{3\pi}} \approx 4.61 \, \text{m}.$$

Using this value of r to compute the corresponding height h from Formula (3.4.11) gives

$$h = \frac{200 - \pi r^2}{\pi r} = \frac{200 - \pi \left(\frac{200}{3\pi}\right)}{\pi \sqrt{\frac{200}{3\pi}}} = \frac{\frac{400}{3}}{\pi \sqrt{\frac{200}{3\pi}}} = 2\sqrt{\frac{200}{3\pi}} \approx 9.21 \, \text{m}.$$

Thus, the maximum volume is

$$V = \pi r^2 h = \pi \cdot \frac{200}{3\pi} \cdot 2 \cdot \sqrt{\frac{200}{3\pi}} = 2\pi \left(\frac{200}{3\pi}\right)^{3/2} \approx 614.2 \, \text{m}^3$$

It is important to note that in the optimal solution the height is twice the radius

$$h = 2r.$$

and thus the cylinder with maximum volume is proportioned as shown in Figure 3.4.11 above. This is a general result: *Out of all cylinders with the same surface area (including the circular top and bottom), the one with maximum volume has $h = 2r$.* See the exercises for more details.

Miscellaneous

Unlike the problems presented above, there are many extremal problems which do *not* naturally involve a function of two variables and a constraint equation. Rather, the function to be maximized or minimized is written as a function of a single variable directly from the geometry of the problem. The following are several examples.

Example 3.4.6 (Carrying a Ladder Around a Corner)

Problem: A painting crew has to move several very long ladders down a hallway in the Pentagon Building and their foreman wonders if they will have trouble getting them around a corner where the width of the hallway changes from 2 meters to 3.5 meters. Figure 3.4.13 shows one long ladder that the crew successfully carried around the corner.

Before attempting to carry more ladders around the corner, the foreman, wishing to save his crew some effort, poses the problem of determining the longest ladder that can be carried around this corner. It is agreed that the ladders must be carried *horizontally*, that is, they cannot be tilted up to take advantage of the ceiling height when moving them around the corner.

Solution: One of the painters, who is a programmer and prone to experimental endeavors, decides to solve the problem in an approximate, and applied, way. He writes a program that takes as input the length of the ladder L, in meters, and a positive integer n, and produces a movie with n frames as output. For example, the following command produces a movie, with 20 frames, of a 6 meter ladder being carried around the corner.

```
> hallway(6,2,3.5,20);
```

As you can see when viewing the movie, the ladder is initially placed flat against the west wall with its bottom touching the south wall. Then the bottom is pulled along the south wall until the ladder either clears the corner (which it does in this case) or hits the corner, knocking a chunk out of the plaster. This painter uses his program to experimentally guess at the answer to the problem. He runs the

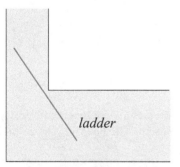

Figure 3.4.13: *A ladder that makes it around the corner.*

ladder

following two movies, finding that a 7 meter ladder is possible, but an 8 meter ladder is not:

```
> hallway(7,2,3.5,20);
> hallway(8,2,3.5,20);
```

Next, he narrows the search for the longest ladder, by choosing one that is halfway between 7 and 8 meters:

```
> hallway(7.5,2,3.5,20);
```

He finds that the 7.5 meter ladder will make it around the corner, and since it just barely clears the corner, he declares that the approximate answer is 7.5 meters.

The foreman congratulates him, but declares that the problem is still open until the *exact* answer to it is found. After all, perhaps the painter's program is faulty or incorrect.

Another painter in the crew, having had calculus in school, solves the problem exactly as follows. She reasons that the longest ladder that makes its around the corner is the same as the shortest of all the ladders that do not. That is, out of all ladders that get stuck, which is the shortest one? She reasons that "getting stuck" amounts to the ladder touching both outside walls while simultaneously touching the corner. She draws several typical ladders that get stuck as shown in Figure 3.4.14.

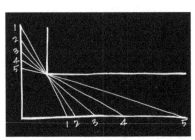

Figure 3.4.14: *Some typical ladders that get stuck.*

These sketches tell her that the length of a ladder that gets stuck depends on the angle it makes with the corner. See Figure 3.4.15.

The length L of such a ladder is then divided into two parts x and y as shown ($L = x + y$). Using trigonometry on the two right triangles, the second painter finds that

$$\cos\theta = \frac{2}{x}, \sin\theta = \frac{3.5}{y}.$$

Thus,

$$x = 2\sec\theta, \ y = 3.5\csc\theta,$$

and so

$$L = 2\sec\theta + 3.5\csc\theta,$$

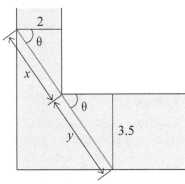

Figure 3.4.15: *The angle θ determines the length of a ladder that gets stuck.*

This gives L as a function of the single variable θ, and θ can vary over the interval $[0, \pi/2]$. Now the problem is to find the absolute minimum of L. For this, the second painter looks at the critical point equation

$$\frac{dL}{d\theta} = 2\sec\theta\tan\theta - 3.5\csc\theta\cot\theta = 0$$

which she rewrites as

$$2\sec\theta\tan\theta = 3.5\csc\theta\cot\theta,$$

or

$$\frac{2\sin\theta}{\cos^2\theta} = \frac{3.5\cos\theta}{\sin^2\theta}$$

Rearranging this, she gets

$$\tan^3\theta = 1.75$$

Thus, the angle for the shortest ladder is

$$\theta = \arctan\left((1.75)^{1/3}\right) \approx 0.878\,\text{rad},$$

and this ladder has length

$$L = 2\sec\theta + 3.5\csc\theta \approx 7.68 \,\text{m}.$$

The first painter mentions that his experimental methods gave an answer of about 7.5 meters, very close to the exact answer above. The second painter agrees, but prefers the exact methods provided by calculus. The foreman awards both of them a prize of an extra hour for lunch.

Example 3.4.7 (Least Time Path)

There are many situations in physics where the motion of an object is governed by the requirement that it takes the least time to go from point P to point Q. Often, in moving from P to Q, the object must reflect from an interface, or change speed as it passes through the interface. The laws of reflection and refraction of light (viewing light as composed of particles) is one example, and this will be covered in the exercises. Here we present an example which on first glance doesn't appear connected with the Law of Reflection, but in fact is.

Problem: A cross-country running team is training for an upcoming race by running between towns P and Q, where town Q is located 2 miles south and 3 miles east of town P and the country-side is flat and open between the towns. Generally the team members run together at a training pace of 8 miles per hour and run directly from P to Q. But, one day for the sake of variation, Jake suggests that they first run to a point S on the edge of an east-west highway that lies 1 mile south of town Q and from there continue on to Q.

To make it interesting, Jake suggests that they each pick a different point S, run at the same training pace, and see who gets to Q first. Jake, being the only one of them who is presently taking calculus, picks a point that gets him to Q first. Vanessa, an expert programmer, comes in right behind him. How did Vanessa use a computer program to approximate the best point S? How did Jake use calculus to find the optimal point S?

Solution: Working together, Jake and Vanessa select a coordinate system with P on the y-axis at point $(0, 2)$ and Q on the x-axis at point $(3, 0)$. Then the highway's edge is represented by the line $y = -1$, and a point S on the highway's edge has coordinates $(x, -1)$.

Vanessa's program (a Maple procedure) is quite general and works like this. For each choice of x the program creates a movie of the runner going from $P = (0, b)$ to $S = (x, c)$ and then to $Q = (a, 0)$, where $a = 3, b = 2, c = -1$. To make it more general, she allows for the runner to change speed after reaching the road's edge (speed v_1 from P to S and speed v_2 from S to Q). Finally, instead of a single choice for x, she allows for an input of a list of choices, one for each runner. Thus, to use her procedure, called paths, you make the command:

paths(a,b,c,v1,v2,[x1,x2,..,xk],N)

The argument N is the number of frames in the movie. In addition to returning the movie as an output, her procedure prints out the time each path takes. She decides to run a simulation with five equally spaced choices of x and N = 20 frames:

```
> paths(3,2,-1,8,8,[.5,1,1.5,2,2.5],20);
```

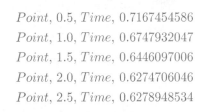

Point, 0.5, *Time*, 0.7167454586

Point, 1.0, *Time*, 0.6747932047

Point, 1.5, *Time*, 0.6446097006

Point, 2.0, *Time*, 0.6274706046

Point, 2.5, *Time*, 0.6278948534

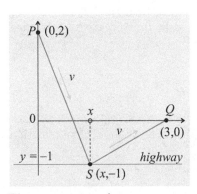

Figure 3.4.16: *A cross-country run from P to the highway and then to Q.*

The output of times above suggests to Vanessa that she choose $x = 2$, giving her a time of $T = 0.627$ hours, the least of all the times shown. The movie also confirms that, with this choice, she will beat the others.

Jake, however, is lucky that Vanessa didn't stumble upon the *exact* solution with her computer approximation. He found the optimal x using calculus as follows. First he determined the time T it takes to run the path PSQ as a function of x, where $P = (0, 2)$, $S = (x, -1)$, $Q = (3, 0)$. Using the distance formula, he found

$$
\begin{aligned}
|PS| &= \sqrt{(x-0)^2 + (-1-2)^2} = \sqrt{x^2 + 9} \\
|SQ| &= \sqrt{(3-x)^2 + (0-(-1))^2} = \sqrt{(3-x)^2 + 1}
\end{aligned}
$$

Each runner's speed is $v = 8$ mph, and $v = \frac{D}{T}$, where D is the total distance traveled. Thus,

$$
T = \frac{D}{v} = \frac{1}{8}\left(\sqrt{x^2 + 9} + \sqrt{(3-x)^2 + 1}\right)
$$

This function T is defined for all real numbers x. Jake, in order to minimize T and find the least time, calculated the 1st derivative and set it equal to 0:

$$
\frac{dT}{dx} = \frac{1}{8}\left(\frac{x}{\sqrt{x^2 + 9}} - \frac{3-x}{\sqrt{(3-x)^2 + 1}}\right) = 0
$$

The critical numbers x are then the solutions of

$$
\frac{x}{\sqrt{x^2 + 9}} = \frac{3-x}{\sqrt{(3-x)^2 + 1}}
$$

Note that there are no solutions to this if $x \geq 3$, since then the left side of this equation would be positive and the right side would be 0 or negative. Jake then squared each side of the above equation to get

$$
\frac{x^2}{x^2 + 9} = \frac{(3-x)^2}{(3-x)^2 + 1}
$$

To solve this, Jake used a little-known identity for working with ratios (dating back to Euclid's time), namely if $\frac{A}{B} = \frac{C}{D}$ then $\frac{A}{B-A} = \frac{C}{D-C}$. Thus, the previous equation reduces to

$$
\frac{x^2}{9} = \frac{(3-x)^2}{1}, \quad \text{or} \quad x^2 = 9(9 - 6x + x^2).
$$

Rearranging gives

$$
0 = 8x^2 - 54x + 81 = (4x - 9)(2x - 9)
$$

So the solutions are

$$
x = \frac{9}{4}, \frac{9}{2} = 2.25, \, 4.5
$$

Jake thus found that the only critical number is $x = 2.25$ miles. (The number $x = 4.5$ doesn't work in the original critical point equation, even though it is a solution of the derived equation he obtained by squaring.) Using this x gives a path that takes the least time. This least time is

$$
T_{least} = \frac{1}{8}\left(\sqrt{\left(\frac{9}{4}\right)^2 + 9} + \sqrt{\left(3 - \frac{9}{4}\right)^2 + 1}\right) = \frac{1}{8}(5) = 0.625 \text{ hr} = 2250 \text{ s}
$$

Compare this with Vanessa's time $T = 0.627$ hr ≈ 2257 s. Jake beats her by about 7 seconds.

Exercises: 3.4 (Optimization)

```
> with(code_ch3_new);
```

$[Printmax Afences, Printmax Vbox, Printmin Pfences$
$Printmin Sbox, hallway, isosceles$
$maxAfences, maxVbox, mean\_value$
$minPfences, minSbox, paths, print\_mean\_value]$

Area-Perimeter Problems: Exercises 1–12 deal with maximizing area and minimizing perimeter.

1. Fencing a Corral (Maximum Area)

A rancher has 1200 yards of fencing available to construct a rectangular corral next to a river (no fencing is to be used along the river-side of the corral). As in Example 3.4.1, she wants to maximize the area that the corral encloses. Do the following to determine the optimal corral.

(a) CAS: Use `maxAfences(1200,8,river,0)` to generate a movie of 11 such corrals. Use the movie to take data and construct a table like Table 3.4.1, showing the bases b, heights h, and areas A of the 8 corrals in the movie. Out of these 8 corrals, find the one with the largest area.

(b) Use calculus to find the dimensions of the corral with largest area that can be made with 1200 yards of fencing. For this determine the area function A that must be maximized and the interval on which it is defined. Find all the critical points of A and give the values of b, h, and A for the optimal corral. Draw a picture of the optimal configuration.

2. Geometry (Isoperimetrical Problem)

Out of all rectangles having perimeter 1200, find the one with the greatest area.

3. Fencing a Corral (Minimum Fencing)

The rancher in Example 3.4.1 has to build another corral 5 miles downstream from the the first one, but now she has to buy her own fencing at a cost of a dollar a yard. She wants to enclose an area of $A = 260,000$ square yards and, as before, will use the river to form the fourth side of the corral. In order to minimize costs, she want to use the least amount of fencing to enclose the given area. Solve this problem experimentally and exactly as follows:

(a) CAS: Use `minPfences(260000,11,river,0);` to generate a movie with 11 corrals, all with area 260,000 square yards. Use the movie to determine, approximately, the bases b, the heights h, and the amount of fencing $P = b + 2h$ of each corral. Record your data in a table. Find the one that requires the least amount of fencing P.

(b) Use calculus to find the dimensions of the corral using the least amount of fencing and enclosing the given amount of area. For this write $P = b + 2h$ as a function of a single variable, using the constraint that $A = 260,000$. Determine the interval for the independent variable (b or h) and then find all the critical points in this interval. Give the values of b, h, and A for the optimal corral and draw a picture of the optimal configuration.

4. Geometry:

Out of all rectangles having area $A = 250,000$ square meters, find the one has the least perimeter.

5. Fencing a Corral with Interior Partitions (Maximum Area)

As a variation on the fencing problem in Example 3.4.1 consider the following. The rancher has the same 1600 yards of fencing with which to construct the corral next to the river, but now she wants to use a portion of the fencing to divide the corral into three sections with 2 partitions of fencing which perpendicular to the river as shown in Figure 3.4.1x.

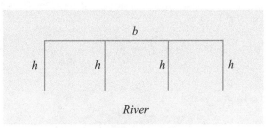

Figure 3.4.1x: *A corral next to a river divided by 2 partitions.*

Her problem is the same as before: Under these requirements (constraints), which coral encloses the largest total area?

(a) CAS: To get a feel for how this problem is different from Example 3.4.1, execute the command `maxAfences(1600,11,river,2);` to produce a movie illustrating 11 such corrals. Use the movie to take data and construct a table like Table 3.4.1, showing the bases b, heights h, and areas A of the 11 corrals in the movie. Out of these 11 corrals, find the one with the largest area.

(b) Use calculus to find the dimensions of the largest (area-wise) corral which can be made with 1600 yards of fencing with the three required sections. For this determine the area function A that must be maximized and the interval on which it is defined. Find all the critical points of A, give the values of b,

h, and A for the optimal corral and draw a picture of the optimal configuration. Compare the exact answer here with the approximate answer in Part (a) and with the exact answer in Example 3.4.1.

6. Fencing a Corral with Interior Partitions (Maximum Area) (GENERAL)

As a generalization of the Example 3.4.1 and Problem 5 above, consider the following problem. A rancher has 1600 yards of fencing to build a rectangular corral next to a river. He does not need to use fencing along the river side, but does need to use fencing to divide the interior of the corral with k sections of fencing perpendicular to the river. See Figure 3.4.2x.

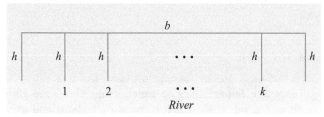

Figure 3.4.2x: *A corral next to a river divided by k partitions.*

(a) For a typical corral as shown in Figure 3.4.2x, write the expression for the amount of fencing P in terms of b, h, and k.

(b) Write the area function A as a function of h only. (It will also involve k, but k is fixed for the moment.) Find the interval of appropriate values of h on which to maximize A.

(c) Find the dimensions (h and b) for the corral of this type which has the largest enclosed area $A = bh$. Determine the relative proportion $\dfrac{b}{h} = m$ (i.e., $b = mh$) of the optimal rectangular corral. Your answers should depend on k.

(d) Check that your answers in Part (c) give the results for $k = 0$ in Example 3.4.1 and for $k = 2$ in Problem 5 above. Sketch the optimal corrals, at the same scale, for each of the cases $k = 0, 1, 2, 3$. Does it make sense that the optimal value for the base b does not depend on k?

7.   Fencing a Corral with Interior Partitions-Parallel to River (Maximum Area)

Consider the following variation of the fencing problem in Problem 5 above. A rancher has 1600 yards of fencing with which to construct a corral next to the river, but now she wants to use a portion of the fencing to divide the corral into three sections with 2 partitions of fencing which run *parallel* to the river as shown in Figure 3.4.3x.

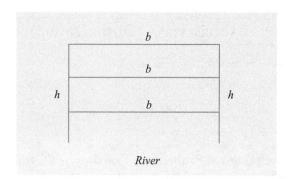

Figure 3.4.3x: *A corral with 2 partitions running parallel to the river.*

Out of all such corrals, determine the one that encloses the greatest amount of area.

8.   Fencing a Corral with Interior Partitions-Parallel to River (Maximum Area) (GENERAL)

Formulate and solve the generalization of Problem 7 above, where now there are k partitions running *parallel* to the river.

9. Fencing a Corral-No River (Maximum Area)

This problem is the same as Example 3.4.1, except that there is no river to form the fourth side of the corral. A rancher has 1600 yards of fencing available to construct a rectangular corral and he wants to maximize the area that the corral encloses. Solve this problem experimentally and exactly as follows:

(a) **CAS:** Use `maxAfences(1600,7,noriver,0)` to generate a movie of 7 such corrals. Use the movie to take data and construct a table like Table 3.4.1, showing the bases b, heights h, and areas A of the 7 corrals in the movie. Out of these 7 corrals, find the one with the largest area.

(b) Use calculus to find the dimensions of the corral with largest area that can be made with 1600 yards of fencing. For this determine the area function A that must be maximized and the interval on which it is defined. Find all the critical points of A, give the values of b, h, and A for the optimal coral and draw a picture of the optimal configuration. Compare the answer here with the answers in Part (a) and Example 3.4.1.

10. Fencing a Corral with Interior Partitions-No River (Maximum Area)

Rework Problem 5 above but this time assume there is no river to form the fourth side of the corral. For Part (a) of that problem, use the command `maxAfences(1600,11,noriver,2);` Compare your result here with those in Problems 5,7, and Example 3.4.1.

11. Geometry (An Isoperimetrical Problem)

Solve the following isoperimetrical problem: *Out of all right triangles with perimeter $P = 1$, which one has the largest area.*

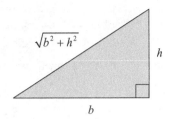

Is your answer what you expected (or might have expected had you thought about it in advance)? Can you make an argument for obtaining the correct answer based on the symmetry of the various expressions in b and h?

12. General Fencing Problem-River/No River (Maximum Area)

Consider the various fencing problems studied here, with and without a river to form the fourth side of the rectangular corral. Solve the general version of these problems:

(a) For a rectangular corral, next to a river, with k interior partitions, find the one enclosing the largest area with a given amount P of fencing. Your answer should involve P as a basic parameter.

(b) For a rectangular corral (NOT bounded by a river), with k interior partitions, find the one enclosing the largest area with a given amount P of fencing.

Volume and Surface-Area Problems: Exercises 13–24 are optimization problems of two types: (1) minimizing surface area for a given volume and (2) maximizing volume for a given surface area.

13. Minimum Surface Area Box (no Top) with given Volume

The pecan company in Example 3.4.4 decides to increase the volume of the box for its pecans to $V = 1728$. Assuming, as before, that the container base (i.e., the bottom and four sides) is made of aluminum and that the company wants to minimize the amount of aluminum used (the surface area of the bottom plus the four sides), find the optimal dimensions of the box.

Solve this problem experimentally and exactly as in Example 3.4.4. Specifically:

(a) CAS: Use `minSbox(1728,11,notop)` to generate an animation of 11 boxes all with the same volume $V = 1728$. Use the last frame in the animation to collect data on the bases x and heights h of the boxes, and use this to compile a table like Table 3.4.3. NOTE: If you want to print out the last frame in the movie, use the command `printminSbox(1728,11,notop)` to generate a single figure, which you can then print. You can also use this figure to point and click and

obtain the data for x and h. Alternatively, you can measure the data off the printout.

ALSO NOTE: If you use the animation to collect the data, you should change the last frame in the animation to a wire frame style and use a view with orientation [0, 90].

Out of the 11 boxes in the movie, determine the one with the least surface area (bottom plus four sides). This will be an approximation to the exact solution of the problem in Part (b) below.

(b) Use calculus to find the dimensions of the aluminum container with given volume $V = 1728$, no top, and minimum surface area S. For this determine the surface area function S that must be minimized and the interval on which it is defined. Find all the critical points of S, give the values of x, h, and S for the optimal box, and draw a picture of the optimal configuration.

14. Minimum Surface Area Box (with Top) with given Volume

As a variant of the problem in Example 3.4.4 consider the following. The pecan company wants a box with a volume of 1000 cubic inches and it is to have a top as well as a bottom (both square). Out of all such boxes, which one has the least surface area? Solve this problem experimentally and exactly as in Example 3.4.4. Specifically:

(a) CAS: Use `minSbox(1000,9,top)` to generate an animation of 9 boxes all with the same volume $V = 1000$. Use the last frame in the animation to collect data on the bases x and heights h of the boxes, and use this to compile a table like Table 3.4.3. NOTE: If you want to print out the last frame in the movie, use the command `PrintminSbox(1000,9,top)` to generate a single figure, which you can then print. You can also use this figure to point and click and obtain the data for x and h. Alternatively, you can measure the data off the printout.

ALSO NOTE: If you use the animation to collect the data, you should change the last frame in the animation to a wire frame style and use a view with orientation [0, 90].

Out of the 9 boxes in the movie, determine the one with the least surface area (top and bottom and four sides). This will be an approximation to the exact solution of the problem in Part (b) below.

(b) Use calculus to find the dimensions of the aluminum container with given volume $V = 1000$, and minimum surface area S. For this determine the surface area function S that must be maximized and the interval on which it is defined. Find all the critical points of S, give the values of x, h, and S for the optimal box, and draw a picture of the optimal configuration. Compare the exact answer here with the approximate answer in Part (a). Also compare the answers here with that in Example 3.4.4. Comment on how adding the top changes things.

15. Maximum Volume Box (no Top) with given Surface Area

Here is a problem that is dual to that in Exercise 13. The pecan company wants to construct a display box out of 2700 square inches of Plexiglas and build it so that the maximum volume is enclosed (it holds the most number of pecans). If the box is to have a square base and no top (so customers can scoop out a sample of pecans), what should the dimensions of the box be? Do an experimental and exact study of this problem. Specifically:

(a) CAS: Use `maxVbox(2700,11,notop)` to generate an animation of 11 boxes, all with surface area $S = 2700$. Use the last frame in the animation to collect data on the bases x and heights h of the boxes, and use this to compile a table like Table 3.4.3. You can also use the command `PrintmaxVbox(2700,11,notop)` to help in the data collection.

Out of the 11 boxes in the movie, determine the one with the maximum volume. This will be an approximation to the exact solution of the problem in Part (b) below.

(b) Use calculus to find the dimensions of the container with given surface area $S = 2700$ square inches and maximum volume.

16. Maximum Volume Box (no Top) with given Surface Area (General)

Consider the general problem of making a box with square base of side x and height h and no top, using a given amount of material, i.e., with given surface area S. Out of all such boxes, find the one with maximum volume V. Specifically, show that the maximum volume box has

$$x = \left(\frac{S}{3}\right)^{1/2}, \quad h = \frac{1}{2}\left(\frac{S}{3}\right)^{1/2}, \quad V = \left(\frac{S}{3}\right)^{3/2}$$

17. Maximum Volume Box (with Top) with given Surface Area (General)

As in Exercise 16, solve the general problem of finding the maximum volume V for a box with given surface area S, but now assume the box has a top. The base (and top) is a square of side x and the height is h. Show that out of all such boxes, the one with maximum volume has

$$x = \left(\frac{S}{6}\right)^{1/2}, \quad h = \left(\frac{S}{6}\right)^{1/2}, \quad V = \left(\frac{S}{6}\right)^{3/2}$$

Thus, the box is a cube.

18. Minimum Surface Area Box (no Top) with given Volume (General)

Consider the general problem of making a box with square base of side x, with height h, with no top, and with a given volume V. Out of all such boxes, find the one that has the minimum amount of surface area S. Specifically:

(a) Show that the minimum surface area box with given volume V has

$$x = (2V)^{1/3}, \quad h = \frac{1}{2}(2V)^{1/3}, \quad S = 3(2V)^{2/3}$$

(b) Show that this problem is dual to the one in Exercise 16. Namely, the formula for the minimum S:

$$S = 3(2V)^{2/3}$$

when solved for V, gives the formula for the maximum volume

$$V = \frac{1}{2}\left(\frac{S}{3}\right)^{3/2}.$$

in Exercise 16. This is a general result relating certain minimization and maximization problems.

19. Maximum Volume Can

Suppose the storage-tank company in Example 3.4.5 decides to donate twice as much material: $S = 800\,m^3$ of steel for the surface area of the cylindrical tank. Out of all tanks with this surface area which one has the greatest volume? Compare the answer here with that in Example 3.4.5.

20. Maximum Volume Can (General)

Solve the general version of Example 3.4.5 and Exercise 19 above. Namely, Out of all cylindrical cans, with r as the radius of the base, h as the height, and with given surface area S, which one contains the greatest volume V? Specifically, show that the can with maximum volume for the given surface area S has

$$r = \left(\frac{S}{6\pi}\right)^{1/2}, \quad h = 2\left(\frac{S}{6\pi}\right)^{1/2}, \quad V = 2\pi\left(\frac{S}{6\pi}\right)^{3/2}$$

21. Minimum Surface Area Can (Oatmeal Containers)

An oatmeal company wants to package and sell its oatmeal in cardboard, cylindrical containers with volume $V = 226\,in^3$. The manufacturer of the containers charges 20 cents per square foot for the cardboard material used in making the containers. Find the dimensions, surface area, and cost of the cheapest such container.

22. Minimum Surface Area Can (General Problem)

Out of all cylindrical cans with volume V find the one with the least surface area (circular top/bottom and cylindrical side). In particular show that the minimum surface area can has dimensions and area:

$$r = \left(\frac{V}{2\pi}\right)^{1/3}, \quad h = 2\left(\frac{V}{2\pi}\right)^{1/3}, \quad S = 6\pi\left(\frac{V}{2\pi}\right)^{2/3}$$

Also show that this minimization problem is dual to the maximization problem in Exercise 20. Namely that the formula for S:

$$S = 6\pi\left(\frac{V}{2\pi}\right)^{2/3}$$

when solved for V, gives the maximum volume:

$$V = 2\pi\left(\frac{S}{6\pi}\right)^{3/2}$$

23. Maximum Volume Box, Folded, No Top

Suppose you want to make an open-top box from a rectangular sheet of cardboard with dimensions $b = 30$ inches and $h = 20$ inches. One way to do this, as shown in the figure below, is to cut squares out of each corner of the cardboard sheet, fold along the dotted lines, and turn up the four resulting flaps.

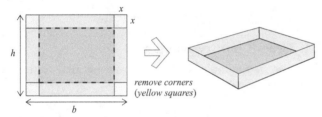

remove corners
(yellow squares)

You can get many different boxes from this construction, depending on the size of the square you remove from each corner. The problem here is to determine, out of all possible such boxes, which one has the largest volume.

24. Maximum Volume Box-Folded-No Top (General)

Solve the general version of Exercise 23. Namely, starting with a cardboard sheet of dimensions b inches by h inches and using the construction of removing squares of side x from each corner, find the open-top box which has the maximum volume. Specifically, show that the maximum volume box occurs for

$$x = \frac{b + h - \sqrt{b^2 - bh + h^2}}{6}$$

Ladder Problems: Exercises 25–28 are problems about carrying a ladder around a corner for two types of corners: square and rounded.

25. Longest Ladder

As a variation of Example 3.4.6, find the length of the longest ladder that can be carried around a corner if the two hallways are each 3 meters wide. Do this both experimentally and exactly. Specifically:

(a) CAS: Use the special-purpose Maple command `hallway(L,a,b,n,r)` to generate a movie with n frames that shows a ladder of length L being carried from a hallway of width a into one of width b. The fifth argument r should be set to 0 for square inside corners. Otherwise it is the radius (in meters) of the inside rounded corner. For the other arguments: use, say $n = 20$ frames and $a = b = 3$. Start with a length L that is small enough for the ladder to make it around the corner. Gradually increase L until the ladder gets stuck. That will give an approximate answer to the problem.

(b) As in Example 3.4.6, let L be a length of a ladder that gets stuck at the corner and express L in terms of the angle θ shown in Figure 3.4.15. Use calculus to minimize L as a function of θ.

26. Longest Ladder (General Problem)

Solve the general longest ladder problem. Namely, for hallways of widths a and b, find the length L of the longest ladder that can be carried around the corner where these hallways meet. (Assume the ladder is carried horizontally. No tilting is allowed.) Specifically, do the following:

(a) Show that the longest ladder makes an angle of

$$\theta = \tan^{-1}\left((b/a)^{1/3}\right)$$

with the corner as it squeezes by. Here θ is the angle shown in Figure 3.4.15.

(b) Show that the length of the longest ladder is

$$L_{\max} = \left(a^{2/3} + b^{2/3}\right)^{3/2}$$

(c) Use the formulas in (a) and (b) to check the results in Example 3.4.6 and Exercise 25 above (if you did that exercise).

27. Longest Ladder with Rounded Corner

As a more complicated variant of Example 3.4.6, suppose the inside corner where the hallways meet is rounded using a quarter of a circle of radius $r = 2$ meters. See Figure 3.4.xx below.

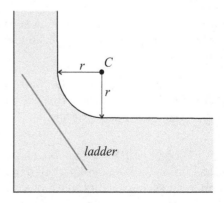

Figure 3.4.xx: *Two hallways meeting with a rounded inside corner.*

Assuming the widths of the hallways are $a = 2$ meters and 3.5 meters, find the length of the longest ladder that can be carried around the corner. Do this both experimentally and analytically. Specifically:

(a) CAS: Use the special-purpose Maple command `hallway(L,a,b,n,r)` to generate a movie with n frames that shows a ladder of length L being carried from a hallway of width a into one of width b where the inside corner is rounded by a quarter arc of radius r. Here n is the number of frames in the animation.

(b) As in Example 3.4.6, let L be a length of a ladder that gets stuck on the corner and express L in terms of an appropriate angle θ. Use calculus to minimize L as a function of θ.

28. Longest Ladder with Rounded Corner (General Problem)

Solve the general problem for carrying a ladder from one hallway to the next past a rounded corner. Assume the hallways have widths a, b, and the inside corner where they meet is rounded with a quarter circle of radius r. See the figures for the answer to Exercise 27 above.

(a) Show that the length of any ladder that gets stuck is given by
$$L(\theta) = \frac{(a+r)\sin\theta + (b+r)\cos\theta - r}{\sin\theta\cos\theta},$$
where θ is the angle shown in the answer to to Exercise 27.

(b) Find an equation for the critical numbers of L. Show that this equation is exactly solvable in the case where the hallways are of the same width: $a = b$. Comment on why the critical number θ in this case makes sense. Show that in this case $(a = b)$ the maximum length ladder that can be carried around the corner is
$$L_{\max} = 2\sqrt{2}\,(a + r) - 2\,r$$

(c) Show that everything reduces to the square corner case when $r = 0$ (as in Example 3.4.6 and Exercise 25 above).

Least-Time Problems: Exercises 29–35 are least-time problems dealing with cross-country runners and light reflecting and refracting at an interface.

29. Cross-Country Runners–1

Suppose the runners in Example 3.4.7 run to a a point on an east-west road that is 6 miles south of town Q. Find the path that takes the least time. Do this as in Example 3.4.7, approximately by using the special-purpose Maple procedure `paths` or exactly by using calculus.

30. Cross-Country Runners–2

You may have noticed in Example 3.4.7 that the least time path has the property that the lines PS and SQ make equal angles with the highway (or the perpendicular to the highway). Use right-triangle geometry and the analysis in Example 3.4.7 to prove that this is indeed the case.

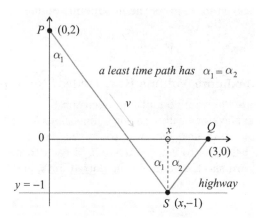

31. Cross-Country Runners-3

Suppose in Example 3.4.7, the east-west road is 1 mile *north* of town Q.

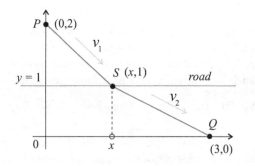

(a) Show that the least-time path that goes from P to the road to Q is now a straight line (i.e., P, S, Q are collinear). This is typical of any road north of town Q, *provided* the speed of the runner is the same before and after reaching the road ($v_1 = v_2$).

(b) Suppose that after a heavy rain, the field south of the road becomes muddy and the runners can only maintain a pace of $v_2 = 6$ miles per hour on that section. Assuming that north of the road their pace is still $v_1 = 8$ miles per hour, find the least-time path that goes from P to the road to Q.

Do Parts (a) and (b) exactly, using calculus. Also show that in Part (a) where the speeds are the same, before and after reaching the road, that the least-time path is the same as the shortest path, and therefore the result doesn't require calculus. CAS: Also work Parts (a) and (b) approximately, using the procedure `paths`, and NOTE: In part (b) the equation for the optimal x cannot be solved exactly by hand. Use Maple to get approximate solutions.

32. Reflection of Light-Fermat's Principle

The behavior of light rays as they travel through space, reflecting off of or refracting through an interface, is governed by Fermat's Principle of Least Time: A light ray, traveling at constant speed v through a medium, travels from point-to-point along a path that minimizes the time. Consider the case of reflection. Light rays emanate from point P, spreading out in all directions, and in the absence of reflecting or refraction interfaces, the rays travel in a straight lines (with no change of speed and no change in direction, the least time path is the one with shortest distance). However, assume a reflecting interface is located at $y = c$ as shown in the figure below.

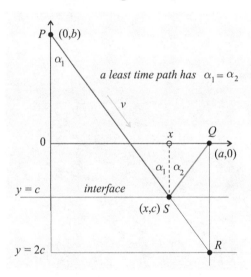

Then one of the light rays from P will reach Q directly, traveling along a straight line, and an additional ray from P will pass through Q by traveling along a path PSQ that reflects off the interface.

Show that if S is the point on the interface such that PSQ is the least time path, then the lines PS, SQ make equal angles α_1, α_2 with the normal line to the interface. Show also that the point S can be constructed geometrically as the intersection of the lines PR and $y = c$, where R is the point $R = (a, 2c)$. EXTRA CREDIT: Show the converse, i.e., if PSQ is a path such that lines PS, SQ make equal angles α_1, α_2 with the normal line to the interface, then PSQ is the least time path.

33. Cross-Country Runners–4

Suppose in Example 3.4.7, the east-west road runs directly through town Q as shown in the figure below,

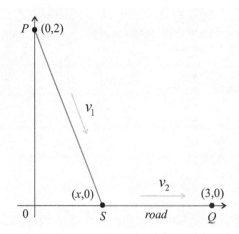

The runners run to a point on the road and then along the road to town Q. Assume that the hard surface of the road allows the runners to increase their pace to $v_2 = 12$ miles per hour, as they run along the road. If their pace before reaching the road is still $v_1 = 8$ miles per hour, find the least-time path that goes from P to the road and then along the road to Q. Solve this problem exactly, using calculus. CAS: Solve this problem approximately, using the `paths` procedure.

34. Refraction of Light

As indicated in Exercise 32, Fermat's Principle also governs the behavior of light rays which, traveling with speed v_1, strike an interface and pass through it, continuing on with speed v_2. See the figure below.

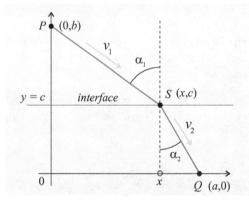

A common situation for this is the refraction of light as it passes from air into water where its speed is less. (or the other way around, passing from water into air.)

Show that if PSQ is a least time path, then the lines PS, SQ make equal angles, α_1, α_2 (relative to the normal line) such that

$$\frac{\sin \alpha_1}{\sin \alpha_2} = \frac{v_1}{v_2} \quad \text{(Snell's Law)}$$

35. Cross-Country Runners–General

Solve the general problem for cross-country runners. Namely, suppose an east-west road is located at $y = c$

(north of town Q if $c > 0$, south of town Q if $c < 0$, and directly through town Q if $c = 0$). The figure below shows the case for $c > 0$.

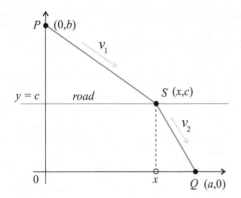

The runners start at town P and run with speed v_1 to a point S on the road, after which they run directly to town Q with speed v_2. As in the figure, we assume that a and b are positive and that $c < b$. Find the least time path PSQ. Specifically, do the following:

(a) (Equal Speeds: $v_1 = v_2$ Case): Show that the point $S = (x, c)$ giving the least time path has

$$(i) \quad x = \frac{a\,(b - c)}{b - 2c}, \quad \text{if } c < 0$$

and

$$(ii) \quad x = \frac{a\,(b - c)}{b}, \quad \text{if } c \ge 0$$

Draw pictures for each of these cases and show that in the former case (i) the path PSQ is an equal angles reflection and in the latter case (ii) the path PSQ is a straight line.

(b) (Non-Equal Speeds $v_1 \ne v_2$ and $c = 0$ Case): Show that the point $S = (x, c)$ giving the least time path has

$$(i) \quad x = \frac{bv_1}{\sqrt{v_1^2 - v_2^2}}, \quad \text{if } v_1 < \frac{a}{\sqrt{a^2 + b^2}} \cdot v_2$$

and

$$(ii) \quad x = a, \quad \text{if } v_1 \ge \frac{a}{\sqrt{a^2 + b^2}} \cdot v_2$$

Calculus *Concepts & Computation*

3.5 The Mean Value Theorem

> with(code_ch3_new,mean_value,print_mean_value);

$$[mean\_value,\ print\_mean\_value]$$

In this section we discuss a theorem, called the *mean value theorem*, which is extremely important in mathematics. Its importance comes from the fact that it instrumental in proving a great many other theorems and results. You will see some applications of this theorem in this section and throughout the book.

The content of the mean value theorem is very easy to understand geometrically and the proof of this theorem is fairly simple too (using the extreme value theorem and the critical value theorem). To understand the geometric content of the mean value theorem execute the following commands and view the resulting movie.

> f:=x->4-x^2;

$$f := x \mapsto 4 - x^2$$

> mean_value(f,-1,2,30,4);

The movie displays 31 tangent lines to the graph of $f(x) = 4 - x^2$ on the interval $[-1, 2]$. They move along the graph changing their slopes as they move from left-to-right. Also shown (in turquoise) is the secant line joining the two endpoints $A = (-1, 3)$ and $B = (2, 0)$ on the graph of f. If you step through the animation frame-by-frame you will see that when $x = 0.5$, the tangent line appears to be parallel to the secant line AB. This occurs in the 15th frame as shown in Figure 3.5.1. (Note: The initial frame of the movie is the 0th frame.)

The movie illustrates the content of the mean value theorem which says, under appropriate hypotheses on the function f, there will be at least one place where the tangent line is parallel to the secant line. Otherwise said, the *slope* of the tangent line is that same as the *slope* of the secant line. In this example, with $f(x) = 4 - x^2$ on the interval $[-1, 2]$, the secant line through the endpoints A, B on its graph has slope

$$m_{\text{sec}} = \frac{f(2) - f(-1)}{2 - (-1)} = \frac{(4 - 2^2) - (4 - (-1)^2)}{2 - (-1)} = \frac{0 - 3}{3} = -1.$$

And the tangent line at any point $(x, f(x))$ has slope $f'(x) = -2x$. Equating these two slopes gives the equation

$$-2x = -1$$

Thus, $x = \frac{1}{2} = 0.5$, as we found above from watching the movie. *Note*: The slopes in Figure 3.5.1 are distorted since the scales on the x-axis and y-axis are not the same. With the above example as a guide, we now formally state (and prove) the mean value theorem:

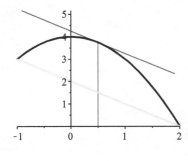

Figure 3.5.1: *The* 15*th frame of the moving tangent line animation.*

THEOREM 3.5.1 (Mean Value Theorem)

Suppose f is continuous on the closed interval $[a,b]$ and differentiable on the open interval (a,b). Then there is a number c between a and b such that

$$f'(c) = \frac{f(b) - f(a)}{b - a} \qquad (3.5.1)$$

Proof: Define a function H on the $[a, b]$ interval by

$$H(x) = [f(b) - f(a)](x - a) - [f(x) - f(a)](b - a).$$

for x in $[a, b]$. Then H is continuous on the closed interval $[a, b]$ and differentiable on the open interval (a, b) (since f is). It is also easy to see that

$$H(a) = 0 = H(b).$$

We will show that $H'(c) = 0$ for some c between a and b. If H is a constant function, then it is clear that $H'(c) = 0$ for *all* c between a and b. So we may as well assume that H is not a constant function. By the extreme value theorem (in Section 3.3), H has a maximum value and a minimum value in the interval $[a, b]$. Since H is not a constant function, the maximum and minimum values must be different. Thus, at least one of these values must be different from 0 and so must occur at a point c different from a and b (since $H(a) = 0 = H(b)$). Thus, by the critical number theorem: $H'(c) = 0$. But, from the definition of H above we find

$$H'(x) = \frac{d}{dx}\left[(f(b) - f(a))(x - a) - (f(x) - f(a))(b - a)\right]$$

$$= (f(b) - f(a)) - f'(x)(b - a)$$

for all x in (a, b). So, by taking $x = c$ in this we get

$$0 = (f(b) - f(a)) - f'(c)(b - a)$$

Rearranging gives

$$f'(c) = \frac{f(b) - f(a)}{b - a},$$

which is what we wanted to prove.

Example 3.5.1 (Validating the Mean Value Theorem (MVT))

To illustrate the validity of the mean value theorem, we look at several more examples. In each example, we verify that the hypotheses of the theorem are satisfied and then find all numbers c in the interval (a, b), that satisfy

$$f'(c) = \frac{f(b) - f(a)}{b - a}.$$

Part (a): $f(x) = x^3 - x^2 - 2x$, $[1, 2]$.

Here f is a polynomial and so is continuous and differentiable everywhere. Also

$$f'(x) = 3x^2 - 2x - 2 \quad \text{and} \quad \frac{f(2) - f(1)}{2 - 1} = \frac{0 - (-2)}{1} = 2$$

Equating these gives the equation

$$3x^2 - 2x - 2 = 2, \quad \text{which gives} \quad 3x^2 - 2x - 4 = 0,$$

Thus, there are two places where the tangent line is parallel to the secant line. Using the quadratic formula, gives

$$x = \frac{2 \pm \sqrt{4 + 48}}{6} = \frac{2 \pm \sqrt{52}}{6} = \frac{1 \pm \sqrt{13}}{3}$$

Part (b): $f(x) = x \ln x - x$, $[1, 2]$

The natural log function and the identity function $g(x) = x$ are continuous on the closed interval and differentiable on the open interval. So the product of these is also, as well as the function f obtained by subtracting the identity function. Next

$$f'(x) = \frac{d}{dx}\left(x\ln x - x\right) = 1\cdot\ln x + x\cdot\frac{1}{x} - 1 = \ln x + 1 - 1 = \ln x$$

and

$$\frac{f(2) - f(1)}{2 - 1} = \frac{2\ln 2 - 2 - (1\ln 1 - 1)}{1} = 2\ln 2 - 1$$

So the equation

$$\ln x = 2\ln 2 - 1$$

gives where the tangent line is parallel to the secant line. Solving for x yields

$$x = e^{2\ln 2 - 1} = e^{\ln\left(2^2\right)}e^{-1} = 4e^{-1} \approx 1.47$$

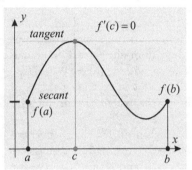

Figure 3.5.2: *A horizontal secant line implies the existence of at least one horizontal tangent line.*

A SPECIAL CASE OF THE MVT:

An interesting special case of the mean value theorem is when $f(a) = f(b)$. This means that the secant line through the endpoints of the graph is a horizontal line as shown in Figure 3.5.2.

In this case the mean value theorem guarantees the existence of a number c between a and b where the first derivative is 0 (the tangent line is horizontal). This special case of the mean value theorem is called Rolle's theorem:

COROLLARY 3.5.1 (Rolle's Theorem)

Suppose f is continuous on the closed interval $[a,b]$ and differentiable on the open interval (a,b). If $f(a) = f(b)$ then there is a number c between a and b such that $f'(c) = 0$

NOTE: In Rolle's theorem, if f is not a constant function then the number c guaranteed by the theorem is a place where f has a local maximum or local minimum. This result doesn't follow directly from the mean value theorem, but rather comes from the *proof* of the mean value theorem.

Example 3.5.2 (An Illustration of Rolle's Theorem)

Consider the function $f(x) = 4 + x^2 - x^4$ on the interval $[-1.5, 1.5]$. Since f is a polynomial it is differentiable on any open interval and continuous on any closed interval. Also,

$$f(-1.5) = 1.1875 = f(1.5)$$

and so f satisfies the hypotheses of Rolle's theorem. Thus, there is at least one c between -1.5 and 1.5 such that

$$f'(c) = 0$$

But $f'(x) = 2x - 4x^3 = 2x\left(1 - 2x^2\right)$, so the above equation is

$$2c\left(1 - 2c^2\right) = 0.$$

Hence

$$c = 0, \pm\frac{1}{\sqrt{2}} \approx 0, \pm 0.707106781$$

This verifies the validity of Rolle's theorem in this particular example. An animation of the situation is given by the following command:

```
> f:=x->4+x^2-x^4;
```

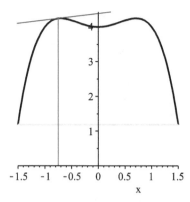

Figure 3.5.3: *The 10th frame of the animation.*

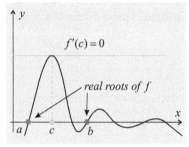

Figure 3.5.4: *Two successive roots a, b imply the existence of an intermediate value c where $f'(c) = 0$.*

$$f := x \mapsto 4 + x^2 - x^4$$

```
> mean_value(f,-1.5,1.5,40,2);
```

Using a probe with the cursor position selected on the appropriate frames in the movies gives us that the tangent line is horizontal at $c \approx -0.7, 0, 0.7$, which coincide with the exact values found above. The following creates the 10th frame in the animation, showing the tangent line right before it becomes horizontal.

```
> print_mean_value(f,-1.5,1.5,40,2,10);
```

Applications of Rolle's Theorem

A common use of Rolle's theorem is in determining the nonexistence of additional roots of a function f. The discussion here will be limited to roots which are real numbers and functions which are differentiable on their domains. If we know one root, say a, then $f(a) = 0$. Any additional root, say b, gives $f(b) = 0 = f(a)$, and so by Rolle's theorem there exists a c between a and b such that $f'(c) = 0$. Geometrically this is clear. The real roots are the places where the graph of f crosses the x-axis. See Figure 3.5.4.

If the graph crosses the x-axis a $x = a$ and then again at $x = b$, then there must be a horizontal tangent line somewhere in between. Turning the discussion around, suppose the graph of f crosses the x-axis at $x = a$ and that $f'(x) \neq 0$ for any x (other than possibly $x = a$), then the graph if f cannot cross the x-axis at any other point.

Example 3.5.3 (An Application of Rolle's Theorem)

The polynomial function $f(x) = x^5 + x + 2$ clearly has $x = -1$ as one real root since $f(-1) - (-1)^5 + (-1) + 2 = 0$. Also,

$$f'(x) = 5x^4 + 1 > 0,$$

for all x. Thus, f cannot have another real root.

Example 3.5.4 (The Intermediate Value Theorem & Rolle's Theorem)

Problem: Show that the function $f(x) = e^{-x} - x + 1$ has one and only one root in the interval $[1, 2]$.

Solution: First we use the intermediate value theorem to get the existence of at least one root. The values of f at the endpoints of the interval are

$$\begin{aligned} f(1) &= e^{-1} - 1 + 1 = e^{-1} \approx 0.368 \\ f(2) &= e^{-2} - 2 + 1 = e^{-2} - 1 \approx -0.865 \end{aligned}$$

Since 0 is between -0.865 and 0.368, the intermediate value theorem guarantees that 0 is a value of the function f. So there is a number r between 1 and 2 such that $f(r) = 0$. To show that r is the only root of f in the given interval, we argue by contradiction. Suppose s is another root in the interval different from r. Then $f(s) = 0 = f(r)$ and so by Rolle's theorem, there is a number c between r and $s$such that $f'(c) = 0$. But

$$f'(x) = \frac{d}{dx}\left(e^{-x} - x + 1\right) = -e^{-x} - 1 = -\left(e^{-x} + 1\right) < 0,$$

for every x. This contradiction shows that our assumption of the existence of an additional root s is wrong. There are no other roots in the interval.

Applications of The MVT

You will see many applications of the mean value theorem throughout the book. As mentioned, the MVT is principally used to prove other results. Two important ones are: (a) the constant function is the only function whose derivative is identically zero and (b) (consequently) two functions which have the same derivative function differ by a constant. These are our first two examples, which we state as theorems.

THEOREM 3.5.2 (Zero Derivative Theorem)

Suppose f is differentiable on the interval (a,b) and

$$f'(x) = 0$$

for all x in (a,b). Then f is a constant function, i.e., there exists a constant C such that

$$f(x) = C$$

for all x in (a,b).

Proof: All we have to show is that if x_1 and x_2 are any two distinct points in the interval, then f has the same value at each of them: $f(x_1) = f(x_2)$. To show this we use the MVT to get the existence of a number c between x_1 and x_2 such that

$$\frac{f(x_1) - f(x_2)}{x_1 - x_2} = f'(c) = 0.$$

Hence, $f(x_1) - f(x_2) = 0$ and this gives us what we need.

An immediate corollary of the zero derivative theorem is the following result, which says that two functions with the same derivative are essentially the same function.

THEOREM 3.5.3 (Equal Derivatives Theorem)

Suppose f and g are differentiable on the interval (a,b) and

$$f'(x) = g'(x)$$

for all x in (a,b). Then f and g differ by a constant, i.e., there exists a constant C such that

$$f(x) = g(x) + C$$

for all x in (a,b).

Proof: Define a function h on (a, b) by $h(x) = f(x) - g(x)$, for all x in (a, b). Then

$$h'(x) = f'(x) - g'(x) = 0,$$

for all x in (a, b). Hence, by the zero derivative theorem, h is a constant function, i.e., there is a constant C such at $h(x) = C$, for all x in (a, b). But, by definition of h, this is

$$f(x) - g(x) = C$$

for all x in (a, b). Rearranging gives the result of the theorem.

Example 3.5.5 (A Law of Logarithms)

Problem: Use the equal derivatives theorem to prove that

$$\ln(AB) = \ln A + \ln B,$$

for all positive numbers A, B.

Solution: Fix A and let f and g be the two functions:

$$f(x) = \ln(Ax) \quad \text{and} \quad g(x) = \ln x,$$

for x in $(0, \infty)$. Then by the chain rule

$$f'(x) = \frac{1}{Ax} \cdot \frac{d}{dx}(Ax) = \frac{1}{Ax} \cdot A = \frac{1}{x} = g'(x).$$

Hence, f and g have the same derivative on the interval $(0, \infty)$ and so by the equal derivatives theorem, there is a constant C such that

$$\ln(Ax) = C + \ln x \qquad (3.5.1)$$

for all $(0, \infty)$. But if the above equation holds for all positive x, then in particular it holds for $x = 1$. This gives the value of the constant C, namely:

$$\ln(A) = C + \ln 1 = C.$$

With this value of C, equation (3.5.1) becomes

$$\ln(Ax) = \ln A + \ln x,$$

for all x in $(0, \infty)$. Taking $x = B$ gives the required identity:

$$\ln(AB) = \ln A + \ln B,$$

Example 3.5.6 (Functional Identities)

Problem: Suppose that f and g are differentiable on the interval $I = (a, b)$. Show that if

$$f' = g \quad \text{and} \quad g' = f \qquad (3.5.2)$$

on I, then there is a constant C such that

$$f^2 - g^2 = C,$$

on I. Also show that the particular functions: $f = \sinh$ and $g = \cosh$ (hyperbolic sine and cosine functions) satisfy identity (3.5.2) and determine the value of the constant C in this case.

Solution: If we let h be the function

$$h = f^2 - g^2,$$

then

$$h' = \left(f^2\right)' - \left(g^2\right)' = 2ff' + 2gg' = 2fg - 2gf = 0$$

So by the zero derivative theorem, h is a constant function, i.e., there exists a constant C such that

$$f^2 - g^2 = C,$$

on I. Recall that the hyperbolic sine and cosine functions were defined by

$$\sinh x = \frac{1}{2}\left(e^x - e^{-x}\right) \quad \text{and} \quad \cosh x = \frac{1}{2}\left(e^x + e^{-x}\right)$$

for x in $\mathbb{R}$. From this it is clear that

$$\frac{d}{dx}(\sinh x) = \cosh x \quad \text{and} \quad \frac{d}{dx}(\cosh x) = \sinh x$$

So by the general result above, there is a constant C such that

$$\sinh^2 x - \cosh^2 x = C,$$

for all x. Taking $x = 0$ gives $C = -1$ and thus the identity:

$$\sinh^2 x - \cosh^2 x = -1,$$

i.e.,

$$\cosh^2 x - \sinh^2 x = 1.$$

Interpretations of the MVT

We used a geometric interpretation to motivate and introduce the content of the mean value theorem. This is always a good approach, but has several drawbacks when we try to generalize the mean value theorem to other types of functions (such as vector-valued functions and functions of several variables, to be considered later in the book). Additionally, the geometry (tangent line slope at some point equals secant line slope) doesn't explain the origin of the name "mean value" for this theorem. As we shall see in Chapter 4 on integrals, the *integral version* of the mean value theorem readily exhibits where the mean value (or average value) name comes from. Likewise, the integral version of the MVT generalizes to all types of functions (as we will see).

Another interpretation of the MVT arises when the function f is the position function for an object moving in 1-dimension (a falling ball, an accelerating car, etc.). Then $s = f(t)$ gives the position s of the object at time t. For the motion from time a to time b, the displacement (change in position) is $\Delta s = f(b) - f(a)$ and the average velocity over the time interval $[a, b]$

$$v_{ave} = \frac{\Delta s}{\Delta t} = \frac{f(b) - f(a)}{b - a}.$$

The MVT says that at some time c during the motion, the object's (instantaneous) velocity must be equal to this average velocity:

$$f'(c) = \frac{f(b) - f(a)}{b - a}$$

Example 3.5.7 (A Speeding Motorist)

Problem: At 10 AM a policeman observes a red SUV traveling along a highway well within the 70 mph speed limit. At 10:30 AM, 40 miles down the highway, another policeman, in radio contact with the first one, observes the same SUV traveling within the speed limit. Should the second policeman arrest the motorist for speeding?

Solution: Yes. In the elapsed time of half an hour ($\frac{1}{2}$ hour), the SUV's displacement was 40 miles. So its average velocity is

$$\frac{\Delta s}{\Delta t} = \frac{40}{\frac{1}{2}} = 80\text{mph}.$$

By the MVT, the SUV's velocity (speedometer reading) must have been 80 mph at some time c during the trip.

Figure 3.5.5: *Speed Trap.*

Exercises: 3.5 (The Mean Value Theorem)

```
> with(code_ch3_new,mean_value,print_mean_value);
           [mean_value,print_mean_value]
```

Using `mean_value` **to Visualize the Mean Value Theorem**

In Exercises 1–22, a function f is given which satisfies the hypotheses of the MVT (mean value theorem) on the given interval $[a, b]$. The MVT asserts the *existence* of at least one number c between a and b such that:

$$f'(c) = \frac{f(b) - f(a)}{b - a} \qquad (3.5.1x)$$

Verify that this is indeed true in each particular case by finding explicitly all numbers c which satisfy this equation. Do this in two ways:

(a) CAS: Use the special-purpose Maple procedure `mean_value` to create an animation of the tangent line moving along the graph of f. Step through the movie frame-by-frame until you get to the frame (or frames) where the tangent line appears to be parallel to the secant line through the points $(a, f(a))$ and $(b, f(b))$. Then use the cursor probe on the graph to determine the x-value where this occurs. This gives, approximately, one of the numbers $x = c$ which satisfies Equation (3.5.1x). NOTE: In using the procedure `mean_value`, first define the function f in Maple as usual. Then it becomes the first argument in the procedure call: `mean_value(f,a,b,N,h)`. The argument N is the number of frames in the movie (not counting the 0th frame). 20 or 30 frames are usually sufficient, but use more if the movie appears to skip the place where the tangent line is parallel to the secant line. The argument h controls the length of the tangent line. Experiment with several values $(h = 1, 2, \text{ say})$ until you get a suitable picture.

(b) Where possible, use algebra to solve equation (3.5.1x) to find exactly all numbers c that satisfy it.

1. $f(x) = 3 + 2x - x^2$, $[-1, 2]$

2. $f(x) = 10 + 3x - x^2$, $[-2, 4]$

3. $f(x) = x + \dfrac{1}{x}$, $[0.5, 4]$ 4. $f(x) = x^2 + \dfrac{1}{x^2}$, $[0.5, 2]$

5. $f(x) = \sqrt{1 - x}$, $[-3, 1]$ 6. $f(x) = \sqrt[3]{1 - x}$, $[-28, 0]$

7. $f(x) = \dfrac{x}{x + 2}$, $[-1, 2]$ 8. $f(x) = \dfrac{x - 1}{x + 1}$, $[0, 3]$

9. $f(x) = \frac{1}{2}x - \sqrt{x}$, $[0, 4]$ 10. $f(x) = \frac{1}{9}x - \sqrt[3]{x}$, $[0, 27]$

11. $f(x) = 3x^{2/5} - x^{7/5}$, $[0, 3]$

12. $f(x) = 5x^{2/3} - x^{5/3}$, $[0, 5]$

13. $f(x) = \dfrac{1}{x^2} - \dfrac{4}{2x} + \dfrac{1}{3}$, $[1, 3]$

14. $f(x) = \dfrac{1}{x^2} - \dfrac{7}{5x} + \dfrac{2}{5}$, $[1, 5]$

15. $f(x) = \dfrac{e^x}{e^x + 1}$, $[\ln(0.1), \ln 50]$

16. $f(x) = \dfrac{e^x - e^{-x}}{e^x + e^{-x}}$, $[0, \ln 8]$

17. $f(x) = x + \sin x$, $[0, 4\pi]$

18. $f(x) = x - \cos x$, $[0, 4\pi]$

19. $f(x) = \sin^{-1} x$, $[-1, 1]$ **20.** $f(x) = \tan^{-1} x$, $[0, 5]$

21. $f(x) = x^2\sqrt{36 - x^2}$, $[0, 6]$

22. $f(x) = x^3\sqrt{27 - x^3}$, $[0, 3]$

Applying Rolle's Theorem

In Exercises 23–28 use the Intermediate Value Theorem and Rolle's theorem to show that the given function has one and only one real root on the given interval.

23. $f(x) = x^7 + x + 1$, $[-1, 1]$

24. $f(x) = x^3 + x - 1$, $[-1, 1]$

25. $f(x) = x \ln x - 3$, $[2, 4]$

26. $f(x) = x^2 \ln x - 5$, $[2, 5]$

27. $f(x) = \sin x + 3x + 1$, $[-1, 1]$

28. $f(x) = \cos x + 3x + 1$, $[-1, 1]$

Proving Identities

In Exercises 29–36 use the equal derivatives theorem to prove the identities.

29. $\ln(x^r) = r \ln x$ **30.** $\ln\left(\dfrac{x}{a}\right) = \ln x - \ln a$

31. $\cot^{-1} x = \tan^{-1}\left(\dfrac{1}{x}\right)$

32. $\sec^{-1}\left(\dfrac{1}{x}\right) = \cos^{-1}(x)$

33. $\sin^{-1} x = -\tan^{-1}\left(\dfrac{\sqrt{1 - x^2}}{x}\right) + C$

34. $\cos^{-1} x = \tan^{-1}\left(\dfrac{\sqrt{1 - x^2}}{x}\right) + C$

35. $\sec^{-1} x = \tan^{-1}\left(\sqrt{x^2 - 1}\right) + C$

36. $\csc^{-1} x = -\tan^{-1}\left(\sqrt{x^2 - 1}\right) + C$

NOTE: Formulas 31, 33–36 show how all the inverse trig functions can expressed in terms of the inverse tangent function. The constant C depends on the interval being considered.

3.6 L' Hospital's Rule

```
> with(limit_tools,L_Hospital);
```

$$[L\_Hospital]$$

Geometric Motivation for L' Hospital's Rule

In Chapter 1 we presented several limit theorems which gave us methods for computing limits exactly. One of these theorems told us that the limit of a quotient is the quotient of the limits, assuming that the limit of the numerator and the limit of the denominator exist and that the limit of the denominator is *not* zero. There was also an extension of this limit theorem to quotients where the denominator has limit zero, but the numerator has nonzero limit L. In this case, we interpreted the limit of the quotient in the extended sense $\frac{L}{0} = \pm\infty$.

In addition to these results there is another limit theorem, called *L' Hospital's rule*, that sometimes can be used for finding the limit of certain types of quotients. It applies when the limit of the denominator is zero. In this section we will study L' Hospital's rule and we will see that it involves taking derivatives first and then passing to the limit.

Before stating L' Hospital's rule, we look at a few typical examples where it can be readily employed to simply and quickly discern the value of the limit. In Chapter 1 we evaluated

$$\lim_{x \to 0} \frac{\sin x}{x} = 1, \qquad (3.6.1)$$

numerically and graphically and concluded that its value was 1, as indicated. This was a guess since we offered no algebraic way of verifying it or otherwise proving this result was true. Another example of this same type is

$$\lim_{x \to 0} \frac{1 - \cos x}{x} = 0, \qquad (3.6.2)$$

which we used in Chapter 2 to prove that the derivative of $\cos x$ is $-\sin x$. Again, the tools we used to verify the validity of this result were the graphical and numerical methods. A third example, which we will study below, is the limit

$$\lim_{x \to 1} \frac{x^2 - 1}{\ln x} = 2. \qquad (3.6.3)$$

In all three of the above examples, we are taking the limit of a quotient $\frac{f(x)}{g(x)}$, where the numerator and denominator both tend to zero. A naive application of the limit laws for quotients leads to an indeterminate result:

$$\lim_{x \to a} \frac{f(x)}{g(x)} = \frac{\lim_{x \to a} f(x)}{\lim_{x \to a} g(x)} = \frac{0}{0} = \text{? (indeterminate)}$$

Such limits are called *indeterminate forms* of type $\frac{0}{0}$. The problem here is the interpretation of the indeterminate expression $\frac{0}{0}$. Without some justification, we cannot say the value of the limit is zero, even though it might be (as in (3.6.2)), and we cannot say it is some other value (as in (3.6.1) and (3.6.3)). L' Hospital's rule provides way to find the correct value of the limit and a proper justification of it. Using L' Hospital's rule does not rely on the guess-work involved in the graphical and numerical methods of evaluating limits.

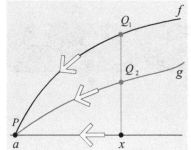

Figure 3.6.1: *Points Q_1 and Q_2 slide along the graphs of f and g toward the point P.*

To motivate the statement of L' Hospital's rule (which is a rather surprising rule), and also to indicate why it works, we look at the situation geometrically. We start with what we know for sure, namely the assumption that we have two functions f and g that both tend to 0 as x approaches the number a:

$$\lim_{x \to a} f(x) = 0 \quad \text{and} \quad \lim_{x \to a} g(x) = 0.$$

Geometrically, this looks something like the situation shown in Figure 3.6.1.

The points $Q_1 = (x, f(x))$ and $Q_2 = (x, g(x))$, on the graphs of f and g respectively, both tend toward the point $P = (a, 0)$ as $x \to a$. Our concern is with what happens to the ratio $\frac{f(x)}{g(x)}$ in this limiting process. Geometrically, this ratio is the ratio $\frac{Q_1 x}{Q_2 x}$ of the line segments $Q_1 x$, $Q_2 x$ shown in Figure 3.6.1, and of course, the lengths of these line segments tend to zero as $x \to a$. To better understand this ratio of vanishing quantities, we view $Q_1 x$, $Q_2 x$, as the sides of two right triangles $Q_1 x P$, $\Delta Q_2 x P$ as shown in Figure 3.6.2.

These triangles are actually difference triangles for the functions f and g, with

$$\begin{aligned} \Delta x &= x - a \\ \Delta y_1 &= |Q_1 x| = f(x) - 0 = f(x) \\ \Delta y_2 &= |Q_2 x| = g(x) - 0 = g(x) \end{aligned}$$

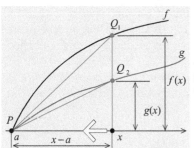

Figure 3.6.2: *Triangles $\Delta Q_1 x P$, $\Delta Q_2 x P$ are difference triangles for f and g, respectively.*

As we saw in Section 2.5, each of these difference triangles become smaller and smaller, ultimately vanishing, as $x \to a$, but the ratios of their respective sides can tend to definite values

$$\frac{\Delta y_1}{\Delta x} \to L_1 \quad \text{and} \quad \frac{\Delta y_2}{\Delta x} \to L_2.$$

This argument suggests that

$$\lim_{x \to a} \frac{f(x)}{g(x)} = \lim_{x \to a} \frac{\Delta y_1}{\Delta y_2} = \lim_{x \to a} \frac{\frac{\Delta y_1}{\Delta x}}{\frac{\Delta y_2}{\Delta x}} = \frac{L_1}{L_2}.$$

We can lend visual credence to the dynamics involved in these ideas by using the special-purpose Maple command L_Hospital. For this, we return to the third example above:

$$\lim_{x \to 1} \frac{x^2 - 1}{\ln x} = 2,$$

and define the two functions f and g by:

```
> f:=x->x^2-1;g:=x->ln(x);
```

$$f := x \mapsto x^2 - 1$$
$$g := x \mapsto \ln(x)$$

Then we look at the dynamics on the interval by using the L_Hospital command as follows:

```
> L_Hospital(f,g,1,1.5);
```

Figure 3.6.3 shows the 7th frame in this animation. At each time (or frame) during the animation, the triangles $\Delta Q_1 x P$, $\Delta Q_2 x P$ are similar to the triangles $\Delta R_1 S P$, $\Delta R_2 S P$ (respectively). The former pair of triangles ultimately vanishes as $\Delta x \to 1$, but the latter pair tends to a definite pair of triangles. Using the cursor probe on the last frame in the animation, you will see that the vertical sides of triangles have lengths

$$|R_1 S| = 1, \quad |R_2 S| = 0.5,$$

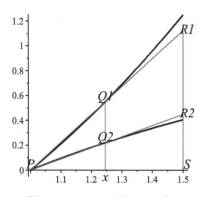

Figure 3.6.3: *The 7th frame in the animation* L_Hospital(f,g,1,1.5).

approximately. (Note: You might have to use the full-screen display of the last frame to get accurate data from the cursor probes). The triangles have a common horizontal side of length $|PS| = 1.5 - 1 = 0.5$. Thus, the slopes of the hypotenuses of the vanishing triangles $\Delta Q_1 x P$, $\Delta Q_2 x P$ tend to

$$\frac{\Delta y_1}{\Delta x} \to \frac{1}{0.5} = 2 \quad \text{and} \quad \frac{\Delta y_2}{\Delta x} \to \frac{0.5}{0.5} = 1,$$

respectively. By definition of the derivative, the above two values are $f'(1)$ and $g'(1)$, where $f(x) = x^2 - 1$ and $g(x) = \ln x$. All of this is evidence for the validity of L' Hospital's rule, which says

$$\lim_{x \to a} \frac{f(x)}{g(x)} = \lim_{x \to a} \frac{f'(x)}{g'(x)}.$$

(Of course, we need to impose appropriate hypotheses on the functions involved for this to be true.) In this particular example, L' Hospital's rule looks like

$$\lim_{x \to 1} \frac{x^2 - 1}{\ln x} = \lim_{x \to 1} \frac{\frac{d}{dx}(x^2 - 1)}{\frac{d}{dx}(\ln x)} = \lim_{x \to 1} \frac{2x}{\frac{1}{x}} = \lim_{x \to 1} 2x^2 = 2$$

Note that the correct limiting value 2 can also be estimated by cursor probing on the last frame in the movie `L_Hospital(f,g,1,1.5)`, measuring $|R_1 S| = 1$, $|R_2 S| = 0.5$, and taking their ratio $|R_1 S|/|R_2 S| = 1/(0.5) = 2$. Do you see why?

L' Hospital's Rule for Indeterminate Forms

Having discussed the geometrical motivation for L' Hospital's rule in the first subsection above, we now present the statement of this rule and illustrate its use with a number of examples.

THEOREM 3.6.1 (L' Hospital's Rule)

Suppose f and g are differentiable on an open interval I about a, and that

$$\lim_{x \to a} f(x) = 0 \quad and \quad \lim_{x \to a} g(x) = 0$$

Then

$$\lim_{x \to a} \frac{f(x)}{g(x)} = \lim_{x \to a} \frac{f'(x)}{g'(x)}$$

provided the latter limit exists and $g'(x) \neq 0$ for x near a but distinct from a.

NOTE 1: L' Hospital's rule is valid also for one-sided limits and limits at infinity. In other words, in the theorem $x \to a$ can be replaced by $x \to a^-$, $x \to a^+$, $x \to \infty$, $x \to -\infty$.

NOTE 2: L' Hospital's rule says that, under the stated conditions, the limit of a quotient can be replaced by the limit of the quotient of the respective derivatives. *It is important to stress here that this is NOT related to the quotient rule for derivatives.* In L' Hospital's rule, the derivatives of each of f and g are taken separately and then the new quotient $\frac{f'(x)}{g'(x)}$ is formed.

A proof of a special case of this theorem is given in the last subsection below. You will see that the proof is entirely similar to geometrical argument given in the first subsection.

Example 3.6.1 (Applying L' Hospital's Rule)

Problem: Find the following limits using L' Hospital's rule:

(a) $\lim_{x \to 1} \dfrac{x^3 + 3x^2 - x - 3}{x^3 - x^2 - 4x + 4}$ (b) $\lim_{x \to 4} \dfrac{\sqrt{x} - 2}{x - 4}$ (c) $\lim_{x \to 0} \dfrac{\tan x}{e^{2x} - 1}$

Solution: You can readily check in each of these that the numerators and denominators tend to zero. Thus, we have indeterminate forms $\frac{0}{0}$ to evaluate. Applying L' Hospital's rule, we get

Part(a):

$$\lim_{x\to1}\frac{x^3+3x^2-x-3}{x^3-x^2-4x+4}\overset{L'Hosp}{=}\lim_{x\to1}\frac{\frac{d}{dx}\left(x^3+3x^2-x-3\right)}{\frac{d}{dx}\left(x^3-x^2-4x+4\right)}=\lim_{x\to1}\frac{3x^2+6x-1}{3x^2-2x-4}$$

$$=\frac{3\left(1\right)^2+6\left(1\right)-1}{3\left(1\right)^2-2\left(1\right)-4}=\frac{8}{-3}=-\frac{8}{3}$$

Part (b):

$$\lim_{x\to4}\frac{\sqrt{x}-2}{x-4}\overset{L'Hosp}{=}\lim_{x\to4}\frac{\frac{d}{dx}\left(\sqrt{x}-2\right)}{\frac{d}{dx}\left(x-4\right)}=\lim_{x\to4}\frac{\frac{1}{2\sqrt{x}}}{1}=\frac{1}{2\sqrt{4}}=\frac{1}{4}$$

Part (c):

$$\lim_{x\to0}\frac{\tan x}{e^{2\,x}-1}\overset{L'Hosp}{=}\lim_{x\to0}\frac{\frac{d}{dx}(\tan x)}{\frac{d}{dx}\left(e^{2x}-1\right)}=\lim_{x\to0}\frac{\sec^2x}{2e^{2\,x}}=\frac{\sec^2(0)}{2e^0}=\frac{1}{2}$$

You should note that the limits in Parts (a) and (b) can be done algebraically by factoring (in Part (a)) and rationalizing the numerator (in Part (b)). However, we think that you will find using L' Hospital's is a quicker and more pleasant way to evaluate these limits.

Also note that Part (c) *cannot* be done algebraically, so L' Hospital's rule is the only way of showing, rigorously, that the limit exists and is equal to 1/2. (Numerical and graphical methods will lead you to the same answer, but that is only guess-work.)

SPECIAL NOTE: With practice you should be able to skip the step in L' Hospital's rule where $\frac{d}{dx}$ is inserted in the numerator and denominator, especially when the derivatives are easy to do in your head.

Example 3.6.2 (Two Famous Limits)

Problem: Use L' Hospital's rule to calculate the following famous limits:

(a) $\lim_{x\to0}\dfrac{\sin x}{x}$ (b) $\lim_{x\to0}\dfrac{1-\cos x}{x}$

Solution: It is clear that we get $\frac{0}{0}$ if we take the limit of the numerators over the limit of the denominators, so we have indeterminate forms in each case. Thus, we can apply L' Hospital's rule:

$$\lim_{x\to0}\frac{\sin x}{x}\overset{L'Hosp}{=}\lim_{x\to0}\frac{\cos x}{1}=\frac{\cos\left(0\right)}{1}=\frac{1}{1}=1,$$

in the first case, and

$$\lim_{x\to0}\frac{1-\cos x}{x}\overset{L'Hosp}{=}\lim_{x\to0}\frac{\sin x}{1}=\frac{\sin(0)}{1}=\frac{0}{1}=0,$$

in the second case. These are the famous limits we used in Chapter 2 Section 7 to prove that $\frac{d}{dx}(\sin x)=\cos x$ and $\frac{d}{dx}(\cos x)=-\sin x$. So it is important for you to realize that the above derivation of the results 1 and 0 for these limits is rather circular – to get the results we need to know the derivatives of sine and cosine, but to know these derivatives requires using the results! You should not worry too much about all of this. Rather you should view L' Hospital's rule as a quick and easy way of getting the results of these limits.

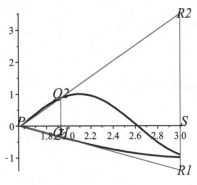

Figure 3.6.4: *The 11th frame in the animation* `L_Hospital(f,g,1.57,3).`

Example 3.6.3 (Using the `L_Hospital` Command)

Problem: Use the special-purpose Maple command `L_Hospital` to estimate the limit $\displaystyle\lim_{x\to\pi/2}\frac{\cos x}{\cos 3x}$. Then use L' Hospital's rule to verify and check your estimate.

Solution: We define the two functions and then use the `L_Hospital` command as follows.

```
> f:=x->cos(x);g:=x->cos(3*x);
```
$$f := \cos$$
$$g := x \mapsto \cos(3\,x)$$
```
> L_Hospital(f,g,1.57,3);
```

Figure 3.6.4 shows the 11th frame in this movie.

We use the mouse to probe the points in the last frame in this movie and find that $R_1 S = -1.55$, $R_2 S = 4.27$, approximately. Thus, we estimate the limit is

$$\lim_{x\to\pi/2}\frac{\cos x}{\cos 3x} = \frac{R_1 S}{R_2 S} = -\frac{1.55}{4.27} \approx -0.363$$

Using L' Hospital's rule verifies that this is approximately the right value. It gives the exact value as follows:

$$\lim_{x\to\pi/2}\frac{\cos x}{\cos 3x} \overset{L'Hosp}{=} \lim_{x\to\pi/2}\frac{-\sin x}{-3\sin 3x} = \frac{\sin\left(\frac{\pi}{2}\right)}{3\sin\left(\frac{3\pi}{2}\right)} = -\frac{1}{3}$$

Example 3.6.4 (Using L' Hospital's Rule Twice)

Problem: Find the limit: $\displaystyle\lim_{x\to 0}\frac{\sin x - x}{x^2}$.

Solution: It is easy to check that this limit is indeterminate of type $\frac{0}{0}$. So we apply L' Hospital's rule to get

$$\lim_{x\to 0}\frac{\sin x - x}{x^2} \overset{L'Hosp}{=} \lim_{x\to 0}\frac{\cos x - 1}{2x}.$$

However, you see that the new limit is also indeterminate of type $\frac{0}{0}$. So we apply L' Hospital's rule a second time to get

$$\lim_{x\to 0}\frac{\cos x - 1}{2x} \overset{L'Hosp}{=} \lim_{x\to 0}\frac{-\sin x}{2} = \frac{0}{2} = 0.$$

This problem illustrates that some limits require repeated application of L' Hospital's rule before they become determinate.

Other Indeterminate Forms

L' Hospital's rule was discussed above for indeterminate form of type $\frac{0}{0}$. Here we look at how this rule can be applied to other types of indeterminate forms. The box in the margin shows the various types which we handle in one way or another by using L' Hospital's rule.

The first line lists indeterminate forms that arise from limits involving quotients, products, and differences, while the second line lists the ones that come from limits involving exponents. The reason these forms are indeterminate is that, as we saw with $\frac{0}{0}$, there is no one value that we can definitely assign to the form. For example, it might be tempting to say that $\frac{\infty}{\infty}$ is equal to 1 (or perhaps ∞), and that 0^0 is equal to 1. But, as we shall see, this could be wrong, since some limits of these forms give answers different from these. Contrast what we have said about indeterminate forms with what we found Section 1.8 for certain forms involving the extended real numbers $\pm\infty$. See the margin box. These are *definite* results that you can always use in evaluating limits. It is just the indeterminate ones that you must investigate using L' Hospital's rule.

Indeterminate Forms

$$\frac{0}{0} \quad \frac{\infty}{\infty} \quad \infty\cdot 0 \quad \infty-\infty$$

$$0^0 \quad 1^\infty \quad \infty^0$$

Extended Arithmetic

For a positive real number k:

$$\frac{k}{+0} = +\infty \qquad \frac{k}{-0} = -\infty$$

$$\pm\infty\cdot k = \pm\infty \qquad \frac{k}{\pm\infty} = 0$$

Forms of Type $\dfrac{\infty}{\infty}$

A limit of the form $\lim_{x \to a} \dfrac{f(x)}{g(x)}$ is called *indeterminate of type* $\dfrac{\infty}{\infty}$, if

$$\lim_{x \to a} f(x) = \pm\infty \quad \text{and} \quad \lim_{x \to a} g(x) = \pm\infty.$$

Note that there are four possibilities for the $\pm$ signs here. It does not matter what they are. L' Hospital's rule still holds for this type of indeterminate form and the rule looks exactly like it did for the form $\frac{0}{0}$, namely:

L' Hospital's Rule for Type $\dfrac{\infty}{\infty}$

$$\lim_{x \to a} \frac{f(x)}{g(x)} = \lim_{x \to a} \frac{f'(x)}{g'(x)} \qquad (3.6.4)$$

The same hypotheses as before must hold for the rule (3.6.4) to work: (1) The functions f, g must be differentiable on an open interval about a, (2) they must not be zero for x near a, but distinct from a, and (3) the limit on the right-side of (3.6.4) must exist.

Note also that L' Hospital's rule (3.6.4) holds for one-sided limits $x \to a^{+}$, $x \to a^{-}$ and for limits at infinity $x \to \pm\infty$.

Example 3.6.5

Problem: Find the following limits using L' Hospital's rule:

(a) $\displaystyle\lim_{x \to 1^{+}} \frac{\frac{1}{x-1}}{\ln(x-1)}$ (b) $\displaystyle\lim_{x \to \infty} \frac{x}{e^{5x}}$ (c) $\displaystyle\lim_{x \to \infty} \frac{x^3}{e^{5x}}$ (d) $\displaystyle\lim_{x \to -\infty} \frac{2x^3 - x + 5}{x^2 - 5x^3}$

Solution: It is easy to check that, in each case, we have an indeterminate form of type $\frac{\infty}{\infty}$. Applying L' Hospital's rule in each case gives

(a) $\displaystyle\lim_{x \to 1^{+}} \frac{\frac{1}{x-1}}{\ln(x-1)} = \lim_{x \to 1^{+}} \frac{\frac{-1}{(x-1)^2}}{\frac{1}{x-1}} = \lim_{x \to 1^{+}} -\frac{1}{(x-1)^2} \cdot (x-1) = \lim_{x \to 1^{+}} \frac{-1}{x-1} = -\infty$

(b) $\displaystyle\lim_{x \to \infty} \frac{x}{e^{5x}} = \lim_{x \to \infty} \frac{1}{5e^{5x}} = 0$

(c) In this one, we have to use L' Hospital's rule three times:

$$\lim_{x \to \infty} \frac{x^3}{e^{5x}} = \lim_{x \to \infty} \frac{3x^2}{5e^{5x}} = \lim_{x \to \infty} \frac{6x}{25e^{5x}} = \lim_{x \to \infty} \frac{6}{125e^{5x}} = 0$$

(d) Again, we use L' Hospital's rule three times.

$$\lim_{x \to -\infty} \frac{2x^3 - x + 5}{x^2 - 5x^3} = \lim_{x \to -\infty} \frac{6x^2 - 1}{2x - 15x^2} = \lim_{x \to -\infty} \frac{12x}{2 - 30x} = \lim_{x \to -\infty} \frac{12}{-30} = -\frac{2}{5}$$

Note that you could also evaluate this limit using the algebraic technique from Chapter 1. Namely, divide numerator and denominator by x^3 and then take the limit.

Forms of Type $0 \cdot \infty$ and $\infty - \infty$

Indeterminate forms of types $0 \cdot \infty$ and $\infty - \infty$ arise from limits such as

$$\lim_{x \to a} f(x) g(x) \quad \text{and} \quad \lim_{x \to a} [h(x) - k(x)],$$

where

$$\lim_{x \to a} f(x) = 0, \ \lim_{x \to a} g(x) = \infty, \ \lim_{x \to a} h(x) = \infty \quad \text{and} \quad \lim_{x \to a} k(x) = \infty.$$

There is *no* L' Hospital's rule for these types of indeterminate forms. However, if we can convert these limits, using algebra, into ones that are indeterminate of types $\frac{0}{0}$ or $\frac{\infty}{\infty}$, then we can use L' Hospital's rule on the converted forms. This is easiest to explain using examples as follows.

Example 3.6.6

Problem: Identify the types of indeterminacy of the following limits. Then convert them into types $\frac{0}{0}$ or $\frac{\infty}{\infty}$ and use L' Hospital's rule to evaluate them. Use Maple to do a quick graphical check of your answers.

(a) $\lim\limits_{x\to 0^+} x\ln x$ (b) $\lim\limits_{x\to\infty} e^{-5x}x^3$ (c) $\lim\limits_{x\to 0^+} \csc x - \cot x$

Solution (a): Here $\lim_{x\to 0^+} x = 0$, $\lim_{x\to 0^+} \ln x = -\infty$, and so this is an indeterminate form of type $0\cdot\infty$. We convert it into a form of type $\frac{\infty}{\infty}$ by using the fact that multiplying x is equivalent to dividing by $1/x$:

$$\lim_{x\to 0^+} x\ln x = \lim_{x\to 0^+} \frac{\ln x}{\frac{1}{x}} \overset{L'Hosp}{=} \lim_{x\to 0^+} \frac{\frac{1}{x}}{-\frac{1}{x^2}} \overset{alg}{=} \lim_{x\to 0^+} \frac{1}{x}\cdot\left(-x^2\right)$$
$$= \lim_{x\to 0^+} (-x) = 0$$

NOTE: Any product can be converted to a quotient in this manner:

$$AB = \frac{B}{\frac{1}{A}} = \frac{A}{\frac{1}{B}}$$

Usually one of these conversions is preferred over the other when using L'Hospital's rule. For example, in this problem we could have used the conversion

$$x\ln x = \frac{x}{\frac{1}{\ln x}}.$$

This gives an indeterminate form of type $\frac{0}{0}$, but use of L' Hospital's rule on this doesn't work out so well. With practice and experience you will learn to chose the best conversion.

Finally, as a quick graphical check on our answer $\lim_{x\to 0^+} x\ln x = 0$, we graph $f(x) = x\ln x$ on an interval with 0 as the left endpoint. See Figure 3.6.5.

```
> f:=x->x*ln(x);
```
$$f := x \mapsto x\ln(x)$$
```
> plot(f(x),x=0..2,color=red,thickness=2);
```

Solution (b): The limit $\lim_{x\to\infty} e^{-5x}x^3$ is again this is a form of type $0\cdot\infty$. Here it is natural to convert the product into the quotient as follows

$$e^{-5x}x^3 = \frac{x^3}{e^{5x}}.$$

Then we use the result of Part (c) in Example 3.6.5 above:

$$\lim_{x\to\infty} e^{-5x}x^3 = \lim_{x\to\infty} \frac{x^3}{e^{5x}} = 0.$$

A plot of the function $f(x) = e^{-5x}x^3$ shows the limiting behavior as x gets large:
```
> f:=x->exp(-5*x)*x^3;
```
$$f := x \mapsto e^{-5x}x^3$$
```
> plot(f(x),x=0..3,color=red,thickness=2);
```

We see from Figure 3.6.6 that the limit goes to 0 rather rapidly because of the fast exponential decay of e^{-5x}.

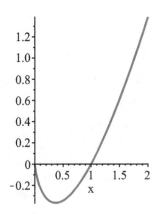

Figure 3.6.5: *The graph of $f(x) = x\ln x$ near 0.*

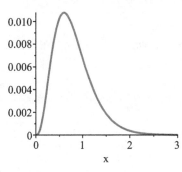

Figure 3.6.6: *The graph of $f(x) = e^{-5x}x^3$ on $[0,3]$.*

Solution (c): Here, for $\lim_{x\to 0^+} \csc x - \cot x$, the separate limits are

$$\lim_{x\to 0^+} \csc x = \lim_{x\to 0^+} \frac{1}{\sin x} = \frac{1}{+0} = +\infty$$

and

$$\lim_{x\to 0^+} \cot x = \lim_{x\to 0^+} \frac{\cos x}{\sin x} = \frac{1}{+0} = +\infty$$

So this is an indeterminate form of type $\infty - \infty$. The conversion of this into something where L' Hospital's rule applies involves combining fractions:

$$\csc x - \cot x = \frac{1}{\sin x} - \frac{\cos x}{\sin x} = \frac{1 - \cos x}{\sin x}.$$

The latter fraction gives an indeterminate form of type $\frac{0}{0}$. Thus, we can use L' Hospital's rule as follows

$$\lim_{x\to 0^+} (\csc x - \cot x) = \lim_{x\to 0^+} \frac{1 - \cos x}{\sin x} \overset{L'Hosp}{=} \lim_{x\to 0^+} \frac{\sin x}{\cos x} = \frac{\sin(0)}{\cos(0)} = \frac{0}{1} = 0.$$

A plot of $f(x) = \csc x - \cot x$ near 0 is shown in Figure 3.6.7. This provides a graphical check of our work.

```
> f:=x->csc(x)-cot(x);
```
$$f := x \mapsto \csc(x) - \cot(x)$$
```
>plot(f(x),x=0..3,color=red,thickness=2);
```

Figure 3.6.7: *Plot of $f(x) = \csc x - \cot x$.*

Forms of Types 0^0, 1^∞, and ∞^0.

Limits such as $\lim_{x\to a} f(x)^{g(x)}$ will give indeterminate forms of types 0^0, 1^∞, and ∞^0 when the respective limits

$$\lim_{x\to a} f(x) \qquad \text{and} \qquad \lim_{x\to a} g(x)$$

A Fundamental Identity

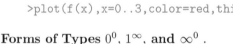
$$b^a = e^{a\ln b}$$

are 0, 0, or 1, $\pm\infty$, or $\pm\infty$, 0, respectively. These limits can be converted into ones which are indeterminate of type $e^{0\cdot\infty}$ by using the identity shown in the margin box. From the continuity of e^x, we can thus get

$$\lim_{x\to a} f(x)^{g(x)} = \lim_{x\to a} e^{g(x)\ln f(x)} = e^{\lim_{x\to a} g(x)\ln f(x)}.$$

Problems of this type then reduce to evaluating indeterminate limits of the type

$$\lim_{x\to a} g(x)\ln f(x) = L.$$

We find L as we did in the last subsection. Then the answer to the original limit is e^L.

CAUTION: It is a common mistake to use L as the answer for the original limit.

Example 3.6.7

Problem: Identify the types of indeterminacy of the following limits. Then evaluate each limit. Use Maple to produce a graphical check of your answers.

(a) $\lim_{x\to 0^+} x^x$ (b) $\lim_{x\to\infty} x^{1/x}$ (c) $\lim_{x\to\infty} \left(1 + \frac{1}{x}\right)^x$ (d) $\lim_{x\to 0^+} (1 + 2\sin x)^{1/x}$

Solution (a): This is clearly an indeterminate form of type 0^0. When we convert to base e, the limit becomes:

$$\lim_{x\to 0^+} x^x = \lim_{x\to 0^+} e^{x\ln x} = e^{\lim_{x\to 0^+} x\ln x}.$$

The limit in the exponent here was found in part (a) of Example 3.6.6. above:

$$\lim_{x \to 0^+} x \ln x = 0$$

So the value of the original limit is $e^0 = 1$. That is,

$$\lim_{x \to 0^+} x^x = 1$$

To check this, we plot $f(x) = x^x$ on an interval with 0 as the left endpoint:

```
> f:=x->x^x;
```
$$f := x \mapsto x^x$$
```
> plot(f(x),x=0..1,color=red,thickness=2);
```

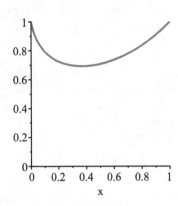

Figure 3.6.8: *Plot of* $f(x) = x^x$ *near* 0 .

Solution (b): This limit $\lim\limits_{x \to \infty} x^{1/x}$ is an indeterminate form of type ∞^0. Converting to base e gives

$$\lim_{x \to \infty} x^{1/x} = \lim_{x \to \infty} e^{\frac{\ln x}{x}} = e^{\lim_{x \to \infty} \frac{\ln x}{x}}$$

The limit in the exponent here is indeterminate of type $\frac{\infty}{\infty}$, so we can use L' Hospital's rule:

$$\lim_{x \to \infty} \frac{\ln x}{x} = \lim_{x \to \infty} \frac{\frac{1}{x}}{1} = 0.$$

Thus, the original limit is $e^0 = 1$, i.e.,

$$\lim_{x \to \infty} x^{1/x} = 1.$$

We check this by plotting $f(x) = x^{1/x}$.

```
> f:=x->x^(1/x);
```
$$f := x \mapsto x^{1/x}$$
```
> plot([0,1,f(x)],x=2..200,color=[black,black,red]);
```

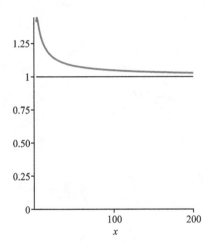

Figure 3.6.9: *Plot of* $f(x) = x^{1/x}$ *near* 0 .

Solution (c): The limit $\lim_{x \to \infty} \left(1 + \frac{1}{x}\right)^x$ is an indeterminate form of type 1^∞. It converts to base e as follows

$$\lim_{x \to \infty} \left(1 + \frac{1}{x}\right)^x = e^{\lim_{x \to \infty} x \ln(1 + 1/x)}$$

The limit in the exponent is

$$\lim_{x \to \infty} x \ln\left(1 + \frac{1}{x}\right) = \lim_{x \to \infty} \frac{\ln\left(1 + \frac{1}{x}\right)}{\frac{1}{x}} = \lim_{x \to \infty} \frac{\frac{1}{1+\frac{1}{x}} \cdot \left(-\frac{1}{x^2}\right)}{-\frac{1}{x^2}} = \lim_{x \to \infty} \frac{1}{1 + \frac{1}{x}} = 1$$

Thus, the answer is $e^1 = e$ and from this we get a famous limit expression for the number e:

$$\lim_{x \to \infty} \left(1 + \frac{1}{x}\right)^x = e$$

The following plot illustrates this

```
> f:=x->(1+1/x)^x;
```
$$f := x \mapsto \left(1 + x^{-1}\right)^x$$
```
> plot([0,exp(1),f(x)],x=0..20,color=[black,black,red]);
```

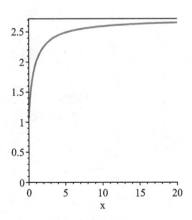

Figure 3.6.10: *Plot of* $f(x) = \left(1 + \frac{1}{x}\right)^x$.

Solution (d): The limit here is $\lim\limits_{x\to0^+} (1+2\sin x)^{1/x}$ and is indeterminate of type 1^∞. It converts to base e as

$$\lim_{x\to0^+} (1+2\sin x)^{1/x} = e^{\lim_{x\to0^+} \frac{\ln(1+2\sin x)}{x}}$$

The limit in the exponent is indeterminate of type $\frac{0}{0}$ and so we can use L'Hospital's rule on it:

$$\lim_{x\to0^+} \frac{\ln(1+2\sin x)}{x} = \lim_{x\to0^+} \frac{\frac{2\cos x}{1+2\sin x}}{1} = 2$$

Hence the original limit is

$$\lim_{x\to0^+} (1+2\sin x)^{1/x} = e^2 \approx 7.4$$

Again we check the result by plotting $f(x) = (1+2\sin x)^{1/x}$ near the origin.

```
>f:=x->(1+2*sin(x))^(1/x);
```
$$f := x \mapsto (1+2\sin(x))^{x^{-1}}$$
```
> plot([0,f(x)],x=0.1..7*Pi/6,color=[black,red]);
```

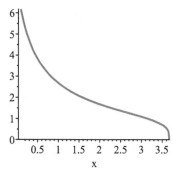

Figure 3.6.11: *Plot of $f(x) = (1+2\sin x)^{1/x}$.*

Proof of L'Hospital's Rule

We will only look at a special case of the proof. Suppose that $f(a) = 0 = g(a)$, that both f', g' are continuous, and that $g'(a) \ne 0$. Then

$$\lim_{x\to a} \frac{f(x)}{g(x)} = \lim_{x\to a} \frac{f(x) - f(a)}{g(x) - g(a)} = \lim_{x\to a} \frac{\frac{f(x)-f(a)}{x-a}}{\frac{g(x)-g(a)}{x-a}}$$

$$= \frac{f'(a)}{g'(a)} = \lim_{x\to a} \frac{f'(x)}{g'(x)} .$$

The last equality follows because f' and g' are both continuous at $x = a$.

Exercises: 3.6 (L' Hospital's Rule)

Using L' Hospital's Rule: Indeterminate Forms of Type $\frac{0}{0}$ or $\frac{\infty}{\infty}$.

In Exercises 1–48 use, where possible, L' Hospital's rule (repeatedly if necessary) to evaluate the limit.

1. $\lim\limits_{x \to 1} \dfrac{5\,x^4 - 7\,x^3 + 2\,x^2}{3\,x^2 + 7\,x - 10}$ **2.** $\lim\limits_{x \to 1} \dfrac{5\,x^3 - 7\,x^2 + 2\,x}{4\,x^2 + 3\,x - 7}$

3. $\lim\limits_{x \to 2} \dfrac{2\,x^4 - 7\,x^3 + 3\,x^2 + 8\,x - 4}{x^4 - 4\,x^3 + 3\,x^2 + 4\,x - 4}$

4. $\lim\limits_{x \to 3} \dfrac{2\,x^4 - 7\,x^2 - 5\,x^3 + 10\,x + 6}{2\,x^3 - 5\,x^2 - 7\,x + 12}$

5. $\lim\limits_{x \to 1} \dfrac{x^2 - 1}{2\,x + 1}$ **6.** $\lim\limits_{x \to 1} \dfrac{x^2 + 3\,x - 4}{x - 1}$

7. $\lim\limits_{x \to 16} \dfrac{x - 16}{\sqrt{x} - 4}$ **8.** $\lim\limits_{x \to 25} \dfrac{x - 25}{\sqrt{x} - 5}$

9. $\lim\limits_{x \to 27} \dfrac{\sqrt[3]{x} - 3}{x - 27}$ **10.** $\lim\limits_{x \to 32} \dfrac{\sqrt[5]{x} - 2}{x - 32}$

11. $\lim\limits_{x \to 1} \dfrac{\ln x}{x^2 - 1}$ **12.** $\lim\limits_{x \to 1} \dfrac{x^p \ln x}{x^2 - 1}$

13. $\lim\limits_{x \to 1} \dfrac{x^3 \ln x}{\sin 2\pi x}$ **14.** $\lim\limits_{x \to 1} \dfrac{x^3 \ln x}{x - \cos 2\pi x}$

15. $\lim\limits_{x \to 0} \dfrac{\sin x^2)}{3\,x^2}$ **16.** $\lim\limits_{x \to 1} \dfrac{\tan\left(x^2 - 1\right)}{1 - x^2}$

17. $\lim\limits_{x \to 0} \dfrac{\sin^2 x}{1 - \cos x}$ **18.** $\lim\limits_{x \to \pi/2} \dfrac{\cos^2 x}{1 - \sin x}$

19. $\lim\limits_{x \to 0} \dfrac{\cos 3x - 1}{x^2}$ **20.** $\lim\limits_{x \to \pi} \dfrac{\sin 5x}{1 + \cos x}$

21. $\lim\limits_{x \to 0} \dfrac{\sec x - 1}{\tan x}$ **22.** $\lim\limits_{x \to \pi/2} \dfrac{\csc x - 1}{\cot x}$

23. $\lim\limits_{x \to 0} \dfrac{\sec x - 1}{x^2}$ **24.** $\lim\limits_{x \to 0} \dfrac{\sec 4x^2 - 1}{x^2}$

25. $\lim\limits_{x \to 0} \dfrac{\tan x}{x}$ **26.** $\lim\limits_{x \to \pi/2} \dfrac{\cot x}{x - \frac{\pi}{2}}$

27. $\lim\limits_{x \to 0} \dfrac{\tan x - x}{x^3}$ **28.** $\lim\limits_{x \to 0} \dfrac{\cos x - 1}{x^2}$

29. Show that $\lim\limits_{x \to 0} \dfrac{\sin ax}{x} = a$

30. Show that $\lim\limits_{x \to \pi/2} \dfrac{\cos[a\ x - \frac{\pi}{2})] - 1}{x - \frac{\pi}{2}} = 0$

31. $\lim\limits_{x \to 0} \dfrac{\sin x \sin 3x}{x^2}$ **32.** $\lim\limits_{x \to 0} \dfrac{\tan x \tan 3x}{x}$

33. $\lim\limits_{x \to 0} \dfrac{\sin(x^2) - x^2}{x^3}$ **34.** $\lim\limits_{x \to 0} \dfrac{\cos(x^2) - 1}{x^2}$

35. $\lim\limits_{x \to 0} \dfrac{\cos x \cos 2x - 1}{x^2}$ **36.** $\lim\limits_{x \to 0} \dfrac{\sec^2 3x - 1}{x^2}$

37. $\lim\limits_{x \to 0} \dfrac{2^x - 1}{3^x - 1}$ **38.** $\lim\limits_{x \to 0} \dfrac{5^x - 1}{7^x - 1}$

39. $\lim\limits_{x \to 1} \dfrac{x^2 - 1}{x^3 - 1}$ **40.** $\lim\limits_{x \to 0} \dfrac{\tan \pi x}{e^x - 1}$

41. $\lim\limits_{x \to \infty} \dfrac{\ln x}{x}$ **42.** $\lim\limits_{x \to \infty} \dfrac{\ln x}{x + 1}$

43. $\lim\limits_{x \to \infty} \dfrac{\ln x}{\sqrt{x}}$ **44.** $\lim\limits_{x \to \infty} \dfrac{\ln x}{x^{1/3}}$

45. $\lim\limits_{x \to \infty} \dfrac{e^{3x}}{x^2}$ **46.** $\lim\limits_{x \to \infty} \dfrac{e^{3x}}{x^5}$

47. $\lim\limits_{x \to \infty} \dfrac{5\,x^2 - 4\,x + 6}{1 - 3\,x^2}$ **48.** $\lim\limits_{x \to \infty} \dfrac{9\,x^2 - 14\,x + 10}{4 - 3\,x + 6\,x^2}$

Using L' Hospital's Rule: Indeterminate Forms of Type $0 \cdot \infty,\ 0^0,\ 1^\infty,\ \infty^0,$ or $\infty - \infty$.

In Exercises 49–82 evaluate the limit, where possible, using L' Hospital's rule. Identify the limit's type of indeterminate form before using L' Hospital's rule.

49. $\lim\limits_{x \to 0^+} \sqrt{x} \ln x$ **50.** $\lim\limits_{x \to 0^+} x^{1/3} \ln x$

51. $\lim\limits_{x \to 0^+} x\,(\ln x)^2$ **52.** $\lim\limits_{x \to 0^+} x^k\,(\ln x)^p$

53. $\lim\limits_{x \to 0} \dfrac{\tan^{-1} x}{x}$ **54.** $\lim\limits_{x \to 0} \dfrac{\tan^{-1} x}{x^2}$

55. $\lim\limits_{x \to 0^+} \sin x \ln x$ **56.** $\lim\limits_{x \to 0^+} \tan x \ln x$

57. $\lim\limits_{x \to 0^+} x \ln (\sin x)$ **58.** $\lim\limits_{x \to 0^+} x \ln (\tan x)$

59. $\lim\limits_{x \to 0^+} (\sin x)^x$ **60.** $\lim\limits_{x \to 0^+} (\tan x)^x$

61. $\lim\limits_{x \to 0^+} x^{\sin x}$ **62.** $\lim\limits_{x \to 0^+} x^{\tan x}$

63. $\lim\limits_{x \to 0} (1 - 5\,x)^{1/(3x}.$ **64.** $\lim\limits_{x \to 0} (1 + x)^{1/x}$

65. $\lim\limits_{x \to \infty} \left(1 + \dfrac{3}{x^2}\right)^x$ **66.** $\lim\limits_{x \to \infty} \left(1 - \dfrac{3}{x^2}\right)^x$

67. $\lim\limits_{x \to \infty} \left(1 + \dfrac{4}{x^2}\right)^{x^2}$ **68.** $\lim\limits_{x \to \infty} \left(1 - \dfrac{4}{x^2}\right)^{x^2}$

69. $\lim\limits_{x \to \infty} x \sin \left(\dfrac{1}{x}\right)$ **70.** $\lim\limits_{x \to \infty} x \cos \left(\dfrac{1}{x}\right)$

71. $\lim\limits_{x \to \infty} x^2 \sin \left(\dfrac{1}{x}\right)$ **72.** $\lim\limits_{x \to \infty} x^2 \cos \left(\dfrac{1}{x}\right)$

73. $\lim\limits_{x \to 0} (1 - \cos x)^{\sin x}$ **74.** $\lim\limits_{x \to 0} (\tan x)^{\sin x}$

75. $\lim\limits_{x \to 0^+} \left(\dfrac{1}{x} - \dfrac{1}{\sin x}\right)$ **76.** $\lim\limits_{x \to 0^+} \left(\csc x - \dfrac{1}{x}\right)$

77. $\lim\limits_{x \to 0^+} \left(\dfrac{1}{x^2} - \dfrac{\cos 3x}{x^2}\right)$ **78.** $\lim\limits_{x \to 0^+} \left(\dfrac{1}{x^2} - \dfrac{\cos 5x}{x^2}\right)$

79. $\lim\limits_{x \to \infty} \left(\sqrt{x^2 + 1} - x\right)$ **80.** $\lim\limits_{x \to \infty} \left(\sqrt{x^2 + 2} - x\right)$

81. $\lim\limits_{x \to 0^+} \left(\dfrac{1}{x} - \dfrac{1}{e^x - 1}\right)$ **82.** $\lim\limits_{x \to 0^+} \left(\dfrac{1}{x} - \dfrac{\ln 2}{2^x - 1}\right)$

Calculus Concepts & Computation

3.7 Antiderivatives and Integrals

This Section begins a new phase of your calculus experience. So far you have been studying the *differential calculus* which consists of finding derivatives of functions and using these derivatives in various applications. Now you will begin a study of what is known as the *integral calculus* and you will learn many interesting and important applications of this aspect of calculus.

In a sense, the integral calculus is the reverse of the differential calculus. Instead of differentiating functions we now want to learn how to *un*differentiate them, that is, we want to find *antiderivatives* of functions. The next subsection clarifies what we mean by this, and the ensuing sections motivate why antiderivatives, which are also called *integrals*, are useful.

Antiderivatives

By now you should have had a lot of practice and experience with the process of differentiating a given function f to get the derivative function f'. Symbolically the differentiation process operates on functions:

$$f \to f'$$

to give new functions. Now we want to reverse this process and go the other way:

$$? \leftarrow f$$

Specifically, the question mark stands for the question: *What function G has derivative equal to f?* That is, can we find a function G such that

$$G' = f.$$

Such a function G is called an *antiderivative* of f.

DEFINITION 3.7.1 (Antiderivatives)

Suppose f is a function defined on an interval I. A function G, defined and differentiable on I, is called an antiderivative *of f if*

$$G'(x) = f(x)$$

for all x in I.

Since finding antiderivatives of functions is the inverse of the differentiation process, and since inverse processes are usually more difficult to do than the process itself, you can expect that antidifferentiation will be harder than differentiation. In later chapters you will learn many techniques to help you more easily calculate antiderivatives of given functions, but for now the only technique you have is guesswork, which will depend heavily on your ability to remember the derivatives of all the basic functions. For example,

$\cos x$ is the derivative of $\sin x$.
$3x^2$ is the derivative of x^3.
$\sec^2 x$ is the derivative of $\tan x$
$\sec x \tan x$ is the derivative of $\sec x$.
e^x is the derivative of e^x .

Now read each of these statements backwards, replacing the word "derivative" with the word "antiderivative."

$$\sin x \text{ is an antiderivative of } \cos x$$
$$x^3 \text{ is an antiderivative of } 3x^2\,,$$

and so forth. In general, finding an antiderivative amounts to filling in the blank:

$$f(x) \text{ is the derivative of _____ },$$

where $f(x)$ is a given function. For example, can you fill in the blank for the following?

$$\frac{1}{2\sqrt{x}} \text{ is the derivative of _____ }.$$

Hopefully, you quickly remembered that $\sqrt{x}$ is the correct answer here. An alternative format to the fill-in-the-blank-format is the equation format. We write the equation

$$G'(x) = f(x)\,,$$

where $f(x)$ is a given function, and ask: What is $G(x)$? Namely, solve the above equation for G. The equation here is what is known as a *differential equation*, and G is the unknown in this equation. The designation "differential equation" comes from the Leibniz form of the above equation, i.e.,

$$\frac{d}{dx}(G(x)) = f(x)\,.$$

In any event, finding G, for now, relies on your memory and some basic algebra, provided that the given function f is not too different from one of the basic functions in your vocabulary. Later you will learn many rules, formulas, and techniques that will allow you to find G when f is fairly complicated.

Example 3.7.1 (Finding Antiderivatives)

Problem (a): Find an antiderivative of $5x^7$, i.e., solve

$$\frac{d}{dx}(G(x)) = 5x^7,$$

for G. Using our understanding of the power rule for derivatives, we know that

$$\frac{d}{dx}\left(x^8\right) = 8x^7.$$

This is close, but not exactly what we need. However, if we multiply both sides of this equation by $\frac{5}{8}$, we get

$$\frac{5}{8} \cdot \frac{d}{dx}\left(x^8\right) = \frac{5}{8} \cdot 8x^7.$$

or

$$\frac{d}{dx}\left(\frac{5}{8}x^8\right) = 5x^7.$$

Thus, an antiderivative of $5x^7$ is

$$G(x) = \frac{5}{8}x^8.$$

It is instructive to check our work. We recommend that you do this often, since it helps reinforce the distinction between differentiation and antidifferentiation.

CHECK: $\dfrac{d}{dx}(G(x)) = \dfrac{d}{dx}\left(\dfrac{5}{8}x^8\right) = \dfrac{5}{8}\dfrac{d}{dx}\left(x^8\right) = \dfrac{5}{8}\cdot 8x^7 = 5x^7$.

Problem(b): Find a function G whose derivative is $f(x) = 1 + \sin x$. Here we have to solve the equation

$$\dfrac{d}{dx}(G(x)) = 1 + \sin x,$$

for G. We search our memory and recall that

$$\dfrac{d}{dx}(x) = 1 \quad \text{and} \quad \dfrac{d}{dx}(\cos x) = -\sin x$$

The last expression is not quite right because of the minus sign, but we can multiply both sides by -1 to get what we need.

$$\dfrac{d}{dx}(-\cos x) = \sin x.$$

Thus, since differentiation is a linear operation, we see that the function

$$G(x) = x - \cos x,$$

has the desired derivative.

CHECK: $\dfrac{d}{dx}(G(x)) = \dfrac{d}{dx}(x - \cos x) = 1 - (-\sin x) = 1 + \sin x$.

Problem(c): Find an antiderivative of the function $f(x) = \dfrac{x + 4x^{1/3}}{x^2}$.

To solve this problem write it as a differential equation

$$\dfrac{d}{dx}(G(x)) = \dfrac{x + 4x^{1/3}}{x^2}$$

and simplify the fraction on the right side of this equation.

$$\dfrac{x + 4x^{1/3}}{x^2} = \dfrac{x}{x^2} + 4\cdot\dfrac{x^{1/3}}{x^2} = x^{-1} + 4x^{-5/3}.$$

Now we can state the problem in the preferred form: Find a solution G of the differential equation

$$\dfrac{d}{dx}(G(x)) = x^{-1} + 4x^{-5/3}.$$

We handle each part separately. Recall that the derivative of the natural log function is

$$\dfrac{d}{dx}(\ln x) = \dfrac{1}{x} = x^{-1}.$$

So the natural log function $\ln x$ is an antiderivative of the first part. For the second part, we use

$$\dfrac{d}{dx}\left(x^{-2/3}\right) = -\dfrac{2}{3}x^{-5/3}.$$

Multiplying both sides of this equation by -6 gives

$$\dfrac{d}{dx}\left(-6x^{-2/3}\right) = -6\left(-\dfrac{2}{3}x^{-5/3}\right) = 4x^{-5/3},$$

which is what we need. From the above work we conclude that

$$\dfrac{d}{dx}\left(\ln x - 6x^{-2/3}\right) = x^{-1} + 4x^{-5/3}.$$

and so
$$G(x) = \ln x - 6x^{-2/3}$$

is an antiderivative of the given function.

In our discussion and in the above example you should notice that we continually referred to G as *an* antiderivative of the given function f rather than referring to it as *the* antiderivative. This is because a given function will generally have more than one antiderivative. In fact there will be infinitely many of them. This is due to the fact that the derivative of any constant C is zero:

$$\frac{d}{dx}(C) = 0.$$

Thus, adding a constant C to any antiderivative gives another antiderivative. For example, we saw above that

$$\frac{d}{dx}\left(\frac{5}{8}x^8\right) = 5x^7$$

So clearly

$$\frac{d}{dx}\left(\frac{5}{8}x^8 + 1\right) = 5x^7 \quad \text{and} \quad \frac{d}{dx}\left(\frac{5}{8}x^8 + 2\right) = 5x^7.$$

This means that

$$\frac{5}{8}x^8, \ \frac{5}{8}x^8 + 1, \ \text{and} \ \frac{5}{8}x^8 + 2$$

are three different antiderivatives of the function $5\,x^7$.

More generally, it is easy to see that if $G(x)$ is one antiderivative of a given function $f(x)$, then so is $G(x) + C$, for any constant C. Thus, there is no unique antiderivative of a given function $f(x)$. Accepting this non-uniqueness, a natural question for us to ask is: Can we describe all the possible antiderivatives of $f(x)$ in some fashion? The next theorem tell us how to do this.

THEOREM 3.7.1 (Non-Uniqueness of Antiderivatives)

Suppose G is an antiderivative for the function f on the interval $I = (a, b)$. If H is any other antiderivative of f on I, then there exists a constant C such that

$$H(x) = G(x) + C,$$

for all x in I.

Proof: This theorem is just a variation of Theorem 3.5.3 (Equal Derivatives Theorem) which says that if two functions have the same derivative on an interval, then they are the same up to a constant. That is, since $H'(x) = f(x) = G'(x)$ for all x in I, there exists a constant C such that $H(x) = G(x) + C$, for all x in I. .

Integrals

The process of finding antiderivatives G of a given function f amounts to solving the equation

$$G'(x) = f(x),$$

for G. While at this point we do not have many techniques for solving such equations, it will be helpful to introduce some operator notation for the antidifferentiation process. A natural notation might be to use the standard notation for the inverse of an operator. In this case, view the above equation as

$$\frac{d}{dx}(G(x)) = f(x) \qquad (3.7.1)$$

which says that differentiating $G(x)$ gives $f(x)$. Suppose the operator $\frac{d}{dx}$ has an inverse, and denote this inverse in the standard way by $\left(\frac{d}{dx}\right)^{-1}$. Then we can turn Equation (3.7.1) around, so that it expresses the concept that undifferentiating $f(x)$ gives $G(x)$:

$$\left(\frac{d}{dx}\right)^{-1} f(x) = G(x).$$

One difficulty with this notation is that the operator $\frac{d}{dx}$ is not one-to-one, and so technically does not have an inverse. We saw this above, when we found that if $G(x)$ is one antiderivative of $f(x)$, then $G(x) + C$ is also an antiderivative for any choice of the constant C. Thus, there are infinitely many functions whose derivatives are the given function f. So we modify the last equation, writing

$$\left(\frac{d}{dx}\right)^{-1} f(x) = G(x) + C. \qquad (3.7.2)$$

and think of this as giving a formula for the *general antiderivative*. (It is one particular antiderivative plus an arbitrary constant C.) Equation (3.7.2) is more convenient than Equation (3.7.1) since it expresses the direct effect of the operator acting on the given function $f(x)$, to give the result $G(x) + C$. For example,

$$\left(\frac{d}{dx}\right)^{-1} x^2 = \frac{1}{3} x^3 + C.$$

Next, we want to make one more change in the notation for the anti-differentiation operator. For historical reasons, which will be discussed later, the inverse differentiation operator $\left(\frac{d}{dx}\right)^{-1}$, is denoted by $\left(\frac{d}{dx}\right)^{-1} = \int (\ \ ) \, dx$. Thus, we rewrite Equation (3.7.2) as follows.

THE INTEGRAL NOTATION

For a given function f, the notation

$$\int f(x)dx$$

stands for the general antiderivative of f. Thus, if G is one particular antiderivative then

$$\int f(x)dx = G(x) + C \qquad (3.7.3)$$

The symbol $\int$ is called the *integral sign*, and the process of applying the integral sign to $f(x)$ is known as *integrating $f(x)$*. The result:

$$\int f(x)dx,$$

is called the *integral of $f(x)$ with respect to x*. The function f is called the *integrand* of the integral. The differential dx is included with the integrand for several reasons, which will be explained later. For now just think of dx as indicating which variable to integrate with respect to. Later you will learn how to change variables in the integrand, which often helps in computing the integral.

Now, instead of antidifferentiating $f(x)$, we will be speaking of *integrating* $f(x)$ to get the expression for the general antiderivative. It is all the same thing, except integrating, by applying $\int$ to $f(x)$, seems more analogous to the concept of differentiating, by applying $\frac{d}{dx}$ to $f(x)$. Let's see how this new notation works with the previous examples, as well as some new ones.

In Example 3.7.1, we found that the general antiderivative of $f(x) = 5x^7$ is $G(x) = \frac{5}{8}x^8 + C$. With the integral notation this can be written more clearly and directly as

$$\int 5x^7 \, dx = \frac{5}{8}x^8 + C.$$

The other two antiderivatives that we found in Example 3.7.1 can be expressed in the integral notation as

$$\int (1 + \sin x) \, dx = x - \cos x + C,$$

$$\int \frac{x + 4x^{1/3}}{x^2} \, dx = \int \left(\frac{x}{x^2} + 4\frac{x^{1/3}}{x^2} \right) dx = \int \left(x^{-1} + 4x^{-5/3} \right) dx = \ln x - 6x^{-2/3} + C.$$

NOTE: Often when integrating, as in the last example, you will have to algebraically simplify the integrand (such as $\frac{x + 4\sqrt[3]{x}}{x^2}$) before integrating.

You should find the integral notation easier and more convenient to work with than the differential notation. Just remember that integrating $f(x)$ gives an antiderivative of $f(x)$. Symbolically, $\int f(x) \, dx$ stands for an antiderivative of $f(x)$ (technically the general antiderivative).

The fact that integration and differentiation are inverse processes to one another is recorded by the important formulas shown in the margin box.

The Formula (1) says that if we integrate a function f and then differentiate the result, we get f back again. Formula (2) says that if we differentiate a function f and then integrate the result, then we get f back again, up to an arbitrary constant C. This expresses the idea that, when applied in succession, one operation undoes what the other one does. This is only approximately true in the second identity, since antiderivatives are only determined up to an arbitrary constant C. For example, suppose $f(x) = x^2$. Then the two identities (1)–(2), in this case, look like

$$\frac{d}{dx} \int x^2 \, dx = \frac{d}{dx} \left(\frac{1}{3}x^3 + C \right) = x^2$$

$$\int \frac{d}{dx} \left(x^2 \right) \, dx = \int 2x \, dx = x^2 + C$$

INVERSE OPERATORS

$$\frac{d}{dx} \int f(x) \, dx = f(x) \qquad (1)$$

$$\int \frac{d}{dx} f(x) \, dx = f(x) + C \qquad (2)$$

Some Integration Formulas

The integrals of power functions occur very often in applications, and so it is convenient to have a general formula for such integrals. The next theorem gives such a formula.

THEOREM 3.7.2 (The Integral of a Power Function)

For any real number $n \neq -1$

$$\int x^n \, dx = \frac{x^{n+1}}{n+1} + C \qquad (3.7.4)$$

While for $n = -1$

$$\int x^{-1} \, dx = \int \frac{1}{x} \, dx = \ln x + C \qquad (3.7.5)$$

Proof: The validity of these formulas is easy to prove. We just take the derivatives of the right sides:

$$\frac{d}{dx}\left(\frac{x^{n+1}}{n+1}\right) = \frac{d}{dx}\left(\frac{1}{n+1}x^{n+1}\right) = \frac{1}{n+1} \cdot \frac{d}{dx}\left(x^{n+1}\right) = \frac{1}{n+1} \cdot (n+1)x^n = x^n.$$

$$\frac{d}{dx}(\ln x) = \frac{1}{x}.$$

NOTE: The integration rule

$$\int x^n \, dx = \frac{x^{n+1}}{n+1} + C,$$

is easily remembered and used. Just *add 1 to the exponent and then divide by this new exponent* to get the antiderivative. This seems reasonable since integration is the opposite of differentiation, and when differentiating a power function you *subtract 1 from the exponent and multiply by the old exponent* to get the derivative. For example,

$$\int x^{23} \, dx = \frac{x^{23+1}}{23+1} + C = \frac{x^{24}}{24} + C = \frac{1}{24}x^{24} + C.$$

$$\int x^{-10} \, dx = \frac{1}{-10+1}x^{-10+1} + C = -\frac{1}{9}x^{-9} + C$$

$$\int x^{-9/5} \, dx = \frac{1}{-9/5+1}x^{-9/5+1} + C = \frac{1}{-4/5}x^{-4/5} + C = -\frac{5}{4}x^{-4/5} + C.$$

With a little practice you should be able to eliminate the intermediate steps in the above calculations.

NOTE: The special case of Formula (3.7.4) for $n = 0$ gives

$$\int 1 \, dx = x + C \qquad (3.7.6)$$

The second equation in the proof of Theorem 3.7.2, i.e.,

$$\frac{d}{dx}(\ln x) = \frac{1}{x},$$

is just one of the basic differentiation formulas. In fact, each of the basic differentiation formulas that you learned in the differential calculus can be restated as an integration formula. Namely, saying that

$$\frac{d}{dx}(G(x)) = f(x),$$

is equivalent to saying

$$\int f(x) \, dx = G(x) + C.$$

Thus, we can restate all the previous differentiation formulas as integral formulas. Table 3.7.1 in the margin below shows some of these.

You should memorize these basic integrals because they will be indispensable in all you future work with more complicated integrals. In addition, you will frequently use the following two integration rules. These come from the corresponding differentiation rules.

THEOREM 3.7.3 (The Sum and Multiples Rules for Integrals)

Suppose $f(x)$ and $g(x)$ are functions and c is a real number. Then

$$\int [f(x) + g(x)]\,dx = \int f(x)\,dx + \int g(x)\,dx \qquad (3.7.7)$$

and

$$\int cf(x)\,dx = c\int f(x)\,dx \qquad (3.7.8)$$

The first formula says that the integral of the sum of two functions is the sum of the integrals of each of the functions. The second formula says that we can factor constants out of the integral.

All of these basic integral formulas, combined with standard algebra, allow us to calculate the integrals of quite few more complicated functions. The following example illustrates some of this.

Example 3.7.2 (Using the Basic Integral Formulas & Integral Rules)

Problem (a): Any polynomial function can be easily integrated:

$$\int \left(5 + 3x - 4x^2 + 7x^3\right) dx = 5\int 1\,dx + 3\int x\,dx - 4\int x^2\,dx + 7\int x^3\,dx$$

$$= 5x + \frac{3}{2}x^2 - \frac{4}{3}x^3 + \frac{7}{4}x^4 + C$$

This suggests the general result that the integral of a polynomial of degree n is a polynomial of degree $n + 1$.

Problem (b): More generally, any linear combination of power functions can be easily integrated:

$$\int \left(4x^{2/3} - 6x^{-8} + 3x^{7/2}\right) dx = 4 \cdot \frac{3}{5}x^{5/3} - 6\left(-\frac{1}{7}x^{-7}\right) + 3 \cdot \frac{2}{9}x^{9/2} + C$$

$$= \frac{12}{5}x^{5/3} + \frac{6}{7}x^{-7} + \frac{2}{3}x^{9/2} + C$$

Problem (c): Often you will have to do some algebra before calculating the integral:

$$\int \left(3x^2 - \frac{1}{\sqrt[3]{x}}\right)\sqrt{x}\,dx = \int \left(3x^2 - x^{-1/3}\right)x^{1/2}\,dx$$

$$= \int \left(3x^{2+1/2} - x^{-1/3+1/2}\right) dx = \int \left(3x^{5/2} - x^{1/6}\right) dx = 3 \cdot \frac{2}{7}x^{7/2} - \frac{6}{7}x^{7/6} + C$$

Problem (d): Another integral that involves doing some algebra first is

$$\int \left(x + \sqrt{x}\right)^2 dx = \int \left(x^2 + 2x\sqrt{x} + x\right) dx = \int \left(x^2 + 2x^{3/2} + x\right) dx$$

$$= \frac{1}{3}x^3 + \frac{4}{5}x^{5/2} + \frac{1}{2}x^2 + C$$

Problem (e): Generally, quotients are hard to integrate since there is *no quotient rule* for integrals. However, if you can convert the quotient into something else, using legitimate algebra, then you might be able to integrate the result. For instance,

$$\int \frac{x - 2\sqrt{x} + 5x^{-7}}{x^2}\,dx = \int \left(\frac{x}{x^2} - 2 \cdot \frac{x^{1/2}}{x^2} + 5 \cdot \frac{x^{-7}}{x^2}\right) dx$$

$$= \int \left(x^{-1} - 2x^{-3/2} + 5x^{-9}\right) dx = \ln x + 4x^{-1/2} - \frac{5}{8}x^{-8} + C$$

SOME BASIC INTEGRALS

$$\int x^n dx = \frac{1}{n+1}x^{n+1} + C \quad (n \neq -1)$$

$$\int \frac{1}{x}\,dx = \ln x + C$$

$$\int a^x dx = \frac{1}{\ln a}a^x + C$$

$$\int e^x dx = e^x + C$$

$$\int \cos x\,dx = \sin x + C$$

$$\int \sin x\,dx = -\cos x + C$$

$$\int \sec^2 x\,dx = \tan x + C$$

$$\int \csc^2 x\,dx = -\cot x + C$$

$$\int \sec x\tan x\,dx = \sec x + C$$

$$\int \csc x\cot x\,dx = -\csc x + C$$

Table 3.7.1

Problem (f): With the rules you have learned so far there are a limited number of trigonometric expressions that you can integrate. For instance:

$$\int (5\sin x + 3\cos x + 7\sec x \tan x)\, dx = -5\cos x + 3\sin x + 7\sec x + C.$$

Sometimes you will have to use some algebra and trig identities:

$$\int \frac{1 + \cos^2 x}{\cos^2 x}\, dx = \int \left(\frac{1}{\cos^2 x} + \frac{\cos^2 x}{\cos^2 x} \right) dx = \int \left(\sec^2 x + 1 \right) dx = \tan x + x + C.$$

Later you will study techniques and methods of integration that will allow you to tackle a wider range of integrals involving trigonometric functions.

Example 3.7.3 (Using Algebra Before Integrating)

Problem (a): Factoring and reducing will sometimes help when dealing with rational functions:

$$\int \frac{x^3 - 8}{x - 2}\, dx \;=\; \int \frac{(x-2)(x^2 + 2x + 4)}{x - 2}\, dx = \int \left(x^2 + 2x + 4 \right) dx$$
$$=\; \frac{1}{3}x^3 + x^2 + 4x + C$$

Problem (b): Exponential expressions can often be put in a form to use the basic integrals:

$$\int \frac{4^x + 6^x}{2^x}\, dx \;=\; \int \frac{(2 \cdot 2)^x + (2 \cdot 3)^x}{2^x} = \int \frac{2^x 2^x + 2^x 3^x}{2^x} = \int \left(2^x + 3^x \right) dx$$
$$=\; \frac{1}{\ln 2} 2^x + \frac{1}{\ln 3} 3^x + C$$

Problem (c): Later we will have another way to do the following integral, but for now we use laws of exponents:

$$\int 3^{4x-3}\, dx \;=\; \int 3^{4x} \cdot 3^{-3}\, dx = \int (3^4)^x \cdot \frac{1}{27}\, dx = \frac{1}{27} \int 81^x\, dx$$
$$=\; \frac{1}{27 \ln 81} 81^x + C$$

Exercises: 3.7 (Antiderivatives and Integrals)

Computing Integrals

In Exercises 1–50, calculate the integrals (i.e., general antiderivatives)

1. $\int \left(10x^4 - 6x^2 + 4x - 5\right) dx$

2. $\int \left(ex^5 - \sqrt{2}x^2 + \pi x - \sqrt[3]{2}\right) dx$

3. $\int \left(10x^{-4} - 6x^{-2} + 4x^{-1} - 5^{-1}\right) dx$

4. $\int \left(10x^{-4/3} - 6\,x^{-2/5} + 4\dfrac{1}{\sqrt{x}} - 8^{-1/3}\right) dx$

5. $\int \left(2\sqrt[3]{x^5} - \dfrac{1}{4\sqrt[5]{x^3}}\right) dx$

6. $\int \left(3\sqrt[4]{x^2} - \dfrac{1}{9\sqrt{x^4}}\right) dx$

7. $\int \sqrt{x}\left(\sqrt[3]{x^2} - x\right) dx$ **8.** $\int \sqrt[3]{x}\left(\sqrt{x} - x\right) dx$

9. $\int \left(x + \sqrt{x}\right)^3 dx$ **10.** $\int \left(x + \dfrac{1}{\sqrt{x}}\right)^3 dx$

11. $\int \dfrac{\left(x + \sqrt{x}\right)^2}{x^6} dx$ **12.** $\int \dfrac{\left(x^2 + 1\right)^2}{\left(\sqrt{x}\right)^2} dx$

13. $\int \dfrac{\left(\sqrt{x^3} - \sqrt{x}\right)^2}{x^4} dx$ **14.** $\int \dfrac{\left(\sqrt{x} - 1\right)^2}{x^4} dx$

15. $\int \dfrac{x + 1}{x} dx$ **16.** $\int \dfrac{x^2 + 1}{x} dx$

17. $\int \dfrac{\left(2 - 5x\right)^2}{x} dx$ **18.** $\int \dfrac{\left(2 - x\right)^3}{x} dx$

19. $\int \dfrac{e^x + 1}{e^x} dx$ **20.** $\int \dfrac{2^x + 1}{2^x} dx$

21. $\int \dfrac{e^{2x} - 1}{e^x + 1} dx$ **22.** $\int \dfrac{4^x - 1}{2^x + 1} dx$

23. $\int \left(2^x + 1\right)^2 dx$ **24.** $\int \left(3^x + 1\right)^3 dx$

25. $\int (\sin x + 2\cos x) dx$ **26.** $\int (\cos x - 5\sin x) dx$

27. $\int \sin x \cos x\, dx$ **28.** $\int (\cos^2 x - \sin^2 x) dx$

29. $\int \dfrac{1}{\cos^2 x} dx$ **30.** $\int \dfrac{1}{\sin^2 x} dx$

31. $\int \sec x(\sec x + \tan x) dx$

32. $\int \csc x(\csc x + \cot x) dx$

33. $\int \dfrac{1 + \tan x}{\sec x} dx$ **34.** $\int \dfrac{1 + \cot x}{\csc x} dx$

35. $\int \left(\tan^2 x + 1\right) dx$ **36.** $\int \tan^2 x\, dx$

37. $\int \left(\dfrac{\sin^2 x}{\cos^2 x} + 1\right) dx$ **38.** $\int \left(\dfrac{\cos^2 x}{\sin^2 x} + 1\right) dx$

39. $\int \dfrac{1 - \sin^2 x}{\cos x} dx$ **40.** $\int \dfrac{1 - \cos^2 x}{\sin x} dx$

41. $\int \dfrac{1 - \sin^2 x}{1 + \sin x} dx$ **42.** $\int \dfrac{1 - \cos^2 x}{1 + \cos x} dx$

43. $\int \dfrac{(1 + \tan^2 x)^2}{\sec^2 x} dx$ **44.** $\int \dfrac{(1 + \cot^2 x)^2}{\csc^2 x} dx$

45. $\int \dfrac{\sin x}{\cos^2 x} dx$ **46.** $\int \dfrac{\cos x}{\sin^2 x} dx$

47. $\int \sin (x - 2) dx$ **48.** $\int \cos (x - 2) dx$

49. $\int 2^{2x-1} dx$ **50.** $\int 4^{3-5x} dx$

Solving Basic Differential Equations by Integration

In Exercises 51–60, the derivative of the function f is given. Find the formula for the function f and equations for the tangent lines to f at the given points. CAS: Also, plot the graph of f and the tangent lines you found in the same figure. If your lines don't look tangent to the graph of f, you should check your calculations. NOTE: Use integrals to find the function f.

51. $f'(x) = 3x^2 - 6x, (1, -1), (-1, 3)$

52. $f'(x) = 6x^2 - 4x^3, (1, 3), (0, 2)$

53. $f'(x) = \dfrac{x - 1}{x}, (1, -1), (2, -\ln 2)$

54. $f'(x) = \dfrac{x - 2}{x}, (1, -1), (2, -2\ln 2)$

55. $f'(x) = \dfrac{e^x + 1}{e^x}, (0, 0), (-1, -e)$

56. $f'(x) = \dfrac{e^x - 1}{e^x}, (0, 0), (1, e^{-1})$

57. $f'(x) = 1 + 2\sin x, (0, -1), (\pi/2, \pi/2 + 1)$

58. $f'(x) = 2x + \sec^2 x, (0, -1), (\pi/4, \pi^2/16)$

59. $f'(x) = \left(e^{x/2} - e^{-x/2}\right)^2, (0, 2), \left(1, e - e^{-1}\right)$

60. $f'(x) = \left(2^{x/2} - 2^{-x/2}\right)^2, (0, 2), \left(1, \dfrac{3}{2\ln 2} - 2\right)$

4 Integrals

Calculus *Concepts & Computation*

4.1 Areas and Sums

```
> with(code_ch4,circle,parabola);with(code_ch1sec1);
```
$$[circle,\ parabola]$$
$$[polygonlimit,\ secantlimit]$$

This chapter begins our study of the integral calculus, which is the counter-part to the differential calculus you learned in Chapters 1–3. The topic of integrals, otherwise known as antiderivatives, was introduced in Section 3.7, and you should read that discussion before continuing here.

A major application of antiderivatives, or integrals, is the measurement of areas of planar regions D. In fact, a principal motive behind the invention of the integral calculus was to solve the area problem. See Figure 4.1.1.

Before we learn how to measure areas of such general regions D, it is best to think about the areas of simple regions, and, indeed, reflect on the very notion of what is meant by "area." This we discuss here. Then, in the next two sections, Sections 4.2 and 4.3 , we look at the details of measuring areas of regions "beneath the graphs of continuous functions." Then in Section 5.1 we tackle the task of finding area of more complicated regions, such as the region D in Figure 4.4.1. We have intuitive notions about what is meant by the area of a region. It is a positive number A which somehow measures the "largeness" of the region and enables us to compare regions with different shapes. Knowing the formula for the area of a rectangle allows us to find the areas of other basic regions, such as parallelograms, triangles, and trapezoids—all of which can be found *without calculus*. If, however, we want to find areas of planar regions with curved boundaries, such as the region D in Figure 4.1.1, then we need to use calculus.

The General Area Problem

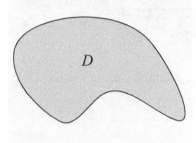

Figure 4.1.1: *Find the area of the region D bounded by a piecewise smooth curve.*

Areas of Basic Regions

You probably "know" that the area of a rectangle is the product of its base times its height $A = bh$. But you should reflect on the fact that this is actually a *definition*, rather than something that can be derived from more primitive notions.

DEFINITION 4.1.1 (Area of a Rectangle)

The area of a rectangle with base b and height h is $A = bh$.

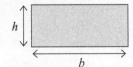

It is said that in ancient times, the measurement of the length of the boundary of a region (its perimeter) was used sometimes to quantify the largeness of the region. After all, length is easier to measure—you just step off along the boundary, counting the paces as you go. But for quantifying the extent of a rectangular piece of property, the area $A = bh$, given as the product of the lengths of its sides, turned out to be a better gauge of the value of the property.

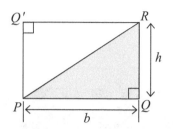

Figure 4.1.2: *The area of a right triangle is $A = \dfrac{1}{2}\,bh$.*

Using this as the definition of the area of a rectangle, we can derive the formulas for the areas of other basic regions. For this, we need to use the primitive notions:

(1) *The areas of congruent figures are the same.*

(2) *If a region is the disjoint union of subregions, then the area of the region is the sum of the areas of the subregions.*

Applying these primitive notions to the case of a right triangle, we get that its area is one-half its base times its height. You can easily prove this as an exercise.

Next, how do we deal with parallelograms that are not rectangles and triangles that are not right triangles? Why is it that the formulas for their areas are $A = bh$ and $A = \frac{1}{2}\,bh$, respectively? To see this, first consider the case of a parallelogram.

DEFINITION: A *parallelogram* is a quadrilateral (four-sided figure) whose opposite sides are parallel (and of equal length).

Figure 4.1.3 shows a rectangle $PQRS$ and parallelogram $PQR'S'$ which have the same base b and height h.

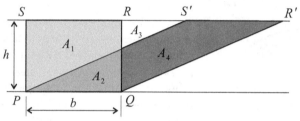

Figure 4.1.3: *The area of a parallelogram is also $A = bh$.*

To show that the rectangle and parallelogram have the same area, label the areas of four of subregions as A_1, A_2, A_3, A_4 as shown. By elementary geometry one can prove that the right triangles PSS' and QRR' are congruent (exercise), and hence they have the same area. So

$$A_1 + A_3 = A_3 + A_4.$$

Hence,

$$A_1 = A_4.$$

Adding A_2 to both sides of this gives

$$A_1 + A_2 = A_2 + A_4.$$

But $A_1 + A_2$ is the area of rectangle $PQRS$ and $A_2 + A_4$ is the area of parallelogram $PQR'S'$. Thus, the two areas are equal. The measure of each is $A = bh$, since that is the measure for the area of the rectangle.

This result for areas of parallelograms leads to the area formula for general triangles (not just right triangles). This is left as an exercise. Using these formulas for the areas of basic regions, we can find formulas for areas of more complicated regions.

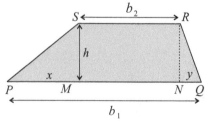

Figure 4.1.4: *A trapezoid with bases b_1, b_2 and height h has area $A = \frac{1}{2}\left(b_1 + b_2\right)h$.*

Example 4.1.1 (The Trapezoidal Area Formula)

Problem: Using area formulas for triangles and rectangles, derive the formula for the area of the trapezoid given in Figure 4.1.4. (Recall that a trapezoid is a quadrilateral with one pair of opposite sides that are parallel.)

The formula is

$$A = \frac{1}{2}\left(b_1 + b_2\right)h.$$

This says that the area is the average of the bases b_1, b_2 times the height h. Also note that when the bases have the same length, $b_1 = b_2 = b$, the trapezoid is a parallelogram and the formula reduces to $A = bh$.

Solution: Dropping perpendiculars from points R and S onto the base PQ gives points M and N. This also divides the trapezoid into a rectangle and two right triangles. Labeling the bases PM and QN of the right triangles by x and y, respectively, gives the areas of these triangles as

$$A_1 = \frac{1}{2}\, xh, \; A_2 = \frac{1}{2}\, yh$$

The area of the rectangle $MNRS$ is

$$A_3 = b_2 h.$$

It is clear that

$$b_1 = x + b_2 + y,$$

or, equivalently

$$x + y = b_1 - b_2.$$

Now use this last expression in the following calculation of the area of the trapezoid.

$$
\begin{aligned}
A &= A_1 + A_2 + A_3 = \frac{1}{2}\, xh + \frac{1}{2}\, yh + b_2 h \\
&= \left[\frac{1}{2}\, (x+y) + b_2\right] h = \left[\frac{1}{2}\, (b_1 - b_2) + b_2\right] h \\
&= \frac{1}{2}\, (b_1 + b_2)\, h.
\end{aligned}
$$

This gives the formula that we were looking for.

Example 4.1.2

Problem: Apply the trapezoid formula from the previous example to find the area of the particular trapezoid in Figure 4.1.5.

Solution: Here the bases are $b_1 = 5$, $b_2 = 3$,and the height is $h = 2$. So the computation is easy enough:

$$A = \frac{1}{2}\, (5 + 3)\, 2 = 8.$$

Example 4.1.3 (Five Adjacent Trapezoids)

Problem: Determine the formula for the area of a region made of 5 trapezoids as shown in Figure 4.1.6.

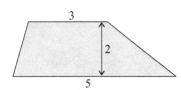

Figure 4.1.5: *A trapezoid.*

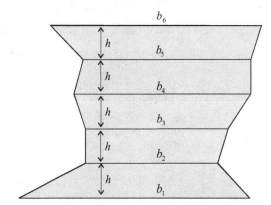

Figure 4.1.6: *A region composed of 5 trapezoids*

Solution: The trapezoids in Figure 4.1.6 all have the same height h and have bases taken in pairs form the sides labeled $b_1, b_2, \ldots, b_6$. Using the formula for the area of a trapezoid, derived in Example 4.1.1, and the additivity principle for areas in general, we find the area of the region in Figure 4.1.6 is

$$
\begin{aligned}
A &= \frac{1}{2}\left(b_1 + b_2\right)h + \frac{1}{2}\left(b_2 + b_3\right)h + \frac{1}{2}\left(b_3 + b_4\right)h + \frac{1}{2}\left(b_4 + b_5\right)h + \frac{1}{2}\left(b_5 + b_6\right)h \\
&= \frac{1}{2}\left(b_1 + b_2 + b_2 + b_3 + b_3 + b_4 + b_4 + b_5 + b_5 + b_6\right)h \\
&= \frac{1}{2}\left(b_1 + 2\,b_2 + 2\,b_3 + 2\,b_4 + 2\,b_5 + b_6\right)h.
\end{aligned}
$$

This is sum of the averages of all the bases (counting the overlapping ones on the interior twice) times the common height h. Note that the formula would not be so simple if the heights of the trapezoids were different.

Areas of Regions Under Graphs

Later we will be interested in finding areas of regions bounded by graphs of functions. For step-functions and polygonal functions we can use the ideas of the previous examples to compute the area. Before doing this note that if $x_1 < x_2$ are points on the x-axis, then we use

$$
\Delta x = x_2 - x_1
$$

to denote the length of the line segment between these points.

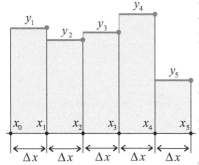

Figure 4.1.7: *The graph of a step function with 5 treads.*

Example 4.1.4

Problem: Find a formula for the aea of the region bounded by the x-axis and graph of a step-function with five treads as shown in Figure 4.1.7.

Solution: The area A is the sum of the areas of the 5 rectangles shown in the figure

$$
A = a_1 + a_2 + a_3 + a_4 + a_5.
$$

The heights of the respective rectangles are y_1, y_2, y_3, y_4, y_5. Each base has the same length, which we have denoted by Δx. This notation will be used often in the next section and stands for the *difference* of the x-coordinates. In this example all the differences are the same:

$$
x_1 - x_0 = x_2 - x_1 = x_3 - x_2 = x_4 - x_3 = x_5 - x_4 = \Delta x.
$$

Note that, in general, we cannot expect the differences $x_i - x_{i-1}$, for $i = 1, 2, 3, 4, 5$, to be the same. Now the area of the ith rectangle is $a_i = y_i \Delta x$, and summing up these areas gives the area A of the region beneath the graph of this step-function.

$$
\begin{aligned}
A &= a_1 + a_2 + a_3 + a_4 + a_5 \\
&= y_1 \Delta x + y_2 \Delta x + y_3 \Delta x + y_4 \Delta x + y_5 \Delta x \\
&= \left(y_1 + y_2 + y_3 + y_4 + y_5\right) \Delta x.
\end{aligned}
$$

The formula is fairly simple and easily extends to a step-function with any number of steps, *provided* all the bases have the same length (here called Δx). Just add all the y-values and multiply by the common base length. When the bases have different lengths, the formula is not as simple. See the exercises.

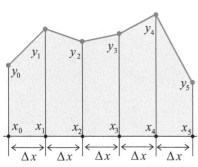

Figure 4.1.8: *The graph of a five-sided polygonal function.*

Example 4.1.5

Problem: Find a formula for the area of the region bounded by the *x-axis* and the graph of the five-sided polygonal function shown in Figure 4.1.8.

Solution: This region is similar to the region in Figure 4.1.6, being composed of five trapezoids, but is oriented differently. The "bases" b_1, b_2, b_3, b_4, b_5, b_6 are now labeled y_0, y_1, y_2, y_3, y_4, y_5, and run vertically, and the common "height" h is now Δx, and runs horizontally. Since orientation does not matter (i.e., congruent regions have the same area), the formula for the area is exactly the same, except for the notation:

$$A = \frac{1}{2}\left(y_0 + 2y_1 + 2y_2 + 2y_3 + 2y_4 + y_5\right)\Delta x.$$

Areas of Curved Regions

When the boundary of the region is curved, the method applied in the above sections is insufficient because the region cannot be divided into subregions whose area formulas we know. This is where calculus comes in. The idea is to approximate the curved region using a sequence of basic regions, such as collections of triangles, rectangles, or trapezoids, and then take the limit of this sequence of approximations.

For example, the following command from Chapter 1 shows a circular region being approximated by a sequence of triangular regions and, indeed served as a motivation for the limit concept in Section 1.1.

```
> polygonlimit;
```

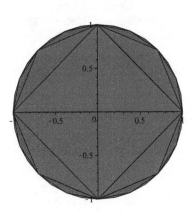

Figure 4.1.9: *The last frame in the movie produced by* polygonlimit.

Here we look at such approximations for circular regions (and for parabolic regions in the exercises), but use only collections of rectangles, triangles, and trapezoids which are appropriately chosen. In the next section we discuss approximations using only rectangles, but do it for fairly general regions bounded on one side by the graph of a continuous function. Then in Section 4.3, we show how to take limits of these approximations to get the exact area.

Example 4.1.6 (Approximations to Circular Area)

Problem: There is a special-purpose command to produce a movie of a circular region of radius r being approximated by either n inscribed rectangles or n inscribed trapezoids. This command has the forms

```
circle(r,n,rectangles)
circle(r,n,trapezoids)
```

Use this command to produce movies for a circular region being approximated by rectangles and trapezoids, respectively. In each case compute the area of the approximation.

For the case of rectangles, we use the command:

```
> circle(4,8,rectangles);
```

This produces the movie whose last frame is shown in the Figure 4.1.10.

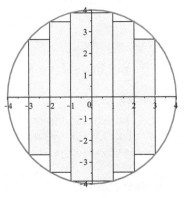

Figure 4.1.10: *The last frame in the movie produced by* circle(4,8,rectangles).

Notice that our approximation technique is such that the first and last rectangles in the movie have zero height and so the rectangles reduce to just line segments. Note also the symmetry about the x-axis, so we can measure the areas of the 6 rectangles above the x-axis and double the result to get the approximation to the area of the circle. Also, the length of each base is one, so that simplifies things too. Using the cursor probe on the above figure, we get the following rectangle heights:

$$2.64, \ 3.45, \ 3.85, \ 3.85, \ 3.45, \ 2.64.$$

Note the symmetry in the numbers here. We could have cut our work in half again by using symmetry with respect to the y-axis as well as the x-axis. Also, beware that using the mouse is not a very accurate measuring tool. So if you repeat this, you may get numbers different from ours. Now the area calculation is (remember to double things)

```
> area1:=2*(2.64+3.45+3.85+3.85+3.45+2.64)*1;
```
$$area1 := 39.76$$

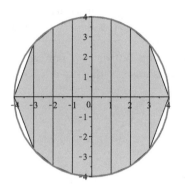

Figure 4.1.11: *The last frame in the movie produced by* `circle(4,8,trapezoids)`.

Next we look at the trapezoidal approximation:

```
> circle(4,8,trapezoids);
```

This gives a movie whose last frame is shown in Figure 4.3.11. Note here that the first and last trapezoids are really triangles (a degenerate case when one base of the trapezoid has zero length). As in the above calculation for rectangles, we exploit symmetry to reduce the work. We use the observation that there is symmetry with respect both the x-axis and y-axis. Therefore, all we have to do is calculate the areas of the three trapezoids and one triangle in the 1st quadrant and then multiply the result by 4 to get the approximating area. Using the cursor probe on the figure gives y-values:

```
> y1:=4;y2:=3.84;y3:=3.47;y4:=2.59;y5:=0;
```
$$y1 := 4$$
$$y2 := 3.84$$
$$y3 := 3.47$$
$$y4 := 2.59$$
$$y5 := 0$$

So the area of the approximation is

```
> area2:=4*(1/2)*(y1+2*y2+2*y3+2*y4+y5)*1;
```
$$area2 := 47.60$$

Compare this approximation with the first one using rectangles. It was 39.76 and, based on examination of the above figures, we conclude that the second approximation is better. Generally: *Using trapezoids rather than rectangles will provide a better approximation to areas of curved regions.*

Of course you know from grade school math the exact formula $A = \pi r^2$ for the area of a circle. But that is only because Greek mathematicians derived this result over 2000 years ago using limiting methods that were the precursors of the calculus invented in the 17th century. For the example here, using this formula gives an exact area (and a better approximate value for it)

$$A = \pi r^2 = \pi(4)^2 = 16\pi \approx 50.26548246.$$

In Chapter 5 we will show you how to use calculus to derive the formula $A = \pi r^2$.

Example 4.1.7 (Three More Rectangular Approximations)

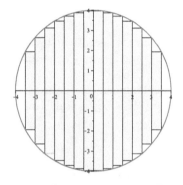

`circle(4,16,rectangles)`.

Problem: For a circle of radius 4, view the movies of the approximations to the circular area using 16, 32, and 64 rectangles respectively. What are the respective lengths of the bases for the rectangles in each case? Explain how the area of the circle might be obtained as a limit.

Solution: The following three commands produce the required movies.

```
> circle(4,16,rectangles);
> circle(4,32,rectangles);
> circle(4,64,rectangles);
```

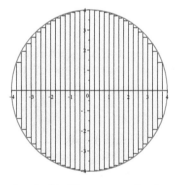

`circle(4,32,rectangles)`.

See the margin figures. In each movie, we examine the last frame to try to discern the common width Δx of the rectangles in the figure. For instance, we look at the rectangle with one side passing through 2 on the x-axis. Probing the point on the x-axis where the other side of this rectangle passes through, we get (approximately): (a) 2.50 in the case for 16 rectangles, (b) 2.25 in the case for 32 rectangles, and (c) 2.125 in the case for 64 rectangles. Thus subtracting 2 gives:

$$\Delta x = 0.5 \quad \text{in the case for 16 rectangles}$$
$$\Delta x = 0.25 \quad \text{in the case for 32 rectangles}$$
$$\Delta x = 0.125 \quad \text{in the case for 64 rectangles}$$

Thus, as the number of rectangles doubles from 16 to 32 to 64, it appears that the method behind the animation is halving the length of their bases.

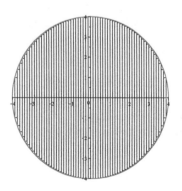

`circle(4,64,rectangles)`.

Suppose we denote the approximating area using n rectangles by A_n. Then as n increases, Δx decreases, and the approximations A_n get closer and closer to the exact area of the circle. Indeed, taking the number n of rectangles to infinity makes Δx go to zero. This is analogous to the limiting process for derivatives, and it seems reasonable that the exact area should be the limit of the approximate areas A_n:

$$A = \lim_{n \to \infty} A_n.$$

Thus: *the limit concept is used to find areas of regions with curved boundaries*.

This is fine in concept, but we have yet to address how to calculate the specific areas A_n so that we can take the above limit. Each is the sum of the areas of n rectangles

$$A_n = a_1 + a_2 + \cdots + a_n \qquad (4.1.1).$$

We computed this sum for $n = 8$ in Example 4.1.6. It might not be too tedious to compute the sum for $n = 16$. But for $n = 32$ and $n = 64$, the calculations (and data gathering from the above animations) can take a while.

So, it will be helpful to develop some notation for computing sums like that in Equation (4.1.1). this we do in the next subsection.

The Sigma Notation

When approximating the area of a curved region using n rectangles, the areas a_i, $i = 1, \ldots, n$, of the n rectangles are computed and then the approximate area of the region is the sum of $a_1, a_2, \ldots, a_n$. That is,

$$A \approx A_n = a_1 + a_2 + \cdots + a_n.$$

An indexed list of numbers such as $a_1, a_2, \ldots, a_n$ is referred to as a *sequence* in mathematics. As you will see, sequences are very common in mathematics and some useful notation has been developed for working with sums of sequences. The Greek symbol for capital S is Σ, pronounced "sigma," and this symbol is associated with the summation operation as follows. If a sequence is denoted by $a_1, a_2, \ldots, a_n$, then in sigma notation the sum of the these terms is written as

$$A_n = a_1 + a_2 + \cdots + a_n = \sum_{i=1}^{n} a_i.$$

Here, the i in the sigma notation is called the *indexing variable* (or *summation index*) since it is used to index the elements in the sequence.

More generally, if a sequence of terms is denoted by $b_1, b_2, \ldots b_n$, then in sigma notation the sum of the mth through the nth terms in the sequence is written as

$$b_m + b_{m+1} + \cdots + b_n = \sum_{i=m}^{n} b_i.$$

The expression $i = m$ below the Σ indicates that the first summand in the sum should be b_m. The n above the Σ indicates that the last summand in the sum should be b_n. The above sum could also be written using a different indexing variable, say k:

$$\sum_{k=m}^{n} b_k.$$

When calculating sums by hand that are written in sigma notation, you have to rewrite the sum without sigma notation. This is done by successively substituting into b_k the values of k between m and n and then adding the results. For instance, suppose we wanted to calculate

$$\sum_{k=3}^{7} (2k+1)^2 .$$

Writing the sum without sigma notation gives

$$(2(3)+1)^2 + (2(4)+1)^2 + (2(5)+1)^2 + (2(6)+1)^2 + (2(7)+1)^2$$

The summands are obtained by taking the expression $(2\,k+1)^2$ and substituting for the indexing variable k the numbers 3, 4, 5, 6, 7. The sum is now easily calculated

$$49 + 81 + 121 + 169 + 225 = 645.$$

Thus, given the sum in sigma notation, we can always write out as many of the summands as we wish (all of them if there are not too many). However, if we are given the summands, expressing their sum in sigma notation can be harder (sometimes impossible) because we must discern the pattern in the summands. For example, consider the sum

$$8 + 27 + 64 + 125 + 216 + 343 + 512.$$

To write this using sigma notation we must be able to write the summands in terms of an indexing variable. Let's call the indexing variable i. Then we need to determine a range of consecutive integers for i and a formula for a_i, the ith term in the sum, so that as i runs through its range of values, the terms 8, 27, 64, . . , 512 are generated by the formula. First we should look for a pattern relating these numbers. Notice that they are all perfect cubes: $2^3, 3^3, 4^3, 5^3, 6^3, 7^3, 8^3$. Now we can see that if we let i take on the integer values from 2 to 8, then the formula $a_i = i^3$ will generate the terms. The sigma notation for this sum is then

$$\sum_{i=2}^{8} i^3 .$$

Computing Sums Using Do-Loops

A sum which can be written in sigma notation can easily be calculated using Maple. For example, if we want to calculate the sum of the cubes of the first 100 natural numbers:

$$\sum_{i=1}^{100} i^3$$

then we can use the following Maple commands:

```
> s:=0:
> for i from 1 to 100 do
>   s:=s+i^3;
> end do:
> s;
```

$$25502500$$

The name s is used to accumulate the final sum and is initially set to 0. The next **three** lines constitute what is called a *do-loop*. This do-loop tells Maple to "do" the calculation repeatedly 100 times as i ranges from 1 to 100 by increments of 1. At each repetition of the loop notice that i^3 is added to the previous value of s so that the final value of s is the desired sum. The last line asks Maple to show us the final value stored in s, that is, the final sum. Thus, we see that the sum of the cubes of the first 100 natural numbers is 25,502,500.

In general we see that a do-loop for calculating the sum $\sum_{i=m}^{n} b_k$, where the values of m and n are known and the formula for b_k is also known, would be the following.

```
> s:=0;
> for k from m to n do
>     s:=s+b(k);
> end do:
> s;
```

Summation Formulas

In some cases we can actually derive a formula for summing up a sequence of numbers. The simplest example of this is the formula that occurs when the terms of the sequence do not depend on the indexing variable. This means that the terms of the sequence are constant with respect to the indexing variable.

$$\sum_{i=1}^{n} c = \underbrace{c + c + \cdots + c}_{n \; summands} = nc \qquad (4.1.2)$$

Here we are just adding up n copies of c, and indeed this indicates that repeated addition of c just gives a multiple of c.

Summation Formulas
(0) $\sum_{i=1}^{n} 1 = n$
(1) $\sum_{i=1}^{n} i = \dfrac{n(n+1)}{2}$
(2) $\sum_{i=1}^{n} i^2 = \dfrac{n(n+1)(2n+1)}{6}$
(3) $\sum_{i=1}^{n} i^3 = \left[\dfrac{n(n+1)}{2} \right]^2$

Example 4.1.8

Formula (4.1.2) above can be used straight-forwardly as follows.

$$\sum_{i=1}^{120} 4 = 120(4) = 480$$

$$\sum_{k=1}^{22} 12y = 22(12y) = 264y$$

$$\sum_{i=1}^{n} 1 = n(1) = n$$

In the second calculation we are assuming that y does not depend on the index variable k, that is, y is constant with respect to k.

Note that Formula (4.1.2) cannot be applied to the summation

$$\sum_{i=1}^{200} i = 1 + 2 + 3 + \cdots + 200,$$

since the ith term of the sequence is i, and this certainly depends on the indexing variable i. There is a famous formula that will allow us to easily compute this sum by hand. This formula, along with some other important ones are given in the margin box.

We can apply Formula (1) from the table to sum the first 200 natural numbers. This is quicker than writing a do loop to compute the sum.

$$\sum_{i=1}^{200} i = 1 + 2 + 3 + \cdots + 200 = \frac{200(201)}{2} = 20,100$$

Summation Formulas
(4) $\sum_{i=1}^{n} ca_i = c\sum_{i=1}^{n} a_i$
(5) $\sum_{i=1}^{n} (a_i + b_i) = \sum_{i=1}^{n} a_i + \sum_{i=1}^{n} b_i$

There are two further summation formulas that are natural and very useful. They are given in the table shown in the margin.

Example 4.1.9

Problem: Use the summation formulas (1)–(5) to calculate $\sum\limits_{i=1}^{35} \left(2i + 7i^3\right)$.

Solution: To do this calculation, notice that this is an algebraic expression and that the rules of algebra apply (i.e., summation formulas (4) and (5)).

$$\sum_{i=1}^{35} \left(2i + 7i^3\right) = \sum_{i=1}^{35} 2i + \sum_{i=1}^{35} 7i^3 = 2\sum_{i=1}^{35} i + 7\sum_{i=1}^{35} i^3$$

Now, we can apply summation formulas (1) and (3):

$$\sum_{i=1}^{35} \left(2i + 7i^3\right) = 2 \cdot \frac{35(36)}{2} + 7\left(\frac{35(36)}{2}\right)^2 = 2,779,560$$

Example 4.1.10

Problem: Use the summation formulas to compute the following sums

(a) $\sum\limits_{i=1}^{50}(i-1)(5i+3)$ (b) $\sum\limits_{i=21}^{100} i^2$

Solution:

(a) Multiply out first and then use the summation formulas;

$$\sum_{i=1}^{50} (i-1)(5i+3) = \sum_{i=1}^{50} \left(5i^2 - 2i - 3\right) = 5\sum_{i=1}^{50} i^2 - 2\sum_{i=1}^{50} i - 3\sum_{i=1}^{50} 1$$

$$= 5 \cdot \frac{50(51)101}{6} - 2 \cdot \frac{50(51)}{2} - 3(50) = 211,925$$

(b) View the given sum as the difference of two sums:

$$\sum_{i=21}^{100} i^2 = \sum_{i=1}^{100} i^2 - \sum_{i=1}^{20} i^2 = \frac{100(101)201}{6} - \frac{20(21)(41)}{6} = 335,480$$

Geometric Sums

Most of the sums that we encounter in calculus do not have formulas (also called, closed-form formulas) to express the result of the sum. An important class of sums that do have summation formulas are *geometric sums*. These are sums of the form

$$r + r^2 + r^3 + r^4 + \cdots + r^n = \sum_{i=1}^{n} r^i.$$

Geometric Sum Formula

(6) $\sum\limits_{i=1}^{n} r^i = r\left[\dfrac{r^n - 1}{r - 1}\right]$

where r is any real number except 1. We exclude $r = 1$, since then the sum is the sum of n ones which, as we saw in Summation Formula (0), is just n. Note that in a geometric sum, each term r^i in the sum is exponential with fixed base r and variable exponent i. Compare this with the sums we studied above, such as $\sum_{i=1}^{n} i^2$ (the sum of the first n squares) where each term i^2 is exponential with variable base i and fixed exponent 2. The summation formula for the general geometric sum is shown in the box in the margin.

Example 4.1.11 (Geometric Sums)

Problem: Use the geometric sum formula to compute the following sums

(a) $\sum\limits_{i=1}^{8} 2^i = 2 + 2^2 + 2^3 + \cdots + 2^8$ (b) $\sum\limits_{i=1}^{10} \left(\dfrac{4}{5}\right)^i = \dfrac{4}{5} + \left(\dfrac{4}{5}\right)^2 + \cdots + \left(\dfrac{4}{5}\right)^{10}$

Solution:

(a) Here $r = 2$, so $\displaystyle\sum_{i=1}^{8} 2^i = 2\left[\dfrac{2^8 - 1}{2 - 1}\right] = 2[4096 - 1] = 8190.$

(b) Here $r = 4/5$, so $\displaystyle\sum_{i=1}^{10}\left(\dfrac{4}{5}\right)^i = \dfrac{4}{5}\left[\dfrac{\left(\frac{4}{5}\right)^{10} - 1}{\frac{4}{5} - 1}\right] = 4\left[1 - \left(\dfrac{4}{5}\right)^{10}\right] = 3.570503270.$

Some Proofs of Summation Formulas

We will prove Formulas (1) and (6) and leave the others as exercises. All the formulas can be proved by mathematical induction, but historically Formulas (1) and (6) are special and can be proven as follows.

Let

$$S_n = 1 + 2 + \cdots + (n - 1) + n.$$

By commutativity of addition this sum can also be written

$$S_n = n + (n - 1) + \cdots + 2 + 1$$

Adding these expressions gives

$$\begin{aligned} 2S_n &= (n + 1) + (n + 1) + \cdots + (n + 1) + (n + 1) \\ &= n(n + 1). \end{aligned}$$

Hence

$$S_n = \frac{n(n + 1)}{2},$$

which is what we wanted to prove.

The proof (6) goes as follows. Again let S_n denote the sum of the n terms:

$$S_n = \sum_{i=1}^{n} r^i = r + r^2 + r^3 + r^4 + \cdots + r^n$$

Multiplying both sides of this by r gives

$$rS_n = r\left(r + r^2 + r^3 + r^4 + \cdots + r^n\right) = r^2 + r^3 + r^4 + r^5 + \cdots + r^{n+1}$$

Thus, taking the difference yields

$$rS_n - S_n = r^{n+1} - r$$

and factoring gives

$$(r - 1)S_n = r\left(r^n - 1\right), \quad \text{and so} \quad S_n = r\left[\dfrac{r^n - 1}{r - 1}\right]$$

This is what we wanted to prove.

Exercises: 4.1 (Areas and Sums)

```
> with(code_ch4);
```
$[DRSplot, RSplot, circle, parabola , printcircle, printparabola]$

Areas Under the Graphs of Step-Functions and Polygonal Functions

In exercises 1–6, determine the area under the graphs of the given step-functions and polygonal functions. Your answers will be approximate since they are based on de-termining the approximate heights and widths from the pictures.

1.

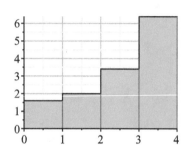

2.

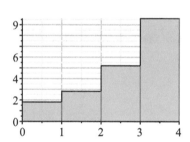

3.

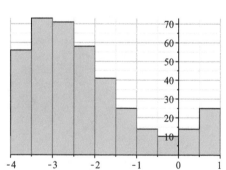

4.

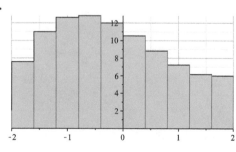

5.

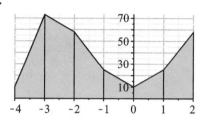

6.

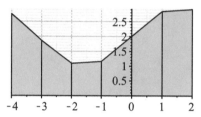

CAS: Approximate Areas of Regions Bounded by Circles and Parabolas

In Exercises 7–12, use the commands below to generate movies of rectangular and trapezoidal approximations to the areas of circles and parabolas. From the final frame in the movie, estimate the approximate area.

7. circle(4,16,rectangles)   **8.** circle(3,9,rectangles)
circle(4,32,rectangles)   circle(3,18,rectangles)
9. circle(5,10,trapezoids)   **10.** circle(2,10,trapezoids)
circle(5,20,trapezoids)   circle(2,20,trapezoids)
11. parabola(4,16,rectangles) **12.** Use trapezoids
parabola(4,16,rectangles)   in Exercise 11

Using the Summation Formulas and Rules

In Exercises 13–26, use the summation formulas to com-pute the following sums.

13. $\displaystyle\sum_{i=1}^{10} \left(2 - 3i + 5i^2\right)$ **14.** $\displaystyle\sum_{i=1}^{10} \left(3 + 2i - 7i^2\right)$

15. $\displaystyle\sum_{i=1}^{20} \left(3i + 1\right)^2$ **16.** $\displaystyle\sum_{i=1}^{20} \left(2i + 1\right)^2$

17. $\displaystyle\sum_{i=1}^{20} \left(2i + 1\right)^3$ **18.** $\displaystyle\sum_{i=1}^{20} \left(2i - 1\right)^3$

19. $\displaystyle\sum_{i=1}^{15} i^2 \left(2i + 5\right)$ **20.** $\displaystyle\sum_{i=1}^{15} i^2 \left(3i + 4\right)$

21. $\displaystyle\sum_{i=1}^{n} \left(\frac{2i}{n} + \frac{7i^3}{n^3}\right) \frac{2}{n}$ **22.** $\displaystyle\sum_{i=1}^{n} \left(\frac{3i}{n} + \frac{5i^3}{n^3}\right) \frac{4}{n}$

23. $\displaystyle\sum_{i=1}^{8} 3^i$ **24.** $\displaystyle\sum_{i=1}^{8} 4^i$

25. $\displaystyle\sum_{i=1}^{10} \left[2i - (2/3)^i\right]$ **26.** $\displaystyle\sum_{i=1}^{10} \left[3i - (3/4)^i\right]$

Calculus Concepts & Computation

4.2 Riemann Sums

```
> with(code_ch4sec2,RSplot,DRSplot);
```
$$[RSplot, DRSplot]$$

In the previous section we discussed the problem of measuring areas of "curved" regions and developed the idea of approximating curved regions by simple geometric regions, such as rectangles, triangles, trapezoids, each having a known area. Our goal in this section and the next is to establish a limiting procedure that gives the exact areas of curved regions as limits of sums of areas of these simple types of approximating regions.

The key to finding the areas of more general "curved regions" is to solve a special case called the *area problem*:

For a continuous function f, which is positive on an interval [a, b], determine the area of the region D bounded by the graph of f, the two vertical lines through a and b, and the x-axis.

We discuss how to solve the area problem using limits of Riemann sums, each Riemann sum being the sum of the areas of certain approximating rectangles.

Riemann Sums using Right Endpoints

The area problem is similar to the tangent line problem in the sense that solving it amounts to determining, or *defining*, what is meant by the area of a curved region. In solving the tangent line problem, we had to set up a limiting process (the slopes of a sequence of secant lines) in order to define the slope of the tangent line as a limit.

Similarly, to solve the area problem, we will set up a limiting process to define the area of the region D beneath the graph of f as a limit. In this case the limit is the limit of approximating areas. Each approximating area will be a sum of rectangular areas. Thus, the limiting process for the area problem is slightly more complicated, even though the concept behind it is quite simple. The concept involves what are known as Riemann sums.

The method of Riemann sums, devised by the German mathematician G. F. Bernhard Riemann (1826-1866), is a method that begins by approximating the region D with a sequence of rectangles and using the sum of the areas of these rectangles as an approximation to the area of D. Indeed, the area of D will then be *defined* as a limit of such sums. This section will help you learn how to set up and calculate Riemann sums, while Section 4.3 will show you how to solve the area problem by taking limits of Riemann sums.

To get started, note that if the function f is a step-function, then the area of the region D beneath its graph is quite easy to determine since it is just the sum of areas of rectangles. Figure 4.2.2 illustrates an example of this where there are five rectangles.

To generalize this, it is natural to devise a systematic way of approximating an arbitrary continuous function f by a step-function s. Then the area of the region beneath s gives an approximation to the area of the region beneath f. This is the Riemann sum method.

So, assume we start with a function f that has graph as shown in Figure 4.2.3. To get a step-function approximation, suppose we divide the interval $[a, b]$ into, say, five subintervals. We do this by choosing four distinct points, x_1, x_2, x_3, x_4, between a and b. Figure 4.2.4 shows one of the many possible choices of these points and the resulting subintervals.

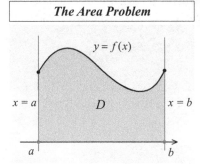

The Area Problem

Figure 4.2.1

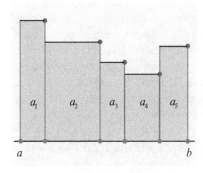

Figure 4.2.2: *The area $A = a_1 + a_2 + \cdots + a_5$ beneath the graph of a step-function.*

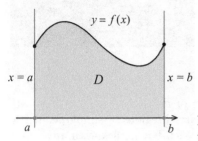

Figure 4.2.3: *The Region beneath the graph of f.*

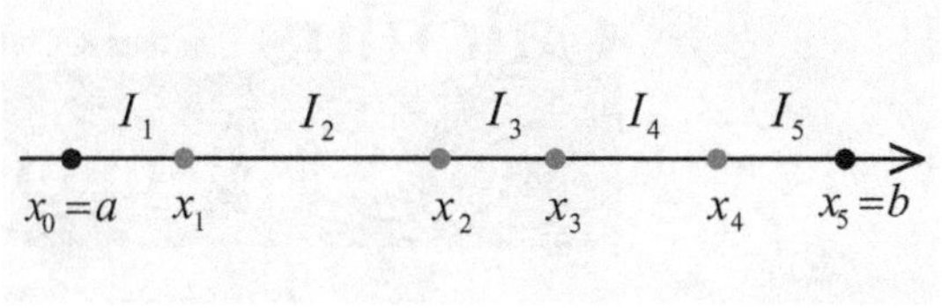

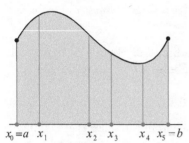

Figure 4.2.5: *Five regions determined by the partition* $P = \{x_i\}_{i=0}^{5}$ *of* $[a, b]$.

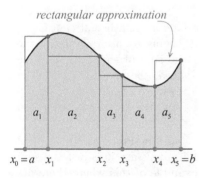

Figure 4.2.6: *Creation of 5 rectangles using right endpoints of the partition.*

Figure 4.2.4

Figure 4.2.4: *A choice of 4 points* x_1, x_2, x_3, x_4 *gives a subdivision of* $[a, b]$ *into 5 subintervals* I_1, I_2, I_3, I_4, I_5.

It is customary to label the endpoints a and b of $[a, b]$ by $x_0 = a$ and $x_5 = b$. Then the five subintervals are

$$I_1 = [x_0, x_1], I_2 = [x_1, x_2], I_3 = [x_2, x_3], I_4 = [x_3, x_4], I_5 = [x_4, x_5].$$

This is called a *subdivision* of $[a, b]$. For the cases when we have a larger number of subintervals than five, it is convenient to use a general subscript index i and refer to the subinterval

$$I_i = [x_{i-1}, x_i],$$

as the ith subinterval, for $i = 1, 2, 3, 4, 5$. The points x_i we have chosen to form the subdivision are called *partition points*, since subdividing is often referred to as partitioning. The set of partition points

$$P = \{x_0, x_1, x_2, x_3, x_4, x_5\} = \{x_i\}_{i=0}^{5}$$

is called a *partition* of $[a, b]$. When the points in the partition are equally spaced (i.e., the distance between any two adjacent ones is the same), then the partition P is called a *regular partition*. Having this subdivision of $[a, b]$ into five subintervals, we now divide the region D beneath the graph into five subregions by drawing vertical lines through each of the partition points. This gives five regions as shown in Figure 4.2.5.

Now approximate each of these five regions by using rectangles based on "right endpoints" of the partition as shown in Figure 4.2.6.

To draw the rectangular approximation shown in Figure 4.2.6, which uses right endpoints, first draw vertical lines upward through all the partition points; stopping each line where it intersects the graph. Then starting with the first subinterval $[x_0, x_1]$, follow the vertical line through the right endpoint x_1 up to where this line intersects the graph and draw a horizontal line *backward* until you reach a point directly over the left endpoint x_0. Complete the rectangle by drawing a vertical line from this point down (or up) to where it intersects the graph. Repeat this process for the second subinterval $[x_1, x_2]$, and so on, until you have constructed rectangles over all the subintervals. With a little practice, you will find it easy to draw such rectangular approximations. *Note* that the height of the ith rectangle is the value $f(x_i)$ of the function at the right endpoint x_i of the ith subinterval $[x_{i-1}, x_i]$.

The area of the rectangular approximation is $a_1 + a_2 + a_3 + a_4 + a_5 = \sum_{i=1}^{5} a_i$, where a_i is the area of the ith rectangle. So the approximation to the area A beneath the graph of f is

$$A \approx \sum_{i=1}^{5} a_i,$$

The approximating sum $\sum_{i=1}^{5} a_i$, which is based on the partition we chose, is called a *Riemann sum*. There are many different Riemann sums, one for each possible partition of $[a, b]$ and each possible choice of heights for the rectangles in the sum. We are interested in obtaining better and better approximations to the area under the graph of f by choosing Riemann sums with more summands in them.

Note: The above rectangular approximation is a fairly good approximation to the area under the graph of f even though the outline of the tops of the rectangles is not very similar to the graph of f. As you can see in Figure 4.2.6, the first and fifth rectangles extend above the graph of f, and so give too large an area. But this is compensated by the fact that the second, third, and fourth rectangles fall beneath the graph of f and thus give too small an area. Thus, the approximating area is relatively good. Of course these observations depend on the nature of the function being approximated. In other examples, using five rectangles to approximate the area under the graph will produce a poor approximation.

Example 4.2.1 (Computing a Riemann Sum from a Given Graph)

Problem: Suppose the graph of f on the interval is as shown in Figure 4.2.7, and we partition $[-2, 3]$ into five subintervals by the partition $P = \{-2, -1, 0, 1, 2, 3\}$, giving the rectangular approximation shown in the figure. Calculate the Riemann sum corresponding to this partition.

Solution: We simply calculate the areas of the five rectangles shown and add them up. That is the Riemann sum in this case. Note that the partition points are equally spaced, so this is a *regular* partition. The points are all a distance of 1 unit apart. Thus, the base of each rectangle has length 1. The heights of the rectangles can be determined (approximately) by looking carefully at the figure or by using the cursor probe on the figure. The heights appear to be approximately

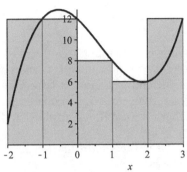

Figure 4.2.7: *The graph of a function and a rectangular approximation.*

$$12, 12, 8, 6, 12.$$

Thus, the Riemann sum is

$$12(1) + 12(1) + 8(1) + 6(1) + 12(1) = 50.$$

Note that it is purely coincidental that three of the heights are the same (the value 12), and while it is convenient that the length of each base is 1, this is not typical.

We extend the previous example to one with twice as many rectangles:

Example 4.2.2 (A Riemann Sum for a Finer Partition)

Problem: Suppose the graph of f on the interval $[-2, 3]$ is as shown in Figure 4.2.8, and we partition $[-2, 3]$ into ten subintervals by the partition

$$P = \{-2, -1.5, -1, -0.5, 0, 0.5, 1, 1.5, 2, 2.5, 3\},$$

giving the approximating step-function shown in the figure. Calculate the Riemann sum corresponding to this partition.

Solution: This partition is also a regular one, with the points spaced 0.5 units apart, and so 0.5 is the length of the base of each of the ten rectangles. The heights we find to be approximately

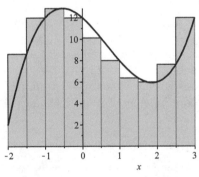

Figure 4.2.8: *The graph of a function and a rectangular approximation.*

$$8.6, 12, 13, 12, 10.1, 8, 6.4, 6, 7.6, 12.$$

The corresponding Riemann sum is

```
>(8.6+12+13+12+10.1+8+6.4+6+7.6+12)*0.5;
                47.85
```

Notice that for regular partitions, we can factor out the common length of the bases (which is 0.5 here) from the Riemann sum and add up the heights separately. For non-regular partitions, we can not do this. Also note that you can easily do this calculation by hand or by calculator. Using Maple, however, will be convenient when we have a great many summands to add together.

The two examples above used figures that were produced by the special-purpose Maple command called `RSapprox`. It will plot the rectangles in any Riemann sum approximation. The next example discusses how to use this command and the corresponding animation command `DRSplot`.

Example 4.2.3 (A Very Fine Partition Requires a Computer)

The function used in Examples 4.2.1–4.2.2 is the cubic polynomial

$$f(x) = x^3 - 2x^2 - 3x + 12.$$

To produce a plot of the approximation shown in Figure 4.2.8, first define this function in Maple:

```
>f:=x->x^3-2*x^2-3*x+12;
```
$$f := x \mapsto x^3 - 2x^2 - 3x + 12$$

Then the plot is produced by the command

```
> RSplot(f,-2,3,10,1);
```

The output from this command is the Figure 4.2.8 above. The input arguments -2 and 3 to this command are the endpoints of the interval and the input 10 specifies a subdivision into ten, equal length, subintervals. The fifth input argument 1 specifies that we want the plot of the 1st *type* of Riemann sum, which is the one based on right endpoints. Later on we will discuss several other types of Riemann sums and will use RSplot for these types as well.

You can also produce an animation of the rectangles in the approximation being drawn, one-by-one, using the command DSRplot. For example,

```
> DRSplot(f,-2,3,10,1);
```

You should study the animation by slowing down the frame-rate and running it several times. Also, go through the animation frame-by-frame, observing how the rectangular approximation is constructed. In the exercises, you will have to draw, by hand, some rectangular approximations, so studying this animation should help you.

Suppose we increase the number of subintervals from 10 to 40. The resulting animation is produced by

```
> DRSplot(f,-2,3,40,1);
```

Figure 4.2.9 shows the last (40th) frame in this animation (or equivalently, the output of RSplot).

You should compare Figure 4.2.9 with Figures 4.2.7 and 4.2.8. Using a partition with 5 subintervals gives an approximating area of 50 (Figure 4.2.7), while increasing to 10 subintervals gives an approximating area of 47.85 (Figure 4.2.8). Based on Figure 4.2.9, it appears that using 40 subintervals would give a better approximation still. However, doing the calculations is somewhat time-consuming (exercise), so we look at more convenient ways to do the computation in the next subsection.

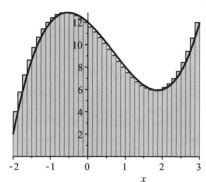

Figure 4.2.9: *The last frame in the animation* DRSplot(f,-2,3,40,1).

Summation Notation for Riemann Sums

Example 4.2.3 suggests that we need to develop some notation for the areas of the approximating rectangles and the sum of these areas. This is especially important for the case shown in Figure 4.2.9 where there are 40 approximating rectangles. Writing out a sum of 40 areas can be tedious, but with the proper notation this task, as well as the calculation of the sum, can be made very easy.

The mathematical notation for the general situation is as follows. We suppose that f is a continuous function on the interval $[a, b]$. For a general partition

$$P = \{x_0, x_1, ..., x_n\} = \{x_i\}_{i=0}^{n}$$

of $[a, b]$ into n subintervals, we let $I_i = [x_{i-1}, x_i]$ denote the ith subinterval and let Δx_i denote the length of this subinterval. Thus,

$$\Delta x_i = x_i - x_{i-1}.$$

Note that we assume that $x_0 = a$, $x_n = b$ and that the x_i are indexed in increasing order:

$$x_0 < x_1 < x_2 < \cdots < x_{n-1} < x_n.$$

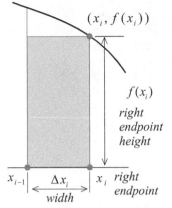

$(x_i, f(x_i))$

$f(x_i)$

right
endpoint
height

x_{i-1} Δx_i x_i *right*
$\underset{width}{\longleftrightarrow}$ *endpoint*

Figure 4.2.10: *The area of the ith rectangle in the Riemann sum for right endpoints.*

Thus, the difference $\Delta x_i = x_i - x_{i-1}$ does measure the actual width of the ith subrectangle. Using Riemann sums based on right endpoints, for each i we evaluate f at the right endpoint of $I_i = [x_{i-1}, x_i]$. Then $f(x_i)$ is the height of the ith subrectangle. Hence the area of the ith subrectangle is

$$a_i = f(x_i)\,\Delta x_i.$$

All of this is illustrated in Figure 4.2.10.

Using the sigma notation for sum, we can write the sum of the areas of the n rectangles as

$$\sum_{i=1}^{n} a_i = \sum_{i=1}^{n} f(x_i)\,\Delta x_i.$$

This is the Riemann sum corresponding to the partition P and based on the selection of *right endpoints* for determining the heights of the rectangles. Since the sum depends on P as well as the selection of points to use in determining heights (in this case the right endpoints, denoted by R), we build this into the following definition of Riemann sums:

Definition 4.2.1 (Riemann Sums for Right Endpoints)

For a function f on an interval [a,b] and for a partition

$$P = \{x_0, x_1, x_2, \ldots, x_n\}$$

of [a,b], the Riemann sum based on right endpoints for rectangle heights is

$$R_P = \sum_{i=1}^{n} f(x_i)\Delta x_i \qquad (4.2.1)$$

Even though the notation for Riemann sums can seem to be rather elaborate and confusing at first, just remember that a Riemann sum is merely a sum of (heights) times (bases) for a collection of rectangles.

Differences of Partition Points

$x_0 = 1$ $\}$ $\Delta x_1 = 2 - 1 = 1$
$x_1 = 2$ $\}$ $\Delta x_2 = 4 - 2 = 2$
$x_2 = 4$ $\}$ $\Delta x_3 = 5 - 4 = 1$
$x_3 = 5$ $\}$ $\Delta x_4 = 6.5 - 5 = 1.5$
$x_4 = 6.5$ $\}$ $\Delta x_5 = 7 - 6.5 = 0.5$
$x_5 = 7$ $\}$ $\Delta x_6 = 8 - 7 = 1$
$x_6 = 8$

Example 4.2.4 (Computing a Riemann Sum and Sketching By-Hand)

Problem: For the function $f(x) = 10x - x^2$ on the interval $[1, 8]$, and for the partition

$$P = \{1, 2, 4, 5, 6.5, 7, 8, \},$$

compute, by hand, the corresponding right endpoint Riemann sum. Also, sketch the graph of the function and approximating rectangles.

Solution: First we label the partition points as $x_i, i = 0, 1, \ldots, 6$, and compute the differences between successive points. See the margin box.

Thus, the corresponding Riemann sum is

$$
\begin{aligned}
R_P &= f(2) \cdot 1 + f(4) \cdot 2 + f(5) \cdot 1 + f(6.5) \cdot 1.5 + f(7) \cdot 0.5 + f(8) \cdot 1 \\
&= 16 \cdot 1 + 24 \cdot 2 + 25 \cdot 1 + 22.75 \cdot 1.5 + 21 \cdot 0.5 + 16 \cdot 1 \\
&= 149.625
\end{aligned}
$$

The computations are easy enough to do by hand once you get used to all the notation and have done a few problems like this. You might also find that using a table to record the intermediate results is useful. Table 4.2.1 shows the results that we calculated in this example.

The tabular method here is simple. Fill in the first column with the partition points. Then evaluate the function at each of these points to get the entries in the

x_i	$f(x_i)$	Δx_i	$f(x_i)\Delta x_i$
1	9	---	---
2	16	1	16
4	24	2	48
5	25	1	25
6.5	22.75	1.5	34.125
7	21	0.5	10.5
8	16	1	16
			$R = 149.625$

Table 4.2.1

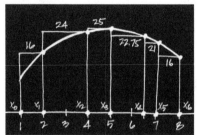

Figure 4.2.11: The graph of $f(x) = 10x - x^2$ and the seven approximating rectangles.

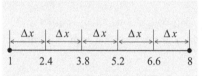

Figure 4.2.12: *A subdivision of* $[1,8]$ *into 5 equal subintervals*

second column. Compute the differences between adjacent partition points to get the entries in the third column. The fourth column is the product of the numbers in the second and third columns. Then sum the numbers in the fourth column to get the Riemann sum. This only takes a few minutes with pencil and paper (no calculators or computers, please!).

Next we sketch the graph of f on $[1,8]$. Note that the total graph of f is a parabola with x-intercepts 0 and 10. So you might want to sketch this first and then cut it off to get the graph on the interval $[1,8]$. Then we just mark the partition points and sketch in the approximating right endpoint rectangles to get the drawing shown in Figure 4.2.11.

Example 4.2.5 (A Regular Partition Riemann Sum)

Problem: For the function $f(x) = 10x - x^2$ on the interval $[1,8]$, construct a *regular* partition of $[1,8]$ into five subintervals and then compute the corresponding Riemann sum based on right endpoints.

Solution: Recall that a regular partition is one where the partition points are equally spaced. In this example, the partition points will divide the interval into five equal parts. The length of the whole interval $[1,8]$ is $8 - 1 = 7$, and so dividing into 5 equal parts gives that each subinterval has length

$$\Delta x = \frac{8-1}{5} = \frac{7}{5} = 1.4$$

Now how do we find the partition x_i points from this? It is easy enough to sketch the location of the partition points–just divide $[1,8]$ into 5 equal parts as shown in Figure 4.2.12.

From the figure we see that if we start with $x_0 = a = 1$ and add $\Delta x = 1.4$ to it we get the first partition point

$$x_1 = a + \Delta x = 1 + 1.4 = 2.4$$

Adding Δx to this, we get the second partition point

$$x_2 = x_1 + \Delta x = 2.4 + 1.4 = 3.8$$

And so forth:

$$x_3 = x_2 + \Delta x = 3.8 + 1.4 = 5.2$$
$$x_4 = x_3 + \Delta x = 5.2 + 1.4 = 6.6$$
$$x_5 = x_4 + \Delta x = 6.6 + 1.4 = 8.0$$

It is important to observe the pattern here, since we will use it many times in other examples: *Keep adding Δx to get the successive partition points.* Also, it is important to phrase this in a slightly different way: Start with x_0 and add Δx a total of i times to get the ith partition point:

$$x_i = a + \Delta x + \Delta x + \cdots + \Delta x = a + i\Delta x.$$

With the partition points 1, 2.4, 3.8, 5.2, 6.6, 8 determined, the corresponding Riemann sum is easily computed:

$$
\begin{aligned}
R_P &= f(2.4)\,\Delta x + f(3.8)\,\Delta x + f(5.2)\,\Delta x + f(6.6)\,\Delta x + f(8)\,\Delta x \\
&= \left(f(2.4) + f(3.8) + f(5.2) + f(6.6) + f(8)\right)\Delta x \\
&= (18.24 + 23.56 + 24.96 + 22.44 + 16)\,\Delta x = 105.2\Delta x = 105.2\,(1.4) = 147.28
\end{aligned}
$$

The computations here involve squaring some two-digit numbers, and the total computation should take about five minutes or so by hand without the use of a computer or calculator. To see how to handle the more tedious cases when there are many more summands than five, we look at how to do the above computations again, but this time using Maple. First define the function

```
> f:=x->10*x-x^2;
```

$$f := x \mapsto 10\,x - x^2$$

Then the result is computed as follows

```
> RS:=(f(2.4)+f(3.8)+f(5.2)+f(6.6)+f(8))*(1.4);
```

$$RS := \ 147.280$$

Well, that's certainly easy enough, but we recommend that you also know how to do the computations here by hand. The above Maple calculations readily lend themselves to cases where there are a great number of subintervals—too many to do the calculations by hand. The next example shows you how to do this.

Before proceeding, we look at, in general, what we learned in the last example. To construct regular partitions of $[a, b]$ into n subintervals, we take the length $b - a$ of the whole interval and divide by n to get the common length Δx of each subinterval

$$\Delta x = \frac{b - a}{n}.$$

Then, to manufacture the partition points x_i, we take the endpoint a and successively add Δx to it

$$x_i = a + i\Delta x,$$

for $i = 0, 1, 2, \ldots, n$. Since the corresponding right endpoint Riemann sum only depends on n, we denote it by R_n instead of R_P. For convenience, we record these formulas in the following box:

Formulas for Regular Partitions

For a regular partition of [a,b] into n subintervals, the length of each subinterval is

$$\Delta x = \frac{b - a}{n} \qquad (4.2.2)$$

The partition points are given by

$$x_i = a + i\Delta x \qquad (4.2.3)$$

for $i = 1, 2, \ldots, n$. The corresponding right endpoint Riemann sum is

$$R_n = \sum_{i=1}^{n} f(x_i)\Delta x \qquad (4.2.4)$$

Example 4.2.6 (Computing R₁₀₀ with a Computer)

Problem: For the function $f(x) = 10\,x - x^2$ on the interval $[1, 8]$, construct the regular partition of $[1, 8]$ into 100 subintervals and compute the corresponding right endpoint Riemann sum R_{100}.

Solution: If you understood how to do the calculations in the previous two examples, the notation below for automating these calculations should seem natural.

Define the function and assign the values for the left and right endpoints of the interval :

```
> f:=x->10*x-x^2;
```

$$f := x \mapsto 10x - x^2$$

```
> a:=1.0;b:=8.0;
```

$$a := 1.0$$
$$b := 8.0$$

Assign the value for the number n of subintervals and set up an array X to store the calculated partition points:

```
> n:=100;X:=array(0..n);
```
$$n := 100$$
$$X := array\ (0..100,[\ ])$$

Compute Δx (which is called dX here), assign the value to the 0th partition point $x_0 = a$, and then use a do loop to calculate the other partition points .

```
> dX:=(b-a)/n;
```
$$dX := 0.07000000000$$

```
> X[0]:=a;
```
$$X_0 := 1.0$$

```
> for i from 1 to n do X[i]:=a+i*dX end do:
```

Now we just use the `sum` command to compute the corresponding Riemann sum $R_n = \sum_{i=1}^{n} f(x_i)\,\Delta x$.

```
> i:=evaln(i);
```
$$i := i$$

```
> R100:=sum(f(X[i])*dX,i=1..n);
```
$$R100 := 144.9059500$$

This is certainly an easy way to compute something that would be tedious to do by hand. However, *the point is*: you must do the calculations by hand for small values of n and try to understand the concept behind all the calculations, otherwise the above automated calculations would be meaningless.

Summary: In the last three examples we have computed right endpoint Riemann sums for $f(x) = 10x - x^2$, on the interval $[1, 8]$. The results were

$$
\begin{aligned}
R_P &= 149.625,\ P \text{ an } irregular \text{ partition of } [1,8] \text{ into 6 subintervals} \\
R_5 &= 147.28,\ P \text{ a } regular \text{ partition of } [1,8] \text{ into 5 subintervals} \\
R_{100} &= 144.9,\ P \text{ a } regular \text{ partition of } [1,8] \text{ into 100 subintervals}
\end{aligned}
$$

The values here represent approximations to the area of the region underneath the graph of f.

Example 4.2.7 (Formulas for R_n)

For certain functions f it is possible to use the summation formulas from Section 4.1 to get a formula for the Riemann sum R_n. We can use the function $f(x) = 10x - x^2$ from the last example to show how this is done. We let n be arbitrary and write out R_n in general. The interval is $[1, 8]$, so the regular partition has subinterval lengths:

$$\Delta x = \frac{8 - 1}{n} = \frac{7}{n},$$

and partition points:

$$x_i = a + i\Delta x = 1 + \frac{7i}{n}$$

Then

$$f(x_i) = f\left(1 + \frac{7i}{n}\right) = 10\left(1 + \frac{7i}{n}\right) - \left(1 + \frac{7i}{n}\right)^2$$

$$= 10 + \frac{70i}{n} - \left(1 + \frac{14i}{n} + \frac{49i^2}{n^2}\right)$$

$$= 9 + \frac{56i}{n} - \frac{49i^2}{n^2}$$

Thus,

$$R_n = \sum_{i=1}^{n}\left(9 + 56\frac{i}{n} - 49\frac{i^2}{n^2}\right)\frac{7}{n} = \left(9\sum_{i=1}^{n}1 + \frac{56}{n}\sum_{i=1}^{n}i - \frac{49}{n^2}\sum_{i=1}^{n}i^2\right)\frac{7}{n}$$

$$= \frac{63}{n} \sum_{i=1}^{n} 1 + \frac{392}{n^2} \sum_{i=1}^{n} i - \frac{343}{n^3} \sum_{i=1}^{n} i^2$$

$$= \frac{63}{n} \cdot n + \frac{392}{n^2} \cdot \frac{n(n+1)}{2} - \frac{343}{n^3} \cdot \frac{n(n+1)(2n+1)}{6}$$

$$= 63 + 196 \cdot \frac{n+1}{n} - \frac{343}{6} \cdot \frac{(n+1)(2n+1)}{n^2}.$$

We leave this resulting formula in this form rather than combining terms. This allows us to more easily determine the limiting behavior as n gets large. We first check that this formula gives us the values R_n that we computed in the previous example. Using Maple for this, we first define R_n as a function of n:

```
> R:=n->63+196*(n+1)/n-(343/6)*(n+1)*(2*n+1)/(n^2);
```

$$R := n \mapsto 63 + \frac{196\,n + 196}{n} - \frac{343}{6} \frac{(n+1)(2\,n+1)}{n^2}$$

This gives

```
> R(5.0);
```
$$147.2800000$$
```
> R(100.);
```
$$144.9059500$$

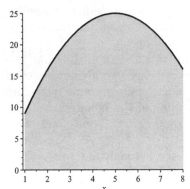

Figure 4.2.13: *The area under the graph of* $f(x) = 10\,x - x^2$ *on* $[1,8]$ *is a limit of Riemann sums:* $\lim_{n \to \infty} R_n = \frac{434}{3} \approx 144.667$.

These are the same values we found in Examples 4.2.5–4.2.6 using other methods. Now to determine the limiting behavior, i.e., $\lim_{n \to \infty} R_n$, we first observe that

$$\lim_{n \to \infty} \frac{n+1}{n} = \lim_{n \to \infty} \left(1 + \frac{1}{n}\right) = 1,$$

and

$$\lim_{n \to \infty} \frac{(n+1)(2n+1)}{n^2} = \lim_{n \to \infty} \frac{n+1}{n} \cdot \frac{2n+1}{n} = \lim_{n \to \infty} \left(1 + \frac{1}{n}\right)\left(2 + \frac{1}{n}\right) = 2.$$

These are two standard limits that will occur often in the next section. Based on these, we see that

$$\lim_{n \to \infty} R_n = \lim_{n \to \infty} \left(63 + 196 \cdot \frac{n+1}{n} - \frac{343}{6} \cdot \frac{(n+1)(2n+1)}{n^2}\right)$$

$$= 63 + 196 \cdot 1 - \frac{343}{6} \cdot 2 = \frac{434}{3} = 144.666 \cdots$$

Thus, the last four examples (Examples 4.2.4–4.2.7), suggest that we define the area under the graph of $f(x) = 10x - x^2$ on the interval $[1,8]$ to be given by this limit of Riemann sums.

Example 4.2.8 (Formulas for R_n)

Problem: For $f(x) = e^x$ on the interval $[0,1]$ find a (closed form) formula for R_n.

Solution: The length of each subinterval is $\Delta x = (1 - 0)/n = 1/n$ and the ith partition point is $x_i = 0 + i\Delta x = i/n$. Then

$$R_n = \sum_{i=1}^{n} f(x_i)\Delta x = \sum_{i=1}^{n} e^{i/n} \cdot \frac{1}{n} = \frac{1}{n} \sum_{i=1}^{n} e^{i/n}$$

While this is a formula for R_n, it is not "closed-form" since the summation index i is present. To get rid of it, we use the Summation Formula (6) for geometric sums (Section 4.1), with $r = e^{1/n}$. This gives

$$\frac{1}{n} \sum_{i=1}^{n} e^{i/n} = \frac{1}{n} \sum_{i=1}^{n} \left(e^{1/n}\right)^i = \frac{1}{n} \cdot e^{1/n} \left[\frac{\left(e^{1/n}\right)^n - 1}{e^{1/n} - 1}\right] = \frac{e^{1/n}}{n\left(e^{1/n} - 1\right)} \cdot (e - 1)$$

We can now use this directly to compute, say, the $n = 5$ and $n = 100$ rectangular approximations to the area under the graph of $f(x) = e^x$ on the interval $[0, 1]$. The are

$$R_5 = 1.103331114(e - 1) \quad \text{and} \quad R_{100} = 1.005008342(e - 1)$$

In the next section we will show that $A = \lim_{n \to \infty} R_n = e - 1$ is the exact area under the graph.

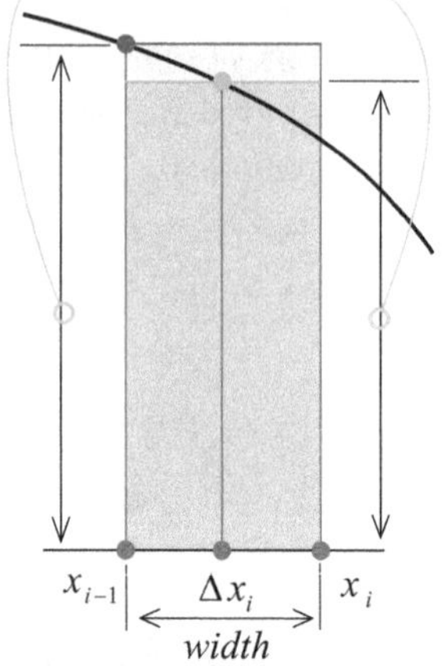

Riemann Sums (Other Choices of Endpoints)

In Section 4.3 we will be taking limits of Riemann sums to determine the area under the graph of a function f (the area problem). For continuous functions it suffices, in this limiting process, to use right endpoint Riemann sums based on a regular partition. These are the types of Riemann sums studied above.

For non-continuous functions and for use in estimation and approximation, it is important to have more general types of Riemann sums, ones that are not based on regular partitions, and ones that have the heights of the approximating rectangles determined by other points besides the right endpoints of the subintervals. Two natural alternatives to using right endpoints are using *left endpoints* and using *midpoints* as illustrated in Figure 4.2.14.

Note that in the ith subinterval $I_i = [x_{i-1}, x_i]$ the left endpoint is x_{i-1}, and the midpoint is the average of the left and right endpoints:

$$midpoint = \frac{x_{i-1} + x_i}{2}.$$

left endpoint
height   midpoint height
$f(x_{i-1})$ $f\left((x_i + x_{i-1})/2\right)$

x_{i-1} | Δx_i | x_i
width

Figure 4.2.14: *The rectangles determined by using left endpoints and midpoints*

Thus, the corresponding Riemann sums are defined as follows.

Definition 4.2.2 (Riemann Sums for Left Endpoints and Midpoints)

For a function f on an interval [a, b] and for a partition

$$P = \{x_0, x_1, x_2, \ldots, x_n\}$$

of [a, b], the Riemann sums based on left endpoints and midpoints for rectangle heights are

$$L_P = \sum_{i=1}^{n} f(x_{i-1}) \Delta x_i \tag{4.2.5}$$

$$M_P = \sum_{i=1}^{n} f((x_i + x_{i-1})/2) \Delta x_i \tag{4.2.6}$$

An important special case of this is when the partition P is a regular partition. Then we have as before,

$$\Delta x_i = \Delta x = \frac{b - a}{n},$$

for each i. So, the Riemann sum only depends on n and the type of endpoint used, and in this case we denote the Riemann sums L_P and M_P by L_n and M_n, respectively. In summary then, we now have three special types of Riemann sums when the partition P is regular:

Riemann Sums for Regular Partitions:

$$R_n = \sum_{i=1}^{n} f(x_i) \Delta x \tag{4.2.7}$$

$$L_n = \sum_{i=1}^{n} f(x_{i-1}) \Delta x \tag{4.2.8}$$

$$M_n \;=\; \sum_{i=1}^{n} f\left((x_{i-1}+x_i)/2\right)\Delta x \qquad (4.2.9)$$

These formulas are as easy to use as the one for right endpoint Riemann sums. The following examples illustrate this and some of the uses of these new types of Riemann sums.

Example 4.2.9 (Left Endpoint & Midpoint Riemann Sums)

Problem: Consider $f(x) = 1 + x^2$ on the interval $[0,1]$. For a regular partition of $[0,1]$ into 5 subintervals, compute, by hand, the corresponding Riemann sums based on left endpoints and midpoints. Sketch the graph of f and the two sets of approximating rectangles.

Solution: Here $a = 0, b = 1$, and $n = 5$. Using the regular partition formulas, we find that

$$\Delta x = \frac{b-a}{n} = \frac{1-0}{5} = \frac{1}{5} = 0.2,$$

is the common length of the subintervals. Then, the partition points are

$$x_i = a + i\Delta x = 0 + i(0.2) = 0.2i,$$

for $i = 0, 1, 2, 3, 4, 5$. Specifically, the partition points are
$$0, 0.2, 0.4, 0.6, 0.8, 1$$
The corresponding left endpoint Riemann sum is

$$\begin{aligned}
L_n &= \sum_{i=1}^{n} f(x_{i-1})\Delta x = [f(x_0) + f(x_1) + f(x_2) + f(x_3) + f(x_4)]\Delta x \\
&= [f(0) + f(0.2) + f(0.4) + f(0.6) + f(0.8)]\,0.2 \\
&= [1 + 1.04 + 1.16 + 1.36 + 1.64]\,0.2 = 1.24
\end{aligned}$$

Next, we average the partition points 0, 0.2, 0.4, 0.6, 0.8, 1.0 to get the midpoints:
$$0.1, 0.3, 0.5, 0.7, 0.9$$
The corresponding midpoint Riemann sum is

$$\begin{aligned}
M_5 &= \sum_{i=1}^{5} f\left((x_{i-1}+x_i)/2\right)\Delta x \\
&= [f((x_0+x_1)/2) + f((x_1+x_2)/2) + \cdots + f((x_4+x_5)/2)]\Delta x \\
&= (f(0.1) + f(0.3) + f(0.5) + f(0.7) + f(0.9))\cdot 0.2 \\
&= (1.01 + 1.09 + 1.25 + 1.49 + 1.81)\cdot 0.2 = 1.33.
\end{aligned}$$

Figure 4.2.15 shows the hand-drawn sketch of the function f and the two sets of approximating rectangles.

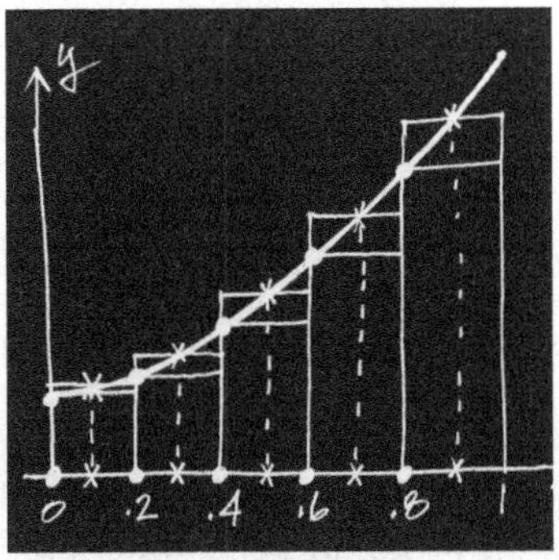

Figure 4.2.15: *Sketch of* $f(x) = 1 + x^2$ *and the 5 left endpoint and midpoint approximating rectangles.*

Example 4.2.10 (Computer Graphics for R_n, L_n, M_n)

Problem: For the function $f(x) = e^{-x}$ on the interval $[0,2]$, compute the right endpoint, left endpoint, and midpoint, regular Riemann sums for $n = 10$. (*Note:* 10 is a small number of rectangles, but a large number makes it hard to distinguish the differences in these three types of approximations.) Use RSplot to display the approximating rectangles of each type in the same figure.

Solution: We automate the procedure just like we did in Example 4.2.6. First, we define the function and the endpoints of the initial interval.

```
> f:=x->exp(-x);
```
$$f := x \mapsto e^{-x}$$
```
> a:=0;b:=2;
```

$$a := 0$$
$$b := 2$$

Next set up an array X to store the partition points and an array M to store the midpoints.

```
> n:=10;X:=array(0..n);M:=array(1..n);
```

$$n := 10$$
$$X := array(0..10), [\ ])$$
$$M := array(0..10), [\ ])$$

Now compute dX, assign a value to X[0], and use a do loop to compute the values of the other partition points .

```
> dX:=evalf((b-a)/n);
```

$$dX := 0.2000000000$$

```
> X[0]:=0;
```

$$X_0 := 0$$

```
> for i from 1 to n do X[i]:=a+i*dX end do:
```

Use another do loop to compute the midpoints of each of the subintervals.

```
> for i from 1 to n do M[i]:=(X[i-1]+X[i])/2 end do:
```

Now we can use Maple's sum command to compute the three types of sums required:

```
> i:=evaln(i);
```

$$i := i$$

```
> R10:=sum(X[i]*dX,i=1..n);
```

$$R10 := 2.200000000$$

```
> L10:=sum(X[i-1]*dX,i=1..n);
```

$$L10 :-\ 1.800000000$$

```
> M10:=sum(M[i]*dX,i=1..n);
```

$$M10 := 2.000000000$$

To interpret the result, we use RSplot three separate times and combine them in one figure.

```
> right:=RSplot(f,0,2,10,1):
> left:=RSplot(f,0,2,10,2):
> mid:=RSplot(f,0,2,10,3):
> with(plots,display);
```

$$[display]$$

```
> display(right,left,mid);
```

Figure 4.2.16 shows the resulting three sets of approximating rectangles: (1) right endpoints (green), (2) left endpoints (yellow), and (3) midpoints (blue). NOTE: The rectangles overlap, so you can only see the tops of the blue and yellow rectangles.

The figure displays three important facts: For *decreasing* functions (1) the right endpoint approximating step-function lies *below* the graph of f, (2) the left endpoint approximating step-function lies *above* the graph of f, and (3) the midpoint approximating step-function lies *between* these other two step-functions. The corresponding Riemann sums satisfy the inequalities

$$R_n \le M_n \le L_n;$$

for all values of n. Furthermore, you can perhaps surmise from the above figure that the midpoint Riemann sum M_{20} will give a better approximation to the area under the graph of f than R_{20} or L_{20}, since each of its rectangles has part that lies above and part that lies below the graph of f, and these parts are approximately equal (in this figure).

You should be able to easily convince yourself that the above result for decreasing functions has an analog for increasing functions: If f is *increasing* on the interval $[a, b]$, then for the regular partition of $[a, b]$ into n subintervals, we have

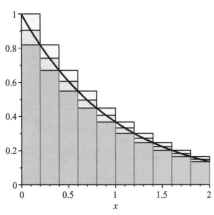

Figure 4.2.16: *Plot of $y = e^{-x}$ and the approximating rectangles for the Riemann sums: (green = right), (yellow = left), and (blue = mid).*

$$L_n \leq M_n \leq R_n,$$

for all n. Furthermore the midpoint, regular Riemann sum M_n, gives the best approximation to the area under the graph of f. CAUTION: If the function f is not monotonic on the interval $[a, b]$, then there is little we can say about the relations of these Riemann sums to each other.

Example 4.2.9 illustrates a good reason for using other types of Riemann sums besides that standard right endpoints Riemann sum. Namely, the midpoint Riemann sum gives a better approximation to the area under the graph than either the right endpoint or left endpoint Riemann sums do.

We can generalize the situation even more by allowing the selection of arbitrary points s_i in the partition's subintervals:

$$s_i \in [x_{i-1}, x_i],$$

$i = 1, 2, \ldots, n$. Then we can use these for the rectangle heights: $f(s_i)$, in the approximating rectangles. The following definition gives the details of this.

General Riemann Sums

Definition 4.2.3 (Riemann Sums for Arbitrary Partition Points)

For a function f on an interval $[a, b]$, for a partition

$$P = \{x_0, x_1, x_2, \ldots, x_n\}$$

of $[a, b]$, and for a selection

$$S = \{s_1, s_2, \ldots, s_n\}$$

of points $s_i \in [x_{i-1}, x_i]$, the corresponding Riemann sum is

$$S_P = \sum_{i=1}^{n} f(s_i)\Delta x_i \qquad (4.2.10)$$

All of these different types of Riemann sums can seem confusing and overwhelming at first. But simply put, each Riemann sum is just a sum of areas of rectangles that serves to approximate the area under the graph of f. All the different types are needed for the theory in the next section.

Exercises: 4.2 (Riemann Sums)

```
> with(code_ch4,RSplot,DRSplot);
                    [RSplot,DRSplot]
```

Right Endpoint Riemann Sums (Given Figure)

In Exercises 1–6, study the given figure to determine the heights and the widths of the n rectangles that approximate the area under the graph. Use this to calculate the regular, right endpoint Riemann sum $R_n = \sum_{i=1}^{n} f(x_i)\Delta x$ to the area under the graph of the function f on the interval $[a, b]$

1. $f(x) = \dfrac{1}{10}(x^3 - 4x + 10), [-1, 3], n = 8$

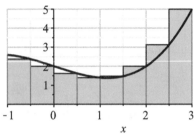

2. $f(x) = 16x^2 - x^4 + 10, [-4, 1], n = 10$

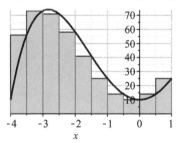

3. $f(x) = \dfrac{1}{2}(4x^2 - x^4 + 5), [-2, 2], n = 10$

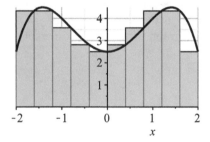

4. $f(x) = x^3 - 2x^2 - 3x + 12, [-2, 3], n = 10$

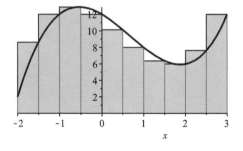

5. $f(x) = (1 + \sin x)^{\cos x}, [1, 5], n = 10$

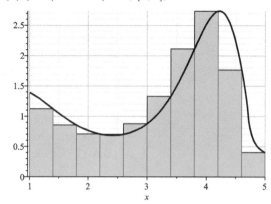

6. $f(x) = (1 + 1/x)^{\cos x}, [1, 5], n = 12$

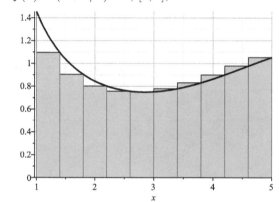

Right Endpoint Riemann Sums (Using RSplot)

CAS: Use RSplot(f,a,b,n,1) to plot the rectangles in the regular, right endpoint Riemann sum approximation to the area under the graph of the function f on the interval $[a, b]$. From the resulting picture, calculate (approximately) the value of the Riemann sum $R_n = \sum_{i=1}^{n} f(x_i)\Delta x$. Then use the command RS(f,a,b,n,1) to have Maple compute a more accurate approximation.

7. $f(x) = e^{-x}\cos(2\pi x) + 2, [0, 1], n = 10$

8. $f(x) = e^{-x}\sin(2\pi x) + 2, [0, 1], n = 10$

9. $f(x) = x^{\sin x}, [1, 5], n = 10$

10. $f(x) = x^{\cos x}, [1, 5], n = 10$

11. $f(x) = (1 + 1/x)^x, [0, 10], n = 10$

12. $f(x) = (1 + 3/x)^x, [0, 10], n = 10$

13. $f(x) = (1 + 1/x)^{\sin x}, [1, 10], n = 10$

14. $f(x) = (1 + 1/x)^{\cos x}, [1, 10], n = 10$

Right Endpoint Riemann Sums (By-Hand Calculations & Sketches)

In Exercises 15–40 calculate, by hand (or calculator), the

regular, right endpoint Riemann sum approximation

$$R_n = \sum_{i=1}^{n} f(x_i)\Delta x$$

to the area under the graph of the function f on the interval $[a, b]$ for the specified values of n. Also sketch, by hand, the graph of the function and the approximating rectangles.

15. $f(x) = 4 - x^2$, $[-2, 2]$, $n = 8$

16. $f(x) = 9 - x^2$, $[-3, 3]$, $n = 12$

17. $f(x) = 4x - x^2$, $[0, 4]$, $n = 8$

18. $f(x) = 5x - x^2$, $[0, 5]$, $n = 10$

19. $f(x) = 5 + 4x - x^2$, $[0, 5]$, $n = 10$

20. $f(x) = 4 + 3x - x^2$, $[0, 4]$, $n = 10$

21. $f(x) = \sqrt{x}$, $[0, 4]$, $n = 8$

22. $f(x) = \sqrt{x + 4}$, $[-4, 0]$, $n = 8$

23. $f(x) = \sqrt{16 - x^2}$, $[0, 4]$, $n = 8$

24. $f(x) = \sqrt{25 - x^2}$, $[0, 5]$, $n = 10$

25. $f(x) = 20 - 10x^3$, $[-1, 1]$, $n = 8$

26. $f(x) = 40x - 10x^3$, $[0, 2]$, $n = 8$

27. $f(x) = 5 + 4x - x^2$, $[-1, 4]$, $n = 10$

28. $f(x) = 3 - 2x - x^2$, $[-3, 1]$, $n = 10$

29. $f(x) = 2^x$, $[0, 1]$, $n = 8$

30. $f(x) = 3^x$, $[0, 1]$, $n = 8$

31. $f(x) = e^x$, $[1, 2]$, $n = 8$

32. $f(x) = e^x$, $[2, 3]$, $n = 8$

33. $f(x) = e^{-x}$, $[0, 1]$, $n = 8$

34. $f(x) = e^{-x}$, $[0, 2]$, $n = 8$

35. $f(x) = 2^{-x}$, $[0, 1]$, $n = 8$

36. $f(x) = 2^{-x}$, $[0, 2]$, $n = 8$

37. $f(x) = 8 - e^x$, $[0, 2]$, $n = 8$

38. $f(x) = 10 - e^x$, $[0, 2]$, $n = 8$

39. $f(x) = \sin \pi x$, $[0, 1]$, $n = 10$

40. $f(x) = \cos(\pi x/2)$, $[-1, 1]$, $n = 10$

Right Endpoint Riemann Sums (General Calculations)

In Exercises 41–54, compute, by hand and for a general n, the regular, right endpoint Riemann sum approximation

$$R_n = \sum_{i=1}^{n} f(x_i)\Delta x$$

to the area under the graph of the function f on the interval $[a, b]$. Simplify using the summation formulas from Section 4.1. ALSO, if you worked one of the exercises

above that involved the function here, use the formula you get here for R_n to check and compare with the result you got there.

41. $f(x) = 1 + x^2$, $[0, 2]$ 42. $f(x) = 1 - x^2$, $[0, 1]$

43. $f(x) = 20 - 10x^3$, $[-1, 1]$

44. $f(x) = 40x - 10x^3$, $[0, 2]$

45. $f(x) = 5 + 4x - x^2$, $[-1, 4]$

46. $f(x) = 3 - 2x - x^2$, $[-3, 1]$

47. $f(x) = 2^x$, $[0, 1]$ 48. $f(x) = 3^x$, $[0, 1]$

49. $f(x) = e^x$, $[1, 2]$ 50. $f(x) = e^x$, $[2, 3]$

51. $f(x) = e^{-x}$, $[0, 1]$ 52. $f(x) = e^{-x}$, $[0, 2]$

53. $f(x) = 2^{-x}$, $[0, 1]$ 54. $f(x) = 2^{-x}$, $[0, 2]$

Right-Left-Mid Riemann Sums (Using RSplot to Create the Figure)

CAS: Use RSplot(f,a,b,n,k) to plot the rectangles in the regular, right endpoint ($k = 1$), left endpoint ($k = 2$), and midpoint ($k = 3$) Riemann sum approximations to the area under the graph of the function f on the interval $[a, b]$. From the resulting picture, calculate (approximately) the value of the three Riemann sums:

$$R_n = \sum_{i=1}^{n} f(x_i)\Delta x, \qquad L_n = \sum_{i=1}^{n} f(x_{i-1})\Delta x,$$

$$M_n = \sum_{i=1}^{n} f\left(\frac{x_i + x_{i-1}}{2}\right)\Delta x.$$

Then use the command RS(f,a,b,n,k) to have Maple compute a more accurate approximations.

55. $f(x) = e^{-x}\cos(2\pi x) + 2$, $[0, 1]$, $n = 10$

56. $f(x) = e^{-x}\sin(2\pi x) + 2$, $[0, 1]$, $n = 10$

57. $f(x) = x^{\sin x}$, $[1, 5]$, $n = 10$

58. $f(x) = x^{\cos x}$, $[1, 5]$, $n = 10$

Right-Left-Mid Endpoint Riemann Sums (Calculating and Sketching By-Hand)

Calculate, by hand, the regular, right endpoint, left endpoint, and midpoint Riemann sum approximations to the area under the graph of the function f on the interval $[a, b]$. for the specified value of n. Also sketch, by hand, the graph of the function and the approximating rectangles for each of the three approximations. NOTE: You may use your work from Exercises 15–40, if you worked those problems.

59. $f(x) = \sqrt{x}$, $[0, 4]$, $n = 8$

60. $f(x) = \sqrt{16 - x^2}$, $[0, 4]$, $n = 8$

61. $f(x) = 20 - 10x^3$, $[-1, 1]$, $n = 8$

62. $f(x) = 40x - 10x^3$, $[0, 2]$, $n = 8$

63. $f(x) = 5 + 4x - x^2$, $[-1, 4]$, $n = 10$

64. $f(x) = 3 - 2x - x^2$, $[-3, 1]$, $n = 10$

Calculus Concepts & Computation

4.3 Definite Integrals

```
> with(code_ch4sec2);
```

$$[RSplot, DRSplot, integral]$$

In this section we solve the special case of the area problem posed in Section 4.2. This problem is to find the area A of the region D *"below the graph of a function f"* on an interval $[a, b]$. Technically D is the region bounded by the curves:

$$y = f(x), y = 0, x = a, x = b,$$

where $0 \leq f(x)$ for all x in $[a, b]$. See Figure 4.3.1. The graph of the curve $y = f(x)$ is the graph of f, while the graph of $y = 0$ is the x-axis. The graphs of $x = a$, $x = b$ are the vertical lines through a and b on the x-axis.

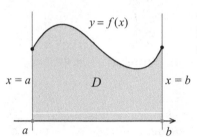

Figure 4.3.1: *The Region D beneath the graph of f.*

In the last section we introduced the concept of a *general* Riemann sum

$$S_P = \sum_{i=1}^{n} f(s_i) \Delta x_i \approx A$$

as an approximation to the area A of the region D. Here $P = \{x_0, x_1, ..., x_n\}$ is partition of $[a, b]$ and $S = \{s_1, s_2, ..., s_n\}$ is a selection of points from each subinterval, $s_i \in [x_{i-1}, x_i]$, for each i. In Example 4.2.7 we indicated that the area A of the region under the graph of $f(x) = 10x - x^2$ on the interval $[1, 8]$ could be found by taking the limit of the right endpoint Riemann sums R_n with regular partitions P. That is,

$$A = \lim_{n \to \infty} R_n = \lim_{n \to \infty} \sum_{i=1}^{n} f(x_i) \Delta x.$$

Here the function $f(x) = 10x - x^2$ is a continuous function and the theory will tell us that the area under the graph of a *continuous* function can *always* be calculated by taking the limits of right endpoint, regular Riemann sums. But what about for non-continuous functions? And what do we take as the definition of the "area" under the graph of a function on an interval? These questions lead us to the notion of the definite integral of f over the interval $[a, b]$.

The Definite Integral

To answer the questions raised above, we need to consider the concept of limits of *general* Riemann sums:

$$\lim_{|P| \to 0} S_P = \lim_{|P| \to 0} \sum_{i=1}^{n} f(s_i) \Delta x_i.$$

Here $|P|$ is the *norm* of the partition $P = \{x_0, x_1, x_2, \ldots, x_n\}$. The norm is defined as the *maximum* of all the lengths of the subintervals determined by the partition. That is,

$$|P| = \max \{\Delta x_1, \Delta x_2, \ldots, \Delta x_n\}.$$

When $|P|$ is small, say $|P| < \delta$, then all the lengths Δx_i of the bases of the rectangles in the Riemann sum are small, $\Delta x_i < \delta$. So, the limiting process indicated above is one where the norm of the partition tends to zero and thus all the lengths Δx_i tend to zero. The other aspects of what we mean by the limit of Riemann sums, as well as the new concept of the definite integral, are given in the following definition.

Definition 4.3.1 (The Definite Integral)

Suppose f is a function on an interval $[a,b]$. We say the limit of Riemann sums for f on $[a,b]$ exists and is the number I:

$$I = \lim_{|P| \to 0} \sum_{i=1}^{n} f(s_i)\Delta x_i$$

if for every $\varepsilon > 0$ there is a $\delta > 0$ such that

$$\left| I - \sum_{i=1}^{n} f(s_i)\Delta x_i \right| < \varepsilon$$

for every partition $P = \{x_0, x_1, x_2, \ldots, x_n\}$ with $|P| < \delta$ and every selection $S = \{s_1, s_2, \ldots, s_n\}$ with s_i in $[x_{i-1}, x_i]$. When the limit exists, we say that f is integrable on $[a, b]$ and the number I is called the definite integral of f from a to b.

The above definition is rather abstract (especially if you did not study the formal ε-δ definition of the limit concept in Section 1.9). Intuitively the definition says that we can make all the Riemann sums $S_P = \sum_{i=1}^{n} f(s_i)\Delta x_i$ close to I (within ε of I) if we take the norm of the partition small enough (less that δ) and this closeness holds regardless of the selection of points $S = \{s_1, s_2, \ldots, s_n\}$ used. The number I, which is called the *definite integral* of f from a to b, has a special notation:

Notation for Definite Integrals

If the function f is integrable on the interval $[a,b]$, then its definite integral I is denoted by

$$I = \int_a^b f(x)\,dx = \lim_{|P| \to 0} \sum_{i=1}^{n} f(s_i)\Delta x_i$$

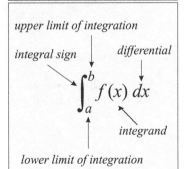

The Definite Integral

upper limit of integration

integral sign   differential

$$\int_a^b f(x)\ dx$$

integrand

lower limit of integration

The notation $\int_a^b f(x)\,dx$ for the definite integral was introduced by Leibniz to stand for the process of integrating (*making whole* in Latin) all the rectangles in the Riemann sums as their bases get infinitesimally small: $\Delta x_i \to dx \approx 0$ In the limiting process, the finite sum $\sum_{i=1}^{n}$ of rectangular areas $f(s_i)\Delta x_i$ turns into a "continuous sum" $\int_a^b$ of infinitesimal areas: $f(x)dx$, one for each x in $[a, b]$. The various elements in the notation for the definite integral are displayed in the margin box.

The notation is designed to indicate all the aspects involved in this complicated number that is the limit of Riemann sums. For instance, in Examples 4.2.4–4.2.7 we developed the motivation for defining the area A of the region under the graph of $f(x) = 10x - x^2$ on the interval $[1, 8]$ by limits. In particular, it was suggested that A is given by the limit of right endpoint Riemann sums and that this area is $\frac{434}{3}$, With the new definite integral notation we can write this as

$$A = \int_1^8 \left(10x - x^2 \right) dx = \frac{434}{3}.$$

Here 1 is the *lower limit* of integration and 8 is the *upper limit*. The *integrand* is the function $10x - x^2$. The *definite integral* is the number $\frac{434}{3}$.

NOTE/CAUTION: In Section 3.7 we used the integral sign $\int$ to denote the process of taking antiderivatives and the process was called indefinite integration. The result of indefinite integration is a *function* (an antiderivative of the integrand). On the otherhand, the result of definite integration is a *number*. For example,

$$\int \left(10x - x^2\right) dx = 5x^2 - \frac{1}{3}x^3 + C \qquad (\textit{Indefinite Integral})$$

and

$$\int_1^8 \left(10x - x^2\right) dx = \frac{434}{3} \qquad (\textit{Definite Integral})$$

In the next section we shall see that the concepts of indefinite and definite integrals are related to each other by what is known as the Fundamental Theorem of Calculus. Hence, the use of the integral sign $\int$ in each should make sense.

When the integrand $f(x)$ is a continuous function on the interval $[a, b]$, then not only is f integrable on $[a, b]$, but its definite integral can be computed by using right endpoint Riemann sums rather than by using general Riemann sums.

Theorem 4.3.1 (Definite Integrals of Continuous Functions)

Suppose f is a continuous function on the interval [a,b]. *Then f is integrable on* [a, b] *and*

its definite integral is the limit of right endpoint, regular partition, Riemann sums:

$$\int_a^b f(x)dx = \lim_{n \to \infty} \sum_{i=1}^n f(x_i)\Delta x$$

A more general theorem can be stated: A continuous function f on $[a, b]$ is integrable and its definite integral $\int_a^b f(x)\,dx$ can be computed by taking limits of right endpoint, left endpoint, or midpoint, regular partition, Riemann sums:

$$
\begin{aligned}
\int_a^b f(x)\,dx &= \lim_{n \to \infty} \sum_{i=1}^n f(x_i)\,\Delta x & (\textit{right endpoint}) \\
&= \lim_{n \to \infty} \sum_{i=1}^n f(x_{i-1})\,\Delta x & (\textit{left endpoint}) \\
&= \lim_{n \to \infty} \sum_{i=1}^n f\left(\frac{x_{i-1} + x_i}{2}\right)\Delta x. & (\textit{midpoint})
\end{aligned}
$$

In practice you will find that the computations are usually simplest using right endpoint Riemann sums.

Example 4.3.1

Problem: Compute the definite integral $\displaystyle\int_1^4 \left(1 + x^2\right) dx$ using Riemann sums.

Solution: Since the integrand, $f(x) = 1 + x^2$, is a continuous function, we can take limits of right endpoint Riemann sums to get the result. In this example the interval $[a, b]$ is $[1, 4]$, so $a = 1$, $b = 4$ and

$$
\begin{aligned}
\Delta x &= \frac{b - a}{n} = \frac{4 - 1}{n} = \frac{3}{n} \\
x_i &= a + i\Delta x = 1 + \frac{3i}{n} \\
f(x_i) &= 1 + (x_i)^2 = 1 + \left(1 + \frac{3i}{n}\right)^2 = 2 + \frac{6i}{n} + \frac{9i^2}{n^2}.
\end{aligned}
$$

Thus,

$$R_n = \sum_{i=1}^n f(x_i)\,\Delta x = \sum_{i=1}^n \left(2 + \frac{6i}{n} + \frac{9i^2}{n^2}\right)\frac{3}{n} = \frac{6}{n}\sum_{i=1}^n 1 + \frac{18}{n^2}\sum_{i=1}^n i + \frac{27}{n^2}\sum_{i=1}^n i^2$$

$$= \frac{6}{n}(n) + \frac{18}{n^2}\left(\frac{n(n+1)}{2}\right) + \frac{27}{n^3}\left(\frac{n(n+1)(2n+1)}{6}\right).$$

We now have to take limits of this as $n \to \infty$. The first term in the expression reduces to 6. The other terms reduce as well:

$$\lim_{n\to\infty} \frac{18}{n^2}\left(\frac{n(n+1)}{2}\right) = 18 \cdot \lim_{n\to\infty} \frac{n+1}{2n} = 18 \cdot \lim_{n\to\infty} \frac{1}{2}\left(1 + \frac{1}{n}\right) = 18 \cdot \frac{1}{2} = 9,$$

and

$$\lim_{n\to\infty} \frac{27}{n^3}\left(\frac{n(n+1)(2n+1)}{6}\right) = 27 \lim_{n\to\infty} \frac{1}{6}\left(1 + \frac{1}{n}\right)\left(2 + \frac{1}{n}\right) = 27 \cdot \frac{2}{6} = 9$$

Thus, we find

$$\int_1^4 \left(1 + x^2\right) dx = \lim_{n\to\infty} R_n$$

$$= \lim_{n\to\infty}\left[\frac{6}{n}(n) + \frac{18}{n^2}\left(\frac{n(n+1)}{2}\right) + \frac{27}{n^3}\left(\frac{n(n+1)(2n+1)}{6}\right)\right]$$

$$= 6 + 9 + 9 = 24$$

It is important to note in the last example that there are some common limits that often occur in taking limits of right endpoint Riemann sums. You can readily check (see the exercises) the validity of the limits shown in the margin box.

Some Special Limits

$$\lim_{x\to\infty} \frac{1}{n^2}\left(\frac{n(n+1)}{2}\right) = \frac{1}{2}$$

$$\lim_{x\to\infty} \frac{1}{n^3}\left(\frac{n(n+1)(2n+1)}{6}\right) = \frac{1}{3}$$

$$\lim_{x\to\infty} \frac{1}{n^4}\left(\frac{n(n+1)}{2}\right)^2 = \frac{1}{4}$$

Box 4.3.1: *Some limits that occur in limits of Riemann sums.*

Example 4.3.2

Problem: Compute the definite integral $\int_0^2 \left(1 - 2x + x^3\right) dx$ using right endpoint Riemann sums.

Solution: Here $a = 0, b = 2$, and so

$$\Delta x = \frac{b-a}{n} = \frac{2-0}{n} = \frac{2}{n}$$

$$x_i = a + i\Delta x = 0 + \frac{2i}{n} = \frac{2i}{n}$$

$$f(x_i) = 1 - 2 \cdot \frac{2i}{n} + \left(\frac{2i}{n}\right)^3 = 1 - \frac{4i}{n} + \frac{8i^3}{n^3}$$

Then

$$R_n = \sum_{i=1}^{n} f(x_i)\,\Delta x = \sum_{i=1}^{n}\left(1 - \frac{4i}{n} + \frac{8i^3}{n^3}\right)\frac{2}{n}$$

$$= \frac{2}{n}\sum_{i=1}^{n} 1 - \frac{8}{n^2}\sum_{i=1}^{n} i + \frac{16}{n^4}\sum_{i=1}^{n} i^3$$

$$= \frac{2}{n} \cdot n - \frac{8}{n^2} \cdot \frac{n(n+1)}{2} + \frac{16}{n^4} \cdot \left[\frac{n(n+1)}{2}\right]^2.$$

Using the special limits from Box 4.3.1 above, we find that

$$\int_0^1 \left(2 - x + x^3\right) dx = \lim_{n\to\infty} R_n = 2 - 8 \cdot \frac{1}{2} + 16 \cdot \frac{1}{4} = 2$$

Example 4.3.3

Problem: Compute the definite integral $\int_0^1 e^x\,dx$ using right endpoint Riemann sums.

Solution: In Example 4.2.8 from the last section we found that

$$R_n = \frac{e^{1/n}}{n\left(e^{1/n} - 1\right)} \cdot (e - 1)$$

Now it is easy to see that

$$\lim_{n \to \infty} e^{1/n} = e^{\lim_{n \to \infty}(1/n)} = e^0 = 1$$

Also one can, using L' hospital's rule, show that

$$\lim_{n \to \infty} n\left(e^{1/n} - 1\right) = 1$$

One can also prove the more general case of this limit, which is shown in the margin Box 4.3.2. See the exercises. Based on these limit calculations we conclude that

$$\int_0^1 e^x\, dx = \lim_{n \to \infty} \frac{e^{1/n}}{n\left(e^{1/n} - 1\right)} \cdot (e - 1) = e - 1$$

Another Special Limit

For any positive number a

$$\lim_{x \to \infty} n\left(a^{1/n} - 1\right) = \ln a$$

Box 4.3.2: *A special limit that occurs in limits of Riemann sums.*

Properties of the Definite Integral

There are a number of properties of the definite integral which are useful to know, both for simplifying computations and for theoretical discussions. Some of these properties are stated in the following theorem, which we do not prove. The proof, as would be expected, follows from properties of Riemann sums and properties of limits.

Theorem 4.3.2 (Properties of Definite Integrals)

Suppose f and g are integrable functions on the interval [a,b] and k is any constant.

Then f + g and k f are integrable functions on [a,b] and

$$(1) \quad \int_a^b \big(f(x) + g(x)\big)dx = \int_a^b f(x)dx + \int_a^b g(x)dx$$

$$(2) \quad \int_a^b k\, f(x)dx = k\int_a^b f(x)dx$$

Furthermore if c is any number between a and b then

$$(3) \quad \int_a^b f(x)dx = \int_a^c f(x)dx + \int_c^b f(x)dx$$

Property (3) is the Additive Property for area (at least for areas of regions of this special type). It says that if, for an integrable function f on an interval $[a, b]$, we split the region D under the graph into two subregions D_1, D_2 by means of a vertical line, then the area A of D is the sum of the areas A_1, A_2 of the subregions

$$A = A_1 + A_2.$$

In the definite integral notation this says

$$\int_a^b f(x)\, dx = \int_a^c f(x)\, dx + \int_c^b f(x)\, dx.$$

See Figure 4.3.2.

There are two additional aspects of the definite integral which should be noted. These are displayed in margin Box 4.3.2. Property (4) in the box is more or less a

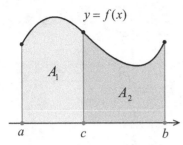

Figure 4.3.2: *Illustration of the additive property of the definite integral.*

$$\int_a^a f(x)dx = 0 \qquad (4)$$

$$\int_b^a f(x)dx = -\int_a^b f(x)dx \qquad (5)$$

Box 4.3.3

definition. In the development of the definite integral it is tacitly assumed that the interval $[a,b]$ has $a < b$. When $a = b$, then of course there is no interval to partition, or otherwise said, all partition points are the same and so all the differences are zero: $\Delta x_i = 0$ and consequently every Riemann sum is zero.

Property (5) in the box is a definition which is necessary for the change of variables formula (substitution method) to hold. See Section 4.5.

Area and Net Area

The definition of the definite integral $\int_a^b f(x)\, dx$ was motivated by the case when f is nonnegative on the interval $[a, b]$, i.e., $f(x) \geq 0$ for all x in $[a, b]$) In this case the number $\int_a^b f(x)\, dx$ gives the "area under the graph of f on the interval $[a, b]$." There are two things to note here:

(1) The definition of the definite integral applies in general to all functions, regardless of whether they are nonnegative or not.

(2) The definition of the definite integral gives meaning to, and indeed defines, what we mean by "area under the graph of f on the interval $[a, b]$."

Definition 4.3.2 (Area and Net Area)

Suppose f is an integrable function on an interval $[a, b]$. Let D be the region bounded by the curves $y = f(x)$, $y = 0$, $x = a$, and $x = b$.

(1) *If $f(x) \geq 0$ on $[a, b]$, then the area A of D is:* $A = \int_a^b f(x)dx$

(2) *If $f(x) \leq 0$ on $[a, b]$, then the area A of D is:* $A = -\int_a^b f(x)dx$

(3) *If f has both positive and negative values on $[a, b]$, then:* $A_{net} = \int_a^b f(x)dx$

is the net area of the region D.

The motivation for Part (2) of the definition comes from Figure 4.3.3. When $f(x) \leq 0$ for x in $[a, b]$, then the graph of f lies below the x-axis as shown. Also shown is a right endpoint Riemann sum which approximates the area of the region D. However, note that in the Riemann sum

$$R_n = \sum_{i=1}^n f(x_i)\, \Delta x,$$

each $f(x_i)$ is negative. So $f(x_i)\Delta x$ is *not* the area of the ith rectangle, but rather the area is $-f(x_i)\, \Delta x$. Thus, the approximation to the *area* of D is

$$\sum_{i=1}^n -f(x_i)\, \Delta x = -\sum_{i=1}^n f(x_i)\, \Delta x = -R_n.$$

Hence, the area of D should be

$$A = \lim_{n \to \infty} -R_n = -\int_a^b f(x)\, dx.$$

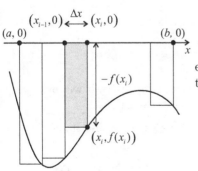

Figure 4.3.3: *The Riemann sum approximations are negative when f is nonpositive on $[a, b]$*

The interpretation of Part (3) of Definition 4.3.2 now follows from Parts (1) and (2). Figure 4.3.4 below shows the graph of a function that is both positive and negative on an interval $[a, b]$.

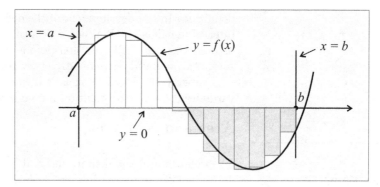

Figure 4.3.4: *The Riemann sum approximations can be both positive and negative for a general function f on $[a, b]$.*

A particular right endpoint Riemann sum is shown. The terms in the sum corresponding to the yellow rectangles are positive, while those terms corresponding to the blue rectangles are negative. Thus, in this particular example, it seems that the total Riemann sum shown in the figure should be approximately zero (or perhaps a small negative number, since the blue area seems slightly larger than the yellow area):

$$\sum_{i=1}^{n} f(x_i)\, \Delta x \approx 0$$

In the limit, for this example, you see that the area A_1 of the region under the graph and above the x-axis is approximately equal to the area A_2 below the x-axis and above the graph. Hence, in this case,

$$\int_a^b f(x)\, dx = A_1 - A_2 \approx 0$$

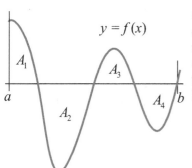

Figure 4.3.5: *A graph of a function*

Generally the value of the definite integral could be any number—positive, negative, or zero. It is positive (negative) when there is more area enclosed above (below) the x-axis than below (above) it. The definite integral is zero when the area enclosed above the x-axis is exactly equal to the area below it. As another example, consider the graph shown in Figure 4.3.5. In the figure the areas of the regions above and below the x-axis labeled as shown. Then the definite integral can be expressed as

$$\int_a^b f(x)\, dx = A_1 - A_2 + A_3 - A_4.$$

From the graph shown in Figure 4.3.5, one would estimate that the value of the definite integral is negative.

Pedagogical Remarks

For the applications of the definite integral, as in measuring areas, it will help your understanding to geometrically view $A = \int_a^b f(x)\, dx$ either as

(1) the limit of sums of areas of approximating rectangles (Riemann sums),

$$\Delta A_i = f(x_i)\, \Delta x \quad \text{and} \quad A = \lim_{n \to \infty} \sum_{i=1}^{n} \Delta A_i = \lim_{n \to \infty} \sum_{i=1}^{n} f(x_i)\, \Delta x$$

or as

(2) the continuous sum of areas of infinitesimal rectangles.

$$dA = f(x)dx \quad \text{and} \quad A = \int dA = \int_a^b f(x)\, dx.$$

For the geometry in (1) we have been using the command `DRSplot(f,a,b,N)` to illustrate the discrete sum $\sum_{i=1}^{n} A_i$ of finitely many discrete areas A_i. The first frame of the movie shows A_1, the second frame $A_1 + A_2$, and so on, down to the last frame showing

$$A_1 + A_2 + \cdots + A_n = \sum_{i=1}^{n} A_i.$$

For example, consider the function

$$f(x) = 2 - 2x + x^3$$

on the interval $[0, 1.5]$. The approximating, right endpoint, regular Riemann sum using 40 rectangles is

$$R_n = \sum_{i=1}^{40} f(x_i)\, \Delta x.$$

A movie showing the 40 approximating rectangles accumulating under the graph is created by the following code. Figure 4.3.6 shows the 25th frame in the movie.

```
> f:=x->2-2*x+x^3;
```
$$f := x \mapsto 2 - 2x + x^3$$

```
> DRSplot(f,0,1.5,40);
```

Similarly, we can use the command `integral(f,a,b,N)` to illustrate the continuous sum $\int_a^b dA$ of infinitely many infinitesimal areas dA. The first frame in the movie shows $dA = f(x)dx$, the first infinitesimal area. (Technically, we cannot see an infinitesimal area, so the first frame is $f(a)\,\Delta x$, with Δx a line thickness of 3 in Maple.) The ensuing frames in the movie show the area (or net area) accumulating as $dA = f(x)dx$, represented by a bright yellow vertical line segment, moves from left-to-right. For example

```
> integral(f,0,1.5,40);
```

creates a movie with 40 frames showing the area $A = \int_0^{1.5} (2 - 2x + x^3)\, dx$ being swept out as x moves from 0 to 1.5. The 25th frame in this movie is shown in Figure 4.3.7.

```
> integral(f,0,1.5,40,25,fig);
```

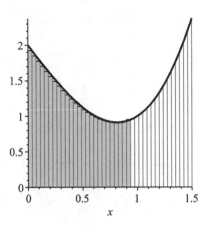

Figure 4.3.6: *The 25th frame in* `DRSplot(f,0,1.5,40)` *showing rectangles in the approximating sum* $\sum_{i=1}^{25} A_i$.

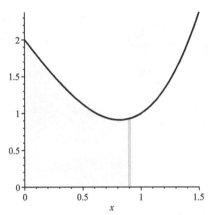

Figure 4.3.7: *The 25th frame in the movie* `integral(f,0,1.5,40)`.

Exercises: 4.3 (Definite Integrals)

Computing Definite Integrals Using the Limit Definition

In Exercises 1–16, compute the definite integral using the limit definition. NOTE: Each integrand is continuous on the given interval, so you can use limits of right endpoint sums

$$\int_a^b f(x)\,dx = \lim_{n\to\infty} R_n = \lim_{n\to\infty} \sum_{i=1}^n f(x_i)\Delta x$$

You may use the special limits in Boxes 4.3.1–4.3.2.

1. $\int_0^2 (x^2 - 1)\,dx$

2. $\int_0^2 (x^3 - 1)\,dx$

3. $\int_0^3 (4x - x^3)\,dx$

4. $\int_0^2 (x^2 - x^3)\,dx$

5. $\int_{-1}^3 (x^2 - 2x)\,dx$

6. $\int_{-1}^1 (x^2 + 2x)\,dx$

7. $\int_{-1}^2 (2x^2 - x^3)\,dx$

8. $\int_{-2}^2 (x^3 + x^2 - 2x)\,dx$

9. $\int_0^1 2^x\,dx$

10. $\int_0^1 3^x\,dx$

11. $\int_1^2 e^x\,dx$

12. $\int_1^2 2^x\,dx$

13. $\int_0^1 e^{-x}\,dx$

14. $\int_0^1 2^{-x}\,dx$

15. $\int_1^2 e^{-x}\,dx$

16. $\int_1^2 2^{-x}\,dx$

Computing Definite Integrals Using Graphs and Known Areas

In Exercises 17–32, compute the definite integral by (a) graphing the integrand, (b) using known area formulas for geometric shapes, such as circles, rectangles, trapezoids, and (c) using the additive property for areas and integrals (See Formula (3) in Theorem 4.3.2). DO NOT use the limit definition of the definite integral as you did in Exercises 1–16.

17. $\int_0^1 (1 + x)\,dx$

18. $\int_0^1 (1 - x)\,dx$

19. $\int_{-1}^2 |x|\,dx$

20. $\int_{-2}^1 |x|\,dx$

21. $\int_0^3 (x - 1)\,dx$

22. $\int_0^4 (x - 2)\,dx$

23. $\int_{-1}^2 f(x)\,dx$, where $f(x) = \begin{cases} 2 + 2x & x < 0 \\ 1 - x & x \geq 0 \end{cases}$

24. $\int_{-2}^1 f(x)\,dx$, where $f(x) = \begin{cases} 1 + x & x < 0 \\ 2 - x & x \geq 0 \end{cases}$

25. $\int_{-2}^2 \sqrt{4 - x^2}\,dx$

26. $\int_{-3}^3 \sqrt{9 - x^2}\,dx$

27. $\int_{-1}^3 f(x)\,dx$, $f(x) = \begin{cases} -\sqrt{4 - x^2} & -2 \leq x < 0 \\ x - 2 & x > 0 \end{cases}$

28. $\int_{-3}^4 f(x)\,dx$, $f(x) = \begin{cases} -\sqrt{9 - x^2} & -3 \leq x < 0 \\ x - 3 & x > 0 \end{cases}$

29. $\int_0^3 f(x)\,dx$, $f(x) = \begin{cases} 1 + x & 0 \leq x < 1 \\ 3 - x & x > 1 \end{cases}$

30. $\int_0^3 f(x)\,dx$, $f(x) = \begin{cases} 2 - x & 0 \leq x < 1 \\ x & x > 1 \end{cases}$

31. $\int_0^2 f(x)\,dx$, $f(x) = \begin{cases} 1 + \sqrt{1 - x^2} & 0 \leq x < 1 \\ x & x > 1 \end{cases}$

32. $\int_0^2 f(x)\,dx$, $f(x) = \begin{cases} 2 + \sqrt{4 - x^2} & 0 \leq x < 2 \\ x & x \geq 2 \end{cases}$

33. Prove that the limits in Boxes 4.3.1–4.3.2 are correct.

34. Use the limit definition of the definite integral and the special limits in Box 4.3.1 to derive the following results:

(a) $\int_0^1 x\,dx = \dfrac{1}{2}$ (b) $\int_0^1 x^2\,dx = \dfrac{1}{3}$ (c) $\int_0^1 x^3\,dx = \dfrac{1}{4}$

Computing Definite Integrals Using Properties of the Integral

In Exercises 35–40, use the results in Exercise 34 and the properties of integrals from Theorem 4.3.2 to compute the integrals:

35. $\int_0^1 4(x - x^2)\,dx$

36. $\int_0^1 (2x - 5x^2)\,dx$

37. $\int_0^1 (x^2 - 1)\,dx$

38. $\int_0^1 (x^2 - 4)\,dx$

39. $\int_0^1 (4x - x^3)\,dx$

40. $\int_0^1 (2x^3 - x)\,dx$

In Exercises 41–48 sketch the graph of the integrand. Then use the results of the corresponding problems above (Exercises 1–16, 35–40, Example 4.3.3) and the additive property of integrals to compute the integral.

41. $\int_1^2 (x^2 - 1)\,dx$

42. $\int_1^2 (x^3 - 1)\,dx$

43. $\int_1^3 (4x - x^3)\,dx$

44. $\int_1^2 (x^2 - x^3)\,dx$

45. $\int_0^2 e^x\,dx$

46. $\int_0^2 2^x\,dx$

47. $\int_0^2 e^{-x}\,dx$

48. $\int_0^2 2^{-x}\,dx$

Calculus *Concepts & Computation*

4.4 The Fundamental Theorem of Calculus

In this section we present a theorem which greatly simplifies the computation of definite integrals. Rather than using a limit of Riemann sums to calculate $\int_a^b f(x)\,dx$, we can, according to this theorem, use an indefinite integral $\int f(x)\,dx$. Thus, this theorem will establish the connection between the $\int_a^b$ and $\int$ notations, i.e., the connection between the definite and indefinite integrals.

Because of its importance, this theorem is called the *Fundamental Theorem of Calculus*. The theorem actually has two parts and, while the second part is the most useful, we begin with the first part which can be used to motivate and prove the second part. As a matter of notation, we use FTC as an abbreviation for "Fundamental Theorem of Calculus."

The Net Area Function (FTC Part 1)

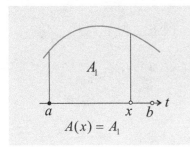

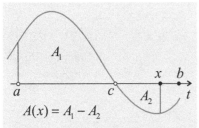

Figure 4.4.1

The notion of net area under the graph of a function f on an interval $[a, b]$ was introduced in the last section. From this concept we can construct a new function called the *net area function*. For this suppose then that f is a continuous function on an interval $[a, b]$. For x in $[a, b]$, define $A(x)$ as the value of the definite integral of f from a to x:

$$A(x) \equiv \int_a^x f(t)\,dt. \qquad (4.4.1)$$

Note that the notation employs the symbol t for the dummy variable of integration in the integrand. This is because we want to use x as the independent variable for the function A and it is suppose to occur as the upper limit of integration in Formula (4.4.1) above. The Figure 4.4.1 shows the situation graphically.

The function f shown in the top part of the figure is nonnegative on the interval $[a, b]$ and so you can see two things: (1) $A(x)$ is the area under the graph from a to x and (2) $A(x)$ increases as x increases. On the otherhand, the function f shown bottom part of the figure is nonnegative until it crosses the x-axis at c, after which it is negative. Thus, $A(x)$ increases until x gets to c, after which it begins to decrease as negative amounts of area are added to $\int_a^c f(x)\,dx$. That is,

$$A(x) = \int_a^x f(t)\,dt = \int_a^c f(t)\,dt + \int_c^x f(t)\,dt,$$

where $\int_c^x f(t)\,dt < 0$.

It is also important to note that the net area function is zero at $x = a$, i.e.,

$$A(a) = \int_a^a f(t)\,dt = 0$$

Example 4.4.1 (A Net Area Function)

Problem: Compute the net area function for $f(x) = 1 - x^3$ on the interval $[0, 2]$. Also, graph A and f on this interval.

Solution: Suppose x is in $[0, 2]$ We have to compute the definite integral

$$A(x) \equiv \int_0^x \left(1 - t^3\right) dt \qquad (4.4.2)$$

This will be easier once we have the FTC Part 2, but for now we must resort to limits of Riemann sums. Even though x is not a definite number, we can still employ the same routine for computing the right endpoint, regular Riemann sum on the interval $[0, x]$. We use the previous notation with t instead of x:

$$\Delta t = \frac{b-a}{n} = \frac{x-0}{n} = \frac{x}{n}$$

$$t_i = a + i\Delta t = \frac{ix}{n} = \frac{xi}{n}$$

$$f(t_i) = 1 - \frac{(xi)^3}{n^3} = 1 - \frac{x^3 i^3}{n^3}$$

Thus,

$$R_n = \sum_{i=1}^{n}\left(1 - \frac{x^3 i^3}{n^3}\right)\frac{x}{n} = \frac{x}{n}\sum_{i=1}^{n} 1 - \frac{x^4}{n^4}\sum_{i=1}^{n} i^3$$

$$= \frac{x}{n}\cdot n - \frac{x^4}{n^4}\left(\frac{n(n+1)}{2}\right)^2 = x - \frac{1}{n^4}\left(\frac{n(n+1)}{2}\right)^2 \cdot x^4$$

Taking the limit as $n \mapsto \infty$ and using the results in Box 4.3.1, gives

$$A(x) \equiv \int_0^x \left(1 - t^3\right) dt = \lim_{n\to\infty} R_n$$

$$= x - \lim_{n\to\infty}\left[\frac{1}{n^4}\left(\frac{n(n+1)}{2}\right)^2\right]\cdot x^4 = x - \frac{1}{4}x^4.$$

Thus, for $f(x) = 1 - x^3$ on $[0, 2]$, the net area function is $A(x) = x - \frac{1}{4}x^4$. NOTE: This example verifies the content of the Fundamental Theorem of Calculus Part 1 (See below). That is, the net area function is always an antiderivative of the function f:

$$A'(x) = \frac{d}{dx}\left(x - \frac{1}{4}x^4\right) = 1 - x^3 = f(x).$$

Finally, we define the function f and its net area function A in Maple and create the combined plot as follows.

```
> f:=x->1-x^3;
```

$$f := x \mapsto 1 - x^3$$

```
> A:=x->x-x^4/4;
```

$$A := x \mapsto x - \tfrac{1}{4}x^4$$

```
> plot([f(x),A(x)],x=0..2,color=[black,red],thickness=[1,2]);
```

Notice that the area function A increases until f becomes zero at $x = 1$ and goes negative thereafter. The area function is zero when x reaches the point where the area above the x-axis is equal to the area below the x-axis. From Figure 4.4.2, this appears to happen at approximately $x = 1.6$. The exact value comes from solving $A(x) = 0$, i.e.,

$$x - \frac{1}{4}x^4 = 0$$

This gives $x = 0$ and $x = 4^{1/3} \approx 1.587401052$. Also note that, in this example, where the integrand f is zero (at $x = 1$), the net area function A changes from increasing to decreasing. Thus, $x = 1$ is a critical number for A, which is to be expected since we have seen that $A'(x) = f(x)$.

Example 4.4.2

Consider the function

$$f(x) = e^{-x}\sin 8x$$

and net area function

$$A(x) = \int_0^x e^{-t}\sin 8t\, dt$$

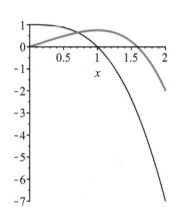

Figure 4.4.2: *Plot of the function $f(x) = 1 - x^3$ on $[0, 2]$ (in black) and its net area function $A(x) = x - \frac{1}{4}x^4$ (in red).*

While we cannot, at this point, compute a formula for this net area function, we can use the special-purpose Maple command `Areafunction` to examine the relationship between f and A.

```
> f:=x->exp(-x)*sin(8*x);
```
$$f := x \mapsto e^{-x} \sin(8x)$$
```
> Areafunction(f,0,1,100,fig);
```

The above code creates a movie showing the net area for f on the interval $[0,1]$ being approximated by 100 rectangles. The red curve in the movie shows how this approximate net area $A_{approx}(x)$ varies as x moves from 0 to 1. The following figure shows the last frame in the movie.

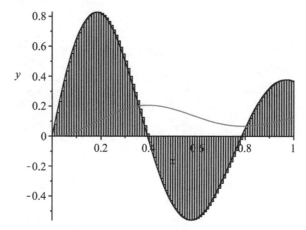

Figure 4.4.3: *The red curve is an approximation to the net area function for $f(x) = e^{-x}\sin 8x$ on the interval$[0,1]$.*

The areas of the green rectangles approximate the area between the graph of f and the x-axis. If you do a signed-sum of the areas of these rectangles, using a plus (+) for those above the x-axis and a minus (-) for those below, going from left to right, the red curve will give the accumulated net area. You can see that the red curve starts at zero and increases, as area is accumulated, reaching a local maximum value where the graph of f first crosses the x-axis (at about $x = 0.4$). After that the net area curve begins to decrease as area is subtracted from the accumulated total. That continues until it reached a local minimum value where f next crosses the x-axis (at about $x = 0.8$).

This analysis of the graphs of f and the approximation to the net area function A suggests, as in the previous example, that A is an antiderivative of f:

$$A'(x) = f(x),$$

for all x in $[0, 1]$. As we saw in Example 4.4.1, the net area function is an antiderivative of the original function. This relationship was also suggested by the graphics in Example 4.4.2. The next theorem, which is the first part of the Fundamental Theorem of Calculus says that this is always the case.

Theorem 4.4.1 (Rate of Change of Net Area) FTC Part 1

Suppose f is a continuous function on the interval $[a,b]$ and A is the net area function

$$A(x) \equiv \int_a^x f(t)\,dt,$$

x in $[a, b]$. Then A is an antiderivative of f:

$$A'(x) = f(x)$$

for all x in (a, b).

A heuristic proof of this theorem goes as follows. We use the limit definition of the derivative to compute the derivative:

$$A'(x) = \lim_{h \to 0} \frac{A(x+h) - A(x)}{h}.$$

For simplicity we assume that f is a nonnegative function and that $h > 0$. Then since $a < x < x + h$, by the additive property of areas, we have

$$A(x+h) = \int_a^{x+h} f(t)\, dt = \int_a^x f(t)\, dt + \int_x^{x+h} f(t)\, dt = A(x) + \int_x^{x+h} f(t)\, dt.$$

Thus,

$$\frac{A(x+h) - A(x)}{h} = \frac{1}{h} \int_x^{x+h} f(t)\, dt.$$

Now consider the figure in the margin.

For h small (and positive), we see from the figure that the area $\int_x^{x+h} f(t)\, dt$ is approximately the same as the area $f(x)\, h$:

$$\int_x^{x+h} f(t)\, dt \approx f(x)\, h$$

and so

$$\frac{1}{h} \int_x^{x+h} f(t)\, dt \approx \frac{1}{h} \left(f(x)\, h \right) = f(x).$$

This argument suggests that in the limit we get $f(x)$:

$$A'(x) = \lim_{h \to 0} \frac{A(x+h) - A(x)}{h} = \lim_{h \to 0} \frac{1}{h} \int_x^{x+h} f(x)\, dx = f(x).$$

This completes the heuristic argument.

NOTE: This first part of the Fundamental Theorem of Calculus guarantees us that any continuous function on $[a, b]$ has an antiderivative on this interval and, indeed, an antiderivative that vanishes at a.

The Evaluation Theorem (FTC Part 2)

The second part of the Fundamental Theorem of Calculus (FTC Part 2) allows us to evaluate any definite integral $\int_a^b f(x)\, dx$ quickly and easily once we know an antiderivative F of f.

Theorem 4.4.2 (Fundamental Theorem of Calculus) FTC Part 2

Suppose f is a continuous function on the interval [a,b] and F is any antiderivative of f. Then

$$\int_a^b f(x)dx = F(b) - F(a)$$

CAUTION: Note the distinction between the lower case f (the integrand) and the upper case F (an antiderivative of the integrand).

Proof: Let A be the net area function

$$A(x) = \int_a^x f(t)\, dt.$$

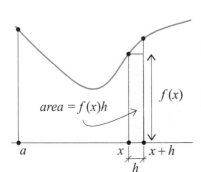

Figure 4.4.4: *The area $\int_h^{x+h} f(t)\, dt$ beneath the graph on the interval $[x, x + h]$ is approximately equal to the rectangular area $f(x)h$ shown.*

Then by Theorem 4.4.1, A is an antiderivative of f. By Theorem 3.7.1, we know that any two antiderivatives differ by a constant. So there exists a constant C such that

$$A(x) = F(x) + C \qquad (4.4.3)$$

for all x in $[a, b]$. Since the above equation holds for all x in $[a, b]$, in particular it holds for $x = a$. So

$$0 = A(a) = F(a) + C.$$

This gives us the value of the constant C, namely, $C = -F(a)$. Then Equation (4.4.3) becomes

$$A(x) = F(x) - F(a),$$

for all x in $[a, b]$. Taking $x = b$ in the above equation gives

$$\int_a^b f(t)\, dt = A(b) = F(b) - F(a),$$

and this completes the proof.

With a little practice and experience, you will find that The Fundamental Theorem of Calculus is a quick way to compute $\int_a^b f(x)\, dx$. Using it involves two steps:

(1) Find an antiderivative F of the integrand f.

(2) Evaluate F at a and b and then take the difference : $F(b) - F(a)$.

The first step is the hard part. As you have seen in Section 3.7, antiderivatives can be difficult to determine. The second step is routine numerical calculation, but you will need to be careful with the minus sign and simplifications.

For the second step, we introduce some standard notation for the evaluation process. This is shown in the margin box.

For example, if $F(x) = x^2 - 4x^3$, then

$$\begin{aligned} F(x)\Big|_1^2 &= F(2) - F(1) = 2^2 - 4(2)^3 - \left(1^2 - 4(1)^3\right) \\ &= 4 - 32 - (1 - 4) = -28 - (-3) = -25 \end{aligned}$$

The Evaluation Notation

upper limit of evaluation

$$F(x)\Big|_a^b = F(b) - F(a)$$

lower limit of evaluation

Example 4.4.3

Problem: Compute the area beneath the graph of $f(x) = \sin x$ on the interval $[0, \pi]$.

Solution: Since the sine function is nonnegative on the given interval, the area is $A = \int_0^\pi \sin x\, dx$. An antiderivative of $f(x) = \sin x$ is $F(x) = -\cos x$. So by the FTC we can evaluate the definite integral as follows:

$$A = \int_0^\pi \sin x\, dx = (-\cos x)\Big|_0^\pi = -\cos(\pi) - (-\cos(0)) = -(-1) - (-1) = 2$$

Remember that the indefinite integral notation $\int f(x)\, dx$ was introduced to stand for the general antiderivative of $f(x)$, i.e., a particular antiderivative $F(x)$ plus an arbitrary constant C (a constant of integration):

$$\int f(x)\, dx = F(x) + C.$$

When we evaluate this expression at $x = a$ and $x = b$ and then take the difference, the constant C subtracts out:

$$\begin{aligned} \left(\int f(x)\, dx\right)\Big|_a^b &= \left(F(x) + C\right)\Big|_a^b = (F(b) + C) - (F(a) + C) = F(b) - F(a) \\ &= F(x)\Big|_a^b \end{aligned}$$

The Definite Integral
Two Steps

definite integral

$\downarrow$

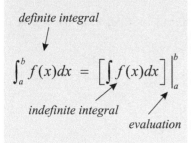

$$\int_a^b f(x)dx = \left[\int f(x)dx\right]\Bigg|_a^b$$

indefinite integral   *evaluation*

Thus, the two step process of computing a definite integral is: (1) Do the indefinite integral (leaving off the constant of integration) and (2) Evaluate the indefinite integral from a to b. In terms of notation, we can write this as shown in the margin box.

This nicely summarizes the connection between the definite integral (a number) and the indefinite integral (a function). Both processes are referred to as integration, but their results are different.

Example 4.4.4 (Using the FTC Part 2)

Problem: Use the Fundamental Theorem of Calculus (Part 2) to calculate the following definite integrals.

$$\text{(a) } \int_{-1}^2 \left(x - x^2\right) dx \quad \text{(b) } \int_1^4 \frac{1 + \sqrt{x^3}}{\sqrt{x}} dx \quad \text{(c) } \int_0^{\frac{\pi}{2}} \cos x \left(1 + \cos x\right) dx \quad \text{(d) } \int_1^x \frac{1}{t} dt$$

Solution (a): By the FTC to calculate the definite integral $\int_{-1}^2 \left(x - x^2\right) dx$ we first do an indefinite integral (leaving off the constant of integration)

$$\int \left(x - x^2\right) dx = \frac{1}{2}x^2 - \frac{1}{3}x^3.$$

Then we evaluate this from -1 to 2:

$$\left(\frac{1}{2}x^2 - \frac{1}{3}x^3\right)\Bigg|_{-1}^2 = \left(\frac{1}{2}(2)^2 - \frac{1}{3}(2)^3\right) - \left(\frac{1}{2}(-1)^2 - \frac{1}{3}(-1)^3\right)$$

$$= \left(2 - \frac{8}{3}\right) - \left(\frac{1}{2} - \left(-\frac{1}{3}\right)\right) = 2 - \frac{8}{3} - \frac{1}{2} - \frac{1}{3} = -\frac{3}{2}.$$

Thus,

$$\int_{-1}^2 \left(x - x^2\right) dx = -\frac{3}{2}.$$

Solution (b): We first convert to exponent notation in the integrand and then use algebra to write it as

$$\frac{1 + \sqrt{x^3}}{\sqrt{x}} = \frac{1 + x^{3/2}}{x^{1/2}} = x^{-1/2} + x.$$

Then

$$\int_1^4 \frac{1 + \sqrt{x^3}}{\sqrt{x}} dx = \int_1^4 \left(x^{-1/2} + x\right) dx = \left(2x^{1/2} + \frac{1}{2}x^2\right)\Bigg|_1^4$$

$$= \left(2(4)^{1/2} + \frac{1}{2}(4)^2\right) - \left(2 + \frac{1}{2}\right) = \left(4 + \frac{16}{2}\right) - \frac{5}{2} = \frac{19}{2}$$

Solution (c): We first use algebra and a trig identity to convert the integrand into something we can find an antiderivative for.

$$\cos x \left(1 + \cos x\right) = \cos x + \cos^2 x = \cos x + \frac{1}{2} + \frac{1}{2}\cos 2x.$$

We know antiderivatives for the first two functions:

$$\int \cos x \, dx = \sin x + C, \quad \int \frac{1}{2} dx = \frac{1}{2}x + C$$

To find an antiderivative for the third function, we note that

$$\frac{d}{dx}\left(\sin 2x\right) = 2\cos 2x$$

so

$$\frac{d}{dx}\left(\frac{1}{2}\sin 2x\right) = \cos 2x, \quad \text{i.e.,} \quad \int \cos 2x\, dx = \frac{1}{2}\sin 2x + C.$$

Having antiderivatives for each of the parts of the integrand, we can now compute the definite integral.

$$\int_0^{\frac{\pi}{2}} \cos x\,(1 + \cos x)\, dx = \int_0^{\frac{\pi}{2}} \left(\cos x + \frac{1}{2} + \frac{1}{2}\cos 2x\right) dx$$

$$= \left(\sin x + \frac{1}{2}x + \frac{1}{2}\cdot\frac{1}{2}\sin 2x\right)\Big|_0^{\frac{\pi}{2}}$$

$$= \left(\sin\left(\frac{\pi}{2}\right) + \frac{\pi}{4} + \frac{1}{4}\sin(\pi)\right) - \left(\sin(0) + 0 + \frac{1}{4}\sin(0)\right)$$

$$= 1 + \frac{\pi}{4}$$

Solution (d): **Since**

$$\int \frac{1}{t}\, dt = \ln t + C$$

the definite integral is

$$\int_1^x \frac{1}{t}\, dt = \ln t \Big|_1^x = \ln x - \ln(1) = \ln x.$$

This shows that $A(x) = \ln x$ is the net area function for $f(x) = \dfrac{1}{x}$ on the interval $[1, \infty)$.

Example 4.4.5 (Calculating Net Areas and Areas)

Problem: For the function

$$f(x) = 4 - x^2 \quad \text{on} \quad [0, 3]$$

find

$$A_{net} = \int_0^3 (4 - x^2)\, dx$$

and then express this net area as the signed sum of actual areas of the region between the graph of f and the x-axis. Also sketch a graph of f and label the regions with these areas.

Solution: Using the FTC, the net area is easy to find:

$$A_{net} = \int_0^3 (4 - x^2)\, dx = \left(4x - \frac{1}{3}x^3\right)\Big|_0^3 = 4(3) - \frac{1}{3}(3)^3 = 12 - 9 = 3$$

A sketch of the graph of f on the given interval is shown In Figure 4.4.5.

In the figure, the region above the x-axis has area

$$A_1 = \int_0^2 (4 - x^2)\, dx = \left(4x - \frac{1}{3}x^3\right)\Big|_0^2 = 4(2) - \frac{1}{3}(2)^3 = 8 - \frac{8}{3} = \frac{16}{3}$$

The region beneath the x-axis has area

$$A_2 = -\int_2^3 (4 - x^2)\, dx = -\left(4x - \frac{1}{3}x^3\right)\Big|_2^3$$

$$= -\left(4(3) - \frac{1}{3}(3)^3\right) + \left(4(2) - \frac{1}{3}(2)^3\right) = -3 + \frac{16}{3} = \frac{7}{3}$$

Thus,

$$A_1 - A_2 = \frac{16}{3} - \frac{7}{3} = \frac{9}{3} = 3 = A_{net}$$

This expresses the net area as the signed sum of actual areas.

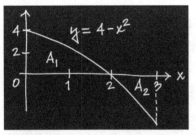

Figure 4.4.5: *Graph of* $f(x) = 4 - x^2$ *on* $[0, 3]$.

Exercises: 4.4 (The Fundamental Theorem of Calculus)

Using the Fundamental Theorem of Calculus

In Exercises 1–44, use the Fundamental Theorem of Calculus (Part 2) to evaluate the definite integrals.

1. $\displaystyle\int_1^2 (2 - 3x + 5x^2)\,dx$ **2.** $\displaystyle\int_1^2 (4 - 2x + 6x^2)\,dx$

3. $\displaystyle\int_{-1}^2 (3x^2 - 4x^3)\,dx$ **4.** $\displaystyle\int_{-1}^2 (5x^4 - 3x^2)\,dx$

5. $\displaystyle\int_0^1 (2x^{1/2} - 4x^{2/3} + 2x)\,dx$

6. $\displaystyle\int_0^1 (4x^{1/5} - 9x^{2/7} + 2)\,dx$

7. $\displaystyle\int_1^2 \frac{u+1}{u^2}\,du$ **8.** $\displaystyle\int_1^2 \frac{u+1}{\sqrt{u}}\,du$

9. $\displaystyle\int_1^2 \frac{(x-2)^2}{x^2}\,dx$ **10.** $\displaystyle\int_1^2 \frac{(x-3)^2}{x^3}\,dx$

11. $\displaystyle\int_0^1 \sqrt{y}\,(y+1)^2\,dy$ **12.** $\displaystyle\int_0^1 \sqrt{y}\,(y^2+1)^2\,dy$

13. $\displaystyle\int_0^1 (2x-1)(x-3)\,dx$ **14.** $\displaystyle\int_0^1 (3x+1)(x-2)\,dx$

15. $\displaystyle\int_0^1 \frac{e^x+1}{e^x}\,dx$ **16.** $\displaystyle\int_0^1 \frac{2^x+1}{2^x}\,dx$

17. $\displaystyle\int_0^1 \frac{e^{2x}-1}{e^x+1}\,dx$ **18.** $\displaystyle\int_0^1 \frac{4^x-1}{2^x+1}\,dx$

19. $\displaystyle\int_{-1}^1 (2^x+1)^2\,dx$ **20.** $\displaystyle\int_{-1}^1 (3^x+1)^2\,dx$

21. $\displaystyle\int_0^1 2^x\,(3^x-5^x)\,dx$ **22.** $\displaystyle\int_0^1 2^{-x}\,(3^x-5^x)\,dx$

23. $\displaystyle\int_0^1 3^{5x-2}\,dx$ **24.** $\displaystyle\int_0^1 2^{3x-2}\,dx$

25. $\displaystyle\int_0^\pi (\sin x - \cos x)\,dx$ **26.** $\displaystyle\int_0^\pi (\sin^2 x - \cos^2 x)\,dx$

27. $\displaystyle\int_0^{2\pi} (1 + 2\sin x)^2\,dx$ **28.** $\displaystyle\int_0^{2\pi} (1 + 2\cos x)^2\,dx$

29. $\displaystyle\int_{\pi/6}^{\pi/4} \sec x\,(\sec x - \tan x)\,dx$

30. $\displaystyle\int_{\pi/6}^{\pi/2} \csc x\,(\csc x - \cot x)\,dx$

31. $\displaystyle\int_0^{\pi/3} \frac{1 + \tan x}{\sec x}\,dx$ **32.** $\displaystyle\int_{\pi/4}^{\pi/3} \frac{1 + \cot x}{\csc x}\,dx$

33. $\displaystyle\int_0^{\pi/4} \frac{\sin x}{\cos^2 x}\,dx$ **34.** $\displaystyle\int_{\pi/4}^{\pi/2} \frac{\cos x}{\sin^2 x}\,dx$

35. $\displaystyle\int_0^{\pi/4} (\tan^2 x + 1)\,dx$ **36.** $\displaystyle\int_0^{\pi/4} \tan^2 x\,dx$

37. $\displaystyle\int_{-\pi/4}^{\pi/4} \left(\frac{\sin^2 x}{\cos^2 x} + 1\right)\,dx$ **38.** $\displaystyle\int_{\pi/6}^{\pi/4} \left(\frac{\cos^2 x}{\sin^2 x} + 1\right)\,dx$

39. $\displaystyle\int_0^{\pi/3} \frac{1 - \sin^2 x}{\cos x}\,dx$ **40.** $\displaystyle\int_{\pi/6}^{\pi/3} \frac{1 - \cos^2 x}{\sin x}\,dx$

41. $\displaystyle\int_{\pi/6}^{\pi/3} \frac{1 - \sin^2 x}{1 + \sin x}\,dx$ **42.** $\displaystyle\int_{\pi/6}^{\pi/3} \frac{1 - \cos^2 x}{1 + \cos x}\,dx$

43. $\displaystyle\int_{\pi/6}^{\pi/3} \frac{(1 + \tan^2 x)^2}{\sec^2 x}\,dx$ **44.** $\displaystyle\int_{\pi/6}^{\pi/3} \frac{(1 + \cot^2 x)^2}{\csc^2 x}\,dx$

Net Area as a Signed Sum of Areas

In Exercises 45–66, find the net area

$$A_{net} = \int_a^b f(x)\,dx$$

between the graph of f on the interval $[a, b]$ and the x-axis and then express this net area as the signed sum of actual areas of the regions between the graph of f and the x-axis. Also sketch a graph of f and label the regions with these areas.

45. $f(x) = x^2 - 2x$, $[0, 3]$ **46.** $f(x) = x^2 - 2x$, $[-1, 3]$

47. $f(x) = x^4 - 3x^3 + 4x$, $[-2, 3]$

48. $f(x) = x^4 + x^3 - 8x^2 - 12x$, $[-3, 3]$

49. $f(x) = 1 - \frac{1}{x}$, $[\frac{1}{2}, 2]$ **50.** $f(x) = 1 - \frac{1}{x^2}$, $[\frac{1}{2}, 2]$

51. $f(x) = 1 - \sqrt{x}$, $[0, 4]$ **52.** $f(x) = 1 - x^{1/3}$, $[0, 8]$

53. $f(x) = e^{-x} - 1$, $[-1, 2]$ **54.** $f(x) = 1 - 2^x$, $[-1, 2]$

55. $f(x) = e^x - 2$, $[-1, 2]$ **56.** $f(x) = 2 - 2^x$, $[-1, 2]$

57. $f(x) = \frac{1}{2} + \cos x$, $[0, \pi]$ **58.** $f(x) = \frac{1}{2} + \sin x$, $[0, \pi]$

59. $f(x) = \sin x - \cos x$, $[0, 2\pi]$

60. $f(x) = \cos x - \sin x$, $[0, 2\pi]$

61. $f(x) = \sin^2 x - \frac{1}{4}$, $[0, \pi]$

62. $f(x) = \cos^2 x - \frac{1}{4}$, $[0, \pi]$

63. $f(x) = \tan x - 1$, $[-\pi/3, \pi/3]$

64. $f(x) = \cot x - 1$, $[\pi/6, 5\pi/6]$

65. $f(x) = \sec x - \frac{2}{\sqrt{3}}$, $[-\pi/3, \pi/3]$

66. $f(x) = \csc x - \frac{2}{\sqrt{3}}$, $[\pi/6, 5\pi/6]$

Sketching the Net Area Function

In Exercises 67–72, the graph of a function f on an interval is given. Use the graph to construct a rough sketch of the net area function

$$A(x) = \int_a^x f(t)\,dt.$$

Remember, the x-intercepts of the graph of f tell you something about the graph of A. (See Figures 4.4.2–4.4.3.) CAS: As optional computer-work, use the special-purpose command Areafunction to check your work. (See Examples 4.4.1–4.4.2)

67. $f(x) = x^3 - 6x^2 + 8x + 1$, $[0, 3]$

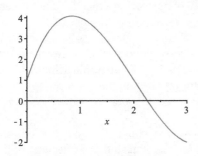

68. $f(x) = x^3 - 7x^2 + 6x + 1$, $[0, 2]$

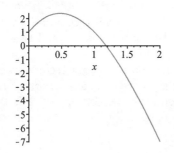

69. $f(x) = e^x + 4e^{-x} - 5$, $[-1, 2]$

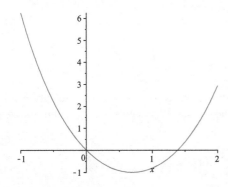

70. $f(x) = e^x - 2e^{-x} - 1$, $[-1', 3]$

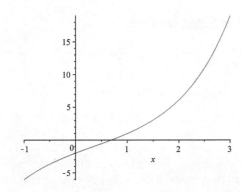

71. $f(x) = \sin x - \cos x$, $[0, 6]$

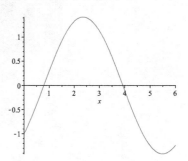

72. $f(x) = \sin^2 x - \frac{1}{4}$, $[0, 3]$

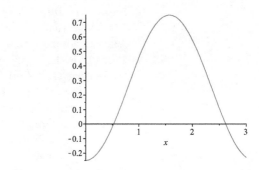

Computing the Net Area Function

In Exercises 73–93, compute, using the Fundamental Theorem of Calculus, the net area function A_{net} for the given function f on the given interval $[a, b]$. CAS: As optional computer work, plot, in the same figure, the graphs of f and A_{net} on $[a, b]$.

73. $f(x) = x^2 - 2x$, $[0, 3]$ **74.** $f(x) = x^2 - 2x$, $[-1, 3]$

75. $f(x) = x^4 - 3x^3 + 4x$, $[-2, 3]$

76. $f(x) = x^4 + x^3 - 8x^2 - 12x$, $[-3, 3]$

77. $f(x) = 1 - \dfrac{1}{x}$, $[\frac{1}{2}, 2]$ **78.** $f(x) = 1 - \dfrac{1}{x^2}$, $[\frac{1}{2}, 2]$

79. $f(x) = 1 - \sqrt{x}$, $[0, 4]$ **80.** $f(x) = 1 - x^{1/3}$, $[0, 8]$

81. $f(x) = e^{-x} - 1$, $[-1, 2]$ **82.** $f(x) = 1 - 2^x$, $[-1, 2]$

83. $f(x) = e^x - 2$, $[-1, 2]$ **84.** $f(x) = 2 - 2^x$, $[-1, 2]$

85. $f(x) = \frac{1}{2} + \cos x$, $[0, \pi]$ **86.** $f(x) = \frac{1}{2} + \sin x$, $[0, \pi]$

87. $f(x) = \cos^2 x - \frac{1}{4}$, $[0, \pi]$

88. $f(x) = \cos^2 x - \frac{3}{4}$, $[0, \pi]$

89. $f(x) = \tan x - 1$, $[-\pi/3, \pi/3]$

90. $f(x) = \cot x - 1$, $[\pi/6, 5\pi/6]$

91. $f(x) = \sec x - \frac{2}{\sqrt{3}}$, $[-\pi/3, \pi/3]$

92. $f(x) = \csc x - \frac{2}{\sqrt{3}}$, $[\pi/6, 5\pi/6]$

93. Those functions in Exercises 67–72 that you did.

Calculus Concepts & Computation

4.5 The Substitution Method

This chapter has introduced the concept of the definite integral (defined as the limit of Riemann sums) to solve the problem of measuring areas (and net areas). The next chapter will show you many additional examples of the use of the definite integral. It can be employed to measure the volumes of certain solids, the surface areas of these solids, the length of curves, the work done against a resisting force, and the centroids of planar regions, to name but a few of the applications of integration. In all cases these quantities (such as volume) are numbers and are given in general by formulas involving a definite integral (and thus can be viewed as limits of certain types of modified Riemann sums).

While Riemann sums are the best way to conceptually *define* certain quantities (such as volume), we have seen in the last section that the Fundamental Theorem of Calculus is the best way to *compute* these quantities. And for this we need to find an antiderivative, or indefinite integral, of the integrand. We have already computed a great many of the basic indefinite integrals and, to move beyond this to more complicated indefinite integrals, we need additional techniques. These techniques are called *techniques of integration* and Chapter 6 is devoted to a comprehensive study of the known techniques of integration.

Here we look at one of the most basic and important techniques of integration. It is called the *substitution method* (or sometimes *u-substitution* or *change of variables*). Heuristically, the technique relies on the concept of differentials. As we have seen in Chapter 2, if a variable u is related to a variable x by the formula

$$u = g(x),$$

then the differentials du, dx are related by the formula

$$du = g'(x)dx.$$

Thus, if we have an integral of the form

$$\int f(g(x)) g'(x)\, dx,$$

then we can use the above formulas to rewrite the integral as an integral involving the variable u. Specifically, make the substitutions embodied in the above formulas to get:

$$\int f(g(x))g'(x)\, dx = \int f(u)\, du.$$

This is the substitution method, and the new integral $\int f(u)\, du$ that results is simpler and is perhaps one of the basic integrals that you know.

Main Steps in Applying the Substitution Method:

(1) Determine what part of the given integral (an integral with respect to x) to choose for $g(x)$. That is, what should you let u be?

(2) Compute the relation: $du = g'(x)dx$ between the differentials.

(3) Rewrite, using correct algebra, the original integral as an integral involving only u and du.

Experience will help you master these steps. Basically, you should study the integrand and try to identify part of it that looks like a composition of two functions

$f(g(x))$. Then let $u = g(x)$ be the function on the inside. After this compute $du = g'(x)\,dx$ and see if that matches the other part of the integrand.

Example 4.5.1

Problem: Compute the integral $\displaystyle\int \frac{2x}{\sqrt{1+x^2}}\,dx$

Solution: We recognize the denominator of the integrand as being the composition of the square root function and the function $g(x) = 1 + x^2$. So we let

$$u = 1 + x^2$$

and

$$du = \frac{d}{dx}\left(1 + x^2\right)dx = 2x\,dx$$

Thus,

$$
\begin{aligned}
\int \frac{2x}{\sqrt{1+x^2}}\,dx &= \int \frac{1}{\sqrt{1+x^2}}\cdot 2x\,dx = \int \frac{1}{\sqrt{u}}\,du \\
&= \int u^{-1/2}\,du = 2u^{1/2} + C = 2\sqrt{u} + C = 2\sqrt{1+x^2} + C.
\end{aligned}
$$

You can easily check this by differentiating using the chain rule.

Often in using the substitution method it is necessary to manipulate the equation that relates the differentials du and dx in order to rewrite, correctly, the integral in x as an integral in u. The next example demonstrates this

Example 4.5.2

Problem: Compute the integral $\displaystyle\int xe^{-x^2}\,dx$.

Solution: Here we choose the substitution

$$u = -x^2$$

because x is essentially the derivative of $-x^2$. From the above equation relating u and x, we get the following equation that relates their differentials:

$$du = -2\,x\,dx$$

or equivalently;

$$-\frac{1}{2}du = x\,dx.$$

Notice that we divided by -2 to get the equation relating the differentials in a better form. Now we can rewrite the original integral as follows.

$$
\begin{aligned}
\int xe^{-x^2}\,dx &= \int e^{-x^2}\,(x\,dx) = \int e^u\left(-\frac{1}{2}du\right) \\
&= -\frac{1}{2}\int e^u\,du = -\frac{1}{2}e^u + C = -\frac{1}{2}e^{-x^2} + C.
\end{aligned}
$$

Sometimes, when using the substitution method it is necessary to solve the equation $u = g(x)$ for x, getting $x = g^{-1}(u)$, and use this result to rewrite everything in terms of u. Here's an example of this:

Example 4.5.3

Problem: Compute the integrals:

(a) $\displaystyle\int 2x^3\sqrt{1+x^2}\,dx$ (b) $\displaystyle\int x^2\,(x+5)^{1/3}\,dx$

Solution(a): As in the first example above, we let

$$u = 1 + x^2$$

so that

$$du = 2x\,dx.$$

Now let's try rewriting the original integral:

$$\int 2x^3\sqrt{1+x^2}\,dx = \int x^2\sqrt{1+x^2}\cdot 2x\,dx = \int x^2\sqrt{u}\,du$$

But what do we do with the x^2 that is still in the integrand? We need to rewrite it in terms of u. For this note that the original substitution was

$$u = 1 + x^2$$

which says that

$$x^2 = u - 1.$$

Thus, the original integral changes to an integral in u only and we integrate as follows:

$$
\begin{aligned}
\int 2x^3\sqrt{1+x^2}\,dx &= \int (u-1)\sqrt{u}\,du = \int (u-1)\,u^{1/2}\,du \\
&= \int \left(u^{3/2} - u^{1/2}\right)du = \frac{2}{5}u^{5/2} - \frac{2}{3}u^{3/2} + C \\
&= \frac{2}{5}\left(1+x^2\right)^{5/2} - \frac{2}{3}\left(1+x^2\right)^{3/2} + C
\end{aligned}
$$

Solution (b): For $\displaystyle\int x^2\,(x+5)^{1/3}\,dx$, we use the substitution

$$u = x + 5$$

so then

$$du = dx.$$

This gives

$$\int x^2\,(x+5)^{1/3}\,dx = \int x^2 u^{1/3}\,du.$$

To remove the x^2 from the last integral, take the substitution equation $u = x + 5$, solve for $x = u - 5$, and substitute this in the last integral. You get

$$
\begin{aligned}
\int x^2 u^{1/3}\,du &= \int (u-5)^2\,u^{1/3}\,du = \int \left(u^2 - 10u + 25\right)u^{1/3}\,du \\
&= \int \left(u^{7/3} - 10u^{4/3} + 25u^{1/3}\right)du \\
&= \frac{3}{10}u^{10/3} - \frac{30}{7}u^{7/3} + \frac{75}{4}u^{4/3} + C \\
&= \frac{3}{10}(x+5)^{10/3} - \frac{30}{7}(x+5)^{7/3} + \frac{75}{4}(x+5)^{4/3} + C
\end{aligned}
$$

There are a number of problems where the appropriate substitution is $u = ax$, with a is a nonzero constant. For example,

$$\int \cos(3x)\,dx.$$

We know that the integral of the cosine is the sine: $\int \cos x\, dx = \sin x + C$, but the appearance of the 3 in the argument for the cosine changes things slightly. However, we can try the substitution

$$u = 3\,x$$

so that

$$du = 3dx$$

or equivalently $\frac{1}{3}du = dx$. Using these substitutions gives

$$\int \cos(3x)\, dx \quad = \quad \int \cos(u) \cdot \left(\frac{1}{3}du\right) = \frac{1}{3}\int \cos(u)\, du$$

$$= \quad \frac{1}{3}\sin(u) + C = \frac{1}{3}\sin(3x) + C$$

Since integrals with expressions like this are common, we can formulate a general rule as shown in the margin box.

Here are some standard examples of this.
Since

$$\int \sec^2 x\, dx = \tan x + C,$$

we have

$$\int \sec^2(5x)\, dx = \frac{1}{5}\tan(5x) + C.$$

And since

$$\int e^x\, dx = e^x + C,$$

we have

$$\int e^{-7x}\, dx = -\frac{1}{7}e^{-7x} + C.$$

> For $a \neq 0$ any nonzero constant.
> If
> $$\int f(x)dx = F(x) + C$$
> then
> $$\int f(ax)dx = \frac{1}{a}F(ax) + C$$

Example 4.5.4

Problem: Compute the integrals: (a) $\int \dfrac{x^2}{1+x^3}\, dx$ (b) $\int \tan x\, dx$

Solution (a): We use the substitution

$$u = 1 + x^3.$$

which gives

$$du = 3x^2\, dx, \quad \text{or equivalently} \quad \frac{1}{3}du = x^2\, dx.$$

This change of variables leads to

$$\int \frac{x^2}{1+x^3}\, dx \quad = \quad \int \frac{1}{1+x^3} \cdot x^2\, dx = \int \frac{1}{u}\left(\frac{1}{3}du\right)$$

$$= \quad \frac{1}{3}\int \frac{1}{u}\, du = \frac{1}{3}\ln u + C = \frac{1}{3}\ln\left(1+x^3\right) + C.$$

NOTE: The result is only valid if we restrict x so that $1 + x^3$ is positive since $\ln u$ is only defined for u positive. However, since

$$\frac{d}{du}\left(\ln|u|\right) = \frac{1}{u},$$

we can get an answer valid for a larger range of values by using absolute values, namely $\ln|1 + x^3| + C$, which is defined for all x except -1.

Solution (b): To compute $\int \tan x \, dx$ it helps to write $\tan x$ in terms of sines and cosines:

$$\int \tan x \, dx = \int \frac{\sin x}{\cos x} \, dx.$$

Now try the substitution

$$u = \cos x.$$

Then

$$du = -\sin x \, dx.$$

So

$$
\begin{aligned}
\int \tan x \, dx &= \int \frac{\sin x}{\cos x} \, dx = \int \frac{1}{\cos x} \cdot \sin x \, dx \\
&= \int \frac{1}{u}(-du) = -\int \frac{1}{u} \, du = -\ln u + C = -\ln(\cos x) + C \\
&= \ln\left((\cos x)^{-1}\right) + C = \ln(\sec x) + C.
\end{aligned}
$$

<u>NOTE</u> 1: We used a law of logarithms and a trig identity to write the original answer, $-\ln(\cos x) + C$, in two other, equivalent ways. When working the exercises, if your answer is different from the answer in the text, try using some identities or some algebra.

<u>NOTE</u> 2: (2) For the result to be valid, x must be restricted so that $\cos x$ (and $\sec x$) are positive. Otherwise, to get the most general result you should use absolute values: $|\cos x|$ (and $|\sec x|$) and restrict to values of x for which $\cos x \neq 0$.

If g is a differentible function, then

$$\int \frac{g'(x)}{g(x)} \, dx = \ln|g(x)| + C$$

The two problems in the previous exercise are of a general type. If the integrand is a fraction and if the numerator is the derivative of the denominator, then the integral involves the natural log function. The margin box summarizes this.

A rather tricky application of this general formula is the following example.

Example 4.5.5

Problem: Compute $\int \sec x \, dx$

Solution: As with the integral of $\tan x$ above, we could try to rewrite in terms of sines and cosines first:

$$\int \sec x \, dx = \int \frac{1}{\cos x} \, dx,$$

but this does not help. The trick here is to rewrite as a ratio of a function divided into its derivative. Recalling that

$$(\sec x)' = \sec x \tan x$$

and

$$(\tan x)' = \sec^2 x$$

We get

$$(\sec x + \tan x)' = \sec x \tan x + \sec^2 x = \sec x(\sec x + \tan x).$$

Dividing each side of this last equation by $\sec x + \tan x$, we get

$$\frac{(\sec x + \tan x)'}{\sec x + \tan x} = \sec x.$$

Consequently

$$\int \sec x \, dx = \int \frac{(\sec x + \tan x)'}{\sec x + \tan x} \, dx = \ln|\sec x + \tan x| + C.$$

Using the techniques of the last two examples, we can determine the integrals of the remaining two standard trigonometric functions, namely $\cot x$ and $\csc x$.

In summary, the following box gives the integrals of the six standard trigonometric functions.

Integrals of the Six Standard Trigonometric Functions

$$\int \sin x \, dx = -\cos x + C \qquad\qquad \int \cos x \, dx = \sin x + C$$

$$\int \tan x \, dx = \ln|\sec x| + C \qquad\qquad \int \cot x \, dx = -\ln|\csc x| + C$$

$$\int \sec x \, dx = \ln|\sec x + \tan x| + C \qquad\qquad \int \csc x \, dx = -\ln|\csc x + \cot x| + C$$

Notice the patterns in these integrals and how the integrals of the co-functions involve a negative sign relative to the integral of the function itself.

Example 4.5.6

Problem: Compute the integrals: (a) $\displaystyle\int \frac{\ln x}{x} \, dx$ (b) $\displaystyle\int \frac{e^{\sqrt{x}}}{\sqrt{x}} \, dx$

Solution (a): If we write the integral as $\int \ln x \cdot \frac{1}{x} \, dx$ and recognize $\frac{1}{x}$ as the derivative of $\ln x$, then the substitution

$$u = \ln x, \, du = \frac{1}{x} dx,$$

leads to

$$\int \frac{\ln x}{x} \, dx = \int \ln x \cdot \frac{1}{x} \, dx = \int u \, du = \frac{1}{2} u^2 + C = \frac{1}{2} (\ln x)^2 + C.$$

Solution(b): This is similar to part (a) since the derivative of $\sqrt{x}$ is $\frac{1}{2\sqrt{x}}$. We use the substitution:

$$u = \sqrt{x}, \quad du = \frac{1}{2\sqrt{x}} dx$$

to get

$$\int \frac{e^{\sqrt{x}}}{\sqrt{x}} \, dx = \int e^{\sqrt{x}} \frac{1}{\sqrt{x}} \, dx = \int e^u \cdot 2 \, du = 2e^u + C = 2e^{\sqrt{x}} + C.$$

The u-substitution technique often occurs when doing *definite* integrals. As we have seen, to compute a definite integral $\int_a^b f(x) \, dx$ we first do an indefinite integral $\int f(x) \, dx$ (leaving off the constant of integration C) and then we evaluate the result from $x = a$ to $x = b$. The u-substitution can be used to calculate the indefinite integral and, as stressed above, after integrating with respect to u and obtaining an answer in terms of u, we substitute back in to obtain the answer in terms of x. This last step is important when doing definite integrals because the original limits of integration, a and b, pertain to x, not u.

However, if we wish, when using a u-substitution on a definite integral problem, we can change the limits of integration for the variable x into limits of integration with respect to u. Then we do not need to return to anything involving x. Thus, if the substitution is

$$u = g(x),$$

then

$$u = g(a) \quad \text{when} \quad x = a$$

and

$$u = g(b) \quad \text{when} \quad x = b$$

Consequently, we get

u-Substitutions for Definite Integrals

$$\int_a^b f(g(x))g'(x)\,dx = \int_{g(a)}^{g(b)} f(u)\,du.$$

Here are some examples of how this works.

Example 4.5.7

Problem: Compute the integrals

$$\text{(a)} \int_0^\pi \frac{\sin x}{2 - \cos x}\,dx \qquad \text{(b)} \int_{-2}^2 (x+2)^5\,x\,dx$$

Solution (a): Write the integral as

$$\int_0^\pi \frac{1}{2 - \cos x} \cdot \sin x\,dx$$

and recognize that $\sin x$ is (up to a sign) the derivative of $\cos x$. This suggests the substitution

$$u = 2 - \cos x, \quad du = \sin x\,dx$$

From which we get

$$\text{when} \quad x = 0,\ u = 2 - \cos(0) = 2 - 1 = 1$$

$$\text{when} \quad x = \pi,\ u = 2 - \cos(\pi) = 2 - (-1) = 3$$

Making these substitutions gives

$$\int_0^\pi \frac{1}{2 - \cos x} \cdot \sin x\,dx = \int_1^3 \frac{1}{u}\,du = \ln u \Big|_1^3 = \ln 3 - \ln 1 = \ln 3$$

Solution (b): Here, to get the 5th power off of the binomial, we make the substitution

$$u = x + 2, \quad \text{so that also} \quad u - 2 = x$$

$$du = dx$$

$$\text{when} \quad x = -2,\ u = -2 + 2 = 0$$

$$\text{when} \quad x = 2,\ u = 2 + 2 = 4$$

Then the integral changes to

$$\begin{aligned}
\int_{-2}^2 (x+2)^5\,x\,dx &= \int_0^4 u^5\,(u-2)\,du = \int_0^4 \left(u^6 - 2u^5\right)du = \left(\frac{1}{7}u^7 - \frac{2}{6}u^6\right)\Big|_0^4 \\
&= \frac{1}{7}(4)^7 - \frac{1}{3}(4)^6 = 4^6\left(\frac{4}{7} - \frac{1}{3}\right) = 4096\left(\frac{5}{21}\right) = \frac{20480}{21}
\end{aligned}$$

Exercises: 4.5 (The Substitution Method)

Using u-Substitutions

In Exercises 1–50, use a substitution to compute the integral. Remember to express your answer in terms of the original variable.

1. $\displaystyle\int x^3\sqrt{1+x^4}\,dx$ 2. $\displaystyle\int \frac{x^3}{\sqrt{1+x^4}}\,dx$

3. $\displaystyle\int \sqrt{x}\left(1+x^{3/2}\right)^5 dx$ 4. $\displaystyle\int \sqrt{x}\left(1+x^{3/2}\right)^5 dx$

5. $\displaystyle\int x\cos\left(x^2\right) dx$ 6. $\displaystyle\int x^{-3}\cos\left(x^{-2}\right) dx$

7. $\displaystyle\int x^2 e^{-x^3}\,dx$ 8. $\displaystyle\int x^{-2} e^{1/x}\,dx$

9. $\displaystyle\int \frac{x}{\sqrt{4-x^2}}\,dx$ 10. $\displaystyle\int \frac{x}{\sqrt{x^2-25}}\,dx$

11. $\displaystyle\int x^2\left(x-1\right)^{2/3}dx$ 12. $\displaystyle\int x^3\left(2x+1\right)^{2/5}dx$

13. $\displaystyle\int \frac{x^2}{\left(x-2\right)^3}\,dx$ 14. $\displaystyle\int \frac{x^2}{\sqrt{x-2}}\,dx$

15. $\displaystyle\int x^{-1}\sin\left(\ln x\right) dx$ 16. $\displaystyle\int x^{-1}\sec^2\left(\ln x\right) dx$

17. $\displaystyle\int \frac{1}{x\ln x}\,dx$ 18. $\displaystyle\int \frac{1}{x\left(\ln x\right)^3}\,dx$

19. $\displaystyle\int \frac{1}{\sqrt{x}\left(\sqrt{x}+1\right)^{3/2}}\,dx$ 20. $\displaystyle\int \frac{1}{\sqrt{x}\left(\sqrt{x}+1\right)^{5/2}}\,dx$

21. $\displaystyle\int \frac{\cos\left(\sqrt{x}\right)}{\sqrt{x}}\,dx$ 22. $\displaystyle\int \frac{\sin\left(\sqrt{x}\right)}{\sqrt{x}}\,dx$

23. $\displaystyle\int \frac{1}{x^2\cos^2\left(x^{-1}\right)}\,dx$ 24. $\displaystyle\int \frac{1}{x^2\sin^2\left(x^{-1}\right)}\,dx$

25. $\displaystyle\int \frac{\sin^2\left(x^{-1}\right)}{x^2\cos^2\left(x^{-1}\right)}\,dx$ 26. $\displaystyle\int \frac{\cos^2\left(x^{-1}\right)}{x^2\sin^2\left(x^{-1}\right)}\,dx$

27. $\displaystyle\int \frac{x^2}{x^3+1}\,dx$ 28. $\displaystyle\int \frac{x^4}{x^5+1}\,dx$

29. $\displaystyle\int \frac{x}{x^4+1}\,dx$ 30. $\displaystyle\int \frac{x^2}{x^6+1}\,dx$

31. $\displaystyle\int \frac{1}{\sqrt{x}\left(x+1\right)}\,dx$ 32. $\displaystyle\int \frac{1}{\sqrt{x}\left(x+4\right)}\,dx$

33. $\displaystyle\int \frac{1}{\sqrt{x}\sqrt{1-x}}\,dx$ 34. $\displaystyle\int \frac{1}{\sqrt{x}\sqrt{25-x}}\,dx$

35. $\displaystyle\int \frac{x^2}{\sqrt{1-x^6}}\,dx$ 36. $\displaystyle\int \frac{x^3}{\sqrt{1-x^8}}\,dx$

37. $\displaystyle\int \sin^3 x\cos x\,dx$ 38. $\displaystyle\int \cos^5 x\sin x\,dx$

39. $\displaystyle\int \tan^2 x\sec^2 x\,dx$ 40. $\displaystyle\int \cot^2 x\csc^2 x\,dx$

41. $\displaystyle\int \tan^3 x\sec x\,dx$ 42. $\displaystyle\int \cot^3 x\csc x\,dx$

43. $\displaystyle\int \frac{\sin 3x}{\sqrt{1+\cos 3x}}\,dx$ 44. $\displaystyle\int \frac{\sec^2 3x}{1+\tan 3x}\,dx$

45. $\displaystyle\int \frac{1}{\sqrt{1-9x^2}}\,dx$ 46. $\displaystyle\int \frac{1}{x\sqrt{9x^2-1}}\,dx$

47. $\displaystyle\int \frac{e^x}{\sqrt{1-e^{2x}}}\,dx$ 48. $\displaystyle\int \frac{e^{2x}}{\sqrt{1-e^{4x}}}\,dx$

49. $\displaystyle\int \frac{\cos x}{1+\sin^2 x}\,dx$ 50. $\displaystyle\int \frac{\sec^2 x}{\sqrt{1-\tan^2 x}}\,dx$

Expressing Net Areas as Signed Sums of Areas

In Exercises 51–58, use the given graph (and the FTC Part 2) to find the *net* area

$$A_{net} = \int_a^b f(x)\,dx$$

between the graph of f on the interval $[a,b]$ and the x-axis. Then express this net area as the signed sum of actual areas of the regions between the graph of f and the x-axis. Note in some cases there is only one region involved. In cases where there are two or more regions involved and you cannot determine the zeros of f exactly, use the approximate values read from the graph.

51. $f(x) = \dfrac{e^x}{1+e^x}$, $[0,10]$

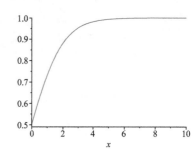

52. $f(x) = \dfrac{2^x}{1+2^x}$, $[0,10]$

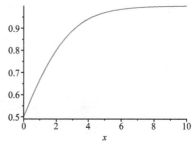

53. $f(x) = x(x-2)^5$, $[0,3]$

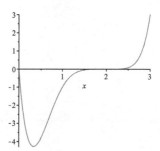

54. $f(x) = x^2 (x-2)^5$, $[0,3]$

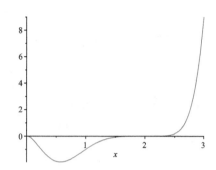

55. $f(x) = \dfrac{\cos x}{1 + \sin^2 x}$, $[0, 3\pi/4]$

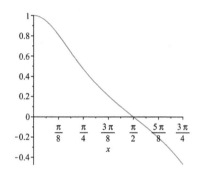

56. $f(x) = \dfrac{\sin x}{1 + \cos^2 x}$, $[0, 3\pi/4]$

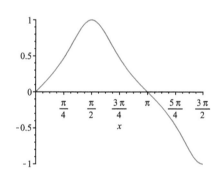

57. $f(x) = \dfrac{90x^2}{(x^3+8)^2}$, $[-1, 2]$

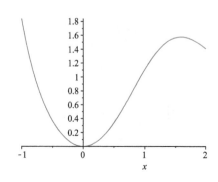

58. $f(x) = \dfrac{60x^3}{(x^4+8)^2}$, $[-1, 2]$

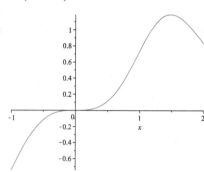

Substitutions Where du is a Multiple of dx

As mentioned in the reading material, there are some commonly occurring integrals that can be computed with a u-substitution that gives $du = a\, dx$, where a *is* a constant. For example:

$$\int \cos 5x \, dx = \frac{1}{5} \sin 5x + C$$

and generally

$$\int f(ax) \, dx = \frac{1}{a} F(ax) + C.$$

where F is an antiderivative of f (and $a \neq 0$). More generally:

$$\int f(ax + b) \, dx = \frac{1}{a} F(ax + b) + C \qquad (4.5.1x)$$

In Exercises 59–78, compute the integrals using Formula (4.5.1x) rather than a u-substitution.

59. $\displaystyle\int \sin 8x \, dx$

60. $\displaystyle\int \sin 10x \, dx$

61. $\displaystyle\int e^{-4x/5} \, dx$

62. $\displaystyle\int e^{-7x/3} \, dx$

63. $\displaystyle\int (x+3)^2 \, dx$

64. $\displaystyle\int (x-5)^3 \, dx$

65. $\displaystyle\int \frac{1}{x+7} \, dx$

66. $\displaystyle\int \frac{2}{x+8} \, dx$

67. $\displaystyle\int \cos(2x+3) \, dx$

68. $\displaystyle\int \sin(5x-4) \, dx$

69. $\displaystyle\int \frac{1}{3x+1} \, dx$

70. $\displaystyle\int \frac{1}{5x-2} \, dx$

71. $\displaystyle\int (2x+5)^{21} \, dx$

72. $\displaystyle\int (3x-4)^{99} \, dx$

73. $\displaystyle\int \frac{1}{1+9x^2} \, dx$

74. $\displaystyle\int \frac{1}{1+25x^2} \, dx$

75. $\displaystyle\int \frac{1}{4x^2+20x+26} \, dx$

76. $\displaystyle\int \frac{1}{9x^2+12x+5} \, dx$

77. $\displaystyle\int \frac{e}{\sqrt{e^{5x/3}}} \, dx$

78. $\displaystyle\int \frac{e}{\sqrt{e^{-7x/5}}} \, dx$

5

Applications of Integrals

Calculus *Concepts & Computation*

5.1 Areas of Planar Regions

In the previous chapter we saw how the area problem led to the introduction of definite integrals as limits of Riemann sums. For a function f which is nonnegative (and continuous) on an interval $[a, b]$, the area of the region D underneath its graph is given (defined) by

$$A = \int_a^b f(x)\,dx = \lim_{n \to \infty} \sum_{i=1}^n f(x_i)\,\Delta x \qquad (5.1.1)$$

You should realize that the region D is rather special and to measure areas of more complicated regions we will have to extend the area Formula (5.1.1). We do this in several steps, beginning with regions that are called Type I regions.

Type I Regions

Suppose f and g are two continuous functions on an interval $[a, b]$ and that $g(x) \leq f(x)$ for all x in $[a, b]$. The *Type I Region* determined by these functions is the region D bounded by the graphs of f and g and the two vertical lines through the endpoints of $[a, b]$. Otherwise said, D is the region bounded by the curves

$$y = f(x), \ y = g(x), \ x = a, \ x = b \qquad (5.1.2)$$

Figure 5.1.1 illustrates an example of a Type I region.

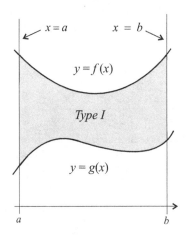

Figure 5.1.1:
A Type I region.

NOTE 1: A special case of this is when the function g is identically zero: $g(x) = 0$, for all x in $[a, b]$. Then the Type I region reduces to just the area under the graph of f on $[a, b]$.

NOTE 2: There are other possibilities for the position of the Type I region in the plane. The graph of g (as well as f) could lie below the x-axis. Also the graphs could come together at one or both endpoints, i.e., $f(a) = g(a)$ or $f(b) = g(b)$.

NOTE 3: In the description of a Type I region, we often refer to f as the "function on the top" and g as the "function on the bottom."

There are several ways to determine the area of a Type I region. One way is to use limits of Riemann sums, which serves not only to motivate the resulting integral formula, but also will be a relevant approach to measuring volumes in later sections of this chapter.

Thus, for a given n, we consider a regular partition $P = \{x_0, x_1, \ldots, x_n\}$ of $[a, b]$ into subintervals of length $\Delta x = (b - a)/n$. Through each of the right endpoints x_i of these subintervals we draw vertical lines to intersect the graphs at $(x_i,\ g(x_i))$ and $(x_i,\ f(x_i))$, respectively. Then we get an approximating rectangle with Δx for the base length and $h_i = f(x_i) - g(x_i)$ for the height. Adding up the areas of these approximating rectangles gives

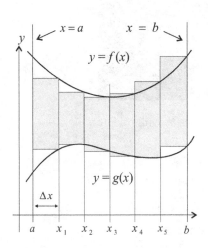

Figure 5.1.2: *A Riemann sum approximation for a Type I region.*

$$R_n = \sum_{i=1}^n h_i \Delta x = \sum_{i=1}^n [f(x_i) - g(x_i)]\Delta x, \qquad (5.1.3)$$

as an approximation to the area of a Type I region. Figure 5.1.2 shows such an approximation using six rectangles for the region in Figure 5.1.1.

As in Chapter 4, study and practice will help you learn how to draw such right endpoint approximations. Using the special-purpose Maple procedure

```
areatype1(f,g,a,b,N,fig)
```

also may help your learning process. This procedure works just like the procedure `RSapprox` from Chapter 4. (In fact it reduces to that procedure if you take `g = 0` for the second argument). Here is an example of its use:

Example 5.1.1 (Approximating the Area)

Problem: Using eight rectangles, calculate the right endpoint, regular Riemann sum approximation to the area of the region between the graphs of $f(x) = 2 - x^2$ and $g(x) = x^2$ on the interval $[0, 1]$.

Solution: The procedure `areatype1` is employed as follows.

```
> f:=x->2-x^2;
```
$$f := x \mapsto 2 - x^2$$

```
> g:=x->x^2;
```
$$g := x \mapsto x^2$$

```
> areatype1(f,g,0,1,8,fig);
```

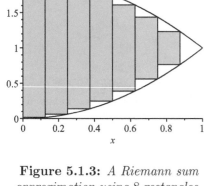

Figure 5.1.3: *A Riemann sum approximation using 8 rectangles. The region bounded by the graphs of $f(x) = 2 - x^2$, $g(x) = x^2$.*

The last frame in the movie is shown in Figure 5.1.3.

Note that the last rectangle in the approximation has zero height and so reduces to a line segment (with zero area). The calculation of the approximate area is easy enough to do by hand.

First $\Delta x = (b - a)/n = 1/8$ and the partition points are

$$0, \frac{1}{8}, \frac{2}{8}, \frac{3}{8}, \frac{4}{8}, \frac{5}{8}, \frac{6}{8}, \frac{7}{8}, 1$$

The results of the by-hand calculation of the heights of the eight rectangles are given in Table 5.1.1.

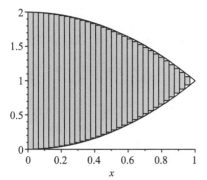

Figure 5.1.4: *A Riemann sum approximation using 32 rectangles (the last of which has zero height).*

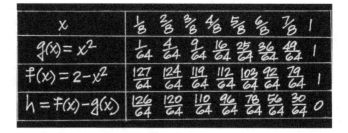

x	$\frac{1}{8}$	$\frac{2}{8}$	$\frac{3}{8}$	$\frac{4}{8}$	$\frac{5}{8}$	$\frac{6}{8}$	$\frac{7}{8}$	1
$g(x) = x^2$	$\frac{1}{64}$	$\frac{4}{64}$	$\frac{9}{64}$	$\frac{16}{64}$	$\frac{25}{64}$	$\frac{36}{64}$	$\frac{49}{64}$	1
$f(x) = 2 - x^2$	$\frac{127}{64}$	$\frac{124}{64}$	$\frac{119}{64}$	$\frac{112}{64}$	$\frac{103}{64}$	$\frac{92}{64}$	$\frac{79}{64}$	1
$h = f(x) - g(x)$	$\frac{126}{64}$	$\frac{120}{64}$	$\frac{110}{64}$	$\frac{96}{64}$	$\frac{78}{64}$	$\frac{56}{64}$	$\frac{30}{64}$	0

Table 5.1.1: *The heights of the rectangles in the approximation.*

The Riemann sum is now calculated as

$$R_8 = h_1 \Delta x + h_2 \Delta x + h_3 \Delta x + h_4 \Delta x + h_5 \Delta x + h_6 \Delta x + h_7 \Delta x + h_8 \Delta x$$

$$= (h_1 + h_2 + h_3 + h_4 + h_5 + h_6 + h_7 + h_8) \, \Delta x$$

$$= \left(\frac{126}{64} + \frac{120}{64} + \frac{110}{64} + \frac{96}{64} + \frac{78}{64} + \frac{56}{64} + \frac{30}{64} + 0 \right) \cdot \frac{1}{8}$$

$$= \frac{616}{64} \cdot \frac{1}{8} = \frac{77}{64} \approx 1.203$$

A better approximation using 32 rectangles is shown in Figure 5.1.4.

The computer-calculated approximation is $R_{32} = 1.301757812$

The above example motivates that, in general, to get the exact area of a Type I region we need to take limits of Riemann sums of the form displayed in Equation (5.1.3). Thus, the area is defined by

$$A = \lim_{n \to \infty} R_n = \lim_{n \to \infty} \sum_{i=1}^{n} h_i \Delta x \qquad (5.1.4)$$

$$= \lim_{n \to \infty} \sum_{i=1}^{n} [f(x_i) - g(x_i)] \Delta x \qquad (5.1.5)$$

This limit gives us a definite integral where the integrand encodes the geometry of the situation. The following box shows the notation.

Areas of Type I Regions

$$A = \int_a^b [f(x) - g(x)] \, dx \qquad (5.1.5a)$$

$$or \qquad A = \int_a^b h \, dx \qquad (5.1.5b)$$

where $h = f(x) - g(x)$.

We have given the integral formula for the area in two different versions: Eq. (5.1.5a) and Eq. (5.1.5b) . The first version is motivated by the discussion about the limit of the Riemann sums. The second version can be viewed as just relabeling the integrand. But it also has a heuristic value that you may find useful in setting up the integrals for specific examples. As in Chapter 4, we can motivate this second integral formula using infinitesimals:

For a given x between a and b, the vertical line through x intersects the Type I region in a line segment of length h. See Figure 5.1.5.

Then the quantity $dA = h \, dx$ represents an infinitesimal amount of area. Doing a continuous sum of these, we get the actual area:

$$A = \int_a^b dA = \int_a^b h \, dx.$$

This is the heuristic (or pedagogical) development of the integral formulas (5.1.5a)–(5.1.5b) for computing the area of a Type I region. There will be a great many formulas in this chapter and it is important that you study the above development so that you understand where the formulas came from. If you do this throughout the chapter, it will be easier for you to pick the right formula to use in each particular situation.

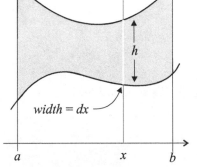

Figure 5.1.5: *An infinitesimal element dA of area A.*

Example 5.1.2 (Using the Integral Formulas)

Problem: Calculate the exact area A of the region between the graphs of $f(x) = 2 - x^2$ and $g(x) = x^2$ on the interval $[0, 1]$. Also compare the exact answer with the two approximations in Example 5.1.1.

Solution: This is an easy calculation:

$$h = f(x) - g(x) = 2 - x^2 - x^2 = 2 - 2x^2.$$

$$A = \int_0^1 \left(2 - 2x^2\right) dx = \left(2x - \frac{2}{3}x^3\right)\Big|_0^1 = 2 - \frac{2}{3} = \frac{4}{3} \approx 1.333$$

Of the two approximations we found above: $R_8 = 1.203$ and $R_{32} = 1.301757812$, only the second one is reasonably close to the exact answer of $A = 4/3$.

To use Formulas (5.1.5a)–(5.1.5b):

$$A = \int_a^b h\,dx = \int_a^b \left[f(x) - g(x)\right] dx$$

you must do three things.

(1) Identify the function on the top (that's f) and the function on the bottom (which is g). To do this you often will need to graph these functions.

(2) Determine the limits of integration a and b. Sometimes the interval $[a, b]$ is given to you, so identifying a and b is easy. Other times you will have to get a and b by determining where the graphs of f and g intersect. This amounts to solving the equation $f(x) = g(x)$ for x. This equation should be written in the form $f(x) - g(x) = 0$, and when this is (reducible to) a polynomial equation or a trigonometric equation, you can use the techniques you learned in precalculus (or algebra and trig) to find the solutions. If these techniques don't work, or the equation is not of this type, then you can try using the numerical techniques of Maple to find the solutions.

(3) Finally, compute the definite integral using the Fundamental Theorem of Calculus.

Example 5.1.3 (Graphing & Setting Up the Integral Formula)

Problem: Find the area of the region enclosed by the graphs of $y = 3 - x^2$ and $y = x + 1$.

Solution: You should recognize that the graphs of these equations are a parabola and a straight line, respectively. A quick by-hand sketch reveals that the line intersects the parabola in two points.

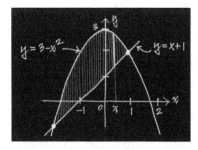

Figure 5.1.6: *A sketch of the curves* $y = 3 - x^2$ *and* $y = x + 1$

To find the x-coordinates of these points, we solve the equation

$$3 - x^2 = x + 1$$

This is a quadratic equation which, rearranged, gives the standard form

$$x^2 + x - 2 = 0,$$

and this factors as

$$(x - 1)(x + 2) = 0$$

Thus, the solutions are $x = -2, 1$. From the by-hand sketch we see that $a = -2$, $b = 1$, $f(x) = 3 - x^2$, $g(x) = x + 1$. So, the area of the enclosed region is

$$A = \int_{-2}^1 \left(3 - x^2 - (x + 1)\right) dx = \int_{-2}^1 \left(2 - x - x^2\right) dx$$

$$= \left(2x - \frac{1}{2}x^2 - \frac{1}{3}x^3\right)\Big|_{-2}^1 = \left(2 - \frac{1}{2} - \frac{1}{3}\right) - \left(-4 - 2 + \frac{8}{3}\right)$$

$$= \frac{7}{6} - \left(-\frac{10}{3}\right) = \frac{27}{6} = \frac{9}{2}$$

Example 5.1.4 (Graphing & Setting Up the Integral Formula)

Problem: Find the area of the region between the graphs of $f(x) = \dfrac{4}{x+3}$ and $g(x) = x^2$.

Solution: The function f is a rational function with a vertical asymptote at $x = -3$. The graph of g is the standard parabola, and to see where it intersects the graph of f we solve the equation:

$$\frac{4}{x+3} = x^2, \quad \text{equivalently,} \quad 4 = x^2(x+3)$$

or

$$x^3 + 3x^2 - 4 = 0$$

A standard way to find roots of a cubic equation is to use the rational roots theorem (and in particular always check to see if $x = \pm 1$ are roots). Here it is easy to see that $x = 1$ is a root. You can continue using the rational roots theorem to find the other roots (if they are rational) or you can do the following (which works in any case).

We have found one root $x = 1$. This means that $x^3 + 3x^2 - 4$ has $x - 1$ as a factor:

$$x^3 + 3x^2 - 4 = (x-1) \cdot q(x),$$

where $q(x)$ is a quadratic polynomial. So the other roots are the root of $q(x) = 0$, which can be found by factoring or the quadratic formula. To find $q(x)$ we use the algorithm for long division of polynomials. We find that

$$\frac{x^3 + 3x^2 - 4}{x - 1} = x^2 + 4x + 4$$

Thus, the remaining roots are the roots of $0 = x^2 + 4x + 4 = (x+2)^2$. This has a single (repeated) root $x = -2$.

In summary, we have found that the graphs of f and g intersect in two points with x-coordinates $x = -2, 1$, respectively. A by-hand sketch of these graphs is shown in Figure 5.1.7.

Now we use the integral formula with $a = -2$, $b = 1$.

$$A = \int_{-2}^{1} \left(\frac{4}{x+3} - x^2 \right) dx = \left(4\ln(x+3) - \frac{1}{3}x^3 \right) \Big|_{-2}^{1}$$

$$= \left(4\ln(4) - \frac{1}{3} \right) - \left(4\ln(1) - \frac{1}{3}(-8) \right) = 4\ln(4) - 3 \approx 2.55.$$

The calculation is relatively straight-forward, but you must be careful with the minus signs in the evaluations. You can check that the answer is reasonable by looking at the above graph and counting square units.

There is an alternative way to motivate the integral formula

$$A = \int_{a}^{b} [f(x) - g(x)] \, dx$$

for the area of a Type I region D. For simplicity we assume that f and g are nonnegative on the interval (a, b). By a property of the definite integral, we have

$$A = \int_{a}^{b} [f(x) - g(x)] \, dx = \int_{a}^{b} f(x) \, dx - \int_{a}^{b} g(x) \, dx = A_1 - A_2.$$

where A_1 is the area of the region D_1 underneath the graph of f and A_2 is the area of the region D_2 underneath the graph of g. This makes sense if we view the region D as the difference of two regions: $D = D_1 - D_2$. This is illustrated in Figure 5.1.8.

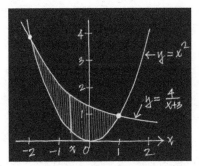

Figure 5.1.7: *A sketch of the graphs of* $f(x) = \dfrac{4}{x+3}$ *and* $g(x) = x^2$.

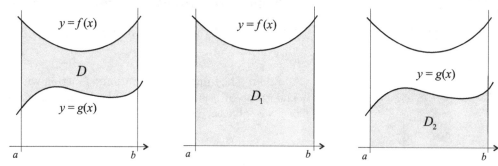

Figure 5.1.8: *The region D is the difference of two regions $D = D_1 - D_2$.*

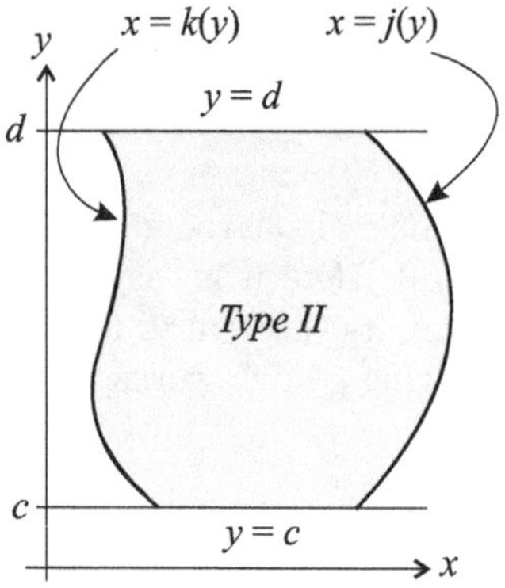

Type II Regions

As we have seen a Type I region is a region bounded by the graphs of two *functions* and two *vertical* lines. In many applications a region is determined by two *horizontal* lines and the graphs of two *curves* whose equations have the special form: $x = j(y)$ and $x = k(y)$. We assume j and k are continuous functions of y for y in an interval $[c, d]$. Thus, we say a region D is a *Type II* region if it is bounded by the graphs of

$$x = j(y), \ x = k(y), \ y = c, \ y = d$$

where $c < d$ and $k(y) \le j(y)$ for all y in $[c, d]$. Figure 5.1.9 shows a typical Type II region.

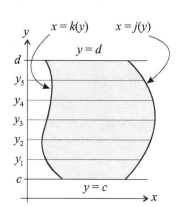

Figure 5.1.9

To determine the area of such a region, it is natural to use limits of Riemann sums. But how do we form the Riemann sums in this case? Since two of the boundary curves of D are horizontal lines and the interval $[c, d]$ lies along the y-axis, it seems reasonable to subdivide $[c, d]$ by a regular partition

$$P = \{y_0, y_1, \ldots, y_n\}$$

giving subintervals of common length $\Delta y = (d - c)/n$. Then we slice up the region D using horizontal lines through the partition points. This is shown for $n = 6$ in Figure 5.1.10. Out of these slices, we construct horizontal rectangles to approximate the area of D. Each rectangle will have Δy as the common height. Their widths, however, will vary. For the width of the ith rectangle we use the right endpoint y_i of the ith subinterval $[y_{i-1}, y_i]$ and evaluate j and k there, to get the ith width as a difference:

$$w_i = j(y_i) - k(y_i).$$

Figure 5.1.11 shows the resulting approximating rectangles for $n = 6$.

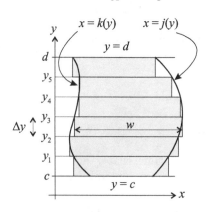

Figure 5.1.10: *Horizontal slices on a Type II region.*

Based on this geometry, the natural Riemann sum to use for the approximate area is

$$R_n = \sum_{i=1}^{n} w_i \Delta y = \sum_{i=1}^{n} [j(y_i) - k(y_i)] \Delta y, \qquad (5.1.6)$$

As for Type I regions, there is a special-purpose Maple routine

```
areatype2(j,k,c,d,N,fig)
```

which may help you visualize these Type II Riemann sum approximations. An example below shows how this is used.

To get the exact area from these approximations, we take the limit of the Riemann sums:

$$A = \lim_{n \to \infty} R_n = \lim_{n \to \infty} \sum_{i=1}^{n} w_i \Delta y \qquad (5.1.7)$$

Figure 5.1.11: *Horizontal approximating rectangles for a Type II region.*

$$= \lim_{n\to\infty} \sum_{i=1}^{n} [j(y_i) - k(y_i)] \Delta y \qquad (5.1.8)$$

Based on this, we get the following formula/definition of the area of a Type II region:

Areas of Type II Regions

$$A = \int_c^d [j(y) - k(y)]\, dy \qquad (5.1.8a)$$

$$or \qquad A = \int_c^d w\, dy \qquad (5.1.8b)$$

where $w = j(y) - k(y)$.

In a certain sense there is no difference between a Type I and a Type II region. You can always obtain one from the other by interchanging x and y in the equation for the bounding curves. Geometrically, interchanging the x-axis and y-axis flips the graph of one onto the other.

However, there are several situations where the Type II region concept and "integrating with respect to y" are useful. One is when the region of interest consists of two or more Type I regions, requiring two or more different integrals to evaluate. If the same region can be viewed as a single Type II region, then a single integral will suffice to measure its area. The next example illustrates this.

Example 5.1.5 (Converting to Type II in Order to Get a Single Integral)

Problem: Find the area of the region D which is bounded by the curves

$$y = x^2, \ y = 2x, \ y = 1, \qquad (5.1.9)$$

with $0 \le x$ and $y \le 1$.

Solution: A sketch of the region D is shown in Figure 5.1.12.

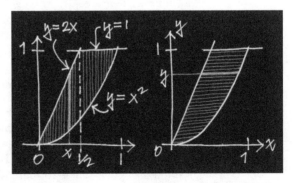

Figure 5.1.12: *A region D consisting of two Type I regions. Alternatively D can be viewed as a single Type II region.*

Note that while the curves $y = x^2, y = 2x$, intersect at $x = 0$ and $x = 2$, the latter is not used because the specification $y \le 1$, indicates the the region D lies below the line $y = 1$.

The region D is not a Type I region, but the vertical line $x = 1/2$ divides the region into two regions, each of which is Type I. While the two integrals needed to find the area are easy enough to calculate (exercise), it is quicker to do a single integral, integrating with respect to y. This is possible because D is a (single) Type

II region. Solving the first two equations in (5.1.9) for x gives the bounding curves for this Type II region:

$$x = \sqrt{y},\ x = \frac{1}{2}\,y,\ y = 1.$$

Thus, $j(y) = \sqrt{y}$, $k(y) = \frac{1}{2}\,y$ and $c = 0$, $d = 1$. The area is then given by

$$A = \int_0^1 \left(\sqrt{y} - \frac{1}{2}y \right) dy = \left(\frac{2}{3}y^{3/2} - \frac{1}{4}y^2 \right)\Big|_0^1 = \frac{2}{3} - \frac{1}{4} = \frac{5}{12}.$$

To get a feel for the change in the geometry and the concept of integrating with respect to y, we use the special-purpose Maple procedure `areatype2`. The code for this is as follows.

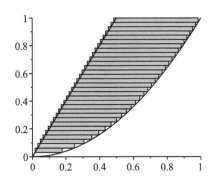

```
>   j:=y->sqrt(y);
```
$$j := y \mapsto \sqrt{y}$$
```
>   k:=y->y/2;
```
$$k := y \mapsto \frac{1}{2}\,y$$
```
>   areatype2(j,k,0,1,32,fig);
```
The approximation using, 32, rectangles is, 0.4233714362

This produces an animation whose last frame is shown in the margin figure.

It is important to note for future applications, that the process of integrating with respect to y involves the limit of approximations where the region is sliced up using with "horizontal" rectangles. See the above figure. The approximation shown uses 32 rectangles (the first of which has 0 width) and gives

$$A \approx 0.4233714362$$

In Type I regions, integrating with respect to x involves the limit of approximations where the region is sliced up using with "vertical" rectangles. See Figures 5.1.3 - 5.1.5.

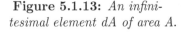

As we did for Type I regions, we can motivate the second version of the integral formula as heuristically arising from a continuous sum of infinitesimal areas dA, each of which is a width w times an infinitesimal height dy. Thus $dA = w\,dy$, and

$$A = \int_c^d dA = \int_c^d w\,dy.$$

Figure 5.1.13 depicts this geometrically.

Figure 5.1.13: *An infinitesimal element dA of area A.*

Compare these infinitesimal elements, which are horizontal slices, one for each y between c and d, with the infinitesimal elements for Type I regions, which are vertical slices, one for each x between a and b. These heuristic viewpoints will be important for us in the multivariable calculus later in the book. Also, the next section uses this vehicle to motivate the measurement of volume by viewing a solid as composed of infinitely many infinitesimal cross-sectional slices.

Often a region can be viewed as either a Type I or a Type II region, but the choice of which integral formula to use (integrating with respect to x or with respect to y) is dictated by which integration is easier. The following example illustrates this.

Example 5.1.6 (Converting to a Type II in Order to Integrate)

Problem: Find the area of the region (in the first quadrant) bounded by

$$y = \tan^{-1} x,\ y = 0,\ x = 1$$

Solution: The figure below shows a sketch of the region.

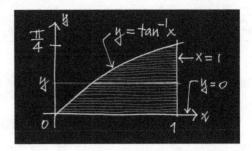

Figure 5.1.14: *The graphs of* $y = \tan^{-1} x$, $y = 0$, $x = 1.0$

As a Type I region $f(x) = \tan^{-1} x$, $g(x) = 0$, $a = 0$, $b = 1$, the area calculation requires evaluating the integral

$$A = \int_0^1 \tan^{-1} x \, dx.$$

You can do this integral using integration by parts, which is an integration technique presented in the next chapter. But, for now, we view the region as a Type II region and integrate with respect to y. The curves bounding the region are

$$x = \tan y, \quad x = 1, \quad y = 0$$

So $j(y) = 1, k(y) = \tan y$. and $c = 0$. To find the upper limit of integration we determine where the first two curves intersect. This gives the equation

$$\tan y = 1$$

to solve. There are infinitely many solutions of this, but the basic one, $y = \pi/4$, is the one we need. Thus, the area of the region can be computed by the integral

$$A = \int_0^{\pi/4} [\,1 - \tan y\,]\, dy = [\,y - \ln(\sec y)\,]\Big|_0^{\pi/4}$$

$$= \frac{\pi}{4} - \ln\left(\frac{2}{\sqrt{2}}\right) = \frac{\pi}{4} - \frac{1}{2}\ln 2$$

Exercises: 5.1 (Areas of Planar Regions)

Calculating The Approximate Area Between Curves

In Exercises 1–4, do the following

(a) Determine the x-coordinates a, b of the points where the graphs of the two functions intersect.

(b) Estimate the area of the region between the graphs by using right endpoint Riemann sum approximations for a partition of $[a,b]$ into $n = 8$ subintervals. Do the calculations by hand. **CAS:** You may use the special-purpose Maple commands `areatype1` and `areatype2` to produce the graphics. Compare your calculation with the one produced by the Maple command.

(c) **CAS:** Use the Maple commands to do the calculations for $n = 32$ subintervals.

1. $f(x) = 4x + 12$, $g(x) = x^2$

2. $f(x) = -4x + 5$, $g(x) = x^2$

3. $j(y) = y^3 - 16y$, $k(y) = 4y^2 - 64$

4. $j(y) = y^3 - 4y$, $k(y) = 2y^2 - 8$

Calculating the Exact Area Between Curves

In Exercises 5–20, find the area of the region bounded by the given curves. Also sketch the region.

5. $y = x + 2$, $y = x^2$ **6.** $y = x^2 - 5$, $y = 4x$

7. $y = -x^2 - 2x$, $y = x^2 - 4$

8. $y = x^2 - 2x$, $y = -x^2 + 4$

9. $y = 1 - x^2$, $y = x^3 - x$ **10.** $y = x^3 - 1$, $y = x - x^2$

11. $y = \sqrt{x}$, $y = \dfrac{2}{x+1}$, $x = 0$

12. $y = 3\sqrt{x}$, $y = \dfrac{6}{x+2}$, $x = 0$

13. $y = e^x - 1$, $y = 1$, $x \geq 0$

14. $y = e^x - 2$, $y = 1$, $x \geq 0$

15. $y = \cos x$, $y = \sin 2x$, for x in $[0, \frac{\pi}{2}]$

16. $y = \sin x$, $y = \cos 2x$, for x in $[0, \frac{\pi}{2}]$

17. $y = \sec x$, $y = 2$, $-\pi/2 < x < \pi/2$

18. $y = \csc x$, $y = 2$, $0 < x < \pi$

19. $y = x^3 - 16x$, $y = 4x^2 - 64$

20. $y = x^3 - 4x$, $y = 2x^2 - 8$

Area of Multiple Type I Regions

In Exercises 21–42, sketch the region bounded by the given curves and find the area of the region. Each region consists of two or more Type I regions and so to find its area you will either have to (a) set up separate integrals for the Type I regions and add the results or (b) convert, where possible, the region to a single Type II region and do a single integral with respect to y.

21. $y = 1/x$, $y = x$, $y = 0$, $x = 3$

22. $y = 1/x$, $y = x^2$, $y = 0$, $x = 3$

23. $y = 2x$, $y = 3 - x$, $y = 0$

24. $y = 3x$, $y = 4 - x$, $y = 0$

25. $y = -4x + 9$, $y = \frac{1}{2}x$, $y = -\frac{2}{5}x + \frac{27}{5}$

26. $y = -2x + 10$, $y = \frac{1}{2}x + \frac{2}{3}$, $y = 5x - 4$

27. $y = \frac{1}{2}x + 1$, $y = \frac{1}{2}x + 3$, $x = 1$, $x = 4$

28. $y = mx + c_1$, $y = mx + c_2$, $x = a$, $x = b$

29. $y = 2x + 1$, $y = x$, $y = 4 - x$, $x = 0$

30. $y = 3x + 1$, $y = \frac{1}{4}x$, $y = 5 - x$, $x = 0$

31. $x^2 \leq y$, $y \leq x + 6$, $-x + 2 \leq y$

32. $x^2 \leq y$, $y \leq -x + 6$, $x + 2 \leq y$

33. $y = \sqrt{x}$, $y = 2 - x$, $y = 0$

34. $y = 2\sqrt{x}$, $y = 3 - x$, $y = 0$

35. $y = 2/\sqrt{x}$, $y = 2x$, $y = 1$

36. $y = 3/\sqrt{x}$, $y = 3x$, $y = 1$

37. $y = x^2$, $y = \ln x$, $y = 0$, $y = 1$

38. $y = x^3$, $y = \ln x$, $y = 0$, $y = 1$

39. $y = x^3$, $y = x - 1$, $y = 1$, $y = -1$

40. $y = -x^3$, $y = 1 - x$, $y = 1$, $y = -1$

41. $y = x^3$, $y = (x - 2)^2$, $y = 1$, $y = 2$

42. $y = x^5$, $y = (x - 2)^4$, $y = 1$, $y = 2$

Finding Areas by Converting to a Type II Region

In Exercises 43–48, the region D is the region beneath the graph of the function on the given interval (a Type I region). Sketch the region D and find the area of D by converting it to a Type II region and integrating with respect to y.

43. $y = \sin^{-1} x$, $0 \leq x \leq 1$ **44.** $y = \cos^{-1} x$, $0 \leq x \leq 1$

45. $y = \ln x$, $1 \leq x \leq 3$ **46.** $y = \ln(x - 1)$, $2 \leq x \leq 5$

47. $y = \ln(1 + \sqrt{x})$, $0 \leq x \leq 1$

48. $y = \ln(1 + \sqrt[3]{x})$, $0 \leq x \leq 1$

Calculus Concepts & Computation

5.2 Solids with Known Sectional Area

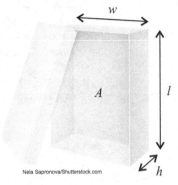

Figure 5.2.1: *A rectangular parallelepiped.*

Another major application of the definite integral is in measuring *volumes* of special types of solids. While measuring areas of regions requires only a single integral (for simple regions), you will see, in an ensuing chapter, that multiple integrals are needed to measure volumes of general solids. However, for a special type of solid, called a *solid of known sectional area*, a single integral of its sectional area function will suffice to get its volume. When this type of solid has a constant sectional area function then the solid is called a *generalized cylinder*. So, we discuss generalized cylinders first.

Generalized Cylinders

The notion of volume for general solids is quite complicated. Starting with the definition of volume for a rectangular parallelepiped (a shoe box) one can use calculus to determine the volume of more general solids.

A solid E is called a *parallelepiped* if it is bounded by three pairs of parallel planes, with each pair intersecting the other two pairs. If each pair of planes intersects the other two pairs in right angles, then E is called a *rectangular parallelepiped (a box)*. For the case of a rectangular parallelepiped it is natural to define its volume V as the product of the lengths of its perpendicular sides: $V = lwh$. See Figure 5.2.1.

Note that the base of the box has area $A = lw$ and so another way to express the volume is

$$V = Ah$$

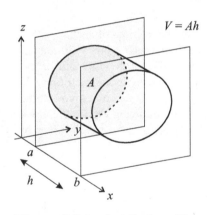

Figure 5.2.2: *A cylinder with base $A = \pi r^2$ and height h.*

The formula $V = Ah$ also extends to a class of solids called *generalized cylinders*. An ordinary cylinder can be viewed as the solid generated by translating a circle in a direction that is perpendicular to the plane in which the circle lies. For example, Figure 5.2.2 shows a circle lying in the plane $x = a$, which is perpendicular to the x-axis. A cylinder is generated when this circle is translated in the x-direction, ending in the plane $x = b$. The area of the circle is $A = \pi r^2$ and the "height" of the cylinder is $h = b - a$. *Note*: Usually a cylinder is oriented with its height in the z-direction, but we have oriented the above cylinder in a non-traditional way so that it coincides with the orientations of the solids in the next subsection. We have used the volume formula $V = \pi r^2 h = Ah$ for cylinders at various places in the book, but the proof of its correctness requires calculus. We will see that the formula is a special case of that for a generalized cylinder.

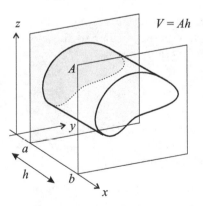

Figure 5.2.3: *A generalized cylinder with "base" area A and "height" h.*

The definition of a *generalized cylinder* is similar to that for the standard cylinder. Start with a region D lying in a plane, say the plane $x = a$, and translate D in the x-direction to the plane $x = b$. This generates a solid E as shown in Figure 5.2.3. The volume of such a solid is given by

$$V = Ah.$$

For now, we will accept this formula as true. Later, in the multivariable part of this book, we will employ double integrals to get a formula for the volumes of very broad class of solids and this formula will reduce to the above formula when the solid is a generalized cylinder.

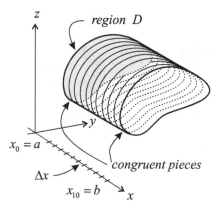

Figure 5.2.4: *A generalized cylinder has cross sections of equal area*

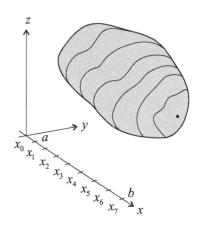

Figure 5.2.5: *A more general solid with varying cross sections.*

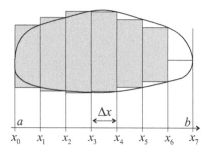

Figure 5.2.6: *Projection of the slices onto the x-z plane.*

Volumes of Solids with Known Cross Sectional Area

To extend the the measurement of volume to solids of known sectional area, we consider first what makes generalized cylinders so special. Suppose, as shown in Figure 5.2.4, E is the generalized cylinder obtained by translation of a region D in the x-direction. Then E has the special property that each cross section of it by a plane perpendicular to the x-axis is a planar region congruent to the region D. Furthermore, slicing E like this gives sub-solids that are generalized cylinders which are all congruent to each other (and thus have the same volume). Figure 5.2.4 shows the solid E sliced into 10 congruent pieces (sub-solids) which we label $E_1, E_2, \ldots, E_{10}$. Each piece E_i has the same volume $V_i = A\Delta x, i = 1, \ldots, 10$. By an additivity property of volume measure, we see that the sum of these volume measures gives the expected volume of E:

$$V = V_1 + V_2 + \cdots + V_{10} = A\Delta x + A\Delta x + \cdots + A\Delta x$$

$$= A(10\Delta x) = A(b-a) = Ah$$

To generalize, suppose we have a solid whose cross sections, by planes $x = k$ perpendicular to the x-axis, vary with k. A good example to consider is a potato, oriented as shown in Figure 5.2.5.

The figure indicates eight cross sections of the potato by planes perpendicular to the x-axis. Two of the cross sections (the ones by planes $x = x_0$, $x = x_7$) are points, while the other six are different regions with different areas. Thus, the potato E is *not* a generalized cylinder. So how can we determine the volume of such a solid? The key to answering this is to consider slicing the potato into a large number of thin pieces, say 50 pieces, much as you would do in making potato chips out of the potato. Each piece (or chip) E_i is *essentially* a generalized cylinder with area A_i and small thickness (height) $h = \Delta x$. The areas A_i of the chips are, as you know from experience, generally different. As in our discussion following Figure 5.2.4, we see that the volume of the potato is approximately the sum of all the volumes of the chips:

$$V \approx A_1\Delta x + A_2\Delta x + \cdots + A_{50}\Delta x = \sum_{i=1}^{50} A_i\Delta x \qquad (5.2.4)$$

This looks like a Riemann sum for a certain definite integral and this argument with the potato suggests that we define the volume of such solids as follows.

Suppose the solid E lies between the planes $x = a$, $x = b$ (with $a < b$) and that for each x between a and b, the cross section through x perpendicular to the x-axis has area $A(x)$. We assume that A is a continuous function of x. If

$$P = \{x_0, x_1, x_2, \ldots, x_n\}$$

is a regular partition of $[a, b]$, then $A(x_i), i = 1, 2, \ldots, n$, are the areas of the cross sections D_i through E with planes $x = x_i$. Translating each section D_i backwards to plane $x = x_{i-1}$ gives a generalized cylinder E_i with volume $V_i = A(x_i)\Delta x$. This construction is indicated for the potato in Figure 5.2.6 (with $n = 7$).

As we have said, the cross sections of E by the planes $x = a$ and $x = b$ are single points (in this example). Also, the right endpoint x_i of each subinterval $[x_{i-1}, x_i]$ is used to make the section and the resulting section is translated back to $x = x_{i-1}$ to generate the ith generalized cylinder. Thus, in the figure for x_7 the generated "solid" is the line segment in the Figure 5.2.6 and has no volume. Figure 5.2.7 is a 3D view of the six generalized cylinders (and one line segment) obtained by the approximation shown in Figure 5.2.6.

This discussion and pictures suggest that, for a general n, an approximate volume of E is

$$V \approx \sum_{i=1}^{n} V_i = \sum_{i=1}^{n} A(x_i)\,\Delta x \qquad (5.2.5)$$

Letting $n \mapsto \infty$ gives the definition of the exact volume V of E in terms of a definite integral, indeed the definite integral of the cross sectional area function A.

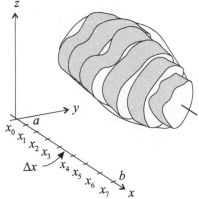

Figure 5.2.7: *Approximation of E by seven generalized cylinders*

DEFINITION 5.2.1 (Volume of a Solid of Known Sectional Area)

Suppose a solid E lies between planes $x = a$, $x = b$, and for each x in $[a,b]$ the

cross section of E by a plane through x perpendicular to the x-axis has area $A(x)$.

If A is an integrable function, then the volume of E is

$$V = \int_a^b A(x)\,dx \qquad (5.2.6)$$

While the discussion leading to this definition is fairly involved, the resulting volume formula (5.2.6) is very simple. Notice how the units of measurement are involved in the formula: If the length x is in meters, then $A(x)$ is in square meters and so

$$dV = A(x)\,dx$$

is in cubic meters. Figure 5.2.8 illustrates, heuristically, the infinitesimal element of volume dV and how a continuous summation of these infinitesimals gives the volume V.

Example 5.2.1 (Ostrich Eggs)

Problem: Ostrich eggs are much larger than chicken eggs, can take as much as 90 minutes to hard boil, and typically have an ellipsoidal shape that is close to spherical. Consider a hard boiled ostrich egg with length 8 inches and having circular sections perpendicular to it length. If the largest circular section has diameter 6 inches, find the volume of the egg.

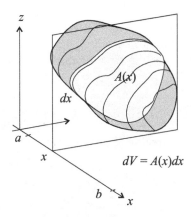

Figure 5.2.8: *A "continuous" sum of infinitesimal elements dV gives the volume* $V = \int_a^b A(x)\,dx$

An ostrich egg and some chicken eggs.

Solution: The shell of the egg can be modeled by the ellipsoidal surface with equation

$$\frac{x^2}{16} + \frac{y^2}{9} + \frac{z^2}{9} = 1$$

where x, y, and z are in inches. See Figure 5.2.9. (You will study ellipsoids in Multivariable Calculus.) Slicing the egg with the plane $x = 0$ gives the equation

$$0 + \frac{y^2}{9} + \frac{z^2}{9} = 1, \text{ equivalently, } y^2 + z^2 = 9.$$

This is a circular section of radius 3 inches (diameter 6 inches) and is the largest circular section. Similarly, slicing the egg with the plane $x = 2$ gives the equation

$$\frac{1}{4} + \frac{y^2}{9} + \frac{z^2}{9} = 1, \text{ equivalently, } y^2 + z^2 = \frac{27}{4},$$

which is a circular section of radius $3\sqrt{3}/2 \approx 2.6$ inches. Generally, for any x between -4 and 4, slicing the egg by such a plane through x will give the equation

$$y^2 + z^2 = \frac{9}{16}\left(16 - x^2\right).$$

This is a circular section of radius r, where

$$r^2 = \frac{9}{16}\left(16 - x^2\right).$$

Thus, the cross sectional area function is

$$A = \pi r^2 = \frac{9}{16}\pi\left(16 - x^2\right),$$

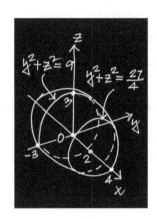

Figure 5.2.9: *An egg with ellipsoidal shape :* $\frac{x^2}{16} + \frac{y^2}{9} + \frac{z^2}{9} = 1$

for x in $[-4.4]$. Now the volume of the egg is easy to calculate. Using symmetry about the origin, we get

$$V = \int_{-4}^{4} A\left(x\right) dx = 2\int_{0}^{4} A\left(x\right) dx = 2\int_{0}^{4} \frac{9\pi}{16}\left(16 - x^2\right) dx$$

$$= \frac{9\pi}{8}\left(16x - \frac{1}{3}x^3\right)\Big|_{0}^{4} = \frac{9\pi}{8}\left(64 - \frac{64}{3}\right) = 48\pi \approx 150.8 \, \text{in}^3$$

<u>NOTE</u>: Many important, every-day solids of known cross section are *solids of revolution*. The ostrich egg in the above example is a solid of revolution. These will be discussed in the next two sections. However, not all solids with circular sections are solids of revolution, as the next example shows.

Example 5.2.2 (A Cone)

Problem: Find the volume of the conical solid shown in Figure 5.2.10.

Solution: We orient the x-axis as shown. Then for an x between 0 and 12, let d be the diameter of the circular section at x. Since the gold and yellow right triangles in the picture are similar, we have that the ratios of their corresponding sides are equal:

$$\frac{d}{8} = \frac{x}{12}.$$

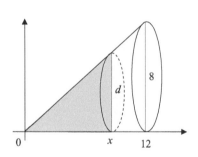

Figure 5.2.10: *A cone with "height" 12 ft and circular base with diameter 8 ft.*

This gives $d = 8x/12 = 2x/3$, and so the area of the circular section at x is

$$A = \pi\left(\frac{d}{2}\right)^2 = \frac{1}{4}\pi\left(\frac{2x}{3}\right)^2 = \frac{\pi}{9}x^2.$$

Then the volume is

$$V = \int_{a}^{b} A\left(x\right) dx = \int_{0}^{12} \frac{\pi}{9}x^2 dx = \frac{\pi}{9}\left(\frac{1}{3}x^3\right)\Big|_{0}^{12} = 64\pi$$

We can write the answer as follows so that it corresponds to the general volume formula for a cone:

$$V = 64\pi = \frac{1}{3}\pi\left(4\right)^2\left(12\right) = \frac{1}{3}\pi r^2 h = \frac{1}{3}Ah$$

Conical volume is one-third the area of the base times the height.

Template Solids

Consider a solid E which is bounded on one side by a Type I region D, called the *template* of the solid. See Figure 5.2.11.

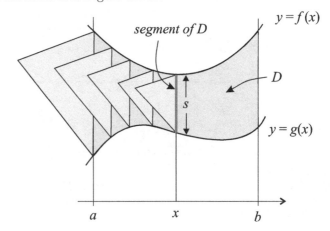

Figure 5.2.11: *A template solid with a Type I region D as its bottom. Here each section is an equilateral triangle with one side coinciding with a segment of D.*

Further, suppose each cross section of E perpendicular to the x-axis is a basic geometrical figure (rectangle, triangle, semicircle) with one of its sides coinciding with the segment of D made by the cross section. For example, Figure 5.2.11 shows such a solid where the cross sections are equilateral triangles with the base of the triangle coinciding with a segment of D.

Note that for each x between a and b, the plane through x which is perpendicular to the x-axis intersects the region D in a line segment, called a *segment of D*. This segment has length s given by

$$s = f(x) - g(x)$$

Since each cross section of E is a basic geometric figure with one side of length s, we can use geometry to determine the cross sectional area first as a function of s and then as a function of x.

As indicated by Figure 5.2.11, we assume each section of E lies above the x-y plane. Thus, one face (namely the bottom) of the solid E is flat and coincides with the template (the region D). Later we will generalize this, allowing the template to lie within the solid.

Example 5.2.3 (Triangular Cross Sections)

Problem: Suppose E is a template solid with template being the region D enclosed by the graphs of

$$f(x) = 2 - \sqrt{x}, \quad g(x) = \sqrt{x}, \quad x = 0.$$

Also suppose that each section of E by a plane perpendicular to the x-axis is an equilateral triangle having one of its sides a segment of D. Find the volume of E.

Solution: First sketch, by hand, a graph of the region D that is the bottom of E. This is shown in the Figure 5.2.12.

The figure also shows, for an x in $[0, 1]$, a segment of the Type I region D and a section of the solid. Here the length s of the segment of D is calculated to be

$$s = f(x) - g(x) = (2 - \sqrt{x}) - (\sqrt{x}) = 2 - 2\sqrt{x}$$

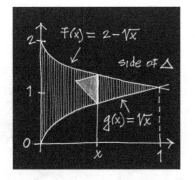

Figure 5.2.12: *A sketch of the template D of the solid and a typical cross section of the solid with template segment of length s.*

So s varies from a maximum of 2 (when $x = 0$) to a minimum of 0 (when $x = 1$). Now try to visualize the cross sections of E. Each is an equilateral triangle, the largest with side $s = 2$ and smallest side $s = 0$. From elementary geometry (See the Table of Geometries in the exercises) the area of an equilateral triangle with side s is

$$A = \frac{\sqrt{3}}{4} s^2.$$

So, as a function of x:

$$A(x) = \frac{\sqrt{3}}{4} s^2 = \frac{\sqrt{3}}{4} \left(2 - 2\sqrt{x}\right)^2 = \frac{\sqrt{3}}{4} \left(4 - 8\sqrt{x} + 4x\right)$$

$$= \sqrt{3}\left(1 - 2\sqrt{x} + x\right)$$

Then the volume of this solid is

$$V = \int_0^1 A(x)\,dx = \int_0^1 \sqrt{3}\left(1 - 2\sqrt{x} + x\right)dx$$

$$= \sqrt{3}\left(x - \frac{4}{3}x^{\frac{3}{2}} + \frac{1}{2}x^2\right)\Big|_0^1 = \sqrt{3}\left(1 - \frac{4}{3} + \frac{1}{2}\right) = \frac{\sqrt{3}}{6}$$

You can use the special-purpose Maple procedure

```
sections(f,g,a,b,N,type,figure,k)
```

to create an animation of the solid being approximated by N slices (cross sections). The procedure assumes the region is a Type I region bounded by

$$y = f(x),\ y = g(x),\ x = a,\ x = b$$

with $g(x) \le f(x)$ for x in $[a, b]$. The sixth argument to the procedure, **type**, indicates the type of cross section. There are four main types:

    1 = squares
    2 = equilateral triangles
    3 = semicircles
    4 = isosceles right triangles with hypotenuse in the base

The seventh and eighth arguments specify the name (**figure**) of a static figure to be produced and the number (k $\le$ N) of approximating cross sections to be shown in the static figure.

For instance, in Example 5.2.3, we can generate an approximation using N = 20 slices by using the following code.

```
>  f:=x->2-sqrt(x);g:=x->sqrt(x);
```

$$f := x \mapsto 2 - \sqrt{x}$$
$$g := x \mapsto \sqrt{x}$$

```
>  sections(f,g,0,1,20,2,fig,13);
```

The animation gives a feel for how the solid is built up out of sectional pieces. The kth frame of the animation is stored in the variable named **fig**. This is shown below for $k = 13$.

```
>  fig;
```

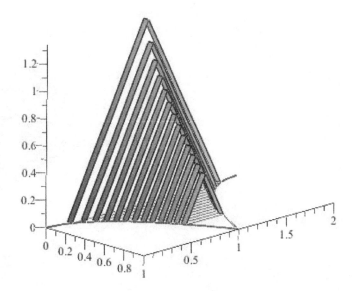

Figure 5.2.13: *An approximation, with 20 cross sections, to the solid in Example 5.2.3. The figure shows the first 13 cross sectional approximations. The boundary curves of the region D are shown in blue and the segments of D in red.*

Example 5.2.4 (Semicircular Cross Sections)

Problem: Suppose that the bottom of a template solid E is the region D bounded by the graphs of

$$f(x) = e^{-x}, \ g(x) = 0, \ x = 0, \ x = 2.$$

Assume that each section of E by a plane perpendicular to the x-axis is an semicircle with its diameter coinciding with a segment of D. Find the volume of E.

Solution: As before, we sketch the template and put in a typical cross section at some point x between $x = 0$ and $x = 2$. Each cross section, being a semicircle has area that is one-half the area of the corresponding circle:

$$A = \frac{1}{2} \pi r^2$$

To find how the radius r depends on x, note that the cross section at a typical x between 0 and 2 has diameter $s = e^{-x}$. Thus, r is one-half of this and so the area function is

$$A(x) = \frac{1}{2} \pi \left(\frac{1}{2} e^{-x} \right)^2 = \frac{\pi}{8} e^{-2x}.$$

The volume is then

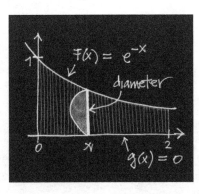

Figure 5.2.14: *A sketch of the template D of the solid and a typical cross section of the solid with template segment of length s.*

$$V = \int_0^2 \frac{\pi}{8} e^{-2x} \, dx = \frac{\pi}{8} \left(-\frac{1}{2} e^{-2x} \right) \Big|_0^2 = \frac{\pi}{8} \left(-\frac{1}{2} e^{-4} + \frac{1}{2} \right) = \frac{\pi}{16} \left(1 - e^{-4} \right)$$

We can again get a better visualization of the solid by using the `sections` command as follows.

```
>   f:=x->exp(-x);g:=x->0;
```

$$f := x \mapsto e^{-x}$$
$$g := x \mapsto 0$$

```
>   sections(f,g,0,2,20,3,fig,10);
```

That gives an animation showing the solid being approximated by 20 semicircular disks. A static picture, showing the first 10 approximating semicircular disks, is shown below.

```
>  fig;
```

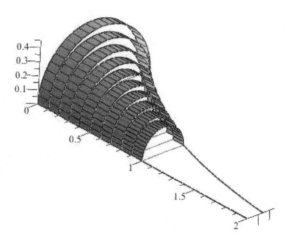

Figure 5.2.15: *The first* 10 *cross sectional approximations to the solid in* Example 5.2.4. *The boundary curves of the region* D *are shown in blue and the segments of* D *in red.*

Example 5.2.5 (Pyramids and Shifted, Twisted Pyramids)

Suppose b and h are positive constants and D is the triangular region bounded by the graphs of

$$f(x) = \frac{b}{2h}x, \qquad g(x) = -\frac{b}{2h}x$$

for x in $[0, h]$. Let E_1 be the template solid with D as the bottom face and having each section perpendicular to the x-axis be a square with one side coinciding with a segment of D. Then E_1 is a pyramid with "height" h and "base" a square of side length b. See Figure 5.2.16.

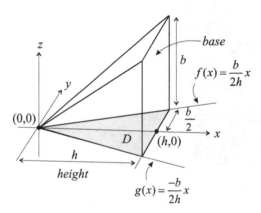

Figure 5.2.16: *A template solid* E_1 *with triangular template* D *and square sections.*

NOTE: This pyramid is not oriented as usual since its square base in not in the x-y plane. But, we still refer to h as its height.

The volume of the pyramid is easy to calculate. The area of a section is simply $A = s^2$ and the section at x has

$$s = f(x) - g(x) = \frac{b}{2h}x - \left(-\frac{b}{2h}x\right) = \frac{b}{h}x.$$

Then

$$A = s^2 = \frac{b^2}{h^2}x^2$$

and

$$V = \int_0^h A(x)\,dx = \int_0^h \frac{b^2}{h^2}x^2\,dx = \frac{b^2}{h^2}\left(\frac{1}{3}x^3\right)\Big|_0^h = \frac{b^2}{h^2}\left(\frac{h^3}{3}\right) = \frac{1}{3}b^2 h$$

This verifies, using calculus, the famous formula from elementary geometry that the volume of a pyramid is

$$V = \frac{1}{3}(\text{Area of the Base})\cdot(\text{Height}).$$

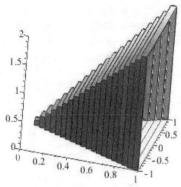

Figure 5.2.17: *Sectional approximation to the pyramid E_1.*

This pyramid can also be visualized using the sectional approximations to it created by the `sections` command. For this we take $h = 1 = b$ and `type=1`.

```
>   f:=x->x;g:=x->-x;
```

$$f := x \mapsto x$$
$$g := x \mapsto -x$$

```
>   sections(f,g,0,1,15,1,fig,15);
>   fig;
```

The pyramid in Figure 5.2.17 is not the standard pyramid because its apex is not centered over its base. To get a *standard pyramid E_2*, we use the same region D and have each section perpendicular to the x-axis be a square whose side length s is the same as the segment of D made by the section. But, we shift the center of the square down a distance of $s/2$ below D. The shape of one such standard pyramid is indicated in the sectional approximation shown in Figure 5.2.18.

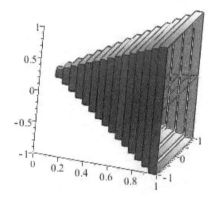

Figure 5.2.18: *Sectional approximation to the pyramid E_2.*

Instead of shifting the centers of the sectional squares down by amounts $\frac{1}{2}s = \frac{b}{2h}x$, we can shift by an amount specified by a function $v(x)$. For example, $v(x) = x^2$. This gives a *curved pyramid E_3* which has a shape indicated by the sectional approximation in Figure 5.2.19.

One final variation on this pyramidal theme is to allow twisting as well as shifting, of the sectional square. Specifically, after shifting the sectional square at x down by amount $v(x)$, we twist it, i.e., rotate it about is center by amount $t(x)$. This gives a twisted *pyramid E_4* which has a shape indicated by the sectional approximation in Figure 5.2.20.

NOTE: The graphics here were produced by a special-purpose Maple procedure like `sections`. See the exercises for this.

One question may have occurred to you when studying the four "pyramids" in Example 5.2.5. How do we measure their volumes? For the first one, E_1, since it is a template solid with D as its bottom face, we can find its volume, as we did, by integrating the area function. The standard pyramid E_2 can be viewed as a double solid and so we could find the volume of the template solid that is its top half and then double it. But what about the volumes of the shifted and shifted-twisted pyramids E_3 and E_4?

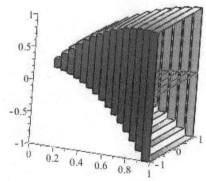

Figure 5.2.19: *Sectional approximation to the pyramid E_3.*

The answer to the last question is quite simple and you can perhaps guess what it is by studying and comparing all four of the sectional approximations to the pyramids as shown in Figures 5.2.17–5.2.20. Each of the four sectional approximations consists of 15 slabs and from one figure to the next each corresponding slab appears to have the same volume; the slab is just shifted or shifted and twisted. Thus, all four sectional approximations have the equal volumes. The same can be surmised about the infinitesimal slabs, the one for the cross section at x, $dV = A(x)\,dx$ is the

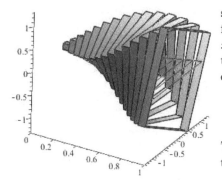

Figure 5.2.20: *Sectional approximation to the shifted, twisted pyramid E_4.*

same for each of the pyramids. More precisely, what we are saying is that the area function $A(x)$ is the same for each of the four pyramids since the cross sections at x are the same square in each case, with the square being shifted or shifted and twisted in pyramids E_2, E_3, and E_4. Shifting and twisting does not change the area of the square. Hence all four pyramids have the same volume

$$V = \int_0^h A(x)\,dx = \frac{1}{3}b^2 h$$

This discussion serves to motivate an old and famous principle first formulated by the Italian mathematician Bonaventure Cavalieri (1498-1547).

Cavalieri's Principle

If two solids have the property that each plane parallel to a given plane produces cross sections with equal areas, then the solids have the same volume.

SUMMARY: To measure the volume of any template solid, whether the template is the bottom face or not, determine its cross sectional area function $A(x)$ and then integrate.

Example 5.2.6 (The Great Pyramid of Giza)

Problem: The ancient pyramid of in Egypt has a base that is approximately 756 ft on a side and is approximately 481 ft high. Find the volume of the pyramid.

Boonsom/Shutterstock.com

Figure 5.2.21: *The Great Pyramid of Giza.*

Solution: By the formula from the previous example, the volume is

$$V = \frac{1}{3}Ah = \frac{1}{3}(756)^2 \cdot 481 = 91,636,272 \text{ ft}^3.$$

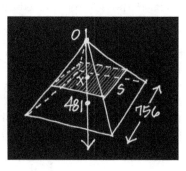

Figure 5.2.22: *A sketch for the ratio method.*

An alternative to using this formula from the discussion of template solids, we can also use the ratio method from Example 5.2.6. For this locate the x-axis vertically with its origin at the apex of the pyramid and directed downward. The sketch in Figure 5.2.22 shows this.

Then for each x between 0 and 481, the cross section at x is a square with side s. By similar triangles

$$\frac{s}{x} = \frac{756}{481}. \text{ So } s = \frac{756}{481}x$$

Thus, the area function is

$$A = s^2 = \left(\frac{756}{481}\right)^2 x^2.$$

Then the volume is

$$V = \int_a^b A\left(x\right) dx = \int_0^{481} \left(\frac{756}{481}\right)^2 x^2 \, dx = \frac{1}{3}\left(\frac{756}{481}\right)^2 x^3 \Big|_0^{481} = \frac{1}{3}\left(756\right)^2 \cdot 481,$$

which gives the same result as before.

Exercises: 5.2 (Solid with Known Sectional Area)

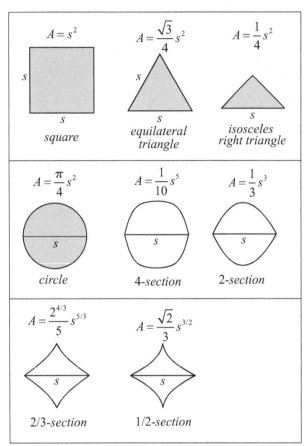

TABLE OF GEOMETRIES

The areas of some standard geometric figures for use in Exercises 11–20 are shown in gold. The other areas pertain to some nonstandard figures for use in Exercises 21–30 and 37.

Eggs, Monuments, and Swimming Pools

In Exercises 1–10 find the indicated volumes. In 3–10, you can use, if you wish, the method of ratios of sides of similar triangles to determine the cross sectional area functions $A(x)$. NOTE: Even if you know a geometrical formula for the volume, you should also set up an integral.

$$V = \int_a^b A(x)\, dx$$

and use calculus to find the volume.

Volumes of Eggs

1. Find the volume of the ostrich egg whose shell has the equation $\dfrac{x^2}{25} + \dfrac{y^2}{16} + \dfrac{z^2}{16} = 1$.

2. A large chicken egg is four inches long and two inches wide. Find the volume of the egg, assuming it is ellipsoidal in shape.

Volumes of Conical Tanks

3. A storage tank is in the shape of a right circular cone with height 12 m and circular base of diameter 12 m. Find the volume of the tank.

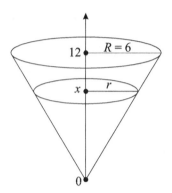

4. The storage tank in Exercise 3 has water in it 1 meter in depth (1 meter from the bottom). How much water will it take to fill the tank to within 2 m of the top?

Volumes of Swimming Pools

5. A 40 ft long by 20 ft wide rectangular swimming pool is filled with water, having a depth of 3 ft at the shallow end and 8 ft at the deep end (40 ft from the shallow end). Calculate the volume of the water in the pool.

6. In Las Vegas, a swimming pool is constructed in the shape of an inverted right circular cone. If the cone has a 20 ft diameter base (the top edge of the pool) and is 2 ft deep, find the volume of water needed to fill it to the top.

Volumes of Monuments

7. A proposed bronze monument honoring Pythagoras is 10 feet high tapering from its base (which is an isosceles right triangle) to a point at its apex. At the base, the sides about the right angle are each 2 feet in length. If each section perpendicular to its axis is an isosceles right triangle, what volume of bronze is needed to cast the monument?

8. A proposed aluminum monument honoring Euclid is 15 feet high tapering from its base (which is an equilateral triangle) to a point at its apex. At the base, all the sides of the triangle are are 3 feet in length. If each section perpendicular to its axis is an equilateral triangle, what volume of aluminum is needed to cast the monument?

9. The Washington monument is an obelisk, a much-used shape for monuments. It has a main shaft which is a truncated pyramid: height 500 ft, base 55 ft square, and top 34 ft square. The shaft is capped by a small pyramid of height 55 ft (and base 34 ft square). Find the volume. *Hint*: Consider the cap and shaft separately.

Zack Frank/Shutterstock.com

10. The Obelisk of Buenos Aires has a main shaft which is a truncated pyramid: height 63 m, base 4.9 m square, and top 3.5 m square. The shaft is capped by a small pyramid of height 4.9 m (and base, 3.5 m square). Find the volume.

meunierd/Shutterstock.com

Volumes of Template Solids

In Exercises 11–20, find the volume of the template solid with template being the region D enclosed by the given curves and with cross sections of the specified geometrical type. Rectangles and triangles have one of their sides coincide with a segment of D. Semicircles have their diameters on a segment of D. ALSO: (a) Sketch the region D and a typical cross section and (b) **CAS:** Use, where possible, the `sections` command to produce an animation that will help you understand the shape of the solid.

11. $y = x^2, y = 2 - x^2, x \geq 0$, squares,

12. $y = x^3, y = 2 - x^3, x \geq 0$, squares

13. $y = 1 - x^3, y = 0, x = 0,$, equilateral triangles

14. $y = 1 - x^4, y = 0, x \geq 0$, equilateral triangles

15. $y = \cos x, y = \sin x, x = 0, x = \pi/4$, semicircles

16. $y = \tan x, y = \sec x, x = 0, x = \pi/4$, semicircles

17. $y = \sin, x, y = 1, x = 0, x = \pi/2$, squares

18. $y = \cos x, y = 1, x = 0, x = \pi/2$, squares

19. $y = e^x, y = e^{-x}, x = 0, x = 1$, isosceles right triangles, hypotenuse in the base.

20. $y = 1 - \sqrt{x}, y = 1 + x, x = 0, x = 1$, isosceles right triangles

Template Solids with p-Sections

In this group of exercises, we consider template solids with cross sections that are called p-sections, where p is any positive number. When $p = 1$, the cross section is a square and for other values of p you can consider a p-section as a generalization of a square, although the sides are curved. One side of the p-section is the graph of the function

$$C(y) = (s/2)^p - y^p$$

on the interval $(0, s/2)$. Here s denotes the length of the *diagonal* of the p-section, The figure below shows the graph of C, which forms one side of the p-section.

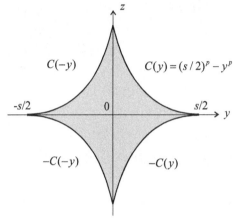

Figure 5.2.1x: *A p-section is the region bounded by the graphs of C and its reflections about the x-axis, y-axis, and the origin.*

Note that the graph of C has $s/2$ as its x-intercept. The other three sides of the p-section are formed by the graphs of the functions shown in the figure. The figure is for $p = 1/2$, in which case

$$C(y) = \sqrt{s/2} - \sqrt{y} \quad (\textit{the 1/2-section function}).$$

Another important case is $p = 2$, in, which case

$$C(y) = (s/2)^2 - y^2 \quad (\textit{the 2-section function}).$$

NOTE: The area of a p-section is 4 times the area of the region under the graph of C:

$$A_p = 4 \int_0^{s/2} C(y)\, dy.$$

The Table of Geometries at the beginning of this exercise set gives these areas for $p = 4, 2, 1/2$, and $3/2$. Exercise 30 below gives the area for a general p.

Exercises with p-Sections

In Exercises 21–29, find the volume of the template solid with the specified region D:

$$y = f(x), y = g(x), \quad x \text{ in } [a, b]$$

as its template and with each cross section a p-section (for the given p) with its *diagonal* coinciding with a segment of D. (Because the segment is a diagonal, the template D is in the core of the solid and divides it in half.) ALSO (1) Sketch the region and a typical cross section, and (2) CAS: Use the command

$$\texttt{psurface(f, g, a, b, p)}$$

to plot the surface that bounds the solid. Or you can use

$$\texttt{psections(f, g, a, b, N, p, figure, k)}$$

to visualize the solid via its sectional approximations (with N sections).

21. $f(x) = \sqrt{x}$, $g(x) = -x$, $[0,1]$, $p = 2$

22. $f(x) = 1 + x^2$, $g(x) = 1 - \sqrt{x}$, $[0,1]$, $p = 2$

23. $f(x) = \sin x$, $g(x) = -f(x)$, $[0,\pi]$, $p = 2$

24. $f(x) = \cos x$, $g(x) = -f(x)$, $[0,\pi]$, $p = 2$

25. $f(x) = \sqrt{x}$, $g(x) = -f(x)$, $[0,1]$, $p = 4$

26. $f(x) = \sqrt[3]{x}$, $g(x) = -f(x)$, $[0,1]$, $p = 4$

27. $f(x) = 1 - x$, $g(x) = -f(x)$, $[0,1]$, $p = 4$

28. $f(x) = 1 - \dfrac{1}{2}x$, $g(x) = -f(x)$, $[0,1]$, $p = 4$

29. $f(x) = x$, $g(x) = -x$, $[0,1]$, $p = 1/2$

30. Show that a p-section with diagonal length s has area $A_p = \dfrac{p}{(p+1)\,2^{p-1}}s^{p+1}$.

Template Solids with q-Regions for Templates (Tents & Teepees)

The next group of exercises deals with template solids having templates that are called *q-regions*. A q-region is the Type I region bounded by the graphs of

$$f(x) = \frac{b}{2h^q}x^q, \qquad g(x) = \frac{-b}{2h^q}x^q$$

on the interval $[0,h]$. Here q, b, and h are any positive numbers. The function f is a basic power function $y = mx^q$ with coefficient $m = \frac{b}{2h^q}$ chosen so that $f(h) = \dfrac{b}{2}$. See the figure below.

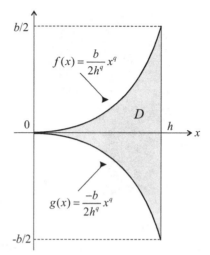

Figure 5.2.2x: *A region D, called a q-region, is bounded by a power function and its negative.*

We can consider a template solid with a q-region as its template, forming the bottom face of the solid. We allow any type of geometric figure as cross sections. Here, for the most part, we only consider cross sections that are squares. The resulting solids are called *generalized pyramids*. The usual type of pyramid, one with flat bounding surfaces, comes from the choice $q= 1$. See Figure 5.2.16 in Example 5.2.5. As mentioned in that example, the standard pyramid arises from having the square cross sections shifted down half a side length as indicated in Figure 5.2.18.

We will do this shifting here for the generalized pyramids. As you will see from the visualizations below, you can think of these solids as tents. Indeed, some native American teepees had the shape of a standard pyramid, being constructed of four poles tilted together and wrapped with animal skins. Other teepees used more poles and were conical in shape.

In Exercises 31–38 find the volume of the generalized pyramid (tent). Also (a) sketch the template region, showing a typical cross section, and (b) CAS: use the `psurface` command to visualize the solid. Compare the result to that for the standard pyramid in Example 5.2.5.

31. $q = 2$, square sections, any b and h.

32. $q = 3$, square sections, any b and h

33. $q = 1/2$, square sections, any b and h

34. $q = 1/3$, square sections, any b and h

35. Twisted Tents

The tent in Exercise 33, after being set up is twisted by a sudden gust of wind. Figure 5.2.4x in that exercise shows the BEFORE shape of the tent. The figure below shows the AFTER shape of the tent. Calculate the volume of each tent. You may use the result from Exercise 33.

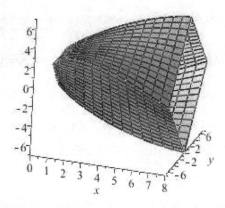

36. Twisted Tents

The tent in Exercise 31, after being set up is twisted by a sudden gust of wind. Figure 5.2.3x in that exercise shows the BEFORE shape of the tent. The figure below shows the AFTER shape of the tent. You may use the result from Exercise 31.

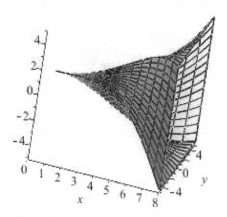

37. $q = 1/2, p = 2$-sections, any b and h
38. $q = 1/3, p = 3$-sections, any b and h

Fixed Perimeter Sections

In this group of exercises, consider template solids whose sections are either (1) rectangles or (2) sectors of circles and assume that each section has the same perimeter $P = 4$. The template is a region D bounded by $y = f(x)$, $y = g(x)$ for x in the interval $[0, 1]$ and the segments of D have lengths $s = f(x) - g(x)$.

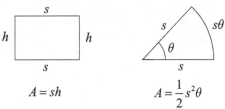

$$A = sh \qquad\qquad A = \frac{1}{2}s^2\theta$$

Each segment D by a plane perpendicular to the x-axis coincides with either (1) the bottom side of the rectangular section or (2) the bottom radius of the sectorial

section. Find the volume of the solid. CAS: You can also use a special-purpose Maple procedure

        FPsections(f,g,a,b,N,type,figure,k)

to produce and animation of the solid being approximated by sections. This works exactly like the `sections` procedure, except now there are two types

type = 1 (rectangles with perimeter 4)
type = 2   (sectors with perimeter 4)

39. $f(x) = x^2$, $g(x) = -x^2$, rectangles
40. $f(x) = \sqrt{x}$, $g(x) = -\sqrt{x}$, rectangles
41. $f(x) = \cos(\pi x/2)$, $g(x) = 0$, rectangles
42. $f(x) = 1 - x^2$, $g(x) = 0$, rectangles
43. $f(x) = 1 + \sqrt{x}$, $g(x) = 0$, sectors
44. $f(x) = 1 + x^{1/3}$, $g(x) = 0$, sectors
45. $f(x) = 1$, $g(x) = -e^{-2x}$, sectors
46. $f(x) = 1$, $g(x) = -e^{-3x}$, sectors

Disk

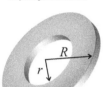

Washer (Annulus)

 Calculus Concepts & Computation

5.3 Solids of Revolution-Disk Method

The most common and important type of a solid with known cross sections is a *solid of revolution*. For solids of revolution, each cross-section perpendicular to the axis of revolution is either a disk or an annulus, centered on the axis of revolution.

The area for a disk, which commonly is called the area of a circle, is given by the well-known formula:

$$A = \pi R^2.$$

An annulus is sometimes called a washer because it is the shape of washers used with nuts and bolts. Being the region between two concentric circles, an annulus has area which is the difference of the areas of the respective concentric disks:

$$A = \pi R^2 - \pi r^2 = \pi \left(R^2 - r^2 \right),$$

where $r < R$ are the radii of the circles. To compute the volume V, which is the integral of the area function A, all we have to do is determine how R (and r, in the washer case) depends on x (or other variables of integration). This determination is aided by an understanding of the geometry of solids of revolution and an ability to visualize them as well. We first discuss these things before computing volumes.

Solids of Revolution (Definition and Discussion)

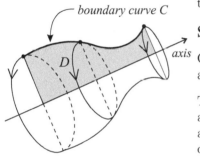

Geometrically a solid of revolution E is generated by revolving a a planar region D about a given line, called the *axis* for the solid. See figure 5.3.1.

The region D is bounded by a curve (or curves) C and during the revolution about the axis, each point on C sweeps out a circle, which is the boundary of a circular disk. The solid E can be considered as being comprised of all these circular disks (They are its cross sections.) It is also important to observe that during the revolution, the curve (or curves) C that bounds the region D generates a surface, called a *surface of revolution*. This surface bounds the corresponding solid of revolution.

Figure 5.3.1: *A Region D revolved about an axis creates a solid of revolution.*

In the simplest case the axis of revolution is the x-axis and D is a Type I region bounded by the graph of a continuous (nonnegative) function f on an interval $[a,b]$, the vertical lines through a and b, and the x-axis. See Figure 5.3.2.

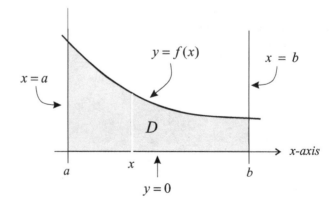

Figure 5.3.2: *The region D beneath the graph of f on $[a, b]$.*

<u>NOTE</u>: The general Type I region (see Section 5.1) is bounded on the bottom by the graph of a function g. The simpler region here has $g(x) = 0$, for all x in the

interval $[a, b]$. This simpler type of region is called *the region beneath the graph of* f (on the given interval).

In the above figure we have indicated (in yellow) a typical line segment in the region D. When the region is revolved about the x-axis, this line segment sweeps out a circular disk. This is shown in yellow in Figure 5.3.3 below.

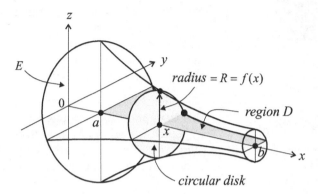

Figure 5.3.3: *The solid of revolution generated by the region beneath the graph of* f.

The circular disk shown in yellow is a typical cross section and it is easy to see that it has radius $R = f(x)$. Observe how this radius varies as x ranges throughout the interval $[a, b]$

We next discuss ways of visualizing these solids.

Drawing Solids of Revolution

We want you to be able to visualize the solids of revolution that occur in the exercises by using hand-drawn sketches (and sometimes computer plots). Here are some directions for doing these activities.

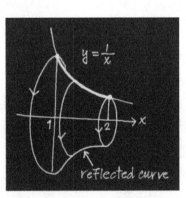

Figure 5.3.4: *A hand-drawn sketch of a solid of revolution.*

Hand-Drawn Sketches: The key to sketching a solid of revolution by hand is to first sketch the curve that generates the corresponding surface of revolution. Thus, plot the graph of f in the x-y plane. Then make this figure look three-dimensional by sketching the circles generated by the two endpoints $(a, f(a))$ and $(b, f(b))$ as they revolve about the axis of revolution. You might want to add an additional circle or two generated by other points on the graph. This will help make the sketch look more three-dimensional. For example, Figure 5.3.4 shows the hand-drawn plot of the function $f(x) = \frac{1}{x}$, on the interval $[1, 2]$, and several circles on the solid of revolution.

Note that as the graph of f is revolved about the x-axis, it sweeps out the surface bounding the solid, and when it has revolved through 180 degrees it reappears in the x-y plane as a curve which is the reflection of the graph of f about the x-axis. It helps to draw this reflected graph when making a sketch of the solid of revolution.

Computer Plots: We have provided several special-purpose Maple commands for plotting surfaces of revolution. The one we want to use here is

```
revolve1X(f,g,a,b)
```

This is for revolving a Type I region about the x-axis. It produces a plot of the surface of revolution that bounds the corresponding solid. Before using this command make sure f, g, a, b are defined as usual in Maple. For example,

```
>   f:=x->1/x;g:=0;
```

$$f := x \mapsto \frac{1}{x}$$

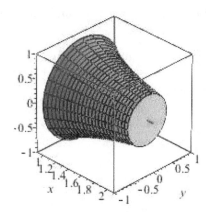

Figure 5.3.5: *A solid of revolution generated by* `revolve1X(f,g,a,b)`.

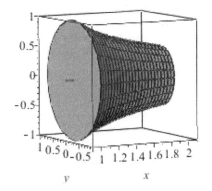

Figure 5.3.6: *Another view of the solid from Figure* 5.3.5.

$$g := 0$$

```
>  a:=1;b:=2;
```

$$a := 1$$
$$b := 2$$

```
>  revolve1X(f,g,a,b);
```

Note how various points on the graph of f generate circles on the surface of revolution. Also note how the graph of f is rotated and displayed at various positions on the surface. The figure also includes plots of the first and last circular disk cross sections. The one at $x = b$ is shown in grey. By rotating the figure you can see the one at $x = a$, which is colored brown in Figure 5.3.6. There are other views

you might want to consider when studying a solid of revolution, but the solid in this example is very simple, and so the first figure perhaps suffices to comprehend it. Later we will look at additional arguments in the `revolve1X` command that allow you to cut away parts of the bounding surface so that the solid is easier to understand. You can also use the special purpose command

```
animate-revolve(f,a,b)
```

to produce a movie of the surface of revolution being swept out as the graph of f is revolved about the x-axis. After becoming familiar with how solids of revolution are generated, you will be able to get by with just using the static `revolve1X` command for studying these solids.

The Disk Method Formula

The last subsection gave you experience with solids of revolution E obtained by revolving the region D beneath the graph of of a function f about the x-axis. Since each cross section of E is a circular disk centered on the x-axis, the cross sectional area function has the form $A = \pi R^2$. Figure 5.3.7 shows a typical example.

As you can see, for each x in $[a, b]$, the cross section at x has radius $R = f(x)$ and so the area function, as a function of x, is

$$A(x) = \pi \left[f(x) \right]^2.$$

This gives the following integral formula for such a solid of revolution:

Volume - Disk Method

If f is nonnegative and continuous on $[a, b]$,

then the volume V of the solid obtained by revolving

the region beneath the graph of f about the x-axis is

$$V = \int_a^b \pi \left[f(x) \right]^2 dx \qquad (5.3.1a)$$

Alternatively

$$V = \int_a^b \pi R^2 dx \qquad (5.3.1b)$$

where $R = f(x)$.

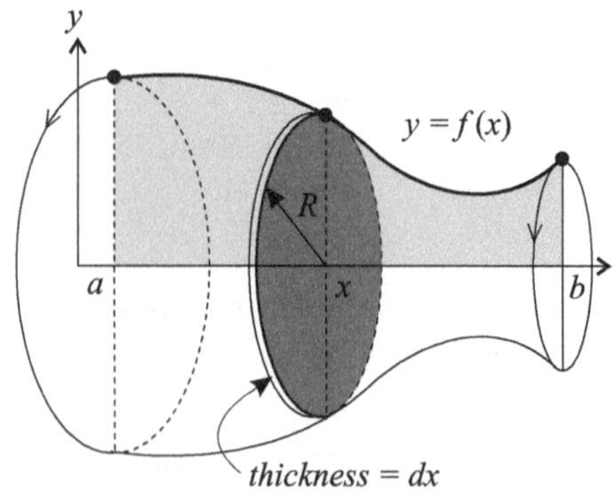

Figure 5.3.7: *The cross section at x has radius $R = f(x)$.*

Measuring volume by using Formula 5.3.1 is called the *disk method* because each cross section is a disk. Heuristically, we can think of the solid as composed of infinitely many thin cylindrical disks with infinitesimal volume

$$dV = \pi R^2 \, dx.$$

See Figure 5.3.7. Doing a continuous sum (integral) of these elements of volume gives the volume:

$$V = \int dV = \int \pi R^2 \, dx.$$

Example 5.3.1 (Using the Integral Formula)

Problem: The region beneath the graph of $f(x) = x^{-1}$ on the interval $[1, 2]$ is revolved about the x-axis. Find the volume of the resulting solid of revolution.

Solution: As far as the algebra and the calculus involved, this is the easiest problem you will see:

$$A = \pi R^2 = \pi \left[x^{-1} \right]^2 = \pi x^{-2}$$

So

$$V = \int_a^b \pi R^2 \, dx = \int_1^2 \pi x^{-2} \, dx = \pi \left(-x^{-1} \right) \Big|_1^2 = \pi \left(-\frac{1}{2} + 1 \right) = \frac{\pi}{2}.$$

Example 5.3.2 (Spinning Tops)

Problem: A toy manufacturer makes a spinning top whose plastic base is the solid of revolution formed by revolving the graph of $f(x) = 2\sqrt{x} - x$ on the interval $[0, 4]$ about the x-axis. With units in inches, find the volume of the top's base and the cost to cast the bases of 1000 tops. Assume the plastic costs 4 cents per cubic inch. Also sketch the graph of f and the corresponding solid of revolution.

Amy Donovan/Shutterstock.com

Solution: The function $f(x) = 2\sqrt{x} - x$ is zero only at $x = 0$, 4, and since

$$f'(x) = \frac{1}{\sqrt{x}} - 1 \quad f''(x) = -\frac{1}{2x^{3/2}},$$

the only critical number is $x = 1$. By the 2nd derivative test, this is where the function has a local maximum. A sketch of the function and corresponding solid of revolution is shown below.

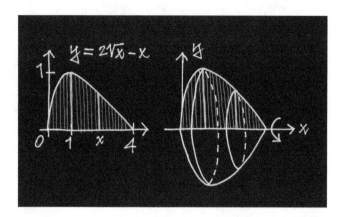

Figure 5.3.8: *Plot of the function $f(x) = 2\sqrt{x} - x$ on the interval $[0, 4]$ and the corresponding solid of revolution.*

Using Integral Formula 5.3.1, with $R = 2\sqrt{x} - x$, to calculate the exact volume gives

$$V = \int_0^4 \pi \left[2\sqrt{x} - x\right]^2 dx = \int_0^4 \pi \left(4x - 4x\sqrt{x} + x^2\right) dx$$

$$= \pi \left(2x^2 - \frac{8}{5}x^{5/2} + \frac{1}{3}x^3\right)\Big|_0^4 = \pi \left(32 - \frac{8}{5}(32) + \frac{64}{3}\right)$$

$$= 32\pi \left(1 - \frac{8}{5} + \frac{2}{3}\right) = \frac{32\pi}{15} \approx 6.7 \text{ cubic inches.}$$

Thus, the cost to cast the base of one top is approximately $4(6.7) = 26.8$ cents. So for 1000 tops the total cost would be 268 dollars.

Computer graphs of the solid of revolution can be plotted as follows.

```
>   f:=x->2*x^(1/2)-x;g:=0;
```
$$f := x \mapsto 2\sqrt{x} - x$$
$$g := 0$$
```
>   a:=0;b:=4;
```
$$a := 0$$
$$b := 4$$
```
>   revolve1X(f,g,a,b);
```

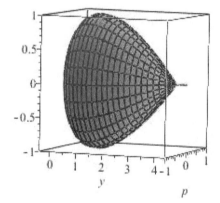

Figure 5.3.9: *Solid of revolution obtained by revolving $f(x) = 2\sqrt{x} - x$, $0 \le x \le 4$, about the x-axis.*

Example 5.3.3 (Using the Integral Formula & Computer Approximations)

Problem: The region beneath the graph of function $f(x) = 1 - e^{-x}$ on the interval $[0, 1]$ is revolved about the x-axis. Sketch the graph of f and the corresponding solid of revolution Then compute its volume. Also use the `diskmethod` command to approximate the solid with 10 cylindrical disks.

Solution: Graph f by graphing the decaying exponential function $g(x) = e^{-x}$, reflecting this about the x-axis to get the graph of $-g(x)$, and then shifting this up 1 unit to get the graph of f. This and the sketch of the corresponding solid are shown below.

Using Integral Formula 5.3.1, with $R = 1 - e^{-x}$, to calculate the exact volume gives

$$V = \int_0^1 \pi \left[1 - e^{-x}\right]^2 dx = \int_0^1 \pi \left(1 - 2e^{-x} + e^{-2x}\right) dx$$

$$= \pi \left(x + 2e^{-x} - \frac{1}{2}e^{-2x}\right)\Big|_0^1 = \pi \left(1 + 2e^{-1} - \frac{1}{2}e^{-2} - 2 + \frac{1}{2}\right)$$

$$= \pi \left(2e^{-1} - \frac{1}{2}e^{-2} - \frac{1}{2} \right) = \frac{\pi}{2} \left(4e^{-1} - e^{-2} - 1 \right) \approx 0.528$$

For solids of revolution, the approximation by *generalized* cylinders, as discussed in Section 5.2, now becomes approximations by *actual cylinders*. Thus, in terms of right endpoint, regular Riemann sums, the volume is

$$V = \int_a^b \pi \left[f(x) \right]^2 dx = \lim_{n \to \infty} \sum_{i=1}^n \pi \left[f(x_i) \right]^2 \Delta x.$$

So, the approximation is

$$V \approx V_n = \sum_{i=1}^n \pi \left[f(x_i) \right]^2 \Delta x$$

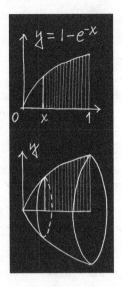

Figure 5.3.10: *An solid of revolution.*

with each term in the sum being the volume of a cylinder of radius $R = f(x_i)$ and "height" Δx. These cylinders are called *cylindrical disks*. You can use a special-purpose Maple command that we have designed to automate the calculation of V_n and to plot ther cylindrical disks in the approximation. This command is

```
diskmethod(f,a,b,n)
```

Inclusion of a 5th argument produces an animation of the approximating solid being constructed from the cylindrical disks. Here's how this works in this example.

```
>  with(plots):
>  f:=x->1-exp(-x);
```
$$f := x \mapsto 1 - e^{-x}$$
```
>  diskmethod(f,0,1,10);
```
    the approximation with, 10, cylindrical disks is, .5920546560

As you can see the approximation visually seems pretty good. Numerically $V_{10} = 0.5920546560$, which also is fairly close to the exact volume,

$$V = \frac{\pi}{2} \left(4e^{-1} - e^{-2} - 1 \right) \approx 0.528,$$

found above. A movie showing the approximation being generated can be produced by

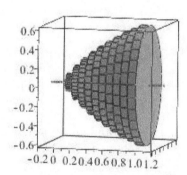

Figure 5.3.11: *An approximation to the solid using 10 cylindrical disks.*

```
>  diskmethod(f,0,1,10,movie);
```

You can "play" the movie by making the command:

```
>  movie;
```

Exercises: 5.3 (Solids of Revolution: The Disk Method)

Part A

For each of the Exercises 1–20 which you are assigned, do the following:

(*i*) Sketch the the region D beneath the graph of $y = f(x)$ on the given interval $[a,b]$ and then sketch the solid obtained by revolving D about the x-axis. Label and annotate your figure.

(*ii*) Use Formula 5.3.1(a)-(b) to calculate the exact volume. Show all your steps and algebraic simplifications.

1. $f(x) = 1 - \sqrt{x}$, for x in $[0, 1]$.
2. $f(x) = 1 - x^{1/3}$, for x in $[0, 1]$.
3. $f(x) = -x^2 + 4x$, for x in $[0, 3]$.
4. $f(x) = -x^2 + 6x$, for x in $[0, 4]$.
5. $f(x) = x^3 + 1$, for x in $[-1, 1]$.
6. $f(x) = x^5 + 1$, for x in $[-1, 1]$.
7. $f(x) = \dfrac{x}{4} + \dfrac{1}{x}$, for x in $[\frac{1}{2}, 4]$.
8. $f(x) = \dfrac{x}{9} + \dfrac{1}{x}$, for x in $[\frac{1}{2}, 9]$.
9. $f(x) = \dfrac{x^3}{3} + \dfrac{1}{4x}$, for x in $[\frac{1}{2}, 2]$.
10. $f(x) = x^3 + \dfrac{1}{12x}$, for x in $[\frac{1}{2}, 2]$.
11. $f(x) = e^x + e^{-x}$, for x in $[-1, 1]$.
12. $f(x) = e^x - e^{-x}$, for x in $[0, 1]$.
13. $f(x) = \sec x$, for x in $[-\frac{\pi}{3}, \frac{\pi}{3}]$.
14. $f(x) = \csc x$, for x in $[\frac{\pi}{3}, \frac{2\pi}{3}]$.
15. $f(x) = \tan x$, for x in $[0, \frac{\pi}{4}]$.
16. $f(x) = \cot x$, for x in $[\frac{\pi}{4}, \frac{\pi}{3}]$.
17. $f(x) = \sin x$, for x in $[0, \pi]$.
18. $f(x) = \cos x$, for x in $[-\frac{\pi}{2}, \frac{\pi}{2}]$.
19. $f(x) = \sin x + 2$, for x in $[0, 2\pi]$.
20. $f(x) = \cos x + 2$, for x in $[0, 2\pi]$.

21. Standard Volume Formulas

Each of the following functions is particularly simple and generates a well-known solid of revolution when the region beneath it is revolved about the x-axis. In these, r and h are positive constants.

(a) $y = r$, for x in $[0, h]$. (a constant function)

(b) $y = \dfrac{r}{h} x$, for x in $[0, h]$. (a straight line)

(c) $y = \sqrt{r^2 - x^2}$, for x in $[-r, r]$.

For each of these functions, do the following

(*i*) Sketch the solid of revolution, label/annotate your sketch, and identify the solid as one of the well-known ones.

(*ii*) Calculate the exact volume and compare the formula you get (which should involve r and h) with a formula from some mathematical reference.

(*iii*) Use the `revolve1X` command to produce a picture of the solid. *Note*: You will have to assign particular values to r and h.

22. Non-Standard Volume Formulas

Part B

CAS: **Computer Plots and Approximations**

The following group of exercises corresponds to the group 1–20 above. Do the following:

(*i*) Use the `revolve1X` command to generate a computer plot of the surface bounding the solid of revolution. Print this out and label/annotate this with the formula for the function, the axes, and the axis of revolution.

(*ii*) Use the `diskmethod` command to compute the approximate volumes V_n, for $n = 5, 10, 100$ (Note: For $n > 25$, the procedure computes the approximate volume, but does not produce any graphics). View the animations. Print out the pictures of the two cylindrical disk approximations and annotate them. Compare the approximate volume V_{100} with the exact volume V.

23. Exercise 1	24. Exercise 2
25. Exercise 3	26. Exercise 4
27. Exercise 5	28. Exercise 6
29. Exercise 7	30. Exercise 8
31. Exercise 9	32. Exercise 10

Part C

Computer Plots and Approximations (Continued)

33. Exercise 11	34. Exercise 12
35. Exercise 13	36. Exercise 14
37. Exercise 15	38. Exercise 16
39. Exercise 17	40. Exercise 18
41. Exercise 19	42. Exercise 20

5.4 The Washer and Shell Methods

In this section we extend the discussion of solids of revolution to allow for more general solids and other axes of revolution. The disk method generalizes to the *washer method*. (A disk is a washer with no hole in it.) The *shell method* is totally different and arises from viewing a solid of revolution as consisting of infinitely many infinitesimal shells.

The Washer Method

In the previous section we generated solids of revolution E by revolving the region beneath the graph of f about the x-axis. This is the special case of a Type I region where $g = 0$. Generally, Type I regions are regions D that are bounded between the graphs of two nonnegative functions f and g on an interval $[a, b]$, with $g(x) \leq f(x)$ on $[a, b]$ and with $g \neq 0$. See Figure 5.4.1.

If we revolve such a region about the x-axis, we get a solid of revolution E which has a "hole" in it. The hole arises because of the graph of the function g. As you can see from Figure 5.4.1, a typical cross section of the solid is generated by revolving the vertical slice (or segment) about the x-axis. This typical cross section looks like a washer and technically is called an *annulus* (the region between two concentric disks)

As an initial example, consider $f(x) = 1 + x^2$ and $g(x) = \sqrt{x}$, on the interval $[0, 1]$. Figure 5.4.3 shows the graphs of these two functions and the corresponding solid of revolution.

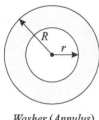

Washer (Annulus)

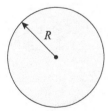

outer disk

inner disk

Figure 5.4.1: *A Type I region determined by two functions f and g.*

Figure 5.4.2: *An annulus is what is left after removing an inner disk from an outer disk.*

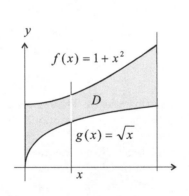

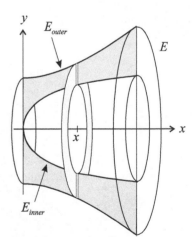

Figure 5.4.3: *The solid generated by revolving a Type I region about the x-axis.*

In general, the cross sectional area function is

$$A = \pi R^2 - \pi r^2 = \pi \left(R^2 - r^2 \right) = \pi \left([f(x)]^2 - [g(x)]^2 \right)$$

and the volume of E is given by Formula (5.4.1a,b) in the box below.

Volume - Washer Method

For a Type I region revolved about the x-axis, the volume

of the resulting solid of revolution is

$$V = \int_a^b \pi([f(x)]^2 - [g(x)]^2)dx \qquad (5.4.1a)$$

Alternatively

$$V = \int_a^b \pi(R^2 - r^2)dx \qquad (5.4.1b)$$

where $R = f(x)$ and $r = g(x)$.

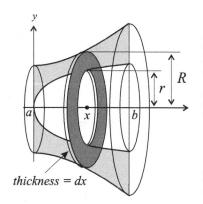

Figure 5.4.4: *A typical washer formed by nearby cross sections.*

<u>NOTE</u> 1: Of course the integral formula for the volume can be motivated by taking limits of certain Riemann sums, each of which is the volume of an approximation to the solid by washers with thickness Δx.

<u>NOTE</u> 2: At the infinitesimal level, we can view the solid E as being comprised of washers (annuli) with infinitesimal thickness dx. See Figure 5.4.4. Then

$$dV = \pi \left([f(x)]^2 - [g(x)]^2\right) dx,$$

is the infinitesimal volume of a thin slice through E at the point x. Adding continuously (i.e., integrating) these

$$V = \int_a^b dV = \int_a^b \pi \left([f(x)]^2 - [g(x)]^2\right) dx$$

gives Formula (5.4.1a,b).

<u>NOTE</u> 3: A third way to get Formula (5.4.1a,b) is to view the solid E as what is left when we take solid E_{outer} and remove the solid E_{inner} from it. See Figure 5.4.3 above. Symbolically,

$$E = E_{outer} - E_{inner}$$

The figure shows this clearly. The region underneath the graph of g when revolved about the x-axis generates a parabolic cup E_{inner}. Removing this cup from the solid E_{outer} creates the solid E. Based on this, we reason that the volume of E should be the difference of the volumes of E_{outer} and E_{inner}, each of which is given by Integral Formula (5.4.1a,b). Hence,

$$V = \int_a^b \pi [f(x)]^2 \, dx - \int_a^b \pi [g(x)]^2 \, dx = \int_a^b \pi \left([f(x)]^2 - [g(x)]^2\right) dx.$$

Example 5.4.1 (Revolving a Type I Region about the x-axis)

Returning to the example above, with $f(x) = 1 + x^2$, $g(x) = \sqrt{x}$, for x in $[0,1]$, we get the following calculation of the volume of E:

$$V = \int_0^1 \pi \left([1 + x^2]^2 - [\sqrt{x}]^2\right) dx = \pi \int_0^1 \left(1 + 2\,x^2 + x^4 - x\right) dx$$

$$= \pi \left(x + \frac{2\,x^3}{3} + \frac{x^5}{5} - \frac{x^2}{2}\right)\Big|_0^1 = \frac{41\pi}{30}.$$

As discussed in Section 5.3, you can use the command `revolve1X(f,g,a,b)` to have Maple plot a picture of the solid E. The picture consists of plots of the two surfaces generated by revolving the graphs of f and g about the x-axis. It also shows the two annuli made by the cross sections at $x = a$ and $x = b$.

```
>  f:=x->1+x^2;g:=x->sqrt(x);
```

$$f := x \mapsto 1 + x^2$$
$$g := x \mapsto \sqrt{x}$$

```
>  revolve1X(f,g,0,1);
```

You should rotate the figure around in order to get other views that may help you better understand the geometry of this solid. Often it helps the visualization if you cut away part of the surfaces, especially if the outer surface completely encloses and obscures the inner one. To do this, include two additional arguments α, β in the command `revolve1X(f,g,a,b,alpha, beta)`

The default values for these two angles are $\alpha = 0$ and $\beta = 2\pi$, so if these arguments are omitted you get a full 360 degree revolution of the graphs generating the surfaces, as shown in the above figure. But if you specify something like $\alpha = -\pi, \beta = \pi/2$, then, in the present example, the `revolve1X` command will give the Figure 5.4.6. With this cut-away view you can see more clearly the inner parabolic cup that has been removed to create the hole in the solid.

So far we have learned only how to measure volumes of solids of revolutions obtained by revolving a Type I region about the x-axis (For an axis parallel to the x-axis, see the exercises). What happens if we revolve a Type I region about the y-axis (or an axis parallel to the y-axis)? And what about Type II regions revolved about axes parallel to either the x-axis or y-axis?

The answers to these questions are fairly simple and the resulting volumes are given by integral formulas. To understand and remember these formulas it is essential that you know the geometry involved.

Revolving Type II Regions about the y-axis (The Washer Method Again)

If we revolve a region D about the y-axis, or an axis parallel to the y-axis, instead of the x-axis, then the volume of the resulting solid can no longer be measured by the preceding formulas. In this subsection we look at a formula that will handle this situation when D is a Type II region bounded by the graphs of two nonnegative functions

$$x = j(y), \ x = k(y), \ y = c, \ y = d$$

where j and k are given functions of y with $k(y) \le j(y)$, for y in $[c, d]$. See Figure 5.4.7.

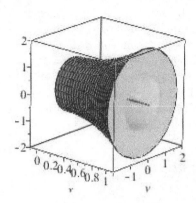

Figure 5.4.5: *A solid produced by* `revolve1X(f,g,a,b)`.

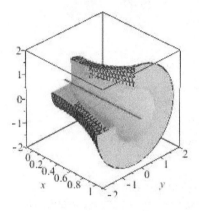

Figure 5.4.6: *A cut-away of Figure 5.4.5 produced by* `revolve(f,g,a,b, α, β )` *with* $\alpha = -\pi$ *and* $\beta = \pi/2$

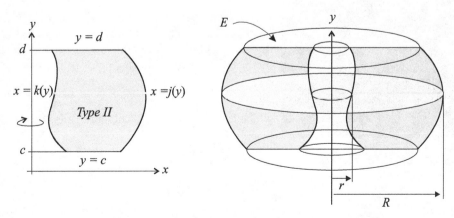

Figure 5.4.7: *A Type II region (left) and the solid of revolution formed by revolving it about the y-axis (right).*

The figure also shows the solid E generated by revolving this region about the y-axis. How is this solid different from one generated by revolving a Type I region about the x-axis? The major difference is that it is oriented differently – the axis of revolution is vertical. Also the variable y is now the independent variable and, relative to the y-axis, the graph of $x = j(y)$, lies "above" the graph of $x = k(y)$. So if you just adjust your thinking (turn your head to the side if necessary), there is really *no difference* between revolving a Type II region about the y-axis and revolving a Type I region about the x-axis. Thus, all the same ideas should apply in reasoning that the volume of E is given by the following formula:

Volume - Washer Method 2

For a Type II region revolved about the y-axis, the volume

of the resulting solid of revolution is

$$V = \int_c^d \pi([j(y)]^2 - [k(y)]^2)\,dy \qquad \text{(5.4.2a)}$$

Alternatively

$$V = \int_c^d \pi(R^2 - r^2)\,dy \qquad \text{(5.4.2b)}$$

where $R = j(y)$ and $r = k(y)$.

The use of this formula is exactly the same as the one for revolving Type I regions about the x-axis.

In Summary: If D is a region of Type I revolved about the x-axis or is Type II region revolved about the y-axis, then we have similar integral formulas for computing the volume of the solid of revolution. In each case we are using the washer method to compute the volume.

Example 5.4.2 (Revolving a Type II Region about the y-axis)

Problem: Suppose D is the region bounded by the graphs of

$$y = \ln x, \ y = \sqrt{4 - x}, \ y = 0, \ y = 1$$

Graph the region D and find the volume of the sold obtained by revolving D about the y-axis.

Solution: A sketch of the first two curves (the graphs of two well-known functions of x) and the two horizontal lines is shown in Figure 5.4.8. Note that the horizontal line $y = 1$ is below the point (x_0, y_0) where the graphs of $y = \ln x$ and $y = \sqrt{4 - x}$ intersect. To determine this point of intersection requires solving

$$\ln x = \sqrt{4 - x},$$

which is not possible to do algebraically. So we use Maple to get an approximate answer.

```
>   x0:=fsolve(ln(x)=sqrt(4-x),x);
```
$$x0 := 2.880622455$$
```
>   y0:=ln(x0);
```
$$y0 := 1.058006401$$

We see from the sketch that the region D is composed of three Type I regions. But, since we are revolving about the y-axis (and using the washer method) we can

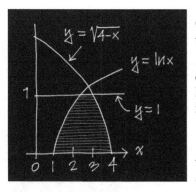

Figure 5.4.8: *The region D.*

express D as a single Type II region and use Formula 5.4.2(a)–(b) once. For this, take the two equations

$$y = \ln x, \; y = \sqrt{4 - x}$$

and solve each for x:

$$x = e^y, \; x = 4 - y^2$$

This gives the functions h and k in the Type II description:

```
>  j:=y->4-y^2;
```
$$j := y \mapsto 4 - y^2$$

```
>  k:=y->exp(y);
```
$$k := y \mapsto e^y$$

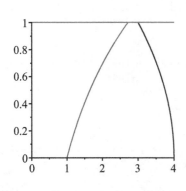

Figure 5.4.9: *A computer plot of the region D.*

A computer plot of these functions and the horizontal lines $y = 0$, $y = 1$ can be done with the following code.

```
>  plot([[j(y),y,y=0..1],[k(y),y,y=0..1],[0,y,y=0..1],
>  [x,1,x=0..4]], color=[black,blue,red,red]);
```

Revolving this region about the y-axis and using the washer method with

$$R = 4 - y^2, \; r = e^y,$$

gives a volume

$$V = \int_0^1 \pi \left(\left[4 - y^2\right]^2 - [e^y]^2 \right) \, dy = \int_0^1 \pi \left(16 - 8y^2 + y^4 - e^{2y} \right) \, dy$$

$$= \pi \left(16y - \frac{8}{3}y^3 + \frac{1}{5}y^5 - \frac{1}{2}e^{2y} \right)\Big|_0^1 = \pi \left(16 - \frac{8}{3} + \frac{1}{5} - \frac{1}{2}e^2 + \frac{1}{2} \right) = \pi \left(\frac{421}{30} - \frac{e^2}{2} \right)$$

To plot this solid of revolution we use a special-purpose Maple command for revolving Type II regions about the y-axis. This command is

$$\texttt{revolve2Y(j,k,c,d,}\alpha\texttt{,}\beta\texttt{)}$$

This is used in the same way as the `revolve1X` command. (NOTE: The 2Y in the command's name indicates a Type II region revolved about the y-axis.) We have already defined the functions j and k above, so we simply enter

```
>  revolve2Y(j,k,0,1,Pi/2,2*Pi);
```

This gives Figure 5.4.10. Notice that when revolving about the y-axis, the use of $\alpha = \pi/2$, $\beta = 2\pi$ often produces the best view in a cut-a-way figure.

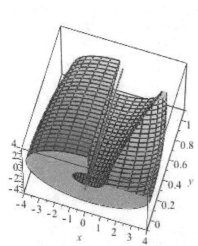

Figure 5.4.10: *The solid of revolution rendered by* `revolve2Y(j,k,c,d,`$\pi/2,2\pi$`)`.

The Shell Method

The *washer/disk method* can be used for *any* solid of revolution. For this you must: (A) when revolving about the x-axis, decompose the region D into a number of Type I regions, or (B) when revolving about the y-axis, decompose the region D into a number of Type II regions. The *washer/disk method* is easiest to use when the solid of revolution is either of the following

a Type I region revolved about the x-axis
a Type II region revolved about the y-axis

The *shell method* is an alternative method which also can be used on any solid of revolution and is easier to use when the solid of revolution is either of the following

a Type I region revolved about the y-axis
a Type II region revolved about the x-axis

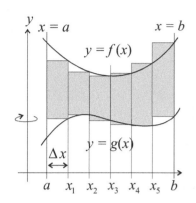

Figure 5.4.11: *Approximating the region between the graphs of f and g.*

The shell method has a totally different integral formula for computing the volume. The formula arises from using approximations and then taking limits, just as we did in 5.2 in deriving the formula for volumes of solids of known cross sectional area. But, now the approximations are cylindrical *shells* (hence the name shell method).

The Formula for the Shell Method

Suppose the region is a Type I region and is revolved about the y-axis. We approximate the region D by rectangles arising from a regular partition

$$P = \{x_0, x_1, x_2, \ldots, x_n\}$$

of $[a,b]$ into subintervals $[x_{i-1}, x_i]$, where $x_i = a + i(b-a)/n$, for $i = 1, 2, \ldots, n$. We let $\Delta x = x_i - x_{i-1} = (b-a)/n$ and use the right endpoint x_i for constructing the height of the ith subrectangle. Figure 5.4.11 shows this for $n = 6$.

The figure illustrates the rectangles that are formed from the approximations, and you can see how the collection of these approximate the region D. When these rectangles are revolved about the y-axis, each of them generates a *cylindrical shell* as shown in Figure 5.4.12

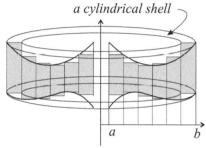

Figure 5.4.12: *Cylindrical shells are formed when rectangles are revolved about the y-axis.*

The collection of these cylindrical shells form what is called the *cylindrical shell approximation* to *the solid E*. To compute this approximate volume, first consider the volume of the ith cylindrical shell. Its volume is the difference of the volumes of two concentric cylinders. See Figure 5.4.13.

The outer one has circular base of radius $R = x_i$ and the inner one has circular base with radius $r = x_{i-1}$. Each cylinder has the same height $h = f(x_i) - g(x_i)$. Since the volume of a cylinder is $\pi r^2 h$, the volume of a cylindrical shell is

$$V_{outher} - V_{inner} = \pi R^2 h - \pi r^2 h = \pi\left(R^2 - r^2\right)h$$

$$= \pi\left(R + r\right)\left(R - r\right)h.$$

If we now use the particular values for R, r, and h in the the ith cylindrical shell, we get the following formula for its volume:

$$V_{outer} - V_{inner} = \pi\left(x_i + x_{i-1}\right)\left(x_i - x_{i-1}\right)[f(x_i) - g(x_i)]$$

$$= \pi\left(x_i + x_{i-1}\right)[f(x_i) - g(x_i)]\Delta x = 2\pi\left(\frac{x_i + x_{i-1}}{2}\right)[f(x_i) - g(x_i)]\Delta x$$

Note: In the last step we have inserted a 2 with the π in order to get the quantity $(x_i + x_{i-1})/2$ in the expression for the volume. This quantity is the midpoint of the interval $[x_{i-1}, x_i]$. The reason for doing this will become apparent later when we take limits. Adding all these volumes gives the volume of the total cylindrical shell approximation:

Approximate Volume using n Cylindrical Shells:

$$V_n = \sum_{i=1}^{n} 2\pi\left(\frac{x_i + x_{i-1}}{2}\right)[f(x_i) - g(x_i)]\Delta x$$

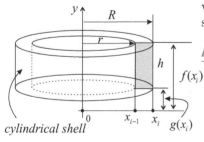

Figure 5.4.13: *The volume of each cylindrical shell is the the difference of volumes of the outer and inner cylinders.*

Taking limits as n tends to ∞ will give us an integral expression for the exact volume of this type of solid of revolution. Before discussing this, we look at some visual evidence to support the idea that the limit will give us the exact volume.

Example 5.4.3 (Cylindrical Shell Approximations)

Suppose $f(x) = (x-2)^2 + 1$ and $g(x) = 0$ on the interval $[1,3]$. (Recall that $f(x) = a(x-h)^2 + k$ is the general expression for a quadratic function. Its graph is a parabola with vertex (h, k).) Figure 5.4.14 shows the graph of f on the interval $[1, 3]$, together with the vertical lines

Figure 5.4.15 shows a hand-drawn sketch of the solid E obtained by revolving the region under the graph of f about the y-axis.

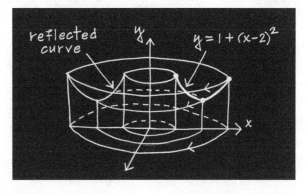

Figure 5.4.15: *A hand-drawn sketch of the solid E.*

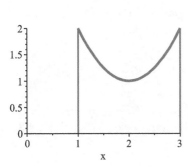

Figure 5.4.14: *A Type I region with*
$f(x) = (x - 2)^2 + 1$, $g(x) = 0$.

It is easy to sketch, for small values of n, the cylindrical shell approximation and compute its volume using Formula 5.4.3.

For large values of n we have provided a special-purpose Maple command called `shellmethod` to draw a picture of the cylindrical shell approximation and compute its volume. This command has the basic form

```
shellmethod(f,g,a,b,n)
```

and works in the same way as `washermethod`. The function on the bottom, which is g, is the second argument (with $g = 0$ when the x-axis bounds the region on the bottom). The picture of the cylindrical shell approximation is not produced when n is larger than 25. You can also use optional arguments α and β to cut-away part of the shell approximation. This results in a revolution of the region between angles α and β. (The default values are $\alpha = 0$, $\beta = 2\pi$). In this example, $g = 0$ and we need to cut-away part of the solid to see it properly.

```
>  f:=x->(x-2)^2+1;g:=0;
```
$$f := x \mapsto (x - 2)^2 + 1$$
$$g := 0$$
```
>  a:=1;b:=3;
```
$$a := 1$$
$$b := 3$$
```
>  shellmethod(f,g,a,b,5,0,3*Pi/2);
```
the approximation with, 5, cylindrical shells is, 39.20707632

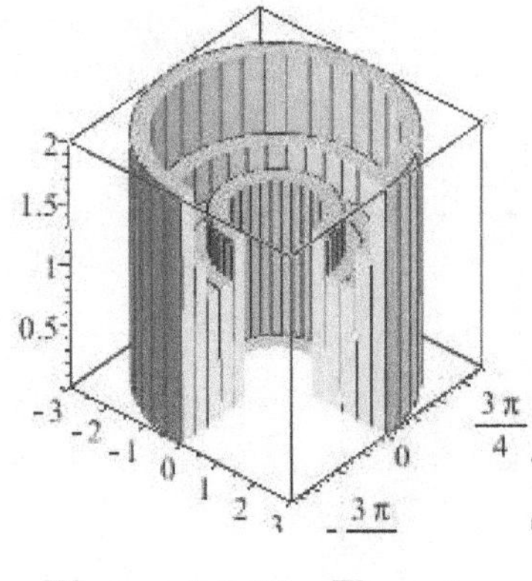

The above output from the `shellmethod` command gives $V_5 = 39.20707632$ as calculated by Formula 5.4.3. The other output from this command is Figure 5.4.16.

As you can see, the `shellmethod` procedure renders each of the five shells totally. When n is large, the thickness of each shell can be very small and the shell appears a "sheet" much like the sheets in a roll of paper towels. In this example, the figure below for $n = 20$ shows this more clearly.

Figure 5.4.16: *The outer shells in the approximation to E with 5 cylindrical shells.*

With the evidence from Example 5.4.3 as a guide, we would guess that the volume

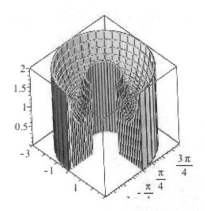

Figure 5.4.17: *The outer shells in the approximation to E with* 20 *cylindrical shells.*

of the nth cylindrical shell approximation

$$V_n = \sum_{i=1}^{n} 2\pi \left(\frac{x_i + x_{i-1}}{2} \right) [f(x_i) - g(x_i)] \Delta x$$

would approach the exact volume V of E as n tends to ∞:

$$V = \lim_{n \to \infty} V_n.$$

Theory tells us that this is true, with the Riemann sums, in the limit, giving us an integral for the volume:

$$V = \lim_{n \to \infty} \sum_{1=1}^{n} 2\pi \left(\frac{x_i + x_{i-1}}{2} \right) [f(x_i) - g(x_i)] \Delta x = \int_a^b 2\pi x [f(x) - g(x)] \, dx$$

You see here how the average $(x_i + x_{i-1})/2$ in the discrete sum turns into x in the integrand. For convenience, we record the integral formula below (Formula 5.4.3):

Volume - Shell Method

For a Type I region revolved about the y-axis, the volume of the resulting solid of revolution is

$$V = \int_a^b 2\pi x [f(x) - g(x)] \, dx \qquad (5.4.3\text{a})$$

Alternatively

$$V = \int_a^b 2\pi R h \, dx \qquad (5.4.3\text{b})$$

where $R = x$ and $h = f(x) - g(x)$.

The derivation of this formula using limits of Riemann sums is the rigorous approach to the problem of finding the volume. A non-rigorous approach, but one that is pedagogically useful involves using cylindrical shells of infinitesimal thickness dx. Figure 5.4.18 shows one such shell located at a typical point x between a and b.

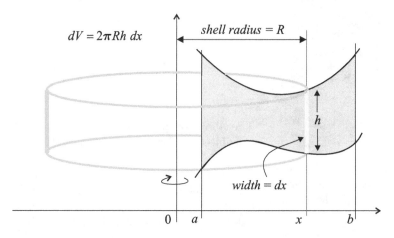

Figure 5.4.18: *An infinitesimal cylindrical shell generated by revolving a line segment.*

The line segment of height $h = f(x) - g(x)$ when revolved about the y-axis generates a cylindrical shell with radius $R = x$ (and infinitesimal thickness dx). To get the volume dV of this infinitesimal shell, slice the cylinder vertically and roll it out as shown below.

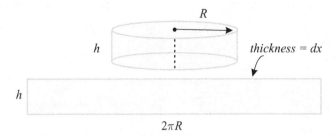

Figure 5.4.19: *Slicing and unrolling a cylindrical shell.*

The corresponding infinitesimal cylindrical shell has infinitesimal volume

$$dV = 2\pi Rh\, dx$$

and so

$$V = \int dV = \int 2\pi Rh\, dx$$

gives the volume of the solid of revolution.

Example 5.4.4 (Exact vs. Approximate Volume)

In Example 5.4.3 above we had the `shellmethod` command calculate the 5 and 20 cylindrical shell approximations

$$V_5 = 39.20707632, \qquad V_{20} = 34.80884662$$

to the exact volume V of E. The region D generating E is the one bounded by $f(x) = (x-2)^2 + 1$, $g(x) = 0$, and the vertical lines $x = 0$, $x = 1$. Let's see what Formula 5.4.3(a)-(b) gives for the exact volume. This will be a simple calculation since it only involves integrating polynomial functions. The radius and height of the shell at x are

$$R = x \text{ and } h = f(x) = (x-2)^2 + 1$$

Then the volume is:

$$V = \int_a^b 2\pi Rh\, dx = \int_1^3 2\pi x \left((x-2)^2 + 1\right) dx = \int_1^3 2\pi x \left(x^2 - 4x + 5\right) dx$$

$$= \int_1^3 2\pi \left(x^3 - 4x^2 + 5x\right) dx = 2\pi \left(\frac{1}{4}x^4 - \frac{4}{3}x^3 + \frac{5}{2}x^2\right)\Big|_1^3$$

$$= \frac{32\pi}{3} = 33.51032165\cdots$$

As an exercise, use `shellmethod` with n large and see how many shells are needed to get an approximate volume of 33.5.

Summary of Washer and Shell Methods

In working a given problem, you will need to develop some way of determining which method to use: washer or shell. We suggest you adopt the following strategy.

There are two basic regions that we can revolve: Type I and Type II regions. There are two basic axes to revolve about: the x-axis and the y-axis. Thus, there are four basic type of solids of revolutions with the following recommended methods:

Type I region revolved about the x-axis (WASHER)

Type II region revolved about the y-axis (WASHER)

Type I region revolved about the y-axis (SHELL)

Type II region revolved about the x-axis (SHELL)

Study Figure 5.4.19 below to understand why the recommended methods work best.

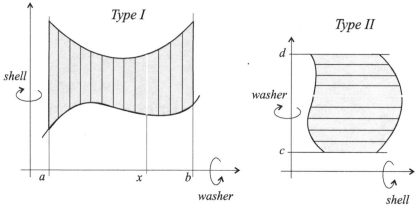

Figure 5.4.19: *The two basic type of regions and the two basic axes to revolve them about.*

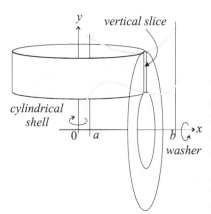

Figure 5.4.20: *A vertical slice revolved about the x-axis and the y-axis.*

We have shown shading lines for the regions: vertical for the Type I region and horizontal for the Type II region. As the figure indicates, the method to use (WASHER or SHELL) is determined by whether the shading line, revolved about an axis, makes a washer or a (cylindrical) shell. For instance, Figure 5.4.20 below shows this situation for a Type I region.

As you can see, a vertical slice (or shading line) through a Type I region creates a washer when revolved about the x-axis, The same slice creates a cylindrical shell when revolved about the y-axis.

Exercises: 5.4 (The Washer and Shell Methods)

Part A

The Washer Method (Type I Revolved about the x-axis)

In each of the exercises 1–18, do the following:

(a) Sketch the region D bounded by the curves and the corresponding solid E obtained by revolving D about the x-axis. Also sketch a typical washer.

(b) Use Formula 5.4.1(a)–(b) to calculate the exact value for the volume of E. Show all your steps and algebraic simplifications.

1. $y = \sqrt{x}$, $y = \dfrac{x}{4}$, $x = 0$, $x = 4$

2. $y = \sqrt{x}$, $y = x^6$, $x = 0$, $x = 1$

3. $y = e^{-x}$, $y = 2 + x^2$, $x = 0$, $x = 1$

4. $y = \dfrac{1}{x}$, $y = 1 + x^2$, $x = 1$, $x = 2$

5. $y = x + 3$, $y = 5 - x^2$

6. $y = x^2$, $y = 4x + 12$

7. $y = x^2$, $y = 8 - x^2$

8. $y = 2x^2$, $y = 9 - x^2$

9. $y = 1 + \sin \pi x$, $y = x$, $x = 0$, $x = 1$

10. $y = 2 + \cos \pi x$, $y = x$, $x = 0$, $x = 1$

11. $y = 4 + \sin x$, $y = 2 + \cos x$, $x = 0$, $x = 2\pi$

12. $y = 2 + \sin x$, $y = 4 + \cos x$, $x = 0$, $x = 2\pi$

13. $y = \tan x$, $y = 1$, $x = 0$

14. $y = \cot x$, $y = 1$, $x = \pi/2$

15. $y = 2 - x$, $y = 1 - e^{-x}$, $x = 0$, $x = 1$

16. $y = 1 + x$, $y = 1 - e^x$, $x = 0$, $x = 1$

17. $y = \sec x$, $y = \cos x$, $x = 0$, $x = \pi/3$

18. $y = \csc x$, $y = \sin x$, $x = \pi/2$, $x = 2\pi/3$

The Washer Method (Type II Revolved about the y-axis)

In each of the Exercises 19–26, do the following:

((a) Sketch the region D bounded by the curves and the corresponding solid E obtained by revolving D about the y-axis. Also sketch a typical washer.

(b) Use the Washer Method Formula 5.4.2(a)-(b) to calculate the exact value for the volume of E. Show all your steps and algebraic simplifications.

19. $y \le x^3$, $y = (x - 2)^2$, $y = 1$, $y = 2$

20. $y \le x^4$, $y = (x - 2)^2$, $y = 1$, $y = 2$

21. $y = x^2$, $y = \ln x$, $y = 0$, $y = 1$

22. $y = x$, $y = \ln x$, $y = 0$, $x = 3$

23. $y = \sin^{-1} x$, $y = 0$, $x = 1$

24. $y = \cos^{-1} x$, $y = 0$, $x = 1$

25. $y = \ln(1 + x^2)$, $y = 0$, $x = 1$

26. $y = \ln(1 + x^{2/3})$, $y = 0$, $x = 1$

The Shell Method (Type I Revolved about the y-axis)

For each of the Exercises 27–48, do the following:

(i) Sketch the region D bounded by the given curves and then sketch the solid of revolution obtained by revolving the region D about the y-axis. Label and annotate your figures.

(ii) Use the Shell Method Integral Formula 5.4.3(a)-(b) to calculate the exact volume. Show all your steps and algebraic simplifications.

27. $y = \sqrt{x}$, $y = 2 - x^3$, $y = 0$

28. $y = \sqrt[3]{x}$, $y = 2 - x^4$, $y = 0$

29. $y = x^3$, $y = 2 - x^2$, $0 \le x$

30. $y = x^4$, $y = 2 - x^2$, $0 \le x$

31. $y = 4x - x^2$, $y = 0$

32. $y = 2x - x^2$, $y = 0$

33. $y = x^3 - 5x^2 + 6x + 1$, $y = 0$, $x = 0$, $x = 3$

34. $y = x^3 - 6x^2 + 8x + 4$, $y = 0$, $x = 0$, $x = 4$

35. $y = \dfrac{2}{1 + x^2}$, $y = 0$, $0 \le x$, $x = 2$

36. $y = \dfrac{3x}{1 + x^3}$, $y = 0$, $0 \le x$, $x = 2$

37. $y = e^{-x^2}$, $y = 0$, $0 \le x$, $x = 2$

38. $y = e^{x^2}$, $y = 0$, $0 \le x$, $x = 1$

39. $y = \dfrac{1}{3 - x}$, $y = 0$, $x = 1$, $x = 2$

40. $y = \dfrac{1}{4 - x}$, $y = 0$, $x = 1$, $x = 2$

41. $y = 2 + x^2$, $y = 1 - x$, $0 \le x$, $x = 1$

42. $y = 2 + x^3$, $y = 1 - x$, $0 \le x$, $x = 1$

43. $y = \sqrt{x}$, $y = 6 - x$, $x = 0$

44. $y = \sqrt[3]{x}$, $y = 6 - x$, $x = 0$

45. $y = \dfrac{1}{\sqrt{1 - x^2}}$, $y = 0$, $0 \le x$, $x = 3/4$

46. $y = \dfrac{1}{\sqrt{1 + x^2}}$, $y = 0$, $0 \le x$, $x = 1$

47. $y = \sin(x^2)$, $y = 0$, $x = 0$, $x = \sqrt{\pi}$

48. $y = \cos(x^2)$, $y = 0$, $x = 0$, $x = \sqrt{\pi/2}$

Part B

Using the Washer or the Shell Methods In Exercises 49–62, find the volume of the solid obtained by revolving the illustrated region about the given axis.

49. $y = \sec x \tan x$, $x = 0$, $x = \frac{\pi}{3}$ (x-axis)

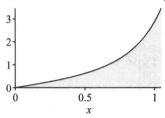

50. $y = \sec x \sqrt{\tan x}$, $x = 0$, $x = \frac{\pi}{3}$ (x-axis)

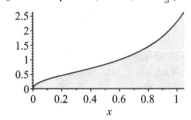

51. $y = \sin x \sqrt{\cos x}$, $x = 0$, $x = \frac{\pi}{3}$ (x-axis)

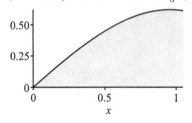

52. $y = \sin x \sqrt{\cos x}$, $x = 0$, $x = \frac{\pi}{3}$ (x-axis)

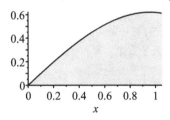

53. $y = x \left(1 + x^3\right)^{1/4}$, $x = 0$, $x = 1$ (x-axis)

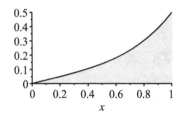

54. $y = x \left(1 + x^5\right)^{1/4}$, $x = 0$, $x = 1$ (x-axis)

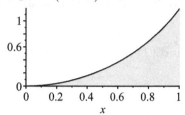

55. $y = \dfrac{3x}{1 + x^3}$, $x = 0$, $x = 2$ (y-axis)

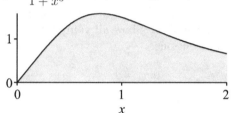

56. $y = \dfrac{5x^3}{1 + x^5}$, $x = 0$, $x = 2$ (y-axis)

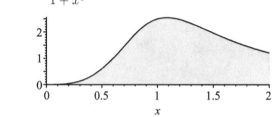

57. $y = x^{-3} e^{x^{-1}}$, $x = 1$, $x = 2$ (y-axis)

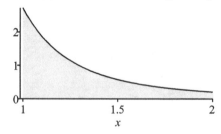

58. $y = x^{-4} e^{x^{-2}}$, $x = 1$, $x = 2$ (y-axis)

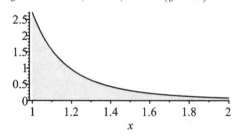

59. $y = x^{-3} \sin^2 \left(x^{-1} \right)$, $x = 0.4$, $x = 1$ (y-axis)

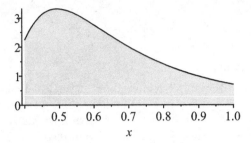

60. $y = x^{-3} \cos^2 \left(x^{-1} \right)$, $x = 0.4$, $x = 1$ (y-axis)

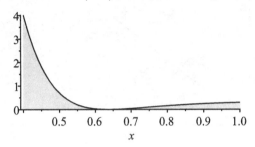

61. $y = 1 + x^{-3/2} \sin \left(10 + 10 \sqrt{x} \right)$, $x = 1$, $x = 4$ (y-axis)

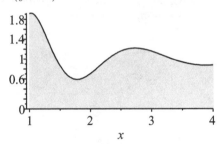

62. $y = 1 + x^{-3/2} \cos \left(10 + 10 \sqrt{x} \right)$, $x = 1$, $x = 4$ (y-axis)

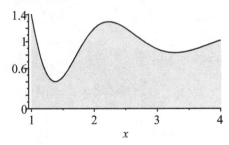

Using *Both* the Washer & Shell Methods

In Exercises 63–72, the region D bounded by the given curves is revolved about the y-axis. Sketch the region and the solid and calculate the exact volume *two* ways. In the first way convert the region D into a Type II region (or possibly several Type II regions if necessary). Then use the washer method to calculate the volume. In the second way, use the shell method directly to calculate the exact volume. Comment on which method you think is more direct, easier, or takes less time.

63. $y = x^3$, $y = 0$, $x = 1$

64. $y = x^4$, $y = 0$, $x = 1$, 1st quadrant

65. $y = x^2$, $y = -2x + 3$, $x = 0$, 1st quadrant

66. $y = x^3$, $y = -2x + 3$, $x = 0$

67. $y = \dfrac{1}{\sqrt{x+1}}$, $y = 0$, $x = 0$, $x = 3$

68. $y = \dfrac{1}{\sqrt{x+2}}$, $y = 0$, $x = 0$, $x = 2$

69. $y = x^3$, $y = x - 1$, $y = 1$, $y = 0$

70. $y = x^5$, $y = x - 1$, $y = 1$, $y = 0$

71. $y = \dfrac{1}{x}$, $y = x$, $y = 0$, $x = 2$

72. $y = \dfrac{1}{x^2}$, $y = x$, $y = 0$, $x = 2$

CAS: Computer Plots and Approximations

For selected exercises you were assigned in group 1–72 above, extend your study of the solid by doing the following:

73. Solid Plots

Use the `revolve1X` or `revolve1Y` commands to generate a computer plot of the surface bounding the solid of revolution. Print this out and label/annotate this with the formula for the function, the axes, and the axis of revolution.

74. Solid Approximations

Use the `diskmethod`, `washermethod`, or `shellmethod` commands to compute the approximate volumes V_n, for $n = 5, 10$. View the pictures (and animations) produced. Print out the pictures of the approximations and annotate them. Compute the approximate volume V_{100}, V_{200} and compare with the exact volume V. Experiment with the values of n needed to get V_n within two decimal places of V.

Other Axes of Revolution

The next group of exercises considers solids generated by revolving about lines *parallel* to either the x-axis or the y-axis.

Discussion & Examples

We suppose a region D is revolved about an axis which is either a horizontal line, $y = c$ or a vertical line $x = d$ (which do not intersect D). This generalizes the situation considered in the reading material (where the axis is the x-axis, $y = 0$ or the y-axis, $x = 0$).

The figure for the resulting solid of revolution looks similar: it is a solid with a hole in it (usually) and centered on the axis of revolution. Also, all cross-sections perpendicular to the axis of revolution are washers (or disks) and, alternatively, the solid can be viewed as consisting of cylindrical shells centered on the axis of revolution. *When properly interpreted*, the integral formulas

$$V = \int_a^b \pi \left(R^2 - r^2\right) dx, \ V = \int_c^d \pi \left(R^2 - r^2\right) dy,$$

$$V = \int_a^b 2\pi Rh \, dx \ V = \int_c^d 2\pi Rh \, dy$$

for the washer and shell methods still apply. But now R, r, and h have to be determined from a drawing.

Horizontal Axes

For example, suppose the region is bounded by $y = x$, $y = \dfrac{1}{x}$, $x = 1$, $x = 2$, and we revolve about the axis $y = 2$. Figure 5.4.1x shows the region D and a section through the region at a typical x in the interval $[1, 2]$.

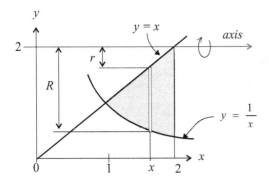

Figure 5.4.1x: *Revolving about any horizontal axis creates a solid whose sections are annuli with radii R and r. After determining how these depend on x, you can then use Formula 5.4.1(b) to compute the volume of the solid.*

From the figure it is easy to see that the two radii for the annular section at x are

$$R = 2 - \frac{1}{x} \quad \text{and} \quad r = 2 - x.$$

Using these gives

$$\begin{aligned}
V &= \int_a^b \pi \left(R^2 - r^2\right) dx \\
&= \int_1^2 \pi \left(\left[2 - \frac{1}{x}\right]^2 - [2 - x]^2\right) dx \\
&= \int_1^2 \pi \left(4 - \frac{4}{x} + \frac{1}{x^2} - \left(4 - 4x + x^2\right)\right) dx \\
&= \int_1^2 \pi \left(-\frac{4}{x} + \frac{1}{x^2} + 4x - x^2\right) dx \\
&= \pi \left(-4\ln x - \frac{1}{x} + 2x^2 - \frac{x^3}{3}\right)\Bigg|_1^2
\end{aligned}$$

$$\begin{aligned}
&= \pi \left(-4\ln 2 - \frac{1}{2} + 8 - \frac{8}{3} + 1 - 2 + \frac{1}{3}\right) \\
&= \pi \left(\frac{25}{6} - 4\ln 2\right)
\end{aligned}$$

Vertical Axes

If we revolve the above region about a vertical line, say $x = 3$, we get a different solid and the shell method will work better. The figure below indicates how the R and h in the shell method formula are determined.

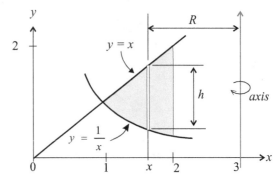

Figure 5.4.2x: *Revolving about any vertical axis creates a solid composed of cylindrical shells with radii R and heights h. After determining how these depend on x, you can then use Formula 5.4.3 (b) to compute the volume of the solid.*

Now we have

$$R = 3 - x, \ h = f(x) - g(x) = x - \frac{1}{x}$$

and

$$2\pi Rh = 2\pi (3 - x)\left(x - \frac{1}{x}\right) = 2\pi \left(3x - \frac{3}{x} - x^2 + 1\right)$$

and the volume is

$$\begin{aligned}
V &= \int_a^b 2\pi Rh \, dx = \int_1^2 2\pi \left(3x - \frac{3}{x} - x^2 + 1\right) dx \\
&= 2\pi \left(\frac{3}{2}x^2 - 3\ln x - \frac{1}{3}x^3 + x\right)\Bigg|_1^2 \\
&= 2\pi \left(6 - 3\ln 2 - \frac{8}{3} + 2 - \frac{3}{2} + \frac{1}{3} - 1\right) \\
&= \pi \left(\frac{19}{3} - 6\ln 2\right)
\end{aligned}$$

After reading the discussion and examples, use what you learned on the following group of exercises. In each one, determine the volume of the solid obtained by revolving the region about the specified axis. Sketch the region and the corresponding solid of revolution.

75. $y = \sqrt{x}, y = 0, x = 0, x = 4$, axis: $y = 3$.

76. $y = x^{1/3}, y = 0, x = 0, x = 4$, axis: $y = 3$.

77. $y = 2 - x$, $y = \sqrt{x}$, $x = 0$, axis: $x = 1$.

78. $y = 2 - x$, $y = x^{1/3}$, $0 \le x$, axis: $x = 1$

79. $y = e^{-x}$, $y = 1 + x^2$, $x \ge 0$, $x = 1$, axis: $y = -1$

80. $y = e^x$, $y = 1 - x$, $x \ge 0$, $x = 1$, axis: $y = -1$

81. $y = 2 - x^2$, $y = x$, $x \ge 0$, axis: $y = 2$.

82. $y = 2 - x^3$, $y = x$, $x \ge 0$, axis: $y = 2$.

83. $y = x - x^2$, $y = 1 + x$, $x = 0$, $x = 1$, axis: $y = 3$.

84. $y = x - x^3$, $y = 1 + x$, $x = 0$, $x = 1$, axis: $y = 3$.

85. $y = \dfrac{1}{x}$, $y = x$, $y = 0$, $x = 2$, axis: $x = 3$.

86. $y = \dfrac{1}{x^2}$, $y = x$, $y = 0$, $x = 2$, axis: $x = 3$.

87. $y = \sin(\frac{\pi}{2}x)$, $y = 2 - x$, $x \ge 0$, $x = 1$,, axis: $y = 2$.

88. $y = \cos(\frac{\pi}{2}x)$, $y = 1 + x$, $x \ge 0$, $x = 1$,, axis: $y = 2$.

89. $y = \sin x$, $y = \cos x$, $x = 0$, $x = \pi/4$, axis: $y = 1$.

90. $y = \sin x$, $y = \cos x$, $x = \pi/4$, $x = \pi/2$, axis: $y = 1$.

91. $y = \tan x$, $y = \sec x$, $x = 0$, $x = \pi/4$, axis: $y = 2$.

92. $y = \cot x$, $y = \csc x$, $x = \pi/4$, $x = \pi/2$, axis: $y = 2$.

93. $y = 1 - x^2$, $y = x^3 - x$, axis: $x = 1$.

94. $y = 1 - x^4$, $y = x^3 - x$, axis: $x = 1$.

Numerical Approximations

In Exercises 95–98, write out the integral formula for the exact volume of the solid of revolution obtained by revolving the region D bounded by the given curves about the y-axis. You will not be able to calculate value of the integral at this time (but will be able to later, after Chapter 6). Use the `shellmethod` command to calculate some approximate volumes V_n. Use small values of n and view the pictures of the cylindrical shell approximations in order to get a feel for how close V_n is to V. Then use `shellmethod` to calculate approximate volumes when n is large. (Recall that when n is bigger than 25, no picture is produced.) Be systematic! List the results of your study and discuss your conclusions from analyzing this data.

95. $y = x \sin x$, $y = 0$, $x = 0$, $x = \pi$

96. $y = x \cos x$, $y = 0$, $x = 0$, $x = \pi/2$

97. $y = 3 x e^{-x}$, $y = 0$, $x = 0$, $x = 2$

98. $y = 4 x^2 e^{-x}$, $y = 0$, $x = 0$, $x = 2$

Project 5.4 (The Frustum Method)

The disk method arose from using step-function approximations to the graph of f. The region beneath an approximating step-function generates a cylindrical disk approximation to E when revolved about the x-axis. Taking limits as the step-functions approach the graph of f gives the integral for the exact volume of E.

This project studies the differences that arise when we approximate the graph of f by *polygonal functions* instead of step-functions. (In a prior section on areas you may have worked a similar project that investigated how approximations to area are better when using polygonal approximations (trapezoids) rather than using step-function approximations).

(*i*) Sketch a generic graph for a function f on an interval $[a,b]$, and for a regular partition of $[a,b]$ into 6 subintervals, sketch the corresponding polygonal approximation. Sketch the solid of revolution that arises by revolving this polygonal approximation about the x-axis. This is called a *conical frustum approximation*.

(*ii*) A *frustum* of a cone is a solid obtained from a cone by cutting through it perpendicular to its axis and removing the smaller cone lying toward the apex. See Figure 5.4.1P.

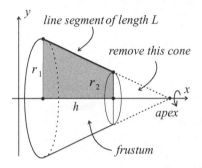

Figure 5.4.1P: *A frustum of a cone.*

Derive the formula

$$V = \frac{\pi}{3} \left(r_1^2 + r_1 r_2 + r_2^2 \right) h \qquad (5.40.1\,\text{P})$$

for the volume of a frustum of a cone based on the quantities r_1, r_2 , and h shown in Figure 5.4.1P. *Hint*: There are several ways to do this. One way is to realize that the frustum shown is the solid obtained by revolving the graph of the linear function

$$y = \frac{(r_2 - r_1)}{h} x + r_1,$$

on the interval $[0,h]$ about the x-axis. Then just compute V using the integral Formula (5.4.1a–b). *Extra Hint*: In computing the integral, use a change of variables to integrate

$$\left[\frac{(r_2 - r_1)}{h} x + r_1 \right]^2 .$$

Another way to get Formula (5.40.2P) is two realize that the frustum of a cone is the difference of two cones. Then, taking for the granted that the volume of a cone is one third the area of its base times its height, a little algebra will get you Formula (5.40.1 P). Try both ways!

(*iii*) Consider the ith subinterval in the polygonal approximation from Part (*i*). On this interval the polygonal approximation is just a straight line and so generates a frustum of a cone when revolved about the x-axis. Use Formula (5.40.1 P) to show that the volume of this ith frustum is

$$\frac{\pi}{3}\left[(f(x_{i-1}))^2 + f(x_{i-1})f(x_i) + (f(x_i))^2\right]\Delta x_i.$$

(*iv*) From Part (*iii*), we get that the conical frustum approximation to E has volume

$$V_n =$$

$$\sum_{i=1}^{n}\frac{\pi}{3}\left[(f(x_{i-1}))^2 + f(x_{i-1})f(x_i) + (f(x_i))^2\right]\Delta x_i$$

What integral formula do you get from the limit: $\lim_{n\to\infty} V_n$? Is it the same as Formula (5.4.1a) (which was derived from cylindrical disk approximations)? Why/why not?

(*v*) There is a special purpose command called frustumapprox that has the

    frustumapprox(f,a,b,n)

and which you can use exactly like diskmethod. However, its output is the volume V_n of the conical frustum approximation and a corresponding picture showing all the frusta is the approximation. Do a comparison of the approximate volumes calculated by the disk method and the frustum method. Specifically, for the function

$$f(x) = x^3 - 5x^2 + 6x + 1,$$

on the interval $[0, 3]$, make a table of values of V_n computed by each method for $n = 5, 10, 20, 50, 100, 300$. For the small values, n = 5, 10, 20, include the corresponding pictures of the cylindrical disk and conical frustum approximations. Calculate the exact volume and compare with approximate volumes in the table. Draw conclusions.

Calculus *Concepts & Computation*

5.5 Lengths of Curves

We have seen how the definite integral, which was developed primarily to measure areas of planar regions, can also be employed to measure volumes of certain types of solids. In this section we will show how the length of a plane curve can be measured using a definite integral.

As might be expected, we start with the basic notion of length and extend it by means of limits. Thus, a line segment Q_0Q_1 in the plane with endpoints

$$Q_0 = (x_0, y_0),\ Q_1 = (x_1, y_1)$$

has length

$$L = |Q_0Q_1| = \sqrt{(x_1 - x_0)^2 + (y_1 - y_0)^2}.$$

This is the basic notion of length. The following figure illustrates a basic line segment and its extension to a polygonal curve.

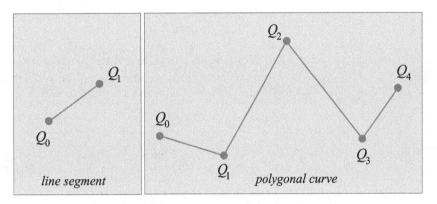

Figure 5.5.1: *Two elementary "curves" whose lengths are computable without calculus.*

A polygon, or polygonal curve, is a geometric figure composed of a sequence of contiguous line segments (its sides). The polygonal curve in Figure 5.5.1 has four sides, Q_0Q_1, Q_1Q_2, Q_2Q_3, Q_3Q_4, and has length defined as the sum of the lengths of its sides:

$$L = |Q_0Q_1| + |Q_1Q_2| + |Q_2Q_3| + |Q_3Q_4|$$

$$= \sum_{i=1}^{4} |Q_{i-1}Q_i| = \sum_{i=1}^{4} \sqrt{(x_i - x_{i-1})^2 + (y_i - y_{i-1})^2}$$

For a more general curve, say one which is the graph of a function, the length of the curve is defined (where possible) by taking limits of the lengths of *approximating* polygonal curves. To develop this idea, suppose that the curve has equation $y=f(x)$, for x in the interval $[a, b]$. Then each partition

$$P = \{x_0, x_1, x_2, \ldots, x_n\}$$

of $[a, b]$ gives a corresponding approximating polygonal curve with vertices

$$Q_i = (x_i, f(x_i)),\ i = 1, \ldots, n.$$

Figure 5.5.2 illustrates this situation for $n = 4$.

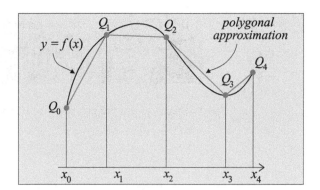

Figure 5.5.2: *A polygonal approximation to the graph of f.*

In general, we let

$$\Delta x_i = x_i - x_{i-1}$$
$$\Delta y_i = f(x_i) - f(x_{i-1})$$

Then the length of the polygonal curve that approximates f is

$$L_P = \sum_{i=1}^{n} |Q_{i-1}Q_i| = \sum_{i=1}^{n} \sqrt{\Delta x_i{}^2 + \Delta y_i{}^2}$$

When we use finer and finer partitions (ones whose norms become smaller and smaller) then the corresponding polygonal curves become better approximations to the graph of f. For example, Figure 5.5.3 shows a partition P' which is finer than the partition P in Figure 5.5.2.

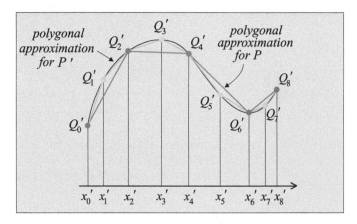

Figure 5.5.3: *A better polygonal approximation arises from a finer partition P' of $[a,b]$.*

In the figure, it is important to note that not only is P' a finer partition, but it is also a *refinement* of P, i.e., it contains the partition points of P. In this case, we see that $Q'_{2j} = Q_j$, $j = 0, 1, 2, 3, 4$. Since P' a refinement of P, it has a greater length:

$$L_P < L_{P'} \qquad (5.5.1)$$

To see this, observe that in Figure 5.5.3, the first line segment arising from the partition P is $Q'_0 Q'_2$ and this is one side in the triangle $\triangle Q'_0 Q'_1 Q'_2$. By elementary geometry, in any triangle, the sum of the lengths of two sides is greater than the length of the remaining side:

$$|Q'_0 Q'_2| < |Q'_0 Q'_1| + |Q'_1 Q'_2|$$

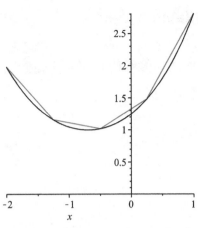

Similar remarks apply to the other line segments arising from the partition P and this leads to Inequality (5.5.1).

Example 5.5.1 (Polygonal Approximations to a Curve)

Problem: For the function

$$f(x) = e^x + \frac{1}{4}\, e^{-x}$$

on the interval $[-2, 1]$, use the special-purpose Maple command

```
> polygonapprox(f,a,b,n)
```

to plot polygonal approximations to the graph of f. Use regular partitions P with $n = 4, 6$ and compute the lengths L_P of these approximations.

Solution: The following code defines the function and then uses `polygonapprox` to produce the graphics and the lengths.

```
> f:=x->exp(x)+exp(-x)/4;
```

$$f := x \mapsto e^x + \frac{1}{4}\, e^{-x}$$

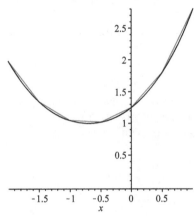

```
> polygonapprox(f,-2,1,4);
```

The length of the polygonal approximation with, 4, sides is, 4.284935631

```
> polygonapprox(f,-2,1,6);
```

The length of the polygonal approximation with, 6, sides is, 4.314695881

The output confirms the theory that $L_P < L_{P'}$, where P, P' are the partitions for $n = 4, 6$, respectively. We can use the procedure `Dpolygonplot(f,a,b,n,fig)` to get a better understanding for how the lengths L_P of the polygonal approximations increase as P becomes finer. The output from this procedure is an animation showing the polygonal approximations with $1, 2, 3, \ldots, n$ sides being plotted in frames $1, 2, 3, \ldots, n$.

```
> Dpolygonapprox(f,-2,6,6,fig);
```

The fifth argument `fig`, which is optional, is a display of the last frame in the animation. This is shown in In Figure 5.5.4.

```
> fig;
```

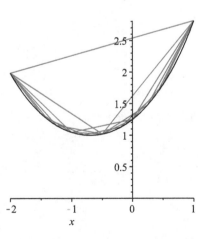

By inspecting all the figures shown in the margin, we can make two important observations. Not only does the length L_P increase as P gets finer, but also any of these lengths appear to be (intuitively) less than the "length" of the curve $y = f(x)$. Symbolically:

$$L_P < \text{"length of the curve"}$$

for all partitions P. So, the situation is this. As we use finer and finer partitions P, the lengths L_P increase and these lengths appear to be bounded above by what we would want to call the length of the curve (which is obtained as the limit of the L_P as $\|P\| \to 0$). This leads to the following definition of length for curves that are graphs of functions.

Figure 5.5.4: *The last frame in the dynamic plot*
`Dpolygonapprox(f,-2,1,6,fig)`

DEFINITION 5.5.1 (Length of a Rectifiable Curve)

Suppose f is a function defined on the interval [a,b]. Consider the set of all lengths of approximating polygonal curves that arise from partitions P of [a,b]:

$$\{ \, L_P \mid P \text{ is a partition of } [a,b] \, \}$$

If this set is bounded above, then we say that the curve: y = f(x), which is the the graph of f on [a,b], is rectifiable. Its length L is defined by

$$L \equiv \lim_{\|P\|\to 0} L_P = \lim_{\|P\|\to 0} \sum_{i=1}^{n} \sqrt{(\Delta x_i)^2 + (\Delta y_i)^2}$$

NOTE 1: The term "rectifiable" just means that we can measure the length of the curve by taking limits of the approximating lengths L_P. There are non-rectifiable curves, namely ones where the set of approximating lengths L_P is not bounded above. (See the Exercises.)

NOTE 2: The length L of a rectifiable curve is also called its *arc length*. This terminology comes from the important special case when the curve is an arc of a circle. See Example 5.5.1(b) below.

In the case when f is a "smooth" function (i.e., has a derivative which is continuous on $[a, b]$) then the curve $y = f(x)$ is rectifiable and there is an integral formula for its length. To motivate the formula, note that each approximating length can be written as

$$L_P = \sum_{i=1}^{n} \sqrt{\Delta x_i^2 + \Delta y_i^2} = \sum_{i=1}^{n} \sqrt{\left(1 + \frac{\Delta y_i^2}{\Delta x_i^2}\right) \Delta x_i^2}$$

$$= \sum_{i=1}^{n} \sqrt{1 + \left(\frac{\Delta y_i}{\Delta x_i}\right)^2} \cdot \Delta x_i.$$

Now as $\|P\| \to 0$, we have $\Delta x_i \to dx$ and $\dfrac{\Delta y_i}{\Delta x_i} \to \dfrac{dy}{dx} = f'(x)$. This leads to the following theorem.

THEOREM 5.5.1 (Lengths of Smooth Curves)

Suppose f has a derivative which is continuous on [a,b]. Then the curve: y = f(x) is rectifiable and its length is given by

$$L = \int_a^b \sqrt{1 + \left[\frac{dy}{dx}\right]^2} \, dx = \int_a^b \sqrt{1 + [f'(x)]^2} \, dx \qquad (5.5.2)$$

Use of the integral formula (5.5.2) requires care be taken in computing the derivative $f'(x)$ and its square $[f'(x)]^2$. The resulting integrand:

$$\sqrt{1 + [f'(x)]^2}$$

can be difficult to integrate because of the square root. There are, however, numerous special types of functions f for which the integral can be computed. We explore these here and in the exercises.

Example 5.5.1 (Using the Arc Length Formula)

Problem: Find the arc lengths for the curves which are the graphs of the following functions:

(a) $f(x) = \dfrac{2}{3} x^{3/2}$ on $[0, 3]$.   (b) $f(x) = \sqrt{1 - x^2}$ on $[\frac{1}{2}, \frac{\sqrt{2}}{2}]$

Solution (a): The derivative is

$$f'(x) = x^{1/2} = \sqrt{x},$$

which is continuous on $[0, 1]$. So we can use Formula 5.5.2. The computations are

$$1 + [f'(x)]^2 = 1 + \left[\sqrt{x}\right]^2 = 1 + x.$$

$$L = \int_0^3 \sqrt{1 + [f'(x)]^2}\, dx = \int_0^3 \sqrt{1 + x}\ dx = \int_0^3 (1 + x)^{1/2}\, dx$$

$$= \frac{2}{3}(1 + x)^{3/2}\Big|_0^3 = \frac{2}{3}(8 - 1) = \frac{14}{3}$$

Solution (b): For

$$f(x) = \sqrt{1 - x^2}$$

the derivative, using the chain rule, is

$$f'(x) = \frac{-x}{\sqrt{1 - x^2}}$$

So

$$1 + [f'(x)]^2 = 1 + \frac{x^2}{1 - x^2} = \frac{1}{1 - x^2}$$

and

$$\sqrt{1 + [f'(x)]^2} = \frac{1}{\sqrt{1 - x^2}}$$

Then the arc length is

$$L = \int_{\frac{1}{2}}^{\frac{\sqrt{2}}{2}} \frac{1}{\sqrt{1 - x^2}}\ dx = \arcsin x \Big|_{\frac{1}{2}}^{\frac{\sqrt{2}}{2}} = \arcsin\left(\frac{\sqrt{2}}{2}\right) - \arcsin\left(\frac{1}{2}\right) = \frac{\pi}{4} - \frac{\pi}{6} = \frac{\pi}{12}$$

Note that the indefinite integral needed in the calculation is the inverse sine function, $\sin^{-1} x$, which we have written using the traditional notation as $\arcsin x$. The reason for this is to emphasize how measuring arc length on the graph of

$$f(x) = \sqrt{1 - x^2}$$

is related to lengths of arcs on a circle of radius 1. Indeed, as you know, the graph of f is the semi-circle shown in Figure 5.5.5.

The length of the graph of f on the interval $[1/2, \sqrt{2}/2]$ (shown in red) is $\pi/12$, which is the difference of the lengths of the graphs on the intervals $[0, \sqrt{2}/2]$ and $[0, 1/2]$ (shown in blue and gold).

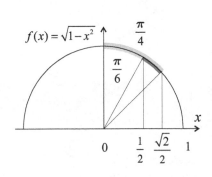

Figure 5.5.5: *The arc length* $L = \frac{\pi}{12} = \frac{\pi}{4} - \frac{\pi}{6}.$

Example 5.5.2 (Arc Length for a Special Class of Curves)

Problem: There is a special class of functions f for which the expression $1 + [f'(x)]^2$ is a perfect square. (See the Exercises.) This greatly simplifies the computation of the arc length. For the following two examples of this, find the arc lengths for the curves which are the graphs of the functions:

(a) $f(x) = \sqrt{x} - \dfrac{1}{3}x^{3/2}$ on $[1, 4]$.   (b) $f(x) = e^x + \dfrac{1}{4}e^{-x}$ on $[-2, 1]$

Solution(a): The derivative is

$$f'(x) = \frac{1}{2\sqrt{x}} - \frac{\sqrt{x}}{2}$$

So

$$1 + [f'(x)]^2 = 1 + \left[\frac{1}{2\sqrt{x}} - \frac{\sqrt{x}}{2}\right]^2 = 1 + \left(\frac{1}{4x} - \frac{1}{2} + \frac{x}{4}\right)$$

$$= \frac{1}{4x} + \frac{1}{2} + \frac{x}{4} = \left(\frac{1}{2\sqrt{x}} + \frac{\sqrt{x}}{2}\right)^2$$

Notice that what makes this work is that the expression $\frac{1}{4x} - \frac{1}{2} + \frac{x}{4}$ is the square of a binomial, $(a - b)^2$, where the middle term is $-2ab = -\frac{1}{2}$. Adding 1 to it changes the middle term from $-\frac{1}{2}$ to $\frac{1}{2}$, thus giving the square $(a + b)^2$. From the above we get

$$L = \int_1^4 \sqrt{\left(\frac{1}{2\sqrt{x}} + \frac{\sqrt{x}}{2}\right)^2} = \int_1^4 \left(\frac{1}{2\sqrt{x}} + \frac{\sqrt{x}}{2}\right) dx$$

$$= \left(\sqrt{x} + \frac{1}{3}x^{3/2}\right)\Big|_1^4 = \left(2 + \frac{8}{3}\right) - \left(1 - \frac{1}{3}\right) = 1 + \frac{9}{3} = 4$$

Solution (b): For the function

$$f(x) = e^x + \frac{1}{4}e^{-x}$$

the derivative is

$$f'(x) = e^x - \frac{1}{4}e^{-x}$$

So

$$1 + [f'(x)]^2 = 1 + \left[e^x - \frac{1}{4}e^{-x}\right]^2 = 1 + \left(e^{2x} - \frac{1}{2} + \frac{1}{16}e^{-2x}\right)$$

$$= e^{2x} + \frac{1}{2} + \frac{1}{16}e^{-2x} = \left(e^x + \frac{1}{4}e^{-x}\right)^2$$

Thus,

$$L = \int_{-2}^1 \sqrt{\left(e^x + \frac{1}{4}e^{-x}\right)^2} dx = \int_{-2}^1 \left(e^x + \frac{1}{4}e^{-x}\right) dx$$

$$= \left(e^x - \frac{1}{4}e^{-x}\right)\Big|_{-2}^1 = e - \frac{1}{4}e^{-1} - e^{-2} + \frac{1}{4}e^2 \approx 4.338240710$$

Compare this exact length and the approximate lengths we found in Example 5.5.1 above:

$$\text{4 sided polygonal approximation} = 4.284935631$$
$$\text{6 sided polygonal approximation} = 4.314695881$$

The Arc Length Function

Suppose f is a differentiable function and has a continuous derivative on the interval $[a, b]$. Then, on this interval, we can define a function s, called an *arc length function* by letting $s(x)$ be the length of the graph of f between the points $(a, f(a))$ and $(x, f(x))$. See Figure 5.5.6.

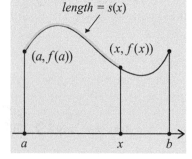

Figure 5.5.6: *The arc length function $s(x)$*

Because of Theorem 5.5.1, the definition of s can also be expressed in terms of a definite integral:

DEFINITION 5.5.2 (Arc Length Function)

Suppose f has a derivative which is continuous on $[a,b]$. Then the arc length length is defined by

$$s(x) = \int_a^x \sqrt{1 + [f'(t)]^2}\, dt \qquad (5.5.3)$$

Notice how, in the definition, the variable x occurs as the upper limit of integration and that the variable of integration is t.

Example 5.5.3 (Computing the Arc Length Function)

Problem: For the function $f(x) = \dfrac{1}{3}\left(x^2 + 2\right)^{3/2}$ on the interval $(0, \infty)$, find the formula for the arc length function.

Solution: The derivative

$$f'(x) = \frac{1}{3} \cdot \frac{3}{2}\left(x^2+2\right)^{1/2} 2x = x\left(x^2+2\right)^{1/2}$$

is continuous on the given interval. So we can compute the arc length function using the Formula 5.5.3. For this we first compute

$$1 + [f'(x)]^2 = 1 + \left[x\left(x^2+2\right)^{1/2}\right]^2 = 1 + x^2\left(x^2+2\right)$$

$$= x^4 + 2x^2 + 1 = \left(x^2+1\right)^2$$

So

$$\sqrt{1 + [f'(x)]^2} = \sqrt{\left(x^2+1\right)^2} = x^2 + 1$$

Thus,

$$s(x) = \int_a^x \sqrt{1+[f'(t)]^2}\,dt = \int_0^x \left(t^2+1\right)\,dt = \left(\frac{1}{3}t^3 + t\right)\Big|_0^x = \frac{1}{3}x^3 + x$$

For example, when $x = 1$, the length of the graph of f between the points $A = (0, f(0))$ and $B = (1, f(1))$ is $s(1) = 4/3$. This is illustrated in the Figure 5.5.7.

The Leibniz Notation: $ds^2 = dx^2 + dy^2$

Since the arc length function is defined by a definite integral with variable upper limit of integration:

$$s(x) = \int_a^x \sqrt{1 + [f'(t)]^2}\,dt,$$

we see (by the first part of the Fundamental Theorem of Calculus) that it is differentiable and has derivative:

$$s'(x) = \frac{d}{dx}\int_a^x \sqrt{1 + [f'(t)]^2}\,dt = \sqrt{1 + [f'(x)]^2}$$

In the Leibniz notation this is

$$\frac{ds}{dx} = \sqrt{1 + \left[\frac{dy}{dx}\right]^2}.$$

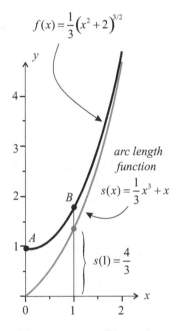

$f(x) = \dfrac{1}{3}\left(x^2+2\right)^{3/2}$

arc length function

$s(x) = \dfrac{1}{3}x^3 + x$

$s(1) = \dfrac{4}{3}$

Figure 5.5.7: *The ordinate at x to the graph of the arc length function s has the same length as the graph of f between $A = (0, f(0))$ and $B = (x, f(x))$*

Viewing this in terms of differentials, we can write, heuristically,

$$ds = \sqrt{1 + \left[\frac{dy}{dx}\right]^2}\, dx = \sqrt{1 + \frac{dy^2}{dx^2}}\, dx = \sqrt{\frac{dx^2 + dy^2}{dx^2}}\, dx.$$

So

$$ds = \sqrt{dx^2 + dy^2}$$

This equation expresses the infinitesimal element of arc length ds in terms of the differentials dx and dy. One can consider it as coming from the Pythagorean theorem applied to a differential triangle (the infinitesimal version of a difference triangle).

By adding together (integrating) all these infinitesimal elements of arc length, we get the total length:

$$s = \int ds.$$

For a specific length of the curve, we can express its length L, given by Formula 5.5.2, in differential form as follows:

$$L = \int_a^b \sqrt{1 + \left[\frac{dy}{dx}\right]^2}\, dx = \int_a^b \sqrt{dx^2 + dy^2} = \int_a^b ds \qquad (5.5.4)$$

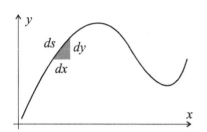

Figure 5.5.8: *A differential triangle.*

While the work here with differentials is mathematical fiction, it offers a useful pedagogical way of computing the quantities in the arc length integral. The following example illustrates this.

Example 5.5.4 (Using Leibniz Differentials)

Problem: Find the length of the curve $x = y^{2/3}$ between the points $(0,0)$ and $(4,8)$

Solution: As in the substitution method, if the variables are related by the equation

$$x = y^{2/3}$$

then their differentials are related by

$$dx = \frac{2}{3} y^{-1/3} dy.$$

So,

$$dx^2 = \left(\frac{2}{3} y^{-1/3} dy\right)^2 = \frac{4}{9} y^{-2/3}\, dy^2$$

and

$$ds^2 = dx^2 + dy^2 = \frac{4}{9} y^{-2/3}\, dy^2 + dy^2 = \left(\frac{4}{9} y^{-2/3} + 1\right) dy^2$$

$$= \left(\frac{4}{9y^{2/3}} + 1\right) dy^2 = \frac{4 + 9y^{2/3}}{9y^{2/3}}\, dy^2$$

Thus, the length is

$$L = \int_0^8 ds = \int_0^8 \sqrt{dx^2 + dy^2} = \int_0^8 \sqrt{\frac{4 + 9y^{2/3}}{9y^{2/3}}}\, dy$$

$$= \int_0^8 \frac{\sqrt{4 + 9y^{2/3}}}{3y^{1/3}}\, dy = \frac{1}{3} \int_0^8 \sqrt{4 + 9y^{2/3}}\; y^{-1/3}\, dy$$

To compute the integral use a substitution:

$$u = 4 + 9\,y^{2/3}, \; du = 6\,y^{-1/3}dy$$

when $y = 0$, $u = 4$ and when $y = 8$, $u = 40$.

Then

$$L = \frac{1}{3} \int_4^{40} \sqrt{u} \cdot \frac{1}{6} \cdot du = \frac{1}{18} \cdot \frac{2}{3} u^{3/2} \Big|_4^{40} = \frac{1}{27} \left(80\sqrt{10} - 8\right) = \frac{8}{27} \left(10\sqrt{10} - 1\right)$$

<u>NOTE</u>: In this example we can solve the equation $x = y^{2/3}$ for y to get $y = x^{3/2}$ (with $0 \le x$). Then, as in all the prior examples, we could use

$$L = \int_a^b \sqrt{1 + \left[\frac{dy}{dy}\right]^2}\, dx$$

to compute the length. However, when solving for y is not possible, such as for the curve:

$$x = y^4 + \frac{1}{32}\,y^{-2}$$

then use the differential method as in Example 5.5.4.

Exercises: 5.5 (Lengths of Curves)

In Exercises 1–8, compute the length of the graph of the function on the given interval.

1. $f(x) = \ln(\sec x)$, $[0, \frac{\pi}{3}]$

2. $f(x) = \ln(\csc x)$, $[\frac{\pi}{6}, \frac{\pi}{2}]$

3. $f(x) = \cosh x$, $[-2, 2]$

4. $f(x) = e^{3x} + \frac{1}{36} e^{-3x}$, $[-\frac{4}{3}, \frac{1}{3}]$

5. $f(x) = \ln(x + \sqrt{x^2 - 1})$, $[1, 2]$

6. $f(x) = \frac{1}{3} \ln(3x + \sqrt{9x^2 - 1}$, $[1, 2]$

7. $f(x) = \sec^{-1}(e^x)$, $(0, \ln 2)$

8. $f(x) = \csc^{-1}(e^x)$, $(0, \ln 2)$

A Special Class of Functions

In Exercises 9–26, the functions $y = f(x)$ constitute a special class of functions for which the expression

$$1 + [f'(x)]^2 = 1 + \left[\frac{dy}{dx}\right]^2$$

is a perfect square. (See Exercise 45 for the theory on construction of such functions.)

Find the length of the graph of $y = f(x)$ on the given interval.

9. $f(x) = \dfrac{x^3}{3} + \dfrac{1}{4x}$, $[1, 3]$

10. $y = \dfrac{x^3}{12} + \dfrac{1}{x}$, $[1, 3]$

11. $y = \dfrac{x^4}{4} + \dfrac{1}{8x^2}$, $[1, 2]$

12. $y = x^4 + \dfrac{1}{32x^2}$, $[1, 2]$

13. $f(x) = \dfrac{x^5}{5} + \dfrac{1}{12x^3}$, $[1, 2]$

14. $f(x) = x^5 + \dfrac{1}{60x^3}$, $[1, 2]$

15. $f(x) = \frac{2}{5} x^{5/2} + \frac{1}{2} x^{-1/2}$, $[1, 4]$

16. $f(x) = \frac{3}{7} x^{7/3} + \frac{3}{4} x^{-1/3}$, $[1, 8]$

17. $y = \ln x - \frac{1}{8} x^2$, $[1, 4]$

18. $y = \ln(1 + e^{2x}) - \frac{1}{8} x + \frac{1}{16} e^{-2x}$, $[0, 2]$

19. $f(x = \ln(\tan x) - \frac{1}{8} \sin^2 x$, $[0, \frac{\pi}{4}]$

20. $f(x = \ln(\sec x) + \frac{1}{4} \ln(\csc x)$, $[\frac{\pi}{6}, \frac{\pi}{3}]$

21. $f(x) = \sin x - \frac{1}{4} \ln(\sec x + \tan x$, $[0, \frac{\pi}{4}]$

22. $f(x) = \ln(1 + x^2) - \frac{1}{8} \ln x - \frac{1}{16} x^2$, $[1, 4]$

23. $f(x) = x + \frac{1}{3} x^3 - \frac{1}{4} \tan^{-1} x$, $[0, 1]$

24. $f(x) = \tan x - \frac{1}{8} x - \frac{1}{16} \sin 2x$, $[0, \frac{\pi}{4}]$

25. $y = \ln(1 + \sqrt{x}) - \frac{1}{3} x^{3/2} - \frac{1}{4} x^2$, $[1, 4]$

26. $y = \ln(1 + \ln x) - \frac{1}{8} x^3 \ln x - \frac{1}{16} x^2$, $[1, 4]$

Using Leibniz Differentials

Follow the method in Example 5.5.4 to compute the lengths of the following curves.

27. $x = y^4 + \frac{1}{32} y^{-2}$, $[1, 2]$ **28.** $x = y^5 + \frac{1}{60} y^{-3}$, $[1, 2]$

29. $x = e^{y/2} + e^{-y/2}$, $[0, 1]$ **30.** $x = e^{y/3} + \frac{1}{4} e^{-y/2}$, $[0, 1]$

31. $x = \dfrac{y}{y + 1} - \dfrac{(y + 1)^3}{12}$, $[0, 2]$

Approximate Arc Length

32. CAS: Select some of those Exercises 1–26 above that you were assigned and use the special-purpose Maple procedure `polygonapprox` to produce approximate values for the arc length as well as the corresponding graphics. Compare the numerical approximations you get with the exact lengths you computed in Exercise 1–26.

Arc Length Functions

In Exercises 33–38:

(a) Compute the arc length function

$$s(x) = \int_a^x \sqrt{1 + [f'(t)]^2}\, dt,$$

for the function f on the given interval $[a, b]$. Also

(b) Pick a point x in the interval $[a, b]$ and compute the length of the graph of f between the point $(a, f(a))$ and $(x, f(x))$.

(c) CAS: Use a computer to plot the function and its arc length function in a single display. Include a graph of the vertical line segment joining the points $(x, 0)$ and $(x, s(x))$. Interpret the results.

33. $f(x) = \ln(\csc x)$, $[\frac{\pi}{2}, \frac{5\pi}{6}]$

34. $f(x = \ln(\sec x)$, $[0, \frac{\pi}{3}]$

35. $f(x) = \cosh x$, $[0, 2]$

36. $f(x) = 2 \ln(x + \sqrt{x^2 - 4})$, $[4, 9]$

37. $f(x) = \sqrt{1 - x^2}$, $[0, 1]$

38. $f(x) = \csc^{-1}(e^x)$, $[0, \ln 2]$

Approximate Arc Length

CAS: In Exercises 39–44, set up the arc length integral that gives the length of the graph of the function on the given interval. You will not be able to compute the integral exactly (by hand), so use the special-purpose Maple procedure polygonapprox to produce approximate values for the arc length as well as the corresponding graphics. Compare the numerical approximations you get with those produced by Maple's int command.

39. $f(x) = x^3$, $[0, 1]$ **40.** $f(x) = x^4$, $[0, 1]$

41. $f(x) = \sin x$, $[0, \pi]$ **42.** $f(x) = \cos x$, $[0, \pi]$

43. $f(x) = x^{\sin x}$, $[1, 5]$ **44.** $f(x) = x^{\cos x}$, $[1, 5]$

A Special Class of Functions (Theory)

45. Suppose g is a differentiable function on an interval $I = [a, b]$ and that its derivative is continuous and positive on I. Let h be an antiderivative of the function $-\dfrac{1}{4g'}$ on the interval I, i.e,

$$h(x) = -\frac{1}{4} \int \frac{1}{g'(x)}\, dx,$$

Further, let
$$f(x) = g(x) + h(x)$$
for x in I. Show that
$$1 + [f'(x)]^2 = [g'(x) - h'(x)]^2$$

for all x in I and use this to compute the arc length function for f.

46. For any real number $p \neq 0, 2$, let f be the function defined for $x > 0$ by

$$f(x) = \frac{x^p}{p} + \frac{1}{4(p-2)}\, x^{2-p}$$

Show that $1 + [f'(x)]^2$ is a perfect square and compute the arc length function for f on the interval $[1, \infty)$. Discuss how this is related to Exercise 45.

47. Suppose that f has a continuous derivative on the interval $[a, b]$ (and for simplicity assume that f is increasing on this interval). Show that the graph of f^{-1} on the interval $[f^{-1}(a), f^{-1}(b)]$ has the same length as the graph of f on the interval $[a, b]$. Make a sketch to convince yourself of the plausibility of this result.

Calculus Concepts & Computation

5.6 Surface Area of Solids of Revolution

We have seen how solids of revolution are created by revolving Type I or Type II regions about various axes. In this section we derive some integral formulas for measuring the *surface area* of such solids. We begin with the special Type I region which is just the region beneath the graph of a *positive* function f on an interval $[a,b]$. As an initial example consider:

Example 5.6.1 (A Las Vegas Urn)

Several large urns outside a Las Vegas hotel are in the shape of a solid of revolution (with units in feet). The function whose graph generates the surface of the urn is

```
>   f:=x->2+sin(x);
```

$$f := x \mapsto 2 + \sin(x)$$

```
>   plot([f(x),0],x=0..7*Pi/4,color=black,filled=[color=turquoise]);
```

Revolving this region about the x-axis gives the solid shown in Figure 5.6.2.

```
>   with(plots):
```

```
>   revolve1X(f,0,7*Pi/4);
```

Note that the *surface* of this solid is generated by the graph of f as it is revolved about the x-axis. Indeed, the rendering in Maple shows this graph at various positions during the revolution. The other curves in the figure are the circles traced out by points on the graph of f as it is revolved.

Each urn is to be repainted in a bright turquoise color. How many gallons of paint will it take to repaint 10 urns if each gallon covers 400 ft²? To answer this question we need to develop a formula for measuring surface area.

As is customary in calculus, exact measurements involve approximations and limits. Thus, to measure the area of a surface of revolution, we approximate the surface with elementary surfaces for which we know the areas and then we take limits. In this case, the appropriate elementary surface is the surface of a *frustum*. Such a surface is obtained by revolving a line segment, lying above the x-axis, about the x-axis. Figure 5.6.3 illustrates this.

Note that the frustum is what is left when you slice, perpendicular to the axis, a full cone below its apex and remove the smaller conical piece at the apex. One can use elementary geometry to determine the area of the surface of such a frustum. (See the Exercises.) This area is

$$A = \pi (r_1 + r_2) L, \qquad (5.6.1)$$

where, as shown in Figure 5.6.3, r_1, r_2 are the radii of the top and bottom circular bases of the frustum and L is the length of the generating line segment. NOTE: L is often called the *slant height* of the frustum. To see how to approximate a surface of revolution with surfaces of frusta, we first approximate the function f with a polygonal curve:

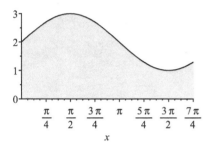

Figure 5.6.1: *The region beneath the graph of* $f(x) = 2 + \sin x$ *on the interval* $[0, 7\pi/4]$.

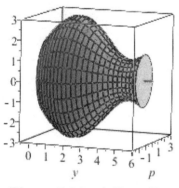

Figure 5.6.2: *A Vegas Urn.*

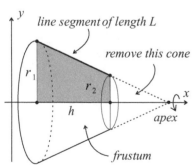

Figure 5.6.3: *A frustum of a cone.*

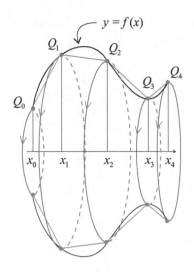

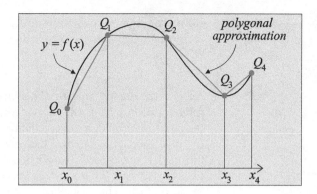

Figure 5.6.4: *A polygonal approximation to the graph of f.*

Figure 5.6.5: *Approximation of the surface of revolution by frusta of cones.*

Each side of the polygonal approximation, when revolved about the x-axis generates a frustum of a cone. See Figure 5.6.5.

The collection of all these frusta forms an approximation to the surface of revolution. Using Formula (5.6.1) on the ith frustum with radii $r_1 = f(x_{i-1})$, $r_2 = f(x_i)$, the slant height is

$$L = \sqrt{\Delta x_i{}^2 + \Delta y_i{}^2} = \sqrt{1 + \frac{\Delta y_i{}^2}{\Delta x_i{}^2}}\, \Delta x_i$$

and the surface area is

$$S_i = \pi\left[f(x_{i-1}) + f(x_i)\right]\sqrt{1 + \frac{\Delta y_i{}^2}{\Delta x_i{}^2}}\, \Delta x_i$$

Adding these gives an approximation to the area S of the surface of revolution:

$$S \approx \sum_{i=1}^{n} \pi\left[f(x_{i-1}) + f(x_i)\right]\sqrt{1 + \frac{\Delta y_i{}^2}{\Delta x_i{}^2}}\, \Delta x_i \qquad (5.6.2)$$

As an example of the approximation with frusta, consider $f(x) = 2 + \sin x$ on the interval $[0, 7\pi/4]$. It is simple enough to use a regular partition of the interval into 5 subintervals and compute, by hand, the approximating sum in (5.6.2). Alternatively, we can use a special-purpose Maple command to do this and also produce a picture of the approximating frusta. The results are shown below.

```
> frustumapprox(f,0,7*Pi/4,5);
```

The approximate surface area using, 5, *frusta is,* 83.49244633

To get the exact area of the surface of revolution, we take limits of such sums:

$$S = \lim_{\|P\|\to 0} \sum_{i=1}^{n} \pi\left[f(x_{i-1}) + f(x_i)\right]\sqrt{1 + \left(\frac{\Delta y_i}{\Delta x_i}\right)^2}\, \Delta x_i$$

This gives the following integral formula for S.

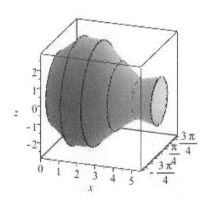

Figure 5.6.6: *The surfaces of five approximating frusta.*

THEOREM 5.6.1 (Area of a Surface of Revolution)

Suppose f is positive on $[a,b]$ and has a derivative which is continuous on $[a,b]$. Then the curve $y = f(x)$, rotated about the x-axis, generates a surface whose area is given by

$$S = \int_a^b 2\pi f(x)\sqrt{1 + [f'(x)]^2}\, dx = \int_a^b 2\pi y\sqrt{1 + \left[\frac{dy}{dx}\right]^2}\, dx \qquad (5.6.3)$$

Note that $\|P\| \to 0$ forces the left and right endpoints x_{i-1} and x_i to approach each other. Thus, to get Formula (5.6.3), we heuristically use

$$\pi[f(x_{i-1}) + f(x_i)] \to 2\pi f(x) = 2\pi y, \ \text{as } \|P\| \to 0.$$

As with the arc length formula, using the surface area Formula (5.6.3) requires carefulness in computing the derivative, squaring, and simplifying using algebra. The resulting integrand can be difficult, if not impossible, to integrate in closed form. In these cases, the integral can be computed using Maple's numerical integration techniques, or can be approximated using the special-purpose Maple procedure `frustumapprox`. There are also many of cases where the integral can be computed in closed form. The following examples (and many in the Exercises) exhibit these cases.

Example 5.6.2 (Using the Surface Area Formula)

Problem: The graph of

$$f(x) = \frac{x^3}{12} + \frac{1}{x} \quad \text{on the interval} \quad [1,4],$$

is revolved about the x-axis. Find the area of the corresponding surface of revolution and plot the surface using `revolve1X`.

Solution: The derivative is

$$f'(x) = \frac{x^2}{4} - \frac{1}{x^2}.$$

So

$$1 + [f'(x)]^2 = 1 + \left[\frac{x^2}{4} - \frac{1}{x^2}\right]^2 = 1 + \left(\frac{x^4}{16} - \frac{1}{2} + \frac{1}{x^4}\right) = \frac{x^4}{16} + \frac{1}{2} + \frac{1}{x^4} = \left[\frac{x^2}{4} + \frac{1}{x^2}\right]^2$$

Thus,

$$\sqrt{1 + [f'(x)]^2} = \sqrt{\left[\frac{x^2}{4} + \frac{1}{x^2}\right]^2} = \frac{x^2}{4} + \frac{1}{x^2}$$

and

$$f(x)\sqrt{1 + [f'(x)]^2} = \left(\frac{x^3}{12} + \frac{1}{x}\right)\left(\frac{x^2}{4} + \frac{1}{x^2}\right) = \frac{x^5}{48} + \frac{x}{12} + \frac{x}{4} + \frac{1}{x^3} = \frac{x^5}{48} + \frac{x}{3} + \frac{1}{x^3}.$$

Consequently

$$S = \int_1^4 2\pi\left(\frac{x^5}{48} + \frac{x}{3} + \frac{1}{x^3}\right) dx = \pi\left(\frac{x^6}{144} + \frac{x^2}{3} - \frac{1}{x^2}\right)\Big|_1^4$$

$$= \pi\left(\frac{256}{9} + \frac{16}{3} - \frac{1}{16} - \frac{1}{144} - \frac{1}{3} + 1\right) = \frac{275\pi}{8}$$

Finally, we plot the surface shown in Figure 5.6.7 using:

```
>  f:=x->x^3/12+1/x;g:=0;
```

$$f := x \mapsto \frac{1}{12}x^3 + \frac{1}{x}$$

$$g := 0$$

```
>  revolve1X(f,g,1,4);
```

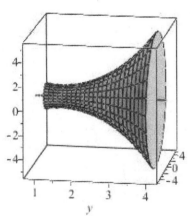

Figure 5.6.7: *The surface of revolution obtained by revolving the graph of* $f(x) = \frac{x^3}{12} + \frac{1}{x}$

Example 5.6.3 (A Football - Using Some Techniques of Integration)

Problem: An American football is approximately 11 inches long and 22 inches around (circumference) at its middle (where your hand grips it).

Assume the surface of the football can be modeled approximately by the surface of revolution obtained by revolving the graph of

$$f(x) = a \cos bx, \text{ on the interval } \left[-\frac{\pi}{2b}, \frac{\pi}{2b}\right],$$

Mtsaride/Shutterstock.com

Figure 5.6.8: *An American football.*

about the x-axis. Find the amount of leather needed to make a football (assuming there is no waste and neglecting the overlap necessary to sew the seams)

Solution: First we determine a and b. The length of the interval for the graph of f is $\frac{\pi}{b}$, so we need $\frac{\pi}{b} = 11$, which gives

$$b = \frac{\pi}{11} \approx 0.286 \text{ inches.}$$

The circumference $2\pi a$ has to be 22 and so

$$a = \frac{11}{\pi} = 3.5 \text{ inches}$$

Note that

$$a = \frac{1}{b}, \text{ So } ab = 1 \text{ and } \frac{a}{b} = a^2$$

We do the calculations in general and then use the above values for a and b.

Since $f(x) = a \cos bx$, $f'(x) = -ab \sin bx = -\sin bx$. So

$$\sqrt{1 + [f'(x)]^2} = \sqrt{1 + \sin^2 bx}$$

For a football, we can use symmetry and double the measure of half the surface area:

$$S = 2 \int_0^{\pi/2b} 2\pi a \cos bx \sqrt{1 + \sin^2 bx} \, dx$$

Use the u-substitution

$$u = \sin bx, \ du = b \cos bx \quad (\text{So } du = \frac{1}{b} \cos bx \, dx)$$

$$\text{when } x = 0, \ u = 0, \text{ and when } x = \frac{\pi}{2b}, \ u = 1$$

This will simplify the integral to

$$S = 4\pi \cdot \frac{a}{b} \int_0^1 \sqrt{1 + u^2} \, du = 4\pi a^2 \int_0^1 \sqrt{1 + u^2} \, du$$

This integral requires techniques of integration which you will study in Chapter 6. One of those techniques relies on the trig identity

$$1 + \tan^2\theta = \sec^2\theta$$

This suggests the substitution (called a trig substitution)

$$u = \tan\theta, \ du = \sec^2\theta \, d\theta$$

$$\text{when } u = 0, \ \theta = 0, \text{ and when } u = 1, \ \theta = \frac{\pi}{4}$$

Then

$$\sqrt{1+u^2} = \sqrt{1+\tan^2\theta} = \sqrt{\sec^2\theta} = \sec\theta$$

Now, in terms of the new variable θ, the surface area integral becomes

$$S = 4\pi a^2 \int_0^{\pi/4} \sec^3\theta\, d\theta$$

This integral in can be computed using a table of integrals (see the Appendix). The table has the formula

$$\int \sec^n x\, dx = \frac{1}{n-1}\sec^{n-2}x\tan x + \frac{n-2}{n-1}\int \sec^{n-2}x\, dx$$

This is known as a *reduction formula* and will be discussed in the next chapter also. Using this with $n=2$ and $x=\theta$ gives

$$\int \sec^3\theta\, d\theta = \frac{1}{2}\sec\theta\tan\theta + \frac{1}{2}\int \sec\theta\, d\theta$$

$$= \frac{1}{2}\sec\theta\tan\theta + \frac{1}{2}\ln(\sec\theta + \tan\theta)$$

Now the final computation of the surface area is, with $a \approx 3.5\text{in}$,

$$S = 4\pi a^2 \cdot \frac{1}{2}\Big[\sec\theta\tan\theta + \ln(\sec\theta+\tan\theta)\Big]\Big|_0^{\pi/4}$$

$$= 2\pi a^2\left[\sqrt{2} + \ln\left(\sqrt{2}+1\right)\right] \approx 176.7\,\text{in}^2.$$

Thus, one football has a surface area of about $177\,\text{in}^2$ and would need that much leather (not counting waste) to construct.

Example 5.6.4 (The Vegas Urn Again - Approximating Surface Area)

Problem: The graph of

$$f(x) = 2 + \sin x, \text{ on the interval } [0, 7\pi/4],$$

is revolved about the x-axis to create the urn in Example 5.6.1. Find the *approximate* area of the corresponding surface of revolution and use this to compute how many gallons of paint are needed to paint 10 urns. (Each gallon covers $400\,\text{ft}^2$.)

Solution: First we compute the derivative. Here $f'(x) = \cos x$ and so

$$S = 2\pi \int_0^{7\pi/4} (2+\sin x)\sqrt{1+\cos^2 x}\, dx$$

While this integral is similar to that in the last example, computing it is much too difficult. (Maple can do it using elliptic functions, but few *people* could do such calculations.) Therefore, we use `frustumapprox` to get an approximate area. For this, we include an optional 5th argument to suppress the graphic output.

```
>   f:=x->2+sin(x);
```
$$f := x \mapsto 2 + \sin(x)$$
```
>   frustumapprox(f,0,7*Pi/4,20,nopic);
```
> *The approximate surface area using*, 20, *frusta is*, 85.03644587
```
>   frustumapprox(f,0,7*Pi/4,100,nopic);
```
> *The approximate surface area using*, 100, *frusta is*, 85.13398051
```
>   frustumapprox(f,0,7*Pi/4,150,nopic);
```

The approximate surface area using, 150, frusta is, 85.13624147

This gives some data that suggests that the surface area is about 85.13. Multiplying this by 10 gives 851.3 ft^2 of surface area to paint on the 10 urns. Thus, dividing by 400 ft^2/gal tells us that we need about 2.13 gallons to paint all the urns.

The Leibniz Notation: $dS = 2\pi r \, ds$

We can write the surface area Formula (5.6.3) as

$$S = \int_a^b 2\pi f(x) \sqrt{1 + [f'(x)]^2} \, dx$$

in abbreviated form as

Areas of Surfaces of Revolution
$S = \int_b^a 2\pi r \, ds$ \qquad (5.6.7)
where $r = f(x)$ and $ds = \sqrt{dx^2 + dy^2}$.

Note that the infinitesimal element of arc length is

$$ds = \sqrt{1 + [f'(x)]^2} \, dx = \sqrt{1 + \left[\frac{dy}{dx}\right]^2} \, dx = \sqrt{dx^2 + dy^2}$$

Heuristically

$$dS = 2\pi r \, ds$$

represents the surface area of an infinitesimal frustum with slant height

$$ds = \sqrt{dx^2 + dy^2}$$

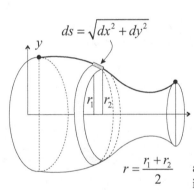

$$ds = \sqrt{dx^2 + dy^2}$$

$$r = \frac{r_1 + r_2}{2}$$

Figure 5.6.9: *The surface area is the integral of the the infinitesimal elements of area $dS = 2\pi r \, ds$, which are the areas of the infinitesimal frusta.*

and $r = (r_1 + r_2)/2$ being the average of the radii for the bases. This is illustrated in Figure 5.6.9.

Formula (5.6.7) is convenient to use when revolving other types of curves and using other axes of revolution. All you have to do is (1) determine the distance r to the axis of revolution and (2) compute $ds = \sqrt{dx^2 + dy^2}$ in terms of the relevant variable. The following example exhibits one such situation.

NOTE: See Exercise 35 for a proof of the validity of using the integral formula:

$$S = \int_a^b 2\pi r \, ds$$

for situations where r is not $f(x)$.

Example 5.6.5 (Revolving About the y-Axis)

Problem: The graph of the function $f(x) = x^{1/3}$ on the interval $[0, 1]$ is revolved about the y-axis. Find the area of the corresponding surface of revolution

Solution: As shown in Figure 5.6.10, for each x in the interval $[0, 1]$, there is a corre-sponding element of arc length ds at a distance $r = x$ from the axis of revolution. So, we can compute the surface area as

$$S = \int_0^1 2\pi x \, ds.$$

To compute ds, start with $y = x^{1/3}$, so that

$$dy = \frac{1}{3}x^{-2/3}dx = \frac{1}{3x^{2/3}}dx$$

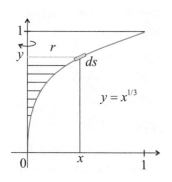

Then

$$ds^2 = dx^2 + dy^2 = dx^2 + \frac{1}{9x^{4/3}}\,dx^2$$

$$= \left(1 + \frac{1}{9x^{4/3}}\right)dx^2 = \left(\frac{9x^{4/3}+1}{9x^{4/3}}\right)dx^2$$

Thus,

$$ds = \sqrt{dx^2 + dy^2} = \frac{\sqrt{9\,x^{4/3}+1}\,dx}{3x^{2/3}}$$

Figure 5.6.10: *The curve $y = x^{1/3}$ is revolved about the y-axis.*

Then the area is

$$S = \int_0^1 2\pi x \frac{\sqrt{9x^{4/3}+1}}{3x^{2/3}}\,dx = \frac{2\pi}{3}\int_0^1 x^{1/3}\sqrt{9x^{4/3}+1}\,dx$$

To compute the integral, we make the substitution

$$u = 9\,x^{4/3} + 1, \ du = 12\,x^{1/3}dx$$

to get

$$S = \frac{2\pi}{3}\int_1^{10}\sqrt{u}\left(\frac{1}{12}\,du\right) = \frac{\pi}{18}\int_1^{10} u^{1/2}\,du = \frac{\pi}{18}\left(\frac{2}{3}u^{3/2}\right)\Big|_1^{10} = \frac{\pi}{27}\left(10\sqrt{10}-1\right)$$

Exercises: 5.6 (Surface Areas of Solids of Revolution)

In Exercises 1–12, compute the area of the surface obtained by revolving the graph of $y = f(x)$, on the interval $[a, b]$ about the x-axis.

1. $f(x) = x^3$, $[0, 1]$ **2.** $y = \frac{1}{3}x^3$, $[0, 1]$

3. $f(x) = \sqrt{x}$, $[1, 4]$ **4.** $f(x) = 2\sqrt{x}$, $[1, 4]$

5. $y = \dfrac{x^4}{4} + \dfrac{1}{8x^2}$, $[1, 2]$ **6.** $y = x^4 + \dfrac{1}{32x^2}$, $[1, 2]$

7. $f(x) = e^x + \frac{1}{4}e^{-x}$, $[0, 1]$

8. $f(x) = e^{2x} + \frac{1}{16}e^{-2x}$, $[0, 1]$

9. $f(x) = \sqrt{x} - \frac{1}{3}x^{3/2}$, $[1, 4]$

10. $f(x) = 2\sqrt{x} - \frac{1}{6}x^{3/2}$, $[1, 4]$

11. $f(x) = \frac{2}{5}x^{5/2} + \frac{1}{2}x^{-1/2}$, $[1, 2]$

12. $f(x) = \frac{3}{7}x^{7/3} + \frac{3}{4}x^{-1/3}$, $[1, 8]$

Surface Areas for Footballs

13. A rugby ball is 30 cm long and has a circumference of 60 cm. at its widest point. Assume the rugby ball can be modeled as a surface of revolution obtained by revolving the graph of $f(x) = a \sin bx$, on the interval $[0, \frac{\pi}{b}]$. about the x-axis. Find the surface area.

14. A nerf ball is 6 in long and has a circumference of 12 in and has a circumference of 12 in at its widest point. Assume the nerf ball can be modeled as a surface of revolution obtained by revolving $f(x) = a \sin bx$, on the interval $[0, \frac{\pi}{b}]$. about the x-axis. Find the surface area.

Surface Area of Airplane Nose Cones

15. The parabolic nose cone of an airplane is 4 m in diameter at its base and 4 m long Assume the nose cone is modeled as a surface obtained by revolving $f(x) = \dfrac{a}{\sqrt{b}}\sqrt{b - x}$, on the interval $[0, b]$, about the x-axis. Find the amount of sheet metal in one nose cone.

16. The parabolic nose cone of airplane is 2 feet in diameter at its base and 3 feet long Assume the nose cone is modeled as a surface of revolution obtained by revolving the graph of revolving the graph of $f(x) = \dfrac{a}{\sqrt{b}}\sqrt{b - x}$, on the interval $[0, b]$ about the x-axis. Find the amount of aluminum used in forming one nose cone.

17. (Inverse Functions) Suppose that f has a continuous derivative on the interval $[a, b]$ and is positive on this interval. (For simplicity you may assume that f is increasing on this interval.) Suppose the graph of inverse function f^{-1} on the interval $[f(a), f(b)]$ is revolved about the x-axis. Show that the surface area of the corresponding solid of revolution is given by

$$S_{inv} = \int_a^b 2\pi x \sqrt{1 + [f'(x)]^2}\, dx \qquad (5.6.1x)$$

Convince yourself of the validity of the result by drawing a sketch showing the geometry involved.

In Exercises 18–27, for the given function f on the interval $[a, b]$ compute the area of the surface obtained by revolving the inverse function f^{-1} on the interval $[f(a), f(b)]$ about the x-axis. See Exercise 17 for the theory and use Formula (5.6.1x) from that exercise for the computations.

18. $f(x) = \dfrac{x^3}{12} + \dfrac{1}{x}$, $[2, 4]$ **19.** $f(x) = \dfrac{x^3}{3} + \dfrac{1}{4x}$, $[1, 4]$

20. $f(x) = x^3 + \dfrac{1}{12x}$, $[1, 4]$

21. $f(x) = \dfrac{x^4}{4} + \dfrac{1}{8x^2}$, $[1, 2]$ **22.** $f(x) = x^4 + \dfrac{1}{32x^2}$, $[1, 2]$

23. $f(x) = \sqrt{x} - \frac{1}{3}x^{3/2}$, $[1, 4]$

24. $f(x) = 3x^{1/3} - \frac{3}{20}x^{5/3}$, $[1, 8]$

25. $f(x) = \frac{3}{7}x^{7/3} + \frac{3}{4}x^{-1/3}$, $[1, 8]$

26. $f(x) = \ln x - \frac{1}{8}x^2$, $[1, 4]$

27. $f(x) = x^2 - \frac{1}{8}\ln x$, $[1, 4]$

Approximate Surface Area (CAS)

28. Select some of those Exercises 1–12 above that you were assigned and use the special-purpose Maple procedures `frustumapprox` and `revolve1X` to produce approximate values for the surface area as well as the corresponding graphics. Compare the numerical approximations you get with the exact areas you computed in Exercises 1–12.

In Exercises 29–32 set up the surface area integral for the surface obtained by revolving the graph of the function on the given interval about the x-axis. You will not be able to compute the integral exactly (by hand), so use the special-purpose Maple procedure `frustumapprox` to produce approximate values for the surface area as well as the corresponding graphics. Compare the numerical approximations you get with those produced by Maple's `int` command.

29. $f(x) = x^4$, $[0, 1]$ **30.** $f(x) = x^{2/5}$, $[0, 1]$
31. $f(x) = \sin^2 x$, $[0, \pi]$ **32.** $f(x) = \cos^2 x$, $[0, \pi]$

A Special Class of Functions (Theory)

33. Suppose g is a differentiable function on an interval $I = [a, b]$ and that its derivative is continuous and positive on I. Let h be an antiderivative of the function $-\dfrac{1}{4g'}$ on the interval I, i.e,

$$h(x) = -\frac{1}{4}\int \frac{1}{g'(x)}\,dx.$$

Further, let
$$f(x) = g(x) + h(x)$$

for x in I. Show that

$$1 + [f'(x)]^2 = [g'(x) - h'(x)]^2$$

for all x in I. Use this to show that the area of the surface of generated by revolving the graph of f about the x-axis is

$$S = \pi\left[(g(x))^2 - (h(x))^2 + 2g(x)h(x) + k(x)\right]\Big|_a^b$$

where k is an antiderivative of the function $\dfrac{g}{g'}$ on the interval I, i.e,

$$k(x) = \int \frac{g(x)}{g'(x)}\,dx.$$

34. For any real number $p \neq 2$, let f be the function defined for $x > 0$ by

$$f(x) = \frac{x^p}{p} + \frac{x^{2-p}}{4p - 8}$$

Consider the graph of f on an interval $[a, b]$, where $a > 0$. Use the result of Exercise 33 to show that the area of the surface of generated by revolving this graph about the x-axis is

$$S = \pi\left[\frac{x^{2p}}{p^2} - \frac{1}{16(p-2)^2}x^{4-2p} + \frac{p-1}{2p(p-2)}x^2\right]\Big|_a^b$$

Revolving about the y-axis equals Revolving the Inverse about the x-axis

35. Illustrate by drawing the graphs of a function f and its inverse f^{-1}, the following facts

(a) Revolving the graph of f about the y-axis and revolving the graph of f^{-1} about the x-axis give surfaces that are the same (congruent). The area of each surface is

$$S_{inv} = \int_a^b 2\pi x\sqrt{1 + [f'(x)]^2}\,dx$$

(b) Revolving the graph of f^{-1} about the y-axis and revolving the graph of f about the x-axis give surfaces that are the same (congruent). The area of each surface is

$$S = \int_a^b 2\pi f(x)\sqrt{1 + [f'(x)]^2}\,dx.$$

Calculus Concepts & Computation

5.7 Force and Work

Work

Work

If the force F is constant then

$$W = Fd$$

where d is the distance moved

The concept of *work* originated in physics as a means of quantifying the *effort* it takes to move an object that is being acted on by a force F. Here we will assume that the motion of the object is along a straight line (usually the x-axis or the y-axis). When the force acting on the object is *constant* during the motion, then the work done to move the object a distance d along the line is by definition just the product of the force times the distance: $W = Fd$.

In the metric system the units are: F is in Newtons (N) and d is in meters (m), so the work W is in Newton-meters (N-m). In the English system the units are: F is in pounds (lb) and d is in feet (ft), so the work W is in foot-pounds (ft-lb).

Example 5.7.1 (Lifting a Calculus Book)

Suppose you lift your calculus book, which is laying on the floor, and place it on the desktop. How much work does this require? Assuming the calculus book weighs six and a half pounds, $F = 6.5$ lb, and the desktop is 30 inches from the floor, $d = 2.5$ ft, then the work done is simply

$$W = 6.5(2.5) = 16.25 \text{ ft-lb}$$

This calculation seems reasonable. However, it is somewhat a simplification of the true work because the book has a thickness and so different layers of the book are moved different distances. But, for practical purposes, in this problem, we can assume all the weight of the book is concentrated at its center.

NOTE: An object's *weight* is the force F acting on it near the earth's surface. By Newton's 2nd law $F = mg$, where m is the object's mass and g is the acceleration of gravity near the earth's surface. So weight is *not* the same as mass. Also, the weight of the same object would be different on another planet. The mass m remains the same while the acceleration of gravity g varies from planet to planet.

Example 5.7.2 (Lifting a Stack of Calculus Books)

Problem: Suppose there is a stack of 15 calculus books resting on the floor and that each one weighs 6.5 lb and is 2 inches thick. How much total work is done to lift all the books and place them on a tabletop that is 30 inches off the floor?

Solution: We assume that the total work is equal to the sum of all the separate efforts of lifting each book to the tabletop. The first book (the one on top) we only have to lift 2 inches, so the work done for that is

$$W_1 = 6.5 \left(\frac{2}{12} \right) = \frac{13}{12} \text{ ft-lb}$$

The second book we have to lift a distance of 4 inches, so the work for that is

$$W_1 = 6.5 \left(\frac{4}{12} \right) = \frac{26}{12} \text{ ft-lb}$$

Continuing like this we see that the work done to lift the i-th book to the tabletop (a distance of $2i$ inches) is

$$W_i = 6.5 \left(\frac{2i}{12} \right) = \frac{13i}{12} \text{ ft-lb}$$

Figure 5.7.1: *A stack of calculus books.*

Using the postulate that work is cumulative, the total work done in lifting all the calculus books is the sum of the work done on each:

$$W = \sum_{i=1}^{15} W_i = \sum_{i=1}^{15} \frac{13}{12}\, i = \frac{13}{12} \sum_{i=1}^{15} i = \frac{13}{12} \cdot \frac{15(16)}{2} = 130 \text{ ft-lb}$$

To extend the concept of work to more complicated situations, we need calculus. One such situation is when the force is not constant.

Work Done When The Force Varies

Imagine what would happen in Example 1 if the calculus book magically got lighter and lighter as you lifted it. Intuitively then, to lift it to the desktop would require less effort, i.e., less work. But how could we quantify this? To answer this, we consider the general situation.

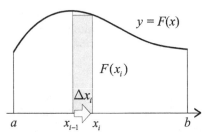

Figure 5.7.2: *An object moves from a to b subject to a variable force F.*

Suppose that an object moves from left-to-right along the x-axis, starting at a and finishing at b, and that when it is in position x, the force acting on it is $F(x)$. If the force is variable, then we can break the distance moved, $d = b - a$, into a number of smaller distances, using a partition $P = \{x_i\}_{i=1}^{n}$. For a very fine partition, each of the incremental distances $\Delta x_i = x_i - x_{i-1}$ is small enough so that the force F is almost constant, say $F(x_i)$, as the object moves from x_{i-1} to x_i. See Figure 5.7.2. Thus, the work done in moving over the i-th subinterval is approximately $F(x_i)\Delta x_i$ and therefore the total work done in moving from a to b is approximately:

$$W \approx \sum_{i=1}^{n} F(x_i)\Delta x_i$$

Otherwise said, right endpoint Riemann sums for F on the interval $[a,b]$ approximate the work done in moving an object from a to b. This suggests that we take limits to get the following definition of work done against a variable force.

DEFINITION 5.7.1 (Work Done Against a Variable Force)

The work W done as an object moves from a to b subject to a force F is

$$W = \int_{a}^{b} F(x)dx$$

Thus, computing the work amounts to integrating the force function over the interval of the motion. Often, in problems, you must determine the formula for the force function.

Example 5.7.3 (Lifting Bags of Concrete Mix)

Problem: A crane is lifting a pallet stacked with bags of concrete mix to the top of a 20 ft tall building. The pallet and all the bags of concrete mix weigh 500 lb at the beginning of the lift and the crane is lifting them at a constant rate of 1 ft/s. Unknown to the crane's operator, a number of the bags have holes in them, allowing the concrete mix to leak out during the lift and causing the load to lose weight at the rate of 4 lb/s. Calculate the work done in lifting the pallet of concrete bags to the top of the building. Compare this to the work done if the bags do not leak.

Solution: We determine a formula for the force function F by placing the x-axis directed vertically with its origin at the ground. Each second the load loses 4 lb and in that time it moves 1 ft. So when the load has moved x ft, it has lost $4x$ lbs

of its weight. Thus,
$$F(x) = 500 - 4x.$$

So the work done is

$$W = \int_0^{20} \left(500 - 4x\right) dx = \left(500x - 2x^2\right) \Big|_0^{20}$$

$$= \left(500\,(20) - 2\,(20)^2\right) = 10{,}000 - 800 = 9{,}200 \text{ ft-lb}$$

If the bags do not leak, then the force is constant, $F = 500$. The work is $W = 500(20) = 10{,}000$ ft-lb.

Example 5.7.4 (Hooke's Law)

Robert Hooke, a contemporary of Newton, discovered by direct experimentation that the magnitude of the force F needed to stretch a given spring is directly proportional to the distance x it is stretched:

$$F = kx. \qquad \text{(Hooke's Law)}$$

Here k is the *spring constant* (a positive constant that indicates the stiffness of the spring). Of course, this law only holds for relatively small stretches of the spring. The same law holds when you compress the spring a distance x: The magnitude of the force required is $F = kx$.

Problem: Suppose a 10 lb weight stretches a spring 2 inches. Find the work done in stretching the spring 8 inches.

Solution: The first sentence in the problem gives us the information needed to determine the spring constant k:

$$k = \frac{F}{x} = \frac{10}{\frac{2}{12}} = 60$$

Then for this particular spring, the force function is $F = 60x$ and the work done to stretch it 8 inches (i.e., 2/3 ft) is

$$W = \int_0^{2/3} 60x \, dx = 30x^2 \Big|_0^{2/3} = 30 \left(\frac{4}{9}\right) - 0 = \frac{40}{3} \text{ ft-lb.}$$

Work Done in Emptying Tanks

There is a category of problems involving pumping fluids out of storage tanks and calculating the work done. At first thought it may seem to be a vague, ill-defined problem. What is the force that is acting? What is the object being moved? But using calculus, we can analyze what the (definition of) work is in this situation.

Consider a storage tank with shape as shown in Figure 5.7.3. Orient the x-axis upward through the center of the tank with the origin at the bottom of the tank.

The height of the tank is T and the top of the fluid is at b on the x-axis (fluid depth $= b$). Assume the fluid has a (constant) density ρ (pounds per cubic foot). Now consider two cross sections through the fluid, one at x on the axis and the other an infinitesimal distance dx below x. These cross sections bound an infinitesimal slab of the fluid (shown in blue) with volume $dV = A(x)\,dx$, where $A(x)$ is the area of the first cross section.

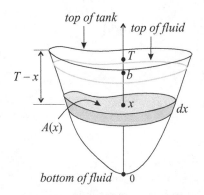

Figure 5.7.3: *A general tank containing a fluid.*

As in Example 2 above on lifting a stack of calculus books, we consider the fluid in the tank as being a stack of these infinitesimal slabs of fluid. We calculate the work done to lift each one to the top of the tank and then add up all these increments of work. The weight of the infinitesimal slab at x is

$$w = \rho A(x)dx$$

and the distance it is lifted is

$$T - x$$

So the increment of work for it is

$$dW = (T - x)\,\rho A(x)\,dx$$

Doing a continuous sum (integral) of these, as x ranges from the bottom ($x = 0$) to the top of the fluid ($x = b$) gives the total work done. See the margin.

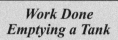

**Work Done
Emptying a Tank**

$$W = \int\limits_{0}^{b} \rho(T - x)A(x)dx$$

To use this integral formula for the work, you will need to determine the cross sectional area function A, which typically comes from the geometry of the tank.

Example 5.7.5 (Pumping Oil out of a Tank)

Problem: Suppose a large steel tank in the shape of an inverted cone is filled to within 2 feet of its top with oil having density $\rho = 50$ lb/ft^3 (pounds per cubic foot). The tank is 20 ft high and has a 10 ft radius at the top. See Figure 5.7.4. Find the work done in pumping all the oil out of the tank.

Solution: The figure shows a typical slab at an x between 0 and 18. This slab is lifted (by the pump) a distance of $20 - x$ feet. Each cross section that bounds the slab is a circle of radius r and area $A = \pi r^2$. But how does r depend on the variable x? To determine this we look at the two right triangles in Figure 5.7.4 and use similar triangles. The large right triangle has sides 10 and 20 and the corresponding sides in the smaller right triangle are r and x, respectively. So,

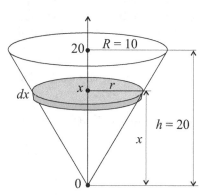

Figure 5.7.4: *A conical tank containing oil.*

$$\frac{r}{x} = \frac{10}{20} = \frac{1}{2} \quad \text{and thus} \quad r = \frac{1}{2}x$$

This gives the area function as a function of x:

$$A(x) = \pi \left(\frac{1}{2}x\right)^2 = \frac{\pi}{4}x^2$$

Also note that in using the integral formula for the work, $T = 20$ and $b = 18$, since the tank is "filled to within 2 ft of its top." Additionally $\rho = 50$. Thus, the work required to pump all the oil out of the tank is

$$W = \int_0^{18} 50\,(20 - x)\,\frac{\pi}{4}\,x^2\,dx = \frac{50\pi}{4} \int_0^{18} \left(20x^2 - x^3\right)\,dx$$

$$= \frac{25\pi}{2} \left(\frac{20}{3}x^3 - \frac{1}{4}x^4\right)\Bigg|_0^{18} = \frac{25\pi}{2}\left(\frac{20}{3}\cdot 18^3 - \frac{1}{4}\cdot 18^4\right)$$

$$= \frac{25\pi}{2}\cdot 18^3 \left(\frac{20}{3} - \frac{18}{4}\right) = \frac{25\pi}{2}\cdot 18^3 \left(\frac{13}{6}\right) = 157,950\,\pi$$

$$\approx 496,214.56 \text{ ft-lb}$$

Fluid Pressure

An object immersed in a fluid, like a scuba diver in the ocean, experiences forces on its surfaces due to *pressure* from the fluid. Pressure p is measured as force per unit area and if the pressure on a surface of area A is constant, then the magnitude of the force acting perpendicularly to the surface is

$$F = pA.$$

Commonly, tires for automobiles are inflated with air to achieve a pressure of 30-40 psi (pound per square inch) on the inner tubes. On earth, at sea level, the atmospheric pressure is approximately 17 psi and this is due to the weight of all the air (atmosphere) above us. At the tops of mountains, the air pressure is less, due to less air above you.

Your ear drums are a sensitive gauge to air pressure, as you may have noticed when driving up a mountain. Similarly when diving in the ocean, the pressure on your ear drums becomes greater with depth. Experiment shows that, in general, fluid pressure p can be modeled as a simple linear function of the depth h:

$$p = \rho h$$

where ρ is the density of the fluid (weight per unit volume). For example, seawater has a typical density of 64 lb/ft^3 and so the fluid pressure varies as $p = 64\,h$, where h is the depth in feet. Thus, at a depth of 90 ft, the pressure on your ear drums is

$$p = 64(90) = 5760\,\text{lb/ft}^2 = \frac{5760}{144}\,\text{psi} = 40\,\text{psi}$$

Assuming that an ear drum is approximately 1/4 square inches in area, the force on it would be

$$F = pA = 40(1/4) = 4\,\text{lb}.$$

NOTE: We generally will neglect the extra pressure due to the atmosphere. When diving in the ocean, you have the weight of the water above you *and* the weight of the atmosphere above that creating the pressure on you.

Calculus comes into play when the submerged object is large enough so that you cannot neglect, as in the ear drum calculation, the variation of the pressure from the top to the bottom of the object.

Example 5.7.6 (Total Force on a Drainage Gate)

Problem: A dam at one end of a small reservoir has a rectangular drainage gate (4 ft wide and 1 ft deep) located with its top at a depth of 4 ft from the water surface. Assuming the fresh water density is 62.4 lb/ft^3, find the total force exerted by the water on the gate.

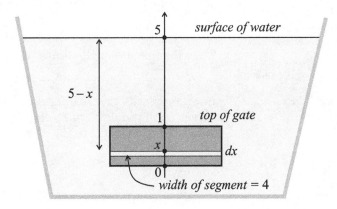

Figure 5.7.5: *A drainage gate for a dam.*

Solution: We set up the problem by taking x-axis oriented vertically with the origin at the bottom of the gate. Then the top of the gate is at $x = 1$ and the water surface is at $x = 5$. For a general x between 0 and 1, consider an infinitesimal horizontal segment of the rectangular gate. The width of the segment is 4 and its height is the infinitesimal dx. Thus, the area of the segment is $4\,dx$ and it is located at a depth of $5 - x$ from the surface of the water. The pressure at this depth is $p = \rho h = 62.4(5 - x)$. Then the (infinitesimal) element of force on this segment is

$$dF = pdA = 62.4\,(5 - x)\,4dx$$

Integrating gives the total force on the gate:

$$F = \int dF = \int_0^1 62.4\,(5 - x)\,4dx$$

$$= 249.6 \int_0^1 (5 - x)\,dx = 249.6\left(5x - \frac{1}{2}x^2\right)\bigg|_0^1 = 249.6\,(4.5) = 1123.2 \text{ lb.}$$

Total Force on a Submerged Plate

It is easy to generalize the situation in Example 5.7.6 to the calculation of the total force on a flat plate of any shape submerged vertically in a liquid of density . See Figure 5.7.6 below.

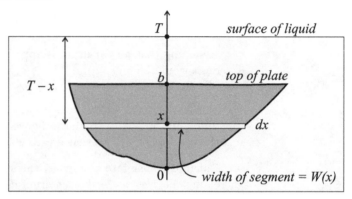

Figure 5.7.6: *A flat plate submerged vertically in a liquid.*

As in the example, we take the x-axis oriented vertically with the origin at the bottom of the plate. Suppose the top edge of the plate, assumed to be flat, is located at $x = b$ and that the surface of the liquid is located at $x = T$. For an x between 0 and b, the width of of the horizontal segment at x is $W(x)$ and its height is the infinitesimal dx. Thus, the area of the segment is $W(x)dx$ and it is located at a depth of $h = T - x$ from the surface of the liquid. The pressure at this depth is

$$p = \rho h = \rho\,(T - x)\,.$$

Then the (infinitesimal) element of force on this segment is

$$dF = pdA = \rho\,(T - x)\,W(x)dx$$

Integrating gives the total force on the plate. See the margin.)

Using this integral formula generally will require determining the width function W as a function of x. See the exercises.

Total Force on a Submerged Plate

$$F = \int_0^b \rho(T - x)W(x)dx$$

Exercises: 5.7 (Force and Work)

Constant Force Problems

1. You lift a 60 lb bucket of paint from the pavement to the tailgate of your truck. If the tailgate is 28 inches above the payment, how much work is done?

2. In lifting a 15 lb carry-on suitcase 7 feet to the overhead luggage rack, how much work is done?

3. A stack of 12 sacks of 25 lb concrete mix must be lifted from the pavement to a truck bed that is four feet above the pavement. If each sack is 4 inches thick, how much total work is done in loading the bags, one-by-one onto the truck?

4. A stack of fifteen concrete pavers, sitting on the floor, is lifted one-by-one and placed on a 30 inch high shelf. If each paver weighs 15 lbs and is 2 inches thick, how much total work is done?

5. A stack of twelve biology books, sitting on the floor, is lifted one-by-one and placed on a 40 inch high table. If each book weighs 7.2 lbs and is 3 inches thick, how much total work is done?

6. A stack of 10 sacks of 25 lb concrete mix must be lifted from the pavement to a truck bed that is four feet above the pavement. If each sack is 4 inches thick, how much total work is done in loading the bags, one-by-one onto the truck?

Spring Problems

7. A 3 lb force stretches a spring 4 inches. How much work is done in stretching the spring 10 inches?

8. A 4 lb force stretches a spring 6 inches. How much work is done in stretching the spring 16 inches?

9. A force of 212 N stretches a spring 20 cm. How much work is done in compressing the spring from 10 cm to 40 cm.

10. Same as Exercise 9 except with a force of 250 N.

Variable Force Lifting Problems

11. A 500 lb tank of water is is being lifted by a crane from the ground to the roof of a 12 story building (144 ft above the ground). The crane is lifting at the rate of 2 feet per second and the tank, due to a small hole, is leaking at the rate of 1/12 lb per second. How much work is done in lifting the leaking tank to the roof? Compare this with the work done if the tank does not leak.

12. A 400 lb tank of sand is is being lifted by a crane from the ground to the roof of a 12 story building (144 ft above the ground). The crane is lifting at the rate of 3 feet per second and the tank, due to a small hole, is leaking at the rate of 1/12 lb per second. How much work is done in lifting the leaking tank to the roof? Compare this with the work done if the tank does not leak.

13. A 20 foot long, industrial-strength cable, weighing 5 lb per foot, is hanging from a platform inside a warehouse. How much work is done in hauling the entire cable up to the platform?

14. A 30 foot long anchor chain (without the anchor) weighing 8 lb per foot, is hanging from the deck of a ship. How much work is done in hauling the entire chain up to the deck of the ship?

Emptying Tanks

15. The conical tank shown in Figure 5.7.1x is 10 m high and has a base of radius 4 m. It is full of water which has density 9200 N/m^3. How much work is done in pumping all the water out of the tank?

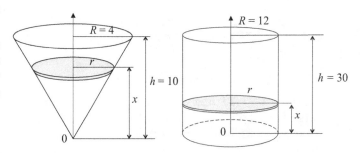

Figure 5.7.1x: *A conical tank containing water* (Exercise 15) *and a cylindrical tank containing oil* (Exercise 17)

16. Suppose the tank in Exercise 15 is only filled to within 2 meters of the top. How much work is done in pumping all the water out of the tank?

17. The cylindrical tank shown in Figure 5.7.1x is 30 ft high and has a base of radius 12 ft. It is half full of oil which has density 60 lb/ft^3. How much work is done in pumping all the oil out of the tank?

18. A cylindrical tank is 12 m high and has a circular base of radius 4 m. It is 2/3 full of water which has density 9200 N/m^3. How much work is done in pumping all the water out of the tank?

19. The parabolic tank shown in Figure 5.7.2x is obtained by revolving the graph of $y = 2\sqrt{x}$ about the x-axis (which is oriented vertically). The tank is 16 ft high and is filled to the top with gasoline, which has a density of 42 lb/ft^3. Find the work done in pumping all the gasoline from the tank.

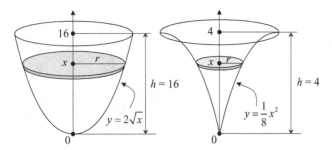

Figure 5.7.2x: *A parabolic tank containing gasoline (Exercise 19) and a trumpet-shaped tank containing seawater (Exercise 21).*

20. The parabolic tank in Exercise 19 is filled to the 8 ft level. Find the work done in pumping all the gasoline out of the tank.

21. A casino in Las Vegas has glass aquarium shaped like a trumpet. See Figure 5.7.2x. The tank is 4 m high and is filled to the top with seawater having a density of 9200 N/m^3. After removing all the tropical fish in the tank, find the work done in pumping all the seawater out of the tank.

22. The tank in Exercise 21 is filled to within 1 meter of the top. Find the work done in pumping out all the seawater.

Fluid Pressure on Submerged Plates

In Exercises 23–30, find the total force on the submerged plate. The fluid is seawater with density 64 lb/ft^3 and the distances shown in the figure are in feet. You can consider the plate as a drainage gate in the face of a dam.

23. Rectangle

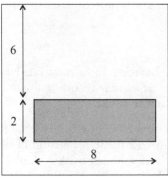

24. Rectangle

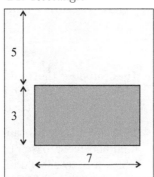

25. Isosceles Triangle

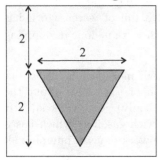

26. Isosceles Triangle

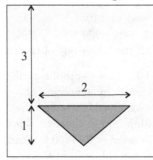

27. Isosceles Triangle

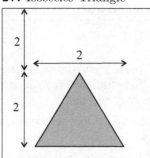

28. Isosceles Triangle

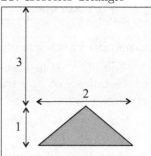

29. Right Triangle

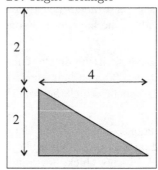

30. Right Triangle

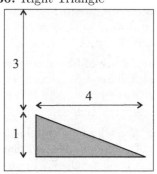

Plates that are Type I Regions

Suppose a submerged plate has the shape of a Type I region with the x-axis oriented vertically and $a = 0$. See the figure below.

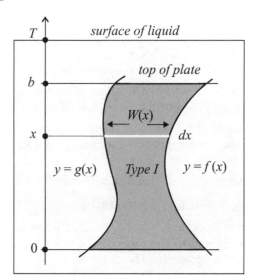

In this situation, the width function is $W(x) = f(x) - g(x)$. In Exercises 31–38, find the total force exerted on the Type I region submerged in seawater with the bottom of the plate at the depth T feet below the surface. Also SKETCH the region.

31. $f(x) = \frac{1}{2}x^2$, $g(x) = -\frac{1}{2}x^2$, $b = 2$, $T = 10$

32. $f(x) = \frac{1}{2}x^3$, $g(x) = -\frac{1}{2}x^3$, $b = 2$, $T = 10$

33. $f(x) = \sqrt{x}$, $g(x) = -\sqrt{x}$, $b = 1$, $T = 10$

34. $f(x) = x^{1/3}$, $g(x) = -x^{1/3}$, $b = 8$, $T = 10$

35. $f(x) = 4 - x^2$, $g(x) = 0$, $b = 2$, $T = 6$

36. $f(x) = 8 - x^3$, $g(x) = 0$, $b = 2$, $T = 12$

37. $f(x) = 2 - \sqrt{x}$, $g(x) = -f(x)$, $b = 4$, $T = 10$

38. $f(x) = 2 - x^{1/3}$, $g(x) = -f(x)$, $b = 8$, $T = 10$

Fluid Pressure on Dams

39. A dam has a vertical face, on the water side, in the shape of a regular trapezoid. The trapezoid has bases of 2200 ft (at the top) and 1600 ft (at the bottom) and a height of 400 ft. The water has a density of 62 lb/ft^3 Assuming the water level reaches the top of the dam, find the total force on the face of the dam.

Zeljko Radojko/Shutterstock.com

40. A dam has a vertical face, on the side, in the shape of a regular trapezoid. The trapezoid has bases of 800 m (at the top) and 600 m (at the bottom) and a height of 100 m. The water has a density of 9000 N/m^3. Assuming the water level reaches the top of the dam, find the total force on the face of the dam.

Pavle Marjanovic/Shutterstock.com

Calculus Concepts & Computation

5.8 Moments and Center of Mass

A composite body consists of several materials of different shapes bound together to form a single solid. As an example, consider a hatchet, which is made of a wooden handle with a steel head attached. In a hatchet tossing contest, the motion of the hatchet as it is pitched toward a tree is a complicated motion. But the motion can be more simply analyzed by following the motion of its center of mass, The center of mass moves in a parabolic arc while the hatchet itself spins uniformly about its center of mass. See Figure 5.8.1. The center of mass is indicated by a black dot in the figure.

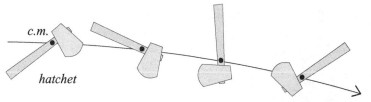

Figure 5.8.1: *Motion of the center of mass (c.m.) of a hatchet.*

The same can be said for a homogeneous body, such as a wooden (uncorked) baseball bat being tossed toward the dugout. The center of mass is an important point to follow when analyzing the motion.

The center of mass is also an important point to know when you want the body to be stationary – the center of mass does not move and the body does not rotate about it.

In this section we will learn how to determine the center of mass for various sorts of bodies. We begin first with bodies that are a system of discrete particles (which does not require calculus) and then discuss bodies that are a continuous distribution of particles (which does require calculus).

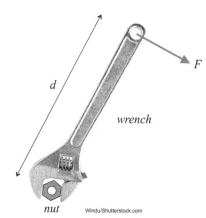

Figure 5.8.2: *Torquing a nut with a wrench.*

Torque and Moments

When using a wrench to tighten a nut, you are torquing the nut by means of the wrench. Namely, you are rotating (twisting) the nut by applying a force near the end of the wrench's handle.

The magnitude of the torque is typically measured by the magnitude of the force times the distance of the force from the center of the nut.

Torque
The torque T created at a point in a body by a force F at a distance d from the point is $T = Fd$

In this definition, T, F, and d are the *magnitudes* of the torque, force, and position *vectors*. We will discuss vectors in a later chapter. (Also the equation $T = Fd$ assumes that the force is applied perpendicularly to the position vector.) That the amount of twist should depend on F and d in this manner is common experience, It is easier to achieve more torque with a longer wrench and, with a given wrench, a greater force results in a greater torque.

Another simple situation where torques occur is in a playground with two children on a seesaw. If the seesaw is balanced, not turning one way or the other, then the torque at the balance point (the fulcrum) created by each child must be the same. Here the forces F_1, F_2 are the weights of the children, and for balance

$$F_1 d_1 = F_2 d_2$$

where d_1, d_2 are the respective distances of the children from the fulcrum.

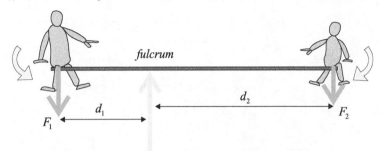

Figure 5.8.3: *Two children balanced on a seesaw.*

Neglecting the weight of the board in the seesaw, we have a body consisting of two weights $F_1 = m_1 g$ and $F_2 = m_2 g$, with m_1, m_2 the masses of the children and g the acceleration of gravity near the earth's surface. The point of balance (fulcrum) is the *center of gravity* for this body. If we write the equation for equal torques as

$$m_1 g d_1 = m_2 g d_2$$

and divide out the g, we get

$$m_1 d_1 = m_2 d_2.$$

This simplification always occurs when the forces acting are weights and suggests that we introduce the concept of a *moment* as being mass times distance.

Moment
The moment M created at a point in a body by a weight F = mg acting at a distance d is $$M = md$$

Often we refer to the moment $M = md$ as being *created by the mass m acting at a distance d*. In this setting, the balance point of the seesaw is called the *center of mass* of the body composed of the two children located at their respective positions (again, neglecting the weight of the seesaw).

Center of Mass (Discrete Systems of Mass)

To develop some notation to handle more complicated situations than this, we introduce the x-axis oriented along the seesaw and let x_1 be the coordinate of the position of the first child and x_2 the coordinate for the second. Also let x^* denote the coordinate for the center of mass. See Figure 5.8.4.

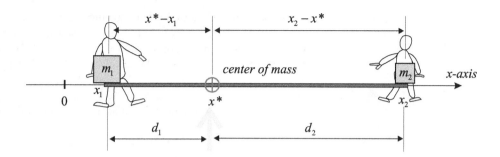

Figure 5.8.4: *Center of mass notation.*

From the figure we determine that

$$d_1 = x^* - x_1$$

$$d_2 = x_2 - x^*$$

and so the equal moments equation $m_1 d_1 = m_2 d_2$ can be written as

$$m_1 (x^* - x_1) = m_2 (x_2 - x^*) \qquad (5.8.1)$$

We solve this for x^*. First

$$m_1 x^* - m_1 x_1 = m_2 x_2 - m_2 x^*$$

and so

$$(m_1 + m_2)x^* = m_1 x_1 + m_2 x_2$$

This gives

$$x^* = \frac{m_1 x_1 + m_2 x_2}{m_1 + m_2} \qquad \text{(center of mass coordinate)}$$

In this formula $m_1 x_1 + m_2 x_2$ is called the *moment* of the system of masses about the origin and $m_1 + m_2$ is the *total mass* of the system. It is also important to note that Eq. (5.8.1) can be written as

$$m_1 (x_1 - x^*) + m_2 (x_2 - x^*) = 0 \qquad (5.8.2)$$

This form of the equation for balance is better if we want to generalize to more than two weights (masses). It says that the moment of the system of masses about the point with coordinate x^* (the left side of the equation) is zero.

Example 5.8.1 (Children on a Seesaw)

Problem: Suppose two children sit at opposite ends of a 10 ft long seesaw. If the weights of the children are 96 lb and 64 lb, find the point where the seesaw will balance (the center of mass)

Solution: Since $g = 32$, from $96 = m_1 (32)$ and $64 = m_2 (32)$, we get $m_1 = 3$, $m_2 = 2$. It does not matter where we locate the seesaw on the x-axis. (See the Exercises.) We put the left end at 4, so that the right end is at 14. Thus, $x_1 = 4$, $x_2 = 14$. Then

$$x^* = \frac{3(4) + 2(14)}{2 + 3} = \frac{40}{5} = 8 \, \text{ft}.$$

This says that the center of mass is 4 ft from the largest child and 6 ft from the smaller child.

The calculation of the coordinate x^* for the center of mass of any number of masses $m_1, m_2, m_3, \ldots, m_k$ positioned along the x-axis can be done in a similar way. Suppose that $x_1, x_2, x_3, \ldots, x_k$ are the coordinates of the positions for these masses. For a given number c, we define

Moment of the System of Masses About Point c

$$M_c = \sum_{i=1}^{k} m_i (x_i - c) \qquad (5.8.3)$$

Up to the factor g, this moment is the same as the torque of the system about the point c. NOTE: Some of the quantities $x_i - c$ can be negative. See Figure 5.8.5.

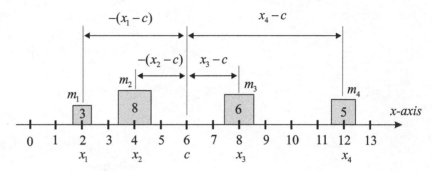

Figure 5.8.5: *A system of four masses on the x-axis.*

In the figure $c = 6$ and the moment of the system of four masses about c is

$$M_c = 3(2 - 6) + 8(4 - 6) + 6(8 - 6) + 5(12 - 6) = -12 - 16 + 12 + 30 = 14$$

Because the moment about c is positive the system will turn clockwise about c if we attempt to balance at that point. Naturally enough, the center of mass of the system will be the point x^* where the moment is zero:

$$M_{x^*} = 0$$

that is,

$$\sum_{i=1}^{k} m_i (x_i - x^*) = 0$$

Solving this for x^* gives

$$x^* = \frac{\sum_{i=1}^{k} m_i x_i}{\sum_{i=1}^{k} m_i}.$$

Note that the numerator is the moment of system about 0 and the denominator is the total mass. We denote these quantities by M_0 and m respectively. Then

Center of Mass - 1d

$$x^* = \frac{\sum_{i=1}^{k} m_i x_i}{\sum_{i=1}^{k} m_i} = \frac{M_0}{m} \qquad (5.8.4)$$

This formula is the direct extension of the one for two masses (the seesaw) and is easy to use. For example, the center of mass for the system shown in Figure 5.8.5 is

$$x^* = \frac{3\,(2) + 8\,(4) + 6\,(8) + 5\,(12)}{3 + 8 + 6 + 5} = \frac{146}{22} = \frac{73}{11} \approx 6.6$$

Center of Mass in 2-Dimensions

For a system of masses $m_1, m_2, m_3, \ldots, m_k$ distributed about at various positions in the x-y plane, the location of the center of mass (the balancing point) requires two coordinates (x^*, y^*). Now we have a two-dimensional seesaw, considered as a sheet of plywood with the fulcrum located beneath. See Figure 5.8.6.

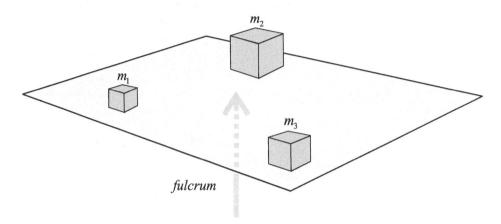

Figure 5.8.6: *A two-dimensional seesaw.*

The theory for balancing the masses on the fulcrum now requires the notion of *moment about a line* in the x-y plane. This arises as follows. Instead of balancing the 2-d seesaw (sheet of plywood) on a single point (the fulcrum point), we first consider balancing it from below on a vertical sheet of plywood. See Figure 5.6.7.

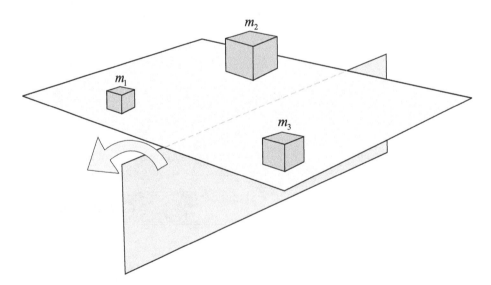

Figure 5.8.7: *The moment (turning) of the seesaw about a line.*

This vertical sheet makes contact with the 2-d seesaw in a line below it. Unless the seesaw balances, it has a tendency to turn one way or another about that line of contact. That tendency is the *moment of the system* about that line. To simplify the mathematics we only consider lines that are either vertical or horizontal.

Moments of the System of Masses About Lines x = c and y = d

$$M_{x,c} \;=\; \sum_{i=1}^{k} m_i \, (x_i - c)$$

$$M_{y,d} \;=\; \sum_{i=1}^{k} m_i\,(y_i - d)$$

For example, in Figure 5.8.8 below, the three masses create a moment about the line $x = c$ which is measured as follows.

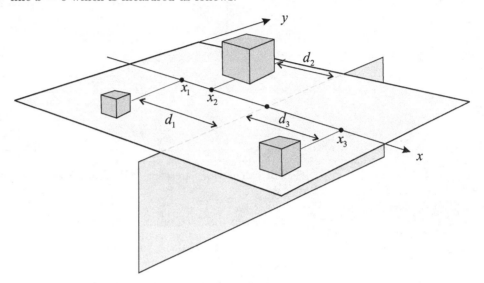

Figure 5.8.8: *The moment of three masses about the line $x = c$.*

The three distances to the line $x = c$ are d_1, d_2, d_3, respectively. Distances are positive numbers and so, in terms of these distances, the moment about the line is

$$M_{x,c} = m_1\,(x_1 - c) + m_2\,(x_2 - c) + m_3\,(x_3 - c) = -m_1 d_1 - m_2 d_2 + m_3 d_3$$

For the masses and distances depicted in the figure, this moment appears to be negative, which means the seesaw will rotate about the line in the counter-clockwise direction. To achieve balance we need to move the supporting plane closer to the largest mass. Similarly, if we use support planes whose lines of support are lines parallel to the x-axis, then we can find one about which the seesaw balances.

Thus, there is one vertical line $x = x^*$ about which the seesaw balances (has moment 0) and one horizontal line $y = y^*$ about which the seesaw balances. The two lines intersect in a point (x^*, y^*) which is the fulcrum point where the seesaw will also balance, supported at this single point. This fulcrum point is the center of mass of the 2-d system. Thus, we get equations

$$M_{x,x^*} = 0, \qquad M_{y,y^*} = 0$$

and solving for x^* and y^* gives

$$x^* = \frac{\displaystyle\sum_{i=1}^{k} m_i x_i}{\displaystyle\sum_{i=1}^{k} m_i} \quad \text{and} \quad y^* = \frac{\displaystyle\sum_{i=1}^{k} m_i y_i}{\displaystyle\sum_{i=1}^{k} m_i}$$

Note that the first numerator is $M_{x,0}$, which is the moment of the system about the line $x = 0$. (This line is the y-axis and so some calculus book denote this by M_y, calling it the moment about the y-axis.) The second numerator is $M_{y,0}$, which is the moment of the system about the line $y = 0$ (also called the moment about the x-axis, since the line $y = 0$ is the x-axis). Each denominator is the total mass m of the system. In summary:

Center of Mass - 2d

$$x^* = \frac{\displaystyle\sum_{i=1}^{k} m_i x_i}{\displaystyle\sum_{i=1}^{k} m_i} = \frac{M_{x,0}}{m} \qquad (5.8.5)$$

$$y^* = \frac{\displaystyle\sum_{i=1}^{k} m_i y_i}{\displaystyle\sum_{i=1}^{k} m_i} = \frac{M_{y,0}}{m} \qquad (5.8.6)$$

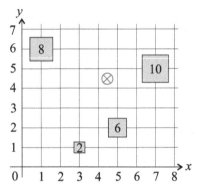

Figure 5.8.9: *A system of four masses in the plane.*

The calculations are easy to do and are entirely similar to the ones done in the 1-d case.

Example 5.8.2 (Center of Mass in 2d)

Problem: Compute the coordinates of the center of mass for the system shown in Figure 5.8.9.

Solution: The total mass of the system is

$$m = 8 + 2 + 6 + 10 = 26$$

The coordinates of the center of mass are

$$x^* = \frac{8\,(1) + 2\,(3) + 6\,(5) + 10\,(7)}{26} = \frac{114}{26} = \frac{57}{13} \approx 4.4$$

$$y^* = \frac{8\,(6) + 2\,(1) + 6\,(2) + 10\,(5)}{26} = \frac{112}{26} = \frac{56}{13} \approx 4.3$$

Center of Mass (Continuous Systems of Mass)

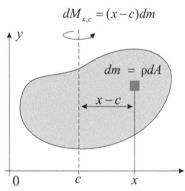

Figure 5.8.10: *A lamina is a region D in the x-y plane with a density function ρ.*

Your experience above with the concepts of moments and centers of mass for finitely many, discrete masses $m_1, m_2, m_3, \ldots, m_k$ located at various points in the x-y plane should help you understand the extension of these concepts to continuous distributions of infinitely many masses constituting a body known as a *plane lamina*. This is a two-dimensional region D in the x-y plane that comes with a mass density function ρ, which gives the mass per unit area at each point on the region. You can think of the lamina as a thin sheet of material cut in the shape of D and having its density vary according to ρ.

Thus, an infinitesimal element of area dA has mass $dm = \rho\, dA$ and the total mass of the lamina is

$$m = \int dm = \int \rho\, dA$$

where the integral is over the region D.

<u>NOTE</u> 1: Here the notion of the "integral over D" is heuristic. We will make this precise when we discuss multivariable calculus in later chapters.

<u>NOTE</u> 2: For the most part, we will deal only with *homogeneous* laminas. These have constant density functions: $\rho = $ constant. Then the total mass is just

$$m = \int \rho\, dA = \rho \int dA = \rho A$$

For a homogeneous lamina, the center of mass is called the *centroid*. As we shall see, the location of the center of mass (centroid) of a homogeneous lamina depends only on its geometry, or shape.

NOTE 3: The regions used here will be either Type I or Type II and so the area A of the lamina can be computed as we did in Section 5.1.

The moment about a horizontal or vertical line is analogous to the discrete case, although to define it properly we again need the notion of the "integral over D" from multivariable calculus. Informally, to define the moment of the lamina about the line $x = c$, we start with an infinitesimal element of mass ρdA located at a point (x,y) in the region D. See Figure 5.8.10. Then $x - c$ is the signed distance to the line and so $(x - c)\rho\, dA$ is an infinitesimal element of the moment. The total moment would be

$$M_{x,c} = \int \rho\,(x - c)\, dA$$

Similarly, the moment about $y = d$ is

$$M_{y,d} = \int \rho\,(y - d)\, dA$$

As in the discrete case, to balance the lamina from below by a support, such as a sheet of plywood, the moment about the support's line of contact must be zero. There is one vertical line $x = x^*$ and one horizontal line $y = y^*$ for which the respective moments are zero:

$$M_{x,x^*} = 0, \qquad M_{y,y^*} = 0$$

The values of y^* can be found by solving these equations (using properties of integrals in the process). The results are given in the following box.

Center of Mass - 2d Laminas	
General	**Constant Density**
$x^* \;=\; \dfrac{M_{x,0}}{m} \;=\; \dfrac{\int \rho x dA}{\int \rho dA}$	$=\; \dfrac{\int x dA}{A} \qquad (5.8.7)$
	when ρ is constant
$y^* \;=\; \dfrac{M_{y,0}}{m} \;=\; \dfrac{\int \rho y dA}{\int \rho dA}$	$=\; \dfrac{\int y dA}{A} \qquad (5.8.8)$

NOTE 1: The left pane in the box gives the general formula for the coordinates of the center of mass. The right pane gives what these formulas reduce to when ρ is constant (which is primarily what we assume here). Because ρ is eliminated from the formulas, the center of mass (or centroid) is a purely geometrical aspect of the lamina's shape.

NOTE 2: To find the center of mass, you will have to compute three integrals – one for the total mass m, which you should do first, and then two for the coordinates:

$$x^* = \frac{1}{m} \int \rho x\, dA$$

$$y^* = \frac{1}{m} \int \rho y \, dA$$

<u>NOTE</u> 3: To find the centroid (i.e., the center of mass when ρ = constant), you will have to compute three integrals –one for the area A, which you should do first, and two for the coordinates:

$$x^* = \frac{1}{A} \int x \, dA$$

$$y^* = \frac{1}{A} \int y \, dA$$

In order to specialize these formulas to regions D that are Type I or II, we first consider three principles that can be derived from these formulas.

Center of Mass Principles

(1) If the lamina is divided into two parts, then the moment of the lamina about any line is the sum of the moments of the two parts about that line.

(2) If the total mass of the lamina is concentrated at its center of mass, then the resulting point mass creates the same moment about any line as the lamina does.

(3) If the lamima is symmetric about a line *and* the lamina has constant density, then the centroid lies on that line.

The centroids for many laminas can be determined directly from these principles, without using integrals. The following example illustrates this.

Example 5.8.3 (Use of the CM Principles)

Problem: Use the Center of Mass Principles to find the centroids of the laminas shown in the following figure.

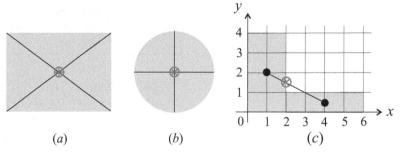

Figure 5.8.11: *A rectangular, circular, and L shaped homogeneous lamina.*

Solution (a): The rectangle is symmetric about each of its diagonals, so by CM Principle (3), the centroid of a rectangle lies on each diagonal. Thus, the centroid coincides with the point of intersection of the two diagonals. This point is the center of the rectangle.

Solution (b): A circle is symmetric about any line through its center (a diameter) and so the centroid lies on any such line. Thus, the centroid coincides with the point of intersection any two diameters. This point is the center of the circle.

Solution (c): We divide the L-shaped lamina into two rectangular sub-laminas. The one on the left, by Part (a) of this problem, has centroid at $(x_1, y_1) = (1, 2)$ and has total mass $m_1 = 8\rho$. (Here 8 is the area of the rectangle and ρ is the mass density of the lamina). The rectangle on the right has centroid at $(x_2, y_2) = (4, 1/2)$ and has total mass $m_2 = 4\rho$. By CM Principle (2), we can find the center of mass of the whole lamina by replacing it by the system of two masses m_1, m_2 located at (x_1, y_1), (x_2, y_2), shown as black dots in Figure 5.8.11. Thus, the coordinates of the center of mass (centroid) of the lamina are

$$x^* = \frac{8\rho\,(1) + 4\rho\,(4)}{8\rho + 4\rho} = \frac{8\,(1) + 4\,(4)}{8 + 4} = \frac{24}{12} = 2$$

$$y^* = \frac{8\rho\,(2) + 4\rho\,(1/2)}{8\rho + 4\rho} = \frac{8\,(2) + 4\,(1/2)}{8 + 4} = \frac{18}{12} = \frac{3}{2}$$

<u>NOTE</u>: Because the mass density ρ divides out, we can, when working such problems, just use the respective areas (8 and 4) instead of the masses (8ρ and 4ρ).

Homogeneous Laminas with Type I Shapes

The general formulas for the center of mass of a lamina specialize when it is homogeneous and its shape D is a Type I region. The heuristic argument is as follows.

The lamina is viewed as being composed of infinitesimal vertical segments. At a point x between a and b, the vertical segment has finite height $f(x) - g(x)$, but infinitesimal width dx. So the mass of this segment is

$$dm = \rho\,dA = \rho\,[f(x) - g(x)]\,dx$$

In computing the moments about the axes, we can consider (by the CM principles) this element of mass as concentrated at the center of mass of the segment, The segment, being an infinitesimal rectangle, has its center of mass at its center, which is the point

$$\left(x, \frac{1}{2}\,[f(x) + g(x)]\right)$$

Note that the y-coordinate of the center comes from using the midpoint formula.

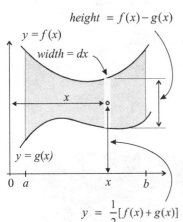

$$\text{height} = f(x) - g(x)$$
$$y = f(x)$$
$$\text{width} = dx$$
$$y = g(x)$$
$$y = \frac{1}{2}[f(x) + g(x)]$$

Figure 5.8.12: *The moments of an infinitesimal strip about the axes.*

Based on this we have

$$M_{x,0} = \int x\rho\,dm = \int_a^b x\rho\,[f(x) - g(x)]\,dx = \rho\int_a^b x\,[f(x) - g(x)]\,dx$$

and

$$M_{y,0} = \int y\rho\,dm = \int_a^b \frac{1}{2}\,[f(x) + g(x)]\,\rho\,[f(x) - g(x)]\,dx$$

$$= \rho\int_a^b \frac{1}{2}\left([f(x)]^2 - [g(x)]^2\right)dx$$

Here we have used the identity: $(u + v)(u - v) = u^2 - v^2$ to simplify the integrand. From Section 5.1, the total mass of the lamina is

$$m = \int dm = \int_a^b \rho\,[f(x) - g(x)]\,dx = \rho\int_a^b [f(x) - g(x)]\,dx = \rho A$$

Dividing m into each of the moments above and noting that the ρ cancels in each case, we get the following specialized formulas.

Centroid - Type I Regions

$$x^* \;=\; \frac{M_{x,0}}{m} \;=\; \frac{1}{A} \int_a^b x\,[f(x) - g(x)]\,dx \qquad (5.8.9)$$

$$y^* \;=\; \frac{M_{y,0}}{m} \;=\; \frac{1}{A} \int_a^b \frac{1}{2}\big([f(x)]^2 - [g(x)]^2\big)\,dx \qquad (5.8.10)$$

$$A \;=\; \int_a^b [f(x) - g(x)]\,dx \qquad (5.8.11)$$

Example 5.8.4 (Centroid of a Homogeneous Lamina)

Problem: Find the centroids of the homogeneous laminas whose shapes are the following Type I regions.

(a) $y = \dfrac{1}{x^2}$, $y = x$, $x = 1$, $x = 2$ (b) $y = e^x$, $x = 0$, $x = 1$

Sketches of these two regions are given in Figure 5.8.12 below.

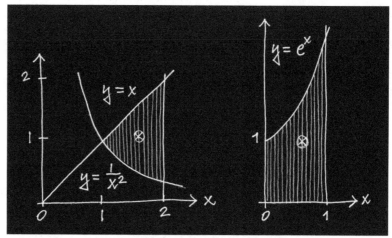

Figure 5.8.13: *Sketches of the regions in Problem (a) (left) and Problem (b) (right).*

Solution (a): From the sketch we see that the function bounding the top of the region is $f(x) = x$ and the one for the bottom boundary is $g(x) = x^{-2}$. The three integrals that we need to calculate are: the area integral

$$A = \int_a^b [f(x) - g(x)]\,dx = \int_1^2 \left(x - \frac{1}{x^2}\right) dx = \left(\frac{1}{2}x^2 + \frac{1}{x}\right)\bigg|_1^2$$

$$= \left(2 + \frac{1}{2}\right) - \left(\frac{1}{2} + 1\right) = 1$$

and the coordinate integrals

$$x^* = \frac{1}{A}\int_a^b x\,[f(x) - g(x)]\,dx = \frac{1}{1}\int_1^2 x\left(x - \frac{1}{x^2}\right) dx = \int_1^2 \left(x^2 - \frac{1}{x}\right) dx$$

$$= \left(\frac{1}{3}x^3 - \ln x\right)\bigg|_1^2 = \left(\frac{8}{3} - \ln 2\right) - \left(\frac{1}{3} - 0\right) = \frac{7}{3} - \ln 2 \approx 1.62$$

$$y^* = \frac{1}{A} \int_a^b \frac{1}{2} \left([f(x)]^2 - [g(x)]^2 \right) dx = \frac{1}{1} \int_1^2 \frac{1}{2} \left[x^2 - \left(\frac{1}{x^2} \right)^2 \right] dx$$

$$= \int_1^2 \frac{1}{2} \left[x^2 - \frac{1}{x^4} \right] dx = \frac{1}{2} \left(\frac{1}{3} x^3 + \frac{1}{3} \frac{1}{x^3} \right) \Big|_1^2$$

$$= \frac{1}{2} \left[\left(\frac{8}{3} + \frac{1}{24} \right) - \left(\frac{1}{3} + \frac{1}{3} \right) \right] = \frac{49}{48} \approx 1.02$$

Thus, the centroid is

$$\left(\frac{7}{3} - \ln 2, \frac{49}{48} \right) \approx (1.62, 1.02)$$

Looking at the graph of the region in Figure 5.8.13 above, we see that these coordinates appear to be approximately correct.

Solution (b): Here D is the region beneath the graph of $f(x) = e^x$ on the interval $[0, 1]$. Since $g(x) = 0$, the general formulas simplify. The three integrals we need are

$$A = \int_a^b f(x) \, dx, \quad x^* = \frac{1}{A} \int_a^b x f(x) \, dx, \quad y^* = \frac{1}{A} \int_a^b \frac{1}{2} [f(x)]^2 \, dx.$$

The area integral is

$$A = \int_0^1 e^x \, dx = e^x \Big|_0^1 = e - 1.$$

Computation of the second integral $\int_0^1 xe^x \, dx$ requires knowing an antiderivative of xe^x. One could use the technique of integration called *integration by parts* to determine an antiderivative. (See Chapter 6.) But it is easy to check that

$$\frac{d}{dx} (xe^x - e^x) = xe^x.$$

Thus, the first coordinate integral is

$$x^* = \frac{1}{A} \int_a^b x f(x) \, dx = \frac{1}{e-1} \int_0^1 xe^x \, dx = \frac{1}{e-1} (xe^x - e^x) \Big|_0^1 = \frac{1}{1-e} \approx 0.582$$

The second coordinate integral is

$$y^* = \frac{1}{A} \int_a^b \frac{1}{2} [f(x)]^2 \, dx = \frac{1}{e-1} \int_0^1 \frac{1}{2} [e^x]^2 \, dx = \frac{1}{e-1} \int_0^1 \frac{1}{2} e^{2x} \, dx$$

$$= \frac{1}{4(e-1)} e^{2x} \Big|_0^1 = \frac{1}{4(e-1)} (e^2 - 1) = \frac{(e-1)(e+1)}{4(e-1)} = \frac{e+1}{4} \approx 0.93$$

Thus the centroid is

$$\left(\frac{1}{e-1}, \frac{e+1}{4} \right) \approx (0.58, 0.93).$$

The sketch in Figure 5.8.13 above shows the location of the centroid based on these calculations.

Example 5.8.5 (Centroids of Standard Geometric Figures)

Problem: Find the centroids of the following geometric figures

(a) A right triangle with base b and height h (b) A quarter-circle of radius r.

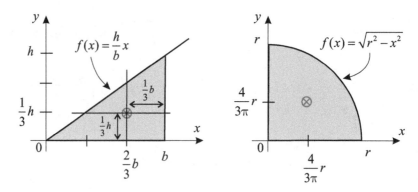

Figure 5.8.14: *Two homogeneous laminas with standard geometric shapes.*

Solution (a): As shown in the figure the hypotenuse is the graph of $f(x) = \dfrac{hx}{b}$ for $x = 0$ to $x = b$. In this problem $g(x) = 0$ and so the general formulas simplify. The three integrals we need are

$$A = \int_a^b f(x)\, dx, \quad x^* = \frac{1}{A}\int_a^b x f(x)\, dx, \quad \text{and} \quad y^* = \frac{1}{A}\int_a^b \frac{1}{2}\left[f(x)\right]^2 dx.$$

In this example:

$$A = \int_0^b \frac{h}{b} x\, dx = \frac{h}{2b} x^2 \Big|_0^b = \frac{h}{2b} \cdot b^2 = \frac{bh}{2}$$

(Of course, we did not need to integrate to find this area of a right triangle.)

$$x^* = \frac{2}{bh}\int_0^b x\left(\frac{h}{b}x\right) dx = \frac{2}{bh}\int_0^b \frac{h}{b} x^2\, dx = \frac{2}{bh}\left(\frac{h}{3b}x^3\right)\Big|_0^b = \frac{2}{bh}\left(\frac{hb^2}{3}\right) = \frac{2}{3}b$$

$$y^* = \frac{2}{bh}\int_0^b \frac{1}{2}\left(\frac{h}{b}x\right)^2 = \frac{2}{bh}\left(\frac{h^2}{6b^2}x^3\right)\Big|_0^b = \frac{2}{bh}\left(\frac{h^2 b}{6}\right) = \frac{1}{3}h$$

<u>NOTE</u>: As indicated in Figure 5.8.14, the centroid for a right triangle can be located as follows. For each side about the right angle, draw a line perpendicular to it and at a distance 1/3 of its length away from the right angle. The two perpendiculars will intersect in the centroid.

Solution (b): For the quarter-circle, we use the graph of $f(x) = \sqrt{r^2 - x^2}$ on the interval $[0, r]$, and of course $g(x) = 0$. So again, we just have to compute the integrals

$$A = \int_a^b f(x)\, dx, \quad x^* = \frac{1}{A}\int_a^b x f(x)\, dx, \quad \text{and} \quad y^* = \frac{1}{A}\int_a^b \frac{1}{2}\left[f(x)\right]^2 dx.$$

The area integral

$$A = \int_0^r \sqrt{r^2 - x^2}\, dx$$

requires a technique of integration from the next chapter. However, if we use the well-known formula for the area of a circle, then we get (for a quarter circle)

$$A = \frac{1}{4}\pi r^2.$$

Next,

$$x^* = \frac{4}{\pi r^2}\int_0^r x\sqrt{r^2 - x^2}\, dx,$$

which can be computed with the u-substitution

$$u = r^2 - x^2, \, du = -2\,x dx$$

$$u = r^2, \text{ when } x = 0, \quad u = 0, \text{ when } x = r$$

Then

$$x^* = \frac{4}{\pi r^2} \int_0^r x\sqrt{r^2 - x^2}\,dx = \frac{4}{\pi r^2} \int_0^r \sqrt{r^2 - x^2} \cdot x\,dx = \frac{4}{\pi r^2} \int_{r^2}^0 \sqrt{u}\left(-\frac{1}{2}\,du\right)$$

$$= \frac{2}{\pi r^2} \int_0^{r^2} \sqrt{u}\,du \; = \; \frac{2}{\pi r^2}\left(\frac{2}{3}u^{\frac{3}{2}}\right)\bigg|_0^r \; = \; \frac{4}{3\pi}r \; \approx \; 0.42r.$$

Finally

$$y^* = \frac{1}{A}\int_0^r \frac{1}{2}\left(\sqrt{r^2-x^2}\right)^2 dx = \frac{4}{\pi r^2}\int_0^r \frac{1}{2}\left(r^2 - x^2\right)\,dx$$

$$= \frac{2}{\pi r^2}\left(r^2 x - \frac{1}{3}x^3\right)\bigg|_0^r = \frac{2}{\pi r^2}\left(\frac{2}{3}r^3\right) = \frac{4}{3\pi}r \approx 0.42r$$

Exercises: 5.8 (Moments and Center of Mass)

Seesaws

1. Two children sit on a 12-ft long seesaw. They weigh 48 lb and 80 lb, respectively. Where must the fulcrum be placed so that the seesaw balances?

2. Two children sit on a 10-ft long seesaw. They weigh 42 lb and 66 lb, respectively. Where must the fulcrum be placed so that the seesaw balances?

Center of Mass in 1d

3. Find the moment of the system of masses about the points $c = 2$ and $c = 6$. In each case, which way does the system rotate? Find the center of mass of the system.

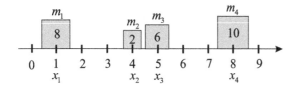

4. Find the moment of the system of masses about the points $c = 2$ and $c = 6$. In each case, which way does the system rotate? Find the center of mass of the system.

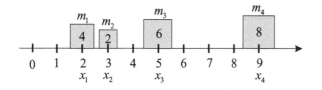

Center of Mass in 2d

5. Find the center of mass of the system of four masses shown in the figure. The distances are in feet.

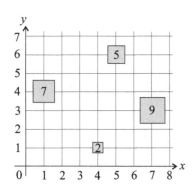

6. Find the center of mass of the system of four masses shown in the figure. The distances are in meters.

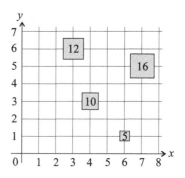

Reducing a System of 3 Masses to a System of 2 Masses

7. Find the center of mass X for the first *two* masses m_1, m_2 in the following system of three masses. Form a new system with two masses–the first being $M = m_1 + m_2$ located at X and the second being m_3 located at x_3 as originally shown in the figure. Sketch the new system of two masses and find its center of mass x'. Show that x' is the same as the center of mass x^* of the original system of three masses.

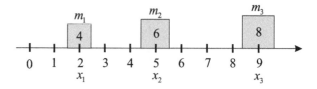

8. Consider a general system of three masses m_1, m_2, m_3 located at x_1, x_2, x_3. Let X be the center of mass of the first two masses. Form a new system with two masses— the first being being $M = m_1 + m_2$ located at X and the second m_3 located at x_3. Show that the center of mass x' of the new system is the same as the center of mass x^* of the of the original system of three masses.

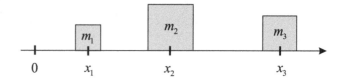

Reducing a System of 3 Masses to a System of 2 Masses

9. Find the center of mass (X, Y) for the first two masses in the following system of three masses. Form a new system with two masses — the first being $M = m_1 + m_2$ located at (X, Y) and the second being m_3 located at (x_3, y_3) as originally shown in the figure. Sketch the new system of two masses and find its center of mass (x', y'). Show that (x', y') is the same as the center of mass (x^*, y^*) of the original system of three masses.

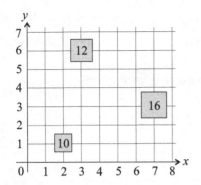

10. Find the center of mass (X, Y) for the first two masses in the following system of three masses. Form a new system with two masses—the first being $M = m_1 + m_2$ located at (X, Y) and the second being m_3 located at (x_3, y_3) as originally shown in the figure. Sketch the new system of two masses and find its center of mass (x', y'). Show that (x', y') is the same as the the center of mass (x^*, y^*) of the original system of three masses.

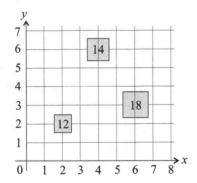

Reducing a System of n Masses to a System of n-1 Masses

11. Consider a general system of three masses m_1, m_2, m_3 located at (x_1, y_1), (x_2, y_2), (x_3, y_3), respectively. Let (X, Y) the center of mass of the first two masses. Form a new system with two masses – the first being $M = m_1 + m_2$ located at (X, Y) and the second being m_3 located at (x_3, y_3). Show that the center of mass (x', y') of the new system is the same as the center of mass (x^*, y^*) of the original system of three masses.

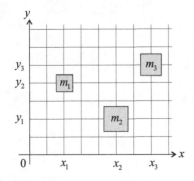

12. Consider a general system of n masses $m_1, m_2, \ldots, m_n$ located at $(x_1, y_1), (x_2, y_2), \ldots, (x_n, y_n)$, respectively. Let (X, Y) be the center of mass of the first two

masses. Form a new system with $n - 1$ masses – the first being $M = m_1 + m_2$ located at (X, Y) and the rest being $m_3, \ldots, m_n$ located at $(x_3, y_3), \ldots, (x_n, y_n)$. Show that the center of mass (x', y') of the new system is the same as the center of mass (x^*, y^*) of the original system of n masses.

In Exercises 13–20, find, using the Center of Mass Principles, the centroid of the homogeneous lamina. See Example 5.8.3.

13. Figure (a)   **14.** Figure (b)

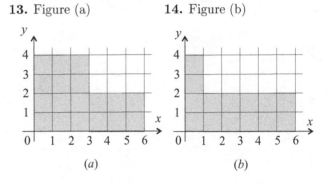

(a)   (b)

15. Figure (a)

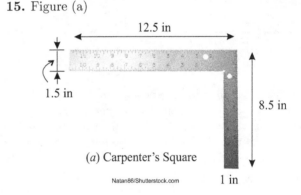

(a) Carpenter's Square

Natan86/Shutterstock.com

16. Figure (b)

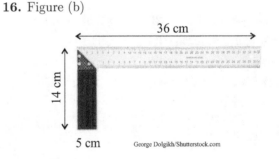

George Dolgikh/Shutterstock.com

17. Figure (a)   **18.** Figure (b)

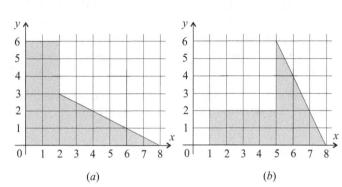

(a)   (b)

19. Figure (a)   **20.** Figure (b)

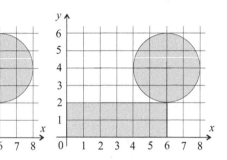

(a)   (b)

42. $y = 4 - e^x$, $y = 0$, $[0, 1]$

43. $y = \sin x$, $y = 0$, $[0, \pi]$ **44.** $y = \cos x$, $y = 0$, $[0, \frac{\pi}{2}]$

Hint: $\int x \sin x \, dx = -x \cos x + \sin x$
and $\int x \cos x \, dx = x \sin x - \cos x$.

45. $y = 1 + \sin x$, $y = 0$, $[0, \pi]$

46. $y = 1 + \cos x$, $y = 0$, $[0, \frac{\pi}{2}]$

In Exercises 21–46, a homogeneous plane lamina has the shape of the region D bounded by the graphs of $y = f(x)$ and $y = g(x)$ on the interval $[a, b]$. Sketch the region D and find the centroid of the lamina. Also mark the approximate location of the centroid on your sketch. NOTE: In the cases where the interval $[a, b]$ is not given, determine a and b by finding where the graphs intersect.

21. $y = x^2$, $y = 0$, $[0, 2]$ **22.** $y = x^3$, $y = 0$, $[0, 2]$

23. $y = \sqrt{x}$, $y = 0$, $[0, 4]$ **24.** $y = \sqrt[3]{x}$, $y = 0$, $[0, 8]$

25. $y = 4x - x^2$, $y = 0$ **26.** $y = 8x - x^2$, $y = 0$

27. $y = 2 - \sqrt{x}$, $y = 0$, $[0, 4]$

28. $y = 2 - \sqrt[3]{x}$, $y = 0$, $[0, 8]$

29. $y = \dfrac{1}{\sqrt{x}}$, $y = x$, $[1, 4]$ **30.** $y = \dfrac{1}{\sqrt[3]{x}}$, $y = x$, $[1, 8]$

31. $y = \dfrac{1}{x}$, $y = x$, $[1, 2]$ **32.** $y = \dfrac{1}{x}$, $y = \sqrt{x}$, $[1, 4]$

33. $y = 2\sqrt{x}$, $y = x$, $[0, 1]$ **34.** $y = 2x^{1/3}$, $y = x$, $[0, 1]$

35. $y = 2\sqrt{x}$, $y = x^2$, $[0, 1]$

36. $y = 2x^{1/3}$, $y = x^3$, $[0, 1]$

37. $y = x - x^2$, $y = -x$ **38.** $y = 2x - x^2$, $y = -x$

39. $y = \dfrac{1}{\sqrt{x}}$, $y = \sqrt{x}$, $[1, 4]$

40. $y = x^{-1/3}$, $y = x^{1/3}$, $[1, 8]$

41. $y = 3 - e^x$, $y = 0$, $[0, 1]$

6

Techniques of Integration

Calculus Concepts & Computation

6.1 Integration by Parts

As we have seen, the processes of differentiation and integration of functions f are related, and are essentially the inverses of one another. This relationship is is embodied in the formulas:

$$\frac{d}{dx} \int f(x)\,dx = f(x) \qquad (6.1.1)$$

$$\int f'(x)\,dx = f(x) \qquad (6.1.2)$$

The second formula should more precisely be written as $\int f'(x)\,dx = f(x) + C$, but for simplicity we have listed only $f(x)$ as an antiderivative of $f'(x)$ rather than the most general antiderivative.

Because differentiation and integration are related, you might expect that all the differentiation rules you learned in Chapter 2 would have analogous integration rules. This is true to a certain extent. The sum and difference rules, as well as the constant multiple rule translate directly into corresponding integration rules:

$$\int (f(x) \pm g(x))\,dx = \int f(x)\,dx \pm \int g(x)\,dx$$

$$\int cf(x)\,dx = c \int f(x)\,dx$$

However, the product and quotient rules for differentiation do NOT translate directly into an integration rules. Nevertheless, if we start with the product rule for differentiation,

$$(f(x)G(x))' = f'(x)G(x) + f(x)G'(x), \qquad (6.1.3)$$

we can develop a corresponding integration rule for the product of two functions. This rule is called *integration by parts*

First note that we used a capital G in (6.1.3). That's because we want to use lower case g for the derivative. Thus, we let $g(x) = G'(x)$ in Equation (6.1.3). Then integrate both sides of Equation (6.1.3) to get

$$\int (f(x)G(x))'\,dx = \int f'(x)G(x)\,dx + \int f(x)g(x)\,dx$$

By Formula (6.1.2), the left side of the last equation is just $f(x)G(x)$. So we get

$$f(x)G(x) = \int f'(x)G(x)\,dx + \int f(x)g(x)\,dx$$

Rearranging this last equation gives

$$\int f(x)g(x)\,dx = f(x)G(x) - \int f'(x)G(x)\,dx$$

where $g(x) = G'(x)$. Properly interpreted this is the integration by parts formula.

Integration by Parts Formula

For differentiable functions f and g

$$\int f(x)g(x)\,dx \;=\; f(x)G(x) - \int f'(x)G(x)\,dx \qquad (6.1.4)$$

where $\;G(x) = \int g(x)dx$

In Formula 6.1.4, we view $f(x)$ and $g(x)$ as given functions, the product of which we want to integrate. The function G is an antiderivative of g, i.e.,

$$G(x) = \int g(x)dx.$$

To use Formula (6.1.4) you must first integrate the given function g to get G and also differentiate the given function f to get f'. Then you use these in the right side of Formula (6.1.4). This gives a part that is integrated, namely $f(x)G(x)$, and another integral. Thus, the original integral is partially integrated. You have integrated the part $g(x)$. All of this indicates the origin of the name: *integration by parts.*

Example 6.1.1

Problem: Calculate the integral $\int xe^{5x}\,dx$.

Solution: Here

$$f(x) = x, \qquad g(x) = e^{5x}.$$

So we compute

$$f'(x) = 1, \qquad G(x) = \int e^{5x}dx = \frac{1}{5}e^{5x}.$$

Substituting these in Formula (6.1.4) gives

$$\int xe^{5x}dx = x(\frac{1}{5}e^{5x}) - \int 1 \cdot (\frac{1}{5}e^{5x})dx = \frac{1}{5}xe^{5x} - \frac{1}{5}\int e^{5x}dx$$

Now we compute the remaining integral to get

$$\int xe^{5x}dx = \frac{1}{5}xe^{5x} - \frac{1}{5}(\frac{1}{5}e^{5x}) = \frac{1}{5}xe^{5x} - \frac{1}{25}e^{5x} + C.$$

<u>NOTE</u>: In computing $G(x)$ and in computing the second integral in the integration by parts formula, we did not use a constant of integration C. But at the final step we added the constant of integration.

Example 6.1.2

Problem: Use integration by parts on the following integrals.

Part (a): $\int x \cos 2x\,dx$

Solution (a): Here

$$f(x) = x, \qquad g(x) = \cos 2x.$$

So we compute

$$f'(x) = 1, \qquad G(x) = \int \cos 2x\,dx = \frac{1}{2}\sin 2x.$$

Thus, by the IP formula

$$\int x\cos 2x\,dx \;=\; x(\frac{1}{2}\sin 2x) - \int 1(\frac{1}{2}\sin 2x)dx = \frac{1}{2}x\sin 2x - \frac{1}{2}\int \sin 2x\,dx$$

$$=\; \frac{1}{2}x\sin 2x - \frac{1}{2}(-\frac{1}{2}\cos 2x) = \frac{1}{2}x\sin 2x + \frac{1}{4}\cos 2x + C$$

Part (b): $\displaystyle\int \sqrt{x}\cos x\,dx$

Solution (b): Here

$$f(x) = \sqrt{x}, \qquad g(x) = \cos x.$$

So we compute

$$f'(x) = \frac{1}{2\sqrt{x}}, \qquad G(x) = \int \cos x\,dx = \sin x.$$

Thus, by the IP formula.

$$\int \sqrt{x}\cos x\,dx = \sqrt{x}\sin x - \int \frac{1}{2\sqrt{x}}\sin x\,dx$$

We see that integration by parts results in a new integral which is not possible to calculate by known integration techniques. This example illustrates that you can always use integration by parts on a given integral (provided you can compute the integral $G(x) = \int g(x)dx$). However, the remaining integral in the formula may be as difficult as the original integral.

Part (c): $\displaystyle\int (\ln x)\frac{1}{x}\,dx$

Solution (c): Here

$$f(x) = \ln x, \qquad g(x) = \frac{1}{x}.$$

So we compute

$$f'(x) = \frac{1}{x}, \qquad G(x) = \int \frac{1}{x}\,dx = \ln x.$$

Using this in the IP formula gives

$$\int (\ln x)\frac{1}{x}\,dx = \ln x(\ln x) - \int \frac{1}{x}(\ln x)dx$$

This is interesting. The new integral is the same as the one we started with. Thus, if we add it to both sides of the above equation we get

$$2\int (\ln x)\frac{1}{x}dx = (\ln x)^2$$

Dividing by 2 gives

$$\int (\ln x)\frac{1}{x}dx = \frac{1}{2}(\ln x)^2$$

NOTE: We could also get the same result by using a substitution:

$$u = \ln x, \qquad du = \frac{1}{x}\,dx.$$

Then,

$$\int (\ln x)\frac{1}{x}\,dx = \int u\,du = \frac{1}{2}u^2 = \frac{1}{2}(\ln x)^2.$$

There is an alternative notation for the integration by parts formula that is often useful (and that some people prefer). This notation is similar to the u-substitution notation. It employs Leibniz's differential notation, but now there are two functions u and v and their differentials du and dv. To use this notation we start with the integral $\int f(x)g(x)dx$ that we want to compute. We introduce u and dv by the assignments:

$$u = f(x) \quad \text{and} \quad dv = g(x)dx \qquad (6.1.5a)$$

Then

$$du = f'(x)dx \quad \text{and} \quad v = \int g(x)dx \qquad (6.1.5b)$$

Making these substitutions in the Integration by Parts Formula (6.1.4) gives the following alternative version of it.

Integration by Parts Formula - Leibniz's Version

For differentiable functions f and g

$$\underbrace{\int f(x)}_{u}\underbrace{g(x)\,dx}_{dv} = \underbrace{f(x)}_{u}\underbrace{G(x)}_{v} - \int \underbrace{G(x)}_{v}\underbrace{f'(x)\,dx}_{du}$$

where $G(x) = \int g(x)dx = \int dv = v$. Thus,

$$\int u\,dv = uv - \int v\,du \qquad (6.1.6)$$

Formula (6.1.6) is the Leibniz version of the integration by parts formula. While it is less complicated looking than Formula (6.1.4), it still takes some practice to use correctly. The first step in using it is to write down the expressions in (6.1.5a) for the particular f and g that you choose. Then carefully compute du and v from (6.15b). After this, substitute u, v, and du in the right side of Formula (6.1.6). That will leave you with one integral, namely $\int v\,du$, to compute. Diagram 6.1.1 may help you remember which products you must form from your calculations for use in the IP formula.

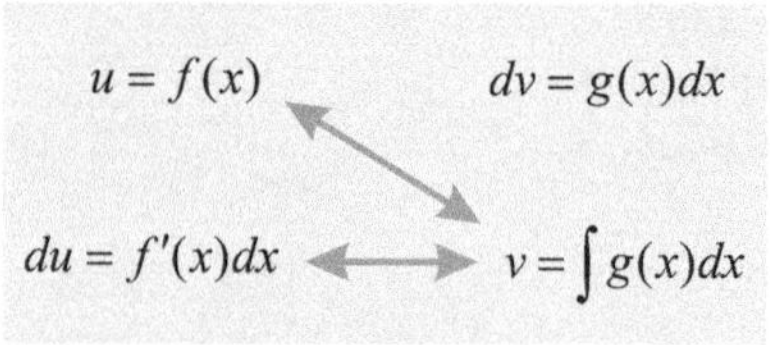

$$u = f(x) \qquad dv = g(x)dx$$
$$du = f'(x)dx \longleftrightarrow v = \int g(x)dx$$

Diagram 6.1.1

CAUTION: Regardless of which version of the integration by parts formula that you use, you will have to differentiate the function you choose for f and integrate the function you choose for g. When doing this, it is a common error to integrate where you should differentiate and to differentiate where you should integrate.

Example 6.1.3 (Logs and Powers of x)

Problem: Calculate $\int (\ln x)x^2 dx$

Solution: With the Leibniz notation we let

$$u = \ln x, \quad dv = x^2 dx.$$

Then we compute

$$du = \frac{1}{x}\,dx, \quad v = \int x^2 dx = \frac{1}{3}x^3$$

Using the integration by parts formula, we get

$$\int (\ln x) x^2 dx \;=\; \int u\,dv = uv - \int v\,du$$

$$=\; (\ln x)(\frac{1}{3}x^3) - \int (\frac{1}{3}x^3)\cdot(\frac{1}{x})dx$$

$$=\; \frac{1}{3}x^3 \ln x - \frac{1}{3}\int x^2 dx = \frac{1}{3}x^3 \ln x - \frac{1}{9}x^3 + C$$

NOTE: As in Example 6.1.1, when using integration by parts, the constant of integration C is added in the last step of the calculation. So here, when we computed v by integration, we wrote $v = \dfrac{1}{3}x^3$, rather than the more general $v = \dfrac{1}{3}x^3 + C$.

The examples above illustrate the basic technique, but the following issues can occur to complicate IP (Integration by Parts)

(1) (Switch the Functions in the Integrand) In applying integration by parts, you have to choose one part of the integrand for $u = f(x)$ and then the other part becomes $dv = g(x)dx$. In some problems you will need to switch the functions $f(x)$ and $g(x)$. For instance, in the last example the integral can be written with the functions in either order:

$$\int (\ln x) x^2 dx = \int x^2 \ln x\, dx$$

The latter way is the more typical way to write the integral, but if you try taking

$$u = x^2, \quad dv = \ln x\, dx,$$

then

$$du = 2x\, dx, \quad v = \int \ln x\, dx.$$

This assignment requires that you know how to compute $\int \ln x\, dx$. We will see how to do this below.

(2) (Only One Function in the Integrand) For example, can you apply IP to $\int \ln x\, dx$?

(3) (Integration by Parts Two or More Times) Applying IP once gives: $\int u\,dv = uv - \int v\,du$, which still leaves an integral to evaluate. If this is an integral that you know, or one which you can compute using a u-substitution (or other methods), then you are done. Otherwise consider applying IP again.

The following examples illustrate how these issues arise.

Example 6.1.4 (Switch the Functions)

Problem: Compute $\displaystyle\int x \tan^{-1} x\, dx$

Solution: We switch the functions in the integrand: $\int x \tan^{-1} x\, dx = \int (\tan^{-1} x) x\, dx$ and take

$$u = \tan^{-1} x, \quad dv = x\, dx$$

Then

$$du = \frac{1}{x^2 + 1}dx, \quad v = \int x\, dx = \frac{1}{2}x^2.$$

Putting these in the IP formula gives

$$\int (\tan^{-1} x) x\, dx \;=\; (\tan^{-1} x)\cdot\frac{1}{2}x^2 - \int \frac{1}{x^2+1}\cdot\frac{1}{2}x^2 dx$$

$$=\; \frac{1}{2}x^2 \tan^{-1} x - \frac{1}{2}\int \frac{x^2}{x^2+1}dx.$$

To compute the remaining integral we use long division to divide x^2 by $x^2 + 1$. The result is

$$\frac{x^2}{x^2 + 1} = 1 - \frac{1}{x^2 + 1}.$$

Then

$$\int \frac{x^2}{x^2 + 1} \, dx = \int (1 - \frac{1}{x^2 + 1}) dx = x - \tan^{-1} x.$$

Using this in the previous calculation, we find that

$$\int x \tan^{-1} x \, dx = \frac{1}{2} x^2 \tan^{-1} x - \frac{1}{2}(x - \tan^{-1} x) + C = \frac{1}{2}(x^2 + 1) \tan^{-1} x - \frac{1}{2} x + C$$

Example 6.1.5 (Only One Function in the Integrand)

Problem: The natural log function $f(x) = \ln x$ is one of our basic functions. What is its integral?

Solution: To compute $\int \ln x \, dx$ we use integration by parts with

$$u = \ln x, \quad dv = dx.$$

Then

$$du = \frac{1}{x} \, dx, \quad v = x.$$

So

$$\int \ln x \, dx \ = \ uv - \int v \, du = (\ln x) x - \int x \cdot \frac{1}{x} \, dx$$

$$= \ x \ln x - \int 1 \, dx = x \ln x - x + C.$$

$$\boxed{\int \ln x \, dx \ = \ x \ln x - x + C}$$

Box 6.1.1: *The integral of the natural log funtion.*

In summary we get the memorable result shown in the margin box.

Example 6.1.6 (Integration by Parts Multiple Times)

Problem: Compute $\int x^2 \cos x \, dx$.

Solution: For multiple uses of integration by parts, we think that the first version of IP:

$$\int f(x) g(x) dx = f(x) G(x) - \int f'(x) G(x) dx.$$

is quicker and easier to use.

$$\int x^2 \cos x \, dx \ = \ x^2 \sin x - \int 2x \sin x \, dx$$

$$= \ x^2 \sin x - \left[2x(-\cos x) - \int 2(-\cos x) dx \right]$$

$$= \ x^2 \sin x + 2x \cos x - 2 \sin x + C$$

Example 6.1.7 (Integration by Parts Multiple Times)

Problem: Here's an example

$$I = \int e^{2x} \cos x \, dx$$

where, after integration by parts twice, the integral that you are left with is the same as the one you started with. So clearly, continuing with the integration by parts will lead nowhere. What can you do? (See Example 6.1.2(c).)

Solution: Label the integral you start with I as shown and solve for I in the equation you get. On the first use of IP, we use the *fg*-version

$$\int f(x)g(x)dx = f(x)G(x) - \int f'(x)G(x)dx.$$

with $f(x) = e^{2x}$ and $g(x) = \cos x$. So $G(x) = \int \cos x\, dx = \sin x$.

$$
\begin{aligned}
I &= \int e^{2x} \cos x\, dx = e^{2x} \sin x - \int 2e^{2x} \sin x\, dx \\
&= e^{2x} \sin x - \left[2e^{2x}(-\cos x) - \int 4e^{2x}(-\cos x)dx\right] \\
&= e^{2x} \sin x + 2e^{2x} \cos x - 4\int e^{2x} \cos x\, dx \\
&= e^{2x} \sin x + 2e^{2x} \cos x - 4I.
\end{aligned}
$$

Thus, we have found that

$$I = e^{2x} \sin x + 2\,e^{2x} \cos x - 4I.$$

We solve this for I.

$$5I = e^{2x} \sin x + 2e^{2x} \cos x,$$

and so

$$I = \frac{1}{5}(e^{2x} \sin x + 2e^{2x} \cos x).$$

In summary:

$$I = \int e^{2x} \cos x\, dx = \frac{1}{5}e^{2x} \sin x + \frac{2}{5}e^{2x} \cos x + C.$$

<u>NOTE</u> 1: In these types of problems, introduce the symbol I for the original integral. After integration by parts twice, I should occur again. Then solve for I.

<u>NOTE</u> 2: We added the constant of integration C at the last step, after we found integral I.

Example 6.1.8 (Reduction Formula)

Problem: For an integer $n \geq 2$, use integration by parts to express $I = \int \cos^n x dx$ in terms of an integral of cosine with a reduced (lesser) power.

Solution: View the integral as

$$I = \int \cos^n x\, dx = \int \cos^{n-1} x \cdot \cos x\, dx$$

and let

$$u = \cos^{n-1} x, \qquad dv = \cos x\, dx$$

Then (using the chain rule on the derivative)

$$du = (n-1)\cos^{n-2} x \cdot (-\sin x)\, dx, \qquad v = \sin x$$

So the IP is

$$I = \int \cos^n x \, dx \;\; = \;\; \int \cos^{n-1} x \cdot \cos x \, dx$$

$$= \;\; \cos^{n-1} x \cdot \sin x - \int (n-1) \cos^{n-2} x \cdot (-\sin x) \cdot \sin x \, dx$$

$$= \;\; \cos^{n-1} x \cdot \sin x + (n-1) \int \cos^{n-2} x \cdot \sin^2 x \, dx$$

Next, rewrite the last integral above using the trig identity: $\sin^2 x = 1 - \cos^2 x$.

$$I \;\; = \;\; \int \cos^n x \, dx = \cos^{n-1} x \sin x + (n-1) \int \cos^{n-2} x (1 - \cos^2 x) dx$$

$$= \;\; \cos^{n-1} x \sin x + (n-1) \int \cos^{n-2} x \, dx - (n-1) \int \cos^n x \, dx$$

$$= \;\; \cos^{n-1} x \sin x + (n-1) \int \cos^{n-2} x \, dx - (n-1)I$$

Solving this for I gives

$$nI = \cos^{n-1} x \, \sin x + (n-1) \int \cos^{n-2} x \, dx$$

Dividing by n gives the reduction formula

$$\int \cos^n x \, dx = \frac{1}{n} \cos^{n-1} x \, \sin x + \frac{n-1}{n} \int \cos^{n-2} x \, dx$$

Example 6.1.9 (Volume of a Sinesoidal Bundt Cake)

Problem: A bundt cake can be considered as a solid of revolution obtained by revolving a certain Type I region D about the y-axis. The cake is actually formed by pouring batter into a mold (the "bundt" pan, trademarked by Nordic Ware), baking, and then flipping the mold over to extract the cake.

Heike Brauer\Shutterstock.com

Ffolas/Shutterstock.com

The American Mathematical Society (AMS), at an upcoming banquet for 100 guests, is considering serving slices of bundt cake for dessert. To honor Ptolemy, an astronomer who compiled the first table of sines, the bunt cakes are to have the form created using the region D:

$$y = \frac{1}{3} \sin 6x, \quad x \text{ in } \left[\frac{\pi}{36}, \frac{\pi}{6} \right],$$

where the units are in feet. If 10 bunt cakes are needed, how many gallons of batter must the cook prepare for baking all the cakes?

Solution: The graph of the region D is shown below on the left. Revolving this about the y-axis creates the solid that is the bundt cake. This is shown on the right,

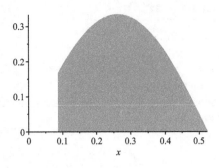
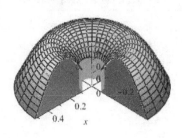

The figure on the right shows the cake after $1/4$ of it has been eaten. Note that the slices of a bundt cake are usually taken in planes through the axis of revolution. Thus, the face of each slice of cake is the region D.

To find the volume, we assume, for simplicity, that batter does not increase in volume when baked. Then we use the shell method with $f(x) = \frac{1}{3}\sin 6x$ on the interval $\left[\frac{\pi}{36}, \frac{\pi}{6}\right]$:

$$V = \int_a^b 2\pi x f(x)\, dx = \int_{\pi/36}^{\pi/6} \frac{2\pi}{3} x \sin 6x\, dx = \frac{2\pi}{3} \int_{\pi/36}^{\pi/6} x \sin 6x\, dx$$

This requires IP (Integration by Parts). We let

$$u = x, \qquad dv = \sin 6x\, dx$$

Then

$$du = dx, \qquad v = \int \sin 6x\, dx = -\frac{1}{6}\cos 6x$$

So

$$\int x \sin 6x\, dx = -\frac{1}{6}x\cos 6x + \frac{1}{6}\int \cos 6x\, dx = -\frac{1}{6}x\cos 6x + \frac{1}{36}\sin 6x$$

Thus, the volume of one bunt cake is

$$
\begin{aligned}
V &= \frac{2\pi}{3}\left[-\frac{1}{6}x\cos 6x + \frac{1}{36}\sin 6x\right]\Bigg|_{\pi/36}^{\pi/6} \\
&= \frac{2\pi}{3}\left[\frac{\pi}{36} + 0\right] - \frac{2\pi}{3}\left[-\frac{1}{6}\left(\frac{\pi}{36}\right)\frac{\sqrt{3}}{2} + \frac{1}{72}\right] \\
&= \frac{\pi}{54}\left[\pi\left(1 + \frac{\sqrt{3}}{12}\right) - \frac{1}{2}\right] = \frac{\pi^2}{54} + \frac{\pi^2\sqrt{3}}{648} - \frac{\pi}{108} \\
&\approx 0.1800622734 \text{ ft}^3.
\end{aligned}
$$

To convert this to gallons, we use the fact that 1 gallon = 231 in^3 . Then

$$V \approx 1.346959344 \text{ gallons}$$

Thus, for ten cakes, the cook needs to prepare 13.5 gallons of batter.

Exercises: 6.1 (Integration by Parts)

Use integration by parts (IP) to compute the following integrals. NOTE: In some of the problems you will have to switch your assignment of what you call the the first function $f(x)$ and what you call the second function $g(x)$.

1. $\displaystyle\int x\sin 2x\,dx$ **2.** $\displaystyle\int x\sin 3x\,dx$

3. $\displaystyle\int xe^{3x}\,dx$ **4.** $\displaystyle\int xe^{2x}\,dx$

5. $\displaystyle\int x\sec^2 x\,dx$ **6.** $\displaystyle\int x\csc^2 x\,dx$

7. $\displaystyle\int x\sec x\tan x\,dx$ **8.** $\displaystyle\int x\csc x\cot x\,dx$

9. $\displaystyle\int \frac{xe^x}{(1+e^x)^2}\,dx$ **10.** $\displaystyle\int \frac{xe^{-x}}{(1+e^{-x})^2}\,dx$

11. $\displaystyle\int \ln(\sec x)\sec^2 x\,dx$ **12.** $\displaystyle\int \ln(\csc x)\csc^2 x\,dx$

13. $\displaystyle\int x^3\ln x\,dx$ **14.** $\displaystyle\int x^n\ln x\,dx$

15. $\displaystyle\int x^2(\ln x)^2\,dx$ **16.** $\displaystyle\int x^{-3}(\ln x)^2\,dx$

17. $\displaystyle\int x^2(\ln x)^3\,dx$ **18.** $\displaystyle\int x^{-1/2}(\ln x)^2\,dx$

19. $\displaystyle\int x^n(\ln x)^p$ (Find a reduction formula.)

20. $\displaystyle\int x^{-2}(\ln x)^4\,dx$

21. $\displaystyle\int e^{-x}\ln(1+e^x)\,dx$ **22.** $\displaystyle\int e^{-2x}\ln(1+e^{2x})\,dx$

23. $\displaystyle\int \frac{\ln x\cos(\ln x)}{x}\,dx$ **24.** $\displaystyle\int \frac{\ln x\sin(\ln x)}{x}\,dx$

25. $\displaystyle\int \frac{\ln x\sec^2(\ln x)}{x}\,dx$ **26.** $\displaystyle\int \frac{\ln x\csc^2(\ln x)}{x}\,dx$

27. $\displaystyle\int \sec^2 x\ln(\cos x)\,dx$ **28.** $\displaystyle\int \sec^2 x\ln(\sin x)\,dx$

29. $\displaystyle\int \sec x\tan x\ln(\cos x)\,dx$

30. $\displaystyle\int \sec x\tan x\ln(\sin x)\,dx$

31. $\displaystyle\int \cos x\ln(\cos x)\,dx$ **32.** $\displaystyle\int \sin x\ln(\sin x)\,dx$

33. $\displaystyle\int \cos x\ln(1+\cos x)\,dx$ **34.** $\displaystyle\int \sin x\ln(1+\sin x)\,dx$

35. $\displaystyle\int x^{-1/2}\tan^{-1}\left(x^{-1/2}\right)\,dx$

36. $\displaystyle\int x^{-3/2}\tan^{-1}\left(x^{-3/2}\right)\,dx$

37. $\displaystyle\int x^2\tan^{-1}x\,dx$ **38.** $\displaystyle\int x\tan^{-1}x\,dx$

39. $\displaystyle\int x^3\tan^{-1}x\,dx$ **40.** $\displaystyle\int x^4\tan^{-1}x\,dx$

41. $\displaystyle\int x^n\tan^{-1}x\,dx$ **42.** $\displaystyle\int x^5\tan^{-1}x\,dx$

43. $\displaystyle\int x^2\ln(x^2+1)\,dx$ **44.** $\displaystyle\int x^n\ln(x^2+1)\,dx$

Single Function Integrands

The integral $\displaystyle\int \ln x\,dx$, as illustrated in the reading material, is a standard example where integration by parts is effective when the integrand is not the product of two functions (unless you consider $\ln x$, as $(\ln x)\cdot 1$). Exercises 45–58 are further examples of this (and also exhibit the integrals of some basic functions). NOTE: In Exercises 55–58, first do a substitution of the form $u=x^{1/2}$ and then integrate by parts.

45. $\displaystyle\int \tan^{-1}x\,dx$ **46.** $\displaystyle\int \cot^{-1}x\,dx$

47. $\displaystyle\int \sin^{-1}x\,dx$ **48.** $\displaystyle\int \cos^{-1}x\,dx$

49. $\displaystyle\int \ln(x^2+1)\,dx$ **50.** $\displaystyle\int \cos(\ln x)\,dx$ (Use IP)

51. $\displaystyle\int \ln(\sqrt{x}+1)\,dx$ **52.** $\displaystyle\int \cos(\ln x)\,dx$ (Use IP)

53. $\displaystyle\int \sin(\ln x)\,dx$ **54.** $\displaystyle\int \cos(\ln x)\,dx$

55. $\displaystyle\int \tan^{-1}(\sqrt{x})\,dx$ **56.** $\displaystyle\int \cot^{-1}(\sqrt{x})\,dx$

57. $\displaystyle\int e^{\sqrt{x}}\,dx$ **58.** $\displaystyle\int e^{2\sqrt{x}}\,dx$

IP Multiple Times

Sometimes integration by parts applied two or more times will successfully compute an integral. Since reduction formulas are derived from integration by parts, their use is really integration by parts multiple times. Exercises 59–86 exhibit some of this. NOTE: In Exercises 79–86, first do a substitution of the form $u=x^{1/n}$ (for $n=3$ or 4) and then integrate by parts multiple times.

59. $\displaystyle\int x^2e^{-3x}\,dx$ **60.** $\displaystyle\int x^2e^{4x}\,dx$

61. $\displaystyle\int x^2\sin 5x\,dx$ **62.** $\displaystyle\int x^2\cos 3x\,dx$

63. $\displaystyle\int x^2\tan x\sec^2 x\,dx$ **64.** $\displaystyle\int x^2\cot x\csc^2 x\,dx$

65. $\displaystyle\int x^3e^{2x}\,dx$ **66.** $\displaystyle\int x^3e^{3x}\,dx$

67. $\displaystyle\int x^ne^{ax}\,dx$ (Derive a reduction formula.)

68. $\displaystyle\int x^n\cos ax\,dx$ (Derive a reduction formula.)

69. $\displaystyle\int x^4e^{2x}\,dx$ (Use Exercise 67)

70. $\int x^5 e^{-2x}\, dx$ (Use Exercise 65)

71. $\int e^x \cos x\, dx$

72. $\int e^x \sin x\, dx$

73. $\int e^{-x} \sin x\, dx$

74. $\int e^{-x} \cos x\, dx$

75. $\int e^{4x} \cos 3x\, dx$

76. $\int e^{-4x} \sin 2x\, dx$

77. $\int e^{ax} \sin bx\, dx$

78. $\int e^{ax} \cos bx\, dx$

79. $\int \tan^{-1}(x^{1/3})\, dx$

80. $\int \cot^{-1}(x^{1/3})\, dx$

81. $\int \tan^{-1}(x^{1/4})\, dx$

82. $\int \cot^{-1}(x^{1/4})\, dx$

83. $\int e^{(x^{1/3})}\, dx$

84. $\int e^{(2x^{1/3})}\, dx$

85. $\int e^{(x^{1/4})}\, dx$

86. $\int e^{(2x^{1/4})}\, dx$

Applications (Volumes)

In Exercises 87–98, the region beneath the graph of $y = f(x)$ on the interval $[a, b]$ is revolved about the y-axis. Find the volume of the resulting solid of revolution.

87. $f(x) = e^{-x}$, $[0, 2]]$

88. $f(x) = e^{-2x}$, $[0, 1]$

89. $f(x) = xe^{-x}$, $[0, 3]]$

90. $f(x) = xe^{-2x}$, $[0, 2]$

91. $f(x) = x \sin 3x$, $[0, \pi/3]]$

92. $f(x) = x \sin 4x$, $[0, \pi/4]$

93. $f(x) = x^3 \ln x$, $[1, e]$

94. $f(x) = x \ln x$, $[1, e]$

95. $f(x) = 1 + \cos x$, $[0, \pi]$

96. $f(x) = 1 + \sin x$, $[0, \pi]$

97. $f(x) = \tan^{-1} x$, $[0, 1]$

98. $f(x) = \sec^{-1} x$, $[1, 2]$

Theory (Some Integral Formulas)

99. (IP for Definite Integrals)

By the Fundamental Theorem of Calculus, any definite integral can be computed in two steps. First compute the indefinite integral and then evaluate that from a to b. Therefore, there is really no reason to have an integration by parts formula for definite integrals. However, sometimes you may find it useful. The formula is

$$\int_a^b f(x)g(x)\, dx = f(x)G(x)\Big|_a^b - \int_a^b f'(x)G(x)\, dx, \quad (1)$$

where

$$G(x) = \int g(x)\, dx.$$

The Leibniz version of IP for definite integrals is

$$\int_a^b u\, dv = uv\Big|_a^b - \int_a^b v\, du \quad (2)$$

Verify the validity of these IP formulas for definite integrals.

100. (Integrating Inverse Functions - Complementary Areas)

Suppose that f is increasing on $[a, b]$ and has continuous derivative on (a, b). Show that

$$\int_{f(a)}^{f(b)} f^{-1}(y)\, dy = bf(b) - af(a) - \int_a^b f(x)\, dx \quad (3)$$

Also give a geometric interpretation, in terms of areas, for this integral formula. The geometric interpretation can serve as verification of the validity of the formula, but generally, does not comprise a proof of it.

101. (Integrating Squares of Inverse Functions - Complementary Volumes)

Suppose that f is increasing on $[a, b]$ and has continuous derivative on (a, b). Show that

$$\int_{f(a)}^{f(b)} \left(f^{-1}(y)\right)^2 dy = b^2 f(b) - a^2 f(a) - \int_a^b 2x\, f(x)\, dx \quad (4)$$

Also give a geometric interpretation, in terms of volumes of solids of revolution, for this integral formula. The geometric interpretation can serve as verification of the validity of the formula.

102. (Integrating Powers of Inverse Functions.

Suppose that f is increasing on $]a, b]$. For a positive real number p consider

$$\int_{f(a)}^{f(b)} \left(f^{-1}(y)\right)^p dy.$$

Based on Exercises 100 and 101, make a conjecture about an integral formula for this definite integral. Prove your conjecture.

Areas and Volumes Generated by Inverse Functions.

Suppose that f is increasing on $[a, b]$ and has continuous derivative on (a, b). Consider the inverse function f^{-1} on the interval $[f(a), f(b)]$. The region D_1 which is bounded by

$$x = f^{-1}(y),\ y = f(a),\ y = f(b),\ x = 0,$$

is just the region "beneath" the graph of $f^{-1}(y)$ for y in $[f(a), f(b)]$. Note that to sketch the region D_1, just graph $y = f(x)$ for x in $[a, b]$ (which is the same as the graph of $x = f^{-1}(y)$ for y in $[f(a), f(b)]$) and the draw the two horizontal lines: $y = f(a)$, $y = f(b)$ and the vertical line: $x = 0$. The curve and three lines bound the region D_1.

Areas: In Exercises 103–108, sketch the region D_1 and use the integral formula from Exercise 100 to find its area.

103. $f(x) = \sec x$, $[0, \frac{\pi}{3}]$ **104.** $f(x) = \csc x$, $[\pi, \frac{5\pi}{6}]$

105. $f(x) = \tan x$, $[0, \frac{\pi}{4}]$ **106.** $f(x) = -\cot x$, $[\frac{\pi}{2}, \frac{3\pi}{4}]$

107. $f(x) = x^3 + x + 1$, $[0, 1]$

108. $f(x) = x^3 + 2x + 1$, $[0, 1]$

Volumes: In Exercises 109–114, sketch the solid obtained by revolving D_1 about the y-axis and then use the integral formula from Exercise 101 to find its volume.

109. $f(x) = \sin x$, $[0, \frac{\pi}{2}]$ **110.** $f(x) = \cos x$, $[\frac{3\pi}{2}, 2\pi]$

111. $f(x) = e^x$, $[0, 1]$ **112.** $f(x) = e^{2x}$, $[0, 1]$

113. $f(x) = x^3 + x + 1$, $[0, 1]$

114. $f(x) = x^3 + 2x + 1$, $[0, 1]$

Applications (Centroids)

In Exercises 115–128, the region D beneath the graph of $y = f(x)$ on the interval $[a, b]$ is a homogeneous lamina. Find the centroid of D.

115. $f(x) = \cos x$, $[0, \pi/2]$ **116.** $f(x) = \sin x$, $[0, \pi/2]$

117. $f(x) = e^{-x}$, $[0, \ln 2]$ **118.** $f(x) = e^{-2x}$, $[0, 2/\ln 2]$

119. $f(x) = \ln x$, $[1, e]$ **120.** $f(x) = x^2 \ln x$, $[1, e]$

121. $f(x) = xe^{-x}$, $[0, 1]$ **122.** $f(x) = xe^{-2x}$, $[0, 1]$

123. $f(x) = x \ln x$, $[1, e]$ **124.** $f(x) = x \ln(x^2)$, $[1, \sqrt{e}]$

125. $f(x) = x^{-3} \ln x$, $[1, e]$ **126.** $f(x) = x^{-4} \ln x$, $[1, e]$

127. $f(x) = x \sin x$, $[0, \frac{\pi}{2}]$ **128.** $f(x) = x \cos x$, $[0, \frac{\pi}{2}]$

Application (Euler's Bundt Cake)

129. The famous swiss mathematician Leonhard Euler (1707–1783) discovered the number e as the most appropriate base to use for logarithms. In honor of this discovery (and countless others), the Mathematical Association of America (MAA) is baking 10 bundt cakes for its annual banquet. The shape for the cakes is the solid of revolution obtained by revolving a region D beneath the graph of a natural logarithm function about the y-axis. Specifically, D is the region beneath the graph of

$$f(x) = 2 \ln x, \text{ for } x \text{ in } [1, 2e],$$

with units in inches. (The scaling by 2 is to get a cake of appropriate size.) Find the number of gallons of cake batter the cook must prepare in order to bake 10 bundt cakes in this shape.

Theory (Integrating by Parts Multiple Times)

130. Show that

$$\int x g(x) \, dx = x G(x) - H(x) + C, \qquad (5)$$

where

$$G(x) = \int g(x)\,dx, \ H(x) = \int G(x)\,dx = \int \left(\int g(x)\,dx \right) dx$$

Roughly speaking, to compute $\int xg(x)\,dx$ completely, you must be able to integrate $g(x)$ twice, i.e., compute its 2nd integral. How many functions g do you know that can be integrated twice? What about starting with a function H and letting $g(x) = H''(x)$?

131. (The Table Method)

Show that

$$\int x^n g(x)\,dx = x^n g_1(x) - \int n x^{n-1} g_1(x)\,dx, \qquad (6)$$

where

$$g_1(x) = \int g(x)\,dx$$

Show how, when n is a positive integer, repeated use of Formula (6) can complete the computation of $\int x^n g(x)\,dx$. Indicate how repeated use of the formula can be arranged in a table for convenience of computation.

132. The generalization of Formula (6) above is the f-g version of IP:

$$\int f(x) g(x)\,dx = f(x) g_1(x) - \int f'(x) g_1(x)\,dx, \qquad (7)$$

Show how a table method works for this. Is it a useful method other than in the case when $f(x) = x^n$?

Using the Table Method

Use the result of Exercise 131 to compute the integrals in Exercises 133–146

133. $\int x^2 e^{-3x}\,dx$ **134.** $\int x^2 e^{4x}\,dx$

135. $\int x^3 e^{2x}\,dx$ **136.** $\int x^3 e^{3x}\,dx$

137. $\int x^4 e^{-2x}\,dx$ **138.** $\int x^4 e^{-3x}\,dx$

139. $\int x^6 e^{-2x}\,dx$ **140.** $\int x^6 e^{2x}\,dx$

141. $\int x^2 \sin 3x\,dx$ **142.** $\int x^2 \cos 3x\,dx$

143. $\int x^4 \sin 2x\,dx$ **144.** $\int x^4 \cos 2x\,dx$

145. $\int x^6 \sin x\,dx$ **146.** $\int x^6 \cos x\,dx$

In Exercises 147–150, n and k are positive integers. Show that the substitution $u = x^{1/n}$ reduces the integrals to ones that can be computed using integration by parts multiple times. For the latter, consult Exercises 41 and 67.

147. $\int e^{(x^{1/n})}\,dx$ **148.** $\int x^k e^{(x^{1/n})}\,dx$

149. $\int \tan^{-1}(x^{1/n})\,dx$ **150.** $\int x^k \tan^{-1}(x^{1/n})\,dx$

Calculus *Concepts & Computation*

6.2 Trigonometric Integrals

In this section we look at several techniques that can be used to integrate certain products involving powers of trigonometric functions. The use of trigonometric identities, as you might expect, plays a fundamental role in these techniques.

Being able to compute the trig integrals in this section is not only important in its own right but also is an essential part of the integration technique you will study in the next section.

Integrals Involving Powers of Sine and Cosine

There is a general technique (procedure) that can be used to compute integrals of the form

$$\int \sin^n x \cos^k x \, dx$$

for certain powers (exponents) n and k. This technique involves using some basic trig identities for sine and cosine and the u-substitution technique from Section 4.5. You will need the identity $\sin^2 x + \cos^2 x = 1$, but will use it in one of the following forms

$$\sin^2 x = 1 - \cos^2 x$$
$$\cos^2 x = 1 - \sin^2 x$$

Before discussing the general technique, we look at a few typical examples.

Example 6.2.1

Problem: Compute $\int \sin^2 x \cos^3 x \, dx$

Solution: The idea behind integrating this is to write $\cos^3 x = \cos^2 x \cos x$ and use the fact that $\cos x$ is the derivative of $\sin x$. Then replacing $\cos^2 x$ by $1 - \sin^2 x$ and employing the u-substitution $u = \sin x$, $du = \cos x \, dx$ will lead to an easy expression in u to integrate:

$$\int \sin^2 x \cos^3 x \, dx = \int \sin^2 x \cos^2 x \cdot \cos x \, dx = \int \sin^2 x \left(1 - \sin^2 x\right) \cdot \cos x \, dx$$

$$= \int u^2 \left(1 - u^2\right) \, du = \int \left(u^2 - u^4\right) du = \frac{1}{3} u^3 - \frac{1}{5} u^5 + C$$

$$= \frac{1}{3} \sin^3 x - \frac{1}{5} \sin^5 x + C$$

NOTE: Even though there is a $\sin^2 x$ factor in the integrand, we do not use the half angle identity in this type of problem. Doing so would complicate the integral and lead nowhere. As you can see, using the sine substitution is the best way to compute the integral and will work whenever there is an odd power of the cosine in the integrand. (See the rules below.)

The last example is indicative of the general technique for integrating $\int \sin^n x \cos^k x \, dx$ when one of the powers, n or k, is an odd integer. If both n and k are even, then the technique is different and usually takes longer to apply. The rules for the general technique are as follows:

Technique for Integrating $\int \sin^n x \cos^k x \, dx$

(1) Odd Power of the Sine ($n = 2p + 1$) Use the substitution $u = \cos x$:

$$\int \sin^{2p+1} x \, \cos^k x \, dx = \int \underbrace{\left(\sin^2 x\right)^p}_{\left(1-u^2\right)^p} \underbrace{\cos^k x}_{u^k} \underbrace{\sin x \, dx}_{-du}$$

(2) Odd Power of Cosine ($k = 2p + 1$) Use the substitution $u = \sin x$:

$$\int \sin^n x \, \cos^{2p+1} x \, dx = \int \underbrace{\sin^n x}_{u^n} \underbrace{\left(\cos^2 x\right)^p}_{\left(1-u^2\right)^p} \underbrace{\cos x \, dx}_{du}$$

Table 6.2.1

NOTE 1: (**OSOC Cases**) The two cases given in the table are the easy cases. There is either an odd power on the sine (OS) or an odd power on the cosine (OC). The remaining case, Case (3), is where both powers on the sine and cosine are even. In this case, the technique is to first rewrite (if necessary) the integrand in terms of the sine only (using $\cos^2 x = 1 - \sin^2 x$ or in terms of the cosine only (using $\sin^2 x = 1 - \cos^2 x$). Then, after doing some algebra, use a reduction formula from the following table.

Reduction Formulas (*sine and cosine*)

$$\int \sin^n x \, dx = -\frac{1}{n}\sin^{n-1} x \, \cos x + \frac{n-1}{n}\int \sin^{n-2} x \, dx \qquad (6.2.1)$$

$$\int \cos^n x \, dx = \frac{1}{n}\cos^{n-1} x \, \sin x + \frac{n-1}{n}\int \cos^{n-2} x \, dx \qquad (6.2.2)$$

Table 6.2.2

NOTE 2: The reduction formulas in the above Table are for $n \geq 2$. For $n = 1$ there's no need to reduce.

NOTE 3: Some calculus books use the half-angle formulas:

$$\sin^2 x = \frac{1}{2} - \frac{1}{2}\cos 2x \qquad (6.2.3)$$

$$\cos^2 x = \frac{1}{2} + \frac{1}{2}\cos 2x \qquad (6.2.4)$$

for the case when both powers are even. Generally this takes longer and is algebraically more intensive than using the reduction formulas.

Example 6.2.2 (Using a Reduction Formula)

Problem: Compute $\int \cos^4 x \, dx$.

Solution: We use the cosine reduction formula twice:

$$\int \cos^4 x\,dx \;=\; \frac{1}{4}\cos^3 x \sin x + \frac{3}{4}\int \cos^2 x\,dx$$

$$=\; \frac{1}{4}\cos^3 x \sin x + \frac{3}{4}\left(\frac{1}{2}\cos x \sin x + \frac{1}{2}\int 1\,dx\right)$$

$$=\; \frac{1}{4}\cos^3 x \sin x + \frac{3}{8}\cos x \sin x + \frac{3}{8}x + C$$

Example 6.2.3 (Even Powers of the Sine and Cosine)

Problem: Compute $\int \sin^2 x \cos^2 x\,dx$

Solution: We convert everything to sines and use the sine reduction formula.

$$\int \sin^2 x \cos^2 x\,dx \;=\; \int \sin^2 x \left(1 - \sin^2 x\right) dx = \int \left(\sin^2 x - \sin^4 x\right) dx$$

$$=\; \int \sin^2 x\,dx - \int \sin^4 x\,dx$$

$$=\; \int \sin^2 x\,dx - \left(-\frac{1}{4}\sin^3 x \cos x + \frac{3}{4}\int \sin^2 x\,dx\right)$$

$$=\; \frac{1}{4}\sin^3 x \cos x + \frac{1}{4}\int \sin^2 x\,dx$$

$$=\; \frac{1}{4}\sin^3 x \cos x + \frac{1}{4}\left(-\frac{1}{2}\sin x \cos x + \frac{1}{2}\int 1\,dx\right)$$

$$=\; \frac{1}{4}\sin^3 x \cos x - \frac{1}{8}\sin x \cos x + \frac{1}{8}x + C$$

NOTE: We applied the reduction formula first to the integral with $\sin^4 x$, which gives an integral with $\sin^2 x$. Then we combined this with the other integral of $\sin^2 x$ and used the reduction formula on the result.

Example 6.2.4 (Special non-OSOC Cases)

Problem: Compute $\int \cos^2 x\,dx$

Solution: You can easily compute this using the reduction formula for the cosine. However, if you are good at remembering trig identities you could do it with the half-angle formula (6.2.4) discussed above. Using this, we get

$$\int \cos^2 x\,dx \;=\; \int \left(\frac{1}{2} + \frac{1}{2}\cos 2x\right) dx = \frac{1}{2}x + \frac{1}{2}\int \cos 2x\,dx$$

$$=\; \frac{1}{2}x + \frac{1}{2}\cdot\frac{1}{2}\sin 2x + C = \frac{1}{2}x + \frac{1}{4}\sin 2x + C$$

NOTE: When integrating trigonometric expressions, the answers can often be expressed in alternative ways. This arises because of the various trig identities that allow us to turn one trig expression into another. For example, the answer above can be expressed as

$$\frac{1}{2}x + \frac{1}{2}\sin x \cos x + C$$

by using the double angle formula: $\sin 2x = 2\sin x \cos x$. This is what you get if you use the reducton formula (6.2.2) directly to compute the integral.

CAUTION: In the exercises, after working a trigonometric integral problem, your answer may look different from the one in the Solutions Manual. Your answer could be correct and, if so, can be converted into the one in the Solutions Manual using trig identities. Or, maybe your answer is incorrect because of some error you made in the calculations.

Integrals Involving Powers of Tangent and Secant

As with sine and cosine, there is a general technique to compute integrals of the form

$$\int \sec^n x \tan^k x \, dx$$

for certain powers n and k. The technique has two *easy* cases. In one case you use the substitution $u = \tan x$, $du = \sec^2 x \, dx$ and the trig identity: $\sec^2 x = 1 + \tan^2 x$. In the other case you use the substitution $u = \sec x$, $du = \sec x \tan x \, dx$ and the trig identity $\tan^2 x = \sec^2 x - 1$. Before looking at the general technique, we examine a few particular examples.

Example 6.2.5 (Odd Power of the Tangent - OT case)

Problem: Compute the integral $\int \sec^3 x \tan^3 x \, dx$.

Solution: The power of the tangent is odd and there is a secant term present. So we can use the following technique. Take one of the secant terms and one of the tangent terms and put them with dx. This gives

$$\sec x \tan x \, dx = du, \quad \text{where} \quad u = \sec x$$

Thus, we just convert the remaining tangent terms to secants using $\tan^2 x = \sec^2 x - 1$. Then we can rewrite everything entirely in terms of u and du.

$$
\begin{aligned}
\int \sec^3 x \tan^3 x \, dx &= \int \sec^2 x \tan^2 x \sec x \tan x \, dx = \int \sec^2 x \left(\sec^2 x - 1 \right) \sec x \tan x \, dx \\
&= \int u^2 \left(u^2 - 1 \right) du = \int \left(u^4 - u^2 \right) du = \frac{1}{5} u^5 - \frac{1}{3} u^3 + C \\
&= \frac{1}{5} \sec^5 x - \frac{1}{3} \sec^3 x + C
\end{aligned}
$$

Example 6.2.6 (Even Power of Secant - ES case)

Problem: Compute $\int \sec^6 x \tan^4 x \, dx$.

Solution: The power of the secant is $n = 6$ and so we can do the following technique (which works whenever n is even). We write

$$\sec^6 x = \sec^4 x \cdot \sec^2 x = \left(\sec^2 x \right)^2 \sec^2 x = \left(1 + \tan^2 x \right)^2 \sec^2 x.$$

Using this we rewrite the integral and make the substitution $u = \tan x, \, du = \sec^2 x \, dx$.

$$
\begin{aligned}
\int \sec^6 x \tan^4 x \, dx &= \int \left(1 + \tan^2 x \right)^2 \sec^2 x \tan^4 x \, dx \\
&= \int \left(1 + \tan^2 x \right)^2 \tan^4 x \sec^2 x \, dx = \int \left(1 + u^2 \right)^2 u^4 \, du \\
&= \int \left(1 + 2u^2 + u^4 \right) u^4 \, du = \int \left(u^4 + 2u^6 + u^8 \right) du \\
&= \frac{1}{5} u^5 + \frac{2}{7} u^7 + \frac{1}{9} u^9 + C = \frac{1}{5} \tan^5 x + \frac{2}{7} \tan^7 x + \frac{1}{9} \tan^9 x + C
\end{aligned}
$$

The last two examples motivate the general technique which is summarized in the following table.

Technique for Integrating $\displaystyle\int \sec^n x \tan^k x\, dx$

---

(1) Odd Power of Tangent ($k = 2p + 1$) and $n \geq 1$. Use the substitution $u = \sec x$:

$$\int \sec^n x \tan^{2p+1} x\, dx = \int \underbrace{\sec^{n-1} x}_{u^{n-1}} \underbrace{\left(\tan^2 x\right)^p}_{\left(u^2-1\right)^p} \underbrace{\sec x \tan x\, dx}_{du}$$

(2) Even Power of the Secant ($n = 2p$). Use the substitution $u = \tan x$:

$$\int \sec^{2p} x \tan^k x\, dx = \int \underbrace{\sec^{2(p-1)} x}_{\left(u^2+1\right)^{p-1}} \underbrace{\tan^k x}_{u^k} \underbrace{\sec^2 x\, dx}_{du}$$

Table 6.2.3

NOTE 1: As a means of remembering the Cases (1) and (2) use the acronym OTES, which stands for Odd Tangent (OT) or Even Secant (ES).

NOTE 2: The OTES cases are the easy ones. The remaining possibility, Case (3), is when the power of the tangent is even and the power of the secant is odd. This is a harder case. If there is no secant term, use a reduction formula for the tangent function. Otherwise, rewrite the integrand entirely in terms of the secant (using $\tan^2 x = \sec^2 x - 1$) and employ the reduction formula for the secant.

Reduction Formulas (*secant and tangent*)

$$\int \sec^n x\, dx = \frac{1}{n-1}\sec^{n-2} x \tan x + \frac{n-2}{n-1}\int \sec^{n-2} x\, dx \qquad (6.2.5)$$

$$\int \tan^n x\, dx = \frac{1}{n-1}\tan^{n-1} x - \int \tan^{n-2} x\, dx \qquad (6.2.6)$$

Table 6.2.4

NOTE 3: In Case (1) from Table 6.2.3 (the OT case of OTES) it is required that $n \geq 1$, i.e., there is at least one secant term in the integrand. When $n = 0$, then use the tangent reduction formula from the above table.

NOTE 4: The reduction formulas in the Table 6.2.4 require that $n \geq 2$. For $n = 1$, there is no need to reduce.

Example 6.2.7 (A non OTES case)

Problem: Compute $\displaystyle\int \sec x \tan^2 x\, dx$

Solution: First use the identity: $\tan^2 x = \sec^2 x - 1$, then the reduction formula:

$$\int \sec x \tan^2 x\, dx = \int \sec x \left(\sec^2 x - 1\right) dx = \int \left(\sec^3 x - \sec x\right) dx.$$

Now use a reduction formula for powers of the secant:

$$\int \sec^3 x\, dx - \int \sec x\, dx = \frac{1}{2} \sec x \tan x + \frac{1}{2} \int \sec x\, dx - \int \sec x\, dx$$

$$= \frac{1}{2} \sec x \tan x - \frac{1}{2} \int \sec x\, dx = \frac{1}{2} \sec x \tan x - \frac{1}{2} \ln\left(\sec x + \tan x\right) + C$$

<u>NOTE</u>: When the integrand contains several powers of the secant, use the reduction formula on the highest power first (in this case the 3rd power). This will give lower powers of the secant that can be combined with the other lower powers.

Example 6.2.8 (An Application to Finding Volumes)

Problem: The region below the graph of $f(x) = \tan^2 x \sec^2$ on the interval $[0, \pi/4]$ is revolved about the x-axis. Find the volume of the resulting solid of revolution.

Solution: Before computing the volume, we look at the graphs of the region and the solid. The following code plots the region.

```
> f:=x->(tan(x))^2*(sec(x))^2;
```
$$f := x \mapsto (\sec(x))^2 (\tan(x))^2$$
```
> plot(f(x),x=0..Pi/4,thickness=2,color=black,filled=[color=grey]);
```

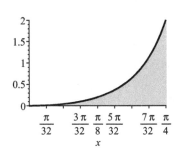

Figure 6.2.1: The graph of $f(x) = \tan^2 x \sec^2 x$ on the interval $[0, \frac{\pi}{4}]$.

To display the solid of revolution we use the special procedure `revolve1X` (Section 5.3) and cut away part of the solid to better exhibit the bounding curve $y = \tan x \sec x$.

```
> revolve1X(f,0,Pi/4,-Pi,Pi/2);
```

The computation of the volume uses the disk-method formula $V = \int_a^b \pi\, [f(x)]^2\, dx$ from Section 5.3. In this case the volume is

$$V = \int_0^{\frac{\pi}{4}} \pi \tan^4 x \sec^4 x\, dx.$$

This is the Even Secant (ES) case of OTES. So we can compute the integral by (1) using the substitution: $u = \tan x$, $du = \sec^2 x\, dx$, and (2) changing the limits of integration: when $x = 0$, $u = \tan(0) = 0$ and when $x = \pi/4$, $u = \tan(\pi/4) = 1$. This gives

$$
\begin{aligned}
V &= \int_0^{\frac{\pi}{4}} \pi \tan^4 x \sec^4 x\, dx = \int_0^{\frac{\pi}{4}} \pi \tan^4 x \sec^2 x \sec^2 x\, dx \\
&= \int_0^{\frac{\pi}{4}} \pi \tan^4 x \left(1 + \tan^2 x\right) \sec^2 x\, dx = \int_0^1 \pi u^4 \left(1 + u^2\right)\, du \\
&= \int_0^1 \pi \left(u^4 + u^6\right)\, du = \pi \left(\frac{1}{5} u^5 - \frac{1}{7} u^7\right)\Big|_0^1 = \frac{2\pi}{35}.
\end{aligned}
$$

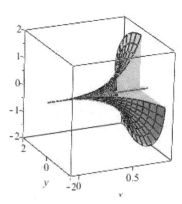

Figure 6.2.2: *The solid obtained by revolving the region below the graph of $f(x) = \tan^2 x \sec^2 x$ on the $[0, \pi/4]$ about the x-axis.*

Exercises: 6.2 (Trigonometric Integrals)

In Exercises 1–24, compute the given trigonometric integral.

1. $\int \sin^3 x \cos^2 x \, dx$

2. $\int \sin^2 x \cos^3 x \, dx$

3. $\int \sin^5 x \cos^4 x \, dx$

4. $\int \sin^4 x \cos^5 x \, dx$

5. $\int \sin^3 x \, dx$

6. $\int \cos^3 x \, dx$

7. $\int \sin^9 x \cos^3 x \, dx$

8. $\int \sin^3 x \cos^{15} x \, dx$

9. $\int \sin^4 x \cos^2 x \, dx$

10. $\int \sin^2 x \cos^4 x \, dx$

11. $\int \tan^3 x \sec x \, dx$

12. $\int \tan^3 x \sec^2 x \, dx$

13. $\int \tan^5 x \sec x \, dx$

14. $\int \tan^5 x \sec^2 x \, dx$

15. $\int \tan^3 x \sec^3 x \, dx$

16. $\int \tan^3 x \sec^7 x \, dx$

17. $\int \sec^4 x \tan^2 x \, dx$

18. $\int \sec^6 x \tan^2 x \, dx$

19. $\int \sec^8 x \tan^3 x \, dx$

20. $\int \sec^6 x \tan^3 x \, dx$

21. $\int \sec^3 x \, dx$

22. $\int \sec^5 x \, dx$

23. $\int \tan^2 x \sec^3 x \, dx$

24. $\int \tan^4 x \sec^3 x \, dx$

Trig Integrals with Negative & Fractional Powers

When integrating powers of sines and cosines or secants and tangents,

$$\int \sin^n x \cos^k x \, dx, \qquad \int \sec^n x \tan^k x \, dx,$$

we have been assuming that the powers are positive integers. When n or k is negative, or more generally, any real number, the trigonometric integral can often be evaluated by using the same techniques as those we have employed so far. Exercises 25–48 exhibit this for the OSOC and OTES cases.

25. $\int \dfrac{\sin^3 x}{\cos^2 x} \, dx$

26. $\int \dfrac{\cos^3 x}{\sin^2 x} \, dx$

27. $\int \dfrac{\sin^2 x}{\cos^2 x} \, dx$

28. $\int \dfrac{\cos^2 x}{\sin^2 x} \, dx$

29. $\int \dfrac{\sin^4 x}{\cos^2 x} \, dx$

30. $\int \dfrac{\cos^4 x}{\sin^2 x} \, dx$

31. $\int \dfrac{\cos^5 x}{\sin^4 x} \, dx$

32. $\int \dfrac{\cos^5 x}{\sin^2 x} \, dx$

33. $\int \dfrac{\sin^3 x}{\sqrt{\cos x}} \, dx$

34. $\int \cos^5 x \sin^{3/2} x \, dx$

35. $\int \dfrac{\sec^3 x}{\tan^4 x} \, dx$

36. $\int \dfrac{\tan^4 x}{\sec^3 x} \, dx$

37. $\int \dfrac{\sec^4 x}{\tan^4 x} \, dx$

38. $\int \dfrac{\sec^4 x}{\tan^6 x} \, dx$

39. $\int \dfrac{\tan^3 x}{\sec^3 x} \, dx$

40. $\int \dfrac{\tan^5 x}{\sec^5 x} \, dx$

41. $\int \dfrac{\tan^5 x}{\sec x} \, dx$

42. $\int \dfrac{\tan^5 x}{\sec^2 x} \, dx$

43. $\int \dfrac{\tan^4 x}{\sec^5 x} \, dx$

44. $\int \dfrac{\tan^4 x}{\sec^7 x} \, dx$

45. $\int \dfrac{\tan^2 x}{\sec^5 x} \, dx$

46. $\int \dfrac{\tan^2 x}{\sec^7 x} \, dx$

47. $\int \dfrac{1}{\sec x \tan^2 x} \, dx$

48. $\int \dfrac{1}{\sec x \tan^4 x} \, dx$

49. Show, in general, how integrals involving products of integer powers of sines and cosines can be computed using either u-substitutions or reduction formulas.

50. Show, in general, how integrals involving products of integer powers of secants and tangents can be reduced to integrals involving products of integer powers of sines and cosines. Thus, these integrals can be computed as shown in Exercise 49.

Reduction Formulas

51. Suppose n and k are nonnegative integers. Using integration by parts (and trig identities) derive the following Cosecant-Secant Reduction Formulas (CSRFs):

CSRF 1. $(k \geq 2)$

$\int \csc^n x \sec^k x \, dx$
$= \frac{1}{k-1} \csc^n x \sec^{k-2} x \tan x + \frac{n+k-2}{k-1} \int \csc^n x \sec^{k-2} x \, dx$

CSRF 2. $(n > 1)$

$\int \csc^n x \sec x \, dx$
$= -\frac{1}{n-1} \csc^{n-2} x \sec x \cot x + \frac{n-2}{n-1} \int \csc^{n-2} x \sec x \, dx$

CSRF 3. $(n > 1)$

$\int \csc^n x \, dx = -\frac{1}{n-1} \csc^{n-2} x \cot x + \frac{n-2}{n-1} \int \csc^{n-2} x$

52. Use a trig identity to show that

$$\int \csc x \sec x \, dx = -\ln (\csc 2x + \cot 2x) + C$$

This is the remaining case not covered by the reduction formula (CSRF 3) in Exercise 51.

Volumes: The graphs of the following functions on the given intervals are revolved about the x-axis to create solids of revolution. Find the volumes of these solids.

53. $f(x) = \sec^2 x$, $[0, \frac{\pi}{3}]$

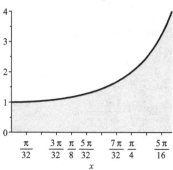

54. $f(x) = \csc^2 x$, $[\frac{\pi}{6}, \frac{\pi}{2}]$

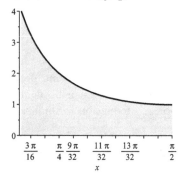

55. $f(x) = \sin^2 x$, $[0, \pi]$

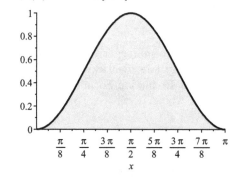

56. $f(x) = \cos^2 x$, $[0, \frac{\pi}{2}]$

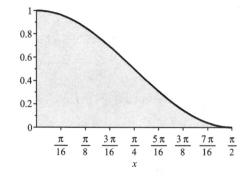

57. $f(x) = \tan^2 x$, $[0, \frac{\pi}{4}]$

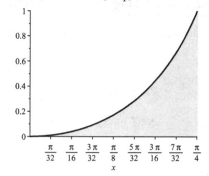

58. $f(x) = \cot^2 x$, $[\frac{\pi}{6}, \frac{\pi}{2}]$

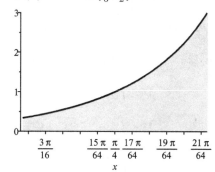

59. $f(x) = \sin^2 x \cos x$, $[0, \frac{\pi}{2}]$

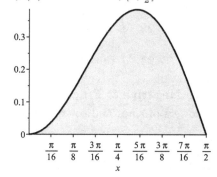

60. $f(x) = \sin x \cos^2 x$, $[0, \frac{\pi}{2}]$

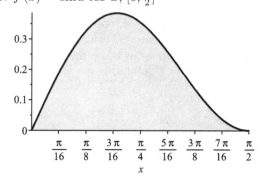

Calculus *Concepts & Computation*

6.3 Trigonometric Substitutions

The u-substitution method, or change of variables, is one of the most valuable techniques of integration. This section studies another change of variables method which involves trigonometric functions and, hence, is called the method of *trigonometric substitutions* (trig substitutions). If the integral you wish to compute is

$$\int f(x)\,dx, \qquad (6.3.1)$$

then the change of variables involves a new variable θ, which is related to the variable x by one of the three equations:

$$x = a\sin\theta, \quad x = a\tan\theta, \quad \text{or} \quad x = a\sec\theta. \qquad (6.3.2)$$

The choice of the constant a and the use of the sine or tangent or secant are determined by the particular problem. The relation between the differentials will be one of the following three:

$$dx = a\cos\theta\,d\theta, \quad dx = a\sec^2\theta\,d\theta, \quad \text{or} \quad dx = \sec\theta\tan\theta\,d\theta. \qquad (6.3.3)$$

For example, if we use the trig substitution $x = a\sin\theta$, then the integral in (6.3.1) becomes

$$\int f(x)\,dx = \int f(a\sin\theta)a\cos\theta\,d\theta.$$

While this new integral in terms of θ is generally more complicated, in the particular class of examples studied here it will simplify, using trigonometric identities, to a trigonometric integral of the type you encountered in the previous section.

Example 6.3.1 (A Secant Substitution)

Problem: Use a trig substitution to compute $\displaystyle\int \frac{1}{\sqrt{x^2-1}}\,dx$.

Solution: We are motivated to use a secant substitution because of the expression $x^2 - 1$ and the fact that

$$\sec^2\theta - 1 = \tan^2\theta$$

for all θ. Thus, letting

$$x = \sec\theta, \quad \text{we get} \quad dx = \sec\theta\tan\theta\,d\theta$$

and

$$x^2 - 1 = \sec^2\theta - 1 = \tan^2\theta.$$

Then the integral becomes

$$
\begin{aligned}
\int \frac{1}{\sqrt{x^2-1}}\,dx &= \int \frac{1}{\sqrt{\tan^2\theta}}\sec\theta\tan\theta\,d\theta = \int \frac{1}{\tan\theta}\sec\theta\tan\theta\,d\theta \\
&= \int \sec\theta\,d\theta = \ln|\sec\theta + \tan\theta| + C.
\end{aligned}
$$

Here we are assuming that $x = \sec\theta$ is larger than 1 (so that $\sqrt{x^2-1}$ is defined). For this, we assume that $0 < \theta < \pi/2$, which guarantees that $0 < \tan\theta$. To finish, we have to translate the expression in θ into an expression in x. From above we have

$$\sec\theta = x \quad \text{and} \quad \tan^2\theta = \sec^2\theta - 1 = x^2 - 1, \quad \text{i.e.,} \quad \tan\theta = \sqrt{x^2 - 1}.$$

So, the integral is

$$\int \frac{1}{\sqrt{x^2 - 1}}\,dx = \ln\left|x + \sqrt{x^2 - 1}\right| + C.$$

The most famous example of a trigonometric substitution is the following.

Example 6.3.2 (Application: The Circular Area Formula)

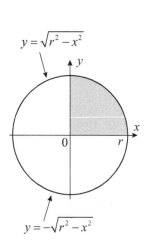

$y = \sqrt{r^2 - x^2}$

$y = -\sqrt{r^2 - x^2}$

Problem: Find the area A of the region enclosed by a circle of radius r.

Solution: Of course you remember from your early days in mathematics that the area is $A = \pi r^2$. This famous formula was derived several thousand years ago by Greek mathematicians using the *method of exhaustion*, which was the precursor to the calculus formulated by Newton and Leibniz in the sixteen hundreds. In this problem, let's see how calculus (and trig substitutions) can prove the validity of this result.

The circle of radius r and center at the origin has equation $x^2 + y^2 = r^2$. Solving for y gives explicitly two functions of x as shown in the margin figure.

Using the plus sign gives a function $f(x) = \sqrt{r^2 - x^2}$, defined on the interval $[-r, r]$, whose graph is a semicircle of radius r. The graph of f on $[0, r]$ is a quarter circle and so the area beneath this graph is one quarter of the area A of the whole circle. Hence,

$$A = 4\int_0^r \sqrt{r^2 - x^2}\,dx.$$

We compute the indefinite integral and then evaluate from 0 to r. For the indefinite integral we use the substitution:

$$x = r\sin\theta, \quad dx = r\cos\theta\,d\theta.$$

The motivation for the substitution is that

$$r^2 - x^2 = r^2 - r^2\sin^2\theta = r^2(1 - \sin^2\theta) = r^2\cos^2\theta.$$

Hence,

$$\sqrt{r^2 - x^2} = \sqrt{r^2\cos^2\theta} = r\cos\theta$$

This gives

$$\int \sqrt{r^2 - x^2}\,dx = \int r\cos\theta \cdot r\cos\theta\,d\theta = r^2\int \cos^2\theta\,d\theta.$$

Now all we have to do is to calculate the trig integral $\int \cos^2\theta\,d\theta$. This we did in Section 6.2 and found that the answer can be expressed in two ways as follows.

$$\int \cos^2\theta\,d\theta = \frac{1}{2}\theta + \frac{1}{4}\sin 2\theta + C = \frac{1}{2}\left(\theta + \sin\theta\cos\theta\right) + C.$$

The second way of expressing the answer is preferable because we have to now translate this expression in into an expression in x. For this, note that the substitution was

$$x = r\sin\theta.$$

Hence

$$\frac{x}{r} = \sin\theta, \quad \text{and} \quad \theta = \sin^{-1}\left(\frac{x}{r}\right).$$

Further, note that $\cos^2 \theta = 1 - \sin^2 \theta$, and thus for $0 \le \theta \le \frac{\pi}{2}$,

$$\cos \theta = \sqrt{1 - \sin^2 \theta} = \sqrt{1 - \frac{x^2}{r^2}} = \frac{\sqrt{r^2 - x^2}}{r}.$$

Putting all this in the answer above gives

$$\int \sqrt{r^2 - x^2}\, dx = r^2 \int \cos^2 \theta\, d\theta = \frac{r^2}{2} \left[\theta + \sin \theta \cos \theta \right] + C$$

$$= \frac{r^2}{2} \left[\sin^{-1} \left(\frac{x}{r} \right) + \frac{x}{r} \frac{\sqrt{r^2 - x^2}}{r} \right] + C.$$

Thus,

$$A = 4 \int_0^r \sqrt{r^2 - x^2}\, dx = 4 \cdot \frac{r^2}{2} \left[\sin^{-1} \left(\frac{x}{r} \right) + \frac{x}{r} \frac{\sqrt{r^2 - x^2}}{r} \right] \Bigg|_0^r$$

$$= 2r^2 \left[\sin^{-1}(1) - \sin^{-1}(0) + 0 - 0 \right] = 2r^2 \left[\frac{\pi}{2} - 0 + 0 - 0 \right]$$

$$= \pi r^2$$

This proves the validity of the famous area formula. The work also exhibits some of the typical parts involved in evaluating an integral using trig substitutions.

The above examples should help motivate the trig substitution technique. The technique is similar to that for u-substitutions, except the relation between the variable x and the new variable θ involves either the sine, tangent, or secant functions.

While you can use the trig substitution technique on any type of integral, there are three types of expressions that occur as integrands which usually will simplify by making such a substitution. These types are shown in the following Table.

Trigonometric Substitutions			
Expression	**Substitution**	**Differentials**	**Identity**
$a^2 - x^2$	$x = a \sin \theta$	$dx = a \cos \theta\, d\theta$	$a^2 - a^2 \sin^2 \theta = a^2 \cos^2 \theta$
$a^2 + x^2$	$x = a \tan \theta$	$dx = a \sec^2 \theta\, d\theta$	$a^2 + a^2 \tan^2 \theta = a^2 \sec^2 \theta$
$x^2 - a^2$	$x = a \sec \theta$	$dx = a \sec \theta \tan \theta\, d\theta$	$a^2 \sec^2 \theta - a^2 = a^2 \tan^2 \theta$

Table 6.3.1

After making one of these three substitutions, you must carefully rewrite the integrand in terms of the new variable θ. It is also important to remember to replace the differential dx by the appropriate expression from Table 6.3.1.

CAUTION: A common mistake is to replace dx by $d\theta$, which is wrong and can make the resulting integral either too easy or too difficult to compute.

Example 6.3.3

Problem: Compute the integral $\int x^3 \sqrt{9 - x^2}\, dx$

Solution: Because of the expression $9 - x^2$, we use the sine substitution from the table: $x = 3 \sin \theta$. The substitution on the differentials is $dx = 3 \cos \theta \, d\theta$. We will use the trig identity

$$9 - 9\sin^2\theta = 9(1 - \sin^2\theta) = 9\cos^2\theta$$

to simplify the integral:

$$
\begin{aligned}
\int x^3 \sqrt{9 - x^2} \, dx &= \int 27 \sin^3 \theta \sqrt{9 - 9\sin^2 \theta} \cdot 3 \cos \theta \, d\theta \\
&= \int 27 \sin^3 \theta \sqrt{9 \cos^2 \theta} \cdot 3 \cos \theta \, d\theta \\
&= \int 27 \sin^3 \theta \cdot 3 \cos \theta \cdot 3 \cos \theta \, d\theta = 243 \int \sin^3 \theta \cos^2 \theta \, d\theta
\end{aligned}
$$

The last integral above is a trig integral which has an odd power of the sine (The OS case of OSOC). We factor out a $\sin \theta$ term and put it with $d\theta$ and then make the substitution $u = \cos \theta$, so that $du = -\sin \theta \, d\theta$. The integral becomes

$$
\begin{aligned}
243 \int \sin^3 \theta \cos^2 \theta \, d\theta &= 243 \int \sin^2 \theta \cos^2 \theta \cdot \sin \theta \, d\theta \\
&= 243 \int \left(1 - \cos^2 \theta\right) \cos^2 \theta \cdot \sin \theta \, d\theta \\
&= 243 \int \left(1 - u^2\right) u^2 \left(-du\right) = 243 \int \left(u^4 - u^2\right) du \\
&= 243 \left(\frac{1}{5} u^5 - \frac{1}{3} u^3\right) + C \\
&= \frac{243}{5} \cos^5 \theta - 81 \cos^3 \theta + C. \qquad (6.3.4)
\end{aligned}
$$

Finally, we need to translate this back into an expression in x to get the answer. For this remember that $x = 3 \sin \theta$, so $\sin \theta = \dfrac{x}{3}$. But Eq, (6.3.4) involves $\cos \theta$ not $\sin \theta$, so we have to use

$$\cos^2 \theta = 1 - \sin^2 \theta = 1 - \frac{x^2}{9} = \frac{9 - x^2}{9}.$$

This gives

$$\cos \theta = \frac{(9 - x^2)^{1/2}}{3} \qquad (6.3.5)$$

Putting this in expression (6.3.4) above gives the following answer.

$$
\begin{aligned}
\int x^3 \sqrt{9 - x^2} \, dx &= \frac{243}{5} \frac{(9 - x^2)^{5/2}}{3^5} - 81 \cdot \frac{(9 - x^2)^{3/2}}{3^3} + C \\
&= \frac{1}{5} (9 - x^2)^{5/2} - 3 (9 - x^2)^{3/2} + C.
\end{aligned}
$$

<u>NOTE</u> 1: Some instructors will want you to factor the above answer.

<u>NOTE</u> 2: This problem and all other in this section can be worked using a u^2-substitution. See the discussion later in this section

The Triangle Technique

At the last step in the computation in Example 6.3.3, we had to rewrite the answer, expressed in terms of θ, as an expression in x. This amounted to determining what

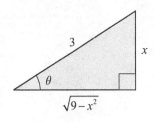

$\cos \theta$ is in terms of x, given that $\sin \theta = \frac{x}{3}$. The result was expression (6.3.5). There is a "triangle technique" for doing things like this. For Example 6.3.3 above, we draw a right triangle and label one of the (non-right) angles with θ as shown in the figure in the margin. Since $\sin \theta = \dfrac{x}{3} = \dfrac{opposite}{hypoteneuse}$, we label the side opposite with x and the hypotenuse with 3. Then by the Pythagorean theorem, the side adjacent to θ is $\sqrt{9 - x^2}$. With all the sides determined, you can now find the expression for any trig function of θ. In particular,

$$\cos \theta = \frac{adjacent}{hypoteneuse} = \frac{\sqrt{9 - x^2}}{3},$$

which is what we found in (6.3.5), using algebra.

In general, the triangle technique for the three respective trig substitutions is shown in the margin boxes.

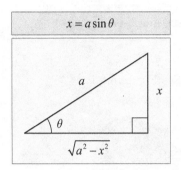

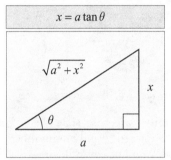

Example 6.3.4

Problem: Calculate $\displaystyle\int \frac{\sqrt{25 + x^2}}{x^4}\, dx$.

Solution: Because of the expression $25 + x^2$, the appropriate trig substitution is $x = 5 \tan \theta$, with $dx = 5 \sec^2 \theta\, d\theta$. Then

$$\sqrt{25 + x^2} = \sqrt{25 + 25 \tan^2 \theta} = \sqrt{25 \left(1 + \tan^2 \theta\right)} = \sqrt{25 \sec^2 \theta} = 5 \sec \theta,$$

and the integral becomes

$$\begin{aligned} I &= \int \frac{\sqrt{25 + x^2}}{x^4}\, dx = \int \frac{5 \sec \theta}{625 \tan^4 \theta} \cdot 5 \sec^2 \theta\, d\theta = \frac{1}{25} \int \frac{\sec^3 \theta}{\tan^4 \theta}\, d\theta \\ &= \frac{1}{25} \int \frac{\frac{1}{\cos^3 \theta}}{\frac{\sin^4 \theta}{\cos^4 \theta}}\, d\theta = \frac{1}{25} \int \frac{1}{\cos^3 \theta} \cdot \frac{\cos^4 \theta}{\sin^4 \theta}\, d\theta = \frac{1}{25} \int \frac{\cos \theta}{\sin^4 \theta}\, d\theta \end{aligned}$$

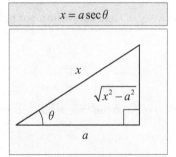

This is a OC (odd cosine) case of OSOC for an integral of powers of sine and cosine. So, we use the u-substitution:

$$u = \sin \theta, \ du = \cos \theta\, d\theta$$

Then

$$\begin{aligned} I &= \frac{1}{25} \int \frac{1}{\sin^4 \theta} \cdot \cos \theta\, d\theta = \frac{1}{25} \int \frac{1}{u^4}\, du = \frac{1}{25} \int u^{-4} du \\ &= \frac{1}{25} \left(-\frac{1}{3} u^{-3} \right) + C = -\frac{1}{75} \cdot \frac{1}{u^3} + C = -\frac{1}{75} \frac{1}{\sin^3 \theta} + C \end{aligned} \qquad (6.3.6)$$

Box 6.3.1: *Triangles for the three types of trigonometric substitutions*

To translate this into an expression in x, we use the original relation between the variables: $x = 5 \tan \theta$, or equivalently

$$\tan \theta = \frac{x}{5} = \frac{opposite}{adjacent}.$$

We draw the triangle shown in the margin and get that

$$\frac{1}{\sin \theta} = \csc \theta = \frac{hypotenuse}{opposite} = \frac{\sqrt{25 + x^2}}{x} = \frac{\left(25 + x^2\right)^{1/2}}{x}.$$

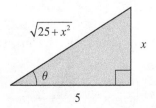

Using this to rewrite (6.3.6), we get the following answer

$$\int \frac{\sqrt{25 + x^2}}{x^4} \, dx = -\frac{1}{75} \frac{\left(25 + x^2\right)^{3/2}}{x^3} + C$$

Example 6.3.5 (Candy Kisses)

Problem: Hershey's candy company, for an upcoming banquet, plans to make 20 giant replicas of its famous candy kisses. The secret formula for a candy kiss's shape is that it is the solid obtained by revolving the graph of

$$f(x) = x \left(1 - x^2\right)^{1/4}, \ 0 \le x \le 1,$$

about the x-axis. Here the units for x are inches. See Figure 6.3.1.

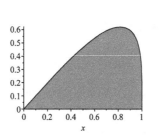
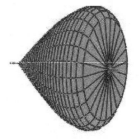

Figure 6.3.1: *A Candy kiss obtained as a solid of revolution.*

To get the giant replica, the company changes the units to feet, so that it is a foot high when placed on a banquet table with its point upward. Find the number of gallons of chocolate that must be melted to form the 20 giant candy kisses.

Solution: Using the volume formula from Chapter 5, we get that the volume of one giant candy kiss is

$$V = \int_a^b \pi \left[f(x)\right]^2 dx = \int_0^1 \pi \left[x \left(1 - x^2\right)^{1/4}\right]^2 dx = \int_0^1 \pi x^2 \left(1 - x^2\right)^{1/2} dx$$

To compute the indefinite integral $\int x^2 \left(1 - x^2\right)^{1/2} dx$ we make the trig substitution:

$$x = \sin\theta, \ dx = \cos\theta \, d\theta.$$

Then we get the trig integral

$$\int x^2 \left(1 - x^2\right)^{1/2} dx = \int \sin^2\theta \cos\theta \cdot \cos\theta d\theta = \int \sin^2\theta \cos^2\theta d\theta$$

The trig integral here is a non-OSOC case. We did this particular one in Example 6.2.3, so we use that result here:

$$\begin{aligned}
\int \sin^2\theta \cos^2\theta d\theta &= \frac{1}{4}\sin^3\theta \cos\theta - \frac{1}{8}\sin\theta \cos\theta + \frac{1}{8}\theta + C \\
&= \frac{1}{4}x^3 \left(1 - x^2\right)^{1/2} - \frac{1}{8}x \left(1 - x^2\right)^{1/2} + \frac{1}{8}\sin^{-1}x + C
\end{aligned}$$

Here we have used $x = \sin\theta$ and $\cos\theta = \sqrt{1 - \sin^2\theta} = (1 - x^2)^{1/2}$. Thus, the volume is

$$V = \pi \left[\frac{1}{4}x^3(1 - x^2)^{1/2} - \frac{1}{8}x(1 - x^2)^{1/2} + \frac{1}{8}\sin^{-1}x\right] \Big|_0^1 = \frac{\pi}{8}\sin^{-1}(1) = \frac{\pi^2}{16} \text{ ft}^3$$

To convert this to gallons, we use the fact that 1 gallon $= 231$ in$^3 = 231 \left(\frac{1}{12}\right)^3$ ft^3. Then

$$V = \frac{\pi^2}{16} \left(\frac{12^3}{231}\right) \approx 4.61 \text{ gallons}$$

Thus, for 20 candy kisses Hershey's needs to prepare $20(4.61) = 92.2$ gallons of chocolate.

An Alternative Method

The essential feature of trig substitutions is that they rationalize the integrands of the four types of integrals to which they apply. These four types are

$$\text{(a)} \int x^n R^k \, dx \quad \text{(b)} \int \frac{x^n}{R^k} \, dx \quad \text{(c)} \int \frac{R^k}{x^n} \, dx, \quad \text{(d)} \int \frac{1}{x^n R^k} \, dx$$

where $n \geq 0, k > 0$ are integers, k is odd, and

$$R = (a^2 - x^2)^{1/2}, \quad \text{or} \quad R = (a^2 + x^2)^{1/2}, \quad \text{or} \quad R = (x^2 - a^2)^{1/2}$$

Trig substitutions, as you have seen, turn these types of integrals into trig integrals, which can be computed by the methods of Section 6.2.

There is an alternative method to trig substitutions which will also rationalize these four types of integrals and, conveniently, does not involve trig functions. This method, called u^2–*substitutions*, is often quicker and easier to use than trig substitutions. The following table shows you what substitution to make in each of the cases

u^2- substitutions			
n odd	$u^2 = a^2 - x^2$	$u^2 = a^2 + x^2$	$u^2 = x^2 - a^2$
n even	$u^2 = \dfrac{a^2 - x^2}{x^2}$	$u^2 = \dfrac{a^2 + x^2}{x^2}$	$u^2 = \dfrac{x^2 - a^2}{x^2}$

Table 6.3.2

Note that the form of the u^2–substitution depends on whether the integer n is even or odd. Regardless of the form involved, you should use the equation relating u^2 and x^2 to (1) compute the relation between the differentials du and dx and (2) rewrite, using these relations, the given integral entirely in terms of u.

The easier case is when n is odd, so we present two examples of this first.

Example 6.3.6 (n odd)

Problem: Compute the integral $\int x^3 \sqrt{9 - x^2} \, dx$

Solution: Because of the expression $9 - x^2$, we use the following substitution from the table:

$$u^2 = 9 - x^2, \quad \text{so that} \quad 2u \, du = -2x \, dx, \quad \text{i.e.,} \quad -\frac{u}{x} \, du = dx$$

Note also that $x^2 = 9 - u^2$. Then

$$\begin{aligned} \int x^3 \sqrt{9 - x^2} \, dx &= \int x^3 u \left(-\frac{u}{x} \, du\right) = -\int x^2 u^2 \, du = -\int (9 - u^2) u^2 \, du \\ &= \int (u^4 - 9u^2) \, du = \frac{1}{5} u^5 - \frac{9}{3} u^3 + C \\ &= \frac{1}{5}(9 - x^2)^{5/2} - 3(9 - x^2)^{3/2} + C \end{aligned}$$

Compare this with the trig substitution method used in Example 6.3.3 on the same integral.

Example 6.3.7 (n **odd**)

Problem: Compute the integral $\displaystyle\int \frac{x^3}{(4-x^2)^{5/2}}\,dx$

Solution: Because of the expression $4-x^2$, we use the following substitution from the table:

$$u^2 = 4 - x^2, \quad \text{so that} \quad u\,du = -x\,dx, \quad \text{i.e.,} \quad -\frac{u}{x}\,du = dx$$

Note that $x^2 = 4 - u^2$. Then

$$
\begin{aligned}
\int \frac{x^3}{(4-x^2)^{5/2}}\,dx &= \int \frac{x^3}{u^5}\left(-\frac{u}{x}\,du\right) = -\int \frac{x^2}{u^4}\,du = -\int \frac{4-u^2}{u^4}\,du \\
&= \int (u^{-2} - 4u^{-4})\,du = -u^{-1} + \frac{4}{3}u^{-3} + C \\
&= -\frac{1}{(4-x^2)^{1/2}} + \frac{4}{3(4-x^2)^{3/2}} + C
\end{aligned}
$$

The case when n is even is a little bit more complicated but works in a similar way.

Example 6.3.8 (n **even**)

Problem: Compute the integral $\displaystyle\int \frac{(16-x^2)^{1/2}}{x^4}\,dx$

Solution: Because of the expression $16-x^2$, we use the following substitution from the table:

$$u^2 = \frac{16-x^2}{x^2} = 16x^{-2} - 1, \quad \text{so that} \quad 2u\,du = -32x^{-3}\,dx \quad \text{i.e.,} \quad -\frac{1}{16}x^3 u\,du = dx$$

From the first equation above, we get: $x^2 u^2 = 16 - x^2$. Then

$$
\begin{aligned}
\int \frac{(16-x^2)^{1/2}}{x^4}\,dx &= \int \frac{xu}{x^4}\left(-\frac{x^3 u}{16}\,du\right) = -\frac{1}{16}\int u^2\,du \\
&= -\frac{1}{48}u^3 + C = -\frac{1}{48}\cdot\frac{(16-x^2)^{3/2}}{x^3} + C
\end{aligned}
$$

We should mention that when using u^2–substitutions on certain integrals, it will be necessary to employ a reduction formula on the resulting integral in u. (See the exercises for the appropriate reduction formulas.) This is similar to what happens with trig substitutions when the resulting trig integral is a non-OSOC or a non-OTES case.

Exercises: 6.3 (Trigonometric Substitutions)

In Exercises 1–50, use the appropriate trigonometric substitution to compute the given integrals.

1. $\displaystyle\int x^3\sqrt{4-x^2}\,dx$

2. $\displaystyle\int x^5\sqrt{4-x^2}\,dx$

3. $\displaystyle\int \frac{x^3}{\sqrt{4+x^2}}\,dx$

4. $\displaystyle\int \frac{x^5}{\sqrt{4+x^2}}\,dx$

5. $\displaystyle\int x^3\left(x^2-1\right)^{3/2}dx$

6. $\displaystyle\int x^5\left(x^2-1\right)^{3/2}dx$

7. $\displaystyle\int \frac{1}{\left(25-x^2\right)^{3/2}}\,dx$

8. $\displaystyle\int \frac{1}{\left(25-x^2\right)^{5/2}}\,dx$

9. $\displaystyle\int \frac{\sqrt{x^2-9}}{x^4}\,dx$

10. $\displaystyle\int \frac{\sqrt{x^2-4}}{x^4}\,dx$

11. $\displaystyle\int \frac{x^2}{\left(x^2-9\right)^{5/2}}\,dx$

12. $\displaystyle\int \frac{x^2}{\left(x^2-9\right)^{7/2}}\,dx$

13. $\displaystyle\int x^2\sqrt{9-x^2}\,dx$

14. $\displaystyle\int x^4\sqrt{9-x^2}\,dx$

15. $\displaystyle\int \frac{1}{x^2\left(1+x^2\right)^{3/2}}\,dx$

16. $\displaystyle\int \frac{1}{x^2\left(x+x^2\right)^{3/2}}\,dx$

17. $\displaystyle\int \frac{\left(4+x^2\right)^{3/2}}{x^6}\,dx$

18. $\displaystyle\int \frac{\left(9+x^2\right)^{3/2}}{x^6}\,dx$

19. $\displaystyle\int \frac{x^3}{\left(9+x^2\right)^{5/2}}\,dx$

20. $\displaystyle\int \frac{x^2}{\left(9+x^2\right)^{5/2}}\,dx$

21. $\displaystyle\int \frac{x^5}{\left(4+x^2\right)^{3/2}}\,dx$

22. $\displaystyle\int \frac{x^3}{\left(4+x^2\right)^{3/2}}\,dx$

23. $\displaystyle\int \frac{x^2}{\left(16-x^2\right)^{3/2}}\,dx$

24. $\displaystyle\int \frac{x^4}{\left(16-x^2\right)^{3/2}}\,dx$

25. $\displaystyle\int \frac{\left(1+x^2\right)^{1/2}}{x^6}\,dx$

26. $\displaystyle\int \frac{\left(4+x^2\right)^{1/2}}{x^6}\,dx$

27. $\displaystyle\int \frac{\left(1+x^2\right)^{1/2}}{x^8}\,dx$

28. $\displaystyle\int \frac{\left(4+x^2\right)^{1/2}}{x^8}\,dx$

29. $\displaystyle\int x^2\sqrt{25+x^2}\,dx$

30. $\displaystyle\int x^4\sqrt{25+x^2}\,dx$

31. $\displaystyle\int \frac{x^2}{\sqrt{x^2-4}}\,dx$

32. $\displaystyle\int \frac{x^3}{\sqrt{x^2-4}}\,dx$

33. $\displaystyle\int \frac{1}{x^2\left(x^2-25\right)^{3/2}}\,dx$

34. $\displaystyle\int \frac{1}{x^3\left(x^2-1\right)^{3/2}}\,dx$

35. $\displaystyle\int \frac{1}{x^2\left(1-x^2\right)^{5/2}}\,dx$

36. $\displaystyle\int \frac{1}{x^4\left(1-x^2\right)^{5/2}}\,dx$

37. $\displaystyle\int \frac{1}{x^5\left(x^2-4\right)^{3/2}}\,dx$

38. $\displaystyle\int \frac{1}{x^5\left(x^2-9\right)^{3/2}}\,dx$

39. $\displaystyle\int \frac{1}{x\left(x^2-25\right)}\,dx$

40. $\displaystyle\int \frac{1}{x^2\left(x^2-25\right)}\,dx$

41. $\displaystyle\int \frac{1}{x^2\left(x^2-9\right)^{5/2}}\,dx$

42. $\displaystyle\int \frac{1}{x\left(x^2-9\right)^{5/2}}\,dx$

43. $\displaystyle\int x^3\sqrt{x^2-4}\,dx$

44. $\displaystyle\int x^5\sqrt{x^2-4}\,dx$

45. $\displaystyle\int \frac{\sqrt{4-x^2}}{x^2}\,dx$

46. $\displaystyle\int \frac{\left(4-x^2\right)^{3/2}}{x^2}\,dx$

47. $\displaystyle\int \frac{\left(x^2-1\right)^{3/2}}{x^6}\,dx$

48. $\displaystyle\int \frac{\left(x^2-1\right)^{3/2}}{x^8}\,dx$

49. $\displaystyle\int \frac{\sqrt{x^2-1}}{x^6}\,dx$

50. $\displaystyle\int \frac{\sqrt{x^2-1}}{x^8}\,dx$

In Exercises 51–74, the integrals are some standard expressions involving a^2-x^2, a^2+x^2, x^2-a^2, which often occur in applications. (Cf. Examples 6.3.1–6.3.2.) Use trigonometric substitutions to compute these integrals.

51. $\displaystyle\int \sqrt{1-x^2}\,dx$

52. $\displaystyle\int \sqrt{a^2-x^2}\,dx$

53. $\displaystyle\int \sqrt{1+x^2}\,dx$

54. $\displaystyle\int \sqrt{a^2+x^2}\,dx$

55. $\displaystyle\int \sqrt{x^2-1}\,dx$

56. $\displaystyle\int \sqrt{x^2-a^2}\,dx$

57. $\displaystyle\int \frac{1}{\sqrt{1-x^2}}\,dx$

58. $\displaystyle\int \frac{1}{\sqrt{a^2-x^2}}\,dx$

59. $\displaystyle\int \frac{1}{\sqrt{1+x^2}}\,dx$

60. $\displaystyle\int \frac{1}{\sqrt{a^2+x^2}}\,dx$

61. $\displaystyle\int \frac{1}{\sqrt{x^2-1}}\,dx$

62. $\displaystyle\int \frac{1}{\sqrt{x^2-a^2}}\,dx$

63. $\displaystyle\int \frac{1}{x\sqrt{1-x^2}}\,dx$

64. $\displaystyle\int \frac{1}{x\sqrt{a^2-x^2}}\,dx$

65. $\displaystyle\int \frac{1}{x\sqrt{1+x^2}}\,dx$

66. $\displaystyle\int \frac{1}{x\sqrt{a^2+x^2}}\,dx$

67. $\displaystyle\int \frac{1}{x\sqrt{x^2-1}}\,dx$

68. $\displaystyle\int \frac{1}{x\sqrt{x^2-a^2}}\,dx$

69. $\displaystyle\int \frac{\sqrt{1-x^2}}{x}\,dx$

70. $\displaystyle\int \frac{\sqrt{a^2-x^2}}{x}\,dx$

71. $\displaystyle\int \frac{\sqrt{1+x^2}}{x}\,dx$

72. $\displaystyle\int \frac{\sqrt{a^2+x^2}}{x}\,dx$

73. $\displaystyle\int \frac{\sqrt{x^2-1}}{x}\,dx$

74. $\displaystyle\int \frac{\sqrt{x^2-a^2}}{x}\,dx$

Applications

75. (Areas Bounded by Hyperpolas) Find the area enclosed by the graphs of the curves

$$y^2 - x^2 = 1,\ x = 0,\ x = 1.$$

The first curve is an hyperbola.

76. (Areas Bounded by Hyperbolas) Find the area enclosed by the graph of the curves

$$x^2 - y^2 = 1, \ x = 1, \ x = 2.$$

The first curve is an hyperbola.

77. (Volumes by the Shell Method) Find the volume of the solid generated by revolving the region D beneath the graph of

$$f(x) = x \sin^{-1} x, \ 0 \le x \le 1,$$

about the y-axis. *Hint*: Integrate by parts first and then do a trig substitution.

78. (Volumes by the Shell Method) Find the volume of the solid generated by revolving the region D beneath the graph of

$$f(x) = x \cos^{-1} x, \ 0 \le x \le 1,$$

about the y-axis. *Hint*: Integrate by parts first and then do a trig substitution.

79. (Centroids) Suppose the region D in Exercise 77 is a homogeneous lamina. Calculate the coordinates of its centroid.

80. (Centroids) Suppose the region D in Exercise 78 is a homogeneous lamina. Calculate the coordinates of its centroid

81. (u²–Substitutions) Derive the following reduction formulas. For $p > 1$ an integer and s any number:

$$(1) \int \frac{u^s}{(1+u^2)^p} \, du =$$

$$\frac{-1}{2(p-1)} \cdot \frac{u^{s-1}}{(1+u^2)^{p-1}} + \frac{s-1}{2(p-1)} \int \frac{u^{s-2}}{(1+u^2)^{p-1}} \, du$$

$$(2) \int \frac{u^s}{(1-u^2)^p} \, du =$$

$$\frac{1}{2(p-1)} \cdot \frac{u^{s-1}}{(1-u^2)^{p-1}} - \frac{s-1}{2(p-1)} \int \frac{u^{s-2}}{(1-u^2)^{p-1}} \, du$$

$$(3) \int \frac{u^s}{(u^2-1)^p} \, du =$$

$$\frac{-1}{2(p-1)} \cdot \frac{u^{s-1}}{(u^2-1)^{p-1}} + \frac{s-1}{2(p-1)} \int \frac{u^{s-2}}{(u^2-1)^{p-1}} \, du$$

Hint: Use integration by Parts. Also show that for $a > 0$, each of the integrals:

$$(i) \int \frac{w^s}{(a^2+w^2)^p} \, dw \quad (ii) \int \frac{w^s}{(a^2-w^2)^p} \, dw$$

$$(iii) \int \frac{w^s}{(w^2-a^2)^p} \, dw$$

can, by the substitution $w = au$, be transformed into a multiple, a^{s-2p+1}, of the corresponding integral (1), (2), or (3) on the left sides of the above reduction formulas. Thus, we do not need separate reduction formulas for integrals (i), (ii), and (iii).

82. (u²–Substitutions) For each of the reduction formulas (1), (2), and (3) in Exercise 81, show that if we start with s and even integer (positive, negative, or 0) and $p > 1$ an integer, then repeated use of the formula will eventually give a similar integral with $p = 1$ and $s = 2m$ still even. If is s is nonnegative then we can use long division to compute this integral and if s is negative then we can use one of the following identities to to compute this integral:

$$(A) \quad \frac{1}{u^{2m}(1+u^2)} =$$

$$\frac{1}{u^{2m}} - \frac{1}{u^{2m-2}} + \cdots + (-1)^{m-1} \frac{1}{u^2} + (-1)^m \frac{1}{1+u^2}$$

$$(B) \quad \frac{1}{u^{2m}(1-u^2)} = \frac{1}{u^{2m}} + \frac{1}{u^{2m-2}} + \cdots + \frac{1}{u^2} + \frac{1}{1-u^2}$$

(Using u²–Substitutions) Make u^2–substitutions to compute the following integrals.

$$83. \int x^3 \left(4 - x^2\right)^{5/2} \, dx \qquad 84. \int x^3 \left(4 - x^2\right)^{3/2} \, dx$$

$$85. \int x^5 \left(x^2 - 9\right)^{3/2} \, dx \qquad 86. \int x^5 \left(x^2 - 9\right)^{7/2} \, dx$$

$$87. \int \frac{x^3}{(9 + x^2)^{5/2}} \, dx \qquad 88. \int \frac{x^3}{(9 + x^2)^{7/2}} \, dx$$

$$89. \int \frac{x^2}{(25 - x^2)^{5/2}} \, dx \qquad 90. \int \frac{x^4}{(16 - x^2)^{7/2}} \, dx$$

$$91. \int \frac{1}{x^2 \left(4 - x^2\right)^{3/2}} \, dx \qquad 92. \int \frac{1}{x^2 \left(9 - x^2\right)^{3/2}} \, dx$$

$$93. \int \frac{1}{x^4 \left(16 + x^2\right)^{3/2}} \, dx \qquad 94. \int \frac{1}{x^4 \left(9 + x^2\right)^{3/2}} \, dx$$

$$95. \int \frac{\left(4 + x^2\right)^{3/2}}{x^6} \, dx \qquad 96. \int \frac{\left(9 + x^2\right)^{5/2}}{x^8} \, dx$$

$$97. \int \frac{1}{x \left(x^2 - 1\right)^{3/2}} \, dx \qquad 98. \int \frac{1}{x \left(1 - x^2\right)^{5/2}} \, dx$$

$$99. \int \frac{1}{x^3 \left(x^2 - 1\right)^{3/2}} \, dx \qquad 100. \int \frac{1}{x^3 \left(1 - x^2\right)^{5/2}} \, dx$$

$$101. \int \frac{1}{x \left(4 - x^2\right)^{3/2}} \, dx \qquad 102. \int \frac{1}{x \left(9 - x^2\right)^{5/2}} \, dx$$

$$103. \int \frac{1}{\sqrt{x^2 - 1}} \, dx \qquad 104. \int \frac{1}{\sqrt{x^2 - 4}} \, dx$$

$$105. \int \frac{1}{x\sqrt{x^2 - 1}} \, dx \qquad 106. \int \frac{1}{x\sqrt{x^2 - 4}} \, dx$$

Calculus *Concepts & Computation*

6.4 Partial Fractions

In this section we consider an integration technique that, in theory, will enable us to integrate any rational function. Recall that a rational function R is the quotient (or ratio) of two polynomial functions:

$$R(x) = \frac{N(x)}{D(x)} \qquad (6.4.1)$$

Here $N(x)$ and $D(x)$ are general polynomials

$$N(x) = a_n x^n + a_{n-1} x^{n-1} + \cdots + a_2 x^2 + a_1 x + a_0, \qquad (6.4.2)$$
$$D(x) = b_k x^k + b_{k-1} x^{k-1} + \cdots + b_2 x^2 + b_1 x + b_0, \qquad (6.4.3)$$

of degrees n and k (notation: $\deg(N(x)) = n$, $\deg(D(x)) = k$). Thus, the integration technique, called *partial fraction decomposition* (or just *partial fractions*) gives a means of computing integrals of the type

$$\int R(x)\, dx = \int \frac{N(x)}{D(x)}\, dx$$

To motivate the partial fraction decomposition technique, we consider the several examples.

Example 6.4.1

From your work with adding fractions in algebra you can easily verify that

$$\frac{2}{x-1} + \frac{3}{x+2} = \frac{5x+1}{(x-1)(x+2)} = \frac{5x+1}{x^2+x-2} \qquad (6.4.4)$$

Having this enables us to easily do the following.

Problem: Compute the integral $\int \dfrac{5x+1}{x^2+x-2}\, dx$.

Solution: The integrand is a rational function which, according to Eq. (6.4.4) splits into the sum of two rational functions $\frac{2}{x-1}$ and $\frac{3}{x+2}$ (called partial fractions since their sum yields the total fraction we started with). The integral is easily computed:

$$\int \frac{5x+1}{x^2+x-2}\, dx = \int \left(\frac{2}{x-1} + \frac{3}{x+2}\right) dx = \int \frac{2}{x-1}\, dx + \int \frac{3}{x+2}\, dx$$

$$= 2\ln|x-1| + 3\ln|x+2| + C.$$

In essence, the partial fraction decomposition technique consists of taking a rational function, such as $\frac{5x+1}{x^2+x-2}$, and decomposing it into a sum of simpler partial fractions, in this case, $\frac{2}{x-1}$ and $\frac{3}{x+2}$. You can understand the motivation for the technique if you read Eq. (6.4.4) backwards (from right-to-left). Start with $\frac{5x+1}{x^2+x-2}$ and factor the denominator $x^2+x-2 = (x-1)(x+2)$. Then the partial fraction decomposition will have the form

$$\frac{A}{x-1} + \frac{B}{x+2}$$

for some numbers A and B. The technique guarantees the existence of A and B and simple algebra allows us to determine that $A = 2$, $B = 3$

The above example illustrates one of the algebraic methods involved in the partial fractions technique, namely factoring. The factorization

$$x^2 + x - 2 = (x - 1)(x + 2)$$

of the denominator determines the denominators of the partial fractions. This is a crucial step in the technique. Another method employed in the technique is long division of polynomials. The following example shows how this occurs.

Example 6.4.2 (Improper Rational Functions)

Problem: Compute the integral $\displaystyle\int \frac{x^3 - 2x^2 + 7}{x^2 + x - 2}\,dx$

Solution: This problem is related to the last. But here the integrand is a rational function which is *improper*, i.e., the degree of its numerator is NOT less than the degree of its denominator (in this case, 3 is not less than 2). Using long division we can divide $N(x) = x^3 - 2\,x^2 + 7$ by $D(x) = x^2 + x - 2$ and a get a quotient $q(x)$ of degree $3 - 2 = 1$ and a remainder $r(x)$ which has degree strictly less than 2 (Thus, $\deg(r(x)) = 1$ or 0). In general

$$\frac{N(x)}{D(x)} = q(x) + \frac{r(x)}{D(x)},$$

with $\deg(r(x)) < \deg(D(x))$. In this example, long division gives

$$\frac{x^3 - 2x^2 + 7}{x^2 + x - 2} = x - 3 + \frac{5x + 1}{x^2 + x - 2}.$$

(Verify this!) Now we can do the integral (easily, since we can use the work in Example 6.4.1):

$$\int \frac{x^3 - 2x^2 + 7}{x^2 + x - 2}\,dx \;=\; \int \left(x - 3 + \frac{5x + 1}{x^2 + x - 2} \right) dx$$

$$=\; \frac{1}{2}x^2 - 3x + 2\ln|x - 1| + 3\ln|x + 2| + C.$$

The examples above illustrate two components of the partial fractions technique: *factoring* and *long division*. By far, the process of factoring can be the most difficult. We recall some of the basics.

A quadratic polynomial $p(x) = ax^2 + bx + c$ can often be factored into the product of two linear factors. For example,

$$p(x) = 2x^2 - 5x - 3 = (2x + 1)(x - 3).$$

The factorization involves a trial-and-error technique. When factoring a quadratic polynomial, it can also happen that the two linear factors are the same (repeated twice). For example,

$$p(x) = x^2 + 2x + 1 = (x + 1)(x + 1) = (x + 1)^2.$$

Also note that a quadratic polynomial $p(x)$ factors into a product of linear factors using real numbers if and only if the roots of $p(x) = 0$ are real numbers. If a quadratic polynomial *cannot* be factored into a product of linear factors (using real numbers), then it is called an *irreducible quadratic factor*. For example,

$$p(x) = x^2 + 2x + 5,$$

does not factor using real numbers, since the roots of $x^2 + 2x + 5 = 0$ are $x = -1 \pm 2i$. Thus, $x^2 + 2x + 5$ is irreducible.

This distinction between reducible (i.e., factorizable over the real number system) and irreducible quadratic polynomials is important when factoring polynomials of higher degree. For example, the following sixth degree polynomial factors as a product of four linear factors (one of which is repeated twice) and one irreducible quadratic factor:

$$
\begin{aligned}
p(x) &= 2x^6 + 3x^5 - 3x^4 - 38x^3 - 80x^2 - 61x - 15 \\
&= (2x+1)(x-3)(x+1)^2(x^2+2x+5)
\end{aligned}
$$

NOTE: The actual factorization of this $p(x)$ would take awhile to do by hand. Usually the ones you will have to do by hand will be simpler than this.

As this last example may indicates, any polynomial with real number coefficients can be factored completely as a product of linear factors (some of which may be repeated) and irreducible quadratic factors (some of which may be repeated). This result is called the factorization theorem.

Factorization Theorem

Suppose

$$p(x) = a_n x^n + a_{n-1} x^{n-1} + \cdots + a_2 x^2 + a_1 x + a_0 \qquad (6.4.5)$$

is a polynomial with coefficients $a_n, a_{n-1}, \ldots, a_2, a_1, a_0$ *that are*

real numbers. Then p(x) factors as the product of linear factors

and irreducible quadratic factors:

$$p(x) = \underbrace{(b_1 x + c_1)^{m_1} \cdots (b_r x + c_r)^{m_r}}_{\text{linear factors}} \underbrace{(d_1 x^2 + e_1 x + f_1)^{k_1} \cdots (d_s x^2 + e_s x + f_s)^{k_s}}_{\text{irreducible quadratic factors}} \qquad (6.4.6)$$

In the theorem, the powers $m_1, \ldots, m_r, k_1, \ldots, k_s$ on the linear and irreducible quadratic factors indicate the number of times those factors appear in the total factorization of $p(x)$. These numbers are commonly called the *multiplicity*, or number of *repeats*, of the factor. For example, suppose a polynomial $p(x)$ factors as

$$p(x) = (3x+5)^2 (x-1)^4 (4x^2 + 4x + 5)^3 (x^2 + 1).$$

Then the linear factor $3x + 5$ is repeated twice ($m = 2$), the linear factor $x - 1$ is repeated four times ($m = 4$), the irreducible quadratic factor $4x^2 + 4x + 5$ is repeated three times ($k = 3$), and the irreducible quadratic factor $x^2 + 1$ is repeated once ($k = 1$).

The next two examples show how to handle irreducible quadratic factors when they occur in an integral.

Example 6.4.3 (Two Term Irreducible Quadratics)

The simplest type of irreducible quadratic is one where the x term is missing. For example: $x^2 + 4$. This is irreducible since the roots of $x^2 + 4 = 0$ are $x = \pm 2i$. Two simple integrals involving this as a denominator are:

Problem: Compute the integrals (a) $\displaystyle\int \frac{x}{x^2 + 4}\, dx$ (b) $\displaystyle\int \frac{1}{x^2 + 4}\, dx$.

Solution (a): Use a u-substitution $u = x^2 + 4$, $du = 2x\, dx$, to get

$$\int \frac{x}{x^2 + 4}\, dx = \int \frac{1}{u} \cdot \frac{1}{2}\, du = \frac{1}{2} \ln |u| + C = \frac{1}{2} \ln \left(x^2 + 4\right) + C.$$

Solution (b): This is a basic integral

$$\int \frac{1}{x^2 + 4}\, dx = \frac{1}{2} \tan^{-1} \left(\frac{x}{2}\right) + C.$$

Generally

$$\int \frac{1}{x^2 + a^2}\, dx = \frac{1}{a} \tan^{-1} \left(\frac{x}{a}\right) + C.$$

When the x term is not missing in an irreducible quadratic $ax^2 + bx + c$, then completing the square and a change of variables will lead to integrals like those in (a) and (b) above. The next example illustrates this.

Example 6.4.4 (Irreducible Quadratics)

Problem: Compute the integral $\displaystyle\int \frac{3x^2 + 7x + 21}{x^2 + 2x + 5}\, dx$.

Solution: Since the integrand is an improper rational function, we use long division to get

$$\frac{3x^2 + 7\, x + 21}{x^2 + 2\, x + 5} = 3 + \frac{x + 6}{x^2 + 2\, x + 5}.$$

So the integral is

$$\int \left(3 + \frac{x + 6}{x^2 + 2x + 5}\right) dx = 3x + \int \frac{x + 6}{x^2 + 2x + 5}\, dx.$$

To do the remaining integral, we attempt to decompose $\frac{x+6}{x^2+2\,x+5}$ into partial fractions. For this we would first have to factor the denominator $x^2 + 2x + 5$. But, as we saw above, this is an irreducible quadratic and thus the fraction $\frac{x+6}{x^2+2\,x+5}$ does not decompose. It is as simple as it gets. So how do we integrate this fraction? First we complete the square on the quadratic in the denominator:

$$x^2 + 2\, x + 5 = x^2 + 2\, x + 1 + 4 = (x + 1)^2 + 4$$

Then the integral is

$$\int \frac{x + 6}{(x + 1)^2 + 4}\, dx,$$

and we use the u-substitution $u = x + 1$, $du = dx$, to simplify it. Note that from $u = x + 1$, we get $x = u - 1$.

$$\int \frac{x + 6}{(x + 1)^2 + 4}\, dx = \int \frac{u - 1 + 6}{u^2 + 4}\, du = \int \frac{u}{u^2 + 4}\, du + \int \frac{5}{u^2 + 4}\, du$$

$$= \int \frac{u}{u^2 + 4}\, du + \frac{5}{2} \tan^{-1} \left(\frac{u}{2}\right) + C.$$

The remaining integral above can be computed using another substitution: $w = u^2 + 4$, $dw = 2u\,du$. This gives

$$\int \frac{u}{u^2 + 4}\,du = \int \frac{1}{w} \cdot \frac{1}{2}\,dw = \frac{1}{2}\ln \mid w \mid = \frac{1}{2}\ln\left(u^2 + 4\right).$$

Putting this with what we found above gives

$$
\begin{aligned}
\int \frac{x+6}{\left(x+1\right)^2 + 4}\,dx &= \frac{1}{2}\ln\left(u^2 + 4\right) + \frac{5}{2}\tan^{-1}\left(\frac{u}{2}\right) + C \\
&= \frac{1}{2}\ln\left((x+1)^2 + 4\right) + \frac{5}{2}\tan^{-1}\left(\frac{x+1}{2}\right) + C \\
&= \frac{1}{2}\ln\left(x^2 + 2x + 5\right) + \frac{5}{2}\tan^{-1}\left(\frac{x+1}{2}\right) + C
\end{aligned}
$$

In summary,

$$\int \frac{3x^2 + 7x + 21}{x^2 + 2x + 5}\,dx = 3x + \frac{1}{2}\ln\left(x^2 + 2x + 5\right) + \frac{5}{2}\tan^{-1}\left(\frac{x+1}{2}\right) + C.$$

In addition to long division and factoring, the third aspect of the partial fraction technique is the actual *decomposition* of a proper fraction into a sum of partial fractions. This requires that you know the correct *form* of the decomposition (i.e., what types of partial fractions to use) and that you be able to use algebra to determine the required numbers in the partial fractions. Here are several examples of what is involved.

Example 6.4.5 (Decomposition into Partial Fractions)

Problem: Compute the integral $\displaystyle\int \frac{2x - 17}{x^2 - 3x - 10}\,dx$.

Solution: The denominator factors as

$$x^2 - 3x - 10 = \left(x + 2\right)\left(x - 5\right).$$

So we try to decompose the integrand into the sum of two fractions, one with denominator $x + 2$ and the other with denominator $x - 5$

$$\frac{2x - 17}{x^2 - 3x - 10} = \frac{2x - 17}{\left(x + 2\right)\left(x - 5\right)} = \frac{A}{x + 2} + \frac{B}{x - 5} \qquad (6.4.7)$$

To determine the numbers A and B, we multiply both sides of Eq. (6.4.7) by the least common denominator $\left(x + 2\right)\left(x - 5\right)$:

$$\frac{2x - 17}{\left(x + 2\right)\left(x - 5\right)} \cdot \left(x + 2\right)\left(x - 5\right) = \frac{A}{x + 2} \cdot \left(x + 2\right)\left(x - 5\right) + \frac{B}{x - 5} \cdot \left(x + 2\right)\left(x - 5\right),$$

which reduces to

$$2\,x - 17 = A\left(x - 5\right) + B\left(x + 2\right).$$

(Note: You can get the same equation by adding the fractions on the right side of Eq. (6.4.7) and then equating the numerator with the original numerator.)

Now we can use this last equation in several ways to determine A and B. For this type of example, the simplest way is as follows. Observe that the equation is valid for all values of x and so in particular it holds for $x = 5$ Substituting this value in the equation reduces it to

$$2\left(5\right) - 17 = B\left(5 + 2\right),$$

or

$$-7 = 7B,$$

Thus, $B = -1$. Next, substitute the value $x = -2$ into Equation (6.4.7) to get

$$2(-2) - 17 = A(-2 - 5),$$

or

$$-21 = -7A,$$

Thus, $A = 3$. Note that the choice of values $x = 5$ and $x = -2$ is motivated by the fact that the first choice makes $x - 5$ zero and the second choice makes $x + 2$ zero, thus reducing Eq. (6.4.7) to one with a single unknown in each case.

With A and B determined, we have the decomposition

$$\frac{2x - 17}{x^2 - 3x - 10} = \frac{3}{x + 2} + \frac{-1}{x - 5}.$$

Thus, the integral is now easy to compute

$$\int \frac{2x - 17}{x^2 - 3x - 10}\, dx = \int \frac{3}{x + 2}\, dx + \int \frac{-1}{x - 5}\, dx$$

$$= 3\ln|x + 2| - \ln|x - 5| + C.$$

Example 6.4.6 (Linear and Irreducible Factors)

Problem: Compute the integral $\displaystyle\int \frac{2x^2 - 3}{(x - 2)(x^2 + 1)}\, dx$.

Solution: Note that the integrand is a proper rational function and so we do not have to use long division. The denominator is already in completely factored since $x^2 + 1$ is irreducible. (The roots of $x^2 + 1 = 0$ are $\pm i$.) The correct form to assume for the partial fraction decomposition is

$$\frac{2x^2 - 3}{(x - 2)(x^2 + 1)} = \frac{A}{x - 2} + \frac{Bx + C}{x^2 + 1}$$

NOTE: For a simple linear factor like $x - 2$, the numerator in the corresponding partial fraction will be a number A. But for an irreducible quadratic factor, such as $x^2 + 1$, the numerator will be a linear expression $Bx + C$, involving two numbers B and C. To determine the numbers A, B, C, we multiply both sides of Eq. (6.4.8) by the least common denominator to get

$$\frac{2x^2 - 3}{(x - 2)(x^2 + 1)} \cdot (x - 2)(x^2 + 1)$$

$$= \frac{A}{x - 2} \cdot (x - 2)(x^2 + 1) + \frac{Bx + C}{x^2 + 1} \cdot (x - 2)(x^2 + 1)$$

or

$$2x^2 - 3 = A(x^2 + 1) + (Bx + C)(x - 2). \qquad (6.4.9)$$

Now we determine the unknowns A, B, and C so that this equation holds for all x. As mentioned in the last example, there are two ways to do this. In the last example we substituted particular values of x to determine the unknowns. We could do that here too. But let's use the alternative method instead. For this, expand the right side of Eq. (6.4.9) and collect like terms:

$$A(x^2 + 1) + (Bx + C)(x - 2) = Ax^2 + A + Bx^2 + Cx - 2Bx - 2C$$

$$= (A + B)x^2 + (-2B + C)x + (A - 2C).$$

Using this, Eq. (6.4.9) becomes

$$2x^2 - 3 = (A + B)\, x^2 + (-2B + C)\, x + (A - 2C).$$

If this is to hold for all x, then the coefficients of x^2 and x on each side of the equation must be the same, and the constant terms on each side must be the same. This leads to

$$\begin{aligned} A + B &= 2 \\ -2B + C &= 0 \\ A - 2C &= -3 \end{aligned}$$

This is a linear system of three equations for the three unknowns A, B, C. There are several methods to solve such systems. The elimination method proceeds by combining the equations to eliminate one of the unknowns, say C, to get a system of two equations in two unknowns, A and B. Eliminating again gives a single equation that determines one unknown. Back-substituting then determines the other two unknowns.

For the system in this example, the second equation says that $C = 2B$. Substitute this in the third equation to eliminate C and get and get $A - 4B = -3$ Then we have a system of two equations in two unknowns:

$$\begin{aligned} A + B &= 2 \\ A - 4B &= -3 \end{aligned}$$

Now subtract the second equation from the first to eliminate A and get a single equation

$$5B = 5$$

Thus, $B = 1$. Substitute this into $A + B = 2$ to get $A = 1$ And since $C = 2B$, we get $C = 2$. In summary $A = 1$, $B = 1$, $C = 2$ and so the partial fraction decomposition is

$$\frac{2\,x^2 - 3}{(x - 2)\,(x^2 + 1)} = \frac{1}{x - 2} + \frac{x + 2}{x^2 + 1}.$$

The integral is now easy to compute

$$\begin{aligned} \int \frac{2x^2 - 3}{(x - 2)\,(x^2 + 1)}\, dx &= \int \frac{1}{x - 2}\, dx + \int \frac{x + 2}{x^2 + 1}\, dx \\ &= \ln|x - 2| + \int \frac{x}{x^2 + 1}\, dx + \int \frac{2}{x^2 + 1}\, dx \\ &= \ln|x - 2| + \frac{1}{2}\ln\left(x^2 + 1\right) + 2\tan^{-1} x + C. \end{aligned}$$

All of the above examples serve to motivate the general partial fractions technique for integrating any rational function. The technique consists of three steps as indicated in the following boxes.

Partial Fraction Decomposition

To compute the integral $\int \dfrac{N(x)}{D(x)}\, dx$ *, where $N(x)$ and $D(x)$ are polynomials*

with no common factors, do the following:

(1) *Use long division (if necessary) to write*

$$\frac{N(x)}{D(x)} = q(x) + \frac{r(x)}{D(x)}$$

where $\deg(r(x)) < \deg(D(x))$.

> (2) *Factor D(x) completely as in Equation* (6.4.6).

---

(3) *In the partial fraction decomposition of* $\dfrac{r(x)}{D(x)}$

(a) *for each linear factor* $(bx + c)^m$, *with m repeats, use*

$$\frac{A_1}{bx + c} + \frac{A_2}{(bx + c)^2} + \cdots + \frac{A_m}{(bx + c)^m} \qquad (6.4.10)$$

(b) *for each irreducible quadratic factor* $(dx^2 + ex + f)^k$, *with k repeats, use*

$$\frac{A_1 x + B_1}{dx^2 + ex + f} + \frac{A_2 x + B_2}{(dx^2 + ex + f)^2} + \cdots + \frac{A_k x + B_k}{(dx^2 + ex + f)^k} \qquad (6.4.11)$$

In Step (3) of the partial fraction technique, it is extremely important that you use the correct *form* of either (6.4.10) or of (6.4.11) for each linear or irreducible quadratic factor. Otherwise you will not be able to determine the unknown numbers A, B, C, etc., in the decomposition. For example, if $(x - 1)^3$ occurs in the factorization of the denominator $D(x)$, then the partial fraction decomposition will contain the sum of *three* fractions involving

$$\frac{A}{x - 1} + \frac{B}{(x - 1)^2} + \frac{C}{(x - 1)^3}.$$

Example 6.4.7 (Correct Form for the PFD)

Problem: What is the *form* of the partial fraction decomposition (PFD) for

$$\frac{2 x^6 + 12 x^4 + 13 x^2 - 5 x^5 - 14 x^3 + 13 x + 7}{(x + 2)(x - 3)^2 (x^2 + 1)^2}$$

Solution: Note that the denominator has degree $1 + 2 + 2(2) = 7$ and so the fraction is proper. The numerator and denominator have no common factors because if you evaluate the numerator at $x = -2$, 3, $\pm i$ you do not get zero. Thus, we can apply Step (3) of the partial fractions technique to get that the given fraction decomposes as

$$\frac{2 x^6 + 12 x^4 + 13 x^2 - 5 x^5 - 14 x^3 + 13 x + 7}{(x + 2)(x - 3)^2 (x^2 + 1)^2}$$

$$= \frac{A}{x + 2} + \frac{B}{x - 3} + \frac{C}{(x - 3)^2} + \frac{Dx + E}{x^2 + 1} + \frac{Fx + G}{(x^2 + 1)^2}.$$

This is the form that was asked for. Determining the numbers A, B, C, D, E, F, G is another question. (Exercise.). In summary:

(1) The multiplicity of $x + 2$ is 1 and so there is one fraction in the decomposition corresponding to it.

(2) The multiplicity of $x - 3$ is 2 and so there are two fractions in the decomposition corresponding to it.

(3)   The multiplicity of $x^2 + 1$ is 2 and so there are two fractions in the decomposition corresponding to it.

Example 6.4.8 (Repeated Linear Factors)

Problem: Compute the integral $\displaystyle\int \frac{2x^2 - 3x}{(x-1)^3}\,dx$

Solution: As we saw above, the correct form for the partial fraction decomposition is

$$\frac{2\,x^2 - 3\,x}{(x-1)^3} = \frac{A}{x-1} + \frac{B}{(x-1)^2} + \frac{C}{(x-1)^3}$$

To determine A, B, C, we multiply each side of the above equation by $(x-1)^3$.

$$\frac{2x^2 - 3x}{(x-1)^3} \cdot (x-1)^3 = \left[\frac{A}{x-1} + \frac{B}{(x-1)^2} + \frac{C}{(x-1)^3}\right](x-1)^3,$$

or

$$2\,x^2 - 3\,x = A\,(x-1)^2 + B\,(x-1) + C \qquad (6.4.12)$$

By multiplying out and collecting like terms, the right side of the above equation can be written as

$$\begin{aligned}
A\,(x-1)^2 + B\,(x-1) + C &= A\,(x^2 - 2\,x + 1) + Bx - B + C \\
&= Ax^2 + (-2A + B)\,x + (A - B + C)
\end{aligned}$$

Then Eq. (6.4.12) is

$$2\,x^2 - 3\,x = Ax^2 + (-2\,A + B)\,x + A - B + C$$

Equating coefficients of the powers of x on each side gives

$$\begin{aligned}
A &= 2 \\
-2A + B &= -3 \\
A - B + C &= 0
\end{aligned}$$

The value $A = 2$ substituted in the second equation gives $-4 + B = -3$. So $B = 1$. Then the third equation above gives $C = -A + B = -1$. This determines all the numbers: $A = 2$, $B = 1$, $C = -1$ Then the decomposition is:

$$\frac{2\,x^2 - 3\,x}{(x-1)^3} = \frac{2}{x-1} + \frac{1}{(x-1)^2} + \frac{-1}{(x-1)^3},$$

and the integral is

$$\begin{aligned}
\int \frac{2x^2 - 3x}{(x-1)^3}\,dx &= \int \left(\frac{2}{x-1} + \frac{1}{(x-1)^2} + \frac{-1}{(x-1)^3}\right) dx \\
&= 2\ln|x - 2| - \frac{1}{x-1} + \frac{1}{2}\cdot\frac{1}{(x-1)^2} + C.
\end{aligned}$$

Note that only one of the terms in the answer involves the natural logarithm function. The others are power functions. Look for this whenever you have a repeated linear factor.

Example 6.4.9 (Repeated Irreducible Quadratic Factor)

Problem: Compute the integral $\displaystyle\int \frac{x^2 + x + 4}{(x^2 + 4)^2}\,dx$

Solution: The correct assumed form for the partial fraction decomposition is

$$\frac{x^2 + x + 4}{\left(x^2 + 4\right)^2} = \frac{Ax + B}{x^2 + 4} + \frac{Cx + D}{\left(x^2 + 4\right)^2}$$

Multiplying both sides of this equation by $\left(x^2 + 4\right)^2$ gives

$$
\begin{aligned}
x^2 + x + 4 &= (Ax + B)\left(x^2 + 4\right) + Cx + D \\
&= Ax^3 + Bx^2 + (4A + C)\,x + (4B + D)\,.
\end{aligned}
$$

Equating coefficients of like powers of x on each side of this equations, gives us the following very simple system of equations.

$$
\begin{aligned}
A &= 0 \\
B &= 1 \\
4A + C &= 1 \\
4B + D &= 4
\end{aligned}
$$

From this you can easily see that $A = 0, B = 1, C = 1, D = 0$, and so the partial fraction decomposition is

$$\frac{x^2 + x + 4}{\left(x^2 + 4\right)^2} = \frac{1}{x^2 + 4} + \frac{x}{\left(x^2 + 4\right)^2}$$

Thus, the integral is

$$
\begin{aligned}
\int \frac{x^2 + x + 4}{\left(x^2 + 4\right)^2}\,dx &= \int \frac{1}{x^2 + 4}\,dx + \int \frac{x}{\left(x^2 + 4\right)^2}\,dx \\
&= \frac{1}{2}\tan^{-1}\left(\frac{x}{2}\right) - \frac{1}{2}\cdot\frac{1}{x^2 + 4} + C.
\end{aligned}
$$

The second integral was computed using the substitution $u = x^2 + 4,\ du = 2x\,dx$.

Example 6.4.10 (The Three Steps)

Problem: Compute the integral $\displaystyle\int \frac{x^2 - 3x - 6}{x^3 + x^2 - x - 1}\,dx$.

Solution: We go through the three steps in the partial fraction technique:

STEP 1: The degree of the numerator is less than the degree of the denominator and so there is no need to divide.

STEP 2: To factor the denominator, we look for its roots, i.e., solutions of $x^3 + x^2 - x - 1 = 0$. One root is easy to guess. It is $x = 1$. Then we divide $x^3 + x^2 - x - 1$ by $x - 1$ to get a quotient of $x^2 + 2x + 1$ and zero for the remainder. This gives

$$x^3 + x^2 - x - 1 = (x - 1)\left(x^2 + 2x + 1\right) = (x - 1)(x + 1)^2\,.$$

where we have recognized $x^2 + 2x + 1$ as the square of $x + 1$ This completes the factorization.

STEP 3: The correct assumed form of the partial fraction decomposition is

$$\frac{x^2 - 3x - 6}{x^3 + x^2 - x - 1} = \frac{x^2 - 3x - 6}{(x - 1)(x + 1)^2} = \frac{A}{x - 1} + \frac{B}{x + 1} + \frac{C}{(x + 1)^2}.$$

Multiplying both sides of this equation by $(x - 1)(x + 1)^2$ gives

$$x^2 - 3x - 6 = A(x+1)^2 + B(x-1)(x+1) + C(x-1) \qquad (6.4.13).$$

To determine A, B, C from this we use the technique of substituting values of x into the equation. The two convenient values are $x = 1$, $x = -1$ since these make some of the terms on the right side zero.

For $x = 1$ the equation is

$$1 - 3 - 6 = A(1+1)^2,$$

or $-8 = 4A$. So $A = -2$

For $x = -1$ the equation is

$$1 + 3 - 6 = C(-1-1),$$

or $-2 = -2C$. So $C = 1$.

These are the only two "convenient" values of x in the sense that they each make two of the terms zero on the right of Eq. (6.4.13). We need to select one more value for x to substitute in Eq. (6.4.13). This will determine the last unknown B. Since $x = 0$ is easy to compute with, we use it.

For $x = 0$ the equation is

$$-6 = A - B - C.$$

But $A = -2, C = 1$, so the equation is

$$-6 = -3 - B$$

Thus, $B = 3$. With the numbers determined ($A = -2$, $B = 3$, $C = 1$), the partial fraction decomposition is

$$\frac{x^2 - 3x - 6}{(x-1)(x+1)^2} = \frac{-2}{x-1} + \frac{3}{x+1} + \frac{1}{(x+1)^2},$$

and the integral is

$$\int \frac{x^2 - 3x - 6}{(x-1)(x+1)^2}\, dx = \int \frac{-2}{x-1}\, dx + \int \frac{3}{x+1}\, dx + \int \frac{1}{(x+1)^2}\, dx$$

$$= -2\ln|x-1| + 3\ln|x+1| - \frac{1}{x+1} + C.$$

Example 6.4.11 (Halibut Fishing)

Problem: A large area of the northern Pacific near Alaska is prime fishing territory for halibut. The regulation of over-fishing, which can lead to extinction, is guided by several scientific models that predict how the halibut population changes over time. Since counting the number of halibut harvested by large commercial vessels is impossible, these models use bio-mass (the weight, in kilograms of the catch) as a measure of the quantity of fish.

One simple model, known as a logistic differential equation, says that the biomass $y(t)$, of halibut at time t in the Northern Pacific has a time rate of change given by

$$\frac{dy}{dt} = -\frac{0.71}{8}\,(y-8)\,y \qquad (6.4.14)$$

Here the units for y are in ten billions of kilograms and the time t is in years. Starting with Eq. (6.4.14), use Leibniz differentials and partial fractions to get an equation involving y and t (and an arbitrary constant) that implicitly defines y as a function of t

Solution: If we knew the rate of change $\dfrac{dy}{dt}$ as a function of t, we could integrate to find y as a function of t. However, Equation (6.4.14) does not give this. Rather it expresses the rate of change of y in terms of a quadratic expression in y. So we cannot integrate directly. An indirect way to integrate involves using Leibniz differentials and a little algebra. First we multiply both sides of Eq. (6.4.14) by dt to get

$$dy = -\frac{0.71}{8}\,(y-8)\,y\,dt$$

Next dividing both sides by $(y-8)\,y/8$ gives

$$\frac{8}{(y-8)\,y}\,dy = -0.71\,dt$$

Now apply an integral symbol to each side:

$$\int \frac{8}{(y-8)\,y}\,dy = -\int 0.71\,dt \qquad (6.4.15)$$

Even though the manipulations with the Leibniz differentials are not mathematically rigorous, the resulting equation above makes perfectly good sense. The indefinite integral on the right is easy:

$$-\int 0.71\,dt = -0.71t + K \qquad (6.4.16)$$

The integral on the left requires partial fraction decomposition. Doing this, we get

$$\int \frac{8}{(y-8)\,y}\,dy = \int \left(\frac{1}{y-8} + \frac{-1}{y} \right) dy = \ln|y-8| - \ln|y| \qquad (6.4.17)$$

Using the results of Eq. (6.4.16)–(6.4.17), the main Equation (6.4.15) becomes

$$\ln|y-8| - \ln|y| = -0.71t + K$$

If we assume that $y > 8$ (and of course $y > 0$, since its a biomass amount), then we can solve for y in the above equation to get

$$y = \frac{8}{1 - Ce^{-0.71t}}, \qquad (6.4.18)$$

where $C = e^K$. (Exercise) The constant C is determined from the initial biomass $y(0)$. You can see from Equation (6.4.18) that regardless of the initial amount $y(0)$ of halibut (even an amount near zero when there has been over-fishing), the amount of halibut will eventually increase to its limiting amount:

$$\lim_{t \to \infty} y = \lim_{t \to \infty} \frac{8}{1 - Ce^{-0.71t}} = 8 \quad \text{(eighty billion kilograms)}$$

For regulatory agencies, the important thing is knowing the time that it takes for the amount of halibut to get close to its limiting value, say to within 90 percent $(0.9(8) = 7.2)$). You can use Equation (6.4.18) to determine how long it takes. This is the time that the fishing industry must wait before returning to harvest the halibut in the Northern Pacific.

Exercises: 6.4 (Partial Fractions)

Use the partial fraction decomposition technique to compute the following integrals.

1. $\int \dfrac{x^4 - 3x^2}{x - 2}\, dx$ **2.** $\int \dfrac{x^5 - 2x^3 + 3x}{x - 3}\, dx$

3. $\int \dfrac{2x^5}{x^2 - 1}\, dx$ **4.** $\int \dfrac{2x^4}{x^2 - 4}\, dx$

5. $\int \dfrac{x - 7}{x^2 - 2x - 3}\, dx$ **6.** $\int \dfrac{16 - x}{x^2 - 2x - 8}\, dx$

7. $\int \dfrac{2x + 13}{x^2 + 9x + 20}\, dx$ **8.** $\int \dfrac{3x - 1}{x^2 + 4x + 3}\, dx$

9. $\int \dfrac{2}{x^2 + 2x}\, dx$ **10.** $\int \dfrac{5x - 12}{x^2 - 3x}\, dx$

11. $\int \dfrac{2x^3 + x^2 - 3x - 6}{x^2 - 4}\, dx$

12. $\int \dfrac{3x^3 - x^2 - 26x + 18}{x^2 - 4}\, dx$

13. $\int \dfrac{2}{2x^2 - 5x + 3}\, dx$ **14.** $\int \dfrac{x}{3x^2 + 5x + 2}\, dx$

15. $\int \dfrac{x + 1}{x^2 - 2x + 1}\, dx$ **16.** $\int \dfrac{2x + 5}{x^2 + 4x + 4}\, dx$

17. $\int \dfrac{3x^2 + 24x + 50}{x\,(x + 5)^2}\, dx$ **18.** $\int \dfrac{5x^2 + 19x + 18}{x\,(x + 3)^2}\, dx$

19. $\int \dfrac{2x^3 - 2x^2 - 2x + 4}{x^4 - 2x^3}\, dx$

20. $\int \dfrac{x^3 + 2x^2 + 2x - 12}{x^4 + 3x^3}\, dx$

21. $\int \dfrac{x^4 - 2x^3 + 4x^2 - x + 4}{x^2 + 1}\, dx$

22. $\int \dfrac{x^4 - 4x^3 + 2x^2 - 2x - 2}{x^2 + 1}\, dx$

23. $\int \dfrac{x - 2}{x^2 + 4x + 13}\, dx$ **24.** $\int \dfrac{x - 4}{x^2 + 2x + 3}\, dx$

25. $\int \dfrac{2x^2 - 2x + 1}{x^3 + x}\, dx$ **26.** $\int \dfrac{6x^2 - 4x + 3}{x^3 + x}\, dx$

27. $\int \dfrac{6x - 2}{(x + 3)\,(x^2 + 1)}\, dx$ **28.** $\int \dfrac{1 - 13x}{(x - 2)\,(x^2 + 1)}\, dx$

29. $\int \dfrac{3x^2 + 7x + 20}{x^3 + 6x^2 + 10x}\, dx$ **30.** $\int \dfrac{3x^2 + 21x + 52}{x^3 + 10x^2 + 26x}\, dx$

31. $\int \dfrac{2x^3 - 2x^2 + 5x - 2}{(x^2 + 1)\,(x^2 + 4)}\, dx$

32. $\int \dfrac{2x^3 + x^2 + 10x + 9}{(x^2 + 1)\,(x^2 + 9)}\, dx$

33. $\int \dfrac{2x^4 + 5x^2 - 3x + 2}{(x - 3)\,(x^2 + 1)^2}\, dx$

34. $\int \dfrac{3x^4 + 8x^2 - 4x + 3}{(x - 2)\,(x^2 + 1)^2}\, dx$

35. $\int \dfrac{2\,x^4 - 2\,x^3 + 3\,x^2 - x - 1}{(x - 2)\,(x^2 + 1)^2}\, dx$

36. $\int \dfrac{6\,x^4 - 12x^3 + 13x^2 - 29x + 71}{(x - 4)\,(x^2 + 1)^2}\, dx$

Irreducible Quadratic Factors

The theory indicates that when an irreducible quadratic factor $\left(ax^2 + bx + c\right)^k$, repeated k times, occurs in the factorization of the denominator, then the partial fraction decomposition has partial fractions:

$$\frac{A_1 x + B_1}{ax^2 + bx + c} + \frac{A_2 x + B_2}{\left(ax^2 + bx + c\right)^2} + \cdots + \frac{A_k x + B_k}{\left(ax^2 + bx + c\right)^k}$$

This being so, the question becomes: How do we compute integrals of the type:

$$\int \frac{Ax + B}{\left(ax^2 + bx + c\right)^n}\, dx$$

where $ax^2 + bx + c$ is irreducible? Recall that irreducibility means the discriminant is negative: $b^2 - 4ac < 0$. The answer to this question is covered in the next two exercises.

37. Suppose $ax^2 + bx + c$ is irreducible. Show that by completing-the-square and with an appropriate u-substitution we can write

$$\int \frac{Ax + B}{\left(ax^2 + bx + c\right)^n}\, dx = \int \frac{Cu + D}{\left(u^2 + r^2\right)^n}\, du$$

38. Show how to compute an integral of the form

$$\int \frac{Ax + B}{\left(x^2 + a^2\right)^n}\, dx$$

by using a u-substitution and a trig substitution. NOTE: We assume that n is a nonnegative integer.

In Exercises 39–44, use the theory described in Exercises 37–38 to compute the integrals.

39. $\int \dfrac{3x + 2}{\left(x^2 + 1\right)^2}\, dx$ **40.** $\int \dfrac{5x - 3}{\left(x^2 + 4\right)^2}\, dx$

41. $\int \dfrac{1}{\left(x^2 + 1\right)^3}\, dx$ **42.** $\int \dfrac{1}{\left(x^2 + 1\right)^4}\, dx$

43. $\int \dfrac{3x + 2}{\left(x^2 + 4x + 8\right)^2}\, dx$ **44.** $\int \dfrac{4x - 5}{\left(x^2 + 6x + 10\right)^2}\, dx$

Calculus *Concepts & Computation*

6.5 Integrals via Computer Algebra Systems

We have been using Maple throughout this book to illustrate concepts, plot graphs of functions, create 3-D graphics, and handle numerical computations. (Other versions of this book will use Mathematica, MathCad, and MatLab for these things.) Maple was originally created to do symbolic computations, i.e., perform algebraic manipulations on symbols rather than numbers (like you did when solving literal equations in algebra and precalculus classes). Thus, Maple (and Mathematica, MathCad, and MatLab) has come to be known as a *computer algebra system* (CAS).

One thing that Maple does really well is the computation of integrals, both indefinite and definite. This section will show you how to get Maple to compute all the integrals you did in Sections 6.1–6.4.

Maple's `int` Command

You can use the `int` command to compute both indefinite and definite integrals. It's two forms are

Indefinite Integral: `int(f(x),x)`

Definite Integral: `int(f(x),x=a..b)`

Here `f` is the function to be integrated, `x` indicates that the integral is respect to x (there may be other symbols in the indefinite integral), and, for the definite integral, `a` and `b` are the lower and upper limits of integration.

Example 6.5.1 (Using `int`)

Problem: Use Maple to compute the indefinite and definite integrals

$$\int \left(3x^2 - 2x + 4\right)\, dx \quad \text{and} \quad \int_0^1 \left(3x^2 - 2x + 4\right)\, dx$$

Solution: There is really no need to use Maple for such simple integrals, but it's a good idea to try simple ones that you can check by hand before doing the difficult ones. To do the indefinite integral we define the function which is the integrand and then integrate:

```
> f:=x->3*x^2-2*x+4;
```
$$f := x \mapsto 3x^2 - 2x + 4$$
```
> int(f(x),x);
```
$$x^3 - x^2 + 4x$$

If you do not want to define the function f (which we recommend in order to be sure you have typed in the formula correctly) you can just enter the expression for f directly in to the `int` command, namely:

```
> int(3*x^2-2*x+4,x);
```
$$x^3 - x^2 + 4x$$

To integrate this function from 0 to 1 use the following command

```
> int(f(x),x=0..1);
```
$$4$$

NOTE: Some Maple users prefer to do Maple input in Math mode entering expressions using a palette. For example, the last two Maple inputs above (which are in Text mode) can be entered in Math mode as follows:

```
> 
```
$$\int \left(3x^2 - 2x + 4\right) \mathrm{dx}$$

$$x^3 - x^2 + 4x$$

$$> \int_0^1 (3x^2 - 2x + 4)\, \mathrm{dx}$$

$$4$$

To have Maple compute integrals, you do not have to specify what integration technique for it to use (that's only necessary for you to know when doing it by hand). However, it will be convenient to organize the rest of the examples here according to the techniques you learned in the previous sections–Section 6.1 (Integration by Parts), Section 6.2 (Trig Integrals), Section 6.3 (Trig Substitutions and u^2-substitutions), and Section 6.4 (Partial Fractions).

Integration by Parts (Section 6.1)

We look at several examples from the exercises in Section 6.1.

Example 6.5.2 (Exercise 15 in 6.1)

Problem: Use Maple to compute the integral

$$\int x^2 \left(\ln x\right)^2\, dx$$

Solution: Define the function in the integrand and integrate using:

```
> f:=x->x^2*(ln(x))^2;
```
$$f := x \mapsto x^2 \ln(x)^2$$
```
> int(f(x),x);
```
$$\frac{1}{3} x^3 \ln(x)^2 - \frac{2}{9} x^3 \ln(x) + \frac{2}{27} x^3$$

That checks exactly with the answer in the Solutions Manual.

The next example shows that Maple's answer (and those for other CASs) is not so easy to interpret.

Example 6.5.3 (Exercise 31 in 6.1)

Problem: Use Maple to compute the integral

$$\int \cos x \ln\left(\cos x\right)\, dx$$

Solution: Define the function in the integrand and integrate using:

```
> f:=x->cos(x)*ln(cos(x));
```
$$f := x \mapsto \cos(x) \ln\left(\cos(x)\right)$$
```
> int(f(x),x);
```

$$\frac{1}{2} I \ln(2)\, \mathrm{e}^{Ix} - \frac{1}{2} I\mathrm{e}^{Ix} \ln\left(\frac{\left(\mathrm{e}^{Ix}\right)^2 + 1}{\mathrm{e}^{Ix}}\right) + \frac{1}{2} I\mathrm{e}^{Ix} - 2I \arctan\left(\mathrm{e}^{Ix}\right) - \frac{\frac{1}{2} I \ln(2)}{\mathrm{e}^{Ix}}$$

$$+ \frac{1}{2} I \ln\left(\frac{\left(\mathrm{e}^{Ix}\right)^2 + 1}{\mathrm{e}^{Ix}}\right) \left(\mathrm{e}^{ix}\right)^{-1} - \frac{\frac{1}{2} I}{\mathrm{e}^{Ix}}$$

This answer is too general to be of use for our purposes. The I in the answer stands for the complex imaginary unit (denoted by i in mathematics). This indicates that Maple is using techniques from complex analysis to do the computation. The reason for this is that in real analysis, the function $\ln x$ is only defined for real numbers $x > 0$, and so $\ln(\cos x)$ is only defined for those x that make $\cos x > 0$. Complex analysis extends the definition of the log function $\ln z$ to complex numbers z and does integrals in the complex domain. This is basically what is behind the complicated answer given above. The answer given in the Solutions Manual for this integral is

$$\int \cos x \ln(\cos x) \, dx = \sin x \, \ln(\cos x) + \ln|\sec x + \tan x| - \sin x + C$$

This is easy enough to compute by hand (as the Solutions Manual shows).

BOTTOM LINE: Unless you go on to to study and learn many topics in higher level mathematics, answers like the one above will not be of much use to you. But, many of Maple's answers will give you exactly what you want.

Trigonometric Integrals (Section 6.2)

Computing trig integrals with Maple works well for the most part, but remember that because of the abundance of trig identities Maple's answer may differ from yours by a constant.

Example 6.5.4 (Exercise 5 in 6.2)

Problem: Use Maple to compute the integral

$$\int \sin^3 x \, dx$$

Solution: Define the function in the integrand and integrate using:

```
> f:=x->(sin(x))^3;
```
$$f := x \mapsto \sin(x)^3$$
```
> int(f(x),x);
```
$$-\frac{1}{3}\sin(x)^2 \cos(x) - \frac{2}{3}\cos(x)$$

Compare this with the answer given in the Solutions Manual:

$$\int \sin^3 x \, dx = \frac{1}{3}\cos^3 x - \cos x + C$$

Can we use trig identities and a choice of the constant C so that this answer is the same as Maple's? Suppose we write $\cos^3 x = \cos^2 x \cdot \cos x$ and use the trig identity $\cos^2 x = 1 - \sin^2 x$. This gives

$$\frac{1}{3}\cos^3 x - \cos x + C = \frac{1}{3}\cos x \left(1 - \sin^2 x\right) - \cos x + C$$

$$= \frac{1}{3}\cos x - \frac{1}{3}\cos x \sin^2 x - \cos x + C = -\frac{1}{3}\cos x \sin^2 x - \frac{2}{3}\cos x + C$$

Thus, we see that this is the same as Maple's answer if we take $C = 0$

Example 6.5.5 (Exercise 21 in 6.2)

Problem: Use Maple to compute the integrals

$$\text{(a) } \int \sec^3 x \, dx \qquad \text{(b) } \int \sec^7 x \, dx$$

Solution: Normally these non-OTES cases would be done by using the reduction formula:

$$\int \sec^n x \, dx = \frac{1}{n-1}\sec^{n-2} x \tan x + \frac{n-2}{n-1}\int \sec^{n-2} x \, dx \qquad \text{(RF)}$$

For (a) the reduction formula is used once and then we would use the basic integral: $\int \sec x \, dx = \ln(\sec x + \tan x)$. This gives

$$\int \sec^3 x \, dx = \frac{1}{2}\sec x \tan x + \frac{1}{2}\ln(\sec x + \tan x) + C$$

Having Maple do it is not much quicker:

```
> f:=x->(sec(x))^3;
```
$$f := x \mapsto \sec(x)^3$$

```
> int(f(x),x);
```
$$\frac{1}{2}\frac{\sin(x)}{\cos(x)^2} + \frac{1}{2}\ln(\sec(x) + \tan(x))$$

It is easy to convert Maple's answer to the one above since

$$\frac{1}{2}\frac{\sin x}{\cos^2 x} = \frac{1}{2}\frac{1}{\cos x}\cdot\frac{\sin x}{\cos x} = \frac{1}{2}\sec x \tan x$$

To compute $\int \sec^7 x\, dx$ by hand with the above reduction formula would require using it three times. Of course, doing it in Maple does not require a reduction formula:

```
> f:=x->(sec(x))^7;
```
$$f := x \mapsto \sec(x)^7$$

```
> int(f(x),x);
```
$$\frac{1}{6}\frac{\sin(x)}{\cos(x)^6} + \frac{5}{24}\frac{\sin(x)}{\cos(x)^4} + \frac{5}{16}\frac{\sin(x)}{\cos(x)^2} + \frac{5}{16}\ln(\sec(x) + \tan(x))$$

You could, if you know a computer programming language, write a program to compute $\int \sec^n x\, dx$ using the above reduction formula.

Trigonometric Substitutions (Section 6.3)

When using Maple on trig substitution problems, generally the answer will be the factored and/or simplified version of the answer in the the Solutions Manual.

Example 6.5.6 (Exercise 19 in 6.3)

Problem: Use Maple to compute the integral

$$\int \frac{x^3}{(9 + x^2)^{5/2}}\, dx$$

Solution: Define the function in the integrand and integrate using:

```
> f:=x->x^3/(9+x^2)^(5/2);
```
$$f := x \mapsto \frac{x^3}{(9 + x^2)^{5/2}}$$

```
> int(f(x),x);
```
$$-\frac{6 + x^2}{(9 + x^2)^{3/2}}$$

This is what we got in the Solutions Manual by using trig substitutions.

Example 6.5.7 (Exercise 83 in 6.3)

Problem: Use Maple to compute the integral

$$\int x^3 \left(4 - x^2\right)^{5/2}\, dx$$

Solution: Define the function in the integrand and integrate using:

```
> f:=x->x^3*(4-x^2)^(5/2);
```
$$f := x \mapsto x^3 \left(4 - x^2\right)^{5/2}$$

```
> int(f(x),x);
```
$$\frac{1}{63}(x - 2)(x + 2)\left(8 + 7x^2\right)\left(4 - x^2\right)^{5/2}$$

Maple factors the answer, but note that $(x - 2)(x + 2) = x^2 - 4 = -(4 - x^2)$, so Maple's answer can be written as

$$\frac{1}{63}\left(x-2\right)\left(x+2\right)\left(8+7x^2\right)\left(4-x^2\right)^{5/2} = -\frac{1}{63}\left(8+7x^2\right)\left(4-x^2\right)^{7/2}$$

The answer in the Solutions Manual for Exercise 83 is

$$\frac{1}{9}\left(4-x^2\right)^{9/2} - \frac{4}{7}\left(4-x^2\right)^{7/2} + C$$

We can factor $\frac{1}{9}, \frac{1}{7}$, and $\left(4-x^2\right)^{7/2}$: out of the first two terms of the above expression

$$\begin{aligned}\frac{1}{9}\left(4-x^2\right)^{9/2} - \frac{4}{7}\left(4-x^2\right)^{7/2} &= \frac{1}{63}\left[4-x^2\right]^{7/2}\left[7(4-x^2)-9\cdot 4\right]\\ &= \frac{1}{63}\left(4-x^2\right)^{7/2}\left(-7x^2-8\right)\end{aligned}$$

This is clearly the same as Maple's answer.

Partial Fractions (Section 6.4)

The `int` command works very well on rational functions. There is also a command which will take any rational function $\frac{N(x)}{D(x)}$ and (1) do polynomial long division get the quotient polynomial plus a proper rational function

$$\frac{N(x)}{D(x)} = q(x) + \frac{r(x)}{D(x)}$$

and (2) decompose $\frac{r(x)}{D(x)}$ into its partial fractions. This command has the following form

```
convert(f(x),parfrac)
```

where $f(x) = \frac{N(x)}{D(x)}$ is the given rational function.

Example 6.5.8 (Exercises 1 and 5 in 6.4)

Problem: Use Maple to compute the integrals

$$\text{(a)} \int \frac{x^4 - 3x^2}{x-2}\, dx \qquad \text{(b)} \int \frac{x-7}{x^2 - 2x - 3}$$

Also use `convert` to (1) do long division on the integrand in (a) to get a quotient plus a proper rational function and (2) get the partial fraction decomposition of the integrand in (b).

Solution: Define the functions in the integrands and integrate using:

```
> f:=x->(x^4-3*x^2)/(x-2);g:=x->(x-7)/(x^2-2*x-3);
```

$$f := x \mapsto \frac{x^4 - 3x^2}{x-2}$$
$$g := x \mapsto \frac{x-7}{x^2 - 2x - 3}$$

```
> int(f(x),x);int(g(x),x);
```

$$\frac{1}{4}x^4 + \frac{2}{3}x^3 + \frac{1}{2}x^2 + 2x + 4\ln(x-2)$$
$$2\ln(x+1) - \ln(x-3)$$

These are the same as the answers given in the Solutions Manual, so there is no algebraic manipulations needed to verify that they are the same. Next to do long division of $f(x) = \frac{x^4-3x^2}{x-2}$ in Maple use

```
> convert(f(x),parfrac);
```

$$x^3 + 2x^2 + x + 2 + 4\frac{1}{x-2}$$

That's certainly quicker than doing it by hand. The partial fraction decomposition of $g(x) = \frac{x-7}{x^2-2x-3}$ is accomplished by

```
> convert(g(x),parfrac);
```

$$-\frac{1}{x-3} + \frac{2}{x+1}$$

Other Integration Techniques and Definite Integrals

In addition to the techniques you have studied in Sections 6.1–6.4, Maple has a great many more techniques that it employs to compute integrals. In addition, when a definite integral is needed and there is no known antiderivative for the integrand, Maple can use numerical approximation techniques to compute good approximate values. Current books on the subject of numerical analysis contain full discussions of these topics. Here we present several examples that illustrate what is involved.

Example 6.5.9

Problem: Find the area the region beneath the graph of

$$f(x) = \sqrt{x}\,\sin x$$

on the interval $[0, \pi]$. Also find the volume of the solid obtained by revolving this region about the x-axis. Compute the two indefinite integrals involved as well as the definite integrals.

Solution: The area and volume are

$$A = \int_0^\pi \sqrt{x}\,\sin x\,dx$$

$$V = \int_0^\pi \pi x \sin^2 x\,dx$$

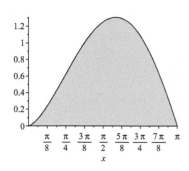

Figure 6.5.1: *The region beneath the graph of* $f(x) = \sqrt{x}\,\sin x.$

Define the function f in the integrand and compute the two indefinite integrals:

```
> f:=x->sqrt(x)*sin(x);
```

$$f := x \mapsto \sqrt{x}\sin(x)$$

```
> int(f(x),x);
```

$$-\sqrt{x}\cos(x) + 1/2\,\sqrt{2}\sqrt{\pi}\,FresnelC\left(\frac{\sqrt{2}\sqrt{x}}{\sqrt{\pi}}\right)$$

The answer here involves what is known as a Fresnel function. The indefinite integral for the volume is

```
> int(Pi*(f(x))^2,x);
```

$$\pi\left(x\left(-1/2\,\cos(x)\sin(x) + 1/2\,x\right) - 1/4\,(\cos(x))^2 - 1/4\,x^2\right)$$

Using the identity $\sin^2 x = \frac{1}{2} - \frac{1}{2}\cos 2x$, you could do this computation without Maple by writing

$$\int x \sin^2 x\,dx = \int x\left[\frac{1}{2} - \frac{1}{2}\cos 2x\right]\,dx = \int \left[\frac{1}{2}x - \frac{1}{2}x\cos 2x\right]\,dx$$

$$= \frac{1}{4}x^2 - \frac{1}{2}\int x\cos 2x\,dx$$

Now use integration by parts on the latter integral

$$\int x\cos 2x\,dx = x\left[\frac{1}{2}\sin 2x\right] - \int 1 \cdot \frac{1}{2}\sin 2x\,dx$$

$$= \frac{1}{2}x\sin 2x - \frac{1}{2}\left[-\frac{1}{2}\cos 2x\right] = \frac{1}{2}x\sin 2x + \frac{1}{4}\cos 2x$$

Putting everything together gives

$$\int x \sin^2 x \, dx = \frac{1}{4}x^2 - \frac{1}{2}\left[\frac{1}{2}x\sin 2x + \frac{1}{4}\cos 2x\right] = \frac{1}{4}x^2 - \frac{1}{4}x\sin 2x - \frac{1}{8}\cos 2x + C$$

Using trig identities one can show (with the right choice of the constant C) that this is the same as Maple's answer (exercise). Finally, using Maple, the area and volume are given by

```
> A:=int(f(x),x=0..Pi);
```

$$A := \sqrt{\pi} + 1/2\,\sqrt{2}\sqrt{\pi}\,FresnelC\left(\sqrt{2}\right)$$

```
> V:=int(Pi*(f(x))^2,x=0..Pi);
```

$$V := \frac{\pi^3}{4}$$

An illustration of this solid of revolution is shown in Figure 6.5.2:

Notice that Maple gives the exact answers. If you want a decimal approximation, use the "evaluate as floating point" command

```
> evalf(A);evalf(V);
```

$$2.435321164$$
$$7.751569172$$

Alternatively, you can use limits of integration that have a decimal point in them:

```
> A:=int(f(x),x=0.0..Pi);
```

$$A := 2.435321164$$

```
> V:=int(Pi*(f(x))^2,x=0.0..Pi);
```

$$V := 7.751569170$$

<u>NOTE:</u> Using `int` like this does more that produce decimal point (or floating point) approximations to the exact values. It forces Maple to use a numerical integration scheme rather than (1) first finding an antiderivative and then (2) evaluating this antiderivative at the limits of integration. The next example illustrates this.

Example 6.5.10 (A Function with No Known Antiderivative)

Problem: Use Maple to compute the integral

$$\int_1^2 x^x \, dx$$

Solution: If we first try to compute the indefinite integral (find an antiderivative), Maple gives us just the symbols for the integral that we want.

```
> int(x^x,x);
```

$$\int x^x dx$$

When this happens it means that Maple cannot find an antiderivative for the integrand. Also note that Maple takes a noticeable amount of time trying all of its techniques to produce an antiderivative. If we try the definite integral, it will not do that either:

```
> int(x^x,x=1..2);
```

$$\int_1^2 x^x dx$$

But using decimals points in the limits of integration forces Maple to give us a decimal approximation:

```
> int(x^x,x=1.0..2.0);
```

$$2.050446235$$

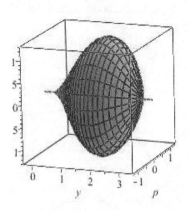

Figure 6.5.2: *The solid obtained by revolving the region beneath the graph of* $f(x) = \sqrt{x}\,\sin x$ *about the x-axis.*

Exercises: 6.5 (Integrals via Computer Algebra Systems)

In Exercises 1–70, use Maple's `int` command to compute the integrals. Compare Maple's answer with the answer in the back of the book. When they are different (and where possible) use algebra and trig identities to to show that they are the same, up to a constant. Determine this constant.

Integration by Parts

1. $\int x \sec x \tan x \, dx$

2. $\int x \csc x \cot x \, dx$

3. $\int \dfrac{xe^x}{(1 + e^x)^2} \, dx$

4. $\int \dfrac{xe^{-x}}{(1 + e^{-x})^2} \, dx$

5. $\int \ln(\sec x) \sec^2 x \, dx$

6. $\int \ln(\csc x) \csc^2 x \, dx$

7. $\int x^n \ln x \, dx$

8. $\int x^3 \ln x \, dx$

9. $\int x^2 (\ln x)^2 \, dx$

10. $\int x^{-3} (\ln x)^2 \, dx$

11. $\int x^2 (\ln x)^3 \, dx$

12. $\int x^{-1/2} (\ln x)^2 \, dx$

13. $\int e^{-x} \ln(1 + e^x) \, dx$

14. $\int e^{-2x} \ln(1 + e^{2x}) \, dx$

15. $\int \dfrac{\ln x \cos(\ln x)}{x} \, dx$

16. $\int \dfrac{\ln x \sin(\ln x)}{x} \, dx$

17. $\int \sec^2 x \ln(\cos x) \, dx$

18. $\int \sec^2 x \ln(\sin x) \, dx$

19. $\int \sec x \tan x \ln(\cos x) \, dx$

20. $\int \sec x \tan x \ln(\sin x) \, dx$

21. $\int \cos x \ln(\cos x) \, dx$

22. $\int \sin x \ln(\sin x) \, dx$

23. $\int \cos x \ln(1 + \cos x) \, dx$ **24.** $\int \sin x \ln(1 + \sin x) \, dx$

25. $\int x^{-1/2} \tan^{-1}\left(x^{-1/2}\right) \, dx$

26. $\int x^{-3/2} \tan^{-1}\left(x^{-3/2}\right) \, dx$

IP Multiple Times

27. $\int x^2 \tan x \sec^2 x \, dx$ **28.** $\int x^2 \cot x \csc^2 x \, dx$

29. $\int x^n e^{ax} \, dx$ (Derive a reduction formula.)

30. $\int x^n \cos ax \, dx$ (Derive a reduction formula.)

Trigonometric Integrals

31. $\int \sin^3 x \cos^2 x \, dx$ **32.** $\int \sin^2 x \cos^3 x \, dx$

33. $\int \sin^5 x \cos^4 x \, dx$ **34.** $\int \sin^4 x \cos^5 x \, dx$

35. $\int \sin^3 x \, dx$

36. $\int \cos^3 x \, dx$

37. $\int \sin^9 x \cos^3 x \, dx$

38. $\int \sin^3 x \cos^{15} x \, dx$

39. $\int \sin^4 x \cos^2 x \, dx$

40. $\int \sin^2 x \cos^4 x \, dx$

41. $\int \tan^3 x \sec x \, dx$

42. $\int \tan^3 x \sec^2 x \, dx$

43. $\int \tan^5 x \sec x \, dx$

44. $\int \tan^5 x \sec^2 x \, dx$

45. $\int \tan^3 x \sec^3 x \, dx$

46. $\int \tan^3 x \sec^7 x \, dx$

Trigonometric Substitution

47. $\int x^3 \sqrt{4 - x^2} \, dx$

48. $\int x^5 \sqrt{4 - x^2} \, dx$

49. $\int \dfrac{x^3}{\sqrt{4 + x^2}} \, dx$

50. $\int \dfrac{x^5}{\sqrt{4 + x^2}} \, dx$

51. $\int x^3 (x^2 - 1)^{3/2} \, dx$

52. $\int x^5 (x^2 - 1)^{3/2} \, dx$

53. $\int x^2 \sqrt{9 - x^2} \, dx$

54. $\int x^4 \sqrt{9 - x^2} \, dx$

55. $\int \dfrac{x^5}{(4 + x^2)^{3/2}} \, dx$

56. $\int \dfrac{x^3}{(4 + x^2)^{3/2}} \, dx$

57. $\int \dfrac{(1 + x^2)^{1/2}}{x^6} \, dx$

58. $\int \dfrac{(4 + x^2)^{1/2}}{x^6} \, dx$

59. $\int \dfrac{(1 + x^2)^{1/2}}{x^8} \, dx$

60. $\int \dfrac{(4 + x^2)^{1/2}}{x^8} \, dx$

Partial Fractions

61. $\int \dfrac{2x + 13}{x^2 + 9x + 20} \, dx$

62. $\int \dfrac{3x - 1}{x^2 + 4x + 3} \, dx$

63. $\int \dfrac{1}{(x^2 + 1)^3} \, dx$

64. $\int \dfrac{1}{(x^2 + 1)^4} \, dx$

Area and Volume

In Exercises 65–70, let D be the region beneath the graph of f on the interval $[a, b]$. Use Maple to find the area of D and the volume of the solid obtained by revolving D about the x-axis. Where possible, compute the definite integrals by hand. Also plot the region and the solid of revolution.

65. $f(x) = \sqrt{x} \cos x$, $[0, \pi/2]$

66. $f(x) = x^{3/2} \cos x$, $[0, \pi/2]$

67. $f(x) = \sqrt{1 + \sin^2 x}$, $[0, \pi]$

68. $f(x) = \sqrt{1 + \cos^2 x}$, $[0, \pi]$

69. $f(x) = \dfrac{x^{3/2}}{1 + x^2}$, $[0, 5]$ **70.** $f(x) = \dfrac{\sqrt{x}}{1 + x}$, $[0, 3]$

Calculus *Concepts & Computation*

6.6 Improper Integrals

In this section we extend the definition of the definite integral $\int_a^b f(x)\,dx$ in two ways:

(A) We allow for the interval $[a, b]$ on which f is defined to be infinite: $[a, \infty)$, $(-\infty, b]$, or $(-\infty, \infty)$.

(B) We allow for f to be undefined at a point c in the in interval $[a, b]$. Usually $\lim_{x \to c} f(x) = \pm\infty$, so that the graph of f has a vertical asymptote at $x = c$.

In each of these two cases, the integral $\int_a^b f(x)\,dx$ is called *improper*. As we shall see, an improper integral *cannot* be evaluated simply by using the fundamental theorem of calculus. Rather, we will have to employ a limit in conjunction with the fundamental theorem of calculus. You may consider this as why these integrals are called improper.

(A) Integrals over Unbounded Intervals

To motivate the first type of improper integral we consider an example:

Example 6.6.1

Problem: Find the area beneath the graph of $f(x) = e^{-x}$ on the intervals $[0, 1]$, $[0, 3]$, $[0, 10]$ and generally $[0, t]$ for any $t > 0$.

Solution: The computations are simple enough:

$$\int_0^1 e^{-x}\,dx = \left. (-e^{-x}) \right|_0^1 = -e^{-1} + 1 = 1 - \frac{1}{e} \approx 0.6321$$

$$\int_0^3 e^{-x}\,dx = \left. (-e^{-x}) \right|_0^3 = -e^{-3} + 1 = 1 - \frac{1}{e^3} \approx 0.9502$$

$$\int_0^{10} e^{-x}\,dx = \left. (-e^{-x}) \right|_0^{10} = -e^{-10} + 1 = 1 - \frac{1}{e^{10}} \approx 0.9999$$

$$\int_0^t e^{-x}\,dx = \left. (-e^{-x}) \right|_0^t = -e^{-t} + 1 = 1 - \frac{1}{e^t}$$

To illustrate the results, we plot the function on the various intervals and combine the plots into one picture. See Figure 6.6.1 in the margin.

```
> with(plots,display):f:=x->exp(-x):
> p1:=plot([f(x),0],x=0..1,filled=[color=yellow]):
> p2:=plot([f(x),0],x=0..3,filled=[color=green]):
> p3:=plot([f(x),0],x=0..10,filled=[color=tan]):
> display([p1,p2,p3]);
```

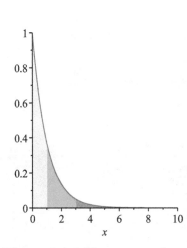

Figure 6.6.1: *The areas under the graph of $f(x) = e^{-x}$ on the intervals $[0, 1]$ (yellow) $[0, 3]$, (yellow+green), and $[0, 10]$ (yellow+green+brown).*

From the above example, we would guess that the area under the graph of $f(x) = e^{-x}$ on the infinite integral $[0, \infty]$ should be 1. This comes from the calculation that

$$\int_0^t e^{-x}\,dx = 1 - \frac{1}{e^t}$$

and the observation that $1/e^t$ is small when t is large. More precisely,

$$\lim_{t \to \infty} \int_0^t e^{-x}\,dx = \lim_{t \to \infty} \left(1 - \frac{1}{e^t} \right) = 1 - 0 = 1.$$

This is the motivation for the following definition

DEFINITION 6.6.1 (improper Integrals)

Suppose f is continuous on the interval $[a,\infty)$. Then we define the improper integral of f over $[a,\infty)$ by

$$\int_a^\infty f(x)dx \equiv \lim_{t\to\infty}\int_a^t f(x)dx \qquad (1)$$

provided the limit exists. In this case we say the improper converges. If the limit does not exist, we say the improper integral diverges.

CONVENTIONS:

(1) When the improper integral converges, its value

$$\int_a^\infty f(x)\,dx = \lim_{t\to\infty}\int_a^t f(x)\,dx = A$$

is the *net area* between the x-axis and the graph of f on the interval $[a, \infty)$.

(2) When the improper integral diverges and does so because $\lim_{t\to\infty}\int_a^t f(x)\,dx = \pm\infty$, then we say the improper integral *diverges to infinity* and write

$$\int_a^\infty f(x)\,dx = \pm\infty.$$

THREE STEPS: There are three steps in computing an improper integral:

(1) Compute the indefinite integral $\int f(x)\,dx$.

(2) Evaluate the indefinite integral from a to t, to get $\int_a^t f(x)\,dx$, which is function of t.

(3) Determine if the resulting function of t has a limit as $t \to \infty$.

Example 6.6.2

Problem: Determine if the following improper integrals converge or diverge. For those that converge find their values.

Part (a): $\displaystyle\int_1^\infty \frac{1}{x^2 + x^4}\,dx$

Solution (a): First use the partial fraction decomposition technique to compute the indefinite integral

$$\int \frac{1}{x^2 + x^4}\,dx = \int \frac{1}{x^2(1 + x^2)}\,dx = \int\left(\frac{1}{x^2} - \frac{1}{1+x^2}\right)dx = -\frac{1}{x} - \tan^{-1}x.$$

Second, use this to get the definite integral:

$$\int_1^t \frac{1}{x^2 + x^4}\,dx = \left(-\frac{1}{x} - \tan^{-1}x\right)\Big|_1^t = 1 + \tan^{-1}(1) - \frac{1}{t} - \tan^{-1}t$$

$$= 1 + \frac{\pi}{4} - \frac{1}{t} - \tan^{-1}t.$$

Third, find the limit of this expression as $t \to \infty$, if it exists. It does and the limit is

$$\lim_{t \to \infty} \left(1 + \frac{\pi}{4} - \frac{1}{t} - \tan^{-1} t\right) = 1 + \frac{\pi}{4} - 0 - \frac{\pi}{2} = 1 - \frac{\pi}{4}.$$

Thus, the improper integral converges and has value

$$\int_1^\infty \frac{1}{x^2 + x^4}\, dx = 1 - \frac{\pi}{4}.$$

Part (b): $\int_1^\infty \dfrac{1}{\sqrt{x} + x}\, dx$

Solution (b): First write the indefinite integral as

$$\int \frac{1}{\sqrt{x} + x}\, dx = \int \frac{1}{\sqrt{x} + \sqrt{x}\sqrt{x}}\, dx = \int \frac{1}{\sqrt{x}\,(1 + \sqrt{x})}\, dx.$$

Then make the substitutions

$$u = 1 + \sqrt{x} \qquad du = \frac{1}{2\sqrt{x}}\, dx$$

to get

$$\int \frac{1}{\sqrt{x} + x} = 2\int \frac{1}{u}\, du = 2\ln u = 2\ln(1 + \sqrt{x}).$$

Thus

$$\int_1^t \frac{1}{\sqrt{x} + x}\, dx = 2\ln\left(1 + \sqrt{t}\right) - 2\ln 2.$$

This expression diverges to infinity as $t \to \infty$ and so the improper integral diverges (to infinity)

$$\int_1^\infty \frac{1}{\sqrt{x} + x}\, dx = \lim_{t \to \infty}\left[2\ln\left(1 + \sqrt{t}\right) - 2\ln 2\right] = \infty.$$

Part (c): $\int_1^\infty \dfrac{\ln x}{x^3}\, dx$

Solution (c): To compute the indefinite integral we use integration by parts:

$$\int \frac{\ln x}{x^3}\, dx \;=\; \int \ln x \cdot x^{-3}\, dx = \ln x \left(-\frac{1}{2}x^{-2}\right) - \int \frac{1}{x}\cdot\left(-\frac{1}{2}x^{-2}\right) dx$$

$$=\; \ln x\left(-\frac{1}{2}x^{-2}\right) + \frac{1}{2}\int x^{-3}\, dx = \ln x\left(-\frac{1}{2}x^{-2}\right) + \frac{1}{2}\left(-\frac{1}{2}x^{-2}\right)$$

$$=\; -\frac{1}{2}\cdot\frac{\ln x}{x^2} - \frac{1}{4}\cdot\frac{1}{x^2} = -\frac{1}{4}\left(\frac{2\ln x + 1}{x^2}\right).$$

Next the definite integral is

$$\int_1^t \frac{\ln x}{x^3}\, dx = -\frac{1}{4}\left(\frac{2\ln x + 1}{x^2}\right)\Big|_1^t = \frac{1}{4} - \frac{1}{4}\left(\frac{2\ln t + 1}{t^2}\right).$$

To evaluate the the limit of this expression, note that

$$\lim_{t \to \infty} 2\ln t + 1 = \infty \quad \text{and} \quad \lim_{t \to \infty} t^2 = \infty$$

and so we can use L' Hospital's rule on the following limit:

$$\lim_{t \to \infty} \lim \left(\frac{2\ln t + 1}{t^2}\right) \overset{L'Hosp}{=} \lim_{t \to \infty}\left(\frac{\frac{2}{t}}{2t}\right) \overset{Alg}{=} \lim_{t \to \infty} \frac{1}{t^2} = 0$$

Thus,

$$\int_1^\infty \frac{\ln x}{x^3}\,dx = \lim_{t\to\infty} \int_1^t \frac{\ln x}{x^3}\,dx = \lim_{t\to\infty} \left[\frac{1}{4} - \frac{1}{4}\left(\frac{2\ln t + 1}{t^2}\right)\right] = \frac{1}{4}.$$

This shows that the improper integral converges and has value $\frac{1}{4}$.

Example 6.6.3 (Gabriel's Horn: Infinite Area and Finite Volume)

Problem: Let D be the region beneath the graph of $f(x) = 1/x$ on the interval $[1,\infty)$. Find the area of D and the volume of the solid obtained by revolving D about the x-axis.

Solution: The area of D, by definition, is the improper integral $A = \int_1^\infty \frac{1}{x}\,dx = \lim_{t\to\infty} \int_1^t \frac{1}{x}\,dx$. But

$$\int_1^t \frac{1}{x}\,dx = \ln x \Big|_1^t = \ln t - \ln 1 = \ln t.$$

So

$$A = \int_1^\infty \frac{1}{x}\,dx = \lim_{t\to\infty} \int_1^t \frac{1}{x}\,dx = \lim_{t\to\infty} \ln t = \infty.$$

Thus, there is an infinite amount of area beneath the graph on the interval $[1,\infty)$. On the other hand, the volume of the solid obtained by revolving the region about the x-axis is, by definition,

$$\begin{aligned} V &= \int_1^\infty \pi R^2\,dx = \int_1^\infty \pi \cdot \frac{1}{x^2}\,dx = \lim_{t\to\infty} \pi \int_1^t \frac{1}{x^2}\,dx \\ &= \lim_{t\to\infty} \pi\left(-\frac{1}{x}\right)\Big|_1^t = \lim_{t\to\infty} \pi\left(1 - \frac{1}{t}\right) = \pi. \end{aligned}$$

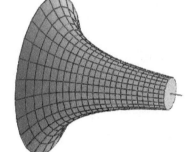

Figure 6.6.2: *A portion of of Gabriel's horn: The solid obtained by revolving $f(x) = 1/x, x$ in $[1,\infty)$ about the x-axis.*

Thus, the volume is $V = \pi$. This is a famous example because the region has infinite area but the volume of the solid it generates is finite.

One can also show (exercise) that the surface area of Gabriel's horn is infinite. Thus, while you could buy enough gallons of paint to fill up the $\pi \approx 3.14$ cubic feet of volume of the horn, that would not suffice to coat all of the surface area. That's a paradox.

Example 6.6.4 (*p*-Integrals)

Problem: Determine the values of p for which the improper integral $\displaystyle\int_1^\infty \frac{1}{x^p}\,dx$ converges.

Solution: We saw in the previous example that this improper integral diverges if $p = 1$, so we assume that $p \neq 1$. In this case, the power rule formula for integrals gives

$$\int_1^t x^{-p}\,dx = \left(\frac{1}{1-p}x^{1-p}\right)\Big|_1^t = \frac{1}{1-p}t^{1-p} - \frac{1}{1-p}.$$

And so

$$\int_1^\infty \frac{1}{x^p}\,dx = \lim_{t\to\infty} \frac{t^{1-p}}{1-p} - \frac{1}{1-p}.$$

But

$$\lim_{t\to\infty} t^{1-p} = \begin{cases} \infty & p < 1 \\ 0 & p > 1 \end{cases}.$$

Thus,

$$\int_1^\infty \frac{1}{x^p}\,dx = \begin{cases} \infty & p < 1 \\ \frac{1}{p-1} & p > 1 \end{cases}$$

The result in Example 6.6.4 is recorded in the following theorem. This will be important for use later when we study series.

THEOREM 6.6.1 (p-integrals)

Suppose p is any real number. Then the improper integral $\int_1^\infty \frac{1}{x^p}\,dx$

(a) *converges to* $\frac{1}{p-1}$ *if* $p > 1$ (b) *diverges to infinity if* $p \leq 1$

Integrals Over Other Unbounded Intervals

Integrals over unbounded intervals of the types: $(-\infty, b]$ and $(-\infty, \infty)$ are also improper. The convergence or divergence of these is defined as follows.

DEFINITION 6.6.2 (Improper Integrals)

Suppose f is continuous on the interval $(-\infty, b]$. Then we define the improper integral of f over $(-\infty, b]$ by

$$\int_{-\infty}^b f(x)dx \equiv \lim_{t \to -\infty} \int_t^b f(x)dx \qquad (2)$$

provided the limit exists. In this case we say the improper converges. If the limit does not exist, we say the improper integral diverges.

If f is continuous on $(-\infty, \infty)$, we define the improper integral of f over $(-\infty, \infty)$ by

$$\int_{-\infty}^\infty f(x)dx = \int_{-\infty}^0 f(x)dx + \int_0^\infty f(x)dx \qquad (3)$$

provided both the improper integrals $\int_0^\infty f(x)dx$, $\int_{-\infty}^0 f(x)dx$ converge

Example 6.6.5

Problem: Determine if the following improper integrals converge or diverge, If they converge find their values.

(a) $\int_{-\infty}^0 (1-x)^{-3/2}\,dx$ (b) $\int_{-\infty}^\infty e^{-x}\cos x\,dx$

Solution (a): First compute

$$\int_t^0 (1-x)^{-3/2}\,dx = 2\,(1-x)^{-1/2}\Big|_t^0 = 2 - \frac{2}{\sqrt{1-t}}.$$

Then

$$\int_{-\infty}^0 (1-x)^{-\frac{3}{2}}\,dx = \lim_{t \to -\infty}\left(2 - \frac{2}{\sqrt{1-t}}\right) = 2$$

Solution (b): We use integration by parts to compute the indefinite integral:

$$I = \int e^{-x}\cos x\,dx = e^{-x}\sin x - \int (-e^{-x})\sin x\,dx$$

$$= e^{-x}\sin x + \int e^{-x}\sin x\,dx$$

$$= e^{-x}\sin x + \left[e^{-x}\left(-\cos x\right) - \int \left(-e^{-x}\right)\left(-\cos x\right)\,dx\right]$$

$$= e^{-x}\sin x - e^{-x}\cos x - \int e^{-x}\cos x\,dx$$

$$= e^{-x}\sin x - e^{-x}\cos x - I$$

Thus,

$$I = \frac{1}{2}e^{-x}\sin x - \frac{1}{2}e^{-x}\cos x = \frac{1}{2}e^{-x}(\sin x - \cos x)$$

Using this, we separately compute each of the improper integrals

$$\int_0^\infty e^{-x}\cos x\,dx, \qquad \int_{-\infty}^0 e^{-x}\cos x\,dx$$

For the first one we have

$$\int_0^t e^{-x}\cos x\,dx = \frac{1}{2}e^{-x}\left(\sin x - \cos x\right)\Big|_0^t = \frac{1}{2}e^{-t}\left(\sin t - \cos t\right) + \frac{1}{2}.$$

To calculate the limit of this note that sine and cosine have values between -1 and 1, and so

$$-2 \le \sin t - \cos t \le 2.$$

So we get the estimate

$$(-2)e^{-t} \le e^{-t}(\sin t - \cos t) \le 2e^{-t}$$

Since $\lim_{t\to\infty}(\pm 2)e^{-t} = 0$, by the squeeze theorem for limits, we have

$$\lim_{t\to\infty} e^{-t}(\sin t - \cos t) = 0$$

Thus, $\int_0^\infty e^{-x}\cos x\,dx = \lim_{t\to\infty}\frac{1}{2}e^{-t}\left(\sin t - \cos t\right) + \frac{1}{2} = \frac{1}{2}$. This improper integral converges to $\frac{1}{2}$, which can be interpreted as the net area between the graph of $f(x) = e^{-x}\cos x$ and the x-axis on the interval $[0,\infty)$. Figure 6.6.3, which is generated by the following command, shows this net area.

```
> plot(exp(-x)*cos(x),x=0..8,filled=[color=yellow]);
```

Note that the graph of $f(x) = e^{-x}\cos x$ essentially coincides with the x-axis beyond $x = 6$. To calculate the other improper integral we can use the work above.

$$\int_t^0 e^{-x}\cos x\,dx = -\int_0^t e^{-x}\cos x\,dx = -\frac{1}{2}e^{-t}\left(\sin t - \cos t\right) - \frac{1}{2}$$

However now $\lim_{t\to -\infty} e^{-t} = \infty$, and so the improper integral $\int_{-\infty}^0 e^{-x}\cos x\,dx$ diverges. This is perhaps clear from inspection of the graph shown Figure 6.6.4, which generated by the following command.

```
> plot(exp(-x)*cos(x),x=-8..0,filled=[color=yellow]);
```

In summary: $\int_0^\infty e^{-x}\cos x\,dx$ converges, but $\int_{-\infty}^0 e^{-x}\cos x\,dx$ diverges, so by definition $\int_{-\infty}^\infty e^{-x}\cos x\,dx$ diverges.

(B) Improper Integrals - Integrands with Vertical Asymptotes

If the function f is not continuous on the interval $[a,b]$, then the definite integral $\int_a^b f(x)\,dx$ may not exist and, even if it does, we cannot compute it by using the fundamental theorem of calculus. In this subsection we consider special cases of this:

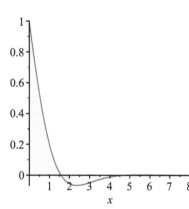

Figure 6.6.3: *The net area between the graph an the x-axis is $\int_0^\infty e^{-x}\cos x\,dx = \frac{1}{2}$.*

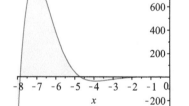

Figure 6.6.4: *The net area on the interval $[-8,0]$ is $\int_{-8}^0 e^{-x}\cos x\,dx \approx 1257$.*

(a) The function fails to be continuous at one of the endpoints a or b of $[a, b]$ and has a vertical asymptote there:

$$\lim_{x \to a^+} f(x) = \pm\infty \quad \text{or} \quad \lim_{x \to b^-} f(x) = \pm\infty$$

(b) The function fails to be continuous at a point c in (a, b) and has a vertical asymptote there:

$$\lim_{x \to c^+} f(x) = \pm\infty \quad \text{or} \quad \lim_{x \to c^-} f(x) = \pm\infty.$$

In either case, the integral $\int_a^b f(x) \, dx$ is called an improper integral. Before defining this type of improper integral we consider a motivating example.

Example 6.6.6 (Area Next to an Asymptote)

Problem: Find the area beneath the graph of $f(x) = 1/\sqrt{x}$ on the intervals $(\frac{1}{4}, 1), (\frac{1}{25}, 1), (\frac{1}{100}, 1)$, and $(t, 1)$.

Solution: Note that the function f has a vertical asymptote at $x = 0$. Before computing the areas, we first plot three of the regions involved:

```
> with(plots,display):
> f:=x->1/sqrt(x);
```

$$f := x \to \frac{1}{\sqrt{x}}$$

```
> p1:=plot([f(x),0],x=1/4..1,filled=[color=yellow]):
> p2:=plot([f(x),0],x=1/25..1,filled=[color=green]):
> p3:=plot([f(x),0],x=1/100..1,filled=[color=tan]):
> display([p1,p2,p3]);
```

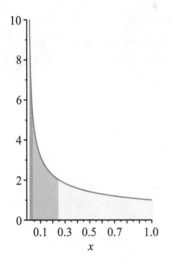

Figure 6.6.5: *The areas under the graph of $f(x) = 1/\sqrt{x}$ on the intervals $[\frac{1}{4}, 1]$ (yellow), $[\frac{1}{25}, 1]$ (yellow+green), and $[\frac{1}{100}, 1]$ (yellow+green+brown).*

The calculations of the areas are straight-forward:

$$\int_{\frac{1}{4}}^{1} \frac{1}{\sqrt{x}} \, dx = 2\sqrt{x} \Big|_{\frac{1}{4}}^{1} = 2\left(1 - \frac{1}{2}\right) = 1$$

$$\int_{\frac{1}{25}}^{1} \frac{1}{\sqrt{x}} \, dx = 2\sqrt{x} \Big|_{\frac{1}{25}}^{1} = 2\left(1 - \frac{1}{5}\right) = 1.6$$

$$\int_{\frac{1}{100}}^{1} \frac{1}{\sqrt{x}} \, dx = 2\sqrt{x} \Big|_{\frac{1}{100}}^{1} = 2\left(1 - \frac{1}{10}\right) = 1.8$$

$$\int_{t}^{1} \frac{1}{\sqrt{x}} \, dx = 2\sqrt{x} \Big|_{t}^{1} = 2\left(1 - \sqrt{t}\right)$$

The above example shows that

$$\int_{t}^{1} \frac{1}{\sqrt{x}} \, dx = 2\left(1 - \sqrt{t}\right)$$

Since $\lim_{t \to 0^+} \sqrt{t} = 0$, the calculations suggest that we define the improper integral $\int_0^1 \frac{1}{\sqrt{x}} \, dx$ as a limit:

$$\int_0^1 \frac{1}{\sqrt{x}} \, dx = \lim_{t \to 0^+} \left[\int_t^1 \frac{1}{\sqrt{x}} \, dx \right] = \lim_{t \to 0^+} \left[2\left(1 - \sqrt{t}\right) \right] = 2$$

The general definition of this type of improper integral is given as follows.

DEFINITION 6.6.3 (Improper Integrals)

Suppose f is continuous on the interval $(a,b]$ and has a vertical asymptote at a.

Then we define

$$\int_a^b f(x)dx \equiv \lim_{t \to a+} \int_t^b f(x)dx \quad (1)$$

provided the limit exists. Similarly if f is continuous on $[a, b)$ and has a vertical asymptote at b, we define

$$\int_a^b f(x)dx \equiv \lim_{t \to b-} \int_a^t f(x)dx \quad (2)$$

provided the limit exists. In each case (1) and (2) the improper integral is said to converge *when the limit exists and otherwise is said to* diverge.

There are several natural extensions of this type of improper integral. One is where the integrand f has a vertical asymptote at a point c between a and b and is continuous on the intervals $[a,c)$ and $(c,b]$. Then we take

$$\int_a^b f(x)\, dx = \int_a^c f(x)\, dx + \int_c^b f(x)\, dx,$$

provided *both* of the improper integrals $\int_a^c f(x)\, dx, \int_c^b f(x)\, dx$ converges.

Example 6.6.7 (Midpoint Vertical Asymptotes)

Problem: Determine if the following improper integral converge or diverges. If they converge, find their values.

Part (a): $\int_{-8}^8 \dfrac{1}{x^{2/3}}\, dx$

Solution (a): The integrand is not defined at $x = 0$ and has a vertical asymptote there. The improper integral consists of two improper integrals

$$\int_{-8}^8 \frac{1}{x^{2/3}}\, dx = \int_{-8}^0 \frac{1}{x^{2/3}}\, dx + \int_0^8 \frac{1}{x^{2/3}}\, dx$$

The second integral is

$$\int_0^8 \frac{1}{x^{2/3}}\, dx = \lim_{t \to 0^+} \int_t^8 x^{-2/3}\, dx = \lim_{t \to 0^+} \left(3x^{1/3}\right)\Big|_t^8 = \lim_{t \to 0^+} \left(6 - 3t^{1/3}\right) = 6$$

The other integral is

$$\int_{-8}^0 \frac{1}{x^{2/3}}\, dx = \lim_{t \to 0^-} \int_{-8}^t x^{-2/3}\, dx = \lim_{t \to 0^-} \left(3x^{1/3}\right)\Big|_{-8}^t = \lim_{t \to 0^-} \left(3t^{1/3} + 6\right) = 6$$

Thus, each of these improper integrals converge and so the original improper integral converges. Its value is

$$\int_{-8}^8 \frac{1}{x^{2/3}}\, dx = \int_{-8}^0 \frac{1}{x^{2/3}}\, dx + \int_0^8 \frac{1}{x^{2/3}}\, dx = 6 + 6 = 12.$$

NOTE: Suppose that we did not recognize that the integral in this problem is improper and used the Fundamental Theorem of Calculus on it anyway.

$$\int_{-8}^{8} \frac{1}{x^{2/3}} \, dx = \left(3x^{1/3}\right)\Big|_{-8}^{8} = 6 - (-6) = 12.$$

So we get the same value, but the reasoning is not justified. If you do this on some improper integrals you will get the wrong answer.

Part(b): $\displaystyle\int_{-8}^{8} \frac{1}{x^{4/3}} \, dx$

Solution (b): As mentioned in the solution to Part (a), you cannot use the Fundamental Theorem of Calculus directly on these types of improper integrals. If we tried to do so in this example we would get (incorrectly) that

$$\int_{-8}^{8} \frac{1}{x^{4/3}} \, dx = -3x^{-1/3}\Big|_{-8}^{8} = -\frac{3}{2} - \frac{3}{2} = -3.$$

However, if we work the problem the correct way we find that the integral diverges. Here are the details.

The integrand is not defined at $x = 0$ and has a vertical asymptote there. The improper integral consists of two improper integrals

$$\int_{-8}^{8} \frac{1}{x^{4/3}} \, dx = \int_{-8}^{0} \frac{1}{x^{4/3}} \, dx + \int_{0}^{8} \frac{1}{x^{4/3}} \, dx$$

The second integral is

$$\begin{aligned}
\int_{0}^{8} \frac{1}{x^{4/3}} \, dx &= \lim_{t \to 0^+} \int_{t}^{8} x^{-4/3} \, dx = \lim_{t \to 0^+} \left(-3x^{-1/3}\right)\Big|_{t}^{8} \\
&= \lim_{t \to 0^+} \left(-6 + 3t^{-1/3}\right) = \infty.
\end{aligned}$$

Thus, because this improper integral diverges, so does the original improper integral $\int_{-8}^{8} \frac{1}{x^{4/3}} \, dx$.

Another variation of improper integrals of the type $\int_{a}^{b} f(x) \, dx$ occurs when f has a vertical asymptote at each endpoint and is continuous on (a, b). Then we choose a point c between a and b and define

$$\int_{a}^{b} f(x) \, dx = \int_{a}^{c} f(x) \, dx + \int_{c}^{b} f(x) \, dx,$$

provided *both* of the improper integrals $\int_{a}^{c} f(x)\,dx$, $\int_{c}^{b} f(x) \, dx$ converge. The most famous example of this type of improper integral comes from measuring the circumference of a circle. The next example gives the details of this,

Example 6.6.8 (A Circular Circumference)

Problem: For a circle of radius 2 centered at the origin, use the arc length formula to find the circumference.

Solution: The equation for this circle is $x^2 + y^2 = 4$ and the top semicircle is the graph of the function

$$y = \sqrt{4 - x^2}$$

for x in $[-2, 2]$. The derivative is

$$\frac{dy}{dx} = -\frac{x}{\sqrt{4 - x^2}}$$

and

$$1 + \left(\frac{dy}{dx}\right)^2 = 1 + \frac{x^2}{4 - x^2} = \frac{4}{4 - x^2}$$

Then

$$\sqrt{1 + \left(\frac{dy}{dx}\right)^2} = \frac{2}{\sqrt{4 - x^2}}.$$

Integrating this from -2 to 2 should give half the circumference. Doubling that will give the circumference:

$$C = 2 \int_{-2}^{2} \frac{2}{\sqrt{4 - x^2}} \, dx = 4 \int_{-2}^{2} \frac{1}{\sqrt{4 - x^2}} \, dx.$$

But integral is improper because, while the integrand is continuous on the open interval $(-2, 2)$, it is not defined at the endpoints. We split the integral into two improper integrals

$$\int_{-2}^{2} \frac{1}{\sqrt{4 - x^2}} \, dx = \int_{-2}^{0} \frac{1}{\sqrt{4 - x^2}} \, dx + \int_{0}^{2} \frac{1}{\sqrt{4 - x^2}} \, dx$$

and use symmetry to get that each of these integrals will have the same value. The second improper integral is

$$\int_{0}^{2} \frac{1}{\sqrt{4 - x^2}} \, dx = \lim_{t \to 2^-} \int_{0}^{t} \frac{1}{\sqrt{4 - x^2}} \, dx = \lim_{t \to 2^-} \left[\sin^{-1}\left(\frac{x}{2}\right) \right]\Big|_{0}^{t}$$

$$= \lim_{t \to 2^-} \left[\sin^{-1}\left(\frac{t}{2}\right) - 0 \right] = \sin^{-1}(1) = \frac{\pi}{2}.$$

Thus, the circumference of a circle of radius 2 is

$$C = 4 \left[\frac{\pi}{2} + \frac{\pi}{2} \right] = 4\pi.$$

which verifies the well-known result $C = 2\pi r$ for $r = 2$.

Exercises: 6.6 (Improper Integrals)

In Exercises 1–44, determine if the improper integrals converges or not. For those that converge, find their values. For those that diverge, indicate the ones that diverge to infinity.

1. $\displaystyle\int_1^\infty \frac{1}{x^{7/5}}\,dx$

2. $\displaystyle\int_1^\infty \frac{1}{x^{8/9}}\,dx$

3. $\displaystyle\int_0^1 \frac{1}{x^{7/5}}\,dx$

4. $\displaystyle\int_0^1 \frac{1}{x^{8/9}}\,dx$

5. $\displaystyle\int_1^\infty \frac{1}{x^{5/6}}\,dx$

6. $\displaystyle\int_1^\infty \frac{1}{x^{7/11}}\,dx$

7. $\displaystyle\int_0^1 \frac{1}{x^{5/6}}\,dx$

8. $\displaystyle\int_0^1 \frac{1}{x^{7/11}}\,dx$

9. $\displaystyle\int_6^\infty \frac{1}{(x-2)^{3/2}}\,dx$

10. $\displaystyle\int_7^\infty \frac{1}{(x-4)^{5/2}}\,dx$

11. $\displaystyle\int_4^\infty \frac{1}{(x-3)^{2/3}}\,dx$

12. $\displaystyle\int_5^\infty \frac{1}{(x-4)^{3/4}}\,dx$

13. $\displaystyle\int_0^4 \frac{1}{(x-1)^{2/3}}\,dx$

14. $\displaystyle\int_0^3 \frac{1}{(x-2)^{3/5}}\,dx$

15. $\displaystyle\int_1^5 \frac{1}{(x-2)^{9/2}}\,dx$

16. $\displaystyle\int_1^7 \frac{1}{(x-3)^{7/2}}\,dx$

17. $\displaystyle\int_0^\infty x e^{-x^2}\,dx$

18. $\displaystyle\int_0^\infty x 10^{-x^2}\,dx$

19. $\displaystyle\int_0^\infty \sin x\,dx$

20. $\displaystyle\int_0^\infty \cos x\,dx$

21. $\displaystyle\int_0^\infty \frac{e^{-x}}{e^{-x}+1}\,dx$

22. $\displaystyle\int_0^\infty \frac{2^{-x}}{2^{-x}+1}\,dx$

23. $\displaystyle\int_0^\infty \frac{e^x}{e^{2x}+1}\,dx$

24. $\displaystyle\int_0^\infty \frac{e^{2x}}{e^{4x}+1}\,dx$

25. $\displaystyle\int_1^\infty \frac{e^{-x}}{\sqrt{1-e^{-2x}}}\,dx$

26. $\displaystyle\int_1^\infty \frac{e^{-2x}}{\sqrt{1-e^{-4x}}}\,dx$

27. $\displaystyle\int_{-\infty}^0 \frac{1}{e^{-x}+1}\,dx$

28. $\displaystyle\int_{-\infty}^0 \frac{1}{e^{-2x}+1}\,dx$

29. $\displaystyle\int_1^\infty \frac{e^{-\sqrt{x}}}{\sqrt{x}}\,dx$

30. $\displaystyle\int_1^\infty \frac{e^{-\sqrt[3]{x}}}{x^{2/3}}\,dx$

31. $\displaystyle\int_0^1 \frac{e^{-\sqrt{x}}}{\sqrt{x}}\,dx$

32. $\displaystyle\int_0^1 \frac{e^{-\sqrt[3]{x}}}{x^{2/3}}\,dx$

33. $\displaystyle\int_2^5 \frac{1}{\sqrt{x^2-4}}\,dx$

34. $\displaystyle\int_3^8 \frac{1}{\sqrt{x^2-9}}\,dx$

35. $\displaystyle\int_1^\infty \frac{1}{\sqrt{x}(x+1)}\,dx$

36. $\displaystyle\int_1^\infty \frac{1}{x^{3/4}(\sqrt{x}+1)}\,dx$

37. $\displaystyle\int_2^\infty \frac{1}{x(\ln x)^2}\,dx$

38. $\displaystyle\int_3^\infty \frac{1}{x(\ln x)^3}\,dx$

39. $\displaystyle\int_0^\infty \tan^{-1} x\,dx$

40. $\displaystyle\int_0^\infty \cot^{-1} x\,dx$

41. $\displaystyle\int_0^\infty \cos x\, e^{-\sin x}\,dx$

42. $\displaystyle\int_0^\infty \sin x\, e^{-\cos x}\,dx$

43. $\displaystyle\int_1^\infty \frac{x}{e^x}\,dx$

44. $\displaystyle\int_1^\infty \frac{x}{e^{3x}}\,dx$

p-k Integrals

This group of exercises deals with improper integrals of the form

$$\int_1^\infty \frac{(\ln x)^k}{x^p}\,dx$$

where p is a positive real number and $k \geq 0$ is an integer. The special case $k = 0$ gives the p-integrals discussed in Example 6.6.3, which led to Theorem 6.6.1. So we will assume assume k is a positive integer.

For the following values of p and k, determine convergence or divergence of the improper integrals and, when they converge, find their values.

45. $\displaystyle\int_1^\infty \frac{\ln x}{x^4}\,dx$

46. $\displaystyle\int_1^\infty \frac{\ln x}{x^3}\,dx$

47. $\displaystyle\int_1^\infty \frac{\ln x}{\sqrt{x}}\,dx$

48. $\displaystyle\int_1^\infty \frac{\ln x}{x^{2/3}}\,dx$

49. $\displaystyle\int_1^\infty \frac{(\ln x)^2}{x^2}\,dx$

50. $\displaystyle\int_1^\infty \frac{(\ln x)^3}{x^2}\,dx$

51. Prove the following result:

THEOREM: For any positive real numbers p and c

$$\lim_{x\to\infty} \frac{(\ln x)^c}{x^p} = 0.$$

NOTE: This says that $(\ln x)^c$ goes to infinity more slowly that any positive power of x. It also leads to the result that for any positive real numbers p and c, there is an M such that

$$(\ln x)^c < x^p,$$

for all $x \geq M$.

52. Based on Exercises 45–50, determine for which values of p and k, the integral

$$\int_1^\infty \frac{(\ln x)^k}{x^p}\,dx$$

converges, and for those that converge find their values.

Damped Power Functions

This group of exercises deals with improper integrals of the form

$$\int_0^\infty x^n e^{-ax}\,dx$$

where n is a nonnegative integer and a is a positive real number. (See Example 6.6.1 for the $n = 0$, $a = 1$, case.) For the following values of n and a, show that the improper integrals converge and find their values.

53. $\int_0^\infty x^2 e^{-x}\, dx$ **54.** $\int_0^\infty x^3 e^{-x}\, dx$

55. $\int_0^\infty x e^{-3x}\, dx$ **56.** $\int_0^\infty x^2 e^{-5x}\, dx$

57. $\int_0^\infty x^3 e^{-ax}\, dx$ **58.** $\int_0^\infty x^4 e^{-ax}\, dx$

59. In general, show that $\int_0^\infty x^n e^{-ax}\, dx$ converges and find the value it converges to.

60. The function $\Gamma(s) = \int_0^\infty x^{s-1} e^{-x}\, dx$, called the *gamma function*, was introduced by Leonhard Euler in the 1700s. Show that the improper integral converges for any positive real number s. Show that $\Gamma(n+1) = n!$ for any positive integer n. Thus, the gamma function can be considered as an extension of the the factorial function to all positive real numbers.

Inverse Tangent Integrals

This group of exercises deals with improper integrals of the form

$$\int_1^\infty \frac{\tan^{-1} x}{x^{m+1}}\, dx$$

where $m \geq 1$ is an integer. For the following values of m, determine convergence or divergence of the improper integrals and, when they converge, find their values.

61. $\int_1^\infty \frac{\tan^{-1} x}{x}\, dx$ **62.** $\int_1^\infty \frac{\tan^{-1} x}{x^4}\, dx$

63. $\int_1^\infty \frac{\tan^{-1} x}{x^2}\, dx$ **64.** $\int_1^\infty \frac{\tan^{-1} x}{x^5}\, dx$

65. $\int_1^\infty \frac{\tan^{-1} x}{x^3}\, dx$

66. Based on your experience with Exercises 61–65, show that the improper integral

$$\int_1^\infty \frac{\tan^{-1} x}{x^{m+1}}\, dx$$

converges for all integers $m \geq 1$ and find the value of the improper integral.

Damped Sines & Cosines

This group of exercises deals with improper integrals of the form

$$\int_1^\infty e^{-ax} \sin bx \, dx \quad \text{and} \quad \int_1^\infty e^{-ax} \cos bx \, dx$$

where a and b are positve real numbers. The integrands are functions that represent damped harmonic motion. Each tends to 0 as $x \to \infty$. To see this note that

$$-1 \leq \sin bx \leq 1$$

for all x and so

$$-e^{-ax} \leq e^{-ax} \sin bx \leq e^{-ax}.$$

Thus, since

$$\lim_{x \to \infty} e^{-ax} = 0.$$

it follows, by the squeeze theorem,

$$\lim_{x \to \infty} e^{-ax} \sin bx = 0 \qquad (1).$$

Similarly

$$\lim_{x \to \infty} e^{-ax} \cos bx = 0 \qquad (2)$$

The improper integrals here measure the net area under the graphs of these damped sine and cosine waves.

For the following values of a and b show that the integrals converge and find their values.

NOTE 1: To compute the indefinite integrals, denoted by I, that occur here you need to integrate by parts twice. This will give an equation involving I which you must solve for I.

NOTE 2: For the integration by parts, it will be quicker to use the *f-g* version of the IP formula:

$$\int f(x)g(x)\, dx = f(x)G(x) - \int f'(x)G(x)\, dx$$

where $G(x) = \int g(x)\, dx$. However, if you wish you can use the *u-v* version of IP.

67. $\int_0^\infty e^{-x} \sin x \, dx$ **68.** $\int_0^\infty e^{-2x} \cos x \, dx$

69. $\int_0^\infty e^{-x} \sin 3x \, dx$ **70.** $\int_0^\infty e^{-x} \cos 4x \, dx$

71. $\int_0^\infty e^{-2x} \sin 5x \, dx$

72. Show that for any positive values of a and b the integrals

$$\int_0^\infty e^{-ax} \sin bx \, dx \quad \text{and} \quad \int_0^\infty e^{-ax} \cos bx \, dx$$

converge and find the values to which they converge.

7

Differential Equations

Calculus Concepts & Computation

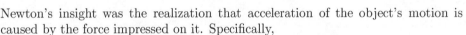

7.1 Introduction to Differential Equations

The study of differential equations dates back to the 1680s when Isaac Newton wrote down, and solved, some of the world's first differential equations. The primary and most important of these differential equations was disguised in his second law of motion, $ma = F$, which he used to explain the motion of planets in the solar system, moons about planets, and projectiles near a planet's surface.

The simplest case of Newton's 2nd Law, easy enough for us to study here, is for 1-dimensional motion, i.e., motion along a straight line, say, the y-axis, with position function $y = f(t)$. (See Sections 2.4–2.5.) Then the object's velocity and acceleration are given by the first and second derivatives

$$v = y' = \frac{dy}{dt} \qquad \text{(velocity)}$$

$$a = y'' = \frac{d^2y}{dt^2} \qquad \text{(acceleration)}$$

Johan Swanepoel/Shutterstock.com

Newton's insight was the realization that acceleration of the object's motion is caused by the force impressed on it. Specifically,

$$my'' = F(t, y, y') \qquad \text{(Newton's 2nd Law)}$$

Here the notation for the force $F = F(t, y, y')$ indicates that the force, in general, can depend on the time t, the position y, and the velocity y'. Since the above equation is an equation involving the unknown function y, and its derivatives y', y'', it is called a *differential equation* (abbreviated DE). This distinguishes it from an algebraic equation, such as $x^2 = x + 2$. To solve an algebraic equation you find all numbers x that "satisfy" it, i.e., numbers such as $x = 2$, which when substituted in the equation make the equality true. To solve a differential equation, you must find all *functions* $y = f(t)$, which when substituted in the equation make the equality true. As you might expect, solving differential equations (DEs) can be more complicated than solving algebraic equations. However, in certain cases solving a DE is simple. For instance, Example 2.5.8 in Chapter 2 shows you how to solve the DE that is Newton's 2nd Law for the special case when the force F is a constant. There are some other easy cases of this, which we will discuss below.

Example 7.1.1 (Solutions of Differential Equations)

Problem: Verify that the given functions are solutions of the differential equations:

(a) $y'' - y' - 2y = 0$, functions: $y = e^{2t}$ and $y = e^{-t}$.

(b) $t^2 y'' + t y' - 4y = 0$, functions: $y = t^2$ and $y = t^{-2}$.

Solution: Just calculate the 1st and 2nd derivatives of each function and substitute it in the equation:

Part (a): For $y' = e^{2t}$, we have $y' = 2e^{2t}$, $y'' = 4e^{2t}$ and so

$$y'' - y' - 2y = 4e^{2t} - 2e^{2t} - 2(e^{2t}) = 0$$

and for $y = e^{-t}$, we have $y' = -e^{-t}$, $y'' = e^{-t}$ and so

$$y'' - y' - 2y = e^{-t} - (-e^{-t}) - 2(e^{-t}) = e^{-t} + e^{-t} - 2e^{-t} = 0$$

Part (b): For $y' = t^2$, we have $y' = 2t$, $y'' = 2$ and so

$$t^2 y'' + ty' - 4y = t^2(2) + t(2t) - 4(t^2) = 2t^2 + 2t^2 - 4t^2 = 0$$

and for $y = t^{-2}$, we have $y' = -2t^{-3}$, $y'' = 6t^{-4}$ and so

$$t^2 y'' + ty' - 4y = t^2(6t^{-4}) + t(-2t^{-3}) - 4(t^{-2}) = 6t^{-2} - 2t^{-2} - 4t^{-2} = 0$$

The general form for first and second order differential equations is given in the following definition.

DEFINITION 7.1.1 (1st and 2nd Order Differential Equations)

(1) *A first-order differential equation for an unknown function y of t has the form*

$$H(t, y, y') = 0 \qquad (7.1.1)$$

(2) *A second-order differential equation for an unknown function y of t has the form*

$$H(t, y, y', y'') = 0 \qquad (7.1.2)$$

Based on the definition it is easy to see that $H(t, y, y', \cdots, y^{(n)}) = 0$ is the form for a general nth order differential equation. We will only study 1st and 2nd order DEs here since they are the ones most commonly occurring in applications. This is because Newton's second law is a 2nd-order DE.

If you can solve Equations (7.1.1)–(7.1.2) for the highest order derivative then you get equivalent DEs expressed in what is called *normal form*:

$$y' = G(t, y) \quad \text{(1st-order)} \qquad y'' = G(t, y, y') \quad \text{(2nd-order)}$$

For example, dividing both sides of Newton's 2nd Law by the constant m puts it in normal form.

NOTE: In many differential equations, ones involving dynamics, the independent variable is the time t. DEs that occur in other applications will use different symbols for the independent variable. The generic independent variable is x and the corresponding 1st- and 2nd-order DEs are

$$H(x, y, y') = 0 \quad \text{and} \quad H(x, y, y', y'') = 0,$$

where $y' = dy/dx$ and $y'' = d^2y/dx^2$.

Solving Differential Equations

Techniques for solving differential equations are many and varied. We will study a few of these techniques in this chapter. They all use calculus. (That's why Newton invented calculus.) In fact every time you compute an integral you are solving the most elementary type of 1st order DE.

Example 7.1.2 (Integrals)

Problem: Solve the following differential equations:

(a) $\dfrac{dy}{dx} = \dfrac{x+1}{x}$ (b) $y'' = \cos t$

Solution: Just integrate once in (a) and twice in (b):

Part (a): Write $\dfrac{dy}{dx} = \dfrac{x+1}{x}$ as

$$dy = \left(\frac{x+1}{x}\right) dx$$

Then

$$y = \int dy = \int \left(\frac{x+1}{x}\right) dx = \int \left(1 + \frac{1}{x}\right) dx = x + \ln x + C$$

Part (b): First

$$y' = \int y'' dt = \int \cos t \, dt = \sin t + C$$

and then

$$y = \int y' dt = \int (\sin t + C) \, dt = -\cos t + Ct + K$$

NOTE 1: In Part (a) the DE is 1st order and its general solution involves one arbitrary constant C (the constant of integration), while in Part (b) the general solution involves two arbitrary constants C and K (two constants of integration, since we integrated twice to get y).

NOTE 2: Using the Leibniz differential notation, as we did in Part (a), is an essential part of many solution techniques for some DEs. Thus, this chapter will show you why this notation is so important. The next two examples illustrates this.

Example 7.1.3 (Chemical Reaction Rates)

Problem: As in Example 2.5.4 from Chapter 2, consider the chemical reaction of hydrogen peroxide decomposing into hydrogen and iodine. Letting $y(t)$ denote the concentration (M/L) of the hydrogen peroxide at time t, chemical theory tells us that y satisfies the 1st order DE

$$\frac{dy}{dt} = -ky^2,$$

where $k = .0012$ is a reaction rate constant found from laboratory data. Chemists call this a *second-order* reaction because of the 2 in the exponent of y^2. Find the general solution of this DE and the particular solution with initial concentration $y(0) = 1$ M/L.

Solution: The technique for solving this DE involves treating dy/dt as a ratio of differentials and multiplying both sides of the DE by dt to get

$$dy = -ky^2 dt$$

Then dividing each side by y^2 results in

$$\frac{1}{y^2} dy = -k \, dt$$

Applying the integral symbol to each side yields the equation

$$\int \frac{1}{y^2} dy = -\int k \, dt$$

So, computing the integral on each side gives

$$-\frac{1}{y} = -kt + C$$

Notice that we only used one constant C of integration. If you use a constant with each of the integrals, they can be combined and relabeled to get just one arbitrary constant. Next solve the last equation explicitly for y, getting

$$y = \frac{1}{kt - C} \qquad (7.1.3)$$

For various choices of C, we get similar, but distinct functions, so there are infinitely many solutions of the DE. See Figure 7.1.1. The ones given in Equation (7.1.3)

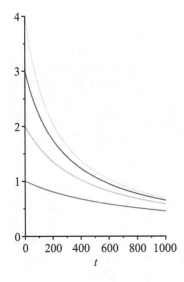

Figure 7.1.1: *Graphs of* $y = \dfrac{1}{kt - C}$ *for* $k = .0012$ *and* $C = -1, -\frac{1}{2}, -\frac{1}{3}, -\frac{1}{4}.$

include all solutions except one. The exceptional solution is the constant function $y = 0$, which you can easily see satisfies $dy/dt = -ky^2$. The graph of this is the t-axis in Figure 7.1.1.

DEFINITION: Constant functions $y = K$ which are solutions of a differential equation are called *equilibrium solutions*.

Note that in this chemical reaction DE, the equilibrium solution $y = 0$ is approached by all other solutions as Figure 7.1.1 indicates. This makes sense because y is the concentration of hydrogen peroxide and, due to the reaction, it eventually goes to 0.

The arbitrary constant C in Formula (7.1.3) is determined from the initial concentration $y(0) = 1$. Taking $t = 0$ in this formula gives

$$1 = \frac{1}{k(0) - C} = -\frac{1}{C},$$

So $C = -1$ and the particular solution this gives is $y = 1/(kt + 1)$.

DEFINITION: An equation specifying an initial-value for a solution of a DE is called *an initial condition* for the DE. Finding a solution of the DE which satisfies an initial condition is called solving an *initial-value problem* (an IVP).

Example 7.1.4 (Drag Forces)

Problem: A 16 lb steel ball is dropped into a large tank containing a fluid with drag constant of 8 lb-s/ft. If the ball enters the fluid with a velocity of 5 ft/sec at time $t = 0$, find the velocity functions v. Find the limiting velocity.

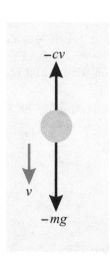

Solution: As you know from experience, motion of a ball through a viscous fluid, such as oil, is retarded by a force (called a drag force) which is in the opposite direction as the motion. Theory and experiment tell us that the drag force is $-cv$ where $c > 0$ is the drag constant. The other force acting on the ball, the one pulling it downward through the fluid, is the force of gravity which, near the earth's surface, has magnitude mg, where g is the acceleration of gravity (32 ft/s^2 in the English system) and m is the mass of the ball (in this case $16/32 = 1/2$ slug). Thus, the total force action on the ball is

$$F = -cv - mg = -8v - \frac{1}{2}(32) = -8v - 16$$

We write the acceleration as the derivative of the velocity and use the Leibniz notation: $my'' = mv' = m\, dv/dt$. Thus, Newton's 2nd Law for the motion of the ball is

$$m\frac{dv}{dt} = -cv - mg,$$

specifically,

$$\frac{1}{2}\frac{dv}{dt} = -8v - 16$$

or more simply.

$$\frac{dv}{dt} = -16(v + 2)$$

The technique for solving this DE is the same as in the last example. Namely treat dv/dt as a ratio of differentials and multiply both sides of the DE by dt to get

$$dv = -16(v + 2)dt$$

Then dividing each side by $v + 2$ results in

$$\frac{1}{v + 2}\, dv = -16\, dt \qquad (7.1.4)$$

NOTE: Dividing by $v+2$ assumes that this quantity is not 0, i.e., $v \neq -2$. You can easily check that the constant function $v = -2$ is a solution of the DE here. Now we proceed to find all the other solutions. Applying the integral symbol to each side of the Equation (7.3.4) yields the equation

$$\int \frac{1}{v+2}\, dv = -\int 16\, dt$$

So, computing the integral on each side gives

$$\ln|v+2| = -16t + C$$

Notice that, again, we only used one constant C of integration. Next consider solving the above equation for v. Applying the exponential function to each side results in

$$e^{\ln|v+2|} = e^{-16t+C}.$$

which is

$$|v+2| = e^{-16t} e^C$$

Here we have used $e^{\ln A} = A$ and $e^{B+C} = e^B e^C$. To simplify this, let r be the positive constant $r = e^C$ and observe that $|v-2| = \pm(v+2)$, so the above equation becomes

$$\pm(v+2) = re^{-16t}, \quad \text{equivalently} \quad v+2 = \pm re^{-16t}$$

Now let $k = \pm r$ to get the following general solution for the velocity function.

$$v = -2 + ke^{-16t} \qquad (7.1.5)$$

This formula gives a whole family of solutions, i.e, infinitely many solutions, one for each choice of k. These together with the equilibrium solution $v = -2$ constitute what is called the *general solution* of this DE. See Figure 7.1.2 for the graphs of six solutions, one of which is the equilibrium solution. It is important to note that each solution approaches the equilibrium solution as t goes to infinity:

$$\lim_{t\to\infty} v = \lim_{t\to\infty}\left(-2 + ke^{-16t}\right) = -2 \text{ ft/s}$$

This means that regardless of the initial velocity with which the ball enters the fluid, the velocity of the ball will approach, due to the drag, a constant velocity of -2. (This, of course assumes the tank is infinitely deep.) For the initial condition $v(0) = -5$, the constant k in Formula (7.1.5) is determined: $-5 = -2 + k$, and so $k = -3$. Thus, the solution of the initial-value problem is

$$v = -2 - 3e^{-16t}$$

INTEGRAL CURVES: A solution of a differential equation is sometimes called an *integral curve* of the DE. Ostensibly this terminology arose from the fact that many solutions of DEs are constructed using integrals. Plotting numerous integral curves in the same figure helps illustrate the dynamics of the situation that the DE describes.

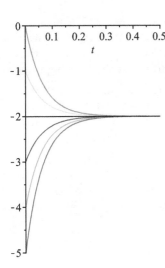

Figure 7.1.2: *Graphs of* $v = -2 + ke^{-16t}$ *for* $k = -3, -2, -1, 0, 1, 2.$

Exercises: 7.1 (Introduction to Differential Equations)

Solutions of DEs

In Exercises 1–18, show that the given DE has the given function(s) as solutions.

1. $xy' + 2y = 4x^2$, $\quad y = x^2 + Cx^{-2}$
2. $xy' + 3y = 5x^2$, $\quad y = x^2 + Cx^{-3}$
3. $y' - (\tan x)y = \sec x$, $\quad y = (x + C)\sec x$
4. $y' + (\cot x)y = \csc x$, $\quad y = (x + C)\csc x$
5. $y'' + 5y' + 6y = 0$, $\quad y = e^{-2t}, y = e^{-3t}$
6. $y'' - y' - 6y = 0$, $\quad y = e^{-2t}, y = e^{3t}$
7. $y'' + 2y' + y = 0$, $\quad y = e^{-t}, y = te^{-t}$
8. $y'' - 2y' + y = 0$, $\quad y = e^{t}, y = te^{t}$
9. $y'' + 4y = 0$, $\quad y = \sin 2t, y = \cos 2t$
10. $y'' + 9y = 0$, $\quad y = \sin 3t, y = \cos 3t$
11. $y'' + 2y' + 5y = 0$, $\quad y = e^{-t}\sin 2t$
12. $y'' + 6y' + 10y = 0$, $\quad y = e^{-3t}\cos t$
13. $x^2y'' - xy' - 3y = 0$, $\quad y = x^{-1}, y = x^3$
14. $x^2y'' + 3xy' - 3y = 0$, $\quad y = x, y = x^{-3}$
15. $x^2y'' + 3xy' = 0$, $\quad y = 1, y = x^{-2}$
16. $x^2y'' + 4xy' = 0$, $\quad y = 1, y = x^{-3}$
17. $4x^2y'' + 4xy' - y = 0$, $\quad y = x^{1/2}, y = x^{-1/2}$
18. $9x^2y'' + 9xy' - y = 0$, $\quad y = x^{1/3}, y = x^{-1/3}$

Finding Solutions of DEs

Find all values of r, so that the suggested function y is a solution of the given DE.

19. $y' + 3y = 0$, $y = e^{rt}$ 20. $y' - 9y = 0$, $y = e^{rt}$
21. $y'' + 3y' = 0$, $y = e^{rt}$ 22. $y'' - 9y' = 0$, $y = e^{rt}$
23. $y'' + y' - 2y = 0$, $y = e^{rt}$
24. $y'' - y' - 2y = 0$, $y = e^{rt}$
25. $y'' + 4y = 0$, $y = \cos rt$ 26. $y'' + 9y = 0$, $y = \sin rt$
27. $y'' - 4y = 0$, $y = e^{rt}$ 28. $y'' - 9y = 0$, $y = e^{rt}$
29. $y'' + 2y' + 10y = 0$, $y = e^{-t}\cos rt$
30. $y'' + 4y' + 13y = 0$, $y = e^{-2t}\sin rt$
31. $x^2y'' - 2xy' + 2y = 0$, $y = x^r$
32. $x^2y'' + 2xy' - 2y = 0$, $y = x^r$
33. $4x^2y'' - 4xy' + y = 0$, $y = x^r$
34. $x^2y'' - 2y = 0$, $y = x^r$

Reaction Rate Equations

Solve the following DEs, which govern certain chemical reactions. Plot a number of the integral curves, including the one that satisfies the given initial condition.

35. $\dfrac{dy}{dt} = -ky$, $k = 0.002$, $y(0) = 2$

36. $\dfrac{dy}{dt} = -ky$, $k = 0.002$, $y(0) = 4$

37. $\dfrac{dy}{dt} = -ky^4$, $k = 0.002$, $y(0) = 2$

38. $\dfrac{dy}{dt} = -ky^n$, for a general $k > 0$, $n > 0$, $y(0) = y_0$.

Motion With Drag

39. An 8 lb steel ball is dropped into a a large tank containing a fluid with drag constant of 8 lb-s/ft. If the ball enters the fluid with a velocity of 6 ft/sec at time $t = 0$, find the velocity function v and the limiting velocity.

40. A 4 lb steel ball is dropped into a large tank containing a fluid with drag constant of 4 lb-s/ft. If the ball enters the fluid with a velocity of 4 ft/sec at time $t = 0$, find the velocity function v and the limiting velocity.

41. A 16 lb steel ball, submerged within a large tank containing a fluid with drag constant of 2 lb-s/ft, is projected upward with an initial velocity of 96 ft/s. (a) Find the velocity function v and the limiting velocity. (b) When is $v = 0$?

42. Solve the general motion with drag DE:

$$m\frac{dv}{dt} = -cv - mg, \qquad (1)$$

with initial velocity $v(0) = v_0$. Find the limiting velocity and the time (if any) when the velocity is zero. Hint: Show that (1) can be written as $\frac{dv}{dt} = -\frac{c}{m}(v + \frac{mg}{c})$.

Reduction of Order

A 2nd-order DE of the form $H(x, y', y'') = 0$ can be reduced to an 1st-order DE by letting $v = y'$. Then $v' = y''$ and so the equation for v is $H(x, v, v') = 0$. (In motion problems this corresponds to introducing the velocity function in place of the derivative of the position function.) Use this to find the general solutions y (involving two arbitrary constants) of the following DEs

43. $y'' = 6x + x^{-1}$ 44. $y'' = 6x^{-3} - x^{-1}$
45. $y'' = x\sin x$ 46. $y'' = x\cos x$
47. $y'' = -8y'$ 48. $y'' = -4y'$
49. $y'' = -8y' - 4$ 50. $y'' = -4y' - 4$
51. $y'' = (y')^2$ 52. $y'' = 2(y')^2$
53. $y'' = (y')^{-2}$ 54. $y'' = 2(y')^{-2}$
55. $y'' = 1 + (y')^2$ 56. $y'' = 4 + (y')^2$

Calculus Concepts & Computation

7.2 Separable DEs and Modeling

While the general form of a 1st order DE is $H(x, y, y') = 0$, there are many special cases of this that have particular forms which allow us to solve them by using algebra and integration techniques. Separable differential equations is one of these special cases. In Section 7.1 we solved the DEs

$$\frac{dy}{dt} = -ky^2 \qquad \text{(Chemical Reaction Rates)}$$

$$m\frac{dv}{dt} = -cv - mg \qquad \text{(Motion with Drag)}$$

Both of these DEs are separable differential equations and the solution technique we used to solve them carries over to the general type of separable differential equation. The general form is given in the following definition.

DEFINITION 7.2.1 (Separable Differential Equations)

A separable differential equation is a first-order DE that can be put in the form

$$G(y)\frac{dy}{dx} + F(x) = 0 \qquad (7.2.1)$$

NOTE 1: The chemical reaction rates and motion with drag DEs are separable since we can write them as

$$\frac{1}{y^2}\frac{dy}{dt} + k = 0$$

$$\frac{m}{cv + mg}\frac{dv}{dt} + 1 = 0$$

NOTE 2: The reason a DE of the form (7.2.1) is called separable is because we can "separate" the variables x, y and their differentials dx, dy. Namely, with the DE in the form (7.2.1), multiplying both sides of it by dx gives

$$G(y)\,dy + F(x)\,dx = 0$$

Applying the integral symbol to this gives the (implicit) solution of the DE:

THEOREM 7.2.1 (The Solution of Separable DEs)

A separable differential equation has its solutions given implicitly by

$$\int G(y)dy + \int F(x)dx = C \qquad (7.2.2)$$

Proof: Suppose g, f are antiderivatives of G, F, respectively: $g'(y) = G(y)$ and $f'(x) = F(x)$ for y and x in intervals J and I, respectively. Then Equation (7.2.2) is

$$g(y) + f(x) = C \qquad (7.2.3)$$

This gives the solutions y of the DE implicitly. We verify this using implicit differentiation. So suppose y is a function of x with values in J for x in I and that

Equation (7.2.3) holds. Then

$$\frac{d}{dx}[g(y)] + \frac{d}{dx}[f(x)] = \frac{d}{dx}[C],$$

or

$$g'(y)\frac{dy}{dx} + f'(x) = 0,$$

which is

$$G(y)\frac{dy}{dx} + F(x) = 0$$

This completes the proof.

NOTE 3: When solving a separable DE, you do not necessarily have to put the DE in Standard Form (7.2.1). Often it convenient to just separate the variables and differentials (using legitimate algebra) and then integrate both sides of the equation. The next example illustrates this.

Example 7.2.1 (Solving Separable DEs)

Problem: Solve the following separable DEs to get an equation for the general solution in implicit form. Solve this equation for y to get an explicit equation for the general solution of the DE. Find a particular solution that satisfies the given initial condition.

(a) $x^3\frac{dy}{dx} = y(x^2 + 2)$, initial condition: $y(1) = 2$

(b) $2\frac{dy}{dt} = y(y - 2)$, initial condition: $y(0) = 1$.

Solution Part (a): First divide both sides by x^3 (so we are assuming $x \neq 0$) and then divide both sides by y (so we are assuming $y \neq 0$). This gives

$$\frac{1}{y}\frac{dy}{dx} = \frac{x^2 + 2}{x^3} = \frac{1}{x} + 2x^{-3}$$

Next, multiply both sides of this by dx and then apply the integral sign:

$$\int \frac{1}{y}\,dy = \int \left(\frac{1}{x} + 2x^{-3}\right)dx$$

This results in

$$\ln|y| = \ln|x| - x^{-2} + C \qquad (7.2.4)$$

This gives, in implicit form, infinitely many solutions of the DE. The process to get (7.2.4) involved, at the first step, dividing by y, so the implicit formula does not contain the equilibrium solution $y = 0$. Next, let's solve Equation (7.2.4) for y. Putting the log terms together gives $\ln|y| - \ln|x| = \ln|y/x|$ and so

$$\ln\left|\frac{y}{x}\right| = -x^2 + C$$

Applying the exponential function to both sides gives

$$e^{\ln\left|\frac{y}{x}\right|} = e^{-x^2 + C},$$

which is (using $e^{\ln A} = A$ and $e^{B+C} = e^B e^C$)

$$\left|\frac{y}{x}\right| = ke^{-x^2},$$

where we let $k = e^C$, for convenience. Now since $|y/x| = \pm(y/x)$ we can write the last equation as

$$\pm\frac{y}{x} = ke^{-x^2}, \quad \text{equivalently,} \quad \frac{y}{x} = \pm ke^{-x^2}$$

If we let $a = \pm k$ and rearrange, the last equation, we get

$$y = axe^{-x^2} \qquad (7.2.5)$$

Note that this explicitly gives all solutions of the DE, since the choice of $a = 0$ gives the equilibrium solution $y = 0$. The arbitrary constant a is determined by the initial condition, which in this case $y(1) = 2$. Substituting 2 for y and 1 for x in the Formula (7.2.5) gives

$$2 = ae^{-1} \quad \text{and so} \quad a = 2e$$

So, the particular solution is $y = 2e\,x\,e^{-x^2} = 2x\,e^{1-x^2}$.

Solution Part (b): Note that $2\dfrac{dy}{dt} = y(y-2)$ has two equilibrium solutions (constant functions) $y = 0$ and $y = 2$. To find non-constant solutions just divide both sides by $y(y-2)$ and then multiply each side by dt. This gives

$$\frac{2}{y(y-2)}\,dy = dt$$

Now apply an integral sign to each side to get

$$\int \frac{2}{y(y-2)}\,dy = \int dt = t + C \qquad (7.2.6)$$

Using partial fractions on the integral with respect y results in

$$\int \frac{2}{y(y-2)}\,dy = \int \left[\frac{-1}{y} + \frac{1}{y-2}\right]\,dy = -\ln|y| + \ln|y-2| = \ln\left|\frac{y-2}{y}\right|$$

Thus, Equation (7.2.6) becomes

$$\ln\left|\frac{y-2}{y}\right| = t + C,$$

and applying the exponential function to each side gives

$$e^{\ln\left|\frac{y-2}{y}\right|} = e^{t+C}, \quad \text{equivalently,} \quad \left|\frac{y-2}{y}\right| = ke^t,$$

where $k = e^C$. As in Part (a), we can remove the absolute value bars and relabel constant in this equation to get

$$\frac{y-2}{y} = ae^t, \quad \text{equivalently,} \quad 1 - \frac{2}{y} = ae^t, \quad \text{i.e.,} \quad 1 - ae^t = \frac{2}{y}$$

Thus, the explicit description of the solutions given implicitly by Equation (7.2.6) is

$$y = \frac{2}{1 - ae^t} \qquad (7.2.7)$$

NOTE 4: The equilibrium solution $y = 2$ is obtained from Equation (7.2.7) by taking $a = 0$. However, the equilibrium solution $y = 0$ is not contained in Equation (7.2.7) (unless you consider taking $a = \infty$ legitimate).

To solve the IVP: $y(0) = 1$, take $y = 1$ and $t = 0$ in Equation (7.2.7) to get $1 = 2/(1-a)$, which gives $a = -1$. Then the corresponding particular solution is

$$y = \frac{2}{1 + e^t}$$

NOTE 5: All the solutions contained in Equation (7.2.7), *except for* $a = 0$, tend to the equilibrium solution $y = 0$:

$$\lim_{t \to \infty} y = \lim_{t \to \infty} \frac{2}{1 - ae^t} = 0$$

COMMENT: Equation (7.2.2) gives after computing the integrals, an equation: $g(y) + f(x) = C$, which implicitly gives the general solution of the separable DE. When you cannot solve this explicitly for y, you can still take this equation as giving a family of integral curves, one for each appropriate value of C. Use of computer plots will help you understand the nature of the solutions. This is what we did Section 2.10 on implicit differentiation, except now we have a whole family of curves.

Example 7.2.2 (An Implicit Description of the General Solution)

Problem: Solve the differential equation:

$$(12y^2 - 4)\frac{dy}{dx} + 8x = 0$$

Use a computer to plot 6 of the integral curves corresponding to $C = 0, 1, 2, 3, 4, 5$. Find the integral curve that satisfies the initial condition $y(1/2) = 0$ and use a computer to plot this curve. Show, graphically, how to split this integral curve up into curves which are graphs of functions.

Solution: Separating variables/differentials and integrating gives

$$\int (12y^2 - 4)dy + \int 8x\,dx = C$$

which is $4y^3 - 4y + 4x^2 = C$, or better, dividing through by 4:

$$y^3 - y + x^2 = C/4 \qquad (7.2.8)$$

This equation is essentially impossible solve for y, so we use `implicitplot` command along with a do loop to plot the curves given by Equation (7.2.8) for the specified values of C. Figure 7.2.1. shows the result.

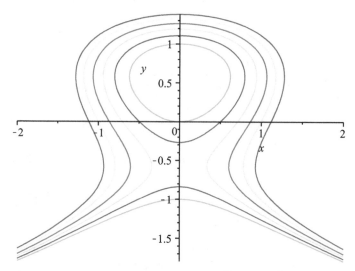

Figure 7.2.1: *The integral curves*: $y^3 - y + x^2 = C/4$ for $C = 0$ (green), 1 (blue), 2 (turquoise), 3 (red), 4 (yellow), 5 (brown)

Note that none of these graphs are the graphs of functions since they do not satisfy the vertical line test.

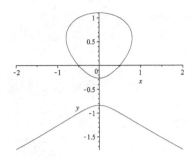

Figure 7.2.2: *The graph of* $y^3 - y + x^2 = 1/4$.

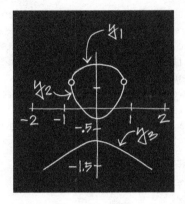

Figure 7.2.3: *The graph of* $y^3 - y + x^2 = 1/4$ *split into graphs of 3 functions.*

For the initial condition $y(1/2) = 0$ take $y = 0$ and $x = 1/2$ in Equation (7.2.8) to get $0 - 0 + 1/4 = C/4$ and so $C = 1$. Thus, the particular integral curve is $y^3 - y + x^2 = 1/4$ and it's graph is the blue curve in Figure 7.2.1. This particular integral curve is shown separately in Figure 7.2.2. There are many ways to break this graph into pieces, each of which is the graph of a function. But since these functions y come from solving the *cubic* Equation (7.2,1), we should view the total graph as the graph of the 3 functions y_1, y_2, y_3. These are are shown in Figure 7.2.3.

Population Models

Differential equations are used to describe a vast and varied number of phenomena which dynamically change over time—such as chemical reactions and motion with drag as discussed in Section 7.1. An interesting and important phenomenon to which DEs have been successfully applied is the growth and decline of populations. We saw this in Example 6.4.11 dealing with the population of halibut in the Northern Pacific. The DE there is

$$y' = -\frac{0.7}{8}(y - 8)y,$$

where y is the biomass of halibut at time t. This is a separable DE, as are the other population models we considered here. These are called *models* because they attempt to capture the dynamics of the changes in populations over time, where there are no general laws, such as Newton's 2nd Law, that can be applied to populations.

Another feature of the populations models studied here is they are *autonomous*, meaning the equation doesn't involve the time:

AUTONOMOUS DEs: $y' = G(y)$ The the general solution of a population model is given implicitly by $F(y) = t + C$, where F is an antiderivative of G. This can often be solved explicitly for y, but regardless, there is a graphical method of sketching the integral curves of the DE using a sketch of the graph of the function G.

Example 7.2.3 (A Population Model)

Problem: Suppose the model for a certain population is

$$y' = -\frac{1}{2} y (y - 1)(y - 2),$$

where $y(t)$ is the population (in millions) at time t (in years). Find the general solution of this separable DE, identify the equilibrium solutions, and sketch a number of the integral curves using the graph of G.

Solution: There are three equilibrium solutions $y = 0$, $y = 1$, and $y = 2$. The other solutions are found as follows. Using Leibniz differentials, the DE is

$$\frac{dy}{dt} = -\frac{1}{2}y(y - 1)(y - 2), \quad \text{so,} \quad \frac{-2}{y(y - 1)(y - 2)} \, dy = dt$$

Using partial fractions on the left side of the above equation, a short computation gives

$$\left[\frac{-1}{y} + \frac{2}{y - 1} + \frac{-1}{y - 2}\right] dy = dt$$

Integrating both sides gives

$$-\ln|y| + 2\ln|y - 1| - \ln|y - 2| = t + C$$

or equivalently

$$\ln\left|\frac{(y - 1)^2}{y(y - 2)}\right| = t + C$$

Applying the exponential function to each side, results in

$$\left| \frac{(y-1)^2}{y(y-2)} \right| = ke^t,$$

where $k = e^C$. As in the above examples we can remove the absolute value bars and write this as

$$\frac{(y-1)^2}{y(y-2)} = ae^t \qquad (7.2.9)$$

This gives the general solution implicitly, but is somewhat tedious to solve explicitly for y. However we can use:

THE GRAPHICAL METHOD: If we let G the function of y defined by

$$G(y) = -\frac{1}{3} y(y-1)(y-2),$$

then a sketch of G will show us how to sketch the integral curves in Equation (7.2.9). The sketch of G, which is a cubic function, doesn't have to be too accurate, but rather just show the qualitative features of the graph. The main feature is its y-intercepts: $G(y) = 0$. (Note that y here denotes the independent variable for the function G.) This gives $y = 0, 1, 2$ (which also identify the equilibrium solutions). Now plot these intercepts on the y-axis, which we orient horizontally in Figure 7.2.4. The intercepts divide the y-axis into four intervals. Determine whether G is positive or negative on each of these, by selecting a test point s in the interval and evaluating $G(s)$. Then you can do the sketch as indicated in Figure 7.2.4.

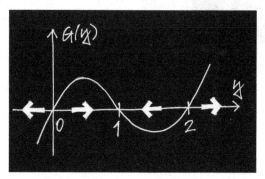

Figure 7.2.4: *A sketch of:* $G(y) = -\frac{1}{3} y(y-1)(y-2)$

Note that we have drawn, on each interval, an arrow in the positive y-direction if G is positive on that interval and in the negative y-direction if G is negative on that interval. We can use this to say where the integral curves are increasing or decreasing because a given integral curve satisfies the DE:

$$y' = G(y).$$

Thus

    (1) Each integral curve with $y(0)$ in $(-\infty, 0)$ decreases as time increases.

    (2) Each integral curve with $y(0)$ in $(0, 1)$ increases as time increases.

    (3) Each integral curve with $y(0)$ in $(1, 2)$ decreases as time increases.

    (4) Each integral curve with $y(0)$ in $(2, \infty)$ increases as time increases.

To use this information to sketch integral curves, choose t as the horizontal axis and y as the vertical axis. First draw in the equilibrium solutions, which are the horizontal lines $y = 0$, $y = 1$, and $y = 2$. These lines create four horizontal strips and an integral curve that has its initial population $y(0)$ in one of the four intervals listed above will remain in this strip. It will increase or decrease (but not both) as t increases. This knowledge allows you sketch the integral curves in each strip. See Figure 7.2.5.

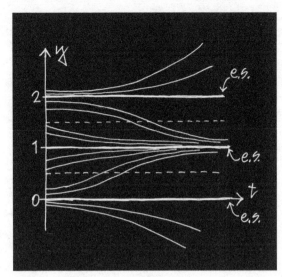

Figure 7.2.5: *Integral curves of*: $y' = -\frac{1}{3}\,y(y-1)(y-2)$

One can show that the integral curves y in the middle strips must all approach the equilibrium solution $y = 1$:

$$\lim_{t \to \infty} y(t) = 1$$

as indicated by the sketch. Also, integral curves y in the outer two strips go to infinity

$$\lim_{t \to \infty} y(t) = \pm\infty$$

For these reasons, the equilibrium solution $y = 1$ is called *asymptotically stable*: *All integral curves that start near it, will approach it asymptotically.* The two other equilibrium solutions $y = 0, y = 2$ are called *unstable*: *All curves starting near them do not stay near them.*

The other feature shown in Figure 7.2.5 is how the integral curves are curveed up or down, i.e., their concavity. From Section 3.2, we know that the concavity of a function y can be determined from its 2nd derivative: (1) concave up where $y'' > 0$, (2) concave down where $y'' < 0$, and (3) inflection points where the concavity changes, forcing $y'' = 0$. In the present setting this can be determined from the graph of G in Figure 7.2.4. To see this, note that since an integral curve satisfies the DE: $y' = G(y)$, differentiating each side of the DE with respect to t (using implicit differentiation on the right side) gives

$$y'' = \frac{d}{dt}\big[G(y)\big] = G'(y)y' = G'(y)G(y)$$

here we used $y' = G(y)$ to get the last expression and employed the notation G' to denote the derivative of G with respect to y. This equation shows us that for an integral curve y in one of the four horizontal strips

(1) If $G'(y)G(y) > 0$, the integral curve y is concave up.

(2) If $G'(y)G(y) < 0$, the integral curve y is concave down.

(3) If $G'(y) = 0$, the integral curve y has a possible inflection point.

Examining Figure 7.2.4 reveals that there are two critical numbers $c_1 < c_2$ (a peak and a valley). Also $G'(y)G(y)$, which is the product of the value of G and the tangent line slope at y, gives us that $G'(y)G(y)$ is (1) negative on $(-\infty, 0)$, (2) positive on $(0, c_1)$, (3) negative on $(c_1 1)$, (4) positive on $(1, c_2)$, (5) negative on $(c_2, 2)$, and (5) positive on $(2, \infty)$. In Figure 7.2.5 we have indicated with dotted lines, the horizontal lines $y = c_1, y = c_2$. An integral curve will have an inflection point where it intersects one of these dotted lines, its concavity changing from up to down (as it crosses $y = c_1$) or from down to up (as it crosses $y = c_2$).

Exercises: 7.2 (Separable Differential Equations and Modeling)

Solving Separable DEs

In Exercises 1–34, find the general solution of the separable DE. Be sure to include the equilibrium solutions, if any, in your answers. Where possible, express the general solution explicitly as a function of y. In either case, find the particular solution that satisfies the given initial condition. CAS: Plot 6–8 integral curves, including the one that satisfies the initial condition.

1. $\dfrac{dy}{dt} = -4y, \quad y(0) = 2$

2. $\dfrac{dy}{dt} = -5y, \quad y(0) = 2$

3. $\dfrac{dy}{dt} = -4y + 12, \quad y(0) = 2$

4. $\dfrac{dy}{dt} = -5y + 15, \quad y(0) = 2$

5. $\dfrac{dy}{dt} = \frac{1}{3}y(y - 3), \quad y(1) = 2$

6. $\dfrac{dy}{dt} = \frac{1}{4}y(y - 4), \quad y(1) = 2$

7. $\dfrac{dy}{dt} = \frac{1}{8}y(y - 2)(y - 4), \quad y(0) = 1$

8. $\dfrac{dy}{dt} = -\frac{1}{8}y(y - 2)(y - 4), \quad y(0) = 3$

9. $\dfrac{dy}{dt} = -\frac{1}{30}y(y - 2)(y - 5), \quad y(0) = 3$

10. $\dfrac{dy}{dt} = \frac{1}{30}y(y - 2)(y - 5), \quad y(0) = 4$

11. $\dfrac{dy}{dt} = \dfrac{(y - 1)^2}{y}, \quad y(2) = 1$

12. $\dfrac{dy}{dt} = \dfrac{(y - 2)^2}{y}, \quad y(1) = 1$

13. $x^2 \dfrac{dy}{dx} = y^2, \quad y(1) = 2$ 14. $x^2 \dfrac{dy}{dx} = -y^2, \quad y(1) = 2$

15. $x^3 \dfrac{dy}{dx} = y^3, \quad y(1) = 2$ 16. $x^3 \dfrac{dy}{dx} = -y^3, \quad y(1) = 2$

17. $2x \dfrac{dy}{dx} = y^2 - 1, \quad y(2) = 1$

18. $2x \dfrac{dy}{dx} = 1 - y^2, \quad y(2) = 1$

19. $\dfrac{dy}{dx} = 2x(y - y^2), \quad y(2) = 1$

20. $\dfrac{dy}{dx} = x(2y - y^2), \quad y(2) = 1$

21. $\dfrac{dy}{dx} = (x - x^2)(y - y^2), \quad y(2) = 1$

22. $\dfrac{dy}{dx} = (2x - x^2)(2y - y^2), \quad y(2) = 1$

23. $(1 + e^x)\dfrac{dy}{dx} = ye^x + e^x, \quad y(2) = 1$

24. $(1 + e^{-x})\dfrac{dy}{dx} = ye^x - e^{-x}, \quad y(2) = 1$

25. $\dfrac{dy}{dx} = (1 + 2x)(1 + y^2), \quad y(2) = 1$

26. $\dfrac{dy}{dx} = (2x - 3)(4 + y^2), \quad y(2) = 1$

27. $(1 + x^2)\dfrac{dy}{dx} = 1 + y^2, \quad y(2) = 1$

28. $(4 + x^2)\dfrac{dy}{dx} = 4 + y^2, \quad y(2) = 1$

29. $\dfrac{dy}{dx} = 3x^2 \cos^2 y, \quad y(2) = 1$

30. $\dfrac{dy}{dx} = 4x^3 \sin^2 y, \quad y(2) = 1$

31. $\sec x \dfrac{dy}{dx} = \csc y, \quad y(2) = 1$

32. $\csc x \dfrac{dy}{dx} = \sec y, \quad y(2) = 1$

33. $\cos^2 x \dfrac{dy}{dx} = \cot y, \quad y(2) = 1$

34. $\sin^2 x \dfrac{dy}{dx} = \tan y, \quad y(2) = 1$

Reduction of Order

Use reduction of order (see Exercises 7.1) to solve the following 2nd-order DEs. Your answer should involve two arbitrary constants.

35. $xy'' + y' = 0$ 36. $xy'' + y' = 0$

37. $(1 + x^2)y'' = 2xy'$ 38. $(1 + x^3)y'' = 3x^2y'$

39. $(x - 2x^3)y'' = (1 - 6x^2)2xy'$

40. $(x + x^3)y'' = (1 + 3x^2)y'$

41. $(1 - x)y'' = (x - 2)y'$ 42. $(1 + x)y'' = (x - 3)y'$

43. $x(1 + x^2)y'' = (1 - x^2)y'$

44. $x(4 + x^2)y'' = (4 - x^2)y'$

45. $(1 + e^x)y'' = y'$ 46. $(1 - e^x)y'' = y'$

47. $\cos x\, y'' = \sin x\, y'$ 48. $\sin x\, y'' = \cos x\, y'$

49. $(\sin x - \cos x)y'' = (\sin x + \cos x)y'$

50. $(\sin x + \cos x)y'' = (\cos x - \sin x)y'$

Population Models

51. In Exercises 1–12 above, consider the differential equation as modeling the evolution of a certain population. (a) Find the general solution of the DE and, where possible, express it in explicit form. (b) Sketch enough of the integral curves to adequately portray the population's behavior based on the initial population. Identify all equilibrium solutions and classify as asymptotically stable, unstable, or semi-stable. (Semi-stable means some the integral curves near it move toward it and others move away.)

Calculus Concepts & Computation

7.3 First-Order Linear DEs

First-order linear differential equations are a very special case of the general 1st-order DE, $H(x, y, y') = 0$. There is a complete theory for the solution of nth-order linear DEs, and for 1st-order linear DEs there is actually a formula for their general solutions. This formula requires computing integrals, as we shall see. The general form of 1st-order linear DEs is given in the following definition.

DEFINITION 7.3.1 (1st Order Linear Differential Equations)

A *1st order linear differential equation* is a DE that can be put in the form

$$\frac{dy}{dx} + p(x)y = q(x) \qquad (7.3.1)$$

Here $p(x)$ and $q(x)$ are given continuous functions on an interval J. We will also use the following form of this where all functions are understood to be functions of x (or whatever the independent variable is):

$$y' + py = q \qquad (7.3.2)$$

This form will be useful for theoretical work and expressing formulas in uncomplicated ways.

Integrating Factor

For the 1st-order linear DE
$$y' + py = q$$
the integrating factor is the function $I = I(x)$ given by
$$I = e^{\int p\,dx} \qquad (7.3.3)$$

NOTE: Often the 1st-order linear DE is not in the standard form (7.3.1) or (7.3.2), but using algebra, you can put it in this form. For example, the DE

$$Ay' + By = C, \quad \text{can be written as} \quad y' + py = q.$$

by dividing by A and taking $p = B/A$ and $q = C/A$. To use the formula we derive below it is imperative that you put the DE in standard form.

The second step in the solution process is to compute a function $I = I(x)$, which is called an *integrating factor*. This is defined in the margin box. Note that since

$$I = e^{\int p\,dx}, \quad \text{the chain rule gives} \quad I' = e^{\int p\,dx} \cdot \left[\int p\,dx\right]' = e^{\int p\,dx} \cdot p = Ip$$

Thus

$$\frac{I'}{I} = p.$$

Using this we can rewrite Equation (7.3.2) as

$$y' + \frac{I'}{I}y = q$$

Now multiply each side of this equation by the integrating factor I to get

$$Iy' + I'y = Iq$$

But by the product rule for derivatives, this equation is

$$(Iy)' = Iq$$

Integrating both sides with respect to x and using $\int (Iy)'\,dx = Iy$ gives

$$Iy = \int Iq\,dx + C$$

Solving this for y gives the formula for the general solution:

$$y = \frac{1}{I}\left[\int Iq\,dx + C\right]$$

This is recorded in the following theorem;

THEOREM 7.3.1 (The Solution of 1st Order Linear DEs)

The general solution of the 1st-order linear DE (7.3.2) is

$$y = \frac{1}{I}\left[\int Iq\,dx + C\right] \qquad (7.3.4)$$

where I is the integrating factor given in (7.3.3) and C is an arbitrary constant.

NOTE: To use Formula (7.3.4), first compute the integrating factor I in (7.3.3). For this you do not need to add a constant of integration. Then compute the integral $\int Iq\,dx$, adding on a constant of integration at this stage.

Example 7.3.1 (Solving 1st-Order DEs)

Problem: Solve the following 1st-order linear DEs, writing down the general solution as given in Formula (7.3.4). For Parts (a) and (b) find a particular solution that satisfies the given initial condition.

Part (a): $y' - \dfrac{3}{x}y = x^2$, initial condition: $y(1) = 2$

Solution Part (a): Here $p(x) = -3/x$ and so

$$\int p\,dx = -3\int \frac{1}{x}\,dx = -3\ln x = \ln(x^{-3})$$

Then the integrating factor is

$$I = e^{\int p\,dx} = e^{\ln(x^{-3})} = x^{-3}$$

Next compute the integral

$$\int Iq\,dx = \int x^{-3}\cdot x^2\,dx = \int x^{-1}\,dx = \int \frac{1}{x}\,dx = \ln x + C$$

Then the general solution is

$$y = \frac{1}{I}\left[\int Iq\,dx + C\right] = x^3\left[\ln x + C\right] = x^3\ln x + Cx^3$$

To choose the constant C so that the initial condition $y(1) = 2$ is satisfied, substitute $x = 1, y = 2$ into this general solution. This gives $2 = (1)^3\ln(1) + C(1)^3 = 0 + C$. So the particular solution whose graph goes through the point $(1, 2)$ is

$$y = x^3\ln x + 2x^3$$

Part (b): $y' - 2(\tan x)\,y = \sec x$, initial condition: $y(0) = 3$.

Solution Part (b): Here $p(x) = -2\tan x$ and so

$$\int p\,dx = -2\int \tan x\,dx = -2\int \frac{\sin x}{\cos x}\,dx = 2\ln(\cos x) = \ln(\cos^2 x)$$

Here, to do the integral, we made the substitution $u = \cos x$ (alternatively you may have memorized the is $\ln(\sec x) = -\ln(\cos x)$. Now the integrating factor is

$$I = e^{\int p\,dx} = e^{\ln(\cos^2)} = \cos^2 x$$

Next compute the integral

$$\int Iq\,dx = \int \cos^2 x \sec x\,dx = \int \cos^2 x \Big[\frac{1}{\cos x}\Big]\,dx = \int \cos x\,dx = \sin x + C$$

Then the general solution is

$$y = \frac{1}{I}\Big[\int Iq\,dx + C\Big] = \frac{1}{\cos^2 x}\big[\sin x + C\big] = \sec x \tan x + C\sec^2 x$$

To choose the constant C so that the initial condition $y(0) = 3$ is satisfied, substitute $x = 0, y = 3$ into this general solution. This gives $3 = \sec(0)\tan(0) + C(\sec(0))^2 = 0 + C$. So the particular solution whose graph goes through the point $(0, 3)$ is

$$y = \sec x \tan x + 3\sec^2 x$$

Part (c): $2x^2 y' - x\,y = 2x^3$, no initial condition.

Solution Part (c): Here we must first put the DE in standard form to identify the functions p and q. So divide both sides by $2x^2$ to get

$$y' - \frac{1}{2x}\,y = x.$$

So now we can identify $p(x) = -1/(2x)$ and then

$$\int p\,dx = -\frac{1}{2}\int \frac{1}{x}\,dx = -\frac{1}{2}\ln x = \ln(x^{-1/2})$$

Then the integrating factor is

$$I = e^{\int p\,dx} = e^{\ln(x^{-1/2})} = x^{-1/2}$$

Next compute the integral

$$\int Iq\,dx = \int x^{-1/2} \cdot x\,dx = \int x^{1/2}\,dx = \frac{2}{3}x^{3/2} + C$$

Then the general solution is

$$y = \frac{1}{I}\Big[\int Iq\,dx + C\Big] = x^{1/2}\Big[\frac{2}{3}x^{3/2} + C\Big] = \frac{2}{3}x^2 + Cx^{1/2}$$

Example 7.3.2 (A Mixing Problem)

Problem: A 1000 gallon storage tank initially contains 100 gallons of water with 10 pounds of salt mixed uniformly throughout. At time $t = 0$, a salt/water solution, with concentration of 0.5 lbs of salt per gallon, begins pouring in at the top of the tank at the rate of 2 gallons per minute and the solution in the tank, after being well-stirred, is allowed to flow out of the bottom of the tank at a rate of 1 gal/min. Let $Q(t)$ denote the number of pounds of salt in the tank at time t. One can show (see the exercises) that the differential equation that models the change in Q is

$$\frac{dQ}{dt} + \frac{1}{100 + t}Q = 1.$$

(a) Find the general solution of this DE and the particular solution that satisfies the initial condition. (b) Determine how long T it takes the tank to fill up and the concentration (lbs/gal) of salt in the tank at this time. (c) If the tank were infinity large, find the limiting concentration of the salt in the tank.

Solution: Here $p(x) = 1/(100 + t)$ and so

$$\int p\, dt = \int \frac{1}{100 + t}\, dx = \ln(100 + t)$$

Now the integrating factor is

$$I = e^{\int p\, dt} = e^{\ln(100+t)} = 100 + t$$

Next compute the integral

$$\int Iq\, dt = \int (100 + t)\, dt = \frac{1}{2}(100 + t)^2 + C$$

Note that we used the substitution $u = 100 + t$ to do the integral. (This makes things work better below.) Then the general solution is

$$Q = \frac{1}{I}\left[\int Iq\, dt + C\right] = \frac{1}{100 + t} \cdot \left[\frac{1}{2}(100 + t)^2 + C\right] = \frac{1}{2}(100 + t) + C(100 + t)^{-1}$$

To choose the constant C so that the initial condition $Q(0) = 10$ is satisfied, substitute $t = 0, Q = 10$ into this general solution. This gives $10 = 50 + C/100$. So $C = -4,000$. Then the particular solution is

$$Q = \frac{1}{2}(100 + t) - 4000(100 + t)^{-1}$$

The time when the tank overflows is when $100 + t = 1000$, so $T = 900$ minutes. The amount of salt in the tank at this time is

$$Q(900) = 500 - \frac{4000}{1000} = 496$$

So the concentration is $Q(900)/1000 = 496/1000 = 0.496$, which is about 1/2 a pound of salt per gallon.

If the tank were infinitely large then it never overflows, so we can take $t \to \infty$ to get

$$\lim_{t \to \infty} \frac{Q(t)}{100 + t} = \lim_{t \to \infty} \frac{1}{2} \cdot \frac{(100 + t) - 4000(100 + t)^{-1}}{100 + t}$$

$$= \lim_{t \to \infty} \frac{1}{2}\left[1 - 4000(100 + t)^{-2}\right] = \frac{1}{2}$$

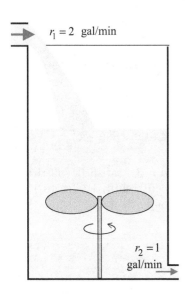

$r_1 = 2$ gal/min

$r_2 = 1$ gal/min

Figure 7.3.1: *A well mixed salt solution.*

Bernoulli Equations

There are differential equations which closely resemble 1st-order linear DEs in form but have a term of the form y^n involving a power n of the unknown function y. These are the Bernoulli differential equations, as the following definition explains:

DEFINITION 7.3.2 (Bernoulli Differential Equations)

A first-order DE that can be put in the form

$$y' + py = qy^n \qquad (7.3.5)$$

is called a Bernoulli DE. Here $p(x)$, $q(x)$ are given continuous functions on an interval J.

NOTE: The power n of y in a Bernoulli DE can be any real number. For $n = 0$ the Bernoulli DE is a 1st-order linear DE and for $n = 1$ it is a separable DE. So we only consider cases $n \neq 0, 1$.

The solution technique for solving a Bernoulli DE is this. First divide each side of the Bernoulli DE (7.3.5) by y^n to get

$$y^{-n}y' + py^{1-n} = q \qquad (7.3.6)$$

Since the first term $y^{-n}y'$ of this DE is essentially the derivative of y^{-n} with respect to the independent variable (either x or t), we let

$$v = y^{1-n} \qquad (7.3.7)$$

Then by the chain rule

$$v' = (1-n)y^{-n}y', \quad \text{equivalently,} \quad \frac{1}{1-n}v' = y^{-n}y'$$

Now use these to rewrite DE (7.3.6) as $\frac{1}{1-n}v' + pv = q$, equivalently,

$$v' + (1-n)pv = (1-n)q \qquad (7.3.8)$$

This is a 1st-order DE for the function v. Solving it by the technique discussed above gives v and then from Equation (7.3.7), we get y:

$$y = v^{1/(1-n)} \qquad (7.3.9)$$

Example 7.3.3 (Solving a Bernoulli DE)

Problem: Find the general solution of the DE:

$$y' - \frac{1}{x}y = -xy^2$$

Solution: The first step is to divide each side by y^2 to get

$$y^{-2}y' - \frac{1}{x}y^{-1} = -x$$

Next let $v = y^{-1}$, so that $v' = -y^{-2}y'$, which is $-v' = y^{-2}y'$. Rewrite the DE in terms of v to get

$$-v' - \frac{1}{x}v = -x \quad \text{equivalently,} \quad v' + \frac{1}{x}v = x$$

This is a linear DE with $p = 1/x, q = x$, so that $I = x$ and $\int Iq\,dx = \int x^2\,dx = x^3/3 + C$. Then

$$v = \frac{1}{I}\left[\int Iq\,dx + C\right] = \frac{1}{x}\left[\frac{1}{3}x^3 + C\right] = \frac{x^3 + 3C}{3x}$$

Then since $v = y^{-1}$, we have $y = v^{-1}$, and so the general solution is

$$y = \frac{3x}{x^3 + 3C}$$

Exercises: 7.3 (First-Order Linear DEs)

Solving 1st-Order Linear DEs

In Exercises 1–34, find the general solution of the the 1st-order linear DE.

1. $y' + 2y = 3e^{-5x}$ **2.** $y' + 3y = 4e^{-7x}$

3. $y' - 3y = x$ **4.** $y' - 4y = x$

5. $y' - 5y = xe^{3x}$ **6.** $y' - 4y = xe^{2x}$

7. $y' + \dfrac{1}{x}y = \sin x$ **8.** $y' + \dfrac{1}{x}y = \cos x$

9. $y' + \dfrac{2}{x}y = \ln xx$ **10.** $y' + \dfrac{2}{x}y = x\ln x$

11. $y' - \dfrac{3}{x}y = x^3 \sin x$ **12.** $y' - \dfrac{3}{x}y = x^3 \cos x$

13. $y' + \dfrac{2}{x}y = \dfrac{1}{1+x^3}$ **14.** $y' + \dfrac{3}{x}y = \dfrac{1}{1+x^4}$

15. $y' + \dfrac{2}{x}y = \dfrac{1}{1-x^2}$ **16.** $y' + \dfrac{2}{x}y = \dfrac{1}{4-x^2}$

17. $y' + \dfrac{2x}{1+x^2}y = e^{-x}$ **18.** $y' + \dfrac{2x}{1+x^2}y = e^{-2x}$

19. $y' + \dfrac{1}{x\ln x}y = x^2$ **20.** $y' + \dfrac{1}{x\ln x}y = x^3$

21. $y' + \dfrac{y}{\sqrt{x}(1+\sqrt{x})} = x^2$ **22.** $y' + \dfrac{y}{\sqrt{x}(1+\sqrt{x})}y = x^3$

23. $y' - (\tan x)\,y = \cos x$ **24.** $y' - (\tan x)\,y = \sin x$

25. $y' - (\tan x)\,y = x\sec x$ **26.** $y' - (\tan x)\,y = x^2 \sec x$

27. $y' + \dfrac{\cos x}{1+\sin x}y = x$ **28.** $y' - \dfrac{\sin x}{1+\cos x}y = x$

29. $y' + \dfrac{\sec^2 x}{2+\tan x}y = \cos x$ **30.** $y' - \dfrac{\csc^2 x}{2+\cot x}y = \sin x$

31. $y' + \dfrac{1+\cos x}{x+\sin x}y = x$ **32.** $y' + \dfrac{1-\sin x}{x+\cos x}y = x$

33. $y' + \dfrac{1}{x(1+\ln x)}y = x^2$ **34.** $y' + \dfrac{1}{x(1+\ln x)}y = x^3$

Mixing Problems

35. A 1000 gallon storage tank initially contains 100 gallons of water with $Q(0) = 15$ pounds of salt mixed uniformly throughout. At time $t = 0$ a salt/water solution, with concentration of $a = 0.4$ lb/gal, begins pouring in at the top of the tank at the rate of $r_1 = 5$ gallons per minute and the solution in the tank, after being well-stirred, is allowed to flow out of the bottom of the tank at a rate of $r_2 = 3$ gal/min. Let $Q(t)$ denote the number of pounds of salt in the tank at time t. The DE that models the change in Q is

$$\frac{dQ}{dt} + \frac{3}{100+2t}Q = 2.$$

(a) Find the general solution of this DE and the particular solution that satisfies the initial condition. (b) Determine the amount of time T it takes the tank to fill up and the concentration (lbs/gal) of salt in the tank at this time. (c) If the tank were infinity large, find the limiting concentration of the salt in the tank.

36. (General Mixing Problem) In the general mixing problem $Q(t)$ and and $V(t)$ are the amounts of salt and water in the tank at time t, while r_1 is the inflow rate of a solution with concentration a lb/gal, and r_2 is the outflow rate with concentration $Q(t)/V(t)$. Show that the DE that models the amount of salt Q in the tank is

$$\frac{dQ}{dt} + \frac{r_2}{V_0 + (r_1 - r_2)t}Q = ar_1.$$

37. Solve the mixing problem where $r_1 = 2, r_2 = 3, a = 3, V_0 = 500$, and $Q_0 = 50$. (See Exercise 36 for notation.) Find the time T when the tank first becomes empty.

38. Solve the mixing problem where $r_1 = 2, r_2 = 4, a = 2, V_0 = 400$, and $Q_0 = 40$. (See Exercise 36 for notation.) Find the time T when the tank first becomes empty.

39. For a 1000 gallon tank, solve the mixing problem where $r_1 = 2, r_2 = 2, a = 3, V_0 = 500$, and $Q_0 = 50$. (See Exercise 36 for notation.) Find the the limiting amount of salt in the tank and the eventual concentration.

40. For a 1000 gallon tank, solve the mixing problem where $r_1 = 3, r_2 = 3, a = 2, V_0 = 400$, and $Q_0 = 40$. (See Exercise 36 for notation.) Find the the limiting amount of salt in the tank and the eventual concentration.

Solving Bernoulli DEs

Find the general solutions of the following DEs.

41. $y' - y = -y^2$ **42.** $y' + y = y^2$

43. $y' + \dfrac{1}{x}y = \dfrac{1}{x}y^{-2}$ **44.** $y' + \dfrac{1}{x}y = \dfrac{1}{x}y^{-4}$

45. $y' + \dfrac{1}{x}y = 2x^2 y^2$ **46.** $y' + y' + \dfrac{1}{x}y = 3x^3 y^2$

47. $y' + \dfrac{1}{x}y = x^3 y^3$ **48.** $y' + y' + \dfrac{1}{x}y = x^4 y^3$

49. $y' - 2y = -e^x y^2$ **50.** $y' - 3y = -e^x y^2$

51. $y' + y = xe^x y^{3/2}$ **52.** $y' + y = x^2 e^x y^{3/2}$

53. $y' - y = -xe^{-2x}y^3$ **54.** $y' - y = -xe^{-3x}y^4$

55. $y' + (\tan x)y = (\cos x)y^2$ **56.** $y' + (\tan x)y = (\cos x)y^2$

8

Sequences and Series

Calculus *Concepts & Computation*

8.1 Sequences

This section introduces the important mathematical concept of a sequence (principally, a sequence of numbers). Informally, a sequence is an ordered list. An example of a sequence of numbers is

$$1, \frac{1}{2}, \frac{1}{3}, \frac{1}{4}, \frac{1}{5}, \ \cdots \ , \frac{1}{n}, \ \cdots$$

which is the sequence of reciprocals of the natural numbers. Another example of a sequence is

$$2, 4, 6, 8, 10, \ \cdots \ , 2n, \ \cdots$$

which is the sequence of even natural numbers. For a general sequence, we will use the notation:

$$a_1, a_2, a_3, a_4, a_5, \ \cdots \ , a_n, \ \cdots$$

The numbers in the sequence are called the *terms* of the sequence: first term, second term, etc, with a_n called the nth term of the sequence. Rather than listing some of the initial terms of the sequence and then using an ellipsis to indicate continuation of the pattern, we will often use the *brace* notation instead. The brace notation: $\{a_n\}_{n=1}^{\infty}$ stands for the sequence

$$\{a_n\}_{n=1}^{\infty} = a_1, a_2, a_3, a_4, a_5, \ \cdots \ , a_n, \ \cdots$$

For example,

$$\left\{ \frac{n}{n+1} \right\}_{n=1}^{\infty} = \frac{1}{2}, \frac{2}{3}, \frac{3}{4}, \frac{4}{5}, \ \cdots \ , \frac{n}{n+1}, \cdots$$

is the brace notation for the sequence of ratios of successive natural numbers. In this notation, the symbol n is called the *index* of the sequence. We can use other symbols for the index and, while the indexing usually starts at 1, we can change that too. For example, the sequence of ratios of successive natural numbers can also be written as

$$\left\{ \frac{k}{k+1} \right\}_{k=1}^{\infty} = \frac{1}{2}, \frac{2}{3}, \frac{3}{4}, \frac{4}{5}, \ \cdots \ , \frac{k}{k+1}, \cdots$$

or as

$$\left\{ \frac{p+1}{p+2} \right\}_{p=0}^{\infty} = \frac{1}{2}, \frac{2}{3}, \frac{3}{4}, \frac{4}{5}, \cdots, \frac{p+1}{p+2}, \ \cdots$$

Sequence

A real-valued function with domain the set of natural numbers

$$f : \mathbb{N} \to \mathbb{R}$$

In the study of sequences, the initial terms of a sequence are not important; it is only the limiting behavior of the sequence that is of concern. Thus, we will often write the brace notation for the sequence in abbreviated form $\{a_n\}$.

A sequence of numbers, more formally, can be defined as a real-valued function f whose domain is the set of natural numbers, $f : \mathbb{N} \to \mathbb{R}$. Then the nth term of the sequence is just $a_n = f(n)$. In this sense, we can consider the graph of the sequence as the plot of the points $\{(n, f(n)) \,|\, n \in \mathbb{N}\}$. For the plot you can use the special-purpose Maple command

```
sequenceplot(f,K)
```

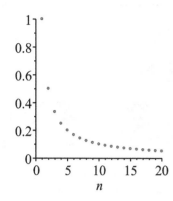

Figure 8.1.1: *A plot of the first* 20 *terms of the sequence* $\left\{\frac{1}{n}\right\}_{n=1}^{\infty}$

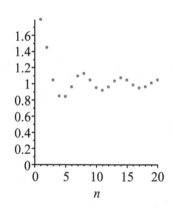

Figure 8.1.2: *A plot of the first* 20 *terms of the sequence* $\left\{(1+\frac{1}{n})^{\sin(n)}\right\}_{n=1}^{\infty}$

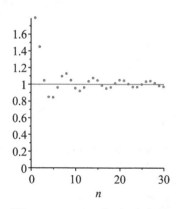

Figure 8.1.3: *A plot of the first* 30 *terms of the sequence* $\left\{(1+\frac{1}{n})^{\sin(n)}\right\}_{n=1}^{\infty}$

where f is the sequence and K is the number of terms you want plotted. Actually, the command gives a dynamic plot of the first K terms of the sequence, or more precisely, a plot of the points

$$\{\, (n, f(n)) \mid n = 1, 2, 3, \ldots, K \,\}$$

We can use this dynamic plot to determine how the sequence behaves as n get large and also get a motivation for the notion of limits of sequences.

Example 8.1.1

Problem: For the sequences:

$$\text{(a) } \left\{\tfrac{1}{n}\right\}_{n=1}^{\infty} \qquad \text{(b) } \left\{\left(1 + \tfrac{1}{n}\right)^{\sin(n)}\right\}_{n=1}^{\infty}$$

use the `sequenceplot` command to plot the first 20 terms of the sequence and use this to make a conjecture as to what number L the terms of the sequence approach as n gets large (as $n \to \infty$).

Solution (a): The following code defines the sequence and creates the dynamic plot.

```
> f:=n->1/n;
```

$$f := n \mapsto \frac{1}{n}$$

```
> sequenceplot(f,20);
```

The `sequenceplot` command produces an animation (movie) of the terms in the sequence. To obtain a static plot of the last frame in the animation use the command:

```
> printsequenceplot(f,20);
```

See Figure 8.1.1. Clearly the terms of this sequence become small as n becomes large and we can make $a_n = 1/n$ as close to 0 as we please by taking n large enough. When this is the case we will say the *limit of the sequence* is zero and write

$$\lim_{n \to \infty} \frac{1}{n} = 0$$

(See the precise definition of this below). This is a standard limit for us, one that we use many times.

Solution (b): We define and plot the sequence as follows.

```
> f:=n->(1+1/n)^(sin(n));
```

$$f := n \mapsto \left(1 + \frac{1}{n}\right)^{\sin(n)}$$

```
> sequenceplot(f,20);
```

The static plot of the first 20 terms is shown in Figure 8.1.2. The plot suggests that the terms of the sequence $\left\{\left(1 + n^{-1}\right)^{\sin(n)}\right\}$ oscillate about the number $L = 1$, approaching it as n gets large. This is more apparent if we use a third argument in the `sequenceplot` command to include a plot of the horizontal line $y = L$ in the figure:

$$\texttt{sequenceplot(f,K,L)}$$

We also include ten more terms in the plot of the sequence.

```
> sequenceplot(f,30,1);
```

The static plot is shown in Figure 8.1.3.

The evidence suggests that the limit of the sequence is 1:

$$\lim_{n \to \infty} \left(1 + \frac{1}{n}\right)^{\sin(n)} = 1$$

Later we will be able to use some limit theorems to prove that the limit is 1.

The above examples motivate the notion of the limit of a sequence. In symbols

$$\lim_{n \to \infty} a_n = L.$$

The concept is exactly the same as the limit of a function at infinity which we studied in Section 1.8:

$$\lim_{x \to \infty} f(x) = L,$$

except now we are dealing with sequences, which are special types of functions. A formal definition of the limit concept for sequences is as follows.

DEFINITION 8.1.1 (Limit of a Sequence)

A sequence $\{a_n\}$ *has a limit* L *if for every* $\varepsilon > 0$, *there is a natural number* N *such that*

$$\left| a_n - L \right| < \varepsilon$$

for all $n \geq N$. *When this is the case, we say the sequence converges (to L) and write*

$$\lim_{n \to \infty} a_n = L$$

One can show that a sequence $\{a_n\}$ can converge to at most one number L (i.e., when the limit $\lim_{n \to \infty} a_n$ exists, it is unique). If there is no number L that satisfies the criterion in Definition 8.1.1, then we say the sequence *diverges* (or the limit $\lim_{n \to \infty} a_n$ does not exist).

The inequality in Definition (8.1.1) says that "the distance between a_n and L is less than ε." By basic algebra, the inequality is equivalent to the compound inequality

$$L - \varepsilon < a_n < L + \varepsilon.$$

This means that a_n is in the interval $(L - \varepsilon, L + \varepsilon)$. Based on these interpretations, we see that the criterion in Definition 8.1.1 says that for a given $\varepsilon > 0$, there is a natural number N such that the plot of the sequence for $n \geq N$ lies between the horizontal lines $y = L + \varepsilon$ and $y = L - \varepsilon$, which is called an *epsilon strip* (ε-*strip*). Figure 8.1.4 below exhibits this.

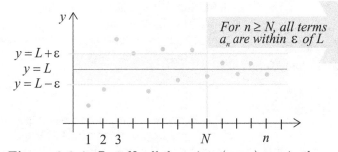

Figure 8.1.4: *Past N, all the points* (n, a_n) *are in the* ε-*strip.*

Example 8.1.2

Problem: For the sequence $\left\{ \left(1 + \frac{1}{n}\right)^{\sin(n)} \right\}$ and values of epsilon: $\varepsilon = 0.5, 0.1, 0.05$ use the plot of the sequence to determine values of N so that $1 - \varepsilon < a_n < 1 + \varepsilon$ for all $n \geq N$.

Solution: Rather than use `sequenceplot` for this, we use a similar special-purpose Maple procedure

```
sequencelimit(f,K,L,ε)
```

which dynamically plots the first K terms of the sequence, the line $y = L$, where L is the conjectured limit, and the lines $y = L + \varepsilon$ and $y = L - \varepsilon$.

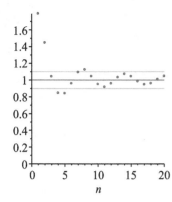

Figure 8.1.5: *A plot of the first 30 terms of the sequence* $\left\{(1+\frac{1}{n})^{\sin(n)}\right\}$ *and the lines* $y = 1, y = 1.1, y = 0.9.$ *The plot suggests that* $0.9 < a_n < 1.1,$ *for* $n > 8.$

```
> f:=n->(1+1/n)^(sin(n));
```

$$f := n \mapsto \left(1 + \frac{1}{n}\right)^{\sin(n)}$$

```
> sequencelimit(f,20,1,0.5);
> sequencelimit(f,20,1,0.1);
> sequencelimit(f,20,1,0.05);
```

Examining the final frames in each of the animations, we see that for $\varepsilon = 0.5$, we can take $N = 2$, for $\varepsilon = 0.1$, we take $N = 9$, and for $\varepsilon = 0.05$, we can take $N = 17$. The last frame of the animation for $\varepsilon = 0.1$ is shown in Figure 8.1.5.

As we did in Section 1.8 for limits of functions, we will encounter special types of divergent sequences, which either increase with out bound or decrease without bound as $n \to \infty$. These types of sequences do not have limits except in the sense of extended real numbers. The terms of the sequence approach either ∞ or $-\infty$, respectively. This is made precise in the following definition

---

DEFINITION 8.1.2 (Diverges to Plus or Minus Infinity)

We say a sequence $\{a_n\}$ *diverges to infinity and write* $\lim\limits_{n\to\infty} a_n = \infty$, *if for every* $M > 0$ *there exists a natural number N such that*

$$a_n > M, \ for \ all \ n \geq N$$

We say the sequence diverges to minus infinity and write $\lim\limits_{n\to\infty} a_n = -\infty$ *if for every* $m < 0$ *there exists a natural number N such that*

$$a_n \leq m, \ for \ all \ n \geq N$$

NOTE: The criterion in Definition 8.1.1 is called the ε-N criterion, or the ε-N definition of the limit of a sequence. Similarly, the criterion in Definition 8.1.2 is called the M-N criterion for divergence to infinity. Using these criteria to *prove* that a limit exists and is a number L (or $\pm\infty$) can be challenging. However, some of the standard limits are easy to prove, such as

$$\lim_{n\to\infty} \frac{1}{n} = 0 \ \text{ and } \ \lim_{n\to\infty} \frac{1}{\sqrt{n}} = 0$$

A Canonical Limit
For any positive number p
$\lim\limits_{n\to\infty} \dfrac{1}{n^p} = 0$

and in general, we get the result shown in the margin box. (See the exercises). The limits of more complicated sequences can be difficult (if not impossible) to prove using the ε-N criterion. However, the use of theorems (proven using the ε-N criterion) makes evaluation of such limits direct and easy. These theorems are entirely similar to those you studied in Chapter 1 for limits of functions. The most basic one is the limit laws theorem for sequences:

THEOREM 8.1.1 (Limit Laws for Sequences)

Suppose that $\{a_n\}$, $\{b_n\}$ *are convergent sequences. Then*

$$(1) \quad \lim_{n \to \infty}(a_n + b_n) = \lim_{n \to \infty} a_n + \lim_{n \to \infty} b_n \qquad \textit{(Sum Law)}$$

$$(2) \quad \lim_{n \to \infty}(a_n - b_n) = \lim_{n \to \infty} a_n - \lim_{n \to \infty} b_n \qquad \textit{(Difference Law)}$$

$$(3) \quad \lim_{n \to \infty} k a_n = k \lim_{n \to \infty} a_n, \textit{ for any constant } k \qquad \textit{(Constant Multiple Law)}$$

$$(4) \quad \lim_{n \to \infty} a_n b_n = \lim_{n \to \infty} a_n \lim_{n \to \infty} b_n \qquad \textit{(Product Law)}$$

$$(5) \quad \lim_{n \to \infty} \frac{a_n}{b_n} = \frac{\lim\limits_{n \to \infty} a_n}{\lim\limits_{n \to \infty} b_n}, \textit{ provided } \lim_{n \to \infty} b_n \neq 0 \qquad \textit{(Quotient Law)}$$

The squeeze theorem for limits also extends to sequences and is often convenient to use:

THEOREM 8.1.2 (The Squeeze Theorem for Sequences)

Suppose that $\{a_n\}, \{b_n\}, \{c_n\}$ *are sequences with* $a_n \leq b_n \leq c_n$ *for all n.*

If $\lim\limits_{n \to \infty} a_n = L = \lim\limits_{n \to \infty} c_n$, *then* $\lim\limits_{n \to \infty} b_n = L$

Additionally, a convergent sequence which is composed with a continuous function gives a convergent sequence whose limit can easily be evaluated. This is the content of the following theorem.

THEOREM 8.1.3 (Continuous Function Law)

Suppose that $\{a_n\}$ *is a sequence whose terms lie in the domain of a function G.*

If $\lim\limits_{n \to \infty} a_n = L$ *and if G is continuous at L, then* $\lim\limits_{n \to \infty} G(a_n) = G(\lim\limits_{n \to \infty} a_n) = G(L)$

Example 8.1.3

Problem: Use the above theorems to find the limits of the following sequences.

$$\text{(a)} \left\{\frac{\sqrt{n}-3}{1+2\sqrt{n}}\right\} \quad \text{(b)} \left\{\left(1+\frac{1}{n}\right)\ln\left(2-\frac{1}{n}\right)\right\} \quad \text{(c)} \left\{\left(1+\frac{1}{n}\right)^{\sin(n)}\right\}$$

Solution (a): Divide numerator and denominator of the nth term by $\sqrt{n}$ and then use the limit laws

$$\lim_{n\to\infty} \frac{\sqrt{n}-3}{1+2\sqrt{n}} = \lim_{n\to\infty} \frac{1-\frac{3}{\sqrt{n}}}{\frac{1}{\sqrt{n}}+2}$$

$$= \frac{\lim\limits_{n\to\infty}\left(1-\frac{3}{\sqrt{n}}\right)}{\lim\limits_{n\to\infty}\left(\frac{1}{\sqrt{n}}+2\right)} = \frac{1-0}{0+2} = \frac{1}{2}.$$

Solution (b): Use the product of the limits rule (Theorem 8.1.1 (4)) and the continuous function rule (Theorem 8.1.3 with $G(x) = \ln x$):

$$\lim_{n \to \infty} \left[\left(1 + \frac{1}{n} \right) \ln \left(2 - \frac{1}{n} \right) \right] = \lim_{n \to \infty} \left(1 + \frac{1}{n} \right) \lim_{n \to \infty} \ln \left(2 - \frac{1}{n} \right)$$

$$= (1 + 0) \cdot \ln \left(\lim_{n \to \infty} \left(2 - \frac{1}{n} \right) \right)$$

$$= 1 \cdot \ln (2 - 0) = \ln 2$$

Solution (c): We **saw** in Examples 8.1 and 8.2 that this sequence appears to have limit 1

$$\lim_{n \to \infty} \left(1 + \frac{1}{n} \right)^{\sin(n)} = 1.$$

To prove this using the theorems above, we first use the base-changing identity

$$B^A = e^{A \ln B}$$

to write the nth term of the sequence as

$$\left(1 + \frac{1}{n} \right)^{\sin(n)} = e^{\sin(n) \ln(1 + 1/n)}$$

Since $G(x) = e^x$ is continuous everywhere, by Theorem 8.1.3 all we have to do is to determine the limit of the sequence

$$a_n = \sin(n) \ln \left(1 + \frac{1}{n} \right)$$

For this we use the Squeeze Theorem. Observe that

$$-1 \le \sin(n) \le 1,$$

for all n. Since $\ln(1 + 1/n)$ is positive, multiplying the above inequalities by this gives

$$-\ln \left(1 + \frac{1}{n} \right) \le \sin(n) \ln \left(1 + \frac{1}{n} \right) \le \ln \left(1 + \frac{1}{n} \right),$$

for all n. By the continuous function rule

$$\lim_{n \to \infty} \ln \left(1 + \frac{1}{n} \right) = \ln \left(\lim_{n \to \infty} 1 + \frac{1}{n} \right) = \ln(1 + 0) = \ln(1) = 0.$$

So, by the Squeeze Theorem

$$L = \lim_{n \to \infty} \sin(n) \ln \left(1 + \frac{1}{n} \right) = 0$$

Consequently

$$\lim_{n \to \infty} \left(1 + \frac{1}{n} \right)^{\sin(n)} = \lim_{n \to \infty} e^{\sin(n) \ln(1 + 1/n)} = e^L = 1.$$

L' Hospital's Rule

As we saw in Chapter 3, L' Hospital's Rule can often be used to evaluate limits of functions at infinity. Thus, you would expect it is often useful for finding limits of sequences. The following theorem states how L' Hospital's rule is employed for sequences.

THEOREM 8.1.4 (L' Hospital's Rule for Sequences)

Suppose $\{f(n)\}_{n=1}^{\infty}, \{g(n)\}_{n=1}^{\infty}$ *are sequences where f, g are defined and differentiable on* $(0, \infty)$.

If $\displaystyle\lim_{x \to \infty} \frac{f(x)}{g(x)}$ *is indeterminate of type* $\dfrac{0}{0}$ *or* $\dfrac{\infty}{\infty}$ *and if* $\displaystyle\lim_{x \to \infty} \frac{f'(x)}{g'(x)}$ *exists, then*

$$\lim_{n \to \infty} \frac{f(n)}{g(n)} = \lim_{n \to \infty} \frac{f'(n)}{g'(n)}$$

NOTE 1: The theorem seems rather obvious and, indeed, follows from the more general result that if H is a function defined on $(0, \infty)$ and if

$$\lim_{x \to \infty} H(x) = L$$

then the sequence $\{H(n)\}_{n=1}^{\infty}$ also converges to L.

$$\lim_{n \to \infty} H(n) = L.$$

NOTE 2: When applying L' Hospital's rule to sequences $a_n = f(n)$ we will treat n as if it were the continuous variable x and write, for instance,

$$f'(n) = \frac{d}{dn}(a_n)$$

Example 8.1.4 (L' Hospital's Rule for Sequences)

Problem: Use Theorem 8.1.4 to evaluate the limits of the following sequences

$$\text{(a) } \left\{ \frac{\ln n}{n} \right\} \quad \text{(b) } \left\{ n \ln \left(1 + \frac{3}{n} \right) \right\} \quad \text{(c) } \{ n^{1/n} \} \quad \text{(d) } \left\{ \left(1 + \frac{3}{n} \right)^n \right\}$$

Solution (a): Clearly $\displaystyle\lim_{x \to \infty} \frac{\ln n}{n}$ is indeterminate of type $\frac{\infty}{\infty}$ and L' Hospital's Rule applies. Thus,

$$\lim_{n \to \infty} \frac{\ln n}{n} \stackrel{L'Hosp}{=} \lim_{n \to \infty} \lim \frac{\frac{d}{dn}(\ln n)}{\frac{d}{dn}(n)} = \lim_{n \to \infty} \lim \frac{\frac{1}{n}}{1} = 0.$$

Solution (b): This limit is indeterminate of type $0 \cdot \infty$, so we convert it to type $\frac{0}{0}$ and apply L' Hospital's Rule

$$\lim_{n \to \infty} n \ln \left(1 + \frac{3}{n} \right) = \lim_{n \to \infty} \frac{\ln \left(1 + \frac{3}{n} \right)}{\frac{1}{n}} \stackrel{L'Hosp}{=} \lim_{n \to \infty} \frac{\frac{d}{dn} \ln \left(1 + \frac{3}{n} \right)}{\frac{d}{dn} \left(\frac{1}{n} \right)}$$

$$= \lim_{n \to \infty} \frac{\frac{1}{1 + \frac{3}{n}} \cdot \left(-\frac{3}{n^2} \right)}{-\frac{1}{n^2}} = \lim_{n \to \infty} \frac{3}{1 + \frac{3}{n}} = 3$$

Solution (c): First we convert $n^{1/n}$, which has a variable base, to base e:

$$n^{1/n} = e^{(1/n) \cdot \ln n} = e^{\frac{\ln n}{n}}$$

Then using the continuous function limit theorem and the result in Part (a), we get

$$\lim_{n \to \infty} n^{1/n} = \lim_{n \to \infty} e^{\frac{\ln n}{n}} = e^{\lim_{n \to \infty} \frac{\ln n}{n}} = e^0 = 1.$$

Solution (d): The limit $\lim_{n \to \infty} \left(1 + \frac{3}{n}\right)^n$ is related to the famous limit

$$\lim_{n \to \infty} \left(1 + \frac{1}{n}\right)^n = e.$$

that we discussed in Section 2.9. As in Part (c) above, we first convert to base e:

$$\left(1 + \frac{3}{n}\right)^n = e^{n \ln(1+3/n)}$$

Then, using the result of Part (b) above, we get

$$\lim_{n \to \infty} \left(1 + \frac{3}{n}\right)^n = \lim_{n \to \infty} e^{n \ln(1+3/n)} = e^{\lim_{n \to \infty} n \ln(1+3/n)} = e^3.$$

Many sequences of importance to us (especially when studying series in the later sections) have expressions involving factorials in them. If you haven't seen this notation before, here's a definition:

DEFINITION 8.1.3 (Factorials)

Factorials of nonnegative integers are defined as follows

$$1! = 1$$
$$2! = 2 \cdot 1 = 2$$
$$3! = 3 \cdot 2 \cdot 1 = 6$$
$$4! = 4 \cdot 3 \cdot 2 \cdot 1 = 24$$
$$5! = 5 \cdot 4 \cdot 3 \cdot 2 \cdot 1 = 120$$

and for a general n

$$n! = n \cdot (n-1) \cdot \ \cdots \ \cdot 3 \cdot 2 \cdot 1$$

Thus, $n!$ is the product of all the integers between n and 1. Also, we define $0! = 1$.

Example 8.1.5 (Sequences with Factorials)

Problem: Find the limits of the following sequences:

$$\text{(a)} \ \left\{\frac{n!}{n^n}\right\} \qquad \text{(b)} \ \left\{\frac{n!}{(n+1)!}\right\}$$

Solution (a): We write out a few of the terms $a_n = \dfrac{n!}{n^n}$ to get a feel for how the sequence behaves

$$
\begin{aligned}
a_1 &= 1 \\[4pt]
a_2 &= \frac{2!}{2^2} = \frac{2 \cdot 1}{2 \cdot 2} = \frac{1}{2} \\[4pt]
a_3 &= \frac{3!}{3^3} = \frac{3 \cdot 2 \cdot 1}{3 \cdot 3 \cdot 3} < \frac{1}{3} \\[4pt]
a_4 &= \frac{4!}{4^4} = \frac{4 \cdot 3 \cdot 2 \cdot 1}{4 \cdot 4 \cdot 4 \cdot 4} < \frac{1}{4}
\end{aligned}
$$

and in general

$$a_n = \frac{n!}{n^n} = \frac{n}{n} \cdot \frac{n-1}{n} \cdot \frac{n-2}{n} \cdots \frac{3 \cdot 2 \cdot 1}{n \cdot n \cdot n} < \frac{1}{n}$$

Thus,

$$0 < a_n \leq \frac{1}{n},$$

for all $n \geq 1$, and so by the Squeeze Theorem

$$\lim_{n \to \infty} \frac{n!}{n^n} = 0$$

Solution (b): As in Part (a), we write out a few terms of the sequence

$$a_1 = \frac{1!}{2!} = \frac{1}{2}$$

$$a_2 = \frac{2!}{3!} = \frac{2 \cdot 1}{3 \cdot 2 \cdot 1} = \frac{1}{3}$$

$$a_3 = \frac{3!}{4!} = \frac{3 \cdot 2 \cdot 1}{4 \cdot 3 \cdot 2 \cdot 1} = \frac{1}{4}$$

$$a_4 = \frac{4!}{5!} = \frac{4 \cdot 3 \cdot 2 \cdot 1}{5 \cdot 4 \cdot 3 \cdot 2 \cdot 1} = \frac{1}{5}$$

$$\vdots$$

$$a_n = \frac{n!}{(n+1)!} = \frac{n}{n+1} \cdot \frac{n-1}{n} \cdot \frac{n-2}{n-1} \cdots \frac{3 \cdot 2 \cdot 1}{3 \cdot 2 \cdot 1} = \frac{n!}{(n+1)\,n!} = \frac{1}{n+1}$$

Thus, the sequence reduces because of the property that $(n+1)! = (n+1)n!$ and this makes the limit easy to evaluate:

$$\lim_{n \to \infty} \frac{n!}{(n+1)!} = \lim_{n \to \infty} \frac{n!}{(n+1)n!} = \lim_{n \to \infty} \frac{1}{n+1} = 0.$$

Basic Factorial Property

$$(n+1)! = (n+1)n!$$

In Part (b) of the last example, we used the important property of factorials shown in the margin box.

CAUTION: This is one of the few properties available to you in working with factorials. Do not assume (and use) some other properties unless you know they are true.

MONOTONE SEQUENCES

There are certain important sequences, called monotone sequences, which occur often and for which their convergence can be tested by observing if their terms are bounded.

DEFINITION 8.1.4 (Monotonicity)

A sequence $\{a_n\}$ is called

(1) *Increasing if* $a_1 \leq a_2 \leq a_3 \leq \cdots \leq a_n \leq a_{n+1} \leq \cdots$

(2) *Strictly Increasing if* $a_1 < a_2 < a_3 < \cdots < a_n < a_{n+1} < \cdots$

(3) *Decreasing if* $a_1 \geq a_2 \geq a_3 \geq \cdots \geq a_n \geq a_{n+1} \geq \cdots$

(4) *Strictly Decreasing if* $a_1 > a_2 > a_3 > \cdots > a_n > a_{n+1} > \cdots$

NOTE 1: A strictly increasing sequence is also an increasing sequence and a strictly decreasing sequence is also a decreasing sequence.

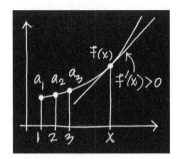

Figure 8.1.6: *If $f'(x) > 0$ on $[0, \infty)$, then $a_n = f(n)$ is an increasing sequence.*

NOTE 2: A *monotone sequence* is, by definition, one that is either increasing or decreasing.

NOTE 3: The requirement in Definition 8.1.4 that *all* the terms of the sequence be ordered as indicated in (1)–(4) is usually relaxed to saying that after some point the terms obey that ordering. For example, if $a_n \le a_{n+1}$, for all $n \ge 43$, then we say the sequence is increasing (or eventually increasing).

NOTE 4: If a sequence $\{a_n\}$ is given by a function: $a_n = f(n)$ and f is differentiable on $[1, \infty)$, then we can use the derivative of f to determine monotonicity. For example if $f'(x) \ge 0$, for $x \ge 1$, then $\{a_n\}$ is increasing (since f is). See Figure 8.1.6.

NOTE 5: If a sequence $\{a_n\}$ is increasing, a little thought shows that only one of two things can happen. Either

(1) The terms are bounded above by some number M, i.e., there is an M such that $a_n < M$, for all n.

(2) The sequence diverges to infinity: $\lim_{n \to \infty} a_n = \infty$.

The number M in Case (1) is called an *upper bound* for the sequence. One can use some theory, usually discussed in advanced calculus, to prove that in Case (1) the sequence must converge.

Similarly, if a sequence is decreasing, it is either (1) bounded below (in which case it converges) or (2) it diverges to minus infinity. All of this is summarized in the following theorem.

THEOREM 8.1.5 (Bounded Monotonic Sequences)

Bounded monotonic sequences $\{a_n\}$ converge

Example 8.1.6 (Monotone Sequences)

The following are monotone sequences. Determine if they are increasing or decreasing and, if they converge, find their limits.

Problem (a): $\left\{ \dfrac{2^n}{n!} \right\}_{n=1}^{\infty}$

Solution (a): One way to determine the monotonicity of a sequence $\{a_n\}$ is to look at the ratio $\dfrac{a_{n+1}}{a_n}$. In this example

$$a_n = \frac{2^n}{n!}, \; a_{n+1} = \frac{2^{n+1}}{(n+1)!}$$

and so

$$\frac{a_{n+1}}{a_n} = \frac{\frac{2^{n+1}}{(n+1)!}}{\frac{2^n}{n!}} = \frac{2^{n+1}}{(n+1)!} \cdot \frac{n!}{2^n} = \frac{2}{n+1} < 1$$

for all $n \ge 2$. Thus, $a_{n+1} < a_n$, for all $n \ge 2$, which says the sequence is strictly decreasing. Since the terms of the sequence are positive, the sequence is bounded below by 0. Hence, by the Bounded-Monotone Theorem (i.e., Theorem 8.1.5), the sequence converges. To determine what it converges to, note that

$$a_1 = \frac{2}{1}$$

$$a_2 = \frac{2}{1} \cdot \frac{2}{2} = \frac{4}{2}$$

$$a_3 = \frac{2}{1} \cdot \left[\frac{2}{2}\right] \cdot \frac{2}{3} = \frac{4}{3}$$

$$a_4 = \frac{2}{1} \cdot \left[\frac{2}{2} \cdot \frac{2}{3}\right] \cdot \frac{2}{4} < \frac{4}{4}$$

$$\vdots$$

$$a_n = \frac{2^n}{n!} = \frac{2}{1} \cdot \left[\frac{2}{2} \cdot \frac{2}{3} \cdot \frac{2}{4} \cdots \frac{2}{n-1}\right] \cdot \frac{2}{n} < \frac{4}{n}$$

We got the above inequality by observing that the product of the terms in the brackets is less than 1. Thus, we have

$$0 < \frac{2^n}{n!} < \frac{4}{n},$$

for all $n \geq 4$. Since $\lim\limits_{n\to\infty} \frac{4}{n} = 0$, we can use the Squeeze Theorem to conclude: $\lim\limits_{n\to\infty} \frac{2^n}{n!} = 0$.

Problem (b): $\left\{\dfrac{n - \ln n}{n + 1}\right\}_{n=1}^{\infty}$

Solution (b): To determine whether the sequence is increasing or decreasing we consider the corresponding function:

$$h(x) = \frac{x - \ln x}{x + 1}$$

and determine if it is increasing or decreasing on some interval of the form $[a, \infty)$. For this, look at the derivative

$$h'(x) = \frac{\left(1 - \frac{1}{x}\right)(x+1) - (x - \ln x)(1)}{(x+1)^2} = \frac{\ln x - \frac{1}{x}}{(x+1)^2}.$$

Now observe that this is positive when $\ln x - \frac{1}{x} > 0$, which occurs for, say, $x \geq 2$. Thus, h is increasing on the interval $[2, \infty)$. Figure 8.1.7 shows a computer plot that helps verify this work.

Consequently, ignoring the first term of the sequence $\left\{\frac{n-\ln n}{n+1}\right\}_{n=1}^{\infty}$, we can say that the resulting sequence is increasing. It is clearly bounded above by 1 since

$$\frac{n - \ln n}{n + 1} \leq \frac{n}{n + 1} < 1,$$

for all n. Thus, the sequence converges. To find its limit, we use L' Hospital's Rule:

$$\lim_{n\to\infty} \frac{n - \ln n}{n + 1} \overset{L'Hosp}{=} \lim_{n\to\infty} \frac{\frac{d}{dn}(n - \ln n)}{\frac{d}{dn}(n + 1)} = \lim_{n\to\infty} \frac{1 - \frac{1}{n}}{1} = 1$$

Use of L' Hospital's rule is valid here since

$$\lim_{n\to\infty}(n - \ln n) = \lim_{n\to\infty} n\left(1 - \frac{\ln n}{n}\right) = \infty \cdot (1 - 0) = \infty$$

See Example 8.1.4 (a) for the basic limit

$$\lim_{n\to\infty} \frac{\ln n}{n} = 0.$$

NOTE: The convergence or divergence of a sequence does not depend its initial terms: $\{a_n\}_{n=1}^{\infty}$ and $\{a_n\}_{n=25}^{\infty}$ both have the same convergence properties.

As in Chapter 1, we will find it convenient to use the arrow notation for limits of sequences. See the margin box,

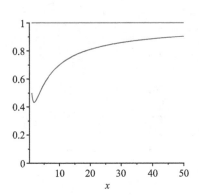

Figure 8.1.7: *Graph of* $h(x) = \dfrac{x - \ln x}{x + 1}$ *on* $[1, 50]$

The Arrow Notation

Suppose $\lim\limits_{n\to\infty} a_n = L$ *, then we write*

$$a_n \to L \quad as \quad n \to \infty$$

This is read as "the sequence tends to L as n tends to infinity." We also write

$$a_n \to L$$

for the same thing since it is understood that n tends to infinity.

Exercises: 8.1 (Sequences)

Some Basic Limits

(1) $\lim\limits_{n\to\infty} \dfrac{1}{n^p} = 0$ (for $p > 0$)

(2) $\lim\limits_{n\to\infty} x^n = 0$ (for $|x| < 1$)

(3) $\lim\limits_{n\to\infty} x^{1/n} = 1$ (for $x > 0$)

(4) $\lim\limits_{n\to\infty} n^{1/n} = 1$

(5) $\lim\limits_{n\to\infty} \dfrac{x^n}{n!} = 0$ (for any x)

(6) $\lim\limits_{n\to\infty} \left(1 + \dfrac{x}{n}\right)^n = e^x$ (for any x)

(7) $\lim\limits_{n\to\pm\infty} \tan^{-1}(n) = \pm\dfrac{\pi}{2}$

Limit Laws & Algebra: Determine whether the following sequences converge and find their limits when they do.

1. $\left\{ \left(\frac{5}{n}\right)^{1/n} \right\}$

2. $\left\{ \left(\frac{3}{n^2}\right)^{1/n} \right\}$

3. $\left\{ (3^n n)^{-2/n} \right\}$

4. $\left\{ (6^n n^3)^{-5/n} \right\}$

5. $a_n = \sqrt[n]{4^n (5^n n)^{-2}}$

6. $a_n = \sqrt[n]{3^n (6^n n)^{-2}}$

7. $a_n = \dfrac{n^2 - 1}{2 - 3n^2} \cdot \dfrac{n}{n+1}$

8. $a_n = \dfrac{n^3 - 4}{1 - 2n^3} \cdot \dfrac{3n}{5n - 1}$

9. $\left\{ e^{-n/(n+1)} \right\}$

10. $\left\{ 2^{-n/(3n+1)} \right\}$

11. $\left\{ \tan^{-1}\left(1 - \frac{1}{n}\right) \right\}$

12. $\left\{ \tan^{-1}\left(\frac{1}{2} - \frac{1}{n}\right) \right\}$

13. $a_n = \dfrac{1 - \frac{1}{n}}{2 + e^{-n}}$

14. $a_n = \dfrac{5 - \frac{2}{n}}{3 + e^{-n}}$

15. $\left\{ \dfrac{\cos(n)}{n} \right\}$

16. $\left\{ \dfrac{\tan^{-1}(n)}{n} \right\}$

17. $\left\{ \dfrac{2e^n - 1}{3e^n + 1} \right\}$

18. $\left\{ \dfrac{4e^n - 1}{5e^n + 1} \right\}$

19. $\left\{ \dfrac{e^n - e^{-n}}{e^n + e^{-n}} \right\}$

20. $\left\{ \dfrac{2e^n - e^{-n}}{3e^n + e^{-n}} \right\}$

21. $\left\{ \dfrac{e^n}{e^{2n} + 1} \right\}$

22. $\left\{ \dfrac{e^{2n}}{e^{3n} + 1} \right\}$

23. $a_n = \dfrac{\sqrt{n} - \frac{1}{\sqrt{n}}}{\sqrt{n} + \frac{1}{n}}$

24. $a_n = \dfrac{n^{1/3} - \frac{1}{n^{1/3}}}{n^{1/3} + \frac{1}{n}}$

25. $\left\{ \dfrac{(\ln n)^2}{n^3} \right\}$

26. $\left\{ \dfrac{(\ln n)^k}{n^p} \right\}$

27. $a_n = (\ln n)^{1/n}$

28. $a_n = (\ln n)^{1/\sqrt{n}}$

29. $a_n = n \sin\left(\frac{1}{n}\right)$

30. $a_n = n \cos\left(\frac{1}{n}\right)$

31. $a_n = \sqrt{n+1} - \sqrt{n}$

32. $a_n = 2\sqrt{n+1} - \sqrt{n}$

33. $a_n = \dfrac{\tan^{-1}(n+1)}{\tan^{-1} n}$

34. $a_n = \dfrac{\cot^{-1}(n+1)}{\cot^{-1} n}$

35. $a_n = e^{n+1} - e^n$

36. $a_n = 2^{n+1} - 2^n$

37. $\left\{ \dfrac{\ln n}{1 + 2\ln n} \right\}$

38. $\left\{ \dfrac{3\ln n}{1 + 2\ln n} \right\}$

39. $\left\{ \dfrac{\ln n}{1 + (\ln n)^2} \right\}$

40. $\left\{ \dfrac{(\ln n)^2}{1 + (\ln n)^3} \right\}$

Squeeze Theorem: In Exercises 41–50, use the Squeeze Theorem to find the limits.

41. $b_n = \dfrac{1 + \cos(n)}{n}$

42. $b_n = \dfrac{1 + \sin(n)}{n}$

43. $b_n = \sin(n) \ln\left(1 + \frac{1}{n}\right)$

44. $b_n = \cos(n) \ln\left(1 + \frac{1}{n}\right)$

45. $b_n = \tan(\sin(n)) \left[1 - \cos\left(\frac{1}{n}\right)\right]$

46. $b_n = \tan(\cos(n)) \left[1 - n\sin\left(\frac{1}{n}\right)\right]$

47. $b_n = (1 + \cos^2 n) \sin\left(\frac{1}{n}\right)$

48. $b_n = (1 + \sin^2 n) \left[1 - \cos\left(\frac{1}{n}\right)\right]$

49. $b_n = (n^2 - 1)^{1/n}$

50. $b_n = (n^3 - 1)^{1/n}$

Exponential Sequences: In Exercises 51–66, use the identity $B^A = e^{A \ln B}$ and either L'Hospital's Rule or the Basic Limits to find the limits.

51. $\left\{ \left(1 + 2\frac{1}{\sqrt{n}}\right)^{\sqrt{n}} \right\}$

52. $\left\{ \left(1 + 2\frac{1}{\sqrt[3]{n}}\right)^{\sqrt[3]{n}} \right\}$

53. $a_n = \left(1 - \frac{\ln 3}{n^2}\right)^{5n^2}$

54. $a_n = \left(1 - \frac{\ln 2}{n^3}\right)^{5n^3}$

55. $\left\{ (1 + 5e^{-n})^{e^n} \right\}$

56. $\left\{ (1 + 6e^{-2n})^{e^{2n}} \right\}$

57. $\left\{ \left(\sqrt{1 + 6/n}\right)^n \right\}$

58. $\left\{ \left(\sqrt{1 + 8/n}\right)^n \right\}$

59. $a_n = \left(1 - \frac{\ln 2}{\ln n}\right)^{\ln n}$

60. $a_n = \left(1 - \frac{\ln 3}{\ln n}\right)^{\ln n}$

61. $a_n = \left(\frac{2}{\pi} \tan^{-1} n\right)^n$

62. $a_n = \left(\frac{2}{\pi} \tan^{-1} n^2\right)^{n^3}$

63. $a_n = \left[\sin\left(\frac{1}{n}\right)\right]^{n-1}$

64. $a_n = \left[\sin\left(\frac{1}{n}\right)\right]^{n-2}$

65. $a_n = \left[\sin\left(\frac{1}{\sqrt{n}}\right)\right]^{1/\sqrt{n}}$

66. $a_n = \left[\sin\left(\frac{1}{\sqrt[3]{n}}\right)\right]^{1/\sqrt[3]{n}}$

Monotone Sequences: Show that the following sequences are monotonic (increasing or decreasing) and find their limits when they exist.

67. $a_n = \dfrac{n+1}{n}$

68. $a_n = \dfrac{n^2 + 1}{n^2}$

69. $a_n = \dfrac{n}{n+1}$

70. $a_n = \dfrac{n^3}{n^3 + 1}$

71. $a_n = \dfrac{n^2 + 1}{n+1}$

72. $a_n = \dfrac{n^3 + 1}{n^2 + n + 1}$

73. $a_n = \dfrac{n}{n^2 - 1}$

74. $a_n = \dfrac{n^2}{n^3 - 1}$

75. $a_n = \dfrac{\sqrt{n}}{\sqrt{n} + 1}$

76. $\left\{ \dfrac{\sqrt[3]{n}}{\sqrt[3]{n} + 1} \right\}$

77. $\left\{ \tan^{-1}\left(\frac{n}{n+1}\right) \right\}$

78. $\left\{ \tan^{-1}\left(\frac{n^2}{n^2 + 1}\right) \right\}$

79. $a_n = \dfrac{n}{2^n}$

80. $a_n = \dfrac{n}{3^n}$

81. $a_n = \dfrac{3^n}{(n+1)!}$

82. $a_n = \dfrac{5^n}{(n+3)!}$

83. $a_n = \dfrac{n!}{n^n}$

84. $a_n = \dfrac{(n+1)!}{n^{n+1}}$

Calculus *Concepts & Computation*

8.2 Infinite Series

In this section we begin our study of series, sometimes called infinite series, which is one of the most important concepts in calculus. Informally, a series is an expression for, or indication of, the process of adding up infinitely many numbers. Symbolically

$$a_1 + a_2 + a_3 + a_4 + \cdots + a_k + \cdots$$

The numbers a_n are called the *terms* of the series. As an alternative to the above ellipsis notation for a series, we also use the notation:

$$\sum_{n=1}^{\infty} a_n$$

for both the series and the indication of the process of adding the infinitely many terms of the series. The process of adding *finitely* many numbers needs no definition and can be indicated using the usual sigma notation from Section 4.1

$$a_1 + a_2 + a_3 + \cdots + a_k = \sum_{n=1}^{k} a_n$$

However, adding infinitely many numbers is an ideal concept, not something that is physically possible, and needs a precise definition. As we have seen before, limits are essential to understanding many concepts in calculus and will be used in in the definition of a series as a infinite summation process. Symbolically we write

$$a_1 + a_2 + a_3 + a_4 + \cdots + a_k + \cdots = \sum_{n=1}^{\infty} a_n = \lim_{k \to \infty} \sum_{n=1}^{k} a_n$$

NOTE: This limiting process of summing infinitely many numbers is entirely similar to the process of calculating improper integrals

$$\int_{1}^{\infty} f(x)\, dx = \lim_{t \to \infty} \int_{1}^{t} f(x)\, dx$$

Before giving the definition, we will consider some motivating examples.

Example 8.2.1 (A Bug's Journey)

Consider the series

$$1 + \frac{1}{2} + \frac{1}{4} + \frac{1}{8} + \frac{1}{16} + \cdots + \frac{1}{2^n} + \cdots$$

The terms of this series and the summation of them can be visualized by the following scenario. A small bug makes a sequence of hops, or jumps, in the forward direction along a straight line. The first hop is a distance of 1 ft, The second is $1/2$ ft, the third hop is $1/4$ ft, and so on. Each hop is half as far as the previous one. Then the above series represents the total distance from the origin the bug travels, assuming the bug could complete the journey in a finite amount of time. Figure 8.2.1 illustrates the situation and gives visual evidence to the fact that the total distance traveled is 2 feet:

$$1 + \frac{1}{2} + \frac{1}{4} + \frac{1}{8} + \frac{1}{16} + \cdots + \frac{1}{2^n} + \cdots = 2.$$

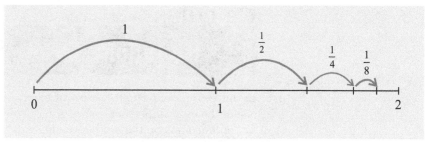

Figure 8.2.1: *The total distance traveled by the bug is* 2 *feet.*

This should seem plausible if you view it as follows. After each hop, the next hop is half the bug's distance from 2. For example, after the first hop, the bug is a distance of 1 from 2, so the next hop is half of that, namely 1/2. Then the bug is a distance of 1/2 from 2, so the next hop is half of that, namely 1/4. And so on. The bug can never get past 2 since it always hops half the remaining distance to 2. But the bug will get as close as it pleases to 2 by executing enough hops. This suggests that the sum of the series is 2. (Later we will prove this.)

We can use a special-purpose Maple procedure `seriesplot` to create a movie of the bug's journey (and illustrate the summation process for any series). To use it, first we define the terms a_n of the series by

```
> a:=n->1/2^(n-1);
```

$$a := n \mapsto \frac{1}{2^{n-1}}$$

Then we create a movie showing the first 10 hops in the bug's journey:

```
>seriesplot(a,10);
```

The sum of the first, 10, *terms of the series is,* 1.998046875

As you can see, the procedure also outputs the sum of the first 10 terms of this series. Figure 8.2.2 shows the last frame in the animation.

The animation represents each term a_n, in the series by a rectangle with height 1 and base length a_n, and so the area of the rectangle is also a_n. The rectangles are placed adjacent to each other, from left-to-right, along the x-axis. Thus, the addition of the terms of the series corresponds to the accumulation of area in the animation. The kth frame of the animation shows a total rectangle (with total area $a_1 + a_2 + \cdots + a_k$) comprised of all the subrectangles (with areas $a_1, a_2, \ldots, a_k$).

As seen in the above figure the first 7 rectangles are clearly discernible, but after that, the rectangles are so thin that their contributions to the total area appear as lines forming a black band. These thin rectangles never extend beyond 2 on the x-axis. Rather, they pile up next to 2, suggesting that the sum of the series is 2.

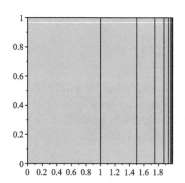

Figure 8.2.2: *The last frame in the movie* `seriesplot(a,10)`.

Example 8.2.2 (Non-Summable Series)

As in the first example, when a series has terms which are all positive, it is intuitively clear that if the series has a finite sum, then the terms must get smaller and smaller as $n \to \infty$ (and in fact go to zero, as we shall later see). For instance, any definition of the sum of a series should give

$$1 + 2 + 3 + 4 + \cdots + n + \cdots = \infty$$

But what about series with positive and negative terms? A famous example, first studied by Euler, is the series whose terms alternate between plus one and minus one:

$$1 - 1 + 1 - 1 + 1 - 1 + 1 - 1 + \cdots = \sum_{n=0}^{\infty} (-1)^n$$

Euler considered the paradox that occurs when one attempts to sum the terms of the series by grouping them in two ways.

First Way: $(1-1)+(1-1)+(1-1)+\cdots = 0+0+0+\cdots = 0$

Second Way: $1+(-1+1)+(-1+1)+\cdots = 1+0+0+\cdots = 1$

This paradox illustrates the need for a precise definition of what it means to sum the terms in a series.

We now turn to the definition of what it means for the terms of a series

$$\sum_{n=1}^{\infty} a_n$$

to be summable, in which case we will call the series *convergent,*. For this, we need to first define the *sequence of partial sums* $\{s_n\}$. This sequence embodies the actual process one would execute in adding up the terms. First, we let $s_1 = a_1$ be the first term of the series. Then add on the second term to get the sum of the first two terms $s_2 = a_1 + a_2$. Adding on the third term gives the sum of the first three terms $s_3 = a_1 + a_2 + a_3$. And so on.

$$
\begin{aligned}
s_1 &= a_1 \\
s_2 &= a_1 + a_2 \\
s_3 &= a_1 + a_2 + a_3 \\
&\vdots \\
s_n &= a_1 + a_2 + \cdots + a_n = \sum_{k=1}^{n} a_k
\end{aligned}
$$

This gives the sequence $\{s_n\}_{n=1}^{\infty}$, which is called the *sequence of partial sums* for the series.

DEFINITION 8.2.0 (The Sequence of Partial Sums)

For a series $\displaystyle\sum_{n=1}^{\infty} a_n$, *its sequence of partial sums is the sequence* $\{s_n\}_{n=1}^{\infty}$

with terms $\qquad s_n = a_1 + a_2 + \cdots + a_n = \displaystyle\sum_{k=1}^{n} a_k$

---

sum of the first n terms

$$s_n = s_{n-1} + a_n$$

sum of the first $n-1$ terms

Box 8.2.1: *A property for generating the sequence of partial sums* $\{s_n\}$

Generally, the terms in the sequence of partial sums can be best computed by noting that

$$s_n = a_1 + a_2 + \cdots + a_{n-1} + a_n = (a_1 + a_2 + \cdots + a_{n-1}) + a_n = s_{n-1} + a_n.$$

This says that having computed s_{n-1}, just add a_n to get s_n. The margin box highlights this property.

Example 8.2.3 (A Sequence of Partial Sums)

Problem: Compute, by hand, the first 5 terms in the sequence of partial sums for the series

$$\sum_{n=1}^{\infty} \frac{1}{n(n+1)} = \frac{1}{2} + \frac{1}{6} + \frac{1}{12} + \frac{1}{20} + \frac{1}{30} + \cdots$$

From your calculations, conjecture a formula for the nth term s_n in general. Prove your conjecture.

Solution: We use the property in Box 8.2.1 to compute $s_1, s_2, \ldots, , s_5$:

$$s_1 = \frac{1}{2}$$

$$s_2 = \frac{1}{2} + \frac{1}{6} = \frac{4}{6} = \frac{2}{3}$$

$$s_3 = \frac{2}{3} + \frac{1}{12} = \frac{9}{12} = \frac{3}{4}$$

$$s_4 = \frac{3}{4} + \frac{1}{20} = \frac{16}{20} = \frac{4}{5}$$

$$s_5 = \frac{4}{5} + \frac{1}{30} = \frac{25}{30} = \frac{5}{6}$$

From these calculations, its easy to conjecture that the general nth term should be

$$s_n = \frac{n}{n+1}.$$

To prove the conjecture we use mathematical induction. The formula is true for $n = 1$, since $s_1 = \frac{1}{2} = \frac{1}{1+1}$. Assuming the formula is true for a given n, we find that

$$s_{n+1} = s_n + a_{n+1} = \frac{n}{n+1} + \frac{1}{(n+1)(n+2)}$$

$$= \frac{n(n+2)+1}{(n+1)(n+2)} = \frac{n^2 + 2n + 1}{(n+1)(n+2)} = \frac{(n+1)^2}{(n+1)(n+2)} = \frac{n+1}{n+2}.$$

Thus, the formula is true for $n+1$. This completes the mathematical induction.

In the last example, we found that for the series

$$\sum_{n=1}^{\infty} \frac{1}{n(n+1)} = \frac{1}{2} + \frac{1}{6} + \frac{1}{12} + \frac{1}{20} + \frac{1}{30} + \cdots$$

the sum of the first 5 terms (the ones shown) is

$$s_5 = \frac{5}{6}$$

and, in general, the sum of the first n terms is

$$s_n = \frac{n}{n+1}.$$

Based on this, it seems reasonable to say that the sum of *all* the terms of the series would ideally be given by the limit

$$\lim_{n\to\infty} s_n = \lim_{n\to\infty} \frac{n}{n+1} = \lim_{n\to\infty} \frac{1}{1+\frac{1}{n}} = \frac{1}{1+0} = 1$$

This leads to concept of a convergent series, namely, a definition of what it means to add up the infinitely many terms of a series.

DEFINITION 8.2.1 (Convergence of a Series)

A series $\sum_{n=1}^{\infty} a_n$ is said to converge if its sequence of partial sums $\{s_n\}_{n=1}^{\infty}$ converges

The number $S = \lim_{n\to\infty} s_n$ is called the sum of the series and we write

$$\sum_{n=1}^{\infty} a_n = S$$

If the sequence $\{s_n\}_{n=1}^{\infty}$ of partial sums does *not* converge (i.e., $\lim\limits_{n\to\infty} s_n$ does not exist) then we say the series $\sum\limits_{n=1}^{\infty} a_n$ *diverges*. Thus, a given series is either convergent or divergent. Much of our effort in the next several sections will be devoted to determining convergence/divergence of series. Even when we can determine that a given series converges, it generally will be difficult to find the sum of the series as we did in the last example. The reason for this is that a specific formula for s_n (the sum of the first n terms of the series) cannot be found. There are a few specific types of series, such as geometric series (discussed below), for which this can be done.

Example 8.2.4 (The Series of Plus/Minus Ones)

The paradox that Euler found in the series

$$1 - 1 + 1 - 1 + 1 - 1 + 1 - 1 + \cdots = \sum_{n=0}^{\infty} (-1)^n$$

can be resolved now that we have a definition of convergence for series. For this series the sequence of partial sums is

$$
\begin{aligned}
s_1 &= 1 \\
s_2 &= 1 - 1 = 0 \\
s_3 &= 1 - 1 + 1 = 1 \\
s_4 &= 1 - 1 + 1 - 1 = 0 \\
s_5 &= 1 - 1 + 1 - 1 + 1 = 1
\end{aligned}
$$

So the sequence of partial sums has terms that alternate between 1 and 0

$$1, 0, 1, 0, 1, 0, 1, 0, \ldots$$

This sequence clearly has no limit and so the series is divergent. The divergence of this series can also be illustrated by a bug's journey as in Example 8.2.1. See Figure 8.2.3.

For the bug's journey, $s_n = 1 - 1 + 1 - \cdots + (-1)^n$ represents the bug's distance from the origin, which is either 1 or 0 depending on whether n is odd or even. Thus, there is no ultimate, single, distance.

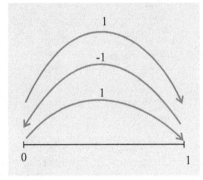

Figure 8.2.3: *A bug hops back and forth from 0 to 1.*

GEOMETRIC SERIES

Geometric series are one of the most important types of series that we will study. The name comes from the special property that a geometric series has: *The ratio of any term to the previous term is the same.* Thus, the series $\sum a_n$ is geometric if there is a number r, called the *common ratio*, such that

$$\frac{a_{n+1}}{a_n} = r,$$

for every n. If we denote the first term of the series by a, then it's not to hard to show (exercise) that a geometric series with common ratio r has the form:

GEOMETRIC SERIES (first term a, common ratio r)

$$\sum_{n=0}^{\infty} ar^n = a + ar + ar^2 + ar^3 + \cdots + ar^{n-1} + \cdots$$

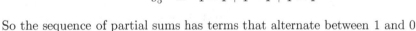

Note that in the form we use, a geometric series begins with 0 and so its nth term is ar^{n-1}. The first example above (The Bug's Journey) involves a geometric series with common ratio $r = 1/2$ and first term $a = 1$:

$$\sum_{n=0}^{\infty} \left(\frac{1}{2}\right)^n = \sum_{n=0}^{\infty} \frac{1}{2^n}.$$

The convergence or divergence of a geometric series is easy to determine. This is because the sum of the first n terms of a geometric series has a well-known formula that is useful in many areas of everyday life (such as business finance).

$$s_n = a + ar + ar^2 + ar^3 + \cdots + ar^{n-1} = \frac{a(1-r^n)}{1-r} \qquad (8.2.1)$$

(Here we assume that r is not 1.) The validity of this formula can be seen as follows. Take

$$s_n = a + ar + ar^2 + \cdots + ar^{n-2} + ar^{n-1}$$

and multiply both sides by r

$$rs_n = ar + ar^2 + ar^3 + \cdots + ar^{n-1} + ar^n$$

Subtracting gives

$$s_n - rs_n = a - ar^n$$

or

$$(1 - r)\, s_n = a\left(1 - r^n\right)$$

Dividing by $1 - r$ gives the result

$$s_n = \frac{a\left(1 - r^n\right)}{1 - r}.$$

Having this explicit formula for the terms in the sequence of partial sums, we can easily determine its limit. As we have seen in Basic Limits Box in the exercises from 8.1,

$$\lim_{n\to\infty} r^n = 0, \quad \text{if } |r| < 1.$$

Also it is clear

$$\lim_{n\to\infty} r^n \quad \text{does not exist, if } |r| > 1.$$

Applying this to the sequence of partial sums, we get

$$\lim_{n\to\infty} s_n = \lim_{n\to\infty} \frac{a\left(1 - r^n\right)}{1 - r} = \frac{a}{1 - r}, \quad \text{if } |r| < 1$$

and

$$\lim_{n\to\infty} s_n \quad \text{does not exist, if } |r| > 1.$$

When $r = 1$

$$s_n = a + a\,(1) + a\,(1)^2 + \cdots + a\,(1)^{n-1} = na,$$

and when $r = -1$

$$s_n = a + a\,(-1) + a\,(-1)^2 + \cdots + a\,(-1)^{n-1} = \begin{cases} 0 & \text{if } n \text{ is even} \\ a & \text{if } n \text{ is odd} \end{cases}$$

and so $\lim_{n\to\infty} s_n$ does not exist in these cases either. Thus, we get the following important theorem.

THEOREM 8.2.1 (Geometric Series)

A geometric series converges if its common ratio r is less than 1 *in absolute value:*
$|r| < 1$ *, and the sum of the series is*

$$\sum_{n=0}^{\infty} ar^n = \frac{a}{1-r} \qquad (8.2.2)$$

For $|r| \geq 1$ *, the series diverges.*

Note in the example above of the Bug's Journey, $a = 1$ and $r = \frac{1}{2}$. So the series is convergent and has sum

$$\sum_{n=0}^{\infty} \frac{1}{2^n} = 1 + \frac{1}{2} + \frac{1}{4} + \frac{1}{8} + \frac{1}{16} + \cdots = \frac{1}{1 - \frac{1}{2}} = 2$$

Example 8.2.5 (Geometric Series)

Problem: Determine which of the following series converge and find the sums of those that do.

(a) $\displaystyle\sum_{n=0}^{\infty} 5\left(\frac{3}{4}\right)^n$ (b) $\displaystyle\sum_{n=0}^{\infty} \left(\frac{11}{10}\right)^n$ (c) $\displaystyle\sum_{n=0}^{\infty} \frac{(-1)^n \, 2^{n+1}}{7^n}$ (d) $\displaystyle\sum_{n=0}^{\infty} \frac{3}{10}\left(\frac{1}{10}\right)^n$

Solution (a): This is geometric series with $a = 5$ and $r = \frac{3}{4}$. So the series converges and has sum

$$\sum_{n=0}^{\infty} 5\left(\frac{3}{4}\right)^n = 5\left(1 + \frac{3}{4} + \frac{9}{16} + \frac{27}{64} + \cdots\right) = \frac{5}{1 - \frac{3}{4}} = 20.$$

Solution (b): Since the common ratio $r = \frac{11}{10} > 1$, the series diverges.

Solution (c): To identify a and r, we rewrite the series as follows to get $r = -\frac{2}{7}$. (So the series converges.)

$$\sum_{n=0}^{\infty} \frac{(-1)^n \, 2^{n+1}}{7^n} = \sum_{n=0}^{\infty} 2\left(-\frac{2}{7}\right)^n = \frac{2}{1 - \left(-\frac{2}{7}\right)} = \frac{2}{\frac{9}{7}} = \frac{14}{9}$$

Solution (d): This is geometric series with $a = 3/10$ and $r = \frac{1}{10}$. So the series converges and has sum

$$\sum_{n=0}^{\infty} \frac{3}{10}\left(\frac{1}{10}\right)^n = \frac{3}{10} + \frac{3}{100} + \frac{3}{100} + \cdots = 0.3 + 0.03 + 0.003 + \cdots$$

$$= 0.33\overline{3} = \frac{\frac{3}{10}}{1 - \frac{1}{10}} = \frac{\frac{3}{10}}{\frac{9}{10}} = \frac{1}{3}$$

This part of the example illustrates an important use of geometric series. It shows that the decimal expansion of $\frac{1}{3}$ is repeating (and never ending, which requires the concept of a series to fully define). The next example explores this more generally.

NOTE: It is important to observe that the first term a of a geometric series does not affect the convergence or divergence of the series and that it can be factored out of the sum when the series converges:

$$\sum_{n=0}^{\infty} ar^n = a + ar + ar^2 + ar^3 + \cdots = a\left(1 + r + r^2 + r^3 + \cdots\right)$$

$$= a\sum_{n=0}^{\infty} r^n = a\left(\frac{1}{1-r}\right) \quad (\text{for} \ |r| < 1)$$

Example 8.2.6 (Repeating Decimals)

Problem: Express the repeating decimal $2.35\overline{35}$ as a fraction.

Solution: The concept of a repeating decimal inherently involves the notion of an infinite series:

$$\begin{aligned}
2.35\overline{35} &= 2 + 0.35 + 0.0035 + 0.000035 + 0.00000035 + \cdots \\
&= 2 + \frac{35}{10^2} + \frac{35}{10^4} + \frac{35}{10^6} + \cdots \\
&= 2 + \frac{35}{10^2}\left(1 + \frac{1}{10^2} + \frac{1}{10^4} + \cdots\right)
\end{aligned}$$

The expression in the parentheses is a convergent geometric series with $a = 1$ and $r = \frac{1}{10^2} = \frac{1}{100}$. Thus,

$$2.35\overline{35} = 2 + \frac{35}{100}\left(\frac{1}{1-\frac{1}{100}}\right) = 2 + \frac{35}{100}\cdot\frac{100}{99} = 2 + \frac{35}{99} = \frac{233}{99}$$

TELESCOPING SERIES

A telescoping series is another special type of series, like geometric series, for which we can determine the convergence and actually find the sum of the series when it converges. The name "telescoping" comes from the fact that these series have terms which, after an initial few terms, all the rest add up to zero (if the addition is carried out indefinitely). Thus, the series collapses to just the sum of those initial few terms. For instance, the series

$$\sum_{n=1}^{\infty} \frac{1}{n(n+1)}$$

that we studied in Example 8.2.3 above is a telescoping series. In that example we saw that the series converges and has sum 1. To come to the same conclusion, we view this series as a telescoping one. To see this, note that it can be written as

$$\begin{aligned}
\sum_{n=1}^{\infty} \frac{1}{n(n+1)} &= \sum_{n=1}^{\infty}\left(\frac{1}{n} - \frac{1}{n+1}\right) \\
&= \left(1 - \frac{1}{2}\right) + \left(\frac{1}{2} - \frac{1}{3}\right) + \left(\frac{1}{3} - \frac{1}{4}\right) + \left(\frac{1}{4} - \frac{1}{5}\right) + \cdots \\
&= 1 - \frac{1}{2} + \frac{1}{2} - \frac{1}{3} + \frac{1}{3} - \frac{1}{4} + \frac{1}{4} - \frac{1}{5} + \cdots \\
&= 1 + 0 + 0 + 0 + \cdots = 1
\end{aligned}$$

Here is a slightly more complicated example of a telescoping series.

Example 8.2.7 (A Telescoping Series)

Problem: Determine if the series $\sum_{n=1}^{\infty} \frac{2}{n^2 + 4n + 3}$ is telescoping and, if it converges, find its sum.

Solution: We use partial fraction decomposition to write the nth term of the series as

$$\frac{2}{n^2 + 4n + 3} = \frac{2}{(n+1)(n+3)} = \frac{1}{n+1} - \frac{1}{n+3}$$

Then we see that

$$\sum_{n=1}^{\infty} \frac{2}{n^2 + 4n + 3} = \sum_{n=1}^{\infty} \frac{1}{n+1} - \frac{1}{n+3}$$

$$= \left(\frac{1}{2} - \frac{1}{4}\right) + \left(\frac{1}{3} - \frac{1}{5}\right) + \left(\frac{1}{4} - \frac{1}{6}\right) + \left(\frac{1}{5} - \frac{1}{7}\right) + \left(\frac{1}{6} - \frac{1}{8}\right) + \left(\frac{1}{7} - \frac{1}{9}\right) + \cdots$$

$$= \frac{1}{2} - \frac{1}{4} + \frac{1}{3} - \frac{1}{5} + \frac{1}{4} - \frac{1}{6} + \frac{1}{5} - \frac{1}{7} + \frac{1}{6} - \frac{1}{8} + \frac{1}{7} - \frac{1}{9} + \cdots$$

$$= \frac{1}{2} + \frac{1}{3} - \frac{1}{4} + \frac{1}{4} - \frac{1}{5} + \frac{1}{5} - \frac{1}{6} + \frac{1}{6} - \frac{1}{7} + \frac{1}{7} - \frac{1}{8} - \frac{1}{9} + \cdots$$

$$= \frac{1}{2} + \frac{1}{3} + 0 + 0 + 0 + 0 - \frac{1}{8} - \frac{1}{9} + \cdots$$

Thus, the series telescopes. The pattern suggests that all the terms add to zero except for $\frac{1}{2}$ and $\frac{1}{3}$ and so the series converges. It has sum $\frac{5}{6}$. You should really look at the sequence of partial sums to verify these assertions. We get

$$s_1 = \frac{1}{2} - \frac{1}{4}$$

$$s_2 = \frac{1}{2} - \frac{1}{4} + \frac{1}{3} - \frac{1}{5}$$

$$s_3 = \frac{1}{2} - \frac{1}{4} + \frac{1}{3} - \frac{1}{5} + \frac{1}{4} - \frac{1}{6} = \frac{1}{2} + \frac{1}{3} - \frac{1}{5} - \frac{1}{6}$$

$$s_4 = s_3 + \frac{1}{3} + \frac{1}{5} - \frac{1}{7} = \frac{1}{2} + \frac{1}{3} - \frac{1}{5} - \frac{1}{6} + \frac{1}{5} - \frac{1}{7} = \frac{1}{2} + \frac{1}{3} - \frac{1}{6} - \frac{1}{7}$$

$$\vdots$$

$$s_n = \frac{1}{2} + \frac{1}{3} - \frac{1}{n+1} - \frac{1}{n+3}$$

Here we have written out enough terms in the sequence to get a good conjecture as to what the n th term s_n is. You can use mathematical induction to prove that the formula for s_n is correct. We see that

$$\lim_{n \to \infty} s_n = \lim_{n \to \infty} \left(\frac{1}{2} + \frac{1}{3} - \frac{1}{n+1} - \frac{1}{n+3}\right) = \frac{1}{2} + \frac{1}{3} = \frac{5}{6},$$

which verifies that the sum of this telescoping series is $\frac{5}{6}$.

Because the convergence of a series is based upon the convergence of its sequence of partial sums, we can use the limit laws for sequences to easily prove the following laws for series.

THEOREM 8.2.2 (Laws for Series)

Suppose that $\sum a_n, \sum b_n$ *are convergent series and k is any constant. Then*

the series $\sum (a_n + b_n)$, $\sum (a_n - b_n)$, $\sum k a_n$ *are convergent and*

(1) $\displaystyle \sum_{n=1}^{\infty} (a_n + b_n) = \sum_{n=1}^{\infty} a_n + \sum_{n=1}^{\infty} b_n$

(2) $\displaystyle \sum_{n=1}^{\infty} (a_n - b_n) = \sum_{n=1}^{\infty} a_n - \sum_{n=1}^{\infty} b_n$

(3) $\displaystyle \sum_{n=1}^{\infty} k a_n = k \sum_{n=1}^{\infty} a_n$

Example 8.2.8 (Applying the Laws for Series)

Problem: Determine if the following series converge. For each one that converges, find the sum of the series.

(a) $\displaystyle \sum_{n=0}^{\infty} \frac{2^{n+1} + 3^n}{5^n}$ (b) $\displaystyle \sum_{n=1}^{\infty} \left[\frac{(-1)^n \, 4^{n-1}}{7^n} - \frac{5}{(n+1)(n+2)} \right]$

Solution (a): We separate this into the sum of two geometric series:

$$\sum_{n=0}^{\infty} \frac{2^{n+1} + 3^n}{5^n} = \sum_{n=0}^{\infty} \frac{2^{n+1}}{5^n} + \sum_{n=0}^{\infty} \frac{3^n}{5^n} = \sum_{n=0}^{\infty} 2 \left(\frac{2}{5} \right)^n + \sum_{n=0}^{\infty} \left(\frac{3}{5} \right)^n$$

$$= \frac{2}{1 - \frac{2}{5}} + \frac{1}{1 - \frac{3}{5}} = \frac{10}{3} + \frac{5}{2} = \frac{35}{6}$$

Solution (b): This series separates into a sum of a geometric series and a telescoping series:

$$\sum_{n=1}^{\infty} \left[\frac{(-1)^n \, 4^{n-1}}{7^n} - \frac{5}{(n+1)(n+2)} \right] = \sum_{n=1}^{\infty} \frac{(-1)^n \, 4^{n-1}}{7^n} - \sum_{n=1}^{\infty} \frac{5}{(n+1)(n+2)}$$

The first series is geometric and we rewrite in standard form as

$$\sum_{n=1}^{\infty} \frac{(-1)^n \, 4^{n-1}}{7^n} = \sum_{n=1}^{\infty} \frac{-1}{7} \left(\frac{-4}{7} \right)^{n-1} = \sum_{k=0}^{\infty} \frac{-1}{7} \left(\frac{-4}{7} \right)^k = \frac{-\frac{1}{7}}{1 - \left(-\left(\frac{4}{7} \right) \right)} = -\frac{1}{11}$$

The second series is telescoping. Using partial fraction decomposition gives

$$\sum_{n=1}^{\infty} \frac{5}{((n+1)(n+2)} = 5 \sum_{n=1}^{\infty} \frac{1}{(n+1)(n+2)} = 5 \sum_{n=1}^{\infty} \left[\frac{1}{n+1} - \frac{1}{n+2} \right]$$

Looking at partial sums

$$s_1 = \frac{1}{2} - \frac{1}{3}$$

$$s_2 = \frac{1}{2} - \frac{1}{3} + \frac{1}{3} - \frac{1}{4} = \frac{1}{2} - \frac{1}{4}$$

$$s_3 = \frac{1}{2} - \frac{1}{4} + \frac{1}{4} - \frac{1}{5} = \frac{1}{2} - \frac{1}{5}$$

$$\vdots$$

$$s_n = \frac{1}{2} - \frac{1}{n+2}$$

Thus,

$$5 \sum_{n=1}^{\infty} \left[\frac{1}{n+1)} - \frac{1}{n+2} \right] = 5 \lim_{n \to \infty} s_n = 5 \lim_{n \to \infty} \left[\frac{1}{2} - \frac{1}{n+2} \right] = 5 \cdot \frac{1}{2} = \frac{5}{2}.$$

Putting both results together gives

$$\sum_{n=1}^{\infty} \left[\frac{(-1)^n \, 4^{n-1}}{7^n} - \frac{5}{(n+1)(n+2)} \right] = -\frac{1}{11} - \frac{5}{2} = -\frac{57}{22}$$

Exercises: 8.2 (Series)

Geometric Series: In Exercises 1–24, find the sum of the geometric series, if it converges, and otherwise say it diverges. NOTE: On some of these the summation begins at other numbers besides $n = 0$.

1. $2 - 2\left(\dfrac{4}{5}\right) + 2\left(\dfrac{4}{5}\right)^2 - 2\left(\dfrac{4}{5}\right)^3 + \cdots$

2. $3 - 3\left(\dfrac{7}{8}\right) + 3\left(\dfrac{7}{8}\right)^2 - 3\left(\dfrac{7}{8}\right)^3 + \cdots$

3. $\displaystyle\sum_{n=0}^{\infty} 5\left(\dfrac{2}{3}\right)^n$
4. $\displaystyle\sum_{n=0}^{\infty} 6\left(\dfrac{5}{7}\right)^n$

5. $\displaystyle\sum_{n=0}^{\infty} 3(-1)^{n+1}\dfrac{2^n}{7^n}$
6. $\displaystyle\sum_{n=0}^{\infty} 2(-1)^{n+1}\dfrac{6^n}{7^n}$

7. $\displaystyle\sum_{n=0}^{\infty} \dfrac{3^{n+1}}{(-5)^n}$
8. $\displaystyle\sum_{n=0}^{\infty} \dfrac{4^{n+1}}{(-9)^n}$

9. $\displaystyle\sum_{n=2}^{\infty} \left(4^{2n}\right)^{-1}$
10. $\displaystyle\sum_{n=2}^{\infty} \left(5^{3n}\right)^{-1}$

11. $\displaystyle\sum_{n=2}^{\infty} (-1)^n \dfrac{2^{n+1}}{3^{n-1}}$
12. $\displaystyle\sum_{n=2}^{\infty} (-1)^n \dfrac{5^{n+1}}{6^{n-1}}$

13. $\displaystyle\sum_{n=0}^{\infty} \left[\dfrac{2^n}{3^{n+1}} + \dfrac{5^{n+1}}{(-6)^n}\right]$
14. $\displaystyle\sum_{n=0}^{\infty} \left[\dfrac{3^{n+1}}{4^n} - \dfrac{2^n}{(-5)^{n+1}}\right]$

15. $\displaystyle\sum_{n=0}^{\infty} \dfrac{(-1)^n \left(4^n - 3^{n+1}\right)}{5^n}$
16. $\displaystyle\sum_{n=0}^{\infty} \dfrac{(-1)^n \left(5^n - 6^{n+1}\right)}{7^n}$

17. $\displaystyle\sum_{n=0}^{\infty} \dfrac{(2^n - 3^n)^2}{10^n}$
18. $\displaystyle\sum_{n=0}^{\infty} \dfrac{(4^n - 5^n)^2}{9^n}$

19. $\displaystyle\sum_{n=0}^{\infty} \dfrac{4^{n/2}}{27^{n/3}}$
20. $\displaystyle\sum_{n=0}^{\infty} \dfrac{9^{n/2}}{125^{n/3}}$

21. $\displaystyle\sum_{n=0}^{\infty} e^{-n\ln 2}$
22. $\displaystyle\sum_{n=0}^{\infty} e^{-n\ln 5}$

23. $\displaystyle\sum_{n=0}^{\infty} e^{-\ln(3^n)}$
24. $\displaystyle\sum_{n=0}^{\infty} e^{-\ln(5^n)}$

Telescoping Series: In Exercises 25–50, find the sum of the convergent telescoping series.

25. $\displaystyle\sum_{n=1}^{\infty} \left[\dfrac{1}{n} - \dfrac{1}{n+2}\right]$
26. $\displaystyle\sum_{n=1}^{\infty} \left[\dfrac{1}{n^2} - \dfrac{1}{(n+2)^2}\right]$

27. $\displaystyle\sum_{n=1}^{\infty} \left[\dfrac{1}{n+1} - \dfrac{1}{n+3}\right]$
28. $\displaystyle\sum_{n=1}^{\infty} \left[\dfrac{1}{(n+2)^2} - \dfrac{1}{(n+3)^2}\right]$

29. $\displaystyle\sum_{n=1}^{\infty} \left[\dfrac{1}{n+1} - \dfrac{1}{n+4}\right]$
30. $\displaystyle\sum_{n=1}^{\infty} \left[\dfrac{1}{(n+1)^2} - \dfrac{1}{(n+4)^2}\right]$

31. $\displaystyle\sum_{n=1}^{\infty} \dfrac{2}{n^2 + 6n + 8}$
32. $\displaystyle\sum_{n=1}^{\infty} \dfrac{2}{n^2 + 8n + 15}$

33. $\displaystyle\sum_{n=1}^{\infty} \left[\dfrac{1}{\sqrt{n}} - \dfrac{1}{\sqrt{n+2}}\right]$
34. $\displaystyle\sum_{n=1}^{\infty} \left[\dfrac{1}{\sqrt{n+1}} - \dfrac{1}{\sqrt{n+3}}\right]$

35. $\displaystyle\sum_{n=1}^{\infty} \left[\dfrac{1}{\ln(n+1)} - \dfrac{1}{\ln(n+3)}\right]$

36. $\displaystyle\sum_{n=1}^{\infty} \left[\dfrac{1}{\ln(n+2)} - \dfrac{1}{\ln(n+5)}\right]$

37. $\displaystyle\sum_{n=1}^{\infty} \left[\dfrac{n+1}{n} - \dfrac{n+2}{n+1}\right]$
38. $\displaystyle\sum_{n=1}^{\infty} \left[\dfrac{n+2}{n+1} - \dfrac{n+3}{n+2}\right]$

39. $\displaystyle\sum_{n=1}^{\infty} \left[\dfrac{n}{n+1} - \dfrac{n+1}{n+2}\right]$

40. $\displaystyle\sum_{n=1}^{\infty} \left[\cos\left(\dfrac{1}{n}\right) - \cos\left(\dfrac{1}{n+1}\right)\right]$

41. $\displaystyle\sum_{n=1}^{\infty} \left[\dfrac{\ln n}{n} - \dfrac{\ln(n+1)}{n+1}\right]$

42. $\displaystyle\sum_{n=1}^{\infty} \left[\ln(n+1) - \ln n\right]$

43. $\displaystyle\sum_{n=1}^{\infty} \left[n^{1/n} - (n+1)^{1/(n+1)}\right]$

44. $\displaystyle\sum_{n=1}^{\infty} \left[(\ln n)^{1/\ln n} - (\ln(n+1))^{1/\ln(n+1)}\right]$

45. $\displaystyle\sum_{n=1}^{\infty} \left[\tan^{-1}(n) - \tan^{-1}(n+1)\right]$

46. $\displaystyle\sum_{n=1}^{\infty} \left[\cot^{-1}(-n) - \cot^{-1}(-n-2)\right]$

47. $\displaystyle\sum_{n=1}^{\infty} \left[n\sin\left(\dfrac{1}{n}\right) - (n+1)\sin\left(\dfrac{1}{n+1}\right)\right]$

48. $\displaystyle\sum_{n=1}^{\infty} \left[n^2\sin\left(\dfrac{1}{n^2}\right) - (n+1)^2\sin\left(\dfrac{1}{(n+2)^2}\right)\right]$

49. $\displaystyle\sum_{n=1}^{\infty} \left[2^{1/n} - 2^{1/(n+2)}\right]$
50. $\displaystyle\sum_{n=1}^{\infty} \left[3^{1/n} - 3^{1/(n+2)}\right]$

Repeating Decimals: In Exercises 51–64, *use geometric series* to convert the repeating decimal to a rational number. There are several ways to handle the geometric series part of the computation. Here, we will generally factor out the the first term and write
$$a + ar + ar^2 + ar^3 + \cdots = a\left(1 + r + r^2 + r^3 + \cdots\right)$$
$$= a \cdot \left(\dfrac{1}{1-r}\right)$$

51. $0.7\overline{77}$ **52.** $0.8\overline{88}$
53. $0.9\overline{99}$ **54.** $1.9\overline{99}$
55. $0.23\overline{23}$ **56.** $0.34\overline{34}$
57. $0.369\overline{69}$ **58.** $0.469\overline{69}$
59. $0.528\overline{787}$ **60.** $0.628\overline{787}$
61. $6.4357\overline{357}$ **62.** $5.2357\overline{357}$
63. $0.099\overline{9}$ **64.** $9.099\overline{9}$

Calculus *Concepts & Computation*

8.3 The *n*th Term & Integral Tests

This section begins our study of methods for determining the convergence or divergence of a given series. These methods are called *tests* and when we use them we are *testing for convergence*. Each test is actually the result of a theorem that says whether the series converges on not, based on some criterion applied to the terms of the series.

Positive Terms Series

Before discussing the various tests for convergence, we consider an important characteristic of series $\sum a_n$ with positive terms: $a_n > 0$. Such series will be very common in this chapter. For positive term series, the corresponding sequence of partial sums $\{s_n\}$ is a strictly increasing sequence and so converges if and only if it is bounded above. (See Theorem 8.1.5). This observation forms the basis for the integral test and many of the other tests for convergence. The following box summarizes the positive term series result.

Positive Terms Series

For a series $\displaystyle\sum_{n=1}^{\infty} a_n$ *with positive terms, the sequence of partial sums is either*

(1) bounded above or (2) diverges to infinity. In the first case the series converges

and has finite sum $\displaystyle\sum_{n=1}^{\infty} a_n < \infty$. *In the second case the series diverges* $\displaystyle\sum_{n=1}^{\infty} a_n = \infty$.

NOTE: Clearly this result also holds for series with nonnegative terms ($a_n \geq 0$, for all n), but we will not need this extra generality here. Elsewhere when we discuss results for positive terms series, these results, for the most part, could be stated more generally for nonnegative term series.

The hard part about using the result is determining whether the sequence of partial sums is bounded above. The integral test discussed later does this by comparing the series with an improper integral. Before looking at this test, we consider the n-th term test for divergence, which applies to any type of series, positive terms or not.

The *n*-th Term Test for Divergence

We have already commented on the intuitive fact that if a series $\sum a_n$ has positive terms and if we can add up all the terms to get a finite number (i.e., if the series converges), then the terms must get smaller and smaller (and in fact, go to zero: $\lim_{n\to\infty} a_n = 0$). This is the content of the next theorem,

---

THEOREM 8.3.1

If the series $\displaystyle\sum_{n=1}^{\infty} a_n$ *converges, then* $\displaystyle\lim_{n\to\infty} a_n = 0$

Proof: Note that for $n > 1$,

$$s_n = \sum_{k=1}^{n} a_k = \sum_{k=1}^{n-1} a_k + a_n = s_{n-1} + a_n$$

Thus,

$$a_n = s_n - s_{n-1}.$$

Since the series converges, its sequence $\{s_n\}_{n=1}^{\infty}$ of partial sums converges, say $\lim\limits_{n \to \infty} s_n = S$. But $\{s_{n-1}\}_{n=2}^{\infty}$ is the same sequence. So by the limit laws for sequences, we get

$$\lim_{n \to \infty} a_n = \lim_{n \to \infty} (s_n - s_{n-1}) = \lim_{n \to \infty} s_n - \lim_{n \to \infty} s_{n-1} = S - S = 0$$

NOTE 1: The way Theorem 8.3.1 is stated is not the most useful. Theorem 8.3.2 below is a better version of it.

NOTE 2: It is important to observe that the implication in Theorem 8.3.1 only goes one way, i.e., the theorem says that

$$\sum_{n=1}^{\infty} a_n \quad converges \quad \Longrightarrow \quad \lim_{n \to \infty} a_n = 0$$

It is NOT TRUE that the convergence of the terms to zero ($\lim\limits_{n \to \infty} a_n = 0$) implies the series $\sum a_n$ converges. The most famous example of this is the harmonic series.

Example 8.3.1 (The Harmonic Series)

The series whose terms are the reciprocals of the natural numbers

$$\sum_{n=1}^{\infty} \frac{1}{n} = 1 + \frac{1}{2} + \frac{1}{3} + \frac{1}{4} + \frac{1}{5} + \cdots$$

is called the *harmonic series*. The terms $a_n = \frac{1}{n}$ of this series clearly go to zero: $\lim_{n \to \infty} \frac{1}{n} = 0$. However, the series diverges. There are several ways to prove this. We could use the integral test, which is discussed below. But here's another way. We look at particular partial sums and group the summands as follows.

$$s_2 = 1 + \frac{1}{2}$$

$$s_4 = 1 + \frac{1}{2} + \left(\frac{1}{3} + \frac{1}{4}\right) > 1 + \frac{1}{2} + \left(\frac{1}{4} + \frac{1}{4}\right) = 1 + \frac{1}{2} + \frac{1}{2} = 1 + 2\left(\frac{1}{2}\right)$$

$$s_8 = s_4 + \left(\frac{1}{5} + \frac{1}{6} + \frac{1}{7} + \frac{1}{8}\right) > s_4 + \left(\frac{1}{8} + \frac{1}{8} + \frac{1}{8} + \frac{1}{8}\right)$$

$$= s_4 + \frac{1}{2} > 1 + 2\left(\frac{1}{2}\right) + \frac{1}{2} = 1 + 3\left(\frac{1}{2}\right)$$

$$s_{16} = s_8 + \left(\frac{1}{9} + \frac{1}{10} + \frac{1}{11} + \frac{1}{12} + \frac{1}{13} + \frac{1}{14} + \frac{1}{15} + \frac{1}{16}\right)$$

$$> s_8 + 8\left(\frac{1}{16}\right) > 1 + 3\left(\frac{1}{2}\right) + \frac{1}{2} = 1 + 4\left(\frac{1}{2}\right)$$

From this you can see the pattern and use mathematical induction to prove that, in general:

$$s_{2^k} > 1 + k\left(\frac{1}{2}\right) = 1 + \frac{k}{2},$$

for every $k > 1$. This estimate says that we can get a sum larger than any given number if we add up enough terms of the series. For instance, if the given number

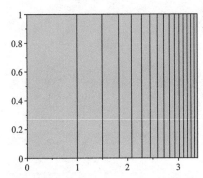

Figure 8.3.1: *The area shown represents the sum* $s_{16} = 1 + \frac{1}{2} + \frac{1}{3} + \frac{1}{4} + \cdots + \frac{1}{16} \approx 3.38.$

is 3. We see from the above that we can take $k = 4$ to get $s_{16} > 1 + \frac{4}{2} = 3$. Using the `seriesplot` routine verifies this and gives us the value $s_{16} \approx 3.38$.

```
> a:=n->1/n;
```
$$a := n \mapsto \frac{1}{n}$$
```
> seriesplot(a,16);
'The sum of the first',16,'terms of the series is', 3.380728993
```

The Figure 8.3.1 shows the last frame in the movie generated by `seriesplot`.

The series diverges very slowly. For, example, to get a sum larger that 100, we would need k to satisfy

$$1 + \frac{k}{2} > 100$$

So we could take $k = 200$. Then $s_{2^{200}} > 100$. But this number of terms: $2^{200} \approx 1.6 \times 10^{60}$ is a huge number. Thus, DO NOT try to use the `seriesplot` command on this.

Theorem 8.3.1 says that if $\sum a_n$ converges, then $\lim a_n = 0$. This is a statement of the form: If P, then Q. So logically, if Q is not true, then P is not true. Thus Theorem 8.3.1 is equivalent to the following theorem.

THEOREM 8.3.2 (The n-th Term Test for Divergence)

For any series $\displaystyle\sum_{n=1}^{\infty} a_n$, *if the limit of the terms is not zero:*

$$\lim_{n \to \infty} a_n \neq 0$$

(which includes the case when the limit of the terms does not exist)

then the series diverges.

This gives us our first test for convergence/divergence of series. In this case, it is a test that tells us that a given series diverges if its terms do not go to zero.

Example 8.3.2 (Using the n-th Term Test)

Problem: Determine if the following series converge or diverge.

(a) $\displaystyle\sum_{n=1}^{\infty} \frac{n}{n+1}$ (b) $\displaystyle\sum_{n=2}^{\infty} \frac{n}{\ln n}$ (c) $\displaystyle\sum_{n=0}^{\infty} \frac{(-1)^n e^n}{e^n + 1}$ (d) $\displaystyle\sum_{n=1}^{\infty} \frac{1}{n^2}$

Solution (a): The series here is

$$\sum_{n=1}^{\infty} \frac{n}{n+1} = \frac{1}{2} + \frac{2}{3} + \frac{3}{4} + \frac{4}{5} + \cdots + \frac{1000}{1001} + \cdots$$

So clearly the terms are getting close to 1 as n gets large:

$$\lim_{n \to \infty} \frac{n}{n+1} = \lim_{n \to \infty} \frac{1}{1 + \frac{1}{n}} = 1 \neq 0$$

So the series diverges by the n-th term test (NTT).

Solution (b): Use L' Hospital's rule to take the limit of the terms

$$\lim_{n \to \infty} \frac{n}{\ln n} \overset{L'Hosp}{=} \lim_{n \to \infty} \frac{1}{\frac{1}{n}} = \lim_{n \to \infty} n = \infty \neq 0$$

Thus, the terms diverge to infinity and so the series diverges by the NTT.

Solution (c): Here, dividing top and bottom by e^n gives

$$\frac{(-1)^n\, e^n}{e^n + 1} = (-1)^n \cdot \frac{1}{1 + e^{-n}} \approx (-1)^n \cdot \frac{1}{1} = (-1)^n$$

for n large. So, for n large, the even terms are close to 1 and the odd terms are close to -1, which means the limit of the terms does not exist. Thus, the series diverges by the NTT.

Solution (d): Here the limit of the terms is 0:

$$\lim_{n \to \infty} \frac{1}{n^2} = 0$$

and so we can not conclude anything because the criterion of the test (i.e., that the limit of the terms is not zero) is not met. When this happens, we say the test fails, and generally try another test on the series. In this case, the integral test, discussed next, will show that this series converges.

The Integral Test

In the **previous** example, we found that the nth term test for divergence failed when applied to the series

$$\sum_{n=1}^{\infty} \frac{1}{n^2} = 1 + \frac{1}{4} + \frac{1}{9} + \frac{1}{16} + \frac{1}{25} + \cdots$$

This series is similar to the harmonic series $\sum \frac{1}{n}$, which also fails the nth term test. However, the harmonic series *was* found to diverge by looking at estimates on the partial sums. Such estimates cannot be developed for

$$\sum_{n=1}^{\infty} \frac{1}{n^2}.$$

So how do we determine the convergence or divergence of this series? Using `seriesplot` can give some insight.

```
> a:=n->1/n^2;
```
$$a := n \mapsto \frac{1}{n^2}$$
```
> seriesplot(a,50);
```
`'The sum of the first',50,'terms of the series is',` 1.625132734

The Figure 8.3.2 shows the last frame in the animation and suggests that perhaps this series converges and has sum less than 1.7.

If you want to sum a large number of terms in this series, you should suppress the graphic output (so as to not lockup the computer). You can do this by using using a `noplot` option as a third argument. For example,

```
> seriesplot(a,100,noplot);
```
$$1.634983900$$
```
> seriesplot(a,200,noplot);
```
$$1.639946546$$

This suggests that the series converges and that its sum is approximately 1.64. To *prove* that the series does indeed converge, we look at the improper integral

$$\int_1^{\infty} \frac{1}{x^2}\, dx = \lim_{t \to \infty} \int_1^t \frac{1}{x^2}\, dx = \lim_{t \to \infty} \left(-\frac{1}{x} \right)\Big|_1^t = \lim_{t \to \infty} \left(1 - \frac{1}{t} \right) = 1.$$

This says that the area under the graph of $f(x) = \frac{1}{x^2}$ on the interval $[1, \infty]$ is exactly 1. If we represent the terms of the series $\sum_{n=1}^{\infty} 1/n^2$ as areas, say as areas of rectangles arranged beneath the graph of f, then we get Figure 8.3.3.

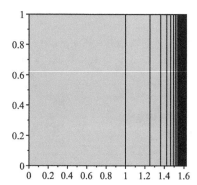

Figure 8.3.2: *The last frame in* `seriesplot(a,50)` *for the series* $\sum_{n=1}^{\infty} \frac{1}{n^2}$.

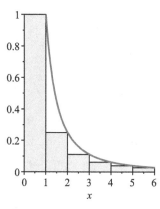

Figure 8.3.3: *Graph of* $f(x) = 1/x^2$ *on the interval* $[1,6]$. *The blue areas represent the first 6 terms in the series* $\sum_{n=1}^{\infty} 1/n^2$

The figure shows that the area under the graph of f on the interval $[1,6]$ is larger than the sum of the 2nd through the 6th terms of the series. This gives the inequality:

$$s_6 = 1 + \frac{1}{4} + \frac{1}{9} + \frac{1}{16} + \frac{1}{25} + \frac{1}{36} < 1 + \int_1^6 \frac{1}{x^2}\,dx = 1 + \left(1 - \frac{1}{6}\right)$$

In general, for any n we have

$$0 < s_n < 1 + \int_1^n \frac{1}{x^2}\,dx = 1 + \left(1 - \frac{1}{n}\right) < 2.$$

As mentioned at the beginning of this section, the sequence of partial sums $\{s_n\}$ is a strictly increasing sequence whenever the terms of the series are positive. The above inequality shows that for this particular series, the sequence $\{s_n\}$ is bounded above by 2, and thus the sequence converges. This proves that the series converges. Note that the inequality also gives

$$\sum_{n=1}^{\infty} \frac{1}{n^2} \le 1 + \int_1^\infty \frac{1}{x^2}\,dx = 2.$$

But this estimate is not very good for the actual sum of the series (which, as we have seen, is closer to 1.64).

A related example involves the corresponding behavior of the following series and improper integral:

$$\sum_{n=1}^{\infty} \frac{1}{\sqrt{n}} \quad \text{and} \quad \int_1^\infty \frac{1}{\sqrt{x}}\,dx.$$

We compute that improper integral diverges to infinity:

$$\int_1^\infty \frac{1}{\sqrt{x}}\,dx = \lim_{t\to\infty}\int_1^t \frac{1}{\sqrt{x}}\,dx = \lim_{t\to\infty}\left(2\sqrt{x}\right)\Big|_1^t = \lim_{t\to\infty}\left(2\sqrt{t} - 2\right) = \infty.$$

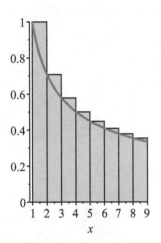

Figure 8.3.4: *Graph of $f(x) = 1/\sqrt{x}$ on the interval $[1,9]$. The green areas represent the first 8 terms in the series $\sum_{n=1}^{\infty} 1/\sqrt{n}$*

To see a similar divergent behavior for the series, we again represent its terms as areas of rectangles, but now with the rectangles lying above the graph of the function $f(x) = 1/\sqrt{x}$. This is illustrated in Figure 8.3.4. From this picture you see that,

$$s_8 = 1 + \frac{1}{\sqrt{2}} + \frac{1}{\sqrt{3}} + \frac{1}{2} + \cdots + \frac{1}{\sqrt{8}} > \int_1^9 \frac{1}{\sqrt{x}}\,dx = 2\sqrt{x}\Big|_1^9 = 6 - 2 = 4$$

In general, we have

$$s_n = 1 + \frac{1}{\sqrt{2}} + \frac{1}{\sqrt{3}} + \cdots + \frac{1}{\sqrt{n}} > \int_1^{n+1} \frac{1}{\sqrt{x}}\,dx - 2\sqrt{x}\Big|_1^{n+1} - 2\sqrt{n+1} - 1$$

This shows the terms in the sequence of partial sums $\{s_n\}$ can be made as large as we please if we take n large enough. For instance to make $s_n > 99$, we need to take $n = 2500$, at least. This is a large number of terms. Thus, we see that the series diverges.

The discussion and examples above lead to a general theorem that can be used for any series with positive terms a_n that arise as values of a function: $a_n = f(n)$, where f is positive, continuous and decreasing. This theorem is the integral test.

THEOREM 8.3.3 (The Integral Test)

Suppose $\displaystyle\sum_{n=1}^{\infty} a_n$ *is a series whose terms are given by* $a_n = f(n)$, *for all n,*

where f is a positive, continuous, decreasing function on the interval $[1,\infty)$.

(1) *If* $\displaystyle\int_{1}^{\infty} f(x)dx$ *converges, then* $\displaystyle\sum_{n=1}^{\infty} a_n$ *converges.*

(2) *If* $\displaystyle\int_{1}^{\infty} f(x)dx$ *diverges, then* $\displaystyle\sum_{n=1}^{\infty} a_n$ *diverges*

The integral test always gives a definitive answer to the question of whether a given series converges. This is so provided (1) the terms of the series satisfy the hypotheses of the theorem and (2) the improper integral can be evaluated. Here are some examples.

Example 8.3.3 (Using the Integral Test)

Problem: Determine whether the following series converge or diverge.

(a) $\displaystyle\sum_{n=1}^{\infty} \frac{n}{e^n}$ (b) $\displaystyle\sum_{n=1}^{\infty} \frac{\ln n}{\sqrt{n}}$ (c) $\displaystyle\sum_{n=1}^{\infty} \frac{1}{\sqrt{n}\,(n+1)}$

Solution (a): Note that $f(x) = \frac{x}{e^x} = xe^{-x}$ is positive, continuous and decreasing on the interval $[1, \infty]$. The corresponding improper integral is

$$\int_{1}^{\infty} \frac{x}{e^x}\,dx = \int_{1}^{\infty} xe^{-x}\,dx.$$

To compute this, we first compute the indefinite integral, which requires integrating by parts:

$$\int xe^{-x}\,dx = x\left(-e^{-x}\right) - \int 1\left(-e^{-x}\right)dx = -xe^{-x} + \int e^{-x}\,dx = -xe^{-x} - e^{-x}$$

$$= -(x+1)\,e^{-x}$$

So the definite integral is

$$\int_{1}^{t} xe^{-x}\,dx = -(x+1)\,e^{-x}\Big|_{1}^{t} = 2e^{-1} - (t+1)\,e^{-t}$$

Taking limits of this (using L' Hospital's rule) gives

$$\int_{1}^{\infty} \frac{x}{e^x}\,dx = 2e^{-1} - \lim_{t\to\infty} (t+1)\,e^{-t} = 2\,e^{-1} - \lim_{t\to\infty} \frac{t+1}{e^t}$$

$$\overset{LHosp}{=} 2e^{-1} - \lim_{t\to\infty} \frac{1}{e^t} = 2e^{-1}.$$

Thus, the improper integral converges and so the series converges by the integral test (IT).

Solution (b): For the series $\displaystyle\sum_{n=1}^{\infty} \frac{\ln n}{\sqrt{n}}$, the corresponding integral is

$$\int_{1}^{\infty} \frac{\ln x}{\sqrt{x}}\,dx = \int_{1}^{\infty} x^{-\frac{1}{2}} \ln x\,dx.$$

Use integration by parts to compute the indefinite integral:

$$\int x^{-\frac{1}{2}} \ln x\,dx = \int \ln x \cdot x^{-\frac{1}{2}}\,dx = \ln x\left(2x^{\frac{1}{2}}\right) - \int \frac{1}{x}\left(2x^{\frac{1}{2}}\right)dx$$

$$= 2\sqrt{x}\ln x - 2\int x^{-\frac{1}{2}}\,dx = 2\sqrt{x}\ln x - 4\sqrt{x} = 2\sqrt{x}\left(\ln x - 2\right)$$

Then
$$\int_1^t \frac{\ln x}{\sqrt{x}}\,dx = 2\sqrt{x}\,(\ln x - 2)\,\Big|_1^t = 2\sqrt{t}\,(\ln t - 2) + 4$$
The limit of this is
$$\int_1^\infty \frac{\ln x}{\sqrt{x}}\,dx = \lim_{t\to\infty}\left[2\sqrt{t}\,(\ln t - 2) + 4\right] = \infty.$$

Thus, the improper integral diverges to infinity and so, by the integral test (IT) the series $\displaystyle\sum_{n=1}^\infty \frac{\ln n}{\sqrt{n}}$ diverges.

Solution (c): For the series $\displaystyle\sum_{n=1}^\infty \frac{1}{\sqrt{n}\,(n+1)}$, we look at the integral
$$\int_1^\infty \frac{1}{\sqrt{x}\,(x+1)}\,dx.$$

To evaluate this, first compute the indefinite integral using a u-substitution $u = \sqrt{x}$, $du = \dfrac{1}{2\sqrt{x}}\,dx$:

$$\int \frac{1}{\sqrt{x}\,(x+1)}\,dx \;=\; \int \frac{1}{\sqrt{x}\,([\sqrt{x}]^2 + 1)}\,dx = 2\int \frac{1}{u^2 + 1}\,du$$
$$=\; 2\tan^{-1}(u) = 2\tan^{-1}\left(\sqrt{x}\right)$$

Then
$$\int_1^t \frac{1}{\sqrt{x}\,(x+1)}\,dx = 2\tan^{-1}\left(\sqrt{x}\right)\Big|_1^t = 2\tan^{-1}\left(\sqrt{t}\right) - \frac{\pi}{2}$$
The limit of this is
$$\int_1^\infty \frac{1}{\sqrt{x}\,(x+1)}\,dx = \lim_{t\to\infty}\left[2\tan^{-1}\left(\sqrt{t}\right) - \frac{\pi}{2}\right] = \pi - \frac{\pi}{2} = \frac{\pi}{2}.$$

Thus, the series converges by the IT.

p-SERIES

Convergence of p-Series

For $p > 0$, the p-series
$$\sum_{n=1}^\infty \frac{1}{n^p} = 1 + \frac{1}{2^p} + \frac{1}{3^p} + \frac{1}{4^p} + \frac{1}{5^p} + \cdots$$
converges if $p > 1$

diverges if $p \le 1$

The series $\displaystyle\sum_{n=1}^\infty \frac{1}{n^2}$, which we used to motivate the introduction of the integral test, and the series $\displaystyle\sum_{n=1}^\infty \frac{1}{n}$, which is the famous harmonic series, are two examples of what are known as p-series:
$$\sum_{n=1}^\infty \frac{1}{n^p}$$

Here the exponent p is any positive real number. Using the integral test and the result of Theorem 6.6.1, we get the result shown in the margin box. Thus, for example, the series
$$\sum_{n=1}^\infty \frac{1}{\sqrt{n^3}} = 1 + \frac{1}{\sqrt{8}} + \frac{1}{\sqrt{27}} + \frac{1}{\sqrt{64}} + \cdots = \sum_{n=1}^\infty \frac{1}{n^{3/2}},$$
is a $p = 3/2$ series and so it converges. On the other hand.
$$\sum_{n=1}^\infty \frac{1}{\sqrt{n}} = 1 + \frac{1}{\sqrt{2}} + \frac{1}{\sqrt{3}} + \frac{1}{\sqrt{4}} + \cdots = \sum_{n=1}^\infty \frac{1}{n^{1/2}},$$

is a $p = 1/2$ series and so it diverges. The theorem gives us another definitive class of series, like the geometric series, for which we know the convergence or divergence. However, unlike the geometric series, for a convergent p-series (i.e., for $p > 1$) we do not know what the value of its sum is.

Exercises: 8.3 (The nth Term and Integral Tests)

In Exercises 1–24, use the nth Term Test (NTT) to see if the series diverges. NOTE: The test fails on some of these, so you can reach no conclusion about convergence or divergence of the series.

1. $\displaystyle\sum_{n=1}^{\infty} \frac{n^5}{3n^5 + 1}$

2. $\displaystyle\sum_{n=1}^{\infty} \frac{n^6}{7n^6 + 1}$

3. $\displaystyle\sum_{n=1}^{\infty} \frac{n^4}{3n^5 - 2}$

4. $\displaystyle\sum_{n=1}^{\infty} \frac{n^5}{5n^6 - 2}$

5. $\displaystyle\sum_{n=1}^{\infty} \frac{\sqrt{n}}{\sqrt{n} + 1}$

6. $\displaystyle\sum_{n=1}^{\infty} \frac{\sqrt[3]{n}}{\sqrt[3]{n} + 1}$

7. $\displaystyle\sum_{n=1}^{\infty} \frac{\sqrt{n}}{n + 1}$

8. $\displaystyle\sum_{n=1}^{\infty} \frac{\sqrt[3]{n}}{n + 1}$

9. $\displaystyle\sum_{n=1}^{\infty} \sin\left(\frac{1}{n}\right)$

10. $\displaystyle\sum_{n=1}^{\infty} \cos\left(\frac{\pi}{2} - \frac{1}{n}\right)$

11. $\displaystyle\sum_{n=1}^{\infty} \cos\left(\frac{1}{n}\right)$

12. $\displaystyle\sum_{n=1}^{\infty} \sin\left(\frac{\pi}{2} + \frac{1}{n}\right)$

13. $\displaystyle\sum_{n=1}^{\infty} \frac{1}{\tan^{-1} n}$

14. $\displaystyle\sum_{n=1}^{\infty} \frac{1}{\cot^{-1} n}$

15. $\displaystyle\sum_{n=1}^{\infty} \frac{1}{n \tan^{-1} n}$

16. $\displaystyle\sum_{n=1}^{\infty} \frac{1}{n \cot^{-1} n}$

17. $\displaystyle\sum_{n=1}^{\infty} \frac{5}{n^{1/n}}$

18. $\displaystyle\sum_{n=1}^{\infty} \frac{7}{n^{2/n}}$

19. $\displaystyle\sum_{n=2}^{\infty} \frac{n^{1/n}}{n^{1/n} - 1}$

20. $\displaystyle\sum_{n=2}^{\infty} \frac{3^{1/n}}{n^{1/n} - 1}$

21. $\displaystyle\sum_{n=1}^{\infty} \frac{2}{\left(1 - \frac{3}{n}\right)^n}$

22. $\displaystyle\sum_{n=1}^{\infty} \frac{4}{\left(1 + \frac{5}{n}\right)^n}$

23. $\displaystyle\sum_{n=1}^{\infty} n \sin\left(\frac{1}{n}\right)$

24. $\displaystyle\sum_{n=1}^{\infty} n \cos\left(\frac{\pi}{2} + \frac{1}{n}\right)$

In Exercises 25–62, use the Integral Test (IT) to determine the convergence/divergence of the series.

NOTE 1: You may assume that the hypotheses of the Integral Test hold.

NOTE 2: If the series is a p-series, you do not have to use the Integral Test. Just use the results about p-series. In 63–66 reduce the terms first.

25. $\displaystyle\sum_{n=1}^{\infty} \frac{n^2}{(n^3 + 1)^2}$

26. $\displaystyle\sum_{n=1}^{\infty} \frac{n^3}{(n^4 + 1)^2}$

27. $\displaystyle\sum_{n=1}^{\infty} \frac{\sqrt{n}}{n^3 + 1}$

28. $\displaystyle\sum_{n=1}^{\infty} \frac{n^{3/2}}{n^5 + 1}$

29. $\displaystyle\sum_{n=1}^{\infty} \frac{n}{n^4 + 1}$

30. $\displaystyle\sum_{n=1}^{\infty} \frac{n^2}{n^6 + 1}$

31. $\displaystyle\sum_{n=1}^{\infty} \frac{1}{\sqrt{n}(n + 1)}$

32. $\displaystyle\sum_{n=1}^{\infty} \frac{\sqrt{n}}{n^3 + 1}$

33. $\displaystyle\sum_{n=1}^{\infty} n^{-5/2}$

34. $\displaystyle\sum_{n=1}^{\infty} n^{-7/3}$

35. $\displaystyle\sum_{n=1}^{\infty} \sqrt{n^{-3}}$

36. $\displaystyle\sum_{n=1}^{\infty} \sqrt{n^{-7}}$

37. $\displaystyle\sum_{n=1}^{\infty} \frac{e^{-n}}{e^{-n} + 1}$

38. $\displaystyle\sum_{n=1}^{\infty} \frac{2^{-n}}{2^{-n} + 1}$

39. $\displaystyle\sum_{n=1}^{\infty} \frac{e^n}{e^{2n} + 1}$

40. $\displaystyle\sum_{n=1}^{\infty} \frac{2^n}{4^n + 1}$

41. $\displaystyle\sum_{n=1}^{\infty} \frac{\ln n}{n}$

42. $\displaystyle\sum_{n=1}^{\infty} \frac{1}{n \ln n}$

43. $\displaystyle\sum_{n=1}^{\infty} \frac{\ln n}{n^4}$

44. $\displaystyle\sum_{n=1}^{\infty} \frac{\ln n}{n^5}$

45. $\displaystyle\sum_{n=1}^{\infty} \frac{(\ln n)^2}{n^{3/2}}$

46. $\displaystyle\sum_{n=1}^{\infty} \frac{(\ln n)^3}{n^{3/2}}$

47. $\displaystyle\sum_{n=1}^{\infty} \frac{\tan^{-1} n}{n^2}$

48. $\displaystyle\sum_{n=1}^{\infty} \frac{\tan^{-1} n}{n^4}$

49. $\displaystyle\sum_{n=1}^{\infty} \frac{\tan^{-1} n}{n^3}$

50. $\displaystyle\sum_{n=1}^{\infty} \frac{\tan^{-1} n}{n^5}$

51. $\displaystyle\sum_{n=2}^{\infty} \frac{1}{n(\ln n)^2}$

52. $\displaystyle\sum_{n=2}^{\infty} \frac{1}{n(\ln n)^3}$

53. $\displaystyle\sum_{n=2}^{\infty} \frac{1}{n\sqrt{\ln n}}$

54. $\displaystyle\sum_{n=2}^{\infty} \frac{1}{n(\ln n)^{3/2}}$

55. $\displaystyle\sum_{n=1}^{\infty} ne^{-n}$

56. $\displaystyle\sum_{n=1}^{\infty} ne^{-2n}$

57. $\displaystyle\sum_{n=1}^{\infty} n^2 e^{-n}$

58. $\displaystyle\sum_{n=1}^{\infty} n^3 e^{-n}$

59. $\displaystyle\sum_{n=1}^{\infty} e^{-n} \cos(e^{-n})$

60. $\displaystyle\sum_{n=1}^{\infty} e^{-n} \sin(e^{-n})$

61. $\displaystyle\sum_{n=1}^{\infty} \frac{e^{-\sqrt{n}}}{\sqrt{n}}$

62. $\displaystyle\sum_{n=1}^{\infty} \frac{e^{-n^{1/3}}}{n^{2/3}.}$

63. $\displaystyle\sum_{n=1}^{\infty} \left[\frac{(n-1)!}{n!}\right]^2$

64. $\displaystyle\sum_{n=1}^{\infty} \left[\frac{(n-1)!}{n!}\right]^3$

65. $\displaystyle\sum_{n=1}^{\infty} \frac{n!}{(2n)!}$

66. $\displaystyle\sum_{n=1}^{\infty} \frac{(n+1)!}{(2n+2)!}$

Calculus *Concepts & Computation*

8.4 The Comparison Tests

The comparison tests apply to positive term series $\sum a_n$ and are again based on Theorem 8.1.5 which determines convergence or divergence from the boundedness or unboundedness of its sequence of partial sums.

The Direct Comparison Test

The series $\sum_{n=1}^{\infty} \frac{1}{n^2+1}$ is not a p-series but is nevertheless convergent, as can be determined from the integral test. An easier way to determine convergence of this series is by direct comparison with the 2-series $\sum_{n=1}^{\infty} \frac{1}{n^2}$. This means the following. Since the terms of the series satisfy

$$\frac{1}{n^2+1} \leq \frac{1}{n^2},$$

for all n, it follows that

$$\sum_{n=1}^{k} \frac{1}{n^2+1} \leq \sum_{n=1}^{k} \frac{1}{n^2} < \sum_{n=1}^{\infty} \frac{1}{n^2} = S,$$

for all k. Thus, the sum S of the 2-series provides an upper bound for the sequence of partial sums of the other series. Therefore by the positive term series result discussed at the beginning of Section 8.3, the other series converges. Clearly the reasoning employed in this example applies in general. This gives the following theorem.

THEOREM 8.4.1 (The Direct Comparison Test)

Suppose $\displaystyle\sum_{n=1}^{\infty} a_n$ *is a series with positive terms.*

(1) *If there is a convergent series* $\displaystyle\sum_{n=1}^{\infty} c_n$ *and* $a_n \leq c_n$ *for all n, then* $\displaystyle\sum_{n=1}^{\infty} a_n$ *converges.*

(2) *If there is a divergent series* $\displaystyle\sum_{n=1}^{\infty} d_n$ *and* $0 < d_n \leq a_n$ *for all n, then* $\displaystyle\sum_{n=1}^{\infty} a_n$ *diverges.*

NOTE: As we have mentioned before, convergence or divergence of a series is not affected by deleting or altering a finite number of its terms, say the first k terms. So the inequalities in Parts (1) and (2) of the theorem only need to hold for all $n > k$.

The next example will give you some experience with using and understanding this new test.

Example 8.4.1 (Using the Direct Comparison Test)

Problem: Determine the convergence/divergence of the following series.

$$\text{(a) } \sum_{n=0}^{\infty} \frac{2^n-1}{3^n+4} \qquad \text{(b) } \sum_{n=2}^{\infty} \frac{n^2}{n^3-1} \qquad \text{(c) } \sum_{n=0}^{\infty} \frac{1}{n!}$$

Solution (a): Without the -1 and 4 in the numerator and denominator, this series would be the geometric series

$$\sum_{n=0}^{\infty} \frac{2^n}{3^n} = \sum_{n=0}^{\infty} \left(\frac{2}{3}\right)^n,$$

which converges since the common ratio is $r = \frac{2}{3}$. We compare the terms and see that

$$\frac{2^n - 1}{3^n + 4} < \frac{2^n}{3^n + 4} < \frac{2^n}{3^n},$$

for all n. Thus, the given series converges by direct comparison with the geometric series.

Solution (b): Without the 1 in the denominator, the series $\sum_{n=2}^{\infty} \frac{n^2}{n^3-1}$ would be the series:

$$\sum_{n=2}^{\infty} \frac{n^2}{n^3} = \sum_{n=2}^{\infty} \frac{1}{n},$$

which is the harmonic series (without its first term). Since the harmonic series diverges, we try to determine if its terms are less than the terms of the given series:

$$\frac{n^2}{n^3 - 1} > \frac{n^2}{n^3} = \frac{1}{n},$$

for all n larger than 1. So the given series diverges by direct comparison with the divergent harmonic series.

Solution (c): For the series $\sum_{n=0}^{\infty} \frac{1}{n!}$, it is a bit trickier to find another series to compare with. The first two terms of the given series are 1, so we look beyond that:

$$a_2 = \frac{1}{2}$$

$$a_3 = \frac{1}{3 \cdot 2} < \frac{1}{2 \cdot 2} = \frac{1}{2^2}$$

$$a_4 = \frac{1}{4 \cdot 3 \cdot 2} < \frac{1}{2 \cdot 2 \cdot 2} = \frac{1}{2^3},$$

and generally we see

$$a_n < \frac{1}{2^{n-1}},$$

for all n larger than 1. But,

$$\sum_{n=1}^{\infty} \frac{1}{2^{n-1}} = \sum_{k=0}^{\infty} \frac{1}{2^k}$$

is a convergent geometric series, and so the given series converges by direct comparison.

Sometimes the obvious comparisons do not work in the sense that the hypotheses necessary to use the direct comparison test are not satisfied. In this case, try another type of test. The following example illustrates this.

Example 8.4.2 (The Direct Comparison Test Fails)

Problem: Determine the convergence/divergence of the following series.

$$\text{(a)} \sum_{n=1}^{\infty} \frac{n^2}{n^3 + 1} \qquad \text{(b)} \sum_{n=1}^{\infty} \frac{1}{\left(1 + \frac{1}{n}\right)^n}$$

Solution (a): The terms in this series are almost identical to those in Example 8.4.1 Part (b) above, but the comparison goes the wrong way

$$\frac{n^2}{n^3 + 1} < \frac{n^2}{n^3} < \frac{1}{n}$$

for all n. Here the terms of the harmonic series $\frac{1}{n}$ are larger that those of the given series and so the divergence of the harmonic series tells us nothing about the given series. We cannot use the direct comparison test. We could use the limit comparison test from the next section below. But we also see that the integral test works:

$$\int_1^t \frac{x^2}{x^3 + 1} dx = \frac{1}{3} \ln\left(x^3 + 1\right)\Big|_1^t = \frac{1}{3} \ln\left(t^3 + 1\right) - \frac{1}{3} \ln 2$$

Thus,

$$\int_1^\infty \frac{x^2}{x^3 + 1} dx = \infty,$$

and so the given series diverges by the integral test.

Solution (b): To find a series to compare $\sum \dfrac{1}{\left(1 + \frac{1}{n}\right)^n}$ with, we first note that, for all n,

$$1 + \frac{1}{n} \leq 1 + 1 = 2,$$

and so

$$\left(1 + \frac{1}{n}\right)^n \leq 2^n.$$

Consequently

$$\frac{1}{2^n} \leq \frac{1}{\left(1 + \frac{1}{n}\right)^n},$$

for all n. So the terms of the given series directly compare with those of the geometric series $\sum \frac{1}{2^n}$, but the comparison goes the wrong way (the convergence of this geometric series does not force the convergence of the given series). We could search for another series to compare with. Trying the integral test seems difficult because

$$\int \frac{1}{\left(1 + \frac{1}{x}\right)^x} dx$$

is not computable. However we see that the nth term test for divergence works, since

$$\lim_{n \to \infty} \left(1 + \frac{1}{n}\right)^n = e$$

is a famous limit. Thus, the limit of the terms of the given series is

$$\lim_{n \to \infty} \frac{1}{\left(1 + \frac{1}{n}\right)^n} = \frac{1}{e} \neq 0$$

So the given series diverges by the NTT for divergence.

The previous example illustrates some of the difficulties with using the direct comparison test. The main one is finding a series to compare the given series with. You will need a series that you know either converges or diverges. So, as a rule of thumb, first try comparing the given series with either a geometric series or a p-series. After this, try another test, at this point either the integral test or the divergence test. The next subsection presents another test, called the *limit comparison test*, which works well and is easy to apply (once you find a series to compare with).

The Limit Comparison Test

When the comparisons in the direct comparison test do not go the right way, you can usually turn to the limit comparison test to get an answer on the convergence/divergence of the given series.

xx

THEOREM 8.4.2 (The Limit Comparison Test)

Suppose $\displaystyle\sum_{n=1}^{\infty} a_n$ *and* $\displaystyle\sum_{n=1}^{\infty} b_n$ *are series with positive terms. If the limit*

$$\lim_{n \to \infty} \frac{a_n}{b_n} = L$$

exist and L is a positive finite number, then either both the series $\displaystyle\sum_{n=1}^{\infty} a_n$, $\displaystyle\sum_{n=1}^{\infty} b_n$ *converge or they both diverge.*

NOTE 1: If the limit in the theorem is zero or infinity (or does not exist) then you cannot use the limit comparison test. However, as an exercise you can show how to extend the theorem to the cases $L = 0$ and $L = \infty$.

NOTE 2: The theorem does not say which of the series $\sum a_n$, $\sum b_n$ is the given series (and it does not matter). However, the choice of a_n, b_n in taking the limit

$$\lim_{n \to \infty} \frac{a_n}{b_n},$$

might be easier with one choice as opposed to the other. (See the next example.)

The following examples illustrate the how this new test works.

Example 8.4.3 (Using the Limit Comparison Test)

Problem: Determine the convergence/divergence of the following series.

(a) $\displaystyle\sum_{n=2}^{\infty} \frac{1}{n^3 - 1}$ (b) $\displaystyle\sum_{n=1}^{\infty} \frac{3n^2 + 4n + 3}{n^5 - n^3 + 1}$ (c) $\displaystyle\sum_{n=0}^{\infty} \frac{3^n}{9^n - 2}$

Solution (a): Clearly we should compare this series with the $p = 3$ series, but the comparisons go the wrong way:

$$\frac{1}{n^3} < \frac{1}{n^3 - 1}$$

for all n. However, using the limit comparison test with

$$a_n = \frac{1}{n^3}, \quad b_n = \frac{1}{n^3 - 1},$$

gives

$$\frac{a_n}{b_n} = \frac{\frac{1}{n^3}}{\frac{1}{n^3-1}} = \frac{1}{n^3} \cdot \left(n^3 - 1\right) = 1 - \frac{1}{n^3}.$$

Thus,

$$L = \lim_{n \to \infty} \frac{a_n}{b_n} = \lim_{n \to \infty} \left[1 - \frac{1}{n^3}\right] = 1$$

So the given series converges by the limit comparison test (LCT).

NOTE: This example illustrates an important strategy involved in using the limit comparison test. The choice of a_n, b_n was made so that the algebra in taking the limit was easier. If we had made the other choice:

$$a_n = \frac{1}{n^3 - 1}, \ b_n = \frac{1}{n^3}$$

then

$$\frac{a_n}{b_n} = \frac{\frac{1}{n^3-1}}{\frac{1}{n^3}} = \frac{n^3}{n^3-1}$$

To calculate the limit of this ratio requires dividing top and bottom by n^3. (Or, you could use L' Hospital's rule.) While this is not much more difficult than the first way, we think you will like the first way better.

Solution (b): The given series

$$\sum_{n=1}^{\infty} \frac{3n^2 + 4n + 3}{n^5 - n^3 + 1}$$

compares naturally to

$$\sum_{n=1}^{\infty} \frac{3n^2}{n^5} = \sum_{n=1}^{\infty} \frac{3}{n^3}$$

The reasoning (and rule of thumb) here is that the highest powers in the numerator and denominator are much larger than the other powers when n is large. For computing the ratio of the respective terms of these series, we take

$$a_n = \frac{1}{n^3}, \qquad b_n = \frac{3n^2 + 4n + 3}{n^5 - n^3 + 1}.$$

Then

$$\frac{a_n}{b_n} = \frac{1}{n^3} \cdot \frac{n^5 - n^3 + 1}{3n^2 + 4n + 3} = \frac{n^2 - 1 + \frac{1}{n^3}}{3n^2 + 4n + 3}$$

$$= \frac{\frac{1}{n^2}}{\frac{1}{n^2}} \cdot \frac{n^2 - 1 + \frac{1}{n^3}}{3n^2 + 4n + 3} = \frac{1 - \frac{1}{n^2} + \frac{1}{n^5}}{3 + \frac{4}{n} + \frac{3}{n^2}}.$$

Thus,

$$\lim_{n \to \infty} \frac{a_n}{b_n} = \frac{1}{3},$$

and so the given series converges by the limit comparison test (LCT).

Solution (c): If the given series $\displaystyle\sum_{n=0}^{\infty} \frac{3^n}{9^n - 2}$ did not have the -2 in the denominator, we would have a geometric series

$$\sum_{n=0}^{\infty} \frac{3^n}{9^n} = \sum_{n=0}^{\infty} \left(\frac{3}{9}\right)^n = \sum_{n=0}^{\infty} \left(\frac{1}{3}\right)^n$$

which is a convergent geometric series. The DCT does not work because the terms compare as

$$\frac{3^n}{6^n} < \frac{3^n}{6^n - 2},$$

for all $n \geq 1$. So, we use the LCT with

$$a_n = \left(\frac{1}{3}\right)^n = \frac{1}{3^n}, \qquad b_n = \frac{3^n}{9^n - 2}$$

This gives

$$\frac{a_n}{b_n} = \frac{1}{3^n} \cdot \frac{9^n - 2}{3^n} = \frac{9^n - 2}{9^n} = 1 - \frac{2}{9^n}$$

Then

$$L = \lim_{n \to \infty} \frac{a_n}{b_n} = \lim_{n \to \infty} \left[1 - \frac{2}{9^n}\right] = 1$$

Since this is a nonzero, finite number, we can use the LCT to conclude that the given series converges.

Exercises: 8.4 (The Comparison Tests)

In Exercises 1–28, use the Direct Comparison Test (DCT) to test the series for convergence or divergence. Show all your steps clearly.

1. $\displaystyle\sum_{n=1}^{\infty} \frac{n^2}{n^5+6}$

2. $\displaystyle\sum_{n=1}^{\infty} \frac{n^3}{n^7+2}$

3. $\displaystyle\sum_{n=1}^{\infty} \frac{1}{n^2+3n+7}$

4. $\displaystyle\sum_{n=1}^{\infty} \frac{1}{(n+4)^2+1}$

5. $\displaystyle\sum_{n=1}^{\infty} \frac{n}{\sqrt{n^5+1}}$

6. $\displaystyle\sum_{n=1}^{\infty} \frac{n^2}{\sqrt{n^7+1}}$

7. $\displaystyle\sum_{n=1}^{\infty} \frac{3^n}{(5^n+1)^2}$

8. $\displaystyle\sum_{n=1}^{\infty} \frac{5^n}{(2^n+1)^2}$

9. $\displaystyle\sum_{n=1}^{\infty} \frac{2^{-n}}{1+2^{-n}}$

10. $\displaystyle\sum_{n=1}^{\infty} \frac{3^{-n}}{1+3^{-n}}$

11. $\displaystyle\sum_{n=1}^{\infty} \frac{2^n+3^n}{6^n+1}$

12. $\displaystyle\sum_{n=1}^{\infty} \frac{4^n+6^n}{10^n+1}$

13. $\displaystyle\sum_{n=1}^{\infty} \frac{\sqrt{9^n+1}}{2^n-1}$

14. $\displaystyle\sum_{n=1}^{\infty} \frac{\sqrt{16^n-1}}{3^n+1}$

15. $\displaystyle\sum_{n=1}^{\infty} \frac{\sqrt{2^n+3^n}}{4^n+5^n}$

16. $\displaystyle\sum_{n=1}^{\infty} \frac{\sqrt{3^n+4^n}}{5^n+6^n}$

17. $\displaystyle\sum_{n=1}^{\infty} \frac{n-1}{n(n+1)(n+2)}$

18. $\displaystyle\sum_{n=2}^{\infty} \frac{n+3}{(n-1)(n-2)}$

19. $\displaystyle\sum_{n=1}^{\infty} \frac{\tan^{-1} n}{n^2}$

20. $\displaystyle\sum_{n=1}^{\infty} \frac{\tan^{-1} n}{n^3}$

21. $\displaystyle\sum_{n=1}^{\infty} \frac{\tan^{-1} n}{\sqrt{n}}$

22. $\displaystyle\sum_{n=1}^{\infty} \frac{\tan^{-1} n}{\sqrt[3]{n^2}}$

23. $\displaystyle\sum_{n=1}^{\infty} \frac{e^n}{e^{2n}+1}$

24. $\displaystyle\sum_{n=1}^{\infty} \frac{3^n}{9^n+1}$

25. $\displaystyle\sum_{n=1}^{\infty} \frac{(n!)^2}{[(n+1)!]^2}$

26. $\displaystyle\sum_{n=1}^{\infty} \frac{[(n+1)!]^2}{[(n+2)!]^2}$

27. $\displaystyle\sum_{n=1}^{\infty} \frac{n!}{(2n)!}$

28. $\displaystyle\sum_{n=1}^{\infty} \frac{(n+1)!}{(2n+2)!}$

In Exercises 29–42, use the Limit Comparison Test (LCT) to test the series for convergence or divergence. Show all your steps clearly.

29. $\displaystyle\sum_{n=2}^{\infty} \frac{n^3}{n^7-1}$

30. $\displaystyle\sum_{n=2}^{\infty} \frac{n^4}{n^9-1}$

31. $\displaystyle\sum_{n=1}^{\infty} \frac{n-1}{n^2+1}$

32. $\displaystyle\sum_{n=1}^{\infty} \frac{n-2}{n^2+4}$

33. $\displaystyle\sum_{n=2}^{\infty} \frac{\sqrt{n}}{n^2-1}$

34. $\displaystyle\sum_{n=2}^{\infty} \frac{\sqrt{n^3}}{n^4-1}$

35. $\displaystyle\sum_{n=1}^{\infty} \frac{2n-1}{(n+2)(n+3)}$

36. $\displaystyle\sum_{n=1}^{\infty} \frac{n^2+1}{(n^2+2)(n^2+3)}$

37. $\displaystyle\sum_{n=1}^{\infty} \frac{4^n}{2\sqrt{25^n-1}}$

38. $\displaystyle\sum_{n=1}^{\infty} \frac{3^n}{3\sqrt{16^n-1}}$

39. $\displaystyle\sum_{n=1}^{\infty} \frac{3(n+1)^2}{n^6}$

40. $\displaystyle\sum_{n=1}^{\infty} \frac{4(n^2+1)^2}{n^7}$

41. $\displaystyle\sum_{n=1}^{\infty} \frac{2^n}{4^n-1}$

42. $\displaystyle\sum_{n=1}^{\infty} \frac{5^n}{4^n+1}$

In Exercises 43–66, determine the convergence or divergence of the series. Use any appropriate test: NTT, IT, DCT, or LCT. State which test you use and show all your steps in using the test.

43. $\displaystyle\sum_{n=1}^{\infty} \frac{2^n}{5^n+1}$

44. $\displaystyle\sum_{n=1}^{\infty} \frac{3^n}{2^n+1}$

45. $\displaystyle\sum_{n=1}^{\infty} \frac{\sqrt{n^3}}{\sqrt[3]{n^{20}+1}}$

46. $\displaystyle\sum_{n=1}^{\infty} \frac{\sqrt{n}}{\sqrt[5]{n^{17}+1}}$

47. $\displaystyle\sum_{n=1}^{\infty} \frac{2n!}{3n!}$

48. $\displaystyle\sum_{n=1}^{\infty} \frac{\sqrt{n!}}{\sqrt{n+3}}$

49. $\displaystyle\sum_{n=1}^{\infty} \frac{e^n}{e^n-1}$

50. $\displaystyle\sum_{n=1}^{\infty} \frac{2^n}{2^{n+1}-1}$

51. $\displaystyle\sum_{n=1}^{\infty} n^2 e^{-n^3}$

52. $\displaystyle\sum_{n=1}^{\infty} \sqrt{n}\, e^{-n^{3/2}}$

53. $\displaystyle\sum_{n=1}^{\infty} \frac{\sin^2 n}{n^{5/4}}$

54. $\displaystyle\sum_{n=1}^{\infty} \frac{\cos^2 n}{n^{5/3}}$

55. $\displaystyle\sum_{n=2}^{\infty} \frac{1}{n(\ln n)^7}$

56. $\displaystyle\sum_{n=2}^{\infty} \frac{1}{n(\ln n)^p}$

57. $\displaystyle\sum_{n=1}^{\infty} \frac{1}{n^{1/n}}$

58. $\displaystyle\sum_{n=1}^{\infty} n^{-(1+1/n.}$

59. $\displaystyle\sum_{n=1}^{\infty} \frac{(n-1)!}{n!+1}$

60. $\displaystyle\sum_{n=2}^{\infty} \frac{(n-1)!}{n!-1}$

61. $\displaystyle\sum_{n=1}^{\infty} \frac{n^{1/n}}{n^2+1}$

62. $\displaystyle\sum_{n=1}^{\infty} \frac{n^{1/n}}{n^3+1}$

63. $\displaystyle\sum_{n=1}^{\infty} \sqrt{\frac{25^{-n}}{4^n}}$

64. $\displaystyle\sum_{n=1}^{\infty} \sqrt[3]{\frac{27^{-n}}{8^n}}$

65. $\displaystyle\sum_{n=1}^{\infty} \frac{3^n+1}{2^n-1}$

66. $\displaystyle\sum_{n=1}^{\infty} \frac{5^n+1}{7^n-1}$

Calculus Concepts & Computation

8.5 The Ratio and Root Tests

The ratio test and root test discussed in this section are for positive terms series. In some respects they are easier to apply to a given series $\sum a_n$ than the comparison tests. This is because we do not have to find another series to compare with the given series.

The Ratio Test

The ratio test is based on the geometric series

$$\sum_{n=0}^{\infty} ar^n = a + a + ar^3 + ar^3 + \cdots$$

whose convergence is determined by the magnitude of the common ratio r (converging when this magnitude is less than 1 and diverging otherwise). When r is positive, the series is a positive-term series and, as we have mentioned previously, the ratio of adjacent terms in the series is constant and equal to the common ratio:

$$\frac{a_{n+1}}{a_n} = \frac{ar^n}{ar^{n-1}} = r.$$

For all other positive term series

$$\sum_{n=1}^{\infty} a_n = a_1 + a_2 + a_3 + a_4 + \cdots$$

the ratio of adjacent terms

$$\frac{a_{n+1}}{a_n},$$

is not constant. However, when this sequence of ratios has a limit

$$\lim_{n \to \infty} \frac{a_{n+1}}{a_n} = \rho,$$

the magnitude of ρ can determine the convergence/divergence of the series. This is the content of the ratio test.

THEOREM 8.5.1 (The Ratio Test)

Suppose $\displaystyle\sum_{n=1}^{\infty} a_n$ *is a series with positive terms and the following limit exists*

$$\rho = \lim_{n \to \infty} \frac{a_{n+1}}{a_n}.$$

(1) If $\rho < 1$*, then* $\displaystyle\sum_{n=1}^{\infty} a_n$ *converges.*

(2) If $\rho > 1$*, then* $\displaystyle\sum_{n=1}^{\infty} a_n$ *diverges.*

(3) If $\rho = 1$*, then the ratio test is inconclusive.*

NOTE: In Case (1), $\rho = 0$ is allowed and the series converges. In Case (2), if the limit exists in the extended sense, i.e., $\rho = \infty$, then the series diverges.

Proof:

Case (1): When $\rho < 1$, we can get a comparison of the given series with a convergent geometric series. We do this as follows. First choose a number r such that $\rho < r < 1$. Then $\varepsilon = r - \rho$ is positive. Since

$$\lim_{n \to \infty} \frac{a_{n+1}}{a_n} = \rho,$$

there is a natural number N such that

$$\left| \frac{a_{n+1}}{a_n} - \rho \right| < \varepsilon = r - \rho,$$

for all $n \geq N$. In particular, this says

$$\frac{a_{n+1}}{a_n} - \rho < r - \rho,$$

or equivalently,

$$\frac{a_{n+1}}{a_n} < r,$$

for $n = N, N + 1, N + 2, \ldots$. Rearranging these inequalities gives

$$
\begin{aligned}
a_{N+1} &< a_N \, r \\
a_{N+2} &< a_{N+1} \, r < (a_N \, r) \, r = a_N \, r^2 \\
a_{N+3} &< a_{N+2} \, r < \left(a_N r^2 \right) r = a_N \, r^3
\end{aligned}
$$

$$\vdots$$

From the first three of these, and induction, we get

$$a_{N+k} < a_N \, r^k,$$

for all $k \geq 1$. Thus, the series

$$\sum_{k=0}^{\infty} a_{N+k} \quad \text{and} \quad \sum_{k=0}^{\infty} a_N r^k$$

compare directly. Since the second series is a convergent geometric series, the first series converges by the direct comparison test. Since the first series is the given series, $\sum a_n$, without its first $N - 1$ terms, the given series converges.

Case (2): When $\rho > 1$, we can choose an r such that $\rho > r > 1$. Then $\varepsilon = \rho - r$ is positive and since the limit of the ratios is ρ, there is an N such that

$$\left| \frac{a_{n+1}}{a_n} - \rho \right| < \varepsilon = \rho - r,$$

for all $n \geq N$. In particular this says that

$$r - \rho = -\varepsilon < \frac{a_{n+1}}{a_n} - \rho$$

or equivalently

$$1 < r < \frac{a_{n+1}}{a_n}$$

for $n = N, N + 1, N + 2, \ldots$ Rearranging these inequalities gives

$$a_N < a_{N+1} < a_{N+2} < a_{N+3} < \cdots$$

Thus, the limit of the terms of the given series is not 0. Hence by the nth term test for divergence, the given series diverges.

<u>Case (3)</u>: When $\rho = 1$, the test is inconclusive. This means that there are examples of convergent series with $\rho = 1$ and examples of divergent series with $\rho = 1$. For instance, consider the general p-series

$$\sum_{n=1}^{\infty} \frac{1}{n^p}.$$

Here $a_n = \frac{1}{n^p}$ and the limit of the ratios of adjacent terms is

$$\rho = \lim_{n \to \infty} \frac{a_{n+1}}{a_n} = \lim_{n \to \infty} \frac{n^p}{(n+1)^p} = \lim_{n \to \infty} \left(\frac{n}{n+1} \right)^p = \left(\lim_{n \to \infty} \frac{n}{n+1} \right)^p = 1^p = 1$$

So the ratio test fails to distinguish which of the p-series converge (those for $p > 1$) and which do not (those for $p \leq 1$).

Example 8.5.1 (Using the Ratio Test)

Determine whether the following series converge or diverge.

Problem (a): $\displaystyle\sum_{n=1}^{\infty} \frac{n^3}{2^n}$

Solution (a): Here $a_n = \dfrac{n^3}{2^n}$, $\quad a_{n+1} = \dfrac{(n+1)^3}{2^{n+1}}$. So

$$\frac{a_{n+1}}{a_n} = \frac{(n+1)^3}{2^{n+1}} \cdot \frac{2^n}{n^3} = \frac{(n+1)^3}{n^3} \cdot \frac{2^n}{2^{n+1}} = \left(\frac{n+1}{n} \right)^3 \cdot \frac{1}{2} = \left(1 + \frac{1}{n} \right)^3 \cdot \frac{1}{2}$$

<u>NOTE</u> 1: When the terms a_n of the series are ratios, then it is useful to consider the ratio of adjacent terms as a product of a term with the reciprocal of the previous term:

$$\frac{a_{n+1}}{a_n} = a_{n+1} \cdot \frac{1}{a_n}.$$

This is what we did above.

<u>NOTE</u> 2: Above we simplified the ratio of adjacent terms by putting the cubic terms together and the powers of 2 together. With the resulting simplification we can now take the limit:

$$\rho = \lim_{n \to \infty} \frac{a_{n+1}}{a_n} = \lim_{n \to \infty} \left(1 + \frac{1}{n} \right)^3 \cdot \frac{1}{2} = \frac{1}{2} < 1$$

Thus, the series converges by the ratio test (RAT).

Problem (b): $\displaystyle\sum_{n=0}^{\infty} \frac{10^n}{n!}$

Solution (b): Here $a_n = \dfrac{10^n}{n!}$, $\quad a_{n+1} = \dfrac{10^{n+1}}{(n+1)!}$. So

$$\frac{a_{n+1}}{a_n} = \frac{10^{n+1}}{(n+1)!} \cdot \frac{n!}{10^n} = \frac{10^{n+1}}{10^n} \frac{n!}{(n+1)!} = 10 \cdot \frac{n!}{(n+1)\, n!} = 10 \cdot \frac{1}{n+1} = \frac{10}{n+1}$$

Thus,

$$\rho = \lim_{n \to \infty} \frac{a_{n+1}}{a_n} = \lim_{n \to \infty} \frac{10}{n+1} = 0 < 1$$

Thus, the series converges by the ratio test (RAT).

Problem (c): $\displaystyle\sum_{n=1}^{\infty} \frac{n^n}{n!}$

Solution (c): Here $a_n = \dfrac{n^n}{n!}, \quad a_{n+1} = \dfrac{(n+1)^{n+1}}{(n+1)!} = \dfrac{(n+1)^n (n+1)}{(n+1)\,n!} = \dfrac{(n+1)^n}{n!}.$

Note that it is sometimes best to simplify a_{n+1} before taking the ratio with a_n. Thus,

$$\frac{a_{n+1}}{a_n} = \frac{(n+1)^n}{n!} \cdot \frac{n!}{n^n} = \frac{(n+1)^n}{n^n} = \left(\frac{n+1}{n}\right)^n = \left(1 + \frac{1}{n}\right)^n.$$

Using the famous limit $\displaystyle\lim_{n\to\infty}\left(1 + \frac{x}{n}\right)^n = e^x$ from Exercise Set 8.1, we get

$$\rho = \lim_{n\to\infty} \frac{a_{n+1}}{a_n} = \lim_{n\to\infty}\left(1 + \frac{1}{n}\right)^n = e > 1$$

So the series diverges by the RAT.

Problem (d): $\displaystyle\sum_{n=1}^{\infty} \frac{(n!)^2}{(2\,n)!}$

Solution (d): Here the terms are $a_n = \dfrac{(n!)^2}{(2n)!}$ and

$$
\begin{aligned}
a_{n+1} &= \frac{[(n+1)!]^2}{(2\,n+2)!} = \frac{[(n+1)n!]^2}{(2n+2)(2n+1)n!} = \frac{(n+1)^2\,(n!)^2}{(2\,n+2)\,(2\,n+1)\,(2\,n)!} \\[2mm]
&= \frac{(n+1)\,(n!)^2}{2\,(2n+1)\,(2n)!} = \frac{n+1}{2(2n+1)} \cdot a_n.
\end{aligned}
$$

With these simplifications of a_{n+1} we get

$$\frac{a_{n+1}}{a_n} = \frac{n+1}{2(2n+1)}.$$

Thus,

$$\rho = \lim_{n\to\infty} \frac{a_{n+1}}{a_n} = \lim_{n\to\infty} \frac{n+1}{2(2n+1)} = \frac{1}{4} < 1$$

So, the series converges by the RAT.

CAUTION: Be careful when working with expressions such as $(2\,n+2)!$. The correct identity to use for this is

$$(2\,n+2)! = (2\,n+2)\,(2\,n+1)\,(2\,n)!$$

The Root Test

The ratio test test is quick and easy to apply to many series and is especially useful in series whose terms involve factorials. The root test is a test for convergence that is particularly useful for series whose nth terms involve a power of n. (The root test is not useful for series involving factorials.) Like the ratio test, the conclusions for the root test depend on the value of a number ρ that arises from a limit.

THEOREM 8.5.2 (The Root Test)

Suppose $\displaystyle\sum_{n=1}^{\infty} a_n$ *is a series with positive terms and the following limit exists*

$$\rho = \lim_{n \to \infty} (a_n)^{1/n}.$$

(1) If $\rho < 1$*, then* $\displaystyle\sum_{n=1}^{\infty} a_n$ *converges.*

(2) If $\rho > 1$*, then* $\displaystyle\sum_{n=1}^{\infty} a_n$ *diverges.*

(3) If $\rho = 1$*, then the root test is inconclusive.*

The proof of the root test is left as an exercise.

Example 8.5.2 (Using the Root Test)

Determine the convergence/divergence of the following series.

Problem (a): $\displaystyle\sum_{n=1}^{\infty} \left(\frac{2n+3}{5n-1}\right)^n$

Solution (a): Here $a_n = \left(\dfrac{2n+3}{5n-1}\right)^n$, and so

$$(a_n)^{\frac{1}{n}} = \left[\left(\frac{2n+3}{5n-1}\right)^n\right]^{\frac{1}{n}} = \left(\frac{2n+3}{5n-1}\right)^{n \cdot \frac{1}{n}} = \frac{2n+3}{5n-1}.$$

Thus,

$$\rho = \lim_{n \to \infty} a_n^{\frac{1}{n}} = \lim_{n \to \infty} \frac{2n+3}{5n-1} = \lim_{n \to \infty} \frac{2 + \frac{3}{n}}{5 - \frac{1}{n}} = \frac{2}{5} < 1$$

So the series converges by the root test (ROT).

Problem (b): $\displaystyle\sum_{n=1}^{\infty} \frac{(\ln n)^n}{n^n}$

Solution (b): Here $a_n = \dfrac{(\ln n)^n}{n^n}$, so $(a_n)^{\frac{1}{n}} = \left(\dfrac{(\ln n)^n}{n^n}\right)^{\frac{1}{n}} = \dfrac{\ln n}{n}$.

Thus,

$$\rho = \lim_{n \to \infty} a_n^{\frac{1}{n}} = \lim_{n \to \infty} \frac{\ln n}{n} \overset{L'\,Hosp}{=} \lim_{n \to \infty} \frac{\frac{1}{n}}{1} = 0 < 1$$

Note that we used L' Hospital's rule on indeterminate limit *undefined* in the next to the last step. Since $\rho = 0 < 1$, the series converges by the root test (ROT).

Problem (c): $\displaystyle\sum_{n=1}^{\infty} \frac{3^n}{n^2}$

Solution (c): This series can be tested using the ratio test, but perhaps you will find the root test is slightly quicker.

$$a_n = \frac{3^n}{n^2}, \quad \text{so} \quad a_n^{\frac{1}{n}} = \left(\frac{3^n}{n^2}\right)^{\frac{1}{n}} = \frac{3}{n^{2/n}}$$

Thus,

$$\rho = \lim_{n \to \infty} a_n^{\frac{1}{n}} = \lim_{n \to \infty} \frac{3}{n^{2/n}} = \lim_{n \to \infty} \frac{3}{(n^{1/n})^2} = \frac{3}{(1)^2} = 3 > 1$$

Here we used the limit result $\lim\limits_{n \to \infty} n^{1/n} = 1$, from the Basic limits Table in Exercise Set 8.1. The series diverges by the ROT. Note that you could also use the divergence test on this series since

$$\lim_{n \to \infty} a_n = \lim_{n \to \infty} \frac{3^n}{n^2} = \infty.$$

(Use L' Hospital's rule twice to evaluate this limit.)

The following table summarizes the tests for convergence that we have discussed in the previous sections (and also contains the alternating series test from the next section).

TESTS FOR CONVERGENCE OF $\sum a_n$		
TEST	**CONDITIONS**[*]	**CONCLUSION**
NTT	$\lim\limits_{n \to \infty} a_n \neq 0$	$\sum a_n$ *diverges*
IT	$a_n = f(n)$ $\int_1^{\infty} f(x)dx = I$ $\quad I < \infty$ $\qquad\qquad\qquad\quad I = \infty$ $f(x) \geq 0$, *continuous, decreasing*	$\sum a_n$ *converges* $\sum a_n$ *diverges*
DCT	*There is a convergent series* $\sum c_n$ *with* $a_n \leq c_n$ *for all large n* *There is a divergent series* $\sum d_n$ *with* $d_n \leq a_n$ *for all large n*	$\sum a_n$ *converges* $\sum a_n$ *diverges*
LCT	$\lim\limits_{n \to \infty} \dfrac{a_n}{b_n} = L \qquad 0 < L < \infty$	$\sum a_n$ *and* $\sum b_n$ *either both converge or both diverge*
RAT	$\lim\limits_{n \to \infty} \dfrac{a_{n+1}}{a_n} = \rho \quad$ $\begin{array}{l} \rho < 1 \\ \rho > 1 \\ \rho = 1 \end{array}$	$\sum a_n$ *converges* $\sum a_n$ *diverges* *no information*
ROT	$\lim\limits_{n \to \infty} a_n^{1/n} = \rho \quad$ $\begin{array}{l} \rho < 1 \\ \rho > 1 \\ \rho = 1 \end{array}$	$\sum a_n$ *converges* $\sum a_n$ *diverges* *no information*
AST	$a_n = (-1)^{n+1} c_n$, *where* $c_n \geq 0$ (1) $c_n \geq c_{n+1}$, *for all large n* (2) $\lim\limits_{n \to \infty} c_n = 0$	$\sum a_n$ *converges*

[*] Note: $a_n > 0$ *in all tests except for NTT and AST*

Exercises: 8.5 (The Ratio and Root Tests)

The Ratio Test: In Exercises 1–24, use the Ratio Test (RAT) to determine the convergence/divergence of the series.

1. $\displaystyle\sum_{n=1}^{\infty} \frac{2^n}{n!}$

2. $\displaystyle\sum_{n=1}^{\infty} \frac{5^n}{n!}$

3. $\displaystyle\sum_{n=1}^{\infty} \frac{(n!)^3}{(3n)!}$

4. $\displaystyle\sum_{n=1}^{\infty} \frac{(n!)^4}{(4n)!}$

5. $\displaystyle\sum_{n=1}^{\infty} \frac{n!}{n^n}$

6. $\displaystyle\sum_{n=1}^{\infty} \frac{n!}{(2n)^n}$

7. $\displaystyle\sum_{n=1}^{\infty} \frac{n^5}{3^n}$

8. $\displaystyle\sum_{n=1}^{\infty} \frac{n^6}{8^n}$

9. $\displaystyle\sum_{n=1}^{\infty} \sqrt{\frac{n^2}{4^n}}$

10. $\displaystyle\sum_{n=1}^{\infty} \sqrt{\frac{n^6}{16^n}}$

11. $\displaystyle\sum_{n=1}^{\infty} \frac{n!}{(2n+1)!}$

12. $\displaystyle\sum_{n=1}^{\infty} \frac{(n+1)!}{(2n+1)!}$

13. $\displaystyle\sum_{n=1}^{\infty} \frac{n!}{(n+1)(2n)!}$

14. $\displaystyle\sum_{n=1}^{\infty} \frac{(2n)!}{(n+1)(3n)!}$

15. $\displaystyle\sum_{n=1}^{\infty} \frac{2^n}{4^n-1}$

16. $\displaystyle\sum_{n=1}^{\infty} \frac{3^n}{5^n-1}$

17. $\displaystyle\sum_{n=1}^{\infty} \frac{n!}{2^{n!}}$

18. $\displaystyle\sum_{n=1}^{\infty} \frac{(2n)!}{3^{n!}}$

19. $\displaystyle\sum_{n=1}^{\infty} \frac{(2n+1)!}{5^n(n!)^2}$

20. $\displaystyle\sum_{n=1}^{\infty} \frac{(2n+1)!}{6^n(n!)^2}$

21. $\displaystyle\sum_{n=1}^{\infty} \frac{(2n)!}{(3^n)^2(n!)^2}$

22. $\displaystyle\sum_{n=1}^{\infty} \frac{(2n)!}{(4^n)^2(n!)^2}$

23. $\displaystyle\sum_{n=1}^{\infty} \frac{n!}{5\cdot7\cdot9\cdots(2n+3)}$

24. $\displaystyle\sum_{n=3}^{\infty} \frac{n!}{3\cdot5\cdot7\cdots(2n-3)}$

The Root Test: In Exercises 25–42, use the Root Test (ROT) to determine the convergence/divergence of the series.

25. $\displaystyle\sum_{n=1}^{\infty} \left(\frac{2n+1}{3n+2}\right)^n$

26. $\displaystyle\sum_{n=1}^{\infty} \left(\frac{3n-1}{5n+2}\right)^n$

27. $\displaystyle\sum_{n=1}^{\infty} \left(\frac{n^2+1}{5n^2+2}\right)^n$

28. $\displaystyle\sum_{n=1}^{\infty} \left(\frac{7n^3+1}{5n^3+2}\right)^n$

29. $\displaystyle\sum_{n=1}^{\infty} \frac{n^3}{4^n}$

30. $\displaystyle\sum_{n=1}^{\infty} \frac{n^5}{6^n}$

31. $\displaystyle\sum_{n=1}^{\infty} \frac{n^{1/n}}{2^n}$

32. $\displaystyle\sum_{n=1}^{\infty} \frac{n^{1/n^2}}{3^n}$

33. $\displaystyle\sum_{n=1}^{\infty} \left(\frac{\ln n}{n}\right)^n$

34. $\displaystyle\sum_{n=1}^{\infty} \left(\frac{\ln n}{\sqrt{n}}\right)^n$

35. $\displaystyle\sum_{n=1}^{\infty} \left(\frac{\sqrt{n}}{n+1}\right)^n$

36. $\displaystyle\sum_{n=1}^{\infty} \left(\frac{\sqrt[3]{n}}{\sqrt{n}+1}\right)^n$

37. $\displaystyle\sum_{n=2}^{\infty} \left(\frac{\sqrt{n}}{\sqrt{n}-1}\right)^n$

38. $\displaystyle\sum_{n=2}^{\infty} \left(\frac{\sqrt[4]{n}}{\sqrt[4]{n}-1}\right)^n$

39. $\displaystyle\sum_{n=1}^{\infty} \frac{n}{\left(1+\frac{2}{n}\right)^{n^2}}$

40. $\displaystyle\sum_{n=3}^{\infty} \frac{n}{\left(1-\frac{2}{n}\right)^{n^2}}$

41. $\displaystyle\sum_{n=1}^{\infty} \frac{\ln n}{n^2}$

42. $\displaystyle\sum_{n=1}^{\infty} \frac{(\ln n)^2}{n^3}$

Your Choice of Tests: In Exercises 43–66, use any of the tests (NTT, IT, DCT, LCT, RAT, or ROT) to determine whether the series converges or not. Often several tests will work, so you have the option of which to use.

43. $\displaystyle\sum_{n=1}^{\infty} \frac{1}{(\sqrt{n}+2)^3}$

44. $\displaystyle\sum_{n=1}^{\infty} \frac{1}{(\sqrt[3]{n}+2)^5}$

45. $\displaystyle\sum_{n=1}^{\infty} \left[\frac{1+e^{-n}}{2+e^{-n}}\right]^n$

46. $\displaystyle\sum_{n=1}^{\infty} \left[\frac{3e^n+1}{5e^n+1}\right]^n$

47. $\displaystyle\sum_{n=5}^{\infty} \frac{1}{(\sqrt{n}-2)^3}$

48. $\displaystyle\sum_{n=9}^{\infty} \frac{1}{(\sqrt[3]{n}-2)^5}$

49. $\displaystyle\sum_{n=1}^{\infty} \frac{(n!)^2}{2^n n^{2n}}$

50. $\displaystyle\sum_{n=1}^{\infty} \frac{(n!)^3}{3^n n^{3n}}$

51. $\displaystyle\sum_{n=1}^{\infty} \frac{1}{\tan^{-1}n}$

52. $\displaystyle\sum_{n=1}^{\infty} \frac{1}{1+\cot^{-1}n}$

53. $\displaystyle\sum_{n=1}^{\infty} \frac{n!}{(2n)!}$

54. $\displaystyle\sum_{n=1}^{\infty} \frac{(2n)!}{(3n)!}$

55. $\displaystyle\sum_{n=1}^{\infty} \frac{n^2}{\sqrt{n^5+1}}$

56. $\displaystyle\sum_{n=1}^{\infty} \frac{n^3}{\sqrt{n^7+1}}$

57. $\displaystyle\sum_{n=1}^{\infty} \frac{\tan^{-1}n}{n}$

58. $\displaystyle\sum_{n=1}^{\infty} \frac{1+\cot^{-1}n}{n}$

59. $\displaystyle\sum_{n=1}^{\infty} \left(\frac{\tan^{-1}n}{n}\right)^2$

60. $\displaystyle\sum_{n=1}^{\infty} \left(\frac{1+\cot^{-1}n}{n}\right)^2$

61. $\displaystyle\sum_{n=1}^{\infty} \frac{2^n+1}{(3^n-1)^2}$

62. $\displaystyle\sum_{n=1}^{\infty} \frac{4^n+1}{(7^n-1)^2}$

63. $\displaystyle\sum_{n=1}^{\infty} \frac{1}{\sqrt{n}(n+1)}$

64. $\displaystyle\sum_{n=1}^{\infty} \frac{\sqrt{n}}{n^3+1}$

65. $\displaystyle\sum_{n=1}^{\infty} \left(\frac{\ln n}{n}\right)^{2n}$

66. $\displaystyle\sum_{n=1}^{\infty} \left(\frac{\ln n}{n}\right)^{3n}$

Calculus *Concepts & Computation*

8.6 Absolute & Conditional Convergence

In this section we move beyond series with positive terms to study series $\sum a_n$ with arbitrary terms, positive and negative. You should note that most of the previous tests for convergence/divergence cannot be applied here since they are for series with positive terms. (The exception is the nth-term test for divergence.) However, all the tests can be applied to the series of absolute values: $\sum |a_n|$ corresponding to the given series, and we shall see that this is sometimes helpful in determining the convergence of $\sum a_n$.

One special type of series with both positive and negative terms is an *alternating series*. Its terms alternate successively from positive to negative. We discuss this type of series first.

Alternating Series

A series $\sum a_n$ is called an alternating series if its terms alternate from positive to negative. We can express this by saying the terms have the form $a_n = (-1)^{n+1} c_n$, where $c_n > 0$ for every n. Then the alternating series is

$$\sum_{n=1}^{\infty} (-1)^{n+1} c_n = c_1 - c_2 + c_3 - c_4 + \cdots$$

We could also allow the first term to be negative

$$\sum_{n=1}^{\infty} (-1)^n c_n = -c_1 + c_2 - c_3 + c_4 - \cdots$$

But since the initial terms of a series do not affect its convergence or divergence, we will use a form of an alternating series where the first term is positive.

Example 8.6.1 (Another Bug's Journey)

Having a series alternate improves its chances of converging (as opposed to having all of its terms positive). Here's a motivating example, one where we can sum both series.

The journey of the bug in Example 8.2.1 consisted of hops in the forward (positive) direction, each hop half the distance as the preceding one.

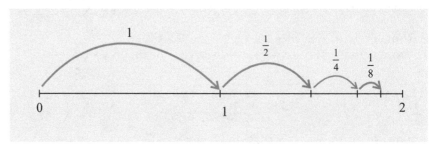

Figure 8.6.1: *The total distance traveled by the bug is 2 feet.*

The total distance of this bug from the origin (after infinitely many hops) is given by the sum of the geometric series

$$1 + \frac{1}{2} + \frac{1}{4} + \frac{1}{8} + \cdots = \sum_{n=0}^{\infty} \left(\frac{1}{2}\right)^n = \frac{1}{1 - \frac{1}{2}} = 2$$

Consider a different bug which executes a sequence of hops, each half the distance as the previous one, but now with the hops alternating forward and backward.

The total distance of this *alternating* bug from the origin (after infinitely many hops) is given by the sum of the geometric series

$$1 - \frac{1}{2} + \frac{1}{4} - \frac{1}{8} + \cdots = \sum_{n=0}^{\infty} (-1)^n \left(\frac{1}{2}\right)^n = \sum_{n=0}^{\infty} \left(-\frac{1}{2}\right)^n = \frac{1}{1 - \left(-\frac{1}{2}\right)} = \frac{2}{3}$$

The picture in the magin indicates why the alternating bug gets less far from the origin that the forwards-only bug, and the calculation confirms this.

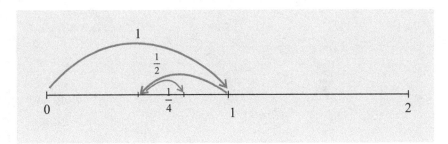

The main convergence test for alternating series has a name that is perhaps misleading. It is called the *alternating series test*, even though not all alternating series satisfy the criteria of the test. The criteria, as the theorem below shows, are that the c_n form a decreasing sequence which tends to zero. This is what occurs for the (alternating) geometric series in Example 8.6.1 where $c_n = \left(\frac{1}{2}\right)^n = \frac{1}{2^n}$

THEOREM 8.6.1 (The Alternating Series Test)

Suppose $\displaystyle\sum_{n=1}^{\infty} (-1)^{n+1} c_n$ *is an alternating series with*

(1) $c_n \geq c_{n+1} \geq 0$, *for every n.*

(2) $\displaystyle\lim_{n \to \infty} c_n = 0$

Then $\displaystyle\sum_{n=1}^{\infty} (-1)^{n+1} c_n$ *converges*

<u>NOTE</u> 1: Criterion (1) of the theorem does not have to hold for every n. It only needs to hold for all $n \geq N$, for some N. As we have stressed repeatedly, the initial terms of a series do not affect whether it converges or not.

<u>NOTE</u> 2: If Criterion (2) does not hold, then $\lim_{n \to \infty} (-1)^{n+1} c_n$ does not exist, and so the series diverges by the NTT.

<u>NOTE</u> 3: When c_n is a fraction, with numerator 1 (or some other number) it is customary to put the alternating signs $(-1)^{n+1}$ in the numerator of c_n. For example, if $c_n = 1/n$, we write

$$\sum_{n=1}^{\infty} (-1)^{n+1} \frac{1}{n} = \sum_{n=1}^{\infty} \frac{(-1)^{n+1}}{n}$$

The proof of Theorem 8.6.1 is left as an exercise.

Example 8.6.2 (Using the Alternating Series Test)

Determine if the following alternating series converge or diverge.

Problem (a): $\displaystyle\sum_{n=1}^{\infty} \frac{(-1)^{n+1}}{n}$

Solution (a): The series

$$\sum_{n=1}^{\infty} \frac{(-1)^{n+1}}{n} = 1 - \frac{1}{2} + \frac{1}{3} - \frac{1}{4} + \frac{1}{5} - \frac{1}{6} + \cdots$$

is known as the *alternating harmonic series* and is the canonical example of an alternating series that satisfies the criteria of the alternating series test. Here is the verification of that.

(1) $c_n = \dfrac{1}{n} > \dfrac{1}{n+1} = c_{n+1}$, for every n.

(2) $\displaystyle\lim_{n\to\infty} c_n = \lim_{n\to\infty} \frac{1}{n} = 0$.

IMPORTANT NOTE: The *alternating* harmonic series converges, but the harmonic series diverges.

Problem (b): $\displaystyle\sum_{n=2}^{\infty} \frac{(-1)^{n+1} n}{n^3 - 1}$

Solution (b): Here

$$c_n = \frac{n}{n^3 - 1}, \qquad c_{n+1} = \frac{n+1}{(n+1)^3 - 1}$$

It is rather difficult to directly see that $c_n \geq c_{n+1}$, so we use the device of looking at the related function:

$$f(x) = \frac{x}{x^3 - 1}.$$

If we can show that f is (eventually) decreasing on $[2, \infty)$, that will show that $c_n = f(n)$ is also (eventually) decreasing. To analyze the monotonicty of f, we use the first derivative

$$f'(x) = \frac{1\left(x^3 - 1\right) - x\left(3x^2\right)}{\left(x^3 - 1\right)^2} = \frac{-1 - 2x^3}{\left(x^3 - 1\right)^2} < 0,$$

for all $x > 0$. Thus, f is decreasing on $[2, \infty)$ and so c_n satisfies the first criterion of the AST (Alternating Series Test). The second criterion is also satisfied since

$$\lim_{n\to\infty} \frac{n}{n^3 - 1} = \lim_{n\to\infty} \frac{1}{3n^2} = 0$$

Here, we used L' Hospital's Rule in limit calculation. Thus, the series converges by the AST.

Problem (c): $\displaystyle\sum_{n=1}^{\infty} (-1)^{n+1} \frac{\ln n}{n}$

Solution (c): In this series

$$c_n = \frac{\ln n}{n}, \qquad c_{n+1} = \frac{\ln(n+1)}{n+1},$$

and again it is difficult to see if $c_n \geq c_{n+1}$, so we look at the corresponding function $f(x) = \frac{\ln x}{x}$. Its derivative is

$$f'(x) = \frac{\frac{1}{x} \cdot x - \ln x \cdot 1}{x^2} = \frac{1 - \ln x}{x^2},$$

and this is negative for all $x > e \approx 2.72$. Therefore, $c_n > c_{n+1}$, for all $n \geq 3$. We can use L' Hospital's rule to verify that criterion (2) holds:

$$\lim_{n \to \infty} \frac{\ln n}{n} = \lim_{n \to \infty} \frac{\frac{1}{n}}{1} = 0$$

Thus, the series converges by the AST,

Problem (d): $\displaystyle\sum_{n=1}^{\infty} \frac{(-1)^{n+1} e^n}{n}$

Solution (d): Here, the sequence $c_n = \dfrac{e^n}{n}$ is not decreasing (Criterion (1) fails). To see this, look at the corresponding function $f(x) = \dfrac{e^x}{x}$, which has derivative

$$f'(x) = \frac{xe^x - e^x}{x^2} = \frac{(x-1)e^x}{x^2} > 0,$$

for all $x > 1$. Thus, f is an increasing function on $(1, \infty)$, and therefore $\{c_n\}$ is an increasing sequence. We conclude that the AST does not apply to the series

$$\sum_{n=1}^{\infty} \frac{(-1)^{n+1} e^n}{n}$$

However, by L' Hospital's rule,

$$\lim_{n \to \infty} \frac{e^n}{n} = \lim_{n \to \infty} \frac{e^n}{1} = \infty.$$

Hence

$$\lim_{n \to \infty} \frac{(-1)^{n+1} e^n}{n} = \text{does not exist,}$$

and so the series diverges by the NTT.

ALTERNATING p-SERIES

Part (a) of the last example illustrates the important result that the alternating harmonic series (alternating 1-series) converges This is true for any *alternating p*-series, as the margin box indicates.

Alternating p-Series

All alternating p-series

$$\sum_{n=1}^{\infty} \frac{(-1)^{n+1}}{n^p} = 1 - \frac{1}{2^p} + \frac{1}{3^p} - \frac{1}{4^p} + \frac{1}{5^p} - \cdots$$

converge.

Example 8.6.3 (Using `seriesplot` on Alternating Sequences)

Problem: Use `seriesplot` on the alternating harmonic series

$$\sum_{n=1}^{\infty} \frac{(-1)^{n+1}}{n} = 1 - \frac{1}{2} + \frac{1}{3} - \frac{1}{4} + \frac{1}{5} - \frac{1}{6} + \cdots$$

to approximate the its sum and to illustrate the manner in which its sequence of partial sums approaches the sum.

Solution: We define the terms $a_n = \dfrac{(-1)^{n+1}}{n}$ and create a movie showing the sequence of partial sums.

```
> a:=n->(-1)^(n+1)/n;
```

$$a := n \mapsto \frac{(-1)^{n+1}}{n}$$

```
> seriesplot(a,16);
```
`'The sum of the first', 16, 'terms of the series is', 0.6628718504`

You should step through the movie, frame by frame, and observe how s_n changes from one frame to the next. Recall that the nth frame shows s_n as an area (in green). Thus, the 1st frame shows

$$s_1 = 1$$

as a green area of 1 square unit. The 2nd frame shows

$$s_2 = 1 - \frac{1}{2} = \frac{1}{2}$$

as a green area of 1/2 square unit. The 3rd frame shows

$$s_3 = 1 - \frac{1}{2} + \frac{1}{3} = \frac{5}{6}$$

as a green area of 5/6 square unit. The 4th frame shows

$$s_3 = 1 - \frac{1}{2} + \frac{1}{3} - \frac{1}{4} = \frac{7}{12}$$

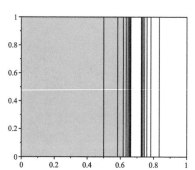

Figure 8.6.2: *The last frame in the movie* `seriesplot(a,16)` *for* $\sum_{n=1}^{\infty} \frac{(-1)^{n+1}}{n}$.

as a green area of 7/12 square unit. And so on. Notice that in going from an odd frame to an even frame the area decreases and in going from an even frame to an odd frame, the area increases (and that the amount of decrease/increase is less each time). Also observe that the even terms, $s_2 < s_4 < s_6 < \ldots$ form an increasing sequence, while the odd terms, $s_1 > s_3 > s_5 \ldots$ form a decreasing sequence. Finally, observe that all the even terms are less that every odd term and that the sum s of the series appears as if it is going to be between all the even and odd terms. The last frame of this 16-frame movie is shown in Figure 8.6.2.

Absolute Convergence & Conditional Convergence

When dealing with series $\sum a_n$ that have both positive and negative terms, we can always look at the corresponding series of absolute values:

$$\sum_{n=1}^{\infty} |a_n|.$$

This series has positive terms and so we can test it for convergence using any of the tests from the previous sections, But what will this tell us about the original series $\sum a_n$? The following theorem gives us an answer to this question.

> **THEOREM 8.6.2 (Absolute Convergence)**
>
> *If* $\sum_{n=1}^{\infty} |a_n|$ *converges, then* $\sum_{n=1}^{\infty} a_n$ *converges.*

The proof of this theorem is left as an exercise. The theorem leads to a new category of series, ones that are absolutely convergent.

> **DEFINITION 8.6.1 (Absolute Convergence)**
>
> *A series* $\sum_{n=1}^{\infty} a_n$ *is called absolutely convergent if* $\sum_{n=1}^{\infty} |a_n|$ *converges*

Think of an absolutely convergent series as being *really* convergent. Not only does it converge, but its series of absolute values converges, Absolute convergence is stronger than just convergence.

Example 8.6.4 (Testing for Absolute Convergence)

Problem: Determine if the following series are absolutely convergent or not.

$$\text{(a) } \sum_{n=1}^{\infty} \frac{\sin(n)}{n^2} \qquad \text{(b) } \sum_{n=1}^{\infty} \frac{(-1)^{n+1}}{n}$$

Solution (a): Note that this is not an alternating series even though it has positive and negative terms. So, we cannot use the alternating series test to see if it converges. The series of absolute values is

$$\sum_{n=1}^{\infty} \left| \frac{\sin(n)}{n^2} \right| = \sum_{n=1}^{\infty} \frac{|\sin(n)|}{n^2}$$

since the values of the sine function are at most 1 in magnitude, we have

$$\frac{|\sin(n)|}{n^2} \leq \frac{1}{n^2},$$

for all n. We can use the direct comparison test, comparing with the convergent $p = 2$ series, to conclude that the series of absolute values converges. Thus, the given series is absolutely convergent.

Solution (b): This series is the alternating harmonic series

$$\sum_{n=1}^{\infty} \frac{(-1)^{n+1}}{n} = 1 - \frac{1}{2} + \frac{1}{3} - \frac{1}{4} + \frac{1}{5} - \frac{1}{6} + \cdots$$

which converges, But its series of absolute values:

$$\sum_{n=1}^{\infty} \frac{\left| (-1)^{n+1} \right|}{n} = \sum_{n=1}^{\infty} \frac{1}{n} = 1 + \frac{1}{2} + \frac{1}{3} + \frac{1}{4} + \frac{1}{5} + \frac{1}{6} + \cdots$$

is the harmonic series, which diverges. The alternating harmonic series is the canonical example of a series that is convergent but not absolutely convergent.

Part (b) of the preceding example leads to the definition of a new class of series.

DEFINITION 8.6.2 (Conditional Convergence)

A series $\sum_{n=1}^{\infty} a_n$ is called conditionally convergent if it converges, but $\sum_{n=1}^{\infty} |a_n|$ diverges

This discussion of general series $\sum a_n$ has led us to a classification scheme for series. A given series is either *absolutely convergent, conditionally convergent, or divergent*. These are mutually exclusive classes and in classifying a given series you should proceed as follows:

(1) First test for absolute convergence (AC) by applying a test from the previous sections to $\sum |a_n|$.

(2) Test for conditional convergence (CC) by applying, if possible, the alternating series test (AST).

(3) If (1) and (2) are inconclusive, try the nth term test (NTT) for divergence.

Example 8.6.5 (Classifying Series)

Problem: Classify the following series as absolutely convergent, conditionally convergent, or divergent.

(a) $\displaystyle\sum_{n=1}^{\infty} \frac{(-1)^{n+1}\, n^2}{(2\,n)!}$ (b) $\displaystyle\sum_{n=1}^{\infty} \frac{(-1)^{n+1}\,\sqrt{n}}{n+1}$ (c) $\displaystyle\sum_{n=1}^{\infty} (-1)^{n+1}\left(1+\frac{5}{n}\right)^{-n}$

Solution (a): The series of absolute values is

$$\sum_{n=1}^{\infty} \frac{n^2}{(2\,n)!},$$

and we use the ratio test on this with

$$a_n = \frac{n^2}{(2\,n)!}, \qquad a_{n+1} = \frac{(n+1)^2}{(2\,n+2)!} = \frac{(n+1)^2}{(2\,n+2)\,(2\,n+1)\,(2\,n)!}.$$

Then

$$\begin{aligned}
\frac{a_{n+1}}{a_n} &= \frac{(n+1)^2}{(2\,n+2)\,(2\,n+1)\,(2\,n)!} \cdot \frac{(2\,n)!}{n^2} \\
&= \frac{(n+1)^2}{n^2} \cdot \frac{1}{(2n+2)\,(2n+1)} = \left(1+\frac{1}{n}\right)^2 \frac{1}{(2n+2)\,(2n+1)}
\end{aligned}$$

Thus,

$$\begin{aligned}
\rho &= \lim_{n\to\infty} \frac{a_{n+1}}{a_n} = \lim_{n\to\infty} \left(1+\frac{1}{n}\right)^2 \frac{1}{(2n+2)\,(2n+1)} \\
&= \lim_{n\to\infty} \left(1+\frac{1}{n}\right)^2 \lim_{n\to\infty} \frac{1}{(2n+2)\,(2n+1)} = 1\cdot 0 = 0 < 1
\end{aligned}$$

So, the series of absolute values converges by the RAT and consequently the given series is absolutely convergent.

Solution (b): The series of absolute values is

$$\sum_{n=1}^{\infty} \frac{\sqrt{n}}{n+1}$$

and we compare this with

$$\sum_{n=1}^{\infty} \frac{\sqrt{n}}{n} = \sum_{n=1}^{\infty} \frac{1}{\sqrt{n}},$$

which is a divergent $p = 1/2$ series. We use the limit comparison test with

$$a_n = \frac{1}{\sqrt{n}}, \qquad b_n = \frac{\sqrt{n}}{n+1},$$

so that

$$\frac{a_n}{b_n} = \frac{1}{\sqrt{n}} \cdot \frac{n+1}{\sqrt{n}} = \frac{n+1}{n} = 1 + \frac{1}{n}$$

Then

$$L = \lim_{n\to\infty} \frac{a_n}{b_n} = \lim_{n\to\infty} \left(1+\frac{1}{n}\right) = 1$$

Since $0 < L < \infty$, by the LCT the series of absolute values of the given series has the same behavior as $\sum \frac{1}{\sqrt{n}}$, which is divergent. Next we test to see if the given series

$$\sum_{n=1}^{\infty} \frac{(-1)^{n+1}\,\sqrt{n}}{n+1}$$

converges. Use the AST, with

$$c_n = \frac{\sqrt{n}}{n+1}, \qquad c_{n+1} = \frac{\sqrt{n+1}}{n+2},$$

and check that $c_n \geq c_{n+1}$ by letting

$$f(x) = \frac{\sqrt{x}}{x+1}.$$

Then

$$f'(x) = \frac{\frac{1}{2\sqrt{x}}(x+1) - \sqrt{x} \cdot 1}{(x+1)^2} = \frac{1-x}{2\sqrt{x}(x+1)} < 0.$$

for $x > 1$. Thus, f is decreasing on the interval $(1, \infty)$, which gives that $\{c_n\}$ is a decreasing sequence. Its limit, using L' Hospital's rule, is

$$\lim_{n \to \infty} c_n = \lim_{n \to \infty} \frac{\sqrt{n}}{n+1} = \lim_{n \to \infty} \frac{\frac{1}{2\sqrt{n}}}{1} = 0$$

So, the given series converges, by the AST, and its series of absolute value diverges. Thus, the given series is conditionally convergent.

Solution (c): The series of absolute values is

$$\sum_{n=1}^{\infty} \left(1 + \frac{5}{n}\right)^{-n}$$

The root test gives

$$\rho = \lim_{n \to \infty} \left[\left(1 + \frac{5}{n}\right)^{-n} \right]^{\frac{1}{n}} \lim_{n \to \infty} \left(1 + \frac{5}{n}\right)^{-1} = (1)^{-1} = 1$$

and so is inconclusive. The ratio test gives the same result. However if we try the nth term test, we get

$$\lim_{n \to \infty} c_n = \lim_{n \to \infty} \left(1 + \frac{5}{n}\right)^{-n} = \lim_{n \to \infty} \frac{1}{\left(1 + \frac{5}{n}\right)^n} = \frac{1}{e^5} \neq 0$$

So the series of absolute values diverges by the NTT and the given series is not absolutely convergent. Looking at the alternating series test, we find that while

$$c_n = \left(1 + \frac{5}{n}\right)^{-n}$$

is a decreasing sequence, the limit of these, as we just saw is not zero. So the AST is not applicable. But if we apply the NTT to the terms of the original series, we get

$$\lim_{n \to \infty} a_n = \lim_{n \to \infty} (-1)^{n+1} c_n = \textit{does not exist}$$

Thus, the given series diverges. Note that if we had the foresight to apply the NTT for divergence at the beginning then we would not need to try the other tests.

Exercises: 8.6 (Absolute and Conditional Convergence)

In Exercises 1–26, use the Alternating Series Test (AST) to determine if the series converges. If the AST does not apply say why and determine if the series diverges or not.

1. $\displaystyle\sum_{n=1}^{\infty} \frac{(-1)^{n+1}}{1+\sqrt{n}}$

2. $\displaystyle\sum_{n=1}^{\infty} \frac{(-1)^{n+1}}{1+n^{3/2}}$

3. $\displaystyle\sum_{n=2}^{\infty} \frac{(-1)^{n}\, n}{n^2-1}$

4. $\displaystyle\sum_{n=2}^{\infty} \frac{(-1)^{n}\, n^2}{n^3-1}$

5. $\displaystyle\sum_{n=2}^{\infty} \frac{(-1)^{n}\,(n^3+n)}{n^4-1}$

6. $\displaystyle\sum_{n=1}^{\infty} \frac{(-1)^{n}\,(2\,n^2+3\,n)}{n^3+1}$

7. $\displaystyle\sum_{n=2}^{\infty} \frac{(-1)^{n}\, n}{n-1}$

8. $\displaystyle\sum_{n=2}^{\infty} (-1)^{n}\, \frac{n^2}{n^2-1}$

9. $\displaystyle\sum_{n=1}^{\infty} (-1)^{n+1}\, n e^{-n}$

10. $\displaystyle\sum_{n=1}^{\infty} (-1)^{n+1}\, n e^{-2n}$

11. $\displaystyle\sum_{n=1}^{\infty} (-1)^{n} \tan^{-1}(1+\tfrac{1}{n})$

12. $\displaystyle\sum_{n=1}^{\infty} (-1)^{n} \cot^{-1}(1+\tfrac{1}{n})$

13. $\displaystyle\sum_{n=2}^{\infty} \frac{(-1)^{n+1} n^{3/2}}{n^2-1}$

14. $\displaystyle\sum_{n=2}^{\infty} \frac{(-1)^{n} n^{5/2}}{n^3-1}$

15. $\displaystyle\sum_{n=1}^{\infty} \frac{(-1)^{n+1}}{e^n+e^{-n}}$

16. $\displaystyle\sum_{n=1}^{\infty} \frac{(-1)^{n+1}}{e^n-e^{-n}}$

17. $\displaystyle\sum_{n=1}^{\infty} \frac{(-1)^{n+1}\,(e^n+e^{-n})}{e^n-e^{-n}}$

18. $\displaystyle\sum_{n=1}^{\infty} \frac{(-1)^{n+1}\,(e^n-e^{-n})}{e^n+e^{-n}}$

19. $\displaystyle\sum_{n=1}^{\infty} \frac{(-1)^{n+1} \ln n}{n^2}$

20. $\displaystyle\sum_{n=1}^{\infty} \frac{(-1)^{n+1} \ln n}{n^3}$

21. $\displaystyle\sum_{n=1}^{\infty} \frac{(-1)^{n+1} (\ln n)^2}{\sqrt{n}}$

22. $\displaystyle\sum_{n=1}^{\infty} (-1)^{n+1} \frac{(\ln n)^2}{n^{2/3}}$

23. $\displaystyle\sum_{n=1}^{\infty} \frac{(-1)^{n+1} \tan^{-1}\left(\frac{1}{n}\right)}{n^2}$

24. $\displaystyle\sum_{n=1}^{\infty} \frac{(-1)^{n+1} \tan^{-1}\left(\frac{1}{n}\right)}{n^{2/3}}$

25. $\displaystyle\sum_{n=1}^{\infty} (-1)^{n} |\sin(1/n)|$

26. $\displaystyle\sum_{n=1}^{\infty} (-1)^{n} |1-\cos(1/n)|$

Classify the following series as either (1) Absolutely Convergent, (2) Conditionally Convergent, or (3) Divergent. Give reasons, say which test you are using, and justify your answers by showing all your work.

27. $\displaystyle\sum_{n=2}^{\infty} \frac{(-1)^{n+1}\, n^4}{n^5-1}$

28. $\displaystyle\sum_{n=2}^{\infty} \frac{(-1)^{n+1}\, n^5}{n^6-1}$

29. $\displaystyle\sum_{n=1}^{\infty} \frac{(-1)^{n+1}\, n^2}{n^4+1}$

30. $\displaystyle\sum_{n=1}^{\infty} \frac{(-1)^{n+1}\, n^3}{n^5+1}$

31. $\displaystyle\sum_{n=2}^{\infty} \frac{(-1)^{n+1}\, \sqrt{n}}{n-1}$

32. $\displaystyle\sum_{n=1}^{\infty} \frac{(-1)^{n+1}\, n^{3/2}}{n^{3/2}+1}$

33. $\displaystyle\sum_{n=1}^{\infty} \frac{(-1)^{n+1}\, \sqrt{n}}{\sqrt{n}+1}$

34. $\displaystyle\sum_{n=2}^{\infty} \frac{(-1)^{n+1}\, n^{3/2}}{n^2-1}$

35. $\displaystyle\sum_{n=1}^{\infty} \frac{(-1)^{n+1} \ln n}{n^{3/2}}$

36. $\displaystyle\sum_{n=1}^{\infty} \frac{(-1)^{n+1} \ln n}{n^{5/2}}$

37. $\displaystyle\sum_{n=1}^{\infty} \frac{(-1)^{n+1} (\ln n)^2}{n^{2/3}}$

38. $\displaystyle\sum_{n=1}^{\infty} (-1)^{n+1} \frac{(\ln n)^2}{n^{4/5}}$

39. $\displaystyle\sum_{n=2}^{\infty} \frac{(-1)^{n}}{n \ln n}$

40. $\displaystyle\sum_{n=2}^{\infty} \frac{(-1)^{n}}{n\sqrt{\ln n}}$

41. $\displaystyle\sum_{n=2}^{\infty} \frac{(-1)^{n}}{n(\ln n)^2}$

42. $\displaystyle\sum_{n=2}^{\infty} \frac{(-1)^{n}}{n(\ln n)^3}$

43. $\displaystyle\sum_{n=1}^{\infty} \frac{(-1)^{n+1}}{e^n-e^{-n}}$

44. $\displaystyle\sum_{n=1}^{\infty} \frac{(-1)^{n+1}}{2^n-2^{-n}}$

45. $\displaystyle\sum_{n=1}^{\infty} \frac{(-1)^{n+1}}{n+\sqrt{n}}$

46. $\displaystyle\sum_{n=1}^{\infty} \frac{(-1)^{n+1}}{n+n^{1/3}}$

47. $\displaystyle\sum_{n=1}^{\infty} \frac{(-1)^{n+1}}{n^2+\sqrt{n}}$

48. $\displaystyle\sum_{n=1}^{\infty} \frac{(-1)^{n+1}}{n^3+n^{1/3}}$

49. $\displaystyle\sum_{n=2}^{\infty} \frac{(-1)^{n+1}}{\ln n}$

50. $\displaystyle\sum_{n=2}^{\infty} \frac{(-1)^{n+1}}{\sqrt{\ln n}}$

51. $\displaystyle\sum_{n=1}^{\infty} \frac{(-1)^{n+1} \ln n}{1+\ln n}$

52. $\displaystyle\sum_{n=1}^{\infty} \frac{(-1)^{n+1} (\ln n)^2}{1+(\ln n)^2}$

53. $\displaystyle\sum_{n=1}^{\infty} \frac{(-1)^{n+1} \ln n}{1+(\ln n)^2}$

54. $\displaystyle\sum_{n=1}^{\infty} \frac{(-1)^{n+1} \ln n}{1+(\ln n)^{3/2}}$

55. $\displaystyle\sum_{n=1}^{\infty} \frac{(-1)^{n+1} \tan^{-1} n}{\sqrt{n}}$

56. $\displaystyle\sum_{n=1}^{\infty} \frac{(-1)^{n+1} \tan^{-1} n}{n^{2/3}}$

57. Prove Theorem 8.6.1 (Alternating Series Test). Hint: Study Example 8.6.3 and use the ideas presented there.

8.7 Power Series

Among all the functions in calculus, polynomial functions

$$p_k(x) = a_0 + a_1 x + a_2 x^2 + a_3 x^3 + \cdots + a_k x^k$$

stand out as the most simple and easy to work with (and in some sense, the most important). In this and the next two sections we will see how many of the other important functions f in calculus (that are not polynomials) can be approximated, on an interval I containing 0, by polynomials

$$f(x) \approx p_k(x) = \sum_{n=0}^{k} a_n x^n,$$

with an appropriate choice of coefficients $\{a_n\}$. Furthermore, using the idea of an "infinitely long" polynomial (one of "infinite degree" $k = \infty$), we often can express f *exactly* on I as

$$f(x) = \sum_{n=0}^{\infty} a_n x^n = a_0 + a_1 x + a_2 x^2 + a_3 x^3 + \cdots.$$

The (infinite) series expression on the right above contains the variable x, and we shall see that the series converges for all x in an interval I, called its interval of convergence. (Clearly the series converges for $x = 0$.) Thus, on this interval the series expression *represents* the function. Since the series involves powers of x, it is called a *power series*.

DEFINITION 8.7.1 (Power Series)

A series of the form

$$\sum_{n=0}^{\infty} a_n x^n = a_0 + a_1 x + a_2 x^2 + a_3 x^3 + \cdots$$

with x variable, is called a power series *(or a* power series in x*).*

Example 8.7.1 (Power Series from Geometric Series)

Relate the following power series to a geometric series

$$\sum_{n=0}^{\infty} a r^n = \begin{cases} \frac{a}{1-r} & |r| < 1 \\ diverges & |r| \geq 1 \end{cases}$$

and use this to determine what function f the power series represents and on what interval the power series represents the function.

Problem (a): $\displaystyle\sum_{n=0}^{\infty} x^n$

Solution (a): This is the most basic and important of the four power series here. It is the geometric series with $a = 1$ and $r = x$. Thus,

$$\sum_{n=0}^{\infty} x^n = \frac{1}{1-x},$$

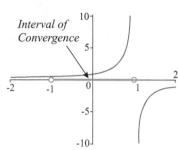

Figure 8.7.1: *The graph of $f(x) = \frac{1}{1-x}$ on the interval $[-2, 2]$ and the interval of convergence $I = (-1, 1)$ for the power series $\sum x^n$.*

provided $|x| = |r| < 1$, i.e., for all x in the interval $I = (-1, 1)$. Note that the function $f(x) = \dfrac{1}{1-x}$ is a rational function which is defined for all x except 1. However, the power series only represents f on the interval I. For example, $f(2) = -1$, but clearly the series does not converge for $x = 2$, since

$$\sum_{n=0}^{\infty} 2^n = 1 + 2 + 4 + 8 + 16 + \cdots = \infty$$

The interval $I = (-1, 1)$ is called the interval of convergence for the power series. Figure 8.7.1 shows this interval along with a graph of the function represented by the power series.

Problem (b): $\displaystyle\sum_{n=0}^{\infty} 3^n x^n$

Solution (b): Since $3^n x^n = (3x)^n$, this is a geometric series with $a = 1$ and $r = 3x$. So,

$$\sum_{n=0}^{\infty} 3^n x^n = \sum_{n=0}^{\infty} (3x)^n = \frac{1}{1-3x},$$

provided $|3x| < 1$. Thus, the series represents the function $f(x) = \dfrac{1}{1-3x}$, for all x in the interval $I = (-\frac{1}{3}, \frac{1}{3})$. This is a smaller interval of convergence than the one for the power series in Part (a). Generally, the interval of convergence for a power series can be any of any size.

Problem (c): $\displaystyle\sum_{n=0}^{\infty} (-1)^n x^{2n}$

Solution (c): Note that $(-1)^n x^{2n} = (-x^2)^n$, so the given series is a geometric series with $a = 1$ and $r = -x^2$. Thus,

$$\sum_{n=0}^{\infty} (-1)^n x^{2n} = \sum_{n=0}^{\infty} (-x^2)^n = \frac{1}{1+x^2},$$

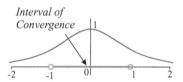

Figure 8.7.2: *The graph of $f(x) = \frac{1}{1+x^2}$ on the interval $[-2, 2]$ and the interval of convergence $I = (-1, 1)$ for the power series $\sum (-1)^n x^{2n}$.*

provided $|x^2| < 1$. Thus, the series represents the function $f(x) = \frac{1}{1+x^2}$ for all x in the interval $I = (-1, 1)$, which the interval of convergence for the power series. (Note: It is coincidental that this is the same interval as in Part (a).) Figure 8.7.2 shows this interval along with a graph of the function that is represented by the power series on that interval.

Again note that while the function $f(x) = 1/(1 + x^2)$ is defined for all x, the power series will not "represent" it outside the interval $I = (-1, 1)$. For example, $f(2) = \frac{1}{5}$, but

$$\sum_{n=0}^{\infty} (-1)^n 2^{2n} = \sum_{n=0}^{\infty} (-1)^n 4^n = 1 - 4 + 16 - 64 + \cdots$$

diverges.

Problem (d): $\displaystyle\sum_{n=0}^{\infty} (-1)^n \frac{x^{3n}}{8^{n+1}}$

Solution (d): We can write the nth term of the series as

$$(-1)^n \frac{x^{3n}}{8^{n+1}} = (-1)^n \frac{x^{3n}}{8^n \cdot 8} = \frac{1}{8}\left(-\frac{x^3}{8}\right)^n$$

so the given series is a geometric series with $a = \frac{1}{8}$, $r = -\frac{x^2}{8}$. Thus,

$$\sum_{n=0}^{\infty} (-1)^n \frac{x^{3n}}{8^{n+1}} = \sum_{n=0}^{\infty} \frac{1}{8}\left(-\frac{x^3}{8}\right)^n = \frac{\frac{1}{8}}{1 + \frac{x^3}{8}} = \frac{1}{8 + x^3},$$

provided $\left|\frac{x^3}{8}\right| < 1$, i.e., $|x| < 2$. So the series represents the function $f(x) = \dfrac{1}{8 + x^3}$ for all x in the interval $I = (-2, 2)$.

NOTE 1: Some power series, such as the one in Part (c) of the last example:

$$\sum_{k=0}^{\infty}(-1)^k x^{2k} = 1 - x^2 + x^4 - x^6 + \cdots = \sum_{n=0}^{\infty} a_n x^n$$

have only selected powers of x occurring. In this case only the even powers occur

$$a_n = \begin{cases} (-1)^k & n = 2k \\ 0 & n = 2k + 1 \end{cases}$$

NOTE 2: The above examples serve as elementary illustrations of how power series can represent functions, specifically the functions

$$f(x) = \frac{1}{1-x}, \quad g(x) = \frac{1}{1-3x}, \quad h(x) = \frac{1}{1+x^2}, \quad k(x) = \frac{1}{8+x^2}.$$

However, these examples fail to motivate the real importance of representing functions by power series. This is because the functions f, g, h, and k are simpler than the power series used to represent them (and are defined on larger domains than the respective power series). The same is not true for the functions

$$fx) = e^x, \quad g(x) = \sin x, \quad h(x) = \tan^{-1} x, \quad k(x) = \ln(x + 1).$$

None of these functions has an explicit formula that defines it. In the ensuing examples, we will determine power series for each of these functions and will look at how the calculus and algebraic operations can be applied to power series. This should serve to demonstrate the usefulness of power series representations of functions in general.

Some functions *cannot* be represented by a power series of the form $\sum a_n x^n$ because they are not defined at $x = 0$. An important example of this is the natural log function $g(x) = \ln x$. Another, more basic, example is the reciprocal function $f(x) = \frac{1}{x}$. The following example shows how to extend the power series concept to allow representations of these functions.

Example 8.7.2 (A Power Series for ln x)

Problem: For the functions $f(x) = \dfrac{1}{x}$, $g(x) = \ln x$ find series representations of the form

$$\sum_{n=0}^{\infty} a_n(x - 1)^n = a_0 + a_1(x - 1) + a_2(x - 1)^2 + a_3(x - 1)^3 + \cdots$$

Solution: We can use an algebraic trick and the geometric series idea to write

$$\begin{aligned}
f(x) &= \frac{1}{x} = \frac{1}{1 + (x - 1)} = \frac{1}{1 - [-(x - 1)]} = \sum_{n=0}^{\infty}[-1(x - 1)]^n \\
&= \sum_{n=0}^{\infty}(-1)^n(x - 1)^n = 1 - (x - 1) + (x - 1)^2 - (x - 1)^3 + \cdots
\end{aligned}$$

The series converges for all x satisfying $|x - 1| < 1$. This last inequality is equivalent to $-1 < x - 1 < 1$, i.e., $0 < x < 2$. So the power series representation is good for all x in the interval $I = (0, 2)$.

Next, we use the above result and a theorem (see Section 8.9) that says that we can integrate a power series *term-by-term*. This gives a power series representation of $\ln x$

$$
\begin{aligned}
\ln x &= \int \frac{1}{x}\,dx = \int \left[\sum_{n=0}^{\infty} (-1)^n (x-1)^n \right] dx = \sum_{n=0}^{\infty} (-1)^n \int (x-1)^n\,dx \\
&= C + \sum_{n=0}^{\infty} (-1)^n \frac{(x-1)^{n+1}}{n+1} = C + \sum_{k=1}^{\infty} (-1)^{k-1} \frac{(x-1)^k}{k} \\
&= C + \sum_{n=1}^{\infty} (-1)^{n+1} \frac{(x-1)^n}{n}
\end{aligned}
$$

In the next to the last step here, we shifted the indexing in the summation, letting $k = n+1$, to get a simpler expression for the series. Then we relabeled with $k = n$ in the resulting series. The constant of integration C can be determined by evaluating each side of the equation at $x = 1$:

$$
0 = \ln(1) = C + \sum_{n=0}^{\infty} (-1)^{n+1} \frac{(1-1)^n}{n} = C
$$

In summary, a power series representation of the natural logarithm function is

$$
\ln x = \sum_{n=1}^{\infty} (-1)^{n+1} \frac{(x-1)^n}{n} = (x-1) - \frac{(x-1)^2}{2} + \frac{(x-1)^3}{3} - \frac{(x-1)^4}{4} + \cdots
$$

NOTE: Later you will learn how to determine that the series only converges for x in the interval $I = (0, 2]$. It does not converges for $x = 0$, since using that value in the series gives the negative of the harmonic series:

$$
(0-1) - \frac{(0-1)^2}{2} + \frac{(0-1)^3}{3} - \frac{(0-1)^4}{4} + \cdots = -1 - \frac{1}{2} - \frac{1}{3} - \frac{1}{4} \cdots = -\sum_{n=1}^{\infty} \frac{1}{n} = -\infty
$$

Of course, we can interpret this as the value of the log function in the extended sense: $\ln(0) = -\infty$. At the other endpoint $x = 2$ of I, we get the interesting result that the sum of the alternating harmonic series is $\ln 2$:

$$
\ln 2 = \sum_{n=1}^{\infty} (-1)^{n+1} \frac{1}{n} = 1 - \frac{1}{2} + \frac{1}{3} - \frac{1}{4} + \frac{1}{5} - \frac{1}{6} + \cdots
$$

The previous example illustrates the need for the following more general notion of a power series.

DEFINITION 8.7.2 (Power Series Centered at c)

A series of the form

$$
\sum_{n=0}^{\infty} a_n (x-c)^n = a_0 + a_1 (x-c) + a_2 (x-c)^2 + a_3 (x-c)^3 + \cdots
$$

with x variable, is called a power series centered at c *(or a* power series in x - c*).*

In addition to using power series to represent all the basic functions in mathematics, power series also serve to define new functions that arise in solving differential equations. The next example illustrates this.

Example 8.7.3 (Series Solutions of Differential Equations)

Depending on your major, you may have to take a course (or two) in differential equations. Such a course deals with methods of solving equations involving an unknown function and its derivatives (hence the name: differential equation). The solutions of a broad class of differential equations can be expressed (or defined) by power series. For example, the differential equation

$$f''(x) - 2xf'(x) - f(x) = 0,$$

has a solution defined by

$$f(x) = 1 + \sum_{n=0}^{\infty} \frac{1 \cdot 5 \cdot 9 \cdots (4n-3)}{(2n)!} x^{2n}.$$

Here, the symbol $1 \cdot 5 \cdot 9 \cdots (4n-3)$ stands for the product of all the integers of the form $4k - 3$ as k ranges from 1 to n. The series converges for all x. To see this, consider any x and apply the ratio test to $|u_n|$, where u_n is the nth term of the power series, Thus,

$$|u_n| = \left| \frac{1 \cdot 5 \cdot 9 \cdots (4n-3)}{(2n)!} x^{2n} \right| = \frac{1 \cdot 5 \cdot 9 \cdots (4n-3)}{(2n)!} |x|^{2n}.$$

Then

$$|u_{n+1}| = \frac{1 \cdot 5 \cdot 9 \cdots (4n-3)(4(n+1)-3)}{(2(n+1))!} |x|^{2(n+1)}$$

$$= \frac{1 \cdot 5 \cdot 9 \cdots (4n-3)(4n+1)}{(2n+2)(2n+1)(2n)!} |x|^{2n}|x|^2$$

And so,

$$|u_{n+1}| \cdot \frac{1}{|u_n|}$$

$$= \frac{1 \cdot 5 \cdot 9 \cdots (4n-3)(4n+1)}{(2n+2)(2n+1)(2n)!} |x|^{2n}|x|^2 \cdot \frac{(2n)!}{1 \cdot 5 \cdot 9 \cdots (4n-3)\,|x|^{2n}}$$

$$= \frac{4n+1}{(2n+2)(2n+1)} |x|^2.$$

Thus,

$$\rho = \lim_{n \to \infty} \frac{|u_{n+1}|}{|u_n|} = \lim_{n \to \infty} \frac{(4n+1)\,|x|^2}{(2n+2)(2n+1)} = 0 < 1$$

So the series converges for any x.

NOTE 1: Here all the powers of x in the power series are even and so we did not need to take absolute values of the terms u_n in order to apply the ratio test. However, in general you will have to use $|u_n|$ since x raised to an odd power can be negative when x is.

NOTE 2: Later we will see that functions defined by power series are differentiable and that the power series can be differentiated (and integrated) term-by-term. This will enable us to show that the function defined here by this power series does, indeed satisfy the differential equation.

The examples above show two of the possibilities for convergence of a power series: either it can converge for all x or or it converges only for x in a bounded interval. An extreme (atypical) case is that the power series converges for only a single value of x. These three possibilities are what we can expect in general, as the following theorem tells us.

> **THEOREM 8.7.1 (Convergence of Power Series)**
>
> *For a given power series,* $\displaystyle\sum_{n=0}^{\infty} a_n(x-c)^n$, *one and only one of the following occurs.*
>
> (1) *The series converges only for* $x = c$.
>
> (2) *The series converges for all* x.
>
> (3) *There is a positive number R such that the series converges if* $|x-c| < R$ *and the series diverges if* $|x-c| > R$.

NOTE 1 (Radius and Interval of Convergence): When Case (3) of the theorem occurs, the series converges for all x in the open interval $(c-R, c+R)$, but the theorem does not tell us whether the series converges or not at the endpoints $c-R$, $c+R$ of this interval. We will have to test the endpoints separately for convergence. (See the examples below.) Depending on whether the series converges at both, only one, or neither of the the endpoints, we get that one of the intervals

$$[c-R, c+R], \quad [c-R, c+R), \quad (c-R, c+R], \quad \text{or} \quad (c-R, c+R)$$

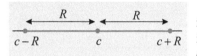

$$\begin{array}{c} R \qquad R \\ \xleftarrow{} \xrightarrow{} \xleftarrow{} \xrightarrow{} \\ c-R \qquad c \qquad c+R \end{array}$$

Figure 8.7.3: *The interval of convergence.*

is the largest set of numbers x for which the series converges. This set of numbers is called the *interval of convergence* (IOC) for the power series. The number R is called the *radius of convergence* for the power series. See the figure in the margin.

NOTE 2: By convention, when the power series converges for all x, the radius of convergence is taken to be $R = \infty$ and the interval of convergence is $(-\infty, \infty)$. In the case when the power series converges only for $x = c$, the radius of convergence is taken to be $R = 0$ and the interval of convergence is $\{c\}$.

For a given power series you can find the radius of convergence using the ratio test (or the root test) on the corresponding series of absolute values. Then the interval of convergence (IOC) can be determined (in Case (3) of the Theorem) by substituting the endpoints $x = c + R$ and $x = c - R$ in the series and using one of the tests for convergence from the previous sections. This is called *testing the endpoints* for convergence. The next example illustrates how to find the radius and interval of convergence.

Example 8.7.4 (Determining the Radius & Interval of Convergence)

Problem: Find the radius of convergence and the interval of convergence for the following power series.

Part (a): $\displaystyle\sum_{n=1}^{\infty} \frac{x^n}{n^2 8^n}$

Solution (a): Here the absolute value of the nth term u_n is

$$|u_n| = \frac{|x|^n}{n^2 8^n}.$$

So

$$\frac{|u_{n+1}|}{|u_n|} = \frac{|x|^{n+1}}{(n+1)^2 \, 8^{n+1}} \cdot \frac{n^2 \, 8^n}{|x|^n} = \frac{|x|}{8} \cdot \frac{n^2}{(n+1)^2}$$

Consequently

$$\rho = \lim_{n\to\infty} \frac{|u_{n+1}|}{|u_n|} = \lim_{n\to\infty} \frac{|x|}{8} \cdot \frac{n^2}{(n+1)^2} = \frac{|x|}{8} \lim_{n\to\infty} \left(\frac{n}{n+1}\right)^2 = \frac{|x|}{8} \cdot (1)^2 = \frac{|x|}{8}.$$

By the ratio test, the series will converge if $\rho < 1$. This translates into the following condition on x:

$$\frac{|x|}{8} < 1, \quad \text{i.e.,} \quad |x| < 8$$

Thus the series converges for all x in the interval $(-8, 8)$. The radius of convergence is $R = 8$. Next we test the endpoints for convergence:

$\underline{x = 8}$: The series becomes

$$\sum_{n=1}^{\infty} \frac{8^n}{n^2 8^n} = \sum_{n=1}^{\infty} \frac{1}{n^2}$$

which converges since it is a $p = 2$ series.

$\underline{x = -8}$: The series becomes

$$\sum_{n=1}^{\infty} \frac{-8^n}{n^2 8^n} = \sum_{n=1}^{\infty} \frac{(-1)^n}{n^2}$$

which converges since it is an alternatiing p-series. Thus, we find that the interval of convergence is $I = [-8, 8]$.

<u>NOTE</u>: On this power series $\sum \frac{x^n}{n^2 8^n}$ (and others like it) you can also use the root test to determine the radius of convergence. Specifically, the absolute value of the nth term u_n is

$$|u_n| = \frac{|x|^n}{n^2 \, 8^n} \quad \text{and so} \quad |u_n|^{\frac{1}{n}} = \frac{|x|}{n^{2/n} \, 8}$$

Since $\lim_{n \to \infty} n^{2/n} = 1$, we get

$$\rho = \lim_{n \to \infty} |u_n|^{\frac{1}{n}} = \lim_{n \to \infty} \frac{|x|}{n^{2/n} \, 8} = \frac{|x|}{8} \stackrel{need}{<} 1$$

So we need $|x| < 8$. to guarantee convergence by the root test. This gives, as with the ratio test, that the radius of convergence is $R = 8$.

Part (b): $\displaystyle\sum_{n=1}^{\infty} \frac{(x+2)^n}{3^n \sqrt{n}}$

Solution (b): Here the absolute value of the nth term u_n is

$$|u_n| = \frac{|x+2|^n}{3^n \sqrt{n}}.$$

So

$$|u_{n+1}| \cdot \frac{1}{|u_n|} = \frac{|x+2|^{n+1}}{3^{n+1} \sqrt{n+1}} \cdot \frac{3^n \sqrt{n}}{|x+2|^n} = \frac{|x+2|}{3} \cdot \frac{\sqrt{n}}{\sqrt{n+1}}$$

Thus,

$$\begin{aligned}
\rho &= \lim_{n \to \infty} \frac{|u_{n+1}|}{|u_n|} = \lim_{n \to \infty} \left[\frac{|x+2|}{3} \cdot \frac{\sqrt{n}}{\sqrt{n+1}} \right] \\
&= \frac{|x+2|}{3} \cdot \lim_{n \to \infty} \sqrt{\frac{n}{n+1}} = \frac{|x+2|}{3} \cdot \sqrt{\lim_{n \to \infty} \frac{n}{n+1}} = \frac{|x+2|}{3}
\end{aligned}$$

Therefore the series converges if

$$\frac{|x+2|}{3} < 1, \quad \text{i.e.,} \quad |x+2| < 3, ,$$

which is equivalent to

$$-3 < x + 2 < 3, \quad \text{i.e.,} \quad -5 < x < 1$$

The series thus converges for all x in the interval $(-5, 1)$. The radius of convergence is $R = 3$. Next we test the endpoints for convergence:

$\underline{x = 1}$: The series becomes

$$\sum_{n=1}^{\infty} \frac{3^n}{3^n \sqrt{n}} = \sum_{n=1}^{\infty} \frac{1}{\sqrt{n}}$$

which diverges because it is a $p = 1/2$ series.

$\underline{x = -5}$: The series becomes

$$\sum_{n=1}^{\infty} \frac{(-3)^n}{3^n \sqrt{n}} = \sum_{n=1}^{\infty} \frac{(-1)^n}{\sqrt{n}}$$

which converges since it is an alternating p-series. Thus, we find that the interval of convergence is $I = [-5, 1)$.

Part (c): $\displaystyle\sum_{n=1}^{\infty} \frac{(-1)^{n+1} x^n}{n^n}$

Solution (c): Here the absolute value of the nth term u_n is

$$|u_n| = \frac{|x|^n}{n^n}.$$

We use the root test on this

$$\rho = \lim_{n \to \infty} |u_n|^{1/n} = \lim_{n \to \infty} \left(\frac{|x|^n}{n^n} \right)^{1/n} = \lim_{n \to \infty} \frac{|x|}{n} = 0.$$

Thus, the series converges regardless of what x is. So the interval of convergence is $I = (-\infty, \infty)$ and the radius of convergence is $R = \infty$.

Part (d): $\displaystyle\sum_{n=1}^{\infty} \frac{2^n (n!)^2 (x-3)^n}{(2n)!}$

Solution (d): Here the absolute value of the nth term u_n is

$$|u_n| = \frac{2^n (n!)^2}{(2n)!} |x - 3|^n \quad \text{and so} \quad |u_{n+1}| = \frac{2^{n+1} [(n+1)!]^2 |x - 3|^{n+1}}{[2(n+1)]!}$$

Note that

$$[(n+1)!]^2 = [(n+1)n!]^2 = (n+1)^2 (n!)^2$$

and

$$[2(n+1)]! = (2n+2)! = (2n+2)(2n+1)(2n)!$$

Then

$$\frac{|u_{n+1}|}{|u_n|} = \frac{2^{n+1}(n+1)^2(n!)^2 |x - 3|^{n+1}}{(2n+2)(2n+1)(2n)!} \cdot \frac{(2n)!}{2^n (n!)^2 |x - 3|^n}$$

$$= \frac{2(n+1)^2 |x - 3|}{(2n+2)(2n+1)} = \frac{(n+1) |x - 3|}{(2n+1)}$$

So

$$\lim_{n \to \infty} \frac{|u_{n+1}|}{|u_n|} = \lim_{n \to \infty} \frac{(n+1)}{2n+1} \cdot |x - 3| = \frac{1}{2} |x - 3|$$

Therefore the series converges if

$$\frac{1}{2} |x - 3| < 1, \quad \text{i.e., if} \quad |x - 3| < 2$$

This is equivalent to

$$-2 < x - 3 < 2, \quad \text{l.e.,} \quad 1 < x < 5$$

Thus the series converges for all x in the interval $(1,5)$. The radius of convergence is $R = 2$. Next we test the endpoints for convergence:

$\underline{x = 5}$: The series becomes

$$\sum_{n=1}^{\infty} \frac{2^n (n!)^2}{(2n)!} 2^n = 2 + \frac{8}{3} + \frac{16}{5} + \cdots$$

Computing a few of the terms b_n of this series, as shown, we would guess that $b_n \geq 1$, for all n. (See the exercises for how to verify this in general.) Thus, $\lim_{n \to \infty} b_n$ is not 0 and so the series diverges by the NTT.

$\underline{x = 1}$: The series becomes

$$\sum_{n=1}^{\infty} \frac{2^n (n!)^2}{(2n)!} (-1)^n 2^n = -2 + \frac{8}{3} - \frac{16}{5} + \cdots$$

The terms of this series are $(-1)^n b_n$, where $1 \leq b_n$, as mentioned in the last discussion above. Thus, $\lim_{n \to \infty} (-1)^n b_n$ is not 0 and so the series diverges by the NTT. All of this shows that the interval of convergence (IOC) for the power series is $I = (1,5)$.

Part (e): $\displaystyle\sum_{n=1}^{\infty} n! (x-4)^n$

Solution (e): Here the absolute value of the nth term u_n is $|u_n| = n!|x-4|^n$. So

$$\frac{|u_{n+1}|}{|u_n|} = \frac{(n+1)! |x-4|^{n+1}}{n! |x-4|^n} = (n+1) |x-4|$$

Consequently,

$$\lim_{n \to \infty} \frac{|u_{n+1}|}{|u_n|} = \lim_{n \to \infty} (n+1) |x-4| = \begin{cases} 0 & x = 4 \\ \infty & x \neq 4 \end{cases}$$

Therefore, the series only converges for $x = 4$. The radius of converge is $R = 0$ and the interval of convergence is $I = \{4\}$.

<u>SUMMARY</u> (Determining the Radius and Interval Of Convergence)

For a given power series $\displaystyle\sum_{n=0}^{\infty} a_n (x-c)^n$,

(1) Use the ratio test (or the root test where its easier) to get an inequality of the form $|x - c| < R$ that x must satisfy to guarantee convergence of the series. Then R will be the radius of convergence.

(2) The endpoints of the interval of convergence are $x = c + R$ and $x = c - R$. Substitute these into the series to get the numerical series

$$\sum_{n=0}^{\infty} a_n R^n \quad \text{and} \quad \sum_{n=0}^{\infty} (-1)^n a_n R^n,$$

respectively. Test convergence or divergence of these series to determine if the end points are or are not in the interval of convergence. This activity is called *testing the endpoints for convergence*.

Exercises: 8.7 (Power Series)

Intervals of Convergence

In Exercises 1–54, determine the radius of convergence and the interval of convergence for each power series.

<u>NOTE</u> 1: Use the ratio or the root tests (whichever you think is easier) to determine the radius of convergence. Test endpoints and determine the Interval of Convergence (IOC).

<u>NOTE</u> 2: When using the root test, the basic limit

$$\lim_{n\to\infty} n^{1/n} = 1$$

often occurs. The generalization of this to:

$$\lim_{n\to\infty} n^{p/n} = \lim_{n\to\infty} \left(n^{1/n}\right)^p = \left(\lim_{n\to\infty} n^{1/n}\right)^p = 1^p = 1,$$

for any real number p, is also useful.

1. $\displaystyle\sum_{n=1}^{\infty} \frac{1}{5^n \sqrt{n}} x^n$

2. $\displaystyle\sum_{n=1}^{\infty} \frac{1}{4^n \sqrt[3]{n}} x^n$

3. $\displaystyle\sum_{n=0}^{\infty} \frac{\sqrt{n}}{n+1} x^n$

4. $\displaystyle\sum_{n=0}^{\infty} \frac{n^{3/2}}{n^2+1} x^n$

5. $\displaystyle\sum_{n=0}^{\infty} \frac{2^n n^2}{n^4+1} x^n$

6. $\displaystyle\sum_{n=0}^{\infty} \frac{4^n n^3}{n^5+1} x^n$

7. $\displaystyle\sum_{n=1}^{\infty} \frac{(x-1)^n}{2^n n^{3/2}}$

8. $\displaystyle\sum_{n=1}^{\infty} \frac{(x-3)^n}{3^n n^{4/3}}$

9. $\displaystyle\sum_{n=0}^{\infty} \frac{n}{n+1} x^n$

10. $\displaystyle\sum_{n=0}^{\infty} \frac{n^2}{n^2+1} x^n$

11. $\displaystyle\sum_{n=1}^{\infty} (2+1/n)^n \frac{x^n}{6^n}$

12. $\displaystyle\sum_{n=1}^{\infty} (3+1/n)^n \frac{x^n}{6^n}$

13. $\displaystyle\sum_{n=0}^{\infty} \frac{2^n}{4^n+1} x^n$

14. $\displaystyle\sum_{n=0}^{\infty} \frac{3^n}{5^n+1} x^n$

15. $\displaystyle\sum_{n=1}^{\infty} \frac{\ln n}{n^2} (x-2)^n$

16. $\displaystyle\sum_{n=1}^{\infty} \frac{\ln n}{n^3} (x-1)^n$

17. $\displaystyle\sum_{n=1}^{\infty} \frac{\ln n}{4^n \sqrt{n}} x^{2n+1}$

18. $\displaystyle\sum_{n=1}^{\infty} \frac{\ln n}{27^n n^{2/3}} x^{3n+1}$

19. $\displaystyle\sum_{n=1}^{\infty} \frac{\tan^{-1} n}{n} x^n$

20. $\displaystyle\sum_{n=1}^{\infty} \frac{\tan^{-1} n}{\sqrt{n}} x^n$

21. $\displaystyle\sum_{n=1}^{\infty} \frac{\tan^{-1} n}{9^n n^2} x^{2n}$

22. $\displaystyle\sum_{n=1}^{\infty} \frac{\tan^{-1} n}{8^n n^3} x^{3n}$

23. $\displaystyle\sum_{n=2}^{\infty} \frac{1}{n(\ln n)^2} (x-3)^n$

24. $\displaystyle\sum_{n=2}^{\infty} \frac{1}{n^2(\ln n)^3} (x-2)^n$

25. $\displaystyle\sum_{n=2}^{\infty} \frac{2^n}{n \ln n} x^n$

26. $\displaystyle\sum_{n=2}^{\infty} \frac{3^n}{\sqrt{n} \ln n} x^n$

27. $\displaystyle\sum_{n=0}^{\infty} \frac{n^2 (x-1)^n}{2^n}$

28. $\displaystyle\sum_{n=0}^{\infty} \frac{n^3 (x-1)^n}{3^n}$

29. $\displaystyle\sum_{n=1}^{\infty} \frac{3^n}{n^3} x^n$

30. $\displaystyle\sum_{n=1}^{\infty} \frac{2^n}{n^2} x^n$

31. $\displaystyle\sum_{n=1}^{\infty} \frac{2^n}{n^n} x^n$

32. $\displaystyle\sum_{n=1}^{\infty} \frac{3^n}{n^n} x^n$

33. $\displaystyle\sum_{n=0}^{\infty} \frac{n!}{3^n} x^n$

34. $\displaystyle\sum_{n=0}^{\infty} \frac{n!}{2^n} x^n$

35. $\displaystyle\sum_{n=0}^{\infty} \frac{27^n}{8^n} x^{3n}$

36. $\displaystyle\sum_{n=0}^{\infty} \frac{15^n}{4^n} x^{3n}$

37. $\displaystyle\sum_{n=0}^{\infty} \frac{(x-2)^n}{3^n}$

38. $\displaystyle\sum_{n=0}^{\infty} \frac{(x-1)^n}{4^n}$

39. $\displaystyle\sum_{n=1}^{\infty} \frac{(1+1/n)^n}{5^n} x^n$

40. $\displaystyle\sum_{n=1}^{\infty} \frac{(1+2/n)^n}{3^n} x^n$

41. $\displaystyle\sum_{n=0}^{\infty} \frac{n^n}{2^n} (x-3)^n$

42. $\displaystyle\sum_{n=0}^{\infty} \frac{n^n}{5^n} (x-2)^n$

43. $\displaystyle\sum_{n=1}^{\infty} \frac{\sin(1/n)}{2^n} x^n$

44. $\displaystyle\sum_{n=1}^{\infty} \frac{\sin(1/n^2)}{3^n} x^n$

45. $\displaystyle\sum_{n=1}^{\infty} \frac{\cos(1/n)}{3^n} x^n$

46. $\displaystyle\sum_{n=1}^{\infty} \frac{\cos(1/n^2)}{4^n} x^n$

47. $\displaystyle\sum_{n=1}^{\infty} \frac{2^n n!}{1 \cdot 3 \cdot 5 \cdots (2n-1)} x^n$

48. $\displaystyle\sum_{n=1}^{\infty} \frac{3^n n!}{2 \cdot 5 \cdot 8 \cdots (3n-1)} x^n$

49. $\displaystyle\sum_{n=0}^{\infty} \frac{(-1)^n}{(2n+1)!} x^{2n}$

50. $\displaystyle\sum_{n=0}^{\infty} \frac{(-1)^n}{(3n+1)!} x^{3n}$

51. $1 + \displaystyle\sum_{n=1}^{\infty} \frac{(1 \cdot 4 \cdot 7 \cdots (3n-2))^2}{(3n)!} x^{3n}$

52. $1 + \displaystyle\sum_{n=1}^{\infty} \frac{(5 \cdot 8 \cdot 11 \cdots (3n+2))^2}{(2n)!} x^{3n}$

53. $\displaystyle\sum_{n=1}^{\infty} \frac{(-3)(-1) \cdot 1 \cdot 3 \cdots (2n-5)}{(2n+1)!} x^{2n+1}$

54. $\displaystyle\sum_{n=1}^{\infty} \frac{(-1)(1) \cdot 3 \cdot 5 \cdots (2n-3)}{(3n+1)!} x^{2n+1}$

55. For $b_n = \frac{2^n (n!)^2}{(2n)!} 2^n$, show that $b_n \geq 1$ for every n.

Calculus *Concepts & Computation*

8.8 Taylor & Maclaurin Series

We have seen in the last section that any power series defines a function on its interval of convergence and that some power series represent, in this way, well-known functions. But what if we start with some of the important functions in mathematics, such as the trigonometric functions, and ask for power series representations of them? How do we find such representations? If the function is differentiable infinitely often on an open interval, then we can compute the *Taylor series expansion* at a point c in this interval. We shall see that the Taylor series expansion, for most functions, represents the function in the sense that, for each x near c, the sum of the series is the value of the function at x. The Taylor series concept is given in the following definition.

DEFINITION 8.8.1 (Taylor & Maclaurin Series)

Suppose that f has derivatives of all orders on an interval about c. Then its
Taylor series at c is the power series

$$\sum_{n=0}^{\infty} \frac{f^{(n)}(c)}{n!}(x-c)^n = f(c) + f'(c)(x-c) + \frac{f''(c)}{2}(x-c)^2 + \frac{f'''(c)}{3!}(x-c)^3 + \cdots$$

In the case when $c = 0$, the Taylor series is called a Maclaurin series and has the form

$$\sum_{n=0}^{\infty} \frac{f^{(n)}(0)}{n!}x^n = f(0) + f'(0)x + \frac{f''(0)}{2}x^2 + \frac{f'''(0)}{3!}x^3 + \frac{f^{(4)}(0)}{4!}x^4 + \cdots$$

NOTE 1: The Maclaurin series expansion of a function is simpler, but to use it the function and all its derivatives must be defined at $x = 0$. For example, the function $f(x) = \sqrt{x}$, while being defined at 0, has none of its derivatives defined at 0. So it has no Maclaurin series expansion. Example 1 below calculates the Taylor series expansion at $x = 1$ for this function.

NOTE 2: Advanced courses discuss the theory for convergence of Taylor series and for what values of x the sum of the series is the value $f(x)$ of the function at x. However, in this section and the next, we will take for granted that the Taylor series represents the function on some interval about $x = c$. Accordingly, we write

$$f(x) = \sum_{n=0}^{\infty} \frac{f^{(n)}(c)}{n!}(x-c)^n \qquad (8.8.1)$$

and

$$f(x) = \sum_{n=0}^{\infty} \frac{f^{(n)}(0)}{n!}x^n \qquad (8.8.2)$$

for the respective Taylor and Maclaurin series expansions of the function f.

NOTE 3: The terminology here concerning series expansions of a function f is that Equation (8.8.1) is the *Taylor series expansion of f about (at)* $x = c$ and that Equation (8.8.2) is the *Maclaurin series expansion of f* (which is always about (at) $x = 0$, when possible).

Example 8.8.1 (Computing a Taylor Series Expansion)

Problem: Compute the Taylor series expansion at $x = 1$ for $f(x) = \sqrt{x}$ and determine its radius of convergence.

Solution: We compute a few derivatives and try to recognize a pattern. Note: To recognize a pattern, we leave the numbers uncomputed.

$$
\begin{aligned}
f(x) &= x^{\frac{1}{2}} \\
f'(x) &= \tfrac{1}{2} x^{\frac{1}{2}-1} \\
f''(x) &= \tfrac{1}{2}\, \tfrac{1}{2}-1) x^{\frac{1}{2}-2} \\
f^{(3)}(x) &= \tfrac{1}{2}\, \tfrac{1}{2}-1) \left(\tfrac{1}{2}-2\right) x^{\frac{1}{2}-3} \\
f^{(4)}(x) &= \tfrac{1}{2} \left(\tfrac{1}{2}-1\right) \left(\tfrac{1}{2}-2\right) \left(\tfrac{1}{2}-3\right) x^{\frac{1}{2}-4}
\end{aligned}
$$

From this, we inductively get

$$
f^{(n)}(x) = \tfrac{1}{2}\, \tfrac{1}{2}-1) \left(\tfrac{1}{2}-2\right) \left(\tfrac{1}{2}-3\right) \cdots \tfrac{1}{2}-(n-1)\right) x^{\frac{1}{2}-n}
$$

For convenience of notation, we use the Pi notation for the above product

$$
\prod_{k=0}^{n-1} \tfrac{1}{2}-k) = \tfrac{1}{2}\, \tfrac{1}{2}-1) \left(\tfrac{1}{2}-2\right) \left(\tfrac{1}{2}-3\right) \cdots \tfrac{1}{2}-(n-1)\right)
$$

This is analogous to the Sigma notation for sums. If we evaluate the nth derivative at $c = 1$ and divide by $n!$, we get what is known as a *binomial coefficient*

$$
\frac{f^{(n)}(1)}{n!} = \frac{\prod_{k=0}^{n-1} \tfrac{1}{2}-k)}{n!} \equiv \binom{\frac{1}{2}}{n}
$$

This is for $n \geq 1$. For $n = 0$, we define

$$
\binom{\frac{1}{2}}{0} \equiv 1
$$

Thus, the Taylor series expansion for $f(x) = \sqrt{x}$ at $x = 1$ is

$$
\begin{aligned}
\sqrt{x} &= \sum_{n=0}^{\infty} \binom{\frac{1}{2}}{n}(x-1)^n \\
&= 1 + \frac{1}{2}(x-1) + \frac{1}{2}\left(\frac{1}{2}-1\right)\frac{1}{2!}(x-1)^2 + \frac{1}{2}\left(\frac{1}{2}-1\right)\left(\frac{1}{2}-2\right)\frac{1}{3!}(x-1)^3 + \cdots \\
&= 1 + \frac{1}{2}(x-1) - \frac{1}{8}(x-1)^2 + \frac{1}{16}(x-1)^3 - \cdots
\end{aligned}
$$

To compute the radius of convergence using the ratio test, note that

$$
|u_n| = \frac{\left|\prod_{k=0}^{n-1} \tfrac{1}{2}-k)\right|}{n!} |x-1|^n
$$

So

$$
\begin{aligned}
\frac{|u_{n+1}|}{|u_n|} &= \frac{\left|\prod_{k=0}^{n} \tfrac{1}{2}-k)\right|}{\left|\prod_{k=0}^{n-1} \left(\tfrac{1}{2}-k\right)\right|} \cdot \frac{n!}{(n+1)!} \frac{|x-1|^{n+1}}{|x-1|^n} \\
&= \frac{\left|\tfrac{1}{2}-n\right|}{n+1} \cdot |x-1| = \frac{n-\tfrac{1}{2}}{n+1} \cdot |x-1|
\end{aligned}
$$

Thus,

$$\lim_{n \to \infty} \frac{|u_{n+1}|}{|u_n|} = \lim_{n \to \infty} \frac{n - \frac{1}{2}}{n + 1} \cdot |x - 1| = |x - 1|$$

Therefore, the radius of convergence is $R = 1$ and the series converges for all x in the interval $(0, 2)$. One can show (exercise) that the series also converges at the endpoints and so the IOC is $[0, 2]$.

Example 8.8.2 (Computing a Maclaurin Series Expansion)

Problem: Compute the Maclaurin series expansion for $f(x) = \sin x$ and determine its interval of convergence.

Solution: As before we compute derivatives until we can deduce a pattern and then formulate the expression for the nth derivative.

$$\begin{aligned}
f(x) &= \sin x \\
f'(x) &= \cos x \\
f''(x) &= -\sin x \\
f'''(x) &= -\cos x \\
f^{(4)}(x) &= \sin x
\end{aligned}$$

At the 4th-order derivative we have the original function back and the process repeats for higher order derivatives. We see that the even-order derivatives $(0, 2, 4, \ldots)$ are plus or minus the sine function and the odd-order derivatives are plus or minus the cosine function. Specifically

$$\begin{aligned}
f^{(2k)}(x) &= (-1)^k \sin x \\
f^{(2k+1)}(x) &= (-1)^k \cos x
\end{aligned}$$

Thus, $f^{(2k)}(0) = (-1)^k \sin(0) = 0$ and so all the even terms of the Maclaurin series are absent. Also, $f^{(2k+1)}(0) = (-1)^k \cos(0) = (-1)^k$. Therefore, the Maclaurin series expansion of the sine function consists of only the odd terms:

$$\sin x = \sum_{k=0}^{\infty} (-1)^k \frac{x^{2k+1}}{(2k+1)!} = x - \frac{x^3}{3!} + \frac{x^5}{5!} - \frac{x^7}{7!} + \cdots$$

This series is easy to remember: It is an alternating series consisting of all the odd powers of x divided by the corresponding factorial. The fact that this series has only odd powers of x accounts for the fact that the sine function is an odd function: $f(-x) = -f(x)$, for all x.

To determine the radius of convergence of this Maclaurin series, apply the ratio test:

$$|u_k| = \left| \frac{(-1)^k x^{2k+1}}{(2k+1)!} \right| = \frac{|x|^{2k+1}}{(2k+1)!}$$

So

$$\begin{aligned}
|u_{k+1}| \cdot \frac{1}{|u_k|} &= \frac{|x|^{2(k+1)+1}}{(2(k+1)+1)!} \cdot \frac{(2k+1)!}{|x|^{2k+1}} = \frac{|x|^{2k+3}}{(2k+3)!} \cdot \frac{(2k+1)!}{|x|^{2k+1}} \\
&= \frac{|x|^{2k+1} |x|^2}{(2k+3)(2k+2)(2k+1)!} \cdot \frac{(2k+1)!}{|x|^{2k+1}} = \frac{|x|^2}{(2k+3)(2k+3)} \to 0.
\end{aligned}$$

as $k \to \infty$. Thus, the radius of convergence is infinite and the series converges for all x. As we mentioned, the proof that, for any x, the sum of the series is $\sin x$ relies on the theory from advanced courses.

Taylor Polynomials & Approximation of Functions

As with any convergent series $\sum a_n$, the sum of the series (what the series converges to) is the limit of the its sequence of partial sums. For a power series $\sum a_n x^n$, the sequence of partial sums is a sequence of *polynomials*, as the next example illustrates.

Example 8.8.3 (A Sequence of Polynomials)

We found in Part (c) of Example 8.7.4 that the power series there defines a function

$$f(x) = \sum_{n=1}^{\infty} (-1)^{n+1} \frac{x^n}{n^n} = x - \frac{1}{4}x^2 + \frac{1}{27}x^3 - \frac{1}{256}x^4 + \cdots$$

on the interval $(-\infty, \infty)$. One y-value of this function is easy to compute: $f(0) = 0$. Computing other y-values requires summing (numerical) series. For example:

$$f(1) = 1 - \frac{1}{4} + \frac{1}{27} - \frac{1}{256} + \cdots$$
$$f(-1) = -1 - \frac{1}{4} - \frac{1}{27} - \frac{1}{256} - \cdots$$

As we have said, the sums for most convergent series are unknown (cannot be determined exactly from the theory) and so the best we can do is approximate by adding a specified number of terms of the series. For this example, we could, say, approximate by using the first four terms:

$$f(1) \approx 1 - \frac{1}{4} + \frac{1}{27} - \frac{1}{256} = \frac{5413}{6912} \approx 0.78$$
$$f(-1) \approx -1 - \frac{1}{4} - \frac{1}{27} - \frac{1}{256} = -\frac{8923}{6912} \approx -1.29$$

More generally, for any x, we can approximate the y-value $f(x)$ by using the first four terms of the powers series that defines f:

$$f(x) \approx x - \frac{1}{4}x^2 + \frac{1}{27}x^3 - \frac{1}{256}x^4 = P_4(x)$$

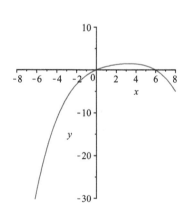

Figure 8.8.1: *A plot of the polynomial P_4 on $(-8, 8)$.*

Thus, we are approximating the values of the function f by the values of a polynomial function, which we have named P_4. This polynomial, as we shall see, is called a *Maclaurin polynomial* for f. While we do not know what the graph of f looks like exactly, we might guess that the graph of P_4 would be an approximate indication of it. The following Maple code creates this graph on the interval, say, $[-8, 8]$.

```
> p4:=x->x-x^2/4+x^3/27-x^4/256;
```
$$p4 := x \mapsto x - \frac{1}{4}x^2 + \frac{1}{27}x^3 - \frac{1}{256}x^4$$
```
> plot(p4(x),x=-8..8,y=-30..10,color=blue);
```

See Figue 8.8.1. Some theory, which we will not discuss here, tells us this graph only approximates the (unknown) graph of f near $x = 0$. This can be verified by using more terms in the power series for f. The following code defines

$$P_k(x) = \sum_{n=1}^{k} (-1)^{n+1} \frac{x^n}{n^n} = x - \frac{1}{4}x^2 + \frac{1}{27}x^3 - \frac{1}{256}x^4 + \cdots + (-1)^k \frac{x^k}{k^k}$$

which is the sum of the first k terms of the power series for f, i.e., the kth partial sum of the series. This is also known as the *Maclaurin polynomial of the k-th order* for the function f.

Maple Code for the kth Order Maclaurin Polynomial

```
> p:=proc(x,k)
```

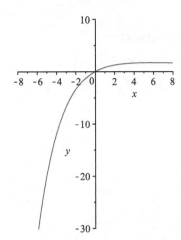

Figure 8.8.2: *A plot of the polynomial P_{100} on $(-8, 8)$.*

```
> local s,n;
> s:=0;
> for n from 1 to k do
> s:=s+(-1)^(n+1)*x^n/(n^n);
> end do;
> end proc;
```

Plotting P_{100} gives the graph in Figure 8.8.2.

```
> plot(p(x,100),x=-8..8,y=-30..10,color=blue);
```

Compare this with the graph of P_4. It is a much better indication of what the true graph of f looks like. The plots of P_4 and P_{100} near $x = 0$ are pretty much the same, but near $x = 6$ they are very different. You would suspect from this that $P_4(6)$ would be a poor approximation to $f(6)$. In summary, this example illustrates that, for a power series, the sequence of partial sums is a sequence of polynomials

$$P_1(x), P_2(x), P_3(x), P_4(x), \ldots, P_k(x), \ldots$$

which converges to the function defined by the series: $\lim_{k \to \infty} P_k(x) = f(x)$, for all x in the interval of convergence.

MACLAURIN POLYNOMIALS

The last example motivates the general definition of Maclaurin polynomials for a function f. The Maclaurin series for f is

$$\sum_{n=0}^{\infty} \frac{f^{(n)}(0)}{n!} x^n$$

and the sequence of partial sums for such a series is a sequence of polynomials:

$P_0(x) = f(0)$	a constant function
$P_1(x) = f(0) + f'(0)x$	a linear function
$P_2(x) = f(0) + f'(0)x + \dfrac{f''(0)}{2}x^2$	a quadratic function
.	.
.	.
.	.
$P_k(x) = f(0) + f'(0)x + \dfrac{f''(0)}{2}x^2 + \cdots + \dfrac{f^{(k)}(0)}{k!}x^k$	a polynomial of the kth degree

More generally, the Taylor series for a function f:

$$f(x) = \sum_{n=0}^{\infty} \frac{f^{(n)}(c)}{n!} (x - c)^n$$

has its sequence of partial sums comprised of a sequence of polynomials $\{P_n(x)\}$, the terms of which are all *Taylor polynomials*. The following definition summarizes all of this.

DEFINITION 8.8.2 (Taylor & Maclaurin Polynomials)

Suppose that f has derivatives of orders $n = 1, 2, \ldots, k$ on an interval about c.

Then its Taylor polynomial of order k *at c is the polynomial*

$$P_k(x) = \sum_{n=0}^{k} \frac{f^{(n)}(c)}{n!}(x-c)^n$$

$$= f(c) + f'(c)(x-c) + \frac{f''(c)}{2}(x-c)^2 + \frac{f'''(c)}{3!}(x-c)^3 + \cdots + \frac{f^{(k)}(c)}{k!}(x-c)^k$$

In the case when $c = 0$, the Taylor polynomial is called a Maclaurin polynomial

$$P_k(x) = \sum_{n=0}^{k} \frac{f^{(n)}(0)}{n!}x^n = f(0) + f'(0)x + \frac{f''(0)}{2}x^2 + \frac{f'''(0)}{3!}x^3 + \cdots + \frac{f^{(k)}(0)}{k!}x^k$$

Example 8.8.4 (Taylor Polynomials for the Square Root Function)

Problem: For $f(x) = \sqrt{x}$, compute the Taylor polynomials $P_k(x)$, $k = 0, 1, 2, 3, 4$, centered at $x = 1$

Solution: We calculate as in Example 1, but now compute the numbers as we proceed.

$$
\begin{array}{llll}
f(x) & = & x^{1/2} & f(1) = 1 \\[2mm]
f'(x) & = & \dfrac{1}{2}x^{-1/2} & f'(1) = \dfrac{1}{2} \\[2mm]
f''(x) & = & -\dfrac{1}{4}x^{-3/2} & \dfrac{f''(1)}{2!} = -\dfrac{1}{4} \cdot \dfrac{1}{2} = -\dfrac{1}{8} \\[2mm]
f^{(3)}(x) & = & \dfrac{3}{8}x^{-5/2} & \dfrac{f^{(3)}(1)}{3!} = \dfrac{3}{8} \cdot \dfrac{1}{6} = \dfrac{1}{16} \\[2mm]
f^{(4)}(x) & = & -\dfrac{15}{16}x^{-7/2} & \dfrac{f^{(4)}(1)}{4!} = -\dfrac{15}{16} \cdot \dfrac{1}{24} = -\dfrac{5}{128}
\end{array}
$$

Then the Taylor polynomials are

$$
\begin{aligned}
P_0(x) & = 1 \\[2mm]
P_1(x) & = 1 + \frac{1}{2}(x-1) \\[2mm]
P_2(x) & = 1 + \frac{1}{2}(x-1) - \frac{1}{8}(x-1)^2 \\[2mm]
P_3(x) & = 1 + \frac{1}{2}(x-1) - \frac{1}{8}(x-1)^2 + \frac{1}{16}(x-1)^3 \\[2mm]
P_4(x) & = 1 + \frac{1}{2}(x-1) - \frac{1}{8}(x-1)^2 + \frac{1}{16}(x-1)^3 - \frac{5}{128}(x-1)^4
\end{aligned}
$$

Example 8.8.5 (Maclaurin Polynomials for the Tangent Function)

Problem: For $f(x) = \tan x$, compute the Maclaurin polynomials $P_k(x)$, $k = 0, 1, 2, 3$.

Solution: A straight-forward computation of the derivatives gives

$$
\begin{array}{lll}
f(x) & = & \tan x \\[2mm]
f'(x) & = & \sec^2 x \\[2mm]
f''(x) & = & 2\sec x(\sec x \tan x) = 2\sec^2 x \tan x
\end{array}
\qquad
\begin{array}{l}
f(0) = 0 \\[2mm]
f'(0) = 1 \\[2mm]
\dfrac{f''(0)}{2!} = \dfrac{0}{2} = 0
\end{array}
$$

$$f^{(3)}(x) \;=\; 4\sec x(\sec x\tan x)\tan x + 2\sec^2 x\sec^2 x \qquad \frac{f^{(3)}(0)}{3!} = \frac{2}{6} = \frac{1}{3}$$

Thus, the Maclaurin polynomials are

$$
\begin{aligned}
P_0(x) &= f(0) = 0 \\
P_1(x) &= f(0) + f'(0)x = x \\
P_2(x) &= f(0) + f'(0)x + \frac{f''(0)}{2}x^2 = x \\
P_3(x) &= f(0) + f'(0)x + \frac{f''(0)}{2}x^2 + \frac{f'''(0)}{3!} = x + \frac{1}{3}x^3
\end{aligned}
$$

NOTE: This example illustrates that a Taylor/Maclaurin polynomial $P_k(x)$ of order k may have degree less than k. Here P_2 has degree 1.

APPROXIMATING with TAYLOR POLYNOMIALS

Taylor polynomials at c are used principally to approximate functions near c. Indeed, the graph of

$$P_1(x) = f(c) + f'(c)(x - c)$$

is the tangent line to the graph of f at the point $(c, f(c))$. The graph of

$$P_2(x) = f(c) + f'(c)(x - c) + \frac{f''(c)}{2}(x - c)^2$$

is a parabola (when $f''(c) \neq 0$) which is the *best* approximation to the graph of f by a parabola. This means that out of all parabolas, the one with equation $y = P_2(x)$ is the only one that (1) passes through the point $Q = (c, f(c))$, (2) has the same tangent line at Q as the graph of f, and (3) has the same circle of curvature at Q as the graph of f. Similarly, $P_3(x)$ is the best approximation to f by a cubic polynomial (when $f^{(3)}(c) \neq 0$). The higher-order polynomials $P_k(x)$ serve as better and better approximations to the function f. The theory shows:

$$\lim_{k\to\infty} P_k(x) = \lim_{k\to\infty} \sum_{n=0}^{k} \frac{f^{(n)}(c)}{n!}(x - c)^n = \sum_{n=0}^{\infty} \frac{f^{(n)}(c)}{n!}(x - c)^n = f(x)$$

when f is representable by a power series on an interval about c.

Example 8.8.6 (Approximating Square Roots with Taylor Polynomials)

Problem: For $f(x) = \sqrt{x}$ graph the function and its Taylor polynomials $P_k(x)$, $k = 1, 2, 3, 4$, at $c = 1$ on an interval about c. In particular compute the approximations $P_k(2)$ to $f(2) = \sqrt{2}$, comparing these with best approximation given by your calculator or by Maple.

Solution: We use the results from Example 4 above. The graph of $P_1(x) = 1 + \frac{1}{2}(x - 1)$ is the tangent line at $Q = (1,1)$. The following code plots the function and its tangent line approximation.

```
> with(plots,display):
> f:=x->sqrt(x);P1:=x->1+(x-1)/2;
```

$$f := x \mapsto \sqrt{x}$$
$$P1 := x \mapsto \frac{1}{2} + \frac{1}{2}x$$

```
> vert:=plot([[1,0],[1,1]],color=tan):
> gr1:=plot([f(x),P1(x)],x=-1..3.5,color=[black,red],
    thickness=[2,1]):
> display({vert,gr});
```

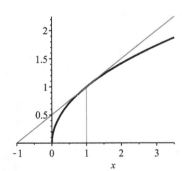

Figure 8.8.3: *Plots of the function $f(x) = \sqrt{x}$ and its tangent line at $Q = (1,1)$.*

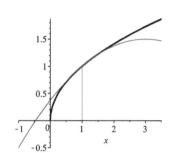

Figure 8.8.4: *Plot of*
$f(x) = \sqrt{x}$ *(in black) and*
the approximating parabola
$P_2(x) = 1 + \frac{1}{2}(x-1) - \frac{1}{8}(x-1)^2$
(in blue) at $Q = (1, 1)$.

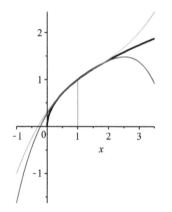

Figure 8.8.5: *Plot of*
$f(x) = \sqrt{x}$ *(in black) and*
approximating polynomials
$P_3(x)$ *(in green) and* $P_4(x)$
(in brown) $Q = (1, 1)$.

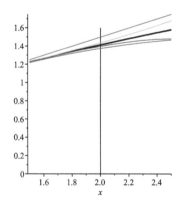

Figure 8.8.6: *Plots of*
$f(x) = \sqrt{x}$ *(in black) and*
the Taylor polynomials $P_k(x)$,
$k = 1, 2, 3, 4$, *near* $x = 2$.

We see from the graph that the value $P_1(2) = 1.5$ is not a very good approximation to $f(2) = \sqrt{2}$. Maple's approximation of the latter value is

```
> f(2.0);
```

$$1.414213562$$

Next we look at the parabolic approximation $P_2 = 1 + \frac{1}{2}(x-1) - \frac{1}{8}(x-1)^2$ to $f(x)$. The following code plots the graphs of f, this parabolic approximation.

```
> P2:=x->1+(x-1)/2-(x-1)^2/8;
```

$$P2 := x \mapsto 1 + \frac{1}{2}(x-1) - \frac{1}{8}(x-1)^2$$

```
> gr2:=plot([f(x),P2(x)],x=-1..3.5,color=[black,blue],
    thickness=[2,1]):
> display(\{gr2,vert\});
```

The use of P_2 to approximate the value of $\sqrt{2}$ gives

$$P_2(2) = 1 + \frac{1}{2} - \frac{1}{8} = \frac{11}{8} = 1.375,$$

which as you can see from the graph is a better approximation than $P_1(2)$ (the tangent line approximation).

The next two Taylor polynomials are

```
> P3:=x->1+(x-1)/2-(x-1)^2/8+(x-1)^3/16;
```

$$P3 := x \mapsto 1 + \frac{1}{2}(x-1) - \frac{1}{8}(x-1)^2 + \frac{1}{16}(x-1)^3$$

```
> P4:=x->1+(x-1)/2-(x-1)^2/8+(x-1)^3/16-5*(x-1)^4/128;
```

$$P4 := x \mapsto 1 + \frac{1}{2}(x-1) - \frac{1}{8}(x-1)^2 + \frac{1}{16}(x-1)^3 - \frac{5}{128}(x-1)^4$$

Plotting these along with the function shows better approximations to the graph of f near $x = 2$, where we want to approximate $f(2) = \sqrt{2}$.

```
> gr3:=plot([f(x),P3(x),P4(x)],x=-1..3.5,color=[black,green,brown],
    thickness=[2,1,1]):
> display({gr3,vert});
```

The use of P_3, P_4 gives much better approximations to $\sqrt{2}$:

$$P_3(x) = 1 + \frac{1}{2} - \frac{1}{8} + \frac{1}{16} = \frac{23}{16} = 1.4375$$

$$P_4(x) = 1 + \frac{1}{2} - \frac{1}{8} + \frac{1}{16} - \frac{5}{128} = \frac{178}{128} = 1.3984375$$

Plotting $P_k(x)$, $k = 1, 2, 3, 4$ near $x = 2$, gives a picture of these approximations.

```
> vert2:=plot([[2,0],[2,1.6]],color=black):
> gr4:=plot([f(x),P1(x),P2(x),P3(x),P4(x),0],x=1.5..2.5,
    color=[black,red,blue,green,brown],thickness=[2,1,1,1,1,1,1]):
> display(\{gr4,vert2\});
```

In general $P_k(2)$ is a better approximation to $\sqrt{2}$ the larger k is. The advanced theory allows one to estimate how good a particular approximation is and enable one to prove that

$$\lim_{k \to \infty} P_k(2) = \sqrt{2}$$

Binomial Series

One of Issac Newton's early contributions in calculus was the discovery of the binomial series. This series generalizes the customary binomial theorem which gives the result of raising a binomial to a positive integer power. For example,

$$(a+b)^2 = a^2 + 2ab + b^2$$
$$(a+b)^3 = a^3 + 3a^2b + 3ab^2 + b^3$$
$$(a+b)^4 = a^4 + 4a^3b + 6a^2b^2 + 4ab^3 + b^4$$

The coefficients: 1 2 1, 1 3 3 1, and 1 4 6 4 1 of the terms are called the *binomial coefficients* and are generally given by

---

DEFINITION 8.8.3 (Binomial Coefficients)

For nonnegative integers $n \le p$, the binomial coefficient is defined by

$$\binom{p}{n} \equiv \frac{p!}{n!(p-n)!} \qquad (8.8.1)$$

Note that $p!$ is divisible by both $n!$ and $(p-n)!$ So, in computing a particular binomial coefficient you should choose the larger of these and reduce. For example

$$\binom{7}{3} = \frac{7!}{3! \, 4!} = \frac{7 \cdot 6 \cdot 5 \cdot 4!}{3!4!} = \frac{7 \cdot 6 \cdot 5}{3!} = \frac{7 \cdot 6 \cdot 5}{3 \cdot 2 \cdot 1}$$

In general, we have the identity

DEFINITION 8.8.4 (Binomial Coefficients - 2nd Definition)

$$\binom{p}{n} \equiv \frac{p(p-1)(p-2)\cdots(p-n+1)}{n!} \qquad (8.8.2)$$

NOTE 1: The numerator in Equation (8.8.2) is the product of n numbers, starting with p and subtracting 1 successively until you have n numbers.

NOTE 2: Equation (8.8.2) makes sense for *any* real number p and any nonnegative integer n. So this is a more general definition of a binomial coefficient and is the one needed in the binomial series.

The binomial theorem gives, for any positive integer p, the expansion of $(a+b)^p$ in terms of the binomial coefficients and powers of a and b:

THEOREM 8.8.1 (Binomial Theorem)   *For any positive integer p,*

$$(a+b)^p = \sum_{n=0}^{p} \binom{p}{n} a^{p-n} b^n \qquad (8.8.3)$$

Newton's crucial observation was that he could use series to extend the binomial theorem to powers p that were *not* positive integers, say to fractional powers such as $1/2$:

$$(a+b)^{1/2} = ?$$

To see how to do this, we switch to the special binomial $1+x$ and let $f(x) = (1+x)^p$. Then we expand f in its Maclaurin series. The result is the following

THEOREM 8.8.2 (Binomial Series)

For any real number p,

$$(1+x)^p = \sum_{n=0}^{\infty} \binom{p}{n} x^n = 1 + px + \frac{p(p-1)}{2!} x^2 + \frac{p(p-1)(p-2)}{3!} x^3 + \cdots \qquad (8.8.4)$$

with the series converging to $(1+x)^p$ for all x in (-1,1).

Proof: First we compute the Maclaurin series for $f(x) = (1+x)^p$. This is similar to the work we did in Example 1:

$$
\begin{aligned}
f(x) &= (1+x)^p \\
f'(x) &= p(1+x)^{p-1} \\
f''(x) &= p(p-1)(1+x)^{p-2} \\
f^{(3)}(x) &= p(p-1)(p-2)(1+x)^{p-3} \\
f^{(4)}(x) &= p(p-1)(p-2)(p-3)(1+x)^{p-4}
\end{aligned}
$$

From this, we inductively get

$$f^{(n)}(x) = p(p-1)(p-2)(p-3)\cdots(p-(n-1))(1+x)^{p-n}$$

Thus, the nth coefficient in the Maclaurin series expansion is

$$\frac{f^{(n)}(0)}{n!} = \frac{p(p-1)(p-2)(p-3)\cdots(p-(n-1))}{n!} = \binom{p}{n}$$

and the Maclaurin series is

$$\sum_{n=1}^{\infty} \binom{p}{n} x^n$$

To get the radius of convergence, use the ratio test with

$$u_n = \frac{p(p-1)(p-2)(p-3)\cdots(p-(n-1))}{n!} x^n.$$

Then

$$\frac{|u_{n+1}|}{|u_n|} = \frac{|p(p-1)(p-2)(p-3)\cdots(p-n)|\,|x|^{n+1}}{|p(p-1)(p-2)(p-3)\cdots(p-n+1)|\,|x|^n} \cdot \frac{n!}{(n+1)!} = \frac{|p-n|}{n+1}|x|$$

Consequently

$$\rho = \lim_{n\to\infty} \frac{|u_{n+1}|}{|u_n|} = \lim_{n\to\infty} \frac{|p-n|}{n+1}|x| = \lim_{n\to\infty} \frac{\left|\frac{p}{n}-1\right|}{1+\frac{1}{n}}|x| = |x| <^{need} 1$$

Thus, the series converges for $|x| < 1$, i.e, for x in the interval $(-1,1)$, and the radius of convergence is $R = 1$. Testing the endpoints and determining the IOC for the binomial series is a little complicated and will not be discussed here.

Example 8.8.7 (Expanding in a Binomial Series)

Problem: Find the Maclaurin series expansion for $f(x) = \dfrac{1}{\sqrt{1+x}}$

Solution: Writing f as

$$f(x) = \frac{1}{\sqrt{1+x}} = (1+x)^{-1/2},$$

we get a straight-forward application of the binomial series theorem with $p = -1/2$:

$$\frac{1}{\sqrt{1+x}} = \sum_{n=0}^{\infty} \binom{-\frac{1}{2}}{n} x^n$$

This is one answer. But can we get a more explicit formula for the binomial coefficients? The nth one is

$$\binom{-\frac{1}{2}}{n} = \frac{-\frac{1}{2}(-\frac{1}{2}-1)(-\frac{1}{2}-2)\cdots(-\frac{1}{2}-(n-1))}{n!}$$

$$= \frac{-\frac{1}{2}(-\frac{3}{2})(-\frac{5}{2})\cdots\left(-\frac{(2n-1)}{2}\right)}{n!} = (-1)^n \frac{1\cdot 3\cdot 5\cdots(2n-1)}{2^n n!}$$

This is a better answer. But we can do better still. Note that the numerator is the product of consecutive odd integers and we can express this as

$$1\cdot 3\cdot 5\cdots(2n-1) = \frac{1\cdot 2\cdot 3\cdot 4\cdot 5\cdots(2n-1)(2n)}{2\cdot 4\cdot 6\cdots(2n)}$$

$$= \frac{(2n)!}{(2\cdot 2\cdot 2\cdots 2)(1\cdot 2\cdot 3\cdots n)} = \frac{(2n)!}{2^n n!}$$

Thus,

$$\binom{-\frac{1}{2}}{n} = \frac{(-1)^n(2n)!}{4^n(n!)^2}$$

Consequently the binomial series is

$$\frac{1}{\sqrt{1+x}} = \sum_{n=0}^{\infty} \frac{(-1)^n(2n)!}{4^n(n!)^2} x^n$$

FINAL NOTE: The extension of the usual binomial formula for $(a+b)^p$ given in Theorem 8.8.1 for p a positive integer can easily be done using Theorem 8.8.2. Specifically:

$$(a+b)^p = \left(a\left[1+\frac{b}{a}\right]\right)^p = a^p\left[1+\frac{b}{a}\right]^p = a^p\sum_{n=0}^{\infty}\binom{p}{n}\frac{b^n}{a^n} = \sum_{n=0}^{\infty}\binom{p}{n}a^{p-n}b^n$$

Of course, for convergence (unless p is a positive integer) this requires that $\left|\frac{b}{a}\right| < 1$.

Exercises: 8.8 (Taylor and Maclaurin Series)

Calculating Maclaurin Series

Find the Maclaurin series for each of the following functions and determine the radius of convergence of the series.

NOTE: Exercises 7 and 9 involve the hyperbolic sine and cosine functions. (See Section 2.12.) These are defined in terms of the natural exponential function as:

$$\sinh x \equiv \frac{1}{2}\left(e^x - e^{-x}\right), \cosh x \equiv \frac{1}{2}\left(e^x + e^{-x}\right).$$

It is easy to check that

$$\frac{d}{dx}\left(\sinh x\right) = \cosh x, \frac{d}{dx}\left(\cosh x\right) = \sinh x$$

Also, $\sinh(0) = 0$, $\cosh(0) = 1..$

1. $f(x) = e^x$
2. $f(x) = (e^x)^3$
3. $f(x) = \cos x$
4. $f(x) = \cos 3x$
5. $f(x) = \ln(1 + x)$
6. $f(x) = \ln(1 + 2x)$
7. $f(x) = \sinh x$
8. $f(x) = \sinh 2x$
9. $f(x) = \cosh x$
10. $f(x) = \cosh 3x$
11. $f(x) = 2^x$
12. $f(x) = 10^x$
13. $f(x) = e^{-x}$
14. $f(x) = 2^{-x}$
15. $f(x) = e^{2x}$
16. $f(x) = 2^{2x}$
17. $f(x) = \sin 2x$
18. $f(x) = \sin 3x$
19. $f(x) = 1 + 3x - 5x^2 + 2x^3$
20. $f(x) = 2 + 4x - 3x^2 + x^3$
21. $f(x) = \sin(x + \pi)$
22. $f(x) = \sin(x - \pi)$
23. $f(x) = \cos(x + 1)$
24. $f(x) = \cos(x - 1)$
25. $f(x) = e^{x+1}$
26. $f(x) = e^{x-1}$
27. $f(x) = 2^x - 2^{-x}$
28. $f(x) = 3^x - 3^{-x}$
29. $f(x) = 2^x + 2^{-x}$
30. $f(x) = 3^x + 3^{-x}$
31. $f(x) = xe^x$
32. $f(x) = xe^{-x}$

Taylor Series Expansions

For each of the following functions, find the Taylor series expansion at the point $x = c$. Also determine the radius of convergence of the series.

33. $f(x) = \ln x, c = 2$
34. $f(x) = \ln x, c = 3$
35. $f(x) = \sin x, c = \pi/3$
36. $f(x) = \cos x, c = \pi/3$
37. $f(x) = \sin x, c = \pi/4$
38. $f(x) = \cos x, c = \pi/4$
39. $f(x) = e^x, c = 1$
40. $f(x) = e^x, c = 2$
41. $f(x) = 2^x, c = 2$
42. $f(x) = 3^x, c = 3$
43. $f(x) = \sqrt[3]{x}, c = 1$
44. $f(x) = \sqrt[5]{x}, c = 1$
45. $f(x) = 1/\sqrt{x}, c = 1$
46. $f(x) = 1/\sqrt[3]{x}, c = 1$

47. $f(x) = x^{-1}, c = 1$
48. $f(x) = (x - 1)^{-1}, c = 2$
49. $f(x) = x^{-2}, c = 1$
50. $f(x) = (x - 1)^{-2}, c = 2$
51. $f(x) = 1 + 3x - 5x^2 + 2x^3, c = 1$
52. $f(x) = 5 - 4x - 6x^2 + 7x^3, c = 1$

Approximating Functions by Taylor/Maclaurin Polynomials

For each of the given functions

(a) Compute the Taylor Polynomials $P_k(x)$ at c for the specified values of k.

(b) Use the polynomials to compute $P_k(a)$ for the specified a and compare with $f(a)$.

(c) **CAS:** Use Maple to plot, in the same figure, the graphs of the polynomials and f on an interval containing c and a.

53. $f(x) = \sin x, c = 0, k = 1, 3, 5, 7, a = 1$
54. $f(x) = \cos x, c = 0, k = 2, 4, 6, 8, a = 1$
55. $f(x) = \sin x, c = 0, k = 1, 2, 3, 4, a = \pi/8$
56. $f(x) = \cos x, c = 0, k = 1, 2, 3, 4, a = \pi/8$
57. $f(x) = \sqrt[3]{x}, c = 1, k = 1, 2, 3, 4, a = 2$
58. $f(x) = \sqrt[4]{x}, c = 1, k = 1, 2, 3, 4, a = 2$
59. $f(x) = \ln x, c = 1, k = 1, 2, 3, 4, a = 2$
60. $f(x) = \ln x, c = 2, k = 1, 2, 3, 4, a = 3$
61. $f(x) = \sec x, c = 0, k = 2, 4, 6, a = \pi/3$
62. $f(x) = \sec x, c = 0, k = 2, 4, 6, a = \pi/4$

Binomial Series

As in Example 8.8.7, use the general binomial series expansion

$$(1 + x)^p = \sum_{n=0}^{\infty} \binom{p}{n} x^n$$

to find the particular expansions for the following binomials. Simplify the binomial coefficients $\binom{p}{n}$ as was done in Example 8.8.7.

63. $(1 + x)^{-3/2}$
64. $(1 + x)^{-5/2}$
65. $\sqrt[3]{1 + x}$
66. $\sqrt[5]{1 + x}$
67. $(1 + x)^{3/2}$
68. $(1 + x)^{5/2}$
69. $\sqrt{a + b}$
70. $(a + b)^{3/2}$
71. $(1 - x)^{-3/2}$
72. $(1 - x)^{-5/2}$
73. $\sqrt[3]{1 + x^2}$
74. $\sqrt[5]{1 + x^2}$
75. $(1 + 2x)^{3/2}$
76. $(1 + 2x)^{5/2}$
77. $\sqrt{a - b}$
78. $(a - b)^{3/2}$

Calculus Concepts & Computation

8.9 Operations on Power Series

In this section we discuss how to apply the standard functional operations to power series. In particular, we consider the algebraic operations (addition, subtraction, multiplication, division, composition) and the operations from calculus (differentiation and integration).

These operations are often useful in determining the Taylor or Maclaurin series for new functions where applying the definition (computing all the derivatives) would be too tedious. Instead, we can take the known power series for the basic functions (see the table at the end of the section) and get the power series for the new functions by using algebra and calculus.

To simplify the notation, we just look at Maclaurin series, even though the results apply to Taylor series as well. Thus, if f and g are two functions represented by power series

$$f\left(x\right) = \sum_{n=0}^{\infty} a_n x^n, \quad g\left(x\right) = \sum_{n=0}^{\infty} b_n x^n$$

Then on the intersection of their intervals of convergence, the functions $f + g$, $f - g$ are represented by the power series

$$f\left(x\right) + g\left(x\right) = \sum_{n=0}^{\infty} \left(a_n + b_n\right) x^n$$

and

$$f\left(x\right) - g\left(x\right) = \sum_{n=0}^{\infty} \left(a_n - b_n\right) x^n$$

This is clear from Theorem 8.2.2.

Example 8.9.1 (The Sum of Two Maclaurin Series)

Problem: Find the Maclaurin series for $f\left(x\right) = \dfrac{5}{6 + x - x^2}$ and determine its interval of convergence.

Solution: The trick here is to use the partial fraction decomposition technique to write

$$\frac{5}{6 + x - x^2} = \frac{5}{\left(2 + x\right)\left(3 - x\right)} = \frac{1}{2 + x} + \frac{1}{3 - x}$$

Next, from the geometric series result:

$$\frac{a}{1 - r} = \sum_{n=0}^{\infty} a r^n, \quad \text{for } |r| < 1,$$

we can expand each partial fraction into a Maclaurin series:

$$\frac{1}{2 + x} = \frac{\frac{1}{2}}{1 + \frac{x}{2}} = \sum_{n=0}^{\infty} \frac{1}{2} \left(-\frac{x}{2}\right)^n = \sum_{n=0}^{\infty} \frac{\left(-1\right)^n}{2^{n+1}} x^n$$

Here we used $r = -\frac{x}{2}$. This series converges only for $\left|\frac{x}{2}\right| < 1$, i.e, for $|x| < 2$. The other partial fraction has $a = \frac{1}{3}$ and $r = \frac{x}{3}$.

$$\frac{1}{3 - x} = \frac{\frac{1}{3}}{1 - \frac{x}{3}} = \sum_{n=0}^{\infty} \frac{1}{3} \left(\frac{x}{3}\right)^n = \sum_{n=0}^{\infty} \frac{1}{3^{n+1}} x^n$$

which converges only for $\left|\frac{x}{3}\right| < 1$, i.e., for $|x| < 3$. Thus,

$$\frac{5}{6 + x - x^2} = \sum_{n=0}^{\infty} \frac{(-1)^n}{2^{n+1}} x^n + \sum_{n=0}^{\infty} \frac{1}{3^{n+1}} x^n = \sum_{n=0}^{\infty} \left(\frac{(-1)^n}{2^{n+1}} + \frac{1}{3^{n+1}} \right) x^n$$

which converges only for $|x| < 2$ and so the IOC is $(-2, 2)$.

The product of two power series is slightly more complicated than the sum or the difference. However, if one of the power series is just a polynomial, then the product is easy to compute, as the following example illustrates.

Example 8.9.2 (The Product of a Polynomial and a Power Series)

Problem: Compute the Maclaurin series for the following functions

(a) $h(x) = x^2 e^x$ (b) $h(x) = (x + x^3) \sin x$

Solution(a): Just use the infinite version of the distributive law. (See Theorem 8.2.2 Part (3).)

$$x^2 e^x = x^2 \sum_{n=0}^{\infty} \frac{x^n}{n!} = \sum_{n=0}^{\infty} \frac{x^2 x^n}{n!} = \sum_{n=0}^{\infty} \frac{x^{n+2}}{n!}$$

Solution(b): Again, use the distributive law

$$\begin{aligned}
(x + x^3) \sin x &= x \sin x + x^3 \sin x = x \sum_{n=0}^{\infty} \frac{(-1)^n x^{2n+1}}{(2n+1)!} + x^3 \sum_{n=0}^{\infty} \frac{(-1)^n x^{2n+1}}{(2n+1)!} \\
&= \sum_{n=0}^{\infty} (-1)^n \frac{x^{2n+2}}{(2n+1)!} + \sum_{n=0}^{\infty} (-1)^n \frac{x^{2n+4}}{(2n+1)!}
\end{aligned}$$

To combine these series we need re-index so that the powers of x are the same. We do this by adjusting the first series as follows

$$\begin{aligned}
\sum_{n=0}^{\infty} \frac{(-1)^n x^{2n+2}}{(2n+1)!} &= x^2 + \sum_{n=1}^{\infty} \frac{(-1)^n x^{2n+2}}{(2n+1)!} = x^2 + \sum_{k=0}^{\infty} (-1)^{k+1} \frac{x^{2(k+1)+2}}{(2(k+1)+1)!} \\
&= x^2 + \sum_{k=0}^{\infty} (-1)^{k+1} \frac{x^{2k+4}}{(2k+3)!}
\end{aligned}$$

Here, after separating off the zeroth term of the series, we re-indexed by making the substitution $n = k + 1$. Just relabeling the index n to k on the second series allows us to combine the series and get the final result.

$$\begin{aligned}
(x + x^3) \sin x &= x^2 + \sum_{k=0}^{\infty} \left(\frac{(-1)^{k+1}}{(2k+3)!} + \frac{(-1)^k}{(2k+1)!} \right) x^{2k+4} \\
&= x^2 + \sum_{k=0}^{\infty} (-1)^k \left(1 - \frac{1}{(2k+3)(2k+2)} \right) \frac{x^{2k+4}}{(2k+1)!}
\end{aligned}$$

When both factors in the product are full power series, the best we can do is to calculate the first few terms in the product. To illustrate the technique, suppose we want to compute the terms in the product up to order three. First we write the series in the dot-dot-dot notation, displaying the terms in each up to order three. Then we use the distributive law and arrange the work as follows.

Multiplication of Power Series

$$f(x)g(x) = (a_0 + a_1 x + a_2 x^2 + a_3 x^3 + \cdots)(b_0 + b_1 x + b_2 x^2 + b_3 x^3 + \cdots)$$

$$= \begin{cases} a_0 b_0 + a_0 b_1 x + a_0 b_2 x^2 + a_0 b_3 x^3 + \cdots \\ \quad + a_1 b_0 x + a_1 b_1 x^2 + a_1 b_2 x^3 + \cdots \\ \quad\quad + a_2 b_0 x^2 + a_2 b_1 x^3 + \cdots \\ \quad\quad\quad + a_3 b_0 x^3 + \cdots \end{cases}$$

$$= a_0 b_0 + (a_0 b_1 + a_1 b_0)x + (a_0 b_2 + a_1 b_1 + a_2 b_0)x^2 + (a_0 b_3 + a_1 b_2 + a_2 b_1 + a_3 b_0)x^3 + \cdots$$

Note how we have put the initial results in an array of rows. The first row is the result of distributing a_0 across all the terms in the second series (and only displaying the results up to order 3). The second row is the result of distributing $a_1 x$ across all the terms in the second series (and only displaying the results up to order 3). Continuing this pattern for four lines (or rows) gives us a display of all the terms in the product series which have order less than or equal to three. Notice also how each successive row of the computation has been shifted over one so that the like powers of x line up in the same column. Adding columnwise then gives us the terms up to order three in the product power series.

As you can see from the work, there is a general formula for the coefficients in the product power series. Thus, if

$$\left[\sum_{n=0}^{\infty} a_n x^n\right]\left[\sum_{n=0}^{\infty} b_n x^n\right] = \sum_{k=0}^{\infty} c_n x^n,$$

then

$$c_n = \sum_{j=0}^{n} a_j b_{n-j}$$

This formula is useful for theoretical work, but not for any particular example. Instead, we just write out the terms as we did above and use the distributive law. The following example illustrates this technique.

Example 8.9.3 (The Product of Two Power Series)

Problem: Compute the first four terms of the Maclaurin series for $h(x) = \dfrac{e^x}{1-x}$.

Solution: View the function as a product of $\frac{1}{1-x}$ and e^x. We write out the first few terms in the Maclaurin series for each function and then use the distributive law.

$$\frac{1}{1-x} \cdot e^x = \left(1 + x + x^2 + x^3 + \cdots\right)\left(1 + x + \frac{x^2}{2} + \frac{x^3}{6} + \cdots\right)$$

$$= \begin{cases} 1 + x + \frac{1}{2}x^2 + \frac{1}{6}x^3 + \cdots \\ \quad + x \ + \ x^2 + \frac{1}{2}x^3 + \cdots \\ \quad\quad + x^2 \ + x^3 + \cdots \\ \quad\quad\quad + x^3 + \cdots \end{cases}$$

$$= 1 + 2x + \frac{5}{2}x^2 + \frac{8}{3}x^3 + \cdots$$

Division of one power series by another is generally more difficult. To compute a Maclaurin series for

$$\frac{f(x)}{g(x)} = \frac{\sum_{n=0}^{\infty} a_n x^n}{\sum_{n=0}^{\infty} b_n x^n} = \frac{a_0 + a_1 x + a_2 x^2 + \cdots}{b_0 + b_1 x + b_2 x^2 + \cdots}$$

The quotient function must be defined at $x = 0$, which means that we must assume that $g(0) \neq 0$. Thus, we require that $b_0 \neq 0$. Because of this, we can assume that the divisor series has leading coefficient $b_0 = 1$. (If not, we can always divide the series by b_0.)

As with multiplication, division is modeled on the technique of long division for polynomials. But, there is one major difference: the divisor and dividend are arranged in *ascending* powers of x, rather than descending powers. Clearly, this is so because a power series has no highest power of x. Thus, in general we arrange the work as follows.

Division of Power Series

$$a_0 + (-a_0 b_1 + a_1)x + [a_0(-b_2 + b_1^2) - a_1 b_1 + a_2]x^2 + \cdots$$

$$1 + b_1 x + b_2 x^2 + \cdots \overline{\smash{\big)}\ a_0 \quad + \quad a_1 x \quad + \quad a_2 x^2 \quad + \quad \cdots}$$

$$a_0 \quad + \quad a_0 b_1 x \quad + \quad a_0 b_2 x^2 \quad + \quad \cdots$$

remainder 1 $\longrightarrow$ $\quad (-a_0 b_1 + a_1)x + (-a_0 b_2 + a_2)x^2 + \cdots$

$$(-a_0 b_1 + a_1)x + (-a_0 b_1 + a_1)b_1 x^2 + \cdots$$

remainder 2 $\longrightarrow$ $\quad [a_0(-b_2 + b_1^2) - a_1 b_1 + a_2]x^2 + \cdots$

To get the first term in the quotient, divide the first term in the divisor (i.e., 1) into the first term in the dividend (i.e., a_0) to get the first term in the quotient (i.e., a_0). Then multiply this (a_0) into all the terms in the divisor, putting the result below the dividend. Drawing a line and then subtracting gives the first remainder. Then repeat the process (forever). Thus, divide 1 into the first term $(-a_0 b_1 + a_1)x$ to get the second term $(-a_0 b_1 + a_1)x$ in the quotient. Etc. Note that because the leading coefficient of the divisor is 1, the first term of each remainder, at each stage, becomes the next term in the quotient.

As with multiplication of power series, there is a general formula for the nth coefficient c_n in the quotient power series. (See the exercises.) However, the formula is only useful for theoretical developments, and so to work any particular example just proceed with the long division as indicated above.

Example 8.9.4 (Division of Power Series)

Problem: Use long division to compute the first four nonzero terms in the quotient power series

(a) $\dfrac{4 + x^2}{\cos x}$ (b) $\dfrac{1}{1 - x}$

Solution (a): Arrange the work as follows.

$$
1 - \frac{1}{2}x^2 + \frac{1}{24}x^4 - \frac{1}{720}x^6 + \cdots \overline{\Big)\ \begin{array}{l} 4 + 3x^2 + \dfrac{4}{3}x^4 + \dfrac{197}{360}x^6 + \cdots \\[2mm] 4 + x^2 \\[2mm] \underline{4 - 2x^2 + \dfrac{1}{6}x^4 - \dfrac{1}{180}x^6 + \cdots} \\[2mm] 3x^2 - \dfrac{1}{6}x^4 + \dfrac{1}{180}x^6 + \cdots \\[2mm] \underline{3x^2 - \dfrac{3}{2}x^4 + \dfrac{1}{8}x^6 + \cdots} \\[2mm] \dfrac{4}{3}x^4 - \dfrac{43}{360}x^6 + \cdots \\[2mm] \underline{\dfrac{4}{3}x^4 - \dfrac{2}{3}x^6 + \cdots} \\[2mm] \dfrac{197}{360}x^6 + \cdots \end{array}}
$$

Again, note how the first term of each remainder, at each stage, becomes the next term in the quotient.

Solution (b): This example is merely to indicate that the well-known geometric series expression for $\frac{1}{1-x}$ can be derived by long division.

$$
1 - x \,\overline{\Big)\ \begin{array}{l} 1 + x + x^2 + x^3 + \cdots \\[2mm] 1 \\[2mm] \underline{1 - x} \\[2mm] x \\[2mm] \underline{x - x^2} \\[2mm] x^2 \\[2mm] \underline{x^2 - x^3} \\[2mm] x^3 \end{array}}
$$

The operation of composition of a power series with a continuous function is a useful way of obtaining Taylor series for new functions. In most cases this operation is quite simple. The following theorem states the general result.

THEOREM 8.9.1 (Substitution into Power Series)

Suppose f is representable by power series

$$
f(x) = \sum_{n=0}^{\infty} a_n x^n = a_0 + a_1 x + a_2 x^2 + a_3 x^3 + a_4 x^4 + \cdots
$$

which is absolutely convergent for $|x| < R$. Suppose g is a continuous function

on an interval I such that $|g(x)| < R$ for all x in I. Then the series

$$
f(g(x)) = \sum_{n=0}^{\infty} a_n (g(x))^n = a_0 + a_1 g(x) + a_2 (g(x))^2 + a_3 (g(x))^3 + a_4 (g(x))^4 + \cdots
$$

converges absolutely for x in I and represents the composite function $f \circ g$.

Here's an important example of the theorem. One of the basic Taylor series that we found in Section 8.7 was

$$
f(x) = \ln x = \sum_{n=1}^{\infty} \frac{(-1)^{n+1}(x-1)^n}{n}
$$

which has radius of convergence 1 and IOC $(0,2]$. See Example 8.7.2 and Exercise 5 in Section 8.8. Letting $g(x) = 1 + x$ and restricting x to $(-1, 1]$, we get from the theorem that

$$\ln(1 + x) = \sum_{n=1}^{\infty} (-1)^{n+1} \frac{x^n}{n},$$

with IOC $(-1, 1]$. This is, in a sense, an equivalent series representation for the natural logarithm function. It is the one listed in Table 8.9.1 (page 573) and can be used in deriving power series for other related functions.

Example 8.9.5 (Composition)

Problem: Use the composition operation and the well-known Maclaurin series from Table 8.9.1 to find the indicated type of power series for the following functions.

(a) $f(x) = \sin 5x$ (Maclaurin)   (b) $f(x) = e^{-x^2/2}$ (Maclaurin)

(c) $f(x) = \ln\ 1 + x^3)$ (Maclaurin)   (d) $f(x) = e^x$ (Taylor at $c = 1$)

Solution (a):

$$\sin 5x = \sum_{n=0}^{\infty} (-1)^n \frac{(5x)^{2n+1}}{(2n+1)!} = \sum_{n=0}^{\infty} (-1)^n\, 5^{2n+1} \frac{x^{2n+1}}{(2n+1)!}$$

Solution (b):

$$e^{-x^2/2} = \sum_{n=0}^{\infty} \frac{\left(-x^2/2\right)^n}{n!} \sum_{n=0}^{\infty} \frac{(-1)^n\, x^{2n}}{n!\, 2^n}$$

Solution (c):

$$\ln\ 1 + x^3) = \sum_{n=1}^{\infty} \frac{(-1)^n\ x^3)^n}{n} = \sum_{n=1}^{\infty} \frac{(-1)^n\, x^{3n}}{n}$$

Solution (d): First substitute $x - 1$ into the Maclaurin series for the natural exponential function:

$$e^{x-1} = \sum_{n=0}^{\infty} \frac{(x-1)^n}{n!}$$

Then use the laws of exponents $e^{x-1} = e^x e^{-1} = \dfrac{e^x}{e}$ and multiply both sides of the above equation by e to get

$$e^x = \sum_{n=0}^{\infty} \frac{e\,(x-1)^n}{n!}.$$

Of course, this result is easy enough to derive directly.

The remaining operations that we can do on powers series are differentiation and integration.

THEOREM 8.9.2 (Term-By-Term Calculus for Power Series)

A function represented by a power series

$$f(x) = \sum_{n=0}^{\infty} a_n(x-c)^n = a_0 + a_1(x-c) + a_2(x-c)^2 + a_3(x-c)^3 + \cdots,$$

with interval of convergence I, is differentiable and integrable on the interior of I. Its derivative and integral are represented by the power series

$$f'(x) = \sum_{n=1}^{\infty} n a_n(x-c)^{n-1} = a_1 + 2a_2(x-c) + 3a_3(x-c)^2 + 4a_4(x-c)^3 + \cdots$$

$$\int f(x)\,dx = C + \sum_{n=0}^{\infty} \frac{a_n}{n+1}(x-c)^{n+1} = C + a_0(x-c) + \frac{a_1}{2}(x-c)^2 + \frac{a_2}{3}(x-c)^3 + \frac{a_3}{4}(x-c)^4 + \cdots$$

These power series have the same radius of convergence as the power series for f, but their intervals of convergence may be different.

Example 8.9.6 (Differentiating a Power Series)

Problem: Let $y = f(x)$ be the function defined by the power series

$$y = \sum_{n=0}^{\infty} \frac{x^{3n}}{(3n)!} = 1 + \frac{x^3}{3!} + \frac{x^6}{6!} + \frac{x^9}{9!} + \cdots$$

Find the interval of convergence for the series and show that, on this interval, y satisfies the differential equation

$$y''' = y$$

Solution: The ratio test easily gives an infinite radius of convergence, so the IOC is $(-\infty, \infty)$. The first derivative is

$$y' = \sum_{n=1}^{\infty} \frac{3n x^{3n-1}}{(3n)!} = \sum_{n=1}^{\infty} \frac{3n x^{3n-1}}{(3n)\,(3n-1)!} = \sum_{n=1}^{\infty} \frac{x^{3n-1}}{(3n-1)!}$$

The second derivative is

$$y'' = \sum_{n=1}^{\infty} \frac{(3n-1)\,x^{3n-2}}{(3n-1)!} = \sum_{n=1}^{\infty} \frac{x^{3n-2}}{(3n-2)!}$$

The third derivative is

$$y''' = \sum_{n=1}^{\infty} \frac{(3n-2)\,x^{3n-3}}{(3n-2)!} = \sum_{n=1}^{\infty} \frac{x^{3n-3}}{(3n-3)!} = \sum_{k=0}^{\infty} \frac{x^{3k}}{(3k)!} = y$$

Note that in the computation for the 1st, 2nd, and 3rd derivatives the summation index starts at 1. This is because the second (nonzero) term in the series for y has x to the 3rd power. Also note that in the last line above, we introduced a new index, letting $n = k + 1$. This was to enable us to recognize the series as the original one for y.

Example 8.9.7 (Integrating a Power Series)

Problem: Find the Maclaurin series for $f(x) = \tan^{-1} x$ and determine its interval of convergence.

Solution: We use the fact $\tan^{-1} x = \displaystyle\int \frac{1}{1 + x^2}\, dx$ and expand the integrand in its Maclaurin series (using a geometric series with $a = 1, r = -x^2$). Then we integrate term-by-term.

$$\begin{aligned}
\tan^{-1} x &= \int \frac{1}{1 + x^2}\, dx = \int \left[\sum_{n=0}^{\infty} (-1)^n\, x^{2n} \right] dx \\
&= C + \sum_{n=0}^{\infty} (-1)^n \int x^{2n}\, dx = C + \sum_{n=0}^{\infty} (-1)^n \frac{x^{2n+1}}{2n + 1}
\end{aligned}$$

To determine the constant C of integration, we evaluate both sides of the above equation at $x = 0$:

$$0 = \tan^{-1}(0) = C$$

Thus, we get the following power series representation of the inverse tangent function

$$\tan^{-1} x = \sum_{n=0}^{\infty} (-1)^n \frac{x^{2n+1}}{2n + 1} = x - \frac{x^3}{3} + \frac{x^5}{5} - \frac{x^7}{7} + \cdots$$

This series is easy to remember. It is an alternating series of all the odd powers of x divided by that odd power. Since we used the geometric series with $r = -x^2$ to get this result, we have, with Theorem 8.9.2, that the series for the inverse tangent converges for $\left| -x^2 \right| < 1$, i.e., for $|x| < 1$. Thus $(-1, 1)$ is contained in the IOC. Testing the endpoint $x = 1$, gives a famous series for the number $\tan^{-1}(1) = \frac{\pi}{4}$. It is

$$\frac{\pi}{4} = \sum_{n=0}^{\infty} (-1)^n \frac{1}{2n + 1} = 1 - \frac{1}{3} + \frac{1}{5} - \frac{1}{7} + \cdots$$

The series converges since it satisfies the criteria of the AST (Alternating Series Test). Testing the endpoint $x = -1$ also gives a convergent series (which is the negative of the one above). So, the IOC for the power series is $[-1, 1]$.

The following table lists all the basic Maclaurin series for some of the important functions in calculus. As you have seen in the examples above, you can use these basic power series to derive Maclaurin series for many other functions.

Basic Maclaurin Series

(1) $\displaystyle e^x = \sum_{n=0}^{\infty} \frac{x^n}{n!} = 1 + x + \frac{x^2}{2} + \frac{x^3}{3!} + \frac{x^4}{4!} + \frac{x^5}{5!} + \cdots$ $\qquad |x| < \infty$

(2) $\displaystyle \sin x = \sum_{n=0}^{\infty} (-1)^n \frac{x^{2n+1}}{(2n+1)!} = x - \frac{x^3}{3!} + \frac{x^5}{5!} - \frac{x^7}{7!} + \frac{x^9}{9!} + \cdots$ $\qquad |x| < \infty$

(3) $\displaystyle \cos x = \sum_{n=0}^{\infty} (-1)^n \frac{x^{2n}}{(2n)!} = 1 - \frac{x^2}{2!} + \frac{x^4}{4!} - \frac{x^6}{6!} + \frac{x^8}{8!} + \cdots$ $\qquad |x| < \infty$

(4) $\displaystyle \ln(1+x) = \sum_{n=1}^{\infty} (-1)^{n+1} \frac{x^n}{n} = x - \frac{x^2}{2} + \frac{x^3}{3} - \frac{x^4}{4} + \frac{x^5}{5} + \cdots$ $\qquad -1 < x \le 1$

(5) $\displaystyle \tan^{-1} x = \sum_{n=0}^{\infty} (-1)^n \frac{x^{2n+1}}{2n+1} = x - \frac{x^3}{3} + \frac{x^5}{5} - \frac{x^7}{7} + \frac{x^9}{9} + \cdots$ $\qquad |x| \le 1$

(6) $\displaystyle \sin^{-1} x = \sum_{n=0}^{\infty} \frac{1 \cdot 3 \cdot 5 \cdots (2n-1)}{2^n n! \, (2n+1)} x^{2n+1} = \sum_{n=0}^{\infty} \frac{(2n)!}{4^n (n!)^2 (2n+1)} x^{2n+1}$ $\qquad |x| \le 1$

(7) $\displaystyle (1+x)^p = \sum_{n=0}^{\infty} \binom{p}{n} x^n = 1 + px + \frac{p(p-1)}{2!} x^2 + \frac{p(p-1)(p-2)}{3!} x^3 + \cdots$

(8) $\displaystyle \frac{1}{1-x} = \sum_{n=0}^{\infty} x^n = 1 + x + x^2 + x^3 + x^4 + x^5 + \cdots$ $\qquad |x| < 1$

(9) $\displaystyle \sinh x = \sum_{n=0}^{\infty} \frac{x^{2n+1}}{(2n+1)!} = x + \frac{x^3}{3!} + \frac{x^5}{5!} + \frac{x^7}{7!} + \frac{x^9}{9!} + \cdots$ $\qquad |x| < \infty$

(10) $\displaystyle \cosh x = \sum_{n=0}^{\infty} \frac{x^{2n}}{(2n)!} = 1 + \frac{x^2}{2!} + \frac{x^4}{4!} + \frac{x^6}{6!} + \frac{x^8}{8!} + \cdots$ $\qquad |x| < \infty$

Table 8.9.1

Exercises: 8.9 (Operations on Power Series)

In Exercises 1–48, use the Maclaurin series in Table 8.9.1 for the basic functions to find Maclaurin series for the following functions. For this you may employ algebraic operations (addition, subtraction, multiplication, division, composition) and calculus operations (differentiation, integration) as indicated in the reading material. Where possible determine the interval of convergence for the series.

1. $f(x) = \dfrac{1}{1 + x^4}$ **2.** $f(x) = \dfrac{1}{1 + x^3}$

3. $f(x) = \dfrac{2}{2 + x - x^2}$ (Use partial fractions)

4. $f(x) = \dfrac{4}{3 + 2x - x^2}$

5. $f(x) = \dfrac{1}{e^{5x}}$ **6.** $f(x) = \dfrac{1}{e^{3x}}$

7. $f(x) = e^{x^2} + \dfrac{1}{1 - x^2}$ **8.** $f(x) = e^{-3x^2} + \dfrac{1}{4 - x^2}$

9. $f(x) = e^{2x} + e^{-3x}$ **10.** $f(x) = e^{5x} + e^{-6x}$

11. $f(x) = e^x + e^{-x}$ **12.** $f(x) = e^x - e^{-x}$

13. $f(x) = x \ln(1 + x)$ **14.** $f(x) = x^2 \ln(1 + x)$

15. $f(x) = x^2 \cos x$ **16.** $f(x) = x^3 \sin x$

17. $f(x) = x \sin(2x^3)$ **18.** $f(x) = x^2 \cos(3x^2)$

19. $f(x) = x^3 e^{-5x}$ **20.** $f(x) = x^4 e^{-2x}$

21. $f(x) = (1 + x)e^x$ **22.** $f(x) = (x + x^2)e^x$

23. $f(x) = \ln(1 + x^2)$ **24.** $f(x) = \ln(1 + x^4)$

25. $f(x) = \ln(1 + 2x)$ **26.** $f(x) = \ln(1 + 5x)$

27. $f(x) = \ln(2 + x^4)$ **28.** $f(x) = \ln(3 + x^6)$

29. $f(x) = (x + x^3) \tan^{-1}(2x)$

30. $f(x) = (1 + x^2) \tan^{-1}(3x)$

31. $f(x) = (1 + x^2) \sin^{-1}(3x)$

32. $f(x) = (x + x^3) \sin^{-1}(2x)$

33. $f(x) = \cos(\sqrt{x})$ **34.** $f(x) = \cos(x^{3/2})$

35. $f(x) = \dfrac{\sin x}{x}$ **36.** $f(x) = \dfrac{1 - \cos x}{x}$

37. $f(x) = \dfrac{e^x - 1}{x}$ **38.** $f(x) = \dfrac{\ln(1 + x)}{x}$

39. $f(x) = \dfrac{1}{2^x}$ (First express in base e)

40. $f(x) = \dfrac{1}{10^x}$ (First express in base e)

41. $f(x) = e^{-x} \ln(1 + x)$ **42.** $f(x) = e^{2x} \ln(1 + x)$

43. $f(x) = e^{-x} \sin x$ **44.** $f(x) = e^{-x} \cos x$

45. $f(x) = \tan x$ **46.** $f(x) = \cot x$

47. $f(x) = \dfrac{\ln(1 + x)}{\sqrt{1 + x}}$ **48.** $f(x) = \dfrac{\ln(1 + x)}{\sqrt[3]{1 + x}}$

In Exercises 49–60, find the Maclaurin series for the function defined by the indefinite integral. In 49–54, also find the formula for the function by computing the integral.

49. $F(x) = \displaystyle\int \dfrac{2}{1 - x^2} \, dx$ **50.** $F(x) = \displaystyle\int \dfrac{2}{1 - 4x^2} \, dx$

51. $F(x) = \displaystyle\int \dfrac{1}{\sqrt{1 + x^2}} \, dx$ **52.** $F(x) = \displaystyle\int \dfrac{x^3}{\sqrt{1 + x^4}} \, dx$

53. $F(x) = \displaystyle\int \dfrac{1}{\sqrt{1 - x^2}} \, dx$ **54.** $F(x) = \displaystyle\int \dfrac{x}{\sqrt{1 - x^2}} \, dx$

55. $F(x) = \displaystyle\int \dfrac{1}{1 + x^3} \, dx$ **56.** $F(x) = \displaystyle\int \dfrac{1}{1 + x^4} \, dx$

57. $F(x) = \displaystyle\int e^{-x^2} \, dx$ **58.** $F(x) = \displaystyle\int e^{-x^3} \, dx$

59. $F(x) = \displaystyle\int \cos(x^2) \, dx$ **60.** $F(x) = \displaystyle\int \sin(x^2) \, dx$

Verify, by differentiating the series term-by-term, that the function defined by the series satisfies the differential equation.

61. $y = \displaystyle\sum_{n=0}^{\infty} \dfrac{(-1)^n x^{3n}}{(3n)!}, \quad y''' = -y$

62. $y = \displaystyle\sum_{n=0}^{\infty} \dfrac{(-1)^n x^{3n+1}}{(3n + 1)!}, \quad y''' = -y$

63. $y = x + \displaystyle\sum_{n=0}^{\infty} \dfrac{x^{3n+4}}{(3n + 4)!}, \quad y''' = y$

64. $y = x^2 + \displaystyle\sum_{n=0}^{\infty} \dfrac{x^{3n+5}}{(3n + 5)!}, \quad y''' = y$

65. $y = x + \displaystyle\sum_{n=0}^{\infty} \dfrac{(-1)^{n+1} x^{4n+5}}{(4n + 5)!}, \quad y^{(4)} = -y$

66. $y = \displaystyle\sum_{n=0}^{\infty} \dfrac{(-1)^n}{(4n)!} x^{4n}, \quad y^{(4)} = -y$

67. $y = \displaystyle\sum_{n=0}^{\infty} \dfrac{(-1)^n x^{2n}}{2^n n!}, \quad y'' + xy' + y = 0$

68. $y = \displaystyle\sum_{n=0}^{\infty} \dfrac{(-1)^n 2^n n! \, x^{2n+1}}{(2n + 1)!}, \quad y'' + xy' + y = 0$

9

Plane Curves & Polar Coordinates

Calculus *Concepts & Computation*

9.1 Parametric Equations

Recall that $\mathbb{R}^2$ denotes the set of all ordered pairs (x, y) of real numbers x, y, and that this set can be identified with the set of all points in the plane by choosing an origin point $O = (0, 0)$ and two mutually perpendicular lines through O (called the *coordinate axes*). Then each point P in the plane is assigned coordinates (x, y), called its *Cartesian coordinates*, by the process outlined in Appendix A.

In this chapter we will study the geometry of curves in the plane (called *plane curves*). We will do this both in general and in the particular case for curves known as *conic sections*. In addition, we introduce a new concept of describing curves by *parametric equations* and this leads to an adaptation of the usual calculus of derivatives and integrals.

Also, we will see how the use of *polar coordinates*, as an alternative to Cartesian coordinates, allows us to simplify the description of and calculus for certain types of plane curves.

Cartesian Equations for Plane Curves

As in Section 2.10, a curve in $\mathbb{R}^2$ is defined to be the set of points whose coordinates (x, y) satisfy an equation $H(x, y) = 0$. Specifically, the curve C given by the equation is the set of points

$$C = \left\{ (x, y) \in \mathbb{R}^2 \mid H(x, y) = 0 \right\}$$

The equation $H(x, y) = 0$ defining the curve is known as a *Cartesian equation* for the curve. Cartesian equations for some standard curves, such as (straight) lines, parabolas, and circles, are shown in the margin. For these standard curves, as well as the ellipses and hyperbolas studied in Section 9.6, the Cartesian equations are easy to use when plotting the curves by hand. This is because the numbers h and k give a point (h, k) which is on the line, is the vertex of the parabola, or is the center of the circle. The number m is the slope of the line, while the number a tells us which way the parabola is turned and, of course, the number r is the radius of the circle. So, with this geometric information and the plots of several points, it is easy to sketch the curve by hand.

However, in general, a Cartesian equation for a curve can be difficult to work with by hand. For example, the equation

$$xy^2 + x^2 y - x^2 + 1 = 0,$$

gives a rather complicated curve. To find points on the curve, the general routine would be to take a value for x (or for y), substitute in the Cartesian equation, and then solve the resulting equation for y (or for x). For example, taking $x = 1$, gives $y^2 + y = 0$, which has solutions $y = 0, -1$. Thus, $(1, 0), (1, -1)$ are two points on the curve. Taking $y = 0$ gives $-x^2 + 1 = 0$, which has solutions $x = \pm 1$, and so $(-1, 0), (1, 0)$ are two more points on the curve (the second of which we already found). Continuing like this, one could generate more points, but connecting these properly to get a hand-drawn sketch of the curve is difficult. Of course, as we did in Section 2.10, we can always use Maple to plot the curve (which still takes a little experimentation with ranges for x and y and grid sizes):

Lines

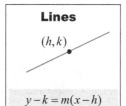

$$y - k = m(x - h)$$

Parabolas

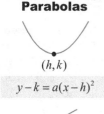

$$y - k = a(x - h)^2$$

$$x - h = a(y - k)^2$$

Circles

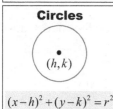

$$(x - h)^2 + (y - k)^2 = r^2$$

```
> H:=(x,y)->x*y^2+x^2*y-x^2+1;
```
$$H := (x, y) \rightarrow xy^2 + yx^2 - x^2 + 1$$
```
> implicitplot(H(x,y)=0,x=-2..3,y=-3..3,grid=[50,50]);
```
This produces the curve shown in the margin Figure 9.1.1.

An alternative, and more direct, method for describing curves is to use parametric equations.

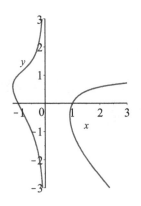

Figure 9.1.1: *The curve with equation* $xy^2 + x^2y - x^2 + 1 = 0$.

Parametric Equations for Plane Curves

Suppose f and g are functions defined on an interval $[a, b]$, then

$$x = f(t), \quad y = g(t), \quad (9.1.1)$$

t in $[a, b]$, are called *parametric equations* for the curve given formally by

$$C = \{\, (f(t), g(t)) \mid t \text{ in } [a, b] \,\}$$

The independent variable t here is called a *parameter* and the set of points C comprising the curve is said to be *parametrized* by Equations (9.1.1). These equations are also called a *parameterization* of the curve C. (We will see that there can be many different parametrizations of the same curve.) We let $P(t) = (f(t), g(t))$ denote the point on the curve corresponding to parameter value t.

Example 9.1.1 (Sketching a Curve Given by Parametric Equations)

Problem: Sketch, by hand, the curve given by the parametric equations:

$$x = 2t^2 - 2, \quad y = t^3 - 4t, \quad \text{for } t \text{ in } [-3, 3].$$

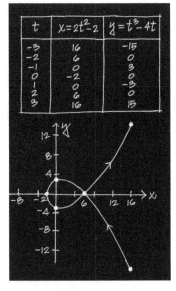

Figure 9.1.2: *The curve with parametric equations* $x = 2t^2 - 2$, $y = t^3 - 4t$, *for* t *in* $[-3, 3]$.

Solution: Unlike curves given by Cartesian equations, we can easily generate points $P(t) = (2t^2 - 2, t^3 - 4t)$ on this curve. We just take a few values for the parameter t, say $t = -3, -2, -1, 0, 1, 2, 3$, and compute the corresponding values of $x = 2t^2 - 2$ and $y = t^3 - 4t$. Figure 9.1.2 shows a table containing these calculations and a sketch of the curve obtained by plotting the points in the table. NOTE: When connecting the plotted points, we do it in the order listed in the table. For instance, connect the one for $t = -3$ to the one for $t = -2$, and so forth. In fact, we can view the parameter t as representing the *time* and the corresponding point $(x, y) = (f(t), g(t)) = P(t)$ as the *position* of a particle moving in the plane. The curve shown in Figure 9.1.2 is then the *trajectory* or *path* this particle. We have also marked the *direction of travel* for this particle on the curve as the time increases from $t = -3$ to $t = 3$.

Example 9.1.2 (Dynamic Aspects of Parametrically Defined Curves)

Problem: Use the dcurve command to create a dynamic plot (i.e., a movie) of the curve in Example 9.1.1.

Solution: We first define the two functions f, g in Maple and then use the dcurve command as follows.

```
> f:=t->2*t^2-2;g:=t->t^3-4*t;
```
$$f := t \rightarrow 2t^2 - 2$$
$$g := t \rightarrow t^3 - 4t$$
```
> dcurve(f,g,-3,3,30);
```
This produces the desired movie. Figure 9.1.3 shows the next to the last frame in this movie. Note how the vertical and horizontal red lines in the movie indicate the positions of the x-coordinate and y-coordinate on the x- and y-axes during the motion. These show how $x = f(t)$ and $y = g(t)$ change over time. Also note the particle is at the point $(6, 0)$ at two distinct times, $t = -2$ and $t = 2$.

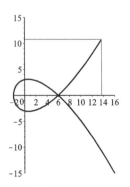

Figure 9.1.3: *A dynamic plot using* dcurve.

In general, parametrically defined curves are easier to plot (by hand or by computer) than curves given by Cartesian equations and they also come with a direction. The parametric equations for many curves originate in physics where they arise as solutions of Newton's 2nd Law of motion.

Example 9.1.3 (Motion Near the Earth's Surface)

Problem: The parametric equations

$$x = 16t, \quad y = -16t^2 + 32t + 12, \quad \text{for } t \text{ in } [0, T],$$

describe the motion of a ball thrown from the top of a 12 ft high building with initial velocities $v_x = 16$ ft/s in the x-direction and $v_y = 32$ ft/s in the y-direction. (a) Find the time T when the ball hits the ground and the place where it hits the ground. (b) Show that the trajectory of the ball lies on a parabola and find the quantities h, k, a that determine this parabola. (c) Find how high the ball goes and when it achieves this maximum height. (d) Create a movie with `dcurve` showing the flight of the ball and use it to verify, approximately, your answers in Parts (a), (b), and (c).

Solution

Part (a): Note that at time zero: $(x, y) = (0, 12)$, which is the top of the building and the ball hits the ground when $y = 0$, i.e., when

$$-16t^2 + 32t + 12 = 0, \quad \text{which is} \quad 4t^2 - 8t - 3 = 0.$$

Using the quadratic formula on this gives $t = 1 \pm \sqrt{7}/2$. So $T = 1 + \sqrt{7}/2 \approx 2.32$ s and at this time the ball is $x = 16T = 16 + 8\sqrt{7} \approx 37.17$ ft from the building.

Part (b): We put the parametric equations together and eliminate the parameter t to get a Cartesian equation for the curve (trajectory of the ball). The first equation $x = 16t$ can be solved for t to give $t = x/16$ and this can be substituted in the second equation to give

$$
\begin{aligned}
y &= -16\left(\tfrac{x}{16}\right)^2 + 32\left(\tfrac{x}{16}\right) + 12 = -\tfrac{1}{16}x^2 + 2x + 12 \\
&= -\tfrac{1}{16}(x^2 - 32x) + 12 = -\tfrac{1}{16}(x^2 - 32x + 256) + 16 + 12 \\
&= -\tfrac{1}{16}(x - 16)^2 + 28
\end{aligned}
$$

Here we used the *completing the square* process to put this Cartesian equation in the standard form for a parabola. We see that $a = -1/16$ and so the parabola is turned downward (as expected) and the vertex is $(h, k) = (16, 28)$.

Part (c): Since the vertex is $(16, 28)$ the ball achieves its maximum height of 28 feet when $x = 16$. Since $x = 16t$ in general, the time t when the maximum height occurs can be found by solving $16t = 16$, which gives $t = 1$.

Part (d): Define the parametric equations and create a dynamic plot of the trajectory using

```
> f:=t->16*t;g:=t->-16*t^2+32*t+12;
```
$$f := t \rightarrow 16t$$
$$g := t \rightarrow -16t^2 + 32t + 12$$
```
> dcurve(f,g,0,2.5,50);
```

This produces a movie, the 30th frame of which is shown in Figure 9.1.4. Note that the time interval $[0, 2.5]$ extends beyond the time $T \approx 2.32$ when the ball hits the ground. We have used 50 frames in the movie, so the frames are spaced $2.5/50 = 1/20$ seconds apart. Thus, the 30th frame corresponds to time $t = 30(1/20) = 1.5$ seconds. The position of the ball should be $(x, y) = (24, 24)$, which appears to be the case in Figure 9.1.4. We found that the maximum height occurs at time $t = 1$, so this should occur in the 20th frame in the movie. Using the cursor probe on this frame, you can check that the maximum height is 28 ft. From the last frame of the

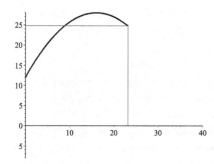

Figure 9.1.4: *Trajectory of the ball with parametric equations* $x = 16t$, $y = -16t^2 + 32t + 12$.

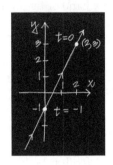

Figure 9.1.5: *The line* $x = 2 + 2t$, $y = 3 + 2t$.

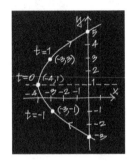

Figure 9.1.6: *The curve* $x = t^2 - 4$, $y = 2t + 1$.

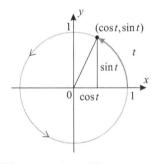

Figure 9.1.7: *The curve* $x = \cos t$, $y = \sin t$.

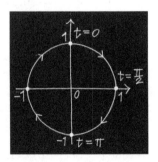

Figure 9.1.8: *The curve* $x = \sin t$, $y = \cos t$.

movie you can check that the ball hits the ground a little more that 37 ft from the bottom of the building.

Eliminating the Parameter

In the previous example, the parametric equations $x = 16t$, $y = -16t^2 + 32t + 12$ described a projectile motion on part of the parabola with Cartesian equation $y = -\frac{1}{16}(x - 16)^2 + 28$. We found this Cartesian equation by the process known as eliminating the parameter. While eliminating the parameter is not always possible, it often allows us to more readily identify the curve when the resulting Cartesian equation is more well-known. Here are some examples of this.

Example 9.1.4 (Lines and Parabolas)

Problem: For each of the parametric equations: (a) Eliminate the parameter to obtain a Cartesian equation for the curve. (b) Sketch the curve and, viewing the curve as the trajectory of a moving particle, describe motion on the curve.

Part (a): $x = 2 + 2t$, $y = 3 + 2t$, for t in $(-\infty, \infty)$.

Solution: Solve $x = 2 + 2t$ for t to get $t = (x - 2)/2$. Substituting this in the equation for y gives

$$y = 3 + 2(x - 2), \quad \text{equivalently:} \quad y = 2x - 1.$$

This is a straight line. The first Cartesian equation says this line passes through $(2, 3)$ and has slope 2. The second equation is the slope-y-intercept version of the line. The y-intercept is $(0, -1)$. Figure 9.1.5 shows a sketch of this line, with the direction in which it is traced out by a particle as t goes from $-\infty$ to ∞. The particle is at the y-intercept at time $t = -1$ and is at $(2, 3)$ at time $t = 0$.

Part (b): $x = t^2 - 4$, $y = 2t + 1$, for t in $(-\infty, \infty)$.

Solution: In this case it is easier to solve $y = 2t + 1$ for t to get $t = (y - 1)/2$. Substituting this in the equation for x gives

$$x = \tfrac{1}{4}(y - 1)^2 - 4.$$

This is an equation for a parabola with vertex $(-4, 1)$, axis $y = 1$ and turned in the positive direction of the axis. Figure 9.1.6 shows a sketch of this parabola, with the direction in which it is traced out by a particle as t goes from $-\infty$ to ∞. The particle is at the vertex $(-4, 1)$ at time $t = 0$.

Example 9.1.5 (Circles)

Problem: Show that by eliminating the parameter in each of the following parametric equations the resulting Cartesian equation is the same. Sketch the curve and describe motion on the curve.

Part (a): $x = \cos t$, $y = \sin t$, for t in $(-\infty, \infty)$.

Solution: This is the standard parametrization of the circle of radius 1 centered at the origin. As shown in figure 9.1.7, the parameter t represents an angle, or arc, on this circle. Some Algebra/Trig books use this to define the trig functions $\cos t$ and $\sin t$. (See the Appendix.). To eliminate the parameter, rather than solving $x = \cos t$ for t, we use the standard trig identity connecting the sine and cosine:

$$x^2 + y^2 = \cos^2 t + \sin^2 t = 1.$$

Thus, the Cartesian equation $x^2 + y^2 = 1$ is the standard unit circle (radius 1, center at the origin). Figure 9.1.7 shows this circle, with the direction in which it is traced out by a particle as t goes from $-\infty$ to ∞. The particle, at time $t = 0$, is at $(1, 0)$ and transverses the circle counter-clockwise, completing one circuit at t goes from 0 to 2π.

Part (b): $x = \sin t$, $y = \cos t$, for t in $(-\infty, \infty)$.

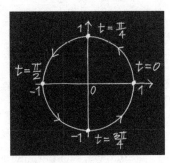

Figure 9.1.9: *The curve* $x = \cos 2t$, $y = \sin 2t$.

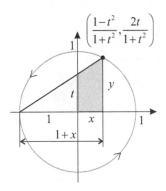

Figure 9.1.10: *The curve* $x = \frac{1-t^2}{1+t^2}$, $y = \frac{2t}{1+t^2}$.

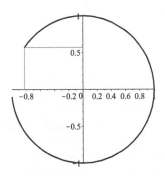

Figure 9.1.11: *The Weierstrass parameterization.*

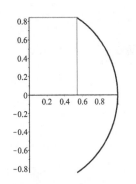

Figure 9.1.12: *The curve* $x = \cos(\sin t)$, $y = \sin(\sin t)$.

Solution: As in Part (a): $x^2 + y^2 = \sin^2 t + \cos^2 t = 1$ gives us that the Cartesian equation is the standard unit circle. But now, as t goes from $-\infty$ to ∞ the circle is traced out clockwise, completing one circuit at t goes from 0 to 2π. See figure 9.1.8.

Part (c): $x = \cos 2t$, $y = \sin 2t$, for t in $(-\infty, \infty)$.

Solution: As in Part (a): $x^2 + y^2 = \cos^2 2t + \sin^2 2t = 1$ gives us that the Cartesian equation is the standard unit circle. But now, as t goes from $-\infty$ to ∞ the circle is traced out twice as fast, completing one circuit at t goes from 0 to π. See Figure 9.1.9.

Part (d): $x = \dfrac{1 - t^2}{1 + t^2}$, $y = \dfrac{2t}{1 + t^2}$, for t in $(-\infty, \infty)$.

Solution: This is the Weierstrass parametrization of the unit circle. (See Section 6.4). Here the parameter t has a geometric meaning as shown in Figure 9.1.10. As in Part (a):

$$x^2 + y^2 = \frac{(1-t^2)^2}{(1+t^2)^2} + \frac{4t^2}{(1+t^2)^2} = \frac{1 - 2t^2 + t^4 + 4t^2}{(1+t^2)^2} = \frac{1 + 2t^2 + t^4}{(1+t^2)^2} = 1$$

gives us that the Cartesian equation is the standard unit circle. But now, as t goes from $-\infty$ to ∞ the circle is traced out *just once*, starting at $(-1, 0)$ at time $t = -\infty$, going to $(0, -1)$ at time $t = -1$, then to $(1, 0)$ at time $t = 0$, then to $(0, 1)$ at time $t = 1$, and ending at $(-1, 0)$ again at time $t = \infty$. If you observe the motion on the circle using the command `dcurve(f,g,-30,30,50)`, you can see that motion is very slow at first, becomes more rapid as t goes from -1 to 1, and slows down again as t approaches ∞. Figure 9.1.11 shows the 30th frame of this movie.

Part (e): $x = \cos(\sin t)$, $y = \sin(\sin t)$, for t in $(-\infty, \infty)$.

Solution: As in Part (a): $x^2 + y^2 = \cos^2 \theta + \sin^2 \theta = 1$, where $\theta = \sin t$, gives us that the Cartesian equation is the standard unit circle. But now, as t goes from $-\infty$ to ∞, only the part of the circle between $\theta = -1$ rad and $\theta = 1$ rad is traced out. This is because $\theta = \sin t$ varies between ± 1. If you observe the motion on the circle using the command `dcurve(f,g,-Pi/2,Pi/2,50)`. Figure 9.1.12 shows the 50th frame of this movie.

NOTE: Example 9.1.5 was designed to illustrate several things: (1) Many different parameterizations give the same Cartesian equation when the parameter is eliminated. Otherwise said, the same Cartesian curve can be parameterized in many different ways. (2) Sometimes the set of points given by the parametric equations is different than the set of points for the corresponding Cartesian equation. (3) Whether or not the parametric and Cartesian equations give the same set of points, the parametric equations can be viewed as describing a motion of a particle on the Cartesian curve. (4) While the parameter t can be viewed as representing time, it can also have a geometric meaning, as in Part (d) of Example 9.1.5.

Cycloids

If you paint a dot on the side of a bicycle tire and watch the path that the dot traces out as a cyclist rides with uniform speed on a flat road, the resulting curve will be a *cycloid* with parametric equations

$$x = rt - r\sin t, \quad y = r - r\cos t,$$

for t in $[0, \infty)$. Figure 9.1.13 shows part of this curve, for a child's bike of radius $r = 1$ foot. The figure is the 45th frame in the movie produced by the special-purpose Maple command `cycloid(1,0,4*Pi,50)`. As you can see, after one full rotation of the tire, the dot returns to the ground, having swept out one "arch" of the cycloid. The dot is then a distance of $2\pi r = 2\pi \approx 6.28$ feet from its starting point (in this case $x = 0$).

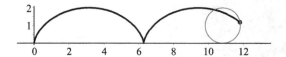

Figure 9.1.13: *Two arches of a cycloid produced by the command* `cycloid(1,0,4*Pi,50)`.

The parametric equations for the cycloid are derived as follows. The parameter t denotes an angle and r is the radius of the wheel. It is assumed that the wheel rolls without slipping, which means that as the wheel turns through a certain angle t, the length rt of the arc on the circumference of the wheel is the same as the length that the wheel rolls on the flat road.

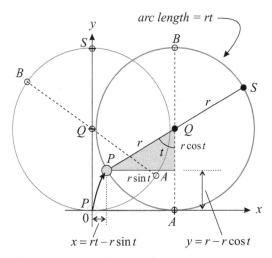

Figure 9.1.14: A cycloid rolls a distance rt.

Starting at time t with the dot, labeled by P, at the origin, the wheel rolls, turning through an angle t shown as $\angle PQA$ in Figure 9.1.14. The arc on the circle subtended by this angle has measure rt. This arc joining points P and A on the circle has the same length as the line segment joining 0 and A on the x-axis. Notice how initially the diameter $\overline{PS}$ is vertical and the diameter $\overline{AB}$ is inclined at angle t to the vertical. After rolling a distance rt, the diameter $\overline{AB}$ is vertical and the diameter $\overline{PS}$ is inclined at angle t to the vertical. The gold right triangle in the figure has one angle of measure t and sides about the right angle of measures $r\sin t$ and $r\cos t$. Subtracting theses from rt and r, respectively, gives the x- and y-coordinates of P after when the wheel has rolled a distance rt.

Exercises: 9.1 (Parametric Equations)

Plotting Curves with Parametric Equations

In Exercises 1–14, sketch the graph of the curve on the given parameter interval by using the parametric equations to plot points. Plot at least 7 points and indicate the direction of the curve with arrow heads on the sketch.

1. $x = t^2$, $y = 1 + t$, $[-3, 3]$ **2.** $x = t^2$, $y = 1 - t$, $[-3, 3]$

3. $x = \frac{1}{2}t + 1$, $y = t + 2$, $[-3, 3]$

4. $x = -\frac{1}{2}t + 1$, $y = t + 2$, $[-3, 3]$

5. $x = 2(t^2 - 1)$, $y = t(t^2 - 4)$, $[-3, 3]$

6. $x = 2(t^2 - 1)$, $y = t(t^2 - 3)$, $[-3, 3]$

7. $x = -t^2$, $y = (t - 1)(t - 2)(t + 3)$, $[-3, 3]$

8. $x = -t^2$, $y = (t - 2)(t - 3)(t + 2)$, $[-3, 3]$

9. $x = \cos t$, $y = \cos t + \sin t$, $[0, 2\pi]$

10. $x = \sin t$, $y = \cos t - \sin 2t$, $[0, 2\pi]$

11. $x = \sin t$, $y = \cos t + \sin 2t$, $[0, 2\pi]$

12. $x = -\sin t$, $y = \cos t + \sin 2t$, $[0, 2\pi]$

13. $x = \cos t$, $y = \cos t + \sin 2t$, $[0, 2\pi]$

14. $x = -\cos t$, $y = \cos t + \sin 2t$, $[0, 2\pi]$

Eliminating the Parameter

In Exercises 15–38, (a) Find, by eliminating the parameter, a Cartesian equation for the curve with given parametric equations. (b) Identify and sketch the curve determined by the Cartesian equation. (c) Describe the motion on this curve of a particle with position $x = f(t), y = g(t)$ at time t. (d) CAS: Use the dynamic curve plotting command dcurve to study and understand more fully the particle's motion on the curve given by the Cartesian equation.

15. $x = 2t - 3$, $y = 4t - 5$, **16.** $x = 3t - 2$, $y = 5t - 4$

17. $x = t^2 - 1$, $y = t + 2$ **18.** $x = t^2 + 2$, $y = t - 1$

19. $x = \sqrt{t}$, $y = t - 1$ **20.** $x = t - 1$, $y = \sqrt{t}$

21. $x = t^6 + 2$, $y = t^3 + 1$ **22.** $x = t^{10} + 2$, $y = t^5 + 1$

23. $x = -\cos t$, $y = \sin t$ **24.** $x = -\sin t$, $y = \cos t$

25. $x = \cos 3t$, $y = \sin 3t$ **26.** $x = \cos 4t$, $y = \sin 4t$

27. $x = 1 + 3\cos t$, $y = 2 + 3\sin t$

28. $x = 3 + 2\cos t$, $y = 1 - 2\sin t$

29. $x = 2 + \cos t$, $y = 1 + \cos^2 t$

30. $x = 1 + \sin t$, $y = 2 + \sin^2 t$

31. $x = \cos\left(\frac{\pi t^2}{1+t^2}\right)$, $y = \sin\left(\frac{\pi t^2}{1+t^2}\right)$

32. $x = \sin\left(\frac{\pi t^2}{1+t^2}\right)$, $y = \cos\left(\frac{\pi t^2}{1+t^2}\right)$

33. $x = \cos(\tan^{-1} t)$, $y = \sin(\tan^{-1} t)$

34. $x = \sin(\tan^{-1} t)$, $y = \cos(\tan^{-1} t)$

35. $x = \cos t$, $y = 1 + 2\cos t$ **36.** $x = \sin t$, $y = 1 + \sin t$

37. $x = t^2$, $y = 2t^2 + 1$ **38.** $x = 2t^2 + 1$, $y = t^2$

Motion Near the Earth's Surface

In Exercses 39–44, the parametric equations describe motion of a ball thrown near the earth's surface. In each exercise: (a) Find the time T when the ball hits the ground and the place where it hits the ground. (b) Show that the trajectory of the ball lies on a parabola and find the quantities h, k, a that determine this parabola. (c) Find how high the ball goes and when it achieves this maximum height. CAS: (d) Create a movie with dcurve showing the flight of the ball and use it to verify, approximately, your answers in Parts (a), (b), and (c).

39. $x = 20t$, $y = -16t^2 + 32t + 24$

40. $x = 32t$, $y = -16t^2 + 16t + 28$

41. $x = 16t$, $y = -16t^2 + 64t$

42. $x = 16t$, $y = -16t^2 + 128t$

43. $x = 16t$, $y = -16t^2 + 20$

44. $x = 32t$, $y = -16t^2 + 32$

Calculus *Concepts & Computation*

9.2 Parametric Calculus - Derivatives

So far we have learned how to apply the derivative and integral calculus to *functions* and have used these derivatives and integrals in many applications. But for a function f, its graph is a special type of curve, one with a very simple equation $y = f(x)$. In this section we extend the calculus, and its applications, to general curves $H(x, y) = 0$ given by parametric equations $x = f(t)$, $y = g(t)$.

Eliminating the Parameter in General

We have seen in a number of examples how to eliminate the parameter t in the parametric equations $x = f(t)$, $y = g(t)$ defining a curve and obtain a corresponding Cartesian equation $H(x, y) = 0$ for the curve. In practice this can be difficult, if not impossible, to do, but in *theory* this is always possible.

To see how this works, suppose t_0 is a time when not both of the derivatives f', g' are zero. Say, $f'(t_0) \neq 0$. Then there is an interval $I = [t_1, t_2]$ about t_0 on which f is either strictly increasing ($x' = f'(t) > 0$) or strictly decreasing ($x' = f'(t) < 0$). This means that f has an inverse f^{-1} on I and, letting $a = f(t_1)$, $b = f(t_2)$, the domain of f^{-1} is either $J = [a, b]$ (in the strictly increasing case) or $J = [b, a]$ (in the strictly decreasing case). See Figure 9.2.1. In either case, we can solve, theoretically, the first parametric equation $x = f(t)$ for t to get $t = f^{-1}(x)$ and this will give the Cartesian equation

$$y = g(f^{-1}(x)) \qquad (9.2.1)$$

This is the standard parametrization for this piece of the curve:

$$\{(f(t), g(t)) \mid t \text{ in } I\} = \{(x, g(f^{-1}(x))) \mid x \text{ in } J\}$$

See Figure 9.2.2.

Slopes and Concavity

With a standard parametrization we can find dy/dx directly by differentiating Eq. (9.2.1) with respect to x using both the chain rule and the inverse function derivative formula: $\frac{d}{dx}[f^{-1}(x)] = 1/f'(f^{-1}(x))$. This gives

$$\frac{dy}{dx} = g'(f^{-1}(x)) \cdot \frac{1}{f'(f^{-1}(x))} = \frac{g'(f^{-1}(x))}{f'(f^{-1}(x))} = \frac{g'}{f'}(f^{-1}(x)) \qquad (9.2.2)$$

Differentiating again with respect to x (using the chain rule, quotient rule, and inverse function derivative formula) results in a formula for the 2nd derivative:

$$\frac{d^2y}{dx^2} = \Big[\frac{g''f' - g'f''}{(f')^2}\Big](f^{-1}(x)) \cdot \frac{1}{f'(f^{-1}(x))} = \Big[\frac{g''f' - g'f''}{(f')^3}\Big](f^{-1}(x)) \qquad (9.2.3)$$

NOTE: Since we cannot usually in practice write y as a function of x as in Equation (9.2.1), we will let $x = f(t)$ in Equations (9.2.2)–(9.2.3) to get

$$\frac{dy}{dx}\Big|_{x=f(t)} = \frac{g'(t)}{f'(t)} \qquad (9.2.4)$$

$$\frac{d^2y}{dx^2}\Big|_{x=f(t)} = \frac{f'(t)g''(t) - f''(t)g'(t)}{(f'(t))^3} \qquad (9.2.5)$$

NOTATION: Since the parametric equations are $x = f(t)$, $y = g(t)$, it will simplify the above formulas greatly if we just use the notation:

$$x' = f'(t), \quad y' = g'(t)$$

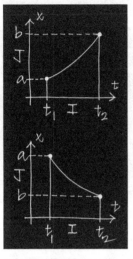

Figure 9.2.1: *The interval J when $x' = f'(t) > 0$ (top) and when $x' = f'(t) < 0$ (bottom).*

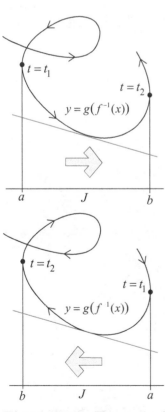

Figure 9.2.2: *The graph of $y = g(f^{-1}(x))$ on J.*

Additionally, we will suppress the t from the notation and write the two formulas as shown in the following box.

PARAMETRIC VERSIONS of the 1st and 2nd Derivatives

Suppose $x = f(t)$, $y = g(t)$ are parametric equations for a plane curve with f and g having continuous first and second derivatives. Then we use the notation

$$\frac{dy}{dx} = \frac{y'}{x'} \qquad (9.2.6) \qquad and \qquad \frac{d^2y}{dx^2} = \frac{x'y'' - x''y'}{(x')^3} \qquad (9.2.7)$$

for the slope and concavity functions (considered as functions of t).

CONVENTION: Formulas (9.2.6)–(9.2.7) use the symbols dy/dx and d^2y/dx^2 to stand for two functions of t which we will call the slope and concavity functions. Thus, the *slope of the curve* (or the tangent line) at time t is $\frac{dy}{dx}|_t$. While, the *concavity of the curve* at time t is $\frac{d^2y}{dx^2}|_t$. Recall that $P(t) = (f(t), g(t)) = (x(t), y(t))$ denotes the point on the curve corresponding to parameter value (time) t. So the slope and concavity refer to this point on the curve.

Example 9.2.1

Problem: Consider the curve in Example 9.1.1, with parametric equations

$$x = 2t^2 - 2, \quad y = t^3 - 4t.$$

(a) Find the slope and concavity functions. (b) Use these to find an equation for the tangent line and the concavity at time $t = 1$. (c) Find all times when the tangent line is horizontal and all times when it is vertical. (d) Show that there are two tangent lines to the curve at the point $(6, 0)$ and find equations for these lines.

Solution:

Part (a): The derivatives are

$$x' = 4t, \quad y' = 3t^2 - 4$$
$$x'' = 4, \quad y'' = 6t$$

Then the slope function is

$$\frac{dy}{dx} = \frac{y'}{x'} = \frac{3t^2 - 4}{4t}$$

and the concavity function is

$$\frac{d^2y}{dx^2} = \frac{x'y'' - x''y'}{(x')^3} = \frac{(4t)6t - 4(3t^2 - 4)}{(4t)^3} = \frac{12t^2 + 16}{64t^3} = \frac{3t^2 + 4}{16t^3}$$

Part (b): The point on the curve for $t = 1$ is $P(1) = (0, -3)$ and, by the above, the slope and concavity at this time are

$$\frac{dy}{dx}\bigg|_{t=1} = -\frac{1}{4}, \qquad \frac{d^2y}{dx^2}\bigg|_{t=1} = \frac{7}{16} > 0$$

Thus, an equation for the tangent line is $y + 3 = -\frac{1}{4}(x - 0)$. Equivalently: $y = -\frac{1}{4}x - 3$. The curve is concave up at this point $(0, -3)$.

Part (c): The tangent line is horizontal when

$$\frac{dy}{dx} = \frac{3t^2 - 4}{4t} = 0,$$

which occurs only when the numerator is zero: $3t^2 - 4 = 0$ (and the denominator is not zero). So $t = \pm 2/\sqrt{3} \approx \pm 1.16$ and the corresponding points are $P(\pm\frac{2}{\sqrt{3}}) = (\frac{2}{3}, \mp\frac{16}{3\sqrt{3}}) \approx (0.67, \mp 3.08)$.

The slope of the curve become infinite at time $t = 0$, since

$$\lim_{t \to 0^+} \frac{3t^2 - 4}{4t} = \frac{-4}{+0} = -\infty \quad \text{and} \quad \lim_{t \to 0^-} \frac{3t^2 - 4}{4t} = \frac{-4}{-0} = \infty$$

So the tangent line is vertical when $t = 0$, which is the point $P(0) = (-2, 0)$ on the curve.

Part (d): Note that $P(-2) = (6, 0) = P(2)$, so that a particle moving on the curve according to the parametric equations will be at $(6, 0)$ at times $t = -2$ and $t = 2$. The slopes at these times are:

$$\left.\frac{dy}{dx}\right|_{t=-2} = \frac{8}{-8} = -1, \quad \left.\frac{dy}{dx}\right|_{t=2} = \frac{8}{8} = 1$$

and equations for the two tangent lines at the point $(6, 0)$ are $y = -x + 6$ and $y = x - 6$.

Tools for Sketching Curves

Just as we did in Sections 3.1–3.2 for graphs of functions, we can construct, for graphs of general curves, two types of diagrams that describe their behavior and help us more accurately sketch their graphs (with a small selection of plotted points). We begin with:

Slope-Direction Diagrams: As in the last example, we can use the slope function $dy/dx = y'/x'$ to determine the times when the parametrized curve is horizontal and vertical:

$$\frac{dy}{dx} = 0 \quad \text{(horizontal)}, \qquad \frac{dy}{dx} = \pm\infty \quad \text{(vertical)}$$

The vertical equation is more precisely $\lim\limits_{t \to a^+} \frac{dy}{dx} = \pm\infty = \lim\limits_{t \to a^-} \frac{dy}{dx}$. Commonly occurring times for a curve to turn vertical are when $x'(t) = 0$ and $y'(t) \neq 0$.

After determining the times $t = h_1, h_2, \ldots, h_m$ when the curve is horizontal and the times $t = v_1, v_2, \ldots, v_n$, when it is vertical, mark these points on the time axis, using a small disk (dot) for the h_i and a small cross for the v_j. This divides the interval of time into a number of subintervals. For example:

We can choose test times in each subinterval to determine if the slope function is positive at that time or negative. Then draw a small line segment with positive or negative slope above the interval. For example:

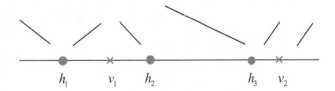

Next use x' to determine the direction a particle with this parametrization would move on the curve: (1) $x' > 0$ indicates rightward motion and (2) $x' < 0$ indicates leftward motion. Record this on the line segments you drew above by placing an arrow-head on the segment: on right end if $x' > 0$ or on the left end if $x' < 0$.

Also determine all the times $t_1, t_2, \ldots, t_p$, when $x'(t) = 0$ and x' changes sign at t. These are known as *turn-around times*, indicating a change of direction. Mark these times on the time line using small circles. This gives the final slope-direction diagram, which could look like the following diagram:

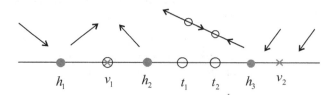

NOTE: Between two successive times when the curve is horizontal (or vertical) there may be several turn-around times. This indicates a *retracing* of the curve by the particle motion. In the diagram above there are two turn-around times between the horizontal times h_2, h_3 and so we have marked the slope segment over the interval (h_2, h_3) with two additional arrow heads.

Having constructed the slope-direction diagram, you can draw (without plotting points) a preliminary sketch of the curve as follows. Pick an arbitrary starting point P and, going from left-to-right on the time line in the diagram, draw curved lines following the slopes and directions between where the curve turns horizontal or vertical. For the above diagram this will give something like the following picture:

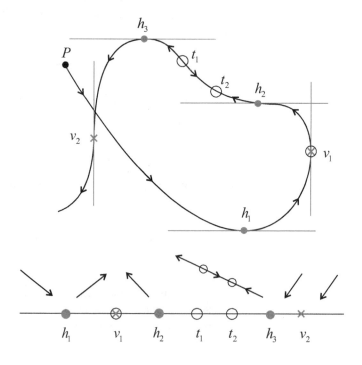

Figure 9.2.3: *A curve and its slope-direction diagram.*

Example 9.2.2

Problem: For the curve with parametric equations

$$x = t^2, \quad y = t^5 - 3t^3 + 2t,$$

construct a slope-direction diagram and sketch a rough graph of the curve, showing directions and horizontal/vertical tangent lines.

Solution: The derivatives are

$$x' = 2t, \qquad y' = 5t^4 - 9t^2 + 2$$

and the slope function is

$$\frac{dy}{dx} = \frac{y'}{x'} = \frac{5t^4 - 9t^2 + 2}{2t}$$

The numerator of dy/dx is zero when $5t^4 - 9t^2 + 2 = 0$. Letting $s = t^2$, we get a quadratic equation $5s^2 - 9s + 2 = 0$ for s. Using the quadratic formula on this yields

$$t^2 = s = \frac{9 \pm \sqrt{41}}{10}, \quad \text{and so} \quad t = \pm\sqrt{\frac{9 \pm \sqrt{41}}{10}} \approx \pm 0.51, \pm 1.24$$

The denominator of dy/dx is zero for $t = 0$. In summary:

Horizontal Times: $t \approx -0.124, -0.51, 0.51, 1.24$

Vertical Times: $t = 0$.

This divides the time line into six intervals: $(-\infty, -1.24), (-1.24, -.51), (-.51, 0),$ $(0, 0.51), (.51, 1.24), (1.24, \infty)$ shown in the margin. As indicated, we choose test times $t = -2, -1, -0.25, 0.25, 1, 2$, respectively, in these intervals and evaluate dy/dx at these times:

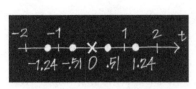

t	-2	-1	$-.25$	$.25$	1	2
$\frac{dy}{dx}$	-11.5	1	-2.9	2.9	-1	11.5
$\pm$	$-$	$+$	$-$	$+$	$-$	$+$

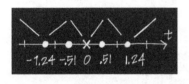

The actual values of dy/dx in the table are not important, but the signs (negative, positive) are. Using this we draw line segments with negative/positive slopes to get the diagram shown in the margin.

Recognizing that $x' = 2t = 0$ only for $t = 0$, that $x' < 0$ for negative times, and that $x' > 0$ for positive times, we see the motion on the curve is leftward initially, turns around at time $t = 0$, where the curve is vertical, and then moves rightward. Using all of this information, we draw the final slope-direction diagram and sketch the curve as shown in Figure 9.2.4. NOTE: The point P chosen as the starting point for the sketch is arbitrary. The sketch is only a rough indication of what the curve looks like and can be used in doing a more accurate sketch by plotting exact points on the curve.

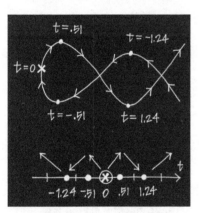

Figure 9.2.4: *A slope-direction diagram and sketch of the curve.*

Example 9.2.3 (A Retraced Curve)

Problem: For the curve with parametric equations

$$x = 2t^2 - 2, \qquad y = t^4 - 4t^2,$$

construct a slope-direction diagram and sketch a rough graph of the curve, showing directions and horizontal/vertical tangent lines. Also eliminate the parameter and find a Cartesian equation for the curve on which the motion takes place.

Solution: The derivatives are

$$x' = 4t, \qquad y' = 4t^3 - 8t = 4t(t^2 - 2)$$

and the slope function is

$$\frac{dy}{dx} = \frac{y'}{x'} = \frac{4t(t^2 - 2)}{4t} = t^2 - 2$$

Thus, dy/dx is zero when $t^2 - 2 = 0$, which gives $x = \pm\sqrt{2} \approx \pm 1.4$. These, then are the times when the slope is horizontal. There are no times when the curve is vertical. As with the last example, $x' = 4t = 0$ gives $t = 0$ as the only turn-around time. In the intervals $(-\infty, -\sqrt{2}), (-\sqrt{2}, \sqrt{2}), (\sqrt{2}, \infty)$, we choose test times $t = -2, 0, 2$, and evaluate dy/dx at these times to get

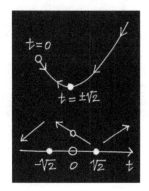

Figure 9.2.5: *A slope-direction diagram and sketch of the curve.*

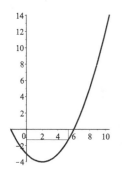

Figure 9.2.6: *A frame in the* dcurve *movie.*

t	-2	0	2
$\frac{dy}{dx}$	2	-2	2
$\pm$	$+$	$-$	$+$

Thus, the slopes alternate from positive to negative to positive. However, there is a turn-around time $t = 0$ in the middle interval $(-\sqrt{2}, \sqrt{2})$, which means the curve is being retraced during these times. The slope-direction diagram and a sketch of the curve is shown in Figure 9.2.5.

Whenever there is a retrace on a curve, it is instructive to do a dynamic plot of the curve using the dcurve command:

```
> f:=t->2*t^2-2;g:=t->t^4-4*t^2;
```
$$f := t \to 2t^2 - 2$$
$$g := t \to t^4 - 4t^2$$

```
> dcurve(f,g,-2.5,2,50);
```

This produces the desired movie. Figure 9.2.6 shows the next to the last frame in this movie. You may perhaps discern for this figure that the particle motion given by these parametric equations lies on a parabola. To prove this, we eliminate the parameter t. Take the equation $x = 2t^2 - 2 = 2(t^2 - 1)$ and solve for t^2 to get $t^2 = \frac{x}{2} + 1$. Then take the 2nd parametric equation: $y = t^4 - 4t^2 = t^2(t^2 - 4)$ and substitute in the value of t^2 we just found. This gives

$$y = (\tfrac{x}{2} + 1)(\tfrac{x}{2} - 3) = \tfrac{1}{4}(x+2)(x-6) = \tfrac{1}{4}(x^2 - 4x - 12) = \tfrac{1}{4}(x-2)^2 - 4$$

Thus, this Cartesian equation is for a parabola with vertex $(2, -4)$ and turned upward. This appears to agree with the data exhibited in Figure 9.2.6.

Concavity Diagrams: Using the 2nd derivative

$$\frac{d^2y}{dx^2} = \frac{x'y'' - x''y'}{(x')^3}$$

to draw a concavity diagram is similar to what was done in Section 3.1. We determine the times when $d^2y/dx^2 = 0$ and mark these on the time line. But, we must also take into account the possibility of times when $d^2y/dx^2 = \pm\infty$ and mark these on the time line too.

Example 9.2.4 (Slope-Direction & Concavity Diagrams)

Problem: For the curve with parametric equations

$$x = \sin t, \quad y = \sin t + \cos t,$$

for t in $[0, 2\pi]$, construct slope-direction and concavity diagrams and sketch a rough graph of the curve, showing directions and horizontal/vertical tangent lines. Also eliminate the parameter and find a Cartesian equation for the curve on which the motion takes place.

Solution: The derivatives are

$$x' = \cos t, \quad y' = \cos t - \sin t$$
$$x'' = -\sin t, \quad y'' = -\sin t - \cos t$$

Then the slope function is

$$\frac{dy}{dx} = \frac{y'}{x'} = \frac{\cos t - \sin t}{\cos t}$$

and the concavity function is

$$\frac{d^2y}{dx^2} = \frac{x'y'' - x''y'}{(x')^3} = \frac{\cos t(-\sin t - \cos t) - (-\sin t)(\cos t - \sin t)}{\cos^3 t}$$
$$= \frac{-\cos^2 t - \sin^2 t}{\cos^3 t} = \frac{-1}{\cos^3 t}$$

First consider drawing the slope-direction diagram. Look for times in $[0, 2\pi]$ when $dy/dx = 0$, in this case, when $\cos t - \sin t = 0$ and for times when $dy/dx = \pm\infty$, in this case, when $\cos t = 0$. You should get:

Horizontal Times: $t = \dfrac{\pi}{4}, \dfrac{5\pi}{4}$

Vertical Times: $\dfrac{\pi}{2}, \dfrac{3\pi}{2}$.

NOTE: The vertical times are also the turn-around times. These times divide the time line into five intervals: $(0, \pi/4), (\pi/4, \pi/2), (\pi/2, 5\pi/4), (5\pi/4, 3\pi/2), (3\pi/2, 2\pi)$ shown in the margin. We choose test times $t = \pi/6, \pi/3, \pi, 4\pi/3, 7\pi/4$, respectively, in these intervals and evaluate dy/dx at these times:

t	$\pi/6$	$\pi/3$	π	$4\pi/3$	$7\pi/4$
$\dfrac{dy}{dx}$	$\dfrac{\frac{\sqrt{3}}{2} - \frac{1}{2}}{\frac{\sqrt{3}}{2}}$	$\dfrac{\frac{1}{2} - \frac{\sqrt{3}}{2}}{\frac{1}{2}}$	$\dfrac{-1-0}{-1}$	$\dfrac{-\frac{1}{2} + \frac{\sqrt{3}}{2}}{-\frac{1}{2}}$	$\dfrac{\frac{\sqrt{2}}{2} + \frac{\sqrt{2}}{2}}{\frac{\sqrt{2}}{2}}$
$\pm$	$+$	$-$	$+$	$-$	$+$

From the table we see that the slopes, from left to right, alternate from positive to negative. There are two turn-around times $t = \pi/2, 3\pi/2$ (when $\cos t = 0$), which coincide with the two vertical times. Using all of this allows us to draw the slope-direction diagram and sketch the curve as shown in Figure 9.2.7.

Next we analyze the concavity. We see that

$$\frac{d^2y}{dx^2} = \frac{-1}{\cos^3 t} = \pm\infty \quad \text{for } t = \frac{\pi}{2}, \frac{3\pi}{2}$$

(and that d^2y/dx^2 is never zero). These times, which are also vertical and turn-around times, divide the interval $[0, 2\pi]$ into three subintervals $[0, \pi/2), (\pi/2, 3\pi/2), (3\pi/2, 2\pi]$. Using test time $t = \pi/4, \pi, 7\pi/4$, we get the following values of the 2nd derivative.

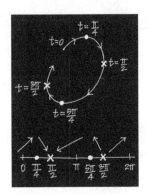

Figure 9.2.7: *A slope-direction diagram and sketch of the curve.*

t	$\pi/4$	π	$7\pi/4$
$\dfrac{d^2y}{dx^2}$	$-\dfrac{4}{\sqrt{2}}$	1	$-\dfrac{4}{\sqrt{2}}$
$\pm$	$-$	$+$	$-$

This gives us the concavity diagram shown in Figure 9.2.8 and verifies the concavity changes at $t = \pi/2, 3\pi/2$ shown in the sketch of the curve in Figure 9.2.7.

To get a Cartesian equation from the parametric equations $x = \sin t$, $y = \sin t + \cos t$, note that $y - x = \cos t$. Thus,

$$x^2 + (y - x)^2 = \sin^2 t + \cos^2 t = 1$$

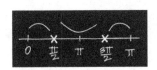

Figure 9.2.8: *A concavity diagram for the curve.*

This equation, or equivalently the equation $2x^2 - 2xy + y^2 = 1$, is a quadratic equation in x and y. In Section 9.6 we will see that any such quadratic equation describes a curve known as a conic section (or a degenerate case). This particular equation describes an ellipse with its major axis rotated.

A dynamic plot of the curve using dcurve is created by the following commands:

```
> f:=t->sin(t);g:=t->sin(t)+cos(t);
```
$$f := t \to \sin(t)$$
$$g := t \to \sin(t) + \cos(t)$$

```
> dcurve(f,g,0,2*Pi,30);
```

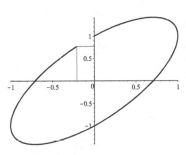

Figure 9.2.9: *Next to the last frame in the movie* dcurve(f,g,0,2*Pi,30).

This produces the desired movie. Figure 9.2.9 shows the next to the last frame in this movie.

xx

Exercises: 9.2 (Parametric Calculus - Derivatives)

Computing Slopes and Tangent Line Equations

In Exercises 1–18, for the curve with the given parametric equations on the given interval $[t_1, t_2]$: (a) Compute the slope function dy/dx and use it to find an equation for the tangent line at the given time t_0. (b) Find all times when the tangent line is horizontal and all times when it is vertical. (c) In 1–6, show that there are two tangent lines to the curve at the given point (x_0, y_0) and find equations for these lines. (d) CAS: Use Maple to plot the curve. Indicate all the information from Parts (a)–(c) on a printout of the plot.

1. $x = t^2$, $y = t(t^2 - 5)$, $[-3, 3]$, 1, $(5, 0)$

2. $x = t^2 - 2$, $y = t(t^2 - 5)$, $[-3, 3]$, 1, $(5, 0)$

3. $x = t^2$, $y = (t - 1)(t^2 - 4)$, $[-3, 3]$, -1, $(4, 0)$

4. $x = t^2 - 2$, $y = (t - 1)(t^2 - 4)$, $[-3, 3]$, -1, $(4, 0)$

5. $x = t^2$, $y = t(t^2 - 2)(t^2 - 3)$, $[-2, 2]$, 1, $(2, 0)$

6. $x = t^2$, $y = t(t^2 - 2)(t^2 - 4)$, $[-2.1, 2.1]$, 1, $(2, 0)$

7. $x = \cos t$, $y = \sin t - \cos t$, $[0, 2\pi]$, $\frac{\pi}{2}$

8. $x = \sin t - \cos t$, $y = \cos t$, $[0, 2\pi]$, $\frac{\pi}{2}$

9. $x = \sin t + \cos t$, $y = \sin t - \cos t$, $[0, 2\pi]$, $\frac{\pi}{2}$

10. $x = \cos t - \sin t$, $y = \cos t + \sin t$, $[0, 2\pi]$, $\frac{\pi}{2}$

11. $x = \sin 2t$, $y = \sin t + \cos t$, $[0, 2\pi]$, $\frac{\pi}{4}$

12. $x = \sin t + \cos t$, $y = \sin 2t$, $[0, 2\pi]$, $\frac{\pi}{4}$

13. $x = \sin 2t$, $y = \frac{1}{4}\cos 2t + \sin t$, $[0, 2\pi]$, 0

14. $x = \sin 2t$, $y = \frac{1}{4}\cos 2t + \cos t$, $[0, 2\pi]$, $\frac{\pi}{2}$

15. $x = \cos t$, $y = \sin t + \cos 2t$, $[0, 2\pi]$, $\frac{\pi}{4}$

16. $x = \sin t + \cos 2t$, $y = \cos t$, $[0, 2\pi]$, $\frac{\pi}{4}$

17. $x = \cos t$, $y = \cos t + \sin 2t$, $[0, 2\pi]$, $\frac{\pi}{4}$

18. $x = -\cos t$, $y = \cos t + \sin 2t$, $[0, 2\pi]$, $\frac{\pi}{4}$

Slope-Direction Diagrams and Sketching

In Exercises 19–36, for the curve with parametric equations, construct a slope-direction diagram and sketch a rough graph of the curve, showing directions and horizontal/vertical tangent lines. Where possible, eliminate the parameter and find a Cartesian equation for the curve on which the motion takes place. You may use the work for the corresponding problem in Exercises 1–18 above.

19. $x = t^2$, $y = t(t^2 - 5)$, $[-3, 3]$
20. $x = t^2 - 2$, $y = t(t^2 - 5)$, $[-3, 3]$

21. $x = t^2$, $y = (t - 1)(t^2 - 4)$, $[-3, 3]$

22. $x = t^2 - 2$, $y = (t - 1)(t^2 - 4)$, $[-3, 3]$

23. $x = t^2$, $y = t(t^2 - 2)(t^2 - 3)$, $[-2, 2]$

24. $x = t^2$, $y = t(t^2 - 2)(t^2 - 4)$, $[-2.1, 2.1]$

25. $x = \cos t$, $y = \sin t - \cos t$, $[0, 2\pi]$

26. $x = \sin t - \cos t$, $y = \cos t$, $[0, 2\pi]$

27. $x = \sin t + \cos t$, $y = \sin t - \cos t$, $[0, 2\pi]$

28. $x = \cos t - \sin t$, $y = \cos t + \sin t$, $[0, 2\pi]$

29. $x = \sin 2t$, $y = \sin t + \cos t$, $[0, 2\pi]$

30. $x = \sin t + \cos t$, $y = \sin 2t$, $[0, 2\pi]$

31. $x = \sin 2t$, $y = \frac{1}{4}\cos 2t + \sin t$, $[0, 2\pi]$

32. $x = \sin 2t$, $y = \frac{1}{4}\cos 2t + \cos t$, $[0, 2\pi]$

33. $x = \cos t$, $y = \sin t + \cos 2t$, $[0, 2\pi]$

34. $x = \sin t + \cos 2t$, $y = \cos t$, $[0, 2\pi]$

35. $x = \cos t$, $y = \cos t + \sin 2t$, $[0, 2\pi]$

36. $x = -\cos t$, $y = \cos t + \sin 2t$, $[0, 2\pi]$

Concavity Diagrams

In Exercises 37–46, for the curve with parametric equations, compute the concavity function d^2y/dx^2 and use it to construct a concavity diagram. If you did a sketch for this curve in Exercises 19–26 above, check that the concavity in the diagram matches that in the sketch.

37. $x = t^2$, $y = t(t^2 - 5)$, $[-3, 3]$

38. $x = t^2 - 2$, $y = t(t^2 - 5)$, $[-3, 3]$

39. $x = t^2$, $y = (t - 1)(t^2 - 4)$, $[-3, 3]$

40. $x = t^2 - 2$, $y = (t - 1)(t^2 - 4)$, $[-3, 3]$

41. $x = t^2$, $y = t(t^2 - 2)(t^2 - 3)$, $[-2, 2]$

42. $x = t^2$, $y = t(t^2 - 2)(t^2 - 4)$, $[-2.1, 2.1]$

43. $x = \cos t$, $y = \sin t - \cos t$, $[0, 2\pi]$

44. $x = \sin t - \cos t$, $y = \cos t$, $[0, 2\pi]$

45. $x = \sin t + \cos t$, $y = \sin t - \cos t$, $[0, 2\pi]$

46. $x = \cos t - \sin t$, $y = \cos t + \sin t$, $[0, 2\pi]$

Calculus Concepts & Computation

⊳ 9.3 Parametric Calculus - Integrals

We have seen in Chapter 5 how to use the definite integral to measure certain quantities connected with a curve C which is a graph of a function $y = f(x)$ on an interval $[a, b]$. In particular, the area A of the region beneath the curve (assuming $f(x) > 0$ on $[a, b]$), the length L of the curve, and the surface area S of the surface obtained by revolving the curve about the x-axis. In this section we extend these calculations to the more general situation where the curve C is given by parametric equations $x = f(t)$, $y = g(t)$.

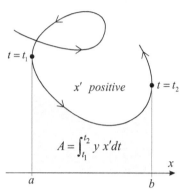

The Area Beneath Part of a Curve

We return to the discussion at the beginning of Section 9.2 concerning eliminating the parameter t in the parametric equations $x = f(t)$, $y = g(t)$. Suppose on a time interval $I = [t_1, t_2]$ that $y = g(t) > 0$ and that $x' = f'(t)$ is either positive (rightward motion) or negative (leftward motion). See Figure 9.3.1.

Then f has an inverse f^{-1} on I and, letting $a = f(t_1), b = f(t_2)$, the domain of f^{-1} is either $J = [a, b]$ (in the $x' > 0$ case) or $J = [b, a]$ (in the $x' < 0$ case) as indicated in Figure 9.3.1. In either case, we can solve, theoretically, the first parametric equation $x = f(t)$ for t to get $t = f^{-1}(x)$ and this will give the function $h(x) = g(f^{-1}(x))$ whose graph on the interval J is the part of the curve C shown in Figure 9.3.1.

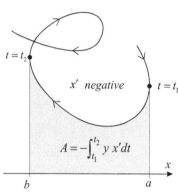

How do we get the area formulas shown for the region beneath this part of the curve? Note how the formulas differ only by a sign: $+$ in the $x' > 0$ case (the yellow region) and $-$ in the $x' < 0$ case (the brown region).

Case 1 $(x' > 0)$: The area beneath the graph of $h(x) = g(f^{-1}(x))$ on $J = [a, b]$ is

$$A = \int_a^b g(f^{-1}(x)) \, dx$$

Figure 9.3.1: *An area beneath a parametric curve.*

To change this into an integral in terms of t we use the substitution (change of variables):

$$t = f^{-1}(x), \quad dt = \frac{1}{f'(f^{-1}(x))} dx = \frac{1}{f'(t)} dx,$$

so that $dx = f'(t)dt$. Also change the limits of integration: when $x = a$ then $t = f^{-1}(a) = t_1$ and when $x = b$ then $t = f^{-1}(b) = t_2$. Thus, the integral in terms of t is

$$A = \int_a^b g(f^{-1}(x)) \, dx = \int_{t_1}^{t_2} g(t) f'(t) \, dt = \int_{t_1}^{t_2} yx' \, dt$$

This gives the area in this case.

Case 2 $(x' < 0)$: The area beneath the graph of $h(x) = g(f^{-1}(x))$ on $J = [b, a]$ is

$$A = \int_b^a g(f^{-1}(x)) \, dx$$

Note that in this case $b < a$ even though $t_1 < t_2$. So, using the same substitution as above we get

$$A = \int_b^a g(f^{-1}(x)) \, dx = \int_{t_2}^{t_1} yx' \, dt = -\int_{t_1}^{t_2} yx' \, dt$$

Thus, the integrals for the area have the same form but differ by a sign. This is summarized in the following box:

PARAMETRIC VERSION of AREA

Suppose $x = f(t)$, $y = g(t)$ *are parametric equations for a plane curve with* f *and* g *having continuous first derivatives. Suppose on the interval* $I = [t_1, t_2]$ *that* $y = g(t) > 0$ *and* $x' = f'(t)$ *is never zero. Then the area of the region beneath the curve is*

$$A = \int_{t_1}^{t_2} y\, x'\, dt \qquad \text{if } x' > 0 \text{ on } I \qquad (9.3.1a)$$

$$A = -\int_{t_1}^{t_2} y\, x'\, dt \qquad \text{if } x' < 0 \text{ on } I \qquad (9.3.1b)$$

COMMENTS: The Formulas 9.3.1a-b are easy enough to use, but you must be careful to discern when the curve is moving rightward ($x' > 0$) and when it is moving leftward ($x' < 0$). Also, on intervals I when $y = g(t)$ is *not* positive, the formulas give the *net area* A_{net}, not the area, and you can look at subintervals of I to get actual areas (as you have done before in Section 4.3)

Example 9.3.1 (Area Under One Arch of a Cycloid)

Problem: Find the area beneath one arch of the cycloid:

$$x = rt - r\sin t, \qquad y = r - r\cos t.$$

Solution:

One arch of the cycloid is swept out for t in $[0, 2\pi]$. Also, since $-1 \le \cos t \le 1$, for all t, it follows that

$$x' = r - r\cos t = r(1 - \cos t) \ge 0,$$

for all t. Thus, the motion is rightward and we can use Formula 9.3.1a to get the area:

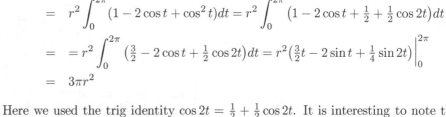

$$A = \int_{t_1}^{t_2} x' y\, dt = \int_0^{2\pi} (r - r\cos t)(r - r\cos t)\, dt = \int_0^{2\pi} r^2(1 - \cos t)^2 dt$$

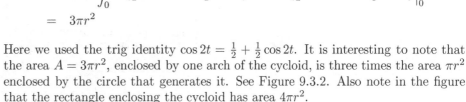

$$= r^2 \int_0^{2\pi} (1 - 2\cos t + \cos^2 t)\, dt = r^2 \int_0^{2\pi} \left(1 - 2\cos t + \tfrac{1}{2} + \tfrac{1}{2}\cos 2t\right) dt$$

$$= r^2 \int_0^{2\pi} \left(\tfrac{3}{2} - 2\cos t + \tfrac{1}{2}\cos 2t\right) dt = r^2 \left(\tfrac{3}{2}t - 2\sin t + \tfrac{1}{4}\sin 2t\right)\Big|_0^{2\pi}$$

$$= 3\pi r^2$$

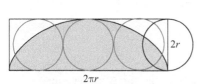

Figure 9.3.2: *One arch of a cycloid bounds an area 3 times that of the circle that generates it.*

Here we used the trig identity $\cos 2t = \tfrac{1}{2} + \tfrac{1}{2}\cos 2t$. It is interesting to note that the area $A = 3\pi r^2$, enclosed by one arch of the cycloid, is three times the area πr^2 enclosed by the circle that generates it. See Figure 9.3.2. Also note in the figure that the rectangle enclosing the cycloid has area $4\pi r^2$.

Example 9.3.2 (Area Enclosed by a Loop)

Problem: Graph the curve with parametric equations:

$$x = t^2, \qquad y = t(t^2 - 4).$$

and find the area enclosed by the loop in the curve.

Solution: Note that because of the form of the parametric equations, for times $\pm t$ the corresponding x-values are the same $x = (\pm t)^2 = t^2$, while the y-values are $y = \pm t((\pm t)^2 - 4) = \pm t(t^2 - 4)$. This means the graph is symmetric with respect to the x axis. Also, times for $t = \pm 2$ the corresponding point is the same: $(4, 0)$.

Figure 9.3.3 shows a graph of the curve for times in $[-3, 3]$. We see that the loop is traced out for t in $[-2, 2]$. The upper part is traced for t in $[-2, 0]$ with a leftward motion $(x' < 0)$, so the area between it and the x-axis is

$$A_1 = -\int_{t_1}^{t_2} x'y\,dt = -\int_{-2}^{0} (t^3 - 4t)(2t)\,dt = \int_{-2}^{0}(8t^2 - 2t^4)\,dt$$

$$= \left(\tfrac{8}{3}t^3 - \tfrac{2}{5}t^5\right)\Big|_{-2}^{0} = \frac{128}{15}$$

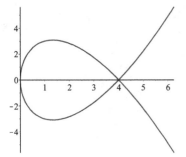

Figure 9.3.3: *The curve in* Example 9.3.2.

Now we could use symmetry and declare that the area A_2 between the x-axis and the lower part of the loop is the same as what we just found $A_2 = A_1$. But let's check this by doing the calculation. The lower part is traced for t in $[0, 2]$ with a rightward motion $(x' > 0)$, but $y < 0$. So the area is

$$A_2 = -\int_{t_1}^{t_2} x'y\,dt = -\int_{0}^{2}(t^3 - 4t)(2t)\,dt = -\int_{0}^{2}(2t^4 - 8t^2)\,dt$$

$$= -\left(\tfrac{2}{5}t^5 - \tfrac{8}{3}t^3\right)\Big|_{0}^{2} = \frac{128}{15}$$

Thus, the area enclosed by the loop is $A_1 + A_2 = \frac{128}{15} + \frac{128}{15} = \frac{256}{15}$.

The Length of a Parametrized Curve

To get a formula for the arc length of a curve given by parametric equations $x = f(t)$, $y = g(t)$ we proceed as we did in getting the area formula. Suppose on a time interval $I = [t_1, t_2]$ that $x' = f'(t)$ is either positive (rightward motion) or negative (leftward motion). Then f has an inverse f^{-1} on I and, letting $a = f(t_1), b = f(t_2)$, the domain of f^{-1} is either $J = [a, b]$ (in the $x' > 0$ case) or $J = [b, a]$ (in the $x' < 0$ case). In either case, we can solve, theoretically, the first parametric equation $x = f(t)$ for t to get $t = f^{-1}(x)$ and this will give the function $y = g(f^{-1}(x))$ whose derivative is

$$\frac{dy}{dx} = \frac{g'}{f'}(f^{-1}(x))$$

See Equation (9.2.2) in the previous section. In the case when $x' > 0$, $J = [a, b]$, the length of the graph of y is

$$L = \int_{a}^{b} \sqrt{1 + \left[\frac{g'}{f'}(f^{-1}(x))\right]^2}\,dx$$

Now on this integral, as we did above, use the substitution $t = f^{-1}(x)$ so that $f'(t)dt = dx$. Also change the limits of integration, and the integral becomes

$$
\begin{aligned}
L &= \int_{a}^{b} \sqrt{1 + \left[\frac{g'}{f'}(f^{-1}(x))\right]^2}\,dx = \int_{t_1}^{t_2} \sqrt{1 + \left[\frac{g'(t)}{f'(t)}\right]^2} \cdot f'(t)\,dt \\
&= \int_{t_1}^{t_2} \sqrt{1 + \frac{[g'(t)]^2}{[f'(t)]^2}} \cdot f'(t)\,dt = \int_{t_1}^{t_2} \sqrt{\frac{[f'(t)]^2 + [g'(t)]^2}{[f'(t)]^2}} \cdot f'(t)\,dt \\
&= \int_{t_1}^{t_2} \frac{\sqrt{[f'(t)]^2 + [g'(t)]^2}}{|f'(t)|} \cdot f'(t)\,dt = \int_{t_1}^{t_2} \sqrt{[f'(t)]^2 + [g'(t)]^2} \cdot \frac{f'(t)}{|f'(t)|}\,dt \\
&= \int_{t_1}^{t_2} \sqrt{[f'(t)]^2 + [g'(t)]^2}\,dt
\end{aligned}
$$

In the last step we used the assumption $x' = f'(t) > 0$ on I to get that $|f'(t)| = f'(t)$.

In the case when $x' = f'(t) < 0$, $J = [b, a]$, the calculations above are much the same, except at the last step we have $|f'(t)| = -f'(t)$ on I.

$$
\begin{aligned}
L &= \int_b^a \sqrt{1 + \left[\frac{g'}{f'}(f^{-1}(x))\right]^2} \, dx = \int_{t_2}^{t_1} \sqrt{1 + \left[\frac{g'(t)}{f'(t)}\right]^2} \cdot f'(t) \, dt \\
&= -\int_{t_1}^{t_2} \sqrt{[f'(t)]^2 + [g'(t)]^2} \cdot \frac{f'(t)}{|f'(t)|} \, dt = -\int_{t_1}^{t_2} \sqrt{[f'(t)]^2 + [g'(t)]^2} \cdot \frac{f'(t)}{-f'(t)} \, dt \\
&= \int_{t_1}^{t_2} \sqrt{[f'(t)]^2 + [g'(t)]^2} \, dt
\end{aligned}
$$

Thus, we see that the arc length formula is the same for the rightward motion case ($x' > 0$) and leftward motion case ($x' < 0$). The following box summarizes the result using the notation $x' = dx/dt$ and $y' = dy/dt$ for $f'(t)$ and $g'(t)$.

PARAMETRIC VERSION of ARC LENGTH

Suppose $x = f(t)$, $y = g(t)$ are parametric equations for a plane curve with f and g having continuous first derivatives. If $x' = f'(t)$ is either positive or or negative on the entire interval $I = (t_1, t_2)$, then the length of the curve traced out over this time interval is

$$
L = \int_{t_1}^{t_2} \sqrt{[x']^2 + [y']^2} \, dt = \int_{t_1}^{t_2} \sqrt{\left[\frac{dx}{dt}\right]^2 + \left[\frac{dy}{dt}\right]^2} \, dt \qquad (9.3.2)
$$

COMMENTS: Sometimes Formula (9.3.2) can be used when there are one or more turn-around times in the interval I. As long as the curve does not retrace part of itself. So, just be careful to analyze (maybe using dcurve) how the curve is being traced.

Example 9.3.3 (Length of a Curve with a Loop)

Problem: Find the length of the curve

$$
x = 4\sqrt{1 + t^2} - 4, \qquad y = \tfrac{4}{3}t^3 - \tan^{-1} t.
$$

for t in $I = [-1, 1]$.

Solution: The derivatives are

$$
x' = \frac{4t}{\sqrt{1 + t^2}}, \qquad y' = 4t^2 - \frac{1}{1 + t^2}
$$

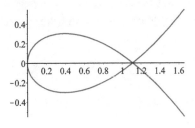

Figure 9.3.4: *The curve in* Example 9.3.3.

There is one turn-around time at time $t = 0$, but the curve is not retraced as seen from the plot in Figure 9.3.4. Alternatively, you can see that $y = g(t) = \tfrac{1}{3}t^3 - \tfrac{1}{4}\tan^{-1} t$ is an odd function: $g(-t) = g(t)$. This means that the part of the curve traced out for t in $[-1, 0]$ is the reflection through the x-axis of the part traced out for t in $[0, 1]$. The calculation of the integrand for the arc length integral goes as follows. First

$$
\begin{aligned}
(x')^2 + (y')^2 &= \frac{16t^2}{1 + t^2} + \left[4t^2 - \frac{1}{1 + t^2}\right]^2 \\
&= \frac{16t^2}{1 + t^2} + 16t^4 - \frac{8t^2}{1 + t^2} + \frac{1}{(1 + t^2)^2}
\end{aligned}
$$

$$= 16t^4 + \frac{8t^2}{1+t^2} + \frac{1}{(1+t^2)^2}$$

$$= \left[4t^2 + \frac{1}{1+t^2}\right]^2$$

Thus, $\sqrt{(x')^2 + (y')^2} = 4t^2 + \frac{1}{1+t^2}$. By the symmetry about the x-axis mentioned above, we get the total length by doubling the integral over $[0, 1]$

$$L = 2\int_0^1 \sqrt{(x')^2 + (y')^2}\, dt = 2\int_0^1 \left[4t^2 + \frac{1}{1+t^2}\right] dt$$

$$= 2\left[\tfrac{4}{3}t^3 + \tan^{-1} t\right]\Big|_0^1 = 2\left[\tfrac{4}{3} + \tfrac{\pi}{4}\right] = \tfrac{16+3\pi}{6} \approx 4.24$$

You can verify, by inspecting Figure 9.3.4, that the length $L \approx 4.24$ appears to be about right.

NOTE: The curve in Example 9.3.3 is one from a special class of parametrized curves that have exactly computable arc lengths. (See the exercises.) The mechanism behind this is that $(x')^2 + (y')^2$ turns out to be a perfect square. By studying the calculation of $(x')^2 + (y')^2$ in the previous example you can see y' is a binomial: $y' = a - b$, such that

$$(x')^2 + (y')^2 = (x')^2 + [a - b]^2 = [a + b]^2$$

The next example works like this too, but is a little bit trickier.

Example 9.3.4 (Length of a Sinusoidal Curve)

Problem: Find the length of the curve

$$x = 4(t - \sin t), \qquad y = \tfrac{5}{2}t + 2\sin t - \tfrac{1}{4}\sin 2t.$$

for t in $I = [0, 4\pi]$.

Solution: A plot of the curve is shown in Figure 9.3.5. The derivatives are

$$x' = 4(1 - \cos t), \qquad y' = \tfrac{5}{2} + 2\cos t - \tfrac{1}{2}\cos 2t$$

There are no turn-around times since $x' = 4(1 - \cos t) \geq 0$ for all times. If you compute $(x')^2 + (y')^2$ directly from the above it is difficult to recognize the result as a perfect square. So, first we rewrite y' as:

$$\begin{aligned}
y' &= \tfrac{5}{2} + 2\cos t - \tfrac{1}{2}\cos 2t = 3 + 2\cos t - (\tfrac{1}{2} + \tfrac{1}{2}\cos 2t) \\
&= 3 + 2\cos t - \cos^2 t = 4 - (1 - 2\cos t + \cos^2 t) \\
&= 4 - (1 - \cos t)^2
\end{aligned}$$

NOTE 1: In the rewrite we used the trig identity: $\tfrac{1}{2} + \tfrac{1}{2}\cos 2t = \cos^2 t$.

NOTE 2: This rewrite of y' also makes it easier to identify when the curve is horizontal and vertical. Namely, since

$$\frac{dy}{dx} = \frac{4 - (1 - \cos t)^2}{4(1 - \cos t)},$$

the curve is horizontal when t is an odd multiple of π and is vertical when t is an even multiple of π. See Figure 9.3.5.

Returning now to the calculation of $(x')^2 + (y')^2$, we find:

$$\begin{aligned}
(x')^2 + (y')^2 &= 16(1 - \cos t)^2 + \left[4 - (1 - \cos t)^2\right]^2 \\
&= 16(1 - \cos t)^2 + 16 - 8(1 - \cos t)^2 + (1 - \cos t)^4 \\
&= 16 + 8(1 - \cos t)^2 + (1 - \cos t)^4 \\
&= \left[4 + (1 - \cos t)^2\right]^2
\end{aligned}$$

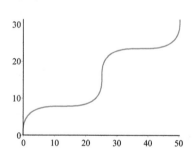

Figure 9.3.5: *The curve in* Example 9.3.4.

With this, the arc length integral is

$$
\begin{aligned}
L &= \int_0^{4\pi} \sqrt{(x')^2 + (y')^2} \, dt = \int_0^{4\pi} \left[4 + (1 - \cos t)^2 \right] \, dt \\
&= \int_0^{4\pi} \left[4 + 1 - 2\cos t + \cos^2 t \right] \, dt = \int_0^{4\pi} \left[5 - 2\cos t + \tfrac{1}{2} + \tfrac{1}{2}\cos 2t \right] \, dt \\
&= \int_0^{4\pi} \left[\tfrac{11}{2} - 2\cos t + \tfrac{1}{2}\cos 2t \right] \, dt = \left[\tfrac{11}{2}t - 2\sin t + \tfrac{1}{4}\sin 2t \right] \Big|_0^{4\pi} = 22\pi
\end{aligned}
$$

The length of the curve, $L = 22\pi \approx 69.12$, appears to agree with what we could estimate from Figure 9.3.5.

Exercises: 9.3 (Parametric Calculus - Integrals)

Areas and Parametrically Defined Curves

In Exercises 1–12, for the curve with the given parametric equations, find the specified area. Use symmetry, where possible, to find half the area and then double it. You will have to determine the times for the integration.

1. $x = t^2 - 2$, $y = t(t^2 - 5)$, $[-3, 3]$, inside loop

2. $x = t^2$, $y = t(t^2 - 5)$ $[-3, 3]$, inside loop

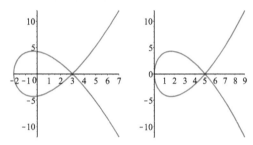

#1   #2

3. $x = t^2$, $y = t(t^2 - 2)(t^2 - 3)$, $[-2, 2]$, inside big loop

4. $x = -\frac{1}{2}t + 1$, $y = t + 2$, $[-2.1, 2.1]$, inside big loop

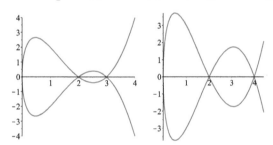

#3   #4

5. $x = t^3$, $y = (t-1)(t-2)(t+3)$, $[-3, 3]$
beneath the curve, in 2nd quadrant

6. $x = t^3$, $y = (t-1)(t-1)(t+2)$, $[-2, 2]$
beneath the curve, in 2nd quadrant

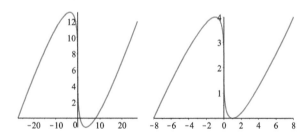

#5   #6

7. $x = \sin t$, $y = \sin 2t + \cos t$, $[0, 2\pi]$, inside big loop

8. $x = -x = \sin t$, $y = \sin 2t + \cos t$, $[0, 2\pi]$,
inside big loop

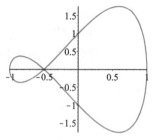 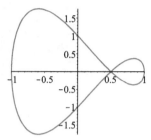

#7   #8

9. $x = \sin t + \frac{1}{4}\cos 2t$, $y = \sin 2t$, $[0, 2\pi]$, inside small loop

10. $x = \sin t - \frac{1}{4}\cos 2t$, $y = \sin 2t$, $[0, 2\pi]$, inside small loop

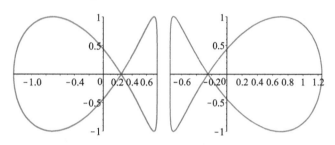

#9   #10

11. $x = t^2$, $y = (t-1)(t^2 - 4)$, $[-2.5, 2.5]$, inside loop

12. $x = -\cos t$, $y = \cos t + \sin 2t$, $[0, 2\pi]$, inside right loop

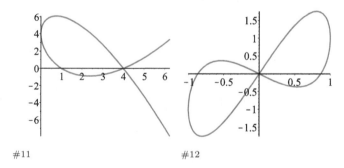

#11   #12

Lengths of Parametrically Defined Curves

In Exercises 13–34, find the length of the curve with the given parametric equations on the specified intervals $[a, b]$.

13. $x = t^2$, $y = t - \frac{1}{3}t^3$, $[0, 2]$

14. $x = t^2$, $y = t^3 - \frac{1}{3}t$, $[0, 2]$

15. $x = t^4$, $y = t^2 - \frac{1}{3}t^6$, $[0, \frac{3}{2}]$

16. $x = t^4$, $y = t^6 - \frac{1}{3}t^2$, $[0, \frac{3}{2}]$

17. $x = t^3$, $y = t - \frac{9}{20}t^5$, $[0, \frac{3}{2}]$

18. $x = t^4$, $y = t^2 - \frac{1}{3}t^6$, $[0, \frac{3}{2}]$

19. $x = \ln t$, $y = t + \frac{1}{4}t^{-1}$, $[1, 2]$

20. $x = \ln t, y = t^2 + \frac{1}{16} t^{-2}$, $[1, 2]$

21. $x = \ln t, y = \sqrt{t} + \frac{1}{\sqrt{t}}$, $[1, 4]$

22. $x = \ln t, y = t^{1/3} + \frac{9}{4} t^{-1/3}$, $[1, 8]$

23. $x = e^t, y = e^{-t} + \frac{1}{12} e^{3t}$, $[0, 1]$

24. $x = e^t, y = e^{3t} + \frac{1}{12} e^{-t}$, $[0, 1]$

25. $x = e^t, y = \ln(1 + e^t) - \frac{1}{4} e^t - \frac{1}{8} e^{2t}$, $[0, 1]$

26. $x = e^{-t}, y = \ln(1 + e^t) + \frac{1}{12} e^{-3t} + \frac{1}{8} e^{-2t}$, $[0, 1]$

27. $x = t - \sin t, y = 1 - \cos t$, $[0, 2\pi]$ (cycloid)

28. $x = t + \sin t, y = 1 - \cos t$, $[0, 2\pi]$ (inverted cycloid)

29. $x = 1 - \cos t, y = t - \frac{1}{8}[t - \frac{1}{2} \sin 2t]$, $[0, 2\pi]$
(smooth cycloid)

30. $x = 1 - \sin t, y = t - \frac{1}{8}[t + \frac{1}{2} \sin 2t]$, $[0, 2\pi]$
(smooth cycloid))

31. $x = t - \frac{1}{4}[t - \frac{1}{2} \cos 2t], y = 1.5 + \sin t - \cos t$, $[0, 2\pi]$
(smooth cycloid)

32. $x = t - \frac{1}{4}[t + \frac{1}{2} \cos 2t], y = 1.5 + \sin t + \cos t$, $[0, 2\pi]$
(smooth cycloid)

33. $x = \sin t - \cos t$
$y = \sin t - \frac{1}{4}[\ln(\sec t + \tan t) - 2\cos t]$, $[0, \pi/3]$

34. $x = \sin t + \cos t$
$y = \cos t - \frac{1}{4}[\ln(\csc t + \cot t) + 2\sin t]$, $[\pi/6, \pi/2]$

35. **(A Special Class of Curves)** Suppose $x = f(t)$ and $G(t)$ are differentiable functions on an interval $I = [a, b]$. Let

$$H(t) = -\frac{1}{4} \int \frac{[x'(t)]^2}{G'(t)} \, dt \qquad (9.3.1x)$$

Consider the curve with parametric equations

$$x = f(t), \ y = G(t) + H(t), \qquad (9.3.2x)$$

for t in $[a, b]$. Show that

$$(x')^2 + (y')^2 = (G' - H')^2 \qquad (9.3.3x)$$

Thus, the parametrization gives a curve whose length is easy to compute.

Calculus Concepts & Computation

9.4 Polar Coordinates

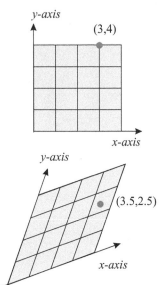

Figure 9.4.1: *Cartesian coordinate systems.*

The Cartesian coordinate system was introduced by Rene Descartes in the 1600s for the purpose of making geometry *analytic*, i.e., making it possible to describe points, curves, and other figures by numbers, symbols, and equations. Descartes coordinate axes were more general than what we do today in that he allowed them to intersect at any angle, rather than just at 90 degrees. This gives a 'slanted' coordinate system. This generality is not as convenient or useful as having axes perpendicular to each other, but illustrates the possibility of setting up other types of coordinate systems on the plane. See Figure 9.4.1.

Another coordinate system for the plane that *is* very useful is the *polar coordinate system*. It works like this. To describe where a point P is relative to the origin O (which is called the *pole*) take the x-axis and rotate it through an angle θ (in radians) so that it goes though the point P. (The rotation angle can be positive or negative and can include multiple full rotations.) Then measure the distance r from the pole O to the point P. This then gives an ordered pair of numbers (r, θ) called *polar coordinates* which determine the position of P. See Figure 9.4.2.

NOTE 1: For technical reasons, we have allowed that the angle of rotation be any angle that places the x-axis on P. Thus, the polar coordinates of a point are not unique.

NOTE 2: Also, we allow the number r to be negative. In this case, to locate the point P with polar coordinates (r, θ), rotate the x-axis through angle θ and then go a distance of $|r|$ in the negative direction along this rotated axis.

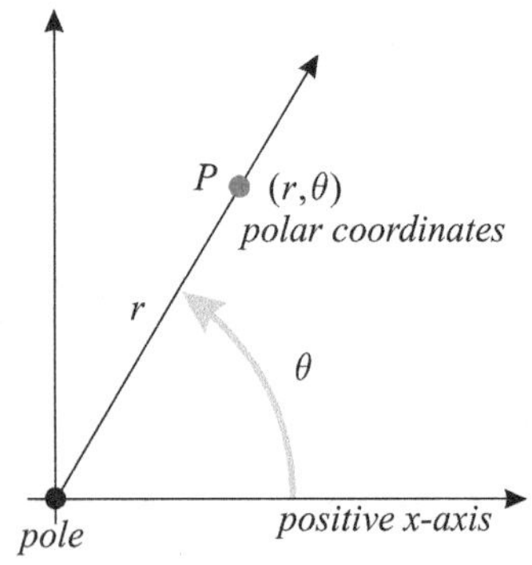

Example 9.4.1

Problem: Plot the points with points with polar coordinates:

$$\left(2, \frac{\pi}{4}\right), \ \left(1, \frac{5\pi}{6}\right), \ \left(-2, -\frac{3\pi}{4}\right), \ \left(1, -\frac{7\pi}{6}\right)$$

Solution: Even though polar coordinates (r, θ) traditionally list r as the first coordinate and θ as the second, you might find it easier to plot $P = (r, \theta)$ by first rotating the x-axis through the angle θ and then going forward/backwards a distance $|r|$ from the pole O to get P. Figure 9.4.3 below shows that the four given polar coordinates above only give two distinct points.

Figure 9.4.2: *polar coordinates of P.*

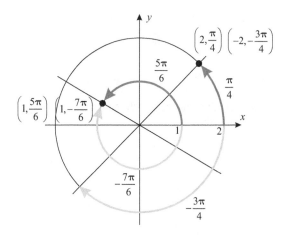

Figure: 9.4.3 *Plotting points with given polar coordinates.*

Polar Coordinate Geometry

In Section 2.10 we studied curves in the plane given by equations such as $H(x,y) = 0$, which now, for the sake of distinction, we will call *Cartesian equations*. Formally speaking, C is the set of all points in the plane whose Cartesian coordinates satisfy $H(x,y) = 0$. This is written as:

$$C = \{\, (x,y) \text{ in } \mathbb{R}^2 \mid H(x,y) = 0 \,\}$$

In Cartesian coordinates, vertical and horizontal lines are called *coordinate lines* and are described by simple equations, such as: $x = \sqrt{3}/2$ and $y = 1/2$. See Figure 9.4.4. Formally speaking, these equations stand for the sets of points:

$$L_1 = \{\, (\tfrac{\sqrt{3}}{2}, y) \mid y \text{ in } \mathbb{R} \,\} \quad \text{and} \quad L_2 = \{\, (x, \tfrac{1}{2}) \mid x \text{ in } \mathbb{R} \,\},$$

respectively. The coordinate lines $x = \frac{\sqrt{3}}{2}$, $y = \frac{1}{2}$ locate a point $P = (\frac{\sqrt{3}}{2}, \frac{1}{2})$ as their point of intersection. Further, the vertical lines $x = 0, \pm 1, \pm 2, \ldots$ and horizontal lines $y = 0, \pm 1, \pm 2, \ldots$ provide a grid on the plane, like a sheet of graph paper. See Figure 9.4.1.

For polar coordinates the situation is entirely analogous. Equations such as $K(r,\theta) = 0$ describe curves C in the plane and these are called *polar equations* for the curves. Now, C is the set of all points in the plane whose polar coordinates satisfy $K(r,\theta) = 0$, i.e.:

$$C = \{\, (r,\theta) \text{ in } \mathbb{R}^2 \mid K(r,\theta) = 0 \,\}$$

In polar coordinates, the *coordinate lines* are circles centered at the origin and straight lines through the origin (called *radial lines*). They are described by the polar equations such as: $r = 1$ and $\theta = \frac{\pi}{6}$. The polar coordinate "lines" $r = 1$, $\theta = \frac{\pi}{6}$ locate a $P = (1, \frac{\pi}{6})$ as their point of intersection. See Figure 9.4.4. Note further that the circles $r = 1, 2, 3, \ldots$ and radial lines $\theta = 0, \pi/6, \pi/4 \ldots$ provide a grid on the plane, which forms the basis for polar coordinate graph paper, which you can buy in the bookstore. See Figure 9.4.5.

Polar coordinate lines are simple to plot, but how do we plots curves with polar equations such as $r = 2\cos 2\theta$? See Figure 9.4.6.

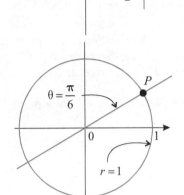

Figure 9.4.4: *Cartesian and polar coordinate lines.*

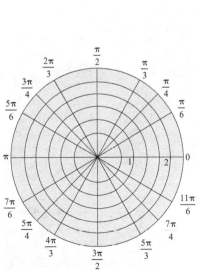

Figure 9.4.5: *Polar coordinate grid.*

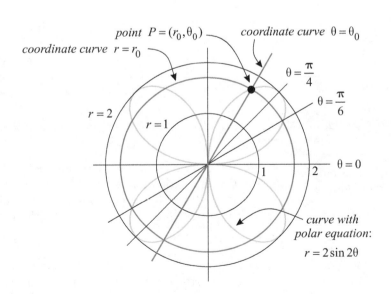

Figure 9.4.6: *Plotting points for the curve $r = 2\cos 2\theta$.*

You can always plot this curve by calculating a number of pairs (r_0, θ_0) which satisfy the polar equation and then plot the corresponding points. Unless you are systematic in plotting the points, it may be confusing how to connect them with a smoothly drawn curve. So, let's develop some methods for understanding and sketching curves given by polar equations $K(r, \theta) = 0$.

Converting Coordinates and Equations

Some well-known curves, such as circles, straight lines, parabolas, have polar equations that are perhaps new to you. But, you can always convert a polar equation to a Cartesian equation and, in the cases where this gives the Cartesian equation for a well-known curve, you can identify and sketch it.

Converting Polar Equations to Cartesian Equations and Vice-Versa

COORDINATE CONVERSIONS
Polar to Cartesian
$x = r\cos\theta$ (9.4.1a)
$y = r\sin\theta$ (9.4.1b)
Cartesian to Polar
$r = \pm\sqrt{x^2 + y^2}$ (9.4.2a)
$\theta = \tan^{-1}\left(\dfrac{y}{x}\right)$ (9.4.2b)

Table 9.4.1: *Formulas for converting coordinates.*

Table 9.4.1 in the margin gives the relationships between Cartesian coordinates and polar coordinates. (See Table 9.4.2 for a derivation of these formulas.) Equations (9.4.1a-b) allow you to convert polar coordinates to Cartesian coordinates, i.e., given the polar coordinates (r, θ) of a point P, then P has Cartesian coordinates given by $x = r\cos\theta$, $y = r\sin\theta$.

Conversely, Equations 9.4.2a-b allow you to find polar coordinates of a point P given its Cartesian coordinates (x, y).

NOTE: To use Formulas 9.4.2a-b proceed as follows:
(1) If $x = 0$, take $\theta = \pi/2$ and $r = y$.
(2) If $x \neq 0$, take $\theta = \tan^{-1}(y/x)$ and choose the plus or minus sign in $r = \pm\sqrt{x^2 + y^2}$ to be plus (+) if $x > 0$ and minus (−), if $x < 0$.

Example 9.4.2 (Converting Coordinates)

Problem: Do the following coordinate conversions.

(a) Convert the polar coordinates $\left(2, \frac{\pi}{4}\right)$, $\left(-2, -\frac{3\pi}{4}\right)$ to Cartesian coordinates.

(b) Convert the Cartesian coordinates $(1, \sqrt{3})$, $(-1, -\sqrt{3})$, $(0, -2), (-2, 0)$ to polar coordinates.

Solution:

Part (a): For $\left(2, \frac{\pi}{4}\right)$ and $\left(-2, -\frac{3\pi}{4}\right)$, the formulas give

$$x = 2\cos(\tfrac{\pi}{4}) = 2(\tfrac{\sqrt{2}}{2}) = \sqrt{2} \;\; \text{and} \;\; y = 2\sin(\tfrac{\pi}{4}) = 2(\tfrac{\sqrt{2}}{2}) = \sqrt{2}$$
$$x = -2\cos(\tfrac{-3\pi}{4}) = -2(-\tfrac{\sqrt{2}}{2}) = \sqrt{2} \;\; \text{and} \;\; y = -2\sin(\tfrac{-3\pi}{4}) = -2(\tfrac{-\sqrt{2}}{2}) = \sqrt{2}$$

So, both polar coordinate pairs refer to the same point, which has Cartesian coordinates $(\sqrt{2}, \sqrt{2})$.

Part (b): For $(1, \sqrt{3})$ and $(-1, -\sqrt{3})$, the formulas give

$$\theta = \tan^{-1}(\tfrac{\sqrt{3}}{1}) = \frac{\pi}{3} \;\; \text{and} \;\; r = \pm\sqrt{(\sqrt{3})^2 + 1^2} = \sqrt{4} = 2$$
$$\theta = \tan^{-1}(\tfrac{-\sqrt{3}}{-1}) = \frac{\pi}{3} \;\; \text{and} \;\; r = \pm\sqrt{(\sqrt{3})^2 + 1^2} = -\sqrt{4} = -2$$

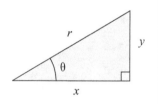

$$\cos\theta = \frac{x}{r} \;\rightarrow\; x = r\cos\theta$$

$$\sin\theta = \frac{y}{r} \;\rightarrow\; y = r\sin\theta$$

$$r^2 = x^2 + y^2 \;\rightarrow\; r = \pm\sqrt{x^2 + y^2}$$

$$\tan\theta = \frac{y}{x} \;\rightarrow\; \theta = \tan^{-1}\left(\frac{y}{x}\right)$$

Table 9.4.2: *Derivation of conversion formulas.*

So, the two points have polar coordinates $(2, \frac{\pi}{3})$ and $(-2, \frac{\pi}{3})$, respectively. For the Cartesian coordinates $(0, -2)$, since $x = 0$, by the note above, $\theta = \pi/2$ and $r = y = -2$, which gives the polar coordinates $(-2, \pi/2)$, For $(-2, 0)$, since $x \neq 0$, take $\theta = \tan^{-1}(\frac{0}{-2}) = \tan^{-1}(0) = 0$. Also, since $x = -2$ we use the (−) to get $r = -\sqrt{(-2)^2 + (0)^2} = -\sqrt{4} = -2$. So the polar coordinates are $(-2, 0)$.

Converting polar *equations* to Cartesian *equations* and vice-versa is slightly different than converting coordinates. The easy direction is converting a Cartesian equation $H(x, y) = 0$ to a polar equation. Substituting in the expressions $x = r\cos\theta$ and $y = \sin\theta$ gives $H(r\cos\theta, r\sin\theta) = 0$.

NOTE: $x^2 + y^2$ is commonly occurring expression in Cartesian equations. It converts to just r^2 in polar coordinates. (Here's why: $x^2 + y^2 = r^2\cos^2\theta + r^2\sin^2\theta =$

$r^2(\cos^2\theta + \sin^2\theta) = r^2(1) = r^2$.) REMEMBER THIS: $r^2 = x^2 + y^2$. For example, the Cartesian equation

$$x(x^2 + y^2)^3 - y = 0$$

converts to

$$r\cos\theta\,(r^2)^3 - r\sin\theta = 0, \text{ i.e., } r^7\cos\theta - r\sin\theta = 0$$

We could do a similar thing to convert a polar equation $K(r,\theta) = 0$ to a Cartesian equation, except that Formula 9.4.2a has a $\pm$ sign in it and Formula 9.4.2b is not usable when $x = 0$. So, we use some standard tricks as exhibited in the next example.

Example 9.4.3 (Converting Polar Equations)

Problem: Convert the following polar equations to Cartesian equation and identify the curve as a standard curve. Also sketch the curve.

(1) $r = 2\sec\theta$ (2) $r = 4\cos\theta$ (3) $r^2\cos\theta\sin\theta = 1$

Solution (1): Since $\sec\theta = 1/\cos\theta$, we rewrite the equations in terms of the cosine:

$$r = \frac{2}{\cos\theta}, \quad \text{equivalently: } r\cos\theta = 2$$

This converts directly to $x = 2$, which is a vertical line through 2 on the x-axis.

Solution (2): The trick here is to multiply both sides of $r = 4\cos\theta$ by r to get:

$$r^2 = 4r\cos\theta, \quad \text{which converts to: } x^2 + y^2 = 4x$$

To identify the curve given by this Cartesian equation, we use the completing-the-square procedure.

$$x^2 + y^2 = 4x \longrightarrow (x-2)^2 + y^2 = 4$$

Thus, the curve is a circle of radius 2 centered at $(2,0)$. Note that this circle is tangent to the y-axis, as shown in Figure 9.4.7.

Solution (3): Even though $r^2 = x^2 + y^2$, we do not use that here. Rather, rewrite the left side as: $r^2\cos\theta\sin\theta = r\cos\theta\, r\sin\theta$. Then the equation is:

$$r\cos\theta\, r\sin\theta = 1, \quad \text{which converts to: } xy = 1$$

The Cartesian equation can be written as $y = \frac{1}{x}$, which is the equation for the graph of the reciprocal function. See Figure 9.4.7.

In the last example, the first two polar equations, $r = 2\sec\theta$ and $r = 4\cos\theta$, are of the special form $r = f(\theta)$, where f is some function. As we shall see, many important curves have such polar equations and there is a special sketching technique for curves described like this. Additionally, as shown in Section 9.5, the calculus is easily applied to such curves.

Also, there are special-purpose Maple procedures that we have written for curves with polar equations $r = f(\theta)$. These are

     `polarcurve(f,a,b)` and `dpolarcurve(f,a,b,N)`

The second one is a dynamic version of the first one and creates a movie that displays the way curve $r = f(\theta)$ is traced out as θ varies. The following code creates such movies for the curves $r = 2\sec\theta$ (a straight line) and $r = 4\cos\theta$ (a circle) in the previous example.

```
> f:=t->2/cos(t);
> dpolarcurve(f,-Pi/3,Pi/3,50);
> f:=t->4*cos(t);
> dpolarcurve(f,0,Pi,50);
```

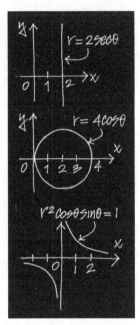

Figure 9.4.7: *Sketches for Parts (1),(2),(3) in Example 9.4.3.*

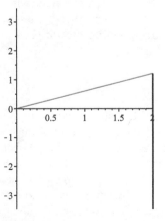

Figure 9.4.8: *The 40th frame in a dynamic plot of $r = 2\sec\theta$.*

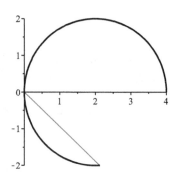

Figure 9.4.9: *The 40th frame in a dynamic plot of* $r = 4\cos\theta$.

You should view these movies because they will help you understand the sketching technique discussed below. Figures 9.4.7-9.4.8 show the 40th frame in these movies.

Sketching Curves in Polar Coordinates

One of the principal reasons for using polar coordinates is that certain curves are easier to describe, sketch, and understand in terms of their polar equations. Also, a polar equation $K(r,\theta) = 0$ for a curve C is often simpler in form than the corresponding Cartesian equation $H(x,y) = 0$ for C. For example the curve in Figure 9.4.6 has polar equation and Cartesian equation given by

$$r = 2\sin 2\theta, \quad (x^2 + y^2)^{3/2} = 4xy,$$

respectively. Here, not only is the polar equation simpler looking, but also it is much simpler to use in sketching the curve. We will do this below after doing some simpler examples first.

A Sketching Technique

As you have seen, when plotting points (r,θ) in polar coordinates it is best to think of first turning the x-axis through the angle θ and then going forward/backward along this rotated axis a distance $|r|$ to locate the point (r,θ).

When the points you want to plot come from a polar equation $K(r,\theta) = 0$, it is helpful to first solve this equation (if possible) for r to get a polar equation of the form $r = f(\theta)$. Then you can easily generate a table of θ-r values by choosing a sequence of values for θ and computing the corresponding values $r = f(\theta)$ for r. Start with $\theta = 0$ and proceed through the standard positive angles:

$$\theta = 0, \frac{\pi}{6}, \frac{\pi}{4}, \frac{\pi}{3}, \frac{\pi}{2}, \frac{2\pi}{3}, \frac{3\pi}{4}, \frac{5\pi}{6}, \pi, \frac{7\pi}{6}, \frac{5\pi}{4}, \frac{4\pi}{3}, \frac{3\pi}{2}, \frac{5\pi}{3}, \frac{7\pi}{4}, \frac{11\pi}{6}, 2\pi$$

and compute the corresponding radii $r = f(\theta)$. (In some cases you can get by with using fewer angles.) To plot the resulting points, think about how the radius r varies as you rotate the x-axis through the angles $\theta = 0, \frac{\pi}{6}, \frac{\pi}{4}, \frac{\pi}{3}, \frac{\pi}{2}, \ldots$ This variation in the radii is exhibited in a `dpolarcurve`, such as the one above for $r = 2\cos\theta$. To aid in seeing how the radius r varies with θ we can use an *auxiliary graph*.

Auxiliary Graphs: Take the function f and plot it as you would any function, with θ as the independent variable and r as the dependent variable. As usual, make a table of θ and r values (as we just discussed) and plot these with the θ axis horizontal and the r-axis vertical (perpendicular to the θ-axis).

The upper part of Figure 9.4.9 exhibits the graph of a function f that is nonnegative on the interval $[0, \pi]$. The graph shows how the radius $r = f(\theta)$ varies, increasing from $r = r_1$ at $\theta = 0$ to a maximum values of r_3, after which it decreases, becoming zero at $\theta = \pi$. In the graph of f the vertical red lines with lengths r_1, r_2, r_3, r_4, r_5, become radial lines in the corresponding plot of the polar curve, which is shown in the lower part of Figure 9.4.9.

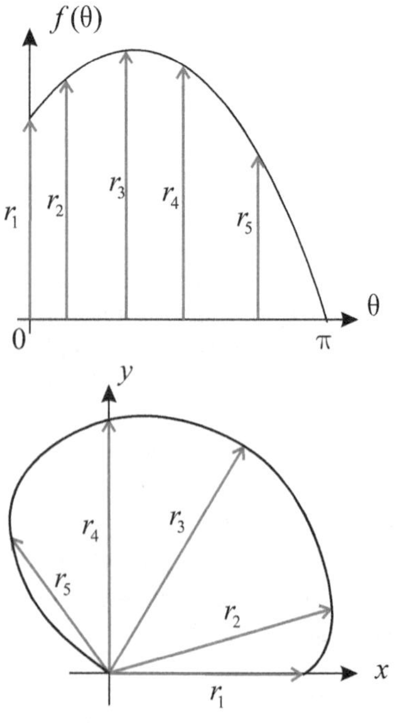

Example 9.4.4 (Parabolic Spiral)

Problem: Sketch the curve with polar equation $r = \sqrt{\theta}$

Solution: The auxiliary graph is just the graph of the standard square root function: $f(\theta) = \sqrt{\theta}$. A sketch of it is shown in Figure 9.4.10. Note that θ must be nonnegative and that as θ increases, r increases. This is typical of a spiral. A sketch of the polar curve is shown in Figure 9.4.10. Note that since the auxiliary graph is very simple, we can use just the angles $\theta = 0, \frac{\pi}{2}, \pi, \frac{3\pi}{2}, 2\pi$ when doing the polar plot. This is part of the value of the auxiliary graph: It tells you what to expect in the polar plot. As we did in the last example, it is instructive to view the movie of the curve being drawn dynamically:

```
> f:=t->sqrt(t);
> dpolarcurve(f,0,2*Pi,50);
```

Figure 9.4.10: *An auxiliary graph used for plotting a curve with polar equation* $r = f(\theta)$.

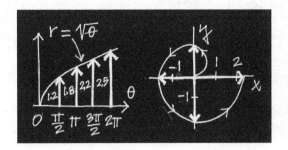

Figure 9.4.11: *Sketch of the parabolic spiral $r = \sqrt{\theta}$.*

Example 9.4.5 (A Two-Loop Polar Curve)

Problem: Sketch the curve with polar equation $r = 2\sin^2\theta$. Also, convert this polar equation to a Cartesian equation.

Solution: To do the auxiliary plot, first use the trig identity $\sin^2\theta = \frac{1}{2} - \frac{1}{2}\cos 2\theta$ to rewrite f as follows:

$$f(\theta) = 2\sin^2\theta = 2(\tfrac{1}{2} - \tfrac{1}{2}\cos 2\theta) = 1 - \cos 2\theta$$

This last expression for f will be easier to work with. The graph of f can be obtained as follows as follows. Sketch the cosine wave: $g(\theta) = \cos 2\theta$ through one period (which is $\frac{2\pi}{2} = \pi$). Flip this graph over to get the graph of $-g(\theta)$. Then translate this up 1 unit to get the graph of $f(\theta)$ shown in Figure 9.4.12.

Using this we see that the radius r varies from $r = 0$ initially, increasing to a maximum value of $r = 2$ when $\theta = \frac{\pi}{2}$, and then it decreases until $r = 0$ when $\theta = \pi$. Thus, we get the top loop of the curve as shown in Figure 9.4.13. The bottom loop is traced out as θ varies through one more period of f, i..e., through $[\pi, 2\pi]$. This gives the complete polar curve, which keeps being retraced as θ varies through further intervals of length 2π.

To convert the polar equation $r = 2\sin^2\theta$ to a Cartesian equation, we multiply both sides by r^2 to get

$$r^3 = 2r^2\sin^2\theta, \quad \text{which converts to} \quad (x^2 + y^2)^{3/2} = 2y^2$$

Note that the original equation $r = 2\sin^2\theta$ requires that $r = \pm\sqrt{x^2 + y^2}$ be nonnegative, so we chose the plus (+) sign. Again, it is instructive to view the movie of the curve being drawn dynamically as follows. (See Figure 9.4.14.)

```
> f:=t->2*(sin(t))^2;
> dpolarcurve(f,0,2*Pi,50);
```

Rose Curves

The curve shown in Figure 9.4.6 with polar equation $r = 2\sin 2\theta$ is an example of what are called *rose curves*. Before discussing rose curves in general, let's sketch this one using the auxiliary graph technique.

Example 9.4.6 (A Rose Curve with Four Petals)

Problem: Sketch the curve with polar equation $r = 2\sin 2\theta$.

Solution: The auxiliary graph is the graph of the sine wave: $f(\theta) = 2\sin 2\theta$, which has amplitude 2 and period $\frac{2\pi}{2} = \pi$. A sketch of f on its basic period is shown in Figure 9.4.15. We see from this that the radius increases from $r = 0$ at $\theta = 0$ to a maximum of $r = 2$ at $\frac{\pi}{4}$ before decreasing back to $r = 0$ at $\frac{\pi}{2}$. This creates one loop, i.e., one petal, of this rose curve. As θ goes from $\frac{\pi}{2}$ to π a second petal of the rose is traced out. See Figure 9.4.16. NOTE: The two petals correspond the to the

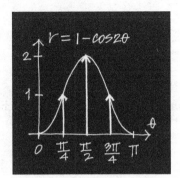

Figure 9.4.12:
An auxiliary graph.

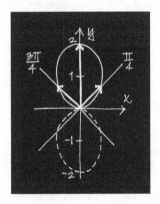

Figure 9.4.13:
The curve with polar equation $r = 2\sin^2\theta$ $= 1 - \cos 2\theta$.

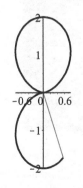

Figure 9.4.14

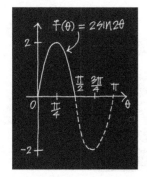

Figure 9.4.15:
An auxiliary graph.

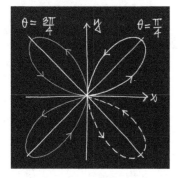

Figure 9.4.16:
Graph of $r = 2\sin 2\theta$.

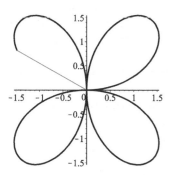

Figure 9.4.17: *A dynamic plot of $r = 2\sin 2\theta$.*

two "humps" in the graph f, the parts of the graph above and below the horizontal θ-axis.

The graph of f on the interval $[\pi, 2\pi]$ corresponds to the final two petals in this 4-petal rose. A movie of the curve being drawn dynamically is create by the following code. (See Figure 9.4.17.)

```
> f:=t->2sin(2*t);
> dpolarcurve(f,0,2*Pi,50);
```

Polar Equations for Rose Curves

There are two types of polar equations that give rose curves. They are

$$r = a\sin n\theta \quad \text{and} \quad r = a\cos n\theta$$

Here $a > 0$ determines the "length" of each petal and n is a positive integer which determines the number of petals: When n is odd there are n petals, but when n is even there are $2n$ petals. (As we just saw $r = 2\sin 2\theta$ gives a rose curve with 4 petals.) Table 9.4.3 on page 608 displays the rose curves for $n = 2, 3, 4$.

Note that the rose curve you get by using the cosine function is just a rotation of the corresponding one for the sine function. Also there are formulas for determining how the petals are arranged (located). See the Exercises for these things. You can use these generalities to guide your sketching of rose curves if you wish. But, as a bare minimum, you should (1) know how many petals to expect and (2) sketch the auxiliary graph (which will indicate where the petals are located).

Example 9.4.7 (A Rose Curve with Three Petals)

Problem: Sketch the curve with polar equation $r = \cos 3\theta$.

Solution: The auxiliary graph is the graph of the cosine wave: $f(\theta) = \cos 3\theta$, which has amplitude 1 and period $\frac{2\pi}{3}$. A sketch of f on its basic period is shown in Figure 9.4.18. We see from this that the three petals are located symmetrically about the lines $\theta = 0$, $\theta = \frac{\pi}{3}$, and $\theta = \frac{2\pi}{3}$. Draw these lines in to prepare for the sketch of the curve. The *petal points*, which are the points on the petals at a distance 1 from the origin, also can be determined from looking at the auxiliary graph. They are the points with polar coordinates $(1, 0)$, $(-1, \frac{\pi}{3})$, and $(1, \frac{2\pi}{3})$. Mark these points on the three lines you just drew. This, then, should be sufficient for you to do a rough sketch of the curve $r = \cos 3\theta$. See Figure 9.4.18.

It is also important to know how the curve is traced out as θ varies through one period, i.e., from $\theta = 0$ to $\theta = \frac{2\pi}{3}$. The sketch in Figure 9.4.17. indicates that, in this example, 2/3 of the curve is traced out during this variation in θ. To get the other 1/3 (the curve shown with dashed lines) you must take θ though another 1/3 of the period (from $\theta = \frac{2\pi}{3}$ to $\theta = \pi$).

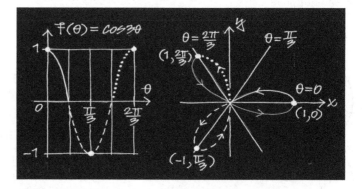

Figure 9.4.18: *An auxiliary graph and sketch of $r = \cos 3\theta$.*

Also shown in Figure 9.4.18 is the direction in which the curve is traced out. You are expected to mark your sketch with direction arrows like those shown. Of course, a dynamic plot of the curve helps you understand this better:

```
> f:=t->cos(3*t);
> dpolarcurve(f,0,Pi,60);
```

See Figure 9.4.19 for a picture of the next to the last frame in this movie.

Limaçons

In addition to the rose curves, which are important for us, there are curves are called limaçons, named after a small snail-like mollusk of Latin genus *limax*. These curves, like the rose curves, have polar equations involving either a cosine or a sine:

$$r = a + b\cos\theta \quad \text{and} \quad r = a + b\sin\theta$$

The constants a and b determine the shape of the limaçon. For $a > b$, the curve is oval in shape. For $a = b$, the curve looks somewhat like a heart and is therefore called a *cardioid*. For $a < b$, the curve has an inner loop. These three cases are displayed in Table 9.4.4 (page 609), which you should study as an aid to identifying and sketching limaçons. Generally, you can sketch a limaçon curve directly, without using an auxiliary graph. Just plot the four or five points (r, θ), with $\theta = 0, \pi/2, \pi, 3\pi/2$, as indicated on the curves in Table 9.4.4 on page 609.

Example 9.4.8 (A Cardioid)

Problem: Sketch the curve with polar equation $r = 1 + \cos\theta$.

Solution: Since $a = 1 = b$, the curve is a cardioid. For $\theta = 0, \pi/2, \pi, 3\pi/2$, the corresponding values of the radius are $r = 2, 1, 0, 1$. A quick sketch is shown in Figure 9.4.20. Of course, a dynamic plot of the curve helps you understand this better:

```
> f:=t->1+cos(t);
> dpolarcurve(f,0,2*Pi,50);
```

See Figure 9.4.21 for a picture of the next to the last frame in this movie.

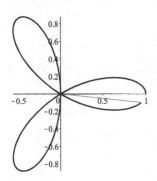

Figure 9.4.19: *59th frame in a dynamic plot of $r = \cos 3\theta$.*

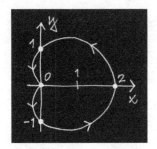

Figure 9.4.20: *A sketch of the cardioid $r = 1 + \cos\theta$*

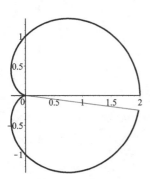

Figure 9.4.21: *49th frame in a dynamic plot of $r = 1 + \cos\theta$.*

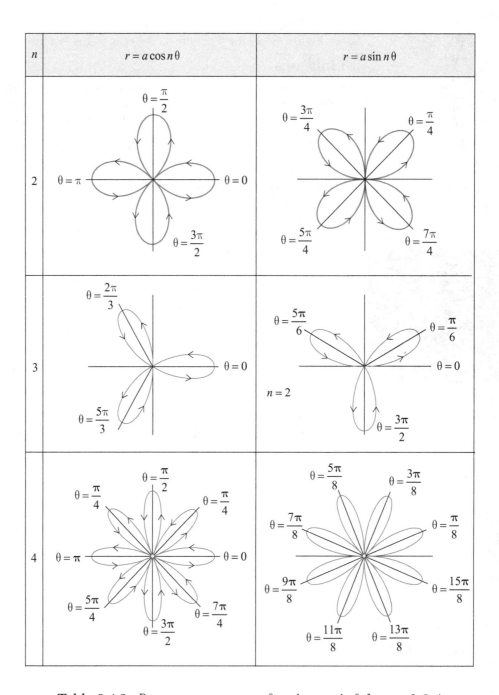

Table 9.4.3: *Rose curves $r = a \cos n\theta$ and $r = a \sin \theta$ for $n = 2, 3, 4$.*

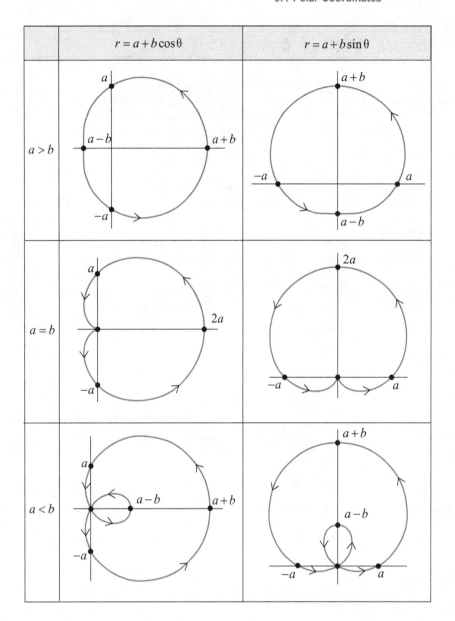

Table 9.4.4: *Limaçons $r = a + b\cos\theta$ and $r = a + b\sin\theta$.*

Exercises: 9.4 (Polar Coordinates)

In Exercises 1–2, convert the given polar coordinates to Cartesian coordinates. Give exact answers.

1. (a) $(2, \pi/6)$ (b) $(2, 13\pi/6)$ (c) $(-2, -5\pi/6)$

2. (a) $(3, 5\pi/3)$ (b) $(3, 7\pi/3)$ (c) $(-3, -4\pi/3)$

In Exercises 3–4, convert the given Cartesian coordinates to to polar coordinates. Give exact answers.

3. (a) $(\sqrt{2}, \sqrt{2})$ (b) $(1, -\sqrt{3})$ (c) $(-2, 0)$

4. (a) $(\sqrt{3}, \sqrt{3})$ (b) $(-\sqrt{3}, 1)$ (c) $(0, -2)$

In Exercises 5–12, sketch the region in the plane described by the given inequalities.

5. $1 \leq r \leq 2$ **6.** $2 \leq r \leq 4$

7. $r \geq 0, \frac{\pi}{6} \leq \theta \leq \frac{\pi}{3}$ **8.** $r \geq 0, \frac{2\pi}{3} \leq \theta \leq \frac{5\pi}{6}$

9. $\frac{\pi}{6} \leq \theta \leq \frac{\pi}{3}$ **10.** $\frac{2\pi}{3} \leq \theta \leq \frac{5\pi}{6}$

11. $1 \leq r \leq 2, 0 \leq \theta \leq \frac{\pi}{3}$ **12.** $2 \leq r \leq 4, \frac{\pi}{6} \leq \theta \leq \frac{\pi}{3}$

In Exercises 13–26, convert the polar equation to a Cartesian equation. Use the Cartesian equation to identify and sketch the curve. Mark the direction on the curve.

13. $r = 3 \csc \theta$ **14.** $r = -3 \sec \theta$

15. $r = 2 \sin \theta$ **16.** $r = -6 \cos \theta$

17. $r = -4 \cos \theta$ **18.** $r = -4 \sin \theta$

19. $r = 4 \cos \theta + 2 \sin \theta$ **20.** $r = 2 \cos \theta - 6 \sin \theta$

21. $r = \tan \theta \sec \theta$ **22.** $r = \cot \theta \csc \theta$

23. $r \sin^2 \theta = 4 \sin \theta + 2 \cos \theta$

24. $r \cos^2 \theta = 2 \sin \theta + 4 \cos \theta$

25. $r^3 \cos^2 \theta \sin \theta = 1$ **26.** $r^3 \sin^2 \theta \cos \theta = 1$

In Exercises 27–34, convert the Cartesian equation to a polar equation.

27. $y = 1$ **28.** $y = -1$

29. $x^2 + y^2 = 4$ **30.** $x^2 + y^2 = 9$

31. $(x - 2)^2 + y^2 = 4$ **32.** $x^2 + (y - 4)^2 = 16$

33. $y + 1 = (x - 1)^2$ **34.** $x + 4 = (y - 2)^2$

In Exercises 35–40, a sketch of an auxiliary graph for a polar curve $r = f(\theta)$ is given. Use this to sketch the graph of the polar curve.

35.
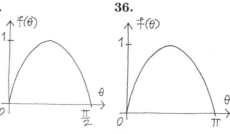

36.

37.
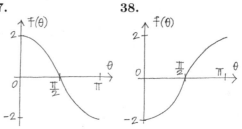

38.

39.
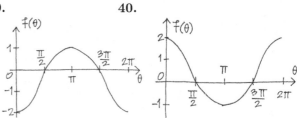

40.

In Exercises 41–58, for the curve with polar equation $r = f(\theta)$, (a) Sketch the graph of the curve, using a sketch of the auxiliary curve if necessary. Mark, with arrows, the direction that the curve is swept out as θ increases. (b) **CAS:** Use `dpolarplot` to check your work.

41. $r = \theta^{1/4}, [0, 2\pi]$ **42.** $r = \theta^{1/3}, [0, 2\pi]$

43. $r = 2 \cos^2 \theta, [0, 2\pi]$ **44.** $r = 3 \sin 2\theta, [0, \pi]$

45. $r = 2 \cos 2\theta, [0, 2\pi]$ **46.** $r = 4 \sin 2\theta, [0, 2\pi]$

47. $r = \sin 3\theta, [0, \pi]$ **48.** $r = 2 \cos 3\theta, [0, \pi]$

49. $r = 2 \sin 4\theta, [0, 2\pi]$ **50.** $r = 3 \cos 4\theta, [0, 2\pi]$

51. $r = 1 + \sin \theta, [0, 2\pi]$ **52.** $r = 2 + 2 \cos \theta, [0, 2\pi]$

53. $r = 1 + 2 \cos \theta, [0, 2\pi]$ **54.** $r = 1 - 2 \sin \theta, [0, 2\pi]$

55. $r = 1 - 2 \cos \theta, [0, 2\pi]$ **56.** $r = 1 - 2 \sin \theta, [0, 2\pi]$

57. $r = 2 + \cos \theta, [0, 2\pi]$ **58.** $r = 2 + \sin \theta, [0, 2\pi]$

Calculus *Concepts & Computation*

9.5 Polar Coordinate Calculus

A curve given by a polar equation of the form $r = f(\theta)$ can be easily parametrized using θ as the parameter. Perhaps you noticed this when sketching polar curves and viewing the dynamic plots of them created by `dpolarcurve` in Section 9.4. To get the parametrization, use the formulas: $x = r\cos\theta$ and $y = r\sin\theta$ that convert from polar to Cartesian coordinates. This gives:

$$x = f(\theta)\cos\theta \quad y = f(\theta)\sin\theta \qquad (9.5.1)$$

All the previous calculus we did with parametrized curves can now be applied to polar curves and we shall see that the formulas for slopes, areas, and lengths will have special forms that depend on $r = f(\theta)$ and its derivative: $r' = f'(\theta)$. For simplicity of notation, we will suppress the f from the notation and write the formulas using r and $r' = \frac{dr}{d\theta}$.

Slopes of Curves Given by Polar Equations

To specialize the slope formula $dy/dx = y'/x'$ to polar curves, start with
$$x = r\cos\theta \quad y = r\sin\theta$$
and differentiate using the product rule:
$$x' = r'\cos\theta - r\sin\theta \quad y' = r'\sin\theta + r\cos\theta \qquad (9.5.2)$$

Thus,

Polar Slope Formula:

$$\frac{dy}{dx} = \frac{r'\sin\theta + r\cos\theta}{r'\cos\theta - r\sin\theta} \qquad (9.5.3)$$

Rather than memorizing this formula, it might best, for a given problem, to just write out $x = f(\theta)\cos\theta$ and $y = f(\theta)\sin\theta$ and then compute x' and y'. After this you can form the ratio y'/x'.

Example 9.5.1

Problem: For the cardioid with polar equation: $r = 1 - \sin\theta$

(a) Find an equation for the tangent line at the point corresponding to $\theta = 0$.

(b) Find all points on the cardioid where the tangent line is either horizontal or vertical.

(c) Sketch the cardioid and the tangent lines in (a) and (b).

Solution: The parametric equations are

$$
\begin{aligned}
x &= (1 - \sin\theta)\cos\theta = \cos\theta - \sin\theta\cos\theta \\
y &= (1 - \sin\theta)\sin\theta = \sin\theta - \sin^2\theta
\end{aligned}
$$

and so

$$
\begin{aligned}
x' &= -\sin\theta - \cos^2\theta + \sin^2\theta & (9.5.4a) \\
y' &= \cos\theta - 2\sin\theta\cos\theta & (9.5.4b)
\end{aligned}
$$

Part (a): From the calculations above, we get

$$x(0) = 1,\ y(0) = 0,\ x'(0) = -1,\ y'(0) = 1$$

So, the tangent line goes through the point $(1, 0)$ and has slope

$$\left.\frac{dy}{dx}\right|_{\theta=0} = \frac{y'(0)}{x'(0)} = \frac{1}{-1} = -1$$

An equation for the tangent line is $y - 0 = -(x - 1)$, which is $y = -x + 1$.

Part (b): It will help if we factor Equations (9.5.4a)–(9.5.4b), using the trig identity $\cos^2 \theta = 1 - \sin^2 \theta$ in the first one. We get

$$x' = -\sin\theta - (1 - \sin^2\theta) + \sin^2\theta = 2\sin^2\theta - \sin\theta - 1 = (2\sin\theta + 1)(\sin\theta - 1)$$

and $y' = \cos\theta - 2\sin\theta\cos\theta = \cos\theta(1 - 2\sin\theta)$. Thus, the slope formula for this cardioid is, in general,

$$\frac{dy}{dx} = \frac{y'}{x'} = \frac{\cos\theta(1 - 2\sin\theta)}{(2\sin\theta + 1)(\sin\theta - 1)}$$

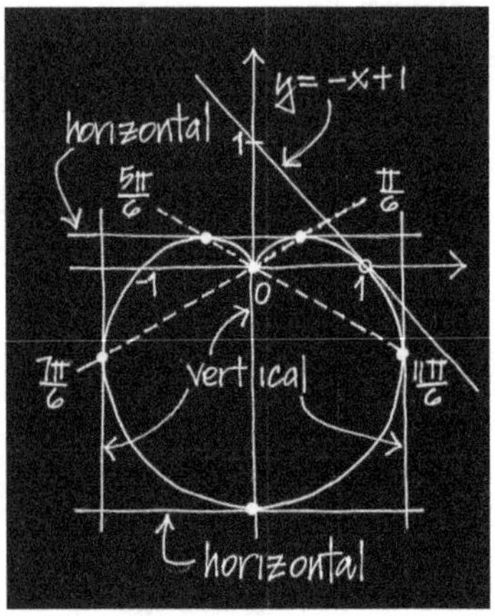

The horizontal tangent lines possibly occur where $\cos\theta(1 - 2\sin\theta) = 0$, which means that either $\cos\theta = 0$ or $\sin\theta = \frac{1}{2}$, These give angles $\frac{\pi}{2}, \frac{3\pi}{2}, \frac{\pi}{6}$, and $\frac{5\pi}{6}$ in the interval $[0, 2\pi]$. The angle $\frac{\pi}{2}$ also makes the denominator 0, so we have an indeterminate form of type $\frac{0}{0}$. Using L'Hospital's rule gives

$$\begin{aligned}
\lim_{\theta \to \pi/2} \frac{dy}{dx} &= \lim_{\theta \to \pi/2} \frac{\cos\theta(1 - 2\sin\theta)}{(2\sin\theta + 1)(\sin\theta - 1)} \\
&\overset{L'Hosp}{=} \lim_{\theta \to \pi/2} \frac{-\sin\theta(1 - 2\sin\theta) - 2\cos^2\theta}{2\cos\theta(\sin\theta - 1) + (2\sin\theta + 1)\cos\theta} \\
&= \frac{-1(1 - 2) - 0}{0 - 0} = \frac{1}{0} = \infty
\end{aligned}$$

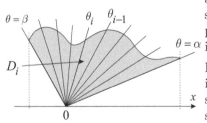

Figure 9.5.1: *Tangents to the cardioid $r = 1 - \sin\theta$.*

This indicates the presence of a vertical tangent line, as we will see in the next paragraph.

The vertical tangent lines possibly occur where $(2\sin\theta + 1)(\sin\theta - 1) = 0$, which means that either $\sin\theta = -\frac{1}{2}$ or $\sin\theta = 1$. These give the angles: $\frac{7\pi}{6}, \frac{11\pi}{6}$, and $\frac{\pi}{2}$ (in the interval $[0, 2\pi]$). The latter of these we found above. A sketch of this cardioid and the tangent lines helps verify our calculations. See Figure 9.5.1.

Areas of Polar Regions

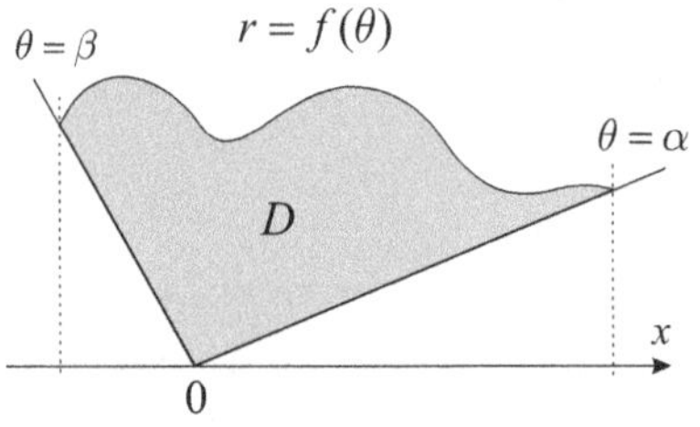

We could use the area formulas $A = \pm \int_{t_1}^{t_2} y\,x'\,dt$ from Formulas (9.3.1a)–(9.3.1b) to measure the area of the region *beneath* the graph of a polar curve $r = f(\theta)$ for θ in $[\alpha, \beta]$ and the x-axis (assuming $f(\theta) \geq 0$). However, for the type of region considered here we need a new integral formula for its area. Such a region, called a *polar region*, consists of all points P whose polar coordinates (r, θ) satisfy the inequalities:

$$0 \leq r \leq f(\theta), \quad \alpha \leq \theta \leq \beta,$$

where we assume that $\alpha \geq 0$ and $\beta \leq \alpha + 2\pi$. See Figure 9.5.2. This is called *the region bounded by the curve $r = f(\theta)$ and the* radial lines $\theta = \alpha$, $\theta = \beta$.

To derive an integral formula for the area of such a region, we use a Riemann sum argument. For a positive integer n, we partition the interval $[\alpha, \beta]$ into n equal subintervals of length $\Delta\theta = (\beta - \alpha)/n$ and let $\theta_i = \alpha + i\Delta\theta$, $i = 1, 2, \ldots, n$ be the partition points. The coordinate lines $\theta = \theta_i$, $i = 1, 2, \ldots, n$ divide the region D into subregions D_i as shown in Figure 9.5.3.

It is natural to approximate each subregion D_i by a sector of a circle. While the indicated D_i in Figure 9.5.3 is not too close to being a sector, several other of those shown are. Further, you can see that for very large n the subregions are very nearly sectors.

Another way to see this is to view a dynamic plot of the polar curve being traced out with the radial lines $\theta = \theta_i$ being retained after appearing in a frame of the movie. The special-purpose Maple procedure `dpolartrace` works like `dpolarcurve`

Figure 9.5.2: *A polar region.*

Figure 9.5.3: *Partitioning D into subregions D_i.*

except that the polar lines are retained. For example, consider the region below the cardioid $r = 1 + \cos\theta$ and above the x-axis. Technically, this is the region

$$0 \leq r \leq 1 + \cos\theta, \quad 0 \leq \theta \leq \pi/2$$

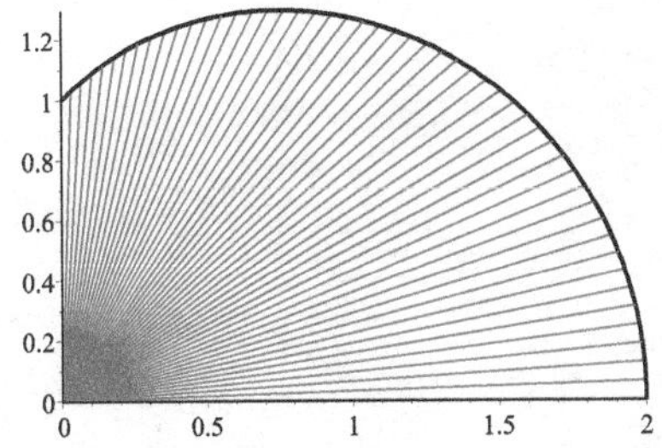

Use the following code

```
> f:=t->1+cos(t);
> dpolartrace(f,0,Pi/2,100);
```

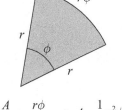

Figure 9.5.4: 50 *subregions of the region* $0 \leq r \leq 1 + \cos\theta,$ $0 \leq \theta \leq \pi/2.$

to produce a movie whose last frame is shown in Figure 9.5.4. As you can see, the 50 subregions D_i are all very nearly circular sectors. You would guess that larger values of n would produce even better results.

So, based on this idea, we approximate each of the subregions D_i shown in Figure 9.5.3 by sectors (using right endpoint). The approximating sectors are shown in Figure 9.5.5.

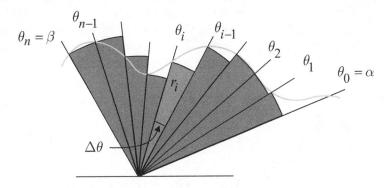

Figure: 9.5.5 *Approximating D with sectors of circles.*

NOTE: The area of a circular sector which has radius r and subtends an angle ϕ is $A = \frac{1}{2}r^2\phi$. The proof of this is indicated in Figure 9.5.6. Using this, we see from Figure 9.5.5 that the area of the sector that approximates subregion D_i is $A_i = \frac{1}{2}r_i^2\Delta\theta$. Adding these up gives the following sectorial approximation to the area of the region D:

$$\frac{A}{\pi r^2} = \frac{r\phi}{2\pi r} \rightarrow A = \frac{1}{2}r^2\phi$$

Figure 9.5.6: *Formula for the area A of a sector.*

$$A \approx \sum_{i=1}^{n} A_i = \sum_{i=1}^{n} \frac{1}{2}r_i^2\Delta\theta$$

Taking the limit yields the integral formula for the area:

AREAS OF POLAR REGIONS

Suppose f is a continuous, nonnegative function on the interval $[\alpha, \beta]$, where $0 \leq \alpha \leq \beta \leq \alpha + 2\pi$. Then the area bounded by the curve with polar equation $r = f(\theta)$ and the radial lines $\theta = \alpha$, $\theta = \beta$ is

$$A = \int_\alpha^\beta \frac{1}{2}r^2 d\theta \qquad (9.5.5)$$

Example 9.5.2 (Areas of Polar Regions)

Problem: Find the areas of the following polar regions.

(a) The region shown in Figure 9.5.4.

(b) The region enclosed by one petal of the rose curve $r = 2\sin 3\theta$.

Solution:

Part (a): After squaring, use the trig identity: $\cos^2 A = \frac{1}{2} + \frac{1}{2}\cos 2A$ to compute the integral:

$$
\begin{aligned}
A &= \int_0^{\pi/2} \frac{1}{2}(1 + \cos\theta)^2\, d\theta = \int_0^{\pi/2} (1 + 2\cos\theta + \cos^2\theta)\, d\theta \\
&= \int_0^{\pi/2} \left(1 + 2\cos\theta + \frac{1}{2} + \frac{1}{2}\cos 2\theta\right) d\theta = \int_0^{\pi/2} \left(\frac{3}{2} + 2\cos\theta + \frac{1}{2}\cos 2\theta\right) d\theta \\
&= \left(\frac{3}{2}\theta + 2\sin\theta + \frac{1}{4}\sin 2\theta\right)\Bigg|_0^{\pi/2} = \frac{3\pi}{4} + 2
\end{aligned}
$$

Part (b): By symmetry we can choose any of the three petals. Note that the first petal, with tip at $\theta = \pi/6$, is traced out as θ goes from 0 to $\pi/3$. Also note that while the radial lines $\theta = 0$, $\theta = \pi/3$ will be the limits of integration in the area integral, these lines do not bound the region. This is because $r = 0$ for each of these angles. After squaring, use the trig identity: $\sin^2 A = \frac{1}{2} - \frac{1}{2}\cos 2A$ to compute the integral:

$$
\begin{aligned}
A &= \int_0^{\pi/3} \frac{1}{2}(2\sin 3\theta)^2\, d\theta = \int_0^{\pi/3} \frac{1}{2}\cdot 4\sin^2 3\theta\, d\theta = 2\int_0^{\pi/3}\left(\frac{1}{2} - \frac{1}{2}\cos 6\theta\right) d\theta \\
&= \int_0^{\pi/3} (1 - \cos 6\theta)\, d\theta = \left(\theta - \frac{1}{6}\sin 6\theta\right)\Bigg|_0^{\pi/3} = \frac{\pi}{3}
\end{aligned}
$$

A More General Polar Region

It is easy to extend the measurement of areas to more general types of polar regions. Suppose f and g are continuous and nonnegative on the interval $[\alpha, \beta]$. Consider a region D consisting of all points P whose polar coordinates (r, θ) satisfy

$$g(\theta) \le r \le f(\theta), \qquad \alpha \le \theta \le \beta,$$

where we assume that $\alpha \ge 0$ and $\beta \le \alpha + 2\pi$. See Figure 9.5.7. This is called *the region bounded by the curves $r = f(\theta)$, $r = g(\theta)$ and* the radial lines $\theta = \alpha$, $\theta = \beta$.

As indicated in Figure 9.5.7, the region D can be viewed as the difference $D = D_1 - D_2$ of two regions D_1, D_2 which have areas A_1, A_2 given by Formula (9.5.5). Thus, the area A of D is

$$A = A_1 - A_2 = \int_\alpha^\beta \frac{1}{2}r_1^2\, d\theta - \int_\alpha^\beta \frac{1}{2}r_2^2\, d\theta = \int_\alpha^\beta \frac{1}{2}\left(r_1^2 - r_2^2\right) d\theta$$

We record this result in the following box.

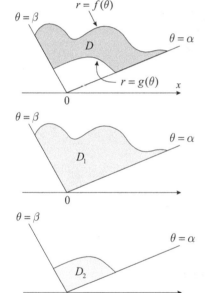

Figure 9.5.7: *A polar region D that is the difference of two polar regions D_1, D_2.*

AREAS OF POLAR REGIONS - PART 2

Suppose f and g are continuous and nonnegative on the interval $[\alpha, \beta]$, where $0 \le \alpha \le \beta \le \alpha + 2\pi$. If $g(\theta) \le f(\theta)$ for all θ in $[\alpha, \beta]$, Then the area bounded by the curves $r_1 = f(\theta)$, $r_2 = g(\theta)$ and the radial lines $\theta = \alpha$, $\theta = \beta$ is

$$A = \int_\alpha^\beta \frac{1}{2}\left(r_1^2 - r_2^2\right) d\theta \qquad (9.5.6)$$

Example 9.5.3 (Areas of Polar Regions - Part 2)

Problem: Find the area enclosed between the two cardioids $r = 1 + \cos\theta$ and $r = 1 + \sin\theta$ for θ in $[0, \pi]$.

Solution: As you can see from a by-hand sketch (Figure 9.5.8) or a computer plot (Figure 9.5.9), these two cardioids change their relative positions from being the outer/inner curve somewhere in the interval $[0, \pi]$. This occurs where the curves intersect in the 1st quadrant. At the point of intersection the r-values are the same, which means $1 + \cos\theta = 1 + \sin\theta$, or equivalently, $\cos\theta = \sin\theta$. This gives $\theta = \pi/4$ for the angle in the 1st quadrant.

Using this we set up two integrals to measure the area. With $R = 1 + \cos\theta$ and $r = 1 + \sin\theta$, we first compute

$$
\begin{aligned}
R^2 - r^2 &= (1 + \cos\theta)^2 - (1 + \sin\theta)^2 = 1 + 2\cos\theta + \cos^2\theta - (1 + 2\sin\theta + \sin^2\theta) \\
&= 2\cos\theta - 2\sin\theta + \cos^2\theta - \sin^2\theta = 2\cos\theta - 2\sin\theta + \cos 2\theta
\end{aligned}
$$

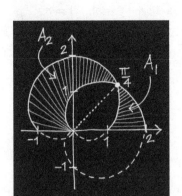

Figure 9.5.8: *A sketch of cardioids* $r = 1 + \cos\theta$ *and* $r = 1 + \sin\theta$.

Then

$$
\begin{aligned}
A_1 &= \int_0^{\pi/4} \frac{1}{2}\left[R^2 - r^2\right] d\theta = \int_0^{\pi/4} \frac{1}{2}\left[2\cos\theta - 2\sin\theta + \cos 2\theta\right] \\
&= \left(\sin\theta + \cos\theta + \frac{1}{4}\sin 2\theta\right)\Big|_0^{\pi/4} = \frac{\sqrt{2}}{2} + \frac{\sqrt{2}}{2} + \frac{1}{4} - 1 = \sqrt{2} - \frac{3}{4}
\end{aligned}
$$

We can reuse much of this to compute

$$
\begin{aligned}
A_2 &= \int_{\pi/4}^{\pi} \frac{1}{2}\left[r^2 - R^2\right] d\theta = -\int_{\pi/4}^{\pi} \frac{1}{2}\left[R^2 - r^2\right] d\theta \\
&= -\left(\sin\theta + \cos\theta + \frac{1}{4}\sin 2\theta\right)\Big|_{\pi/4}^{\pi} \\
&= -\left(-1 - \left[\frac{\sqrt{2}}{2} + \frac{\sqrt{2}}{2} + \frac{1}{4}\right]\right) = \sqrt{2} + \frac{5}{4}
\end{aligned}
$$

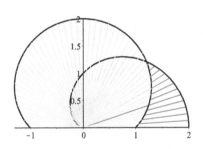

Figure 9.5.9: *The polar region between* $r = 1 + \cos\theta$ *and* $r = 1 + \sin\theta$.

Thus, the total area between the cardioids on the interval $[0, \pi]$ is

$$
A = A_1 + A_2 = 2\sqrt{2} + \frac{1}{2}
$$

NOTE: In Figure 9.5.8, A_2 is the area of the purely yellow region, while A_1 is the area of the purely red region. On the overlap, the shading lines should appear to be orange.

Arc Length of Polar Curves

The arc length Formula 9.3.2 applied to polar curves has a particularly simple form. Using the calculations in (9.5.2) above gives

$$
\begin{aligned}
(x')^2 + (y')^2 &= (r'\cos\theta - r\sin\theta)^2 + (r'\sin\theta + r\cos\theta)^2 \\
&= (r')^2 + r^2 = r^2 + r'^2
\end{aligned}
$$

Thus, we get the integral formula $L = \int_\alpha^\beta \sqrt{r^2 + r'^2}\, d\theta$ for the length. See the next page.

Example 9.5.4 (Length of Polar Curves)

Problem: Find the length of the cardioid $r = 1 - \cos\theta$, for θ in $[0, \pi]$.

Solution: Here $r' = \frac{dr}{d\theta} = \sin\theta$ and so

$$
\begin{aligned}
r^2 + r'^2 &= (1 - \cos\theta)^2 + \sin^2\theta = 1 - 2\cos\theta + \cos^2\theta + \sin^2\theta \\
&= 1 - 2\cos\theta + 1 = 2 - 2\cos\theta = 2(1 - \cos\theta) \\
&= 2(2\sin^2\tfrac{\theta}{2}) = 4\sin^2\tfrac{\theta}{2}
\end{aligned}
$$

Here we have used the trig identity: $2\sin^2 A = 1 - \cos 2A$ with $A = \theta/2$. Thus, the arc length integral is

$$L = \int_0^{2\pi} \sqrt{4\sin^2 \tfrac{\theta}{2}}\, d\theta = \int_0^{2\pi} 2\sin \tfrac{\theta}{2}\, d\theta = \left. \left(-4\cos \tfrac{\theta}{2}\right)\right|_0^{2\pi} = 4 + 4 = 8$$

Note: In taking the square root in the first integrand, we used the fact that $\sin \tfrac{\theta}{2} \geq 0$ for θ in $[0, 2\pi]$.

The following box summarizes the arc length integral formula for curves given in polar coordinates.

ARC LENGTH OF POLAR CURVES

Suppose f is continuously differentiable on the interval $[\alpha, \beta]$, where
$0 \leq \alpha \leq \beta \leq \alpha + 2\pi$. Then the length of the curve $r = f(\theta)$, for θ in $[\alpha, \beta]$, is

$$L = \int_\alpha^\beta \sqrt{r^2 + r'^2}\; d\theta \qquad (9.5.7)$$

Exercises: 9.5 (Polar Coordinate Calculus)

Tangent Lines to Polar Curves

In Exercises 1–14, find an equation for the tangent line to the polar curve at the given angle θ_0. Also sketch the curve and the tangent line.

1. $r = \cos\theta$, $\theta_0 = \frac{\pi}{3}$
2. $r = \sin\theta$, $\theta_0 = \frac{\pi}{3}$

3. $r = 1 - \cos\theta$, $\theta_0 = \frac{\pi}{2}$
4. $r = 1 + \sin\theta$, $\theta_0 = 0$

5. $r = 1 + 2\cos\theta$, $\theta_0 = \frac{\pi}{2}$
6. $r = 1 + 2\sin\theta$, $\theta_0 = \pi$

7. $r = \sin 3\theta$, $\theta_0 = \frac{\pi}{6}$
8. $r = \cos 3\theta$, $\theta_0 = \frac{2\pi}{3}$

9. $r = \sin 3\theta$, $\theta_0 = \frac{\pi}{3}$
10. $r = \cos 3\theta$, $\theta_0 = \frac{\pi}{6}$

11. $r = 1 - 2\cos\theta$, $\theta_0 = \frac{\pi}{3}$
12. $r = 1 + 2\sin\theta$, $\theta_0 = \frac{4\pi}{3}$

13. $r = \cos 2\theta$, $\theta_0 = \frac{\pi}{6}$
14. $r = \sin 2\theta$, $\theta_0 = \frac{\pi}{3}$

Horizontal and Vertical Tangent Lines

In Exercises 15–20, find angles for all the points where the tangent line to the polar curve is either horizontal or vertical. Recall that to solve trig equations involving both sines and cosines, you should use trig identities to rewrite the equation as one with only sines or one with only cosines. Check your answers approximately by looking at the sketches given in the answers for Exercises 1–14.

15. $r = \cos\theta$
16. $r = 3\cos\theta$

17. $r = 1 - \cos\theta$
18. $r = 1 + \sin\theta$

19. $r = \cos 2\theta$
20. $r = \sin 2\theta$

Areas Inside Polar Curves

In Exercises 21–30, find the areas of the shaded polar region. You will have to determine the limits of integration α, β from the picture and the polar equation.

21. $r = 6\cos\theta$
22. $r = 6\sin\theta$

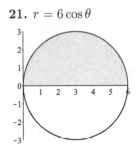

#21

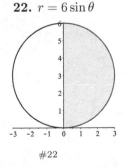

#22

23. $r = 3(1 + \cos\theta) = 6\cos^2\frac{\theta}{2}$
24. $r = 3(1 - \sin\theta) = 6\cos^2(\frac{\theta}{2} - \frac{\pi}{4})$

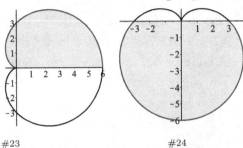

#23   #24

25. $r = 6\cos^3\frac{\theta}{3}$, $[0, \pi]$
26. $r = 6\sin^3\frac{\theta}{3}$, $[\pi, 2\pi]$

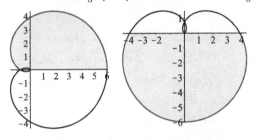

#25   #26

27. $r = 10\,\theta^{1/2}e^{-\theta^2/4}$
28. $r = 10\,\theta^{3/2}e^{-\theta^2/12}$

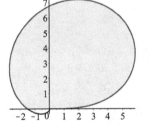

#27

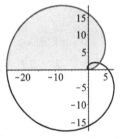

#28

29. $r = 10\cos^{1/2}\frac{\theta}{2}\sin^2\frac{\theta}{2}$
30. $r = 10\cos^{3/2}\frac{\theta}{6}\sin^6\frac{\theta}{6}$

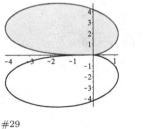

#29

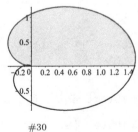

#30

Areas of Polar Regions

In Exercises 31–54, sketch the polar region and find its area.

31. $r = 1 + \cos\theta$, $[0, \pi]$ (Half Cardioid)

32. $r = 1 + \sin\theta$, $[\frac{\pi}{2}, \frac{3\pi}{2}]$ (Half Cardioid)

33. Inner loop of $r = 1 + 2\cos\theta$

34. Inner loop of $r = 2 + 4\sin\theta$

35. Inside $r = 2\cos 3\theta$ **36.** Inside $r = 3\sin 3\theta$

37. Between $r = 2 + 2\cos\theta$, $r = 1 + \cos\theta$, θ in $[0, \frac{\pi}{4}]$

38. Between $r = 2 + 2\sin\theta$, $r = 1 + \sin\theta$, θ in $[\frac{\pi}{4}, \frac{\pi}{2}]$

39. Between $r = 2 + 2\cos\theta$, $r = 2\sin 2\theta$, θ in $[0, \frac{\pi}{2}]$

40. Between $r = 2 + 2\cos\theta$, $r = 2\cos 2\theta$, θ in $[0, \frac{\pi}{4}]$

41. Between $r = 4\sin\theta$, $r = 2$, 1st and 2nd quadrants

42. Between $r = 4\cos\theta$, $r = 2$, 1st and 4th quadrants

43. Between $r = 2 + 2\cos\theta$, $r = 3$, 1st quadrant

44. Between $r = 2 + 2\sin\theta$, $r = 3$, 1st quadrant

45. Inside $r = 2\sin 3\theta$, outside $r = 1$, 1st quadrant

46. Inside $r = 2\cos 3\theta$, outside $r = 1$, 1st quadrant

47. Inside $r = 1$, outside $r = \cos 3\theta$, 2nd quadrant

48. Inside $r = 1$ outside $r = \sin 3\theta$, 1st quadrant

49. Between $r = 2\sin 2\theta$, $r = \sin 2\theta$, 1st quadrant

50. Between $r = 2\cos 2\theta$, $r = \cos 2\theta$, 1st quadrant

51. Inside $r = 1$, outside $r = \cos 2\theta$, 1st quadrant

52. Inside $r = 1$, outside $r = \cos 3\theta$, 2nd quadrant

53. Inside $r = 1$, outside $r = \sin 3\theta$, 1st quadrant

54. Inside $r = 1$, outside $r = \cos 2\theta$, 1st quadrant

Lengths of Polar Curves

In Exercises 55–80, find the length of the curve with the given polar equation on the specified interval $[\alpha, \beta]$.

55. $r = 1 + \cos\theta$, $[0, \pi]$ (Half Cardioid)

56. $r = 1 + \sin\theta$, $[\frac{\pi}{2}, \frac{3\pi}{2}]$ (Half Cardioid) Use $\cos(\theta - \frac{\pi}{2}) = \sin\theta$.

57. $r = \theta^2$, $[0, \pi]$ **58.** $r = \theta^8$, $[0, \pi]$

59. $r = \theta^4$, $[0, \pi]$ **60.** $r = \theta^6$, $[0, \pi]$

61. $r = \theta$, $[0, \pi]$ **62.** $r = \theta^3$, $[0, \pi]$

63. $r = \theta^2 e^{-\theta^2/16}$, $[0, 10]$ **64.** $r = \theta^4 e^{-\theta^2/32}$, $[0, 100]$

65. $r = 10\sin\frac{\theta}{4}\cos^4\frac{\theta}{4}$, $[0, 2\pi]$

66. $r = 10\cos\frac{\theta}{4}\sin^4\frac{\theta}{4}$, $[0, 2\pi]$

67. $r = 100\cos^2\frac{\theta}{8}\sin^8\frac{\theta}{8}$, $[0, 4\pi]$

68. $r = 100\sin^2\frac{\theta}{8}\cos^8\frac{\theta}{8}$, $[0, 4\pi]$

69. $r = 10\cos^{1/2}\frac{\theta}{2}\sin^2\frac{\theta}{2}$, $[0, \pi]$

70. $r = 10\sin^{1/2}\frac{\theta}{2}\cos^2\frac{\theta}{2}$, $[0, \pi]$

71. $r = 10\cos^{3/2}\frac{\theta}{6}\sin^6\frac{\theta}{6}$, $[0, 3\pi]$

72. $r = 10\sin^{3/2}\frac{\theta}{6}\cos^6\frac{\theta}{6}$, $[0, \pi]$

73. $r = 6\sin^3\frac{\theta}{3}$, $[0, \pi]$ **74.** $r = 6\cos^3\frac{\theta}{3}$, $[0, \pi]$

75. $r = 6\sin^4\frac{\theta}{4}$, $[0, \pi]$ **76.** $r = 6\cos^4\frac{\theta}{4}$, $[0, \pi]$

77. $r = \sec\theta$, $[0, \frac{\pi}{4}]$ **78.** $r = \csc\theta$, $[\frac{\pi}{4}, \frac{\pi}{2}]$

79. $r = \sec^2\frac{\theta}{2}$, $[0, \frac{\pi}{3}]$ **80.** $r = \csc^2\frac{\theta}{2}$, $[\frac{\pi}{4}, \frac{\pi}{2}]$

81. (A Special Class of Polar Curves) Suppose $k(\theta)$ is continuously differentiable on an interval $I = [\alpha, \beta]$, with $k'(\theta) \neq 0$ on I. Let

$$h(\theta) = -\frac{1}{4}\int \frac{k(\theta)}{k'(\theta)}\,d\theta \qquad (9.5.1x)$$

Consider the polar curve with equation

$$r = k\,e^h, \qquad (9.5.2x)$$

Show that

$$r^2 + r'^2 = \left[(k' - kh')e^h\right]^2 \qquad (9.5.2x)$$

Thus, for such curves the arc length integrand has no square root.

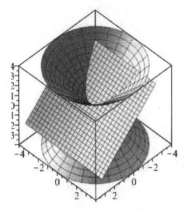

Figure 9.6.1: *A parabola.*

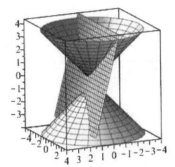

Figure 9.6.2: *A hyperbola.*

Calculus Concepts & Computation

9.6 Conic Sections

The conic sections: parabolas, ellipses, and hyperbolas are the oldest and most important of all the plane curves. Their introduction and study over two thousand years ago by the Greek mathematicians was largely an academic enterprise. However, when Newton, in the 1600s, proved that all objects in the universe move on trajectories which are conic sections, these classic curves became practically indispensable in our space endeavors, from orbiting satellites to moon shots and missions to Mars.

The conic sections got their name as curves that arise by taking sections of a (double) cone by planes inclined at various angles to the cone. To visualize the how such planes intersect the cone to create these curves, you can view the movie produced by `conic-sections`. Figures 9.6.1-9.6.2 show two of the frames from this movie. The axis of the cone is vertical and the seven frames in the movie show planes inclined (relative to horizontal) at angles $\theta = 0, \frac{\pi}{12}, \frac{\pi}{6}, \frac{\pi}{4}, \frac{\pi}{3}, \frac{5\pi}{12}, \frac{\pi}{2}$. Stepping through the movie one frame at a time, you can see the different curves that arise from the sections. These seven curves are: a circle ($\theta = 0$), two ellipses ($\theta = \frac{\pi}{12}, \frac{\pi}{6}$), a parabola ($\theta = \frac{\pi}{4}$), and three hyperbolas ($\theta = \frac{\pi}{3}, \frac{5\pi}{12}, \frac{\pi}{2}$).

Notice that the surface of this cone is generated by taking a line inclined at an angle $\theta = \frac{\pi}{4}$ to the cone's axis and revolving it about this axis. Thus, the parabolic curves arise from planes inclined at this angle. For lesser angles, the planes only intersect the upper half of the cone, giving ellipses. For greater angles, the planes intersect both halves of the cone, giving hyperbolas.

To study conic sections analytically, it is simpler to dispense with this sections-of-a-cone description and instead first define them geometrically in terms of foci and then use the distance formula to get Cartesian equations for them.

Parabolas

Geometrically, we can define a parabola as the set of points in the plane that are at an equal distance from a given line (the directrix) and a given point (the focus).

DEFINITION 9.6.1 (Parabolas)

Suppose D is a line in the plane and F is a point not on D. Then the parabola with directrix D and focus F consists of all points P in the plane such that

$$\overline{PF} = \overline{PD}$$

i.e., the distance from P to the focus is that same as distance from P to the directrix

---

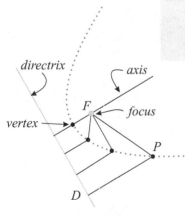

Figure 9.6.3: *A parabola.*

NOTE: The distance from a point to a line is the perpendicular distance.

With a little practice you can actually sketch a number of points that satisfy the equal distance criterion in the definition. One such point is easy to locate. It is the point V that is half-way between the focus and directrix (on the line L through the focus that is perpendicular to the directrix D); The point V is called the *vertex* of the parabola and the line L is the *axis* of the parabola. NOTE: A parabola is symmetric about its axis and both the focus and vertex lie on the axis. See Figure 9.6.3.

To get a Cartesian equation for the parabola, we use the distance formula. The equation will be as simple as possible if we choose the coordinate system so that origin is located at the vertex, i.e., $V = (0, 0)$ and either the x-axis or y-axis coincides with the axis of the parabola. Let's first take the y-axis along the parabolic axis. This gives the setup shown in Figure 9.6.4.

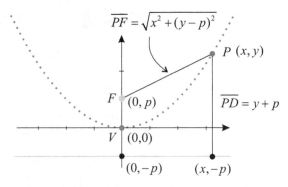

Figure 9.6.4: *A parabola with focus on the y-axis and vertex at the origin.*

The figure assumes that the focus is located on the positive y-axis with coordinates $(0, p)$. In this case $p > 0$ (while $p < 0$ in the case where the focus is on the negative part of the y-axis). As you can see from the figure, a point $P = (x, y)$ satisfies the equi-distance criterion $\overline{PF} = \overline{PD}$ if and only if

$$\sqrt{x^2 + (y - p)^2} = y + p \qquad \text{(P1)}$$

PARABOLAS
(Standard Forms)

(1) $y = \dfrac{1}{4p} x^2$ (9.6.1a)
axis on the y-axis

(2) $x = \dfrac{1}{4p} y^2$ (9.6.1b)
axis on the x-axis

Squaring both sides of this equation and simplifying leads to the equation

$$y = \frac{1}{4p} x^2$$

(Exercise). In the case where the focus is on the x-axis we get an equation like this with the x and y interchanged. The margin box summarizes these derivations.

NOTE 1: In the equation $y = ax^2$, the constant a has no geometric significance. However, in the equation $y = \frac{1}{4p} x^2$, the constant p has the following meaning:

$$|p| = \textit{distance from the vertex to the focus (or the directrix)}$$

NOTE 2 (Latus Rectum): The points $(2p, p), (-2p, p)$ are on the parabola with Equation (9.6.1a), The line segment joining these two points is called the *latus rectum*. Similarly, the points $(p, \pm 2p)$ are on the parabola with Equation (9.6.1b) and the latus rectum is the line segment joining them.

NOTE 3 (Sketching Technique): (a) From the form of the equation determine whether the axis of the parabola is the x-axis or the y-axis. (b) Determine p and use it to locate the focus on the parabola's axis. (c) Draw the latus rectum and a line segment through the vertex parallel to it and of the same length. Join the endpoints of these line segments to get a rectangle (box). Sketch a curve within the box that goes through the vertex and the two endpoints of the latus rectum (corners of the box). Extend the curve outside the box.

Example 9.6.1 (Sketching Parabolas)

Problem: Find the focus, directrix, and axis for each of the following parabolas. Also sketch the parabolas, showing their foci and directrices.

(a) $x = -\frac{1}{8} y^2$ (b) $2x + y^2 = 0$

Solution:

Part (a): Comparing with the standard form $x = \frac{1}{4p} y^2$ gives that x-axis is the axis of the parabola and that $4p = -8$. Thus, $p = -2$ and the focus is $F = (-2, 0)$.

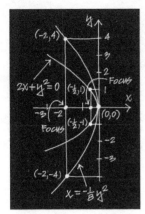

Figure 9.6.5: *The parabolas $x = -\frac{1}{8}y^2$ and $2x + y^2 = 0$*

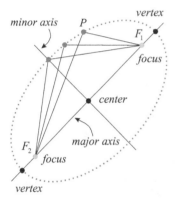

Figure 9.6.6: *An ellipse.*

Source: Mylan Redfern

Figure 9.6.7: *String drawing.*

ELLIPSES
(Standard Forms)

(1) $\dfrac{x^2}{a^2} + \dfrac{y^2}{b^2} = 1$ (9.6.2a)

major axis on the x-axis

(2) $\dfrac{y^2}{a^2} + \dfrac{x^2}{b^2} = 1$ (9.6.2b)

major axis on the y-axis

The directrix is the line $x = 2$. The endpoints of the latus rectum are $(-2, \pm 4)$. A sketch of this parabola is shown in Figure 9.6.5.

Part (b): Rearrange the given equation to get $x = -\frac{1}{2}y^2$. Comparing with the standard form $x = \frac{1}{4p}y^2$ gives that x-axis is the axis of the parabola and that $4p = -2$. Thus, $p = -1/2$ and the focus is $F = (-1/2, 0)$. The directrix is the line $x = 1/2$. The endpoints of the latus rectum are $(-1/2, \pm 1)$. A sketch of this parabola is shown in Figure 9.6.5.

Ellipses

Geometrically, we can define an ellipse as the set of points in the plane such that the sum of the distances to two fixed points (the foci) is constant. See Figure 9.6.6.

DEFINITION 9.6.2 (Ellipses)

Suppose F_1 and F_2 are two distinct points in the plane and $a > 0$ a given constant. The ellipse with foci F_1, F_2, consists of all points P in the plane which satisfy

$$\overline{PF_1} + \overline{PF_2} = 2a \qquad (9.6.2)$$

i.e., the sum of the distances of P to the foci is constant.

NOTE 1: An ellipse can be constructed mechanically by attaching a string of length $2a$ to two nails, one at each focus. With a pencil pressed against the string as shown in Figure 9.6.7, draw a curve while keeping the string tautly stretched.

NOTE 2: As you can perhaps discover from the pencil and string construction, there are two points during the construction when the pencil and the two nails all lie on the same line. The points V_1, V_2 are called the *vertices* of the ellipse and, because the string has length $2a$, a little thought will lead you to the conclusion that the vertices are that far apart: $\overline{V_1 V_2} = 2a$. The line segment $V_1 V_2$ joining the vertices is called the *major axis* of the ellipse. The *center* of the ellipse is the midpoint of the major axis. See Figure 9.6.6.

NOTE 3: Beside the vertices, there are two other prominent points on the ellipse. These are the points W_1, W_2 that are equidistant from the foci: $W_1 F_1 = W_1 F_2 = a$ and $W_2 F_1 = W_2 F_2 = a$. The line segment $W_1 W_2$ joining the vertices is called the *minor axis* of the ellipse. One can prove (exercise) that the minor axis is perpendicular to the major axis and that its midpoint is also the center of the ellipse. This is shown in Figure 9.6.6.

To get a Cartesian equation for an ellipse, one that is as simple as possible, we choose a coordinate system with the origin at the center and, say, the x-axis passing through the foci. See Figure 9.6.8. Let $(c, 0), (-c, 0)$ be the coordinates of the foci and $(a, 0), (-a, 0)$ be the coordinates of the vertices. Then for a point $P = (x, y)$ on the ellipse, the condition that $\overline{PF_1} + \overline{PF_2} = 2a$, is

$$\sqrt{(x - c)^2 + y^2} + \sqrt{(x + c)^2 + y^2} = 2a \qquad (E1)$$

By isolating radicals and squaring, one gets from this an equation with one remaining radical. Isolating it, squaring, and rearranging, one gets

$$\frac{x^2}{a^2} + \frac{y^2}{a^2 - c^2} = 1$$

From Figure 9.6.8., we see that $a^2 - c^2 = b^2$. Thus, we get the first of the two standard forms of the equation of an ellipse. See the margin box.

NOTE 4 (Sketching Technique): (a) Put the equation in one of the standard forms (9.6.2a)–(9.6.2b) and identify a. It is the largest of the numbers ($a > b$). If a^2

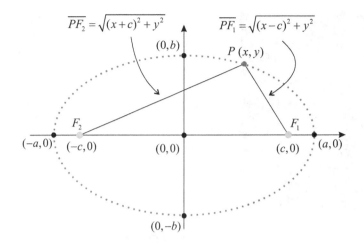

$$\overline{PF_2} = \sqrt{(x+c)^2 + y^2} \qquad \overline{PF_1} = \sqrt{(x-c)^2 + y^2}$$

Figure 9.6.8: *An ellipse in a standard position.*

occurs as the denominator of the x^2 term, then the major axis is on the x-axis. Otherwise it is on the y-axis. (b) Mark the two vertices on the major axis at a distance a from the center (which is $(0,0)$). (c) Mark the two points on the minor axis at a distance b from the center. (d) Sketch a rectangular box with sides passing through these four points and parallel to the major and minor axes, respectively. (e) Within the box sketch the ellipse having it pass through the four points you marked and making sure the sides of the box at these four points are tangent to the ellipse.

NOTE 5: (Locating the Foci) The foci are on the major axis at a distance c from the center of the ellipse. Remember the relation $a^2 = b^2 + c^2$ among the constants a, b, c and use this relation to calculate c, given a and b. The foci are not needed for sketching the ellipse (unless you are drawing it by the string method), but you should mark them on your sketch anyway. They do have geometric significance, which we will discuss below.

Example 9.6.2 (Sketching Ellipses)

Problem: Find the foci and vertices for each of the following ellipses. Also sketch the ellipses, showing the foci and vertices.

$$\text{(a)} \ \frac{x^2}{16} + \frac{y^2}{25} = 1 \qquad \text{(b)} \ x^2 + 9y^2 = 9$$

Solution:

Part (a): Here $25 = 5^2$ is the largest number and so $a = 5$ and $b = 4$. Thus, the vertices are $(0,5), (0,-5)$ and the endpoints of the minor axis are $(4,0), (-4,0)$. Drawing a box centered at the origin with sides $2a = 10$ and $2b = 8$ allows us to sketch the ellipse shown in Figure 9.6.9. Finally to find the foci, use $c^2 = a^2 - b^2 = 25 - 16 = 9$. So $c = \sqrt{9} = 3$ and the foci are $(0,3), (0,-3)$.

Part (b): Divide by 9 to get $\frac{x^2}{9} + y^2 = 1$. Thus, $a = 3$ and $b = 1$. Since $9 = 3^2$ occurs with the x^2, the major axis is on the x-axis. So, the vertices are $(3,0), (-3,0)$. The ends of the minor axis are the points $(0,1), (0,-1)$. Drawing a box centered at the origin with sides $2a = 6$ and $2b = 2$ allows us to sketch the ellipse shown in Figure 9.6.9. Finally to find the foci, use $c^2 = a^2 - b^2 = 9 - 1 = 8$. So $c = \sqrt{8} = 2\sqrt{2}$ and the foci are $(2\sqrt{2}, 0), (-2\sqrt{2}, 0)$.

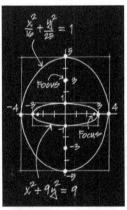

Figure 9.6.9: *The ellipses $\frac{x^2}{16} + \frac{y^2}{25} = 1$ and $x^2 + 9y^2 = 9$*

Hyperbolas

Geometrically, we can define a hyperbola as the set of points P in the plane such that the absolute value of the *difference* of the distances to two fixed points F_1, F_2 (the foci) is constant, say $2a$, where $a > 0$. Since an equation of the form $|x| = 2a$ is equivalent to the two equations $x = \pm 2a$, we see that the criterion defining points on a hyperbola is that given in Equation (9.6.3). See Definition 9.6.3 below.

DEFINITION 9.6.3 (Hyperbolas)

Suppose F_1 and F_2 are two distinct points in the plane and $a > 0$ a given constant. The hyperbola with foci F_1, F_2, consists of all points P in the plane which satisfy

$$\overline{PF_1} - \overline{PF_2} = \pm 2a \qquad (9.6.3)$$

i.e., the difference of the distances of P to the foci is constant.

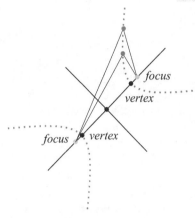

Figure 9.6.10: *A hyperbola.*

NOTE 1: The *focal axis* of a hyperbola lies along the line joining the two foci and the *center* is the midpoint of the line segment joining the foci.

NOTE 2: If we let c denote the distance between the center and either focus, then one can prove that $c > a$ and that there are two points, called the *vertices*, on the hyperbola, each of which is on the focal axis at a distance a from the center. (Exercise.)

To get a Cartesian equation for a hyperbola, we choose a coordinate system with the origin at the center and, say, the x-axis passing through the foci. See Figure 9.6.11. Let $(c,0), (-c,0)$ be the coordinates of the foci and $(a,0), (-a,0)$ be the coordinates of the vertices. Then for a point $P = (x,y)$ on the hyperbola, the condition that $\overline{PF_1} - \overline{PF_2} = \pm 2a$, is

$$\sqrt{(x-c)^2 + y^2} - \sqrt{(x+c)^2 + y^2} = \pm 2a \qquad \text{(H1)}$$

By isolating radicals and squaring, one gets from this an equation with one re-

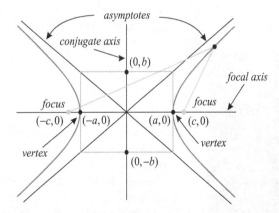

Figure 9.6.11: *A hyperbola with foci on the x-axis*

HYPERBOLAS
(Standard Forms)

(1) $\dfrac{x^2}{a^2} - \dfrac{y^2}{b^2} = 1$ (9.6.3a)

axis on the x-axis

(2) $\dfrac{y^2}{a^2} - \dfrac{x^2}{b^2} = 1$ (9.6.3b)

axis on the y-axis

maining radical. Isolating it, squaring, and rearranging, one gets

$$\frac{x^2}{a^2} - \frac{y^2}{c^2 - a^2} = 1.$$

If we let $b^2 = c^2 - a^2$, then we get the first of the two standard forms of the equation of a hyperbola. See the margin box.

NOTE 3: While the focal axis of a hyperbola is the line segment joining the two vertices, the *conjugate axis* is the line segment through the center, perpendicular to the focal axis, and having endpoints a distance of b from the center. Thus, $2a$ is the length of the focal axis and $2b$ is the length of the conjugate axis. It is important to observe that these axes can have any length relative to one another. When they are of the same length, the hyperbola is called a *rectangular hyperbola*. Also observe that in the standard forms, a^2 occurs with the positive term involving either x^2 or y^2 and it indicates whether the focal axis is along the x-axis or the y-axis.

NOTE 4 (Asymptotes): As indicated in Figure 9.6.11 there are two lines $y = \frac{b}{a}x$ and $y = -\frac{b}{a}x$ that the hyperbola appears to approach as $x \to \pm\infty$. These are the *asymptotes* of the hyperbola. To verify the asymptotic property for the first standard form, solve the equation for y to get two explicitly defined functions (cf. Section 2.10):

$$y = \frac{b}{a}\sqrt{x^2 - a^2} \quad \text{and} \quad y = -\frac{b}{a}\sqrt{x^2 - a^2}$$

Then for, say, the first function, it is easy to show (exercise) that

$$\lim_{x \to \infty} \left(\frac{b}{a}\sqrt{x^2 - a^2} - \frac{b}{a}x \right) = 0$$

NOTE 5 (Sketching Technique): (a) Put the equation in one of the standard forms (9.6.3a)–(9.6.3b) and identify whether the focal axis is on the x-axis or on the y-axis. (b) Mark the two vertices on the focal axis at a distance a from the center (which is $(0,0)$). (c) Mark the two points on the conjugate axis at a distance b from the center. (d) Sketch a rectangular box with sides passing through these four points and parallel to the focal axis and conjugate axis, respectively. (e) Draw the diagonals of the box and extend them in each direction. These are the asymptotes for the hyperbola. Sketch the two branches of the hyperbola passing through the respective vertices and becoming asymptotic to the asymptotes.

NOTE 6 (Locating the Foci): The foci are on the focal axis (naturally) at a distance c from the center of the hyperbola. Remember the relation $c^2 = a^2 + b^2$ among the constants a, b, c and use this relation to calculate c, given a and b. The foci are not needed for sketching the hyperbola, but you should mark them on your sketch anyway. They do have geometric significance, which we will discuss below.

Example 9.6.3 (Sketching Hyperbolas)

Problem: Find the foci and vertices for each of the following hyperbolas. Also sketch the hyperbolas, showing the foci, vertices, and asymptotes.

$$\text{(a)} \quad \frac{y^2}{16} - \frac{x^2}{4} = 1 \qquad \text{(b)} \quad 4x^2 = y^2 + 16$$

Solution:

Part (a): Here we identify $a = 4$, $b = 2$, and, since a^2 is with the y^2, the focal axis is along the y-axis. The vertices are $(0, \pm 4)$ and the points at the end of the conjugate axis are $(\pm 2, 0)$. Since $c^2 = a^2 + b^2 = 16 + 4 = 20$, we find that the distance from the origin to either focus is $c = \sqrt{20} = 2\sqrt{5} \approx 4.47$. The foci are at the points $(0, \pm 2\sqrt{5})$. Sketch a rectangular box with side lengths $2a = 8$, $2b = 4$, passing through the vertices and the conjugate axis points. Extend the diagonals of the box to form the asymptotes. Using this information, we sketch the hyperbola as shown in Figure 9.6.12. As you can see from the figure, the asymptotes have equations $y = \pm\frac{4}{2}x = \pm 2x$.

Part (b): Put the equation $4x^2 = y^2 + 16$ in standard for to get $\frac{x^2}{4} - \frac{y^2}{16} = 1$. So, we identify $a = 2$, $b = 4$, and, since a^2 is with the x^2, the focal axis is along the x-axis. The vertices are $(\pm 2, 0)$ and the points at the end of the conjugate axis are $(0, \pm 4)$. Since $c^2 = a^2 + b^2 = 16 + 4 = 20$, we find that the distance from the origin to either focus is $c = \sqrt{20} = 2\sqrt{5} \approx 4.47$. The foci are at the points $(\pm 2\sqrt{5}, 0)$. Sketch a rectangular box with side lengths $2a = 4$, $2b = 8$, passing through the vertices and the conjugate axis points. This gives the same box as in Part (a.) Extend the diagonals of the box to form the asymptotes (which are the same as in Part(a)). Using this information, we sketch the hyperbola as shown in Figure 9.6.12. As you can see from the figure, the asymptotes have equations $y = \pm\frac{4}{2}x = \pm 2x$, which are the same as in Part (a).

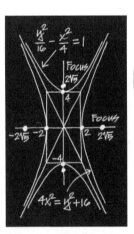

Figure 9.6.12: *The hyperbolas $\frac{y^2}{16} - \frac{x^2}{4} = 1$ and $4x^2 = y^2 + 16$*

Translation of Axes

Table 9.6.1 in the margin gives some equations for parabolas, ellipses, and hyperbolas that are slightly more general than the standard forms we have considered so far. The axes of the conics with these equations are parallel to the coordinate axes, but, for the parabola the vertex is now at (h, k) and for the ellipses and hyperbolas, the centers are at (h, k). The sketching technique is the same, except now you draw the rectangular boxes relative to the point (h, k).

The following figure serves as an additional aid for working with ellipses and hyperbolas where the numbers a, b have slightly different meanings and are used in different ways to find the distance c from a focus to the center.

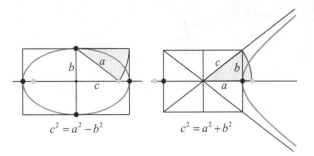

$$c^2 = a^2 - b^2 \qquad\qquad c^2 = a^2 + b^2$$

Figure 9.6.13: *Finding the number c, geometrically and analytically*

PARABOLAS

(1) $y - k = \dfrac{1}{4p}(x-h)^2$

(2) $x - h = \dfrac{1}{4p}(y-k)^2$

vertex (h,k)

ELLIPSES

(3) $\dfrac{(x-h)^2}{a^2} + \dfrac{(y-k)^2}{b^2} = 1$

(4) $\dfrac{(y-k)^2}{a^2} + \dfrac{(x-h)^2}{b^2} = 1$

center (h,k)

HYPERBOLAS

(5) $\dfrac{(x-h)^2}{a^2} - \dfrac{(y-k)^2}{b^2} = 1$

(6) $\dfrac{(y-k)^2}{a^2} - \dfrac{(x-h)^2}{b^2} = 1$

center (h,k)

Table 9.6.1

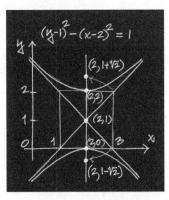

Figure 9.6.14:
A sketch of the conic
$y^2 - x^2 + 4x - 2y - 4 = 0$

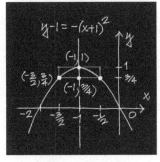

Figure 9.6.15:
A sketch of the conic
$y + x^2 + 2x = 0$

Example 9.6.4 (Identifying Conics)

Problem: Put each of the following equations in standard form (Table 9.6.1) and identify the conic. Find the vertices, foci, and any asymptotes or directrices and sketch the conic.

(a) $y^2 - x^2 + 4x - 2y - 4 = 0$ (b) $y + x^2 + 2x = 0$ (c) $4x^2 + y^2 - 8x + 4y + 4 = 0$

Solution:

Part (a): We complete the square on the x and y terms separately:

$$y^2 - x^2 + 4x - 2y - 4 = 0 \implies y^2 - 2y - (x^2 - 4x) = 4 \implies$$
$$y^2 - 2y + 1 - (x^2 - 4x + 4) = 4 + 1 - 4 \implies (y-1)^2 - (x-2)^2 = 1$$

Thus, the conic is a hyperbola with $a = 1$, $b = 1$ and center at $(2, 1)$. The focal axis is parallel to the y-axis and so the vertices are $(2, 1 \pm 1) = (2, 0), (2, 2)$. Also, $c^2 = a^2 + b^2 = 1 + 1 = 2$. So $c = \sqrt{2}$ and the foci are $(2, 1 \pm \sqrt{2})$. To sketch the hyperbola, plot the center $(2, 1)$ and the vertices, which are 1 unit away in the positive and negative y-directions. Also, plot the points at the ends of the conjugate axis, which are 1 unit away from the center in the positive and negative x-directions. Draw the box determined by these four points and then the asymptotes through the diagonals of the box. Finally, sketch the hyperbola passing through the vertices and approaching the asymptotes. See Figure 9.6.14.

Part (b): We complete the square on the x terms to get:

$$y + x^2 + 2x = 0 \implies y + x^2 + 2x + 1 = 1 \implies$$
$$y + (x+1)^2 = 1 \implies y - 1 = -(x+1)^2$$

Thus, the conic is a parabola with $\frac{1}{4p} = -1$, so $p = -\frac{1}{4}$. The vertex is at $(-1, 1)$ and the parabolic axis is parallel to the y-axis. Also, the focus is $(-1, 1 - \frac{1}{4}) = (-1, \frac{3}{4})$. To sketch the parabola, plot the vertex $(-1, 1)$ and two other points on the parabola, say, for $x = -2$ and $x = 0$. This gives $(-2, 0)$ and $(0, 0)$, Then sketch the parabola as shown in Figure 9.6.15.

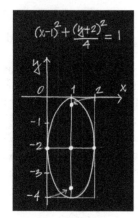

Figure 9.6.16:
A sketch of the conic
$4x^2 + y^2 - 8x + 4y + 4 = 0$

Part (c): We complete the square on the x and y terms separately:

$$4x^2 + y^2 - 8x + 4y + 4 = 0 \implies 4(x^2 - 2x) + y^2 + 4y = -4 \implies$$
$$4(x^2 - 2x + 1) + y^2 + 4y + 4 = -4 + 4 + 4 \implies 4(x-1)^2 + (y+2)^2 = 4$$
$$\implies (x-1)^2 + \frac{(y+2)^2}{4} = 1$$

Thus, the conic is an ellipse with $a = 2, b = 1$ and center at $(1, -2)$. The focal axis is parallel to the y-axis and so the vertices are $(1, -2 \pm 2) = (1, 0), (1, -4)$. Also, $c^2 = a^2 - b^2 = 4 - 1 = 3$. So $c = \sqrt{3}$ and the foci are $(1, -2 \pm \sqrt{3})$, which are approximately $(1, -0.27), (1, -3.7)$. To sketch the ellipse, plot the center $(1, -2)$ and the vertices, which are 2 units away in the positive and negative y-directions. Also, plot the points at the ends of the minor axis, which are 1 unit away from the center in the positive and negative x-directions. Draw the box determined by these four points and sketch the ellipse within this box passing through the vertices and the two points in the ends of the minor axis. The sides of the box should appear to be tangent to the ellipse. The sketch is shown in Figure 9.6.16.

Exercises: 9.6 (Conic Sections)

In Exercises 1–26, identify and sketch the conic section. For parabolas, find and label the focus, directrix, and latus rectum. For ellipses find and label the foci and the vertices. For hyperbolas find and label the foci, vertices, and asymptotes.

1. $\dfrac{x^2}{100} + \dfrac{y^2}{36} = 1$ 2. $\dfrac{x^2}{64} + \dfrac{y^2}{100} = 1$

3. $\dfrac{x^2}{64} - \dfrac{y^2}{36} = 1$ 4. $\dfrac{x^2}{144} - \dfrac{y^2}{81} = 1$

5. $\dfrac{y^2}{9} - \dfrac{x^2}{16} = 1$ 6. $\dfrac{y^2}{144} - \dfrac{x^2}{256} = 1$

7. $x^2 = 4y$ 8. $x^2 = 8y$

9. $y^2 + 2x = 0$ 10. $y^2 + 3x = 0$

11. $36x^2 - 9y^2 = 324$ 12. $9x^2 - 36y^2 = 324$

13. $25x^2 + 4y^2 = 100$ 14. $36x^2 + 9y^2 = 324$

15. $\dfrac{(x-1)^2}{25} + \dfrac{(y+1)^2}{9} = 1$

16. $\dfrac{(x-1)^2}{36} + \dfrac{(y+1)^2}{16} = 1$

17. $(x-1)^2 = -2(y-2)$

18. $(x+1)^2 = 6(y-1)$

19. $\dfrac{(x+2)^2}{4} - \dfrac{(y-1)^2}{4} = 1$

20. $\dfrac{(x+2)^2}{9} - \dfrac{(y-1)^2}{9} = 1$

21. $16x^2 + 9y^2 - 32x + 18y = 119$

22. $4x^2 + 25y^2 + 8x - 150y + 141 = 0$

23. $9x^2 - 16y^2 + 36x + 64y = 116$

24. $16x^2 - 9y^2 - 32x + 36y = 164$

25. $y^2 - 4y - x = -3$ 26. $y^2 + 4y - x = -5$

Finding Equations for Conics

In Exercises 27–44, find the equation, in standard form, for the conic that satisfies the given conditions.

Ellipses

27. The ellipse with foci $(-2, 1)$, $(4, 1)$ and distance between the vertices $= 10$.

28. The ellipse with foci $(1, -2)$, $(1, 4)$ and distance between the vertices $= 10$.

29. The ellipse with foci $(1, 2 \pm \sqrt{7})$ and distance between the vertices $= 8$.

30. The ellipse with vertices $(2, 1 \pm 2\sqrt{3})$ and distance between the vertices $= 8$.

31. The ellipse with vertices $(1, -3)$, $(1, 7)$ and passing through the point $(4, 2)$.

32. The ellipse with vertices $(-2, 3)$, $(6, 3)$ and passing through the point $(2, 0)$.

Hyperbolas

33. The hyperbola with foci $(-4, 1)$, $(6, 1)$ and distance between the vertices $= 6$.

34. The hyperbola with foci $(-4, 1)$, $(6, 1)$ and distance between the vertices $= 8$.

35. The hyperbola with foci $(1, 2 \pm \sqrt{41})$ and distance between the vertices $= 8$.

36. The hyperbola with foci $(1, 2 \pm \sqrt{41})$ and distance between the vertices $= 10$.

37. The hyperbola with vertices $(0, 2)$, $(8, 2)$ and passing through the point $(4 + 2\sqrt{5}, 0)$.

38. The hyperbola with vertices $(0, 1)$, $(4, 1)$ and passing through the point $(2 + \sqrt{5}, 0)$.

Parabolas

39. The parabola with vertex $(1, 2)$ and focus $(\frac{9}{8}, 2)$.

40. The parabola with vertex $(2, 1)$ and focus $(2, \frac{9}{8})$.

41. The parabola with focus $(3, 3)$ and directrix $x = 1$.

42. The parabola with focus $(2, 4)$ and directrix $y = 2$.

43. The parabola with axis $y = 1$ and passing through points $(-2, 0)$, $(-8, 3)$.

44. The parabola with axis $y = 2$ and passing through points $(-2, 1)$, $(-11, 4)$.

Derivations of the Equations for Conics

45. Complete the derivation of Equation (9.6.2a) starting with Equation (E1).

46. Complete the derivation of Equation (9.6.1a) starting with Equation (P1).

47. Complete the derivation of Equation (9.6.3a) starting with Equation (H1).

Vectors and Geometry

Calculus Concepts & Computation

10.1 Three-Dimensional Coordinate Systems

The analytic geometry done so far has been concerned primarily with the study of objects in two-dimensions. These objects, such as lines, curves, and planar regions, are described analytically by setting up a (Cartesian) coordinate system on the plane. This allows us to identify the set of all points P in the plane with the set of all ordered pairs (x, y) in $\mathbb{R}^2$ and leads to the description of lines and curves by equations in x and y and planar regions by inequalities in x and y.

Doing analytic geometry in three-dimensions is an easy extension of this (but can be visually more challenging). We take the plane, now called the *x-y plane*, with its mutually perpendicular x-axis and y-axis intersecting at the origin O, and add a third axis, called the *z-axis*. The z-axis is the line through O which is perpendicular to the x-y plane. In space we think of the x-y plane as being horizontal, like the floor of a room, and the positive direction of the z-axis extending in the direction from floor to ceiling. See Figure 10.1.1.

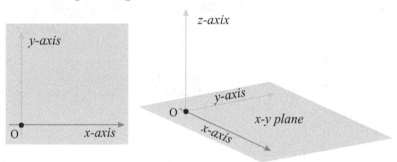

Figure 10.1.1: *The x-y plane as part of 3-dimensional space*

The figure shows a natural view of 3-dimensional space–obtained by rotating slightly and tilting down the plane (x-y plane) to get it as part of 3-dimensional space. Alternatively, one could use the "standard" view of the axes in 3-dimensional space by rotating first through $90 + 45 = 135$ degrees and then tilting it down. See Figure 10.1.2. This view is often not the best view for examining some objects in space and we will often use the one in Figure 10.1.1 (called the *Euler view*). Using a CAS (Computer Algebra System) to create an interactive view, one that you can rotate, is optimum. Many of the figures in this book can be studied like this. For example, Figure 10.1.3 has a corresponding interactive Maple Figure.

Regardless of the view, the assignment of coordinates in 3-dimensions is similar to that in 2-dimensions. Now we use $\mathbb{R}^3$ which is the set of all ordered triples (x, y, z) of real numbers x, y, and z. To each point P in space we assign such a triple (x, y, z), called the *coordinates* of P as follows.

The points in the x-y plane are given coordinates $(x, y, 0)$, where x and y are assigned as usual for points in the plane. For a point P not in the x-y plane, let z be the number on the z-axis obtained by dropping a perpendicular from P to the this axis. Also, let $(x, y, 0)$ be the coordinates of the point obtained by dropping a perpendicular from P onto the x-y plane. Then the ordered triple (x, y, z) gives the coordinates of P. See Figure 10.1.4.

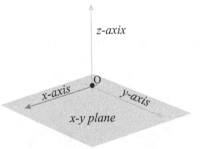

Figure 10.1.2: *The standard view of 3-D space.*

Figure 10.1.3: *A Maple view of 3-D space.*

Note that for the point P in Figure 10.1.4, the three coordinate numbers x, y, z are all positive because the feet of the three perpendiculars shown are on the positive parts of the coordinate axes.

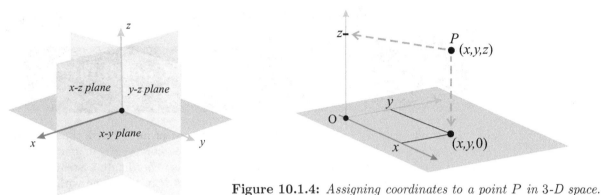

Figure 10.1.4: *Assigning coordinates to a point P in 3-D space.*

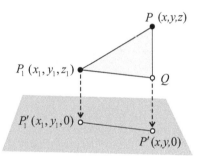

Figure 10.1.5: *Standard view of the coordinate planes.*

As shown in Figure 10.1.4, the point P lies in the 1st *octant* of space. The octants of space are determined much like the quadrants of the plane, except now we use coordinate planes instead of coordinate axes to divide space up. A *coordinate plane* is a plane passing through one pair of the coordinate axes. Thus, there are three coordinate planes: the *x-y plane*, the *x-z plane*, and the *y-z plane*. These are shown in Figure 10.1.5. These three planes divide space into eight parts, called *octants*. The first four octants lie above the x-y plane and the last four octants lie below it.

The Distance Formula in Space

The distance formula for points in the plane is easy to extend to points in space. Thus, suppose that $P_1 = (x_1, y_1, z_1)$ and $P = (x, y, z)$ are two points in space and let $P_1' = (x_1, y_1, 0), P' = (x, y, 0)$ be the points obtained by projecting P_1, P onto the x-y plane (i.e., drop perpendiculars from P_1, P to the plane to get P_1', P'). See Figure 10.1.6. Then by the distance formula for the plane, the distance between P_1', P' is

$$|P_1'P'| = \sqrt{(x - x_1)^2 + (y - y_1)^2}$$

But from Figure 10.1.6 we see that $|P_1'P'| = |P_1Q|$, which is the length of one of the sides about the right angle in the right triangle $\triangle P_1QP$. Also, since Q and P lie in a vertical line at heights z_1 and z above the x-y plane, respectively (in this picture) we have $|QP| = z - z_1$. Thus, by the Pythagorean theorem

$$
\begin{aligned}
|P_1P|^2 &= |P_1Q|^2 + |QP|^2 = \left(\sqrt{(x - x_1)^2 + (y - y_1)^2}\right)^2 + (z - z_1)^2 \\
&= (x - x_1)^2 + (y - y_1)^2 + (z - z_1)^2
\end{aligned}
$$

This gives the formula we need:

Figure 10.1.6: *Measuring the distance between points.*

DISTANCE FORMULA

The distance between points $P_1 = (x_1, y_1, z_1)$ *and* $P = (x, y, z)$ *is*

$$|P_1P| = \sqrt{(x - x_1)^2 + (y - y_1)^2 + (z - z_1)^2} \qquad (10.1.1)$$

NOTE: In using the distance formula it does not matter which point you identify with P_1 and which you identify with P. The formula says to take the squares of the differences of the coordinates, add them, and take the square root:

$$|P_1P| = \sqrt{(\Delta x)^2 + (\Delta y)^2 + (\Delta z)^2} \qquad (10.1.2)$$

Example 10.1.1 (Using the Distance Formula)

Problem: Find the distance between the points $Q = (1, 5, -2)$ and $R = (3, -2, 1)$

Solution: $\Delta x = 3 - 1 = 2$, $\Delta y = -2 - 5 = -7$, $\Delta z = 1 - (-2) = 3$. So

$$|QR| = \sqrt{(2)^2 + (-7)^2 + (3)^2} = \sqrt{4 + 49 + 9} = \sqrt{62}$$

NOTE: Since the formula involves the square of the differences $\Delta x, \Delta y, \Delta z$, these differences can be computed in either order. Generally, we recommend in computing $|QR|$ you subtract the coordinates of Q from the coordinates of R.

Projections

In the discussions above, we have used the term "projection" several times. Geometrically, we can project any point P in space onto a given line or plane in space by drawing a projecting line through P that is perpendicular to the given line or plane. The point P' where the projecting line intersects the given line or plane is called the *orthogonal projection* of P onto the given line or plane. This is a geometrical operation. Later we will learn how to do this analytically.

Equations for Objects in Space

The analytic description of points P in space by means of coordinates (x, y, z) allows us to describe *sets* of points in space by means of equations involving x, y and z. Generally, a *surface* in $\mathbb{R}^3$ is described by a single equation: $H(x, y, z) = k$, where k is a constant. Technically the surface is the set of all points P whose coordinates satisfy the equation:

$$S = \{ (x, y, z) \text{ in } \mathbb{R}^3 \mid H(x, y, z) = k \}$$

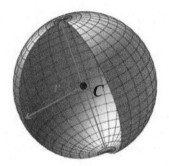

Figure 10.1.7: *A sphere of radius r and center C.*

A well-known type of surface is a sphere. Geometrically a sphere is defined as the set of all points $P = (x, y, z)$ in space at a given distance r from a given point $C = (x_1, y_1, z_1)$. The positive number r is called the *radius* of the sphere and the point C is called its *center*. Using the distance formula we see that the sphere can be described as the set of points (x, y, z) in $\mathbb{R}^3$ which satisfy the equation

$$\sqrt{(x - x_1)^2 + (y - y_1)^2 + (z - z_1)^2} = r$$

Squaring both sides of this equation gives the following equivalent, and simpler looking, equation for the sphere:

STANDARD EQUATION FOR A SPHERE

The sphere of radius r and center $C = (x_1, y_1, z_1)$ *has equation*

$$(x - x_1)^2 + (y - y_1)^2 + (z - z_1)^2 = r^2 \qquad (10.1.2)$$

Example 10.1.2 (Spheres)

Problem:

    (a) Find the standard equation of the sphere of radius 2 and center $(1, -3, 5)$.

    (b) Find the radius and center of the sphere: $x^2 + y^2 + z^2 + 4x + 2y - 2z = 5$.

Solution (a): Direct substitution into Formula (10.1.2) gives the equation

$$(x - 1)^2 + (y + 3)^2 + (z - 5)^2 = 4.$$

Solution (b): We complete-the-square on the x, y, and z terms separately.

$$x^2 + y^2 + z^2 + 4x + 2y - 2z = 5 \longrightarrow x^2 + 4x + y^2 + 2y + z^2 - 2z = 5$$

$$\longrightarrow (x^2 + 4x + 4) + (y^2 + 2y + 1) + (z^2 - 2z + 1) = 5 + 4 + 1 + 1$$
$$\longrightarrow (x + 2)^2 + (y + 1)^2 + (z - 1)^2 = 11$$

Thus, the equation is for a sphere of radius $r = \sqrt{11}$ and center $C = (-2, -1, 1)$.

Another type of surface in $\mathbb{R}^2$, which is well-known, is a plane

STANDARD EQUATION FOR A PLANE

The standard equation for a plane in space is $Ax + By + Cz = D$ (10.1.3)

The constants A, B, C (assumed to not all be zero) and D determine the intercepts of the plane: The x-intercept is $x = D/A$ (assuming $A \neq 0$), the y-intercept is $y = D/B$ (assuming $B \neq 0$), and the z-intercept is $z = D/C$ (assuming $C \neq 0$)

NOTE 1: The x-intercept of a plane is the point where the plane intersects the x-axis. Similarly for the y-intercept and z-intercept.

NOTE 2: If a line and plane in space do not intersect, they are called *parallel*. Thus, a plane may not have an x-intercept (or a y-intercept, or a z-intercept). Any plane has at least one intercept.

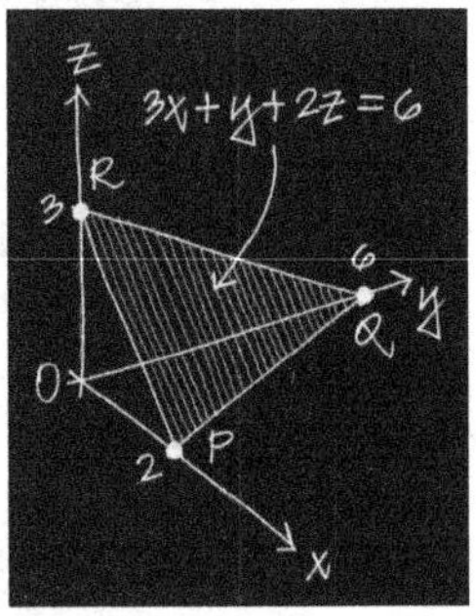

Example 10.1.3 (Planes)

Problem: (a) Find the intercepts for the plane $3x + y + 2z = 6$ and draw a rough sketch of the plane. (b) Find equations for the three coordinate planes.

Solution (a): Rather than remember the formulas for the intercepts given above, just use the fact that the x-intercept is where the plane intersects the x-axis and points on the x-axis have $y = 0, z = 0$. Substituting $y = 0, z = 0$ into the equation for the plane gives $3x = 6$, i.e., $x = 2$. So, the x-intercept is $P = (2, 0, 0)$. Similarly, you can find that the y-intercept and z-intercept are $Q = (0, 6, 0)$ and $R = (0, 0, 3)$, respectively. To sketch the plane, we plot P, Q, and R, which are points on the plane, and then join them with line segments to get a triangle $\triangle PQR$, which forms a portion of the plane. See Figure 10.1.8.

Another view of this plane is shown in Figure 10.1.9, which was created in Maple (with a corresponding Maple Figure that you can rotate interactively). In this figure, a rectangular portion of the plane is rendered and the intersection of the plane with the y-z plane is the red line shown in the figure. You can also discern the intersections of the plane with the other two coordinate planes, giving the other two sides of the triangle $\triangle PQR$. Compare this with the other view of $\triangle PQR$ shown in Figure 10.1.8.

Solution (b): The x-y plane consists of all points whose z-coordinate is zero. Thus, its equation is $z = 0$ (special case of Equation (10.1.3) with $A = B = D = 0$ and $C = 1$). Similarly, the y-z plane has equation $x = 0$ and the x-z plane has equation $y = 0$.

NOTE: Generally, the equation $z = k$ is an equation for a plane perpendicular to the z-axis at the point $(0, 0, k)$. Likewise, the equations $x = k$ and $y = k$ represent planes perpendicular to the x-axis and y-axis, respectively.

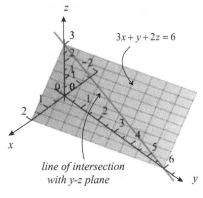

Figure 10.1.8: *A sketch of the plane $3x + y + 2z = 6$.*

Figure 10.1.9: *A Maple version of $3x + y + 2z = 6$.*

Line of Intersection of Two Planes

If two distinct planes in space intersect, then the set of intersection points will be a line in space. Generally, a line in space cannot be described by a (single) Cartesian equation, but it can always be specified by parametric equations. Here, we look at how to determine parametric equations for the line of intersection of two planes.

Example 10.1.4 (Line of Intersection of Two Planes)

Problem: Find parametric equations for the line of intersection of the two planes

$$\begin{aligned} x + 2y - 4z &= 8 \\ x - y + 8z &= 2 \end{aligned}$$

Solution: If you take a linear algebra course, you will learn a systematic process (Gaussian elimination) to solve problems like this. Here, we take a simplistic approach (which works whenever the line of intersection is not horizontal) and let $z = t$ be the parameter. Then, we can write the equations for the two plane as

$$\begin{aligned} x + 2y &= 8 + 4t \\ x - y &= 2 - 8t \end{aligned}$$

With t being arbitrary, we can view the above as a system of two equations in two unknowns and solve it for x and y. If we subtract the bottom equation from the top equation, that will eliminate x and give $3y = 6 + 12t$, and so $y = 2 + 4t$. Then substitute this in the 2nd equation above to get $x - (2 + 4t) = 2 - 8t$. So $x = 4 - 4t$. In summary, we get the following parametric equations for the line of intersection:

$$x = 4 - 4t, \ y = 2 + 4t, \ z = t$$

In Section 10.5, we will have an alternative geometrical way of parametrizing lines of intersections of two planes.

A final formula which is useful in solving some geometrical problems in space is:

MIDPOINT FORMULA

The midpoint of the line segment PQ, with $P = (x_1, y_1, z_1)$ *and* $Q = (x_2, y_2, z_2)$, *is*

$$M = \left(\frac{x_1 + x_2}{2}, \frac{y_1 + y_2}{2}, \frac{z_1 + z_2}{2} \right) \qquad (10.1.4)$$

Exercises: 10.1 (Three-Dimensional Coordinate Systems)

Points & Distances: In Exercises 1–10, plot the points P, Q, the line segment PQ and their projections $P', Q', P'Q'$ on the x-y plane. Do the sketches in the standard view and Euler view of 3-D space. ALSO, compute the distances $|PQ|, |P'Q'|$ between the plotted points.

1. $(3, 1, 4)$, $(1, 2, 2)$ **2.** $(1, 4, 3)$, $(2, 2, 1)$

3. $(2, 1, 4)$, $(-1, -1, 2)$ **4.** $(2, 4, 3)$, $(-2, 2, -1)$

5. $(1, 1, 3)$, $(3, 3, 3)$ **6.** $(3, 2, 4)$, $(1, 3, 4)$

7. $(0, 1, 3)$, $(0, 3, 3)$ **8.** $(0, 3, 1)$, $(0, 1, 1)$

9. $(0, 0, 1)$, $(0, 0, 3)$ **10.** $(0, 0, 2)$, $(0, 0, 6)$

Triangles: In Exercises 11–14, determine if the triangle with given vertices P, Q, R is an equilateral triangle or a right triangle (Identify the right angle).

11. $P = (1, 0, 5)$, $Q = (3, 6, 8)$, $R = (7, 4, -7)$

12. $P = (3, 2, 7)$, $Q = (5, 8, 19)$, $R = (9, 6, -5)$

13. $P = (2, 8, 4)$, $Q = (5, 6, 3)$, $R = (3, 5, 6)$

14. $P = (3, 4, 1)$, $Q = (0, 6, 2)$, $R = (1, 3, 4)$

Spheres: In Exercises 15–26, find the center and radius of the sphere with the given equation or conditions.

15. $(x - 2)^2 + (y + 1)^2 + (z - 3)^2 = 4$

16. $(x - 1)^2 + (y + 3)^2 + (z - 2)^2 = 9$

17. $\frac{x^2}{9} + \frac{y^2}{9} + \frac{(z-2)^2}{9} = 1$ **18.** $\frac{x^2}{16} + \frac{(y-3)^2}{16} + \frac{z^2}{16} = 1$

19. $x^2 + y^2 + z^2 - 6x + 4y - 2z = 2$

20. $x^2 + y^2 + z^2 - 4x + 10y + 8z = 4$

21. Diameter $= |PQ|$, $P = (1, -3, 6)$, $Q = (3, 5, 2)$

22. Diameter $= |PQ|$, $P = (-3, 6, 1)$, $Q = (5, 2, 3)$

23. Center $= (1, -2, 2)$, passes through $(1, 0, 2 + \sqrt{5})$

24. Center $= (2, -1, 3)$, passes through $(1, 0, 3 + \sqrt{2})$

25. Intersects the x-y plane in a circle with radius $r = \sqrt{8}$ and center $(3, 2, 0)$ and the x-z plane in a circle with radius $r = \sqrt{5}$ and center $(3, 0, 1)$

26. Intersects the x-y plane in a circle with radius $r = \sqrt{7}$ and center $(2, -1, 0)$ and the x-z plane in a circle with radius $r = \sqrt{15}$ and center $(2, 0, 3)$

Planes: In Exercises 27–34, find the intercepts of the given plane with the coordinate axes and sketch the plane.

27. $5x + 2y + 3z = 30$ **28.** $4x + 5y + 2z = 40$

29. $\frac{x}{3} + \frac{y}{5} + \frac{z}{2} = 1$ **30.** $\frac{x}{2} + \frac{y}{3} + \frac{z}{5} = 1$

31. $2x + y = 4$ **32.** $3x + 2y = 6$

33. $4x = 8$ **34.** $6y = 18$

Equations for Planes: In Exercises 35–38, find an equation for the plane shown in the figure.

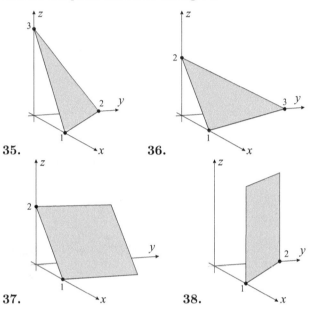

35.   **36.**

37.   **38.**

Intersecting Planes: In Exercises 39–44, find parametric equations for the line of intersection of the given planes.

39. $x - y + 2z = 4$ and $x + y - 6z = 2$

40. $x - 2y + z = 2$ and $x + y - 2z = -4$

41. $x - y = 4$ and $y - 6z = 2$

42. $x - 2y = 2$ and $y - 2z = -4$

43. $x = 4$ and $y = 2$ **44.** $x = 2$ and $y = 3$

Calculus Concepts & Computation

10.2 Vectors

In the sciences and engineering, we can use a single number to quantify and measure many phenomena, such as the temperature of the air, the weight of a ball, or the length of a baseball bat. In physics this number is called a *scalar* quantity. However, to adequately quantify the nature of wind forces applied to the sail of a boat, we need to record not only the strength (magnitude) of the wind but also its direction. In physics, forces are known as *vector* quantities. They require more than just a single number to quantify.

Geometrically, we can represent a vector as a *directed line segment* in space. A *line segment* is the set of points between two points P and Q on a line. We denote the line segment by PQ and its length is, of course, the distance $|PQ|$ between its endpoints P and Q. The line segment becomes *directed* if we designate one point, say P as the *initial* point and then the other point Q as its *terminal* point. We denote this vector (directed line segment) by $\mathbf{v} = \overrightarrow{PQ}$ and graphically represent it by drawing the line segment between P and Q and putting a caret (arrowhead) on the end at Q. See Figure 10.2.1. The word "vector" comes from the Latin word for "carry." Think of a force $\mathbf{v}$ applied to an object at P carrying it to Q.

NOTE: Typically vectors are denoted by boldface, such as $\mathbf{v}$, $\mathbf{w}$. In writing vectors by hand, you can indicate that they are vector quantities in two ways: (1) Put an arrow over the letter, such as $\vec{v}$, $\vec{w}$. (2) Use what is known as *blackboard bold*, such as $\mathbb{V}$, $\mathbb{W}$.

Magnitude: The *magnitude* of a vector $\mathbf{v}$ is denoted by $\|\mathbf{v}\|$ and is the length of the directed line segment that represents $\mathbf{v}$. Thus,

$$\|\mathbf{v}\| = |\overrightarrow{PQ}| = |PQ|$$

GEOMETRIC OPERATIONS ON VECTORS

Even though vectors are different than scalars (numbers) we can do some operations on them like we do on numbers. These operations are addition, subtraction, and scalar multiplication. Before defining these, we discuss what is meant by *equal* vectors.

Equality of Vectors (Geometrically)

In essence, equal vectors have the same magnitude and direction. Thus, $\mathbf{v}$ and $\mathbf{w}$ are equal: $\mathbf{v} = \mathbf{w}$ if $\|\mathbf{v}\| = \|\mathbf{w}\|$ and $\mathbf{v}, \mathbf{w}$ lie in parallel lines, pointing in the same direction. See Figure 10.2.2. Defining equality of vectors in this manner allows us to take a given vector and "move it around" in space. Thus, moving the vector $\mathbf{v} = \overrightarrow{PQ}$ so that its initial point P coincides with the origin O, without changing its direction or magnitude, gives an equal vector $\mathbf{v} = \overrightarrow{OS}$. This vector is known as a *position vector*. This terminology comes from the description of motion in space. We saw in Section 9.1 that parametric equations $x = f(t)$, $y = g(t)$ for a curve can be thought of as describing the motion of a particle on that curve, with $P(t) = (f(t), g(t))$ giving the particle's position at time t. Then the vector $\mathbf{r} = \mathbf{r}(t) = \overrightarrow{OP}$ points from the origin to the particle at each time t. See Figure 10.2.3. Also shown in the figure is the *velocity vector* $\mathbf{v}$, which is discussed in more detail below. It has magnitude which is the speed of the particle and, when located with initial point at P, is tangent to the curve (more specifically lies in the tangent line, pointing in the direction of motion). This discussion about motion of a particle

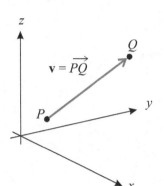

Figure 10.2.1: *A vector* $\mathbf{v}$ *is a directed line segment between points* P *and* Q.

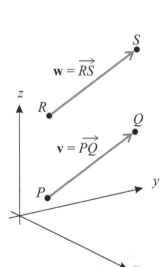

Figure 10.2.2: *Equality of two vectors* $\mathbf{v}$ *and* $\mathbf{w}$.

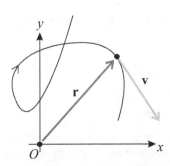

Figure 10.2.3: *Position and velocity vectors* $\mathbf{r}, \mathbf{v}$ *for a planar motion.*

in the plane also applies to motions of particles in space, which we will discuss later.

The first algebraic operation that we do on vectors is vector addition. This is motivated by combining forces by letting them act in secession on an object.

Addition of Vectors (Geometrically)

For vectors **u** and **v**, their sum **u** + **v** is the vector obtained geometrically by moving **v** so that its initial point is at the terminal point of **u**. Then **u** + **v** is the vector that goes from the initial point of **u** to the terminal point of **v**. See Figure 10.2.4.

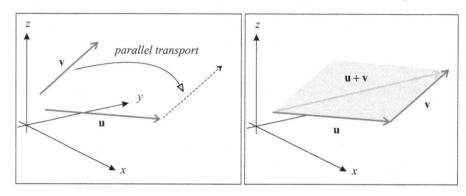

Figure 10.2.4: *Addition of vectors* **u** *and* **w**

NOTE: After we move **v** by *parallel transport* (i.e, keeping it parallel to the original **v** during the move), the two vectors **u, v** lie in the same plane. A portion of this plane is indicated by the brown parallelogram shown in Figure 10.2.4. The vectors **u, v** form two sides of this parallelogram, which is called the *parallelogram determined by* **u** *and* **v**. Then the sum **u** + **v**, which is called the *resultant*, lies along one of the diagonals of this parallelogram. For this reason, when we add vectors geometrically it is known as adding using the *parallelogram rule*.

We can use the parallelogram in Figure 10.2.4 to illustrate the addition **v** + **u** of **u** and **v** in the opposite order. Move (parallel transport) **v**, **u** to the other two sides of the parallelogram. Then **v** + **u** goes from the initial point of **v** to the terminal point of **u**, which gives the same diagonal of the parallelogram as the computation of **u** + **v**. This is the geometric proof of the commutative law of vector addition: **u** + **v** = **v** + **u**.

Scalar Multiplication (Geometrically)

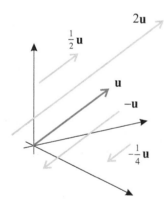

Figure 10.2.5: *Scalar multiples of* **u**.

If **u** is a vector and $k \neq 0$ is a scalar (a real number), then $k\mathbf{u}$ is the vector with magnitude $|k|\|\mathbf{u}\|$ and direction either the same as **u** (if $k > 0$) or the opposite of **u** (if $k < 0$). Thus, 2**u** is twice as long as **u** and in the same direction. While $\frac{1}{2}\mathbf{u} = 0.5\mathbf{u}$ and $-\frac{1}{4}\mathbf{u} = -0.25\mathbf{u}$ have lengths that are one half and one quarter that of **u** and in the same and opposite directions, respectively. See Figure 10.2.5. Also shown in the figure is the vector $-\mathbf{u} \equiv (-1)\mathbf{u}$. This is known as the *negative* of the vector **u**.

NOTE (The Zero Vector): For any point P the vector $\mathbf{0} = \overrightarrow{PP}$ is called the *zero vector*. It has magnitude 0 and no direction. Also (by definition)

$$0\mathbf{u} = \mathbf{0} \quad \text{and} \quad \mathbf{0} + \mathbf{u} = \mathbf{u} = \mathbf{u} + \mathbf{0}$$

for any vector **u**.

Subtraction of Vectors (Geometrically)

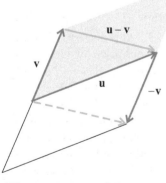

Figure 10.2.6: *Subtraction of* **v** *from* **u**.

For vectors **u, v**, their *difference* is defined as $\mathbf{u} - \mathbf{v} \equiv \mathbf{u} + (-\mathbf{v})$. Geometrically, this has an interpretation in terms of the parallelogram determined by **u** and **v**.

Namely, $\mathbf{u} - \mathbf{v}$ is the other diagonal in the parallelogram. See Figure 10.2.6. Note that a convenient way to construct $\mathbf{u} - \mathbf{v}$ is to put their initial points together and then draw the vector that goes from the terminal point of $\mathbf{v}$ to the terminal point of $\mathbf{u}$. This is shown in Figure 10.2.6.

NOTE: $\mathbf{u} - \mathbf{u} = \mathbf{u} + (-\mathbf{u}) = \mathbf{0}$, for any vector $\mathbf{u}$. This says that $-\mathbf{u}$ is the additive inverse of $\mathbf{u}$.

ALGEBRAIC OPERATIONS ON VECTORS

If we represent vectors *analytically* (rather than geometrically), then we can add, subtract, and scale them by using algebra (which you may find easier than doing these operations geometrically).

DEFINITION 10.2.1 (Analytic Representation of Vectors)

Suppose $P = (x_1, y_1, z_1)$ *and* $Q = (x_2, y_2, z_2)$. *Then the vector* $\mathbf{v} = \overrightarrow{PQ}$ *is given analytically by*

$$\mathbf{v} = \langle v_1, v_2, v_3 \rangle \qquad (10.2.1)$$

where

$$v_1 = x_2 - x_1, \quad v_2 = y_2 - y_1, \quad v_3 = z_2 - z_1 \qquad (10.2.2)$$

The numbers v_1, v_2, v_3 *are called the* components *of* $\mathbf{v}$.

NOTE 1: The components of $\mathbf{v}$ are the three numbers gotten by subtracting the three coordinates of P from the three coordinates of Q.

NOTE 2: When working in two-dimensions (the plane) the analytic representation of vectors can be done with just two components. So in the special case, we write $\mathbf{v} = \langle v_1, v_2 \rangle$.

NOTE 3: If a vector is a position vector, say $\mathbf{r} = \overrightarrow{OQ}$ with $Q = (x, y, z)$, then analytically $\mathbf{r} = \langle x, y, z \rangle$. Thus, the components of a position vector are the same as the coordinates of its terminal point.

NOTE 4: In terms of components, the magnitude of $\mathbf{v}$ is $\|\mathbf{v}\| = \sqrt{v_1^2 + v_2^2 + v_3^2}$

Example 10.2.1 (Finding Components)

Problem: For the points $P = (5, 2, -1)$, $Q = (3, -4, 6)$, find he components of the vectors $\overrightarrow{PQ}$, $\overrightarrow{OP}$ and $\overrightarrow{OQ}$.

Solution: These are easy calculations:

$$\overrightarrow{PQ} = \langle 3 - 5, -4 - 2, 6 - (-1) \rangle = \langle -2, -6, 7 \rangle$$
$$\overrightarrow{OP} = \langle 5, 2, -1 \rangle, \quad \overrightarrow{OQ} = \langle 3, -4, 6 \rangle$$

Doing operations on vectors when they are given analytically is as easy as doing arithmetic on numbers. The following theorem exhibits this.

THEOREM 10.2.1 (Algebraic Operations on Vectors)

Suppose

$$\mathbf{u} = \langle u_1, u_2, u_3 \rangle, \quad \mathbf{v} = \langle v_1, v_2, v_3 \rangle$$

are vectors and k *is a scalar. Then*

and

$$\mathbf{u} + \mathbf{v} = \langle u_1 + v_1, u_2 + v_2, u_3 + v_3 \rangle \qquad (10.2.3a)$$

$$k\mathbf{u} = \langle ku_1, ku_2, ku_3 \rangle \qquad (10.2.3b)$$

Example 10.2.2 (Vector Operations Done Algebraically)

Problem: For the vectors $\mathbf{u} = \langle 3, -2, 4 \rangle$, $\mathbf{v} = \langle 2, 1, -5 \rangle$ compute the following vectors (analytically):

(a) $\mathbf{u} + \mathbf{v}$ (b) $3\mathbf{u}$ (c) $\mathbf{u} - \mathbf{v}$ (d) $2\mathbf{u} + 7\mathbf{v}$

Solution: The computations are:

$$
\begin{aligned}
\mathbf{u} + \mathbf{v} &= \langle 3, -2, 4 \rangle + \langle 2, 1, -5 \rangle = \langle 3+2, -2+1, 4-5 \rangle = \langle 5, -1, -1 \rangle \\
3\mathbf{u} &= 3\langle 3, -2, 4 \rangle = \langle 3(3), 3(-2), 3(4) \rangle = \langle 9, -6, 12 \rangle \\
\mathbf{u} - \mathbf{v} &= \langle 3, -2, 4 \rangle - \langle 2, 1, -5 \rangle = \langle 3-2, -2-1, 4-(-5) \rangle = \langle 1, -3, 9 \rangle \\
2\mathbf{u} + 7\mathbf{v} &= 2\langle 3, -2, 4 \rangle + 7\langle 2, 1, -5 \rangle = \langle 6, -4, 8 \rangle + \langle 14, 7, -35 \rangle = \langle 20, 3, -27 \rangle
\end{aligned}
$$

Example 10.2.3 (Vector Operations Done Geometrically)

Problem: For the vectors in the plane $\mathbf{u} = \langle 2, 1 \rangle$, $\mathbf{v} = \langle -1, 4 \rangle$ compute the following vectors geometrically by sketching the vectors. Check your results by doing the operations algebraically.

(a) $\mathbf{u} + \mathbf{v}$ (b) $\frac{1}{2}\mathbf{u} - \frac{3}{4}\mathbf{v}$

Solution: Figure 10.2.7 shows a sketch of the results done geometrically. To check them, we compute the vectors algebraically:

$$
\begin{aligned}
\mathbf{u} + \mathbf{v} &= \langle 2, 1 \rangle + \langle -1, 4 \rangle = \langle 1, 5 \rangle \\
\tfrac{1}{2}\mathbf{u} - \tfrac{3}{4}\mathbf{v} &= \tfrac{1}{2}\langle 2, 1 \rangle - \tfrac{3}{4}\langle -1, 4 \rangle = \langle 1, \tfrac{1}{2} \rangle + \langle \tfrac{3}{4}, -3 \rangle = \langle 1\tfrac{3}{4}, -2\tfrac{1}{2} \rangle
\end{aligned}
$$

Comparing these vectors with those in the drawing shows that our sketch is approximately correct.

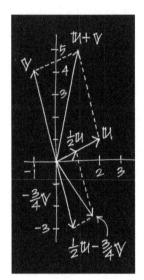

Figure 10.2.7:
Vector operations done geometrically.

The following Theorem summarizes the properties of vector operations, many of which we have mentioned already. The properties are easy to prove using algebra on the analytical representation of vectors.

THEOREM 10.2.2 (Properties of Vector Operations)

Suppose $\mathbf{u}$, $\mathbf{v}$, $\mathbf{w}$ are vectors and k, l are scalars. Then

(1) $\mathbf{u} + \mathbf{v} = \mathbf{v} + \mathbf{u}$ (2) $\mathbf{u} + (\mathbf{v} + \mathbf{w}) = (\mathbf{u} + \mathbf{v}) + \mathbf{w}$

(3) $\mathbf{u} - \mathbf{u} = \mathbf{u} + (-\mathbf{u}) = 0$ (4) $\mathbf{u} + \mathbf{0} = \mathbf{u}$

(5) $k(\mathbf{u} + \mathbf{v}) = k\mathbf{v} + k\mathbf{u}$ (6) $(k+l)\mathbf{u} = k\mathbf{u} + l\mathbf{u}$

(7) $0\mathbf{u} = \mathbf{0}$ (8) $1\mathbf{u} = \mathbf{u}$

(9) $k(l\mathbf{u}) = (kl)\mathbf{u}$ (10) $\| k\mathbf{u} \| = |k| \, \| \mathbf{u} \|$

Unit Vectors

In mathematics the scalar (number) 1 is called the *unit* (and is related to units in physics, which are scales for measurement in either the English or metric systems). In terms of vectors, we say that a vector $\mathbf{u}$ is a *unit vector* if it has unit length (or magnitude). Specifically, its length is $\|\mathbf{u}\| = 1$. A unit vector can have any direction, but there are three special unit vectors, called the *standard unit vectors*, which when located at the origin, are position vectors directed along the three coordinate axes. Specifically:

$$\mathbf{i} = \langle 1, 0, 0 \rangle, \quad \mathbf{j} = \langle 0, 1, 0 \rangle, \quad \mathbf{k} = \langle 0, 0, 1 \rangle$$

The important aspect of these unit vectors is that any vector $\mathbf{v} = \langle v_1, v_2, v_3 \rangle$ can easily be expressed in terms of them. To see this note that

$$v_1\mathbf{i} + v_2\mathbf{j} + v_3\mathbf{k} = v_1\langle 1, 0, 0 \rangle + v_2\langle 0, 1, 0 \rangle + v_2\langle 0, 0, 1 \rangle$$

$$= \langle v_1, 0, 0 \rangle + \langle 0, v_2, 0 \rangle + \langle 0, 0, v_3 \rangle = \langle v_1, v_2, v_3 \rangle$$

This gives us an alternative notation for expressing vectors in terms of their components:

> ### i-j-k Notation for Vectors
>
> *Any vector* $\mathbf{v}$ *in* $\mathbb{R}^3$ *can be expressed in component form as*
>
> $$\mathbf{v} = \langle v_1, v_2, v_3 \rangle = v_1\mathbf{i} + v_2\mathbf{j} + v_3\mathbf{k} \qquad (10.2.4)$$

In Equation (10.2.4), the first notation is called the *bracket notation* for $\mathbf{v}$ in terms of its components and the second notation is called the *i-j-k notation* for $\mathbf{v}$. Most physics books prefer the *i-j-k* notation, so we will use this notation, as well as the bracket notation, throughout this book. Figure 10.2.8 illustrates the *i-j-k* vectors and how, using the parallelogram law, the vector operations $(v_1\mathbf{i} + v_2\mathbf{j}) + v_3\mathbf{k}$ give resultant vector $\mathbf{v}$.

NOTE: For vectors in the x-y plane $v_3 = 0$ and so $\mathbf{v} = \langle v_1, v_2, 0 \rangle = v_1\mathbf{i} + v_2\mathbf{j}$. Since we are identifying such vectors with vectors in $\mathbb{R}^2$ (the plane), we write

Vectors in the Plane: The standard unit vectors in $\mathbb{R}^2$ are $\mathbf{i} = \langle 1, 0 \rangle, \mathbf{j} = \langle 0, 1 \rangle$ and so the bracket and *i-j* notation for vectors in $\mathbb{R}^2$ are

$$\mathbf{v} = \langle v_1, v_2 \rangle = v_1\mathbf{i} + v_2\mathbf{j}$$

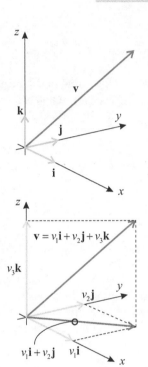

Figure 10.2.8: *The* $\mathbf{i}$, $\mathbf{j}$, $\mathbf{k}$ *vectors and the linear combination of them that gives* $\mathbf{v}$.

The following examples illustrate the use of the *i-j-k* notation when doing vector operations.

Example 10.2.4 (Using the i-j-k notation)

Problem: For the vectors $\mathbf{u} = 2\mathbf{i} - \mathbf{j} + 4\mathbf{k}$, $\mathbf{v} = 3\mathbf{i} + 5\mathbf{j} - 7\mathbf{k}$ compute the following vectors (analytically):

(a) $\mathbf{u} + \mathbf{v}$ (b) $\mathbf{u} - \mathbf{v}$ (c) $3\mathbf{u}$ (d) $\|\mathbf{u}\|$

Solution: The computations are:

$$\begin{aligned}
\mathbf{u} + \mathbf{v} &= (2\mathbf{i} - \mathbf{j} + 4\mathbf{k}) + (3\mathbf{i} + 5\mathbf{j} - 7\mathbf{k}) = 5\mathbf{i} + 4\mathbf{j} - 3\mathbf{k} \\
\mathbf{u} - \mathbf{v} &= (2\mathbf{i} - \mathbf{j} + 4\mathbf{k}) - (3\mathbf{i} + 5\mathbf{j} - 7\mathbf{k}) = -\mathbf{i} - 6\mathbf{j} + 11\mathbf{k} \\
3\mathbf{u} &= 3(2\mathbf{i} - \mathbf{j} + 4\mathbf{k}) = 6\mathbf{i} - 3\mathbf{j} + 12\mathbf{k} \\
\|\mathbf{u}\| &= \|2\mathbf{i} - \mathbf{j} + 4\mathbf{k}\| = \sqrt{4 + 1 + 16} = \sqrt{21}
\end{aligned}$$

Forces and Statics: In mechanics when a number of forces act on an object and it doesn't move (it is static), then the (vector) sum of all the forces is zero (the zero vector). In the special case when all the forces lie in the same plane, it is common in the analysis to assume the plane is the x-y plane with the object located at the origin and the y axis directed upward.

Example 10.2.5 (Balance of Planar Forces)

Problem: A 200 lb weight hangs from two ropes as shown in Figure 10.2.9. The weight $\mathbf{W} = -200\mathbf{j}$ is balanced by forces $\mathbf{F}_1, \mathbf{F}_2$ (tensions) in the ropes, with directions directed along the ropes and magnitudes $F_1 = \|\mathbf{F}_1\|, F_2 = \|\mathbf{F}_2\|$ determined by $\mathbf{F}_1 + \mathbf{F}_2 - 200\mathbf{j} = \mathbf{0}$. Find the magnitudes F_1, F_2 of these two forces.

Solution: By elementary geometry (see Figure 10.2.10) the two forces are

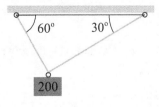

Figure 10.2.9: *A weight suspended from ropes.*

$$\begin{aligned}
\mathbf{F}_1 &= -F_1 \cos(60)\mathbf{i} + F_1 \sin(60)\mathbf{j} = -\tfrac{1}{2}F_1\mathbf{i} + \tfrac{\sqrt{3}}{2}F_1\mathbf{j} \\
\mathbf{F}_2 &= F_2 \cos(30)\mathbf{i} + F_1 \sin(30)\mathbf{j} = \tfrac{\sqrt{3}}{2}F_2\mathbf{i} + \tfrac{1}{2}F_2\mathbf{j}
\end{aligned}$$

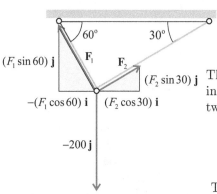

Figure 10.2.10: *A weight suspended from ropes.*

Note: In mechanics it is common to use degrees rather than radians for angles (as we have done here). The condition for statics is

$$
\begin{aligned}
\mathbf{0} &= \mathbf{F}_1 + \mathbf{F}_2 - 200\mathbf{j} \\
&= \left[-\tfrac{1}{2}F_1\mathbf{i} + \tfrac{\sqrt{3}}{2}F_1\mathbf{j} \right] + \left[\tfrac{\sqrt{3}}{2}F_2\mathbf{i} + \tfrac{1}{2}F_2\mathbf{j} \right] - 200\mathbf{j} \\
&= \left[-\tfrac{1}{2}F_1 + \tfrac{\sqrt{3}}{2}F_2 \right]\mathbf{i} + \left[\tfrac{\sqrt{3}}{2}F_1 + \tfrac{1}{2}F_2 - 200 \right]\mathbf{j}
\end{aligned}
$$

Thus, in order for the last vector above to be the zero vector each of the expressions in the square brackets must be 0. This gives the following two equations for the two unknowns F_1, F_2:

$$
\begin{aligned}
-\tfrac{1}{2}F_1 + \tfrac{\sqrt{3}}{2}F_2 &= 0 \\
\tfrac{\sqrt{3}}{2}F_1 + \tfrac{1}{2}F_2 &= 200
\end{aligned}
$$

The first equations says that $F_1 = \sqrt{3}F_2$. Substituting this value of F_1 into the second equation gives $\tfrac{\sqrt{3}}{2} \cdot \sqrt{3}F_2 + \tfrac{1}{2}F_2 = 200$, which is $2F_2 = 200$. Thus, $F_2 = 100$ lb and so $F_1 = \sqrt{3}F_2 = 100\sqrt{3}$ lb.

Normalizing Vectors: For a vector $\mathbf{v}$ the number $\|\mathbf{v}\|$, which gives its length or its magnitude, is sometimes called the *norm* of $\mathbf{v}$. If we scale $\mathbf{v}$ by the reciprocal of its length (assuming $\mathbf{v} \neq 0$), then we get a vector

$$
\mathbf{u} = \frac{1}{\|\mathbf{v}\|}\mathbf{v} \qquad (10.2.5)
$$

which is called *the unit vector in the direction of* $\mathbf{v}$. This vector is also called the *direction* (or *direction vector*) for the given vector $\mathbf{v}$.

This process of scaling $\mathbf{v}$ to get a unit vector in the same direction is called *normalizing* $\mathbf{v}$. In physics, it is often convenient to express a force vector or a velocity vector as a magnitude times a direction, the direction being the unit vector in the direction of the force or velocity. This amounts to normalizing as in Equation (10.2.5) to get $\mathbf{u}$ and then rewriting Equation (10.2.5) as:

$$
\mathbf{v} = \|\mathbf{v}\|\,\mathbf{u} = \|\mathbf{v}\|\left(\frac{\mathbf{v}}{\|\mathbf{v}\|}\right) \qquad (10.2.6)
$$

NOTE: Scaling a vector by the reciprocal of its length is thought of as dividing a vector by it length. So it is natural to use the notation $\frac{\mathbf{v}}{\|\mathbf{v}\|}$ for the normalization.

Example 10.2.6 (Normalization)

Problem: Find the unit vector in the same direction as

$$
\mathbf{v} = \langle 1, -3, 4 \rangle = \mathbf{i} - 3\mathbf{j} + 4\mathbf{k}
$$

Solution: First compute $\|\mathbf{v}\| = \sqrt{1 + 9 + 16} = \sqrt{26}$, Then

$$
\mathbf{u} = \frac{1}{\|\mathbf{v}\|}\mathbf{v} = \frac{1}{\sqrt{26}}\langle 1, -3, 4 \rangle = \left\langle \frac{1}{\sqrt{26}}, \frac{-3}{\sqrt{26}}, \frac{4}{\sqrt{26}} \right\rangle
$$

Example 10.2.7 (Magnitude Times Direction)

Problem: Write the force $\mathbf{F}_2$ found in Example 10.2.5 as a scalar (the magnitude of the force) times a unit vector (the direction of the force).

Solution: We found

$$
\mathbf{F}_2 = \tfrac{\sqrt{3}}{2}F_2\mathbf{i} + \tfrac{1}{2}F_2\mathbf{j} = F_2\left(\tfrac{\sqrt{3}}{2}\mathbf{i} + \tfrac{1}{2}\mathbf{j}\right) = 100\left(\tfrac{\sqrt{3}}{2}\mathbf{i} + \tfrac{1}{2}\mathbf{j}\right)
$$

The magnitude of the force is 100 lb and its direction is $\mathbf{u} = \tfrac{\sqrt{3}}{2}\mathbf{i} + \tfrac{1}{2}\mathbf{j}$

Exercises: 10.2 (Vectors)

Combining Vectors Geometrically: In Exercises 1–2, copy the grid with the vectors **u**, **v** and use it to find, geometrically, the vectors $\mathbf{w}_1, \mathbf{w}_2, \mathbf{w}_3$

1. $\mathbf{w}_1 = 2\mathbf{u} + \frac{1}{2}\mathbf{v},\ \mathbf{w}_2 = \frac{1}{2}\mathbf{u} + 2\mathbf{v},\ \mathbf{w}_3 = \frac{1}{2}\mathbf{u} - \mathbf{v}$

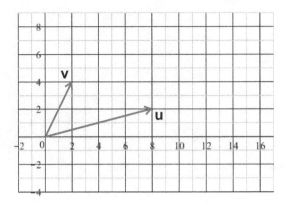

2. $\mathbf{w}_1 = 2\mathbf{u} + \frac{1}{3}\mathbf{v},\ \mathbf{w}_2 = \frac{1}{3}\mathbf{u} + 2\mathbf{v},\ \mathbf{w}_3 = \frac{1}{3}\mathbf{u} - \mathbf{v}$

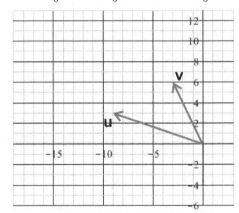

Analytic Representation of Vectors: In Exercises 3–12, find the specified vector. Give your answer in either component form or in terms of **i**, **j**, **k**.

3. $\overrightarrow{PQ}$, where $P = (1, 3)$, $Q = (5, 2)$

4. $\overrightarrow{PQ}$, where $P = (2, 4)$, $Q = (6, 1)$

5. $\overrightarrow{PQ}$, where $P = (-1, 1, 3)$, $Q = (2, 6, -2)$

6. $\overrightarrow{PQ}$, where $P = (5, -3, 2)$, $Q = (-1, 6, -4)$

7. $\overrightarrow{PX}$, where $P = (2, 5, -1)$ and X = midpoint of the line segment between $Q = (-1, 2, -4)$, $R = (3, 6, 2)$.

8. $\overrightarrow{PX}$, where $P = (3, 6, -2)$ and X = midpoint of the line segment between $Q = (2, 3, -6)$, $R = (-4, 7, 2)$.

9. $\overrightarrow{PX}$, where X = center of the parallelogram with vertices $P = (1, 2)$, $Q = (4, 3)$, $R = (5, 8)$, $S = (2, 7)$.

10. $\overrightarrow{PX}$, where X = center of the parallelogram with vertices $P = (3, 4)$, $Q = (6, 5)$, $R = (4, 9)$, $S = (7, 10)$.

11. **v** = the longer diagonal of the parallelogram with vertices $P = (1, 2)$, $Q = (4, 3)$, $R = (5, 8)$, $S = (2, 7)$.

12. **v** = the longer diagonal of the parallelogram with vertices $P = (3, 4)$, $Q = (6, 5)$, $R = (4, 9)$, $S = (7, 10)$.

Combining Vectors Algebraically: In Exercises 13–20, let $\mathbf{u} = \langle\, 3 - 2, 1\,\rangle$ and $\mathbf{v} = \langle\, -2, 4, -5\,\rangle$. Find the specified vector **w** and its length $\|\mathbf{w}\|$.

13. $\mathbf{w} = -2\mathbf{u}$

14. $\mathbf{w} = -3\mathbf{u}$

15. $\mathbf{w} = 3\mathbf{u} + 5\mathbf{v}$

16. $\mathbf{w} = 5\mathbf{u} + 3\mathbf{v}$

17. $\mathbf{w} = 4\mathbf{u} - 3\mathbf{v}$

18. $\mathbf{w} = 6\mathbf{u} - 2\mathbf{v}$

19. $\mathbf{w} = \mathbf{u} + \mathbf{u} + \mathbf{v} + \mathbf{v} + \mathbf{v}$

20. $\mathbf{w} = \mathbf{u} + \mathbf{u} - \mathbf{v} - \mathbf{v} - \mathbf{v}$

Unit Vectors: In Exercises 21–26, find the direction of **v**, that is, a unit vector in the same direction as **v**. Hint: Normalize **v**.

21. $\mathbf{v} = \langle 3, 1 \rangle$

22. $\mathbf{v} = \langle 4, 1 \rangle$

23. $\mathbf{v} = \langle 2, -1, 4 \rangle$

24. $\mathbf{v} = \langle\, -1, 3, -2 \rangle$

25. $\mathbf{v} = 3\mathbf{i} - 2\mathbf{j} + 4\mathbf{k}$

26. $\mathbf{v} = 2\mathbf{i} - 3\mathbf{j} + \mathbf{k}$

Linear Algebra: In Exercises 27–32, solve the vector equation(s) for unknown vectors **x**, **y**, **z**

27. $2\mathbf{x} + \langle 1, 2 \rangle = \langle 3, 6 \rangle$

28. $3\mathbf{x} + \langle 2, 3 \rangle = \langle 14, 6 \rangle$

29. $\begin{cases} \mathbf{x} + \mathbf{y} = \langle 2, 3 \rangle \\ \mathbf{x} - \mathbf{y} = \langle 4, 5 \rangle \end{cases}$

30. $\begin{cases} \mathbf{x} + \mathbf{y} = \langle 3, 4 \rangle \\ \mathbf{x} - \mathbf{y} = \langle 5, 8 \rangle \end{cases}$

31. $\begin{cases} \mathbf{x} + \mathbf{y} + \mathbf{z} = \langle 1, 4, 2 \rangle \\ \mathbf{x} - \mathbf{y} - \mathbf{z} = \langle 3, -2, 4 \rangle \\ \mathbf{y} - \mathbf{z} = \langle 3, 5, 7 \rangle \end{cases}$

32. $\begin{cases} \mathbf{x} - \mathbf{y} + \mathbf{z} = \langle 3, 6, 3 \rangle \\ \mathbf{x} + \mathbf{y} - \mathbf{z} = \langle 1, 2, 5 \rangle \\ \mathbf{y} + \mathbf{z} = \langle 7, 8, 9 \rangle \end{cases}$

Force Diagrams: Find the tensions $\mathbf{F}_1$, $\mathbf{F}_2$ in the ropes holding the suspended weight (in pounds).

33.

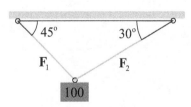

34.

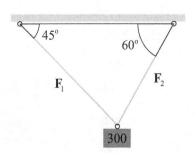

Calculus Concepts & Computation

10.3 The Dot Product

This section introduces another type of operation that we can do on vectors $\mathbf{u}, \mathbf{v}$ in $\mathbb{R}^3$ (and in $\mathbb{R}^2$). The operation is called the *dot product* and is denoted by $\mathbf{u} \cdot \mathbf{v}$ (hence the name dot product) and the result of this operation is a number (not a vector).

DEFINITION 10.3.1 (The Dot Product of Vectors)

Suppose $\mathbf{u} = \langle u_1, u_2, u_3 \rangle$ *and* $\mathbf{v} = \langle v_1, v_2, v_3 \rangle$ *are vectors in* $\mathbb{R}^3$. *Then the dot product of* $\mathbf{u}$ *and* $\mathbf{v}$ *is the number*

$$\mathbf{u} \cdot \mathbf{v} = u_1 v_1 + u_2 v_2 + u_3 v_3 \qquad (10.3.1)$$

NOTE 1: For vectors in the plane, $\mathbf{u} = \langle u_1, u_2 \rangle$, $\mathbf{v} = \langle v_1, v_2 \rangle$, the dot product is defined as $\mathbf{u} \cdot \mathbf{v} = u_1 v_1 + u_2 v_2$.

NOTE 2: The dot product of vectors is sometimes called the *scalar product* to emphasize that the result of the operation is a number and also to contrast it with another type of product of vectors (the *cross product*, which is introduced in Section 10.4).

NOTE 3: The dot product of vectors is also called their *inner product*. In advanced mathematics courses, one studies abstract vector spaces which have an inner product operation on vectors. Such spaces are called *inner product spaces* and the inner product gives a metric structure to the space because it is used to define the length of vectors. For $\mathbb{R}^3$ with the dot product, this is seen from the following:

Dot Products and Length

The dot product of a vector with itself is the square of its length:

$$\mathbf{v} \cdot \mathbf{v} = v_1 v_1 + v_2 v_2 + v_3 v_3 = v_1^2 + v_2^2 + v_3^2 = \|\mathbf{v}\|^2$$

Thus,

$$\sqrt{\mathbf{v} \cdot \mathbf{v}} = \|\mathbf{v}\| \qquad (10.3.2)$$

Example 10.3.1 (Calculating Dot Products)

Problem: Find the dot products of the following vectors:

    (a) $\mathbf{u} = \langle 2, -3, 5 \rangle$, $\mathbf{v} = \langle 4, 1, -6 \rangle$ (b) $\mathbf{w} = 5\mathbf{i} + 2\mathbf{j}$, $\mathbf{w}^\perp = -2\mathbf{i} + 5\mathbf{j}$

Solution: These are easy calculations:

$$\begin{aligned}
\mathbf{u} \cdot \mathbf{v} &= \langle 2, -3, 5 \rangle \cdot \langle 4, 1, -6 \rangle = 2(4) + (-3)1 + 5(-6) = 8 - 3 - 30 = -25 \\
\mathbf{w} \cdot \mathbf{w}^\perp &= (5\mathbf{i} + 2\mathbf{j}) \cdot (-2\mathbf{i} + 5\mathbf{j}) = 5(-2) + 2(5) = -10 + 10 = 0
\end{aligned}$$

As the above example shows, the calculation of dot products is easy. But what do these numbers mean? Of course, as mentioned, the dot product of a vector with itself is the square of its length. But what about the case when the vectors are different?

Each case involves the geometric quantity called the *angle between the vectors*, which for vectors $\mathbf{u}$, $\mathbf{v}$ is the angle θ formed when the vectors are positioned with the same initial point. See Figure 10.3.1. NOTE: θ is always taken to be the smaller of the angles formed: $0 \le \theta \le \pi$. Also recall that for acute angles $(0 < \theta < \pi/2)$,

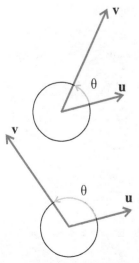

Figure 10.3.1: *The angle* θ *between* $\mathbf{u}$ *and* $\mathbf{v}$.

such as the one at the top of Figure 10.3.1, the cosine is positive $\cos\theta > 0$. While for obtuse angles ($\pi/2 < \theta < \pi$), such as the one at the bottom of Figure 10.3.1, the cosine is negative $\cos\theta < 0$. The Law of Cosines can be used to derive the following relation between $\cos\theta$ and the dot product $\mathbf{u} \cdot \mathbf{v}$:

THEOREM 10.3.1 (The Angle Between Vectors)

For vectors $\mathbf{u} = \langle u_1, u_2, u_3 \rangle$, $\quad \mathbf{v} = \langle v_1, v_2, v_3 \rangle$

$$\mathbf{u} \cdot \mathbf{v} = \|\mathbf{u}\| \, \|\mathbf{v}\| \cos\theta \qquad (10.3.3)$$

where θ is the angle between $\mathbf{u}$ and $\mathbf{v}$.

In words the theorem says: *The dot product of two vectors is equal to the product of their lengths and the cosine of the angle between them.*

NOTE: Since $\|\mathbf{u}\|$ and $\|\mathbf{v}\|$ are positive (we assume neither of the vectors is the zero vector) Formula 10.3.3 shows that θ is acute when $\mathbf{u} \cdot \mathbf{v} > 0$ and is obtuse when $\mathbf{u} \cdot \mathbf{v} < 0$.

Solving Equation 10.3.3 for θ gives the following useful formula for computing the angle θ between vectors $\mathbf{u}$ and $\mathbf{v}$:

Angle Formula: $\theta = \cos^{-1}\left(\dfrac{\mathbf{u} \cdot \mathbf{v}}{\|\mathbf{u}\| \, \|\mathbf{v}\|}\right) \qquad (10.3.4)$

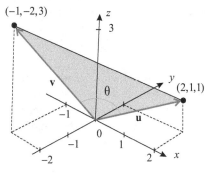

Figure 10.3.2: *The angle between* $\mathbf{u}$ *and* $\mathbf{v}$.

The following two examples illustrate the value of this angle formula.

Example 10.3.2 (Finding Angles)

Problem: Find the angle between the vectors $\mathbf{u} = \langle 2, 1, 1 \rangle$, $\mathbf{v} = \langle -1, -2, 3 \rangle$

Solution: Figure 10.3.2 show the two vectors. The angle between them appears to be obtuse. To be sure we do the computations:

$$\mathbf{u} \cdot \mathbf{v} = \langle 2, 1, 1 \rangle \cdot \langle -1, -2, 3 \rangle = -2 - 2 + 3 = -1$$
$$\|\mathbf{u}\| = \sqrt{4 + 1 + 1} = \sqrt{6}, \; \|\mathbf{v}\| = \sqrt{1 + 4 + 9} = \sqrt{14}$$

and so

$$\theta = \cos^{-1}\left(\frac{-1}{\sqrt{6}\sqrt{14}}\right) \approx 96.26° \approx 1.68 \text{ rad}$$

We also can use Formula 10.3.4 to find the angles in a triangle:

Example 10.3.3 (Finding Angles in a Triangle)

Problem: Suppose, in the plane, $P = (2, 1)$, $Q = (1, 5)$, and $R = (-2, 3)$ are the vertices of the triangle $\triangle PQR$. Find the angle at vertex P.

Solution: At vertex P compute the two vectors

$$\mathbf{u} = \overrightarrow{PQ} = \langle 1 - 2, 5 - 1 \rangle = \langle -1, 4 \rangle$$
$$\mathbf{v} = \overrightarrow{PR} = \langle -2 - 2, 3 - 1 \rangle = \langle -4, 2 \rangle$$

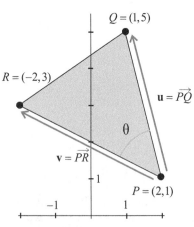

Figure 10.3.3: *The angle at P in triangle $\triangle PQR$.*

See Figure 10.3.3. Then

$$\mathbf{u} \cdot \mathbf{v} = \overrightarrow{PQ} \cdot \overrightarrow{PR} = 4 + 8 = 12$$

$$\|\mathbf{u}\| = \|\overrightarrow{PQ}\| = \sqrt{1 + 16} = \sqrt{17} \; \text{ and } \; \|\mathbf{v}\| = \|\overrightarrow{PR}\| = \sqrt{16 + 4} = \sqrt{20}$$

and so

$$\theta = \cos^{-1}\left(\frac{12}{\sqrt{17}\sqrt{20}}\right) \approx 49.4° \approx 0.862 \text{ rad}$$

An important geometrical concept is orthogonality of vectors. Two vectors $\mathbf{u}$ and $\mathbf{v}$ are *orthogonal* (also known as *perpendicular*) if the angle between them is a right angle. Thus, we get the following important corollary of Theorem 10.3.1, which gives an easy method for determining if two vectors are orthogonal.

COROLLARY 10.3.1 (Orthogonal Vectors)

Two nonzero vectors $\mathbf{u}$ and $\mathbf{v}$ are orthogonal, i.e., perpendicular, if and only if $\mathbf{u} \cdot \mathbf{v} = 0$

The dot product, as with products of numbers, has the commutative and distributive properties. These are stated in the following theorem.

THEOREM 10.3.2 (Properties of the Dot Product)

Suppose $\mathbf{u}$, $\mathbf{v}$, $\mathbf{w}$ are vectors and k is a scalar. Then

(1) $\mathbf{u} \cdot \mathbf{v} = \mathbf{v} \cdot \mathbf{u}$ (2) $\mathbf{u} \cdot (\mathbf{v} + \mathbf{w}) = \mathbf{u} \cdot \mathbf{v} + \mathbf{u} \cdot \mathbf{w}$ (3) $(k\mathbf{u}) \cdot \mathbf{v} = k(\mathbf{u} \cdot \mathbf{v}) = \mathbf{v} \cdot (k\mathbf{u})$

All of these are easily proved using the Definition 10.3.1 of the dot product (Exercise). The distributive property in (2) is the most useful of the three properties. The other two are more or less taken for granted when working with expressions involving dot products.

Vector Projections

Each (nonzero) vector $\mathbf{v}$ in space determines a line in space, namely the line that passes through the initial and terminal points of $\mathbf{v}$. A useful operation on vectors is to be able to project them on this *line through* $\mathbf{v}$.

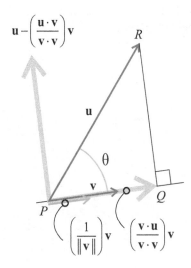

Figure 10.3.4: *The vector projection of $\mathbf{u}$ onto $\mathbf{v}$.*

Thus, suppose $\mathbf{u}$ is another vector and we move it so that it's initial point coincides with the initial point P of $\mathbf{v}$. Then $\mathbf{u}$, $\mathbf{v}$, and the line through $\mathbf{v}$ all lie in the same plane. See Figure 10.3.4. In this plane drop a perpendicular from the terminal point of $\mathbf{u}$ to the line through $\mathbf{v}$. This gives a point Q and the vector $\overrightarrow{PQ}$ is called the *vector projection* of $\mathbf{u}$ onto $\mathbf{v}$. The notation for this vector is $\text{proj}_{\mathbf{v}}\,\mathbf{u}$. This is the vector shown in brown in Figure 10.3.4.

To determine a formula for $\text{proj}_{\mathbf{v}}\,\mathbf{u} = \overrightarrow{PQ}$, we note that it has length $\|\overrightarrow{PQ}\|$ and is in the direction of the unit vector $\frac{1}{\|\mathbf{v}\|}\mathbf{v}$. Thus,

$$\text{proj}_{\mathbf{v}}\,\mathbf{u} = \|\overrightarrow{PQ}\| \frac{1}{\|\mathbf{v}\|}\mathbf{v} \qquad (10.3.5)$$

But $\|\overrightarrow{PQ}\|$ is the length of side adjacent to angle θ in the right triangle $\triangle PQR$ with hypotenuse length $\|\mathbf{u}\|$. See Figure 10.3.4. Thus, by trig and Formula (10.3.3),

$$\|\overrightarrow{PQ}\| = \|\mathbf{u}\|\cos\theta = \|\mathbf{u}\|\left(\frac{\mathbf{v}\cdot\mathbf{u}}{\|\mathbf{v}\|\,\|\mathbf{u}\|}\right) = \frac{\mathbf{v}\cdot\mathbf{u}}{\|\mathbf{v}\|}$$

Using this value in Equation (10.3.5) and the identity $\|\mathbf{v}\|^2 = \mathbf{v}\cdot\mathbf{v}$ gives

$$\text{proj}_{\mathbf{v}}\,\mathbf{u} = \frac{\mathbf{v}\cdot\mathbf{u}}{\|\mathbf{v}\|}\frac{1}{\|\mathbf{v}\|}\mathbf{v} = \frac{\mathbf{v}\cdot\mathbf{u}}{\|\mathbf{v}\|^2}\mathbf{v} = \left(\frac{\mathbf{v}\cdot\mathbf{u}}{\mathbf{v}\cdot\mathbf{v}}\right)\mathbf{v} \qquad (10.3.6)$$

This is the vector projection of $\mathbf{u}$ onto to $\mathbf{v}$ (or more properly, onto the line through $\mathbf{v}$). We can also project $\mathbf{u}$ onto the *plane* that is perpendicular to $\mathbf{v}$. The resulting vector is simply $\mathbf{w} = \mathbf{u} - \text{proj}_{\mathbf{v}}\mathbf{u}$. To see that this vector is perpendicular to $\mathbf{v}$, we simply compute the dot product:

$$\mathbf{v} \cdot \mathbf{w} \;=\; \mathbf{v} \cdot (\mathbf{u} - \mathrm{proj}_{\mathbf{v}}\mathbf{u}) = \mathbf{v} \cdot \left(\mathbf{u} - \left(\frac{\mathbf{v} \cdot \mathbf{u}}{\mathbf{v} \cdot \mathbf{v}} \right) \mathbf{v} \right)$$

$$=\; \mathbf{v} \cdot \mathbf{u} - \left(\frac{\mathbf{v} \cdot \mathbf{u}}{\mathbf{v} \cdot \mathbf{v}} \right) (\mathbf{v} \cdot \mathbf{v}) = \mathbf{v} \cdot \mathbf{u} - \mathbf{v} \cdot \mathbf{u} = 0$$

These two vectors $\mathrm{proj}_{\mathbf{v}}\mathbf{u}$ and $\mathbf{w}$ give what is know as a *decomposition* of any given vector $\mathbf{u}$ into a sum:

$$\mathbf{u} = \mathrm{proj}_{\mathbf{v}}\mathbf{u} + \mathbf{w}$$

of vectors parallel and perpendicular to $\mathbf{v}$. This is summarized in the following theorem.

THEOREM 10.3.3 (Vector Projections)

The vector projection of $\mathbf{u}$ *onto* $\mathbf{v}$ *is given by*

$$\mathrm{proj}_{v}\mathbf{u} = \left(\frac{\mathbf{v} \cdot \mathbf{u}}{\mathbf{v} \cdot \mathbf{v}} \right) \mathbf{v} \qquad (10.3.7)$$

The vector

$$\mathbf{w} = \mathbf{u} - \left(\frac{\mathbf{v} \cdot \mathbf{u}}{\mathbf{v} \cdot \mathbf{v}} \right) \mathbf{v} \qquad (10.3.8)$$

is perpendicular to $\mathbf{v}$ *and is the projection of* $\mathbf{u}$ *into a the plane perpendicular to* $\mathbf{v}$.

NOTE: These projections are sometimes referred to as *orthogonal projections* since there are many other ways to project a vector onto a line or onto a plane.

Example 10.3.4 (Vector Projections)

Problem: Suppose $\mathbf{u} = \langle 3, 1, 1 \rangle$ and $\mathbf{v} = \langle 1, 2, 3 \rangle$. Find the projection of $\mathbf{u}$ onto the line through $\mathbf{v}$ and onto the plane which is perpendicular to $\mathbf{v}$.

Solution: These are easy computations:

$$\mathrm{proj}_{\mathbf{v}}\mathbf{u} = \frac{\langle 1,2,3 \rangle \cdot \langle 3,1,1 \rangle}{\langle 1,2,3 \rangle \cdot \langle 1,2,3 \rangle} \langle 1,2,3 \rangle = \frac{8}{14} \langle 1,2,3 \rangle = \frac{4}{7} \langle 1,2,3 \rangle = \langle \frac{4}{7}, \frac{8}{7}, \frac{12}{7} \rangle$$

and

$$\mathbf{w} = \mathbf{u} - \mathrm{proj}_{\mathbf{v}}\mathbf{u} = \langle 3,1,1 \rangle - \langle \frac{4}{7}, \frac{8}{7}, \frac{12}{7} \rangle = \langle \frac{17}{7}, \frac{-1}{7}, \frac{-5}{7} \rangle$$

Exercises: 10.3 (The Dot Product)

Dot Products: In Exercises 1–12, compute $\mathbf{u} \cdot \mathbf{v}$.

1. $\mathbf{u} = \langle 3, -1 \rangle, \mathbf{v} = \langle 2, 4 \rangle$ **2.** $\mathbf{u} = \langle 3, -1 \rangle, \mathbf{v} = \langle 2, 4 \rangle$

3. $\mathbf{u} = \langle 5, 2 \rangle, \mathbf{v} = \langle -2, 5 \rangle$ **4.** $\mathbf{u} = \langle 4, 1 \rangle, \mathbf{v} = \langle -1, 4 \rangle$

5. $\mathbf{u} = 2\mathbf{i} + 3\mathbf{j}, \mathbf{v} = 5\mathbf{i} + 2\mathbf{j}$ **6.** $\mathbf{u} = 3\mathbf{i} + 4\mathbf{j}, \mathbf{v} = 6\mathbf{i} + \mathbf{j}$

7. $\mathbf{u} = \langle 1, -2, 5 \rangle, \mathbf{v} = \langle 3, 4, -2 \rangle$

8. $\mathbf{u} = \langle 3, -1, 6 \rangle, \mathbf{v} = \langle 2, 4, 7 \rangle$

9. $\mathbf{u} = \mathbf{i} + 2\mathbf{j} - 4\mathbf{k}, \mathbf{v} = 3\mathbf{i} + 2\mathbf{j} + 5\mathbf{j}$

10. $\mathbf{u} = \mathbf{i} + 2\mathbf{j} - 4\mathbf{k}, \mathbf{v} = 3\mathbf{i} + 2\mathbf{j} + 5\mathbf{j}$

11. $\mathbf{u} = \langle 1, 4, 6 \rangle, \mathbf{v} = \langle 2, -2, 1 \rangle$

12. $\mathbf{u} = \langle 3, -1, 2 \rangle, \mathbf{v} = \langle 2, 4, -1 \rangle$

Angle Between Vectors: In Exercises 13–24, compute the angle θ (in degrees) between $\mathbf{u}$ and $\mathbf{v}$.

13. $\mathbf{u} = \langle 3, -1 \rangle, \mathbf{v} = \langle 2, 4 \rangle$ **14.** $\mathbf{u} = \langle 3, -1 \rangle, \mathbf{v} = \langle 2, 4 \rangle$

15. $\mathbf{u} = \langle 5, 2 \rangle, \mathbf{v} = \langle -2, 5 \rangle$ **16.** $\mathbf{u} = \langle 4, 1 \rangle, \mathbf{v} = \langle -1, 4 \rangle$

17. $\mathbf{u} = 2\mathbf{i} + 3\mathbf{j}, \mathbf{v} = 5\mathbf{i} + 2\mathbf{j}$ **18.** $\mathbf{u} = 3\mathbf{i} + 4\mathbf{j}, \mathbf{v} = 6\mathbf{i} + \mathbf{j}$

19. $\mathbf{u} = \langle 1, -2, 5 \rangle, \mathbf{v} = \langle 3, 4, -2 \rangle$

20. $\mathbf{u} = \langle 3, -1, 6 \rangle, \mathbf{v} = \langle 2, 4, 7 \rangle$

21. $\mathbf{u} = \mathbf{i} + 2\mathbf{j} - 4\mathbf{k}, \mathbf{v} = 3\mathbf{i} + 2\mathbf{j} + 5\mathbf{j}$

22. $\mathbf{u} = \mathbf{i} + 2\mathbf{j} - 4\mathbf{k}, \mathbf{v} = 3\mathbf{i} + 2\mathbf{j} + 5\mathbf{j}$

23. $\mathbf{u} = \langle 1, 4, 6 \rangle, \mathbf{v} = \langle 2, -2, 1 \rangle$

24. $\mathbf{u} = \langle 3, -1, 2 \rangle, \mathbf{v} = \langle 2, 4, -1 \rangle$

The Angles in a Triangle: In Exercises 25–30, find the three angles (in degrees) in the triangle $\triangle PQR$. Note: The sum of the angles is $180°$.

25. Vertices: $P = (3, 4), Q = (6, 5), R = (4, 9)$

26. Vertices: $P = (3, 4), Q = (6, 5), R = (4, 9)$

27. Vertices: $P = (2, 1, 1), Q = (0, 4, 2), R = (-1, 1, 6)$

28. Vertices: $P = (3, 1, 1), Q = (0, 5, 2), R = (-2, 1, 6)$

29. Vertices: $P = (3, 1, 5), Q = (4, 3, 11), R = (5, -1, 6)$

30. Vertices: $P = (2, 1, 1), Q = (0, 4, 2), R = (-1, 1, 6)$

Parallel and Orthogonal (Perpendicular) Vectors: In Exercises 31–38, determine if the vector vectors are parallel, orthogonal, or neither.

31. $\mathbf{u} = \langle 3, -1 \rangle, \mathbf{v} = \langle 1, 3 \rangle$ **32.** $\mathbf{u} = \langle 4, 5 \rangle, \mathbf{v} = \langle -5, 4 \rangle$

33. $\mathbf{u} = 6\mathbf{i} - 2\mathbf{j}, \mathbf{v} = 3\mathbf{i} - \mathbf{j}$ **34.** $\mathbf{u} = 3\mathbf{i} + 4\mathbf{j}, \mathbf{v} = 6\mathbf{i} + 8\mathbf{j}$

35. $\mathbf{u} = \langle 3, -2, 5 \rangle, \mathbf{v} = \langle 6, -4, 10 \rangle$

36. $\mathbf{u} = \langle 3, -5, 6 \rangle, \mathbf{v} = \langle 6, -10, 12 \rangle$

37. $\mathbf{u} = 2\mathbf{i} - 5\mathbf{j} + 2\mathbf{k}, \mathbf{v} = 3\mathbf{i} + 2\mathbf{j} + 2\mathbf{k}$

38. $\mathbf{u} = \mathbf{i} + 2\mathbf{j} - 4\mathbf{k}, \mathbf{v} = 3\mathbf{i} + 2\mathbf{j} + 5\mathbf{k}$

Projecting Vectors: In Exercises 39–48, find $\text{proj}_{\mathbf{v}} \mathbf{u}$ (the projection of $\mathbf{u}$ onto $\mathbf{v}$) and $\mathbf{w} = \mathbf{u} - \text{proj}_{\mathbf{v}} \mathbf{u}$ (the projection of $\mathbf{u}$ onto the plane perpendicular to $\mathbf{v}$).

39. $\mathbf{u} = \langle 1, 4 \rangle, \mathbf{v} = \langle 3, 1 \rangle$ **40.** $\mathbf{u} = \langle 2, 6 \rangle, \mathbf{v} = \langle 5, 2 \rangle$

41. $\mathbf{u} = \langle 2, 4, 3 \rangle, \mathbf{v} = \langle 1, 1, 2 \rangle$

42. $\mathbf{u} = \langle 5, 0, 8 \rangle, \mathbf{v} = \langle 2, 2, 1 \rangle$

43. $\mathbf{u} = \langle 3, 2, 7 \rangle, \mathbf{v} = \langle 2, -2, 1 \rangle$

44. $\mathbf{u} = \langle 0, 4, 1 \rangle, \mathbf{v} = \langle 2, 2, 1 \rangle$

45. $\mathbf{u} = \langle 1, 5, 2 \rangle, \mathbf{v} = \langle 2, -1, 3 \rangle$

46. $\mathbf{u} = \langle 1, 4, 3 \rangle, \mathbf{v} = \langle 2, 1, 4 \rangle$

47. $\mathbf{u} = \langle 1, -1, -1 \rangle, \mathbf{v} = \langle 1, 3, -2 \rangle$

48. $\mathbf{u} = \langle 2, -1, 1 \rangle, \mathbf{v} = \langle 3, 2, -3 \rangle$

Calculus Concepts & Computation

10.4 The Cross Product

In the last section we saw the many geometrical uses of the number $\mathbf{u} \cdot \mathbf{v}$, which is the dot product of two vectors $\mathbf{u}, \mathbf{v}$. In this section we look at another type of product, $\mathbf{u} \times \mathbf{v}$, of vectors $\mathbf{u}, \mathbf{v}$. This product is called the *cross product*. The result $\mathbf{u} \times \mathbf{v}$ is *vector* (not a number). The definition, and computation, of the cross $\mathbf{u} \times \mathbf{v}$ is slightly more complicated than that of the dot product, but this complexity results in a wide variety of geometrical applications (normal lines to planes, volumes of parallelepipeds, areas of triangles in space, etc.).

DEFINITION 10.4.1 (The Cross Product of Vectors)

Suppose $\mathbf{u} = \langle u_1, u_2, u_3 \rangle$ *and* $\mathbf{v} = \langle v_1, v_2, v_3 \rangle$ *are vectors in* $\mathbb{R}^3$. *Then the*

cross product of $\mathbf{u}$ *and* $\mathbf{v}$ *is the vector*

$$\mathbf{u} \times \mathbf{v} = \langle u_2 v_3 - u_3 v_2, u_3 v_1 - u_1 v_3, u_1 v_2 - u_2 v_1 \rangle \qquad (10.4.1)$$

To help ease the memorization and use of this complicated formula (10.4.1), we relate it to the important subject of *determinants*, which you will study (or have studied) in Linear Algebra.

Determinants of Matrices

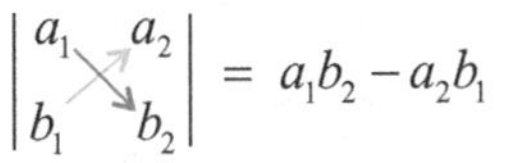

$$\begin{vmatrix} a_1 & a_2 \\ b_1 & b_2 \end{vmatrix} = a_1 b_2 - a_2 b_1$$

Figure 10.4.1: *Computing a* 2×2 *determinant.*

A matrix A is an array, or table, of numbers (called the entries of A) and the determinant of A (when A is square) is a number $|A|$ computed from the entries of A in a very special way. For example:

$$A = \begin{bmatrix} a_1 & a_2 \\ b_1 & b_2 \end{bmatrix} \qquad |A| = \begin{vmatrix} a_1 & a_2 \\ b_1 & b_2 \end{vmatrix} = a_1 b_2 - a_2 b_1$$

This matrix has two rows and two columns and is known as a 2×2 matrix. The determinant of this matrix is the number $a_1 b_2 - a_2 b_1$. This is called a 2×2 *determinant*. Figure 10.4.1 indicates how the four entries in the 2×2 matrix are combined to compute its determinant.

Example 10.4.1 (Calculating a 2×2 Determinant)

For $A = \begin{bmatrix} 2 & 4 \\ 1 & 5 \end{bmatrix}$, we get $|A| = \begin{vmatrix} 2 & 4 \\ 1 & 5 \end{vmatrix} = 2(5) - 4(1) = 10 - 4 = 6$

Next, a 3×3 matrix and its determinant are

$$A = \begin{bmatrix} a_1 & a_2 & a_3 \\ b_1 & b_2 & b_3 \\ c_1 & c_2 & c_3 \end{bmatrix}$$

$$|A| = \begin{vmatrix} a_1 & a_2 & a_3 \\ b_1 & b_2 & b_3 \\ c_1 & c_2 & c_3 \end{vmatrix} = a_1 \begin{vmatrix} b_2 & b_3 \\ c_2 & c_3 \end{vmatrix} - a_2 \begin{vmatrix} b_1 & b_3 \\ c_1 & c_3 \end{vmatrix} + a_3 \begin{vmatrix} b_1 & b_2 \\ c_1 & c_2 \end{vmatrix}$$

$$= a_1(b_2 c_3 - b_3 c_2) - a_2(b_1 c_3 - b_3 c_1) + a_3(b_1 c_2 - b_2 c_1)$$

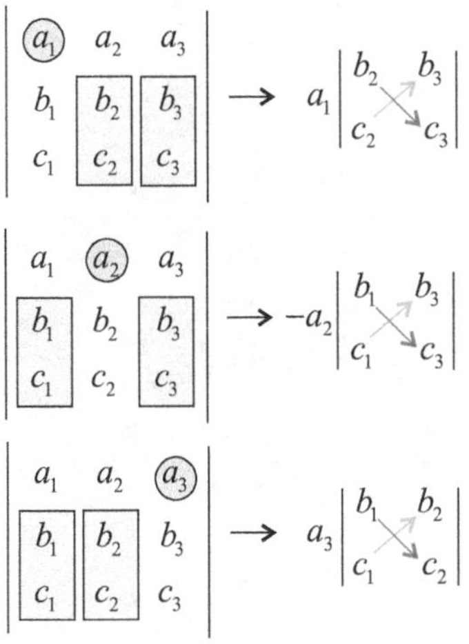

Figure 10.4.2: *Computing a* 3×3 *determinant.*

As you can see, the 3×3 determinant involves combining the three entries in the 1st row with three 2×2 determinants from the 2nd and 3rd rows. Figure 10.4.2 indicates how these 2×2 determinants are formed.

Example 10.4.2 (Calculating a 3×3 Determinant)

$$A = \begin{bmatrix} 3 & 2 & 4 \\ 1 & 8 & 3 \\ 4 & 6 & 2 \end{bmatrix}$$

$$|A| = \begin{vmatrix} 3 & 2 & 4 \\ 1 & 8 & 3 \\ 4 & 6 & 2 \end{vmatrix} = 3 \begin{vmatrix} 8 & 3 \\ 6 & 2 \end{vmatrix} - 2 \begin{vmatrix} 1 & 3 \\ 4 & 2 \end{vmatrix} + 4 \begin{vmatrix} 1 & 8 \\ 4 & 6 \end{vmatrix}$$

$$= 3(16 - 18) - 2(2 - 12) + 4(6 - 32) = -90$$

If you study Formula (10.4.1) for the cross product $\mathbf{u} \times \mathbf{v}$ you will see that each component of this vector is a 2×2 determinant, as indicated in the following box.

$$\mathbf{u} = \langle u_1, u_2, u_3 \rangle$$
$$\mathbf{v} = \langle v_1, v_2, v_3 \rangle$$

$$\mathbf{u} \times \mathbf{v} = \langle u_2 v_3 - u_3 v_2, u_3 v_1 - u_1 v_3, u_1 v_2 - u_2 v_1 \rangle$$

$$\begin{vmatrix} u_2 & u_3 \\ v_2 & v_3 \end{vmatrix} \quad - \begin{vmatrix} u_1 & u_3 \\ v_1 & v_3 \end{vmatrix} \quad \begin{vmatrix} u_1 & u_2 \\ v_1 & v_2 \end{vmatrix}$$

(10.4.2)

The three particular 2×2 determinants shown in Formula (10.4.2) can be explained by looking at 3×3 determinants. If we allow the entries in the first row to be vectors instead of numbers and replace a_1, a_2, a_3 by $\mathbf{i}, \mathbf{j}, \mathbf{k}$, then the computation outlined in Figure 10.4.2 gives

The Cross Product as a Determinant

$$\mathbf{u} \times \mathbf{v} = \begin{vmatrix} \mathbf{i} & \mathbf{j} & \mathbf{k} \\ u_1 & u_2 & u_3 \\ v_1 & v_2 & v_3 \end{vmatrix} = \begin{vmatrix} u_2 & u_3 \\ v_2 & v_3 \end{vmatrix} \mathbf{i} - \begin{vmatrix} u_1 & u_3 \\ v_1 & v_3 \end{vmatrix} \mathbf{j} + \begin{vmatrix} u_1 & u_2 \\ v_1 & v_2 \end{vmatrix} \mathbf{k} \qquad (10.4.3)$$

NOTE 1: There is a minus sign in the second term of Formula (10.4.3). You can view the vectors as being combined with alternating signs: $+, -, +$

NOTE 2: You will be computing a lot of cross products, so you need to make sure you understand how to do it.

Example 10.4.3 (Calculating Cross Products)

Problem: Find the cross products of the following vectors

(a) $\mathbf{u} = \langle 2, 3, 5 \rangle$, $\mathbf{v} = \langle 4, 1, 6 \rangle$ (b) $\mathbf{w} = \langle 4, 1, 0 \rangle$, $\mathbf{F} = \langle 1, 6, 0 \rangle$

Solution: The calculations are:

$$\mathbf{u} \times \mathbf{v} = \begin{vmatrix} \mathbf{i} & \mathbf{j} & \mathbf{k} \\ 2 & 3 & 5 \\ 4 & 1 & 6 \end{vmatrix} = \begin{vmatrix} 3 & 5 \\ 1 & 6 \end{vmatrix} \mathbf{i} - \begin{vmatrix} 2 & 5 \\ 4 & 6 \end{vmatrix} \mathbf{j} + \begin{vmatrix} 2 & 3 \\ 4 & 1 \end{vmatrix} \mathbf{k}$$

$$= (18 - 5)\mathbf{i} - (12 - 20)\mathbf{j} + (2 - 12)\mathbf{k} = 13\mathbf{i} + 8\mathbf{j} - 10\mathbf{k}$$

$$\mathbf{w} \times \mathbf{F} = \begin{vmatrix} \mathbf{i} & \mathbf{j} & \mathbf{k} \\ 4 & 1 & 0 \\ 1 & 6 & 0 \end{vmatrix} = \begin{vmatrix} 1 & 0 \\ 6 & 0 \end{vmatrix} \mathbf{i} - \begin{vmatrix} 4 & 0 \\ 1 & 0 \end{vmatrix} \mathbf{j} + \begin{vmatrix} 4 & 1 \\ 1 & 6 \end{vmatrix} \mathbf{k}$$

$$= (0)\mathbf{i} - (0)\mathbf{j} + (23)\mathbf{k} = 23\mathbf{k} = \langle 0, 0, 23 \rangle$$

NOTE: For vectors $\mathbf{u} = \langle u_1, u_2 \rangle$, $\mathbf{v} = \langle v_1, v_2 \rangle$ in $\mathbb{R}^2$ there is no cross product. However, if we identify $\mathbb{R}^2$ with the x-y plane in $\mathbb{R}^3$, so that $\mathbf{u} = \langle u_1, u_2, 0 \rangle$ and $\mathbf{v} = \langle v_1, v_2, 0 \rangle$, then $\mathbf{u} \times \mathbf{v} = \langle 0, 0, u_1 v_2 - u_2 v_1 \rangle$.

Geometry and the Cross Product

We have seen how the dot product is useful geometrically in discerning when two vectors $\mathbf{u}, \mathbf{v}$ are perpendicular ($\mathbf{u} \cdot \mathbf{v} = 0$) and, more generally, in computing the angle θ between $\mathbf{u}$ and $\mathbf{v}$. This comes from the formula $\mathbf{u} \cdot \mathbf{v} = \|\mathbf{u}\| \|\mathbf{v}\| \cos\theta$.

Similarly, the cross product allows us to compute several geometrical quantities connected with two vectors $\mathbf{u}, \mathbf{v}$. (We assume $\mathbf{v}$ is not a scalar multiple of $\mathbf{u}$.) Recall that when these vectors are positioned so that they have the same initial point, then there is a parallelogram determined by $\mathbf{u}$ and $\mathbf{v}$, which we call the *u-v parallelogram*. Additionally, this parallelogram lies in the plane determined by $\mathbf{u}$ and $\mathbf{v}$, which we call the *u-v plane*. See Figure 10.4.3.

In this situation, there are two things we would like to do geometrically:

(1) Determine a normal line to the *u-v* plane, i.e., a line that is perpendicular to this plane.

(2) Compute the area of the *u-v* parallelogram.

The next theorem tells us how to get each of these things from the cross product $\mathbf{u} \times \mathbf{v}$.

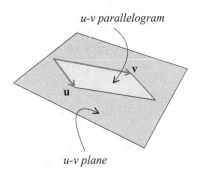

Figure 10.4.3: *The plane and the parallelogram determined by* $\mathbf{u}$ *and* $\mathbf{v}$.

THEOREM 10.4.1 (The Direction and Length of u×v)

For vectors $\mathbf{u}$ *and* $\mathbf{v}$ *in* $\mathbb{R}^3$

(1) *The cross product* $\mathbf{u} \times \mathbf{v}$ *is perpendicular to both* $\mathbf{u}$ *and* $\mathbf{v}$ *and, hence, also to the plane determined by these vectors (the u-v plane)*

(2) *The length* $\|\mathbf{u} \times \mathbf{v}\|$ *of the cross product is equal to the area of the parallelogram determined by* $\mathbf{u}$ *and* $\mathbf{v}$ *(the u-v parallelogram). That is to say,*

$$\|\mathbf{u} \times \mathbf{v}\| = \|\mathbf{u}\| \|\mathbf{v}\| \sin\theta \qquad (10.4.4)$$

where θ *is the angle between* $\mathbf{u}$ *and* $\mathbf{v}$.

The geometric content of the theorem is illustrated in the following figure.

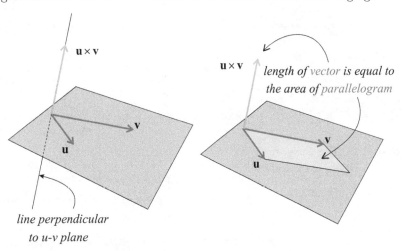

Figure 10.4.4: *The cross product* $\mathbf{u} \times \mathbf{v}$ *is perpendicular to the u-v plane and its length* $\|\mathbf{u} \times \mathbf{v}\|$ *is the area of the u-v parallelogram*

On the line perpendicular to the *u-v* plane there are two directions that we could select for the direction of $\mathbf{u} \times \mathbf{v}$. The direction we chose in Figure 10.4.4 is based on the right-hand rule.

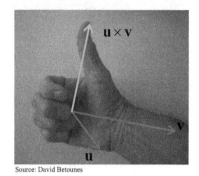

Figure 10.4.5: *The right-hand rule determines the direction on the normal line of* $\mathbf{u} \times \mathbf{v}$.

Right-Hand Rule: To determine the direction of $\mathbf{u} \times \mathbf{v}$, visualize wrapping your right-hand around the normal line and turning $\mathbf{u}$ onto $\mathbf{v}$. Then $\mathbf{u} \times \mathbf{v}$ will be in the direction that your thumb is pointing. See Figure 10.4.5.

Proof of Theorem 10.4.1: For Part (1) we use Formula (10.4.1) in Definition 10.4.1.

$$
\begin{aligned}
\mathbf{u} \cdot (\mathbf{u} \times \mathbf{v}) &= \langle u_1, u_2, u_3 \rangle \cdot \langle u_2 v_3 - u_3 v_2, -(u_1 v_3 - u_3 v_1), u_1 v_2 - u_2 v_1 \rangle \\
&= u_1(u_2 v_3 - u_3 v_2) - u_2(u_1 v_3 - u_3 v_1) + u_3(u_1 v_2 - u_2 v_1) \\
&= 0
\end{aligned}
$$

This shows that $\mathbf{u}$ and $\mathbf{u} \times \mathbf{v}$ are perpendicular. Similarly one shows that $\mathbf{v} \cdot (\mathbf{u} \times \mathbf{v}) = 0$ and so $\mathbf{v}$ and $\mathbf{u} \times \mathbf{v}$ are perpendicular.

To prove Part (2) of the theorem, note that the area of the u-v parallelogram is $A = \|\mathbf{u}\| \, \|\mathbf{v}\| \sin \theta$. See Figure 10.4.6. We look at the square of A and use Formula (10.3.3): $\mathbf{u} \cdot \mathbf{v} = \|\mathbf{u}\| \, \|\mathbf{v}\| \cos \theta$, and the trig identity: $\sin^2 \theta = 1 - \cos^2 \theta$. This gives

$$
\begin{aligned}
A^2 &= \|\mathbf{u}\|^2 \|\mathbf{v}\|^2 \sin^2 \theta = \|\mathbf{u}\|^2 \|\mathbf{v}\|^2 (1 - \cos^2 \theta) = \|\mathbf{u}\|^2 \|\mathbf{v}\|^2 - \|\mathbf{u}\|^2 \|\mathbf{v}\|^2 \cos^2 \theta \\
&= \|\mathbf{u}\|^2 \|\mathbf{v}\|^2 - (\mathbf{u} \cdot \mathbf{v})^2 \\
&= (u_1^2 + u_2^2 + u_3^2)(v_1^2 + v_2^2 + v_3^2) - (u_1 v_1 + u_2 v_2 + u_3 v_3)^2 \\
&= \left\{ \begin{array}{l} u_1^2 v_1^2 + u_1^2 v_2^2 + u_1^2 v_3^2 \\ + u_2^2 v_1^2 + u_2^2 v_2^2 + u_2^2 v_3^2 \\ + u_3^2 v_1^2 + u_3^2 v_2^2 + u_3^2 v_3^2 \end{array} \right\} - \left\{ \begin{array}{l} u_1^2 v_1^2 + 2 u_1 u_2 v_1 v_2 + u_2^2 v_2^2 \\ + 2 u_1 u_3 v_1 v_3 + 2 u_2 u_3 v_2 v_3 + u_3^2 v_3^2 \end{array} \right\} \\
&= (u_2 v_3 - u_3 v_2)^2 + (u_1 v_3 - u_3 v_1)^2 + (u_1 v_2 - u_2 v_1)^2 \\
&= \|\mathbf{u} \times \mathbf{v}\|^2
\end{aligned}
$$

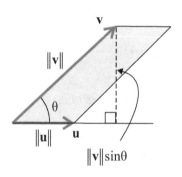

Figure 10.4.6: *The area of the u-v parallelogram.*

Example 10.4.4 (Finding Normals to and Areas of Parallelograms)

Problem: For $\mathbf{u} = \langle 2, 1, 1 \rangle$ and $\mathbf{v} = \langle -1, 2, 1 \rangle$ find a normal to the u-v plane and the area of the u-v parallelogram.

Solution: We first compute the cross product:

$$
\begin{aligned}
\mathbf{u} \times \mathbf{v} &= \begin{vmatrix} \mathbf{i} & \mathbf{j} & \mathbf{k} \\ 2 & 1 & 1 \\ -1 & 2 & 1 \end{vmatrix} = \begin{vmatrix} 1 & 1 \\ 2 & 1 \end{vmatrix} \mathbf{i} - \begin{vmatrix} 2 & 1 \\ -1 & 1 \end{vmatrix} \mathbf{j} + \begin{vmatrix} 2 & 1 \\ -1 & 2 \end{vmatrix} \mathbf{k} \\
&= (1 - 2)\mathbf{i} - (2 + 1)\mathbf{j} + (4 + 1)\mathbf{k} = -\mathbf{i} - 3\mathbf{j} + 5\mathbf{k} = \langle -1, -3, 5 \rangle
\end{aligned}
$$

This gives a vector $\mathbf{n} = \langle -1, -3, 5 \rangle$, which is normal to the u-v plane. The length of this vector is the area of the u-v parallelogram:

$$
A = \|\mathbf{u} \times \mathbf{v}\| = \|\mathbf{n}\| = \|\langle -1, -3, 5 \rangle\| = \sqrt{1 + 9 + 25} = \sqrt{35} \approx 5.9
$$

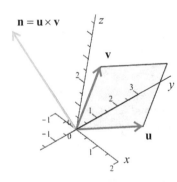

Figure 10.4.7: *The u-v parallelogram in Example 10.4.4.*

Figure 10.4.7 shows the u-v parallelogram and normal vector for this example. It is an annotated version of a Maple Figure that you can produce with the command `cross_product(u1,u2,u3,v1,v2,v3)`. This command also outputs the components of $\mathbf{n} = \mathbf{u} \times \mathbf{v}$ and the area of the u-v parallelogram. You can use it to visualize and check your by-hand computations.

Some algebraic properties of the cross product are given in the following theorem.

THEOREM 10.4.2 (Properties of the Cross Product)

Suppose $\mathbf{u}$, $\mathbf{v}$, $\mathbf{w}$ *are vectors and* k *is a scalar. Then*

(1) $\mathbf{v} \times \mathbf{u} = -\mathbf{u} \times \mathbf{v}$ (2) $\mathbf{u} \times (\mathbf{v} + \mathbf{w}) = \mathbf{u} \times \mathbf{v} + \mathbf{u} \times \mathbf{w}$ (3) $k(\mathbf{u} \times \mathbf{v}) = (k\mathbf{u}) \times \mathbf{v} = \mathbf{v} \times (k\mathbf{u})$

(4) $\mathbf{w} \times (\mathbf{u} \times \mathbf{v}) = (\mathbf{w} \cdot \mathbf{v})\mathbf{u} - (\mathbf{w} \cdot \mathbf{u})\mathbf{v}$

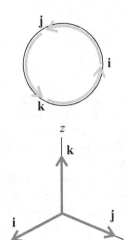

Figure 10.4.8: *Circle diagram for cross products of **i-j-k** vectors .*

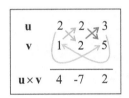

Figure 10.4.9: *Quick way to compute cross products of vectors.*

NOTE 1 (Non-Commutative): Property (1) in the theorem says that the cross product is *not* commutative, i.e., the order of the product makes a difference.

NOTE 2 (Distributivity): Property (2) is the standard distributive property for products and sums.

NOTE 3: We know that $\mathbf{w} \times (\mathbf{u} \times \mathbf{v})$ is perpendicular to $\mathbf{u} \times \mathbf{v}$ and so must lie in the u-v plane. Property (4) tells us what linear combination of $\mathbf{u}$ and $\mathbf{v}$ it is.

NOTE 4 **(Corollary)**: $\mathbf{v} \times \mathbf{v} = \mathbf{0}$ for any vector $\mathbf{v}$. This follows from Property (1) with $\mathbf{u} = \mathbf{v}$, so that $\mathbf{v} \times \mathbf{v} = -\mathbf{v} \times \mathbf{v}$. But the only vector that is the negative of itself is the zero vector.

Cross Products of the i-j-k Vectors: Since the i-j-k vectors are unit vectors that are mutually perpendicular, it follows that the parallelogram determined by any two of them is a square with area 1. Thus, the cross product of two of them is a unit vector and, by the right-hand rule, is $\pm$ one of the i-j-k vectors. In particular, one can show that

$$\mathbf{i} \times \mathbf{j} = \mathbf{k}, \quad \mathbf{j} \times \mathbf{k} = \mathbf{i}, \quad \mathbf{k} \times \mathbf{i} = \mathbf{j}$$

These products are easy to remember if you draw the circle-diagram shown in Figure 10.4.8. Of course, by Property (1) in Theorem 10.4.2, $\mathbf{j} \times \mathbf{i} = -(\mathbf{i} \times \mathbf{j}) = \mathbf{k}$, etc. Knowing the cross products of these standard unit vectors, you could use it to compute the cross product of any two vectors. For example,

$$(2\mathbf{i} + 2\mathbf{j} + 3\mathbf{k}) \times (\mathbf{i} + 2\mathbf{j} + 5\mathbf{k}) = \left\{ \begin{array}{l} 2(\mathbf{i} \times \mathbf{i}) + 4(\mathbf{i} \times \mathbf{j}) + 10(\mathbf{i} \times \mathbf{k}) \\ +2(\mathbf{j} \times \mathbf{i}) + 4(\mathbf{j} \times \mathbf{j}) + 10(\mathbf{j} \times \mathbf{k}) \\ +3(\mathbf{k} \times \mathbf{i}) + 6(\mathbf{k} \times \mathbf{j}) + 15(\mathbf{k} \times \mathbf{k}) \end{array} \right\}$$

$$= \left\{ \begin{array}{l} 4\mathbf{k} - 10\mathbf{j} \\ -2\mathbf{k} + 10\mathbf{i} \\ +3\mathbf{j} - 6\mathbf{i} \end{array} \right\} = 4\mathbf{i} - 7\mathbf{j} + 2\mathbf{k}$$

However, this is not the quickest way to compute cross products. After you have studied the above example and the Definition 10.4.1 of the cross product and the determinant way of computing it (Formula 10.4.3), you may discover a computational method that is quicker than any of these three. Figure 10.4.9 indicates a very quick way to compute the cross product in the above example.

Example 10.4.5 (Areas of Triangles)

Problem: Suppose $P = (1, -1, 2), Q = (3, 1, 1)$, and $R = (-1, 2, 3)$ are three points in space. Find the area of triangle $\triangle PQR$.

Solution: In the last section we used the dot product to measure the angles in a triangle. Here we can use the cross product to measure the area. The strategy is to pick a vertex, say P and look at the vectors $\overrightarrow{PQ}, \overrightarrow{PR}$. Then the length $\|\overrightarrow{PQ} \times \overrightarrow{PR}\|$ of the cross product is the area of the parallelogram determined by $\overrightarrow{PQ}, \overrightarrow{PR}$. By geometry the area of triangle is half the area of the parallelogram $A = \frac{1}{2}\|\overrightarrow{PQ} \times \overrightarrow{PR}\|$. So the computations, using the quick method in Figure 10.4.9, are:

$$\overrightarrow{PQ} = \langle 3-1, 1-(-1), 1-2 \rangle = \langle 2, 2, -1 \rangle$$
$$\overrightarrow{PR} = \langle -1-1, 2-(-1), 3-2 \rangle = \langle -2, 3, 1 \rangle$$
$$\overrightarrow{PQ} \times \overrightarrow{PR} = \begin{vmatrix} 2 & 2 & -1 \\ -2 & 3 & 1 \end{vmatrix} = \langle 2+3, -(2-2), 6+4 \rangle = \langle 5, 0, 10 \rangle$$

Thus, the area is

$$A = \tfrac{1}{2}\|\overrightarrow{PQ} \times \overrightarrow{PR}\| = \tfrac{1}{2}\|\langle 5, 0, 10 \rangle\| = \tfrac{1}{2}\sqrt{25+0+100} = \tfrac{1}{2}\sqrt{125} = \frac{5\sqrt{5}}{2}$$

THE SCALAR TRIPLE PRODUCT

With three vectors $\mathbf{u}, \mathbf{v}, \mathbf{w}$ we can combine both the cross product and the dot product to get a scalar (number) called the *scalar triple product* of the vectors:

DEFINITION 10.4.2 (Scalar Triple Product)

The scalar triple product of vectors $\mathbf{u}$, $\mathbf{v}$, $\mathbf{w}$ *is the number* $(\mathbf{u} \times \mathbf{v}) \cdot \mathbf{w}$.

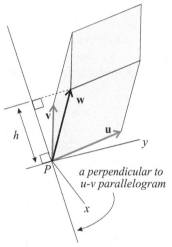

Figure 10.4.10: *The u-v parallelepiped determined by vectors* $\mathbf{u}, \mathbf{v}, \mathbf{w}$.

The vectors $\mathbf{u}, \mathbf{v}, \mathbf{w}$, located so that their initial points coincide, say at the point P, determine a parallelepiped, which is called the *u-v-w parallelepiped*. See Figure 10.4.10. A rectangular parallelepiped is like a shoe box, its sides are pairs of parallel congruent rectangles. You can think of a general parallelepiped as a squashed shoe box, its sides are pairs of parallel congruent parallelograms.

If we select the *u-v* parallelogram as the "base" of the *u-v-w* parallelepiped, then the distance h between the base and the parallelogram opposite it is called the "height" of the parallelepiped. From geometry, the volume of a parallelepiped is the area of the base times the height: $V = Ah$. The geometric significance of the scalar triple product is that its absolute value $|(\mathbf{u} \times \mathbf{v}) \cdot \mathbf{w}|$ is the volume V of the *u-v-w* parallelepiped.

To see this, note that Theorem 10.4.1, says that the area of the base is $A = \|\mathbf{u} \times \mathbf{v}\|$. To measure the height of the parallelepiped, let θ be the angle between $\mathbf{w}$ and $\mathbf{u} \times \mathbf{v}$. If we drop a perpendicular from the terminal point Q of $\mathbf{w}$ to the line through $\mathbf{u} \times \mathbf{v}$ to get the point R on this line, then triangle ΔPQR is a right triangle. See Figure 10.4.11.

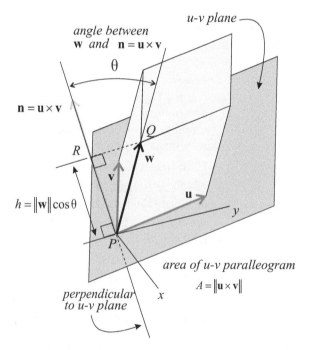

Figure 10.4.11: *Why* $|(\mathbf{u} \times \mathbf{v}) \cdot \mathbf{w}|$ *measures the volume of the u-v-w parallelepiped.*

The hypotenuse of this triangle has length $\|\mathbf{w}\|$. Also, the length of side PR is the height of the parallelepiped, $|PR| = h$ and, by trigonometry, this length is the same as $\|\mathbf{w}\| \cos\theta$. All of this shows that $h = \|\mathbf{w}\| \cos\theta$. Thus, the calculation of the volume is

$$V \quad = \quad Ah = \|\mathbf{u} \times \mathbf{v}\| \, \|\mathbf{w}\| \cos\theta$$

$$= \|\mathbf{u} \times \mathbf{v}\| \, \|\mathbf{w}\| \left(\frac{(\mathbf{u} \times \mathbf{v}) \cdot \mathbf{w}}{\|\mathbf{u} \times \mathbf{v}\| \, \|\mathbf{w}\|} \right)$$

$$= (\mathbf{u} \times \mathbf{v}) \cdot \mathbf{w}$$

NOTE 1: In the next to the last line above, we used the result (Formula (10.3.3) rearranged) that the *cosine of the angle between two vectors is equal to their dot product divided by their lengths.*

NOTE 2: The above volume calculation was based on Figure 10.4.11 where the angle θ between $\mathbf{w}$ and the normal $\mathbf{n} = \mathbf{u} \times \mathbf{v}$ is acute, so that $\cos \theta \geq 0$. When θ is obtuse, then $\cos \theta$ is negative and we should replace it by $|\cos \theta|$ in the expression for h. This will result in getting $|(\mathbf{u} \times \mathbf{v}) \cdot \mathbf{w}|$ in the last line.

From the above calculations we get the following theorem.

THEOREM 10.4.3 (Volumes of Parallelepipeds)

Suppose $\mathbf{u}$, $\mathbf{v}$, $\mathbf{w}$ *are vectors. Then the volume* V *of the u-v-w parallelepiped is*

$$V = |(\mathbf{u} \times \mathbf{v}) \cdot \mathbf{w}| \qquad (10.4.5)$$

NOTE 3: In the theorem, we include the degenerate case when the volume is zero because the vectors $\mathbf{u}$, $\mathbf{v}$, $\mathbf{w}$ all lie in the same plane (or on the same line, which also means they are in the same plane). Thus, when $(\mathbf{u} \times \mathbf{v}) \cdot \mathbf{w} = 0$, we have that $\mathbf{u}$, $\mathbf{v}$, $\mathbf{w}$ are *coplanar*.

Example 10.4.6 (Volumes of Parallelepipeds)

Problem: Suppose $\mathbf{u} = \langle 2, 1, 1 \rangle$, $\mathbf{v} = \langle -1, 2, 1 \rangle$, $\mathbf{w} = \langle 0, 1, 4 \rangle$ are three vectors in space. Find the volume V of the *u-v-w* parallelepiped. Check your answer by computing $V = Ah$ using the area of the base (the *u-v* parallelogram in Example 10.4.4) and the height h.

Solution: In Example 10.4.4, we found $\mathbf{u} \times \mathbf{v} = \langle -1, -3, 5 \rangle$. So, the scalar triple product is

$$(\mathbf{u} \times \mathbf{v}) \cdot \mathbf{w} = \langle -1, -3, 5 \rangle \cdot \langle 0, 1, 4 \rangle = 0 - 3 + 20 = 17$$

Since this is positive, we do not need to take absolute values. Thus, $V = 17$. To check this, we use $A = \sqrt{35} \approx 5.9$ for the area of the *u-v* parallelogram, as found in Example 10.4.4. Next compute

$$h = \|\mathbf{w}\| \cos \theta = \|\mathbf{w}\| \left(\frac{(\mathbf{u} \times \mathbf{v}) \cdot \mathbf{w}}{\|\mathbf{u} \times \mathbf{v}\| \, \|\mathbf{w}\|} \right) = \frac{(\mathbf{u} \times \mathbf{v}) \cdot \mathbf{w}}{\|\mathbf{u} \times \mathbf{v}\|} = \frac{17}{\sqrt{35}} \approx 2.87$$

So clearly, $V = Ah = \sqrt{35} \cdot \frac{17}{\sqrt{35}} = 17$. See figure 10.4.12, which is the annotated version of the Maple Figure produced by the command

```
> scalar_triple_product(u1,u2,u3,v1,v2,v3,w1,w2,w3);
```

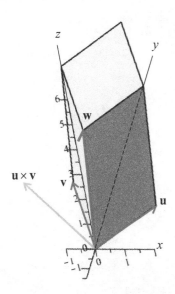

Figure 10.4.12: *The u-v-w parallelepiped in Example* 10.4.6.

Looking back at the definition of a 3×3 determinant at the beginning of this section, you would perhaps guess that it is related to the scalar-triple product, taking the rows of the determinant to be the components of the vectors. This is indeed the case as the next result shows.

The Scalar Triple Product as a Determinant

$$(\mathbf{u} \times \mathbf{v}) \cdot \mathbf{w} = \begin{vmatrix} w_1 & w_2 & w_3 \\ u_1 & u_2 & u_3 \\ v_1 & v_2 & v_3 \end{vmatrix} = w_1 \begin{vmatrix} u_2 & u_3 \\ w_2 & w_3 \end{vmatrix} - w_2 \begin{vmatrix} u_1 & u_3 \\ v_1 & v_3 \end{vmatrix} + w_3 \begin{vmatrix} u_1 & u_2 \\ v_1 & v_2 \end{vmatrix} \qquad (10.4.6)$$

Exercises: 10.4 (The Cross Product)

Determinants: In Exercises 1–6, compute the determinant.

1. $\begin{vmatrix} 2 & 1 & 4 \\ 3 & 6 & 1 \\ 5 & 2 & 6 \end{vmatrix}$ 2. $\begin{vmatrix} 5 & 2 & 2 \\ 1 & 7 & 3 \\ 4 & 1 & 2 \end{vmatrix}$ 3. $\begin{vmatrix} 1 & -2 & 5 \\ 2 & 6 & -3 \\ -3 & 1 & -2 \end{vmatrix}$

4. $\begin{vmatrix} -1 & 2 & 4 \\ 1 & -5 & 3 \\ 4 & 1 & -2 \end{vmatrix}$ 5. $\begin{vmatrix} 3 & 0 & 0 \\ 1 & 8 & 0 \\ 4 & 6 & 2 \end{vmatrix}$ 6. $\begin{vmatrix} 5 & 1 & 4 \\ 0 & 2 & 7 \\ 0 & 0 & 3 \end{vmatrix}$

Cross Products: In Exercises 7–18, compute $\mathbf{u} \times \mathbf{v}$. Remember, for vectors in the plane, $\langle u_1, u_2 \rangle \equiv \langle u_1, u_2, 0 \rangle$

7. $\mathbf{u} = \langle 3, -1 \rangle, \mathbf{v} = \langle 2, 4 \rangle$ 8. $\mathbf{u} = \langle 3, -1 \rangle, \mathbf{v} = \langle 2, 4 \rangle$

9. $\mathbf{u} = \langle 5, 2 \rangle, \mathbf{v} = \langle -2, 5 \rangle$ 10. $\mathbf{u} = \langle 4, 1 \rangle, \mathbf{v} = \langle -1, 4 \rangle$

11. $\mathbf{u} = 2\mathbf{i} + 3\mathbf{j}, \mathbf{v} = 5\mathbf{i} + 2\mathbf{j}$ 12. $\mathbf{u} = 3\mathbf{i} + 4\mathbf{j}, \mathbf{v} = 6\mathbf{i} + \mathbf{j}$

13. $\mathbf{u} = \langle 1, -2, 5 \rangle, \mathbf{v} = \langle 3, 4, -2 \rangle$

14. $\mathbf{u} = \langle 3, -1, 6 \rangle, \mathbf{v} = \langle 2, 4, 7 \rangle$

15. $\mathbf{u} = \mathbf{i} + 2\mathbf{j} - 4\mathbf{k}, \mathbf{v} = 3\mathbf{i} + 2\mathbf{j} + 5\mathbf{j}$

16. $\mathbf{u} = \mathbf{i} + 2\mathbf{j} - 4\mathbf{k}, \mathbf{v} = 3\mathbf{i} + 2\mathbf{j} + 5\mathbf{j}$

17. $\mathbf{u} = \langle 1, 4, 6 \rangle, \mathbf{v} = \langle 2, -2, 1 \rangle$

18. $\mathbf{u} = \langle 3, -1, 2 \rangle, \mathbf{v} = \langle 2, 4, -1 \rangle$

Orthogonal Vectors: In Exercises 19–26, find a vector that is perpendicular (orthogonal) to both $\mathbf{u}$ and $\mathbf{v}$.

19. $\mathbf{u} = \langle 3, -1 \rangle, \mathbf{v} = \langle 2, 4 \rangle$ 20. $\mathbf{u} = \langle 3, -1 \rangle, \mathbf{v} = \langle 2, 4 \rangle$

21. $\mathbf{u} = 2\mathbf{i} + 3\mathbf{j}, \mathbf{v} = 5\mathbf{i} + 2\mathbf{j}$ 22. $\mathbf{u} = 3\mathbf{i} + 4\mathbf{j}, \mathbf{v} = 6\mathbf{i} + \mathbf{j}$

23. $\mathbf{u} = \langle 1, -2, 5 \rangle, \mathbf{v} = \langle 3, 4, -2 \rangle$

24. $\mathbf{u} = \langle 3, -1, 6 \rangle, \mathbf{v} = \langle 2, 4, 7 \rangle$

25. $\mathbf{u} = \mathbf{i} + 2\mathbf{j} - 4\mathbf{k}, \mathbf{v} = 3\mathbf{i} + 2\mathbf{j} + 5\mathbf{j}$

26. $\mathbf{u} = \mathbf{i} + 2\mathbf{j} - 4\mathbf{k}, \mathbf{v} = 3\mathbf{i} + 2\mathbf{j} + 5\mathbf{j}$

The Area of a Triangle: In Exercises 27–32, find (a) the area of the triangle ΔPQR, (b) the length of the altitude from vertex R to side PQ.

27. Vertices: $P = (2, 3), Q = (6, 5), R = (4, 9)$

28. Vertices: $P = (3, 4), Q = (6, 5), R = (4, 9)$

29. Vertices: $P = (2, 1, 1), Q = (0, 4, 2), R = (-1, 1, 6)$

30. Vertices: $P = (3, 1, 1), Q = (0, 5, 2), R = (-2, 1, 6)$

31. Vertices: $P = (3, 1, 5), Q = (4, 3, 11), R = (5, -1, 6)$

32. Vertices: $P = (2, 1, 1), Q = (0, 4, 2), R = (-1, 1, 6)$

Scalar Triple Products: In Exercises 33–36, compute the scalar triple product $(\mathbf{u} \times \mathbf{v}) \cdot \mathbf{w}$. Check your answer by computing the corresponding 3×3 determinant.

33. $\mathbf{u} = \langle 2, 4, 3 \rangle, \mathbf{v} = \langle 1, 1, 2 \rangle, \mathbf{w} = \langle 3, -2, 1 \rangle$

34. $\mathbf{u} = \langle 1, 5, 2 \rangle, \mathbf{v} = \langle 2, 1, -2 \rangle, \mathbf{w} = \langle 4, 3, -1 \rangle$

35. $\mathbf{u} = \langle 1, -1, 0 \rangle, \mathbf{v} = \langle 0, 1, 1 \rangle, \mathbf{w} = \langle 1, 0, -1 \rangle$

36. $\mathbf{u} = \langle -1, 1, 0 \rangle, \mathbf{v} = \langle 0, -1, 1 \rangle, \mathbf{w} = \langle 1, 0, 1 \rangle$

Volumes, Areas, and Heights: In Exercises 37–42, consider the u-v-w parallelepiped S with $\mathbf{u} = \overrightarrow{OP}$, $\mathbf{v} = \overrightarrow{OQ}$, $\mathbf{w} = \overrightarrow{OR}$

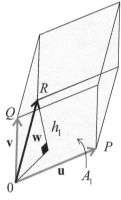

(a) Find the volume of S.

(b) Find the areas A_1, A_2, A_3 of the three faces of S with edges $\mathbf{u}$ and $\mathbf{v}$, $\mathbf{u}$ and $\mathbf{w}$, $\mathbf{v}$ and $\mathbf{w}$.

(c) Find the distance h_1 from R to the face of S with edges $\mathbf{u}$ and $\mathbf{v}$.

37. $\mathbf{u} = \langle 2, 0, 1 \rangle, \mathbf{v} = \langle 1, 2, 1 \rangle, \mathbf{w} = \langle 3, -2, 2 \rangle$

38. $\mathbf{u} = \langle 1, 0, 2 \rangle, \mathbf{v} = \langle 2, 1, -2 \rangle, \mathbf{w} = \langle 1, 3, -1 \rangle$

39. $\mathbf{u} = \langle 2, 1, 1 \rangle, \mathbf{v} = \langle 0, -1, 1 \rangle, \mathbf{w} = \langle -1, 1, 2 \rangle$

40. $\mathbf{u} = \langle 1, 2, 1 \rangle, \mathbf{v} = \langle -1, 0, 1 \rangle, \mathbf{w} = \langle 2, -1, 2 \rangle$

41. $\mathbf{u} = \langle -1, 1, 0 \rangle, \mathbf{v} = \langle 0, -1, 1 \rangle, \mathbf{w} = \langle 1, 0, 1 \rangle$

42. $\mathbf{u} = \langle 1, 1, 0 \rangle, \mathbf{v} = \langle 0, 1, -1 \rangle, \mathbf{w} = \langle 1, 0, 1 \rangle$

Calculus Concepts & Computation

10.5 Lines and Planes in Space

This section studies the geometry of lines and planes in space: $\mathbb{R}^3$. This is an extension of the geometry done in the plane: $\mathbb{R}^2$, but now we find it convenient to also employ *vector methods* to describe objects analytically. We will see that the dot product and cross product are central to these vector methods.

In addition to using vectors, we will see (as we did in Chapter 9) that lines and planes in space can be represented by Cartesian equations as well a parametric equations. Later in the book, these representations will also be used for curves and surfaces in space.

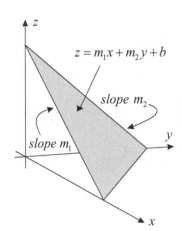

Figure 10.5.1: *The slopes-z-intercept equation for a plane.*

Planes in Space

The various descriptions of planes in $\mathbb{R}^3$ are analogous to the descriptions you studied for lines in $\mathbb{R}^2$. These latter descriptions are: $Ax + By = C$, (standard equation), $y = mx + b$ (slope-y intercept equation), and $y - y_0 = m(x - x_0)$ (point-slope equation).

As discussed in Section 10.1, the equation $Ax + By + Cz = D$ is the *standard equation* for a plane in $\mathbb{R}^3$. When $C \neq 0$ we can solve the standard equation for z to express z as a function of x and y. This gives

$$z = m_1 x + m_2 y + b \quad \text{(slopes-}z\text{-intercept equation)}$$

Figure 10.5.1 shows the geometric significance of the numbers m_1, m_2, and b. Of course, b is the where the plane intersects the z-axis. The intersection of the plane with the x-z plane gives a line with slope m_1 and its intersection with the y-z plane gives a line with slope m_2.

It is important to note that the numbers A, B, C in the standard equation $Ax + By + Cz = D$ for a plane have geometric significance. Specifically, the vector $\mathbf{n} = \langle A, B, C \rangle$ is normal (i.e., perpendicular) to the plane. To prove this, suppose $P = (x_0, y_0, z_0)$ is a given point on this plane. If we take another, general, point $Q = (x, y, z)$ on this plane, then

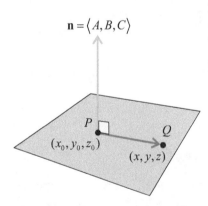

Figure 10.5.2: $\mathbf{n} = \langle A, B, C \rangle$ *is normal to the plane* $Ax + By + Cz = D$.

$$Ax_0 + By_0 + Cz_0 = D \quad \text{and} \quad Ax + By + Cz = D$$

and this gives that $\overrightarrow{PQ} = \langle x - x_0, y - y_0, z - z_0 \rangle$ is perpendicular to $\mathbf{n}$:

$$\begin{aligned} \mathbf{n} \cdot \overrightarrow{PQ} &= \langle A, B, C \rangle \cdot \langle x - x_0, y - y_0, z - z_0 \rangle \\ &= A(x - x_0) + B(y - y_0) + C(z - z_0) \\ &= Ax + By + Cz - (Ax_0 + By_0 + Cz_0) = D - D = 0 \end{aligned}$$

See Figure 10.5.2. This result leads to the following definition:

DEFINITION 10.5.1 (Point-Normal Equation for a Plane)

Suppose $P = (x_0, y_0, z_0)$ *is a given point and* $\mathbf{n} = \langle A, B, C \rangle$ *is a given vector in* $\mathbb{R}^3$.

Then an equation for the plane passing through P with normal $\mathbf{n}$ *is*

$$A(x - x_0) + B(y - y_0) + C(z - z_0) = 0 \quad \textit{Point-Normal Form} \quad (10.5.1)$$

Alternatively, a vector version of this equation is

$$\mathbf{n} \cdot \overrightarrow{PQ} = 0 \quad \textit{Vector Point-Normal Form} \quad (10.5.2)$$

where $Q = (x, y, z)$ *is any point in the plane.*

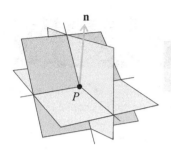

Figure 10.5.3:
Planes through P.

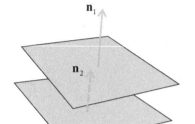

Figure 10.5.4: *Parallel planes have parallel normals.*

NOTE 1: There are infinitely planes passing through the point P, but specifying a normal $\mathbf{n}$ selects a unique plane from all of these. See Figure 10.5.3.

DEFINITION 10.5.2 (Parallel Planes)

Two planes are called parallel if they do not intersect.

NOTE 2: One can show (Exercises) that two distinct planes are parallel if and only if their normals are parallel. See Figure 10.5.4. Parallel vectors are defined as follows.

DEFINITION 10.5.3 (Parallel Vectors)

Two vectors $\mathbf{u}$ and $\mathbf{v}$ are called parallel if one is a scalar multiple of the other:

$$\mathbf{v} = t\,\mathbf{u}$$

for some $t \neq 0$. If $t > 0$, we say $\mathbf{u}$ and $\mathbf{v}$ have the same direction.

Example 10.5.1 (Finding Equations for Planes)

Problem: Find equations for the planes described as follows.

(a) The plane through the point $P = (3, 2, 1)$ with normal $\mathbf{n} = \langle 2, -3, 4 \rangle$.

(b) The plane through $P = (2, 4, 1)$ parallel to the plane $3x + 5y + 2z = 1$.

(c) The plane through the point $P = (-1, 3, 2)$ parallel to the u-v-plane, where $\mathbf{u} = \langle 2, 1, 1 \rangle$, $\mathbf{v} = \langle 1, 4, 2 \rangle$.

(d) The plane through the points $P = (1, 1, 1)$, $Q = (3, 4, 2)$, $R = (2, 2, 6)$.

Solution (a): Using Formula (10.5.1) directly gives

$$2(x - 3) - 3(y - 2) + 4(z - 1) = 0, \quad \text{equivalently:}\quad 2x - 3y + 4z = 4$$

Solution (b): By NOTE 2 above, we can use $\mathbf{n} = \langle 3, 5, 2 \rangle$ as a normal to the requested plane. Then the point-normal equation is

$$3(x - 2) + 5(y - 4) + 2(z - 1) = 0, \quad \text{equivalently:}\quad 3x + 5y + 2z = 28$$

Solution (c): By NOTE 2 above we can use the normal vector to the u-v plane as the normal for the requested plane. The u-v plane has normal

$$\mathbf{n} = \mathbf{u} \times \mathbf{v} = \langle 2, 1, 1 \rangle \times \langle 1, 4, 2 \rangle = \begin{vmatrix} 2 & 1 & 1 \\ 1 & 4 & 2 \end{vmatrix} = \langle -2, -3, 7 \rangle$$

Now use this in the point-normal equation (10.5.1):

$$-2(x + 1) - 3(y - 3) + 7(z - 2) = 0, \quad \text{equivalently:}\quad -2x - 3y + 7z = 7$$

Solution (d): The specified plane is the one containing the triangle $\triangle PQR$. Two vectors along adjacent sides of this triangle are

$$\mathbf{u} \;=\; \overrightarrow{PQ} = \langle 3 - 1, 4 - 1, 2 - 1 \rangle = \langle 2, 3, 1 \rangle$$

$$\mathbf{v} \;=\; \overrightarrow{PR} = \langle 2 - 1, 2 - 1, 6 - 1 \rangle = \langle 1, 1, 5 \rangle$$

Thus, a normal to the plane of the triangle is

$$\mathbf{n} = \mathbf{u} \times \mathbf{v} = \langle 2, 3, 1 \rangle \times \langle 1, 1, 5 \rangle = \begin{vmatrix} 2 & 3 & 1 \\ 1 & 1 & 5 \end{vmatrix} = \langle 14, -9, -1 \rangle$$

Now use this in the point-normal formula (10.5.1). You can choose any one of the points P, Q, R for use in the formula. We choose $P = (1, 1, 1)$ and get:

$$14(x - 1) - 9(y - 1) - (z - 1) = 0, \quad \text{equivalently:} \quad 14x - 9y - z = 4$$

Note how we used the data in Parts (b), (c), and (d) in this example to find a normal $\mathbf{n} = \langle A, B, C \rangle$ to the requested plane.

Lines in Space

A line in $\mathbb{R}^3$ cannot be described by a *single* Cartesian equation. However, using two equations $A_1 x + B_1 y + C_1 z = D_1$ and $A_2 x + B_2 y + C_2 z = D_2$, which are equations for planes, we can describe a line as the intersection of these two planes. But, this is not very convenient since the planes involved are not unique, i.e., a line can be the intersection of many different pairs of planes.

The best way to describe a line in $\mathbb{R}^3$ is parametrically, and, in analogy with the point-normal version of the plane, we have the *point-direction* version of a line.

Point-Direction Equation for a Line: For a given point $P = (x_0, y_0, z_0)$, and a given vector $\mathbf{u}$, consider the line through P in the direction of $\mathbf{u}$ (or parallel to $\mathbf{u}$). This line consists of all points $Q = (x, y, z)$ such that $\overrightarrow{PQ}$ is in the direction of (or parallel to) $\mathbf{u} = \langle u_1, u_2, u_3 \rangle$. Thus,

$$\overrightarrow{PQ} = t\mathbf{u},$$

for some scalar t. Note that for the position vectors $\overrightarrow{OP}, \overrightarrow{OQ}$, we have $\overrightarrow{PQ} = \overrightarrow{OQ} - \overrightarrow{OP}$, and so the above equation can be written as

$$\overrightarrow{OQ} = \overrightarrow{OP} + t\mathbf{u}$$

See Figure 10.5.5. In terms of components, this is

$$\langle x, y, x \rangle = \langle x_0, y_0, z_0 \rangle + t\langle u_1, u_2, u_3 \rangle$$

Equating the components in the vector equation above, gives the parametric equation version of the line

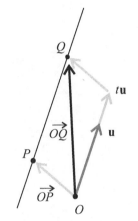

Figure 10.5.5: *The line through P in the direction of $\mathbf{u}$.*

DEFINITION 10.5.4 (Point-Direction Equation for a Line)

Suppose $P = (x_0, y_0, z_0)$ is a given point and $\mathbf{u} = \langle u_1, u_2, u_3 \rangle$ is a given vector in $\mathbb{R}^3$.

Then the vector equation for the line passing through P in direction $\mathbf{u}$ is

$$\overrightarrow{OQ} = \overrightarrow{OP} + t\mathbf{u} \qquad (10.5.3)$$

where t is a scalar and $\overrightarrow{OQ}$ is a position vector for a point $Q = (x, y, z)$ on the line.

Since $\overrightarrow{OQ} = \langle x, y, z \rangle$ and $\overrightarrow{OP} = \langle x_0, y_0, z_0 \rangle$, the component form of (10.5.3) is

$$x = x_0 + u_1 t, \quad y = y_0 + u_2 t, \quad z = z_0 + u_3 t \qquad (10.5.4)$$

NOTE 1: Equation (10.5.3) is known as the *vector version* of the equation for the line through P in the direction of $\mathbf{u}$. It is sometimes written as

$$\mathbf{r} = \mathbf{r}_0 + t\mathbf{u}$$

where $\mathbf{r} = \langle x, y, z \rangle$ is the position vector to an arbitrary point on the line and $\mathbf{r}_0 = \langle x_0, y_0, z_0 \rangle$ is the position vector to the given point P on the line.

NOTE 2: Equation (10.5.4) gives the *parametric equations* of a line in space in terms of the coordinates of a given point on the line and the components of the direction vector of the line.

Example 10.5.2 (Finding Equations for Lines)

Problem: Find equations for the lines described as follows:

(a) The line through the point $P = (2, 5, -3)$ in the direction of $\mathbf{u} = \langle 6, 4, 8 \rangle$.

(b) The line through $P = (2, 4, 1)$ perpendicular to the plane $5x + 7y + 3z = 6$.

(c) The line through the points $P = (1, 2, 1)$, $Q = (3, 5, 4)$.

Solution (a): This is a straight-forward use of Equation (10.5.4):

$$x = 2 + 6t, \; y = 5 + 4t, \; z = -3 + 8t$$

Solution (b): Since the line is perpendicular to the plane, the normal $\mathbf{n} = \langle 5, 7, 3 \rangle$ to the plane can serve as the direction of the line. Thus, the parametric equations for the line are

$$x = 2 + 5t, \; y = 4 + 7t, \; z = 1 + 3t$$

Solution (c): Since P and Q are points on the line, we can use $\overrightarrow{PQ}$ for the direction of the line:

$$\mathbf{u} = \overrightarrow{PQ} = \langle 3 - 1, 5 - 2, 4 - 1 \rangle = \langle 2, 3, 3 \rangle$$

Then for the parametric equations we choose $P = (1, 2, 1)$ for the given point on the line:

$$x = 1 + 2t, \; y = 2 + 3t, \; z = 1 + 3t$$

NOTE 1: The parametric equations for a line are not unique. For example, in the solution to Part (c) in this example, we could have chosen $Q = (3, 5, 4)$ for the given point on the line. Then the parametric equations would be $x = 3 + 2t$, $y = 5 + 3t$, $z = 4 + 3t$. So, beware of this when checking answers to homework problems.

NOTE 2 (Vector-Valued Functions): The solution to Part (c) of the Example , written in vector form: $\mathbf{r} = \mathbf{r}_0 + t\mathbf{u}$ is

$$\mathbf{r}(t) = \langle 1, 2, 1 \rangle + t\langle 2, 3, 3 \rangle = \langle 1 + 2t, 2 + 3t, 1 + 3t \rangle$$

This gives a formula for what is known as a *vector-valued function* $\mathbf{r}$. For each value of the independent variable t we get a vector $\mathbf{r}(t)$, which is the dependent variable. The vector $\mathbf{r}(t)$ gives the position of a point on the line corresponding to t.

NOTE 3 (Line Segments): For the vector-valued function in NOTE 2, we have

$$\mathbf{r}(0) = \langle 1, 2, 1 \rangle = \overrightarrow{OP} \; \text{ and } \; \mathbf{r}(1) = \langle 3, 5, 4 \rangle = \overrightarrow{OQ}$$

Thinking of the parameter t as the time, we get a motion of a particle on the line segment PQ where the particle is at P at time $t = 0$ and at Q at time $t = 1$. One can show that $\mathbf{r}(\frac{1}{2})$ is the position vector for the midpoint of the line segment. Generally, the line segment PQ consists of points with position vectors $\mathbf{r}(t)$ for t in $[0, 1]$.

Distances

There are several types of distances connected with the geometry of points, lines, and planes in $\mathbb{R}^3$. The distance between two points is given by the distance formula. The distance from a point to a line and from a point to a plane can be computed with formulas involving the cross product and dot product. Similarly, we can use vector methods to compute the distances between parallel planes, parallel lines, and skew lines.

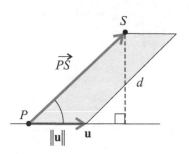

Figure 10.5.6: *The distance from S to the line through P in the direction* **u**.

1. Distance from a Point to a Line

To compute the distance d from a point S to the line $\mathbf{r} = \overrightarrow{OP} + t\mathbf{u}$ (the line through P in direction $\mathbf{u}$), we use the cross product. For this, consider the parallelogram determined by $\mathbf{u}$ and $\mathbf{v} = \overrightarrow{PS}$. See Figure 10.5.6. As we have seen, the area of this parallelogram is given by $A = \|\mathbf{u} \times \overrightarrow{PS}\|$. On the other hand, by elementary geometry, the area is the length of the base times the height $A = bh = \|\mathbf{u}\|d$. Putting these together gives $\|\mathbf{u}\|d = \|\mathbf{u} \times \overrightarrow{PS}\|$. Solving for d gives the desired distance formula.

Distance from a Point to a Line

The distance d from the point S to the line through P in the direction **u** *is*

$$d = \frac{\|\mathbf{u} \times \overrightarrow{PS}\|}{\|\mathbf{u}\|} \qquad (10.5.5)$$

Example 10.5.3 (Distance from a Point to a Line)

Problem: Find distance from the point $S = (3, 5, 2)$ to.

(a) The line through the point $P = (1, 3, 4)$ in the direction of $\mathbf{u} = \langle 2, 1, 3 \rangle$.

(b) The line $x = 2 + 5t$, $y = 4 + 7t$, $z = 1 + 3t$.

Solution (a): This is a straight-forward use of Equation (10.5.5). First compute $\overrightarrow{PS} = \langle 3 - 1, 5 - 3, 2 - 4 \rangle = \langle 2, 2, -2 \rangle$. Then compute

$$\mathbf{u} \times \overrightarrow{PS} = \langle 2, 1, 3 \rangle \times \langle 2, 2, -2 \rangle = \begin{vmatrix} 2 & 1 & 3 \\ 2 & 2 & -2 \end{vmatrix} = \langle -8, 10, 2 \rangle$$

Then $\|\mathbf{u} \times \overrightarrow{PS}\| = \sqrt{64 + 100 + 4} = \sqrt{168} = 2\sqrt{42}$ and $\|\mathbf{u}\| = \sqrt{4 + 1 + 9} = \sqrt{14}$. So the distance is $d = 2\sqrt{42}/\sqrt{14} \approx 3.46$.

Solution (b): Here $P = (2, 4, 1)$ and $\mathbf{u} = \langle 5, 7, 3 \rangle$. So $\overrightarrow{PS} = \langle 3 - 2, 5 - 4, 2 - 1 \rangle = \langle 1, 1, 1 \rangle$. Then compute

$$\mathbf{u} \times \overrightarrow{PS} = \langle 5, 7, 3 \rangle \times \langle 1, 1, 1 \rangle = \begin{vmatrix} 5 & 7 & 3 \\ 1 & 1 & 1 \end{vmatrix} = \langle 4, -2, -2 \rangle$$

Then $\|\mathbf{u} \times \overrightarrow{PS}\| = \sqrt{16 + 4 + 4} = \sqrt{24} = 2\sqrt{6}$ and $\|\mathbf{u}\| = \sqrt{25 + 49 + 9} = \sqrt{83}$. So the distance is $d = 2\sqrt{6}/\sqrt{83} \approx 0.538$.

2. Distance from a Point to a Plane

The computation of the distance d from a point S to the plane through P with normal $\mathbf{n}$ is a straight-forward application of the projection of one vector onto another (Section 10.3). As you can see from Figure 10.5.7, the length of $\text{proj}_{\mathbf{n}}\overrightarrow{PS}$ is the same as d. Thus,

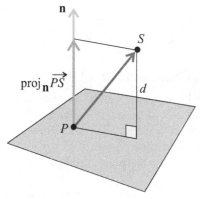

Figure 10.5.7: *The distance from S to the plane through P with normal* **n**.

$$d = \|\text{proj}_{\mathbf{n}}\overrightarrow{PS}\| = \left\| \frac{(\mathbf{n} \cdot \overrightarrow{PS})}{(\mathbf{n} \cdot \mathbf{n})}\mathbf{n} \right\| = \frac{|\mathbf{n} \cdot \overrightarrow{PS}|}{\mathbf{n} \cdot \mathbf{n}}\|\mathbf{n}\| = \frac{|\mathbf{n} \cdot \overrightarrow{PS}|}{\|\mathbf{n}\|}$$

Here we have used $\mathbf{n} \cdot \mathbf{n} = \|\mathbf{n}\|^2$ to simplify the expression at the last step. We record this result in the following box.

Distance from a Point to a Plane

The distance d from the point S to the plane through P with normal **n** *is*

$$d = \frac{\left| \mathbf{n} \cdot \overrightarrow{PS} \right|}{\|\mathbf{n}\|} \qquad (10.5.6)$$

Example 10.5.4 (Distance from a Point to a Plane)

Problem: Find distance from the point $S = (3, 1, 5)$ to.

(a) The plane through the point $P = (2, -1, 1)$ with normal $\mathbf{n} = \langle 3, 2, 4 \rangle$.

(b) The plane through the points $P = (4, 1, 0)$, $Q = (1, 5, 1)$, $R = (2, 2, 4)$.

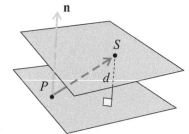

Figure 10.5.8: *The distance between parallel planes.*

Solution (a): First compute $\overrightarrow{PS} = \langle 3 - 2, 1 - (-1), 5 - 1 \rangle = \langle 1, 2, 4 \rangle$ and $\|\mathbf{n}\| = \sqrt{9 + 4 + 16} = \sqrt{29}$. Then

$$d = \frac{\left| \mathbf{n} \cdot \overrightarrow{PS} \right|}{\|\mathbf{n}\|} = \frac{|\langle 3, 2, 4 \rangle \cdot \langle 1, 2, 4 \rangle|}{\sqrt{29}} = \frac{3 + 4 + 16}{\sqrt{29}} = \frac{23}{\sqrt{29}}$$

Solution (b): We need a normal **n** to the plane containing $\triangle PQR$, so we look at vectors going along two sides of this triangle

$$
\begin{aligned}
\overrightarrow{PQ} &= \langle 1 - 4, 5 - 1, 1 - 0 \rangle = \langle -3, 4, 1 \rangle \\
\overrightarrow{PR} &= \langle 2 - 4, 2 - 1, 4 - 0 \rangle = \langle -2, 1, 4 \rangle
\end{aligned}
$$

Then, a normal to the plane of the triangle is

$$\mathbf{n} = \overrightarrow{PQ} \times \overrightarrow{PR} = \langle -3, 4, 1 \rangle \times \langle -2, 1, 4 \rangle = \begin{vmatrix} -3 & 4 & 1 \\ -2 & 1 & 4 \end{vmatrix} = \langle 15, 10, 5 \rangle$$

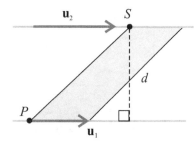

Figure 10.5.9: *The distance between parallel lines.*

So $\|\mathbf{n}\| = \sqrt{225 + 100 + 25} = \sqrt{350}$. Also $\overrightarrow{PS} = \langle 3 - 4, 1 - 1, 5 - 0 \rangle = \langle -1, 0, 5 \rangle$. Then

$$d = \frac{\left| \mathbf{n} \cdot \overrightarrow{PS} \right|}{\|\mathbf{n}\|} = \frac{|\langle 15, 10, 5 \rangle \cdot \langle -1, 0, 5 \rangle|}{\sqrt{350}} = \frac{-15 + 0 + 25}{\sqrt{350}} = \frac{10}{\sqrt{350}} = \frac{2}{\sqrt{14}}$$

3. Distances Between Parallel Planes, Parallel Lines, and Skew Lines

Measuring the three types of distances here can be done by using the distance formulas (10.5.5)–(10.5.6). For instance, to find the distance between two parallel planes, choose a point S on one of the planes and measure the distance from S to the other plane. See Figure 10.5.8. Similarly, to find the distance between two parallel lines, pick a point S on one of the lines and compute the distance from S to the other line. See Figure 10.5.9.

The topic of the distance between skew lines is slightly different. By definition, two lines are *skew* if *they do not intersect and are not parallel*. Thus, skew lines lie in parallel planes and the distance between the lines is the distance between the parallel planes in which they lie. See Figure 10.5.10.

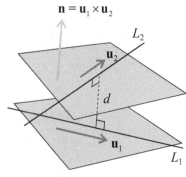

Figure 10.5.10: *The distance between skew lines.*

Example 10.5.5 (Distance Between Skew Lines)

Problem: Show that the lines

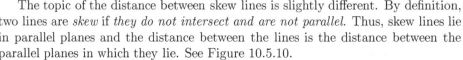
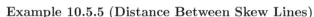

$$L_1: x = 1 + t, \ y = 1 - t, z = 1 \quad \text{and} \quad L_2: x = 2 + t, \ y = 2 + t, z = -1 - t$$

are skew and find the distance between these lines.

Solution: Let $\mathbf{r}_1(t) = \langle 1+t, 1-t, 1 \rangle$ and $\mathbf{r}_2(t) = \langle 2+t, 2+t, -1-t \rangle$ be the two position vectors for the respective lines. If these lines were to intersect, say at P, then $\mathbf{r}_1(t) = \overrightarrow{OP}$ for some parameter value t and $\mathbf{r}_2(s) = \overrightarrow{OP}$ for some parameter value s. Note that the parameter values t and s, generally will be different. Thus, there would be values of t and s so that $\mathbf{r}_1(t) = \mathbf{r}_2(s)$, i.e.,

$$\langle 1+t, 1-t, 1 \rangle = \langle 2+s, 2+s, -1-s \rangle$$

This gives three equations: $1+t = 2+s$, $1-t = 2+s$, and $1 = -1-s$, which t and s must satisfy. The third equation involves only s and gives $s = -2$. Substituting this value of s in the first and second equations gives $t = -1$ and $t = 1$, respectively. This is a contradiction and so the lines do not intersect.

The direction vectors for lines L_1 and L_2 are $\mathbf{u}_1 = \langle 1, -1, 0 \rangle$ and $\mathbf{u}_2 = \langle 1, 1, -1 \rangle$. Clearly $\mathbf{u}_1$ is not a multiple of $\mathbf{u}_2$ and so the lines are not parallel. Thus, the lines are skew.

To find the distance between these two lines, we need to find the parallel planes in which they lie (or at least one of these planes. For this, note that a normal for these planes is

$$\mathbf{n} = \mathbf{u}_1 \times \mathbf{u}_2 = \langle 1, -1, 0 \rangle \times \langle 1, 1, -1 \rangle = \begin{vmatrix} 1 & -1 & 0 \\ 1 & 1 & -1 \end{vmatrix} = \langle 1, 1, 2 \rangle$$

To choose points on the lines (and in the respective planes) take $t = 0$ in the parameterizations to get $P_1 = (1,1,1)$, $P_2 = (2,2,-1)$. Now compute the distance from the point $S = P_2$ (on the second plane) to the first plane (plane through P_1 with normal $\mathbf{n}$). For this, $\overrightarrow{P_1S} = \overrightarrow{P_1P_2} = \langle 1, 1, -2 \rangle$ and

$$d = \frac{|\mathbf{n} \cdot \overrightarrow{P_1S}|}{\|\mathbf{n}\|} = \frac{|\langle 1,1,2 \rangle \cdot \langle 1,1,-2 \rangle|}{\|\langle 1,1,2 \rangle\|} = \frac{2}{\sqrt{6}}$$

Even though we do not need the equations of the two planes to solve this problem, it is instructive to compute them. Then the point normal forms for the planes are

$$(x-1) + (y-1) + 2(z-1) = 0 \quad \text{and} \quad (x-2) + (y-2) + 2(z+1) = 0$$

which simplify to

$$x + y + 2z = 4 \quad \text{and} \quad x + y + 2z = 2,$$

respectively.

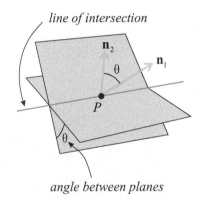

line of intersection

angle between planes

Figure 10.5.11: *The angle between planes and their line of intersection.*

Line of Intersection and Angle Between Planes

If two (distinct) planes are not parallel, then their normals $\mathbf{n}_1$, $\mathbf{n}_2$ are not parallel. As shown in Figure 10.5.11, the angle θ between the planes is the same as the angle between their normals. Thus, we can use the angle measurement technique from Section 10.3 to find θ.

The Angle Between Planes with Normals $\mathbf{n}_1$ and $\mathbf{n}_2$

$$\theta = \cos^{-1}\left(\frac{\mathbf{n}_1 \cdot \mathbf{n}_2}{\|\mathbf{n}_1\| \|\mathbf{n}_2\|} \right) \qquad (10.5.7)$$

Also, you can perhaps see from Figure 10.5.11, that the line of intersection of the two planes has direction $\mathbf{u} = \mathbf{n}_1 \times \mathbf{n}_2$.

Direction of Line of Intersection of Planes with Normals $\mathbf{n}_1$ and $\mathbf{n}_2$

$$\mathbf{u} = \mathbf{n}_1 \times \mathbf{n}_2 \qquad (10.5.8)$$

Example 10.5.6 (Angle Between Planes and Line of Intersection)

Problem: Find the angle between planes $x + y + z = 4$ and $2x + y - z = 2$ and their line of intersection.

Solution: Normals for the planes are $\mathbf{n}_1 = \langle 1, 1, 1 \rangle$ and $\mathbf{n}_2 = \langle 2, 1, -1 \rangle$. The angle between these vectors (i.e., the angle between the planes) is

$$\theta = \cos^{-1}\left(\frac{\mathbf{n}_1 \cdot \mathbf{n}_2}{\|\mathbf{n}_1\| \, \|\mathbf{n}_2\|}\right) = \cos^{-1}\left(\frac{2}{\sqrt{3}\sqrt{6}}\right) \approx 61.87°$$

The line of intersection of these planes has direction

$$\mathbf{u} = \mathbf{n}_1 \times \mathbf{n}_2 = \langle 1, 1, 1 \rangle \times \langle 2, 1, -1 \rangle = \begin{vmatrix} 1 & 1 & 1 \\ 2 & 1 & -1 \end{vmatrix} = \langle -2, 3, -1 \rangle$$

To finish, we need to find a point $P = (x, y, z)$ on the line of intersection. Any such point will be on both planes and so will satisfy both equations $x + y + x = 4$ and $2x + y - z = 2$. An easy way to find such a point is to, say, take $x = 0$. Then the two equations are $y + z = 4$ and $y - z = 2$. Adding the two equations gives $2y = 6$. So $y = 3$. Using this in the first equation gives $3 + z = 4$. So $z = 1$. Thus, we found that the point $(0, 3, 1)$ is on the line of intersection. Thus, the line has parametric equations

$$x = -2t, \ y = 3 + 3t, \ z = 1 - t$$

Exercises: 10.5 (Lines and Planes in Space)

Lines in Space: In Exercises 1–8, find parametric equations for the specified lines.

1. The line through $P = (4, 1, 2)$ in the direction of $\mathbf{v} = \langle 1, 3, 6 \rangle$.

2. The line through $P = (5, 2, 1)$ in the direction of $\mathbf{v} = \langle 2, 4, 7 \rangle$.

3. The line through $P = (5, 2, 1)$ and $Q = (1, 4, 5)$.

4. The line through $P = (6, 2, 2)$ and $Q = (1, 7, 6)$.

5. The line through $P = (4, -1, 2)$ parallel to the line $x = 1 + 3t$, $y = -3 + t$, $z = 2 - 4t$.

6. The line through $P = (-2, 1, 3)$ parallel to the line $x = 1 - 2t$, $y = 2 + t$, $z = 4 - 3t$.

7. The line through $P = (2, -1, 4)$ perpendicular to the plane $2x + 3y + 7z = 8$.

8. The line through $P = (-3, 4, 1)$ perpendicular to the plane $3x + 2y + 6z = 8$.

Planes in Space: In Exercises 9–18, find equations for the specified planes.

9. The plane through $P = (5, 2, 3)$ with normal vector $\mathbf{n} = \langle 2, -4, 3 \rangle$.

10. The plane through $P = (1, 4, 2)$ with normal vector $\mathbf{n} = \langle 3, -2, 4 \rangle$.

11. The plane through $P = (1, 2, 1), Q = (3, 1, 4)$ and $R = (2, 3, 5)$.

12. The plane through $P = (5, 1, 1), Q = (3, 2, 4)$ and $R = (2, 5, 4)$.

13. The plane through $P = (5, -2, 3)$ parallel to $2x - 5y + 2z = 4$.

14. The plane through $P = (6, -2, 4)$ parallel to $3x - 4y + 2z = 5$.

15. The plane through $P = (-2, 1, 3)$ parallel to u-v-plane with $\mathbf{u} = \mathbf{i} + 2\mathbf{j}$, $\mathbf{v} = \mathbf{i} + \mathbf{j} + 3\mathbf{k}$.

16. The plane through $P = (1 - 3, 5)$ parallel to u-v-plane with $\mathbf{u} = 2\mathbf{i} + \mathbf{j}$, $\mathbf{v} = \mathbf{i} + 3\mathbf{j} + \mathbf{k}$.

17. The plane through $P = (4, -1, 2)$ perpendicular to the line $x = 1 + 3t$, $y = -3 + t$, $z = 2 - 4t$.

18. The plane through $P = (-2, 1, 3)$ perpendicular to the line $x = 1 - 2t$, $y = 2 + t$, $z = 4 - 3t$.

Intersecting Lines and Planes: In Exercises 19–28, find equations (Cartesian or parametric) for the specified geometric object.

19. The line of intersection of $x - 2y + z = 2$ and $2x + y - z = 4$.

20. The line of intersection of $3x - y + z = 3$ and $x + y - 3z = 6$.

21. The point of intersection of the lines
$x = 5 + 4t$, $y = 3 + t$, $z = 2 + t$
$x = -1 + s$, $y = -8 + 5s$, $z = -3 + 2s$

22. The point of intersection of the lines
$x = 8 + 3t$, $y = 3 + t$, $z = 1 - t$
$x = 1 + s$, $y = -3 + 4s$, $z = 1 - 2s$

23. The plane containing the lines in #21.

24. The plane containing the lines in #22.

25. The acute angle between the planes in #19

26. The acute angle between the planes in #20.

27. The acute angle between the lines in #21

28. The acute angle between the lines in #22.

Distances: In Exercises 29–36, find the indicated distances.

29. Distance from $S = (4, -1, 2)$ to the line $x = 1 + 3t$, $y = -3 + t$, $z = 2 - 4t$.

30. Distance from $S = (1, -2, 2)$ to the line $x = 1 - t$, $y = -2 + t$, $z = 3 - 2t$.

31. Distance from $S = (2, -1, 1)$ to $2x + y - 3z = 6$

32. Distance from $S = (1, 3, -1)$ to $x + 3y - 2z = 12$

33. Distance from $2x + y - 3z = 10$ to $2x + y - 3z = 6$

34. Distance from $x + 2y - 4z = 8$ to $x + 2y - 4z = 12$

35. Distance between the lines
$x = 5 + 4t$, $y = 3 + t$, $z = 2 + 2t$
$x = -1 + s$, $y = -8 + s$, $z = -3 + 3s$

36. Distance between the lines
$x = 2 + 4t$, $y = 3 + 2t$, $z = 2 + t$
$x = -1 + s$, $y = -8 + 5s$, $z = -3 + 2s$

Calculus *Concepts & Computation*

10.6 Cylinders and Quadric Surfaces

This section discusses two special types of surfaces in $\mathbb{R}^3$: *cylinders* (also known as *generalized cylinders*, or as *surfaces of translation*) and *quadric surfaces*. Cylinders are easy to visualize and sketch. Quadric surfaces are the analogs of the curves called conic sections, which were discussed in Chapter 9.

The study of these surfaces, while important in its own right, has the secondary goal of increasing your ability to visualize objects, such as surfaces, in three dimensions. When you study functions of several variables, you will see that the graph of a function of two variables and the graph of the points of constant value for a function of three variable are both surfaces in $\mathbb{R}^3$.

Cylinders

If you take a curve in the x-y plane and translate it parallel to the z-axis it will sweep out a surface known as a *cylinder*. The standard cylinder shown in Figure 10.6.1 is "generated" in this way by translating a circle, but the technique works for any curve, as indicated on the right side of Figure 10.6.1.

The figure also indicates how to sketch such a surface. First sketch the curve in the x-y plane and then draw straight lines parallel to the z-axis through, say, the endpoints A, B on the curve. Marking points A', B' on these lines at equal distances from the respective points A, B, you can then draw a duplicate of the original curve, but now with endpoints A', B'. This new curve is a "translate" of the original curve. To further enhance the sketch, you can draw five to ten additional lines parallel to AA' and BB' as indicated in Figure 10.6.1.

These additional lines, as well as AA', BB' are called *generators* of the surface (or *rulings* on the surface). Such a surface is also called a *generalized cylinder*, a *surface of translation* (in analogy with a surface of revolution), and a *ruled surface*. If the curve you translate to generate the surface is not too complicated (and doesn't intersect itself), then you can easily construct the surface from a flat sheet of paper by bending it so that opposite edges of the paper follow the shape of the curve and its translate. You have, no doubt, formed standard cylinders in this way. Figure 10.6.2 shows another example of this.

Example 10.6.1 (Sketching Cylinders)

Problem: Sketch the cylinder generated by translating, parallel to the z-axis, the curve (parabola) $y = x^2$ in the x-y plane.

Solution: We use a rotated orientation of the coordinate axes and sketch a portion of the parabola as shown in Figure 10.6.3. Drawing vertical lines through the endpoints up to a certain height and replicating at this height the sketch of the original parabola gives a fairly good picture of the surface. If you wish you can use dotted or dashed lines to indicate parts of the surface that are hidden in this view.

NOTE 1: The equation for the parabola in this example is $y = x^2$ and this is also commonly used as the equation for the cylinder S generated by this parabola. More specifically,

$$S = \{ (x, y, z) \text{ in } \mathbb{R}^3 \mid y = x^2, z \text{ is arbitrary} \}$$

NOTE 2: Generally, an equation such as $H(x, y, z) = 0$ involving x, y, and z represents a surface in $\mathbb{R}^3$. However, when the equation does not contain the variable z, say, $H(x, y) = 0$, then the equation is interpreted as representing a cylinder with rulings parallel to the z-axis. Thus, depending on which variable is missing, there are three types of cylinders we could consider:

$$H_1(x, y) = 0 \quad \text{(Cylinder with rulings parallel to the } z\text{-axis)}$$

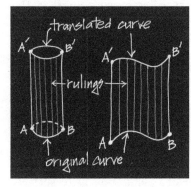

Figure 10.6.1: *A surface generated by translating a curve parallel to the z-axis.*

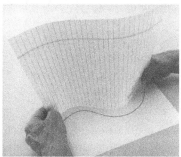

Source: Mylan Redfern

Figure 10.6.2: *Making a cylinder from a sheet of paper.*

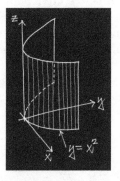

Figure 10.6.3: *A cylinder generated by a parabola.*

$$H_2(x, z) \;=\; 0 \qquad \text{(Cylinder with rulings parallel to the y-axis)}$$
$$H_3(y, z) \;=\; 0 \qquad \text{(Cylinder with rulings parallel to the x-axis)}$$

Example 10.6.2 (Sketching Cylinders)

Problem: Sketch the surfaces with the following equations:

(a) $x^2 + z^2 = 1$ (b) $z = y^3$.

Solution: For Part (a) we sketch a circle of radius 1 in the x-z plane and then translate it in both directions along a y-axis to generate the standard cylinder shown in Figure 10.6.4. For Part (b) we sketch the cubic curve $z = y^3$ in the y-z plane and then translate it in both directions along the x-axis to generate the surface shown in Figure 10.6.5.

Before studying quadric surfaces we look at a technique called *taking traces* which is useful in studying any type of surface.

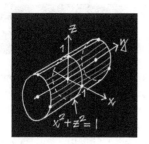

Figure 10.6.4: *A cylinder generated by* $x^2 + z^2 = 1$.

Traces

In the last section we saw that non-parallel planes intersect in a straight line called the line of intersection of the two planes. Generally, one could discuss the curve (or curves) that results from the intersection of any two surfaces. A somewhat simpler situation involves a curve obtained as the intersection of a plane and a given surface. This curve is known as a *trace* on the surface (i.e., the mark made by slicing the surface with a plane).

Taking a series of planes, say parallel to the coordinate planes, and looking at the traces made on the given surface allows us to study (or visualize) the nature of the surface. Recall that $x = k$ and $y = k$ are planes perpendicular to the x-axis and y-axis respectively (and parallel to the y-z plane and x-z plane, respectively). These are the two types of vertical planes that we will use in taking traces. Figure 10.6.6 shows, in each direction, 15 vertical traces, for the surface $z = x^3 e^{-x^2-y^2}$. One trace is highlighted in red. Similarly, $z = k$ is the equation of a plane perpendicular to the z-axis and is a horizontal plane that we will use in taking horizontal slices of surfaces.

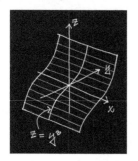

Figure 10.6.5: *A cylinder generated by* $z = y^3$.

Example 10.6.3 (Slicing a Squeezed Standard Cylinder)

Problem: For the surface $x^2 + y^2 - z^2 = 1$ (which is a quadric surface called a hyperboloid of 1 sheet) determine the traces made by a sequence of horizontal planes and by the two vertical planes $x = 0$ and $y = 0$.

Solution: The trace made by a horizontal plane $z = k$ is the curve whose equation is obtained by substituting k for z in the equation for the surface. This gives,

$$x^2 + y^2 - k^2 = 1, \quad \text{or equavalently,} \quad x^2 + y^2 = 1 + k^2$$

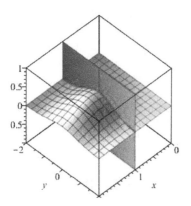

Figure 10.6.6: *Vertical traces on* $z = x^3 e^{-x^2-y^2}$.

This is a circle of radius $r = \sqrt{1 + k^2}$. So the horizontal traces are circles with larger and larger radii, the further we slice from the origin. Compare this with the standard vertical cylinder (with equation $x^2 + y^2 = 1$) whose horizontal traces are circles, all with the *same* radius ($r = 1$). The trace from the vertical plane $x = 0$ gives a curve with equation $0^2 + y^2 - z^2 = 1$, i.e., $y^2 - z^2 = 1$, which is an equation for a hyperbola in the y-z plane. Similarly, the trace from the vertical plane $y = 0$ gives a curve with equation $x^2 + 0^2 - z^2 = 1$, which is an equation for a hyperbola in the x-z plane. Figure 10.6.7 shows a sketch of this surface and some of the traces on the surface.

Quadric Surfaces

We have seen that a quadratic equation, $Ax^2 + By^2 + Cx + Dy + E = 0$, in two variables x and y describes a curve in the plane called a conic section. (The equation can also give the degenerate cases of lines and points.) By analogy, a

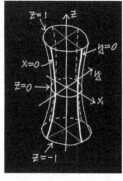

Figure 10.6.7: *The surface* $x^2 + y^2 - z^2 = 1$.

quadratic equation in three variables x, y, and z gives what is known as a *quadric surface* in $\mathbb{R}^3$.

Quadric Surfaces

The equation

$$Ax^2 + By^2 + Cz^2 + Dxy + Exz + Fyz + Gx + Hy + Iz + J = 0 \qquad (10.6.1)$$

describes a quadric surface in $\mathbb{R}^3$. *The six standard quadric surfaces are*

(1) $\dfrac{x^2}{a^2} + \dfrac{y^2}{b^2} + \dfrac{z^2}{c^2} = 1$ *(ellipsoid)*   (4) $\dfrac{x^2}{a^2} + \dfrac{y^2}{b^2} - \dfrac{z^2}{c^2} = 0$ *(elliptic cone)*

(2) $\dfrac{x^2}{a^2} + \dfrac{y^2}{b^2} - \dfrac{z^2}{c^2} = 1$ *(hyperboloid - 1 sheet)*   (5) $z = \dfrac{x^2}{a^2} + \dfrac{y^2}{b^2}$ *(elliptic paraboloid)*

(3) $\dfrac{z^2}{c^2} - \dfrac{x^2}{a^2} - \dfrac{y^2}{b^2} = 1$ *(hyperboloid - 2 sheets)*   (6) $z = \dfrac{x^2}{a^2} - \dfrac{y^2}{b^2}$ *(hyperbolic paraboloid)*

NOTE 1: The general equation (10.6.1) for quadric surfaces contains many *degenerate* cases, such as when the constants A, B, C, D, E, F are zero, which gives a plane $Gx + Hy + Iz + J = 0$. The degenerate cases are not usually considered as quadric surfaces.

NOTE 2: The non-degenerate cases of Equation (10.6.1) lead to the six standard types of quadric surfaces (1)–(6) in the box above. Using linear algebra one can show that by rotating, translating, and interchanging the x, y, z axes, any non-degenerate case of Equation (10.6.1) can be put in one of the six standard forms.

NOTE 3: The six standard types of quadric surfaces: ellipsoids, two types of hyperboloids, cones, and two types of paraboloids, have names that are derived from the horizontal and vertical traces. So taking traces will not only help you identify which type of surface a given equation represents but also will help you sketch it.

NOTE 4: If we interchange the variables x, y, z in the standard equations (1)–(6), the equations change and the orientation of the quadric surface changes. For example, $x = z^2/a^2 - y^2/b^2$ is a hyperbolic paraboloid which is similar to that for equation (6) but oriented differently.

Example 10.6.4 (Sketching Quadric Surfaces)

Problem: Sketch the quadric surfaces represented by the following equations.

(a) $\dfrac{x^2}{9} + \dfrac{y^2}{16} + \dfrac{z^2}{9} = 1$ (b) $x^2 - \dfrac{y^2}{4} - z^2 = 1$ (c) $z = x^2 - y^2$

Solution Part (a): Clearly this is an ellipsoid. Some horizontal traces are the ellipses: $\frac{x^2}{9} + \frac{y^2}{16} = 1$ (for $z = 0$) and $\frac{x^2}{9} + \frac{y^2}{16} = 1 - \frac{4}{9} = \frac{5}{9}$, i.e., $\frac{x^2}{5} + \frac{y^2}{80/9} = 1$ (for $z = \pm 2$). Two vertical traces are: a circle $\frac{x^2}{9} + \frac{z^2}{9} = 1$ (for $y = 0$) and an ellipse $\frac{y^2}{16} + \frac{z^2}{9} = 1$ (for $x = 0$). Thus, these traces are ellipses (with circles being a special case of an ellipse) Sketching these traces, located in their respective slicing planes gives a picture of the surface as shown in Figure 10.6.8.

Solution Part (b): The equation here $x^2 - \frac{y^2}{4} - z^2 = 1$ is similar to that for a Type (3) quadric except that the variables are interchanged. There are 2 minus signs in the equation which helps identify this surface as a 2-sheeted hyperboloid. Since the two minus signs occur with y and z, leaving the plus sign to occur with x, the "axis" of the hyperboloid is the x-axis. We shall see that the two sheets of this

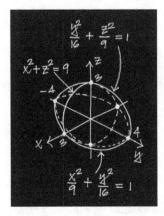

Figure 10.6.8: *The ellipsoid* $\frac{x^2}{9} + \frac{y^2}{16} + \frac{z^2}{9} = 1$.

surface are centered on the axis and turned away from the origin.

All horizontal traces are hyperbolas: $x^2 - \frac{y^2}{4} = k^2 + 1$ (for $z = k$). In particular we get the hyperbola: $x^2 - \frac{y^2}{4} = 1$ (for $z = 0$) and $x^2 - \frac{y^2}{4} = 4 + 1 = 5$, i.e., $\frac{x^2}{5} - \frac{y^2}{20} = 1$ (for $z = \pm 2$).

The vertical traces along the axis of the hyperboloid are $k^2 - \frac{y^2}{4} - z^2 = 1$ (for $x = k$). Rearranging this gives elliptical traces: $\frac{y^2}{4} + z^2 = k^2 - 1$, *provided that* $|k| > 1$. When $k = \pm 1$, we get a pair of points $(\pm 1, 0, 0)$ for the traces. These points are the vertices for this 2-sheeted hyperboloid

The vertical traces with planes $y = k$ are all hyperbolas: $\frac{x^2}{1+k^2/4} - \frac{z^2}{1+k^2/4} = 1$. Putting all of these observations together gives sketch shown in Figure 10.6.9.

Solution Part (c): The equation here, $z = x^2 - y^2$, is that for a Type (6) quadric with $a = b = 1$. The surface is a hyperbolic paraboloid. The key traces to take in order to sketch this surface are: (1) For the plane $y = 0$ the trace is $z = x^2$. So sketch this standard parabola in the x-z plane. (2) The traces with planes $x = 0, x = \pm 1$ are also parabolas $z = -y^2$, $z = 1 - y^2$, but are turned down (and the latter two shifted up 1 unit). Sketch these three parabolas in their respective tracing planes. These are shown in Figure 10.6.10. The horizontal traces are: a pair of lines $x^2 - y^2 = 0$ (for $z = 0$) and hyperbolas $x^2 - y^2 = k$ for ($z = k$, $k \neq 0$). One of these hyperbolas is shown in Figure 10.6.10.

Sketching Quadric Surfaces

It is important that you be able to sketch the six types of quadric surfaces (and name them as well). Doing this by hand will force you to study and understand these surfaces, much more so than looking at the computer-drawn ones in the Table 10.6.1 on the next page. Here are some suggestions for constructing your drawings:

(1) First study the equation for the quadric and identify which type of surface it represents.

(2) **(Ellipsoids)** $\frac{x^2}{a^2} + \frac{y^2}{b^2} + \frac{z^2}{c^2} = 1$. These are easy to sketch. The points $(\pm a, 0, 0)$, $(0, \pm b, 0)$, $(0, 0, \pm c)$ on the ellipsoid are its vertices. Mark these on the x, y, z axes, respectively. Then sketch the elliptical traces made by the planes $z = 0$ and $x = 0$. Put in several more traces made by $x = \pm k$ for $0 < k < a$. Finally add the trace made by $y = 0$.

(3) **(Elliptic Cones)** $\frac{x^2}{a^2} + \frac{y^2}{b^2} - \frac{z^2}{c^2} = 0$. These are easy to sketch. First identify the axis of the cone. For the equation here, the axis is the z-axis. For the equations $\frac{x^2}{a^2} - \frac{y^2}{b^2} + \frac{z^2}{c^2} = 0$ and $-\frac{x^2}{a^2} + \frac{y^2}{b^2} + \frac{z^2}{c^2} = 0$, the axes are the y-axis and x-axis, respectively. (Do you see why this is so?) The traces by planes perpendicular to the axis are ellipses (or circles). Draw in two of these, centered on the axis and located the same distance from the origin. Then complete the drawing by putting in two straight lines through the origin that touch each ellipse.

(4) **(Hyperboloid)** $\frac{x^2}{a^2} + \frac{y^2}{b^2} - \frac{z^2}{c^2} = 1$ (1-sheet) $\frac{z^2}{c^2} - \frac{x^2}{a^2} - \frac{y^2}{b^2} = 1$ (2-sheets).

First identify the axis, which for these two equations is the z-axis. The traces by planes perpendicular to the axis are ellipses (or circles). Draw in two of these, centered on the axis and located the same distance from the origin (For the 2-sheet hyperboloid here the trace must be taken above and below the vertices $(0, 0, \pm c)$). Then complete the drawing by putting in the two branches of a hyperbola made by a vertical trace through the z-axis.

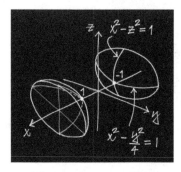

Figure 10.6.9: *The hyperboloid $x^2 - \frac{y^2}{4} - z^2 = 1$.*

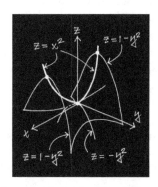

Figure 10.6.10: *The hyperbolic paraboloid $z = x^2 - y^2$.*

(5) **(Elliptic Paraboloid)** $z = \dfrac{x^2}{a^2} + \dfrac{y^2}{b^2}$. First identify the axis, which for this equation is the z-axis. The traces by planes perpendicular to the axis are ellipses (or circles). Draw in one of these centered on the axis and located at a distance from the vertex $(0,0,0)$. The vertical traces made by planes through the z-axis are parabolas all with vertex $(0,0,0)$. Draw in a couple of these.

(6) **(Hyperbolic Paraboloid a.k.a A Saddle)** $z = \dfrac{x^2}{a^2} - \dfrac{y^2}{b^2}$. First identify the axis, which for this equation is the z-axis. The traces by planes perpendicular to the axis are hyperbolas, however we will use only one of these in the sketch. The best way to visualize this surface is as a saddle (for a horse). Sitting in the saddle, your torso will be directed along the axis (the z-axis in this case). The trace made by the plane $y = 0$ is the parabola $z = \frac{x^2}{a^2}$. Sketch this (in the x-z plane). This is the direction of the horse. The trace with the plane $x = 0$ is the parabola $z = -\frac{y^2}{b^2}$. Sketch this (in the y-z plane). This parabola is turned downwards with high point (vertex) at the origin, which is known as the *saddle point* of the saddle. It is where you sit on the saddle with your legs following the downward curve of the parabola $z = -\frac{y^2}{b^2}$. Next sketch two downward-directed parabolic traces $z = k^2 - \frac{y^2}{b^2}$ made by the planes $x = \pm ka$. This gives a fair representation of the saddle. To finish sketch the two branches of the hyperbola $\frac{x^2}{a^2} - \frac{y^2}{b^2} = -k$ made by sectioning the surface with the plane $z = -k$ (with $k > 0$).

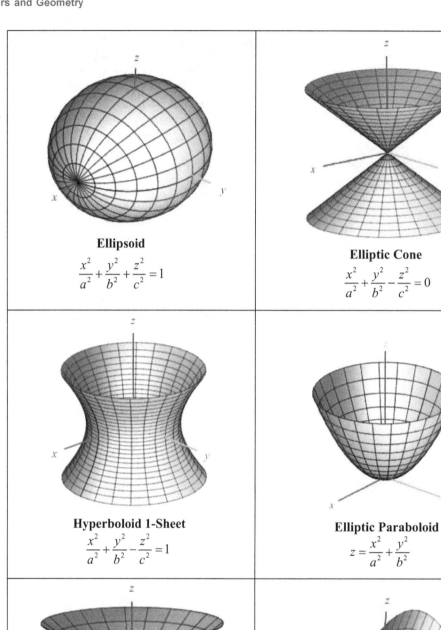

Ellipsoid

$$\frac{x^2}{a^2} + \frac{y^2}{b^2} + \frac{z^2}{c^2} = 1$$

Elliptic Cone

$$\frac{x^2}{a^2} + \frac{y^2}{b^2} - \frac{z^2}{c^2} = 0$$

Hyperboloid 1-Sheet

$$\frac{x^2}{a^2} + \frac{y^2}{b^2} - \frac{z^2}{c^2} = 1$$

Elliptic Paraboloid

$$z = \frac{x^2}{a^2} + \frac{y^2}{b^2}$$

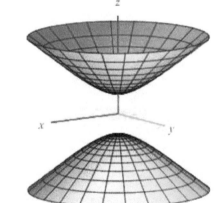

Hyperboloid 2-Sheets

$$\frac{z^2}{c^2} - \frac{x^2}{a^2} - \frac{y^2}{b^2} = 1$$

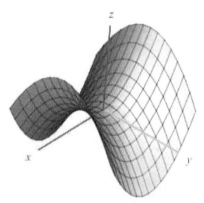

Hyperbolic Paraboloid

$$z = \frac{x^2}{a^2} - \frac{y^2}{b^2}$$

Exercises: 10.6 (Cylinders and Quadric Surfaces)

Matching Surfaces and Equations: In Exercises 1–8, match the graph with its corresponding equation and give the name for the quadric surface.

A. $z^2 = 4x^2 + y^2 + 4$ **B.** $x = y^2 - z^2$

C. $16x^2 + 16y^2 = 4z^2 + 64$ **D.** $4x^2 + 4y^2 + 25z^2 = 100$

E. $z = y^2 - x^2$ **F.** $4x^2 + 4z^2 = y^2 - 1$

G. $49x^2 + 49y^2 + 16z^2 = 784$ **H.** $9y^2 + 9z^2 = 4x^2 + 36$

1.   **2.**

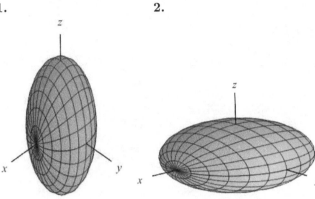

Generalized Cylinders: In Exercises 9–20, sketch the surface with the given equation.

9. $x^2 - y^2 = 1$ **10.** $y^2 - x^2 = 4$ **11.** $z = e^{-x}$

12. $x = e^{-y}$ **13.** $z = \ln y$ **14.** $z = \ln x$

15. $y = \tan^{-1} x$ **16.** $z = \tan^{-1} y$ **17.** $z = y + 1$

18. $x = y + 1$ **19.** $z = \sin y$ **20.** $z = \sin x$

3.   **4.**

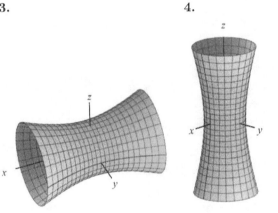

Traces of Quadratic Surfaces: Sketch (in 3-D if you can) the specified traces of the following quadric surfaces. Identify the traces and the quadric surface.

21. $2x - 4y^2 - z^2 = 0$, traces: $z = 0$, $y = 0$

22. $2y - 4x^2 - z^2 = 0$, traces: $z = 0$, $x = 0$

23. $4y^2 - 16x^2 - 16z^2 = 64$, traces: $z = 0$, $y = 8$

24. $4x^2 - 16y^2 - 16z^2 = 64$, traces: $z = 0$, $x = 8$

25. $25x^2 + 25y^2 - 9z^2 = 0$, traces: $y = 0$, $x = 5$

26. $25z^2 + 25y^2 - 9x^2 = 0$, traces: $y = 0$, $z = 5$

5.   **6.**

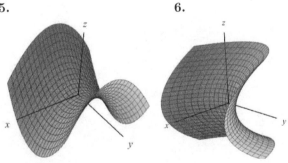

Sketching Quadratic Surfaces: Sketch the following quadratic surfaces. Put the equation for the surface in standard form and identify the quadric surface.

27. $64x^2 - 16y^2 + 64z^2 = 0$ **28.** $16y^2 - 4x^2 + 16z^2 = 0$

29. $2y - 4x^2 - 4z^2 = 0$ **30.** $4x - 8y^2 - 8z^2 = 0$

31. $64x^2 + 16y^2 + 4z^2 = 64$ **32.** $4x^2 + 16y^2 + 64z^2 = 64$

33. $4x^2 - 16y^2 - 16z^2 = 64$ **34.** $4y^2 - 16x^2 - 16z^2 = 64$

35. $z = y^2 - x^2$ **36.** $x = z^2 - y^2$

7.   **8.**

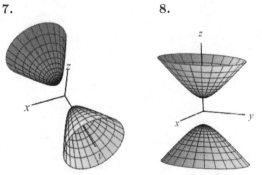

11
Partial Derivatives

Calculus *Concepts & Computation*

11.1 Functions of Two or More Variables

This chapter begins the study of what is known as the *multi-variable calculus*. This involves extending the derivative and integral calculus to functions f that depend on two or more variables. Such functions occur naturally in many application areas (science, engineering, business) and, because of the extra variables, their study is more complicated than the calculus of functions of a single variable. So, we begin with the simplest of the multi-variable cases.

Functions of Two Variables

A function f of two variables has two independent variables, typically denoted by x, y, and the *domain* of f is a subset D of ordered pairs (x, y) in $\mathbb{R}^2$. The *value* of f at an element, or point, (x, y) in its domain is denoted by $f(x, y)$, and, with z typically denoting the *dependent variable*, we write $z = f(x, y)$ to symbolize the functional relationship between the dependent and independent variables. The *graph* of f is the subset of points in $\mathbb{R}^3$ given by

$$G_f = \{\, (x, y, z) \text{ in } \mathbb{R}^3 \mid (x, y) \text{ is in } D \text{ and } z = f(x, y) \,\}$$

Thus, the graph of f is the surface in $\mathbb{R}^3$ associated with the equation $z = f(x.y)$. As such, it is a very special type of surface (satisfies the vertical line test) as compared with a general surface associated with equation $H(x, y, z) = 0$. You can sketch the graph of a function of two variables much like you do for functions of one variable except that now there are two principal directions to plot in.

Plotting and Visualizing Graphs

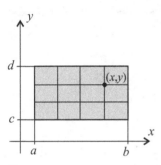

Figure 11.1.1: *A Rectangular domain D for a function.*

The domain D of f can be complicated, but the simplest case is when D is a rectangle $D = \{\, (x, y) \mid a \le x \le b \text{ and } c \le y \le d \,\} = [a, b] \times [c, d]$ (which is analogous to an interval domain for a function of a single variable). See Figure 11.1.1. To make a table of values for the function we need to select points in D and compute the corresponding z-values $z = f(x, y)$. For this, it is convenient to partition (divide) the rectangle D into subrectangles by first partitioning the intervals $I = [a, b]$ and $J = [c, d]$ into subintervals and then drawing vertical and horizontal lines through the partition points. This gives a grid on D as shown in Figure 11.1.1 and delineates its partition into to subrectangles. We then evaluate f at the vertices (x, y) of these subrectangles (i.e., at the grid points) to get a table of $x, y, z = f(x, y)$ values.

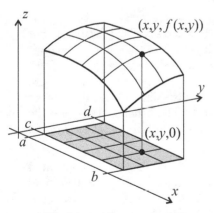

Figure 11.1.2: *The graph of f over a rectangular domain.*

To plot the points on the graph of f from this table of values, note that for each grid point (x, y) in the subdivision of D, we get a point $(x, y, 0)$ in $\mathbb{R}^3$. Above (or below) this point is the corresponding point $(x, y, f(x, y))$ on the graph of f. See Figure 11.1.2.

Having plotted the points $(x, y, f(x, y))$, we naturally get a 'grid' on the surface $z = f(x, y)$ by sketching a series of curves through the points, first going, say, in the x-direction, and then in the y-direction. Figure 11.1.2 shows four curves on the surface going in the x-direction and five curves going in the y-direction. More precisely, these are curves (traces) made by intersecting the surface $z = f(x, y)$ with vertical planes parallel to the x-axis (i.e., planes with equations $y = k$) and with vertical planes parallel to the y-axis (i.e., planes with equations $x = k$).

NOTE: The curves on the surface forming the grid are graphs of functions of one variable: those going in the x-direction are the graphs of $z = f(x, k)$, for various values of k, while those going in the y-direction are the graphs of $z = f(k, y)$. For convenience, these curves will be called *x-traces* and *y-traces*, respectively. More generally it will be useful to have the terminology in the following definition.

DEFINITION 11.1.1 (X Y Z Traces)

For a surface in $\mathbb{R}^3$, *the traces (curves) made by intersecting it with the vertical planes* $y = k$ *and* $x = k$ *are called* x-traces *and* y-traces, *respectively. The traces made by horizontal planes* $z = c$ *are called* z-traces.

Sketching Technique: X-Traces and Y-Traces

If the function f is not too complicated, its graph over a rectangle $R = [a, b] \times [c, d]$ can easily be accomplished by plotting the vertical x-traces and y-traces as indicated in Figure 11.1.2.

First plot the x-traces over the sides of the rectangle. These are called the *boundary traces*. That is, plot the curves $z = f(x, c)$ and $z = f(x, d)$, for x in $[a, b]$, in the planes $y = c$ and $y = d$. These will form two edges of the surface $z = f(x, y)$. Then plot the curves $z = f(a, y)$ and $z = f(b, y)$, for y in $[c, d]$, in the planes $x = a$ and $x = b$. These form the other two edges of the surface $z = f(x, y)$.

Next plot some other x-traces $z = f(x, k)$, for several values of k (with $c < k < d$). Finally, do a similar thing for additional y-traces. The result should give a fairly good picture of the surface which is the graph of f.

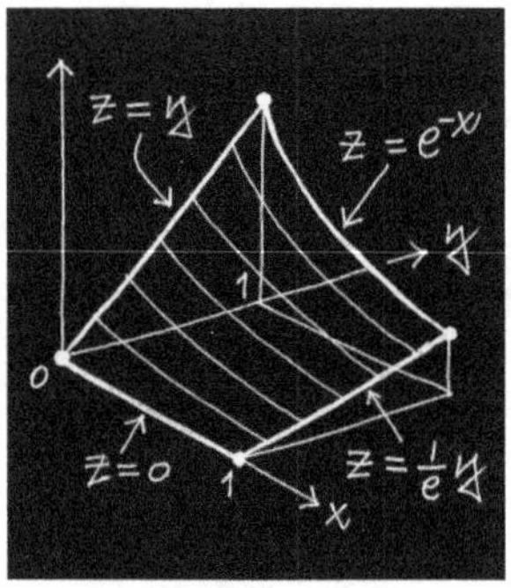

Example 11.1.1 (Sketching Graphs)

Problem: Sketch the graph of $z = f(x, y)$ over the given rectangle R.

(a) $z = ye^{-x}$, $R = [0, 1] \times [0, 1]$ (b) $z = x^2 y^3$, $R = [-1, 1] \times [-1, 1]$
(c) $z = \sin \pi x \cos \pi y$, $R = [0, 1] \times [0, 1]$.

Solution (a): The x-traces have equations $z = ke^{-x}$. For $k = 0$, the x-trace is the graph of $z = 0$, which is a horizontal line. For $k = 1$, the x-trace is the graph of the curve $z = e^{-x}$, which is an exponential decay function. Figure 11.1.3 shows these two curves sketched above two sides of the square R. The y-traces have equations $z = ye^{-k}$, which for $k = 0$ is the straight line $z = y$ and for $k = 1$ is the straight line $z = e^{-1}y$. These are easily sketched above the other two sides of the square R as shown in Figure 11.1.3. The other x-traces are the graphs of decaying exponential functions $z = ke^{-x}$, for $0 < k < 1$, and the other y-traces are all straight lines.

Solution (b): The x-traces have equations $z = mx^2$, where $m = k^3$. For $k = 1$, the x-trace is the graph of the curve $z = x^2$, which is the standard parabola. For $k = -1$, the x-trace is the graph of $z = -x^2$, which is the negative of the standard parabola. Figure 11.1.4 shows these two parabolas sketched above (and below) two sides of the square R. The y-traces have equations $z = my^3$, where $m = k^2$, which for $k = \pm 1$ is the standard cubic $z = y^3$. These are easily sketched above the other two sides of the square R as shown in Figure 11.1.4. The other x-traces are the graphs of parabolas, turned up or down with vertices at the origin. The exceptional case is for $k = 0$ which gives the horizontal line $z = 0$.

Solution (c): The graph of $z = \sin \pi x \cos \pi y$ over the whole plane is a complicated wavy surface, but restricting to its graph just over the square $R = [0, 1] \times [0, 1]$ gives a simpler surface. The x-traces have equations $z = A \sin \pi x$, where $A = \cos \pi k$. For $k = 0$, the x-trace is the graph of $z = \sin \pi x$, which is half the standard sine wave. For $k = 1$, the x-trace is the graph of $z = -\sin \pi x$, which is half the negative of the standard sine wave. Figure 11.1.5 shows these two partial sine waves sketched above two sides of the square R. The y-traces have equations $z = A \cos \pi y$, where

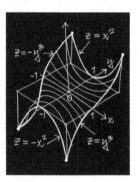

Figure 11.1.3: *A graph of* $z = ye^{-x}$ *showing the boundary and x-traces.*

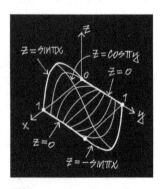

Figure 11.1.4: *x-traces for* $z = x^2 y^3$.

Figure 11.1.5: *x-traces for* $z = \sin \pi x \cos \pi y$.

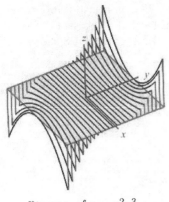

`Xtrace` *of* $z = x^2 y^3$.

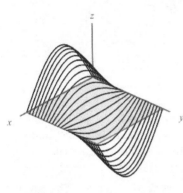

`Xtrace` *of* $z = \sin \pi x \, \cos \pi y$.

Figure 11.1.6

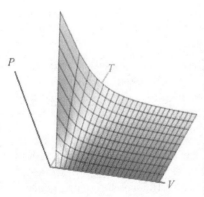

Figure 11.1.7: *Graph of the ideal gas law* $P = RT/V$.

$A = \sin \pi k$, which for $k = 0, 1$ is a horizontal line $z = 0$. See Figure 11.1.5, which also contains a sketch of the y-trace $z = \cos \pi y$ (occurring for $k = 1/2$). The other x-traces are the graphs of half sine waves, turned up or down. The exceptional case is for $k = 1/2$ which gives the horizontal line $z = 0$.

To supplement your visualization and understanding of the surfaces in Example 11.1.1, you can use the special-purpose Maple procedure:

```
Xtrace(f,a,b,c,d,N,x1,y1,z1)
```

This creates a dynamic plot of the x-traces being drawn for the graph of f over the rectangle $R = [a, b] \times [c, d]$. There are $N + 1$ frames in the movie (counting the zeroth frame) and the same number of x-traces. The numbers `x1`, `y1`, `z1` specify the length of the three coordinate axes, which you may want to adjust by experimentation. Figure 11.1.6 shows the last frames in the movies for the two of the functions in Example 11.1.1.

Computer Plots

When the x-traces and y-traces are well-known curves, ones that you can sketch without plotting points, then using them to render the surface is generally the quickest way to sketch the graph of a function of two variables.

If the traces are not familiar, you can always calculate a table of $x, y, z = f(x, y)$ values and plot the corresponding points. Then join these points with straight-line segments, going first, point-by-point in the x-trace directions. This will give polygonal approximations to the x-traces. Then doing the same thing in the y-trace directions will give polygonal approximations to the y-traces. The resulting picture will look like a mesh (or grid) of rectangles approximating the surface. However, each "rectangle" is generally not a rectangle because, for one thing, all four of its vertices may not lie in the same plane. However, putting a diagonal in for each "rectangle" in the mesh, will give a mesh of triangles that approximate the surface. This is how most computer plots of graphs of functions of two variables are constructed. The triangles in the mesh are given colors according to some coloring scheme and the resulting plot will look like a smooth surface if the partition of $R = [a, b] \times [c, d]$ into subrectangles is fine enough (a large number of grid points).

Example 11.1.2 (Ideal Gases)

Problem: A good physical example of function of two variables is the pressure $P = f(V, T)$ of a gas as a function of its volume V and its absolute temperature T (assuming there is 1 Mole of the substance forming the gas). For an ideal gas, f has a simple form:

$$P = \frac{RT}{V} \qquad \text{(Ideal Gas Law)},$$

where R is the gas constant depending on the substance of the gas. Describe how the pressure varies with changing volume when the gas is held at a constant temperature T_0. Compare that with how the pressure varies with changing temperature when the volume is constant V_0.

Solution: The pressure is $P = RT_0/V$ when the temperature of the gas is held at T_0 and so varies inversely with the volume (large volume, low pressure; small volume, high pressure). Figure 11.1.7 shows a computer plot of the graph of the pressure function. The V-traces exhibit this inverse variation of pressure with volume. Likewise the graph shows that the T-traces are straight lines, indicating a linear variation of pressure with temperature.

Level Curves (Horizontal Traces)

Another useful way to visualize the graph of a function of two variables is to look at horizontal traces, i.e., the curves made by intersecting the surface $z = f(x, y)$ with horizontal planes $z = c$, for various choices of c.

The standard name for a horizontal trace is *level curve*. The name ostensibly comes from the fact that a level curve is located at a certain level above (when $c > 0$) or below (when $c < 0$) the x-y plane (which is level $c = 0$). Figure 11.1.8 shows one of the level curves for the function $f(x, y) = x^3 e^{-x^2 - y^2}$.

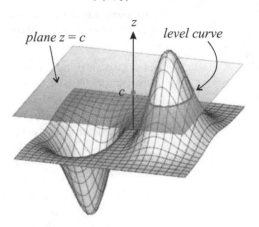

Figure 11.1.8: *The level curve made by plane $z = c$.*

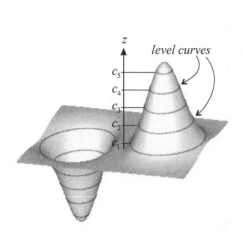

Figure 11.1.9: *A graph of* $f(x, y) = x^3 e^{-x^2 - y^2}$ *showing ten level curves.*

Another reason for the name *level curve* comes from viewing the graph of the function as representing a portion of the earth's surface (the mountain range analogy) and taking $z = 0$ as sea level. Then the level curve made by intersecting the surface with $z = c$ represents all points on the surface at height c above sea level.

The computer plot in Figure 11.1.8 was done with a style that renders the surface with x-traces and y-traces. You can change the style so that the rendering shows the level curves instead. Figure 11.1.9 illustrates this.

The level curve at height c, being the intersection of the graph $z = f(x, y)$ with the plane $z = c$, has equation $f(x, y) = c$. This can be viewed as an equation for a curve in the x-y plane, which is the projection of the actual level curve into this plane. It is traditional to consider each of these curves, the one on the graph of f and the one on the x-y plane, as being the level curve with equation $f(x, y) = c$. Figure 11.1.10 exhibits the 10 level curves in the x-y plane that result from projecting the corresponding ones on the surface in Figure 11.1.9.

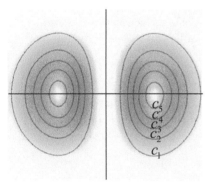

Figure 11.1.10: *Level curves of* $f(x, y) = x^3 e^{-x^2 - y^2}$ *projected into the x-y plane.*

Such a collection of projected level curves form what is called a *contour map* (or a *topographic map*) for the surface. The level curves are called *contour lines* and the collection of them (usually taken at equally spaced heights) gives us another way to visualize the graph of f. Drawing a contour map in two dimensions is perhaps easier than sketching a three-dimensional picture of the surface

Contour Maps - Sketching Level Curves: To draw a contour map for a function, sketch a series of level curves $f(x, y) = c$ (in $\mathbb{R}^2$) by selecting appropriate values of c (positive, zero, and negative). As we saw in Section 2.10, sketching such general curves can be difficult. Here are a few easy ones.

Example 11.1.3 (Sketching Level Curves)

Problem: For the following functions $z = f(x, y)$, sketch a series of level curves using the specified values of c. Label each curve with the respective value of c.

(a) $z = ye^{-x}$, $R = [0, 1] \times [0, 1]$, $c = 0, 0.2, 0.4, 0.6, 0.8$

(b) $z = x^2 y^3$, $R = [-1, 1] \times [-1, 1]$ $c = 0.01, 0.15, 0.5$

(c) $z = y^2 - x^2$, $R = [-3, 3] \times [-3, 3]$, $c = -4, -1, 0, 1, 4$.

Solution (a): The level curves for this function have equations

$$ye^{-x} = c, \quad \text{or equvalently} \quad y = ce^x,$$

which, in this latter form, are recognized as a horizontal line $y = 0$ (for $c = 0$) and graphs of exponential functions (for $c = 0.2, 0.4, 0.6, 0.8$). Figure 11.1.11 shows sketches of these level curves both in the x-y plane and on the surface that is the graph of $z = ye^{-x}$, which we sketched in Figure 11.1.3 using x-traces. You should compare Figure 11.1.3 to the one here and also try to visualize the surface from the two-dimensional sketch of the level curves in the x-y plane.

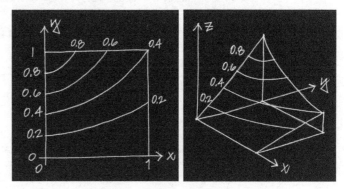

Figure 11.1.11: *Some level curves for $f(x, y) = ye^{-x}$.*

Solution (b): The level curves for this function have equations

$$x^2 y^3 = c, \quad \text{or equivalently} \quad y = \frac{c^{1/3}}{x^{2/3}},$$

which, in this latter form, are recognized as a horizontal line $y = 0$ (for $c = 0$) and graphs of power functions (for $c = 0.01, 0.15, 0.5$). Figure 11.1.12 shows sketches of these level curves both in the x-y plane and on the surface that is the graph of $z = x^2 y^3$, which we sketched in Figure 11.1.4 using x-traces.

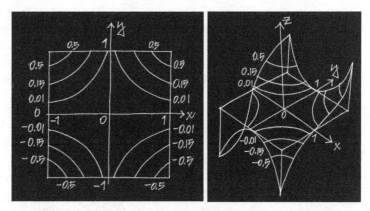

Figure 11.1.12: *Some level curves of $f(x, y) = x^2 y^3$.*

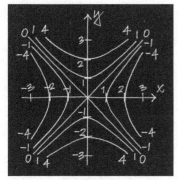

Figure 11.1.13: *Some level curves of $f(x, y) = y^2 - x^2$.*

Solution (c): The level curves for this function have equations $y^2 - x^2 = c$, which, for $c \neq 0$, are recognized as equations for hyperbolas (Section 9.6). For $c = 0$, the equation is $y^2 - x^2 = 0$, which gives $y^2 = x^2$. So, $y = \pm x$ and this represents a pair of lines through the origin, which are the asymptotes for the hyperbolas represented by the other equations. These other equations are $y^2 - x^2 = 1$, $y^2 - x^2 = 4$, $x^2 - y^2 = 1$, and $x^2 - y^2 = 4$. Figure 11.1.13 shows sketches of these level curves. The surface here $z = y^2 - x^2$ you should recognize as a hyperbolic paraboloid (Section 10.6). The sketches of the level curves show, for this saddle-shaped surface, the saddle point is at $(0, 0)$ and the direction of the horse is along the y-axis.

Contour Maps and Computer Plots

Plotting the level curves for functions of two variables is often very difficult to do by hand, but we can always use a computer for plotting both the graph and the level curves. Additionally, some functions of two variables come from measurements of physical data, such as weather and survey data (temperature, pressure, and elevation) for a section of the earth and so are not given directly by a formula for $f(x, y)$. In either of theses cases, it is important for you to be able to analyze a given plot and interpret the information that it contains.

For example, Figure 11.1.14 shows a barometric pressure weather map of the United States (lower forty eight) at a particular time and date.

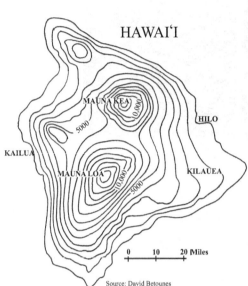

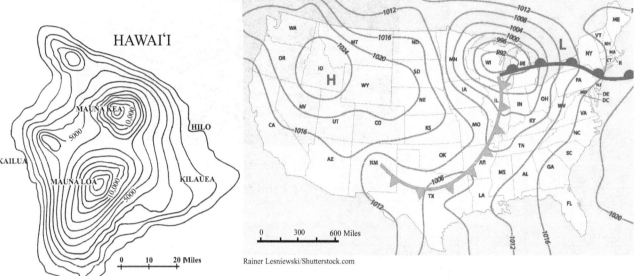

Rainer Lesniewski/Shutterstock.com

Figure 11.1.14: *Atmospheric pressures over the United States.*

Figure 11.1.15: *Elevations above sea level in Hawai'i.*

The contour lines shown are known as *isobars*, namely, lines of equal barometric pressure. Thus, the contour line labeled 1024 that encircles Idaho indicates that all points along that line have barometric pressure 1024 bar. This is an area of high-pressure. Whereas, a low-pressure area is centered over Wisconsin as indicated by the isobar labeled 992. The other isobars occur at increments of 4 units between the high 1024 and the low 992. While there is no formula for the pressure function $p = f(x, y)$ which has these isobars as its level curves, you can nevertheless view the graph of f as a surface which, in the mountain range analogy, has a peak over Idaho, a valley over Wisconsin, and a saddle point on the eastern edge of Nebraska.

Figure 11.1.15 shows a topographic map of Hawai'i where the contour lines are elevations (in feet) above sea level. As you can see, the two major mountain peaks, Muana Kea and Mauna Loa, are over 10,000 feet. Between them there is a saddle point at 6,500 feet . The elevation contours are spaced at intervals of 1000 feet and where they are more closely spaced, say near the peak of Kea, the hillside is more steep than where they are more widely spaced, such as near Kilauea.

Figure 11.1.16 shows a different type of visualization activity that you should master. From the graph of the function in the top part of the figure, you should be able to see that the surface, as a mountain range, has two valleys near $(\pm 0.66, 0)$ and a saddle point at $(0, 0)$. Thus, the contour map shown below the surface is identified as one that displays these features. Looking at the Maple Movie/Figure for Figure 11.1.16 will help you understand this better.

Functions of Three Variables

A function f of three-variables has three independent variables, typically denoted by x, y, z, and the *domain* of f is a subset D of ordered triples of numbers (x, y, z) in $\mathbb{R}^3$. The *value* of f at an element, or point, (x, y, z) in its domain is denoted by $f(x, y, z)$, and, with w typically denoting the *dependent variable*, we write $w = f(x, y, z)$ to symbolize the functional relationship between the dependent and independent

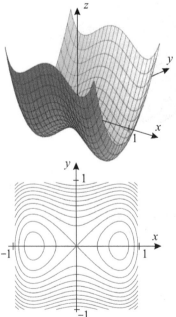

Figure 11.1.16: *Graph of* $f(x, y) = x^4 - x^2 + y^2$ *and some level curves.*

variables. The *graph* of f is the subset of points in $\mathbb{R}^4$ given by

$$G_f = \{\, (x, y, z, w) \text{ in } \mathbb{R}^4 \mid (x, y, z) \text{ is in } D \text{ and } w = f(x, y, z) \,\}$$

The graph of f, sometimes called a *three manifold*, is a subset in $\mathbb{R}^4$. Therefore, we cannot directly visualize the graphs of functions of three variables since we would need to be able to draw four mutually perpendicular axes. We can, however, look at the analog of level curves for functions of two variables. These analogs are called *level surfaces*.

Level Surfaces: If f is a function of three variables and c is a constant, the corresponding *level surface* of f is

$$S = \{\, (x, y, z) \text{ in } \mathbb{R}^3 \mid f(x, y, z) = c \,\}$$

The equation $f(x, y, z) = c$ for a level surface of a function of three variables is the general form for a surface in $\mathbb{R}^3$ and can be much more difficult to sketch than the surfaces considered above (which are graphs of functions of two variables). While we could use x-traces, y-traces, and z-traces to help visualize a given level surface, we need to be able to render a whole series of level surfaces (sketch $f(x, y, z) = c$ for a series of values of c). This will give us an understanding of how the values $w = f(x, y, z)$ vary in space.

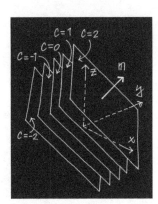

Figure 11.1.17:
Level surfaces of
$f(x, y, z) = x + y + z.$

Example 11.1.4 (Sketching Level Surfaces)

Problem: For the following functions $w = f(x, y, z)$, sketch a series of level surfaces using the specified values of c. Label each surface with the respective value of c.

(a) $f(x, y, z) = x + y + z$, $c = -2, -1, 0, 1, 2$

(b) $f(x, y, z) = \dfrac{z}{x^2 + y^2}$, $c = -2, -1, 0, 1, 2$

Solution (a): The level surfaces $x + y + z = c$ are planes, all with the same normal $\mathbf{n} = \langle\, 1, 1, 1 \,\rangle$. Thus, they are all parallel to one another. Figure 11.1.17 shows a sketch of the requested five level surfaces. Viewing $T = f(x, y, z)$ as a temperature function, we see that each level surface (called an *isotherm* in this situation) consists of all points in space that have the same temperature. Thus, temperatures rise as you move in the direction of $\mathbf{n}$.

Solution (b): To sketch the level surfaces $z/(x^2 + y^2) = c$, we rewrite this equation as $z = c(x^2 + y^2)$. We recognize these surfaces as a plane for $c = 0$ (specifically the x-y plane) and as circular paraboloids for $c \neq 0$ (turned up or down for c positive or negative, respectively). See Figure 11.1.18. Again we can view this function as a temperature function $T = z/(x^2 + y^2)$, with the plane and paraboloids in Figure 11.1.18 being the isotherms.

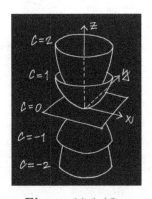

Figure 11.1.18:
Level surfaces of
$f(x, y, z) = z/(x^2 + y^2).$

Functions of n Variables

The extension of the discussion of functions of two or three variable to functions of n variables is easy enough conceptually, but visualization techniques are scarce.

A function f of n-variables has n independent variables, typically denoted by $x_1, x_2, \ldots, x_n$, and the *domain* of f is a subset D of ordered n-tuples of numbers $(x_1, x_2, \ldots, x_n)$ in $\mathbb{R}^n$. The *value* of f at an element, or point, $(x_1, x_2, \ldots, x_n)$ in its domain is denoted by $f(x_1, x_2, \ldots, x_n)$, and, with w typically denoting the *dependent variable*, we write $w = f(x_1, x_2, \ldots, x_n)$ to symbolize the functional relationship between the dependent and independent variables.

Exercises: 11.1 (Functions of Two or More Variables)

Using x-traces and y-traces to Sketch Graphs

In Exercises 1–38, use x-traces and y-traces to sketch the graph of the function $z = f(x, y)$ for (x, y) in the square $R = [-1, 1] \times [-1, 1]$. Do this by first sketching the two x-traces $y = \pm 1$ and the two y-traces $x = \pm 1$. Then complete the sketch by putting in a number of additional x-traces or y-traces (or some of each).

1. $z = yx^2$

2. $z = xy^2$

3. $z = x^2y^2$

4. $z = x^2y^4$

5. $z = xy^3$

6. $z = x^3y$

7. $z = y^2e^{-x}$

8. $z = x^2e^y$

9. $z = y^3e^{-x}$

10. $z = x^3e^y$

11. $z = y^2 \cos \pi x$

8. $z = y^2 \sin \pi x$

13. $z = (1 - x^3)y^2$

14. $z = (1 - y^3)x^2$

15. $z = (1 - x^2)y^2$

16. $z = (1 - y^2)x^2$

17. $z = (1 - x^2)y^3$

18. $z = (1 - y^2)x^3$

19. $z = (1 - x^3)y^3$

20. $z = (1 - y^3)x^3$

21. $z = x^2\sqrt{|y|}$

22. $z = y^2\sqrt{|x|}$

23. $z = (1 - x)\sqrt{|y|}$

24. $z = (1 - y)\sqrt{|x|}$

25. $z = x^2 + y$

26. $z = y^2 + x$

27. $z = x^2 + y^2$

28. $z = x^2 + y^2 + 1$

29. $z = x^2 - y^2$

30. $z = y^2 - x^2$

31. $z = x^3 + y^3$

32. $z = x^3 + y^3 + 1$

33. $z = y^3 - x^3$

34. $z = x^3 - y^3$

35. $z = y^3 - x^2 + 1$

36. $z = x^3 - y^1 + 1$

37. $z = x^3 + y^2$

38. $z = x^2 + y^3 + 1$

Sketching Level Curves (Horizontal Traces)

In Exercises 39–60, sketch the specified level curves for the given function.

39. $z = 2x + 3y$, $c = 0, \pm 6, \pm 12$

40. $z = 3x - 2y$, $c = 0, \pm 6, \pm 12$

41. $z = y + x^2$, $c = 0, 1, 2, 3, 4$

42. $z = y + x^3$, $c = 0, \pm 1, \pm 2$

43. $z = y/(1 + x^2)$, $c = 0, \pm\frac{1}{2}, \pm 1, \pm 2$

44. $z = y/(1 + x^3)$, $c = 0, \pm\frac{1}{2}, \pm 1, \pm 2$

45. $z = yx^2$, $c = 0, \pm\frac{1}{4}, \pm 1$

46. $z = yx^4$, $c = 0, \pm\frac{1}{16}, \pm 1$

47. $z = xy^{-2}$, $c = 0, \pm\frac{1}{2}, \pm 1, \pm 2$

48. $z = xy^{-3}$, $c = 0, \pm\frac{1}{2}, \pm 1, \pm 2$

49. $z = y^2e^x$, $c = 0, \frac{1}{4}, 1, 4$

50. $z = y^2e^{-x}$, $c = 0, \frac{1}{4}, 1, 4$

51. $z = x^3e^y$, $c = 0, \frac{1}{4}, 1, 8$

52. $z = x^3e^{-y}$, $c = 0, \frac{1}{4}, 1, 8$

53. $z = x^2 + y^2$, $c = 1, 2, 3, 4$

54. $z = 2x^2 + 2y^2$, $c = 4, 6, 8, 10$

55. $z = x^2 - y^2$, $c = 0, \pm 1, \pm 2, \pm 4$

56. $z = 2x^2 - 2y^2$, $c = 0, \pm 2, \pm 6, \pm 8$

57. $z = y^3 - x^2 + 1$, $c = -1, -\frac{1}{2}, 0, 1, \frac{3}{2}$

58. $z = x^3 - y^2 + 1$, $c = -1, -\frac{1}{2}, 0, 1, \frac{3}{2}$

59. $z = y^3 - x^3$, $c = 0, \pm 1, \pm\frac{3}{2}$

60. $z = x^3 - y^3$, $c = 0, \pm 1, \pm\frac{3}{2}$

In Exercises 61–66, for the given (hypothetical) contour map, determine the number of peaks, valleys, and saddle points on the corresponding mountain. Copy the map and mark these features on it.

61.   **62.**

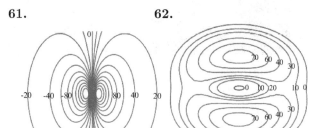

63.   **64.**

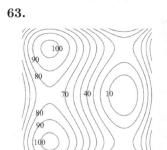
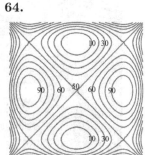

65.   **66.**

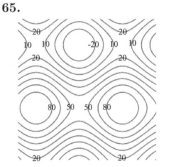
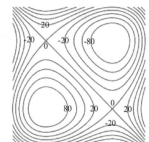

67. Match the following plots of level curve with the corresponding graphs of the function.

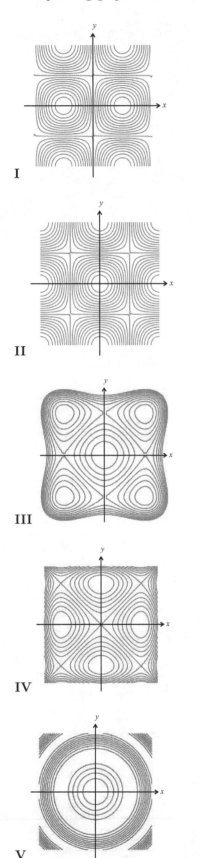

I

II

III

IV

V

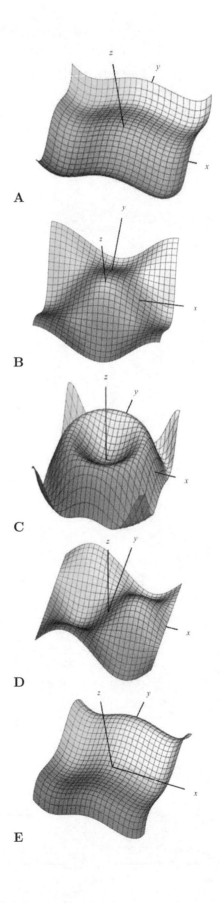

A

B

C

D

E

Calculus Concepts & Computation

11.2 Multivariable Limits & Continuity

In this section we extend the concept of limits to functions of two or more variables. Then we can use the limits to define what it means for a multi-variable function to be continuous at a point and continuous on a domain.

Limits for Functions of Two Variables

Suppose $z = f(x, y)$ is a function of two variables with domain D and $P_0 = (x_0, y_0)$ a given point. The intuitive notion of a limit involves an analysis of the "behavior of f near P_0" (which may not be in D). By "behavior" we mean: What does the graph of f look like near P_0 (even though $f(P_0)$ may not be defined). Saying that a point $P = (x, y)$ in the domain of f, is "near" P_0 means that the distance:

$$|P_0 P| = \sqrt{(x - x_0)^2 + (y - y_0)^2}$$

is small. In this case, we ask if the z-value $z = f(P)$ is "near" a particular value L. Here, nearness of values (i.e., real numbers) is measured by absolute values: $|f(P) - L|$. If we choose points P (in the domain D) nearer and nearer to P_0 and the corresponding function values $f(P)$ get nearer and nearer to L, then we would consider L as a *limit* of f at P_0. Thus, an intuitive definition of a limit might be formulated as follows:

DEFINITION 11.2.1 (Limits - Intuitive Version)

The function f is said to have limiting numerical value L as the variable point P tends to the given point P_0, if the function values $f(P)$ can be made as near to L as we wish by restricting P to being sufficiently near to P_0. When this is the case we use the notation

$$\lim_{P \to P_0} f(P) = L.$$

We say "L is the limit of f as P tends to P_0." Alternatively, we say that f approaches L as P approaches P_0 and write $f(P) \to L$ as $P \to P_0$

It is important to note that since the domain of f is two dimensional, there are lot more "ways" that the variable point P can approach P_0. For a function of a single variable, there are only two ways for $P \to P_0$: from the left side or the right side. This is the concept of one-sided limits discussed in Section 1.6. With functions of two variables $P \to P_0$ can be from either side along *any* line through P_0. Or more generally, the approach can be along any curve through P_0.

Visualization Tools

To get a visual feel for the behavior of f as $P \to P_0$, we can use several animation tools which are analogous to those used in Chapter 1 for functions of a single variable. In that chapter we had `dplot`, which produces an animation of the graph of $y = f(x)$ being drawn from left to right as x goes from a to b. This helped reveal the presence of jump discontinuities and vertical asymptotes in the graph of f on $[a, b]$. We also used `twosidelimit`, `leftlimit` and `rightlimit`, which give movies of the graph of f being drawn as x approaches a given point in $[a, b]$ from both sides, from the left side, or from the right side. These helped us analyze limiting values (if any).

For a function $z = f(x, y)$ of two variables, we can use `dplot3d` to create a movie where the ith frame is a plot of the graph of f on the rectangle $[a, g(t_i)] \times [c, h(t_i)]$. Here $x = g(t)$, $y = h(t)$ is a parametric curve in a rectangle $[a, b] \times [c, d]$ which is contained in the domain of f.

Example 11.2.1 (Using `dplot3d` to Study Function Behavior)

Problem: For the function

$$f(x, y) = \frac{x^4 + x^2 y + y^2}{x^4 + y^2},$$

with $(x, y) \neq (0, 0)$ in $R = [-1, 1] \times [-1, 1]$, study the behavior of the graph of f on the rectangle R.

Solution: First we do a simple dynamic plot of the graph of f having it be swept out in the y-direction, say, with $x = \frac{1}{2}$, $y = t$, parametrizng a straight line that runs from the bottom to top of R as t runs through the interval $I = [-1, 1]$. Figure 11.2.1 shows the last frame in a movie created by `dplot3d`.

By viewing the movie several times you will notice that a crinkling of the surface occurs near the origin and as you can see from the formula for f, the origin $P_0 = (0, 0)$ is a point of interest, because this is the only place (x, y) where $f(x, y)$ does not exist.

Next let's use `dplot3d` with the curve parametrized by $x = t$, $y = t^2$, for t in I again. The movie, the last frame of which is shown in Figure 11.2.2, exhibits the graph of f being plotted as the point $P(t) = (t, t^2)$ moves toward and through the point $(0, 0)$. This moving point traces out the parabola $y = x^2$ shown in black. At the same time a parabola, shown in red, and parametrized by $x = t$, $y = t^2$, $z = f(t, t^2)$, is traced out on the graph of f. Notice that the red parabola is horizontal because f has the same value at all points on the black parabola: $f(t, t^2) = 1.5$, for all $t \neq 0$. This is why we chose this curve to use in the dynamic plot. It passes through the point of interest, $P_0 = (0, 0)$, which is where we want to take the limit, and it happens that f has constant value at points $P \neq P_0$ on this curve. Below we will discuss how to choose such curves and how they can be used to show that a limit does not exist.

But first we need a more precise definition of multivariable limits:

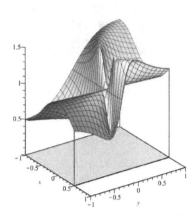

Figure 11.2.1: *Last frame in a* `dplot3d` *movie.*

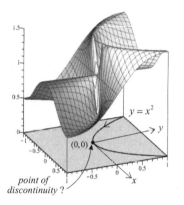

Figure 11.2.2: *A* `dplot3d` *using a parabolic path.*

DEFINITION 11.2.2 (The $\varepsilon - \delta$ Definition of a Limit)

Let f be defined for all points P in an open region D, except possibly at the point P_0 in D.

For a real number L, we say that

$$\lim_{P \to P_0} f(P) = L \qquad \text{(i.e., f has limit L as P approaches P_0)}$$

if for any number $\varepsilon > 0$, there exists a number $\delta > 0$, so that

$$\left| f(P) - L \right| < \varepsilon$$

whenever $P \neq P_0$ satisfies $\left| P_0 P \right| < \delta$.

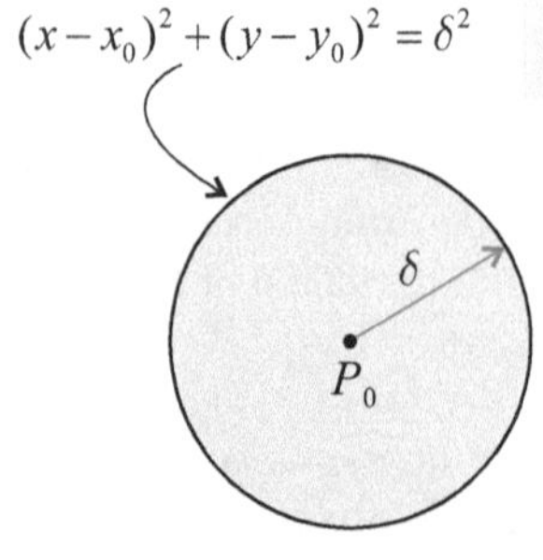

$(x - x_0)^2 + (y - y_0)^2 = \delta^2$

Figure 11.2.3: *The disk $B(P_0, \delta)$.*

NOTE: Saying that a point P satisfies $|P_0 P| < \delta$ means that the distance between P and P_0 is less than δ. Equivalently, this says that P lies in the set

$$B(P_0, \delta) = \{ (x, y) \mid (x - x_0)^2 + (y - y_0)^2 < \delta^2 \},$$

which is called the *open disk of radius δ centered at P_0*. See Figure 11.2.3. This disk gets smaller and smaller as δ gets smaller and smaller. So, this process governs the notion of how points P get nearer and nearer to P_0. This leads to another visualization tool:

More Visualization

For a function $z = f(x, y)$ of two variables the analog of `twosidedlimit` is the animation tool `radial_dplot3d`. This produces a movie in the following fashion. For a given point P_0 and two radii $R > r > 0$, the *ith* frame of `radial_dplot3d` is a plot of that part of the graph of f which lies above/below the annulus centered at P_0 with radii $R \geq r_i$. See Figure 11.2.4. Here r is taken to be very small, but not 0 (remember f may not be defined at P_0) and $R = r_0 > r_1 > r_2 > \cdots > r_N = r$. The resulting sequence of surfaces will show how the graph of f behaves as P approaches P_0 radially in all directions.

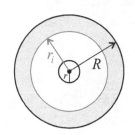

Figure 11.2.4: *An annulus in a radial plot.*

Example 11.2.2 (Using `radial_dplot3d` to Estimate Limits)

Problem: Estimate the following limits using `radial_dplot3d`:

$$(a) \quad \lim_{(x,y)\to(0,0)} (1 + x^2 - y^2) \qquad (b) \quad \lim_{(x,y)\to(0,0)} \frac{2x^2}{x^2 + y^2}$$

Solution (a): Here $f(x, y) = 1 + x^2 - y^2$ is a simple polynomial in two variables whose graph is a standard saddle (hyperbolic paraboloid) shifted up 1 unit. The function is defined everywhere and in particular $f(0, 0) = 1$. You would expect this to be the value of the limit

$$\lim_{(x,y)\to(0,0)} (1 + x^2 - y^2) = 1 + (0)^2 - (0)^2 = 1$$

Using `radial_dplot3d` produces a movie, the last frame of which is shown in Figure 11.2.5. Watching the movie adds evidence to our guess that the limit is $L = 1$.

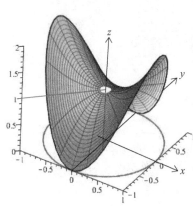

Figure 11.2.5: *Last frame in a* `radial_dplot3d`*.*

Solution (b): Here $f(x, y) = \frac{2x^2}{x^2 + y^2}$ is a rational function in two variables which is defined everywhere except at the point $(0, 0)$, where use of the formula gives $f(0, 0) = \frac{0}{0}$, an indeterminate form (as we saw many times in Chapter 1). If we use `radial_dplot3d` to graphically analyze the existence of the limit, we get a movie, the last frame of which is shown in Figure 11.2.6. Looking closely at the movie, you should be able to discern a number of horizontal lines at various heights, each of which approaching the z-axis. These lines are given parametrically by $x = t$, $y = mt$, $z = f(t, mt)$, where m is a constant and is the slope of a radial line $y = mx$ in the x-y plane (which is parametrized by $x = t$, $y = mt$). Note that at points along each of these latter lines, the values of f are the same:

$$f(t, mt) = \frac{2t^2}{t^2 + m^2 t^2} = \frac{2t^2}{t^2(1 + m^2)} = \frac{2}{1 + m^2}$$

For example, when $m = 0$, we get $f(t, 0) = \frac{2}{1+0} = 2$ as the constant value of f at points along the x-axis (except at $(0, 0)$). Also, for $m = 1$, we get $f(t, t) = \frac{2}{1+1} = 1$ as the constant value of f at points along the line $y = x$ (except at $(0, 0)$).

Based on these last two observations, we can conclude that

$$\lim_{(x,y)\to(0,0)} \frac{2x^2}{x^2 + y^2} = \text{ does not exist}$$

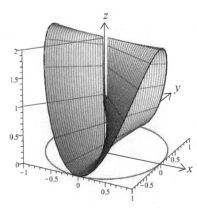

Figure 11.2.6: *Last frame in a* `radial_dplot3d`*.*

This is because no matter what value L we guess for the possible limit, we can always choose m so that $2/(1 + m^2)$ is different than L. It is an exercise to now prove that the limit does not exist using the ε-δ definition of the limit.

The technique used in the last example to ascertain the nonexistence of a limit is a valuable tool. In the example we found a particular family of curves (actually straight lines): $x = t$, $y = mt$ passing through the point P_0 and along each of which the function f had a constant value. If the constant values are different along different curves, then that indicates nonexistence of the limit at P_0. This is summarized in the following box:

TWO CURVES TEST (For Nonexistence of a Limit)

If a function f has two different limits along two different curves in D which pass through P_0, then

$$\lim_{P \to P_0} f(P) = \text{does not exist}$$

NOTE: This is somewhat like the result in Section 1.6 which says that if the two one-sided limits exist and are different numbers, then the two-sided limit does not exist.

To apply the above test you have to find two such curves, which may not be possible for many limits. Here's an example where it is possible:

Example 11.2.3 (Applying the Two Curves Test for Nonexistence)

Problem: Show that the limit

$$\lim_{(x,y) \to (0,0)} \frac{x^4 + x^2 y + y^2}{x^4 + y^2},$$

does not exist.

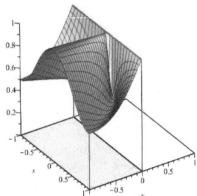

Figure 11.2.7: *A constant value of* 1 *for f along the x-axis:* $(t, 0)$, $t \neq 0$.

Solution: The function f involved in this limit is the one we studied graphically in Example 11.2.1. There we found that f had a constant value of 1.5 at points along the parabola $y = x^2$ (which we parametrized by $x = t$, $y = t^2$). So, more generally, suppose we look at the parabolas $y = ax^2$, parametrized by $x = t$, $y = at^2$, where a is any constant. Then the values of f along such a curve are

$$f(t, at^2) = \frac{t^4 + t^2 at^2 + (at^2)^2}{t^4 + (at^2)^2} = \frac{t^4 + at^4 + a^2 t^4}{t^4 + a^2 t^4} = \frac{1 + a + a^2}{1 + a^2},$$

for all $t \neq 0$. Thus, f has a constant value along any such curve. In Example 11.2.1, we used $a = 1$ and the constant value is $\frac{3}{2} = 1.5$, as we saw. If we take $a = 0$, then the "parabola" degenerates into a straight line (the x-axis) and f has constant value $f(t, 0) = 1$ for all $t \neq 0$. See Figure 11.2.7. Applying the Two Curves Test we see that the limit does not exist.

Just as in Chapter 1, there are limit laws for multivariable limits:

THEOREM 11.2.1 (Limit Laws)

Suppose that c is a constant and that the limits $\lim_{P \to P_0} f(P)$ *and* $\lim_{P \to P_0} g(P)$ *exist. Then*

(1) $\displaystyle \lim_{P \to P_0}[f(P) + g(P)] = \lim_{P \to P_0} f(P) + \lim_{P \to P_0} g(P)$ \hspace{1cm} (Sum Law)

(2) $\displaystyle \lim_{P \to P_0}[f(P) - g(P)] = \lim_{P \to P_0} f(P) - \lim_{P \to P_0} g(P)$ \hspace{1cm} (Difference Law)

(3) $\displaystyle \lim_{P \to P_0}[cf(P)] = c \lim_{P \to P_0} f(P)$ \hspace{1cm} (Constant Multiple Law)

(4) $\displaystyle \lim_{P \to P_0}[f(P)g(P)] = \lim_{P \to P_0} f(P) \cdot \lim_{P \to P_0} g(P)$ \hspace{1cm} (Product Law)

(5) $\displaystyle \lim_{P \to P_0} \frac{f(P)}{g(P)} = \frac{\lim_{P \to P_0} f(P)}{\lim_{P \to P_0} g(P)}$, $\quad if \lim_{P \to P_0} g(P) \neq 0$ \hspace{1cm} (Quotient Law)

These laws together with algebra (factoring, rationalizing, reducing, etc.) enable us to evaluate many of the limits that occur for functions of several variables. It is not hard to show, using Laws 1–4, that $\lim_{P \to P_0} f(P) = f(P_0)$ for any polynomial in two (or more) variables. Since a rational function f in several variables is the ratio of two such polynomial, it follows from Law 5, that $\lim_{P \to P_0} f(P) = f(P_0)$ at any point P_0 in the domain of f. These two assertions give us a two broad classes of functions for which the limits are easy to determine Just evaluate the function at P_0.

Example 11.2.4 (Using the Limit Laws)

Problem: Determine the following limits (if they exist):

Part (a): $\lim_{(x,y) \to (1,-1)} \dfrac{x^2 y - 3x^3 y^2 + y^3}{x^4 + 2y^2}$

Solution (a): This is a rational function and $(1, -1)$ is in its domain. So

$$\lim_{(x,y) \to (1,-1)} \frac{x^2 y - 3x^3 y^2 + y^3}{x^4 + 2y^2} = \frac{(1)^2(-1) - 3(1)^3(-1)^2 + (-1)^3}{(1)^4 + 2(-1)^2} = \frac{-5}{3}$$

Part (b): $\lim_{(x,y) \to (2,3)} \dfrac{x^2 - 2x + xy - 2y}{x - 2}$

Solution (b): Substituting in $x = 2$, $y = 3$ gives $\frac{0}{0}$, an indeterminate form. So, we try using algebra to simplify. Here factoring and reducing will work. We factor the numerator as

$$x^2 - 2x + xy - 2y = x(x - 2) + y(x - 2) = (x + y)(x - 2)$$

Now we can reduce and take the limit:

$$\lim_{(x,y) \to (2,3)} \frac{x^2 - 2x + xy - 2y}{x - 2} = \lim_{(x,y) \to (2,3)} \frac{(x + y)(x - 2)}{x - 2} \lim_{(x,y) \to (2,3)} (x + y) = 5$$

Part (c): $\lim_{(x,y) \to (1,1)} \dfrac{\sqrt{x} - \sqrt{y}}{x - y}$

Solution (c): Substituting in $x = 1$, $y = 1$ gives $\frac{0}{0}$, an indeterminate form. So, we try using algebra to simplify. Here rationalizing the numerator works

$$\begin{aligned}
\lim_{(x,y) \to (1,1)} \frac{\sqrt{x} - \sqrt{y}}{x - y} &= \lim_{(x,y) \to (1,1)} \frac{\sqrt{x} - \sqrt{y}}{x - y} \cdot \frac{\sqrt{x} + \sqrt{y}}{\sqrt{x} + \sqrt{y}} \\
&= \lim_{(x,y) \to (1,1)} \frac{x - y}{(x - y)(\sqrt{x} + \sqrt{y})} = \lim_{(x,y) \to (1,1)} \frac{1}{\sqrt{x} + \sqrt{y}} \\
&= \frac{1}{\sqrt{1} + \sqrt{1}} = \frac{1}{2}
\end{aligned}$$

CONTINUITY

As in Section 1.7, we can define continuity of a multivariable function using limits:

DEFINITION 11.2.3 (Continuity at a Point)

A function f is called continuous at P_0 when

  (i) $f(P_0)$ *is defined, and*

  (ii) $\lim_{P \to P_0} f(P)$ *exists, and*

  (iii) $\lim_{P \to P_0} f(P) = f(P_0)$

If either (i) ,(ii), or (iii) is not true, then f is said to be discontinuous at P_0.

The definition above is the same as before, except for the presence of more variables. However, the extension from continuity at a point to continuity on a function's domain D requires a discussion of the concept of an open region.

A point P_0 in a region D is called an *interior point* of D, if there is a $\delta > 0$ so that the open disk $B(P_0, \delta)$ is contained entirely in D. A region D is called an *open region* if every point in D is an interior point.

With this notion of openness, we extend the concept of continuity to open regions. Simply: a function f defined on an open region D is called *continuous on D* if it is continuous at each point in D.

From the remarks after the Limit Laws Theorem about polynomial and rational functions, we can conclude that these types of functions are continuous on their domains, which are open regions.

To get additional classes of continuous functions, we can use the following results (which are the sane as those discussed in Section 1.7 for single variable functions).

THEOREM 11.2.2 (Algebraic Combinations of Continuous Functions)

Suppose that f and g are continuous on a set D. Then,

(i) $(f \pm g)$ *is continuous on D*

(ii) $(f \cdot g)$ *is continuous on D*

(iii) $\dfrac{f}{g}$ *is continuous on $D' = \{x \in D \mid g(x) \neq 0\}$*

This theorem says that the standard four algebraic operations (addition, subtraction, multiplication, and division) applied to continuous functions yield continuous functions.

The fifth operation we can apply to functions is that of composition. To prove that continuity is preserved under composition of functions, one needs the following theorem:

THEOREM 11.2.3

Suppose that $\lim\limits_{P \to P_0} g(P) = L$ and that f is continuous at L. Then,

$$\lim_{P \to P_0} f(g(P)) = f(\lim_{P \to P_0} g(P)) = f(L)$$

Using this and the definition of multivariable continuity on a region gives:

COROLLARY 11.2.1 (Composition of Continuous Functions)

If f is continuous on D and g is continuous on E, with $g(E) \subseteq D$, then the composite
$$f \circ g$$
is continuous on E

All these theorems and corollary make the work of determining continuity (and discontinuities) easier. That's why we prove theorems.

Example 11.2.5 (Determining Continuity)

Problem: Determine all points where the following functions are discontinuous.

Part (a): $f(x, y) = \dfrac{xy + 1}{x^2 + y^2}$

Solution (a): This is a rational function, so it is continuous on its domain, which in this case consists of all points (x, y) in the plane except for which $x^2 + y^2 \neq 0$, i.e., $(x, y) \neq (0, 0)$. Thus the origin is the only point of discontinuity.

Part (b): $f(x, y) = \dfrac{xy}{2x - y + 1}$

Solution (b): As in Part (a), f is continuous at all points (x, y), except for those that satisfy $2x - y + 1 = 0$. Thus, the points of discontinuity lie on the line $y = 2x + 1$.

Part (c): $f(x, y) = \sec(x^2 + y^2)$

Solution (c): Since $\sec(x^2 + y^2) = \frac{1}{\cos(x^2 + y^2)}$, the discontinuities occur at points (x, y) where $\cos(x^2 + y^2) = 0$. But the cosine is zero only at odd multiples of $\frac{\pi}{2}$. So, the points of discontinuity for f lie on the concentric circles $x^2 + y^2 = \frac{(2n-1)\pi}{2}$, for $n = 0, 1, 2, \ldots$

Part (d): $f(x, y) = \begin{cases} 0 & \text{if } y \leq 1 + x^3 \\ 1 & \text{if } y > 1 + x^3 \end{cases}$

Solution (d): Here you have jump discontinuities at points (x, y) on the curve $y = 1 + x^3$. As you go from one side of this curve to the other, the values of f change from 0 to 1 (or vice versa),

Limits and Continuity in Higher Dimensions

For functions f of n variables: $x_1, x_2, \ldots, x_n$, the definitions, theorems, and corollaries concerning limits and continuity are the same as those discussed above for functions of two variables. In those results just take

$$P = (x_1, x_2, \ldots, x_n) \quad \text{and} \quad P_0 = (x_{01}, x_{02}, \ldots, x_{0n})$$

Exercises: 11.2 (Multivariable Limits and Continuity)

Finding Limits for Two-Variable Functions

In Exercises 1–26, use the Limit Laws and algebra to find the limits.

1. $\displaystyle \lim_{(x,y)\to(1,2)} (2x^2 - 3xy + 4y^2)$

2. $\displaystyle \lim_{(x,y)\to(1,3)} (4x^2 + 5xy - 3y^2)$

3. $\displaystyle \lim_{(x,y)\to(1,2)} \frac{x^2 - 4y + 2}{xy + 1}$ **4.** $\displaystyle \lim_{(x,y)\to(2,1)} \frac{3x^3 - 5y + 3}{xy + 1}$

5. $\displaystyle \lim_{(x,y)\to(1,2)} \sqrt{3xy^2 + 4}$ **6.** $\displaystyle \lim_{(x,y)\to(2,1)} \sqrt{3x^2y + 4}$

7. $\displaystyle \lim_{(x,y)\to(1,-1)} 2xye^{-x^2-y^2}$ **8.** $\displaystyle \lim_{(x,y)\to(1,2)} 3xye^{x^2-y^2}$

9. $\displaystyle \lim_{(x,y)\to(3,2)} \frac{x^2 - 3x - xy + 3y}{x - 3}$

10. $\displaystyle \lim_{(x,y)\to(4,2)} \frac{x^2 - 4x + xy - 4y}{x - 4}$

11. $\displaystyle \lim_{(x,y)\to(1,1)} \frac{(x+y)^2 - 4}{x + y - 2}$

12. $\displaystyle \lim_{(x,y)\to(3,-2)} \frac{(x-y)^2 - 25}{x - y - 5}$

13. $\displaystyle \lim_{(x,y)\to(1,1)} \frac{x^4 - y^4}{x - y}$ **14.** $\displaystyle \lim_{(x,y)\to(1,1)} \frac{x^4 - y^4}{y - x}$

15. $\displaystyle \lim_{(x,y)\to(2,4)} \frac{\sqrt{x+2} - \sqrt{y}}{x + 2 - y}$

16. $\displaystyle \lim_{(x,y)\to(8,16)} \frac{\sqrt{x+8} - \sqrt{y}}{x + 8 - y}$

17. $\displaystyle \lim_{(x,y)\to(1,4)} \frac{2\sqrt{x} - \sqrt{y}}{4x - y}$ **18.** $\displaystyle \lim_{(x,y)\to(1,16)} \frac{4\sqrt{x} - \sqrt{y}}{16x - y}$

19. $\displaystyle \lim_{(x,y)\to(1,1)} \frac{\frac{1}{\sqrt{y}} - \frac{1}{\sqrt{x}}}{x - y}$ **20.** $\displaystyle \lim_{(x,y)\to(1,1)} \frac{\frac{1}{\sqrt{x}} - \frac{1}{\sqrt{y}}}{x - y}$

21. $\displaystyle \lim_{(x,y)\to(1,-1)} \frac{x^3 + y^3}{x + y}$ **22.** $\displaystyle \lim_{(x,y)\to(1,1)} \frac{x^3 - y^3}{x - y}$

23. $\displaystyle \lim_{(x,y)\to(2,2)} \frac{\frac{1}{y} - \frac{1}{x}}{x - y}$ **24.** $\displaystyle \lim_{(x,y)\to(2,2)} \frac{\frac{1}{x} - \frac{1}{y}}{x - y}$

25. $\displaystyle \lim_{(x,y)\to(3,3)} \frac{x - y}{\frac{1}{y} - \frac{1}{x}}$ **26.** $\displaystyle \lim_{(x,y)\to(3,3)} \frac{x - y}{\frac{1}{x} - \frac{1}{y}}$

Applying the Two Curves Test

In Exercises 27–38, (a) Use the Two Curves Test to show that the limit of the function at $P_0 = (0,0)$ does not exist. (b) **CAS:** Use either `dplot3d` or `radialplot` to visually augment your work in Part (a).

27. $f(x, y) = \dfrac{x^2 + xy + y^2}{x^2 + y^2}$ **28.** $f(x, y) = \dfrac{x^2 + xy + y^2}{x^2 + xy}$

29. $f(x, y) = \dfrac{x^3 y}{x^4 + y^4}$ **30.** $f(x, y) = \dfrac{xy^3}{x^4 + y^4}$

31. $f(x, y) = \dfrac{2x^2 y}{x^4 + y^2}$ **32.** $f(x, y) = \dfrac{2xy^2}{x^2 + y^4}$

33. $f(x, y) = \dfrac{x^6 - y^2}{x^6 + y^2}$ **34.** $f(x, y) = \dfrac{x^8 - y^2}{x^8 + y^2}$

35. $f(x, y) = \dfrac{x^2}{\sqrt{x^4 + y^4}}$ **36.** $f(x, y) = \dfrac{x^3}{\sqrt{x^6 + y^6}}$

37. $f(x, y) = \dfrac{xy}{|xy|}$ **38.** $f(x, y) = \dfrac{x^3 y}{|x^3 y|}$

Points of Discontinuities

In Exercises 39–60, describe all points of discontinuity (if any) for the following functions.

39. $f(x, y) = \sin(x^2 + y^2)$ **40.** $f(x, y) = \cos(x^2 + y^2)$

41. $f(x, y) = \cot(x^2 + y^2)$ **42.** $f(x, y) = \tan(x^2 + y^2)$

43. $f(x, y) = \dfrac{x + y}{x - y}$ **44.** $f(x, y) = \dfrac{x - y}{x + y}$

45. $f(x, y) = \dfrac{2x^2 y}{x^2 - y}$ **46.** $f(x, y) = \dfrac{2xy^2}{x - y^2}$

47. $f(x, y) = \sqrt{x^2 - y}$ **48.** $f(x, y) = \sqrt{y - x^3}$

49. $f(x, y) = \begin{cases} 0 & \text{if } y \le x \\ 1 & \text{if } y > x \end{cases}$

50. $f(x, y) = \begin{cases} 0 & \text{if } y \le -x \\ 1 & \text{if } y > -x \end{cases}$

51. $f(x, y) = \begin{cases} 0 & \text{if } y \le x^2 \\ 1 & \text{if } y > x^2 \end{cases}$

Calculus *Concepts & Computation*

11.3 Partial Derivatives

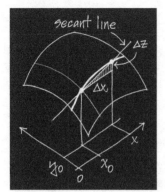

Figure 11.3.1: *A secant line in the x-direction.*

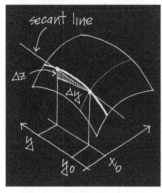

Figure 11.3.2: *A secant line in the y direction.*

The notion of the derivatives for functions f of several variables involves limits, much as it did for single variable functions. We select one of the variables, form the difference (or Newton) quotient with respect to that variable, hold the other variables fixed, and take the limit to get what is known as a *partial derivative* with respect to the selected variable. This section will discuss the geometric significance of partial derivatives, as well as the formulas and rules you can use to calculate such derivatives. We begin with the simplest case–functions of two variables.

Partial Derivatives for Functions of Two Variables

Suppose $z = f(x,y)$ is a function of two variables and (x_0, y_0) is a point in the domain D of f. Letting x vary and holding y fixed, $y = y_0$, gives a function $x \mapsto f(x, y_0)$ of a single variable with difference quotient

$$\frac{\Delta z}{\Delta x} = \frac{f(x, y_0) - f(x_0, y_0)}{x - x_0}$$

Geometrically this gives the slope of a secant line to the curve which is the x-trace made by the plane $y = y_0$. So you would expect that in the limit as $x \to x_0$, this Newton quotient would give the slope of a tangent line to this curve. See Figure 11.3.1. Similarly, letting y vary and holding x fixed, $x = x_0$, gives a function $y \mapsto f(x_0, y)$ of a single variable with difference quotient

$$\frac{\Delta z}{\Delta y} = \frac{f(x_0, y) - f(x_0, y_0)}{y - y_0}$$

See Figure 11.3.2. These two difference quotients give, in the limit, the two partial derivatives of f as stated in the following definition.

DEFINITION 11.3.1 (Partial Derivatives)

For a function $z = f(x,y)$ of two variables and point (x_0, y_0) in its domain, the two partial derivatives of f at (x_0, y_0) are (assuming the limits exists):

$$\frac{\partial z}{\partial x}\bigg|_{(x_0, y_0)} = \lim_{x \to x_0} \frac{\Delta z}{\Delta x} = \lim_{x \to x_0} \frac{f(x, y_0) - f(x_0, y_0)}{x - x_0} \tag{11.3.1}$$

$$\frac{\partial z}{\partial y}\bigg|_{(x_0, y_0)} = \lim_{y \to y_0} \frac{\Delta z}{\Delta y} = \lim_{y \to y_0} \frac{f(x_0, y) - f(x_0, y_0)}{y - y_0} \tag{11.3.2}$$

Geometrically, these two partial derivatives give the slopes of the two tangent lines to the curves that are the x-trace and y-trace at the point (x_0, y_0). Figures 11.3.1–11.3.2 exhibit this.

From Definition 11.3.1, we get two new *functions* $\frac{\partial z}{\partial x}$ and $\frac{\partial z}{\partial y}$ associated with the function $z = f(x,y)$, which are defined at all points (x_0, y_0) in the domain of f where the limits (11.3.1)–(11.3.2) exist. Some other common notation for these functions is

FUNCTIONS: $\frac{\partial z}{\partial x} = \frac{\partial f}{\partial x} = f_x$ and $\frac{\partial z}{\partial y} = \frac{\partial f}{\partial y} = f_y$

Evaluating these functions at a point $(x, y) = (x_0, y_0)$ in their domains gives numbers which are the slopes of the x- and y-traces. The other notation for this is

SLOPES: $\dfrac{\partial z}{\partial x}(x, y) = \dfrac{\partial f}{\partial x}(x, y) = f_x(x, y)$ and $\dfrac{\partial z}{\partial y}(x, y) = \dfrac{\partial f}{\partial y}(x, y) = f_y(x, y)$

Practically speaking, you can think of the partial derivatives $\frac{\partial z}{\partial x}$ and $\frac{\partial z}{\partial x}$ as ordinary derivatives with respect to x and y. The use of ∂, the "curly d," in the notation is just to emphasize that the derivative is only partially with respect to one of the variables. For calculations, we will *not* be using limits to find partial derivatives, but rather we will employ all the theorems and rules (sum, difference, product, quotient, and chain rules) from Calculus I.

Further, as with the Leibniz notation $\frac{d}{dx}$ symbolizing differentiation of a function of one variable, we will use $\frac{\partial}{\partial x}$ and $\frac{\partial}{\partial y}$ as the operators indicating derivatives (partially) with respect to x and y.

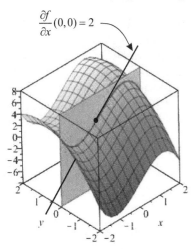

$\dfrac{\partial f}{\partial x}(0,0) = 2$

Figure 11.3.3: *Slope of a tangent to an x-trace.*

Example 11.3.1 (Calculating Partial Derivatives)

Problem: For the function $z = f(x, y) = 4 + 2x - x^3 + y - y^2$, find the two partial derivatives and use these to find the slopes of the x- and y-traces at the point $(x_0, y_0) = (0, 0)$.

Solution: The calculations of $\frac{\partial f}{\partial x}$ and $\frac{\partial f}{\partial y}$ are easy

$$\begin{aligned}
\frac{\partial f}{\partial x} &= \frac{\partial}{\partial x}(4 + 2x - x^3 + y - y^2) \\
&= \frac{\partial}{\partial x}(4 + 2x - x^3) + \frac{\partial}{\partial x}(y - y^2) = 2 - 3x^2 + 0 = 2 - 3x^2 \\
\frac{\partial f}{\partial y} &= \frac{\partial}{\partial y}(4 + 2x - x^3 + y - y^2) \\
&= \frac{\partial}{\partial y}(4 + 2x - x^3) + \frac{\partial}{\partial y}(y - y^2) = 0 + 1 - 2y = 1 - 2y
\end{aligned}$$

Evaluating these two functions at $(0, 0)$ gives

$$\frac{\partial f}{\partial x}(0,0) = (2 - 3x^2)\big|_{(0,0)} = 2 \quad \text{and} \quad \frac{\partial f}{\partial y}(0,0) = (1 - 2y)\big|_{(0,0)} = 1$$

Figures 11.3.3–11.3.4 show the graph of f and the two curves which are the x- and y-traces at $(0, 0)$, respectively. Also shown are the two tangent lines with slopes $f_x(0, 0) = 2$ and $f_y(0, 0) = 1$.

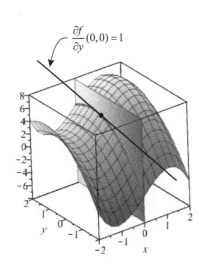

$\dfrac{\partial f}{\partial y}(0,0) = 1$

Figure 11.3.4: *Slope of a tangent to a y-trace.*

NOTE 1: Computing the partial derivatives in the above example was easy. We used the fact that the derivative of a constant is zero. In terms of partial derivatives with respect to x, this means that any expression $g(y)$ involving only y is viewed as a constant and so $\frac{\partial}{\partial x}[g(y)] = 0$. Similarly $\frac{\partial}{\partial y}[h(x)] = 0$, where $h(x)$ is an expression involving x only.

NOTE 2: Even though an expression of the form $h(x)g(y)$ is a product, the partial derivatives are simply $\frac{\partial}{\partial x}[h(x)g(y)] = h'(x)g(y)$ and $\frac{\partial}{\partial y}[h(x)g(y)] = h(x)g'(y)$.

The following example has functions, in Parts (b) and (c), where use of the product, quotient and chain rules is necessary.

Example 11.3.2 (Calculating Partial Derivatives)

Problem: Find the partial derivatives f_x and f_y of the functions:

(a) $f(x, y) = x^2 y^3 - x^5 + y^2$ (b) $f(x, y) = (xy^2 + 2)\sqrt{x^2 + y^3}$

(c) $f(x, y) = \dfrac{x^3 y^5}{x^2 + y^4}$ (d) $f(x, y) = xe^{-\frac{1}{2}(x^2 + y^2)}$

Solution Part (a): The calculations of f_x, f_y are

$$f_x = \frac{\partial}{\partial x}(x^2y^3 - x^5 + y^2) = \frac{\partial}{\partial x}(x^2y^3) - \frac{\partial}{\partial x}(x^5) + \frac{\partial}{\partial x}(y^2) = 2xy^3 - 5x^4$$

$$f_y = \frac{\partial}{\partial y}(x^2y^3 - x^5 + y^2) = \frac{\partial}{\partial y}(x^2y^3) - \frac{\partial}{\partial y}(x^5) + \frac{\partial}{\partial y}(y^2) = 3x^2y^2 + 2y$$

For the partial derivatives of x^2y^3, see NOTE 2 above.

Solution Part (b): The calculations of f_x, f_y involve the product and chain rules:

$$f_x = \frac{\partial}{\partial x}\left((xy^2 + 2)\sqrt{x^2 + y^3}\right)$$

$$= \left(\frac{\partial}{\partial x}(xy^2 + 2)\right)\sqrt{x^2 + y^3} + (xy^2 + 2)\frac{\partial}{\partial x}\left(\sqrt{x^2 + y^3}\right)$$

$$= y^2\sqrt{x^2 + y^3} + (xy^2 + 2)\cdot\frac{2x}{2\sqrt{x^2 + y^3}} = y^2\sqrt{x^2 + y^3} + \frac{x(xy^2 + 2)}{\sqrt{x^2 + y^3}}$$

$$= \frac{y^2(x^2 + y^3) + x(xy^2 + 2)}{\sqrt{x^2 + y^3}} = \frac{2x^2y^2 + y^5 + 2x}{\sqrt{x^2 + y^3}}$$

$$f_y = \frac{\partial}{\partial y}\left((xy^2 + 2)\sqrt{x^2 + y^3}\right)$$

$$= \left(\frac{\partial}{\partial y}(xy^2 + 2)\right)\sqrt{x^2 + y^3} + (xy^2 + 2)\frac{\partial}{\partial y}\left(\sqrt{x^2 + y^3}\right)$$

$$= 2xy\sqrt{x^2 + y^3} + (xy^2 + 2)\cdot\frac{3y^2}{2\sqrt{x^2 + y^3}} = 2xy\sqrt{x^2 + y^3} + \frac{3y^2(xy^2 + 2)}{2\sqrt{x^2 + y^3}}$$

$$= \frac{4xy(x^2 + y^3) + 3y^2(xy^2 + 2)}{2\sqrt{x^2 + y^3}} = \frac{4x^3y + 7xy^4 + 6y^2}{2\sqrt{x^2 + y^3}}$$

Solution Part (c): The calculations of f_x, f_y involve the quotient rule:

$$f_x = \frac{\partial}{\partial x}\left(\frac{x^3y^5}{x^2 + y^4}\right) = \frac{\frac{\partial}{\partial x}(x^3y^5)\cdot(x^2 + y^4) - x^3y^5\frac{\partial}{\partial x}(x^2 + y^4)}{(x^2 + y^4)^2}$$

$$= \frac{3x^2y^5(x^2 + y^4) - x^3y^5(2x)}{(x^2 + y^4)^2} = \frac{x^4y^5 + 3x^2y^9}{(x^2 + y^4)^2}$$

$$f_y = \frac{\partial}{\partial y}\left(\frac{x^3y^5}{x^2 + y^4}\right) = \frac{\frac{\partial}{\partial y}(x^3y^5)\cdot(x^2 + y^4) - x^3y^5\frac{\partial}{\partial y}(x^2 + y^4)}{(x^2 + y^4)^2}$$

$$= \frac{5x^3y^4(x^2 + y^4) - 4x^3y^8}{(x^2 + y^4)^2} = \frac{5x^5y^4 + x^3y^8}{(x^2 + y^4)^2}$$

Solution Part (d): The calculations of f_x, f_y involve the chain rule:

$$f_x = \frac{\partial}{\partial x}\left(xe^{-\frac{1}{2}(x^2+y^2)}\right) = \left(\frac{\partial}{\partial x}(x)\right)e^{-\frac{1}{2}(x^2+y^2)} + x\frac{\partial}{\partial x}\left(e^{-\frac{1}{2}(x^2+y^2)}\right)$$

$$= e^{-\frac{1}{2}(x^2+y^2)} + xe^{-\frac{1}{2}(x^2+y^2)}\frac{\partial}{\partial x}\left(-\frac{1}{2}(x^2 + y^2)\right)$$

$$= e^{-\frac{1}{2}(x^2+y^2)} + xe^{-\frac{1}{2}(x^2+y^2)}(-x) = (1 - x^2)e^{-\frac{1}{2}(x^2+y^2)}$$

$$f_y = \frac{\partial}{\partial y}\left(xe^{-\frac{1}{2}(x^2+y^2)}\right) = x\frac{\partial}{\partial y}\left(e^{-\frac{1}{2}(x^2+y^2)}\right)$$

$$= xe^{-\frac{1}{2}(x^2+y^2)}\frac{\partial}{\partial y}\left(-\frac{1}{2}(x^2 + y^2)\right) = xe^{-\frac{1}{2}(x^2+y^2)}(-y) = -xye^{-\frac{1}{2}(x^2+y^2)}$$

More Geometry: The partial derivatives $\frac{\partial f}{\partial x}$, $\frac{\partial f}{\partial y}$, as we have mentioned, give the slopes $\frac{\partial f}{\partial x}(x_0, y_0)$, $\frac{\partial f}{\partial y}(x_0, y_0)$ of the tangent lines for the x- and y-traces at the point

$(x_0, y_0, f(x_0, y_0))$ on the graph of f. They also allow us to solve the *tangent plane problem*:

The Tangent Plane Problem

For a function $z = f(x, y)$ of two variables and a point $P = (x_0, y_0, f(x_0, y_0))$ on its graph, find an equation for the tangent plane at P.

Example 11.3.3 (Tangent Plane to a Graph)

Problem: For the function $f(x, y) = 4 + 2x - x^3 + y - y^2$, find an equation for the tangent plane to the graph at the point $P = (0, 0, f(0, 0)) = (0, 0, 4)$.

Solution: We can view the tangent plane to the graph at P as arising from a *limit of secant planes* (just as we found, in Chapter 2, the tangent line as a limit of secant lines). Figures 11.3.1–11.3.2 show two secant lines at P to the graph of a function. Putting these two secant lines together (in the same picture) determines a secant plane at P and we take limits of such planes to get the tangent plane.

As in Chapter 2, we can motivate the limiting process by using a special-purpose Maple procedure, which in this case is `secant_planes(f,a,b,c,d,x0,y0,N)`. For this problem we define the function and use the procedure as follows:

```
> f:=(x,y)->4+2*x-x^3+y-y^2;
> secant_planes(f,-1,2,-1,2,0,0,20);
```

These commands produce a movie showing a sequence of 20 secant planes passing through P and cutting the surface, less and less, as they approach the tangent plane in the last frame of the movie. Figure 11.3.5 shows the 10th frame in this movie. As you can see, in each frame, two adjacent edges of the secant plane are formed by two secant lines to the x-trace and y-trace. In the limit, these two secant lines give two tangent lines, one for the x-trace at P and one for the y-trace at P. These two tangent lines form two adjacent edges of the tangent plane at P.

In Example 11.3.1, we found that the slopes of these two tangent lines are

$$\frac{\partial f}{\partial x}(0, 0) = 2 \quad \text{and} \quad \frac{\partial f}{\partial y}(0, 0) = 1$$

We can use these numbers to get two vectors $\mathbf{u}$ and $\mathbf{v}$ that are parallel to the respective tangent lines as shown in Figure 11.3.6. A little thought shows that we can take, say,

$$\mathbf{u} = \langle 1, 0, 2 \rangle \quad \text{and} \quad \mathbf{v} = \langle 0, 1, 1 \rangle$$

Then a normal to the tangent plane is

$$\mathbf{n} = \mathbf{u} \times \mathbf{v} = \langle -2, -1, 1 \rangle,$$

and so an equation for the tangent plane (the plane through $P = (0, 0, 4)$ with normal $\mathbf{n}$) is

$$-2(x - 0) - 1(y - 0) + 1(z - 4) = 0, \quad \text{equivalently:} \quad -2x - y + z = 4$$

NOTE: In Section 11.6 we will discuss tangent planes to surfaces in general.

Partial Derivatives of Functions of n Variables

Partial derivatives of functions $w = f(x_1, x_2, \ldots, x_n)$ of n variables are defined in terms of limits in an entirely analogous way as we did for $n = 2$ variables. For the ith variable x_i $(1 \leq i \leq n)$:

$$\frac{\partial f}{\partial x_i}(x_1, x_2, \ldots, x_n) = \lim_{h \to 0} \frac{f(x_1, x_2, \ldots, x_i + h, \ldots, x_n) - f(x_1, x_2, \ldots, x_i, \ldots, x_n)}{h}$$

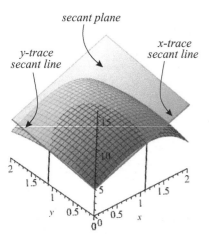

Figure 11.3.5: *Frame 10 in the movie* `secant_planes`.

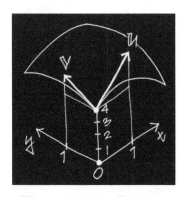

Figure 11.3.6: *Tangent vectors to the graph of f.*

From this, we get n new functions $\frac{\partial f}{\partial x_1}, \frac{\partial f}{\partial x_1}, \ldots, \frac{\partial f}{\partial x_n}$. The notation for these new functions is the same as before: $\frac{\partial w}{\partial x_i} = \frac{\partial f}{\partial x_i} = f_{x_i}$, for each $i = 1 \ldots, n$.

As above for two variables, we do not use the limit definition when computing the partial derivatives in particular examples. Rather, just use all the rules and formulas to compute $\frac{\partial f}{\partial x_i}$ by taking an ordinary derivative with respect to x_i, viewing all the other variables as constants.

Example 11.3.4 (Partial Derivatives of Functions of Three Variables)

Problem: Find the partial derivatives f_x, f_y and f_z of the functions:

(a) $f(x, y, z) = x^2 y^3 z + xy^2 z^5$ (b) $f(x, y, z) = xy^2 z^3 \sqrt{x^2 + y^2 + z^2}$

(c) $f(x, y, z) = \dfrac{x}{y^2 + z^2}$ (d) $f(x, y, z) = \sin(x^2 + y^3 + z^4)$

Solution Part (a): The calculations of f_x, f_y, f_z are

$$f_x = \frac{\partial}{\partial x}\left(x^2 y^3 z + xy^2 z^5\right) = 2xy^3 z + y^2 z^5$$

$$f_y = \frac{\partial}{\partial y}\left(x^2 y^3 z + xy^2 z^5\right) = 3x^2 y^2 z + 2xyz^5$$

$$f_z = \frac{\partial}{\partial z}\left(x^2 y^3 z + xy^2 z^5\right) = x^2 y^3 + 5xy^2 z^4$$

Solution Part (b): Using the product and chain rules, f_x, f_y, f_z are

$$
\begin{aligned}
f_x &= \frac{\partial}{\partial x}\left(xy^2 z^3 \sqrt{x^2 + y^2 + z^2}\right) = y^2 z^3 \sqrt{x^2 + y^2 + z^2} + xy^2 z^3 \frac{x}{\sqrt{x^2 + y^2 + z^2}} \\
&= y^2 z^3 \left[\sqrt{x^2 + y^2 + z^2} + \frac{x^2}{\sqrt{x^2 + y^2 + z^2}}\right] = y^2 z^3 \left[\frac{x^2 + y^2 + z^2 + x^2}{\sqrt{x^2 + y^2 + z^2}}\right] \\
&= \frac{y^2 z^3 [2x^2 + y^2 + z^2]}{\sqrt{x^2 + y^2 + z^2}} \\
f_y &= \frac{\partial}{\partial y}\left(xy^2 z^3 \sqrt{x^2 + y^2 + z^2}\right) = 2xyz^3 \sqrt{x^2 + y^2 + z^2} + xy^2 z^3 \frac{y}{\sqrt{x^2 + y^2 + z^2}} \\
&= xyz^3 \left[2\sqrt{x^2 + y^2 + z^2} + \frac{y^2}{\sqrt{x^2 + y^2 + z^2}}\right] = xyz^3 \left[\frac{2(x^2 + y^2 + z^2) + y^2}{\sqrt{x^2 + y^2 + z^2}}\right] \\
&= \frac{xyz^3 [2x^2 + 3y^2 + 2z^2]}{\sqrt{x^2 + y^2 + z^2}} \\
f_z &= \frac{\partial}{\partial z}\left(xy^2 z^3 \sqrt{x^2 + y^2 + z^2}\right) = 3xy^2 z^2 \sqrt{x^2 + y^2 + z^2} + xy^2 z^3 \frac{z}{\sqrt{x^2 + y^2 + z^2}} \\
&= xy^2 z^2 \left[3\sqrt{x^2 + y^2 + z^2} + \frac{z^2}{\sqrt{x^2 + y^2 + z^2}}\right] = xy^2 z^2 \left[\frac{3(x^2 + y^2 + z^2) + z^2}{\sqrt{x^2 + y^2 + z^2}}\right] \\
&= \frac{xy^2 z^2 [3x^2 + 3y^2 + 4z^2]}{\sqrt{x^2 + y^2 + z^2}}
\end{aligned}
$$

Solution Part (c): Finding f_x is easy but f_y, f_z require the quotient rule

$$
\begin{aligned}
f_x &= \frac{\partial}{\partial x}\left(\frac{x}{y^2 + z^2}\right) = \frac{\partial}{\partial x}\left(\frac{1}{y^2 + z^2}\, x\right) = \frac{1}{y^2 + z^2} \\
f_y &= \frac{\partial}{\partial y}\left(\frac{x}{y^2 + z^2}\right) = \frac{\frac{\partial}{\partial y}(x)(y^2 + z^2) - x\frac{\partial}{\partial y}(y^2 + z^2)}{(y^2 + z^2)^2} \\
&= \frac{0(y^2 + z^2) - x2y}{(y^2 + z^2)^2} = \frac{-2xy}{(y^2 + z^2)^2}
\end{aligned}
$$

$$f_z = \frac{\partial}{\partial z}\left(\frac{x}{y^2 + z^2}\right) = \frac{\frac{\partial}{\partial z}(x)(y^2 + z^2) - x\frac{\partial}{\partial z}(y^2 + z^2)}{(y^2 + z^2)^2}$$

$$= \frac{0(y^2 + z^2) - x2z}{(y^2 + z^2)^2} = \frac{-2xz}{(y^2 + z^2)^2}$$

Solution Part (d): Using the chain rule, f_x, f_y, f_z are

$$f_x = \frac{\partial}{\partial x}\left[\sin(x^2 + y^3 + z^4)\right] = \cos(x^2 + y^3 + z^4)\frac{\partial}{\partial x}(x^2 + y^3 + z^4)$$

$$= \cos(x^2 + y^3 + z^4)\, 2x = 2x\cos(x^2 + y^3 + z^4)$$

$$f_y = \frac{\partial}{\partial y}\left[\sin(x^2 + y^3 + z^4)\right] = \cos(x^2 + y^3 + z^4)\frac{\partial}{\partial y}(x^2 + y^3 + z^4)$$

$$= \cos(x^2 + y^3 + z^4)\, 3y^2 = 3y^2\cos(x^2 + y^3 + z^4)$$

$$f_z = \frac{\partial}{\partial z}\left[\sin(x^2 + y^3 + z^4)\right] = \cos(x^2 + y^3 + z^4)\frac{\partial}{\partial z}(x^2 + y^3 + z^4)$$

$$= \cos(x^2 + y^3 + z^4)\, 4z^3 = 4z^3\cos(x^2 + y^3 + z^4)$$

NOTE 1: After you get used to taking partial derivatives of functions of several variables, you can use some of the short cuts you learned for ordinary derivatives. For instance in using the quotient rule above in Part (c), you could have done the special case of it (when the numerator is a constant c): $\frac{d}{dx}\left(\frac{c}{g(x)}\right) = \frac{-cg'(x)}{[g(x)]^2}$.

NOTE 2: In each of the calculations for Part (d), we put in all the steps, but after you are experienced with partial derivatives, you could do these calculations with one step. The next example illustrates this.

Example 11.3.5 (Partial Derivatives of Functions of Four Variables)

Problem: Find the partial derivatives f_x, f_y, f_z, f_w of the function

$$f(x, y, z, w) = \sin(x^2 + y^3)\cos(z^4 + w^5)$$

Solution: The calculations are a simple use of the chain rule:

$$f_x = \frac{\partial}{\partial x}\left[\sin(x^2 + y^3)\cos(z^4 + w^5)\right] = 2x\cos(x^2 + y^3)\cos(z^4 + w^5)$$

$$f_y = \frac{\partial}{\partial y}\left[\sin(x^2 + y^3)\cos(z^4 + w^5)\right] = 3y^2\cos(x^2 + y^3)\cos(z^4 + w^5)$$

$$f_z = \frac{\partial}{\partial z}\left[\sin(x^2 + y^3)\cos(z^4 + w^5)\right] = -4z^3\sin(x^2 + y^3)\sin(z^4 + w^5)$$

$$f_w = \frac{\partial}{\partial w}\left[\sin(x^2 + y^3)\cos(z^4 + w^5)\right] = -5w^4\sin(x^2 + y^3)\sin(z^4 + w^5)$$

Higher-Order Partial Derivatives

Just as with ordinary derivatives, we apply the partial differentiation process multiple times in succession. Doing so produces what are known as the *higher-order partial derivatives* of the function.

Since the majority of applications of partial derivatives in science, engineering, and business involve, at most, 2nd-order partial derivatives, we stress here just 'second-order partials.'

For a function $z = f(x, y)$ of two variables, the 1st-order partials are symbolized by applying the two partial derivative operators $\frac{\partial}{\partial x}$ and $\frac{\partial}{\partial y}$ to f. If we apply these operators twice to f, the Leibniz notation for the 2nd-order partial derivative operators becomes:

$$\frac{\partial}{\partial x}\frac{\partial}{\partial x} = \frac{\partial\partial}{\partial x\partial x} = \frac{\partial^2}{\partial x^2} \quad \text{and} \quad \frac{\partial}{\partial y}\frac{\partial}{\partial y} = \frac{\partial\partial}{\partial y\partial y} = \frac{\partial^2}{\partial y^2}$$

$$\frac{\partial}{\partial x}\frac{\partial}{\partial y} = \frac{\partial\partial}{\partial x \partial y} = \frac{\partial^2}{\partial x \partial y} \quad \text{and} \quad \frac{\partial}{\partial y}\frac{\partial}{\partial x} = \frac{\partial\partial}{\partial x \partial y} = \frac{\partial^2}{\partial y \partial x}$$

Thus, we have four 2nd-order partials for a function of two variables:

$$\frac{\partial^2 f}{\partial x^2} = f_{xx}, \quad \frac{\partial^2 f}{\partial y^2} = f_{yy}, \quad \frac{\partial^2 f}{\partial x \partial y} = f_{yx}, \quad \text{and} \quad \frac{\partial^2 f}{\partial y \partial x} = f_{xy}$$

The subscripting notation is very convenient to use. Thus, f_{xx} is the function you get by differentiating (partially) f twice with respect to x. Similarly for f_{yy}. More interesting are the partials f_{xy} and f_{yx}, which are called the *mixed partial derivatives* since they involve both the variables x and y. NOTE: In computing f_{xy}, you differentiate f first with respect to x and then with respect to y. (See the Leibniz notation above.) However for f_{yx} you do the derivatives in the opposite order. Having pointed this out, the following theorem tells us that the order makes no difference.

THEOREM 11.3.1 (Order of Partial Derivatives)

Suppose f and its partial derivatives f_x, f_y, f_{xy}, f_{yx} are defined and continuous on an open set D. Then $f_{xy} = f_{yx}$ on D.

Computing 2nd-order partials is easy but involves more work (since you must compute a 1st-order partial first). Examples also show that for a mixed partial derivative, computing f_{yx} might be easier than computing f_{xy}, and vice versa. Since $f_{yx} = f_{xy}$ you might take advantage of this.

Example 11.3.6 (2nd-Order Partial Derivatives)

Problem: Find the 2nd-order partials f_{xx}, f_{xy} and f_{yy} of the functions:

(a) $f(x,y) = x^3y^5 - 4x^2y^2 + 2xy$ (b) $f(x,y) = \sin(x^2y^3)$

Solution Part (a): The 1st-order partials are

$$f_x = \frac{\partial}{\partial x}(x^3y^5 - 4x^2y^2 + 2xy) = 3x^2y^5 - 8xy^2 + 2y$$

$$f_y = \frac{\partial}{\partial y}(x^3y^5 - 4x^2y^2 + 2xy) = 5x^3y^4 - 8x^2y + 2x$$

Then the 2nd-order partials are

$$f_{xx} = \frac{\partial}{\partial x}(3x^2y^5 - 8xy^2 + 2y) = 6xy^5 - 8y^2$$

$$f_{yy} = \frac{\partial}{\partial y}(5x^3y^4 - 8x^2y + 2x) = 20x^3y^3 - 8x^2$$

$$f_{xy} = \frac{\partial}{\partial y}(3x^2y^5 - 8xy^2 + 2y) = 15x^2y^4 - 16xy + 2$$

Solution Part (b): The 1st-order partials are

$$f_x = \frac{\partial}{\partial x}\left[\sin(x^2y^3)\right] = 2xy^3\cos(x^2y^3)$$

$$f_y = \frac{\partial}{\partial y}\left[\sin(x^2y^3)\right] = 3x^2y^2\cos(x^2y^3)$$

Then the 2nd-order partials are

$$f_{xx} = \frac{\partial}{\partial x}\left[2xy^3\cos(x^2y^3)\right] = 2y^3\cos(x^2y^3) - 4x^2y^6\sin(x^2y^3)$$

$$f_{yy} = \frac{\partial}{\partial y}\left[3x^2 y^2 \cos(x^2 y^3)\right] = 6x^2 y \cos(x^2 y^3) - 9x^4 y^4 \sin(x^2 y^3)$$

$$f_{xy} = \frac{\partial}{\partial y}\left[2xy^3 \cos(x^2 y^3)\right] = 6xy^2 \cos(x^2 y^3) - 6x^3 y^5 \sin(x^2 y^3)$$

The next example illustrates that computing f_{xy} maybe easier to do by computing f_{yx} instead.

Example 11.3.7 (Computing a Mixed Partial)

Problem: Find the 2nd-order partial f_{xy} of $f(x,y) = xy + \dfrac{x}{1+x^2}$:

Solution: Note that the function depends on y in a very simple way. So we compute f_y first.

$$f_y = \frac{\partial}{\partial y}\left(xy + \frac{x}{1+x^2}\right) = x$$

Now the rest is easy: $f_{xy} = f_{yx} = (f_y)_x = \frac{\partial}{\partial x}(x) = 1$.

The 3rd- and 4th-order partials of a function $z = f(x,y)$ of two variables are easy extensions of 2nd-order partials. A generalization of Theorem 11.3.1 allows us to identify many of the mixed, higher-order partials. For example, here is a complete list of the distinct third and fourth-order partial derivatives of a function of two variables x, y:

3rd-Order Partials: $f_{xxx}, f_{yyy}, f_{xxy}, f_{yyx}$

4th-Order Partials: $f_{xxxx}, f_{yyyy}, f_{xxxy}, f_{yyyx}, f_{xxyy}$

So, for instance, we have the identifications $f_{xxyy} = f_{xyxy} = f_{yxxy} = f_{yxyx} = f_{yyxx}$.

For higher-order partial derivatives and for the general nth-order partials one has to introduce some addition notation. This is discussed in the exercises.

Having discussed the higher-order partial derivatives for a function of two variables, we just briefly indicate the extension to functions of more than three variables. Again, because of physics, the second-order partials are the most important.

For a function $w = f(x,y,z)$ of three variables, its 2nd-order partials are (assuming the extension of Theorem 11.3.1 to three variables):

$$f_{xx}, f_{yy}, f_{zz}, f_{xy}, f_{xz}, f_{yz}$$

Similarly for a function $u = f(x,y,z,w)$ of four variables, its 2nd-order partials are

$$f_{xx}, f_{yy}, f_{zz}, f_{ww}, f_{xy}, f_{xz}, f_{xw}, f_{yz}, f_{yw}, f_{zw}$$

Other Variables

The standard notation for the variables is x, y, z, etc. But in applications you will encounter other designations for the variables, such as s, t, u, v, etc. For example, in the chemical theory of gases, the pressure is a function of the volume and temperature: $P = f(V, T)$. Then the rates of change of P with respect to volume and temperature are denoted by

$$\frac{\partial P}{\partial V} = P_V, \; \frac{\partial P}{\partial T} = P_T,$$

respectively. In the exercises and elsewhere we will sometimes use this other notation for the variables so that you will become familiar with it when computing partial derivatives.

Exercises: 11.3 (Partial Derivatives)

Computing (1st-Order) Partial Derivatives

In Exercises 1–78, compute the partial derivatives (i.e., 1st-order partials) of the given functions.

1. $f(x,y) = x^3y^4 + 6x^5 - 3y^3$

2. $f(x,y) = x^2y^6 - 5x^4 + 4y^5$

3. $f(x,y) = 4x^2y^{1/2} - 6x^{5/2}y^3$

4. $f(x,y) = 6x^4y^{1/3} - 6x^{2/3}y^2$

5. $f(x,y) = \sqrt{xy}$ **6.** $f(x,y) = \sqrt[3]{xy}$

7. $f(x,y) = \sqrt{x^2 + y^2}$ **8.** $f(x,y) = \sqrt{x^4 + y^4}$

9. $f(x,y) = \dfrac{1}{\sqrt{x^2 + y^2}}$ **10.** $f(x,y) = \dfrac{1}{\sqrt{x^4 + y^4}}$

11. $f(x,y) = \dfrac{1}{x^2 + y^2}$ **12.** $f(x,y) = \dfrac{1}{x^4 + y^4}$

13. $f(x,y) = (3x + 4y)\sqrt{x^2 + y^2}$

14. $f(x,y) = (2x + 3y)\sqrt{x^4 + y^4}$

15. $f(x,y) = (2x^3 - y^2)\sqrt{x^2 + y^2}$

16. $f(x,y) = (3x^5 - y^4)\sqrt{x^4 + y^4}$

17. $f(x,y) = \dfrac{2x + 5y}{3x + 7y}$ **18.** $f(x,y) = \dfrac{5x + 3y}{4x + 6y}$

19. $f(x,y) = \dfrac{x^4y^3}{x^3 + y^2}$ **20.** $f(x,y) = \dfrac{x^6y^5}{x^2 + y^2}$

21. $f(x,y) = \dfrac{x^2 + y^3}{x^3 + y^2}$ **22.** $f(x,y) = \dfrac{x^4 + y^5}{x^2 + y^3}$

23. $f(x,y) = \dfrac{\sqrt{x}}{\sqrt{x} + \sqrt{y}}$ **24.** $f(x,y) = \dfrac{\sqrt{x}}{\sqrt{x} - \sqrt{y}}$

25. $f(x,y) = \dfrac{e^x + e^y}{e^x - e^y}$ **26.** $f(x,y) = \dfrac{e^x - e^y}{e^x + e^y}$

27. $f(x,y) = \dfrac{e^x - e^{-y}}{e^{-x} + e^y}$ **28.** $f(x,y) = \dfrac{e^{-x} - e^y}{e^x + e^{-y}}$

29. $f(x,y) = \dfrac{\cos x + \sin y}{\cos x + \cos y}$ **30.** $f(x,y) = \dfrac{\cos x + \cos y}{\sin x + \sin y}$

31. $f(x,y) = \dfrac{\cos x \cos y}{\sin x + \sin y}$ **32.** $f(x,y) = \dfrac{\sin x \sin y}{\cos x + \cos y}$

33. $f(x,y) = \dfrac{\sin xy}{1 + \sin xy}$ **34.** $f(x,y) = \dfrac{\cos xy}{1 + \cos xy}$

35. $f(x,y) = \tan(x^2y^3)$ **36.** $f(x,y) = \tan(x^4y^5)$

37. $f(x,y) = \sec(x^2y^3)$ **38.** $f(x,y) = \sec(x^4y^5)$

39. $f(x,y) = \sin(e^{-xy^2})$ **40.** $f(x,y) = \cos(e^{-x^2y})$

41. $f(x,y) = e^{\sin(xy^2)}$ **42.** $f(x,y) = e^{\cos(x^2y)}$

43. $f(x,y) = e^{xy^2}\sin(xy^2)$ **44.** $f(x,y) = e^{xy^2}\sin(xy^2)$

45. $f(x,y) = y^2e^{-(x^2+y^2)}$ **46.** $f(x,y) = x^2e^{-(x^2+y^2)}$

47. $f(x,y) = \ln(x^2 + y^2)$ **48.** $f(x,y) = \ln(x^4 + y^4)$

49. $f(x,y) = \ln(x^2y^2)$ **50.** $f(x,y) = \ln(x^4y^4)$

51. $f(x,y) = \ln(x^2 \ln y)$ **52.** $f(x,y) = \ln(y^2 \ln x)$

53. $f(x,y) = (x + \ln y)(y + \ln x)$

54. $f(x,y) = (x - \ln y)(y - \ln x)$

55. $f(x,y) = \dfrac{x + \ln y}{y + \ln x}$ **56.** $f(x,y) = \dfrac{x - \ln y}{y - \ln x}$

57. $f(x,y) = \tan^{-1}(\sqrt{xy})$ **58.** $f(x,y) = \cot^{-1}(\sqrt{xy})$

59. $f(x,y) = \tan^{-1}\left(\dfrac{\sqrt{x}}{\sqrt{y}}\right)$ **60.** $f(x,y) = \tan^{-1}\left(\dfrac{\sqrt{y}}{\sqrt{x}}\right)$

61. $f(x,y) = \tan^{-1}(\sqrt{x^2 + y^2})$

62. $f(x,y) = \tan^{-1}(\sqrt{x^4 + y^4})$

63. $f(x,y,z) = x^3y^2z^5 - 4x^2yz^3$

64. $f(x,y,z) = x^4y^3z^2 - 5x^3y^2z$

65. $f(x,y,z) = \sqrt{x^2 + y^2 + z^2}$

66. $f(x,y,z) = \sqrt{x^4 + y^4 + z^4}$

67. $f(x,y,z) = x^2y^3z^4\sqrt{x^3 + y^3 + z^3}$

68. $f(x,y,z) = x^4y^3z^2\sqrt{x^4 + y^4 + z^4}$

69. $f(x,y,z) = xy^2z^3\sin(xyz)$

70. $f(x,y,z) = x^2yz^3\cos(xyz)$

71. $f(x,y,z) = \dfrac{x + y}{y + z}$ **72.** $f(x,y,z) = \dfrac{y + z}{x + z}$

73. $f(x,y,z) = \dfrac{xyz}{x^2 + y^2 + z^2}$

74. $f(x,y,z) = \dfrac{xyz}{x^3 + y^3 + z^3}$

75. $f(x,y,z) = \dfrac{xy^2z^3}{x + y^2 + z^3}$

76. $f(x,y,z) = \dfrac{x^3y^2z}{x^3 + y^2 + z}$

77. $f(x,y,z) = xye^{-2yz^3}$ **78.** $f(x,y,z) = xze^{-2y^3z}$

Computing 2nd Order Partial Derivatives

In Exercises 79–94, find all the 2nd-order partial derivatives of the given functions.

79. $f(x,y) = 3x^4y - 5x^2y^3$ **80.** $f(x,y) = 3x^4y - 5x^2y^3$

81. $f(x,y) = \sin(x^3y^4)$ **82.** $f(x,y) = \sin(x^4y^5)$

83. $f(x, y) = \ln(x^2 + y^2)$ **84.** $f(x, y) = \ln(x^4 + y^4)$

85. $f(x, y) = \dfrac{1}{x^2 + y^2}$ **86.** $f(x, y) = \dfrac{1}{x^3 + y^3}$

87. $f(x, y) = e^{-x^2 y^3}$ **88.** $f(x, y) = e^{-x^3 y^4}$

89. $f(x, y) = \tan^{-1}(xy)$ **90.** $f(x, y) = \cot^{-1}(xy)$

91. $f(x, y, z) = (x^2 + y^2 + z^2)^{-1/2}$

92. $f(x, y, z) = (x^2 + y^2 + z^2)^{-1/3}$

93. $f(x, y, z, w) = (x^2 + y^2 + z^2 + w^2)^{-1}$

94. $f(x, y, z, w) = (x^2 + y^2 + z^2 + w^2)^{-2}$

Mixed Partial Derivatives

In Exercises 95–104, find the indicated partial derivatives.
NOTE: In some of these, doing the partials in a different
order will make it easier.

95. $f(x, y) = e^{-2xy}$, f_{xxxx}, f_{xxy}

96. $f(x, y) = e^{-3xy}$, f_{xxxx}, f_{xxy}

97. $f(x, y) = \sin(xy)$, f_{xxxx}, f_{xxyy}

98. $f(x, y) = \cos(xy)$, f_{xxxx}, f_{xxyy}

99. $w = s^2 t e^{-s^3}$, w_{sstt}, w_{tss}

100. $w = s^3 t e^{-s^2}$, w_{sstt}, w_{tss}

101. $P = TV^{-1}$, $\partial^3 P / \partial V^3$, $\partial^3 P / \partial T \partial V^2$

102. $P = TV^{-2}$, $\partial^3 P / \partial V^3$, $\partial^3 P / \partial T \partial V^2$

103. $w = u^{-1} v^{-2}$, $\partial^3 w / \partial u \partial v^2$, $\partial^3 w / \partial u^2 \partial v$

104. $w = u^{-2} v^{-1}$, $\partial^3 w / \partial u \partial v^2$, $\partial^3 w / \partial u^2 \partial v$

Calculus *Concepts & Computation*

11.4 The Chain Rule

In Calculus I, the chain rule was an indispensable tool for differentiating composite functions: $f \circ g$, where both f and g are functions of a single variable, say, $y = f(u)$ and $u = g(x)$. The chain rule says the derivative function of such a composite function has its value at x given by (in the prime notation)

$$(f \circ g)'(x) = f'(g(x)) \cdot g'(x)$$

and (in the Leibniz notation)

$$\frac{dy}{dx}\Big|_x = \frac{dy}{du}\Big|_{u=g(x)} \cdot \frac{du}{dx}\Big|_x$$

In this section we extend the formulas to composite functions $f \circ g$, where f and g can be functions of several variables.

The chain rule formula in the multi-variable case is mainly a theoretical tool (which we will use the ensuing sections). As you saw in the previous section, calculating partial derivatives amounts to taking ordinary derivatives with respect to one of the variables while holding the other variables fixed (viewed as constants). Because of this, knowing how to use the chain rule in the single variable case is all you will ever need when working with functions of several variables.

The Chain Rule for Functions of Two Variables

Suppose $w = f(x, y)$ is a function of two variables x and y. The simplest case of the multi-variable chain rule occurs when each of these variables is a function of t, say $x = g(t)$ and $y = h(t)$. Then as a composite function $w = f(g(t), h(t))$ is a function of a single variable t. To see how the chain rule formula arises from the computation of dw/dt, we look at several examples.

These examples involve the basic chain rule for functions of a single variable. For instance, if x is a function of t, then

$$\frac{d}{dt}\left(x^2\right) = 2x\frac{dx}{dt} \quad \text{and} \quad \frac{d}{dt}\left(\sin x\right) = \cos x\frac{dx}{dt}$$

Table 11.4.1 in the margin shows some more of these basic chain rule derivatives.

Example 11.4.1 (Calculating Derivatives)

Problem: For each of the following functions $w = f(x, y)$, assume that x and y are functions of t. Using the derivative rules from Calculus I, find dw/dt. Group together the terms involving dx/dt and dy/dt respectively.

(a) $w = x^2y^3 + 2x^4y^5$ (b) $w = \dfrac{x}{x^2 + y^2}$ (c) $w = x\sqrt{x+y}$

Solution Part (a): Using the basic chain rule and the product rule gives

$$\begin{aligned}
\frac{dw}{dt} &= \frac{d}{dt}\left(x^2y^3 + 2x^4y^5\right) = \frac{d}{dt}\left(x^2y^3\right) + \frac{d}{dt}\left(2x^4y^5\right) \\
&= 2x\frac{dx}{dt}\,y^3 + x^2\,3y^2\frac{dy}{dt} + 8x^3\frac{dx}{dt}\,y^5 + 2x^4\,5y^4\frac{dy}{dt} \\
&= \left(2xy^3 + 8x^3y^5\right)\frac{dx}{dt} + \left(3x^2y^2 + 10x^4y^4\right)\frac{dy}{dt}
\end{aligned}$$

Solution Part (b): Using the basic chain rule and the quotient rule gives

$$\frac{dw}{dt} = \frac{d}{dt}\left(\frac{x}{x^2 + y^2}\right) = \frac{\frac{dx}{dt}(x^2 + y^2) - x\frac{d}{dt}(x^2 + y^2)}{(x^2 + y^2)^2}$$

BASIC CHAIN RULE

$$\frac{d}{dt}\left(x^n\right) = nx^{n-1}\frac{dx}{dt}$$

$$\frac{d}{dt}\left(\sqrt{x}\right) = \frac{1}{2\sqrt{x}}\frac{dx}{dt}$$

$$\frac{d}{dt}\left(e^x\right) = e^x\frac{dx}{dt}$$

$$\frac{d}{dt}\left(\ln x\right) = \frac{1}{x}\frac{dx}{dt}$$

$$\frac{d}{dt}\left(\sin x\right) = \cos x \cdot \frac{dx}{dt}$$

$$\frac{d}{dt}\left(\cos x\right) = -\sin x \cdot \frac{dx}{dt}$$

$$\frac{d}{dt}\left(\tan x\right) = \sec^2 x \cdot \frac{dx}{dt}$$

$$\frac{d}{dt}\left(\sec x\right) = \sec x \tan x \cdot \frac{dx}{dt}$$

$$\frac{d}{dt}\left(\sin^{-1} x\right) = \frac{1}{\sqrt{1-x^2}} \cdot \frac{dx}{dt}$$

$$\frac{d}{dx}\left(\tan^{-1} x\right) = \frac{1}{1+x^2} \cdot \frac{dx}{dt}$$

$$\frac{d}{dt}\left(\sec^{-1} x\right) = \frac{1}{|x|\sqrt{x^2-1}} \cdot \frac{dx}{dt}$$

Table 11.4.1

$$= \frac{\frac{dx}{dt}(x^2 + y^2) - x(2x\frac{dx}{dt} + 2y\frac{dy}{dt})}{(x^2 + y^2)^2} = \frac{(y^2 - x^2)\frac{dx}{dt} - 2xy\frac{dy}{dt}}{(x^2 + y^2)^2}$$

$$= \frac{y^2 - x^2}{(x^2 + y^2)^2}\frac{dx}{dt} + \frac{-2xy}{(x^2 + y^2)^2}\frac{dy}{dt}$$

Solution Part (c): Using the basic chain rule and the product rule gives

$$\frac{dw}{dt} = \frac{d}{dt}\left(x\sqrt{x + y}\right) = \frac{dx}{dt}\sqrt{x + y} + x\frac{d}{dt}\left(\sqrt{x + y}\right)$$

$$= \frac{dx}{dt}\sqrt{x + y} + x\frac{\frac{dx}{dt} + \frac{dy}{dt}}{2\sqrt{x + y}}$$

$$= \left(\sqrt{x + y} + \frac{x}{2\sqrt{x + y}}\right)\frac{dx}{dt} + \frac{x}{2\sqrt{x + y}}\frac{dy}{dt}$$

$$= \frac{3x + 2y}{2\sqrt{x + y}}\frac{dx}{dt} + \frac{x}{2\sqrt{x + y}}\frac{dy}{dt}$$

If you examine the results in each of the three calculations, you will see that in each the end result has the form

$$\frac{dw}{dt} = A\frac{dx}{dt} + B\frac{dy}{dt} \quad \text{where} \quad A = f_x, \quad B = f_y$$

This leads to the general rule in the next Theorem.

THEOREM 11.4.1 (Chain Rule - Part 1)

Suppose $w = f(x, y)$ is differentiable and x, y are differentiable functions of t.

Then w is a differentiable function of t and

$$\frac{dw}{dt} = f_x\frac{dx}{dt} + f_y\frac{dy}{dt} \qquad (11.4.1)$$

Some students and instructors prefer to write this two-variable chain rule as

$$\frac{dw}{dt} = \frac{\partial f}{\partial x}\frac{dx}{dt} + \frac{\partial f}{\partial y}\frac{dy}{dt} \qquad (11.4.2)$$

Both versions (11.4.1) and (11.4.2) show how the partial derivatives of f are involved in the derivative of the composite function. As mentioned above, these formulas are very important for theoretical work. They are also often of practical use in differentiating a composite function $w = f(x, y)$, $x = g(t)$, $y = h(t)$. For this, first compute f_x, f_y, $\frac{dx}{dt} = g'(t)$, $\frac{dy}{dt} = h'(t)$. Then write out

$$\frac{dw}{dt} = f_x\frac{dx}{dt} + f_y\frac{dy}{dt} \quad \text{and substitute in } x, y, \frac{dx}{dt}, \frac{dy}{dt}$$

This is known as the "CR way" of computing the derivative dw/dt. One can also compute dw/dt directly by first calculating, and perhaps simplifying, the composite function $w = f(g(t), h(t))$. Then just differentiate the resulting function of t. This is known as the "non-CR way" of computing the derivative. Each way has its advantages. Sometimes one way is quicker than the other, as the following examples illustrate.

Example 11.4.2 (Using the CR and non-CR Ways)

Problem: For each of the functions

(a) $w = x^3y^4$ (b) $w = \dfrac{x}{x + y}$ (c) $w = x\sqrt{x + y}$

find dw/dt, where x and y are the following functions of t:

(i) $x = t$, $y = t^2$ and   (ii) $x = \cos t$, $y = \sin t$

Do this both by using the chain rule (the CR way) and directly (the non-CR way).

Solution Part (a): The partial derivatives are

$$f_x = \frac{\partial}{\partial x}(x^3 y^4) = 3x^2 y^4, \quad f_y = \frac{\partial}{\partial y}(x^3 y^4) = 4x^3 y^3$$

So

$$\frac{dw}{dt} = f_x \frac{dx}{dt} + f_y \frac{dy}{dt} = 3x^2 y^4 \frac{dx}{dt} + 4x^3 y^3 \frac{dy}{dt} \qquad (11.4.3)$$

Part (i): For $x = t$, $y = t^2$ the derivatives are $\frac{dx}{dt} = 1$, $\frac{dy}{dt} = 2t$. Substituting these four things into Equation (11.4.3) gives

$$\frac{dw}{dt} = 3t^2 (t^2)^4 (1) + 4t^3 (t^2)^3 2t = 3t^{10} + 8t^{10} = 11t^{10}$$

This is the CR way of computing dw/dt. The non-CR way is easier in this case because

$$w = x^3 y^4 = t^3 (t^2)^4 = t^3 t^8 = t^{11} \quad \text{and so} \quad \frac{dw}{dt} = \frac{d}{dt}(t^{11}) = 11t^{10}$$

Part (ii): For $x = \cos t$, $y = \sin t$ the derivatives are $\frac{dx}{dt} = -\sin t$, $\frac{dy}{dt} = \cos t$. Substituting these four things into Equation (11.4.3) gives

$$\begin{aligned}
\frac{dw}{dt} &= 3\cos^2 t \sin^4 t (-\sin t) + 4\cos^3 t \sin^3 t (\cos t) \\
&= -3\cos^2 t \sin^5 t + 4\cos^4 t \sin^3 t
\end{aligned}$$

This is the CR way of computing dw/dt. The non-CR way is just as complicated:

$$\begin{aligned}
w &= x^3 y^4 = \cos^3 t \sin^4 t \\
\frac{dw}{dt} &= \frac{d}{dt}(\cos^3 t \sin^4 t) = 3\cos^2 t(-\sin t)\sin^4 t + \cos^3 t(4\sin^3 t \cos t) \\
&= -3\cos^2 t \sin^5 t + 4\cos^4 \sin^3 t
\end{aligned}$$

Solution Part (b): The partial derivatives are

$$\begin{aligned}
f_x &= \frac{\partial}{\partial x}\left(\frac{x}{x+y}\right) = \frac{1(x+y) - x(1)}{(x+y)^2} = \frac{y}{(x+y)^2} \\
f_y &= \frac{\partial}{\partial y}\left(\frac{x}{x+y}\right) = \frac{0(x+y) - x(1)}{(x+y)^2} = \frac{-x}{(x+y)^2}
\end{aligned}$$

So

$$\frac{dw}{dt} = f_x \frac{dx}{dt} + f_y \frac{dy}{dt} = \frac{y}{(x+y)^2}\frac{dx}{dt} + \frac{-x}{(x+y)^2}\frac{dy}{dt} \qquad (11.4.4)$$

Part (i): For $x = t$, $y = t^2$ the derivatives are $\frac{dx}{dt} = 1$, $\frac{dy}{dt} = 2t$. Substituting these four things into Equation (11.4.4) gives

$$\frac{dw}{dt} = \frac{t^2}{(t+t^2)^2}(1) + \frac{-t}{(t+t^2)^2}(2t) = \frac{-t^2}{(t+t^2)^2} = \frac{-1}{(1+t)^2}$$

This is the CR way of computing dw/dt. The non-CR way is easier in this case because

$$w = \frac{x}{x+y} = \frac{t}{t+t^2} = \frac{1}{1+t} \quad \text{and so} \quad \frac{dw}{dt} = \frac{d}{dt}\left(\frac{1}{1+t}\right) = \frac{-1}{(1+t)^2}$$

Part (ii): For $x = \cos t$, $y = \sin t$ the derivatives are $\frac{dx}{dt} = -\sin t$, $\frac{dy}{dt} = \cos t$. Substituting these four things into Equation (11.4.4) gives

$$\frac{dw}{dt} = \frac{\sin t}{(\cos t + \sin t)^2}(-\sin t) + \frac{-\cos t}{(\cos t + \sin t)^2}(\cos t)$$

$$= \frac{-\sin^2 t - \cos^2 t}{(\cos t + \sin t)^2} = \frac{-1}{(\cos t + \sin t)^2}$$

This is the CR way of computing dw/dt. The non-CR way is just as complicated:

$$w = \frac{x}{x+y} = \frac{\cos t}{\cos t + \sin t}$$

$$\frac{dw}{dt} = \frac{d}{dt}\left(\frac{\cos t}{\cos t + \sin t}\right) = \frac{-\sin t(\cos t + \sin t) - \cos t(-\sin t + \cos t)}{(\cos t + \sin t)^2}$$

$$= \frac{-\sin^2 t - \cos^2 t}{(\cos t + \sin t)^2} = \frac{-1}{(\cos t + \sin t)^2}$$

Solution Part (c): First note that throughout this book we have used:

$$\frac{d}{dx}(\sqrt{x}) = \frac{1}{2\sqrt{x}}$$

for this special case of the power rule. In words the formula says: *the derivative of the square root function is one over two times the square root function.* This will occur many times in the calculations below.

The partial derivatives are

$$f_x = \frac{\partial}{\partial x}(x\sqrt{x+y}) = \frac{\partial}{\partial x}(x) \cdot \sqrt{x+y} + x \cdot \frac{\partial}{\partial x}\sqrt{x+y} = \sqrt{x+y} + x\left(\frac{1}{2\sqrt{x+y}}\right)$$

$$= \sqrt{x+y} + \frac{x}{2\sqrt{x+y}} = \frac{2(x+y) + x}{2\sqrt{x+y}} = \frac{3x + 2y}{2\sqrt{x+y}}$$

$$f_y = \frac{\partial}{\partial y}(x\sqrt{x+y}) = x\frac{\partial}{\partial y}(\sqrt{x+y}) = x\left(\frac{1}{2\sqrt{x+y}}\right) = \frac{x}{2\sqrt{x+y}}$$

So

$$\frac{dw}{dt} = f_x\frac{dx}{dt} + f_y\frac{dy}{dt} = \frac{3x+2y}{2\sqrt{x+y}}\frac{dx}{dt} + \frac{x}{2\sqrt{x+y}}\frac{dy}{dt} \qquad (11.4.5)$$

Part (i): For $x = t$, $y = t^2$ the derivatives are $\frac{dx}{dt} = 1$, $\frac{dy}{dt} = 2t$. Substituting these four things into Equation (11.4.5)gives

$$\frac{dw}{dt} = \frac{3t + 2t^2}{2\sqrt{t+t^2}}(1) + \frac{t}{2\sqrt{t+t^2}}(2t) = \frac{3t + 4t^2}{2\sqrt{t+t^2}}$$

This is the CR way of computing dw/dt. The non-CR way is slightly more difficult:

$$w = x\sqrt{x+y} = t\sqrt{t+t^2}$$

$$\frac{dw}{dt} = \frac{d}{dt}(t\sqrt{t+t^2}) = 1 \cdot \sqrt{t+t^2} + t\left(\frac{1+2t}{2\sqrt{t+t^2}}\right) = \sqrt{t+t^2} + \frac{t+2t^2}{2\sqrt{t+t^2}}$$

$$= \frac{2(t+t^2) + t + 2t^2}{2\sqrt{t+t^2}} = \frac{3t + 4t^2}{2\sqrt{t+t^2}}$$

Part (ii): For $x = \cos t$, $y = \sin t$ the derivatives are $\frac{dx}{dt} = -\sin t$, $\frac{dy}{dt} = \cos t$. Substituting these four things into Equation (11.4.5) gives

$$\frac{dw}{dt} = \frac{3\cos t + 2\sin t}{2\sqrt{\cos t + \sin t}}(-\sin t) + \frac{\cos t}{2\sqrt{\cos t + \sin t}}(\cos t) = \frac{-3\cos t \sin t - 2\sin^2 t + \cos^2 t}{2\sqrt{\cos t + \sin t}}$$

This is the CR way of computing dw/dt. The non-CR way is just as complicated:

$$w = x\sqrt{x+y} = \cos t\sqrt{\cos t + \sin t}$$

$$\frac{dw}{dt} = \frac{d}{dt}(\cos t\sqrt{\cos t + \sin t}) = -\sin t\sqrt{\cos t + \sin t} + \cos t\left(\frac{-\sin t + \cos t}{2\sqrt{\cos t + \sin t}}\right)$$

$$= -\sin t\sqrt{\cos t + \sin t} + \frac{-\cos t\sin t + \cos^2 t}{2\sqrt{\cos t + \sin t}}$$

$$= \frac{-2\sin t(\cos t + \sin t) - \cos t\sin t + \cos^2 t}{2\sqrt{\cos t + \sin t}} = \frac{-3\cos t\sin t - 2\sin^2 t + \cos^2 t}{2\sqrt{\cos t + \sin t}}$$

An Extension

The next simplest case of the multi-variable chain rule involves two independent variables s and t. Thus, suppose $w = f(x, y)$ is a function of two variables x and y and each of these variables is a function of variables s and t, say $x = g(s, t)$ and $y = h(s, t)$. Then as a composite function $w = f(g(s, t), h(s, t))$ is a function of two variables s and t. To see how the chain rule formula arises from the computation of $\partial w/\partial s$ and $\partial w/\partial t$, we look at several examples.

These examples involve the basic chain rule for functions of a single variable. For instance, if $w = f(x, y) = 5x^3 y^7$, where x and y are functions of s and t, then

$$\frac{\partial w}{\partial s} = \frac{\partial}{\partial s}\left(5x^3 y^7\right) = \left(15x^2\frac{\partial x}{\partial s}\right)y^7 + 5x^3\left(7y^6\frac{\partial y}{\partial s}\right)$$

$$= (15x^2 y^7)\frac{\partial x}{\partial s} + (35x^3 y^6)\frac{\partial y}{\partial s} = f_x\frac{\partial x}{\partial s} + f_y\frac{\partial y}{\partial s}$$

You can readily see that the calculations and results are the same for the partial derivative with respect to t. Namely, $\frac{\partial w}{\partial t} = (15x^2 y^7)\frac{\partial x}{\partial t} + (35x^3 y^6)\frac{\partial y}{\partial t}$. This simple example indicates the validity of the following theorem.

THEOREM 11.4.2 (Chain Rule - Part 2)

Suppose $w = f(x, y)$ is differentiable and x, y are differentiable functions of s and t.

Then w is a differentiable function of s and t with partial derivatives given by

$$\frac{\partial w}{\partial s} = f_x\frac{\partial x}{\partial s} + f_y\frac{\partial y}{\partial s} \qquad (11.4.6)$$

$$\frac{\partial w}{\partial t} = f_x\frac{\partial x}{\partial t} + f_y\frac{\partial y}{\partial t} \qquad (11.4.7)$$

NOTE 1: Formulas (11.4.6)–(11.4.7) in the theorem are essentially the same. The only difference is the independent variable names (s and t, respectively). Formula (11.4.7) is the same as Formula (11.4.1): $\frac{dw}{dt} = f_x\frac{dx}{dt} + f_y\frac{dy}{dt}$ except that now there are two independent variables (s and t) and so we use ∂ instead of d. *However*, as you have learned, taking partial derivatives, $\frac{\partial}{\partial t}$ is the same as ordinary derivatives, $\frac{d}{dt}$, with the other variables held fixed.

NOTE 2: The names s and t for the independent variables are ones that are commonly used. However, in many examples and applications other names, such as u and v, are used as names for the independent variables.

NOTE 3: Based on what was said in NOTE 1 the calculation of $\partial w/\partial s$ or $\partial w/\partial t$ is the same as the calculations we did for dw/dt in Example 11.4.2. We can use the chain rule or we can use the direct way by first calculating the composite function $w = f(g(s, t), h(s, t))$, simplifying, and then taking the partials.

Based on NOTES 1–3 above, we could dispense with examples. However, because of the multitude of symbols (s and t instead of just t), it is best to look at the following example.

Example 11.4.3 (Composite Function Partial Derivatives - 2 Independent Variables)

Problem: For each of the functions $w = f(x, y)$ and each choice of x and y as functions of variables s, t (or u, v) find $\partial w/\partial s$ and $\partial w/\partial t$ (or $\partial w/\partial u$ and $\partial w/\partial v$) by using (i) the chain rule in Formulas (11.4.6)–(11.4.7) and (ii) the non-chain rule way by directly calculating w as a function of s and t (or of u and v) and then taking partials.

(a) $w = \dfrac{x}{x+y}, \quad x = s^4 t^5, \quad y = s^6 t^2$

(b) $w = e^{2x} \ln y, \quad x = uv, \quad y = u^2 + v^2$

Solution Part (a): In Example 11.4.2 (b) we found that

$$f_x = \frac{\partial}{\partial x}\left(\frac{x}{x+y}\right) = \frac{y}{(x+y)^2} \quad \text{and} \quad f_y = \frac{\partial}{\partial y}\left(\frac{x}{x+y}\right) = \frac{-x}{(x+y)^2}$$

So

$$\frac{\partial w}{\partial s} = f_x \frac{\partial x}{\partial s} + f_y \frac{\partial y}{\partial s} = \frac{y}{(x+y)^2}\frac{\partial x}{\partial s} + \frac{-x}{(x+y)^2}\frac{\partial y}{\partial s} \qquad (11.4.8)$$

$$\frac{\partial w}{\partial t} = f_x \frac{\partial x}{\partial t} + f_y \frac{\partial y}{\partial t} = \frac{y}{(x+y)^2}\frac{\partial x}{\partial t} + \frac{-x}{(x+y)^2}\frac{\partial y}{\partial t} \qquad (11.4.9)$$

As we have said, these equations are the same except for the s and t. The partials of x and y are

$$\frac{\partial x}{\partial s} = \frac{\partial}{\partial s}(s^4 t^5) = 4s^3 t^5, \quad \frac{\partial y}{\partial s} = \frac{\partial}{\partial s}(s^6 t^2) = 6s^5 t^2$$

$$\frac{\partial x}{\partial t} = \frac{\partial}{\partial t}(s^4 t^5) = 5s^4 t^4, \quad \frac{\partial y}{\partial t} = \frac{\partial}{\partial t}(s^6 t^2) = 2s^6 t$$

Substituting these results and $x = s^4 t^5$, $y = s^2 t^3$ into (11.4.8)–(11.4.9) gives

$$\frac{\partial w}{\partial s} = \frac{s^6 t^2}{(s^4 t^5 + s^6 t^2)^2}(4s^3 t^5) + \frac{-s^4 t^5}{(s^4 t^5 + s^6 t^2)^2}(6s^5 t^2) = \frac{4s^9 t^7 - 6s^9 t^7}{(s^4 t^5 + s^6 t^2)^2}$$

$$= \frac{-2s^9 t^7}{(s^4 t^5 + s^6 t^2)^2} = \frac{-2s^9 t^7}{(s^4 t^2[t^3 + s^2])^2} = \frac{-2s^9 t^7}{s^8 t^4 (t^3 + s^2)^2} = \frac{-2st^3}{(t^3 + s^2)^2}$$

$$\frac{\partial w}{\partial t} = \frac{s^6 t^2}{(s^4 t^5 + s^6 t^2)^2}(5s^4 t^4) + \frac{-s^4 t^5}{(s^4 t^5 + s^6 t^2)^2}(2s^6 t) = \frac{5s^{10} t^6 - 2s^{10} t^6}{(s^4 t^5 + s^6 t^2)^2}$$

$$= \frac{3s^{10} t^6}{(s^4 t^5 + s^6 t^2)^2} = \frac{3s^{10} t^6}{(s^4 t^2[t^3 + s^2])^2} = \frac{3s^{10} t^6}{s^8 t^4 (t^3 + s^2)^2} = \frac{3s^2 t^2}{(t^3 + s^2)^2}$$

This is the CR way of calculating the partials of the composite function. For the non-CR way, we first compute the composite function and simplify:

$$w = \frac{s^4 t^5}{s^4 t^5 + s^6 t^2} = \frac{s^4 t^5}{s^4 t^2 (t^3 + s^2)} = \frac{t^3}{t^3 + s^2}$$

Now take partials of this

$$\frac{\partial w}{\partial s} = \frac{\partial}{\partial s}\left(\frac{t^3}{t^3 + s^2}\right) = \frac{-2st^3}{(t^3 + s^2)^2}$$

$$\frac{\partial w}{\partial t} = \frac{\partial}{\partial t}\left(\frac{t^3}{t^3 + s^2}\right) = \frac{3t^2(t^3 + s^2) - t^3(3t^2)}{(t^3 + s^2)^2} = \frac{3s^2 t^2}{(t^3 + s^2)^2}$$

Solution Part (b): The partial derivatives of f are

$$f_x = \frac{\partial}{\partial x} \left(e^{2x} \ln y \right) = 2e^{2x} \ln y \quad \text{and} \quad f_y = \frac{\partial}{\partial y} \left(e^{2x} \ln y \right) = e^{2x} \cdot \frac{1}{y} = \frac{e^{2x}}{y}$$

Recall in this part $w = f(x(u,v), y(u,v))$ so the independent variables are u and v. So the chain rule in this part is

$$\frac{\partial w}{\partial u} = f_x \frac{\partial x}{\partial u} + f_y \frac{\partial y}{\partial u} = (2e^{2x} \ln y)\frac{\partial x}{\partial u} + (\frac{e^{2x}}{y})\frac{\partial y}{\partial u} \qquad (11.4.10)$$

$$\frac{\partial w}{\partial v} = f_x \frac{\partial x}{\partial v} + f_y \frac{\partial y}{\partial v} = (2e^{2x} \ln y)\frac{\partial x}{\partial v} + (\frac{e^{2x}}{y})\frac{\partial y}{\partial v} \qquad (11.4.11)$$

These equations are the same except for the u and v. The partials of $x = uv$ and $y = u^2 + v^2$ are simply

$$\frac{\partial x}{\partial u} = \frac{\partial}{\partial u}(uv) = v, \qquad \frac{\partial y}{\partial u} = \frac{\partial}{\partial u}(u^2 + v^2) = 2u$$

$$\frac{\partial x}{\partial v} = \frac{\partial}{\partial v}(uv) = u, \qquad \frac{\partial y}{\partial v} = \frac{\partial}{\partial v}(u^2 + v^2) = 2v$$

Substituting these results and $x = uv$, $y = u^2 + v^2$ into (11.4.10)–(11.4.11) gives

$$\frac{\partial w}{\partial u} = = [2e^{2uv}\ln(u^2+v^2)]v + (\frac{e^{2uv}}{u^2+v^2})\,2u = 2ve^{2uv}\ln(u^2+v^2) + \frac{2ue^{2uv}}{u^2+v^2}$$

$$\frac{\partial w}{\partial v} = = [2e^{2uv}\ln(u^2+v^2)]u + (\frac{e^{2uv}}{u^2+v^2})\,2v = 2ue^{2uv}\ln(u^2+v^2) + \frac{2ve^{2uv}}{u^2+v^2}$$

This is the CR way of calculating the partials of the composite function. For the non-CR way, we first compute the composite function:

$$w = e^{2uv}\ln(u^2 + v^2)$$

Now take partials of this

$$\frac{\partial w}{\partial u} = \frac{\partial}{\partial u}\left(e^{2uv}\ln(u^2+v^2)\right) = 2ve^{2uv}\ln(u^2+v^2) + e^{2uv} \cdot \frac{2u}{u^2+v^2}$$

$$\frac{\partial w}{\partial v} = \frac{\partial}{\partial v}\left(e^{2uv}\ln(u^2+v^2)\right) = 2ue^{2uv}\ln(u^2+v^2) + e^{2uv} \cdot \frac{2v}{u^2+v^2}$$

These are the same as what we got above using the multivariable chain rule.

The Chain Rule for Functions of Three Variables

With the experience you have had in the above examples, it might not be hard for you to guess how the chain rule extends to functions of three variables $w = f(x, y, z)$, where x, y, z are functions either of a single variable t or of two variables s, t. The composite function will then be of the form

$$w = f(g(t), h(t), k(t)) \quad \text{or} \quad w = f(g(s,t), h(s,t), k(s,t))$$

Now, when differentiating, ordinarily or partially, with respect to t, the composite function depends on t through the three functions x, y, z (these are the "functions on the inside" of the composite function) and so the derivative will naturally involve $dx/dt, dy/dt, dz/dt$ or $\partial x/\partial t, \partial y/\partial t, \partial z/\partial t$. Moreover, f is the "function on the outside" and so the derivative of the composite function will also involve the functions f_x, f_y, f_z.

The following theorem shows how these six functions are combined to get the multivariable chain rule in this case.

THEOREM 11.4.3 (Chain Rule - Part 3)

Suppose $w = f(x, y, z)$ is a differentiable function of x, y, z.

(a) If x, y, z are differentiable functions of t, then w is a differentiable function of t and

$$\frac{dw}{dt} = f_x \frac{dx}{dt} + f_y \frac{dy}{dt} + f_z \frac{dz}{dt} \qquad (11.4.12)$$

(b) If x, y, z are differentiable functions of s and t, then w is a differentiable function of s and t with partial derivatives given by

$$\frac{\partial w}{\partial s} = f_x \frac{\partial x}{\partial s} + f_y \frac{\partial y}{\partial s} + f_z \frac{\partial z}{\partial s} \qquad (11.4.13)$$

$$\frac{\partial w}{\partial t} = f_x \frac{\partial x}{\partial t} + f_y \frac{\partial y}{\partial t} + f_z \frac{\partial z}{\partial t} \qquad (11.4.14)$$

You can see that these formulas are straight-forward extensions of the chain rule formulas when f is only a function of two variables. These formulas are used in the same way as above and only involve slightly more work. However, because of the presence of more symbols (x, y, z, s, t) calculating partials can be a little confusing at first. So, in the next example, we look at what is involved.

Example 11.4.4 (Partial Derivatives for $w = f(x, y, z)$)

Problem: For each of the functions $w = f(x, y, z)$ and each choice of x, y, z as functions of variables: t (Part (a)) or u, v (Part (b)), find dw/dt or $\partial w/\partial u$ by using (i) the chain rule in Formulas (11.4.12)–(11.4.14) and (ii) the non-chain rule way by directly calculating w as a function of s and t (or of u and v) and then taking partials. Also find the numerical values of these ordinary/partial derivatives at the specified values of the independent variables (t or u, v).

(a) $w = \dfrac{x}{y+z}$, $x = t$, $y = t^2$, $z = t^3$, value: $t = 1$

(b) $w = xyz$, $x = u/v$, $y = u + v$, $z = u - v$, values: $u = 1, v = 1$

Solution Part (a): The partials of f are easy to compute, but in doing so, you must stay focused on which variables are held constant.

$$f_x = \; = \frac{\partial}{\partial x}\left(\frac{x}{y+z}\right) = \frac{1}{y+z}, \; f_y = \frac{\partial}{\partial y}\left(\frac{x}{y+z}\right) = \frac{-x}{(y+z)^2}, \quad \text{and}$$

$$f_z = \frac{\partial}{\partial z}\left(\frac{x}{y+z}\right) = \frac{-x}{(y+z)^2}$$

Using these and

$$x = t, \; y = t^2, \; z = t^3, \; \text{and} \; \frac{dx}{dt} = 1, \; \frac{dy}{dt} = 2t, \; \frac{dz}{dt} = 3t^2$$

in the chain rule Formula (11.4.12) gives

$$\frac{dw}{dt} = f_x \frac{dx}{dt} + f_y \frac{dy}{dt} + f_z \frac{dz}{dt}$$

$$= \frac{1}{y+z}\frac{dx}{dt} + \frac{-x}{(y+z)^2}\frac{dy}{dt} + \frac{-x}{(y+z)^2}\frac{dz}{dt}$$

$$= \frac{1}{t^2+t^3}(1) + \frac{-t}{(t^2+t^3)^2}(2t) + \frac{-t}{(t^2+t^3)^2}(3t^2)$$

$$= \frac{t^2+t^3}{(t^2+t^3)^2} + \frac{-2t^2}{(t^2+t^3)^2} + \frac{-3t^3}{(t^2+t^3)^2}$$

$$= \frac{-t^2 - 2t^3}{(t^2 + t^3)^2} = \frac{-t^2(1 + 2t)}{t^4(1 + t)^2} = \frac{-(1 + 2t)}{t^2(1 + t)^2}$$

This is the calculation of dw/dt using the chain rule. In the non-CR way we substitute $x = t, y = t^2, z = t^3$ into $w = x/(y + z)$, simplify, and differentiate:

$$w = \frac{t}{t^2 + t^3} = \frac{t}{t^2(1 + t)} = \frac{1}{t(1 + t)} \quad \text{so} \quad \frac{dw}{dt} = \frac{-(1 + t + t)}{t^2(1 + t)^2} = \frac{-(1 + 2t)}{t^2(1 + t)^2}$$

This gives the same result as before. Evaluating this at $t = 1$ gives the slope of the tangent line to graph of the composite function: $(dw/dt)|_{t=1} = -3/4$.

Solution Part (b): The partial derivatives of $w = xyz$ are easy to calculate:

$$f_x = \frac{\partial}{\partial x}(xyz) = yz, \quad f_y = \frac{\partial}{\partial y}(xyz) = xz, \quad f_z = \frac{\partial}{\partial z}(xyz) = xy$$

Use these and

$$x = \frac{u}{v}, \ y = u + v, \ z = u - v, \ \text{and} \ \frac{\partial x}{\partial u} = \frac{1}{v}, \ \frac{\partial y}{\partial u} = 1, \ \frac{\partial z}{\partial u} = 1$$

in the chain rule Formula (11.4.12). Also use $yz = (u + v)(u - v) = u^2 - v^2$

$$\begin{aligned}
\frac{\partial w}{\partial u} &= f_x \frac{\partial x}{\partial u} + f_y \frac{\partial y}{\partial u} + f_z \frac{\partial z}{\partial u} \\
&= yz \frac{\partial x}{\partial u} + xz \frac{\partial y}{\partial u} + xy \frac{\partial z}{\partial ut} \\
&= (u^2 - v^2)\frac{1}{v} + \frac{u(u - v)}{v}(1) + \frac{u(u + v)}{v}(1) \\
&= \frac{u^2 - v^2 + u^2 - uv + u^2 + uv}{v} = \frac{3u^2 - v^2}{v}
\end{aligned}$$

This is the calculation of $\partial w/\partial u$ using the chain rule. In the non-CR way we substitute $x = u/v, y = u + v, z = u - v$ into $w = xyz$, simplify, and differentiate:

$$\begin{aligned}
w &= \frac{u}{v} \cdot (u + v) \cdot (u - v) = \frac{u(u^2 - v^2)}{v} = \frac{u^3 - uv^2}{v} \\
\frac{\partial w}{\partial u} &= \frac{\partial}{\partial u}\left(\frac{u^3 - uv^2}{v}\right) = \frac{3u^2 - v^2}{v}
\end{aligned}$$

This gives the same result. Next, evaluating this partial derivative at $u = 1, v = 1$, gives $(\partial w/\partial u)|_{u=1,v=1} = 2$, which, as indicated in Section 11.3, is one of the numbers used in finding a normal vector to tangent plane to graph of the composite function.

The Chain Rule for Functions of m Variables

The cases of the chain rule that we have covered so far will be the most important ones for us. These cases are: $w = f(x, y)$ or $w = f(x, y, z)$, with x, y, z being functions of either one or two variables. However, many applications occur where $w = f(x, y, z, \ldots, q)$ is a function of any number of variables $x, y, z, \ldots, q$ and each of these variables is a function of, say, m variables: $t_1, t_2, \ldots, t_m$. Then the composite function has the form

$$w = f\Big(g(t_1, t_2, \ldots, t_m), h(t_1, t_2, \ldots, t_m), k(t_1, t_2, \ldots, t_m), \ldots, r(t_1, t_2, \ldots, t_m)\Big)$$

In computing the derivative of such a composite function with respect to, say, the ith independent variable t_i, the "outside function" is f and so the chain rule will involve all of its partials: $f_x, f_y, f_z, \ldots, f_q$. The "inside functions" are $x, y, z, \ldots q$ and so we will need all of their partials $\partial x/\partial t_i, \partial y/\partial t_i, \partial z/\partial t_i, \ldots, \partial q/\partial t_i$. Combining all these functions in a natural way gives the general version of the chain rule as shown in the following theorem.

THEOREM 11.4.4 (Chain Rule - General Case)

Suppose $w = f(x, y, z, \ldots, q)$ is a differentiable function of any number of variables $x, y, z, \ldots, q$ and that each of these is a differentiable function of $t_1, t_2, \ldots, t_m$.

Then w is a differentiable function of $t_1, t_2, \ldots, t_m$, with partial derivatives given by

$$\frac{\partial w}{\partial t_i} = f_x \frac{\partial x}{\partial t_i} + f_y \frac{\partial y}{\partial t_i} + f_z \frac{\partial z}{\partial t_i} + \cdots + f_q \frac{\partial q}{\partial t_i} \qquad (11.4.15)$$

for $i = 1, 2, \ldots, m$

Exercises: 11.4 (The Chain Rule)

Using the Chain Rule with x, y Arbitrary

In Exercises 1–10, find $\frac{dw}{dt}$ where $w = f(x, y)$ and x, y are unspecified, differentiable functions of the single variable t. Write your answer with the terms involving dx/dt and dy/dt grouped together.

1. $w = 3x^2y^3 - 5x^4y^2$ **2.** $w = 2x^3y^2 - 4x^4y^3$

3. $w = x^2\sqrt{x^2 + y^2}$ **4.** $w = y^2\sqrt{x^2 + y^2}$

5. $w = x^3y^2e^{-x}$ **6.** $w = x^2y^3e^{-y}$

7. $w = x\ln(x^2 + y^4)$ **8.** $w = y\ln(x^2 + y^4)$

9. $w = \sin(x^2)\cos(x + y)$ **10.** $w = \sin(y^2)\sin(x + y)$

Using the Chain Rule with x, y Given

In Exercises 11–24, find $\frac{dw}{dt}$ where $w = f(x, y)$ and x, y are the following functions of t:

  (i) $x = t$, $y = t^2$ (ii) $x = \cos t$, $y = \sin t$.

Do this using the chain rule (CR) and check your answer using the direct (non-CR) way.

11. $w = x^5y^6$ **12.** $w = x^7y^8$

13. $w = x\sqrt{1 + y}$ **14.** $w - y\sqrt{1 + x}$

15. $w = x^2e^{-xy}$ **16.** $w = y^2e^{-xy}$

17. $w = \ln(1 + x^2y^3)$ **18.** $w = \ln(1 + x^3y^2)$

19. $w = \dfrac{1}{x + y^2}$ **20.** $w = \dfrac{1}{x^2 + y}$

21. $w = \dfrac{x - y}{x + y}$ **22.** $w = \dfrac{x + y}{x - y}$

23. $w = \dfrac{xy^2}{1 + xy^2}$ **24.** $w = \dfrac{x^2y}{1 + x^2y}$

In Exercises 25–42, find all the partial derivatives (or the ordinary derivative) of the composite function w. Do this using the chain rule (CR) and check your answer using the direct (non-CR) way.

25. $w = \dfrac{x}{x^2 + y^2}$, $x = st$, $y = s^2t^2$

26. $w = \dfrac{y}{x^2 + y^2}$, $x = st$, $y = s^2t^2$

27. $w = \dfrac{xy}{x + y}$, $x = uv$, $y = u^2 + v^2$

28. $w = \dfrac{xy}{x - y}$, $x = uv$, $y = u^2 + v^2$

29. $w = x^2\sqrt{x + y}$, $x = st^2$, $y = s^2t$

30. $w = x^3\sqrt{x + y}$, $x = s^2t$, $y = st^2$

31. $w = e^{3x}\sin 2y$, $x = uv$, $y = u^2 + v^2$

32. $w = e^{4x}\cos 2y$, $x = uv$, $y = u^2 + v^2$

33. $w = xy^2z^3$, $x = t$, $y = t^2$, $z = t^3$

34. $w = x^3y^2z$, $x = t$, $y = t^2$, $z = t^3$

35. $w = \dfrac{x^2}{y^2 + z^2}$, $x = t$, $y = t^2$, $z = t^3$

36. $w = \dfrac{y^2}{x^2 + z^2}$, $x = t$, $y = t^2$, $z = t^3$

37. $w = \dfrac{x}{yz}$, $x = uv$, $y = u + v$, $z = u - v$

38. $w = \dfrac{x^2}{yz}$, $x = uv$, $y = u + v$, $z = u - v$

39. $w = \dfrac{y + z}{x + y}$, $x = uv$, $y = u + v$, $z = u - v$

40. $w = \dfrac{y - z}{x - y}$, $x = uv$, $y = u + v$, $z = u - v$

41. $w = \dfrac{x}{y} + \dfrac{y}{z}$, $x = uv$, $y = u + v$, $z = u - v$

42. $w = \dfrac{x}{z} + \dfrac{z}{y}$, $x = uv$, $y = u + v$, $z = u - v$

Calculus Concepts & Computation

11.5 Directional Derivatives & Gradients

The main purpose of this section is to introduce the concept of the gradient ∇f associated with a function f of several variables and to explain the geometric significance of this new function (which is actually a vector-valued function). To motivate how ∇f arises, we first discuss the notion of directional directives.

Directional Derivatives

The idea behind directional derivatives of functions f of several variables is best understood (and motivated) by the case when f is a function of two-variables: $z = f(x, y)$. Then the graph of f is a special type of surface S in $\mathbb{R}^3$. As we saw in Section 11.3, the partial derivatives $f_x(x_0, y_0)$ and $f_y(x_0, y_0)$ at a point $P_0 = (x_0, y_0)$ are the slopes of the tangent lines to the curves on S made by intersecting S with the vertical planes $y = y_0$ (an x-trace) and $x = x_0$ (a y-trace). See Figure 11.5.1.

These two numbers, $f_x(x_0, y_0)$ and $f_y(x_0, y_0)$, can be thought of as the rates of change of the values $z = f(x, y)$ of f as the point (x, y) moves away from (x_0, y_0) in the x-direction and y-direction, respectively. These two directions are indicated by the two standard unit vectors $\mathbf{i} = \langle 1, 0 \rangle$ and $\mathbf{j} = \langle 0, 1 \rangle$.

To generalize, consider how the values of f change by moving away from (x_0, y_0) in the direction indicated by some other unit vector $\mathbf{u} = \langle u_1, u_2 \rangle$, $\|\mathbf{u}\| = 1$. More specifically, "moving away from (x_0, y_0) in the direction of $\mathbf{u}$" means going along the line L through $P_0 = (x_0, y_0)$ in the direction of $\mathbf{u}$. This line can be given parametrically by $x = x_0 + tu_1$, $y = y_0 + tu_2$. Thus, the variation of the z values of f along this line is given by the function

$$k(t) = f(x_0 + tu_1, y_0 + tu_2), \quad (\text{for } 0 \le t \le b)$$

Note that for $t = 0$, the z value is $k(0) = f(x_0, y_0)$ and b is suitably chosen. Also, if we look at the vertical plane through the line L, its trace is a curve on the surface with equation $z = k(t)$ and this curve exhibits how the z-values of f vary as we move away from (x_0, y_0) in the direction of $\mathbf{u}$. See Figure 11.5.2.

Naturally enough, $\frac{dk}{dt}\big|_{t=0} = k'(0)$ is the *rate of change of the z values of f at* (x_0, y_0) *in the direction* $\mathbf{u}$. This rate of change has a special name and symbol which indicates the elements f, $\mathbf{u}$, and (x_0, y_0) involved:

The Directional Derivative: $\quad D_{\mathbf{u}}f(x_0, y_0) = \frac{dk}{dt}\big|_{t=0}$ $\qquad$ (11.5.1)

Technically, $D_{\mathbf{u}}f(x_0, y_0)$ is called the directional derivative of f in direction $\mathbf{u}$ at (x_0, y_0). Since we can change the point $P_0 = (x_0, y_0)$ we get a function $D_{\mathbf{u}}f$ of two variables whose value at (x, y) is $D_{\mathbf{u}}f(x, y)$. Equation (11.5.1) defines this quantity, but we will soon derive an alternative way of computing it.

NOTE: In calculating directional derivatives it is important to use a *unit* vector $\mathbf{u}$ for the direction. If the direction is specified by a vector $\mathbf{v}$ which is not a unit vector, then use $\mathbf{u} = \mathbf{v}/\|\mathbf{v}\|$ in the calculation.

Example 11.5.1 (Directional Derivatives Using the Definition)

Problem: Find the directional derivative of $f(x, y) = 4 + xy^2 + x^3$ at the point $(1, 1)$ in the direction of $\mathbf{v} = \langle 3, 4 \rangle$. Use the definition in Formula (11.5.1).

Solution: First we compute the unit vector $\mathbf{u}$ in the direction of the given vector $\mathbf{v}$, which has length $\|\mathbf{v}\| = \sqrt{(3)^2 + (4)^2} = \sqrt{9 + 16} = \sqrt{25} = 5$. So $\mathbf{u} = \mathbf{v}/5 = \langle \frac{3}{5}, \frac{4}{5} \rangle$. Next, the line through $(x_0, y_0) = (1, 1)$ in the direction of $\mathbf{u}$ can be given parametrically by $x = 1 + \frac{3}{5}t$, $y = 1 + \frac{4}{5}t$. Then the variation of values function is

$$k(t) = f(1 + \tfrac{3}{5}t, 1 + \tfrac{4}{5}t) = 4 + (1 + \tfrac{3}{5}t)(1 + \tfrac{4}{5}t)^2 + (1 + \tfrac{3}{5}t)^3$$

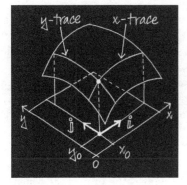

Figure 11.5.1: *The partials* $f_x(x_0, y_0)$, $f_y(x_0, y_0)$ *give the rates of change of f at* (x_0, y_0) *in directions* $\mathbf{i}, \mathbf{j}$.

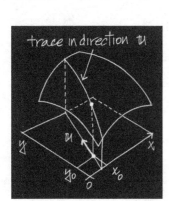

Figure 11.5.2: *A directional derivative gives the the rate of change of f at* (x_0, y_0) *in direction* $\mathbf{u}$

Rather than using algebra to simplify k before taking derivatives, it will be quicker to differentiate first (using the chain rule) and then take $t = 0$ in the result. For this, use the product and chain rules.

$$\frac{dk}{dt} = \frac{d}{dt}\left[4 + (1 + \tfrac{3}{5}t)(1 + \tfrac{4}{5}t)^2 + (1 + \tfrac{3}{5}t)^3\right]$$

$$= \tfrac{3}{5}(1 + \tfrac{4}{5}t)^2 + (1 + \tfrac{3}{5}t) \cdot 2(1 + \tfrac{4}{5}t) \cdot \tfrac{4}{5} + 3(1 + \tfrac{3}{5}t)^2 \cdot \tfrac{3}{5}$$

$$\left.\frac{dk}{dt}\right|_{t=0} = \tfrac{3}{5}(1)^2 + (1)2 \cdot \tfrac{4}{5} + 3(1) \cdot \tfrac{3}{5} = \frac{3 + 8 + 9}{5} = \frac{20}{5} = 4$$

Thus, the directional derivative is $D_{\mathbf{u}}f(1, 1) = 4$.

The geometric interpretation of the number $D_{\mathbf{u}}f(1, 1) = 4$ has two aspects: (*i*) The number 4 is the slope of the tangent line to the trace (curve on the surface) made by the vertical plane through the line $x = 1 + \tfrac{3}{5}t$, $y = 1 + \tfrac{4}{5}t$. (*ii*) The number 4 is the rate of change of f at $P_0 = (1, 1)$ in the direction $\mathbf{v} = \langle 3, 4 \rangle$. Figure 11.5.3 shows a plot of the graph of f near $P_0 = (1, 1)$ and the curve on its graph made by the vertical plane through P_0 in the direction of $\mathbf{u}$.

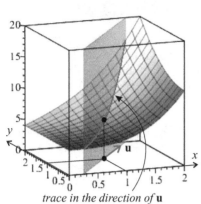

trace in the direction of **u**

Figure 11.5.3: *A directional derivative of* $f(x, y) = xy^2 + x^3$ *at* $(1, 1)$

An Alternative Formula for the Directional Derivative

As opposed to using Formula (11.5.1), there is a somewhat easier and more informative way of computing directional derivatives. It involves the important concept of the *gradient* of a function of several variables:

DEFINITION 11.5.1 (The Gradient Vector)

Suppose f is function of two variables and is differentiable at all points (x, y)
in an open set R. Then the gradient *of f at* (x, y) *is the vector*

$$\nabla f(x, y) = \left\langle f_x(x, y), f_y(x, y) \right\rangle \qquad (11.5.2)$$

This defines a function, denoted by

$$\nabla f = \left\langle f_x, f_y \right\rangle \qquad (11.5.3)$$

whose value at a point (x, y) *in R is the vector* $\nabla f(x, y)$ *given by Formula (11.5.2)*

NOTE: The function ∇f is what is known as a *vector-valued* function. Sometimes ∇f is referred to as the *gradient vector* of f.

Example 11.5.2 (Computing Gradient Vectors)

Problem: Find the gradient vectors of the following functions.

(a) $f(x, y) = x^5 y^2 - 3x^2 y^3$ $f(x, y) = \dfrac{1}{\sqrt{x^2 + y^2}}$

Solution Part (a): The partials are

$$f_x = 5x^4 y^2 - 6xy^3 \quad \text{and} \quad f_y = 2x^5 y - 9x^2 y^2$$

So

$$\nabla f = \langle f_x, f_y \rangle = \langle 5x^4 y^2 - 6xy^3, \, 5x^4 y^2 - 6xy^3 \rangle$$

Solution Part (b): The partials are

$$f_x = \frac{\partial}{\partial x}\left((x^2 + y^2)^{-1/2}\right) = -\frac{1}{2}(x^2 + y^2)^{-3/2}(2x) = \frac{-x}{(x^2 + y^2)^{3/2}}$$

$$f_y = \frac{\partial}{\partial y}\left((x^2 + y^2)^{-1/2}\right) = -\frac{1}{2}(x^2 + y^2)^{-3/2}(2y) = \frac{-y}{(x^2 + y^2)^{3/2}}$$

So

$$\nabla f = \langle\, f_x, f_y\,\rangle = \left\langle \frac{-x}{(x^2 + y^2)^{3/2}}, \frac{-y}{(x^2 + y^2)^{3/2}} \right\rangle$$

Vector-Valued Functions:

In Chapter 9 we studied parameterized plane curves, $x = g(t)$, $y = h(t)$, for t in $[t_1, t_2]$, and viewed them as describing the trajectory of a moving point $P(t) = \mathbf{r}(t) = (g(t), h(t))$ in $\mathbb{R}^2$. In this sense you can think of $\mathbf{r}$ as a *point-valued* function. Then in Chapter 10 we identified points P in $\mathbb{R}^2$ with the vectors $\overrightarrow{OP}$ in the plane going from the origin O to P. From this identification, we can view the position vector $\mathbf{r}(t) = \overrightarrow{OP}(t)$ and its velocity vector $\mathbf{v}(t) = \mathbf{r}'(t)$ as vector-valued functions. Namely,

$$\mathbf{r}(t) = \langle\, g(t), h(t)\,\rangle, \quad \mathbf{v}(t) = \mathbf{r}'(t) = \langle\, g'(t), h'(t)\,\rangle$$

Taking the dot product of the velocity vector with the gradient vector evaluated the corresponding point on the curve gives

$$
\begin{aligned}
\nabla f(\mathbf{r}(t)) \cdot \mathbf{v}(t) &= \langle\, f_x(\mathbf{r}(t)), f_y(\mathbf{r}(t))\,\rangle \cdot \langle\, g'(t), h'(t)\,\rangle \\
&= f_x(\mathbf{r}(t)) g'(t) + f_y(\mathbf{r}(t)) h'(t) \\
&= f_x(g(t), h(t)) g'(t) + f_y(g(t), h(t)) h'(t) \\
&= \frac{d}{dt}[f(g(t), h(t))] = \frac{d}{dt}[f(\mathbf{r}(t))]
\end{aligned}
$$

Here in the first part of the last line we used the multivariable chain rule. Specifically it is Formula (11.4.1), written backwards,

$$f_x \frac{dx}{dt} + f_y \frac{dy}{dt} = \frac{dw}{dt}$$

with $dx/dt = g'(t)$, $dy/dt = h'(t)$, and $w = f(g(t), h(t))$. The derivation above allows us to write Formula (11.4.1) in vector form as follows.

THE CHAIN RULE - PART 1 (VECTOR VERSION)

With position vector $\mathbf{r}(t) = \langle g(t), h(t) \rangle$ *and velocity vector* $\mathbf{v}(t) = \mathbf{r}'(t) = \langle g'(t), h'(t) \rangle$

The chain rule Formula (11.4.1) *can be written as*

$$\frac{d}{dt}[f(\mathbf{r}(t))] = \nabla f(\mathbf{r}(t)) \cdot \mathbf{r}'(t) \qquad (11.5.4)$$

This way of phrasing the chain rule for $w = f(x, y)$, $x = g(t)$, $y = h(t)$ has several theoretical uses. One of these is that it allows us to write directional derivatives in terms of gradients and this will exhibit an important geometrical aspect of the gradient vector ∇f.

To see this, suppose $\mathbf{u} = \langle u_1, u_2 \rangle$ is a unit vector and $P_0 = (x_0, y_0)$ is a point in th domain of f. Then the standard parameterization of the line through P_0 in the direction $\mathbf{u}$ has position and velocity vectors given by

$$\mathbf{r}(t) = \langle\, x_0 + tu_1, y_0 + tu_2\,\rangle \quad \text{and} \quad \mathbf{r}'(t) = \langle\, u_1, u_2\,\rangle = \mathbf{u}$$

So, since the variation function is $k(t) = f(x_0 + tu_1, y_0 + tu_2) = f(\mathbf{r}(t))$, we have

$$
\begin{aligned}
D_{\mathbf{u}} f(x_0, y_0) &= \left. \frac{dk}{dt}\right|_{t=0} = \left.\frac{dk}{dt}[f(\mathbf{r}(t))]\right|_{t=0} = \left.\nabla f(\mathbf{r}(t)) \cdot \mathbf{r}'(t)\right|_{t=0} \\
&= \nabla f(\mathbf{r}(0)) \cdot \mathbf{r}'(0) = \nabla f(x_0, y_0) \cdot \mathbf{u}
\end{aligned}
$$

This then establishes the following result.

THE DIRECTIONAL DERIVATIVE & THE GRADIENT

Suppose f is differentiable on an open set R and $\mathbf{u}$ is a unit vector. Then the directional derivative of f in the direction $\mathbf{u}$ is given by

$$D_{\mathbf{u}}f = \nabla f \cdot \mathbf{u} \qquad (11.5.5)$$

Formula (11.5.5) gives us an easier way (easier than the definition in Formula (11.5.1)) to compute directional derivatives, as the following example shows.

Example 11.5.3 (Directional Derivatives Using the Gradient Vector)

Problem: Find the directional derivative of $f(x,y) = 4 + xy^2 + x^3$ at the point $(1,1)$ in the direction of $\mathbf{v} = \langle 3, 4 \rangle$. Use the gradient vector (Formula (11.5.5)) for this.

Solution: The gradient vector and its value at $(1,1)$ are easy to compute:

$$\nabla f = \langle f_x, f_y \rangle = \langle y^2 + 3x^2, \, 2xy \rangle, \quad \text{and so,} \quad \nabla f(1,1) = \langle 4, 2 \rangle$$

As we saw in Example 11.4.2, the unit vector $\mathbf{u}$ in the direction of $\mathbf{v}$ is $\mathbf{u} = \langle \frac{3}{5}, \frac{4}{5} \rangle$. Thus

$$D_{\mathbf{u}}f(1,1) = \nabla f(1,1) \cdot \mathbf{u} = \langle 4, 2 \rangle \cdot \langle \tfrac{3}{5}, \tfrac{4}{5} \rangle = \tfrac{12}{5} + \tfrac{8}{5} = \tfrac{20}{5} = 4$$

This is the result we got before in Example 11.5.2 and we think you will agree that it is much easier to compute directional derivatives using the gradient vector.

Geometric Interpretation of $D_{\mathbf{u}}f = \nabla f \cdot \mathbf{u}$

In the above example we found that $D_u f(1,1) = 4$. What does this number 4 mean? Well, the original intent of the directional derivative is that 4 is the rate of change of f at $(1,1)$ in the direction $\mathbf{u}$. But, now because of Identity (11.5.5) and the identity $\mathbf{v} \cdot \mathbf{u} = \|\mathbf{v}\|\|\mathbf{u}\| \cos \theta$ from Section 10.3, we can say that

$$4 = D_u f(1,1) = \nabla f(1,1) \cdot \mathbf{u} = \|\nabla f(1,1)\|\|\mathbf{u}\| \cos \theta = \|\nabla f(1,1)\| \cos \theta,$$

where θ is the angle between $\nabla f(1,1)$ and $\mathbf{u}$. NOTE: In the above we used the fact that $\mathbf{u}$ is a unit vector, $\|\mathbf{u}\| = 1$, to simplify. Also, the angle θ is $\theta = \cos^{-1}(4/\|\nabla f(1,1)\|) = \cos^{-1}(4/\sqrt{20}) \approx 26.565° \approx 0.456$ rad.

Now in the above equation, the gradient vector $\nabla f(1,1)$ and its length $\|\nabla f(1,1)\| = \sqrt{20} = 2\sqrt{5} \approx 4.47$ are fixed, but if we vary the direction of $\mathbf{u}$, the angle θ, and therefore the number $\cos \theta$, will vary. Thus,

(1) $D_u f(1,1) = \|\nabla f(1,1)\| = 2\sqrt{5}$, when $\theta = 0$,

(2) $D_u f(1,1) = 0$, when $\theta = \pi/2$,

(3) $D_u f(1,1) = -\|\nabla f(1,1)\| = -2\sqrt{5}$, when $\theta = \pi$,

Since all the values of the cosine function are between one and minus one: $-1 \leq \cos \theta \leq 1$, we see from the above discussion that (a) the maximum value of the directional derivative is $2\sqrt{5}$ and occurs when $\mathbf{u}$ is in the direction of the gradient vector $\nabla f(1,1)$ and (b) the minimum value of the directional derivative is $-2\sqrt{5}$ and occurs when $\mathbf{u}$ is in the direction opposite to the gradient vector $-\nabla f(1,1)$. Since directional derivatives measure the rates of change of f in various directions, we see that the maximum/minimum rate of change of f occur in the direction $\pm \nabla f(1,1)$. This is a general result and is summarized in the following box.

THE DIRECTIONS OF MOST RAPID INCREASE & DECREASE

At a point (x_0, y_0) *in the domain of* f *where it is differentiable* :

(a) $\nabla f(x_0, y_0)$ *is the direction in which* f *increases most rapidly.*

(b) $-\nabla f(x_0, y_0)$ *is the direction in which* f *decreases most rapidly.*

(c) *Any direction perpendicular to* $\nabla f(x_0, y_0) \neq 0$ *is a direction of zero increase for* f.

Example 11.5.4 (Directions of Greatest Increase/Decrease)

Problem: For the function $f(x, y) = \dfrac{18x}{1 + x^2 + y^2}$ find:

(a) The directions of greatest increase and decrease at the point $(1, 2)$ and

(b) The values of the directional derivatives in those directions at $(1, 2)$.

Solution: Using the quotient rule, we easily calculate the two partials f_x, f_y and form the gradient vector

$$\nabla f = \langle f_x, f_y \rangle = \left\langle \frac{18(1 - x^2 + y^2)}{(1 + x^2 + y^2)^2}, \frac{-36xy}{(1 + x^2 + y^2)^2} \right\rangle$$

Thus,

$$\nabla f(1, 2) = \left\langle \frac{18(4)}{36}, \frac{-36(2)}{36} \right\rangle = \langle 2, -2 \rangle$$

So $\pm \langle 2, -2 \rangle$ are the directions of greatest increase/decrease of f at $P_0 = (1, 2)$, while

$$\pm \|\nabla f(1, 2)\| = \pm \sqrt{(2)^2 + (-2)^2} = \pm \sqrt{8} = \pm 2\sqrt{2}$$

are the rates of change (directional derivatives) in those directions. Figure 11.5.- shows a plot of some level curves of f along with the gradient vector $\mathbf{n} = \nabla f(1, 2)$ at the point $(1, 2)$.

The Mountain Slope Analogy: Viewing the graph of f as a mountain slope, the above results tell us that $\nabla f(1, 2)$ points "uphill" and $-\nabla f(1, 2)$ (not shown) points "downhill." By looking at Figure 11.5.4, we see that this uphill direction together with the contour lines (level curves) indicates there is a mountain peak near the point $(1, 0)$. Also note that this gradient vector appears to be normal (perpendicular) to the level curve of f that passes through the point $(1, 2)$. This is a general result, as stated in the following theorem.

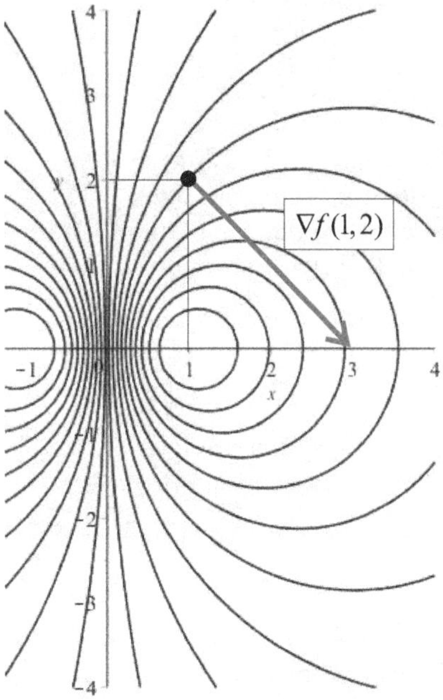

Figure 11.5.4: *The direction of greatest increase at* $(1, 2)$ *of* $f(x, y) = 18x/(1 + x^2 + y^2)$

THEOREM 11.5.1 (Gradient Vectors are Normal to Level Curves)

For each point $P_0 = (x_0, y_0)$ *in the domain of* f, *the gradient vector* $\nabla f(x_0, y_0)$ *is normal to the level curve of* f *which passes through* P_0. *Thus, the direction of greatest increase of* f *at* P_0 *is normal to the level curve passing through* P_0.

NOTE 1: We are assuming, of course, that f is differentiable at P_0,

NOTE 2: Saying that the gradient vector $\nabla f(x_0, y_0)$ is normal to a level curve means that it is normal (or perpendicular) to the tangent line to the curve at (x_0, y_0).

PROOF: The proof uses the vector version of the chain rule given in Formula (11.5.4). For this, suppose the level curve through (x_0, y_0) is $f(x, y) = c$ and that this curve is parametrized by $\mathbf{r}(t) = (g(t), h(t))$, with $\mathbf{r}(0) = (x_0, y_0)$. Note also that $\mathbf{r}'(0)$ is a tangent vector to the curve at the point (x_0, y_0). Now since f has a constant value, namely c, at points on the level curve, we get that $f(\mathbf{r}(t)) = c$

for all t in the parameter interval. Using this and Formula (11.5.4), reading it in reverse order gives

$$\nabla f(\mathbf{r}(t)) \cdot \mathbf{r}'(t) = \frac{d}{dt}\left[f(\mathbf{r}(t))\right] = \frac{d}{dt}[c] = 0$$

for all t. In particular for $t = 0$, we get $\nabla f(x_0, y_0) \cdot \mathbf{r}'(0) = 0$ and this is what we wanted to prove.

In the mountain slope analogy it makes sense that the gradient vector ∇f would be normal to the level curves (contour lines) since ∇f "points' directly uphill, which is the direction of greatest increase of f. Hiking in that direction is the steepest way up the mountain. Perpendicular to ∇f is the direction of the tangent vector $\mathbf{r}'$ to the contour line and that is a direction of zero increase of f. By hiking in that direction on the mountain, you stay at the same level.

Tangent Lines to Level Curves: We can describe, analytically a line in $\mathbb{R}^2$ by specifying a point $P_0 = (x_0, y_0)$ that it goes through and a vector $\mathbf{n} = \langle a, b \rangle$ that is normal to the line. This is entirely analogous to what we did for planes in $\mathbb{R}^3$ (see Section 10.5). A vector equation for the line through P_0 with normal $\mathbf{n}$ is then $\mathbf{n} \cdot \overrightarrow{PP_0} = 0$, where $P = (x, y)$ is a general point on the line. This gives

$$\langle a, b \rangle \cdot \langle x - x_0, y - y_0 \rangle = 0, \quad \text{i.e.,} \quad a(x - x_0) + b(y - y_0) = 0 \qquad (11.5.6)$$

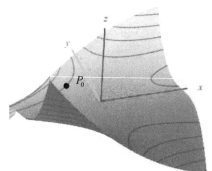

Figure 11.5.5: *The graph of* $f(x, y) = 2x^3 - x^2y$ *with some level curves shown*

We can use Formula (11.5.6) to easily find equations for tangent lines to level curves of f. In this case the normal vector is $\mathbf{n} = \langle a, b \rangle = \langle f_x(x_0, y_0), f_y(x_0, y_0) \rangle$

Example 11.5.5 (Tangent Lines to Level Curves)

Problem: For the function $f(x, y) = 2xy^3 - x^2y$ find:

(a) The direction of greatest increase at the point $(-1, 1)$ and

(b) An equation for the tangent line to the level curve passing through $(-1, 1)$.

Solution Part (a): Figure 11.5.5 shows the graph of f and the point $P_0 = (-1, 1)$. It appears from the graph that uphill is toward the origin. So, we expect the gradient vector to point in that direction. We calculate the two partials f_x, f_y and form the gradient vector

$$\nabla f = \langle f_x, f_y \rangle = \langle 2y^3 - 2xy, 6xy^2 - x^2 \rangle$$

Thus, $\nabla f(-1, 1) = \langle 2 + 2, -6 - 1 \rangle = \langle 4, -7 \rangle$ is the direction of greatest increase. NOTE: You can use any (nonzero) vector to specify a direction. Some calculus books only use unit vectors to indicate directions. So in this example, since $\|\nabla f(-1, 1)\| = \sqrt{16 + 49} = \sqrt{65}$, the direction could be specified by the unit vector $\mathbf{u} = \langle 4/\sqrt{65}, -7/\sqrt{65} \rangle$. See Figure 11.5.6.

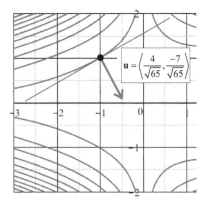

Figure 11.5.6: *The direction of greatest increase of* f *is is indicated by a unit vector in the direction of* $\nabla f(-1, 1)$ $= \langle 4, -7 \rangle$

Solution Part (b): Since $\mathbf{n} = \nabla f(-1, 1) = \langle 4, -7 \rangle$ is a normal to the tangent line at the point $P_0 = (-1, 1)$, an equation for the tangent line (Formula (11.5.6)) is

$$4(x - (-1)) - 7(y - 1) = 0, \quad \text{i.e.,} \quad 4x - 7y + 11 = 0$$

FUNCTIONS OF THREE OR MORE VARIABLES

All that we have done above for functions of two variables extends quite naturally to functions of any number of variables. We restrict the discussion here to functions of three variables since that is the other most commonly occurring case.

Suppose $w = f(x, y, z)$ is a differentiable function of three variables on an open set R. Then the gradient vector of f is the vector-valued function:

The Gradient Vector: $\nabla f = \langle f_x, f_y, f_z \rangle = \langle \dfrac{\partial f}{\partial x}, \dfrac{\partial f}{\partial y}, \dfrac{\partial f}{\partial z} \rangle$ $\qquad (11.5.7)$

Next, considering the directional derivative, suppose $P_0 = (x_0, y_0, z_0)$ is a point in R. If $\mathbf{u} = \langle u_1, u_2, u_3 \rangle$ is unit vector in $\mathbb{R}^3$, then the line through P_0 in the direction of $\mathbf{u}$ is given parametrically by

$$\mathbf{r}(t) = \langle x_0 + tu_1, y_0 + tu_2, z_0 + tu_3 \rangle, \quad (\text{for } -\infty < t < \infty)$$

and the variation of the values of f and the rate of change of these values along this line are measured by the functions:

$$
\begin{aligned}
k(t) &= f(\mathbf{r}(t)), \\
D_{\mathbf{u}}f(x_0, y_0, z_0) &= \frac{dk}{dt}\Big|_{t=0} = \frac{d}{dt}[f(\mathbf{r}(t))]\Big|_{t=0} \\
&= \nabla f(x_0, y_0, z_0) \cdot \mathbf{u}
\end{aligned}
$$

Thus, the directional derivative is expressed in terms of the gradient exactly as before

The Directional Derivative: $D_{\mathbf{u}}f = \nabla f \cdot \mathbf{u}$ (11.5.8)

In the above derivation we used the extension, to three variables, of Formula (11.5.4) which is the vector version of the Chain Rule - Part 1:

The Chain Rule - Part 1: $\dfrac{d}{dt}[f(\mathbf{r}(t))] = \nabla f(\mathbf{r}(t)) \cdot \mathbf{r}'(t)$ (11.5.9)

The geometric interpretation and use of the gradient vector ∇f are the same for functions of three variables as they were for functions of two variables:

Directions of Greatest Increase and Decrease: $\nabla f(x_0, y_0, z_0)$ is the direction in which f increases most rapidly at (x_0, y_0, z_0) and $-\nabla f(x_0, y_0, z_0)$ is the direction in which f decreases most rapidly at (x_0, y_0, z_0).

The Gradient and Level Surfaces: $\mathbf{n} = \nabla f(x_0, y_0, z_0)$ is normal to the level surface of f passing through the point (x_0, y_0, z_0).

Recall that a level surface of f is the set of all points in space where f has the same value. If this value is c, then the equation for the level surface is $f(x, y, z) = c$. Consider a number of these level surfaces $f(x, y, z) = c_i$, $i = 1, 2, \ldots, k$, with the values: $c_i < c_{i+1}$, increasing with i. The the last result above says that if (x_0, y_0, z_0) is point on the ith surface, then $\nabla f(x_0, y_0, z_0)$ points in the direction of the $(i+1)$st surface. The next example illustrates this.

Example 11.5.6 (Normal Lines to Level Surfaces)
Problem: For the function $f(x, y, z) = z^2 - x^2 - y^2$, find

(a) The direction of greatest increase at the point $P_0 = (\frac{\sqrt{2}}{2}, \frac{\sqrt{2}}{2}, \sqrt{5})$ and

(b) Parametric equations for the normal line to the level surface through P_0.

Solution Part (a): The gradient is $\nabla f = \langle -2x, -2x, 2z \rangle$ and so the direction of greatest increase at P_0 is

$$\mathbf{n} = \nabla f(\tfrac{\sqrt{2}}{2}, \tfrac{\sqrt{2}}{2}, \sqrt{5}) = \langle -\sqrt{2}, -\sqrt{2}, 2\sqrt{5} \rangle,$$

Solution Part (b): The gradient vector $\mathbf{n} = \langle -\sqrt{2}, -\sqrt{2}, 2\sqrt{5} \rangle$ is normal (perpendicular) to the level surface of f passing through P_0. So the normal line can be parametrized by

$$x = \frac{\sqrt{2}}{2} - \sqrt{2}\,t, \;\; y = \frac{\sqrt{2}}{2} - \sqrt{2}\,t, \;\; z = \sqrt{5} + 2\sqrt{5}\,t$$

NOTE: The level surfaces for f are $z^2 - x^2 - y^2 = c$, for various values of c. These are all quadric surfaces. For $c = 0$ the level surface is a cone and for $c > 0$, it is a hyperboloid of 2-sheets. While, for $c < 0$, the level surface is a hyperboloid of 1-sheet.

The level surface that passes though $P_0 = (\frac{\sqrt{2}}{2}, \frac{\sqrt{2}}{2}, \sqrt{5})$ has $c = f(\frac{\sqrt{2}}{2}, \frac{\sqrt{2}}{2}, \sqrt{5}) = 4$. Figure 11.5.7 shows this level surface as well as those for $c = 0$ and $c = 1$. The normal vector $\mathbf{n}$ is also shown in red. NOTE: The surfaces have been cut away for the sake of visualization.

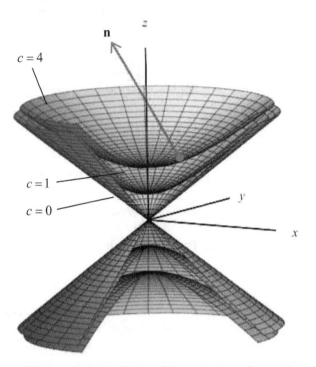

Figure 11.5.7: *Plots of three level surfaces of $f(x, y, z) = z^2 - x^2 - y^2$, for $c - 0, 1, 4$. The red vector shown is normal to the $c = 4$ level surface.*

Exercises: 11.5 (Directional Derivatives & Gradients)

Calculating Gradients

In Exercises 1–32, find the gradient ∇f of the function f and then evaluate it at the point P_0.

1. $f(x, y) = x^2 y^3 + 4xy^2$, $P_0 = (2, -1)$

2. $f(x, y) = x^4 y^2 + 3x^2 y^3$, $P_0 = (3, -1)$

3. $f(x, y) = \sqrt{1 + x^2 y^2}$, $P_0 = (2, -3)$

4. $f(x, y) = \sqrt{1 + x^4 y^4}$, $P_0 = (3, -2)$

5. $f(x, y) = xy\sqrt{x + y}$, $P_0 = (4, 5)$

6. $f(x, y) = xy\sqrt{x - y}$, $P_0 = (9, 5)$

7. $f(x, y) = \dfrac{x - y}{x + y}$, $P_0 = (1, 1)$

8. $f(x, y) = \dfrac{y - x}{x + y}$, $P_0 = (2, 2)$

9. $f(x, y) = \dfrac{xy}{1 + xy}$, $P_0 = (1, 1)$

10. $f(x, y) = \dfrac{xy}{1 - xy}$, $P_0 = (2, 1)$

11. $f(x, y) = \dfrac{e^{xy}}{1 + e^{xy}}$, $P_0 = (0, 0)$

12. $f(x, y) = \dfrac{e^{xy}}{1 + e^{-xy}}$, $P_0 = (0, 0)$

13. $f(x, y) = x^y$, $P_0 = (2, 1)$

14. $f(x, y) = y^x$, $P_0 = (1, 2)$

15. $f(x, y) = \sin \pi x \sin \pi y$, $P_0 = (1, 1/4)$

16. $f(x, y) = \cos \pi x \cos \pi y$, $P_0 = (1/2, 1/4)$

17. $f(x, y, z) = 2x^3 y^2 z^2$, $P_0 = (1, -1, 1)$

18. $f(x, y, z) = 3x^2 y^3 z^3$, $P_0 = (1, -1, 1)$

19. $f(x, y, z) = \sqrt{1 + x^2 y^2 z^2}$, $P_0 = (2, -3, -1)$

20. $f(x, y, z) = \sqrt{1 + x^4 y^4 z^4}$, $P_0 = (3, -2, 1)$

21. $f(x, y, z) = xyz\sqrt{x + y + z}$, $P_0 = (1, 1, 2)$

22. $f(x, y, z) = xyz\sqrt{x - y - z}$, $P_0 = (1, 1, -4)$

23. $f(x, y, z) = \dfrac{x - y - z}{x + y + z}$, $P_0 = (1, 1, 2)$

24. $f(x, y, z) = \dfrac{y - x - z}{x + y + z}$, $P_0 = (2, 2, 1)$

25. $f(x, y, z) = \dfrac{xyz}{1 + xyz}$, $P_0 = (1, -1, -1)$

26. $f(x, y, z) = \dfrac{xyz}{1 - xyz}$, $P_0 = (1, 1, -1)$

27. $f(x, y, z) = \dfrac{e^{xyz}}{1 + e^{xyz}}$, $P_0 = (0, 0, 0)$

28. $f(x, y, z) = \dfrac{e^{xyz}}{1 + e^{-xyz}}$, $P_0 = (0, 0, 0)$

29. $f(x, y, z) = x^{yz}$, $P_0 = (2, 1, 1)$

30. $f(x, y, z) = y^{xz}$, $P_0 = (1, 2, 1)$

31. $f(x, y, z) = \sin \pi x \sin \pi y \sin \pi z$, $P_0 = (1, 1/4, 1/4)$

32. $f(x, y, z) = \cos \pi x \cos \pi y \cos \pi z$, $P_0 = (1/2, 1/4, 1/2)$

Calculating Directional Derivatives

In Exercises 33–44, find the directional derivative $D_{\mathbf{u}} f(P_0)$ of f at P_0 in the direction $\mathbf{v}$. *Note:* $\mathbf{u} = \mathbf{v}/\|\mathbf{v}\|$.

33. $f(x, y) = x^2 y - 3x^3 y^4$, $P_0 = (1, 1)$, $\mathbf{v} = \langle 1, -1 \rangle$

34. $f(x, y) = xy^2 - 5x^4 y^3$, $P_0 = (1, 1)$, $\mathbf{v} = \langle -1, 1 \rangle$

35. $f(x, y) = x^2\sqrt{x + y}$, $P_0 = (3, 6)$, $\mathbf{v} = 3\mathbf{i} + 4\mathbf{j}$

36. $f(x, y) = y^2\sqrt{x - y}$, $P_0 = (9, 5)$, $\mathbf{v} = 3\mathbf{i} + 4\mathbf{j}$

37. $f(x, y) = x\sqrt{x^2 + y^2}$, $P_0 = (3, 4)$, $\mathbf{v} = \langle 1, 3 \rangle$

38. $f(x, y) = y\sqrt{x^2 + y^2}$, $P_0 = (5, 12)$, $\mathbf{v} = \langle 1, 4 \rangle$

39. $f(x, y) = \ln(1 + xy)$, $P_0 = (1, 2)$, $\mathbf{v} = -\mathbf{i} + 2\mathbf{j}$

40. $f(x, y) = \ln(1 - xy)$, $P_0 = (1, -2)$, $\mathbf{v} = -\mathbf{i} + 2\mathbf{j}$

41. $f(x, y, z) = x\sqrt{x^2 + y^2 + z^2}$, $P_0 = (1, 1, 1)$, $\mathbf{v} = \langle -1, 3, 1 \rangle$

42. $f(x, y, z) = y\sqrt{x^2 + y^2 + z^2}$, $P_0 = (1, 1, 1)$, $\mathbf{v} = \langle 2, -4, 2 \rangle$

43. $f(x, y, z) = \ln(1 + xyz)$, $P_0 = (1, 2, 1)$, $\mathbf{v} = 3\mathbf{i} - 2\mathbf{k}$

44. $f(x, y, z) = \ln(1 - xyz)$, $P_0 = (1, -2, 1)$, $\mathbf{v} = 2\mathbf{j} - 3\mathbf{k}$

In Exercises 45–58, find the directions in which the function f increases/decreases most rapidly at P_0 and the values of the directional derivative in those directions. Use unit vectors for the directions.

45. $f(x, y) = xy^2 - 3x^2 y$, $P_0 = (1, -1)$

46. $f(x, y) = x^3 y + 3xy^3$, $P_0 = (1, -1)$

47. $f(x, y) = \dfrac{x}{x + y}$, $P_0 = (1, 1)$

48. $f(x, y) = \dfrac{y}{x + y}$, $P_0 = (2, 2)$

49. $f(x, y) = \dfrac{x}{x^2 + y^2}$, $P_0 = (1, 2)$

50. $f(x, y) = \dfrac{y}{x^2 + y^2}$, $P_0 = (1, 2)$

51. $f(x, y) = \dfrac{xy}{x + y}$, $P_0 = (2, 1)$

52. $f(x, y) = \dfrac{xy}{x - y}$, $P_0 = (3, 1)$

53. $f(x, y) = x\sqrt{x + y}$, $P_0 = (2, 2)$

54. $f(x, y) = y\sqrt{x + y}$, $P_0 = (2, 2)$

55. $f(x, y, z) = 2x^3 y^3 z^2$, $P_0 = (1, -1, 1)$

56. $f(x, y, z) = 3x^2 y^2 z^3$, $P_0 = (1, -1, 1)$

57. $f(x, y, z) = \dfrac{xyz}{x + y + z}$, $P_0 = (2, -1, 3)$

58. $f(x, y, z) = \dfrac{xyz}{x - y + z}$, $P_0 = (2, -1, 3)$

In Exercises 59–70, Compute the gradient $\nabla f(P_0)$ at the point $P_0 = (x_0, y_0)$. Sketch the level curve of f which passes through P_0 and find an equation for the tangent line to the level curve at P_0. Put $\nabla f(P_0)$ in your sketch with its initial point at P_0. Use equal scales on both axes.

59. $f(x, y) = y + x^2$, $P_0 = (1, 1)$

60. $f(x, y) = y + x^3$, $P_0 = (1, 1)$

61. $f(x, y) = \dfrac{y}{1 + x^2}$, $P_0 = (1, 2)$

62. $f(x, y) = \dfrac{y}{1 + x^3}$, $P_0 = (1, 1)$

63. $f(x, y) = y^2 e^x$, $P_0 = (0, -1)$

64. $f(x, y) = y^2 e^{-x}$, $P_0 = (0, 1)$

65. $f(x, y) = x^2 + 4y^2$, $P_0 = (2, \sqrt{3})$

66. $f(x, y) = 4x^2 + y^2$, $P_0 = (\sqrt{3}, 2)$

67. $f(x, y) = \dfrac{y^3}{8x^2}$, $P_0 = (1, 2)$

68. $f(x, y) = \dfrac{x^3}{8y^2}$, $P_0 = (2, 1)$

69. $f(x, y) = \dfrac{y^2}{4(1 - x^2)}$, $P_0 = (1/2, \sqrt{3})$

70. $f(x, y) = \dfrac{x^2}{4(1 - y^2)}$, $P_0 = (\sqrt{3}, 1/2)$

In Exercises 71–78, verify that $\nabla f(P) = \langle 0, 0 \rangle$ at the point $P = (1, 1)$. Such points are of special significance to the graph of f (See Section 11.7).

71. $f(x, y) = (x - 1)^2 + (y - 1)^2$

72. $f(x, y) = 4(x - 1)^2 + (y - 1)^2$

73. $f(x, y) = \ln x \ln y$ **74.** $f(x, y) = \log_2 x \log_2 y$

75. $f(x, y) = \cos \pi x \cos \pi y$ **76.** $f(x, y) = \cos 2\pi x \cos \pi y$

77. $f(x, y) = \dfrac{\cos \pi x}{\cos \pi y}$ **78.** $f(x, y) = \dfrac{\cos 2\pi x}{\cos \pi y}$

Calculus *Concepts & Computation*

11.6 Tangent Planes

There are two types of surfaces in $\mathbb{R}^3$ that we have studied:

- **Graphs of Functions:** Surfaces with equations of the form: $z = f(x, y)$. These are graphs of functions of two variables (in this case the graph of f). See Figure 11.6.1.

- **General Surfaces:** Surfaces with equations of the form: $H(x, y, z) = 0$, where H is a function of three variables, are (can be) more general than surfaces that are graphs of functions of two variables. See Figure 11.6.2.

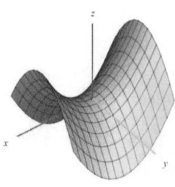

graph of a function

Figure 11.6.1: *The surface* $z = x^2 - y^2$

For the graph of a function $z = f(x, y)$, we can always take $H(x, y, z) = z - f(x, y)$ to get a general surface. So, the graph of f is a special type of general surface. But conversely, a general surface $H(x, y, z) = 0$ need *not* be the graph of a function of two variables. As we did in Section 2.10, we could consider the equation $H(x, y, z) = 0$ as *implicitly* defining one or more functions z of x and y and in some cases we could solve this equation for z to get one or more functions *explicitly* given by equations: $z = f_1(x, y), \ z = f_2(x, y), \ldots, f_k(x, y)$.

The General Tangent Plane Problem

The tangent plane problem discussed in Section 11.3 is for surfaces that are graphs of functions $z = f(x, y)$. The general tangent plane problem is for general surfaces $H(x, y, z) = 0$ and so if we solve this problem, the problem for surfaces that are graphs will be solved as well.

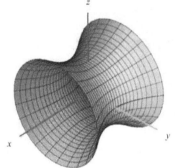

a general surface

Figure 11.6.2: *The surface* $z^2 + y^2 - x^2 - 1 = 0$

The general problem is to find an equation for the tangent plane to a surface $H(x, y, z) = 0$, at a given point (x_0, y_0, z_0) on the surface. But, the surface $H(x, y, z) = 0$ is a *level surface* for the function H and we know that the gradient vector ∇H is normal to the level surfaces of H (Section 11.5). Thus, $\mathbf{n} = \nabla H(x_0, y_0, z_0)$ is normal to the surface $H(x, y, z) = 0$ at the point (x_0, y_0, z_0). Being normal to the surface at this point means it is perpendicular to the tangent plane at this point. Thus, the solution of the tangent plane problem in the general case is easy:

SOLUTION OF THE TANGENT PLANE PROBLEM

Suppose (x_0, y_0, z_0) *is a point on the surface* $H(x, y, z) = 0$ *and that H is a is a differentiable function on a neighborhood of* (x_0, y_0, z_0). *Then an equation for the tangent plane to the surface at* (x_0, y_0, z_0) *is*

$$n_1(x - x_0) + n_2(y - y_0) + n_3(z - z_0) = 0, \qquad (11.6.1)$$

where the normal **n** *to the plane is given by*

$$\mathbf{n} = \langle n_1, n_2, n_3 \rangle = \nabla H(x_0, y_0, z_0) \qquad (11.6.2)$$

Example 11.6.1 (Tangent Planes and Normal Lines for General Surfaces)

Problem: For the surface $xy^2z + 3x^2yz^3 = 4$, find an equation for the tangent plane to the surface at the point $P_0 = (1, 1, 1)$. Also find parametric equations for the normal line to the surface at this point.

Solution: The solution of both problems involves the gradient vector of the function, say, $H(x, y, z) = xy^2z + 3x^2yz^3 - 4$, which is

$$\nabla H = \langle\, y^2z + 6xyz^3,\ 2xyz + 3x^2z^3,\ xy^2 + 9x^2yz^2 \,\rangle$$

Note: Since a partial derivative of a constant, like the -4 in H, is 0, we could have taken H to be $H(x, y, z) = xy^2z + 3x^2yz^3$. Now the normal to the surface (and tangent plane at $P_0 = (1, 1, 1)$ is

$$\mathbf{n} = \nabla H(1,1,1) = \langle\, 1+6,\ 2+3,\ 1+9 \,\rangle = \langle\, 7, 5, 10 \,\rangle$$

Thus, an equation for the tangent plane is

$$7(x-1) + 5(y-1) + 10(z-1) = 0, \quad \text{i.e.,} \quad 7x + 5y + 10z = 22$$

Also, parametric equations of the normal line to the surface (line through $(1, 1, 1)$ in the direction of $\mathbf{n} = \langle\, 7, 5, 10 \,\rangle$) are

$$x = 1 + 7t,\ y = 1 + 5t,\ z = 1 + 10t, \quad \text{i.e.,} \quad \mathbf{r}(t) = \langle\, 1 + 7t,\ 1 + 5t,\ 1 + 10t \,\rangle$$

The Special Tangent Plane Problem for Graphs of Functions

For the surface $z = f(x, y)$ which is the graph of f, we take $H(x, y, z) = z - f(x, y)$, Then

$$H_x = -f_x,\ H_y = -f_y,\ H_z = 1. \quad \text{So,} \quad \nabla H = \langle\, -f_x,\ -f_y,\ 1 \,\rangle$$

SOLUTION OF THE SPECIAL TANGENT PLANE PROBLEM

Suppose (x_0, y_0) is a point in the domain of the function $z = f(x, y)$ and that f is a is a differentiable function on a neighborhood of (x_0, y_0). Then an equation for the tangent plane to the surface at (x_0, y_0, z_0), where $z_0 = f(x_0, y_0)$, is

$$n_1(x - x_0) + n_2(y - y_0) + n_3(z - z_0) = 0 \qquad (11.6.3)$$

Here the normal $\mathbf{n}$ to the plane is given by

$$\mathbf{n} = \langle n_1, n_2, n_3 \rangle = \langle\, -f_x(x_0, y_0),\ -f_y(x_0, y_0),\ 1 \,\rangle \qquad (11.6.4)$$

Example 11.6.2 (Tangent Planes and Normal Lines for Graphs)

Problem: For the function $z = xe^{-x^2 - y^{-2}}$, find an equation for the tangent plane to the graph of the function at the point $P_0 = (1, 1, e^{-2})$. Also find parametric equations for the normal line to the surface at this point.

Solution: The partial derivatives are

$$f_x = (1 - 2x^2)e^{-x^2 - y^{-2}} \quad \text{and} \quad f_y = -2xye^{-x^2 - y^{-2}}$$

So the normal to the surface (and tangent plane) at $(1, 1, e^{-2})$ is

$$\mathbf{n} = \langle\, -f_x(1, 1),\ -f_y(1, 1),\ 1 \,\rangle = \langle\, e^{-2},\ 2e^{-2},\ 1 \,\rangle$$

Thus, an equation for the tangent plane is

$$e^{-2}(x - 1) + 2e^{-2}(y - 1) + 1(z - e^{-2}) = 0, \quad \text{or,} \quad x + 2y + e^2z = 4$$

Also, parametric equations of the normal line to the surface (line through $(1, 1, e^{-2})$ in the direction of $\mathbf{n} = \langle\, e^{-2},\ 2e^{-2},\ 1 \,\rangle$) are

$$x = 1 + e^{-2}t,\ y = 1 + 2e^{-2}t,\ z = e^{-2} + t, \quad \text{i.e.,} \quad \mathbf{r}(t) = \langle\, 1 + e^{-2}t,\ 1 + 2e^{-2}t,\ e^{-2} + t \,\rangle$$

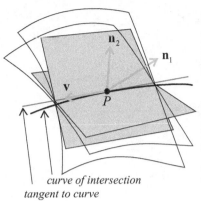

Figure 11.6.3: *A curve of intersection of two surfaces*

curve of intersection tangent to curve

Intersecting Surfaces

In Section 10.6 we discussed determining the line of intersection of two non-parallel planes. We found that if the normals to the planes are $\mathbf{n}_1$ and $\mathbf{n}_2$, respectively, then the line of intersection has direction $\mathbf{v} = \mathbf{n}_1 \times \mathbf{n}_2$.

The generalization of this situation involves two intersecting surfaces, where one would expect that the intersection is a curve (or several curves). Section 11.1 presents a special case of this where one of the surfaces is a plane and the curve of intersection is called a *trace*.

Tangent Line to a Curve of Intersection: Suppose C is a curve of intersection of the surfaces $H(x,y,z) = 0$, $G(x,y,z) = 0$, and $P = (x_0, y_0, z_0)$ is a point on C. The tangent planes to each surface at P have the normal vectors

$$\mathbf{n}_1 = \nabla H(x_0, y_0, z_0) \quad \text{and} \quad \mathbf{n}_2 = \nabla G(x_0, y_0, z_0),$$

respectively. (See Figure 11.6.3.) So, as in Section 10.5, the line of intersection of these planes has direction

$$\mathbf{v} = \mathbf{n}_1 \times \mathbf{n}_2 = \nabla H(x_0, y_0, z_0) \times \nabla G(x_0, y_0, z_0)$$

Assuming the result that this line of intersection is tangent to the curve C at P (See the Exercises), we get the following result:

TANGENT LINE TO THE CURVE OF INTERSECTION

Suppose $P = (x_0, y_0, z_0)$ is a point on a curve C of intersection of the surfaces
$$H(x,y,z) = 0, \quad G(x,y,z) = 0.$$

Then the tangent line to C at P has direction
$$\mathbf{v} = \mathbf{n}_1 \times \mathbf{n}_2 = \nabla H(x_0, y_0, z_0) \times \nabla G(x_0, y_0, z_0)$$

Example 11.6.3 (A Cylinder Intersecting an Ellipsoid)

Problem: The surfaces

$$x^2 + y^2 = 2 \text{ (cylinder)} \quad \frac{x^2}{16} + \frac{y^2}{4} + \frac{z^2}{4} = 1 \text{ (ellipsoid)}$$

have two curves of intersection, one above the x-y plane and the other below. See Figure 11.6.4.

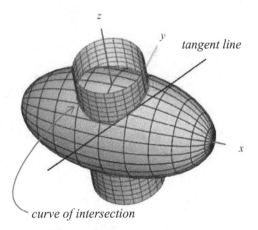

tangent line

curve of intersection

Figure 11.6.4: *A cylinder intersecting an ellipsoid.*

Let C be the curve above the x-y plane and $P = (1, -1, \frac{\sqrt{11}}{2})$ be a point on this curve of intersection. Find parametric equations for the tangent line to C.

Solution: Letting $H(x, y, z) = x^2 + y^2$ and $G(x,, y, z) = \frac{x^2}{16} + \frac{y^2}{4} + \frac{z^2}{4}$, we get

$$\nabla H = \langle 2x, 2y, 0 \rangle, \quad \nabla G = \langle \tfrac{1}{8}x, \tfrac{1}{2}y, \tfrac{1}{2}z \rangle,$$

and so

$$\mathbf{n}_1 = \nabla H(1, -1, \tfrac{\sqrt{11}}{2}) = \langle 2, -2, 0 \rangle, \quad \mathbf{n}_2 = \nabla G(1, -1, \tfrac{\sqrt{11}}{2}) = \langle \tfrac{1}{8}, -\tfrac{1}{2}, \tfrac{\sqrt{11}}{4} \rangle$$

Then the direction of the tangent line is

$$\mathbf{v} = \mathbf{n}_1 \times \mathbf{n}_2 = \langle 2, -2, 0 \rangle \times \langle \tfrac{1}{8}, -\tfrac{1}{2}, \tfrac{\sqrt{11}}{4} \rangle = \begin{vmatrix} 2 & -2 & 0 \\ \tfrac{1}{8} & -\tfrac{1}{2} & \tfrac{\sqrt{11}}{4} \end{vmatrix} = \langle -\tfrac{\sqrt{11}}{2}, -\tfrac{\sqrt{11}}{2}, -\tfrac{3}{4} \rangle$$

Then the line with this direction passing through $P = (1, -1, \tfrac{\sqrt{11}}{2})$ is parametrized by

$$x = 1 - \tfrac{\sqrt{11}}{2}t, \quad y = -1 - \tfrac{\sqrt{11}}{2}t, \quad z = \tfrac{\sqrt{11}}{2} - \tfrac{3}{4}t$$

In the last example we found parametric equations for the tangent line to a curve of intersection C for two surfaces. If the equations for the surfaces are simple enough (as those are), then we can find a parametrization for the curve C itself. The next example exhibits how to do this. NOTE: In Chapter 9 we discussed parametric equations and the calculus for curves in the plane and later we will do the same for curves in space.

Example 11.6.4 (Parametrizing Curves of Intersection)

Problem: Find parametric equations for the curves of intersection for the two surfaces:

$$x^2 + y^2 = 2 \quad \text{(cylinder)} \qquad \frac{x^2}{16} + \frac{y^2}{4} + \frac{z^2}{4} = 1 \quad \text{(ellipsoid)}$$

Use these to check that the direction of the tangent line in Example 11.6.3 is correct.

Solution: We let $x = t$ be the parameter. Putting this in the equation for the cylinder gives

$$t^2 + y^2 = 2, \quad \text{and so} \quad y = \pm\sqrt{2 - t^2}$$

Rewriting the equation for the ellipsoid and substituting in $x = t$ and $y^2 = 2 - t^2$ gives

$$4z^2 = 16 - x^2 - 4y^2 = 16 - t^2 - 4(2 - t^2) = 8 + 3t^2$$

Solving this for z gives the the final equation in the parametrization, which is

$$x = t, \quad y = \pm\sqrt{2 - t^2}, \quad z = \pm\tfrac{1}{2}\sqrt{8 + 3t^2},$$

for t in $[-\sqrt{2}, \sqrt{2}]$. In the parameterization, use the plus sign in the z equation to get the curve of intersection that lies above the x-y plane and use the minus sign to get the curve that lies below. For each of these curves the $\pm$ signs in the y equation give the two halves of the curve.

For $t = 1$, the parametric equations give $x = 1$, $y = -1$, $z = \tfrac{\sqrt{11}}{2}$. So, the parametrization of the piece of the curve that goes through $P = (1, -1, \tfrac{\sqrt{11}}{2})$ is $x = t$, $y = -\sqrt{2 - t^2}$, $z = \tfrac{1}{2}\sqrt{8 + 3t^2}$. From these we get

$$\frac{dx}{dt} = 1, \quad \frac{dy}{dt} = \frac{t}{\sqrt{2 - t^2}}, \quad \frac{dz}{dt} = \frac{3t}{2\sqrt{8 + 3t^2}}$$

For $t = 1$, these give the direction vector $\mathbf{w} = \langle 1, 1, \tfrac{3}{2\sqrt{11}} \rangle$, which you can easy see is parallel to the vector $\mathbf{v}$ found in Example 11.6.3.

Exercises: 11.6 (Tangent Planes)

Tangent Planes for Surfaces which are Graphs

In Exercises 1–18, find find an equation for the tangent plane to the graph of $z = f(x, y)$ at the point $P_0 = (x_0, y_0)$.

1. $f(x, y) = x^4 - x^2 + y^3 - 4y$, $P_0 = (1, 1)$
2. $f(x, y) = x^3 - 2x + y^4 - 3y$, $P_0 = (1, 1)$
3. $f(x, y) = (x^2 - 1)(y^3 - 2y)$, $P_0 = (2, 1)$
4. $f(x, y) = (x^2 - 3)(y^3 - 4y)$, $P_0 = (2, 1)$
5. $f(x, y) = x^2 y^3 + 4xy^2$, $P_0 = (1, -1)$
6. $f(x, y) = x^4 y^2 + 3x^2 y^3$, $P_0 = (1, -1)$
7. $f(x, y) = \sqrt{1 + xy}$, $P_0 = (3, 1)$
8. $f(x, y) = \sqrt{xy - 1}$, $P_0 = (5, 1)$
9. $f(x, y) = x\sqrt{x + y}$, $P_0 = (1, 3)$
10. $f(x, y) = y\sqrt{x + y}$, $P_0 = (3, 1)$
11. $f(x, y) = \ln x \ln y$, $P_0 = (e, e)$
12. $f(x, y) = \log_2 x \log_2 y$, $P_0 = (2, 2)$
13. $f(x, y) = xye^{-3x - 4y}$, $P_0 = (0, 0)$
14. $f(x, y) = xye^{-2x - 5y}$, $P_0 = (0, 0)$
15. $f(x, y) = (x + 1)^y$, $P_0 = (2, 1)$
16. $f(x, y) = (y + 1)^x$, $P_0 = (1, 2)$
17. $f(x, y) = \cos \pi x \sin \pi y$, $P_0 = (1/4, 1/4)$
18. $f(x, y) = \sin \pi x \cos \pi y$, $P_0 = (1/4, 1/4)$

Tangent Planes for General Surfaces

In Exercises 19–26, find equations for the tangent plane and normal line to the given surface at the point P_0.

19. $xy^2 + yz^3 = 6$, $P_0 = (2, -2, 1)$
20. $x^2 y + xz^3 = 6$, $P_0 = (-2, 2, 1)$
21. $\ln(1 + x^2 + y^2 + z^2) = \ln 7$, $P_0 = (-1, 2, 1)$
22. $\ln(1 + x^2 + y^3 + z^4) = \ln 17$, $P_0 = (1, -1, 2)$
23. $xyze^{-x^2 - y^3 - z^4} = e^{-3}$, $P_0 = (1, 1, 1)$
24. $xyze^{-x^3 - y^4 - z^5} = e^{-3}$, $P_0 = (1, 1, 1)$
25. $(x + 1)^{yz} = 4$, $P_0 = (1, 2, 1)$
26. $(y + 1)^{xz} = 4$, $P_0 = (2, 1, 1)$

Tangent Planes for Surfaces of Revolution

If you revolve the graph of $y = f(x)$ on $[a, b]$, about the x-axis, the corresponding surface has equation
$$[f(x)]^2 - y^2 - z^2 = 0.$$

In Exercises 27–34, for the given function f, on the given interval $[a, b]$ and point $P_0 = (x_0, y_0, z_0)$ on its surface of revolution, find an equation for the tangent plane at P_0.

27. $f(x) = 4 - x^2$, $[-2, 2]$, $P_0 = (1, 2, \sqrt{5})$
28. $f(x) = 16 - x^2$, $[-4, 4]$, $P_0 = (2, 2, 2\sqrt{35})$
29. $f(x) = x^2(4 - x^2)$, $[0, 2]$, $P_0 = (1, 1, 2\sqrt{2})$
30. $f(x) = x^2(9 - x^2)$, $[0, 3]$, $P_0 = (1, 5, \sqrt{39})$
31. $f(x) = e^{-2x}$, $[-1, 2]$, $P_0 = (0, \frac{\sqrt{3}}{2}, \frac{1}{2})$
32. $f(x) = e^{2x}$, $[-1, 2]$, $P_0 = (0, \frac{\sqrt{3}}{2}, \frac{1}{2})$
33. $f(x) = \sin x$, $[0, \pi]$, $P_0 = (\frac{3\pi}{4}, \frac{\sqrt{2}}{4}, \frac{\sqrt{6}}{4})$
34. $f(x) = \cos x$, $[\frac{-\pi}{2}, \frac{\pi}{2}]$, $P_0 = (\frac{\pi}{4}, \frac{\sqrt{2}}{4}, \frac{\sqrt{6}}{4})$

Intersecting Surfaces - Tangent Lines

In Exercises 35–42, find parametric equations (a) for the tangent line at the point P on the curve of intersection of the two surfaces and (b) for the curve of intersection.

35. $x^2 + y^2 = 2$, $y^2 + z^2 = 2$, $(1, 1, 1)$

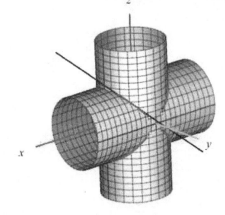

36. $y^2 + z^2 = 1$, $x^2 + y^2 - z^2 = 1$, $(1, \frac{\sqrt{2}}{2}, \frac{\sqrt{2}}{2})$

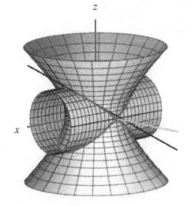

37. $x^2 + y^2 - z^2 = 1$, $y^2 + z^2 - x^2 = 1$, $(1, 1, 1)$

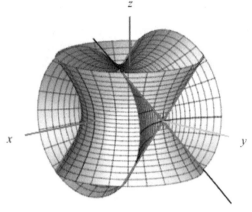

38. $x^2 + y^2 - z^2 = 2$, $y^2 + z^2 - x^2 = 1$, $(1, \frac{\sqrt{6}}{2}, \frac{\sqrt{2}}{2})$

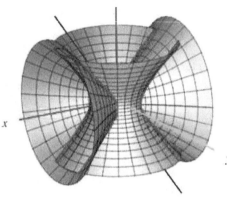

39. $x^2 + y^2 - z^2 = 1$, $\frac{x^2}{16} + \frac{y^2}{4} + \frac{z^2}{4} = 1$, $(1, \frac{\sqrt{15}}{2\sqrt{2}}, \frac{\sqrt{15}}{2\sqrt{2}})$

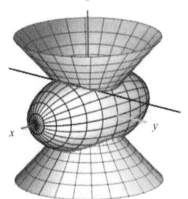

40. $x^2 + y^2 = 1$, $z = x^2 - y^2$, $(\frac{1}{2}, \frac{\sqrt{3}}{2}, -\frac{1}{2})$

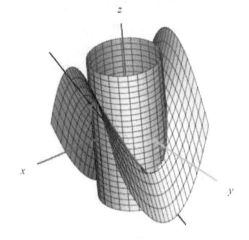

41. $z = x^2 - y^2$, $z = x^2 + y^2 - 2$, $(2, 1, 3)$

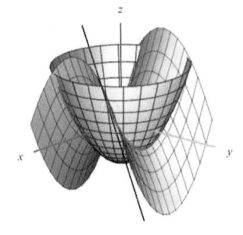

42. $x^2 + y^2 - z^2 = 0$, $y^2 + z^2 = 1$, $(\frac{1}{2}, \frac{\sqrt{6}}{4}, \frac{\sqrt{10}}{4})$

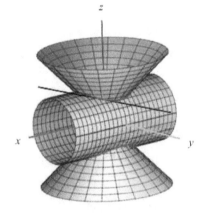

Calculus Concepts & Computation

11.7 Local Extrema & Saddle Points

A primary part of our study of functions f of a single variable was the determination of where, in their domains, they had local maximum and minimum values (local extreme values). These places occur at what are called *critical points* (also called *critical numbers*), which by definition are points x_0 in the domain of f where either (1) $f'(x_0) = 0$ or (2) $f'(x_0)$ does not exist.

Condition (1) indicates the graph of f has a horizontal tangent line at $(x_0, f(x_0))$ and this is what is expected from the "mountain range analogy," which views the graph as mountain range with peaks (local maxima), valleys (local minima), and mountain passes (saddle points).

Local Extrema and Saddle Points for Functions of Two Variables

For functions $z = f(x, y)$ of two variables, the mountain range analogy is not just an an analogy. Since the graph of f is a surface in $\mathbb{R}^3$, it *could* represent an actual mountain range. Figure 11.7.1 shows a well-known mountain range.

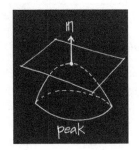

Figure 11.7.2: *A local maximum on the graph of $z = f(x, y)$.*

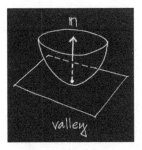

Figure 11.7.3: *A local minimum on the graph of $z = f(x, y)$.*

Nelson Sirlin/Shutterstock.com

Figure 11.7.1: *The Catalina mountain range in Tucson.*

Thus, the local extrema (maxima and minima) and saddle points are actual peaks, valleys, and mountain passes and occur where there is a horizontal tangent plane. See Figures 11.7.2–11.7.4. Notice that on a mountain peak every direction you walk away from the peak leads you down and in a valley every direction you walk away from the valley point leads you up, Compare that with a mountain pass where some directions lead you up and some directions lead you down.

Figures 11.7.2–11.7.4 indicate what the graph of f (a surface) looks like *locally* in a neighborhood of a local extremum or a saddle point. The reason for the designation "local" should be obvious. For example, a peak on a mountain range is only locally a high point. It may not be the highest peak in the mountain range. Figure 11.7.1 shows this for the Catalinas. There are numerous peaks in the photo, but the highest one appears to be one of those that is to the right of center in the picture.

This overview should give you an intuitive idea about what local extrema and saddle points are for functions of two variables (much like those for single variable functions). To find and classify local extrema and saddle points, we apply the calculus in a similar way to what we did in Chapter 3. But now, because the derivatives are partial derivatives, the use of 1st and 2nd-order partials in the

Figure 11.7.4: *A saddle point on the graph of $z = f(x, y)$.*

analysis is much more interesting. We start with a mathematical definition for local maximum and minimum values.

DEFINITION 11.7.1 (Local Extrema)

Suppose $z = f(x, y)$ *is a function of two variables and* (x_0, y_0) *is a point in the domain D of f. Then we say*

(1) *f has a* local maximum *value at* (x_0, y_0) *if there is an circular disk C centered at* (x_0, y_0), *so that*

$$f(x_0, y_0) \geq f(x, y), \quad \text{for all } (x, y) \text{ in } C.$$

(2) *f has a* local minimum *value at* (x_0, y_0) *if there is an circular disk C, centered at* (x_0, y_0), *so that*

$$f(x_0, y_0) \leq f(x, y), \quad \text{for all } (x, y) \text{ in } C.$$

From our intuitive discussion of local extrema at the beginning of this section, you would expect, geometrically, that if f has a local extrema at (x_0, y_0), then at the corresponding peak or valley point on the graph of f the tangent plane would be horizontal.

But, as we saw in Section 11.6, a normal **n** to the tangent plane at the point $(x_0, y_0, f(x_0, y_0))$ is the vector

$$\mathbf{n} = \langle\, -f_x(x_0, y_0), \; -f_x(x_0, y_0), \; 1\,\rangle$$

Thus, for the tangent plane to be horizontal, this normal vector must be vertical: $\mathbf{n} = \langle 0, 0, 1 \rangle$. But this means that the two partial derivative f_x and f_y must be 0 at (x_0, y_0). Of course, we are assuming that f is differentiable at (x_0, y_0). From these geometrical ideas, one can prove the following theorem.

THEOREM 11.7.1 (Horizontal Tangent Planes)

If $z = f(x, y)$ *has a local maximum or local minimum value at* (x_0, y_0) *and if the first-order partial derivatives exist there, then*

$$f_x(x_0, y_0) = 0 \quad \text{and} \quad f_y(x_0, y_0) = 0$$

Another way to phrase the theorem, assuming differentiability, is this: If f has a local extrema at a point then its gradient must be zero there: $\nabla f(x_0, y_0) = 0$. This is the analog of the Calculus I result that the 1st derivative must be zero at local extrema. Points where the gradient ∇f vanishes are called *critical points* of f:

DEFINITION 11.7.2 (Critical Points)

Suppose $z = f(x, y)$ *is a function of two variables. A point* (x_0, y_0) *in the domain of f is called a* critical point of f *if either*

or

(1) $f_x(x_0, y_0) = 0 \quad \text{and} \quad f_y(x_0, y_0) = 0$ (11.7.1)

(2) *f is not differentiable at* (x_0, y_0).

Based on this, Theorem 11.7.1 says that if f has a local extremum at $P_0 = (x_0, y_0)$ and is differentiable at P_0, then P_0 is a critical point.

NOTE: The converse of this last statement is not true. It is possible for f to have critical points P_0 that do not correspond to local maxima or local minima. When there is a horizontal tangent plane at P_0 and there is not a local maximum or minimum, then there must be a saddle point at P_0. This is what we indicated in the introduction to this section. Here is a specific example that illustrates this.

Example 11.7.1 (Saddle Points)

Problem: Show that the function $f(x, y) = 3x - x^3 + y^4 - 8y^2$ has a critical point at $(1, 2)$, but does not have a local maximum or minimum at this point.

Solution: The gradient of f is easy to calculate:

$$\nabla f = \langle 3 - 3x^2, \; 4y^3 - 16y \rangle$$

and so clearly $\nabla f(1, 2) = 0$, which means that $(1, 2)$ is a critical point. The value of f at this point is $f(1, 2) = -14$. Showing that -14 is not a local maximum or minimum value for f would involve demonstrating that every circular disk centered at $(1, 2)$ has points (x, y) where f has both greater and lesser values than -14. This would be a lot of work and so instead we look at a plot of the graph of f near $(1, 2, -14)$. Figure 11.7.5, shows that near $(1, 2)$, the function assumes larger and smaller values than -14. This is not a foolproof way to analyze the nature of critical points. Theorem 11.7.2 below gives us a better tool for this.

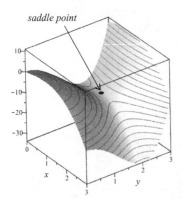

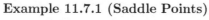

Figure 11.7.5: *A saddle point on the graph of* $f(x, y) = 3x - x^3 + y^4 - 8y^2$

With the previous example as a guide, we define the concept of a saddle point as follows.

DEFINITION 11.7.3 (Saddle Points)

Suppose $z = f(x, y)$ is a differentiable function and (x_0, y_0) is a critical point of f.

Then $(x_0, y_0, f(x_0, y_0))$ is a saddle point if for every circular disk C, centered

at (x_0, y_0), there are points (x, y) in C such that $f(x_0, y_0) > f(x, y)$ and also

points (x, y) in C such that $f(x_0, y_0) < f(x, y)$.

Finding Critical Points

Assuming f is differentiable on its domain, Condition (11.7.1) in Definition 11.7.2 says that critical points arise as solutions of the following system of two equations for two unknowns x, y:

$$f_x(x, y) = 0, \qquad f_y(x, y) = 0 \qquad (11.7.2)$$

Generally, this is a nonlinear system and can be difficult to solve. But there are number of cases, here and in the exercises, that are fairly easy.

Example 11.7.2 (Critical Points)

Problem: Find all critical points of $f(x, y) = 3x - x^3 + y^4 - 8y^2$ and use a computer plot to determine if they give local extrema or saddle points on the graph of f

Solution: As in the last example, the gradient of f is

$$\nabla f = \langle 3 - 3x^2, \; 4y^3 - 16y \rangle$$

Setting each component of ∇f equal to 0 gives, after factoring slightly, the following system of equations:

$$3(1 - x^2) = 0, \quad 4y(y^2 - 4) = 0$$

Each equation involves only one of the unknowns and so the system is easy to solve: $x = \pm 1$ and $y = 0, \pm 2$. The corresponding critical points arise by pairing each of the two x-values with each of the three y-values:

$$(1, 0), \ (1, 2), \ (1, -2), \ (-1, 0), \ (-1, 2), \ (-1, -2)$$

In Example 11.7.1 above we determined, graphically, that the critical point $(1, 2)$ corresponds to a saddle point on the graph of f. Here, we can classify the other five critical points by looking at the larger plot of f in Figure 11.7.6.

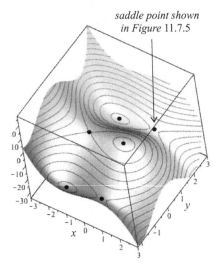

saddle point shown in Figure 11.7.5

Figure 11.7.6: *A graph of* $f(x, y) = 3x - x^3 + y^4 - 8y^2$ *showing 3 local extrema and 3 saddle points.*

The figure indicates the saddle point discussed in Example 11.7.1 and also shows two addition saddle points, as well as a local maximum and two local minima. In summary the classification of the critical points is:

Local Maximum: $(1, 0)$
Local Minima: $(-1, 2), \ (-1, -2)$
Saddle Points: $(-1, 0), \ (1, -2), \ (1, 2)$

Using the graph f in the last example to classify its critical points is easy enough, but lacking graphical capabilities, how would we do the classification?

In analogy with what we did with single variable functions, you would expect that the 2nd-order partial derivatives might provide some information–sort of a 2nd derivative test. Since there are three 2nd-order partials f_{xx}, f_{xy}, f_{yy} it is not clear at first glance how to formulate such a test. However, concepts and theory from the field of differential geometry tell us that the *Hessian* is one of the components we need. The following is a definition of this new function.

DEFINITION 11.7.4 (The Hessian)

Suppose $z = f(x, y)$ *is function of two variables which is differentiable on an open set D.*

Then the Hessian *of* f *is the function defined on D by the following* 2×2 *determinant*

$$H \equiv \begin{vmatrix} f_{xx} & f_{xy} \\ f_{xy} & f_{yy} \end{vmatrix} = f_{xx} f_{yy} - (f_{xy})^2 \qquad (11.7.3)$$

As a function of two variables, the value of the Hessian at a point (x, y) in its domain is the real number computed by

$$H(x, y) = \begin{vmatrix} f_{xx}(x, y) & f_{xy}(x, y) \\ f_{xy}(x, y) & f_{yy}(x, y) \end{vmatrix} = f_{xx}(x, y) f_{yy}(x, y) - (f_{xy}(x, y))^2$$

NOTE: You may find the matrix version of the Hessian (the first expression in Equation (11.7.3)) easier to use and remember.

Example 11.7.3 (Calculating Hessians)

Problem: For the function $f(x,y) = x^2 y - 3xy^2$, find (a) the formula for the Hessian and (b) the value of the Hessian at the point $(1, -1)$.

Solution: First compute the gradient of f

$$\nabla f = \langle 2xy - 3y^2, \ x^2 - 6xy \rangle$$

Then the Hessian is

$$H = \begin{vmatrix} 2y & 2x - 6y \\ 2x - 6y & -6x \end{vmatrix} = -12xy - (2x - 6y)^2 = 12xy - 4x^2 - 36y^2 \quad (11.7.4)$$

and its value at $(1, -1)$ is

$$H(1, -1) = \begin{vmatrix} -2 & 8 \\ 8 & -6 \end{vmatrix} = -52$$

NOTE: You will also get -52 if you use $H = 12xy - 4x^2 - 36y^2$ and substitute in $x = 1$, $y = -1$, but using the matrix form of the determinant in Equation (11.7.4) is easier.

The 2nd Derivative Test for functions of a single variables (Chapter 3, Section 2) extends to functions of two variables. The following theorem shows how the Hessian is a crucial element in this test.

THEOREM 11.7.2 (2nd Derivative Test for Functions of 2 Variables)

Suppose $z = f(x, y)$ is differentiable on an open set R and has continuous partial derivatives on R. Let $P_0 = (x_0, y_0)$ be a critical point in R, i.e., $f_x = 0$, $f_y = 0$ at P_0. Then

(1) *f has a local maximum value at P_0 if $H > 0$ and $f_{xx} < 0$ at P_0.*

(2) *f has a local minimum value at P_0 if $H > 0$ and $f_{xx} > 0$ at P_0.*

(3) *f has a saddle point at P_0 if $H < 0$ at P_0.*

(4) *The test is inconclusive if $H = 0$.*

NOTE: The Hessian determines whether a critical point corresponds to a local extremum ($H > 0$) or a saddle point ($H < 0$). When the there is a local extremum, f_{xx} is used to classify it further as either a local maximum ($f_{xx} < 0$) or a local minimum ($f_{xx} > 0$). This latter classification should make sense if you think of directional derivatives at the critical point: $D_{\mathbf{u}} f(x_0, y_0) = \nabla f(x_0, y_0) \cdot \mathbf{u} = \mathbf{0} \cdot \mathbf{u} = 0$, for every direction $\mathbf{u}$. This is expected since all the traces are curves with horizontal tangent lines (they lie in the horizontal tangent plane at the point). Each of the curves has a local extremum there, and hence (by Section 3.2) is a local maximum if $f_{xx}(x_0, y_0) < 0$ (the curve is concave down) or a local minimum if $f_{xx}(x_0, y_0) > 0$ (the curve is concave up). See Figure 11.7.7.

Example 11.7.4 (Classifying Critical Points)

Problem: Use the 2nd Derivative Test to classify the critical point $(1, 0)$ you found for $f(x,y) = 3x - x^3 + y^4 - 8y^2$ in Example 11.7.2.

Solution: As in the Example 11.7.2, the gradient of f is

$$\nabla f = \langle 3 - 3x^2, \ 4y^3 - 16y \rangle$$

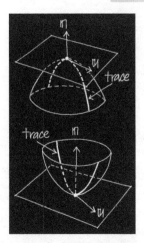

Figure 11.7.7: *Traces that are concave down/up at critical points*

Then the Hessian is

$$H = \begin{vmatrix} -6x & 0 \\ 0 & 12y^2 - 16 \end{vmatrix} \quad \text{and so} \quad H(1,0) = \begin{vmatrix} -6 & 0 \\ 0 & -16 \end{vmatrix} = 96$$

This means that $(1,0)$ corresponds to a local extremum, which in this case is a local maximum because of the -6 entry in the Hessian matrix $(-6 = f_{xx}(1,0) < 0)$

Example 11.7.5 (Finding and Classifying Critical Points)

Problem: For the function $f(x,y) = x^3 + y^3 - 3xy$, find all the critical points and classify them as local maximum, local minimum, or saddle point.

Solution: The gradient is

$$\nabla f = \langle\, 3x^2 - 3y,\ 3y^2 - 3x \,\rangle$$

So the critical point equations are

$$3(x^2 - y) = 0 \quad \text{and} \quad 3(y^2 - x) = 0$$

The first equation says that $y = x^2$ and substituting this in the second equation gives an equation involving only x:

$$3\big((x^2)^2 - x \big) = 0, \quad \text{i.e.,} \quad 3(x^4 - x) = 0, \quad \text{i.e.,} \quad 3x(x^3 - 1) = 0$$

So, either $x = 0$ or $x = 1$. Since $y = x^2$, we see that when $x = 0$ also $y = 0$, which gives $P = (0,0)$ as a critical point. When $x = 1$, we get $y = 1$ and this gives $Q = (1,1)$ as an additional critical point.

To classify the critical points we compute the Hessian

$$H = \begin{vmatrix} 6x & -3 \\ -3 & 6y \end{vmatrix} \quad \text{and so} \quad (a)\ H(0,0) = \begin{vmatrix} 0 & -3 \\ -3 & 0 \end{vmatrix} - -9$$

$$(b)\ H(1,1) = \begin{vmatrix} 6 & -3 \\ -3 & 6 \end{vmatrix} = 27$$

Thus, $(0,0)$ corresponds to a saddle point and $(1,1)$ is where f has a local extremum, which, because in the Hessian $6 = f_{xx}(1,1) > 0$, is a local minimum.

Exercises: 11.7 (Local Extrema and Saddle Points)

Calculating Hessians

In Exercises 1–8, find the Hessian $H = \begin{vmatrix} f_{xx} & f_{xy} \\ f_{xy} & f_{yy} \end{vmatrix}$

of the function f. Leave this in matrix form (i..e., do not evaluate the determinant). Then calculate the value of H at the point P_0, giving your answer first in matrix form and then as a number that result from evaluating the determinant.

1. $f(x,y) = x^2 y^3 + 4xy^2$, $P_0 = (2,-1)$
2. $f(x,y) = x^4 y^2 + 3x^2 y^3$, $P_0 = (3,-1)$
3. $f(x,y) = (x \ln x)(y \ln y)$, $P_0 = (e,e)$
4. $f(x,y) = (x^2 \ln x)(y^2 \ln y)$, $P_0 = (e,e)$
5. $f(x,y) = \cos x \sin y$, $P_0 = (\frac{\pi}{6}, \frac{\pi}{3})$
6. $f(x,y) = \sin x \cos y$, $P_0 = (\frac{\pi}{6}, \frac{\pi}{3})$
7. $f(x,y) = xy e^{-(x^2+y^2)/2}$, $P_0 = (1,1)$
8. $f(x,y) = x^2 y^2 e^{-(x^2+y^2)/2}$, $P_0 = (1,1)$

Finding Local Maxima, Minima, and Saddles

In Exercises 9–60, find the all the critical points P of f and use the Hessian to determine if f has a local maxi-mum, local minimum, or saddle at each of these critical points P.

One Critical Point

9. $f(x,y) = x^2 + ye^{-y}$ 10. $f(x,y) = xe^{-x} + y^2$
11. $f(x,y) = x \ln x + y^2$ 12. $f(x,y) = x^2 + y \ln y$
13. $f(x,y) = xe^{-x} + ye^{-y}$
14. $f(x,y) = (x-1)e^{-x} + (y-1)e^{-y}$
15. $f(x,y) = xe^{-x^3/3} + ye^{-y^3/3}$
16. $f(x,y) = (x-1)e^{-x^3/3} + (y-1)e^{-y^3/3}$
17. $f(x,y) = x^2 + \ln(1+y^2)$
18. $f(x,y) = x^2 + \ln(1+y^4)$
19. $f(x,y) = (e^x + e^{-x})(y^2 - 1)$
20. $f(x,y) = (2^x + 2^{-x})(y^2 - 2)$
21. $f(x,y) = \ln(\ln x) \ln(\ln y)$
22. $f(x,y) = \log_2(\log_2 x) \log_2(\log_2 y)$

Two Critical Points

23. $f(x,y) = x^2 + 3y - y^3$ 24. $f(x,y) = 12x - x^3 + y^2$
25. $f(x,y) = x \ln x + 3y - y^3$
26. $f(x,y) = 3x - x^2 + y \ln y$
27. $f(x,y) = xy e^{-(x+y)}$ 28. $f(x,y) = xy e^{x+y}$
29. $f(x,y) = (1 + x^2)(y^3 - 3y)$
30. $f(x,y) = (x^3 - 27x)(1 + y^2)$

31. $f(x,y) = e^x + e^{-x} + y^3 - 3y$
32. $f(x,y) = 27x - x^3 + e^y + e^{-y}$
33. $f(x,y) = \ln(1 + x^2) + y^3 - 27y$
34. $f(x,y) = 3x - x^2 + \ln(1 + y^2)$

Three Critical Points

35. $f(x,y) = x^2 + y^4 - 2y^2$ 36. $f(x,y) = x^2 + y^4 - y^2$
37. $f(x,y) = (x^2 - 1)ye^{-y}$ 38. $f(x,y) = xe^x(y^2 - 4)$
39. $f(x,y) = e^x + e^{-x} + 8y^2 - y^4$
40. $f(x,y) = e^x + e^{-x} + y^4 - 8y^2$

Four Critical Points

41. $f(x,y) = 3x - x^3 + y^3 - 27y$
42. $f(x,y) = 12x - x^3 + y^3 - 3y$
43. $f(x,y) = x^2 e^{-x} + y^2 e^{-y}$ 44. $f(x,y) = x^2 e^x + y^2 e^y$
45. $f(x,y) = 3x^5 - 25x^3 + 60x + y^2 - 2y$
46. $f(x,y) = 3x^5 - 50x^3 + 135x + 8y - y^2$
47. $f(x,y) = (x^3 - 3x + 18)(y^2 - 1)$
48. $f(x,y) = (x^3 - 12x + 16)(1 - y^2)$

Five Critical Points

49. $f(x,y) = (x^2 - 1)(y^2 - 1)$
50. $f(x,y) = (x^2 - 4)(1 - y^2)$
51. $f(x,y) = (x^3 - 3x + 18)(y^3 - 3y + 18)$
52. $f(x,y) = (x^3 - 12x + 16)(y^3 - 12y + 16)$
53. $f(x,y) = \ln([1 + x^2]/2)(y^2 - 1)$
54. $f(x,y) = (x^2 - 4)\ln([1 + y^2]/2)$
55. $f(x,y) = xy e^{-(x^2+y^2)/2}$ 56. $f(x,y) = xy e^{-(x^4+y^4)/4}$

Six Critical Points

57. $f(x,y) = 3x - x^3 + y^4 - 2y^2$
58. $f(x,y) = 2x^2 - x^4 + y^3 - 12y$

Eight Critical Points

59. $f(x,y) = (x^2 - 1)(y^3 - 3y)$
60. $f(x,y) = (x^3 - 12x)(y^2 - 4)$

12
Multiple Integrals

Calculus *Concepts & Computation*

12.1 Double Integrals and Iterated Integrals

In this chapter we extend the integration theory to functions of two and three variables. This naturally involves using the tools and concepts for integrals of functions of a single variable—antiderivatives and limits of Riemann sums. We begin in this section with the theory for functions $z = f(x, y)$ of two variables.

Suppose $R = [a, b] \times [c, d]$ is a rectangle contained in the domain of f and, for the sake of visualization, suppose $f(x, y) \geq 0$, for all (x, y) in R. In this case, the double integral of f over R, is designed to measure the volume V of the solid S bounded on the top by the graph of f (the surface $z = f(x, y)$), on the bottom by the x-y plane ($z = 0$), and on the sides by the four vertical planes through the sides of R (i.e., $x = a$, $x = b$, $y = c$, $y = d$). See Figure 12.1.1.

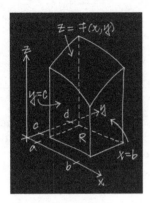

Figure 12.1.1: *The solid S beneath the graph of f and over the rectangle R.*

To measure V, we proceed as usual and approximate S by solids for which we know the volumes. Then we take limits. The simplest solids we could use are rectangular parallelepipeds (boxes), which have volumes equal to the height times the area of the base: $V = hA$.

To get such approximating boxes, we first partition the rectangle R into subrectangles by taking partitions

$$\{x_0, x_1, x_2, \ldots, x_n\} \text{ of } [a, b] \text{ and } \{y_0, y_1, y_2, \ldots, y_m\} \text{ of } [c, d]$$

Drawing vertical lines through the partition points x_i and horizontal lines through the y_j will partition R into subrectangles $R_{ij} = [x_{i-1}, x_i] \times [y_{j-1}, y_j]$. See Figure 12.1.2. This gives the base of an approximating box S_{ij}. See Figure 12.1.3. As shown in the figure, the height of this box is $f(x_i^*, y_j^*)$, where (x_i^*, y_j^*) is any point in the subrectangle R_{ij} (one of the four vertices and the center of R_{ij} are possibilities). The area of the i-jth rectangle is $\Delta A_{ij} = \Delta x_i \Delta y_j$ and so the volume ΔV_{ij} of S_{ij} is

$$\Delta V_{ij} = f(x_i^*, y_j^*)\Delta A_{ij}$$

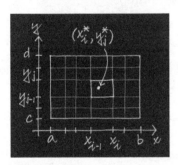

Figure 12.1.2: *A partition of the rectangle R into subrectangles R_{ij}.*

We add all of these up to obtain an approximate volume V_{nm}. To do the addition, note that there are two summation variables, i and j. We can sum first on i, holding j fixed and then sum on j. Or we could do it in the other order. In either case, its not hard to see that the result is the same. Using the sigma notation, we get a *double sum*

$$V_{nm} = \sum_{j=1}^{m}\sum_{i=1}^{n}\Delta V_{ij} = \sum_{j=1}^{m}\sum_{i=1}^{n}f(x_i^*, y_j^*)\Delta A_{ij}$$

This is a typical Riemann sum for $z = f(x, y)$ on a rectangle R. Standard choices for (x_i^*, y_j^*) are (a) right-right hand endpoints (x_i, y_j), (b) left-left hand endpoints (x_{i-1}, y_{j-1}), and (c) centers $([x_i + x_{i-1}]/2, [y_j + y_{j-1}]/2)$.

Based on these approximations one would expect to obtain the exact volume in the limit

$$V = \lim_{m\to\infty}\lim_{n\to\infty}V_{nm} = \lim_{m\to\infty}\lim_{n\to\infty}\sum_{j=1}^{m}\sum_{i=1}^{n}f(x_i^*, y_j^*)\Delta A_{ij},$$

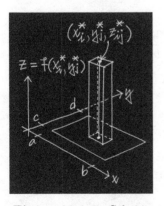

Figure 12.1.3: *Selecting a point (x_i^*, y_j^*) in R_{ij} gives the height z_{ij} of the box.*

provided this limit exists. This motivating discussion for measuring the volume V assumed that $f(x, y) \geq 0$, for all (x, y) in R, but you can see that the double

Riemann sums and limits make sense without this assumption. So, for *any* function f and any rectangle R in the domain of f, the number $\int \int_R f(x,y) dA$ is defined as follows.

DEFINITION 12.1.1 (Double Integrals Over Rectangles)

Suppose R is a rectangle in the domain of f. The double integral of f over R is

$$\iint_R f(x,y)\, dA = \lim_{m \to \infty} \lim_{n \to \infty} \sum_{j=1}^{m} \sum_{i=1}^{n} f(x_i^*, y_j^*) \Delta A_{ij} \qquad (12.1.1)$$

provided this limit exists

NOTE 1: You can see how the double integral notation $\iint$ arises from the double sum notation $\sum\sum$ in the Riemann sums.

NOTE 2: Computing the double integral $\iint_R f(x,y)\, dA$ by taking limits of Riemann sums is only practical when f is continuous on R (a standard assumption) and in this case we can use right-right endpoint, regular Riemann sums

$$\iint_R f(x,y)\, dA = \lim_{m \to \infty} \lim_{n \to \infty} \sum_{j=1}^{m} \sum_{i=1}^{n} f(x_i, y_j) \Delta x\, \Delta y.$$

Here $\Delta x = (b-a)/n$, $\Delta y = (d-c)/m$.

Example 12.1.1 (Calculating Double Riemann Sums)

Problem: For the function

$$f(x,y) = 10 + xy^2 - x^2 \quad \text{on} \quad R = [0,3] \times [0,2],$$

consider the solid S beneath the graph of f and above the rectangle R. Find the volume $V = \iint_R f(x,y)\, dA$ by using the definition of the double integral as a double limit of Riemann sums (Formula 12.1.1). Use regular partitions of $[0,3]$ into n equal subintervals, $[0,2]$ into m equal subintervals, and right endpoints (x_i, y_j), respectively.

Solution: First $\Delta x = \frac{3}{n}$, $\Delta y = \frac{2}{m}$, and so $\Delta x \Delta y = \frac{6}{nm}$. Next, the partition points and values of f at the vertices are

$$x_i = \frac{3i}{n},\ y_j = \frac{2j}{m},\ f(x_i, y_j) = 10 + \frac{3i}{n}\left(\frac{2j}{m}\right)^2 - \left(\frac{3i}{n}\right)^2 = 10 + \frac{3i}{n} \cdot \frac{4j^2}{m^2} - \frac{9i^2}{n^2}$$

Then

$$\begin{aligned}
V_{nm} &= \sum_{j=1}^{m} \sum_{i=1}^{n} f(x_i, y_j) \Delta x\, \Delta y. = \sum_{j=1}^{m} \sum_{i=1}^{n} \left[10 + \frac{3i}{n} \cdot \frac{4j^2}{m^2} - \frac{9i^2}{n^2}\right] \frac{6}{nm} \\
&= \sum_{j=1}^{m} \left[\sum_{i=1}^{n} 10 + \sum_{i=1}^{n} \frac{3i}{n} \cdot \frac{4j^2}{m^2} - \sum_{i=1}^{n} \frac{9i^2}{n^2}\right] \frac{6}{nm} \\
&= \sum_{j=1}^{m} \left[10n + \frac{3}{n} \cdot \frac{n(n+1)}{2} \cdot \frac{4j^2}{m^2} - \frac{9}{n^2} \cdot \frac{n(n+1)(2n+1)}{6}\right] \frac{6}{nm} \\
&= \sum_{j=1}^{m} \left[\frac{60}{m} + \frac{18}{n^2} \cdot \frac{n(n+1)}{2} \cdot \frac{4j^2}{m^3} - \frac{54}{mn^3} \cdot \frac{n(n+1)(2n+1)}{6}\right] \\
&= \frac{60}{m}(m) + \frac{18}{n^2} \cdot \frac{n(n+1)}{2} \cdot \frac{4}{m^3} \cdot \frac{m(m+1)(2m+1)}{6} - \frac{54}{mn^3} \cdot \frac{n(n+1)(2n+1)}{6}(m) \\
&= 60 + \frac{18}{n^2} \cdot \frac{n(n+1)}{2} \cdot \frac{4}{m^3} \cdot \frac{m(m+1)(2m+1)}{6} - \frac{54}{n^3} \cdot \frac{n(n+1)(2n+1)}{6}
\end{aligned}$$

We leave the calculation in this form, because we can use the following Special Limits from Box 4.3.1 (Section 4.3)

$$\lim_{n\to\infty}\frac{1}{n^2}\cdot\frac{n(n+1)}{2}=\frac{1}{2}\quad\text{and}\quad\lim_{n\to\infty}\frac{1}{n^3}\cdot\frac{n(n+1)(2n+1)}{6}=\frac{1}{3}$$

Thus, we get

$$V=\lim_{m\to\infty}\lim_{n\to\infty}V_{nm}=60+\left(18\cdot\frac{1}{2}\cdot4\cdot\frac{1}{3}\right)-\left(54\cdot\frac{1}{3}\right)=60+12-18=54$$

Partial Integrals

As seen in the above example, calculating double integrals using limits of Riemann sums can take some time and in most cases we can not do the sums in closed form. Consequently, Definition 12.1.1 is mainly a theoretical tool which can be used to prove theorems that are the analogs of the Fundamental Theorem of Calculus from Chapter 4. For functions of two variables, these theorems rely on the notion of *partial integrals* introduced in the following definition.

DEFINITION 12.1.2 (Partial Integrals)

For a function f of two variables, the partial integrals

$$\int f(x,y)dx=F(x,y)\quad\text{and}\quad\int f(x,y)dy=G(x,y)\qquad(12.1.2)$$

are functions F and G such that

$$\frac{\partial F}{\partial x}=f\quad\text{and}\quad\frac{\partial G}{\partial y}=f\qquad(12.1.3)$$

NOTE 1: You can, if you wish, think of partial integrals as *anti-partial derivatives*.

NOTE 2: To calculate a partial integral, say with respect to x, do an ordinary indefinite integral with respect to x, treating y and any expressions involving y, as constants.

Example 12.1.2 (Calculating Partial Integrals)

Problem: Compute the following partial integrals:

(a) $\int(6x^2y^3-4xy^2+3y+5)dx$ (b) $\int\cos x\sin y\,dy$

(c) $\int x^2e^{xy}dy$ (d) $\int\frac{x}{x^2+y^2}\,dx$ (e) $\int3x^2\cos(x^3y^3)dx$

Solution Part (a): We use the power rule to integrate the powers of x, treating y^3, y^2 and y as constants:

$$\int(6x^2y^3-4xy^2+3y+5)dx$$

$$=\left(\int6x^2\,dx\right)y^3-\left(\int4x\,dx\right)y^2+\int3y\,dx+\int5\,dx$$

$$=2x^3y^3-2x^2y^2+3xy+5x+\phi(y)$$

NOTE 1: Here ϕ is an arbitrary function of y. Adding an arbitrary function of y to a partial integral with respect to x is the analog of adding a constant of integration C when computing, say, $\int e^{3x}\,dx=\frac{1}{3}e^{3x}+C$. Adding any such ϕ will do, since $\frac{\partial}{\partial x}[\phi(y)]=0$.

NOTE 2: Our use of partial integrals here will usually be in connection with computing *definite* integrals and so adding the arbitrary function ϕ will not be necessary.

Solution Part (b): This is an easy one, since $\cos x$ is treated as a constant when we integrate with respect to y:

$$\int \cos x \sin y \, dy = \cos x \int \sin y \, dy = \cos x(-\cos y) + \psi(x) = -\cos x \cos y + \psi(x)$$

Solution Part (c): We use a u-substitution $u = xy$, $du = \frac{\partial}{\partial y}(xy) = x dy$. Then

$$\int x^2 e^{xy} \, dy = \int x e^{xy} \cdot x dy = \int x e^u du = x e^u = x e^{xy} + \psi(x)$$

Solution Part (d): We use a u-substitution $u = x^2 + y^2$, $du = \frac{\partial}{\partial x}(x^2 + y^2) dx = 2x dx$. So $\frac{1}{2} du = x \, dx$. Then

$$\int \frac{x}{x^2 + y^2} \, dx = \int \frac{1}{x^2 + y^2} \cdot x \, dx = \int \frac{1}{u} \cdot \frac{1}{2} \, du = \frac{1}{2} \ln u = \frac{1}{2} \ln(x^2 + y^2) + \phi(y)$$

Solution Part (e): We use a u-substitution $u = x^3 y^3$, $du = \frac{\partial}{\partial x}(x^3 y^3) dx = 3x^2 y^3 dx$. So $y^{-3} du = 3x^2 dx$. Then

$$\int 3x^2 \cos(x^3 y^3) dx = \int \cos(x^3 y^3) \cdot 3x^2 dx = \int \cos u \cdot y^{-3} du$$

$$= y^{-3} \int \cos u \, du = y^{-3} \sin u = y^{-3} \sin(x^3 y^3) + \phi(y)$$

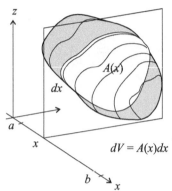

Figure 12.1.4: *Slicing a a potato with a plane per-perpendicular to the x-axis.*

Cross-Sectional Area and Iterated Integrals

In Section 5.2, as an application of single integrals, we measured volumes of solids by integrating the cross-sectional area function $A(x)$:

$$V = \int_a^b A(x) \, dx \qquad (12.1.4)$$

See Figure 12.1.4. which shows a typical cross-section (in yellow) obtained by slicing a potato with a plane through x perpendicular to the x-axis.

The difficulty we had in Chapter 5 with using Formula (12.1.4) was the determination of the area function $A(x)$. However, for the solids S in this section, bounded by the graph of $z = f(x, y)$ on the top, the rectangle $R = [a, b] \times [c, d]$ on the bottom, and the four vertical planes $x = a$, $x = b$, $y = c$, $y = d$, the determination of the cross-sectional area function $A(x)$ is easy. Here's how:

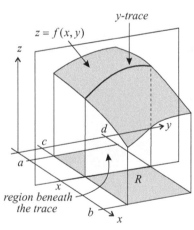

Figure 12.1.5: *Slicing the solid beneath the graph of $z = f(x, y)$ and above R.*

For an x between a and b, the plane through x perpendicular to the x-axis slices the solid S giving a planar region bounded by a y-trace, $z = f(x, y)$, on the top and three line segments on the other sides. See Figure 12.1.5. The area of this region is then given by

$$A(x) = \int_c^d f(x, y) \, dy \equiv \left[\int f(x, y) \, dy \right] \Big|_c^d \qquad (12.1.5)$$

This is a partial integral of f with respect to y evaluated from c to d. Using this in Formula (12.1.4) results in the volume of this type of solid S

$$V = \int_a^b \int_c^d f(x, y) \, dy \, dx \qquad (12.1.6)$$

The expression (12.1.6) for the volume is what is known as an *iterated integral*. The first integral you do is the partial integral with respect to y. The differential

dy being next to $f(x, y)$ indicates that you do this first. Then evaluate the partial integral you get from c to d, which will give you a function of x only (called $A(x)$ in this case). The second integral you do is with respect to x and then you evaluate this from a to b, which will give you a number (the volume V in this case).

We can do an iterated integral in the other order:

$$\int_c^d \int_a^b f(x, y)\, dx\, dy = \int_c^d \left[\int_a^b f(x, y)\, dx \right] dy \qquad (12.1.7)$$

NOTE 1: We put brackets in the expression on the right side of Equation (12.1.7) to clarify what is meant by the expression on the left side. Usually we will leave out the brackets.

NOTE 2: Since there are two different orders to do an iterated integral (integrate 1st with respect to x and 2nd with respect to y or integrate 1st with respect to y and 2nd with respect to x) you might expect to get different results, depending on the order. Fubini's theorem given below says that the result should be the same. But, first we check this out in the next example.

Example 12.1.3 (Calculating Iterated Integrals)

Problem: Compute the following iterated integrals in the order indicated. Then compute, if possible, the iterated integral with the order of integration reversed. Do you get the same number in either order?

$$\text{(a)} \int_1^2 \int_0^1 (12x^2 y - 8xy^3 + 3)\, dy\, dx \quad \text{(b)} \int_2^3 \int_0^1 \frac{2x}{(x^2 + y^2)^2}\, dx\, dy$$

Solution Part (a): In the given order the iterated integral is

$$\int_1^2 \int_0^1 (12x^2 y - 8xy^3 + 3)\, dy\, dx = \int_1^2 \left(12x^2[\tfrac{1}{2}\, y^2] - 8x[\tfrac{1}{4}\, y^4] + 3y \right)\Big|_0^1 dx$$

$$= \int_1^2 \left(6x^2 y^2 - 2xy^4 + 3y \right)\Big|_0^1 dx = \int_1^2 (6x^2 - 2x + 3)\, dx$$

$$= (2x^3 - x^2 + 3x)\Big|_1^2 = (16 - 4 + 6) - (2 - 1 + 3) = 18 - 4 = 14$$

In the reversed order the iterated integral is

$$\int_0^1 \int_1^2 (12x^2 y - 8xy^3 + 3)\, dx\, dy = \int_0^1 \left(12[\tfrac{1}{3}\, x^3]\, y - 8[\tfrac{1}{2}\, x^2]y^3 + 3x \right)\Big|_1^2 dy$$

$$= \int_0^1 \left(4x^3 y - 4x^2 y^3 + 3x \right)\Big|_1^2 dy = \int_0^1 [(32y - 16y^3 + 6) - (4y - 4y^3 + 3)]\, dy$$

$$= \int_0^1 (28y - 12y^3 + 3)]\, dy = (14y^2 - 3y^4 + 3y)\Big|_0^1 = 14$$

So the result 14 is the same for both orders of the iterated integral.

Solution Part (b): In the given order the iterated integral is

$$\int_2^3 \int_0^1 \frac{2x}{(x^2 + y^2)^2}\, dx\, dy = \int_2^3 \left[\frac{-1}{x^2 + y^2} \right]\Big|_0^1 dy$$

Here we used the substitution $u = x^2 + y^2$, $du = \frac{\partial}{\partial x}(x^2 + y^2)dx = 2x\, dx$, to get

$$\int \frac{2x}{(x^2 + y^2)^2}\, dx = \int \frac{1}{(x^2 + y^2)^2} \cdot 2x\, dx = \int \frac{1}{u^2}\, du = -\frac{1}{u} = \frac{-1}{x^2 + y^2}$$

Proceeding with the calculation, we get

$$\int_2^3 \left[\frac{-1}{x^2+y^2}\right]\Bigg|_0^1 dy = \int_2^3 \left[\frac{-1}{1+y^2}+\frac{1}{y^2}\right] dy = \left[-\tan^{-1}y-\frac{1}{y}\right]\Bigg|_2^3$$

$$= -\tan^{-1}(3)+\tan^{-1}(2)-\frac{1}{3}+\frac{1}{2} = -\tan^{-1}(3)+\tan^{-1}(2)+\frac{1}{6}$$

In the reverse order the iterated integral is

$$\int_0^1 \int_2^3 \frac{2x}{(x^2+y^2)^2}\, dy\, dx = ?$$

In this order the first integration involves an inverse tangent function and the total calculation is much more difficult. (See the Exercises.)

Fubini's Theorem and Iterated Integrals

Fubini's theorem for double integrals $\iint_R f(x,y)dA$ can be thought of as the analog of the Fundamental Theorem of Calculus (FTC) for single integrals:

$$\int_a^b f(x)dx = \left[\int f(x)dx\right]\Bigg|_a^b \qquad (12.1.8)$$

The FTC says that to compute a *definite* integral we can first compute an *indefinite* integral $\int f(x)dx$ and then evaluate that from a to b. Fubini's theorem says that to compute a double integrals $\iint_R f(x,y)dA$ we can first compute a partial integral of f with respect to either x or y, evaluate that, do an indefinite integral of the result and evaluate that. But this process is exactly the process of computing an iterated integral.

THEOREM 12.1.1 (Fubini's Theorem for Rectangles)

Suppose f is continuous on a rectangle $R = [a,b]\times[c,d]$ in its domain. Then

$$\iint_R f(x,y)\, dA = \int_c^d \int_a^b f(x,y)dxdy = \int_a^b \int_c^d f(x,y)dydx \qquad (12.1.9)$$

NOTE 1: There are two parts to Fubini's theorem. One part says that the two iterated integrals give the same value. The other part, and most important part, says that the double integral $\iint_R f(x,y)\, dA$ can be computed using an iterated integral rather than a double limit of Riemann sums.

NOTE 2: Since $\iint_R f(x,y)\, dA$ can be computed using an iterated integral, you have two choices of the order of integration when computing it. Often one order of integration is easier than the other. So if you run into difficulty with the integration in one order, try the other order.

NOTE 3: When f is a product of the form $f(x,y) = g(x)h(y)$ it is easy to see that

$$\int_c^d \int_a^b g(x)h(y)\, dxdy = \int_a^b g(x)\, dx \cdot \int_c^d h(y)\, dy \qquad (12.1.10)$$

Exercises: 12.1 (Double Integrals and Iterated Integrals)

Limits of Double Riemann Sums

In Exercises 1–10, use limits of double Riemann sums to compute $\iint_R f(x, y)\, dA$, where $R = [0, 2] \times [0, 5]$ and f is the given function. For Exercises 9-10, use the formula $\lim_{n \to \infty} n(a^n - 1) = \ln a$, for any $a > 0$.

1. $f(x, y) = 2 + 12xy$ 2. $f(x, y) = 3 + 5xy$
3. $f(x, y) = 3x + 4y$ 4. $f(x, y) = 2x + 5y$
5. $f(x, y) = x^2 y - y^2$ 6. $f(x, y) = xy^2 - x^2$
7. $f(x, y) = xy^2 + x^3 y$ 8. $f(x, y) = x^2 y + xy^3$
9. $f(x, y) = e^x e^y$ 10. $f(x, y) = e^{-x} e^{-y}$

Computing Partial Integrals

In Exercises 11–32 , compute the partial integral.

11. $\int (8x^3 y^2 + 9x^2 y^5)\, dx$ 12. $\int (12x^5 y + 8x^3 y^5)\, dx$

13. $\int \left(\frac{x^3 y^2 - 6xy^4}{y^2} \right) dy$ 14. $\int \left(\frac{x^2 y^3 - 6x^4 y}{x^2} \right) dx$

15 $\int \tan x \sec^2 y\, dy$ 16. $\int \tan y \sec^2 x\, dx$

17. $\int xy e^{x^2 y}\, dx$ 18. $\int xy e^{xy^2}\, dy$

19. $\int \left(\frac{y}{\sqrt{x^2 + y^2}} \right) dy$ 20. $\int \left(\frac{x}{\sqrt{x^2 + y^2}} \right) dx$

21 $\int x^2 \tan xy\, dy$ 22. $\int y^2 \tan xy\, dx$

23. $\int \frac{x^3 e^{x\sqrt{y}}}{\sqrt{y}}\, dy$ 24. $\int \frac{y^3 e^{y\sqrt{x}}}{\sqrt{x}}\, dx$

25. $\int \frac{y \sin(y \ln x)}{x}\, dx$ 26. $\int \frac{x \sin(x \ln y)}{y}\, dy$

27. $\int \frac{y^2}{1 + x^2 y^2}\, dx$ 28. $\int \frac{x^2}{1 + x^2 y^2}\, dy$

29. $\int \frac{x e^{xy}}{\sqrt{1 - e^{2xy}}}\, dy$ 30. $\int \frac{y e^{xy}}{\sqrt{1 - e^{2xy}}}\, dx$

31. $\int \frac{xy^3}{(xy - 2)^3}\, dx$ 32. $\int \frac{x^3 y}{(xy - 2)^3}\, dy$

Computing Iterated Integrals

In Exercises 33–50 , compute the iterated integral.

33. $\int_1^2 \int_0^1 (12x^3 y^2 - 16xy^3 + 2)\, dx\, dy$

34. $\int_1^2 \int_0^1 (12x^2 y^3 - 16x^3 y + 3)\, dx\, dy$

35. $\int_4^9 \int_1^2 4x\sqrt{y}\, dx\, dy$ 36. $\int_4^9 \int_1^2 4y\sqrt{x}\, dy\, dx$

37. $\int_4^9 \int_1^2 (4x + 3\sqrt{y})\, dx\, dy$

38. $\int_4^9 \int_1^2 (4y + 3\sqrt{x})\, dy\, dx$

39. $\int_0^1 \int_2^3 x e^{xy}\, dy\, dx$ 40. $\int_0^1 \int_2^3 y e^{xy}\, dy\, dx$

41. $\int_0^1 \int_0^\pi y \cos(xy)\, dx\, dy$ 42. $\int_0^1 \int_0^\pi x \sin(xy)\, dy\, dx$

43. $\int_0^3 \int_0^1 \frac{y}{\sqrt{x + y^2}}\, dy\, dx$ 44. $\int_0^3 \int_0^1 \frac{x}{\sqrt{x^2 + y}}\, dx\, dy$

45. $\int_0^1 \int_1^2 \frac{x}{(x^2 - y^2)^{3/2}}\, dx\, dy$

46. $\int_0^1 \int_1^2 \frac{y}{(y^2 - x^2)^{3/2}}\, dy\, dx$

47. $\int_1^2 \int_1^2 \left(\frac{\ln x}{x} + \frac{\ln y}{y} \right) dx\, dy$

48. $\int_1^2 \int_1^2 \left(\frac{\log_2 x}{x} + \frac{\log_2 y}{y} \right) dx\, dy$

49. $\int_0^1 \int_0^1 4xy \cos(x^2 + y^2)\, dx\, dy$

50. $\int_0^1 \int_0^1 9x^2 y^2 \cos(x^3 + y^3)\, dx\, dy$

Double Integrals over Rectangles

In Exercises 51–64 , compute the double integral over the rectangle $R = [0, 1] \times [0, 1]$.

51. $\iint_R (6x^2 - 8y^3)\, dA$ 52. $\iint_R (8x^3 - 12y^4)\, dA$

53. $\iint_R \frac{x^2}{(y + 1)^3}\, dA$ 54. $\iint_R \frac{y^2}{(x + 1)^3}\, dA$

55. $\iint_R e^{2y} \cos(x e^y)\, dA$ 56. $\iint_R e^{2x} \cos(y e^x)\, dA$

57. $\iint_R \frac{4xy}{(1 + x^2 + y^2)^2}\, dA$ 58. $\iint_R \frac{9x^2 y^2}{(1 + x^3 + y^3)^2}\, dA$

59. $\iint_R \frac{x}{1 + xy}\, dA$ 60. $\iint_R \frac{y}{1 + xy}\, dA$

61. $\iint_R 6y\sqrt{x + y^2}\, dA$ 62. $\iint_R 6x\sqrt{x^2 + y}\, dA$

63. $\iint_R \frac{x e^{x/(y+1)}}{(y + 1)^2}\, dA$ 64. $\iint_R \frac{y e^{y/(x+1)}}{(x + 1)^2}\, dA$

Calculus *Concepts & Computation*

12.2 Double Integrals over General Regions

In this section we extend the double integral $\iint_R f(x, y)\, dA$ of a function f over a rectangles R to double integrals over more general regions.

For suitable regions D in the plane, we can devise a double Riemann sum approximation as follows. We first enclose the entire region in a rectangle R, preferably one as small as possible. Then for each subdivision of R into subrectangles R_{ij}, we produce a "grid" G_0 that covers D by retaining all those subrectangles that overlap (intersect) D and eliminating those that do not. For example, Figure 12.2.1 illustrates such a grid (shown in blue).

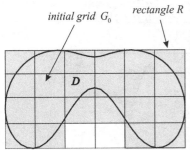

initial grid G_0 *rectangle* R

Figure 12.2.1: *Creating a "grid" (in blue) to approximate the region D.*

Then the approximating Riemann sum for the double integral of f over the region D is taken to be a sum over all the subrectangles in the grid:

$$\sum_{i,\, j \text{ with } R_{ij}\, \in\, G_0} f(x_i, y_j)\, \Delta A_{ij},$$

where $\Delta A_{ij} = \Delta x_i \Delta y_j$. While G_0 is *not* a rectangle it will cover D and be a better approximation to D than the rectangle R, at least if the initial subdivision of R is fine enough.

Having calculated the initial grid G_0, we produce a finer grid G_1 by dividing each rectangle in G_0 into four subrectangles, testing each of these four to see if it intersects D, retaining those that pass the test and tossing out those that do not. The new grid G_1 will still cover D and will be a better approximation to D. See Figure 12.2.2. The corresponding Riemann sum over the rectangles in G_1 should give a better approximation to $\int \int_D f(x, y)\, dA$ as well.

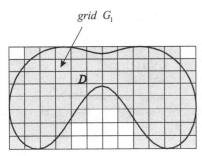

grid G_1

Figure 12.2.2: *Creating a finer grid to approximate the region D.*

This scheme can be continued indefinitely, producing a sequence $\{G_n\}_{n=0}^{\infty}$ of grids which cover D and approximate it better and better as n increases. If we let D_n be the union of all the rectangles in G_n, then in theory $\lim_{n \to \infty} D_n = D$. Thus, D is realized as the limit of a decreasing sequence $D_0 \supset D_1 \supset D_2 \supset \cdots \supset D$ of sets that cover it. The corresponding double integral is defined as the limit of these approximating sums:

DEFINITION 12.2.1 (Double Integrals Over General Regions)

Suppose D is a suitable region in the domain of f. The double integral *of f over D is*

$$\iint_D f(x, y)\, dA \;=\; \lim_{n \to \infty} \sum_{i,\, j \text{ with } R_{ij} \in G_n} f(x_i, y_j) \Delta A_{ij} \qquad (12.2.1)$$

provided this limit exists

Computing double integrals over general regions D using this definition is difficult. Fortunately, one can prove an extended version of Fubini's theorem for rectangles (Theorem 12.1.1). Before looking at this, we consider several other consequences of the definition.

NOTE 1: (**Measuring Volumes**) In (12.2.1), the function f need not be positive on the region D, but when it is, then the volume of the solid beneath the graph of f and above the region D is by definition $V = \iint_D f(x, y)\, dA$.

NOTE 2: (**Measuring Areas**) Since $\lim_{n \to \infty} D_n = D$, we would expect the corresponding sequence of *areas* of the covers D_n to converge to the *area* of D. Thus, we can define the area of such a general region as

$$A = \text{Area of } D = \iint_D 1 \, dA \qquad (12.2.2)$$

The integrand here is $f(x, y) = 1$ and of course its graph is the horizontal plane $z = 1$. Thus, we can also view the double integral $\iint_D 1 \, dA$ as giving the volume of a generalized cylinder of height $h = 1$. See Figure 12.2.3 and Note 3 below.

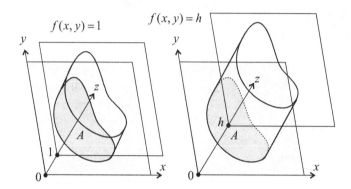

Figure 12.2.3: *The area of the region D is $A = \iint_D 1 \, dA$ and the generalized cylinder of height h has volume $V = hA$*

NOTE 3: (Measuring Volumes of Generalized Cylinders) As in Section 5.2, suppose S is a generalized cylinder obtained by translating a planar region D parallel to itself through a distance h (the height of the generalized cylinder) Then by Definition (12.2.2) in Note 2 above and properties of the double integral, we get

$$V = \text{Volume of } S = \iint_D h \, dA = hA \qquad (12.2.3)$$

This result (12.2.3) gives justification to the method of measuring volumes of solids for which we know the cross-sectional area function $A(x)$ (Sections 5.2 and 12.1) and leads to a generalization of Fubini's Theorem for rectangles (Theorem 12.2.1 below).

Cross-Sectional Area and Iterated Integrals

Recall from Section 12.1 that we used iterated integrals to measure volumes of solids S bounded on the top by the graph of $z = f(x, y)$ (assuming f is positive), on the bottom by the plane of the rectangle R, and on the sides by the four planes $x = a$, $x = b$, $y = c$, $y = d$ (which pass through the sides of R).

To extend this situations from a rectangle R to a general region D, we consider the two types of planar regions introduced in Section 5.1. These were called Type I and Type II regions and we employ the same designations in the corresponding solids they determine:

TYPE I SOLIDS: Suppose D is the Type I region bounded by the graphs of $y = g(x)$, $y = h(x)$ and the vertical lines $x = a$, $x = b$. (We assume that $g(x) \leq h(x)$, for x in $[a, b]$.) See Figure 12.2.4. If $z = f(x, y)$ is a function of two variables that is positive on the region D, then the corresponding *Type I solid* is the solid S bounded by the six surfaces:

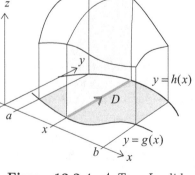

Figure 12.2.4: *A Type I solid based on a Type I region D.*

Top and Bottom: $z = f(x, y)$, $z = 0$
Four Sides: $y = g(x)$, $y = h(x)$, $x = a$, $x = b$

Note that the fours sides of a Type I solid are surfaces of translation (generalized cylinders) as described in Sections 5.2 and 10.6.

Figure 12.2.4 illustrates a Type I solid and shows, for an x between a and b, a cross-section through the solid. The area function $A(x)$ for this cross-section at x is gotten by an integral with respect to y, much like we obtained in Equation (12.1.5) from the last section. But now the limits of integration are not c and d but rather $g(x)$ and $h(x)$. The integral is

$$A(x) = \int_{g(x)}^{h(x)} f(x,y)\,dy \qquad (12.2.4)$$

From Section 5.2, the volume of a solid with known cross-sectional area $A(x)$, for $a \leq x \leq b$, is $V = \int_a^b A(x)\,dx$. Consequently, the volume of a Type I solid is

Type I Volume: $\displaystyle V = \int_a^b \int_{g(x)}^{h(x)} f(x,y)\,dy\,dx \qquad (12.2.5)$

This gives a new kind of iterated integral which is computed in much the same way as before. You first integrate $f(x,y)$ partially with respect to y and then evaluate at $y = h(x)$ and $y = g(x)$, subtracting the latter from the former. This gives a function of x only, which you then integrate from a to b. Here are some examples to illustrate how this is done:

Example 12.2.1 (Iterated Integrals with Variable Limits of Integration)

Problem: Compute the following iterated integrals.

(a) $\displaystyle \int_0^1 \int_{\sqrt{x}}^{3-x^2} 2xy\,dy\,dx$ (b) $\displaystyle \int_0^1 \int_{e^{-x}}^{e^x} \left(1 + \frac{x}{y}\right) dy\,dx$

Solution Part(a): Figure 12.2.5 shows a sketch of the Type I region.

$$\int_0^1 \int_{\sqrt{x}}^{3-x^2} 2xy\,dy\,dx = \int_0^1 \Big[\int_{\sqrt{x}}^{3-x^2} 2xy\,dy\Big]\,dx = \int_0^1 \Big[\,xy^2\,\Big|_{\sqrt{x}}^{3-x^2}\,\Big]\,dx$$

$$= \int_0^1 \Big[\,x(3-x^2)^2 - x(\sqrt{x})^2\,\Big]\,dx = \int_0^1 \Big[\,x(9 - 6x^2 + x^4) - x\cdot x\,\Big]\,dx$$

$$= \int_0^1 \Big[\,9x - x^2 - 6x^3 + x^5\,\Big]\,dx = \Big[\tfrac{9}{2}x^2 - \tfrac{1}{3}x^3 - \tfrac{3}{2}x^4 + \tfrac{1}{5}x^5\Big]\Big|_0^1$$

$$= \tfrac{9}{2} - \tfrac{1}{3} - \tfrac{3}{2} + \tfrac{1}{5} = \tfrac{43}{15}$$

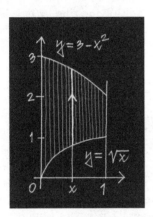

Figure 12.2.5: *A Type I region of integration.*

Solution Part(b): Figure 12.2.6 shows a sketch of the Type I region.

$$\int_0^1 \int_{e^{-x}}^{e^x} \left(1 + \frac{x}{y}\right) dy\,dx = \int_0^1 \Big[\int_{e^{-x}}^{e^x} \left(1 + \frac{x}{y}\right) dy\Big]\,dx = \int_0^1 \Big[\,(y + x\ln y)\,\Big|_{e^{-x}}^{e^x}\,\Big]\,dx$$

$$= \int_0^1 \Big[\,e^x - e^{-x} + x\ln(e^x) - x\ln(e^{-x})\,\Big]\,dx = \int_0^1 \Big[\,e^x - e^{-x} + x\cdot x - x(-x)\,\Big]\,dx$$

$$= \int_0^1 \Big[\,e^x - e^{-x} + 2x^2\,\Big]\,dx = \Big[\,e^x + e^{-x} + \tfrac{2}{3}x^3\,\Big]\Big|_0^1 = e + e^{-1} + \tfrac{2}{3} - 2$$

$$= e + e^{-1} - \tfrac{4}{3}$$

NOTE: Each of the iterated integrals in Example 12.2.1 represents the volume of a Type I solid. The limits of integration determine the region D that forms the base of that solid. The next example reinforces the this observation.

Example 12.2.2 (Sketching the Region of Integration)

Problem: For each of the iterated integrals in Example 12.2.1, sketch the region D of integration,.

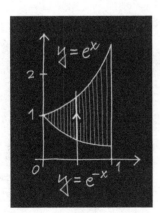

Figure 12.2.6: *A Type I region of integration.*

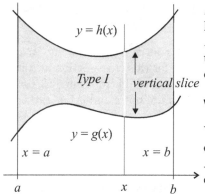

Figure 12.2.7: *A vertical slice through a Type I region D.*

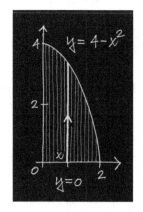

Figure 12.2.8: *A Type I region of integration.*

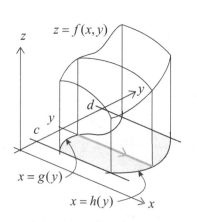

Figure 12.2.9: *A Type II solid based on a Type II region D.*

Solution: For Part (a), sketch the curves $y = 3 - x^2$, $y = \sqrt{x}$ and the two vertical lines $x = 0$, $x = 1$ Then D is the region bounded by these four curves. A sketch of D is shown in Figure 12.2.5. For Part (b), sketch the curves $y = e^x$, $y = e^{-x}$ and the two vertical lines $x = 0$, $x = 1$. Then D is the region bounded by these four curves. A sketch of D is shown in Figure 12.2.6.

Vertical Slices of the Base D and Sections of the Solid S

Visualizing a Type I solid S can be difficult, but sketching its base D (as in the last example) and imagining how the infinitesimal cross-sections with volumes $dV = A(x)dx$ are integrated to give the volume V are things that you should be able to do.

So, as we did in Section 5.2, after sketching the Type I region D, take an x between a and b and draw in a vertical slice through D. Figure 12.2.7 illustrates such a slice (shown in yellow). Now, however, instead of adding the pieces $dA = hdx$ to get the area of D, we instead integrate $f(x,y)$ in the y-direction from $y = g(x)$ to $y = h(x)$, while holding x fixed. This gives $A(x)$. Multiplying this by dx gives volume $dV = A(x)dx$ of the infinitesimal cross-section of S at x, which we integrate to get V.

Example 12.2.3 (Finding Volumes)

Problem: Suppose D is the Type I region in the 1st quadrant bounded by $y = 4 - x^2$, $y = 0$, $x = 0$, $x = 2$. The function $f(x,y) = 12 - 4x - 2y$ has a graph which is a plane above the region D. Sketch D and find the volume of the corresponding Type I solid.

Solution: A sketch of the region D is shown in Figure 12.2.8. As indicated in the figure, for an x between 0 and 2, we integrate $f(x,y) = 12 - 4x - 2y$ with respect to y along the vertical slice at x. The limits of integration for y are $y = 0$ and $y = 4 - x^2$. Then we do another integral (the outer integral) as x goes from 0 to 2. Thus,

$$
\begin{aligned}
V &= \int_0^2 \int_0^{4-x^2} \left[12 - 4x - 2y \right] dy\, dx = \int_0^2 \left[12y - 4xy - y^2 \right] \Big|_0^{4-x^2} dx \\
&= \int_0^2 \left[12(4 - x^2) - 4x(4 - x^2) - (4 - x^2)^2 \right] dx \\
&= \int_0^2 \left[48 - 12x^2 - 16x + 4x^3 - 16 + 8x^2 - x^4 \right] dx \\
&= \int_0^2 \left[32 - 16x - 4x^2 + 4x^3 - x^4 \right] dx = \left[32x - 8x^2 - \tfrac{4}{3}x^3 + x^4 - \tfrac{1}{5}x^5 \right] \Big|_0^2 \\
&= 64 - 32 - \tfrac{32}{3} + 16 - \tfrac{32}{5} = \tfrac{464}{15} = \frac{464}{15}
\end{aligned}
$$

TYPE II SOLIDS: Suppose D is the Type II region bounded by the graphs of $x = g(y)$, $x = h(y)$ and the horizontal lines $y = c$, $y = d$. (We assume that $g(y) \le h(y)$, for y in $[c,d]$.) See Figure 12.2.9. If $z = f(x,y)$ is a function of two variables that is positive on the region D, then the corresponding *Type II solid* is the solid S bounded by the six surfaces:

Top and Bottom: $z = f(x,y)$, $z = 0$
Four Sides: $x = g(y)$, $x = h(y)$, $y = c$, $y = d$

Figure 12.2.9 illustrates a Type II solid and shows, for a y between c and d, a cross-section through the solid. The area function $A(y)$ for this cross-section at y

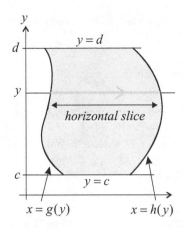

Figure 12.2.10: *A horizontal slice through a Type II region D.*

is gotten by an integral with respect to x, but now the limits of integration are not c and d but rather $g(y)$ and $h(y)$. See Figure 12.2.10. The integral is

$$A(y) = \int_{g(y)}^{h(y)} f(x, y)\, dx \qquad (12.2.6)$$

From Section 5.2, the volume of a solid with known cross-sectional area $A(y)$, for $c \le y \le d$ is $V = \int_c^d A(y)\, dy$. Consequently, the volume of a Type II solid is

Type II Volume: $\qquad V = \int_c^d \int_{g(y)}^{h(y)} f(x, y)\, dx\, dy \qquad (12.2.7)$

Thus, the calculation of volumes for Type I and Type II solids is entirely analogous. We note that the iterated integrals (12.2.5) and (12.2.7) for calculating the respective volumes make sense even when $f(x, y)$ is not positive on the region D. The resulting number, which can be negative or zero, is interpreted as the *net volume* V_{net}.

Whether it is volume or net volume, the iterated integrals over Type I and II regions coincide with the double integrals over these regions. That is the content of Fubini's theorem.

THEOREM 12.2.1 (Fubini's Theorem for Type I & II Regions)

Suppose f is continuous on a region D in its domain. If D is a Type I region, then

$$\iint_D f(x, y)\, dA = \int_a^b \int_{g(x)}^{h(x)} f(x, y)\, dy\, dx \qquad (12.2.8)$$

If D is a Type II region, then

$$\iint_D f(x, y)\, dA = \int_c^d \int_{g(y)}^{h(y)} f(x, y)\, dx\, dy \qquad (12.2.9)$$

NOTE 1: Fubini's theorem extends to more general regions D, provided that D can be decomposed into a number of Type I or Type II regions.

NOTE 2: (Reversing the Order of Integration) If D can be viewed as both a Type I and a Type II region, Theorem 12.2.1 implies that $\iint_D f(x, y)\, dA$ can be computed in two ways—use either Formula (12.2.8) or (12.2.9). Of course there is no need to do the calculation twice, but, as we saw in Example 12.1.1 Part (b), sometimes the iterated integral is easier to do in one order as opposed to the other order. In doing a problem, set up the iterated integral in one order and proceed with the integrations. If one of the integrals becomes too difficult, then reverse the order. Maybe that will help.

NOTE 3: (Caution) When reversing the order of integration in an iterated integral with variable limits of integration, you *cannot* just reverse $dy\, dx$ and the limits of integration. Rather you must analyze the region and change the way you "slice" it: from vertical to horizontal, or vice versa.

Type I: $(\int_a^b \int_{g(x)}^{h(x} f(x, y)\, dy\, dx)$ For an x in $[a, b]$, integrate with respect to y along a *vertical* slice from $g(x)$ to $h(x)$. Then integrate with respect to x.

Type II: $(\int_c^d \int_{g(y)}^{h(y} f(x, y)\, dx\, dy)$ For an x in $[a, b]$, integrate with respect to x along a *horizontal* slice from $g(y)$ to $h(y)$. Then integrate with respect to y.

Example 12.2.4 (Reversing the Order of Integration)

Problem: For each of the following iterated integrals (i) sketch the region D for the corresponding double integral $\iint_D f(x, y)\, dA$, (ii) reverse the order of integration, and (iii) compute the resulting iterated integral.

$$\text{(a)} \int_0^1 \int_1^{e^x} 2ye^{2x}\, dy\, dx \quad \text{(b)} \int_0^4 \int_{\sqrt{x}}^2 3x\sqrt{x^2 + y^4}\, dy\, dx$$

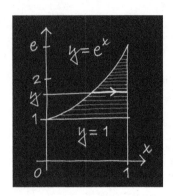

Figure 12.2.11: *A Type II region of integration.*

Solution Part (a): The inner integral with respect to y is from $y = 1$ (the curve on the bottom) up to $y = e^x$ (the curve on the top). We sketch these two curves along with the vertical lines $x = 0$, $x = 1$ and shade the region D with horizontal lines because that's the way we are going to slice it. See Figure 12.2.11. Viewing D as a Type II, the curve on the "left" is $y = e^x$, which we must solve for x. This gives $x = \ln y$. The curve on the "right" is $x = 1$. So for each y between 1 and e, we integrate with respect to x, from left to right, i.e., from $x = \ln y$. to $x = 1$. This gives the inner (or first) integral. The outer integral with respect to y goes from 1 to e. Thus,

$$\int_0^1 \int_1^{e^x} 2ye^{2x}\, dy\, dx = \int_1^e \int_{\ln y}^1 2ye^{2x}\, dx\, dy = \int_1^e \left[ye^{2x} \right]\Big|_{\ln y}^1 dy$$

$$= \int_1^e \left[ye^2 - ye^{2\ln y} \right] dy = \int_1^e \left[ye^2 - y^3 \right] dy = \left[\tfrac{1}{2} y^2 e^2 - \tfrac{1}{4} y^4 \right]\Big|_1^e$$

$$= \left[\tfrac{1}{2} e^2 e^2 - \tfrac{1}{4} e^4 \right] - \left[\tfrac{1}{2} e^2 - \tfrac{1}{4} \right] = \tfrac{1}{4} e^4 - \tfrac{1}{2} e^2 + \tfrac{1}{4}$$

Note: We used $e^{2\ln y} = e^{\ln(y^2)} = y^2$ in the next to the last line above.

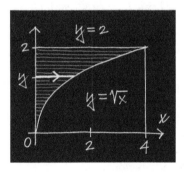

Figure 12.2.12: *A Type II region of integration.*

Solution Part (b): The inner integral with respect to y is from $y = \sqrt{x}$ (the curve on the bottom) up to $y = 2$ (the curve on the top). We sketch these two curves along with the vertical lines $x = 0$, $x = 4$ and shade the region D with horizontal lines because that's way we are going to slice it. See Figure 12.2.12. Viewing D as a Type II, the curve on the "left" is $x = 0$ and The curve on the "right" is $y = \sqrt{x}$, which we must solve for x. This gives $x = y^2$. So for each y between 0 and 2, we integrate with respect to x, from left to right, i.e., from $x = 0$ to $x = y^2$. This gives the inner (or first) integral. The outer integral with respect to y goes from 0 to 2. Thus,

$$\int_0^4 \int_{\sqrt{x}}^2 3x\sqrt{x^2 + y^4}\, dy\, dx = \int_0^2 \int_0^{y^2} 3x\sqrt{x^2 + y^4}\, dx\, dy$$

$$= \int_0^2 \left[(x^2 + y^4)^{3/2} \right]\Big|_0^{y^2} dy = \int_0^2 \left[(2y^4)^{3/2} - (y^4)^{3/2} \right] dy$$

$$= \int_0^2 \left[(2\sqrt{2} - 1)y^6 \right] dy = \left[\tfrac{1}{7}(2\sqrt{2} - 1)\, y^7 \right]\Big|_0^2 = \tfrac{128}{7}(2\sqrt{2} - 1)$$

Note: We used the substitution $u = x^2 + y^4$, $du = \frac{\partial}{\partial x}(x^2 + y^4)dx = 2x\, dx$ in the second line above to get $\int 3x\sqrt{x^2 + y^4}\, dx = (x^2 + y^4)^{3/2}$.

Exercises: 12.2 (Double Integrals over General Regions)

Computing Iterated Integrals

In Exercises 1–52, compute the iterated integral.

1. $\displaystyle\int_0^1 \int_x^{2-x} 2xy \, dy \, dx$ **2.** $\displaystyle\int_0^2 \int_{2x}^{4-x} 2xy \, dy \, dx$

3. $\displaystyle\int_0^1 \int_{x^4}^{x^2} 60x\sqrt{y} \, dy \, dx$ **4.** $\displaystyle\int_0^1 \int_{x^6}^{x^3} 60x\sqrt[3]{y} \, dy \, dx$

5. $\displaystyle\int_0^4 \int_{\sqrt{x}}^2 \frac{x}{y^2} \, dy \, dx$ **6.** $\displaystyle\int_0^9 \int_{\sqrt[3]{x}}^2 \frac{x}{y^2} \, dy \, dx$

7. $\displaystyle\int_1^2 \int_0^{\ln x} 6xe^y \, dy \, dx$ **8.** $\displaystyle\int_1^2 \int_0^{\ln x} 8xe^{2y} \, dy \, dx$

9. $\displaystyle\int_1^2 \int_0^{\ln x} (x + e^y) \, dy \, dx$ **10.** $\displaystyle\int_1^2 \int_0^{\ln x} (x + e^{2y}) \, dy \, dx$

11. $\displaystyle\int_1^2 \int_{1/x}^x (4 + 8xy) \, dy \, dx$ **12.** $\displaystyle\int_1^2 \int_{1/x^2}^x (x + 2y) \, dy \, dx$

13. $\displaystyle\int_0^1 \int_0^{e^x} 3y^2 e^{2x} \, dy \, dx$ **14.** $\displaystyle\int_0^1 \int_0^{e^x} 4y^3 e^{3x} \, dy \, dx$

15. $\displaystyle\int_{\pi/2}^{\pi} \int_0^{1/y} y^2 \cos(xy^2) \, dx \, dy$

16. $\displaystyle\int_{\pi/2}^{\pi} \int_0^{1/y} y^2 \sin(xy^2) \, dx \, dy$

17. $\displaystyle\int_0^1 \int_0^y y^2 e^{xy} \, dx \, dy$ **18.** $\displaystyle\int_0^1 \int_0^y 3y^4 e^{xy^2} \, dx \, dy$

19. $\displaystyle\int_0^1 \int_0^{x^2} 4x^5 \cos(x^2 y) \, dy \, dx$

20. $\displaystyle\int_0^1 \int_0^{x^3} 5x^8 \cos(x^3 y) \, dy \, dx$

21. $\displaystyle\int_0^1 \int_0^{x^2} \frac{3x^6}{(1 + x^4 y)^2} \, dy \, dx$

22. $\displaystyle\int_0^1 \int_0^{x^4} \frac{4x^7}{(1 + x^4 y)^2} \, dy \, dx$

23. $\displaystyle\int_0^1 \int_0^{x^2} \frac{x^3}{(1 - x^2 y)^{3/2}} \, dy \, dx$

24. $\displaystyle\int_0^1 \int_0^{x^4} \frac{3x^4}{(1 - x^2 y)^{3/2}} \, dy \, dx$

25. $\displaystyle\int_0^{\pi/2} \int_0^{\sin x} 6y \cos x \, dy \, dx$

26. $\displaystyle\int_0^{\pi/2} \int_0^{\cos x} 6y \sin x \, dy \, dx$

27. $\displaystyle\int_0^{\pi/2} \int_0^{\sin x} 30y \cos^3 x \, dy \, dx$

28. $\displaystyle\int_0^{\pi/2} \int_0^{\cos x} 30y \sin^3 x \, dy \, dx$

29. $\displaystyle\int_0^{\pi/4} \int_0^{\tan x} 9y^2 \sec x \, dy \, dx$

30. $\displaystyle\int_0^{\pi/4} \int_0^{\tan x} 30y^2 \sec^3 x \, dy \, dx$

31. $\displaystyle\int_0^{\pi/4} \int_0^{\tan x} 30y \sec^4 x \, dy \, dx$

32. $\displaystyle\int_0^{\pi/4} \int_0^{\tan x} 140y^3 \sec^4 x \, dy \, dx$

33. $\displaystyle\int_1^2 \int_0^{1/x} \frac{2}{x + 1} \, dy \, dx$ **34.** $\displaystyle\int_1^2 \int_0^{1/x} \frac{2}{x + 2} \, dy \, dx$

35. $\displaystyle\int_0^1 \int_1^{x^2+1} \frac{4x - 2}{(x + 2)y^2} \, dy \, dx$

36. $\displaystyle\int_0^1 \int_1^{x+3} \frac{8 - 6x}{(x^2 + 4)y^2} \, dy \, dx$

37. $\displaystyle\int_0^1 \int_1^{x+3} \frac{2x^2 - x - 1}{(1 + x^2)y^2} \, dy \, dx$

38. $\displaystyle\int_0^1 \int_1^{x+2} \frac{3x^2 - x + 1}{(1 + x^2)y^2} \, dy \, dx$

39. $\displaystyle\int_0^1 \int_{\sqrt{1-x^2}}^1 \frac{x^3}{y^2} \, dy \, dx$ **40.** $\displaystyle\int_0^1 \int_{\sqrt{1-x^2}}^1 \frac{x^5}{y^2} \, dy \, dx$

41. $\displaystyle\int_0^1 \int_0^{x^{3/2}} 2y\sqrt{1 + x^2} \, dy \, dx$

42. $\displaystyle\int_0^1 \int_0^x 3y^2 \sqrt{1 + x^2} \, dy \, dx$

43. $\displaystyle\int_0^{\pi/2} \int_0^{\cos x} x \, dy \, dx$ **44.** $\displaystyle\int_0^{\pi/2} \int_0^{\sin x} x \, dy \, dx$

45. $\displaystyle\int_1^2 \int_0^{x^2} \ln x \, dy \, dx$ **46.** $\displaystyle\int_1^2 \int_0^{x^3} \ln x \, dy \, dx$

47. $\displaystyle\int_0^{\pi/4} \int_0^x \sec^2 x \, dy \, dx$ **48.** $\displaystyle\int_0^{\pi/4} \int_0^x \csc^2 x \, dy \, dx$

49. $\displaystyle\int_0^1 \int_0^{e^x} \frac{e^{2x}}{(1 + ye^x)^2} \, dy \, dx$

50. $\displaystyle\int_0^1 \int_0^{e^{2x}} \frac{e^{4x}}{(1 + ye^{2x})^2} \, dy \, dx$

51. $\displaystyle\int_0^1 \int_0^{e^x} 2e^{3x} \cos(ye^x) \, dy \, dx$

52. $\displaystyle\int_0^1 \int_0^{e^x} 3e^{5x} \cos(ye^{2x}) \, dy \, dx$

Setting Up Iterated Integrals

In Exercises 53–60, for the region D shown in the sketch, set up the iterated integral $\int_a^b \int_{g(x)}^{h(x)} f(x,y)\,dy\,dx$ that gives the double integral $\iint_D f(x,y)\,dA$.

53.   **54.**

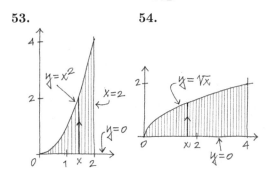

55.   **56.**

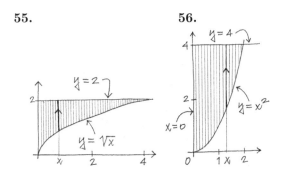

57.   **58.**

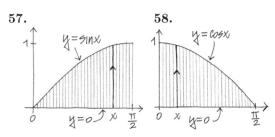

59.   **60.**

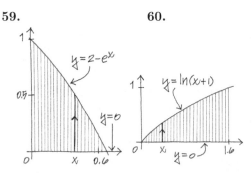

Double Integrals over Type I & II Regions

In Exercises 61–74 , compute the double integral over the specified region D.

61. $\iint_D 6xy\,dA$, D: $y=\sqrt{x}$, $y=2-x$, $x=0$

62. $\iint_D 6xy^2\,dA$, D: $y=x^{1/3}$, $y=2-x$, $x=0$

63. $\iint_D (30x+24y)\,dA$, D: $x=y^2$, $x=2y$

64. $\iint_D (45x+54y)\,dA$, D: $x=y^2$, $x=2y$

65. $\iint_D 27xy^2\,dA$, D: $y=e^x$, $y=1$, $x\ge 0$, $x=1$

66. $\iint_D 64xy^3\,dA$, D: $y=e^x$, $y=0$, $x\ge 0$, $x=1$

67. $\iint_D \dfrac{5x^6}{1+x^2y}\,dA$, D: $y=x^3$, $y=0$, $x\ge 0$, $x=1$

68. $\iint_D \dfrac{7x^{10}}{1+x^4y}\,dA$, D: $y=x^3$, $y=0$, $x\ge 0$, $x=1$

69. $\iint_D 4y^5 e^{xy^2}\,dA$, D: $x=y^2$, $x=0$, $y\ge 0$, $y=1$

70. $\iint_D 5y^7 e^{xy^3}\,dA$, D: $x=y^2$, $x=0$, $y\ge 0$, $y=1$

71. $\iint_D \dfrac{x^3}{(1+x^2y)^2}\,dA$, D: $y=x^2$, $y=0$, $x\ge 0$, $x=1$

72. $\iint_D \dfrac{4x^8}{(1+x^5y)^2}\,dA$, D: $y=x^3$, $y=0$, $x\ge 0$, $x=1$

73 $\iint_D 45y^2 \sin^2 x\,dA$, D: $y=\cos x$, $y=0$, $x\ge 0$, $x\le \frac{\pi}{2}$

74 $\iint_D 105y^2 \sin^4 x\,dA$, D: $y=\cos x$, $y=0$, $x\ge 0$, $x\le \frac{\pi}{2}$

Reverse Order of Integration

In Exercises 75–82 , reverse the order of integration that you set up in Exercises 53–60. Do a sketch of the reverse setup.

75. #53   **76.** #54   **77.** #55   **78.** #56
79. #57   **80.** #58   **81.** #59   **82.** #60

Reverse Order of Integration

In Exercises 83–96, reverse the order of integration and then compute the double integral.

83. $\displaystyle\int_0^4 \int_{\sqrt{x}}^2 3\sec^2(y^3)\,dy\,dx$ **84.** $\displaystyle\int_0^1 \int_x^1 2\sec^2(y^2)\,dy\,dx$

85. $\displaystyle\int_0^4 \int_{\sqrt{x}}^2 3\sqrt{x+y^2}\,dy\,dx$ **86.** $\displaystyle\int_0^4 \int_{\sqrt{x}}^2 \dfrac{9x^2}{32}\sqrt{x^3+y^6}\,dy\,dx$

87. $\displaystyle\int_0^4 \int_{\sqrt{y}}^2 \dfrac{3x^6}{(1+x^4y)^2}\,dx\,dy$ **88.** $\displaystyle\int_0^{16} \int_{\sqrt[4]{y}}^2 \dfrac{4x^7}{(1+x^4y)^2}\,dx\,dy$

89. $\displaystyle\int_0^8 \int_{\sqrt[3]{y}}^2 4x^4 \sin(xy)\,dx\,dy$ **90.** $\displaystyle\int_0^8 \int_{\sqrt{y}}^2 4x^5 \cos(x^2 y)\,dx\,dy$

91. $\displaystyle\int_0^1 \int_{\sin^{-1}y}^{\frac{\pi}{2}} 3y^2 \cos^2 x\,dx\,dy$

92. $\displaystyle\int_0^1 \int_0^{\cos^{-1}y} 3y^2 \sin x\,dx\,dy$

93. $\displaystyle\int_0^1 \int_{\tan^{-1} y}^{\frac{\pi}{4}} 2y \sec^4 x \, dx \, dy$

94. $\displaystyle\int_0^1 \int_{\tan^{-1} y}^{\frac{\pi}{4}} 3y^2 \sec^4 x \, dx \, dy$

95. $\displaystyle\int_0^{\frac{1}{4}} \int_{\sqrt{y}}^{1/2} \frac{4x^3}{(1 - x^2 y)^2} \, dx \, dy$

96. $\displaystyle\int_0^{\frac{1}{8}} \int_{\sqrt[3]{y}}^{1} \frac{6x^5}{(1 - x^3 y)^2} \, dx \, dy$

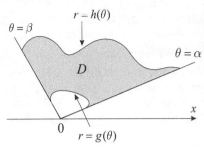

Figure 12.3.1: *A polar region.*

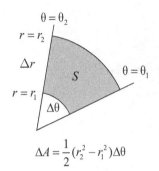

Figure 12.3.2: *A polar rectangle.*

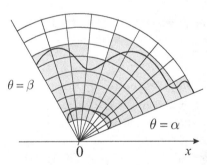

Figure 12.3.3: *Creating a grid to approximate a polar region D.*

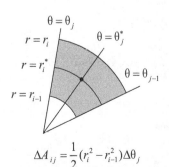

Figure 12.3.4: *The i-jth polar rectangle S_{ij}.*

Calculus *Concepts & Computation*

12.3 Double Integrals in Polar Coordinates

In the previous section we learned how to compute double integrals $\iint_D f(x,y)\,dA$ of functions f over regions D that were either Type I or Type II regions. In this section show how to calculate double integrals over *polar regions*. The technique amounts to changing variables from Cartesian to polar coordinates. We call a region D a *polar region* if it is bounded by the graphs of two polar curves $r = g(\theta)$, $r = h(\theta)$, and two rays with polar equations $\theta = \alpha$, $\theta = \beta$. We assume that $g(\theta) \le h(\theta)$, for θ in $[\alpha, \beta]$, and that $\beta - \alpha < 2\pi$. See Figure 12.3.1.

From Section 12.2, we had the definition of the double integral over general regions D as

$$\iint_D f(x,y)\,dA = \lim_{n \to \infty} \sum_{i,j \text{ with } R_{ij} \in G_n} f(x_i^*, y_j^*)\,\Delta A_{ij},$$

where $\Delta A_{ij} = \Delta x_i \Delta y_j$. The approximating scheme in the limit comes from using grids G_n of rectangles R_{ij} to approximate the region D. But now, since D is a polar region, it is more appropriate to approximate it by what, for lack of a better name, are called *polar rectangles*. They are the differences of two concentric sectors and arise as follows.

A *sector* of a circle of radius r is the region of the circle contained between two rays $\theta = \theta_1$, $\theta = \theta_2$ (with $0 < \theta_1 < \theta_2 < 2\pi$) (Think of a slice of pizza.). The area of such a sector is $A = \frac{1}{2}r^2(\theta_2 - \theta_1) = \frac{1}{2}r^2\Delta\theta$.

For two concentric circles of radii $r_1 < r_2$, the region S between the two circles and the two rays $\theta = \theta_1$, $\theta = \theta_2$ is called a *polar rectangle*. See Figure 12.3.2. It can be thought of as the difference of two sectors, and as such has area

$$\Delta A = \frac{1}{2}r_2^2\Delta\theta - \frac{1}{2}r_1^2\Delta\theta = \frac{1}{2}(r_2^2 - r_1^2)\Delta\theta$$

Now the approximating scheme for polar regions D is as follows. We take D and enclose the entire region in a polar rectangle S, preferably one as small as possible. Then for each subdivision of S into polar subrectangles S_{ij}, we produce a "grid" G_0 that covers D by retaining all those polar subrectangles that overlap (intersect) D and eliminating those that do not. For example, Figure 12.3.3 illustrates such a grid (shown in blue).

Note that the "center" of the i-jth polar rectangle S_{ij} has polar coordinates $r_i^* = \frac{1}{2}(r_i + r_{i-1})$ and $\theta_j^* = \frac{1}{2}(\theta_j + \theta_{j-1})$ and the area of S_{ij} is

$$\Delta A_{ij} = \frac{1}{2}(r_i^2 - r_{i-1}^2)\Delta\theta_j = \frac{1}{2}(r_i + r_{i-1})(r_i - r_{i-1})\Delta\theta_j = r_i^*\Delta r_i\Delta\theta_j$$

See Figure 12.3.4. The approximating Riemann sum for the double integral of f over a *polar* region D is

$$\sum_{i,j \text{ with } S_{ij} \in G_0} f(r_i^*\cos\theta_j^*,\, r_i^*\sin\theta_j^*)\, r_i^*\Delta r_i\Delta\theta_j \approx \iint_D f(x,y)\,dA$$

While G_0 is *not* a rectangle it will cover D and be a better approximation to D than the original polar rectangle S, at least if the initial subdivision of S is fine enough.

Having calculated the initial grid G_0, we produce a finer grid G_1 by dividing each polar subrectangle in G_0 into four polar subrectangles, testing each of these four to see if it intersects D, retaining those that pass the test and tossing out those that do not. The new grid G_1 will still cover D and will be a better approximation to D. See Figure 12.3.5. The corresponding Riemann sum over the rectangles in G_1 should give a better approximation to $\iint_D f(x,y)\,dA$ as well.

This scheme can be continued indefinitely, producing a sequence $\{G_n\}_{n=0}^{\infty}$ of grids which cover D and approximate it better and better as n increases. If we let D_n be the union of all the polar rectangles in G_n, then in theory $\lim_{n\to\infty} D_n = D$. Thus, D is realized as the limit of a decreasing sequence $D_0 \supset D_1 \supset D_2 \supset \cdots \supset D$ of sets that cover it.

The corresponding double integral is the limit of the approximating sums and this limit also gives us the iterated *polar* integrals as a means of computing the double integral. This is the content of the following theorem.

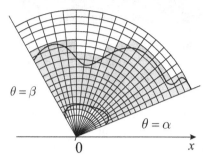

Figure 12.3.5: *A finer grid.*

THEOREM 12.3.1 (Double Integrals in Polar Coordinates)

Suppose D is a polar region, bounded by $r = g(\theta), r = h(\theta), \theta = \alpha, \theta = \beta$, in the domain of f. Then

$$\iint_D f(x,y)\,dA = \lim_{n\to\infty} \sum_{i,j \text{ with } S_{ij} \in G_n} f(r_i^* \cos\theta_j^*, r_i^* \cos\theta_j^*) r_i^* \Delta r_i \Delta \theta_j$$

$$= \int_\alpha^\beta \int_{g(\theta)}^{h(\theta)} f(r\cos\theta, r\sin\theta)\, r\, dr d\theta \qquad (12.3.1)$$

One can consider Formula (12.3.1) as sort of a Fubini type result for double integrals over polar regions. More properly, it is really a change of variables (or substitution) formula. (See Section 12.6.)

Formula (12.3.1) is particularly important when the polar region D is *not* a Type I or a Type II region. The next two examples show you what is involved when this is the case.

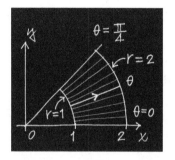

Figure 12.3.6: *The polar rectangle in Example 12.3.1.*

Example 12.3.1 (A Double Integral over a Polar Rectangle)

Problem: Suppose D is the polar rectangle bounded by the circles $r = 1$, $r = 2$ and the lines $\theta = 0, \theta = \pi/4$. For $f(x,y) = xy$, find the volume of the solid beneath the graph of f and above the region D. Also sketch the region D.

Solution: A sketch of the polar rectangle D is shown in Figure 12.3.6. The sketch also indicates the integration process in the iterated integral. Namely, for a θ between $\alpha = 0$ and $\beta = \pi/4$, we do the inner integral with respect to r as r goes from $r = 1$ to $r = 2$. The region D lies in the 1st quadrant and so $f(x,y) \geq 0$ on D. Thus, the volume is given by the double integral

$$
\begin{aligned}
V &= \iint_D xy\,dA = \int_0^{\pi/4} \int_1^2 (r\cos\theta)(r\sin\theta)\, r\, dr\, d\theta \\
&= \int_0^{\pi/4} \int_1^2 r^3 \cos\theta \sin\theta\, dr\, d\theta = \int_0^{\pi/4} \left[\int_1^2 r^3 dr \right] \cos\theta \sin\theta\, d\theta \\
&= \int_0^{\pi/4} \left[\tfrac{1}{4} r^4 \right]\Big|_1^2 \cos\theta \sin\theta\, d\theta = \int_0^{\pi/4} \left[4 - \tfrac{1}{4} \right] \cos\theta \sin\theta\, d\theta \\
&= \tfrac{15}{4} \int_0^{\pi/4} \cos\theta \sin\theta\, d\theta = \tfrac{15}{4} \left[\tfrac{1}{2} \sin^2\theta \right]\Big|_0^{\pi/4} = \tfrac{15}{4} \cdot \tfrac{1}{2} \left(\tfrac{\sqrt{2}}{2} \right)^2 = \tfrac{15}{16}
\end{aligned}
$$

NOTE 1: In the last line above, the trig integral (an OSOC case) is computed using the substitution $u = \sin\theta$, $du = \cos\theta\, d\theta$.

NOTE 2: In setting up the polar integral we used $x = r \cos \theta$, $y = r \sin \theta$ to rewrite the integrand and we replaced the differential dA by $dA = r\, dr\, d\theta$. *Do not forget to include the r in this latter expression.*

The next example has a more complicated polar region, one that is not a polar rectangle, and more complicated double integral.

Example 12.3.2 (A Double Integral over a Rose Petal)

Problem: Suppose D is the region, in the 1st quadrant, which is inside the petal of the rose curve $r = 2 \sin 2\theta$ and outside the circle $r = 1$. For $f(x, y) = \sqrt{x^2 + y^2}$, find the volume of the solid beneath the graph of f and above the region D. Also sketch the region D.

Solution: Since $f(x, y) \geq 0$ everywhere, the volume is given by the double integral. To set this up, we sketch the region D as shown in Figure 12.3.7. The rose curve $r = 2 \sin 2\theta$ and circle $r = 1$ intersect where their r-values are the same, i.e., where

$$2 \sin 2\theta = 1, \quad \text{which gives} \quad \sin 2\theta = \frac{1}{2}$$

There are many solutions of this, but $2\theta = \pi/6$, $5\pi/6$ are two basic ones. Dividing by 2 gives $\theta = \pi/12$, $5\pi/12$. From Figure 12.3.7, these appear to be the two angles we need. Now the setup of the integral, with $r = \sqrt{x^2 + y^2}$, is

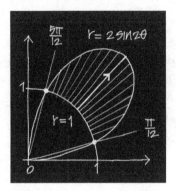

Figure 12.3.7: *The polar region in Example 12.3.2.*

$$
\begin{aligned}
V &= \iint_D \sqrt{x^2 + y^2}\, dA = \int_{\pi/12}^{5\pi/12} \int_1^{2\sin 2\theta} r\, r\, dr\, d\theta = \int_{\pi/12}^{5\pi/12} \int_1^{2\sin 2\theta} r^2\, dr\, d\theta \\
&= \int_{\pi/12}^{5\pi/12} \left[\int_1^{2\sin 2\theta} r^2\, dr \right] d\theta = \int_{\pi/12}^{5\pi/12} \left[\tfrac{1}{3} r^3 \right]\Big|_1^{2\sin 2\theta} d\theta \\
&= \int_{\pi/12}^{5\pi/12} \left[\tfrac{8}{3} \sin^3 2\theta - \tfrac{1}{3} \right] d\theta = \int_{\pi/12}^{5\pi/12} \tfrac{8}{3} \sin^3 2\theta\, d\theta - \int_{\pi/12}^{5\pi/12} \tfrac{1}{3}\, d\theta \\
&= \left[\int_{\pi/12}^{5\pi/12} \tfrac{8}{3} \sin^3 2\theta\, d\theta \right] - \tfrac{\pi}{9}
\end{aligned}
$$

To finish this we need to compute the trig integral

$$
\begin{aligned}
\int_{\pi/12}^{5\pi/12} \tfrac{8}{3} \sin^3 2\theta\, d\theta &= \tfrac{8}{3} \int_{\pi/12}^{5\pi/12} \sin^2 2\theta \cdot \sin 2\theta\, d\theta \\
&= \tfrac{8}{3} \int_{\pi/12}^{5\pi/12} \left[1 - \cos^2 2\theta \right] \sin 2\theta\, d\theta = \tfrac{8}{3} \int_{\sqrt{3}/2}^{-\sqrt{3}/2} \left[1 - u^2 \right] (-\tfrac{1}{2}\, du) \\
&= -\tfrac{4}{3} \left[u - \tfrac{1}{3} u^3 \right]\Big|_{\sqrt{3}/2}^{-\sqrt{3}/2} = -\tfrac{4}{3} u \left[1 - \tfrac{1}{3} u^2 \right]\Big|_{\sqrt{3}/2}^{-\sqrt{3}/2} \\
&= -\tfrac{4}{3} \left(-\tfrac{\sqrt{3}}{2} \right) \left[1 - \tfrac{1}{3} \cdot \tfrac{3}{4} \right] + \tfrac{4}{3} \left(\tfrac{\sqrt{3}}{2} \right) \left[1 - \tfrac{1}{3} \cdot \tfrac{3}{4} \right] = \sqrt{3}
\end{aligned}
$$

Note: In the trig integral (the Odd Sine Case) the technique is to use the substitution $u = \cos 2\theta$, so that $du = -2 \sin 2\theta\, d\theta$. We also changed the limits of integration: when $\theta = \pi/12$, $u = \cos(2(\pi/12)) = \cos(\pi/6) = \sqrt{3}/2$, etc. Hence, the volume is $V = \sqrt{3} - \tfrac{\pi}{9}$.

Type I or Type II Regions that are also Polar Regions

When a Type I or a Type II region D is also a polar region, then we have two ways to compute a double integral $\iint_D f(x, y)\, dA$ over D. We can calculate the iterated integral either (1) in Cartesian coordinates or (2) in polar coordinates. The second way is often preferable when the integrals in with respect to x and y are difficult.

The problems here involve taking a *Cartesian integral* (i.e., an iterated integral in Cartesian coordinates), say, for a Type I region: $\int_a^b \int_{g(x)}^{h(x)} f(x,y)\,dy\,dx$ and changing it into an equivalent *polar integral* (i.e., an iterated integral in polar coordinates).

To do this, carefully sketch the Type I (or II) region D and then try to describe D in terms of polar curves (and lines). Sometimes you might have to break D into two polar regions. Next rewrite the Cartesian integrand in terms of polar coordinates using $x = r\cos\theta$, $y = r\sin\theta$ and replace the differentials $dydx$ (or $dydx$) with $r\,dr d\theta$. *Do not forget to include the r in the last expression.* Remember, also, the commonly occurring expressions $r^2 = x^2 + y^2$ and $r = \sqrt{x^2 + y^2}$.

Example 12.3.3 (Changing Cartesian Integrals to Polar Integrals)

Problem: For each of the following iterated integrals (i) sketch the region D for the corresponding double integral $\iint_D f(x,y)\,dA$, (ii) change the Cartesian integral to an equivalent polar integral and (iii) compute the resulting iterated integral.

$$\text{(a)} \int_{-1}^{1} \int_0^{\sqrt{1-x^2}} \frac{2}{1+x^2+y^2}\,dy\,dx \qquad \text{(b)} \int_1^2 \int_{\sqrt{4-x^2}}^{\sqrt{3}\,x} x\,dy\,dx$$

Solution Part (a): The inner limits of integration (on the inner Cartesian integral) are from $y = 0$ to $y = \sqrt{1-x^2}$. The first equation is for the x-axis and the second is for a semi-circle (square both sides to get $y^2 = 1 - x^2$, i.e., $x^2 + y^2 = 1$, which is a circle of radius 1 centered at the origin.) The outer limits of integration are from $x = -1$ to $x = 1$ and so we see that D is the region between the x-axis and the semi-circle $y = \sqrt{1-x^2}$). See the sketch in Figure 12.3.8. In polar coordinates the region D is bounded by the polar curves: $\theta = 0$, $\theta = \pi$, $r - 0$, $r - 1$. Thus,

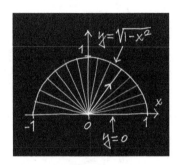

Figure 12.3.8: *The polar region in Example 12.3.3 (a).*

$$\int_{-1}^{1} \int_0^{\sqrt{1-x^2}} \frac{2}{1+x^2+y^2}\,dy\,dx \;=\; \int_0^\pi \int_0^1 \frac{2}{1+r^2}\cdot r\,dr\,d\theta = \int_0^\pi \int_0^1 \frac{2r}{1+r^2}\,dr\,d\theta$$

$$= \int_0^\pi \ln(1+r^2)\Big|_0^1 \, d\theta = \int_0^\pi \ln 2\,d\theta = \pi\ln 2$$

Solution Part (b): The inner limits of integration (on the inner Cartesian integral) are from $y = \sqrt{4-x^2}$ to $y = \sqrt{3}\,x$. The first equation is for a semi-circle (square both sides to get $y^2 = 4 - x^2$, i.e., $x^2 + y^2 = 4$, which is a circle of radius 2 centered at the origin.) The second equation $y = \sqrt{3}\,x$ is for a straight line through the origin with slope $\sqrt{3}$. As shown in Figure 12.3.9, this line intersects the semicircle at the point $(1, \sqrt{3})$. As the sketch indicates, the region D is below this line and above the semicircle. Also indicated are the vertical lines $x = 1$, $x = 2$, which come from the outer limits of integration. In polar coordinates the region D is bounded by the polar curves: $r = 2$ (the semicircle), $r = 2\sec\theta$ (the polar equation for the vertical line $x = 2$), and $\theta = 0$, $\theta = \pi/3$. Thus,

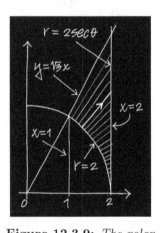

Figure 12.3.9: *The polar region in Example 12.3.3 (b).*

$$\int_1^2 \int_{\sqrt{4-x^2}}^{\sqrt{3}\,x} x\,dy\,dx \;=\; \int_0^{\pi/3} \int_2^{2\sec\theta} r\cos\theta \cdot r\,dr\,d\theta = \int_0^{\pi/3} \int_2^{2\sec\theta} r^2\cos\theta\,dr\,d\theta$$

$$= \int_0^{\pi/3} \left[\tfrac{1}{3}r^3\right]\Big|_2^{2\sec\theta} \cos\theta\,d\theta = \int_0^{\pi/3} \tfrac{1}{3}\left[8\sec^3\theta - 8\right]\cos\theta\,d\theta$$

$$= \tfrac{8}{3}\int_0^{\pi/3}\left[\sec^2\theta - \cos\theta\right]d\theta = \tfrac{8}{3}\left[\tan\theta - \sin\theta\right]\Big|_0^{\pi/3}$$

$$= \tfrac{8}{3}\left[\sqrt{3} - \tfrac{\sqrt{3}}{2}\right] = \tfrac{4}{3}\sqrt{3}$$

Volumes Via Double Integrals in Polar Coordinates

When using the double integral to find volumes of solids (as in Section 12.2) it is also often easier to do the iterated integrals in polar rather than Cartesian coordinates. Many simple solids, regions bounded by quadric surfaces (spheres, cones, paraboloids), cylinders, and planes, have volume integrals of this sort. The next example illustrates this

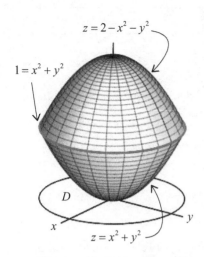

$z = 2 - x^2 - y^2$

$1 = x^2 + y^2$

D

x

y

$z = x^2 + y^2$

Figure 12.3.10: *The solid between two paraboloids.*

Example 12.3.4 (Two Paraboloids)

Problem: Find the volume of the solid enclosed between the paraboloids

$$z = x^2 + y^2 \quad \text{and} \quad z = 2 - x^2 - y^2$$

Solution: To set this up as a Type I solid (see Section 12.2), requires some ability at visualizing objects in 3-D. Figure 12.3.10 shows the two paraboloids intersecting in a curve that appears to be a horizontal circle (shown in red). Note: For clarity the parts of each paraboloid that extend beyond the curve of intersection are not shown.

An equation for the curve of intersection comes from the observation that a point (x, y, z) on this curve of intersection satisfies each equation and so

$$x^2 + y^2 = z = 2 - x^2 - y^2, \text{ i.e., } 2x^2 + 2y^2 = 2, \text{ which gives: } x^2 + y^2 = 1$$

This is a circle and projecting it onto the x-y plane gives a circle (shown in black) with the same equation. The region D for the double integral of this Type I solid consists of the points (x, y) inside, or on, this circle ($x^2 + y^2 \le 1$).

The polar coordinates (r, θ) for such points satisfy $0 \le r \le 1$ and $0 \le \theta \le 2\pi$. The surfaces that bound the top and bottom of the solid are the graphs of $f(x, y) = 2 - x^2 - y^2$ and $H(x, y) = x^2 + y^2$, respectively. So, the integrand of the volume integral is $f(x, y) - H(x, y) = 2 - x^2 - y^2 - (x^2 + y^2) = 2 - 2(x^2 + y^2)$. Thus, the volume is

$$
\begin{aligned}
V &= \iint_D \left[2 - 2(x^2 + y^2) \right] dA = \int_0^{2\pi} \int_0^1 \left[2 - 2r^2 \right] r \, dr d\theta \\
&= \int_0^{2\pi} \int_0^1 \left[2r - 2r^3 \right] dr d\theta = \int_0^{2\pi} \left[r^2 - \tfrac{1}{2}r^4 \right] \Big|_0^1 d\theta \\
&= \int_0^{2\pi} \frac{1}{2} \, d\theta = \frac{1}{2} \cdot 2\pi = \pi
\end{aligned}
$$

Example 12.3.5 (Two Paraboloids, Again)

Problem: Use an iterated integral in Cartesian coordinates to compute the volume of the solid enclosed between the paraboloids in the previous example.

Solution: To simplify the work as much as possible, we use symmetry. Namely, $V = 4V_0$, where V_0 is th portion of the solid in the 1st octant. Thus, we us a double integral over $D_0 = $ the portion of D in the 1st quadrant. This gives

$$
\begin{aligned}
V &= 4 \iint_{D_0} \left[2 - 2(x^2 + y^2) \right] dA = 4 \int_0^1 \int_0^{\sqrt{1-x^2}} \left[2 - 2(x^2 + y^2) \right] dy dx \\
&= 8 \int_0^1 \int_0^{\sqrt{1-x^2}} \left[(1 - x^2) - y^2 \right] dy dx = 8 \int_0^1 \left[(1 - x^2)y - \tfrac{1}{3}y^3 \right] \Big|_0^{(1-x^2)^{1/2}} dx \\
&= 8 \int_0^1 \left[(1 - x^2)(1 - x^2)^{1/2} - \tfrac{1}{3}(1 - x^2)^{3/2} \right] dx = \tfrac{16}{3} \int_0^1 (1 - x^2)^{3/2} \, dx \\
&= \tfrac{16}{3} \int_0^{\pi/2} \cos^4 \theta \, d\theta \quad \text{(got this from a trig substitution: } x = \sin \theta \text{)} \\
&= \left[\tfrac{4}{3} \cos^3 \theta \sin \theta + 2 \cos \theta \sin \theta + 2\theta \right] \Big|_0^{2\pi} = \pi
\end{aligned}
$$

Note: In the last line of the calculation we used a reduction formula (work not shown) to integrate $\cos^4 \theta$. Thus, the calculations in the previous example, using polar coordinates, are considerably shorter than those here.

Exercises: 12.3 (Double Integrals in Polar Coordinates)

Double Integrals over Polar Regions

In Exercises 1–36, compute the double integral $\iint_D f(x,y)\,dA$ over the given polar region D.

1. $\iint_D 4xy\,dA$, inside $r = \sin\theta$, 1st quadrant

2. $\iint_D 5xy^2\,dA$, inside $r = \sin\theta$, 1st quadrant

3. $\iint_D 4xy\,dA$, inside $r = 2\sin\theta$,
outside $r = \sin\theta$, 1st quadrant

4. $\iint_D 5x^2 y\,dA$, inside $r = 2\sin\theta$,
outside $r = \sin\theta$, 1st quadrant

5. $\iint_D (3y + 5x^2 y)\,dA$, inside $r = \cos\theta$, 1st quadrant

6. $\iint_D (3y + 6x^3 y)\,dA$, inside $r = \cos\theta$, 1st quadrant

7. $\iint_D 30x^2 y\,dA$, inside $r = 1 + \cos\theta$, quadrants 1 & 2

8. $\iint_D 30xy^2\,dA$, inside $r = 1 + \sin\theta$, quadrants 1 & 2

9. $\iint_D 3\sqrt{x^2 + y^2}\,dA$, inside $r = 1 + \cos\theta$, quadrant 1

10. $\iint_D 3\sqrt{x^2 + y^2}\,dA$, inside $r = 1 + \sin\theta$, quadrant 2

11. $\iint_D 12\sqrt{x^2 + y^2}\,dA$, below $r = \theta$, for θ in $[0, \pi]$,
above x-axis

12. $\iint_D 30(x^2 + y^2)^{3/2}\,dA$, below $r = \theta$, for θ in $[0, \pi]$,
above x-axis

13. $\iint_D \dfrac{y^2}{\sqrt{x^2 + y^2}}\,dA$, between $r = \theta$, for θ in $[0, \frac{\pi}{4}]$,
and $\theta = 0, \theta = \frac{\pi}{4}$

14. $\iint_D \dfrac{x^2}{\sqrt{x^2 + y^2}}\,dA$, between $r = \theta$, for θ in $[\frac{\pi}{4}, \frac{\pi}{2}]$
and $\theta = \frac{\pi}{4}, \theta = \frac{\pi}{2}$

15. $\iint_D 3x\,dA$, below $r = \theta$, for θ in $[0, \pi]$,
above x-axis

16. $\iint_D 3y\,dA$, below $r = \theta$, for θ in $[0, \pi]$,
above x-axis

17. $\iint_D \cos(\sqrt{x^2 + y^2})\,dA$, between $r = \theta$, for θ in
$[0, \frac{\pi}{2}]$ and $\theta = 0, \theta = \frac{\pi}{2}$

18. $\iint_D \sin(\sqrt{x^2 + y^2})\,dA$, between $r = \theta$, for θ in
$[0, \pi]$ and $\theta = 0, \theta = \pi$

19. $\iint_D e^{2\sqrt{x^2+y^2}}\,dA$, between $r = \theta$, for θ in $[0, 1]$,
and $\theta = 0, \theta = 1$

20. $\iint_D e^{3\sqrt{x^2+y^2}}\,dA$, between $r = \theta$, for θ in $[0, 1]$,
and $\theta = 0, \theta = 1$

21. $\iint_D 35(x^2 + y^2)^{3/2}\,dA$, between $r = \sqrt{\theta}$, for θ in
$[0, \pi]$, and $\theta = 0, \theta = \pi$

22. $\iint_D 63(x^2 + y^2)^{5/2}\,dA$, between $r = \sqrt{\theta}$, for θ in
$[0, \pi]$, and $\theta = 0, \theta = \pi$

23. $\iint_D \dfrac{2}{1 + x^2 + y^2}\,dA$, between $r = \sqrt{\theta}$, for θ in
$[0, \pi]$, and $\theta = 0, \theta = \pi$

24. $\iint_D \dfrac{2}{16 - x^2 - y^2}\,dA$, between $r = \sqrt{\theta}$, for θ in
$[0, \pi]$, and $\theta = 0, \theta = \pi$

25. $\iint_D 2\sin(x^2 + y^2)\,dA$, between $r = \sqrt{\theta}$, for θ in
$[0, \frac{\pi}{2}]$, and $\theta = 0, \theta = \frac{\pi}{2}$

26. $\iint_D 2\cos(x^2 + y^2)\,dA$, between $r = \sqrt{\theta}$, for θ in
$[0, \pi]$, and $\theta = 0, \theta = \pi$

27. $\iint_D 6(x^2 + y^2)^2\,dA$, between $r = \sqrt{\theta}$, $r = 2\sqrt{\theta}$,
for θ in $[0, \frac{\pi}{2}]$, and $\theta = \frac{\pi}{2}$

28. $\iint_D 8(x^2 + y^2)^3\,dA$, between $r = \sqrt{\theta}$, $r = 2\sqrt{\theta}$,
for θ in $[0, \frac{\pi}{2}]$, and $\theta = \frac{\pi}{2}$

29. $\iint_D 9\sqrt{x^2 + y^2}\,dA$, inside $r = \cos 3\theta$,
for θ in $[\frac{\pi}{2}, \frac{5\pi}{6}]$

30. $\iint_D 9\sqrt{x^2 + y^2}\,dA$, inside $r = \sin 3\theta$,
for θ in $[0, \frac{\pi}{3}]$

31. $\iint_D 15(x^2 + y^2)^{3/2}\,dA$, inside $r = \sin 3\theta$,
for θ in $[0, \frac{\pi}{3}]$

32. $\iint_D 15(x^2 + y^2)^{3/2}\,dA$, inside $r = \cos 3\theta$,
for θ in $[0, \frac{\pi}{3}]$

33. $\iint_D 16xy\,dA$, inside $r = \cos 2\theta$, 1st quadrant

34. $\iint_D 16xy\,dA$, inside $r = 3\cos 2\theta$, 1st quadrant

35. $\iint_D 16xy\,dA$, inside $r = \sin 2\theta$, 1st quadrant

36. $\iint_D 16xy\,dA$, inside $r = 3\sin 2\theta$, 1st quadrant

Converting Cartesian Integrals to Polar Integrals

In Exercises 37–44, compute the iterated integral by converting it from Cartesian to polar coordinates. Also sketch the region D of integration for the corresponding double integral.

37. $\displaystyle\int_0^1 \int_0^{\sqrt{1-x^2}} 15xy^2\,dy\,dx$

38. $\displaystyle\int_0^1 \int_0^{\sqrt{1-x^2}} 15x^2 y\,dy\,dx$

39. $\displaystyle\int_{-2}^2 \int_0^{\sqrt{4-x^2}} 14x^2 y^3\,dy\,dx$

40. $\displaystyle\int_0^2 \int_0^{\sqrt{4-x^2}} 14x^3 y^2\,dy\,dx$

41. $\displaystyle\int_0^2 \int_{-\sqrt{2y-y^2}}^{\sqrt{2y-y^2}} x^3 y\,dx\,dy$

42. $\displaystyle\int_0^2 \int_{-\sqrt{2y-y^2}}^{\sqrt{2y-y^2}} x^5 y\,dx\,dy$

43. $\displaystyle\int_{\sqrt{2}}^2 \int_{\sqrt{4-x^2}}^{x} 3x\,dy\,dx$ **44.** $\displaystyle\int_2^4 \int_{\sqrt{6-x^2}}^{\sqrt{3}x} 3x\,dy\,dx$

Volumes of Solids

In Exercises 45-60, use double integrals in polar coordinates to find the volume of the specified solid.

45. The sphere $x^2 + y^2 + z^2 = 25$

46. The sphere $x^2 + y^2 + z^2 = R^2$

47. Inside the cylinder $x^2 + y^2 = 4$ and outside the cone $z = \sqrt{x^2 + y^2}$

48. Inside the cylinder $x^2 + y^2 = R^2$ and outside the cone $z = \sqrt{x^2 + y^2}$

49. Inside the cylinder $x^2 + y^2 = 4$, below the paraboloid $z = x^2 + y^2$, and above $z = 0$

50. Inside the cylinder $x^2 + y^2 = R^2$, below the paraboloid $z = x^2 + y^2$, and above $z = 0$

51. Between the paraboloids $z = x^2 + y^2$ and $z = 18 - x^2 - y^2$

52. Between the paraboloids $z = x^2 + y^2$ and $z = 2R^2 - x^2 - y^2$

53. Inside the cylinder $x^2 + y^2 = 9$ and inside the hemisphere $z = \sqrt{25 - x^2 - y^2}$

54. Inside the cylinder $x^2 + y^2 = a^2$ and inside the hemisphere $z = \sqrt{R^2 - x^2 - y^2}$

55. Outside the cylinder $x^2 + y^2 = 9$ and inside the hemisphere $z = \sqrt{25 - x^2 - y^2}$

56. Outside the cylinder $x^2 + y^2 = a^2$ and inside the hemisphere $z = \sqrt{R^2 - x^2 - y^2}$

57. Above the cone $z = \sqrt{x^2 + y^2}$ and below the hemisphere $z = \sqrt{4 - x^2 - y^2}$

58. Above the cone $z = a\sqrt{x^2 + y^2}$ and below the hemisphere $z = \sqrt{R^2 - x^2 - y^2}$

Calculus *Concepts & Computation*

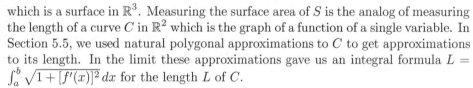

12.4 Applications of Double Integrals

In this section we discuss two applications of the double integral $\iint_D f(x,y)\,dA$. These are (1) surface area and (2) moments and center of mass.

Surface Area

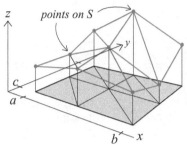

Figure 12.4.1: *A triangular complex approximating the surface $z = f(x,y)$.*

Suppose $z = f(x,y)$ is a function of two variables defined on a rectangle $R = [a,b] \times [c,d]$. Recall that the graph of f is the set of points

$$S = \{\,(x,y,f(x,y)) \mid (x,y) \in R\,\},$$

which is a surface in $\mathbb{R}^3$. Measuring the surface area of S is the analog of measuring the length of a curve C in $\mathbb{R}^2$ which is the graph of a function of a single variable. In Section 5.5, we used natural polygonal approximations to C to get approximations to its length. In the limit these approximations gave us an integral formula $L = \int_a^b \sqrt{1 + [f'(x)]^2}\,dx$ for the length L of C.

Likewise, for the surface S, we construct approximations, which in the limit will give an integral formula, involving double integrals, for the area of S. This formula is a direct extension of the integral formula for length.

We use a scheme that consists of approximating S by a collection of contiguous triangles in space. This collection is called *a triangular complex*. To construct this complex, we first divide the rectangle R into a mesh of contiguous triangles, called a *triangulation* of R. There are many ways to do this and Figure 12.4.1 shows one possible way that consists of first dividing the rectangle R into subrectangles (in this case 4 subrectangles) and then dividing each subrectangle into two triangles using one of its diagonals (in this case giving 8 triangles in the triangulation of R).

Corresponding to any triangle in this triangulation of R, we get a triangle in space that has its three vertices on the surface S, and hence we get a triangular complex that approximates S as indicated in Figure 12.4.1. The triangles in the complex are shown in red.

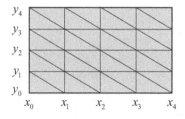

Figure 12.4.2: *A triangular mesh subdividing R.*

The mathematical notation for such a triangular complex is as follows. First, $R = [a,b] \times [c,d]$ is partitioned into subrectangles by using the standard partitions of $[a,b]$ and $[c,d]$ into N subintervals and M subintervals, respectively. Figure 12.4.2 shows a triangulation for the case $N = M = 4$. We will use prior indexing schemes to denote the vertices of the subrectangles and from this we get the indexing of the vertices of the corresponding triangles. The vertices of the subrectangles in the partition of R are $P_{i,j} = (x_i, y_j)$, where $x_i = a + i\Delta x$ and $y_j = c + j\Delta y$, for $i = 0, \ldots, N$, $j = 0, \ldots, M$. Here $\Delta x = (b-a)/N$ and $\Delta y = (d-c)/M$. To these there are corresponding points on the surfaces S:

$$Q_{i,j} = (\,x_i, y_j, f(x_i, y_j)\,).$$

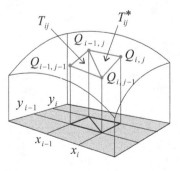

Figure 12.4.3: *Two triangles T_{ij}, T_{ij}^* in the complex approximating $z = f(x,y)$.*

The i-jth subrectangle R_{ij} is (by definition) the rectangle with vertices $P_{i-1,j-1}$, $P_{i,j-1}$, $P_{i,j}$, $P_{i-1,j}$. Corresponding to these vertices are four points $Q_{i-1,j-1}$, $Q_{i,j-1}$, $Q_{i,j}$, $Q_{i-1,j}$ on the surface S. See Figure 12.4.3. From these points we get two triangles T_{ij}, T_{ij}^* which approximate the part of the surface S that lies over the rectangle R_{ij}. The points $Q_{i-1,j-1}$, $Q_{i,j-1}$, $Q_{i-1,j}$ are the vertices of the triangle T_{ij} and $Q_{i-1,j}$, $Q_{i,j}$, $Q_{i,j-1}$ are the vertices of triangle T_{ij}^*, as shown in Figure 12.4.3.

We can now compute the areas of T_{ij} and T_{ij}^* using the vector methods from Chapter 10. For triangle T_{ij}, we let $\mathbf{u}$ and $\mathbf{v}$ be the two vectors with initial point at vertex $Q_{i-1,j-1}$ an terminal points at $Q_{i,j-1}$ and $Q_{i-1,j}$, respectively. Then

$$\mathbf{u} = Q_{i-1,j-1}Q_{i,j-i} = \langle\, x_i - x_{i-1}, 0, f(x_i, y_{j-1}) - f(x_{i-1}, y_{j-1})\,\rangle$$

$$= \; \langle \, \Delta x, \, 0, \, f(x_i, y_{j-1}) - f(x_{i-1}, y_{j-1}) \, \rangle$$
$$\mathbf{v} = Q_{i-1,j-1}Q_{i-1,j} \; = \; \langle \, 0, \, y_j - y_{j-1}, \, f(x_{i-1}, y_j) - f(x_{i-1}, y_{j-1}) \, \rangle$$
$$= \; \langle \, 0, \, \Delta y, \, f(x_{i-1}, y_j) - f(x_{i-1}, y_{j-1}) \, \rangle$$

So,

$$\mathbf{u} \times \mathbf{v} \; = \; \langle \, -[f(x_i, y_{j-1}) - f(x_{i-1}, y_{j-1})]\Delta y, \, -[f(x_{i-1}, y_j) - f(x_{i-1}, y_{j-1})]\Delta x, \, \Delta x \Delta y \, \rangle$$
$$= \; \langle \, -\frac{f(x_i, y_{j-1}) - f(x_{i-1}, y_{j-1})}{\Delta x}, \, -\frac{f(x_{i-1}, y_j) - f(x_{i-1}, y_{j-1})}{\Delta y}, \, 1 \rangle \Delta x \Delta y$$

Thus, the area a_{ij} of T_{ij} is $a_{ij} = \frac{1}{2}\| \, \mathbf{u} \times \mathbf{v} \, \|$, which is

$$a_{ij} = \frac{1}{2}\sqrt{ 1 + \left[\frac{f(x_i, y_{j-1}) - f(x_{i-1}, y_{j-1})}{\Delta x}\right]^2 + \left[\frac{f(x_i, y_j) - f(x_i, y_{j-1})}{\Delta y}\right]^2 } \, \Delta x \, \Delta y$$

As an exercise you can derive a similar formula for the area a_{ij}^* of the triangle T_{ij}^*. Then the total area of the triangular complex is given by the double sum:

$$A_{N,M} = \sum_{i=1}^{N} \sum_{j=1}^{M} (a_{ij} + a_{ij}^*) \qquad (12.4.1)$$

The following example indicates how these approximations work.

Example 12.4.1 (Approximating Surfaces and Their Areas)

Problem: Consider the surface S which is the graph of

$$f(x, y) = \tfrac{3}{4}y + \tfrac{5}{4}(\ln x - \tfrac{1}{8}x^2)$$

on the rectangle $R = [1, 4] \times [0, 2]$. Use the special purpose program `triangleapprox` to (1) plot the triangular complex approximation to S and (2) compute the approximate area $A_{N,M}$, for $N = 10$ and $M = 10$.

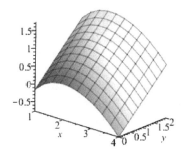

Figure 12.4.4: *A plot of* $f(x, y) = \tfrac{3}{4}y + \tfrac{5}{4}(\ln x - \tfrac{1}{8}x^2)$.

Solution: A plot of the graph of f is shown in Figure 12.4.4. The command

$$\texttt{triangleapprox(f,a,b,c,d,N,M);}$$

will plot the triangular complex that approximates the graph of f using $2NM$ triangles based on the scheme discussed above. (Be careful to not take N or M too large.) The output of the command is a plot of the triangular complex along with the (exact) area of the complex as given by Formula (12.4.1). The following code shows how to use this command:

```
> f:=(x,y)->3*y/4+5*(ln(x)-x^2/8)/4;
```
$$f := x \mapsto \frac{3}{4}y + \frac{5}{4}(\ln x - \frac{1}{8}x^2)$$
```
> triangleapprox(f,1,4,0,2,10,10);
```
the area of the triangular approximation is, 8.146748052

Figure 12.4.5, exhibits the resulting triangular complex approximation containing 200 triangles.

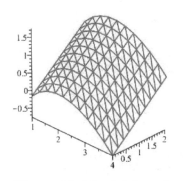

Figure 12.4.5: *A triangular approximation to the plot of* $f(x, y) = \tfrac{3}{4}y + \tfrac{5}{4}(\ln x - \tfrac{1}{8}x^2)$.

NOTE 1: You should understand that the above scheme for plotting approximations to surfaces using triangular complexes is how most computer plotting schemes are designed. That is how Maple rendered the plot shown in Figure 12.4.4, except that (1) it does not put in the diagonal lines (so that the pair T_{ij}, T_{ij}^* appears to be a parallelogram) and (2) it colors the planar face of each triangle.

NOTE 2: Each of the surfaces in Figure 12.4.4 and 12.4.5 appears to be smoothly curved, rather than consisting of a bunch of flat, contiguous triangles. So, you might expect that the approximation $A_{10,10} = 8.146748052$ would be pretty close to the actual area A of the surface. We will see that this is the case after we first discuss the integral formula for A.

This formula results from taking the double limit of the expression in Formula (12.4.1). This gives the *exact* surface area as a double integral:

$$A = \lim_{N \to \infty} \lim_{M \to \infty} A_{N,M}(f) = \lim_{N \to \infty} \lim_{M \to \infty} \sum_{i=1}^{N} \sum_{j=1}^{M} (a_{ij} + a_{ij}^{*})$$

$$= \iint_{R} \sqrt{1 + [f_x(x,y)]^2 + [f_y(x,y)]^2} \, dA \qquad (12.4.2)$$

The surface area integral Formula (12.4.2) extends to the case where the rectangle R is replaced by a general region D (usually of Type I or Type II). So, in summary we have the following theorem:

THEOREM 12.4.1 (Areas of Smooth Surfaces)

Suppose f and its first order partials are continuous on a region D. Then the surface:
$z = f(x,y)$ *has area given by the double integral*

$$A = \iint_{D} \sqrt{1 + [f_x(x,y)]^2 + [f_y(x,y)]^2} \, dA \qquad (12.4.2)$$

Now that we have an integral formula for the exact surface area, let's apply it to the surface we studied with approximate methods in the previous example.

Example 12.4.2 (Computing Surface Area)

Problem: Consider the surface S which is the graph of

$$f(x,y) = \tfrac{3}{4}y + \tfrac{5}{4}(\ln x - \tfrac{1}{8}x^2)$$

on the rectangle $R = [1,4] \times [0,2]$. Find its exact surface area and compare it with the approximate area computed in Example 12.4.1 using a triangular complex.

Solution: The partial derivatives are

$$f_x = \frac{5}{4}\left(\frac{1}{x} - \frac{x}{4} \right), \qquad f_y = \frac{3}{4}$$

and so

$$1 + [f_x]^2 + [f_y]^2 = 1 + \frac{25}{16}\left(\frac{1}{x} - \frac{x}{4} \right)^2 + \frac{9}{16} = \frac{25}{16} + \frac{25}{16}\left(\frac{1}{x} - \frac{x}{4} \right)^2$$

$$= \frac{25}{16}\left[1 + \left(\frac{1}{x} - \frac{x}{4} \right)^2 \right] = \frac{25}{16}\left[1 + \left(\frac{1}{x^2} - \frac{1}{2} + \frac{x^2}{16} \right) \right]$$

$$= \frac{25}{16}\left[\left(\frac{1}{x^2} + \frac{1}{2} + \frac{x^2}{16} \right) \right] = \frac{25}{16}\left(\frac{1}{x} + \frac{x}{4} \right)^2$$

Thus,

$$\sqrt{1 + [f_x]^2 + f_y]^2} = \sqrt{\frac{25}{16}\left(\frac{1}{x} + \frac{x}{4} \right)^2} = \frac{5}{4}\left(\frac{1}{x} + \frac{x}{4} \right)$$

So the surface area is

$$A = \iint_{R} \sqrt{1 + [f_x]^2 + f_y]^2} \, dA = \int_{0}^{2} \int_{1}^{4} \tfrac{5}{4}\left(\frac{1}{x} + \frac{x}{4} \right) dx \, dy$$

$$= \int_{0}^{2} \tfrac{5}{4}\left(\ln x + \tfrac{1}{8}x^2 \right)\Big|_{1}^{4} dy = \int_{0}^{2} \tfrac{5}{4}(\ln 4 + 2 - \tfrac{1}{8}) \, dy$$

$$= 2 \cdot \tfrac{5}{4}(\ln 4 + 2 - \tfrac{1}{8}) = \tfrac{5}{2}\ln 4 + \tfrac{75}{16} \approx 8.153235903$$

Thus, the exact surface area is $\frac{5}{2}\ln 4 + \frac{75}{16} \approx 8.153235903$. In Example 12.4.1 we found an approximate area of 8.146748052 using a triangular complex approximation with 200 triangles. So, that was a fairly good approximation.

The double integral in Formula (11.4.2) for surface area can be difficult to compute for many surfaces, but changing it to a double integral in polar coordinates will work for some surfaces.

Example 12.4.3 (Paraboloids and Spheres)

Problem: Compute the surface area of

    (a) the portion of the paraboloid $z = x^2 + y^2$ which is below the plane $z = 1$.

    (b) the portion of the sphere $x^2 + y^2 + z^2 = 1$ which is above the x-y plane.

Solution Part (a): Here $f(x, y) = x^2 + y^2$ and the intersection of the graph of f with the plane $z = 1$ is a circle, which projected on the x-y plane has equation $x^2 + y^2 = 1$. See Figure 12.4.6. Thus, the region D is a disk of radius 1.

The partials of f are simply $f_x = 2x$ and $f_y = 2y$. So

$$1 + [f_x]^2 + [f_y]^2 = 1 + 4x^2 + 4y^2$$

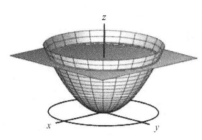

Figure 12.4.6: *The paraboloid $z = x^2 + y^2$ cut by the the plane $z = 1$.*

and since, in polar coordinates, $1 + 4x^2 + 4y^2 = 1 + 4(x^2 + y^2) = 1 + 4r^2$, we use polar coordinates to do the area integral:

$$
\begin{aligned}
A &= \iint_D \sqrt{1 + 4x^2 + 4y^2}\, dA = \iint_D \sqrt{1 + 4(x^2 + y^2)}\, dA \\
&= \int_0^{2\pi}\int_0^1 \sqrt{1 + 4r^2}\, r\, dr d\theta = \int_0^{2\pi} \left[\tfrac{1}{12}(1 + 4r^2)^{3/2} \right]\Big|_0^1 d\theta \\
&= \int_0^{2\pi} \tfrac{1}{12}(5^{3/2} - 1)\, d\theta = \tfrac{1}{12}(5^{3/2} - 1)\cdot 2\pi = \frac{(5^{3/2} - 1)\pi}{6}
\end{aligned}
$$

Solution Part (b): The portion of the sphere $x^2 + y^2 + z^2 = 1$ which is above the x-y plane is, of course, a hemisphere and is the graph of the function

$$z = f(x, y) = \sqrt{1 - x^2 - y^2}, \quad \text{for } (x, y) \text{ in the disk } D\colon x^2 + y^2 \le 1$$

See Figure 12.4.7. The partials of f are

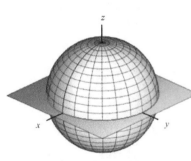

Figure 12.4.7: *The sphere $x^2 + y^2 + z^2 = 1$ cut by the the plane $z = 0$.*

$$f_x = \frac{-x}{\sqrt{1 - x^2 - y^2}}, \qquad f_y = \frac{-y}{\sqrt{1 - x^2 - y^2}}$$

and so

$$
\begin{aligned}
1 + [f_x]^2 + [f_y]^2 &= 1 + \frac{x^2}{1 - x^2 - y^2} + \frac{y^2}{1 - x^2 - y^2} = 1 + \frac{x^2 + y^2}{1 - x^2 - y^2} \\
&= \frac{1}{1 - x^2 - y^2}
\end{aligned}
$$

Again, since in polar coordinates: $1 - x^2 - y^2 = 1 - (x^2 + y^2) = 1 - r^2$, we use polar coordinates to do the area integral:

$$
\begin{aligned}
A &= \iint_D \frac{1}{\sqrt{1 - x^2 - y^2}}\, dA = \iint_D \frac{1}{\sqrt{1 - (x^2 + y^2)}}\, dA \\
&= \int_0^{2\pi}\int_0^1 \frac{1}{\sqrt{1 - r^2}}\, r\, dr d\theta = \int_0^{2\pi} \left[-\sqrt{1 - r^2} \right]\Big|_0^1 d\theta = \int_0^{2\pi} 1\, d\theta = 2\pi
\end{aligned}
$$

By symmetry, the area of the whole sphere (of radius 1) is twice this, i.e., $2\cdot 2\pi = 4\pi$. In general the surface area of a sphere of radius a is $4\pi a^2$. (See the Exercises.)

Often, the double integral in Formula (12.4.2) for surface area either requires techniques of integration from Chapter 6 or (in a great many cases) cannot be computed at all (in closed form). In the latter circumstance we can use numerical techniques, or better yet, use `triangleapprox`. The next example illustrates these things,

Example 12.4.4 (Sun Screens and Paraboloids)

Problem: Compute the surface area of the graph of

(a) $f(x,y) = (e^x - \frac{1}{4}e^{-x})y$ on $R = [-2,1] \times [-1,1]$.

(b) $f(x,y) = x^2 + y^2$ on $R = [-1,1] \times [-1,1]$ (a paraboloid).

Solution Part (a): The graph of this function on the rectangle R is shown in Figure 12.4.8. and, as you can see, could serve as an artistic sun screen to shade a downtown plaza. So, you might want to know how many gallons of paint it would take to paint it (both sides) assuming each unit represents 20 feet (so R is 60 ft by 40 ft).

The partials of f are easy to calculate:

$$f_x = (e^x + \tfrac{1}{4}e^{-x})y, \qquad f_y = (e^x - \tfrac{1}{4}e^{-x})$$

and so

$$\begin{aligned}
1 + [f_x]^2 + [f_y]^2 &= 1 + (e^x + \tfrac{1}{4}e^{-x})^2 y^2 + (e^x - \tfrac{1}{4}e^{-x})^2 \\
&= 1 + (e^x - \tfrac{1}{4}e^{-x})^2 + (e^x + \tfrac{1}{4}e^{-x})^2 y^2 \\
&= 1 + e^{2x} - \tfrac{1}{2} + \tfrac{1}{16}e^{-2x} + (e^x + \tfrac{1}{4}e^{-x})^2 y^2 \\
&= e^{2x} + \tfrac{1}{2} + \tfrac{1}{16}e^{-2x} + (e^x + \tfrac{1}{4}e^{-x})^2 y^2 \\
&= (e^x + \tfrac{1}{4}e^{-x})^2 + (e^x + \tfrac{1}{4}e^{-x})^2 y^2 \\
&= (e^x + \tfrac{1}{4}e^{-x})^2 (1 + y^2)
\end{aligned}$$

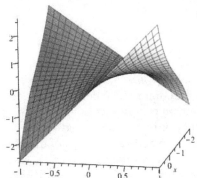

Figure 12.4.8: *The graph of* $f(x,y) = (e^x - \frac{1}{4}e^{-x})y$ *on the rectangle* $R = [-2,1] \times [-1,1]$.

Thus, the surface area integral is

$$\begin{aligned}
A &= \iint_D (e^x + \tfrac{1}{4}e^{-x})\sqrt{1+y^2}\, dA = \int_{-2}^1 \int_{-1}^1 (e^x + \tfrac{1}{4}e^{-x})\sqrt{1+y^2}\, dy\, dx \\
&= \int_{-2}^1 (e^x + \tfrac{1}{4}e^{-x})\, dx \cdot \int_{-1}^1 \sqrt{1+y^2}\, dy \\
&= (e^x - \tfrac{1}{4}e^{-x})\Big|_{-2}^1 \cdot \tfrac{1}{2}\left[y\sqrt{1+y^2} + \ln|\sqrt{1+y^2} + y|\right]\Big|_{-1}^1 \\
&= (e - \tfrac{1}{4}e^{-1} - e^{-2} + \tfrac{1}{4}e^2) \cdot \tfrac{1}{2}\left[\sqrt{2} + \ln(\sqrt{2}+1) - (-\sqrt{2} + \ln(\sqrt{2}-1))\right] \\
&= (e - \tfrac{1}{4}e^{-1} - e^{-2} + \tfrac{1}{4}e^2) \cdot \left[\sqrt{2} + \tfrac{1}{2}\ln(3 + 2\sqrt{2})\right] \approx 9.958809623
\end{aligned}$$

NOTE 1: We used Property (12.1.10) to split the iterated integral in line 1 above into the product of the two integrals in line 2. See Note 3 at the end of Section 12.1.

NOTE 2: We used the trig substitution $y = \tan\theta$ and the reduction formula for powers of the secant to compute

$$\int \sqrt{1+y^2}\, dy = \tfrac{1}{2}\left[y\sqrt{1+y^2} + \ln|\sqrt{1+y^2} + y|\right] \qquad (12.4.3)$$

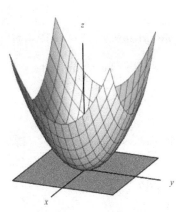

Figure 12.2.9: *The graph of* $f(x,y) = x^2 + y^2$ *on the rectangle* $R = [-1,1] \times [-1,1]$.

NOTE 3: The answer represents an area of approximately $9.958809623(20)(20) = 3983.523849$ sq.ft. Since many paints cover 400 square feet per gallon, we will need about 10 gallons to paint one side of the sun screen (20 gallons for both sides).

Solution Part (b): The graph of this function on the rectangle R is shown in Figure 12.4.9. Even though this function is the same as that in Part (a) of Example 12.4.3, here we are looking at the part of its graph that lies over the rectangle R. For this reason, we cannot switch to polar coordinates and are left with

$$A = \iint_D \sqrt{1 + 4x^2 + 4y^2}\, dA = \int_{-1}^1 \int_{-1}^1 \sqrt{1 + 4x^2 + 4y^2}\, dx\, dy$$

In Cartesian coordinates the iterated integrals are impossible to calculate, so we use `triangleapprox`.

```
> f:=(x,y)->x^2+y^2;
```
$$f := x \mapsto x^2 + y^2$$
```
> triangleapprox(f,-1,1,-1,1,10,10);
```
the area of the triangular approximation is, 7.424775184
```
> triangleapprox(f,-1,1,-1,1,20,20);
```
the area of the triangular approximation is, 7.440890510

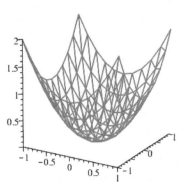

Figure 12.4.10: *A triangular complex approximation to $f(x,y) = x^2 + y^2$ with 200 triangles.*

Figures 12.4.10 and 12.4.11 show the resulting approximating triangular complexes with 200 and 800 triangles, respectively. The two values $A_{10,10} = 7.424775184$ and $A_{20,20} = 7.440890510$ differ by very little and so you would guess that the actual area would be 7.4 something.

Center of Mass for a Plane Lamina

Another standard application of double integrals of functions of two variables involves the notion of the center of mass of a planar lamina, which, by definition, is a region D in the plane $\mathbb{R}^2$, together with a density function ρ. The density function $z = \rho(x,y)$ is a function of two variables whose domain contains D.

We discussed a special case of this application back in Section 5.8 as an application of single integrals. This, of course, was before we had the concept of double integrals. Here we look at the general case, which requires double integrals, and also show how the special case in Section 5.8 arises from double integrals. If you have not done so already, you should read Section 5.8 as an introduction to what we do here.

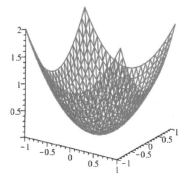

Figure 12.4.11: *A triangular complex approximation to $f(x,y) = x^2 + y^2$ with 800 triangles.*

For simplicity, we will limit the discussion to the case where D is a Type I region. Dealing with Type II regions and combinations of Types I and II is similar.

The lamina D, ρ models the situation where there is a very thin solid, such as sheet metal or plywood, cut in the shape of the planar region D and the density function ρ does not depend on z. Then $\rho(x,y)$ gives the mass per unit area at a point (x,y) in D and $dm = \rho(x,y)\, dA$ gives the infinitesimal element of mass of dA. See Figure12.4.12. Thus, the total mass m of the lamina is defined by the integral of these $m = \iint_D dm$. Specifically:

Total Mass: $\quad m = \iint_D \rho(x,y)\, dA = \int_a^b \int_{y=g(x)}^{y=h(x)} \rho(x,y)\, dy\, dx \qquad (12.4.4)$

The moments of the lamina about a vertical line $x = c$ and horizontal line $y = d$ are given by

Moments:

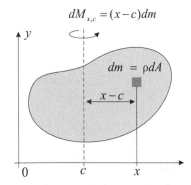

$dM_{x,c} = (x-c)dm$

$dm = \rho dA$

$x - c$

Figure 12.4.12: *A lamina composed of elements dm of mass which create moments $dM_{x,c}$ about the line $x = c$*

$$M_{x,c} = \iint_D \rho(x,y)(x-c)\, dA = \int_a^b \int_{y=g(x)}^{y=h(x)} \rho(x,y)(x-c)\, dy\, dx \qquad (12.4.5)$$

$$M_{y,d} = \iint_D \rho(x,y)(y-d)\, dA = \int_a^b \int_{y=g(x)}^{y=h(x)} \rho(x,y)(y-d)\, dy\, dx \qquad (12.4.6)$$

The numbers $M_{x,c}, M_{y,d}$ give the tendencies of the lamina to turn about the respective lines. The choice for c and d which makes these moments zero defines the coordinates (x^*, y^*) of the center of mass of the lamina. Solving the two equations $M_{x,x^*} = 0$, $M_{y,y^*} = 0$ gives the following formulas.

Center of Mass - 2d Laminas	
General	**Constant Density**

$$x^* = \frac{M_{x,0}}{m} = \frac{\iint_D \rho x\, dA}{\iint_D \rho\, dA} \qquad = \frac{\iint_D x\, dA}{A} \qquad (12.4.7)$$

when ρ is constant

$$y^* = \frac{M_{y,0}}{m} = \frac{\iint_D \rho y\, dA}{\iint_D \rho\, dA} \qquad = \frac{\iint_D y\, dA}{A} \qquad (12.4.8)$$

Table 12.4.1: *Coordinates of the center of mass of a plane lamina.*

This table is essentially the same one used in Section 5.8, except now it has the double integral symbol $\iint$.

Example 12.4.5 (Center of Mass)

Problem: Find the center of mass for each of the following laminas.

(a) $\rho(x,y) = xy$, $\quad D$: bounded by $y = x^2$, $y = 0$, $x = 1$.

(b) $\rho(x,y) = 6\cos x$, $\quad D$: bounded by $y = \sin x$, $y = 0$, $x = \frac{\pi}{2}$.

Solution Part (a): First compute the total mass

$$m = \int_0^1 \int_{y=0}^{y=x^2} xy\, dy dx = \int_0^1 \left[\tfrac{1}{2}xy^2\right]\Big|_{y=0}^{y=x^2} dx = \int_0^1 \tfrac{1}{2}x^5\, dx = \tfrac{1}{12}x^6\Big|_0^1 = \tfrac{1}{12}$$

Then calculate the two moments

$$M_{x,0} = \int_0^1 \int_{y=0}^{y=x^2} x(xy)\, dy dx = \int_0^1 \left[\tfrac{1}{2}x^2 y^2\right]\Big|_{y=0}^{y=x^2} dx = \int_0^1 \tfrac{1}{2}x^6\, dx = \tfrac{1}{14}x^7\Big|_0^1$$

$$= \tfrac{1}{14}$$

$$M_{y,0} = \int_0^1 \int_{y=0}^{y=x^2} y(xy)\, dy dx = \int_0^1 \left[\tfrac{1}{3}xy^3\right]\Big|_{y=0}^{y=x^2} dx = \int_0^1 \tfrac{1}{3}x^7\, dx = \tfrac{1}{24}x^8\Big|_0^1$$

$$= \tfrac{1}{24}$$

Thus, the coordinates of the center of mass are

$$x^* = \frac{M_{x,0}}{m} = \frac{\frac{1}{14}}{\frac{1}{12}} = \frac{12}{14} = \frac{6}{7}, \qquad y^* = \frac{M_{y,0}}{m} = \frac{\frac{1}{24}}{\frac{1}{12}} = \frac{12}{24} = \frac{1}{2}$$

Solution Part (b): First compute the total mass

$$m = \int_0^{\pi/2} \int_{y=0}^{y=\sin x} 6\cos x\, dy dx = \int_0^{\pi/2} (6y\cos x)\Big|_{y=0}^{y=\sin x} dx$$

$$= \int_0^{\pi/2} 6\sin x\cos x\, dx = (3\sin^2 x)\Big|_0^{\pi/2} = 3$$

Then calculate the two moments

$$M_{x,0} = \int_0^{\pi/2} \int_{y=0}^{y=\sin x} 6x\cos x\, dy dx = \int_0^{\pi/2} (6xy\cos x)\Big|_{y=0}^{y=\sin x} dx$$

$$= \int_0^{\pi/2} 6x \sin x \cos x \, dx = \int_0^{\pi/2} 3x \sin 2x \, dx = \left[-\tfrac{3}{2} x \cos 2x + \tfrac{3}{2} \int \cos 2x \, dx \right] \Big|_0^{\pi/2}$$

$$= \left[-\tfrac{3}{2} x \cos 2x + \tfrac{3}{4} \sin 2x \, dx \right] \Big|_0^{\pi/2} = \tfrac{3\pi}{4}$$

$$M_{y,0} = \int_0^{\pi/2} \int_{y=0}^{y=\sin x} 6y \cos x \, dy dx = \int_0^{\pi/2} (3y^2 \cos x) \Big|_{y=0}^{y=\sin x} dx$$

$$= \int_0^{\pi/2} (3 \sin^2 x \cos x) \, dx = \sin^3 x \Big|_0^{\pi/2} = 1$$

In the calculation of m and $M_{y,0}$ above we used the substitution: $u = \sin x$, $du = \cos x \, dx$. Also in the second line of the $M_{x,0}$ calculation, we used the trig identity $2 \sin x \cos x = \sin 2x$ and then integration by parts.

Thus, the coordinates of the center of mass are

$$x^* = \frac{M_{x,0}}{m} = \frac{\tfrac{3\pi}{4}}{3} = \frac{\pi}{4}, \qquad y^* = \frac{M_{y,0}}{m} = \frac{1}{3}$$

Centroids In the special case when the mass density function ρ is constant, the center of mass is called the the centroid of the region D. As shown in Table 12.4.1, the constant ρ cancels out in the ratios defining x^* and y^*. Additionally, the double integrals when computed as iterated integrals are reduced to single integrals after the first iteration. Thus, we get the formulas that we used in Section 5.8. Here is how those formulas arise from the double integrals in Formulas (12.4.7)–(12.4.8):

$$A = \iint_D 1 \, dA = \int_a^b \int_{g(x)}^{h(x)} 1 \, dy dx = \int_a^b [y] \Big|_{g(x)}^{h(x)} dx = \int_a^b [h(x) - g(x)] \, dx$$

$$M_{x,0} = \iint_D x \, dA = \int_a^b \int_{g(x)}^{h(x)} x \, dy dx = \int_a^b [xy] \Big|_{g(x)}^{h(x)} dx$$

$$= \int_a^b x[h(x) - g(x)] \, dx$$

$$M_{y,0} = \iint_D y \, dA = \int_a^b \int_{g(x)}^{h(x)} y \, dy dx = \int_a^b [\tfrac{1}{2} y^2] \Big|_{g(x)}^{h(x)} dx$$

$$= \int_a^b \tfrac{1}{2} \left([h(x)]^2 - [g(x)]^2 \right) \, dx$$

NOTE: There is no reason to remember the above formulas. Just use Formulas (12.4.7)–(12.4.8) as we did in Example 12.4.5.

Exercises: 12.4 (Applications of Double Integrals)

Surface Area

In Exercises 1–18, compute the surface area of the graph of $z = f(x, y)$ on the given region D.

1. $f(x, y) = \frac{3}{4}y + \frac{5}{4}(x^3 + \frac{1}{12}x^{-1})$, $D = [1, 2] \times [0, 1]$

2. $f(x, y) = \frac{3}{4}x + \frac{5}{4}(y^3 + \frac{1}{12}y^{-1})$, $D = [0, 1] \times [1, 2]$

3. $f(x, y) = \frac{15}{8}x + \frac{17}{8}(y^{1/2} - \frac{1}{3}y^{3/2})$, $D = [0, 2] \times [1, 4]$

4. $f(x, y) = \frac{4}{3}y + \frac{5}{3}(x^{1/3} - \frac{9}{20}y^{5/3})$, $D = [1, 8] \times [0, 2]$

5. $f(x, y) = \frac{4}{3}y + \frac{5}{3}(x^4 + \frac{1}{32}y^{-2})$, $D = [1, 2] \times [0, 3]$

6. $f(x, y) = \frac{3}{4}y + \frac{5}{4}(x^5 + \frac{1}{60}y^{-3})$, $D = [1, 2] \times [0, 4]$

7. $f(x, y) = \frac{15}{8}x + \frac{17}{8}(e^y + \frac{1}{4}e^{-y})$, $D = [0, 2] \times [0, \ln 2]$

8. $f(x, y) = \frac{3}{4}y + \frac{5}{x}(e^x + \frac{1}{4}e^{-x})$, $D = [0, \ln 2] \times [0, 2]$

9. $f(x, y) = \frac{5}{4}(x + \frac{1}{3}x^3 - \frac{1}{4}\tan^{-1}x) + \frac{3}{4}y$, $[0, 1] \times [0, 2]$

10. $f(x, y) = \frac{3}{4}x + \frac{5}{4}(y + \frac{1}{3}y^3 - \frac{1}{4}\tan^{-1}y)$, $[0, 2] \times [0, 1]$

11. $f(x, y) = (2e^{2x} + \frac{1}{8}e^{-2x})y$, $D = [-1, 1] \times [-1, 1]$

12. $f(x, y) = (3e^{3x} + \frac{1}{12}e^{-3x})y$, $D = [-1, 1] \times [-1, 1]$

13. $f(x, y) = \sqrt{x} + y$, $D : y = \sqrt{x}$, $y = 0$, $x = 1$

14. $f(x, y) = x^{1/3} + y$, $D : y = x$, $y = 0$, $x = 1$

15. $f(x, y) = x^3 + y$, $D : y = x^3$, $y = 0$, $x = 1$

16. $f(x, y) = x^2 + y$, $D : y = x$, $y = 0$, $x = 1$

17. $f(x, y) = \sqrt{2}\sqrt{xy}$, $D : y = 0$, $y = x^2$, $x = 1$

18. $f(x, y) = \sqrt{2}\sqrt{xy}$, $D : y = 0$, $y = x^3$, $x = 1$

Surface Area - Polar Coordinates

Compute the surface areas of the portions of the surfaces described below in Exercises 19–42. NOTE: Some of these surfaces are shown in Figures A–G below.

19. $z = 4 - x^2 - y^2$, above the plane $z = 0$

20. $z = 9 - x^2 - y^2$, above the plane $z = 0$

21. $z^2 = x^2 + y^2$, between the planes $z = 0$, $z = 2$

22. $z^2 = 4(x^2 + y^2)$, between the planes $z = 0$, $z = 2$

23. $x^2 + y^2 + z^2 = 4$, above the plane $z = 0$

24. $x^2 + y^2 + z^2 = 9$, above the plane $z = 0$

25. $x^2 + y^2 + z^2 = 25$, above the plane $z = 3$

26. $x^2 + y^2 + z^2 = 289$, above the plane $z = 8$

27. $x^2 + y^2 + z^2 = 25$, between the planes $z = 0$, $z = 3$

28. $x^2 + y^2 + z^2 = 289$, between the planes $z = 0$, $z = 8$

29. $z^2 = x^2 + y^2$, inside the cylinder $x^2 + y^2 = 2x$

30. $z^2 = x^2 + y^2$, inside the cylinder $x^2 + y^2 = 4x$

31. $x^2 + y^2 + z^2 = 4$, inside the cylinder $x^2 + y^2 = 2x$

32. $x^2 + y^2 + z^2 = 16$, inside the cylinder $x^2 + y^2 = 4y$

33. $z = x^2 - y^2$, inside the cylinder $x^2 + y^2 = 1$

34. $z = xy$, inside the cylinder $x^2 + y^2 = 1$

35. $z = a^2 - x^2 - y^2$, above the plane $z = 0$

36. $z = x^2 + y^2$, below the plane $z = a^2$

37. $z^2 = m^2(x^2 + y^2)$, between the planes $z = 0$, $z = a$

38. $z^2 = m^2(x^2 + y^2)$, between the planes $z = b$, $z = a$

39. $x^2 + y^2 + z^2 = a^2$, above the plane $z = 0$

40. $x^2 + y^2 + z^2 = a^2$, above the plane $z = -a$

41. $x^2 + y^2 + z^2 = a^2$, above the plane $z = b$, $0 < b < a$

42. $x^2 + y^2 + z^2 = a^2$, between the planes $z = 0$, $z = b < a$

Center of Mass

In Exercises 43–58, compute the total mass and center of mass of the given lamina.

43. $\rho(x, y) = xy^2$, $D : y = x^2$, $y = 0$, $x = 1$

44. $\rho(x, y) = x^2y$, $D : y = x^2$, $y = 0$, $x = 1$

45. $\rho(x, y) = x + y$, $D : y = x$, $y = 0$, $x = 1$

46. $\rho(x, y) = x + y$, $D : y = 2x$, $y = 0$, $x = 1$

47. $\rho(x, y) = x^2 + y^2$, $D : y = \sqrt{x}$, $y = 0$, $x = 1$

48. $\rho(x, y) = x^2 + y^2$, $D : y = x^{1/3}$, $y = 0$, $x = 1$

49. $\rho(x, y) = xy$, $D : y = \sqrt{1 - x^2}$, $y = 0, x \geq 0$

50. $\rho(x,y) = xy, \quad D: y = \sqrt{4-x^2}, y = 0, x \geq 0$

51. $\rho(x,y) = y, \quad D: y = e^{-x}, y = 0, x = 0, x = \ln 2$

52. $\rho(x,y) = y, \quad D: y = e^x, y = 0, x = 0, x = \ln 2$

53. $\rho(x,y) = x, \quad D: y = \ln x, y = 0, x = 1, x = e$

54. $\rho(x,y) = x, \quad D: y = \ln x, y = 0, x = 1, x = e^2$

55. $\rho(x,y) = 6\sin x, \quad D: y = \cos x, y = 0, x = 0, x = \frac{\pi}{2}$

56. $\rho(x,y) = 6\cos x, \quad D: y = \sin x, y = 0, x = 0, x = \frac{\pi}{2}$

57. $\rho(x,y) = \frac{1}{1+x^2}, \quad D: y = 1, y = x, x = 0, x = 1$

58. $\rho(x,y) = \frac{1}{1+x^2}, \quad D: y = 1, y = 2x, x = 0, x = 1$

59. (Matching) Which surfaces in Exercises 19-42 correspond to the following figures?

Figure A:

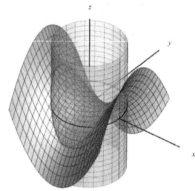

Figure B:

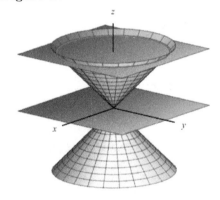

Figure C:

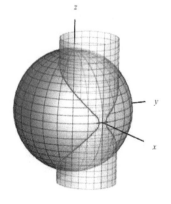

Figure D:

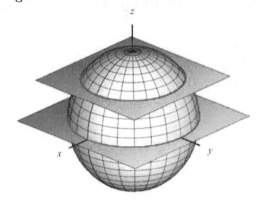

Figure E:

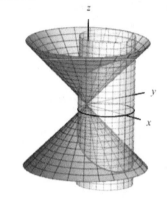

Figure F:

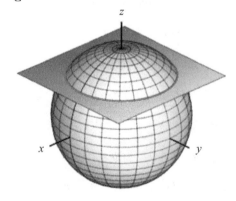

Figure G:

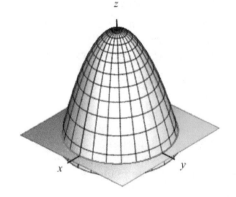

Calculus *Concepts & Computation*

12.5 Triple Integrals

In this section we look at the integration process for functions $w = f(x, y, z)$ of three variables. If E is a suitable solid in $\mathbb{R}^3$ which lies in the domain of f, then we will define $\iiint_E f(x, y, z)\, dV$, which is called the *triple integral of f over E*.

Since we cannot visualize the graph of f in four dimensions, it is hard to motivate what the number $\iiint_E f(x, y, z)\, dV$ means in geometrically as we did for double integrals. When f is a density function (mass per unit volume) then $\iiint_E f(x, y, z)\, dV$ will represent the total mass of the solid E. And, of course, for $f = 1$, we will define the volume of E as $V = \iiint_E 1\, dV$.

We can, however, extend integration to functions of three variables by following the partition and approximate strategy used for functions of one and two variables. Thus, for a solid E contained in the domain of f, a triple Riemann sum approximation can be constructed as follows. We first enclose the entire solid in a "box," $B = [a, b] \times [c, d] \times [p, q]$ (technically B is a rectangular parallelepiped), preferably one as small as possible. We can then subdivide B into a collection of sub-boxes

$$B_{ijk} = [x_{i-1}, x_i] \times [y_{j-i}, y_j] \times [z_{k-1}, z_k],$$

where $\{x_0, x_1, \ldots, x_n\}$, $\{y_0, y_1, \ldots, y_m\}$, $\{z_0, z_1, \ldots, z_\ell\}$ are partitions of the intervals $[a, b]$, $[c, d]$, $[p, q]$, respectively. The volume of B_{ijk} is $\Delta V_{ijk} = \Delta x_i \Delta y_j \Delta z_k$. See Figure 12.5.1.

Then for this initial subdivision of B into sub-boxes B_{ijk}, we produce an initial "grid" G_0 that covers E by retaining all those sub-boxes that overlap (intersect) E and eliminating those that do not. For example, Figure 12.5.2 illustrates such a grid.

From this we get an approximating Riemann sum for the triple integral of f over the solid E. It is taken to be a sum over all the sub-boxes in the grid:

$$\sum_{i,j,k \text{ with } B_{ijk} \in G_0} f(x_i^*, y_j^*, z_k^*)\, \Delta V_{ijk}$$

Here, x_i^*, y_j^*, and z_k^* are arbitrarily selected points in the intervals $[x_{i-1}, x_i]$, $[y_{j-1}, y_j]$, and $[z_{k-1}, z_k]$, respectively.

While G_0 is *not* a box, it will cover E and be a better approximation to E than the box B, at least if the initial subdivision of B is fine enough.

Having constructed the initial grid G_0, we produce a finer grid G_1 by dividing each box in G_0 into eight sub-boxes, testing each of these eight to see if it intersects E, retaining those that pass the test and tossing out those that do not. The new grid G_1 will still cover E and will be a better approximation to E. The corresponding Riemann sum over the boxes in G_1 should give a better approximation to $\iiint_E f(x, y, z)\, dV$ as well.

This scheme can be continued indefinitely, producing a sequence $\{G_n\}_{n=0}^{\infty}$ of grids which cover E and approximate it better and better as n increases. If we let E_n be the union of all the rectangles in G_n, then in theory $\lim_{n \to \infty} E_n = E$. Thus, E is realized as the limit of a decreasing sequence $E_0 \supset E_1 \supset E_2 \supset \cdots \supset E$ of sets that cover it. The corresponding triple integral is defined as the limit of the approximating sums:

Figure 12.5.1: *A subdivision of B into sub-boxes B_{ijk}.*

Figure 12.5.2: *Creating a grid to approximate the solid E.*

DEFINITION 12.5.1 (Triple Integrals Over General Solids)

Suppose E is a suitable solid in the domain of f. The triple integral of f over E is

$$\iiint_E f(x,y,x)\,dV = \lim_{n\to\infty} \sum_{i,j,k \text{ with } B_{ijk} \in G_n} \sum \sum f(x_i, y_j, z_k)\Delta V_{ijk} \qquad (12.5.1)$$

provided this limit exists

As before, with double integrals, the above is just the definition of the triple integral and is only useful for proving theorems and devising numerical approximating schemes. The main theorems that arise from it are Fubini type theorems, the simplest of which is for triple integrals over boxes. This is stated as follows.

THEOREM 12.5.1 (Fubini's Theorem for Rectangles)

Suppose f is continuous on a box $B = [a,b] \times [c,d] \times [p,q]$ in its domain. Then

$$\iiint_B f(x,y,z)\,dV = \int_a^b \int_c^d \int_p^q f(x,y,z)\,dz\,dy\,dx \qquad (12.5.2)$$

All other five orders possible for the iterated integral give the same result.

Example 12.5.1 (Iterated Triple Integrals)

Problem: Compute the triple integral of $f(x,y,z) = 8x^2yz^3 + 15y^2z^4$ over the box $B = [0,3] \times [0,2] \times [0,1]$.

Solution: Because of Fubini's theorem and the fact that solid B is a box, this is an easy calculation.

$$\iiint_B (8x^2yz^3 + 15y^2z^4)\,dV = \int_0^3 \int_0^2 \int_0^1 (8x^2yz^3 + 15y^2z^4)\,dz\,dy\,dx$$

$$= \int_0^3 \int_0^2 (2x^2yz^4 + 3y^2z^5)\Big|_0^1 \,dy\,dx = \int_0^3 \int_0^2 (2x^2y + 3y^2)\,dy\,dx$$

$$= \int_0^3 (x^2y^2 + y^3)\Big|_0^2 \,dx = \int_0^3 (4x^2 + 8)\,dx = \left(\tfrac{4}{3}x^3 + 8x\right)\Big|_0^3 = 36 + 24 = 60$$

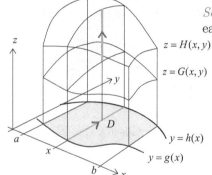

Figure 12.5.3: *A Type I-xy solid.*

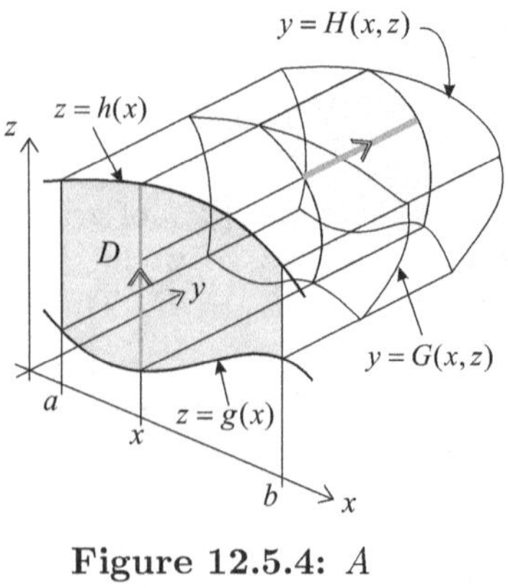

Figure 12.5.4: *A Type I-xz solid.*

For solids E that are more general than boxes, the computation of the triple integral is considerably more complicated. Even with Fubini's theorem, the calculation of $\iiint_E f(x,y,z)\,dV$ can be difficult unless the integrand is simple. In addition, just setting up the iterated integrals correctly requires an analysis of the solid E. We discuss this latter aspect first, before stating the general Fubini theorem.

There are six types of solids E for which we can effectively use Fubini's theorem to compute triple integrals. The "type" nomenclature is based on the type of planar region (Type I or II) and whether that region lies in the x-y plane, the x-z plane, or the y-z plane.

Type I-xy Solids: Suppose D is a Type I region in the x-y plane, bounded by the curves $y = g(x)$, $y = h(x)$, $x = a$, $x = b$, with $a < b$ and $g(x) \le h(x)$, for x in $[a,b]$. Suppose that $z = G(x,y)$, $z = H(x,y)$ are two function whose domains contain D and $G(x,y) \le H(x,y)$ for all (x,y) in D. Then the six surfaces

$$y = g(x),\ y = h(x),\ x = a,\ x = b,\ z = G(x,y),\ z = H(x,y) \qquad (12.5.3)$$

enclose a solid E which we call a *Type I-xy solid*. Note that the first four surfaces in the list (12.5.3) are surfaces of translation (generalized cylinders). Figure 12.5.3 shows a sketch of such a Type I-xy solid.

Type I-xz Solids: These are similar to Type I-xy solids except that the planar region D lies in x-z plane. This means that the bounding surfaces for this type of solid are

$$z = g(x),\ z = h(x),\ x = a,\ x = b,\ y = G(x, z),\ y = H(x, z) \qquad (12.5.4)$$

Figure 12.5.4 shows a sketch of such a Type I-xz solid.

Type I-yz Solids: These are similar to Type I-xy solids except that the planar region D lies in y-z plane. This means that the bounding surfaces for this type of solid are

$$z = g(y),\ z = h(y),\ y = c,\ y = d,\ x = G(y, z),\ x = H(y, z) \qquad (12.5.5)$$

Figure 12.5.5 shows a sketch of such a Type I-yz solid.

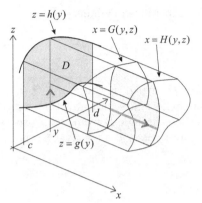

Figure 12.5.5: *A Type I-yz solid.*

NOTE 1: Figures 12.5.3, 12.5.4, 12.5.5 are for Type I xy, xz, yz solids. The sketches for Type II xy, xz, yz solids are similar. Thus, there are six solids in all that Fubini's theorem deals with. We just state the theorem for two of these types of solids.

THEOREM 12.5.2 (Fubini's Theorem for Type I & II Regions)

Suppose f is continuous on a solid E in its domain. If E is a Type I-xy solid, then

$$\iiint_E f(x, y, z)dV = \int_{x=a}^{x=b} \int_{y=g(x)}^{y=h(x)} \int_{z=G(x,y)}^{z=H(x,y)} f(x, y, z)dzdydx \qquad (12.5.6)$$

If E is a Type II-xy solid, then

$$\iiint_E f(x, y, z)dV = \int_{y=c}^{y=d} \int_{x=g(y)}^{x=h(y)} \int_{z=G(x,y)}^{z=H(x,y)} f(x, y, z)dzdxdy \qquad (12.5.7)$$

NOTE 2: To clarify the iterated integration process, we have added more notation to the limits of integration. For instance, in (12.5.6), the inner integration with respect to z goes from $z = G(x, y)$ (lower limit of integration) up to $z = H(x, y)$ (upper limit of integration). Here x and y are fixed and z varies along the vertical line-segment shown in Figure 12.5.3. This line-segment goes between the graph of G (on the bottom) and the graph of H (on the top).

NOTE 3: In an xy type solid, the first (inner) integration is with respect to z. The other integrations are in the order $dydx$ (for Type I) or $dxdy$ (for Type II).

NOTE 4: Figures 12.5.3, 12.5.4, 12.5.5 indicate, with arrows, the integration schemes you will employ when using Fubini's theorem and setting up the iterated integrals. This will be clarified in the example below.

NOTE 5: Some solids E can be analyzed as being any of the six types of solid (Type I xy, xz, yz, Type II xy, xz, yz) Thus, there are six different triple iterated integrals you could use to calculate the triple integral over such a solid. The only compelling reason to use one of these six rather than the others is that one may be easier to compute than the others.

Example 12.5.2 (Integrating Over Type I-xy Solids)

Problem: Compute the following triple integrals over the specified solid E.

(a) $\iiint_E 4xyz\,dV$, where E is the Type I-xy determined by the region D:

$$y = 1, \; y = x^2 \; (\text{with } x \geq 0), \; x = 0, \; x = 1$$

and the graphs of the following functions of two variables:

$$z = 0 \; (\text{the } x\text{-}y \text{ plane}), \qquad z = \sqrt{y} \; (\text{a generalized cylinder})$$

(b) $\iiint_E 8x\,dV$, where E is the tetrahedron shown in Figure 12.5.7.

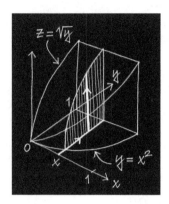

Figure 12.5.6: *The solid bounded by the cylinders* $z = \sqrt{y}$, $y = 1$, $y = x^2$.

Solution Part (a): We first sketch the planar region D, which, because of $x \geq 0$, lies entirely in the 1st quadrant. See Figure 12.5.6. The figure indicates that for an x between $x = 0$ and $x = 1$, and for a y on the slice through D from $y = x^2$ to $y = 1$, we integrate in the z-direction between $z = 0$ and $z = \sqrt{y}$. This gives us the following setup for the iterated integral:

$$\iiint_E 4xyz\,dV = \int_{x=0}^{x=1} \int_{y=x^2}^{y=1} \int_{z=0}^{z=\sqrt{y}} 4xyz\,dz\,dy\,dx$$

$$= \int_{x=0}^{x=1} \int_{y=x^2}^{y=1} \left[2xyz^2\right]\Big|_{z=0}^{z=\sqrt{y}} dy\,dx = \int_{x=0}^{x=1} \int_{y=x^2}^{y=1} 2xy^2\,dy\,dx$$

$$= \int_0^1 \left[\tfrac{2}{3}xy^3\right]\Big|_{y=x^2}^{y=1} dx = \int_0^1 \tfrac{2}{3}\left[x - x^7\right] dx = \tfrac{2}{3}\left[\tfrac{1}{2}x^2 - \tfrac{1}{8}x^8\right]\Big|_0^1 = \tfrac{2}{3}\left[\tfrac{3}{8}\right] = \tfrac{1}{4}$$

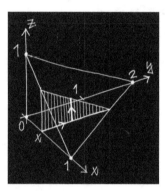

Figure 12.5.7: *The tetrahedron with vertices* $(0,0,0)$, $(1,0,0)$, $(0,2,0)$, $(0,0,1)$.

Solution Part (b): It is easy to see from Figure 12.5.7 that the base of the tetrahedron should be the region D in the setup of the Type I-xy solid. The base is a triangle with two sides on the x-axis and y-axis and third side formed by a line with intercepts $(1,0,0)$, $(0,2,0)$. This line then has slope $m = (2-0)/(0-1) = -2$ and so the point-slope form of its equation is $y - 0 = -2(x-1)$, i.e., $y = -2x + 2$. Thus, the region D is the triangle bounded by the three lines, $y = 0$, $x = 0$, $y = -2x + 2$.

An alternative form of the last equation above is $2x + y = 2$, and this form will give a short-cut way of finding an equation for the plane forming the slanted side of the tetrahedron. A little thought shows us that the equation must have standard form $2x + y + cz = 2$. But, since the plane has z-intercept $(0,0,1)$, we see that $c = 2$. Thus, the slanted side of the tetrahedron has equation

$$2x + y + 2z = 2, \quad \text{equivalently (after solving for } z\text{):} \quad z = 1 - x - \tfrac{1}{2}y$$

So, the tetrahedron is bounded on the top by this plane $z = 1 - x - \tfrac{1}{2}y$ and on the bottom by the plane $z = 0$. The setup and calculation of the triple integral is

$$\iiint_E 8x\,dV = \int_{x=0}^{x=1} \int_{y=0}^{y=2-2x} \int_{z=0}^{z=1-x-\frac{1}{2}y} 8x\,dz\,dy\,dx$$

$$= \int_{x=0}^{x=1} \int_{y=0}^{y=2-2x} \left[8xz\right]\Big|_{z=0}^{z=1-x-\frac{1}{2}y} dy\,dx = \int_{x=0}^{x=1} \int_{y=0}^{y=2-2x} 8x\left[1 - x - \tfrac{1}{2}y\right] dy\,dx$$

$$= \int_{x=0}^{x=1} \int_{y=0}^{y=2-2x} \left(8x[1-x] - 4xy\right) dy\,dx = \int_{x=0}^{x=1} \left(8x[1-x]y - 2xy^2\right)\Big|_{y=0}^{y=2-2x} dx$$

$$= \int_{x=0}^{x=1} \left(8x[1-x](2-2x) - 2x(2-2x)^2\right) dx = \int_0^1 8x(1-x)^2\,dx$$

$$= \int_0^1 8(x - 2x^2 + x^3)\,dx = 8\left(\tfrac{1}{2}x^2 - \tfrac{2}{3}x^3 + \tfrac{1}{4}x^4\right)\Big|_0^1 = 8\left(\tfrac{1}{2} - \tfrac{2}{3} + \tfrac{1}{4}\right) = \tfrac{2}{3}$$

NOTE: Each part of this Example views the solid E as a Type I-xy solid. This is perhaps easiest to visualize and so you should try this first when attempting to determine the limits of integration in the iterated integrals.

MEASURING VOLUMES

The simplest triple integral occurs when the integrand is a constant 1, i.e., $f(x, y, z) = 1$ for all (x, y, z) in E. In this case, we define the *volume* of E as this triple integral:

$$V = \text{Volume of } E = \iiint_E 1 \, dV \qquad (12.5.8)$$

In particular, we can use this formula when E is one of the six types of solids introduced above. For example, the volume formula for a Type I-xy solid is (by Fubini's theorem)

$$\begin{aligned}
V &= \iiint_E 1 \, dV = \int_{x=a}^{x=b} \int_{y=g(x)}^{y=h(x)} \int_{z=G(x,y)}^{z=H(x,y)} 1 \, dz \, dy \, dx \\
&= \int_{x=a}^{x=b} \int_{y=g(x)}^{y=h(x)} z \Big|_{z=G(x,y)}^{z=H(x,y)} dy \, dx \\
&= \int_{x=a}^{x=b} \int_{y=g(x)}^{y=h(x)} \big[H(x, y) - G(x, y) \big] \, dy \, dx \qquad (12.5.9)
\end{aligned}$$

Formula (12.5.9) is a slight generalization of the way we measured volumes using double integrals in Section 12.2. There, the top surface is $z = f(x, y)$ (here it is $z = H(x, y)$) and the bottom surface is $z = 0$ (here we can take $G(x, y) = 0$). So, the next example and many in the Exercises do not involve a new technique, but rather just a change of viewpoint.

Example 12.5.3 (Computing Volumes Using Triple Integrals)

Problem: (a) Use triple integrals to compute the volume

$$V = \iiint_E 1 \, dV = \int_{x=-1}^{x=1} \int_{y=0}^{y=1-x^2} \int_{z=y}^{z=1-x^2} 1 \, dz \, dy \, dx \qquad (12.5.10)$$

Here E is the parabolic wedge bounded by the surfaces:

$$z = y \text{ (slanted plane)}, \quad z = 1 - x^2 \text{(generalized cylinder)}, \quad y = 0 \text{ (x-z plane)},$$

See the sketch in Figure 12.5.8. (b) Rewrite the integral (12.5.10) as equivalent iterated integrals in the orders $dz \, dx \, dy$ and $dy \, dz \, dx$. (c) Compute the integrals in these latter two orders and see if all three results are the same.

Solution Part (a): This is the easy part. Just calculate the iterated integrals.

$$\begin{aligned}
V &= \int_{x=-1}^{x=1} \int_{y=0}^{y=1-x^2} \int_{z=y}^{z=1-x^2} 1 \, dz \, dy \, dx = \int_{x=-1}^{x=1} \int_{y=0}^{y=1-x^2} z \Big|_{z=y}^{z=1-x^2} dy \, dx \\
&= \int_{x=-1}^{x=1} \int_{y=0}^{y=1-x^2} [1 - x^2 - y] \, dy \, dx = \int_{x=-1}^{x=1} \big[(1 - x^2)y - \tfrac{1}{2}y^2 \big] \Big|_{y=0}^{y=1-x^2} dx \\
&= \int_{-1}^{1} [(1 - x^2)(1 - x^2) - \tfrac{1}{2}(1 - x^2)^2] \, dx = \int_{-1}^{1} \tfrac{1}{2}(1 - x^2)^2 \, dx \\
&= \int_{-1}^{1} \tfrac{1}{2}(1 - 2x^2 + x^4) \, dx = 2 \cdot \tfrac{1}{2} \big[x - \tfrac{2}{3}x^3 + \tfrac{1}{5}x^5 \big] \Big|_0^1 = 1 - \tfrac{2}{3} + \tfrac{1}{5} = \tfrac{8}{15}
\end{aligned}$$

NOTE: In the last line, the integral has an integrand which is an even function and we are integrating from -1 to 1. So, we could just integrate from 0 to 1 and double things to get the correct result. See Section 4.3.

Solution Part (b): This is a harder part to the problem since we have to determine the Type I-xy solid that led to the iterated integrals in (12.5.10). For this, note

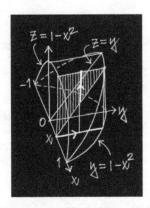

Figure 12.5.8: *The solid bounded by the cylinders $z = 1 - x^2$, $z = y$, $y = 0$.*

that after doing the inner integral with respect to z and evaluating, we are left with a double integral with respect to x and y. This double integral is over the region D bounded by $y = 1 - x^2$, $y = 0$ and is in the order $dy\,dx$. The surface on the top of the solid is $z = 1 - x^2$, while the one on the bottom is $z = y$. So in the sketch shown in Figure 12.5.8, D (not part of the solid) is the parabolic segment shown in the x-y plane. So, if we reverse the order to $dx\,dy$ as shown in Figure 12.5.9, this gives D as the Type II region bounded by $x = -\sqrt{1-y}$, $x = \sqrt{1-y}$, $y = 0$. Thus, the second way of doing the triple integral is

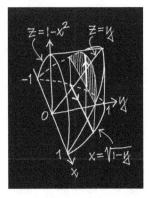

Figure 12.5.9: *Reversing the integration order $dz\,dy\,dx$ in Figure 12.5.8 to integration order $dz\,dx\,dy$.*

$$
\begin{aligned}
V &= \int_{y=0}^{y=1} \int_{x=-\sqrt{1-y}}^{x=\sqrt{1-y}} \int_{z=y}^{z=1-x^2} 1\,dz\,dx\,dy = \int_{y=0}^{y=1} \int_{x=-\sqrt{1-y}}^{x=\sqrt{1-y}} z\,\Big|_{z=y}^{z=1-x^2} dx\,dy \\
&= \int_{y=0}^{y=1} \int_{x=-\sqrt{1-y}}^{x=\sqrt{1-y}} [\,1 - x^2 - y\,]\,dx\,dy = 2\int_{y=0}^{y=1} \Big[\,(1-y)x - \tfrac{1}{3}x^3\,\Big]\Big|_{x=0}^{x=\sqrt{1-y}} dy \\
&= 2\int_0^1 \Big[\,(1-y)\sqrt{1-y} - \tfrac{1}{3}\left(\sqrt{1-y}\right)^3\Big]\,dy = 2\int_0^1 \tfrac{2}{3}(1-y)^{3/2}\,dy \\
&= 2\cdot\tfrac{2}{3}\left(-\tfrac{2}{5}(1-y)^{5/2}\right)\Big|_0^1 = \tfrac{8}{15}
\end{aligned}
$$

Notice how we doubled the evaluation in line two above. See the NOTE above in Part (a).

Solution Part (c): Finally, we setup the iterated integrals in the order $dy\,dz\,dx$. Here, after doing the inner integral with respect to y and evaluating, we are left with a double integral with respect to x and z. This double integral is over a region D in the x-z plane and D, as shown in Figure 12.5.10, forms one side of the solid. This region is bounded by $z = 1 - x^2$ and $z = 0$ and the order of integration in the double integral is $dz\,dx$. The inner integral with respect to y, will be as y goes along a line segment between the surfaces $y = 0$ (the x-z plane) and $y = z$ (an inclined plane). Thus, the third way of doing the triple integral is

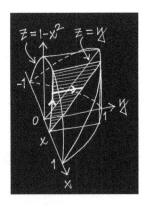

Figure 12.5.10: *Reversing the integration order $dz\,dy\,dx$ in Figure 12.5.8 to integration order $dy\,dz\,dx$.*

$$
\begin{aligned}
V &= \int_{x=-1}^{x=1} \int_{z=0}^{z=1-x^2} \int_{y=0}^{y=z} 1\,dy\,dz\,dx = \int_{x=-1}^{x=1} \int_{z=0}^{z=1-x^2} y\,\Big|_{y=0}^{y=z} dz\,dx \\
&= \int_{x=-1}^{x=1} \int_{z=0}^{z=1-x^2} z\,dz\,dx = \int_{x=-1}^{x=1} \tfrac{1}{2}z^2\,\Big|_{z=0}^{z=1-x^2} dx \\
&= \int_{-1}^{1} \tfrac{1}{2}(1-x^2)^2\,dx = 2\int_0^1 \tfrac{1}{2}(1-x^2)^2\,dx = \int_0^1 (1 - 2x^2 + x^4)\,dx \\
&= \Big[x - \tfrac{2}{3}x^3 + \tfrac{1}{5}x^5\Big]\Big|_0^1 = 1 - \tfrac{2}{3} + \tfrac{1}{5} = \tfrac{8}{15}
\end{aligned}
$$

Thus, all three orders of integration give the same result, which Fubini's theorem guarantees.

APPLICATION: Center of Mass

In section 12.4 we discussed the use of double integrals to determine the total mass and center of mass of a two-dimensional lamina. This is an ideal simplification of the actual situation where objects are three-dimensional. Now that we have triple integrals to employ, we can define the total mass and center of mass of a solid E as follows.

Total Mass: $m = \iiint_E \rho(x, y, z)\,dV$ (12.5.11)

Here, the function ρ is the mass density function for the solid E, with $\rho(x, y, z)$ giving the mass per unit volume at the point (x, y, z).

Moments About the Coordinate Planes:

$$M_{x,0} = \iiint_E x\rho(x,y,z)\,dV \qquad (12.5.12a)$$

$$M_{y,0} = \iiint_E y\rho(x,y,z)\,dV \qquad (12.5.12b)$$

$$M_{z,0} = \iiint_E z\rho(x,y,z)\,dV \qquad (12.5.12c)$$

Coordinates of the Center of Mass:

$$x^* = \frac{M_{x,0}}{m}, \quad y^* = \frac{M_{y,0}}{m}, \quad z^* = \frac{M_{z,0}}{m} \qquad (12.5.13)$$

When the mass density ρ is constant, the center of mass is called the *centroid* and has geometrical significance. A little thought shows that when ρ is constant, then is cancels out in the above ratios, and so we get:

Coordinates of the Centroid:

$$x_c = \frac{\iiint_E x\,dV}{V}, \quad y_c = \frac{\iiint_E y\,dV}{V}, \quad z_c = \frac{\iiint_E z\,dV}{V} \qquad (12.5.14)$$

Here, $V = \iiint_E 1\,dV$ is the volume of the solid E.

Example 12.5.4 (Finding the Centroid)

Problem: Suppose E is the sold bounded by the four surfaces:

$$z = \sqrt{y}\ \text{(cylinder)}, \quad y = \sqrt{x}\ \text{(cylinder)}, \quad z = 0\ \text{(x-y plane)}, \quad x = 1\ \text{(plane)}$$

See Figure 12.5.11. Find the coordinates of the centroid of E.

Solution: First, we setup the iterated triple integral for the volume. Figure 12.5.11 shows the first two bounding surfaces obtained by translating a square root function in the x and z directions. The solid is contained between these and the plane $z = 0$ on the bottom. For clarity, Figure 12.5.11 does not show the plane $x = 1$, but rather shows where it cuts off the other three surfaces,

We view the solid D as a Type I-xy solid with region D bounded by the curves $y = \sqrt{x}$, $y = 0$, $x = 1$ as its base. Then the inner integral with respect to z goes from the surface $z = 0$ (on the bottom) up to the surface $z = \sqrt{y}$ (on the top). Thus, the volume triple integral is

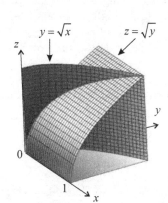

$y = \sqrt{x}$ $z = \sqrt{y}$

Figure 12.5.11: *The solid bounded by the surfaces $z = \sqrt{y}$, $y = \sqrt{x}$, $z = 0$, and $x = 1$.*

$$
\begin{aligned}
V &= \int_{x=0}^{x=1} \int_{y=0}^{y=\sqrt{x}} \int_{z=0}^{z=\sqrt{y}} 1\,dz\,dy\,dx = \int_{x=0}^{x=1} \int_{y=0}^{y=\sqrt{x}} z\Big|_{z=0}^{z=\sqrt{y}}\,dy\,dx \\
&= \int_{x=0}^{x=1} \int_{y=0}^{y=\sqrt{x}} \sqrt{y}\,dy\,dx = \int_0^1 \tfrac{2}{3}y^{3/2}\Big|_{y=0}^{y=\sqrt{x}}\,dx = \int_0^1 \tfrac{2}{3}x^{3/4}\,dx \\
&= \tfrac{2}{3}\cdot\tfrac{4}{7}x^{7/4}\Big|_0^1 = \tfrac{8}{21}
\end{aligned}
$$

The integrals for the three reduced moments ($M_{x,0}$, $M_{y,0}$, $M_{z,0}$, with $\rho = 1$) are similar. They are

$$
\begin{aligned}
M_{x,0} &= \int_{x=0}^{x=1} \int_{y=0}^{y=\sqrt{x}} \int_{z=0}^{z=\sqrt{y}} x\,dz\,dy\,dx = \int_{x=0}^{x=1} \int_{y=0}^{y=\sqrt{x}} xz\Big|_{z=0}^{z=\sqrt{y}}\,dy\,dx \\
&= \int_{x=0}^{x=1} \int_{y=0}^{y=\sqrt{x}} x\sqrt{y}\,dy\,dx = \int_0^1 x\left[\tfrac{2}{3}y^{3/2}\right]\Big|_{y=0}^{y=\sqrt{x}}\,dx = \int_0^1 \tfrac{2}{3}x^{7/4}\,dx \\
&= \tfrac{2}{3}\cdot\tfrac{4}{11}x^{11/4}\Big|_0^1 = \tfrac{8}{33}
\end{aligned}
$$

$$
\begin{aligned}
M_{y,0} &= \int_{x=0}^{x=1} \int_{y=0}^{y=\sqrt{x}} \int_{z=0}^{z=\sqrt{y}} y \, dz \, dy \, dx = \int_{x=0}^{x=1} \int_{y=0}^{y=\sqrt{x}} yz \Big|_{z=0}^{z=\sqrt{y}} dy \, dx \\
&= \int_{x=0}^{x=1} \int_{y=0}^{y=\sqrt{x}} y^{3/2} \, dy \, dx = \int_0^1 \left[\tfrac{2}{5} y^{5/2} \right] \Big|_{y=0}^{y=\sqrt{x}} dx = \int_0^1 \tfrac{2}{5} x^{5/4} \, dx \\
&= \tfrac{2}{5} \cdot \tfrac{4}{9} x^{9/4} \Big|_0^1 = \tfrac{8}{45}
\end{aligned}
$$

and

$$
\begin{aligned}
M_{z,0} &= \int_{x=0}^{x=1} \int_{y=0}^{y=\sqrt{x}} \int_{z=0}^{z=\sqrt{y}} z \, dz \, dy \, dx = \int_{x=0}^{x=1} \int_{y=0}^{y=\sqrt{x}} \tfrac{1}{2} z^2 \Big|_{z=0}^{z=\sqrt{y}} dy \, dx \\
&= \int_{x=0}^{x=1} \int_{y=0}^{y=\sqrt{x}} \tfrac{1}{2} y \, dy \, dx = \int_0^1 \tfrac{1}{4} y^2 \Big|_{y=0}^{y=\sqrt{x}} dx = \int_0^1 \tfrac{1}{4} x \, dx \\
&= \tfrac{1}{8} x^2 \Big|_0^1 = \tfrac{1}{8}
\end{aligned}
$$

Multiplying the above three numbers by the reciprocal of the volume $\frac{1}{V} = \frac{21}{8}$ gives the coordinates of the centroid:

$$
x_c = \frac{21}{33}, \quad y_c = \frac{21}{45}, \quad z_c = \frac{21}{64}
$$

Iterated Integrals and Techniques of Integration: Using Fubini's theorem to compute a triple integral requires you to calculate three single integrals (iterated integrals) and each of these integrals may require the use of one or more of the techniques of integration you learned in Chapter 6. Several instances of this are illustrated in the following example.

Example 12.5.5 (Iterated Integrals & Techniques of Integration)

Problem: Compute the iterated integrals in Parts (a) and (b) below using the suggested technique of integration for some (or one) of the integrals.

Part (a): $\displaystyle \int_0^1 \int_0^{\sqrt{x}} \int_0^{\sqrt{y}} 40x^{12} y z^3 e^{x^4 z^4} \, dz \, dy \, dx$ (substitution)

Solution (a): In the integral with respect to z, let $u = x^4 z^4$ so that $du = 4x^4 z^3 dz$ (remember x is constant during the integration with respect to z. Then

$$
\begin{aligned}
\int_0^1 \int_0^{\sqrt{x}} \int_0^{\sqrt{y}} 40x^{12} y z^3 e^{x^4 z^4} \, dz \, dy \, dx &= \int_0^1 \int_0^{\sqrt{x}} \int_0^{\sqrt{y}} 10x^8 y (4x^4 z^3 e^{x^4 z^4} \, dz) dy \, dx \\
&= \int_0^1 \int_0^{\sqrt{x}} \left[10x^8 y e^{x^4 z^4} \right] \Big|_{z=0}^{z=\sqrt{y}} dy \, dx = \int_0^1 \int_0^{\sqrt{x}} \left[10x^8 y e^{x^4 y^2} - 10x^8 y \right] dy \, dx \\
&= \int_0^1 \left[5x^4 e^{x^4 y^2} - 5x^3 y^2 \right] \Big|_{y=0}^{y=\sqrt{x}} = \int_0^1 \left[5x^4 e^{x^5} - 5x^4 - 5x^4 \right] dx \\
&= \int_0^1 \left[5x^4 e^{x^5} - 10x^4 \right] dx = \left[e^{x^5} - 2x^5 \right] \Big|_0^1 = e - 3
\end{aligned}
$$

Part (b): $\displaystyle \int_0^3 \int_1^{\sqrt{x+1}} \int_0^{\sqrt{y}} \frac{8z}{y^4(x^2+1)} \, dz \, dy \, dx$ (partial fractions)

Solution (b): Here there are two straight forward integrals with respect to z and y and, after the evaluations, we are left with an integrand that is a rational function of x only. Then we use partial fractions:

$$\int_0^3 \int_1^{\sqrt{x+1}} \int_0^{\sqrt{y}} \frac{8z}{y^4(x^2+1)}\,dzdydx = \int_0^3 \int_1^{\sqrt{x+1}} \left[\frac{4z^2}{y^4(x^2+1)} \right] \Bigg|_{z=0}^{z=\sqrt{y}} dydx$$

$$= \int_0^3 \int_1^{\sqrt{x+1}} \frac{4}{y^3(x^2+1)}\,dydx = \int_0^3 \left[\frac{-2}{y^2(x^2+1)} \right]\Bigg|_{y=1}^{y=\sqrt{x+1}} dx$$

$$= \int_0^3 \left[\frac{-2}{(x+1)(x^2+1)} + \frac{2}{x^2+1} \right] dx = \int_0^3 \left[\frac{-1}{x+1} + \frac{x-1}{x^2+1} + \frac{2}{x^2+1} \right] dx$$

$$= \int_0^3 \left[\frac{-1}{x+1} + \frac{x}{x^2+1} + \frac{1}{x^2+1} \right] dx$$

$$= \left[-\ln(x+1) + \tfrac{1}{2}\ln(x^2+1) + \tan^{-1}x \right]\Bigg|_0^3 = \ln(\sqrt{10}/4) + \tan^{-1}(3)$$

Space Curves: When the solid E is bounded by two surfaces that intersect, the curve of intersection C (a curve in $\mathbb{R}^3$, or a space curve) is often needed in the process of changing the order of integration. For this it is convenient to have parametric equations for C. We have discussed parametrizing lines in space and will discuss parametrizing curves in space later. Here, we discuss a special instance of a space curve that arises in changing the order of integration.

Example 12.5.6 (Changing the Order of Integration - Space Curves)

Problem: For the iterated integral in Part (a) of the last example, change the order of integration to $dydzdx$, i.e., view E as a Type I-xz solid.

Solution: As shown Figure 12.5.12, the two surfaces $y = \sqrt{x}$, $z = \sqrt{y}$ intersect in a space curve C (shown in red) which can be parametrized using x as a parameter:

$$x = x, \ y = \sqrt{x}, \ z = \sqrt{\sqrt{x}} = \sqrt[4]{x} = x^{1/4}$$

Then, points on C have the form $(x, \sqrt{x}, x^{1/4})$. Thus, the projection of C onto the x-z plane, gives a curve with parametric equation $(x, 0, x^{1/4})$ and Cartesian equation $z = x^{1/4}$. This curve bounds the region D we need for viewing E as a Type I-xz solid. Thus, as indicated in Figure 12.5.12, changing the order of integration to $dydzdx$ gives

$$\int_0^1 \int_0^{\sqrt{x}} \int_0^{\sqrt{y}} 40x^{12}yz^3 e^{x^4 z^4}\,dzdydx = \int_0^1 \int_0^{x^{1/4}} \int_{z^2}^{\sqrt{x}} 40x^{12}yz^3 e^{x^4 z^4}\,dydzdx$$

Note: In this case the order $dydzdx$ for the iterated integrals is *not* an easy way to calculate the triple integral.

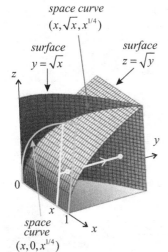

space curve
$(x, \sqrt{x}, x^{1/4})$

surface
$y = \sqrt{x}$

surface
$z = \sqrt{y}$

space curve
$(x, 0, x^{1/4})$

Figure 12.5.12: *Projecting the curve* $(x, \sqrt{x}, x^{1/4})$ *onto the x-z plane to get a curve* $(x, 0, x^{1/4})$ *that bounds the region D.*

Exercises: 12.5 (Triple Integrals)

Computing Iterated Integrals

In Exercises 1–36, compute the iterated triple integrals. Use substitution (1–10, 35, 36), trig integrals (11–16, 19–22), trig substitutions (23–26, 33, 34), partial fractions 27–32), or integration by parts (17, 18).

1. $\displaystyle\int_0^1 \int_0^{\sqrt{x}} \int_0^{\sqrt{y}} \left[168x^3y^3z^3 + 80x^2y^2z \right] dz\,dy\,dx$

2. $\displaystyle\int_0^1 \int_0^{\sqrt{x}} \int_0^{\sqrt{y}} \left[128x^3z + 240x^2y^3z^3 \right] dz\,dy\,dx$

3. $\displaystyle\int_0^1 \int_0^{\sqrt{x}} \int_0^{\sqrt{x}} \left[40xy^3z + 6\sqrt{x}y \right] dz\,dy\,dx$

4. $\displaystyle\int_0^1 \int_0^{\sqrt{x}} \int_0^{\sqrt{x}} \left[36x^2yz^2 + 16\sqrt{x}y^3 \right] dz\,dy\,dx$

5. $\displaystyle\int_0^1 \int_0^x \int_0^{\sqrt{y}} 24x^4yz^3 e^{xz^2} dz\,dy\,dx$

6. $\displaystyle\int_0^1 \int_0^{\sqrt{y}} \int_0^x 72x^4yz^5 e^{xz^6} dz\,dy\,dx$

7. $\displaystyle\int_0^1 \int_0^x \int_0^{\sqrt{y}} 32x^7yz^3 \sin(x^2z^4)\,dz\,dy\,dx$

8. $\displaystyle\int_0^1 \int_0^{\sqrt{x}} \int_0^{\sqrt{y}} 128x^7y^3z^7 \cos(x^2z^8)\,dz\,dy\,dx$

9. $\displaystyle\int_0^1 \int_0^{x^2} \int_0^y \frac{8x^{16}yz}{(1+x^6z^2)^3}\,dz\,dy\,dx$

10. $\displaystyle\int_0^1 \int_0^{\sqrt{x}} \int_0^y \frac{64x^5y^3z^3}{(1+x^2z^4)^3}\,dz\,dy\,dx$

11. $\displaystyle\int_0^\pi \int_0^{\cos x} \int_0^{\sqrt{y}} 60z \sin^3 x\,dz\,dy\,dx$

12. $\displaystyle\int_0^{\pi/2} \int_0^{\sin x} \int_0^{\sqrt{y}} 60z \cos^3 x\,dz\,dy\,dx$

13. $\displaystyle\int_0^{\pi/3} \int_0^{\tan y} \int_0^x 18z \sec y\,dz\,dx\,dy$

14. $\displaystyle\int_0^{\pi/3} \int_0^{\tan y} \int_0^x 6z \sec^3 y\,dz\,dx\,dy$

15. $\displaystyle\int_0^{\pi/4} \int_0^{\tan x} \int_0^y 120z^2 \sec^2 x\,dz\,dy\,dx$

16. $\displaystyle\int_0^{\pi/4} \int_0^{\tan x} \int_0^y 30z^4 \sec^2 x\,dz\,dy\,dx$

17. $\displaystyle\int_0^1 \int_0^{x^2} \int_0^{\sqrt{x}} \frac{16x^3z^3}{1+x^2y}\,dz\,dy\,dx$

18. $\displaystyle\int_0^1 \int_0^{x^2} \int_0^{x^3} \frac{24x^2z^2}{1+x^2y}\,dz\,dy\,dx$

19. $\displaystyle\int_0^\pi \int_0^{\sqrt{x}} \int_0^{\sqrt{y}} 4z \cos(y^2) \sin(y^2) \sin^3 x\,dz\,dy\,dx$

20. $\displaystyle\int_0^\pi \int_0^{\sqrt{x}} \int_0^{\sqrt{y}} 16z \cos^3(y^2) \sin(y^2) \sin^3 x\,dz\,dy\,dx$

21. $\displaystyle\int_0^{\frac{\pi}{4}} \int_0^{\sqrt{x}} \int_0^{\sqrt{y}} 12z \tan^2(y^2) \sec^2(y^2) \sec^2 x\,dz\,dy\,dx$

22. $\displaystyle\int_0^{\frac{\pi}{4}} \int_0^{\sqrt{x}} \int_0^{\sqrt[3]{y}} 15z^2 \tan^4(y^2) \sec^2(y^2) \sec^2 x\,dz\,dy\,dx$

23. $\displaystyle\int_0^1 \int_0^{\sqrt{x}} \int_0^{\sqrt{x}} 4xyz\sqrt{1-x^2}\,dz\,dy\,dx$

24. $\displaystyle\int_0^1 \int_0^{\sqrt{y}} \int_0^{\sqrt{y}} 4xyz\sqrt{1-y^2}\,dz\,dy\,dx$

25. $\displaystyle\int_0^{\sqrt{3}} \int_0^x \int_0^x \frac{60x^2z}{\sqrt{xy+1}}\,dz\,dy\,dx$

26. $\displaystyle\int_0^{\sqrt{3}} \int_0^x \int_0^x \frac{105x^4z}{\sqrt{xy+1}}\,dz\,dy\,dx$

27. $\displaystyle\int_0^1 \int_2^{x+2} \int_1^{y^2} \frac{1}{(x+1)z^2}\,dz\,dy\,dx$

28. $\displaystyle\int_0^1 \int_1^{x+1} \int_1^{y^2} \frac{1}{(x+3)z^2}\,dz\,dy\,dx$

29. $\displaystyle\int_0^3 \int_1^{\sqrt{x+1}} \int_0^{\sqrt{y}} \frac{4z(x-1)}{y^4(x^2+1)}\,dz\,dy\,dx$

30. $\displaystyle\int_0^2 \int_1^{\sqrt{x+2}} \int_0^{\sqrt{y}} \frac{4z(2x-1)}{y^4(x^2+1)}\,dz\,dy\,dx$

31. $\displaystyle\int_0^1 \int_1^{\sqrt{x+2}} \int_0^{\sqrt{y}} \frac{12z}{y^4(x+5)}\,dz\,dy\,dx$

32. $\displaystyle\int_0^1 \int_1^{\sqrt{x+3}} \int_0^{\sqrt{y}} \frac{16z}{y^4(x+7)}\,dz\,dy\,dx$

33. $\displaystyle\int_0^1 \int_1^{\sqrt{x}} \int_0^y \frac{36x^{10}y^3z^3}{(1-x^4z^4)^{5/2}}\,dz\,dy\,dx$

34. $\displaystyle\int_0^1 \int_1^{\sqrt{x}} \int_0^y \frac{24x^5y^3z^3}{(1-x^2z^4)^{5/2}}\,dz\,dy\,dx$

35. $\displaystyle\int_0^1 \int_0^x \int_0^{\sqrt{y}} \frac{48x^4z^3}{(1+xy^3)^2}\,dz\,dy\,dx$

36. $\displaystyle\int_0^1 \int_0^x \int_0^{\sqrt{y}} \frac{120x^6z^5}{(1+x^2y^4)^2}\,dz\,dy\,dx$

Setting Up Iterated Integrals

In Exercises 37–42, use the sketch of the solid E for the triple integral $\iiint_E f(x,y,z)\,dV$ to set up the corresponding triple integral in the order $dz\,dy\,dx$.

37.

38.

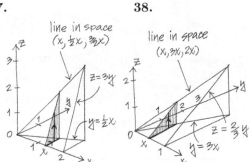

39.

40.

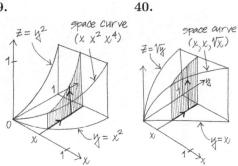

41.

42.

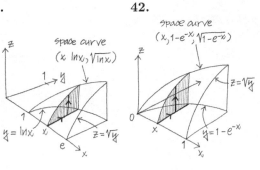

Triple Integrals over Type I-xy Solids

In Exercises 43–52, compute the triple integral over the specified Type I-xy solid E.

43. $\iiint_E 90x^8 y^2 z^5 e^{x^2 z^6}\, dV$, $D: y = x,\ y = 0,\ x = 1$
bounding surfaces: $z = 0,\ z = \sqrt{y}$

44. $\iiint_E 48x^{13} yz^3 e^{x^4 z^4}\, dV$, $D: y = x,\ y = 0,\ x = 1$
bounding surfaces: $z = 0,\ z = \sqrt{y}$

45. $\iiint_E 48x^{15} yz^3 \sin(x^5 z^4)\, dV$,
$D: y = \sqrt{x},\ y = 0,\ x = 1$
bounding surfaces: $z = 0,\ z = \sqrt{y}$

46. $\iiint_E 192x^9 y^3 z^7 \sin(x^4 z^8)\, dV$,
$D: y = \sqrt{x},\ y = 0,\ x = 1$
bounding surfaces: $z = 0,\ z = \sqrt{y}$

47. $\iiint_E 8y^2 z \sec^4 x\, dV$, $D: y = \tan x,\ y = 0,\ x = \frac{\pi}{4}$
bounding surfaces: $z = 0,\ z = \sqrt{y}$

48. $\iiint_E 8y^2 z \csc^4 x\, dV$,
$D: y = \cot x,\ y = 0,\ x = \frac{\pi}{2},\ x = \frac{3\pi}{4}$
bounding surfaces: $z = 0,\ z = \sqrt{y}$

49. $\iiint_E \dfrac{18x^5 z}{(1 + x^3 y^3)^2}\, dV$, $D: y = x,\ y = 0,\ x = 1$
bounding surfaces: $z = 0,\ z = y$

50. $\iiint_E \dfrac{200x^9 z^3}{(1 + x^5 y^5)^2}\, dV$, $D: y = x,\ y = 0,\ x = 1$
bounding surfaces: $z = 0,\ z = y$

51. $\iiint_E \dfrac{24x^9 y}{(1 + x^2 z)^2}\, dV$,
$D: y = x^2,\ y = 0,\ x = 1,\ x \geq 0$
bounding surfaces: $z = 0,\ z = y^2$

52. $\iiint_E \dfrac{24x^{11} y^2}{(1 + x^2 z)^2}\, dV$,
$D: y = x^2,\ y = 0,\ x = 1,\ x \geq 0$
bounding surfaces: $z = 0,\ z = y^3$

Change Order of Integration

In Exercises 53–58, for the triple integral that you set up in Exercises 53–60, change the order of integration $dz\,dy\,dx$ to the other five possible orders.

53. #37 **54.** #38 **55.** #39 **56.** #40
57. #41 **58.** #42

Change Order of Integration

In Exercises 59–64, change the order of integration to $dz\,dx\,dy,\ dy\,dz\,dx,\ dy\,dx\,dz,\ dx\,dy\,dz$ and $dx\,dz\,dy$ and then compute the triple integral using one of these orders.

59. $\displaystyle\int_{z=0}^{z=1} \int_{y=z}^{y=1} \int_{x=\sqrt{y}}^{x=1} 24x^9 yz e^{x^2 z^2}\, dx\, dy\, dz$

60. $\displaystyle\int_{z=0}^{z=1} \int_{y=z}^{y=1} \int_{x=\sqrt{y}}^{x=1} 63x^8 y^2 z^2 e^{x z^3}\, dx\, dy\, dz$

61. $\displaystyle\int_{y=0}^{y=1} \int_{z=0}^{z=y^2} \int_{x=\sqrt{y}}^{x=1} \dfrac{20x^{14} y^5 z}{(1 + x^4 y z^2)^3}\, dx\, dz\, dy$

62. $\displaystyle\int_{y=0}^{y=1} \int_{z=0}^{z=y^2} \int_{x=\sqrt{y}}^{x=1} \dfrac{10x^{19} y^5 z}{(1 + x^6 y z^2)^3}\, dx\, dz\, dy$

63. $\displaystyle\int_{y=0}^{y=1} \int_{z=0}^{z=\sqrt{y}} \int_{x=0}^{x=\cos^{-1} y} 6yz \sin^8 x\, dx\, dz\, dy$

64. $\displaystyle\int_{y=0}^{y=1} \int_{z=0}^{z=\sqrt{y}} \int_{x=0}^{x=\cos^{-1} y} 6yz \cos^8 x\, dx\, dz\, dy$

Calculus Concepts & Computation

12.6 Triple Integrals in Cylindrical and Spherical Coordinates

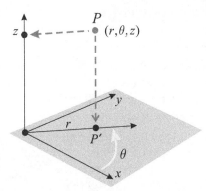

Figure 12.6.1: *Cylindrical coordinates of a point P.*

In addition to using Cartesian coordinates (x, y, z) to study the geometry of curves, surfaces, and solids in space $\mathbb{R}^3$, we can also use cylindrical coordinates (r, θ, z) and spherical coordinates (ρ, θ, ϕ), which, in certain situations, are more advantageous. Employing cylindrical or spherical coordinates instead of Cartesian coordinates is entirely analogous to what we did in Sections 9.4, 9.5, and 12.3. There are two aspects to this.

First, some surfaces and solids are more easily described by cylindrical or spherical coordinate equations. Second, the triple integrals over such solids are easier to compute in cylindrical or spherical coordinates than they would be in Cartesian coordinates.

CYLINDRICAL COORDINATES

We assign cylindrical coordinates to a point P in space as follows. Let (r, θ) be polar coordinates of the orthogonal projection of P onto a point P' in the x-y plane and let z be the number obtained by orthogonally projecting P onto the z axis. Then the cylindrical coordinates of P are (r, θ, z). See Figure 12.6.1.

It is easy to see from the figure that cylindrical coordinates are a direct extension of polar coordinates in the plane to a coordinate system in space. The relationship between the cylindrical coordinates (r, θ, z) and Cartesian coordinates (x, y, z) of a point P in space are shown in the box in the margin. The equations shown allow us, as we did in Section 9.4, to changes coordinates from one system to the other and also to change equations given in Cartesian coordinates to corresponding ones in cylindrical coordinates (and vice versa).

COORDINATE CONVERSIONS
Cylindrical to Cartesian
$x = r\cos\theta$ (12.6.1a)
$y = r\sin\theta$ (12.6.1b)
$z = z$ (12.6.1c)
Cartesian to Cylindrical
$r = \pm\sqrt{x^2 + y^2}$ (12.6.2a)
$\theta = \tan^{-1}\left(\dfrac{y}{x}\right)$ (12.6.2b)
$z = z$ (12.6.2c)

Cylindrical Equations for Surfaces

An equation such as $K(r, \theta, z) = 0$ is called a *cylindrical equation* and the set of all points P in space whose cylindrical coordinates satisfy $K(r, \theta, z) = 0$ is a surface in $\mathbb{R}^3$ (or a degenerate case of a surface). Understanding and plotting surfaces given by cylindrical equations can be difficult, but is somewhat easier for a special class of surfaces whose equations have one of the coordinate variables (either r or θ or z) missing from the equation. These are called *cylinders* (or *generalized cylinders*) in cylindrical coordinates. They are the analogs of the cylinders (or generalized cylinders) discussed in Section 10.6 for Cartesian coordinates. There are three types of such cylinders, depending on which coordinate variable is missing from the equation. We assume the three types of equations can be expressed in functional form (one variable is a function of the other). Thus, the types are

$$
\begin{aligned}
r &= g(\theta) & \text{(Type I: A Polar Cylinder)} \\
r &= h(z) & \text{(Type II: A Surface of Revolution)} \\
z &= k(\theta) & \text{(Type III: A Ribbon Surface)}
\end{aligned}
$$

NOTE 1: In each of these types, the functional relation between the variables could be just the opposite, i.e., $\theta = G(r)$, $z = H(r)$ and $\theta = K(z)$.

NOTE 2: Even though these surfaces are called "cylinders" they are not necessarily cylinders (or generalized cylinders) in the sense discussed in Section 10.6. Type I cylinders *are* generalized cylinders, which we have called *polar cylinders* because they arise by taking the polar curve $r = g(\theta)$ in the x-y plane and translating it to get a generalized cylinder. Type II cylinders are not cylinders at all, but rather are surfaces of revolution and Type III surfaces are ribbon-like surfaces.

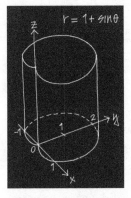

Figure 12.6.2: *A cardioidal cylinder.*

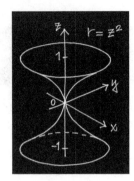

Figure 12.6.3: *A surface of revolution.*

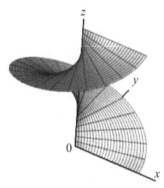

Figure 12.6.4: *The heliocoid $z = \theta$.*

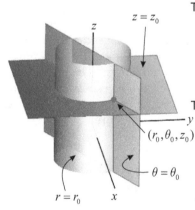

Figure 12.6.5: *Cylindrical coordinate surfaces.*

Being able to visualize these three types of surfaces will help us understand triple integrals over solids E which are bounded by surfaces of these types.

Example 12.6.1 (The Three Types of Cylinders)

Problem: Consider the following cylinders in cylindrical coordinates:

(a) $r = 1 + \sin\theta$ (b) $r = z^2$ (c) $z = \theta$

Sketch the first two cylinders and use a CAS to plot the third one.

Solution Part (a): This is a generalized cylinder in the sense of Section 10.6. We sketch the curve (given by polar equation) $r = 1 + \sin\theta$ (which is a cardioid) in the x-y plane and then translate it in the z-direction to get the surface. The sketch is shown in Figure 12.6.2. We refer to this surface as a *cardioidal cylinder*.

Solution Part (b): We sketch the curve $x = z^2$ in the x-z plane. (Here x represents r). Then revolve this curve about the z-axis to get the surface with cylindrical equation $r = z^2$. The sketch is shown in Figure 12.6.3. It is an exercise to prove that, in general, the cylindrical equation $r = h(z)$ is a surface of revolution.

Solution Part (c): Figure 12.6.4 shows a computer plot of this Type III cylinder.

Coordinate Surfaces: Type I, II, or III cylinders have equations involving only two of the coordinate variables. In the special case of this when the equations involve only *one* variable, we get cylinders that are called *coordinate surfaces*. These are:

$$r = r_0 \quad \text{((A cylinder of radius } r_0 \text{ centered on the } z\text{-axis)}$$
$$\theta = \theta_0 \quad \text{(A vertical plane through } z\text{-axis at angle } \theta_0 \text{ to the } x\text{-axis)}$$
$$z = z_0 \quad \text{(A horizontal plane through } z_0 \text{ on the } z\text{-axis)}$$

These surfaces, as shown in Figure 12.6.5, intersect in the point P with cylindrical coordinates (r_0, θ_0, z_0).

Triple Integrals in Cylindrical Coordinates

As with triple integrals in Cartesian coordinates, a triple integral $\iiint_E f(x, y, z)\, dV$ can be computed by six different iterated triple integrals in cylindrical coordinates. This requires that E be one of the following types of solids:

Type I Solids: These are solids E bounded by the six surfaces:

$$\theta = \alpha,\ \theta = \beta \qquad \text{(Two vertical planes through the } z\text{-axis)}$$
$$r = g(\theta),\ r = h(\theta) \qquad \text{(Two polar cylinders)}$$
$$z = G(r,\theta),\ z = H(r,\theta) \qquad \text{(Two general surfaces)}$$

Type II Solids: These are solids E bounded by the six surfaces:

$$z = a,\ z = b \qquad \text{(Two horizontal planes)}$$
$$r = g(z),\ r = h(z) \qquad \text{(Two surfaces of revolution)}$$
$$\theta = G(r,z),\ z = H(r,z) \qquad \text{(Two general surfaces)}$$

Type III Solids: These are solids E bounded by the six surfaces:

$$\theta = \alpha,\ \theta = \beta \qquad \text{(Two vertical planes through the } z\text{-axis)}$$
$$z = g(\theta),\ z = h(\theta) \qquad \text{(Two ribbon surfaces)}$$
$$r = G(z,\theta),\ r = H(z,\theta) \qquad \text{(Two general surfaces)}$$

NOTE 1: For each of these types of solid, there is related solid where the variables in the first two equations are interchanged. Thus, there are six types of solids we can use iterated integrals on.

NOTE 2: For each type of solid, the equations for the bounding surfaces give the limits of integration in the iterated integrals. This is illustrated in the following theorem.

THEOREM 12.6.1 (Triple Integrals in Cylindrical Coordinates)

Suppose f is continuous on a solid E in its domain. If E is a Type I, II, or III solid, then the triple integral of f over E is given by

TYPE I: $\displaystyle\iiint_E f(x,y,z)\,dV = \int_{\theta=\alpha}^{\theta=\beta}\int_{r=g(\theta)}^{r=h(\theta)}\int_{z=G(r,\theta)}^{z=H(r,\theta)} f(r\cos\theta, r\sin\theta, z)\,r\,dz\,dr\,d\theta$ (12.6.3)

TYPE II: $\displaystyle\iiint_E f(x,y,z)\,dV = \int_{z=a}^{z=b}\int_{r=g(z)}^{r=h(z)}\int_{\theta=G(r,z)}^{\theta=H(r,z)} f(r\cos\theta, r\sin\theta, z)\,r\,d\theta\,dr\,dz$ (12.6.4)

TYPE III: $\displaystyle\iiint_E f(x,y,z)\,dV = \int_{\theta=\alpha}^{\theta=\beta}\int_{z=g(\theta)}^{z=h(\theta)}\int_{r=G(z,\theta)}^{r=H(z,\theta)} f(r\cos\theta, r\sin\theta, z)\,r\,dr\,dz\,d\theta$ (12.6.5)

This theorem can be proven using limits of Riemann sums (as we did for double integrals in polar coordinates) or by using the change of variables formula in Chapter 13.

NOTE 3: After rewriting the expression $f(x,y,z)$ in cylindrical coordinates, be sure to include the expression r with it in the integrand.

Example 12.6.2 (Triple Integrals in Cylindrical Coordinates)

Problem: For each of the following solids E, sketch the solid E and use iterated integrals in cylindrical coordinates to compute the indicated triple integrals.

Part (a): E: Bounded by $\theta = 0, \theta = \frac{\pi}{2}, r = 0, r = 1 + \sin\theta, z = 0, z = r\cos\theta$.

Compute the volume $V = \iiint_E 1\,dV$ and $\iiint_E y\,dV$

Solution Part (a): The equations $\theta = 0, \theta = \frac{\pi}{2}$ are for two coordinate surfaces (planes in this case), and the equation $r = 1 + \sin\theta$ gives a cardioidal cylinder (which we sketched in Figure 12.6.2 by drawing the cardioid $r = 1 + \sin\theta$ in the x-y plane and then translating it in the z-direction). The equation $z = 0$ is a coordinate surface (the x-y plane) and the equation $z = r\cos\theta$ represents a plane as well. To see this, change the cylindrical equation to one in Cartesian coordinates to get $z = x$. You can sketch this plane by drawing the line $z = x$ in the x-z plane and translating it in the y-direction. To sketch the solid, take the cardioidal cylinder in Figure 12.6.2 and cut it off on the sides with the vertical planes $\theta = 0, \theta = \frac{\pi}{2}$ and on top and bottom by the planes $z = x$ and $z = 0$. Figure 12.6.6 shows the result.

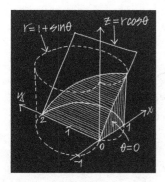

Figure 12.6.6: *A wedge from a cardioidal cylinder.*

The volume of this solid is

$$
\begin{aligned}
V &= \iiint_E 1\,dV = \int_{\theta=0}^{\theta=\pi/2}\int_{r=0}^{r=1+\sin\theta}\int_{z=0}^{z=r\cos\theta} 1\cdot r\,dz\,dr\,d\theta \\
&= \int_{\theta=0}^{\theta=\pi/2}\int_{r=0}^{r=1+\sin\theta} \left[rz\right]\Big|_0^{r\cos\theta}\,dr\,d\theta = \int_{\theta=0}^{\theta=\pi/2}\int_{r=0}^{r=1+\sin\theta} \left[r^2\cos\theta\right]\,dr\,d\theta \\
&= \int_{\theta=0}^{\theta=\pi/2}\left[\tfrac{1}{3}r^3\cos\theta\right]\Big|_0^{1+\sin\theta}\,d\theta = \int_0^{\pi/2}\tfrac{1}{3}(1+\sin\theta)^3\cos\theta\,d\theta \\
&= \int_1^2 \tfrac{1}{3}u^3\,du = \tfrac{1}{12}u^4\Big|_1^2 = \tfrac{1}{12}[16-1] = \frac{5}{4}
\end{aligned}
$$

Note: To get the last line above, we used the substitution $u = 1 + \sin\theta, du =$

$\cos\theta\,d\theta$. Next, for $f(x, y, z) = y$, we have $f(r\cos\theta, r\sin\theta, z) = r\sin\theta$. So,

$$
\begin{aligned}
\iiint_E y\, dV &= \int_{\theta=0}^{\theta=\pi/2} \int_{r=0}^{r=1+\sin\theta} \int_{z=0}^{z=r\cos\theta} r^2\sin\theta\, dzdrd\theta \\
&= \int_{\theta=0}^{\theta=\pi/2} \int_{r=0}^{r=1+\sin\theta} (r^2\sin\theta)\, z\Big|_0^{r\cos\theta}\, drd\theta = \int_{\theta=0}^{\theta=\pi/2} \int_{r=0}^{r=1+\sin\theta} \left[r^3\sin\theta\cos\theta \right] drd\theta \\
&= \int_{\theta=0}^{\theta=\pi/2} \left[\tfrac{1}{4} r^4\sin\theta\cos\theta \right]\Big|_0^{1+\sin\theta}\, d\theta = \int_0^{\pi/2} \tfrac{1}{4}(1+\sin\theta)^4\sin\theta\cos\theta\, d\theta \\
&= \int_1^2 \tfrac{1}{4} u^4(u-1)\, du = \tfrac{1}{4}\left[\tfrac{1}{6} u^6 - \tfrac{1}{5} u^5 \right]\Big|_1^2 = \frac{129}{120}
\end{aligned}
$$

Again, we used the substitution $u = 1 + \sin\theta$, $du = \cos\theta\,d\theta$ to compute the last integral.

Part (b): E: Bounded by $\theta = 0$, $\theta = 2\pi$, $z = -1$, $z = 1$, $r = 0$, $r = z^2$.

Compute the volume $V = \iiint_E 1\, dV$ and $\iiint_E (x + y + 14z^2)\, dV$

Solution Part (b): We did the sketch of this in Part(b) of Example 12.6.1. See Figure 12.6.3.

The volume of this solid is

$$
\begin{aligned}
V &= \iiint_E 1\, dV = \int_{\theta=0}^{\theta=2\pi} \int_{z=-1}^{z=1} \int_{r=0}^{r=z^2} 1 \cdot r\, drdzd\theta \\
&= \int_{\theta=0}^{\theta=2\pi} \int_{z=-1}^{z=1} \left[\tfrac{1}{2} r^2 \right]\Big|_{r=0}^{r=z^2}\, dzd\theta = \int_{\theta=0}^{\theta=2\pi} \int_{z=-1}^{z=1} \left[\tfrac{1}{2} z^4 \right] dzd\theta \\
&= 2\pi \left[\tfrac{1}{10} z^5 \right]\Big|_{-1}^1 = \frac{2\pi}{5}
\end{aligned}
$$

Next for $f(x, y, z) = x + y + 14z^2$, we have $f(r\cos\theta, r\sin\theta, z) = r\cos\theta + r\sin\theta + 14z^2 = r(\cos\theta + \sin\theta) + 14z^2$. So,

$$
\begin{aligned}
\iiint_E (x+y+14z^2)\, dV &= \int_{\theta=0}^{\theta=2\pi} \int_{z=-1}^{z=1} \int_{r=0}^{r=z^2} \left[r^2(\cos\theta+\sin\theta) + 14rz^2 \right] drdzd\theta \\
&= \int_{\theta=0}^{\theta=2\pi} \int_{z=-1}^{z=1} \left[\tfrac{1}{3} r^3(\cos\theta+\sin\theta) + 7r^2z^2 \right]\Big|_{r=0}^{r=z^2}\, dzd\theta \\
&= \int_{\theta=0}^{\theta=2\pi} \int_{z=-1}^{z=1} \left[\tfrac{1}{3} z^6(\cos\theta+\sin\theta) + 7z^6 \right] dzd\theta \\
&= \int_{\theta=0}^{\theta=2\pi} \left[\tfrac{1}{21} z^7(\cos\theta+\sin\theta) + z^7 \right]\Big|_{z=-1}^{z=1}\, d\theta = \int_0^{2\pi} \left[\tfrac{2}{21}(\cos\theta+\sin\theta) + 2 \right] d\theta = 4\pi
\end{aligned}
$$

Part (c): E: Bounded by $\theta = 0$, $\theta = \frac{\pi}{2}$, $z = 0$, $z = \theta$, $r = 1$, $r = 2$.

Compute $V = \iiint_E 1\, dV$ and $\iiint_E 3x\, dV$

Solution Part (c): The top boundary of this solid is the part of the ribbon cylinder $z = \theta$ shown in Figure 12.6.4. The bottom boundary is the plane $z = 0$ (the x-y plane). The side boundaries are the two cylinders $r = 1$, $r = 2$ and two vertical planes $\theta = 0$ (the x-z plane), $\theta = \frac{\pi}{2}$. A sketch of this solid is shown in Figure 12.6.7.

The volume of this solid is

$$
\begin{aligned}
V &= \iiint_E 1\, dV = \int_{\theta=0}^{\theta=\frac{\pi}{2}} \int_{z=0}^{z=\theta} \int_{r=1}^{r=2} 1 \cdot r\, drdzd\theta \\
&= \int_{\theta=0}^{\theta=\frac{\pi}{2}} \int_{z=0}^{z=\theta} \left[\tfrac{1}{2} r^2 \right]\Big|_{r=1}^{r=2}\, dzd\theta = \int_{\theta=0}^{\theta=\frac{\pi}{2}} \int_{z=0}^{z=\theta} \tfrac{3}{2}\, dzd\theta \\
&= \int_{\theta=0}^{\theta=\frac{\pi}{2}} \tfrac{3}{2}\theta\, d\theta = \tfrac{3}{4}\theta^2\Big|_0^{\frac{\pi}{2}} = \frac{3\pi^2}{16}
\end{aligned}
$$

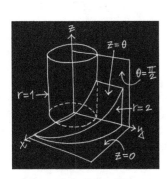

Figure 12.6.7: *A solid bounded by the ribbon cylinder $z = \theta$ on top.*

Next, the polar expression for $3x$ is $x = 3r \cos \theta$, so the triple integral is

$$\iiint_E x \, dV = \int_{\theta=0}^{\theta=\frac{\pi}{2}} \int_{z=0}^{z=\theta} \int_{r=1}^{r=2} 3r^2 \cos \theta \, dr \, dz \, d\theta$$

$$= \int_{\theta=0}^{\theta=\frac{\pi}{2}} \int_{z=0}^{z=\theta} \left[r^3 \cos \theta \right] \Big|_{r=1}^{r=2} dz \, d\theta = \int_{\theta=0}^{\theta=\frac{\pi}{2}} \int_{z=0}^{z=\theta} 7 \cos \theta \, dz \, d\theta$$

$$= \int_{\theta=0}^{\theta=\frac{\pi}{2}} 7\theta \cos \theta \, d\theta = 7 \big[\theta \sin \theta + \cos \theta \big] \Big|_0^{\frac{\pi}{2}} = 7 \big[\tfrac{\pi}{2} - 1 \big]$$

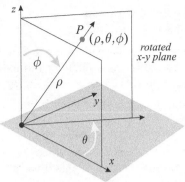

Figure 12.6.8: *Spherical coordinates of a point P.*

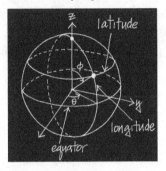

Figure 12.6.9: *A globe.*

Spherical to Cartesian	
$x = \rho \sin \phi \cos \theta$	(12.6.6a)
$y = \rho \sin \phi \sin \theta$	(12.6.6b)
$z = \rho \cos \phi$	(12.6.6c)

Cartesian to Spherical	
$\rho = \pm\sqrt{x^2 + y^2 + z^2}$	(12.6.7a)
$\theta = \tan^{-1}\left(\dfrac{y}{x} \right)$	(12.6.7b)
$\phi = \tan^{-1}\left(\dfrac{\sqrt{x^2 + y^2}}{z} \right)$	(12.6.7c)

Figure 12.6.10: *Half of the surface $\rho = 2 \sin \theta$.*

SPHERICAL COORDINATES

We assign spherical coordinates to a point P in space as follows. Rotate the x-z plane about the z-axis until it contains the point P. Let θ be the angle this rotated plane makes with the original x-z plane, In the rotated plane, rotate the z-axis until it passes through P. Let ϕ be the angle the rotated axis makes with the original z-axis. Finally, let ρ be the distance of P from the origin. Then (ρ, θ, ϕ) are spherical coordinates for P. See Figure 12.6.8.

NOTE 1: The angle ϕ is angle between $\overrightarrow{OP}$ and the unit vector $\mathbf{k}$. So $\phi = 0$ for points on the positive z-axis, $\phi = \pi$ for points on the negative part of the z-axis, and $\phi = \frac{\pi}{2}$ for points in the x-y plane.

NOTE 2: Be cautioned that physics books take ϕ to be the angle between $\overrightarrow{OP}$ and the x-y plane. But, traditionally all math books use ϕ as we have just described it.

NOTE 3: The set of all points P at a given distance ρ_0 from the origin is, of course, a sphere. Then, the two angles θ and ϕ describe the position of P on this sphere. The *latitude* and *longitude* lines on our globe are based on this model. See Figure 12.6.9, Caution: Latitude angles, as in physics books, are measured from the equator. So points along the equator have latitude zero.

The relationship between the spherical coordinates (ρ, θ, ϕ) and Cartesian coordinates (x, y, z) of a point P in space are shown in the box in the margin. The equations shown allow us, as we did in Section 9.4, to changes coordinates from one system to the other and also to change equations given in Cartesian coordinates to corresponding ones in spherical coordinates (and vice versa).

Spherical Equations for Surfaces

An equation such as $K(\rho, \theta, \phi) = 0$ is called a *spherical equation* and the set of all points P in space whose spherical coordinates satisfy $K(\rho, \theta, \phi) = 0$ is a surface in $\mathbb{R}^3$ (or a degenerate case of a surface). Understanding and plotting surfaces given by spherical equations can be difficult, but is somewhat easier for a special class of surfaces whose equations have one of the coordinate variables (either ρ or θ or ϕ) missing from the equation. These are called *cylinders* (or *generalized cylinders*) in spherical coordinates. This concept is analogous that discussed above for cylinders in cylindrical coordinates. Here, however, *none* of these surfaces is a cylinder (or generalized cylinder) in the sense of Section 10.6.

$$\rho = g(\theta) \qquad \text{(Type I: A Polar Surface of Radial Revolution)}$$
$$\rho = h(\phi) \qquad \text{(Type II: A Polar Surface of Revolution)}$$
$$\phi = k(\theta) \qquad \text{(Type III: A Ribbon Surface)}$$

NOTE: In each of these types, the functional relation between the variables could be just the opposite, i.e., $\theta = G(\rho)$, $\phi = H(\rho)$ and $\theta = K(\phi)$.

Example 12.6.3 (The Three Types of Cylinders in Spherical Coordinates)

Problem: Consider the following cylinders in spherical coordinates:

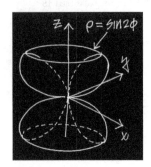

Figure 12.6.11: *A rose surface of revolution.*

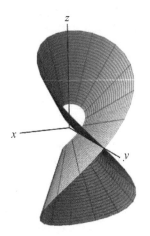

Figure 12.6.12: *The ribbon cylinder $\phi = \theta$.*

(a) $\rho = 2 \sin \theta$ (b) $\rho = \sin 2\phi$, for ϕ in $[0, \pi]$ (c) $\phi = \theta$

Sketch the first two cylinders and use a CAS to plot the third one.

Solution Part (a): The key here is to sketch the curve with polar equation $\rho = 2 \sin \theta$ in the x-y plane (where $\phi = \frac{\pi}{2}$). This curve you recognize as a circle of radius 1 which is tangent to the x-axis. Then for each point P on this curve revolve, in both directions, the vector $\overrightarrow{OP}$ toward the z-axis keeping it in the plane containing $\overrightarrow{OP}$ and the z-axis. This sweeps out a semi-circle on the surface. Sketching a number of these semi-circles will delineate *half* of the surface. Figure 12.6.10 shows the result. NOTE: You must revolve from $\phi = 0$ to $\phi = 2\pi$, so that each point traces out a full circle (passing through the z-axis) to get the *full* surface. All of this illustrates why we have called these surfaces of *radial revolution*.

Solution Part (b): We sketch the polar curve $\rho = \sin 2\phi$ (a rose curve with 4 petals) in the x-z plane. Then revolve this curve about the z-axis to get the surface. A sketch is shown in Figure 12.6.11 It is an exercise to show that, in general, the spherical equation $\rho = h(\phi)$ is a surface of revolution.

Solution Part (c): Figure 12.6.4 shows a computer plot of this Type III cylinder.

Coordinate Surfaces: Type I, II, or III cylinders have equations involving only two of the coordinate variables. In the special case of this when the equations involve only *one* variable, we get cylinders that are called *coordinate surfaces*. These are:

$\rho \;=\; \rho_0$ (A sphere of radius ρ_0 centered at the origin)

$\theta \;=\; \theta_0$ (A vertical plane through z-axis at angle θ_0 to the x-axis)

$\phi \;=\; \phi_0$ (A cone generated by revolving $z = (\cot \phi_0)x$ about the z-axis)

These surfaces, as shown in Figure 12.6.13, intersect in the point P with spherical coordinates $(\rho_0, \theta_0, \phi_0)$.

Triple Integrals in Spherical Coordinates

As with triple integrals in cylindrical coordinates, a triple integral $\iiint_E f(x, y, z)\,dV$ can be computed by six different iterated triple integrals in spherical coordinates. This requires that E be one of the following types of solids:

Type I Solids: These are solids E bounded by the six surfaces:

$\theta = \alpha,\; \theta = \beta$ (Two vertical planes through the z-axis)

$\rho = g(\theta),\; \rho = h(\theta)$ (Two polar spheres)

$\phi = G(\rho, \theta),\; \phi = H(\rho, \theta)$ (Two general surfaces)

Type II Solids: These are solids E bounded by the six surfaces:

$\phi = \alpha,\; \phi = \beta$ (Two cones)

$\rho = g(\phi),\; \rho = h(\phi)$ (Two surfaces of revolution)

$\theta = G(\rho, \phi),\; \theta = H(\rho, \phi)$ (Two general surfaces)

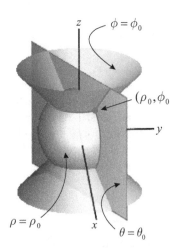

Figure 12.6.13: *Spherical coordinate surfaces.*

Type III Solids: These are solids E bounded by the six surfaces:

$\theta = \alpha,\; \theta = \beta$ (Two vertical planes through the z-axis)

$\phi = g(\theta),\; \phi = h(\theta)$ (Two ribbon surfaces)

$\rho = G(\theta, \phi),\; \rho = H(\theta, \phi)$ (Two general surfaces)

NOTE 1: For each of these types of solid, there is related solid where the variables in the first two equations are interchanged. Thus, there are six types of solids we can use iterated integrals on.

NOTE 2: For each type of solid, the equations for the bounding surfaces give the limits of integration in the iterated integrals. This is illustrated in the following theorem.

THEOREM 12.6.2 (Triple Integrals in Spherical Coordinates)

Suppose f is continuous on a solid E in its domain. If E is a Type I, II, or III solid,

then the triple integral of f over E is given by

TYPE I: (12.6.8)

$$\iiint_E f(x,y,z)\,dV = \int_{\theta=\alpha}^{\theta=\beta} \int_{\rho=g(\theta)}^{\rho=h(\theta)} \int_{\phi=G(\rho,\theta)}^{\phi=H(\rho,\theta)} f(\rho\sin\phi\cos\theta, \rho\sin\phi\sin\theta, \rho\cos\phi)\,\rho^2\sin\phi\,d\phi\,d\rho\,d\theta$$

TYPE II: (12.6.9)

$$\iiint_E f(x,y,z)\,dV = \int_{\phi=\alpha}^{\phi=\beta} \int_{\rho=g(\phi)}^{\rho=h(\phi)} \int_{\theta=G(\rho,\phi)}^{\theta=H(\rho,\phi)} f(\rho\sin\phi\cos\theta, \rho\sin\phi\sin\theta, \rho\cos\phi)\,\rho^2\sin\phi\,d\theta\,d\rho\,d\phi$$

TYPE III: (12.6.10)

$$\iiint_E f(x,y,z)\,dV = \int_{\theta=\alpha}^{\theta=\beta} \int_{\phi=g(\theta)}^{\phi=h(\theta)} \int_{\rho=G(\theta,\phi)}^{\rho=H(\theta,\phi)} f(\rho\sin\phi\cos\theta, \rho\sin\phi\sin\theta, \rho\cos\phi)\,\rho^2\sin\phi\,d\rho\,d\phi\,d\theta$$

This theorem can be proven using limits of Riemann sums (as we did for double integrals in polar coordinates) or by using the change of variables formula in Chapter 13.

NOTE 3: After rewriting the expression $f(x,y,z)$ in spherical coordinates, be sure to include the expression $\rho^2\sin\phi$ with it in the integrand.

Example 12.6.4 (Triple Integrals in Spherical Coordinates)

Problem: For each of the following solids E, sketch the solid E and use iterated integrals in spherical coordinates to compute the indicated triple integrals.

Part (a): E: Bounded by $\theta = 0, \theta = \pi, \phi = 0, \phi = \pi, \rho = 0, \rho = 2\sin\theta$.

Compute the volume $V = \iiint_E 1\,dV$ and $\iiint_E z^2\,dV$

Solution Part (a): The solid E is the one from Part (a) of Example 12.6.3 and a sketch of it is shown in Figure 12.6.10. The volume is computed by

$$
\begin{aligned}
V &= \iiint_E 1\,dV = \int_{\theta=0}^{\theta=\pi} \int_{\phi=0}^{\phi=\pi} \int_{\rho=0}^{\rho=2\sin\theta} 1 \cdot \rho^2\sin\phi\,d\rho\,d\phi\,d\theta \\
&= \int_{\theta=0}^{\theta=\pi} \int_{\phi=0}^{\phi=\pi} \left[\tfrac{1}{3}\rho^3\sin\phi\right]\Big|_{\rho=0}^{\rho=2\sin\theta} d\phi\,d\theta = \int_{\theta=0}^{\theta=\pi} \int_{\phi=0}^{\phi=\pi} \left[\tfrac{8}{3}\sin^3\theta\,\sin\phi\right] d\phi\,d\theta \\
&= \int_{\theta=0}^{\theta=\pi} \tfrac{8}{3}\sin^3\theta\,d\theta \cdot \int_{\phi=0}^{\phi=\pi} \sin\phi\,d\phi = \int_{\theta=0}^{\theta=\pi} \tfrac{8}{3}(1-\cos^2\theta)\sin\theta\,d\theta \cdot \left[-\cos\phi\right]\Big|_0^\pi \\
&= \tfrac{16}{3}\int_1^{-1}(1-u^2)(-du) = \tfrac{16}{3}\int_{-1}^1(1-u^2)\,du = \tfrac{16}{3}\left[u - \tfrac{1}{3}u^3\right]\Big|_{-1}^1 = \frac{64}{9}
\end{aligned}
$$

In the last line above, we used the substitution $u = \cos\theta$, $du = -\sin\theta\,d\theta$. Next, the expression for z^2 in spherical coordinates is $z^2 = (\rho\cos\phi)^2 = \rho^2\cos^2\phi$. So

$$
\begin{aligned}
\iiint_E z^2\,dV &= \int_{\theta=0}^{\theta=\pi} \int_{\phi=0}^{\phi=\pi} \int_{\rho=0}^{\rho=2\sin\theta} \rho^4\cos^2\phi\sin\phi\,d\rho\,d\phi\,d\theta \\
&= \int_{\theta=0}^{\theta=\pi} \int_{\phi=0}^{\phi=\pi} \left[\tfrac{1}{5}\rho^5\cos^2\phi\sin\phi\right]\Big|_{\rho=0}^{\rho=2\sin\theta} d\phi\,d\theta \\
&= \int_{\theta=0}^{\theta=\pi} \int_{\phi=0}^{\phi=\pi} \left[\tfrac{32}{5}\sin^5\theta\,\cos^2\phi\,\sin\phi\right] d\phi\,d\theta
\end{aligned}
$$

$$= \int_{\theta=0}^{\theta=\pi} \tfrac{32}{5} \sin^5 \theta \, d\theta \cdot \int_{\phi=0}^{\phi=\pi} \cos \phi^2 \sin \phi \, d\phi$$

$$= \int_{\theta=0}^{\theta=\pi} \tfrac{32}{5}(1 - \cos^2 \theta)^2 \sin \theta \, d\theta \cdot \left[-\tfrac{1}{3}\cos^3 \phi\right]\Big|_0^\pi$$

$$= \tfrac{32}{5} \int_1^{-1} (1 - u^2)^2 (-du) \cdot \tfrac{2}{3} = \tfrac{64}{15} \int_{-1}^1 (1 - 2u^2 + u^4) du$$

$$= \tfrac{64}{15} \left[u - \tfrac{2}{3}u^3 + \tfrac{1}{5}u^5\right]\Big|_{-1}^1 = \frac{1024}{225}$$

Part (b): E: Bounded by $\theta = 0, \theta = 2\pi, \phi = 0, \phi = \pi/2, \rho = 0, \rho = \sin 2\phi$.
Compute the volume $V = \iiint_E 1 \, dV$ and $\iiint_E \tfrac{45}{32} x^2 \, dV$

Solution Part (b): The solid E is the one from Part (b) of Example 12.6.3 and a sketch of it is shown in Figure 12.6.11. The volume is computed by

$$V = \iiint_E 1 \, dV = \int_{\theta=0}^{\theta=2\pi} \int_{\phi=0}^{\phi=\frac{\pi}{2}} \int_{\rho=0}^{\rho=\sin 2\phi} 1 \cdot \rho^2 \sin \phi \, d\rho d\phi d\theta$$

$$= \int_{\theta=0}^{\theta=2\pi} \int_{\phi=0}^{\phi=\frac{\pi}{2}} \left[\tfrac{1}{3}\rho^3 \sin \phi\right]\Big|_{\rho=0}^{\rho=\sin 2\phi} d\phi d\theta = \int_{\theta=0}^{\theta=2\pi} \int_{\phi=0}^{\phi=\frac{\pi}{2}} \tfrac{1}{3}\sin^3 2\phi \sin \phi \, d\phi d\theta$$

$$= \int_{\theta=0}^{\theta=2\pi} 1 \, d\theta \cdot \int_{\phi=0}^{\phi=\frac{\pi}{2}} \tfrac{1}{3}(2 \sin \phi \cos \phi)^3 \sin \phi \, d\phi = 2\pi \int_{\phi=0}^{\phi=\frac{\pi}{2}} \tfrac{8}{3}\sin^4 \phi \cos^3 \phi \, d\phi$$

$$= \tfrac{16\pi}{3} \int_{\phi=0}^{\phi=\frac{\pi}{2}} \sin^4 \phi (1 - \sin^2 \phi) \cos \phi \, d\phi = \tfrac{16\pi}{3} \int_0^1 u^4 (1 - u^2) \, du$$

$$= \tfrac{16\pi}{3} \left[\tfrac{1}{5}u^5 - \tfrac{1}{7}u^7\right]\Big|_0^1 = \frac{32\pi}{105}$$

In the last line above, we used the substitution $u = \sin \phi$, $du = \cos \phi \, d\phi$. The expression $\tfrac{45}{32}x^2 = \tfrac{45}{32}(\rho \sin \phi \cos \theta)^2 = \tfrac{45}{32}\rho^2 \sin^2 \phi \cos^2 \theta$. So

$$\iiint_E \frac{45}{32} x^2 \, dV = \int_{\theta=0}^{\theta=2\pi} \int_{\phi=0}^{\phi=\frac{\pi}{2}} \int_{\rho=0}^{\rho=\sin 2\phi} \tfrac{45}{32}\rho^4 \sin^3 \phi \cos^2 \theta \, d\rho d\phi d\theta$$

$$= \int_{\theta=0}^{\theta=2\pi} \int_{\phi=0}^{\phi=\frac{\pi}{2}} \left[\tfrac{9}{32}\rho^5 \sin^3 \phi \cos^2 \theta\right]\Big|_{\rho=0}^{\rho=\sin 2\phi} d\phi d\theta$$

$$= \int_{\theta=0}^{\theta=2\pi} \int_{\phi=0}^{\phi=\frac{\pi}{2}} \tfrac{9}{32}\sin^5 2\phi \sin^3 \phi \cos^2 \theta \, d\phi d\theta$$

$$= \int_{\theta=0}^{\theta=2\pi} \cos^2 \theta \, d\theta \cdot \int_{\phi=0}^{\phi=\frac{\pi}{2}} \tfrac{9}{32}(2 \sin \phi \cos \phi)^5 \sin^3 \phi \, d\phi$$

$$= \int_{\theta=0}^{\theta=2\pi} \left(\tfrac{1}{2} + \tfrac{1}{2}\cos 2\theta\right) d\theta \cdot \int_{\phi=0}^{\phi=\frac{\pi}{2}} 9 \sin^8 \phi \cos^5 \phi \, d\phi$$

$$= \left(\tfrac{1}{2}\theta + \tfrac{1}{4}\sin 2\theta\right)\Big|_0^{2\pi} \int_{\phi=0}^{\phi=\frac{\pi}{2}} 9 \sin^8 \phi (1 - \sin^2 \phi)^2 \cos \phi \, d\phi$$

$$= \pi \int_0^1 9u^8 (1 - u^2)^2 \, du = \pi \int_0^1 9(u^8 - 2u^{10} + u^{12}) \, du$$

$$= 9\pi \left[\tfrac{1}{9}u^9 - \tfrac{2}{11}u^{11} + \tfrac{1}{13}u^{13}\right]\Big|_0^1 = \frac{72\pi}{1287}$$

Solids of Revolution

In Section 5.4 we used the washer and shell methods to obtain integral formulas for certain solids of revolution. These solids are obtained by revolving a Type I of

Type II region in the plane about either the x-axis or the y-axis. The analog of this here is a solid obtained by taking a polar region: $\rho = g(\phi)$, $\rho = h(\phi)$, $\phi = \alpha$, $\phi = \beta$, which is graphed in the x-z plane, and revolving it about the z-axis. This is a solid bounded by a Type II cylinder in spherical coordinates. We call these solids *polar solids of revolution*. Figure 12.6.11 illustrates a typical example of such a solid and Example 12.6.4 shows the calculation of its volume.

The general formula for the volume of a polar solid of revolution is easy to derive using triple integrals in spherical coordinates. Namely,

$$
\begin{aligned}
V &= \int_{\theta=0}^{\theta=2\pi} \int_{\phi=\alpha}^{\phi=\beta} \int_{\rho=g(\phi)}^{\rho=h(\phi)} \rho^2 \sin\phi \, d\rho \, d\phi \, d\theta \\
&= \int_{\theta=0}^{\theta=2\pi} \int_{\phi=\alpha}^{\phi=\beta} \frac{1}{3}\rho^3 \sin\phi \Big)\Big|_{\rho=g(\phi)}^{\rho=h(\phi)} d\phi \, d\theta \\
&= \int_{\theta=0}^{\theta=2\pi} 1 \, d\theta \cdot \int_{\phi=\alpha}^{\phi=\beta} \left(\frac{1}{3}[h(\phi)]^3 \sin\phi - [g(\phi)]^3 \sin\phi \right) d\phi \\
&= \frac{2\pi}{3} \int_{\phi=\alpha}^{\phi=\beta} \left([h(\phi)]^3 - [g(\phi)]^3 \right) \sin\phi \, d\phi
\end{aligned}
$$

We record the result in the following box.

Volume of a Polar Solid of Revolution

$$
V = \frac{2\pi}{3} \int_{\phi=\alpha}^{\phi=\beta} \left([h(\phi)]^3 - [g(\phi)]^3 \right) \sin\phi \, d\phi \qquad (12.6.11)
$$

There is another type of solid of revolution that arises from the use of spherical coordinates and it involves a new way of revolving curves or regions to obtain surfaces or solids. Instead of revolving a polar curve $r = g(\theta)$, $\alpha \leq \theta \leq \beta$, in the x-y plane about an axis, we revolve each point on the curve through a full circular arc ($0 \leq \phi \leq 2\pi$) passing through the z-axis. This gives a Type I cylinder $\rho = g(\theta)$, in spherical coordinates, which we call, a polar surface of radial revolution. This surface and planes $\theta = \alpha$, $\theta = \beta$, enclose a *polar solid of radial revolution*. More generally, consider the polar solid of radial revolution bounded by two such surfaces $\rho = g(\theta), \rho = h(\theta)$ and two planes $\theta = \alpha$, $\theta = \beta$ (with $g(\theta) \leq h(\theta)$ for θ in $[\alpha, \beta]$). This type of solid has a special volume formula:

Volume of a Polar Solid of Radial Revolution

$$
V = \frac{4}{3} \int_{\theta=\alpha}^{\theta=\beta} \left([h(\theta)]^3 - [g(\theta)]^3 \right) d\theta \qquad (12.6.12)
$$

As an exercise you can use triple integrals in spherical coordinates to easily derive this formula. HINT: Measure the volume of half the solid by restricting the integral with respect to ϕ to the interval $[0, \pi]$ (which is where $\sin\phi \geq 0$). Then double the result.

CAUTION: Figure 12.6.10 is an example of this where the sketch is *half* of the surface $\rho = 2\sin\theta$. Example 12.6.4 computes the volume of the solid enclosed by this half of the surface. Formula 12.6.12 gives double this. Consult the figures in the Preface and in the answers to Exercises 51 and 53 to view typical *full* solids of this type.

Exercises: 12.6 (Triple Integrals in Cylindrical and Spherical Coordinates)

Triple Integrals in Cylindrical Coordinates

In Exercises 1–10, use cylindrical coordinates to compute the specified triple integral $\iiint_E f(x,,y,z)\,dV$ over the given solid E.

1. $\iiint_E 8y\,dV,\ E: \theta = 0, \theta = \frac{\pi}{2},\ r = 0, r = \sin 2\theta,$
$z = 0, z = r\cos\theta$

2. $\iiint_E 8y\,dV,\ E: \theta = 0, \theta = \frac{\pi}{2},\ r = 0, r = 3\sin 2\theta,$
$z = 0, z = r\cos\theta$

3. $\iiint_E 4y\,dV,\ E: \theta = 0, \theta = \frac{\pi}{2},\ r = 0, r = 2\sin\theta,$
$z = 0, z = r\cos\theta$

4. $\iiint_E 4x\,dV,\ E: \theta = 0, \theta = \frac{\pi}{2},\ r = 0, r = 2\cos\theta,$
$z = 0, z = r\sin\theta$

5. $\iiint_E 4x^2\,dV,\ E: \theta = 0, \theta = 2\pi,\ z = 0, z = 1,$
$r = 0, r = z^3$

6. $\iiint_E 4y^2\,dV,\ E: \theta = 0, \theta = 2\pi,\ z = 0, z = 1,$
$r = 0, r = z^4$

7. $\iiint_E \frac{2}{1+x^2+y^2}\,dV,\ E: \theta = 0, \theta = 2\pi,$
$z = 0, z = 4, r = 0, r = \sqrt{z}$

8. $\iiint_E \frac{2}{2+x^2+y^2}\,dV,\ E: \theta = 0, \theta = 2\pi,$
$z = 0, z = 3, r = 0, r = \sqrt{z}$

9. $\iiint_E 2\cos(x^2+y^2)\,dV,\ E: \theta = 0, \theta = 2\pi,$
$z = 0, z = \pi,\ r = 0, r = \sqrt{z}$

10. $\iiint_E 2\sin(x^2+y^2)\,dV,\ E: \theta = 0, \theta = 2\pi,$
$z = 0, z = \frac{\pi}{2},\ r = 0, r = \sqrt{z}$

Triple Integrals in Spherical Coordinates

In Exercises 11–30, use spherical coordinates to compute the specified triple integral $\iiint_E f(x,,y,z)\,dV$ over the given solid E.

11. $\iiint_E z^2\,dV,\ E: \theta = -\frac{\pi}{2}, \theta = \frac{\pi}{2},\ \phi = 0, \phi = \pi,$
$\rho = 0, \rho = 2\cos\theta$

12. $\iiint_E z^2\,dV,\ E: \theta = -\frac{\pi}{2}, \theta = \frac{\pi}{2},\ \phi = 0, \phi = \pi,$
$\rho = 0, \rho = 4\cos\theta$

13. $\iiint_E 5z^2\,dV,\ E: \theta = 0, \theta = \frac{\pi}{2},\ \phi = 0, \phi = \pi,$
$\rho = 0, \rho = \sin 2\theta$

14. $\iiint_E 5z^2\,dV,\ E: \theta = 0, \theta = \frac{\pi}{2},\ \phi = 0, \phi = \pi,$
$\rho = 0, \rho = 2\sin 2\theta$

15. $\iiint_E 4z\,dV,\ E: \theta = 0, \theta = \pi,\ \phi = 0, \phi = \frac{\pi}{2},$
$\rho = 0, \rho = \theta$

16. $\iiint_E 4z\,dV,\ E: \theta = 0, \theta = \pi,\ \phi = 0, \phi = \frac{\pi}{2},$
$\rho = 0, \rho = \sqrt{\theta}$

17. $\iiint_E 4\sqrt{x^2+y^2+z^2}\,dV,\ E: \theta = 0, \theta = 2\pi,$
$\phi = 0, \phi = \pi,\ \rho = 0, \rho = 2\cos\phi$

18. $\iiint_E 6(x^2+y^2+z^2)^{3/2}\,dV,\ E: \theta = 0, \theta = 2\pi,$
$\phi = 0, \phi = \pi,\ \rho = 0, \rho = 2\cos\phi$

19. $\iiint_E 4\sqrt{x^2+y^2+z^2}\,dV,\ E: \theta = 0, \theta = 2\pi,$
$\phi = 0, \phi = \frac{\pi}{2},\ \rho = 0, \rho = 1+\cos\phi$

20. $\iiint_E 6(x^2+y^2+z^2)^{3/2}\,dV,\ E: \theta = 0, \theta = 2\pi,$
$\phi = 0, \phi = \frac{\pi}{2},\ \rho = 0, \rho = 1+\cos\phi$

21. $\iiint_E 4z\,dV,\ E: \theta = 0, \theta = 2\pi,\ \phi = 0, \phi = \frac{\pi}{2},$
$\rho = 0, \rho = \cos\phi$

22. $\iiint_E 5z^2\,dV,\ E: \theta = 0, \theta = 2\pi,\ \phi = 0, \phi = \frac{\pi}{2},$
$\rho = 0, \rho = \cos\phi$

23. $\iiint_E 5x^2\,dV,\ E: \theta = 0, \theta = 2\pi,\ \phi = 0, \phi = \frac{\pi}{2},$
$\rho = 0, \rho = 1-\cos\phi$

24. $\iiint_E 5y^2\,dV,\ E: \theta = 0, \theta = 2\pi,\ \phi = 0, \phi = \frac{\pi}{2},$
$\rho = 0, \rho = 1-\cos\phi$

25. $\iiint_E 5y^2\,dV,\ E: \theta = 0, \theta = 2\pi,\ \phi = 0, \phi = \frac{\pi}{2},$
$\rho = 0, \rho = \sin 2\phi$

26. $\iiint_E 4z\,dV,\ E: \theta = 0, \theta = 2\pi,\ \phi = 0, \phi = \frac{\pi}{2},$
$\rho = 0, \rho = \sin 2\phi$

27. $\iiint_E \frac{1}{1+\sqrt{x^2+y^2+z^2}}\,dV,\ E: \theta = 0, \theta = 2\pi,$
$\phi = 0, \phi = \pi,\ \rho = 0, \rho = 1+\cos\phi$

28. $\iiint_E \frac{1}{1+\sqrt{x^2+y^2+z^2}}\,dV,\ E: \theta = 0, \theta = 2\pi,$
$\phi = 0, \phi = \frac{\pi}{2},\ \rho = 0, \rho = 1+\sin\phi$

29. $\iiint_E \frac{1}{1+x^2+y^2+z^2}\,dV,\ E: \theta = 0, \theta = 2\pi,$
$\phi = 0, \phi = \frac{\pi}{2},\ \rho = 0, \rho = 2\cos\phi$

30. $\iiint_E \dfrac{1}{1+x^2+y^2+z^2}\,dV,\ E:\theta=0,\theta=2\pi,$
$\phi=0,\phi=\frac{\pi}{2},\ \rho=0,\rho=3\cos\phi$

Volumes of Solids in Cylindrical Coordinates

In Exercises 31–36, compute the volume of the solid E bounded by the following surfaces.

31. $\theta=0,\theta=\frac{\pi}{2},\ r=0,r=\sin 2\theta,\ z=0,z=r\sin\theta$

32. $\theta=0,\theta=\frac{\pi}{2},\ r=0,r=3\sin 2\theta,\ z=0,z=2r\sin\theta$

33. $\theta=0,\theta=\pi,\ r=0,r=\theta^{1/3},\ z=0,z=r\sin\theta$

34. $\theta=0,\theta=\frac{\pi}{2},\ r=0,r=\theta^{1/3},\ z=0,z=r\cos\theta$

35. $\theta=0,\theta=2\pi,\ z=0,z=1,\ r=0,r=1-e^{-z}$

36. $\theta=0,\theta=2\pi,\ z=0,z=1,\ r=0,r=e^z-1$

Volumes of Solids in Spherical Coordinates

In Exercises 37–50, use Formula 12.6.11 or Formula 12.6.12 to compute the volume of the solid E bounded by the following surfaces. **CAS:** Use a computer to plot the surface(s) bounding E.

37. $\theta=0,\theta=2\pi,\ \phi=0,\phi=\pi,\ \rho=0,\rho=1+\cos\phi$

38. $\theta=0,\theta=2\pi,\ \phi=0,\phi=\frac{\pi}{2},\ \rho=0,\rho=1+\cos\phi$

39. $\theta=0,\theta=2\pi,\ \phi=0,\phi=\frac{\pi}{2},\ \rho=1,\rho=1+\cos\phi$

40. $\theta=0,\theta=2\pi,\ \phi=0,\phi=\frac{\pi}{2},\ \rho=2,\rho=2+2\cos\phi$

41. $\theta=0,\theta=2\pi,\ \phi=0,\phi=\pi,\ \rho=0,\rho=\phi^{1/3}$

42. $\theta=0,\theta=2\pi,\ \phi=0,\phi=\pi,\ \rho=0,\rho=\phi^{2/3}$

43. $\theta=0,\theta=2\pi,\ \phi=0,\phi=\frac{\pi}{2},\ \rho=0,\rho=2\cos\phi$

44. $\theta=0,\theta=2\pi,\ \phi=0,\phi=\frac{\pi}{4},\ \rho=0,\rho=2\cos\phi$

45. $\theta=0,\theta=2\pi,\ \phi=0,\phi=\pi,\ \rho=0,\rho=2\sin^{1/3}\phi$

46. $\theta=0,\theta=2\pi,\ \phi=0,\phi=\pi,\ \rho=0,\rho=2\sin^{2/3}\phi$

47. $\theta=0,\theta=2\pi,\ \phi=0,\phi=\frac{\pi}{2},$
$\rho=2\cos\phi,\rho=2+2\cos\phi$

48. $\theta=0,\theta=2\pi,\ \phi=0,\phi=\frac{\pi}{2},$
$\rho=2\cos\phi,\rho=3+3\cos\phi$

49. $\theta=0,\theta=2\pi,\ \phi=0,\phi=\pi,$
$\rho=1+\cos\phi,\rho=2+2\cos\phi$

50. $\theta=0,\theta=2\pi,\ \phi=0,\phi=\pi,$
$\rho=1+\cos\phi,\rho=3+3\cos\phi$

51. $\theta=0,\theta=\frac{\pi}{2},\ \phi=0,\phi=2\pi,\ \rho=0,\rho=2\sin 2\theta$

52. $\theta=-\frac{\pi}{2},\theta=\frac{\pi}{2},\ \phi=0,\phi=2\pi,\ \rho=0,\rho=3\cos 2\theta$

53. $\theta=-\frac{\pi}{2},\theta=\frac{\pi}{2},\ \phi=0,\phi=2\pi,\ \rho=0,\rho=4\cos\theta$

54. $\theta=0,\theta=\pi,\ \phi=0,\phi=2\pi,\ \rho=0,\rho=4\sin\theta$

55. $\theta=0,\theta=\pi,\ \phi=0,\phi=2\pi,\ \rho=2\sin\theta,\rho=4\sin\theta$

56. $\theta=-\frac{\pi}{2},\theta=\frac{\pi}{2},\ \phi=0,\phi=2\pi,\ \rho=\cos\theta,\rho=2\cos\theta$

57. $\theta=-\frac{\pi}{6},\theta=\frac{\pi}{6},\ \phi=0,\phi=2\pi,\ \rho=1,\rho=2\cos 2\theta$

58. $\theta=\frac{\pi}{12},\theta=\frac{5\pi}{12},\ \phi=0,\phi=2\pi,\ \rho=1,\rho=2\sin 2\theta$

Volumes of Snowcones

In Exercises 59–60, use spherical coordinates to describe the solid bounded by the two indicated surfaces and then find the volume of the solid. What is special about the limits of integration in the triple integral for the volume?

59.

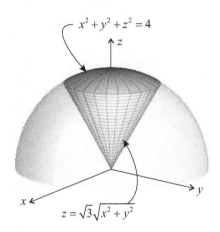

$x^2+y^2+z^2=4$

$z=\sqrt{3}\sqrt{x^2+y^2}$

60.

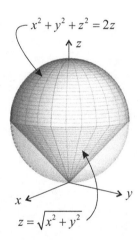

$x^2+y^2+z^2=2z$

$z=\sqrt{x^2+y^2}$

61. Use triple integrals to prove Formula 12.6.12.

62. Use triple integrals in cylindrical coordinates to derive a formula for the solid E bounded by the surfaces: $\theta=\alpha,\theta=\beta,\ z=a,z=b,\ r=g(z),r=h(z)$. Compare the formula you get with Formula 5.4.1a (Washer Method for a solid of revolution).

13

Geometry of Curves and Surfaces

Calculus *Concepts & Computation*

13.1 Space Curves and Arc Length

In this chapter we study in more detail the geometry of curves and surfaces in $\mathbb{R}^3$. As briefly discussed in Section 11.6, a general surface S in $\mathbb{R}^3$ can be described by a Cartesian equation $H(x, y, z) = 0$, while a curve C in $\mathbb{R}^3$ can be given as the intersection of two surfaces: $H(x, y, z) = 0$, $G(x, y, z) = 0$. Specifically

$$
\begin{aligned}
S &= \{ (x, y, z) \text{ in } \mathbb{R}^3 \mid H(x, y, z) = 0 \} \\
C &= \{ (x, y, z) \text{ in } \mathbb{R}^3 \mid H(x, y, z) = 0 \text{ and } G(x, y, z) = 0 \}
\end{aligned}
$$

In chapter 10, using vector methods to analyze properties of lines, planes, and triangles in space, we were doing basic Euclidean geometry. Here, since the curves and surfaces we study are not straight or flat, we will have to use derivatives (and integrals) to determine properties such as length, area, and various curvatures. This is elementary differential geometry.

For all of this, it is convenient to have the curves and surfaces in $\mathbb{R}^3$ be given by parametric equations (*parametrized*), as we did for plane curves in Chapter 9.

This first section discusses space curves and arc length and Section 13.2 does the corresponding things for surfaces in space.

Parametric Equations for Space Curves

Suppose f, g, and h are functions defined on an interval $[a, b]$ and are, where necessary, differentiable at least twice on this interval. Then

$$ x = f(t), \qquad y = g(t), \qquad z = h(t) \qquad (13.1.1) $$

for t in $[a, b]$, are called *parametric equations* for the curve C given formally by

$$ C = \{ \, (f(t), g(t), h(t)) \mid t \text{ in } [a, b] \, \} \qquad (13.1.2) $$

The independent variable t here is called a *parameter* and the set of points C comprising the curve is said to be *parametrized* by Equations (13.1.1). These equations are also called a *parameterization* of the curve C. We let $P(t) = (f(t), g(t), h(t))$ denote the point on the curve corresponding to parameter value t. Plotting the points $P(t)$ as t runs through the parameter interval $[a, b]$, from left-to-right, gives the curve in space as well as a direction on it as illustrated in Figure 13.1.1.

Sketching parametrized curves in space by-hand can be done, but we concentrate here on computer plots to help with the visualization process.

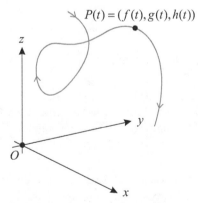

Figure 13.1.1: *A Parametrization of a curve in space.*

Example 13.1.1 (Dynamic Aspects of Parametrized Space Curves)

Problem: Use the `dcurve3d` command to create a dynamic plot (i.e., a movie) of the following curve being drawn in space.

$$ x = (1 + 2\cos t)\cos t, \qquad y = (1 + 2\cos t)\sin t, \qquad z = \tfrac{1}{4}t + \sin t, $$

for t in $[0, 4\pi]$

Solution: We first define the three functions f, g, h in Maple and then use the `dcurve3d` command as follows.

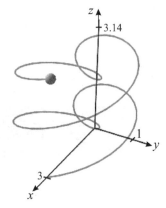

Figure 13.1.2: *A dynamic plot, using* `dcurve3d`*, of the curve:*
$$x = (1 + 2\cos t)\cos t,$$
$$y = (1 + 2\cos t)\sin t,$$
$$z = \tfrac{1}{4}t + \sin t.$$

```
> f:=t->(1+2*cos(t))*cos(t);g:=t->(1+2*cos(t))*sin(t);h:=t->t/4+sin(t);
```
$$f := t \rightarrow (1 + 2\cos t)\cos t$$
$$g := t \rightarrow (1 + 2\cos t)\sin t$$
$$h := t \rightarrow \tfrac{1}{4}t + \sin t$$
```
> dcurve3d(f,g,h,0,4*Pi,100,0);
```

This produces the desired movie and Figure 13.1.2 shows the last frame in this movie.

NOTE 1: This space curve is a particular case of the family of curves of the form:

Limaçonal Helices:

$$
\begin{aligned}
x &= (a + b\cos t)\cos t \\
y &= (a + b\cos t)\sin t \\
z &= \left[\tfrac{1}{4m}(a^2 + b^2) - m\right]t + \tfrac{1}{2m}ab\sin t
\end{aligned}
\qquad (13.1.3)
$$

for t in $[0, 2n\pi]$. The well-known (and most simple) case of this is for $b = 0$, which gives the *standard helix*:

$$x = a\cos t, \qquad y = a\sin t, \qquad z = kt \qquad (13.1.4)$$

NOTE 2: Figure 13.1.3 shows a surface on which this limaçonal helix lies. This surface is the (generalized) cylinder obtained by taking the polar curve $r = 1 + 2\cos\theta$ (a limaçon), graphed in the x-y plane and translating it in the z direction. You can more easily recognize that this space curve lies on this limaçonal surface by rotating the figure so that it is viewed looking down along the z-axis on the x-y plane.

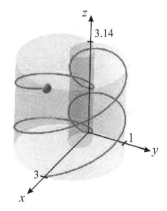

Figure 13.1.3: *A space curve lies on a generalized cylinder.*

Vector-Valued Functions

It will be convenient to think of the parametrization (13.1.1) of C as a map, or function, $\mathbf{r} : [a, b] \rightarrow \mathbb{R}^3$, with domain $[a, b]$ and range in $\mathbb{R}^3$. The function notation for this is

$$\mathbf{r}(t) = (\, f(t),\, g(t),\, h(t)\,) = P(t) \qquad (13.1.5)$$

So, the value of $\mathbf{r}$ at t is the point $P(t)$. Then the curve $C = \{\, P(t)\,|\, t \text{ in } [a, b]\, \}$ is just the graph of this function $\mathbf{r}$.

Additionally, as in Chapter 10, we can identify the point $P(t)$ with the vector $\overrightarrow{OP}(t)$. Thus, we can also view $\mathbf{r} : [a, b] \rightarrow \mathbb{R}^3$ as a *vector-valued function* and write

$$\mathbf{r}(t) = \langle\, f(t),\, g(t),\, h(t)\, \rangle = f(t)\mathbf{i} + g(t)\mathbf{j} + h(t)\mathbf{k} \qquad (13.1.6)$$

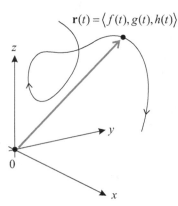

Figure 13.1.4: *A position vector for a particle motion.*

The vector $\mathbf{r}(t) = \overrightarrow{OP}(t)$, from the origin to the point $P(t)$, is called a *position vector*. This is so since the parametric equations can be thought of as describing a motion of a particle on C (which is the trajectory of the particle) and the parameter t is viewed as the time. Then at time t, the vector $\mathbf{r}(t)$ points to the position of the particle. See Figure 13.1.4.

Many parametric equations arise as solutions of Newton's 2nd Law for motion of a particle (or object) in space subject to certain forces. Streamlines in fluid mechanics, heat flow lines in thermodynamics, and charged particle trajectories in electricity and magnetism all involve curves described parametrically.

This kinematic view of parametrized curves in $\mathbb{R}^3$ suggests an extension of the derivative calculus to vector-valued functions.

Position, Velocity, and Tangent Vectors

The velocity of a particle's motion on a curve parametrized by $\mathbf{r} : [a, b] \rightarrow \mathbb{R}^3$ should be the rate of change of the position vector $\mathbf{r}$. To analyze this, consider the position $\mathbf{r}(t)$ of the particle at time t and its position $\mathbf{r}(t + \Delta t)$ at a short time later (with Δt a small increment of time). Then, as we learned in Chapter 10, the vector $\mathbf{r}(t + \Delta t) - \mathbf{r}(t)$ is geometrically the vector that goes from the terminal point of $\mathbf{r}(t)$ to the terminal point of $\mathbf{r}(t + \Delta t)$. See Figure 13.1.5.

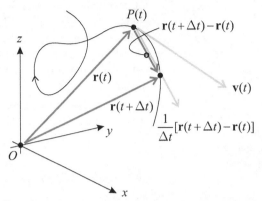

Figure 13.1.5: *The velocity vector for a particle motion in space.*

For Δt small enough this vector would essentially coincide with a portion of the curve. (Indeed, a computer plot of a curve consists a collection of such vectors.) Thus, the *average rate of change* of position for the lapse of time Δt is

$$
\begin{aligned}
\mathbf{v}_{ave}(t, \Delta t) &= \frac{\mathbf{r}(t + \Delta t) - \mathbf{r}(t)}{\Delta t} = \frac{1}{\Delta t}\big[\,\mathbf{r}(t + \Delta t) - \mathbf{r}(t)\,\big] \\
&= \frac{1}{\Delta t}\langle\, f(t + \Delta t) - f(t),\ g(t + \Delta t) - g(t),\ h(t + \Delta t) - h(t)\,\rangle \\
&= \langle\, \frac{f(t + \Delta t) - f(t)}{\Delta t},\ \frac{g(t + \Delta t) - g(t)}{\Delta t},\ \frac{h(t + \Delta t) - h(t)}{\Delta t}\,\rangle
\end{aligned}
$$

Assuming that the limit of a vector-valued function is the limit of it component functions we see from the above that the velocity vector at time t is

$$
\mathbf{v}(t) = \lim_{\Delta t \to 0} \mathbf{v}_{ave}(t, \Delta t) = \langle\, f'(t),\ g'(t),\ h'(t)\,\rangle.
$$

This argument then leads to the definition of the velocity vector for the parametrized curve: $x = f(t)$, $y = g(t)$, $x = h(t)$:

Velocity (Tangent) Vector at Time t:

$$
\begin{aligned}
\mathbf{v}(t) = \mathbf{r}'(t) &= \langle\, f'(t),\ g'(t),\ h'(t)\,\rangle = f'(t)\mathbf{i} + g'(t)\mathbf{j} + h'(t)\mathbf{k} \qquad (13.1.7) \\
&= \langle\, x'(t),\ y'(t),\ z'(t)\,\rangle = x'(t)\mathbf{i} + y'(t)\mathbf{j} + z'(t)\mathbf{k}
\end{aligned}
$$

This, of course, gives a vector-valued function $\mathbf{v} : [a, b] :\to \mathbb{R}^3$, called the *velocity function* and, according to Formula (13.1.7), is easy to calculate if the derivatives f', g', and h' are not too difficult to compute.

It is important to note that the velocity vector $\mathbf{v}(t)$ is usually plotted with its initial point at the point $P(t)$ on the curve and then it is tangent to the curve at this point. See Figure 13.1.5 above. Thus, $\mathbf{v}(t)$ lies in the tangent line and, indeed, can be used as the direction vector for the parametrization of the tangent line. Additionally, $\mathbf{v}(t)$ points in the direction of the particle's motion on the curve at time t.

Compare and contrast these two viewpoints. The *kinematical* point of view involves the velocity vector $\mathbf{v}$, while the *geometrical* point of view emphasizes the tangent vector $\mathbf{r}' = \mathbf{v}$.

Example 13.1.2 (Dynamic Aspects of Velocity Vectors)

Problem: (a) Use the `tanvectors3d` command to create a dynamic plot (i.e., a movie) of the velocity vectors moving along the curve parametrized by:

$$
\mathbf{r}(t) = \langle\, [2 + \cos \tfrac{1}{2}t]\cos t,\ [2 + \cos \tfrac{1}{2}t]\sin t,\ \sin \tfrac{1}{2}t\,\rangle \qquad (13.1.8)
$$

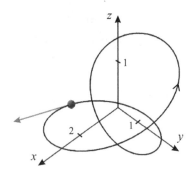

Figure 13.1.6: *A movie of the velocity vector moving along the boundary curve of a Möbius strip.*

for t in $[0, 4\pi]$. (b) Compute the velocity function $\mathbf{v} = \mathbf{r}'$. Find the velocity vectors and their magnitudes at times $t = 0$, π.

Solution (a): Define the three functions f, g, h in Maple as we did in Example 13.1.1 and then use the command `tanvectors3d(f,g,h,0,4*Pi,40,4,4,2);` to create the movie. Figure 13.1.6 shows the 36th frame in the movie. You should run the movie several times from several different viewpoints and note how the length of the velocity vector changes as it moves along the curve. Note: The perspective in a 3D figure may change the way the lengths of lines appear. Hence, rotate through a number of viewpoints.

Solution (b): For the derivatives and the magnitude calculations it will be convenient to introduce the function $M(t) = 2 + \cos\frac{1}{2}t$. Then

$$\mathbf{r}(t) = \langle\, M(t)\cos t,\ M(t)\sin t,\ \sin\tfrac{1}{2}t\,\rangle$$

So,

$$\mathbf{v}(t) = \mathbf{r}'(t) = \langle\, M'(t)\cos t - M(t)\sin t,\ M'(t)\sin t + M(t)\cos t,\ \tfrac{1}{2}\cos\tfrac{1}{2}t\,\rangle,$$

where $M'(t) = -\frac{1}{2}\sin\frac{1}{2}t$. Thus, for $t = 0$, we have $M(0) = 3$, $M'(0) = 0$ and so

$$\mathbf{v}(0) = \mathbf{r}'(0) = \langle\, 0,\ 3,\ \tfrac{1}{2}\,\rangle$$

While, for $t = \pi$, we have $M(\pi) = 2$, $M'(\pi) = -\frac{1}{2}$ and so

$$\mathbf{v}(\pi) = \mathbf{r}'(\pi) = \langle\, \tfrac{1}{2},\ -2,\ 0\,\rangle$$

Thus, the lengths of these velocity vectors are

$$\|\mathbf{v}(0)\| = \sqrt{9 + \tfrac{1}{4}} = \frac{\sqrt{37}}{2} \approx 3.04$$

$$\|\mathbf{v}(\pi)\| = \sqrt{\tfrac{1}{4} + 4} = \frac{\sqrt{17}}{2} \approx 2.06$$

Generally, the magnitude $\|\mathbf{v}(t)\|$ of the velocity vector at time t has units of distance divided by time and is a scalar quantity. So, it is natural to define this as the *speed* of the particle at time t:

Speed (Tangent Vector Length) at Time t:

$$\|\mathbf{v}(t)\| = \|\mathbf{r}'(t)\| = \sqrt{[f'(t)]^2 + [g'(t)]^2 + [h'(t)]^2} \qquad (13.1.9)$$

Viewing the movie in Example 13.1.2 again, you can see that the particle's speed is greater where the velocity vector is longer. We can be more precise about this by calculating the speed function for this curve, which is the boundary curve for a Möbius strip. A Möbius strip is a surface with interesting properties, which we will discuss in Section 13.2.

Example 13.1.3 (Speed Along a Möbius Boundary Curve)

Problem: Calculate the speed function for the Möbius boundary curve in Example 13.1.2 and find the absolute maximum and minimum speeds.

Solution The parametrization used in Example 13.1.2 was

$$\begin{aligned}\mathbf{r}(t) &= \langle\, [2 + \cos\tfrac{1}{2}t]\cos t,\ [1 + \cos\tfrac{1}{2}t]\sin t,\ \sin\tfrac{1}{2}t\,\rangle \\ &= \langle\, M(t)\cos t,\ M(t)\sin t,\ \sin\tfrac{1}{2}t\,\rangle\end{aligned}$$

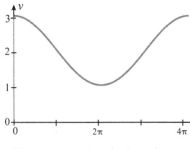

Figure 13.1.7: *A plot of*
$v(t) = \frac{1}{2}\sqrt{1 + 4\left[2 + \cos\frac{1}{2}t\right]^2}.$

where $M(t) = 2 + \cos\frac{1}{2}t$. We found that

$$\mathbf{v}(t) = \mathbf{r}'(t) = \langle\, M'(t)\cos t - M(t)\sin t,\ M'(t)\sin t + M(t)\cos t,\ \tfrac{1}{2}\cos\tfrac{1}{2}t\,\rangle,$$

where $M'(t) = -\frac{1}{2}\sin\frac{1}{2}t$. We first calculate the *square* of the speed:

$$\begin{aligned}\|\mathbf{v}(t)\|^2 &= \left[M'(t)\cos t - M(t)\sin t\right]^2 + \left[M'(t)\sin t + M(t)\cos t\right]^2 + \tfrac{1}{4}\cos^2\tfrac{1}{2}t \\ &= M'(t)^2 + M(t)^2 + \tfrac{1}{4}\cos^2\tfrac{1}{2}t = \tfrac{1}{4}\sin^2\tfrac{1}{2}t + M(t)^2 + \tfrac{1}{4}\cos^2\tfrac{1}{2}t\end{aligned}$$

$$= \tfrac{1}{4} + M(t)^2 = \tfrac{1}{4}\left[1 + 4M(t)^2\right]$$

Hence, the speed is

$$v(t) = \|\mathbf{v}(t)\| = \tfrac{1}{2}\sqrt{1 + 4M(t)^2} = \tfrac{1}{2}\sqrt{1 + 4\left[2 + \cos\tfrac{1}{2}t\right]^2}$$

Figure 13.1.7 is a plot of this speed function on $[0, 4\pi]$ and it shows the maximum speed occurs at times $t = 0$, 4π and the minimum speed occurs at $t = 2\pi$. Thus,

$$\text{Max speed} = v(0) = \tfrac{1}{2}\sqrt{37} \approx 3.04, \qquad \text{Min speed} = v(2\pi) = \tfrac{1}{2}\sqrt{5} \approx 1.12$$

Arc Length

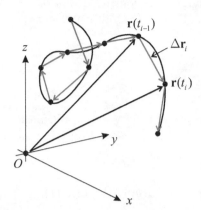

Figure 13.1.8: *A polygonal curve (in red) that approximates the curve C (in black).*

To define the length (or arc length) of a space curve C, we proceed as we did in Section 5.5. Suppose that $\mathbf{r} : [a, b] \to \mathbb{R}^3$ is parametrization of C:

$$\mathbf{r}(t) = \langle\, f(t),\, g(t),\, h(t)\, \rangle$$

Assume that $\mathbf{r}$ is one-to-one on (a, b), i.e., $\mathbf{r}(t_1) \neq \mathbf{r}(t_2)$, for $t_1 \neq t_2$ in (a, b). This is to ensure that the parametrization does not trace out the curve (or parts of it) more than once. (See Examples 9.1.5 and 9.2.3 in Chapter 9.)

Then for each partition $P = \{\, t_0, t_1, t_2, \dots t_n\, \}$ of $[a, b]$ we get a polygonal curve (a polygon) with vertices $\mathbf{r}(t_i)$, $i = 0, \dots, n$, on the curve C. Its sides are

$$\Delta\mathbf{r}_i \equiv \mathbf{r}_i - \mathbf{r}_{i-1} = \langle\, \Delta x_i,\, \Delta y_i,\, \Delta z_i\, \rangle,$$

for $i = 1, \dots, n$, where

$$\begin{aligned} \Delta x_i &= f(t_i) - f(t_{i-1}) \\ \Delta y_i &= g(t_i) - g(t_{i-1}) \\ \Delta z_i &= h(t_i) - h(t_{i-1}) \end{aligned}$$

See Figure 13.1.8. Thus, the length of the polygonal curve that approximates C is

$$L_P = \sum_{i=1}^{n} \|\Delta\mathbf{r}_i\| = \sum_{i=1}^{n} \sqrt{\Delta x_i^2 + \Delta y_i^2 + \Delta z_i^2}$$

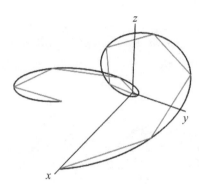

Figure 13.1.9: *A 10-sided polygonal curve that approximates a limaçonal helix.*

When we use finer and finer partitions then the corresponding polygonal curves become better approximations to the curve C. As in Section 5.5, you can easily determine that if P' is a finer partition of P and a refinement $(P \subset P')$, then $L_P < L_{P'}$. The next example verifies this for the limaçonal helix in Example 13.1.1. For simplicity of the graphics, we just use half the curve shown there.

Example 13.1.4 (Polygonal Approximations to a Limaconal Helix)

Problem: Use the command `polygonalplot3d(f,g,h,a,b,N)` to create two polygonal curves approximations to the curve C with parametrization:

$$\mathbf{r}(t) = \langle\, (1 + 2\cos t)\cos t,\, (1 + 2\cos t)\sin t,\, \tfrac{1}{4}t + \sin t\, \rangle \qquad (13.1.10)$$

for t in $[0, 2\pi]$. Use Partitions P and P' with $N = 10$ and $N = 20$ subintervals, respectively. Verify that $L_P < L_{P'}$.

Solution As in Example 13.1.1 define f, g, h and then use the commands:

```
> polygonalapprox3d(f,g,h,0,2*Pi,10);
```
   The length of the polygonal approximation with, 10, sides is, 13.37990090
```
> polygonalapprox3d(f,g,h,0,2*Pi,20);
```
   The length of the polygonal approximation with, 20, sides is, 13.94442426

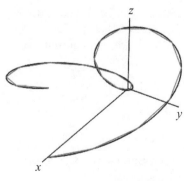

Figure 13.1.10: *A 20-sided polygonal curve that approximates a limaçonal helix.*

The graphics produced by these commands are shown in Figures 13.1.9–13.1.10. The approximate lengths shown verify that $L_P < L_{P'}$ when $P \subset P'$.

Based on these observations and the corresponding discussion in Section 5.5, it seems reasonable to make the following assertion. The set U of all lengths of the polygonal approximations:

$$L_P = \sum_{i=1}^{n} \|\Delta \mathbf{r}_i\| = \sum_{i=1}^{n} \left\|\frac{\Delta \mathbf{r}_i}{\Delta t_i}\right\| \Delta t_i$$

should contain lengths that are as close to the length L of C as we wish. When the set U has an upper bound, we say that the curve C is *rectifiable* and take L to be the least upper bound of U. In symbols:

$$L \equiv \limsup\left\{ L_P = \sum_{i=1}^{n} \left\|\frac{\Delta \mathbf{r}_i}{\Delta t_i}\right\| \Delta t_i \mid P \; a \; partition \; of \; [a,b] \right\} \qquad (13.1.11)$$

For the above discussion the only restriction we have placed on $\mathbf{r} = \langle f, g, h \rangle$ is that it be one-to-one. To get an integral formula for L we need the additional restriction that the component functions $x = f(t)$, $y = g(t)$, $z = h(t)$ have derivatives $x'(t) = f'(t)$, $y'(t) = g'(t)$, $z'(t) = h'(t)$ that are continuous.

THEOREM 13.1.1 (Lengths of Parametrized Curves)

Suppose $\mathbf{r}:[a,b] \to \mathbb{R}^3$ *is a parametrization of a curve C. If* $\mathbf{r}$ *is one-to-one on* (a,b) *and if its component functions* $x = f(t)$, $y = g(t)$, $z = h(t)$ *have continuous derivatives, then C is rectifiable and has length given by*

$$L = \int_{a}^{b} \|\mathbf{r}'(t)\| \, dt = \int_{a}^{b} \sqrt{[x'(t)]^2 + [y'(t)]^2 + [z'(t)]^2} \; dt \qquad (13.1.12)$$

NOTE 1: (Simple and Almost Simple Curves) The condition that $\mathbf{r} : [a, b] \to \mathbb{R}^3$ be one-to-one, except possibly at the end points of $[a, b]$, is meant to ensure that the parametrization does not retrace parts of the curve, in which case the integral formula (13.1.12) would over-measure the length. A curve is called *simple* when the parametrization is one-to-one except possibly at the end points a, b. More generally, a curve C, parametrized by $\mathbf{r} : [a, b] \to \mathbb{R}^3$, is called *almost simple* if $\mathbf{r}$ is one-to-one almost everywhere on $[a, b]$. This latter condition means that there is a subset $Z \subset [a, b]$, of measure zero, such that $\mathbf{r}$ is one-to-one on $[a, b] \setminus Z = \{ t \text{ in } [a, b] \mid t \text{ is not in } Z \}$.

NOTE 2: Formula 13.1.12 holds for almost simple curves.

For some parametrizations, the integral in Formula (13.1.12) can be difficult, if not impossible, to compute exactly (i.e., in closed form) because of the square root in the integrand. However, there is a class of curves for which we can compute the integral exactly because

$$[x'(t)]^2 + [y'(t)]^2 + [z'(t)]^2 = a \; perfect \; sqaure$$

The following example shows you four curves of this type.

Example 13.1.5 (Computing Lengths of Curves Exactly)

Problem: Compute the lengths (arc lengths) of the following curves C with the given parametrizations.

Part (a): $x = t,$ $y = t^2,$ $z = \frac{3}{4}t - \frac{1}{3}t^3,$ t in $[-2, 2]$

Solution (a): The derivatives are

$$x' = 1, \qquad y' = 2t, \qquad z' = \frac{3}{4} - t^2,$$

So,

$$[x'(t)]^2 + [y'(t)]^2 + [z'(t)]^2 = 1 + 4t^2 + (\tfrac{3}{4} - t^2)^2 = 1 + 4t^2 + \tfrac{9}{16} - \tfrac{3}{2}t^2 + t^4$$
$$= \tfrac{25}{16} + \tfrac{5}{2}t^2 + t^4 = (\tfrac{5}{4} + t^2)^2$$

Thus,

$$L = \int_a^b \sqrt{[x'(t)]^2 + [y'(t)]^2 + [z'(t)]^2}\, dt = \int_{-2}^2 \sqrt{(\tfrac{5}{4} + t^2)^2}\, dt = \int_{-2}^2 (\tfrac{5}{4} + t^2)\, dt$$
$$= 2\int_0^2 (\tfrac{5}{4} + t^2)\, dt = 2\big(\tfrac{5}{4}t + \tfrac{1}{3}t^3\big)\Big|_0^2 = 2\big(\tfrac{5}{2} + \tfrac{8}{3}\big) = \frac{31}{3} = 10\tfrac{1}{3}.$$

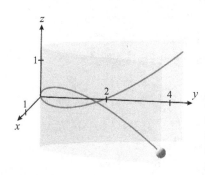

Figure 13.1.11: *The curve* $x = t$, $y = t^2$, $z = \tfrac{3}{4}t - \tfrac{1}{3}t^3$.

Figure 10.3.11 shows a plot of this curve, which lies on the surface (generalized cylinder) obtained by translating, in the z-direction, the plane curve: $x = t$, $y = t^2$ (the standard parabola $y = x^2$). You can see from the figure that a length of $L = 10\tfrac{1}{3}$ seems to be approximately correct. Note: Because of perspective foreshortening, accessing lengths of objects in space can be very inaccurate.

Part (b): $\quad x = (1 + 2\cos t)\cos t, \quad y = (1 + 2\cos t)\sin t, \quad z = \tfrac{1}{4}t + \sin t,$ for t in $[0, 4\pi]$. This is the limaçonal helix from Examples 13.1.1 and 13.1.4.

Solution (b): For the calculations it is convenient to write the parametrization as

$$x = R\cos t, \quad y = R\sin t, \quad z = \tfrac{1}{4}t + \sin t,$$

where $R = 1 + 2\cos t$. Then

$$x' = R'\cos t - R\sin t, \quad y' = R'\sin t + R\cos t, \quad z' = \tfrac{1}{4} + \cos t,$$

where $R' = -2\sin t$. Looking first at the sum of the squares $[x'(t)]^2 + [y'(t)]^2$ gives

$$[x'(t)]^2 + [y'(t)]^2 = (R'\cos t - R\sin t)^2 + (R'\sin t + R\cos t)^2$$
$$= (R')^2\cos^2 t - 2R'R\cos t \sin t + R^2\sin^2 t + (R')^2\sin^2 t - 2R'R\cos t \sin t + R^2\cos^2 t$$
$$= (R')^2 + R^2 = 4\sin^2 t + (1 + 2\cos t)^2 = 4\sin^2 t + 1 + 4\cos t + 4\cos^2 t$$
$$= 5 + 4\cos t$$

Thus,

$$\|\mathbf{r}'(t)\|^2 = [x'(t)]^2 + [y'(t)]^2 + [z'(t)]^2$$
$$= 5 + 4\cos t + (\tfrac{1}{4} + \cos t)^2 = 5 + 4\cos t + \tfrac{1}{16} + \tfrac{1}{2}\cos t + \cos^2 t$$
$$= \tfrac{81}{16} + \tfrac{9}{2}\cos t + \cos^2 t = \big(\tfrac{9}{4} + \cos t\big)^2$$

Consequently,

$$L = \int_a^b \|\mathbf{r}'(t)\|\, dt = \int_0^{4\pi} \sqrt{\big(\tfrac{9}{4} + \cos t\big)^2}\, dt = \int_0^{4\pi} \big(\tfrac{9}{4} + \cos t\big)\, dt$$
$$= \big(\tfrac{9}{4}t + \sin t\big)\Big|_0^{4\pi} = 9\pi \approx 28.27.$$

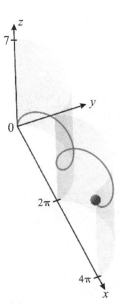

Figure 13.1.12: *The curve* $x = t - \sin t$, $y = 1 - \cos t$, $z = \tfrac{1}{2}(t + \sin t)$ *on a cycloidal cylinder.*

It is difficult to tell from looking at Figure 13.1.2 whether this calculation is approximately the length of the curve. But it does seem plausible. However, this is the same curve as in Example 13.1.4, except here the parameter interval is twice as long and so is (by symmetry) the length of the curve. The approximate length we found using a 20-side polygon was 13.94442426, which compares well with half the exact length we found here: $\tfrac{1}{2}L = \tfrac{1}{2}(9\pi) \approx \tfrac{1}{2}(28.27)$.

Part (c): $\quad x = t - \sin t, \quad y = 1 - \cos t, \quad z = \tfrac{1}{2}(t + \sin t),$

for t in $[0, 4\pi]$. This is what we call a *cycloidal helix* because it lies on the surface (generalized cylinder) obtained by translating, in the z-direction, the cycloid:

$x = t - \sin t$, $y = 1 - \cos t$. See Figure 13.1.12.

Solution (c): The derivatives are

$$x' = 1 - \cos t, \quad y' = \sin t, \quad z' = \tfrac{1}{2}(1 + \cos t),$$

So,

$$
\begin{aligned}
[x'(t)]^2 + [y'(t)]^2 + [z'(t)]^2 &= (1 - \cos t)^2 + \sin^2 t + \tfrac{1}{4}(1 + \cos t)^2 \\
&= 1 - 2\cos t + \cos^2 t + \sin^2 t + \tfrac{1}{4} + \tfrac{1}{2}\cos t + \tfrac{1}{4}\cos^2 t \\
&= 1 - 2\cos t + 1 + \tfrac{1}{4} + \tfrac{1}{2}\cos t + \tfrac{1}{4}\cos^2 t \\
&= \tfrac{9}{4} - \tfrac{3}{2}\cos t + \tfrac{1}{4}\cos^2 t = (\tfrac{3}{2} + \tfrac{1}{2}\cos t)^2
\end{aligned}
$$

Thus,

$$
\begin{aligned}
L &= \int_a^b \sqrt{[x'(t)]^2 + [y'(t)]^2 + [z'(t)]^2}\, dt = \int_0^{4\pi} \sqrt{(\tfrac{3}{2} + \tfrac{1}{2}\cos t)^2}\, dt \\
&= \int_0^{4\pi} (\tfrac{3}{2} + \tfrac{1}{2}\cos t)\, dt = \left(\tfrac{3}{2}t + \tfrac{1}{2}\sin t\right)\Big|_0^{4\pi} = 6\pi \approx 18.85
\end{aligned}
$$

Part (d): $x = t^4$, $y = t^2 - \tfrac{1}{3}x^6$, $z = \left[t + \tfrac{2}{5}t^5 + \tfrac{1}{9}t^9\right] - \tfrac{1}{3}t^3$,

for t in $[0, \tfrac{3}{2}]$.

Solution (d): The derivatives are

$$
\begin{aligned}
x' = 4t^3, \quad y' = 2t - 2t^5, \quad z' &= \left[1 + 2t^4 + t^8\right] - t^2 \\
&= [1 + t^4]^2 - t^2.
\end{aligned}
$$

Looking first at the sum of the squares $[x'(t)]^2 + [y'(t)]^2$ gives

$$
\begin{aligned}
[x'(t)]^2 + [y'(t)]^2 &= 16t^6 + [2t - 2t^5]^2 = 16t^6 + [4t^2 - 8t^6 + 4t^{10}] \\
&= 4t^2 + 8t^6 + 4t^{10} = [2t + 2t^5]^2 = 4t^2[1 + t^4]^2
\end{aligned}
$$

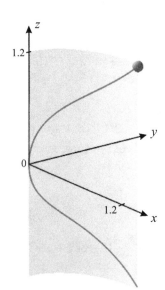

Figure 13.1.13: *The curve*
$x = t^4$, $y = t^2 - \tfrac{1}{3}t^6$,
$z = \left[t + \tfrac{2}{5}t^5 + \tfrac{1}{9}t^9\right] - \tfrac{1}{3}t^3$.

Thus,

$$
\begin{aligned}
\|\mathbf{r}'(t)\|^2 &= [x'(t)]^2 + [y'(t)]^2 + [z'(t)]^2 \\
&= 4t^2[1 + t^4]^2 + \left([1 + t^4]^2 - t^2\right)^2 \\
&= 4t^2[1 + t^4]^2 + [1 + t^4]^4 - 2t^2[1 + t^4]^2 + t^4 \\
&= \left([1 + t^4]^2 + t^2\right)^2
\end{aligned}
$$

Consequently,

$$
\begin{aligned}
L &= \int_a^b \sqrt{[x'(t)]^2 + [y'(t)]^2 + [z'(t)]^2}\, dt = \int_{-1}^1 \sqrt{\left([1 + t^4]^2 + t^2\right)^2}\, dt \\
&= \int_{-1}^1 \left([1 + t^4]^2 + t^2\right) dt = 2\int_0^1 \left(1 + 2t^4 + t^8 + t^2\right) dt \\
&= 2\left(t + \tfrac{2}{5}t^5 + \tfrac{1}{9}t^9 + \tfrac{1}{3}t^3\right)\Big|_0^1 = 2\left(1 + \tfrac{2}{5} + \tfrac{1}{9} + \tfrac{1}{3}\right) = 3\tfrac{31}{45}
\end{aligned}
$$

Figure 13.1.13 shows the last frame in a dynamic plot of this curve using `dcurve3d`.

TIPS FOR THE EXERCISES:

(1) Carefully compute $[x'(t)]^2 + [y'(t)]^2 + [z'(t)]^2$ and try to recognize it as a perfect square.

(2) Sometimes it is best to first compute $[x'(t)]^2 + [y'(t)]^2$ as we did in Parts (b) and (d) of the last example.

(3) If $x = R(t) \cos t$, $y = R(t) \sin t$ is the standard parameterization of a polar curve $r = R(\theta)$, with t replacing θ, then expect $[x'(t)]^2 + [y'(t)]^2 = [R(t)]^2(t) + [R'(t)]^2$. See Part (b) above. *This means you do NOT heave to go through all the intermediate step in computing* $[x'(t)]^2 + [y'(t)]^2$. Just go directly to the computation of $[R(t)]^2 + [R'(t)]^2$. Then add $[z'(t)]^2$ to the result.

(4) Sometimes, as in Part (d) above, it is best not to square things immediately.

(5) Be familiar with using the binomial theorem in reverse: $a^2 + 2ab + b^2 = (a+b)^2$.

(6) Look for $4ab + (a-b)^2 = 4ab + a^2 - 2ab + b^2 = a^2 + 2ab + b^2 = (a+b)^2$

Approximating Arc Length

Example 13.1.5 exhibits four interesting space curves for which we can compute the exact arc length. However, there are many other important (and interesting) space curves for which we cannot calculate their exact lengths. For such curves, we can at least setup the integrals that give the arc lengths and then use a CAS to get numerical approximations (See Section 6.7). Alternatively, we can use polygonapprox3d as the next example illustrates.

Example 13.1.6 (Computing Lengths of Curves Approximately)

Problem: Compute, approximately, the length (arc length) of the boundary curve for the Möbius strip discussed in Examples 13.1.2 and 13.13.

Solution: The curve was given by the parametrization in Equation (13.1.8) and we calculated that

$$v(t) = \|\mathbf{v}(t)\| = \|\mathbf{r}'(t)\| = \tfrac{1}{2}\sqrt{1 + 4\left[2 + \cos\tfrac{1}{2}t\right]^2}$$

Thus,

$$L = \int_0^{4\pi} \tfrac{1}{2}\sqrt{1 + 4\left[2 + \cos\tfrac{1}{2}t\right]^2}\, dt$$

The indefinite integral here is exceedingly difficult to calculate. While a CAS can compute it, the answer is too complex to be of use. Using polygonappraox3d to approximate the curve with polygons gives approximate lengths:

```
> f:=t->(2+cos(t/2))*cos(t);g:=t->(2+cos(t/2))*sin(t);h:=t->sin(t/2);
```
$$f := t \rightarrow (2 + \cos(\tfrac{1}{2}t))\cos t$$
$$g := t \rightarrow (2 + \cos(\tfrac{1}{2}t))\sin t$$
$$h := t \rightarrow \sin(\tfrac{1}{2}t)$$
```
> polygonalapprox3d(f,g,h,0,4*Pi,50);
```
   The length of the polygonal approximation with, 50, *sides is,* 25.94162775
```
> polygonalapprox3d(f,g,h,0,4*Pi,100);
```
   The length of the polygonal approximation with, 100, *sides is,* 25.99552354
```
> polygonalapprox3d(f,g,h,0,4*Pi,200);
```
   The length of the polygonal approximation with, 200, *sides is,* 26.00901163

Maple computes the definite integral numerically as $L \approx 26.01350893$.

Constant Speed Parametrizations:

As you might expect, if $\mathbf{r} : [a, b] \rightarrow \mathbb{R}^3$ is a parametrization of a curve C and the speed is constant, i.e., $\|\mathbf{v}(t)\| = \|\mathbf{r}'(t)\| = constant$, for all t. Then the length of C is easy to compute.

In theory, under suitable conditions, it is possible to obtain a constant speed parametrization of a given curve C (or a portion of C). In almost all of these cases, the theory does not give us the explicit expressions for f, g, h, in the constant speed parametrization $x = f(t)$, $y = g(t)$, $z = h(t)$. See Section 13.3.

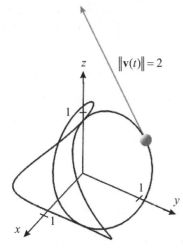

Figure 13.1.14: *A curve with constant speed parametrization.*

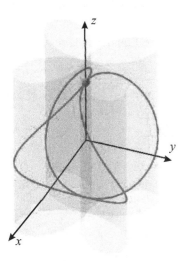

Figure 13.1.15: *The last frame in a movie produced by* `dcurve3d`*.*

It is rare to find *explicitly* given constant-speed parametrizations. However, the following example gives a new one we found to add to the ones that were previously known. There are also, some new ones in the Exercises.

Example 13.1.7 (A Constant Speed Parametrization)

Problem: Consider the paramterization

$$\mathbf{r}(t) = \langle\ \sin 2t \cos t,\ \sin 2t \sin t,\ \tfrac{\sqrt{3}}{2}\cos 2t\ \rangle \qquad (13.1.14)$$

Show that $\|\mathbf{r}'(t)\| = \|\mathbf{v}(t)\| = 2$, for all t in $(-\infty, \infty)$.

Solution: Let

$$R(t) = \sin 2t.$$

Then we see that the first two component functions in the parametrization (13.1.14) are $x = R(t)\cos t$, $y = R(t)\sin t$. This the standard parametrization for the polar curve $r = \sin 2\theta$ (a four petal rose curve) with t replacing θ as the parameter. Thus, as mentioned in TIP (3) above,

$$[x'(t)]^2 + [y'(t)]^2 = [R(t)]^2 + [R'(t)]^2 = \sin^2 2t + 4\cos^2 2t$$

Also, $z' = -\sqrt{3}\sin 2t$ and so

$$[x'(t)]^2 + [y'(t)]^2 + [z'(t)]^2 = [R(t)]^2 + [R'(t)]^2 + [z'(t)]^2$$
$$= \sin^2 2t + 4\cos^2 2t + 3\sin^2 2t = 4\sin^2 2t + 4\cos^2 2t = 4$$

Thus, $\|\mathbf{r}'(t)\| = \|\mathbf{v}(t)\| = 2$.

Figure 13.1.14 shows the 37th frame in a movie created by the `tanvectors3d` command. By rotating the figure you can more-or-less discern that the tangent vector $\mathbf{v}$ has the same length in each of the frames and that the length is 2.

Figure 13.1.15 shows the last frame in a movie produced by `dcurve3d`. Each frame also displays the generalized cylinder on which the curve lies. This surface is obtained by translating the rose curve $r = \sin 2\theta$ in the z-direction. If you rotate the movie so that you are looking almost directly down on the x-y-plane, then you can see more clearly how the curve is traced out on this surface.

A special case of constant-speed parameterization is when the constant is 1, so that $\|\mathbf{v}(t)\| = 1$, for all t in $[a, b]$. We record this in the following box:

Constant Speed Parametrizations

Suppose $\mathbf{r} : [a,b] \rightarrow \mathbb{R}^3$ *is a parametrization of a curve C and assume* $\mathbf{r}$ *has component functions f, g, h that are differentiable. Then* $\mathbf{r}$ *is called a* constant speed parametrization *if there is a positive constant k so that*

$$\|\mathbf{v}(t)\| = k, \qquad (13.1.13)$$

for all t in $[a,b]$*. If* $k = 1$*, then* $\mathbf{r}$ *is called a* unit speed parametrization *and C is said to be* parametrized by arc length*.*

In Section 13.3, we discuss how to parametrize curves by their arc lengths. This, involves inverting the arc length function $s(t) = \int_a^t \|\mathbf{r}'(u)\|\, du$.

Exercises: 13.1 (Space Curves and Arc Lengths)

Velocity (Tangent) Vectors

In Exercises 1–22, for the curve C parametrized by $\mathbf{r} : [a, b] \to \mathbb{R}^3$, find the velocity (tangent) vector $\mathbf{v} = \mathbf{r}'$ function. Also, at the specified time, find the velocity and speed.

1. $\mathbf{r} = \langle\, t, t^2, t^3 \,\rangle$, $t = 1$

2. $\mathbf{r} = \langle\, t^2, t^3, t^4 \,\rangle$, $t = 1$

3. $\mathbf{r} = \langle\, t^{1/2}, t^{3/2}, t^{5/2} \,\rangle$, $t = 4$

4. $\mathbf{r} = \langle\, t^{1/3}, t^{2/3}, t^{4/3} \,\rangle$, $t = 8$

5. $\mathbf{r} = \langle\, e^t, e^{2t}, e^{3t} \,\rangle$, $t = \ln 2$

6. $\mathbf{r} = \langle\, e^{2t}, e^{3t}, e^t \,\rangle$, $t = \ln 2$

7. $\mathbf{r} = \langle\, t^2, t \ln t, t^2 \ln t \,\rangle$, $t = 1$

8. $\mathbf{r} = \langle\, t^2, t^2 + t \ln t, t^3 + t^2 \ln t \,\rangle$, $t = 1$

9. $\mathbf{r} = \langle\, \cos(t^2), \sin(t^2), t^2 \,\rangle$, $t = \sqrt{\pi}$

10. $\mathbf{r} = \langle\, \cos(t^3), \sin(t^3), t^3 \,\rangle$, $t = \sqrt[3]{\pi}$

11. $\mathbf{r} = \langle\, t \cos t, t^2 \sin t, t^3 \,\rangle$, $t = \pi$

12. $\mathbf{r} = \langle\, t^2 \cos t, t^3 \sin t, t \,\rangle$, $t = \pi$

13. $\mathbf{r} = \langle\, \ln(\cos t), \ln(\sin t), \sqrt{2}\, t \,\rangle$, $t = \frac{\pi}{4}$

14. $\mathbf{r} = \langle\, \ln(\sec t), \ln(\csc t), \sqrt{2}\, t \,\rangle$, $t = \frac{\pi}{4}$

15. $\mathbf{r} = \langle\, te^{2t}, te^t, te^{-t} \,\rangle$, $t = 0$

16. $\mathbf{r} = \langle\, te^{3t}, te^{2t}, te^{-2t} \,\rangle$, $t = 0$

17. $\mathbf{r} = \langle\, e^{2t} + e^{-2t}, e^{2t} - e^{-2t}, e^{2t} \,\rangle$, $t = 0$

18. $\mathbf{r} = \langle\, e^{3t} + e^{-3t}, e^{3t} - e^{-3t}, e^{3t} \,\rangle$, $t = 0$

19. $\mathbf{r} = \langle\, \dfrac{t}{1+t^2}, \dfrac{t^2}{1+t^2}, \dfrac{t^3}{1+t^2} \,\rangle$, $t = 1$

20. $\mathbf{r} = \langle\, \dfrac{t^2}{2+t^2}, \dfrac{t}{2+t^2}, \dfrac{t^3}{2+t^2} \,\rangle$, $t = 1$

21. $\mathbf{r} = \langle\, \dfrac{\sin t}{1+\cos t}, \dfrac{\cos t}{1+\sin t}, \cos t - \sin t \,\rangle$, $t = 0$

22. $\mathbf{r} = \langle\, \dfrac{\cos t}{1-\sin t}, \dfrac{\sin t}{1-\cos t}, \cos t + \sin t \,\rangle$, $t = \pi$

Computing Arc Length (Exactly)

In Exercises 23–70, compute the arc length of the curve C parametrized by $x = f(t), y = g(t), z = h(t)$, t in $[a, b]$.

Power Curves

23. $x = t$, $y = \frac{1}{2}t^2$, $z = \frac{3}{4}t - \frac{1}{12}t^3$, $[0, 1]$

24. $x = t$, $y = \frac{1}{2}t^2$, $z = \frac{15}{8}t - \frac{1}{24}t^3$, $[0, 1]$

25. $x = t^2$, $y = t^3$, $z = \frac{3}{4}t^2 - \frac{9}{32}t^4$, $[0, 1]$

26. $x = t^2$, $y = t^3$, $z = \frac{15}{8}t^2 - \frac{9}{64}t^4$, $[0, 1]$

27. $x = t^3$, $y = t^4$, $z = \frac{3}{4}t^3 - \frac{4}{15}t^5$, $[0, 1]$

28. $x = t^3$, $y = t^4$, $z = \frac{7}{24}t^3 - \frac{2}{5}t^5$, $[0, 1]$

29. $x = t$, $y = t^2$, $z = \frac{3}{4}t^2 - \frac{1}{8}\ln t$, $[1, 2]$

30. $x = t$, $y = t^2$, $z = z = \frac{15}{8}t^2 - \frac{1}{16}\ln t$, $[1, 2]$

Exponential Curves

31. $x = t$, $y = e^t$, $z = \frac{3}{4}e^t + \frac{1}{4}e^{-t}$, $[0, 1]$

32. $x = t$, $y = c^{2t}$, $z = \frac{3}{4}e^{2t} + \frac{1}{16}e^{-2t}$, $[0, 1]$

33. $x = t$, $y = e^{3t}$, $z = \frac{3}{4}e^{3t} + \frac{1}{36}e^{-3t}$, $[0, 1]$

34. $x = t$, $y = e^{3t}$, $z = \frac{15}{8}e^{3t} + \frac{1}{72}e^{-3t}$, $[0, 1]$

35. $x = t$, $y = e^t$, $z = \frac{3}{4}t - \frac{1}{8}e^{2t}$, $[0, 1]$

36. $x = t$, $y = e^{2t}$, $z = \frac{3}{4}t - \frac{1}{4}e^{4t}$, $[0, 1]$

Helical Curves

37. $x = \cos t$, $y = \sin t$, $z = t/2$, $[0, 2\pi]$

38. $x = \cos t$, $y = \sin t$, $z = t/4$, $[0, 2\pi]$

39. $x = \cos t$, $y = \sin t$, $z = \frac{1}{3}t^{3/2} - t^{1/2}$, $[0, 9]$

40. $x = \cos t$, $y = \sin t$, $z = \frac{1}{4}t^{4/3} - \frac{9}{8}t^{2/3}$, $[0, 27]$

41. $x = \cos t$, $y = \sin t$, $z = e^t + \frac{1}{4}e^{-t}$, $[0, 1]$

42. $x = \cos t$, $y = \sin t$, $z = e^{2t} + \frac{1}{16}e^{-2t}$, $[0, 1]$

Limaçonal Curves

43. $x = t - \sin t$, $y = 1 - \cos t$, $z = 3\cos(t/2)$, $[0, 2\pi]$

44. $x = t + \sin t$, $y = 1 - \cos t$, $z = 3\sin(t/2)$, $[0, \pi]$

45. $x = t + \sin t$, $y = 1 - \cos t$, $z = \frac{1}{2}(t - \sin t)$, $[0, 2\pi]$

46. $x = t - \sin t$, $y = 1 - \cos t$, $z = t + \sin t$, $[0, 2\pi]$

47. $x = (1 + \cos t)\cos t$, $y = (1 + \cos t)\sin t$, $z = \frac{1}{2}(t - \sin t)$, $[0, 2\pi]$

48. $x = (1 - \cos t)\cos t$, $y = (1 - \cos t)\sin t$, $z = \frac{1}{2}(t + \sin t)$, $[0, 2\pi]$

49. $x = (2 + \cos t)\cos t$, $y = (2 + \cos t)\sin t$,

$z = \frac{11}{8}t - \frac{1}{2}\sin t, \quad [0, 2\pi]$

50. $x = (2 - \cos t)\cos t, \; y = (2 - \cos t)\sin t,$
$z = \sin t - \frac{1}{4}t, \quad [0, 2\pi]$

51. $x = (1 + \cos t)\cos t, \; y = (1 + \cos t)\sin t,$
$z = 3\sin(t/2), \quad [0, \pi]$

52. $x = (1 + \cos t)\cos t, \; y = (1 + \cos t)\sin t,$
$z = 3\sin(t/2), \quad [0, \pi]$

53. $x = (1 + \sin t)\cos t, \; y = (1 + \sin t)\sin t,$
$z = \sqrt{2}\sin^2(t/2), \quad [0, 2\pi]$

54. $x = (1 - \sin t)\cos t, \; y = (1 - \sin t)\sin t,$
$z = \sqrt{2}\sin^2(t/2), \quad [0, 2\pi]$

Spiral Curves

55. $x = t\cos t, \; y = t\sin t, \; z = \frac{3}{4}t - \frac{1}{12}t^3, \quad [0, \pi]$

56. $x = t\cos t, \; y = t\sin t, \; z = \frac{7}{8}t - \frac{1}{24}t^3, \quad [0, \pi]$

57. $x = e^t\cos t, \; y = e^t\sin t, \; z = \frac{1}{12}e^{3t} + e^{-t}, \quad [0, 1]$

58. $x = e^t\cos t, \; y = e^t\sin t, \; z = e^{3t} + \frac{1}{6}e^{-t}, \quad [0, 1]$

59. $x = e^t\cos t, \; y = e^t\sin t, \; z = \frac{1}{16}e^{4t} + e^{-2t}, \quad [0, 1]$

60. $x = e^t\cos t, \; y = e^t\sin t, \; z = e^{4t} + \frac{1}{16}e^{-2t}, \quad [0, 1]$

Astroidal Curves

61. $x = 2\cos^3 t, \; y = 2\sin^3 t, \; z = \frac{7}{16}\cos 2t, \quad [0, \frac{\pi}{2}]$

62. $x = 2\cos^3 t, \; y = 2\sin^3 t, \; z = \frac{7}{16}\cos 2t, \quad [0, 2\pi]$

63. $x = 4\cos^3 t, \; y = 4\sin^3 t, \; z = \frac{9}{8}\sin 4t - \frac{7}{2}t, \; [0, 2\pi]$

64. $x = 4\cos^3 t, \; y = 4\sin^3 t, \; z = \frac{9}{8}\sin 4t - \frac{7}{2}t, \; [0, 2\pi]$

Constant Speed Parametrizations

65. $x = \cos 2t\cos t, \; y = \cos 2t\sin t, \; z = \frac{\sqrt{3}}{2}\sin 2t, \; [0, 2\pi]$

66. $x = \sin 2t\cos t, \; y = \sin 2t\sin t, \; z = \frac{\sqrt{3}}{2}\cos 2t, \; [0, 2\pi]$

67. $x = \sin 3t\cos t, \; y = \sin 3t\sin t, \; z = \frac{2\sqrt{2}}{3}\cos 3t, \; [0, 2\pi]$

68. $x = \cos 3t\cos t, \; y = \cos 3t\sin t, \; z = \frac{2\sqrt{2}}{3}\sin 3t, \; [0, 2\pi]$

69. $x = (1 + \cos t)\cos t, \; y = (1 + \cos t)\sin t,$
$z = 4\cos\frac{1}{2}t, \; [0, 2\pi]$

70. $x = (1 - \cos t)\cos t, \; y = (1 - \cos t)\sin t,$
$z = 4\cos\frac{1}{2}t, \; [0, 2\pi]$

Calculus *Concepts & Computation*

13.2 Surfaces and Surface Area

As in Section 11.6, a *general surface* S in $\mathbb{R}^3$ can be described by a Cartesian equation $H(x, y, z) = 0$. Specifically, S is the set of points

$$S = \{ (x, y, z) \text{ in } \mathbb{R}^3 \mid H(x, y, z) = 0 \}, \qquad (13.2.1)$$

For the special case of a *surface which is graph* of a function $F : D \to \mathbb{R}$ of two variables, the surface is described the equation $z = F(x, y)$ and is the set of points:

$$\begin{aligned} S = G_F &= \{ (x, y, z) \text{ in } \mathbb{R}^3 \mid z = F(x, y) \} & (13.2.2) \\ &= \{ (x, y, F(x, y)) \mid (x, y) \text{ in } D \}. & (13.2.3) \end{aligned}$$

The quadric surfaces studied in Section 10.6 are important examples of general surfaces, although paraboloids such as $z = x^2 + y^2$, and hyperbolic paraboloids, such as $z = x^2 - y^2$, are actually graphs of functions.

In this latter special case where $S = G_F$, the geometry and calculus connected with the study of the surface S are considerably simplified. This is because, in Equation (13.2.3) we can view the points on the surface as being located, or determined, by the values of x, and y, which we now consider as *parameters* rather than as independent variables. As the parameters (x, y) vary over D (which is usually a rectangle) the surface is "swept out" in $\mathbb{R}^3$.

This way of using two parameters to represent a surface $S = G_F$ which is a graph can be extended to general surfaces in a natural way.

Parametric Equations for Surfaces

Suppose f, g, and h are functions defined on a region D in the plane $\mathbb{R}^2$ and are, where necessary, differentiable at least twice on this interval. Then

$$x = f(u, v), \quad y = g(u, v), \quad z = h(u, v) \qquad (13.2.4)$$

for (u, v) in D, are called *parametric equations* for the surface S given formally by

$$S = G_{f,g,h} = \{ (f(u, v), g(u, v), h(u, v)) \mid (u, v) \text{ in } D \} \qquad (13.2.5)$$

The terminology here is similar to that for curves. The variables u, v are called *parameters* and the set of points S comprising the surface is said to be *parametrized* by Equations (13.2.4). These equations are also called a *parameterization* of the surface S. We let $P(u, v) = (f(u, v), g(u, v), h(u, v))$ denote the point on the surface corresponding to point (u, v) in the parameter domain D. Plotting the points $P(u, v)$ as (u, v) runs through the parameter domain gives the surface in space as illustrated in Figure 13.2.1.

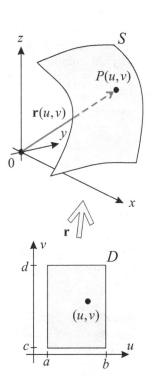

Figure 13.2.1: *A Parametrization of a surface in space.*

Vector-Valued Functions

It will be convenient think of the parametrization (13.2.4) of S as a map, or function, $\mathbf{r} : D \to \mathbb{R}^3$, with domain D and range in $\mathbb{R}^3$. The function notation for this is

$$\mathbf{r}(u, v) = (f(u, v), g(u, v), h(u, v)) = P(u, v) \qquad (13.2.6)$$

So, the value of $\mathbf{r}$ at (u, v) is the point $P(u, v)$. Additionally, as in Chapter 10, we can identify the point $P(u, v)$ with the vector $\overrightarrow{OP}(u, v)$. Thus, we can also view $\mathbf{r} : D \to \mathbb{R}^3$ as a *vector-valued function* and write

$$\mathbf{r}(u, v) = \langle f(u, v), g(u, v), h(u, v) \rangle = f(u, v)\mathbf{i} + g(u, v)\mathbf{j} + h(u, v)\mathbf{k} \qquad (13.2.7)$$

The vector $\mathbf{r}(u,v) = \overrightarrow{OP}(u,v)$, from the origin to the point $P(u,v)$, is called a *position vector*. See Figure 13.2.1.

Coordinate Curves and Grids

For the most part, we will assume the parameter domain is a rectangle: $D = [a,b] \times [c,d]$. Then for each point (u_0, v_0) in D, we get two *coordinate curves* $\mathbf{c}_1(v_0) : [a,b] \to \mathbb{R}^3$ and $\mathbf{c}_2(u_0) : [c,d] \to \mathbb{R}^3$ defined by

$$\mathbf{c}_1(v_0)(t) = \mathbf{r}(t, v_0) \quad \text{and} \quad \mathbf{c}_2(u_0)(t) = \mathbf{r}(u_0, t),$$

where t is in $[a,b]$ for $\mathbf{c}_1(v_0)$ and t is in $[c,d]$ for $\mathbf{c}_2(u_0)$. The notation here makes this concept of *coordinate curves* seem complicated. It is more easily understood if we impose a grid on the rectangular parameter domain D with one of the horizontal and one of the vertical grid lines passing through the point (u_0, v_0) as shown in Figure 13.2.2. Then $\mathbf{c}_1(v_0)$ is the restriction of the function $\mathbf{r}$ to the mentioned horizontal grid line and $\mathbf{c}_2(u_0)$ is the restriction of the function $\mathbf{r}$ to the mentioned vertical grid line. This is illustrated in Figure 13.2.2. The figure also shows how restricting $\mathbf{r}$ to other horizontal and vertical grid lines gives respective coordinate curves on the surface. From this, we get a *curved grid* on the surface S. This should not be unfamiliar. If you look back (or ahead) at any of the computer plots of surfaces in the book you will see the curved grids on the surfaces.

For example, Figure 13.2.3 shows a computer plot of paramatrized surface with a number of coordinate curves on the surface. The coordinate curves are not only important in studying the geometry of the surface (Section 13.4), but also help delineate the features of the surface in the illustration created by the computer.

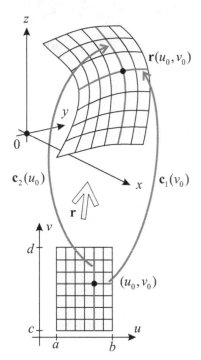

Figure 13.2.2: *Grid lines in the parameter domain get mapped onto coordinate curves.*

The Standard Parametrization of a Surface which is a Graph

For a function $F : D \to \mathbb{R}$ of two variables, the *standard parametrization* of its graph is

$$\mathbf{r}(x,y) = \langle\, x,\, y,\, F(x,y)\,\rangle,$$

for (x,y) in D.

Sketching parametrized surfaces in space by-hand can be done, and in fact you should have already had some experience with this in Chapter 5 where you sketched solids of the revolution. In doing so you were also sketching their surfaces.

So, before continuing with the discussion of general surfaces, we look at this special type. This will show you how parametrizations for surfaces arise naturally.

Surfaces of Revolution

Many of the standard surfaces in mathematics, such as cones, cylinders, spheres, tori, and special cases of the paraboloids and hyperboloids, are surfaces of revolution (as you will soon see). These are generated by revolving a curve C, in some plane, about an axis in that plane.

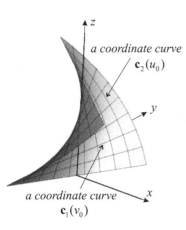

Figure 13.2.3: *Coordinate curves in a computer plot.*

While we could use any plane and any axis, we will assume the curve C is in the x-z-plane and is revolved about the z-axis. This will give us the standard surfaces (cylinders, cones, spheres, tori, etc.) oriented in their customary ways. So, suppose C has is given by parametric equations

$$x = X(t), \quad y = 0, \quad z = Z(t) \qquad (13.2.8)$$

for t in $[c,d]$. We can use elementary geometry to determine a parametrization of the surface of revolution generated by C. This will naturally involve the parameter t that parametrizes C and also an angle parameter θ indicating the amount of revolution. One can show that a point $(X(t), 0, Z(t))$ on C when revolved about the z-axis through angle θ will give the point $(X(t)\cos\theta, X(t)\sin\theta, Z(t))$ on the surface of revolution. Revolving all the points on C through a complete evolution (0 to 2π) will give the surface of revolution, Thus, the natural parametrization is:

$$\mathbf{r}(\theta, t) = \big(X(t)\cos\theta, \, X(t)\sin\theta, \, Z(t) \big), \qquad (13.2.9)$$

for (θ, t) in $D = [0, 2\pi] \times [c, d]$. Figure 13.2.4 below shows the geometry in this construction. The brown triangle in the figure is a right triangle with hypotenuse of length $X(t)$ and with sides adjacent and opposite θ having lengths $x = X(t)\cos\theta$ and $y = X(t)\sin\theta$, respectively. So, x and y are the first two coordinates of the rotated point, while clearly $z = Z(t)$ is its third coordinate. (This analysis assumes, as in the figure, that $X(t) > 0$. But, one can extend the argument to $X(t) \leq 0$, to get that Formula (13.2.9) holds in general.)

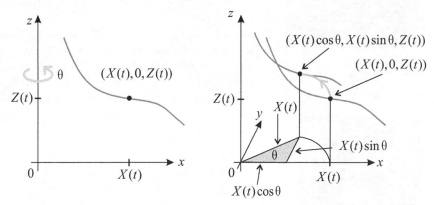

Figure 13.2.4: *A surface of revolution generated by revolving a curve in the x-z-plane about the z-axis.*

NOTE 1: In general, $|X(t)|$ is the distance of the point $(X(t)\cos\theta, X(t)\sin\theta, Z(t))$ from the axis of rotation (the z-axis in this case) and $Z(t)$ is the z-coordinate.

NOTE 2: For surfaces of revolutions, the coordinate curves are easy to understand. The parametrization $\mathbf{r}$ maps horizontal grid lines onto circles and vertical grid lines on to rotated copies of the curve C. See Figure 13.2.5.

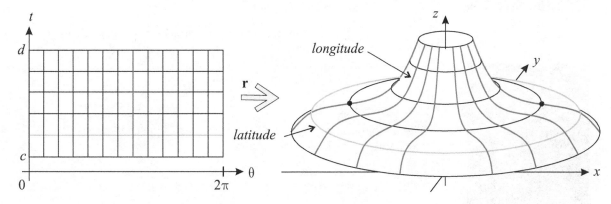

Figure 13.2.5: *The coordinate curves on a surface of revolution are circles and copies of the curve C. They are analogous to latitude circles and longitude half circles on earth.*

NOTE 3: In analogy with the sphere as a model of the earth, we will, in general, refer to the coordinate curves for *any* surface of revolution as *latitudes* and *longitudes*.

Example 13.2.1 (Parametrizing and Sketching Surfaces of Revolution)

Problem: For each of the following curves C in the x-z-plane do the following:

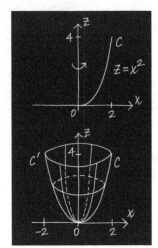

Figure 13.2.6:
A paraboloid.

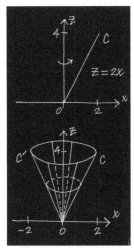

Figure 13.2.7:
A cone.

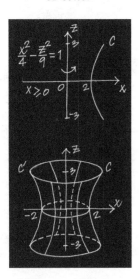

Figure 13.2.8:
A Hyperboloid.

(i) Parametrize C. (ii) Parametrize the surface S obtained by revolving C about the z-axis. (iii) Sketch the surface S along with its latitude and longitude lines (coordinate curves). (iv) Identify the surface S.

In (a) and (b) we use the standard parametrization of a curve which is the graph of a function $z = F(x)$, i.e., we use $x = t$, $z = F(t)$. ALSO: See the discussion under **Drawing Solids of Revolution** in Section 5.3.

Part: (a) $z = x^2$, for x in $[0, 2]$.

Solution (a): The curve C is half of the standard parabola (but in the x-z-plane) and has parametrization: $x = t$, $y = 0$, $z = t^2$, for t in $[0, 2]$. Then the surface S has parametrization

$$\mathbf{r}(\theta, t) = \langle\, t\cos\theta,\, t\sin\theta,\, t^2\,\rangle, \qquad (13.2.10)$$

for (θ, t) in $D = [0, 2\pi] \times [0, 2]$. Figure 13.2.6 shows a sketch of C on the top and on the bottom the surface S, which is drawn as follows. Reflect C through the z-axis to get the curve C' shown. Then for the selected points on C, draw horizontal circles about the z-axis to render the latitude lines. Also sketch in a few additional curves similar to C to give some longitude lines. This surface is a quadric surface called a *circular paraboloid*.

Part: (b) $z = 2x$, for x in $[0, 1]$.

Solution (b): The "curve" C is part of the straight line through the origin with slope 2 and has parametrization: $x = t$, $y = 0$, $z = 2t$, for t in $[0, 1]$. Then the surface S has parametrization

$$\mathbf{r}(\theta, t) = \langle\, t\cos\theta,\, t\sin\theta,\, 2t\,\rangle, \qquad (13.2.11)$$

for (θ, t) in $D = [0, 2\pi] \times [0, 1]$. Figure 13.2.7 shows a sketch of C on the top and on the bottom the surface S, drawn as follows. Reflect C through the z-axis to get the line C' shown. Then for the selected points on C, draw horizontal circles about the z-axis to render the latitude lines. Also sketch a few addition straight lines through the origin, similar to C, to give some longitude lines. This surface is a standard *cone*.

Part: (c) The half hyperbola $\dfrac{x^2}{4} - \dfrac{z^2}{9} = 1$, where $x \geq 2$.

Solution (c): To parametrize hyperbolas we use, naturally, the hyperbolic sine and cosine functions: $\sinh t$ and $\cosh t$. These functions are discussed in Section 2.12 and have many similarities to the trig functions. All we need to know here is the basic hyperbolic identity and the derivatives:

$$\cosh^2 t - \sinh^2 t = 1, \qquad \frac{d}{dt}(\cosh t) = \sinh t, \qquad \frac{d}{dt}(\sinh t) = \cosh t.$$

Then, a parametrization of the indicated half hyperbola is $x = 2\cosh t$, $y = 0$, and $z = 3\sinh t$. To check this, look at

$$\frac{x^2}{4} - \frac{z^2}{9} = \frac{4\cosh^2 t}{4} - \frac{9\sinh^2 t}{9} = \cosh^2 t - \sinh^2 t = 1$$

The surface S has parametrization

$$\mathbf{r}(\theta, t) = \langle\, 2\cosh t\cos\theta,\, 2\cosh t\sin\theta,\, 3\sinh t\,\rangle, \qquad (13.2.12)$$

for (θ, t) in $D = [0, 2\pi] \times (-\infty, \infty)$. Figure 13.2.8 shows a sketch of the curve C on the top (just for $2 \leq x \leq 2\sqrt{2}$) and on the bottom the surface S, drawn as follows. Reflect C through the z-axis to get the curve C' shown. Then for the selected points on C, draw horizontal circles about the z-axis to render the latitude lines. Also sketch in a few addition curves similar to C to give some longitude lines. This surface is a quadric surface called a *circular hyperboloid of one sheet*.

The Torus and Sphere

A *torus* is an important surface of revolution, which is sometimes called a *doughnut* because it bounds a solid that is similar to a well-liked snack in America. It is a surface of revolution described as follows.

For constants $a > 0, k \geq 0$, consider the circle C in the x-z-plane with center $(k, 0, 0)$ and radius a. From the geometry shown in Figure 13.2.9, we see that C can be parametrized using an angle ϕ for the parameter. This gives

$$x = k + a\cos\phi, \quad y = 0, \quad z = a\sin\phi,$$

for ϕ in $[0, 2\pi]$. Then the corresponding surface of revolution is parametrized by

$$\mathbf{r}(\theta, \phi) = \langle (k + a\cos\phi)\cos\theta, \ (k + a\cos\phi)\cos\theta, \ a\sin\phi \rangle, \qquad (13.2.13)$$

for (θ, ϕ) in $[0, 2\pi] \times [0, 2\pi]$. Depending on the relative magnitudes of a and k, the parameterization (13.2.13) describes a torus, a sphere, or something in between:

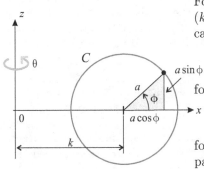

Figure 13.2.9: *The circle C in the x-y-plane with center $(k, 0, 0)$ and radius a.*

Example 13.2.2 (Sketching a Torus et al.)

Problem: Use the `drevplot` command to create a dynamic plot (i.e., a movie) of the torus parametrized by (13.2.13) for $a = 2$ and $k = 4$. Also, use `drevplot` to study the surfaces parametrized by (13.2.13) with $a = 2$ and $k = 1, k = 0$. Comment on the type of surface in these latter two cases.

Solution: We first define the two component functions $X(\phi) = k + a\cos\phi$ and $Z(\phi) = a\sin\phi$ in Maple and then use the `drevplot` command as follows.

```
> X:=phi->k+a*cos(phi);Z:=t->a*sin(phi);
```

$$X := \phi \rightarrow k + a\cos(\phi)$$
$$Z := \phi \rightarrow a\sin(\phi)$$

```
> a:=2;k:=4;
```

$$a := 2$$
$$k := 4$$

```
> drevplot(X,Z,0,2*Pi,10,7.5,7.5,6,5,25);
```

This produces the desired movie. The left side of Figure 13.2.10 shows the 9th frame in this movie. Note: The 0th frame just shows the curve C (a circle). So there are 11 frames in the movie.

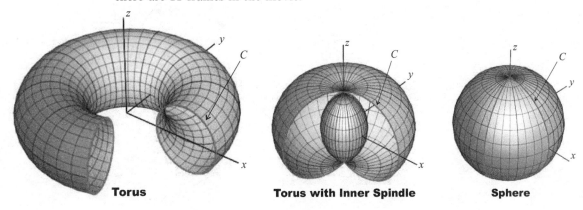

Torus   **Torus with Inner Spindle**   **Sphere**

Figure 13.2.10: *Surfaces generated by revolving a circle C with radius 2 and centers $(4, 0, 0)$ (left), $(1, 0, 0)$ (center), and $(0, 0, 0)$ (right), respectively.*

Next, changing k to $k = 1$ in the `drevplot` command produces a movie, the 9th frame of is shown in the center of Figure 13.2.10. We call this a *torus with inner spindle* because the hole in the actual torus closes up and a new surface is created inside the outer surface. Finally, changing k to $k = 0$ in the `drevplot` command produces a movie, the 9th frame of which is shown in the right side of Figure 13.2.10.

Now the circle C is centered at the origin and so we would expect the surface of revolution to be a sphere of radius 2.

NOTE: It is important to observe, which is apparent in the movie, that the sphere is swept out twice as θ runs through $[0, 2\pi]$. This is because we are revolving the full circle C about the z-axis. If we restrict the parameter ϕ to $[-\frac{\pi}{2}, \frac{\pi}{2}]$, then we get a semi-circle C', which, when revolved about the z-axis, sweeps out the sphere just once. Compare this with Part (c) of Example 9.1.5, where the parametrization of the unit circle traces out the circle twice as the parameter t runs through $[0, 2\pi]$, but only once if we restrict t to $[0, \pi]$.

SUMMARY: Surfaces of revolutions are naturally parametrized by two parameters, the rotation angle θ and the parameter t for the curve being revolved.

In addition to surfaces of revolution, there are many other special types of surfaces that are easy to parametrize. Before looking at these, we return to the discussion of general surfaces and the derivative calculus for them.

Partial Derivatives, Tangent, and Normal Vectors

A surface S parametrized by $\mathbf{r} : D \to \mathbb{R}^3$ has many tangent vectors at a given point $P(u_0, v_0) = \mathbf{r}(u_0, v_0)$. However, there are two special ones, related to the partial derivatives of $\mathbf{r}$, that we call the *standard tangent vectors* at $P(u_0, v_0)$. We assume, for simplicity, that $D = [a, b] \times [c, d]$.

The partial derivatives of a vector-valued function $\mathbf{r}$ are defined just like the partial derivatives in Chapter 11 for scalar-valued functions, that is, in terms of limits:

$$
\begin{aligned}
\frac{\partial \mathbf{r}}{\partial u}(u_0, v_0) &= \lim_{\Delta u \to 0} \frac{1}{\Delta u} \big[\mathbf{r}(u_0 + \Delta u, v_0) - \mathbf{r}(u_0, v_0) \big] \\
&= \langle \frac{\partial f}{\partial u}(u_0, v_0), \frac{\partial g}{\partial u}(u_0, v_0), \frac{\partial h}{\partial u}(u_0, v_0) \rangle
\end{aligned}
$$

Figure 13.2.11 indicates the geometry of this vector limit.

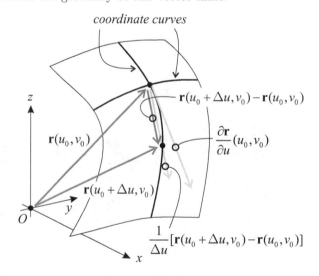

Figure 13.2.11: *A tangent vector to a coordinate curve is the limit of secant vectors.*

The geometry indicates that, for the coordinate curve $\mathbf{c}_1(v_0)$ through the point $P(u_0, v_0)$, the vector $\frac{1}{\Delta u} \big[\mathbf{r}(u_0 + \Delta u, v_0) - \mathbf{r}(u_0, v_0) \big]$ (shown in blue) is a secant vector for the coordinate curve. This secant vector approaches the vector $\frac{\partial \mathbf{r}}{\partial u}(u_0, v_0)$ (shown in green) in the limit as $\Delta u \to 0$. Thus, the vector $\frac{\partial \mathbf{r}}{\partial u}(u_0, v_0)$ is tangent to the coordinate curve (and also to the surface S). Similarly, the vector $\frac{\partial \mathbf{r}}{\partial v}(u_0, v_0)$ is tangent to the coordinate curve $\mathbf{c}_2(u_0)$ through the point $P(u_0, v_0)$.

Standard Tangent Vectors (Notation): $\mathbf{r}_u = \dfrac{\partial \mathbf{r}}{\partial u}$ and $\mathbf{r}_v = \dfrac{\partial \mathbf{r}}{\partial v}$

Technically speaking these are vector-valued functions $\mathbf{r}_u$, $\mathbf{r}_v : D :\to \mathbb{R}^3$, which in terms of component functions are

$$\mathbf{r}_u = \langle\, f_u, g_u, h_u \,\rangle, \qquad \mathbf{r}_v = \langle\, f_v, g_v, h_v \,\rangle.$$

Then for each point (u, v) in the parameter domain $\mathbf{r}_u(u, v)$ and $\mathbf{r}_v(u, v)$ are the standard tangent vectors at $P(u, v)$. Figure 13.2.12 shows these two vectors (without showing their explicit dependence on the point (u, v) in the parameter domain). Also shown is the *standard normal vector* at the point (u, v).

Standard Normal Vector: $\qquad \mathbf{n} = \mathbf{r}_u \times \mathbf{r}_v$

It is important to note that the tangent and normal vectors $\mathbf{r}_u, \mathbf{r}_v, \mathbf{n}$ are usually plotted with their initial points at the point $P(u, v)$ on the surface S.

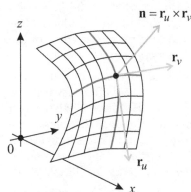

Figure 13.2.12: *The standard tangent vectors $\mathbf{r}_u, \mathbf{r}_v$ and standard normal vector $\mathbf{n}$.*

Example 13.2.3 (Computing the Tangent and Normal Vectors)

Problem: For the surfaces of revolution in Example 13.2.1 Parts (a), (b), and (c), compute the standard tangent vectors $\mathbf{r}_u, \mathbf{r}_v$ and normal vector $\mathbf{n}$.

Solution (a): The parametrization (13.2.10) we found for this paraboloid was

$$\mathbf{r}(\theta, t) = \langle\, t\cos\theta, \, t\sin\theta, \, t^2 \,\rangle,$$

So, the partial derivatives are

$$\mathbf{r}_\theta = \langle\, -t\sin\theta, \, t\cos\theta, \, 0 \,\rangle$$
$$\mathbf{r}_t = \langle\, \cos\theta, \, \sin\theta, \, 2t \,\rangle$$

and the normal vector is

$$\mathbf{n} = \mathbf{r}_\theta \times \mathbf{r}_t = \begin{vmatrix} \mathbf{i} & \mathbf{j} & \mathbf{k} \\ -t\sin\theta & t\cos\theta & 0 \\ \cos\theta & \sin\theta & 2t \end{vmatrix} = \langle\, 2t^2\cos\theta, 2t^2\sin\theta, -t \,\rangle$$

Solution (b): The parametrization (13.2.11) we found for this cone was

$$\mathbf{r} = \langle\, t\cos\theta, \, t\sin\theta, \, 2t \,\rangle,$$

So, the partial derivatives are

$$\mathbf{r}_\theta = \langle\, -t\sin\theta, \, t\cos\theta, \, 0 \,\rangle$$
$$\mathbf{r}_t = \langle\, \cos\theta, \, \sin\theta, \, 2 \,\rangle$$

and the normal vector is

$$\mathbf{n} = \mathbf{r}_\theta \times \mathbf{r}_t = \begin{vmatrix} \mathbf{i} & \mathbf{j} & \mathbf{k} \\ -t\sin\theta & t\cos\theta & 0 \\ \cos\theta & \sin\theta & 2 \end{vmatrix} = \langle\, 2t\cos\theta, 2t\sin\theta, -t \,\rangle$$

Solution (c): The parametrization (13.2.12) we found for this hyperboloid was

$$\mathbf{r} = \langle\, 2\cosh t\cos\theta, \, 2\cosh t\sin\theta, \, 3\sinh t \,\rangle,$$

So, the partial derivatives are

$$\mathbf{r}_\theta = \langle\, -2\cosh t\sin\theta, \, 2\cosh t\cos\theta, \, 0 \,\rangle$$
$$\mathbf{r}_t = \langle\, 2\sinh t\cos\theta, \, 2\sinh t\sin\theta, \, 3\cosh t \,\rangle$$

and the normal vector is

$$\mathbf{n} = \mathbf{r}_\theta \times \mathbf{r}_t = \begin{vmatrix} \mathbf{i} & \mathbf{j} & \mathbf{k} \\ -2\cosh t\sin\theta & 2\cosh t\cos\theta & 0 \\ 2\sinh t\cos\theta & 2\sinh t\sin\theta & 3\cosh t \end{vmatrix}$$

$$= \langle\, 6\cosh^2 t\cos\theta, \, 6\cosh^2 t\sin\theta, \, -4\cosh t\sinh t\sin^2\theta - 4\cosh t\sinh t\cos^2\theta \,\rangle$$

$$= \langle\, 6\cosh^2 t\cos\theta,\ 6\cosh^2 t\sin\theta,\ -4\cosh t\sinh t\,\rangle$$

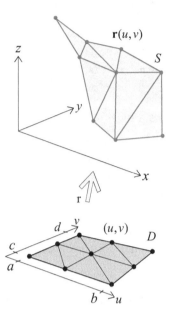

Figure 13.2.13: *A triangular complex approximating a parametrized surface S.*

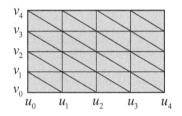

Figure 13.2.14: *A triangular mesh subdividing D.*

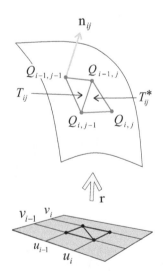

Figure 13.2.15: *Two triangles T_{ij}, T_{ij}^* in the complex approximating S.*

Surface Area

For a general surface S parametrized by $\mathbf{r}: D \to \mathbb{R}^3$, the derivation of an integral formula for the surface area $\mathcal{A}$ of S is a direct extension of what we did in Section 12.4 for a surface $z = F(x, y)$ which is the graph of a function of two variables. Most of the notation and concepts are the same, but for clarity we repeat some of the discussion here. We assume the parameter domain is a rectangle: $D = [a, b] \times [c, d]$.

We use a scheme that consists of approximating S by a collection of contiguous triangles in space. This collection is called *a triangular complex*. To construct this complex, we first divide the parameter D into a mesh of contiguous triangles, called a *triangulation* of D. There are many ways to do this and Figure 13.2.13 shows one possible way that consists of first dividing the rectangle D into subrectangles (in this case 4 subrectangles) and then dividing each subrectangle into two triangles using one of its diagonals (in this case giving 8 triangles in the triangulation of D).

Corresponding to any triangle in this triangulation of D, we get a triangle in space that has its three vertices on the surface S, and hence we get a triangular complex in space that approximates S as indicated in Figure 13.2.13. The sides of these triangles are shown in red.

The mathematical notation for such a triangular complex is as follows. First, $D = [a, b] \times [c, d]$ is partitioned into subrectangles by using the standard partitions of $[a, b]$ and $[c, d]$ into N subintervals and M subintervals, respectively. Figure 13.2.14 shows a triangulation for the case $N = M = 4$. We will use prior indexing schemes to denote the vertices of the subrectangles and from this we get the indexing of the vertices of the corresponding triangles. The vertices of the subrectangles in the partition of D are

$$P_{i,j} = (u_i, v_j),$$

where $u_i = a + i\Delta u$ and $v_j = c + j\Delta v$, for $i = 0, \ldots, N$, $j = 0, \ldots, M$. Here $\Delta u = (b - a)/N$ and $\Delta v = (d - c)/M$. To these there are corresponding points on the surfaces S:

$$Q_{i,j} = \mathbf{r}(u_i, v_j).$$

The i-jth subrectangle D_{ij} is (by definition) the rectangle with vertices $P_{i-1,j-1}$, $P_{i,j-1}$, $P_{i,j}$, $P_{i-1,j}$. Corresponding to these vertices are four points $Q_{i-1,j-1}$, $Q_{i,j-1}$, $Q_{i,j}$, $Q_{i-1,j}$ on the surface S. See Figure 13.2.15. From these points we get two triangles T_{ij}, T_{ij}^* which approximate the part of the surface S that we get by restriction $\mathbf{r}$ to the subrectangle D_{ij}. The points $Q_{i-1,j-1}$, $Q_{i,j-1}$, $Q_{i-1,j}$ are the vertices of the triangle T_{ij} and $Q_{i-1,j}$, $Q_{i,j}$, $Q_{i,j-1}$ are the vertices of triangle T_{ij}^*, as shown in Figure 13.2.15.

We can now compute the areas of T_{ij} and T_{ij}^* using the vector methods from Chapter 10. In the triangle T_{ij}, the two vectors with initial point at vertex $Q_{i-1,j-1}$ and terminal points at $Q_{i,j-1}$ and $Q_{i-1,j}$, are

$$\mathbf{r}(u_i, v_{j-1}) - \mathbf{r}(u_{i-1}, v_{j-1}), \qquad \mathbf{r}(u_{i-1}, v_j) - \mathbf{r}(u_{i-1}, v_{j-1})$$

So, the cross product of these vectors gives a vector $\mathbf{n}_{ij}$ which is normal to the triangle:

$$\mathbf{n}_{ij} \equiv \big[\mathbf{r}(u_i, v_{j-1}) - \mathbf{r}(u_{i-1}, v_{j-1})\big] \times \big[\mathbf{r}(u_{i-1}, v_j) - \mathbf{r}(u_{i-1}, v_{j-1})\big]$$

$$= \left[\frac{\mathbf{r}(u_i, v_{j-1}) - \mathbf{r}(u_{i-1}, v_{j-1})}{\Delta u} \times \frac{\mathbf{r}(u_{i-1}, v_j) - \mathbf{r}(u_{i-1}, v_{j-1})}{\Delta v}\right] \Delta u \Delta v$$

Thus, the area of the triangle T_{ij} is:

$$\tfrac{1}{2}\|\mathbf{n}_{ij}\| = \tfrac{1}{2}\left\|\frac{\mathbf{r}(u_i, v_{j-1}) - \mathbf{r}(u_{i-1}, v_{j-1})}{\Delta u} \times \frac{\mathbf{r}(u_{i-1}, v_j) - \mathbf{r}(u_{i-1}, v_{j-1})}{\Delta v}\right\| \Delta u \Delta v$$

In a similar fashion, for the triangle T_{ij}^* let

$$\mathbf{n}_{ij}^* \equiv \left[\, \mathbf{r}(u_i, v_j) - \mathbf{r}(u_{i-1}, v_j)\,\right] \times \left[\, \mathbf{r}(u_i, v_j) - \mathbf{r}(u_i, v_{j-1})\,\right]$$

$$= \left[\, \frac{\mathbf{r}(u_i, v_j) - \mathbf{r}(u_{i-1}, v_j)}{\Delta u} \times \frac{\mathbf{r}(u_i, v_j) - \mathbf{r}(u_i, v_{j-1})}{\Delta v}\,\right] \Delta u \Delta v$$

Then, the area of the triangle T_{ij}^* is:

$$\tfrac{1}{2}\|\mathbf{n}_{ij}^*\| = \tfrac{1}{2}\left\| \frac{\mathbf{r}(u_i, v_j) - \mathbf{r}(u_{i-1}, v_j)}{\Delta u} \times \frac{\mathbf{r}(u_i, v_j) - \mathbf{r}(u_i, v_{j-1})}{\Delta v}\right\| \Delta u \Delta v$$

Then the total area of the triangular complex is given by the double sum:

$$\mathcal{A}_{N,M} = \sum_{i=1}^{N} \sum_{j=1}^{M} \left[\, \tfrac{1}{2}\|\mathbf{n}_{ij}\| + \tfrac{1}{2}\|\mathbf{n}_{ij}^*\|\,\right] \qquad (13.2.14)$$

$$= \sum_{i=1}^{N} \sum_{j=1}^{M} \left[\begin{array}{l} \tfrac{1}{2}\left\| \frac{\mathbf{r}(u_i, v_{j-1}) - \mathbf{r}(u_{i-1}, v_{j-1})}{\Delta u} \times \frac{\mathbf{r}(u_{i-1}, v_j) - \mathbf{r}(u_{i-1}, v_{j-1})}{\Delta v}\right\| \Delta u \Delta v \\[2mm] + \tfrac{1}{2}\left\| \frac{\mathbf{r}(u_i, v_j) - \mathbf{r}(u_{i-1}, v_j)}{\Delta u} \times \frac{\mathbf{r}(u_i, v_j) - \mathbf{r}(u_i, v_{j-1})}{\Delta v}\right\| \Delta u \Delta v \end{array}\right]$$

This is a complicated looking expression, but it is easy enough to write the code for a special-purpose procedure to do the calculations (and also plot the triangular complex).

Example 13.2.4 (Approximating Surfaces and Their Areas)

Problem: Consider the toroidal surface S which is parametrized by

$$\mathbf{r} = \langle\, (1+\cos\phi)\cos\theta,\ (1+\cos\phi)\sin\theta,\ \sin\phi\,\rangle$$

for parameters (θ, ϕ) in $D = [0, 2\pi] \times [0, 2\pi]$. This is the parametrization (13.2.13) with $a = 1, k = 1$ and is the limiting case of a torus giving a torus without a hole.

Use the special purpose program `TriangleApprox` to (1) plot the triangular complex approximation to S and (2) compute the approximate area $A_{N,M}$, for $N = 15$ and $M = 15$.

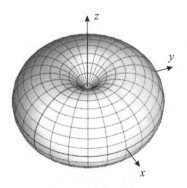

Figure 13.2.16:
A torus with no hole.

Solution: A plot of the surface S is shown in Figure 13.2.16. The command

```
TriangleApprox(f,g,h,a,b,c,d,N,M);
```

will plot the triangular complex that approximates S using $2NM$ triangles based on the scheme discussed above. (Be careful to not take N or M too large.) The output of the command is a plot of the triangular complex along with the (exact) area of the triangular complex as given by Formula (13.2.14). The following code shows how to use this command:

```
> f:=(theta,phi)->(1+cos(phi))*cos(theta);
```
$$f := (\theta, \phi) \mapsto (1 + \cos(\phi))\cos(\theta)$$
```
> g:=(theta,phi)->(1+cos(phi))*sin(theta);
```
$$g := (\theta, \phi) \mapsto (1 + \cos(\phi))\sin(\theta)$$
```
> h:=(theta,phi)->sin(phi);
```
$$h := (\theta, \phi) \mapsto \sin(\phi)$$
```
> TriangleApprox(f,g,h,0,2*Pi,0,2*Pi,15,15);
```
the area of the triangular approximation is, 38.48063894

Figure 13.2.17, exhibits the resulting triangular complex approximation containing 225 triangles.

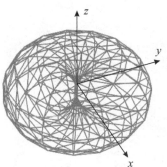

Figure 13.2.17: *A triangular approximation to the plot of a torus with no hole.*

NOTE 1: The procedure `TriangleApprox` used here is an extension of the procedure `triangleapprox` in Section 12.4, which is used for surfaces G_F that are graphs of functions F of two variables. To apply this new procedure to G_F use the standard parametrization $f(u,v) = u, g(u,v) = v, h(u,v) = F(u,v)$.

NOTE 2: You should understand that the above scheme for plotting approximations to surfaces using triangular complexes is how most computer plotting schemes are designed. That is how Maple rendered the plot shown in Figure 13.2.16, except that (1) it does not put in the diagonal lines (so that the pair T_{ij}, T_{ij}^* appears to be a quadrilateral) and (2) it colors the planar face of each triangle.

NOTE 3: Each of the surfaces in Figure 13.2.16 and 13.2.17 appears to be fairly smooth, rather than consisting of a bunch of flat, contiguous triangles. So, you might expect that the approximation $\mathcal{A}_{15,15} = 38.48063894$ would be pretty close to the actual area $\mathcal{A}$ of the surface. We will see that this is the case after we first discuss the integral formula for $\mathcal{A}$.

This formula results from taking the double limit of the expression in Formula (13.2.14). This gives the *exact* surface area as a double integral:

$$
\mathcal{A} = \lim_{N\to\infty}\lim_{M\to\infty} \mathcal{A}_{N,M} = \lim_{N\to\infty}\lim_{M\to\infty} \sum_{i=1}^{N}\sum_{j=1}^{M} \left[\tfrac{1}{2}\|\mathbf{n}_{ij}\| + \tfrac{1}{2}\|\mathbf{n}_{ij}^*\| \right]
$$

$$
= \iint_D \|\mathbf{n}\|\, dA = \iint_D \|\mathbf{r}_u \times \mathbf{r}_v\|\, dA \qquad (13.2.15)
$$

So, in summary we have the following theorem:

THEOREM 13.2.1 (Areas of Parameterized Surfaces)

Suppose $\mathbf{r}: D \to \mathbb{R}^3$ *is a parametrization of a surface S, with* $D = [a,b]\times[c,d]$.
If $\mathbf{r}$ *is one-to-one on D, except possibly on the boundary of D, and if the component functions of* $\mathbf{r}$ *have continuous partial derivatives, then the area of S is*

$$
\mathcal{A} = \iint_D \|\mathbf{n}\|\, dA = \iint_D \|\mathbf{r}_u \times \mathbf{r}_v\|\, dA = \int_c^d \int_a^b \|\mathbf{r}_u(u,v) \times \mathbf{r}_v(u,v)\|\, du\,dv \qquad (13.2.16)
$$

NOTE 1: (Simple and Almost Simple Surfaces) The condition that $\mathbf{r}: D \to \mathbb{R}^3$ be one-to-one, except possibly on the boundary of D, is meant to ensure that the parametrization does not retrace parts of the surface, in which case the integral formula (13.2.16) would over-measure the area. (See Example 13.2.2 where the parametrization of the sphere sweeps out the sphere twice.) A surface is called *simple* when the parametrization is one-to-one except possibly on the boundary of D. More generally, a surface S, parametrized by $\mathbf{r}: D \to \mathbb{R}^3$, is called *almost simple* if $\mathbf{r}$ is one-to-one almost everywhere on D. This latter condition means that there is a subset $Z \subset D$, of measure zero, such that $\mathbf{r}$ is one-to-one on $D \setminus Z = \{(u,v) \text{ in } D \,|\, (u,v) \text{ is not in } Z\}$.

NOTE 2: Formula 13.2.16 holds for almost simple surfaces.

NOTE 3: The surface area Formula (13.2.16) extends to the case where the rectangle D is replaced by a general planar region (usually of Type I or Type II).

Example 13.2.5 (Computing Surface Area)

Problem: Compute the areas of the surfaces with the following paramterizations.

Part (a): $\mathbf{r}(u,v) = \langle\, \frac{1}{3}u^3 + uv^2, \frac{5}{3}v^3, v^5 - \frac{5}{4}v \,\rangle$, for (u,v) in $[-1,1]\times[-1,1]$

Solution (a): First compute the partial derivatives of $\mathbf{r}$:

$$
\mathbf{r}_u = \langle\, u^2 + v^2, 0, 0 \,\rangle
$$
$$
\mathbf{r}_v = \langle\, 2uv, 5v^2, 5v^4 - \tfrac{5}{4} \,\rangle
$$

and the normal vector is

$$
\mathbf{n} = \mathbf{r}_u \times \mathbf{r}_v = \begin{vmatrix} \mathbf{i} & \mathbf{j} & \mathbf{k} \\ u^2 + v^2 & 0 & 0 \\ 2uv & 5v^2 & 5v^4 - \tfrac{5}{4} \end{vmatrix} = \langle\, 0, -(u^2+v^2)(5v^4 - \tfrac{5}{4}), (u^2+v^2)5v^2 \,\rangle
$$

Then

$$\begin{aligned}
\|\mathbf{n}\|^2 &= (u^2 + v^2)^2 (5v^4 - \tfrac{5}{4})^2 + (u^2 + v^2)^2\, 25v^4 \\
&= (u^2 + v^2)^2 \big[(5v^4 - \tfrac{5}{4})^2 + 25v^4 \big] \\
&= (u^2 + v^2)^2 \big[25v^8 - \tfrac{25}{2}v^4 + \tfrac{25}{16} + 25v^4 \big] \\
&= (u^2 + v^2)^2 \big[25v^8 + \tfrac{25}{2}v^4 + \tfrac{25}{16} \big] \\
&= (u^2 + v^2)^2 (5v^4 + \tfrac{5}{4})^2
\end{aligned}$$

Thus,

$$\|n\| = (u^2 + v^2)(5v^4 + \tfrac{5}{4})$$

Consequently

$$\begin{aligned}
\mathcal{A} &= \iint_D \|\mathbf{n}\|\, dA = \int_{-1}^{1}\int_{-1}^{1} (u^2 + v^2)(5v^4 + \tfrac{5}{4})\, dv\, du \\
&= \int_{-1}^{1}\int_{-1}^{1} u^2(5v^4 + \tfrac{5}{4})\, dv\, du + \int_{-1}^{1}\int_{-1}^{1} v^2(5v^4 + \tfrac{5}{4})\, dv\, du = I_1 + I_2
\end{aligned}$$

For the sake of simplicity, we have split the double integral into two separate double integrals. Calculation of the first one gives

$$\begin{aligned}
I_1 &= \int_{-1}^{1}\int_{-1}^{1} u^2(5v^4 + \tfrac{5}{4})\, dv\, du = \int_{-1}^{1} u^2\, du \cdot \int_{-1}^{1} (5v^4 + \tfrac{5}{4})\, dv \\
&= 2\int_{0}^{1} u^2\, du \cdot 2\int_{0}^{1} (5v^4 + \tfrac{5}{4})\, dv = \tfrac{2}{3}u^3 \Big|_0^1 \cdot 2\big(v^5 + \tfrac{5}{4}v\big)\Big|_0^1 \\
&= \tfrac{2}{3} \cdot 2\big(1 + \tfrac{5}{4}\big) = 3
\end{aligned}$$

Here we used the properties: (1) $\int_a^b \int_c^d f(x)g(y)\, dy\, dx = \int_a^b f(x)\, dx \cdot \int_c^d g(y)\, dy$ and (2) If f is an even function, then $\int_{-b}^{b} f(x)\, dx = 2\int_0^b f(x)\, dx$. Consider using these below and in the exercises.

The calculation of the second double integral is

$$\begin{aligned}
I_2 &= \int_{-1}^{1}\int_{-1}^{1} v^2(5v^4 + \tfrac{5}{4})\, dv\, du = \int_{-1}^{1}\int_{-1}^{1} (5v^6 + \tfrac{5}{4}v^2)\, dv\, du \\
&= \int_{-1}^{1} 1\, du \cdot \int_{-1}^{1} (5v^6 + \tfrac{5}{4}v^2)\, dv = 2\int_0^1 1\, du \cdot 2\int_0^1 (5v^6 + \tfrac{5}{4}v^2)\, dv \\
&= 2u\Big|_0^1 \cdot 2\big(\tfrac{5}{7}v^7 + \tfrac{5}{12}v^3\big)\Big|_0^1 = 2 \cdot 2\big(\tfrac{5}{7} + \tfrac{5}{12}\big) = \tfrac{95}{21}
\end{aligned}$$

Thus, the surface area is

$$\mathcal{A} = I_1 + I_2 = 3 + \tfrac{95}{21} = \tfrac{158}{21} = 7\tfrac{11}{21}$$

Figure 13.2.18 shows a plot of this surface and you can check visually that $\mathcal{A} = 7\tfrac{11}{21}$ appears to be approximately correct.

Part (b): $\mathbf{r}(u,v) = \langle\, u^3 v,\ 4\sqrt{1 + v^2} - 4,\ \tfrac{4}{3}v^3 - \tan^{-1} v\, \rangle$, for (u,v) in $[-1,1]\times[-1,1]$.

Solution (b): First compute the partial derivatives of $\mathbf{r}$:

$$\mathbf{r}_u = \langle\, 3u^2 v,\ 0,\ 0\, \rangle$$

$$\mathbf{r}_v = \Big\langle\, u^3,\ \frac{4v}{\sqrt{1 + v^2}},\ 4v^2 - \frac{1}{1 + v^2}\, \Big\rangle$$

and the normal vector is

$$\mathbf{n} = \mathbf{r}_u \times \mathbf{r}_v = \begin{vmatrix} \mathbf{i} & \mathbf{j} & \mathbf{k} \\ 3u^2 v & 0 & 0 \\ u^3 & \frac{4v}{\sqrt{1+v^2}} & 4v^2 - \frac{1}{1+v^2} \end{vmatrix}$$

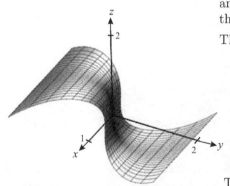

Figure 13.2.18: *The surface* $x = \tfrac{1}{3}u^3 + uv^2,\ y = \tfrac{5}{3}v^3,$ $z = v^5 - \tfrac{5}{4}v.$

$$= \ \langle \, 0, \, -3u^2v\big[\, 4v^2 - \frac{1}{1+v^2} \,\big], \, \frac{3 \cdot 4\, u^2v^2}{\sqrt{1+v^2}} \, \rangle$$

Then

$$\begin{aligned}
\|\mathbf{n}\|^2 \ &= \ 9u^4v^2\big[\, 4v^2 - \frac{1}{1+v^2} \,\big]^2 + \frac{9 \cdot 16\, u^4v^4}{1+v^2} \\
&= \ 9u^4v^2\left[\big[\, 4v^2 - \frac{1}{1+v^2} \,\big]^2 + \frac{16\, v^2}{1+v^2}\right] \\
&= \ 9u^4v^2\left[16v^2 - \frac{8v^2}{1+v^2} + \frac{1}{(1+v^2)^2} + \frac{16\, v^2}{1+v^2} \right] \\
&= \ 9u^4v^2\left[16v^2 + \frac{8v^2}{1+v^2} + \frac{1}{(1+v^2)^2} \right] \\
&= \ 9u^4v^2\big[\, 4v^2 + \frac{1}{1+v^2} \,\big]^2
\end{aligned}$$

Thus,

$$\|n\| = 3u^2|v|\big[\, 4v^2 + \frac{1}{1+v^2} \,\big]$$

Consequently

$$\begin{aligned}
\mathcal{A} \ &= \ \iint_D \|\mathbf{n}\|\, dA = \int_{-1}^{1}\int_{-1}^{1} 3u^2|v|\big[\, 4v^2 + \frac{1}{1+v^2} \,\big]\, dv\, du \\
&= \ \int_{-1}^{1} 3u^2\, du \cdot \int_{-1}^{1} |v|\big[\, 4v^2 + \frac{1}{1+v^2} \,\big]\, dv \\
&= \ 2\int_{0}^{1} 3u^2\, du \cdot 2\int_{0}^{1} v\big[\, 4v^2 + \frac{1}{1+v^2} \,\big]\, dv \\
&= \ 2\int_{0}^{1} 3u^2\, du \cdot 2\int_{0}^{1} \big[\, 4v^3 + \frac{v}{1+v^2} \,\big]\, dv = 2u^3\Big|_0^1 \cdot 2\big[\, v^4 + \tfrac{1}{2}\ln(1+v^2) \,\big]\Big|_0^1 \\
&= \ 2(1) \cdot (2)\big[1 + \tfrac{1}{2}\ln 2\big] = 4 + 2\ln 2 \approx 5.386
\end{aligned}$$

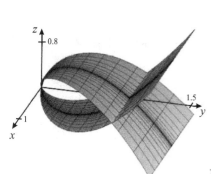

Figure 13.2.19: *The surface*
$x = u^3v,\ y = 4\sqrt{1+v^2} - 4,$
$z = \frac{4}{3}v^3 - \tan^{-1} v.$

Figure 13.2.19 shows a plot of this surface and you can check visually that $\mathcal{A} = 4 + 2\ln 2 \approx 5.386$ appears to be in the ball park.

NOTE: As seen in the figure, this surface S intersects itself and so is not a simple surface. But the curve (actually line) of intersection is a set of measure zero and so S is almost simple. (See NOTES 1 and 2 after Theorem 13.2.1.) Thus, we are justified in using the integral formula (13.2.16).

Example 13.2.6 (Computing Surface Area - Surfaces of Revolution)

Problem: Compute the areas of the surfaces in Example 13.2.1 Part (a) (a paraboloid) and the torus with no hole in Example 13.2.2. Compare this latter area with the approximate area found in Example 13.2.2.

Solution (a): The parametrization (13.2.10) we found for this paraboloid was

$$\mathbf{r}(\theta, t) = \langle \, t\cos\theta, \, t\sin\theta, \, t^2 \, \rangle,$$

for (θ, t) in $D = [0, 2\pi] \times [0, 2]$. In Example 13.2.3, we computed the normal to the surface:

$$\mathbf{n} = \langle \, 2t^2\cos\theta, 2t^2\sin\theta, -t \, \rangle$$

Thus,

$$\|\mathbf{n}\|^2 = 4t^4\cos^2\theta + 4t^4\sin^2\theta + t^2 = 4t^4 + t^2 = t^2(4t^2 + 1)$$

and so the area is

$$\mathcal{A} \ = \ \iint_D \|\mathbf{n}\|\, dA = \int_0^{2\pi}\int_0^2 t\sqrt{4t^2 + 1}\, dt d\theta = 2\pi\int_0^2 t\sqrt{4t^2 + 1}\, dt$$

$$= 2\pi \int_1^5 \sqrt{u}\left(\tfrac{1}{8}\,du\right) = \tfrac{\pi}{4}\left[\tfrac{2}{3}u^{3/2}\right]\Big|_1^5 = \tfrac{\pi}{6}\left[5\sqrt{5}-1\right]$$

In the above, we used the substitution $u = 4t^2 + 1$, $du = 8t\,dt$.

Solution (b): The parametrization for the no hole torus is

$$\mathbf{r} = \langle\,(1+\cos\phi)\cos\theta,\ (1+\cos\phi)\sin\theta,\ \sin\phi\,\rangle$$

for parameters (θ,ϕ) in $D = [0,2\pi]\times[0,2\pi]$. First compute the partial derivatives of $\mathbf{r}$:

$$\mathbf{r}_\theta = \langle\,-(1+\cos\phi)\sin\theta,\ (1+\cos\phi)\cos\theta,\ 0\,\rangle$$
$$\mathbf{r}_\phi = \langle\,-\sin\phi\cos\theta,\ -\sin\phi\sin\theta,\ \cos\phi\,\rangle$$

Then the normal vector is

$$\mathbf{n} = \mathbf{r}_u \times \mathbf{r}_v = \begin{vmatrix} \mathbf{i} & \mathbf{j} & \mathbf{k} \\ -(1+\cos\phi)\sin\theta & (1+\cos\phi)\cos\theta & 0 \\ -\sin\phi\cos\theta & -\sin\phi\sin\theta & \cos\phi \end{vmatrix}$$

$$= \left\langle\, \begin{array}{c} \cos\phi(1+\cos\phi)\cos\theta \\ \cos\phi(1+\cos\phi)\sin\theta \\ \sin\phi(1+\cos\phi)\sin^2\theta + \sin\phi(1+\cos\phi)\cos^2\theta \end{array} \,\right\rangle$$

$$= \langle\,\cos\phi(1+\cos\phi)\cos\theta,\ \cos\phi(1+\cos\phi)\sin\theta,\ \sin\phi(1+\cos\phi)\,\rangle$$

Thus,

$$\begin{aligned} \|\mathbf{n}\|^2 &= \cos^2\phi(1+\cos\phi)^2\cos^2\theta + \cos^2\phi(1+\cos\phi)^2\sin^2\theta + \sin^2\phi(1+\cos\phi)^2 \\ &= \cos^2\phi(1+\cos\phi)^2 + \sin^2\phi(1+\cos\phi)^2 = (1+\cos\phi)^2 \end{aligned}$$

Therefore, the area is

$$\begin{aligned} \mathcal{A} &= \iint_D \|\mathbf{n}\|\,dA = \int_0^{2\pi}\int_0^{2\pi} (1+\cos\phi)\,d\phi\,d\theta = 2\pi\int_0^{2\pi}(1+\cos\phi)\,d\phi \\ &= 2\pi\left[\phi + \sin\phi\right]\Big|_0^{2\pi} = 4\pi^2 \approx 39.4784176 \end{aligned}$$

This exact answer $\mathcal{A} = 4\pi^2 \approx 39.4784176$ shows that $\mathcal{A}_{25,25} = 38.48063894$, which is the area of the 225 triangular approximation, is actually a pretty good approximation.

The last two examples illustrate the standard procedure for computing the integrand $\|\mathbf{n}\| = \|\mathbf{r}_u \times \mathbf{r}_v\|$ of the surface area integral: (1) Calculate the partial derivatives $\mathbf{r}_u, \mathbf{r}_v$. (2) Compute the cross product $\mathbf{n} = \mathbf{r}_u \times \mathbf{r}_v$. (3) Calculate the length $\|\mathbf{n}\|$ of the normal vector. In all three steps you must be careful with the algebra and the calculus. By taking care and simplifying, using the binomial theorem in reverse and certain trig identities where necessary, you should end up with an integrand that you can integrate, *at least for most of the problems and exercises we have selected.* For some of classes of surfaces, such as surfaces of revolution, there is a simplification of the area formula (13.2.16) that we can use:

An Area Formula for Surfaces of Revolution

Consider the general surface of revolution with parametrization

$$\mathbf{r}(\theta,t) = \langle\,X(t)\cos\theta,\ X(t)\sin\theta,\ Z(t)\,\rangle,$$

for (θ,t) in $D = [0,2\pi]\times[c,d]$. First compute the partial derivatives of $\mathbf{r}$:

$$\mathbf{r}_\theta = \langle\,-X(t)\sin\theta,\ X(t)\cos\theta,\ 0\,\rangle$$
$$\mathbf{r}_t = \langle\,X'(t)\cos\theta,\ X'(t)\sin\theta,\ Z'(t)\,\rangle$$

and the normal vector is

$$
\mathbf{n} = \mathbf{r}_u \times \mathbf{r}_v = \begin{vmatrix} \mathbf{i} & \mathbf{j} & \mathbf{k} \\ -X(t)\sin\theta & X(t)\cos\theta & 0 \\ X'(t)\cos\theta & X'(t)\sin\theta & Z'(t) \end{vmatrix}
$$

$$
= \ \langle\ X(t)Z'(t)\cos\theta,\ X(t)Z'(t)\sin\theta,\ -X(t)X'(t)\sin^2\theta - X(t)X'(t)\cos^2\theta\ \rangle
$$

$$
= \ \langle\ X(t)Z'(t)\cos\theta,\ X(t)Z'(t)\sin\theta,\ -X(t)X'(t)\ \rangle
$$

Thus,

$$
\begin{aligned}
\|\mathbf{n}\|^2 &= [X(t)Z'(t)]^2\cos^2\theta + [X(t)Z'(t)]^2\sin^2\theta + [X(t)X'(t)]^2 \\
&= [X(t)Z'(t)]^2 + [X(t)X'(t)]^2 \\
&= [X(t)]^2\big([X'(t)]^2 + [Z'(t)]^2\big)
\end{aligned}
$$

Taking square roots of this gives the integrand $\|\mathbf{n}\|$ for the surface area integral: $\|\mathbf{n}\| = |X(t)|\sqrt{[X'(t)]^2 + [Z'(t)]^2}$. NOTE: This does not depend on θ and so the iterated integral for the area reduces to 2π times a single integral (with respect to t). The following theorem summarizes all of this;

Area of a Surface of Revolution

Suppose S is the surface of revolution obtained by revolving a simple curve

$$x = X(t),\ y = 0,\ z = Z(t),\quad \text{for } t \text{ in } [a,b],$$

about the z-axis. Then the surface area integral formula for S is

$$
\mathcal{A} = \iint_D \|\mathbf{n}\|\, dA = 2\pi\int_a^b |X(t)|\ \sqrt{[X'(t)]^2 + [Z'(t)]^2}\ dt \qquad (13.2.17)
$$

You can try this formula on the two surfaces of revolution in the previous example and see how you like it. Obviously, it eliminates the task of computing $\mathbf{r}_\theta, \mathbf{r}_t$ and $\mathbf{r}_\theta \times \mathbf{r}_t$. Even with this simplification of the surface area formula, the integral is, for most surfaces of revolution, impossible to compute exactly. However, there is a special class of surfaces for which this is possible because

$$
\|\mathbf{n}\|^2 = |X(t)|^2\big([X'(t)]^2 + [Z'(t)]^2\big) = a\ perfect\ sqaure,
$$

for the appropriate choice of X, Z. The following example shows you two surfaces of this type.

Example 13.2.7 (Computing Surface Area - Surfaces of Revolution)

Problem: Compute the surface area of the following surfaces of revolution.

Part (a): $x = (t - \frac{1}{3}t^3)\cos\theta,\qquad y = (t - \frac{1}{3}t^3)\sin\theta,\qquad z = t^2,$

for (θ, t) in $[0, 2\pi] \times [0, 2]$. (*A revolved loop*)

Solution (a): Here $X(t) = t - \frac{1}{3}t^3$, $Z(t) = t^2$, $X'(t) = 1 - t^2$ and $Z'(t) = 2t$. Then

$$
[X'(t)]^2 + [Z'(t)]^2 = (1 - t^2)^2 + 4t^2 = 1 - 2t^2 + t^4 + 4t^2 = (1 + t^2)^2
$$

So, by Formula 13.2.17, the surface area is

$$
\mathcal{A} = 2\pi\int_c^d |X(t)|\sqrt{[X'(t)]^2 + [Z'(t)]^2}\, dt = 2\pi\int_0^2 |t - \tfrac{1}{3}t^3|(1 + t^2)\, dt
$$

Note the absolute value of $t - \frac{1}{3}t^3$ in the integrand. This is needed because $X = t - \frac{1}{3}t^3$ goes from positive to negative on the interval $[0, 2]$ and is zero $X = t - \frac{1}{3}t^3 = 0$,

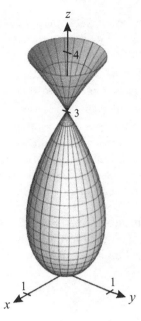

Figure 13.2.20:
The surface
$x = (t - \frac{1}{3}t^3)\cos\theta,$
$y = (t - \frac{1}{3}t^3)\sin\theta,$
$z = t^2.$

when $t = \sqrt{3}$. Thus, we divide the calculation of $\mathcal{A}$ into integrals over $[0, \sqrt{3}]$ (where $|X| = X$) and $[\sqrt{3}, 2]$ (where $|X| = -X$). Looking a Figure 13.2.20, you can see that this gives two areas $\mathcal{A}_1$ and $\mathcal{A}_2$, one of the tear-drop shaped surface and one of the conical surface, respectively. The tear-drop surface has area

$$
\begin{aligned}
\mathcal{A}_1 &= 2\pi \int_c^d |X(t)| \sqrt{[X'(t)]^2 + [Z'(t)]^2}\, dt = 2\pi \int_0^{\sqrt{3}} (t - \tfrac{1}{3}t^3)(1 + t^2)\, dt \\
&= 2\pi \int_0^{\sqrt{3}} \left[t + \tfrac{2}{3}t^3 - \tfrac{1}{3}t^5 \right] dt = 2\pi \left[\tfrac{1}{2}t^2 + \tfrac{1}{6}t^4 - \tfrac{1}{18}t^6 \right] \Big|_0^{\sqrt{3}} \\
&= 2\pi \left[\tfrac{1}{2}(3) + \tfrac{1}{6}(9) - \tfrac{1}{18}(27) \right] = 2\pi \cdot 3 \left[\tfrac{1}{2} + \tfrac{1}{2} - \tfrac{1}{2} \right] = 3\pi
\end{aligned}
$$

We can use the some of the above calculations in the following computation of the area of the conical surface:

$$
\begin{aligned}
\mathcal{A}_2 &= 2\pi \int_c^d |X(t)| \sqrt{[X'(t)]^2 + [Z'(t)]^2}\, dt = 2\pi \int_{\sqrt{3}}^2 -(t - \tfrac{1}{3}t^3)(1 + t^2)\, dt \\
&= -2\pi \left[\tfrac{1}{2}t^2 + \tfrac{1}{6}t^4 - \tfrac{1}{18}t^6 \right] \Big|_{\sqrt{3}}^2 = -2\pi \left[\tfrac{1}{2}(4) + \tfrac{1}{6}(16) - \tfrac{1}{18}(64) \right] + 3\pi \\
&= 3\pi - \tfrac{20}{9}\pi
\end{aligned}
$$

So, the total area is

$$
\mathcal{A} = \mathcal{A}_1 + \mathcal{A}_2 = 6\pi - \tfrac{20}{9}\pi
$$

Part (b): $x = (1 - \cos t)\cos\theta, \quad y = (2 - \cos t)\sin\theta, \quad z = t - \sin t,$
for (θ, t) in $[0, 2\pi] \times [0, 2\pi]$. (*A revolved cycloid*)

Solution (b): Here $X(t) = 1 - \cos t$, $Z(t) = t - \sin t$, and so
$$X'(t) = \sin t, \qquad Z'(t) = 1 - \cos t.$$

Then, using the trig identity $2\sin^2 A = 1 - \cos 2A$, we get

$$
\begin{aligned}
[X'(t)]^2 + [Z'(t)]^2 &= \sin^2 t + (1 - \cos t)^2 = \sin^2 t + 1 - 2\cos t + \cos^2 t \\
&= 2 - 2\cos t = 4\sin^2 \tfrac{1}{2}t
\end{aligned}
$$

So, by Formula 13.2.17, the surface area is

$$
\begin{aligned}
\mathcal{A} &= 2\pi \int_c^d |X(t)| \sqrt{[X'(t)]^2 + [Z'(t)]^2}\, dt = 2\pi \int_0^{2\pi} \left[1 - \cos t \right] 2 \sin \tfrac{1}{2}t\, dt \\
&= 4\pi \int_0^{2\pi} \left[2\sin^2 \tfrac{1}{2}t \right] \sin \tfrac{1}{2}t\, dt = 8\pi \int_0^{2\pi} \left[1 - \cos^2 \tfrac{1}{2}t \right] \sin \tfrac{1}{2}t\, dt \\
&= 8\pi \int_1^{-1} \left[1 - u^2 \right](-2\,du) = 16\pi \int_{-1}^1 \left[1 - u^2 \right] du = 32\pi \int_0^1 \left[1 - u^2 \right] du \\
&= 32\pi \left[u - \tfrac{1}{3}u^3 \right] \Big|_0^1 = \tfrac{64}{3}\pi \approx 67.02
\end{aligned}
$$

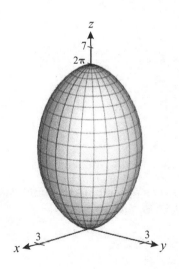

Figure 13.2.21:
The surface
$x = (1 - \cos t)\cos\theta,$
$y = (1 - \cos t)\sin\theta,$
$z = t - \sin t.$

Figure 13.2.21 shows a plot of this surface. You can see from the figure that a surface area of $\mathcal{A} = \frac{64}{3}\pi \approx 67.02$ may be approximately correct, but this one is rather hard to determine.

The Möbius Strip

There is an interesting and important surface, called the *Möbius strip*, which we will use for the theory in Chapter 14. This surface, unlike a sphere or a torus, is easy to construct out of paper, but has a surface area that is impossible to compute exactly.

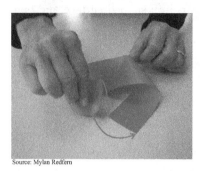

Figure 13.2.22: *Creating a Möbius strip by hand.*

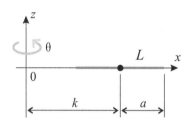

Figure 13.2.23: *Revolve a line segment L while rotating.*

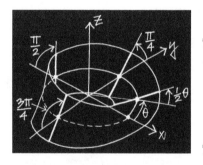

Figure 13.2.24: *A sketch of a Möbius strip.*

To construct a Möbius strip, take a strip of paper, or better yet a piece of masking tape, that is six times longer than it is wide. Holding the ends of the strip, one in each hand, twist one end through a full revolution and join it to the other end. See Figure 13.2.22.

The Möbius strip is *not* a surface of revolution, but is part of a more general class of surfaces (a class which contains the surfaces of revolution).

To describe a Möbius strip S mathematically, let L be the line segment in the x-axis with midpoint at $(k, 0, 0)$ and length $2a$. If we revolve L about the z-axis, we generate an annulus (i.e., a washer), an important but not very complicated surface. However, suppose that, as we revolve L about the z-axis, we also rotate L vertically about its midpoint. Specifically, revolving through angle θ while rotating vertically through angle $\theta/2$, will generate the surface S. See Figures 13.2.23-13.2.24. Parametrizing the line segment L by $x = t$, $y = 0$, $z = 0$, for t in $[-a, a]$, you can easily show (exercise) that the corresponding Möbius strip is parametrized by

$$\mathbf{r}(\theta, t) = \langle\, (k + t\cos\tfrac{\theta}{2})\cos\theta,\ (k + t\cos\tfrac{\theta}{2})\sin\theta,\ t\sin\tfrac{\theta}{2}\,\rangle \qquad (13.2.18)$$
$$= \langle\, R\cos\theta,\ R\sin\theta,\ t\sin\tfrac{\theta}{2}\,\rangle$$

Where, for convenience, we have let $R = k + t\cos\tfrac{\theta}{2}$. Then $R_\theta = -\tfrac{t}{2}\sin\tfrac{\theta}{2}$ and $R_t = \cos\tfrac{\theta}{2}$. Next we calculate the tangent and normal vectors

$$\mathbf{r}_\theta = \langle\, -\tfrac{t}{2}\sin\tfrac{\theta}{2}\cos\theta - R\sin\theta,\ -\tfrac{t}{2}\sin\tfrac{\theta}{2}\sin\theta + R\cos\theta,\ \tfrac{t}{2}\cos\tfrac{\theta}{2}\,\rangle \quad (13.2.19)$$

$$\mathbf{r}_t = \langle\, \cos\tfrac{\theta}{2}\cos\theta,\ \cos\tfrac{\theta}{2}\sin\theta,\ \sin\tfrac{\theta}{2}\,\rangle \qquad (13.2.20)$$

and the normal vector is

$$\mathbf{n} = \begin{vmatrix} \mathbf{i} & \mathbf{j} & \mathbf{k} \\ -\tfrac{t}{2}\sin\tfrac{\theta}{2}\cos\theta - R\sin\theta & -\tfrac{t}{2}\sin\tfrac{\theta}{2}\sin\theta + R\cos\theta & \tfrac{t}{2}\cos\tfrac{\theta}{2} \\ \cos\tfrac{\theta}{2}\cos\theta & \cos\tfrac{\theta}{2}\sin\theta & \sin\tfrac{\theta}{2} \end{vmatrix}$$

$$= \langle\, -\tfrac{t}{2}\sin\theta + R\sin\tfrac{\theta}{2}\cos\theta,\ \tfrac{t}{2}\cos\theta + R\sin\tfrac{\theta}{2}\sin\theta,\ -R\cos\tfrac{\theta}{2}\,\rangle \quad (13.2.21)$$

Thus,

$$\|\mathbf{n}\|^2 = \left[-\tfrac{t}{2}\sin\theta + R\sin\tfrac{\theta}{2}\cos\theta\right]^2 + \left[\tfrac{t}{2}\cos\theta + R\sin\tfrac{\theta}{2}\sin\theta\right]^2 + R^2\cos^2\tfrac{\theta}{2}$$
$$= \tfrac{t^2}{4} + R^2\sin^2\tfrac{\theta}{2} + R^2\cos^2\tfrac{\theta}{2} = \tfrac{t^2}{4} + R^2$$
$$= \tfrac{1}{4}t^2 + \left(k + t\cos\tfrac{\theta}{2}\right)^2 \qquad (13.2.22)$$

Then the area integral for the Möbius strip is

$$\mathcal{A} = \int_0^{2\pi}\int_{-a}^{a} \sqrt{\tfrac{1}{4}t^2 + \left(k + t\cos\tfrac{\theta}{2}\right)^2}\ dt\, d\theta \qquad (13.2.23)$$

There is no known integration technique that will allow us to compute this integral exactly. We can use a CAS to compute it numerically. For this, we take $k = 2$ and $a = 1$. Then in Maple, we get

```
> F:=(theta,t)->sqrt(t^2/4+(1+t*cos(theta/2))^2);
```
$$F := (\theta, t) \to \sqrt{\tfrac{1}{4}t^2 + \left(2 + t\cos\tfrac{\theta}{2}\right)^2}$$
```
> evalf(Int(Int(F(theta,t),t=-1..1),theta=0..2*Pi));
```
$$25.41308559$$

Alternatively we could use `TriangleApprox`. After defining the component functions `f`, `g`, and `h` for the Möbius strip, we use the following commands to obtain two approximations to it surface area:

```
> TriangleApprox(f,g,h,0,2*Pi,-1,1,20,20);
```
the area of the triangular approximation is, 25.15472694

```
> TriangleApprox(f,g,h,0,2*Pi,-1,1,100,100);
```
the area of the triangular approximation is, 25.40269204

A Dynamically Drawn Möbius Strip: There is a special-purpose Maple procedure called dsurfplot that can be used to dynamically plot any parametrized surface (with rectangular parameter domain). After defining the component functions f, g, and h for the Möbius strip, we create a movie of the strip being swept out with the command:

```
> dsurfplot(f,g,h,0,2*Pi,-1,1,10,3.5,4,3.5,5,5);
```

As you view the movie, notice how the inclination of the line segment L (shown in red) changes during the revolution. When $\theta = \frac{\pi}{2}$, the inclination is $\theta = \frac{\pi}{4}$. When $\theta = \pi$, the inclination is $\theta = \frac{\pi}{2}$. When $\theta = \frac{3\pi}{2}$, the inclination is $\theta = \frac{3\pi}{4}$. This twisting of the strip is shown in Figure 13.2.25.

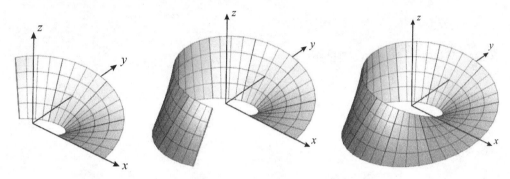

Figure 13.2.25: *Three frames in the dynamic plot of a Möbius strip.*

Exercises: 13.2 (Surfaces and Surface Area)

Standard Tangent and Normal Vectors

In Exercises 1–22, for the surface S parametrized by $\mathbf{r} : D \to \mathbb{R}^3$, find the standard tangent vectors $\mathbf{r}_u, \mathbf{r}_v$, and normal vector $\mathbf{n} = \mathbf{r}_u \times \mathbf{r}_v$. NOTE: The natural order of the parameters is $(u, v), (s, t), (\theta, t), (\theta, \phi), (\phi, t), (x, y)$.

1. $\mathbf{r} = \langle\, uv, u+v, u^2v^2 \,\rangle$ **2.** $\mathbf{r} = \langle\, uv^2, u-v, u^2v \,\rangle$

3. $\mathbf{r} = \langle\, \dfrac{u}{v}, \dfrac{v}{u}, uv \,\rangle$ **4.** $\mathbf{r} = \langle\, \dfrac{u^2}{v}, \dfrac{v^2}{u}, u^2v^2 \,\rangle$

5. $\mathbf{r} = \langle\, u^{1/2}v^{-1/2}, u^{-1/2}v^{1/2}, u^{1/2}v^{1/2} \,\rangle$

6. $\mathbf{r} = \langle\, u^{1/3}v^{-1/3}, u^{-1/3}v^{1/3}, u^{1/3}v^{1/3} \,\rangle$

7. $\mathbf{r} = \langle\, \ln(s^2 + t^2), \tan^{-1}(st), s^2t^2 \,\rangle$

8. $\mathbf{r} = \langle\, \ln(s^4 + t^4), \tan^{-1}(s^2t^2), s^4t^4 \,\rangle$

9. $\mathbf{r} = \langle\, e^{u^2+v^2}, e^{-u^2-v^2}, uv \,\rangle$

10. $\mathbf{r} = \langle\, e^{u^2-v^2}, e^{v^2-u^2}, uv \,\rangle$

11. $\mathbf{r} = \langle\, e^{st}, e^{-st}, s+t \,\rangle$ **12.** $\mathbf{r} = \langle\, e^{st}, e^{-st}, s-t \,\rangle$

13. $\mathbf{r} = \langle\, t\cos\theta, t\sin\theta, \theta \,\rangle$ (helicoid)

14. $\mathbf{r} = \langle\, 2t\cos\theta, 2t\sin\theta, \frac{1}{2}\theta \,\rangle$ (helicoid)

15. $\mathbf{r} = \langle\, 4\cos\theta, 3\sin\theta\cos\phi, 2\sin\theta\sin\phi \,\rangle$ (ellipsoid)

16. $\mathbf{r} = \langle\, 3\sin\theta\cos\phi, 4\cos\theta, 2\sin\theta\sin\phi \,\rangle$ (ellipsoid)

17. $\mathbf{r} = \langle\, 2\cosh t\cos\phi, 3\cosh t\sin\phi, \sinh t \,\rangle$ (hyperboloid)

18. $\mathbf{r} = \langle\, 2\cosh t\cos\phi, \sinh t, 3\cosh t\sin\phi \,\rangle$ (hyperboloid)

19. $\mathbf{r} = \langle\, x, y, \dfrac{x^2}{4} - \dfrac{y^2}{9} \,\rangle$ (hyperbolic parboloid)

20. $\mathbf{r} = \langle\, x, y, \dfrac{y^2}{25} - \dfrac{x^2}{16} \,\rangle$ (hyperbolic parboloid)

21. $\mathbf{r} = \langle\, 2u\cosh v, 3u\sinh v, u^2 \,\rangle$ (hyperbolic parboloid)

22. $\mathbf{r} = \langle\, 5u\sinh v, 4u\cosh v, u^2 \,\rangle$ (hyperbolic parboloid)

Surface Area

In Exercises 23–42, compute the area of the surface S parametrized by $\mathbf{r} : D \to \mathbb{R}^3$, with $D = [a, b] \times [c, d]$. NOTE: $\int_{-a}^{a} f(x)\, dx = 2\int_0^a f(x)\, dx$, if f is an even function.

23. $\mathbf{r} = \langle\, u^3v^2, v^3, v - \frac{9}{20}v^5 \,\rangle$, $[-1, 1] \times [-1, 1]$

24. $\mathbf{r} = \langle\, u^3v^2, v^3, 9v^5 - \frac{1}{20}v \,\rangle$, $[-1, 1] \times [-1, 1]$

25. $\mathbf{r} = \langle\, \frac{1}{3}u^3v^3, v - \frac{1}{3}v^3, 1 - v^2 \,\rangle$, $[-1, 1] \times [-1, 1]$

26. $\mathbf{r} = \langle\, u^3v^2, 5v^3 - \frac{5}{2}v^7, 2v^5 \,\rangle$, $[-1, 1] \times [-1, 1]$

27. $\mathbf{r} = \langle\, u + u^3v^2, v^4, v^6 - \frac{1}{3}v^2 \,\rangle$, $[0, 2] \times [0, 1]$

28. $\mathbf{r} = \langle\, u + u^3v^2, 5v^4, 4v^3 - \frac{5}{3}v^5 \,\rangle$, $[-1, 1] \times [-1, 1]$

29. $\mathbf{r} = \langle\, u^5 + uv^2, v^2, v^3 - \frac{1}{3}v \,\rangle$, $[-1, 1] \times [-1, 1]$

30. $\mathbf{r} = \langle\, u^5 + uv^2, v^3, v - \frac{9}{20}v^5 \,\rangle$, $[-1, 1] \times [-1, 1]$

31. $\mathbf{r} = \langle\, u + \frac{1}{3}u^3v^2, 2v^3, 3v - \frac{3}{5}v^5 \,\rangle$, $[-1, 1] \times [-1, 1]$

32. $\mathbf{r} = \langle\, u + \frac{1}{3}u^3v^2, 2v^3, 9v - \frac{1}{5}v^5 \,\rangle$, $[-1, 1] \times [-1, 1]$

33. $\mathbf{r} = \langle\, \frac{1}{3}u^3 + uv^2, 8v^5, 25v^8 - v^2 \,\rangle$, $[0, 1] \times [0, 1]$

34. $\mathbf{r} = \langle\, \frac{1}{3}u^3 + uv^2, 4v^5, 5v^8 - \frac{5}{4}v^2 \,\rangle$, $[0, 1] \times [0, 1]$

35. $\mathbf{r} = \langle\, u^3 + ue^{-v}, e^v, \frac{1}{12}e^{3v} + e^{-v} \,\rangle$, $[-1, 1] \times [-1, 1]$

36. $\mathbf{r} = \langle\, u^3 + ue^{-v}, e^{-2v}, e^{2v} + \frac{1}{12}e^{-6v} \,\rangle$, $[-1, 1] \times [-1, 1]$

37. $\mathbf{r} = \langle\, u^3 + u\sin\frac{v}{2}, v + \sin v, 1 - \cos v \,\rangle$, $[0, 2] \times [0, \pi]$

38. $\mathbf{r} = \langle\, u^3 + u\cos\frac{v}{2}, v - \sin v, 1 - \cos v \,\rangle$, $[0, 2] \times [0, \pi]$

39. $\mathbf{r} = \langle\, u^5 + uv^2, \ln v, v^{1/3} + \frac{9}{4}v^{-1/3} \,\rangle$, $[-1, 1] \times [1, 8]$

40. $\mathbf{r} = \langle\, u^5 + uv^2, \ln v, v^{1/2} + v^{-1/2} \,\rangle$, $[-1, 1] \times [1, 4]$

41. $\mathbf{r} = \langle\, \frac{1}{3}u^3v, \sqrt{1+v^2}, \tan^{-1}v - \frac{1}{12}v^3 \,\rangle$, $[0, 1] \times [0, 1]$

42. $\mathbf{r} = \langle\, \frac{1}{3}u^3v, \sqrt{1+v^2}, \frac{1}{3}v^3 - \frac{1}{4}\tan^{-1}v \,\rangle$, $[0, 1] \times [0, 1]$

Surface Area - Surfaces of Revolution

In Exercises 43–70, a curve C with parametrization
$$x = X(t),\ y = 0,\ z = Z(t),\ \text{for } t \text{ in } [a, b],$$
is revolved about the z-axis to create a surface S. Find the surface area $\mathcal{A}$ of S. NOTE: Only the first four problems are like Example 13.2.7 (a) and you will have to use integrals over two subintervals of $[a, b]$ to compute $\mathcal{A}$.

43. $X = t^3 - \frac{4}{3}t, Z = 2t^2, \ [0, 1]$

44. $X = t - \frac{1}{3}t^3, Z = t^2, \ [0, 1]$

45. $X = 2t - \frac{3}{2}t^3, Z = 3t^2, \ [0, 2]$

46. $X = t^2 - \frac{1}{3}t^6, Z = t^4, \ [0, \frac{3}{2}]$

47. $X = 2t^3, Z = 9t - \frac{1}{5}t^5, \ [0, 1]$

48. $X = t^3$, $Z = 9t^5 - \frac{1}{20}t$, $[0,1]$

49. $X = t^4$, $Z = t^3 - \frac{4}{15}t^5$, $[0,1]$

50. $X = 5t^4$, $Z = 4t^3 - \frac{5}{3}t^5$, $[0,1]$

51. $X = 4t^5$, $Z = 5t^4 - \frac{5}{6}t^6$, $[0,1]$

52. $X = 2t^5$, $Z = 5t^3 - \frac{5}{21}t^7$, $[0,1]$

53. $X = t^5$, $Z = t^3 - \frac{25}{84}t^7$, $[0,1]$

54. $X = t^5$, $Z = t^7 - \frac{25}{84}t^3$, $[0,1]$

55. $X = t^4$, $Z = t - \frac{4}{7}t^7$, $[0,1]$

56. $X = t^4$, $Z = t^7 - \frac{25}{96}t^4$, $[0,1]$

57. $X = e^{-t} + \frac{1}{12}e^{3t}$, $Z = e^t$, $[-1,1]$

58. $X = e^{2t} + \frac{1}{12}e^{-6t}$, $Z = e^{-2t}$, $[-1,1]$

59. $X = e^{-2t}$, $Z = e^{-t} - \frac{1}{3}e^{-3t}$, $[0,1]$

60. $X = e^{-3t}$, $Z = e^{-4t} - \frac{9}{32}e^{-2t}$, $[0,1]$

61. $X = \frac{1}{2}t^2$, $Z = t^4 - \frac{1}{16}\ln t$, $[1,2]$

62. $X = \frac{1}{3}t^3$, $Z = t^6 - \frac{1}{24}\ln t$, $[1,2]$

63. $X = t + \frac{1}{4}t^{-1}$, $Z = \ln t$, $[1,2]$

64. $X = t^2 + \frac{1}{16}t^{-2}$, $Z = \ln t$, $[1,2]$

65. $X = t^{1/2} + t^{-1/2}$, $Z = \ln t$, $[1,4]$

66. $X = t^{1/3} + \frac{9}{4}t^{-1/3}$, $Z = \ln t$, $[1,8]$

67. $X = \sqrt{1+t^2}$, $Z = t^2 - \frac{1}{16}\ln(1+t^2)$, $[0,1]$

68. $X = \sqrt{1+t^2}$, $Z = \frac{1}{2}\ln(1+t^2) - \frac{1}{8}t^2$, $[0,1]$

69. $X = t + \frac{1}{8}\left[t - \frac{1}{2}\sin 2t\right]$, $Z = 1 - \cos t$, $[0,2\pi]$

70. $X = t - \frac{1}{8}\left[t + \frac{1}{2}\sin 2t\right]$, $Z = 1 - \sin t$, $[0,2\pi]$

14
Vector Analysis

Calculus *Concepts & Computation*

14.1 Vector Fields & Differential Operators

In this chapter we discuss the important topic called *vector analysis*, which is, simply put, calculus applied to vector-valued functions.

A natural place to start in the discussion is in this first section with the topic vector fields. There are two types of these: *vector fields on curves and surfaces* and *vector fields on open sets*.

Vector Fields on Curves and Surfaces

For a curve C in space, parametrized by $\mathbf{r} : [a, b] \to \mathbb{R}^3$, the vector-valued function $\mathbf{r}' : [a, b] \to \mathbb{R}^3$ is a good example of what is called a *vector field on C*. The reason for this name is that if you imagine plotting the tangent vectors $\mathbf{r}'(t)$ with initial points at $P(t) = \mathbf{r}(t)$, for all t in $[a, b]$ (or at least a large number of t), then you get a "field" of vectors, much like a field of Kansas wheat. See Figure 14.1.1, which was produced using the special purpose procedure `vectorfieldplotC`. The general definition of this concept is as follows.

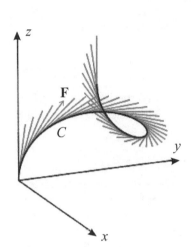

Figure 14.1.1: *A tangential vector field on the curve C in Example 13.1.5 Part (d).*

DEFINITION 14.1.1 (Vector Fields on Curves)

Suppose C is a curve in the plane parametrized by $\mathbf{r} : [a,b] \to \mathbb{R}^2$. *A vector field on C is a vector-valued function* $\mathbf{F} : [a,b] \to \mathbb{R}^2$. *In terms of component functions, we write*

$$\mathbf{F}(t) = \langle M(t), N(t) \rangle = M(t)\mathbf{i} + N(t)\mathbf{j} \qquad (14.1.1)$$

Suppose C is a space curve parametrized by $\mathbf{r} : [a,b] \to \mathbb{R}^3$. *A vector field on C is a vector-valued function* $\mathbf{F} : [a,b] \to \mathbb{R}^3$. *In terms of component functions, we write*

$$\mathbf{F}(t) = \langle M(t), N(t), K(t) \rangle = M(t)\mathbf{i} + N(t)\mathbf{j} + K(t)\mathbf{k} \qquad (14.1.2)$$

We assume, where necessary, that the components of $\mathbf{F}$ have continuous partial derivatives to the first or second order.

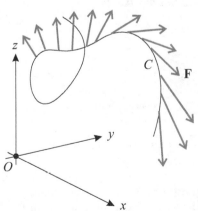

Figure 14.1.2: *A vector field on a curve C.*

Of course the vector field $\mathbf{r}'$ on C is a rather special (and important) vector field on C since each vector in the field is tangent to C. The vector field $\mathbf{r}''$ is another important vector field on C and its vectors, while not tangent to C, do indicate the direction in which C is curving. In general, as the definition indicates, *any* vector-valued function $\mathbf{F} : [a, b] \to \mathbb{R}^3$, unrelated to the parametrization $\mathbf{r}$, qualifies as a vector field on C. See Figure 14.1.2. However, you will soon see, based on topics in physics and engineering, what are the most pertinent vector fields $\mathbf{F}$ for our studies.

Next, we consider the corresponding concept for surfaces. For a surface S, parametrized by $\mathbf{r} : D \to \mathbb{R}^3$, the notion of a *vector field on S* is best motivated by the tangential vector fields $\mathbf{r}_u, \mathbf{r}_v : D \to \mathbb{R}^3$ as well as the normal vector field $\mathbf{n} = \mathbf{r}_u \times \mathbf{r}_v : D \to \mathbb{R}^3$. While these vector-valued functions are related to the geometry of the surface S, we will need to consider, more generally, any vector-valued function $\mathbf{F} : D \to \mathbb{R}^3$ as a vector field on S. This is recorded in the following definition.

DEFINITION 14.1.2 (Vector Fields on Surfaces)

Suppose S is a surface parametrized by $\mathbf{r}:D\to\mathbb{R}^3$. *A vector field on S is a vector-valued function* $\mathbf{F}:D\to\mathbb{R}^3$. *In terms of component functions, we write*

$$\mathbf{F}(u,v)=\langle M(u,v),N(u,v),K(u,v)\rangle = M(u,v)\mathbf{i}+N(u,v)\mathbf{j}+K(u,v)\mathbf{k} \quad (14.1.3)$$

We assume, where necessary, that the components of $\mathbf{F}$ *have continuous partial derivatives to the first or second order.*

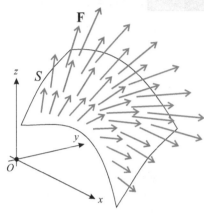

Figure 14.1.3: *A vector field on a surface S.*

Figure 14.1.3 shows a hypothetical example of a general vector field on a surface S. It better illustrates the reason for the name "vector field" because it resembles a wheat field in Kansas.

Vector Fields (in the Plane and in Space)

The most common (and important) type of vector field used in vector analysis is one that describes a field of vectors distributed throughout an open set U in $\mathbb{R}^2$ or an open set U in $\mathbb{R}^3$. The first is called a vector field in the plane and second is called a vector field in space. Further, as we shall see below, there are natural differential operators (the curl and divergence operators) that we can apply directly to vector fields of this type.

The formal definition of planar and spatial vector fields is as follows:

DEFINITION 14.1.3 (Vector Fields)

A vector field $\mathbf{F}$ *in the plane is a vector-valued function* $\mathbf{F}:U\to\mathbb{R}^2$, *where U is an open set in* $\mathbb{R}^2$. *In terms of component functions, we write*

$$\mathbf{F}(x,y)=\langle M(x,y),N(x,y)\rangle = M(x,y)\mathbf{i}+N(x,y)\mathbf{j}$$

for (x,y) *in U. Similarly, in three dimensions,*

A vector field $\mathbf{F}$ *in space is a vector-valued function* $\mathbf{F}:U\to\mathbb{R}^3$, *where U is an open set in* $\mathbb{R}^3$. *In terms of component functions, we write*

$$\mathbf{F}(x,y,z)=\langle M(x,y,z),N(x,y,x),K(x,y,z)\rangle$$
$$= M(x,y,z)\mathbf{i}+N(x,y,z)\mathbf{j}+K(x,y,z)\mathbf{k}$$

We assume, where necessary, that the components of $\mathbf{F}$ *have continuous partial derivatives to the first or second order.*

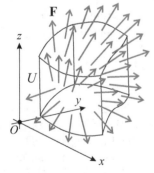

Figure 14.1.4: *A vector field on a open set U.*

NOTE 1: When we refer to $\mathbf{F}$ as a "vector field," we mean that it is the type of vector field in the above definition. When we refer to $\mathbf{F}$ as a "vector field on C" or as a "vector field on S" we mean that it is the type of vector field in Definitions 14.1.1–14.1.2.

NOTE 2: A vector field is a vector-valued function in which the domain U has the same dimension as the codomain.

A vector field $\mathbf{F}$ is just a special type of function and its "graph" can be visualized by plotting a whole field, or collection, of vectors $\mathbf{F}(P)$, one at each point P in U (or at least at a great number of point in U). Figure 14.1.4 illustrates this with a hypothetical plot.

Concrete examples of vector fields occur in many everyday situations, from the wind speed arrows your local meterologist shows you on TV to vortex circulation arrows superimposed on the air flow patterns of hurricanes. In physics, where the vector field concept originated, vector fields describe electromagnetic fields, gravitational fields, and velocity flow fields. The vectors in these vector fields are, of course, invisible (as they would be in wind speed maps on TV, where they not superimposed on the maps). That is the great aspect of this mathematical concept—the arrows in the vector field $\mathbf{F}$ are imaginary, but the use of $\mathbf{F}$ allows us to study and understand many natural phenomena.

Scalar Fields

Also from physics, in accordance with the *number = scalar* nomenclature, we have the following terminology. A real-valued function ψ with domain an open set U in $\mathbb{R}^2$ or in $\mathbb{R}^3$ is called a *scalar field*. Notation:

$$\psi : U \to \mathbb{R} \qquad (14.4.4)$$

Again, the *field* concept can be thought of in this case as attaching a scalar (i.e., a number) $\psi(P)$ to each point P in U. This gives whole field of numbers representing some physical quantity, such as temperature or density per unit volume.

As with vector fields on curves and surfaces, there are corresponding concepts for scalar fields. If C is a curve parameterized by $\mathbf{r} : [a, b] \to \mathbb{R}^3$, then a *scalar field on C* is a function $\psi : [a, b] \to \mathbb{R}$. Similarly, if S is a surface parameterized by $\mathbf{r} : D \to \mathbb{R}^3$, then a *scalar field on S* is a function $\psi : D \to \mathbb{R}$. You will see how these concepts are used in the next section.

Operations on Vector Fields

Many of the algebraic operations on functions and vectors carry over in a natural fashion to vector fields. The calculus operations do as well, but in a new and different way. To discuss this, it will be convenient to first just consider vector fields in space.

Suppose $\mathbf{F}, \mathbf{G}, \mathbf{H} : U \to \mathbb{R}^3$ are vector fields on an open set U in $\mathbb{R}^3$ and that $\psi : U \to \mathbb{R}$ is a scalar field on U. Then the algebraic operations $\mathbf{F} + \mathbf{G}$, $\mathbf{F} - \mathbf{G}$, $\mathbf{F} \times \mathbf{G}$, and $\psi\mathbf{F}$ result in vector fields defined by

(1) $(\mathbf{F} + \mathbf{G})(x, y, z) = \mathbf{F}(x, y, z) + \mathbf{G}(x, y, z)$

(2) $(\mathbf{F} - \mathbf{G})(x, y, z) = \mathbf{F}(x, y, z) - \mathbf{G}(x, y, z)$

(3) $(\mathbf{F} \times \mathbf{G})(x, y, z) = \mathbf{F}(x, y, z) \times \mathbf{G}(x, y, z)$

(4) $(\psi\mathbf{F})(x, y, z) = \psi(x, y, z)\mathbf{F}(x, y, z)$

While the algebraic operations $\mathbf{F} \cdot \mathbf{G}$ and $\det(\mathbf{F}, \mathbf{G}, \mathbf{H})$ give scalar fields defined by

(5) $(\mathbf{F} \cdot \mathbf{G})(x, y, z) = \mathbf{F}(x, y, z) \cdot \mathbf{G}(x, y, z)$

(6) $\det(\mathbf{F}, \mathbf{G}, \mathbf{H})(x, y, z) = \det(\mathbf{F}(x, y, z), \mathbf{G}(x, y, z), \mathbf{H}(x, y, z))$

Next, there are three important differential operators that we can apply to vector and scalar fields. The first of these you have already seen in Chapter 11.

The Gradient Operator: If ψ is a scalar field on U, then the *gradient* of ψ, denoted by $\nabla\psi$, is the vector field on U defined by

$$\nabla\psi = \left\langle \frac{\partial\psi}{\partial x}, \frac{\partial\psi}{\partial y}, \frac{\partial\psi}{\partial z} \right\rangle = \frac{\partial\psi}{\partial x}\mathbf{i} + \frac{\partial\psi}{\partial y}\mathbf{j} + \frac{\partial\psi}{\partial z}\mathbf{k} \qquad (14.1.5)$$

Recall, from Chapter 11, the geometric significance of $\nabla\psi$: At each point (x_0, y_0, z_0) in U, the vector $\nabla\psi(x_0, y_0, z_0)$ is perpendicular to the level surface $\psi(x, y, z) = c$ passing through the point (x_0, y_0, z_0). Here $c = \psi(x_0, y_0, z_0)$.

NOTATION: The symbol ∇ is a differential operator, much like $\frac{\partial}{\partial x}$, and it is instructive to think of ∇ as a vector operator. Namely:

$$\nabla = \left\langle \frac{\partial}{\partial x}, \frac{\partial}{\partial y}, \frac{\partial}{\partial z} \right\rangle \qquad (14.1.6)$$

Then, just as we multiply a vector by a scalar: $\langle v_1, v_2, v_3 \rangle k = \langle v_1 k, v_2 k, v_3 k \rangle$, we can multiply ∇ by ψ to get

$$\nabla \psi = \left\langle \frac{\partial}{\partial x}, \frac{\partial}{\partial y}, \frac{\partial}{\partial z} \right\rangle \psi = \left\langle \frac{\partial \psi}{\partial x}, \frac{\partial \psi}{\partial y}, \frac{\partial \psi}{\partial z} \right\rangle \qquad (14.1.7)$$

The Curl Operator: If $\mathbf{F} = \langle M, N, K \rangle$ is a vector field on U, then the *curl* of $\mathbf{F}$, denoted by $\nabla \times \mathbf{F}$, is the vector field on U defined by

$$
\begin{aligned}
\nabla \times \mathbf{F} &= \begin{vmatrix} \mathbf{i} & \mathbf{j} & \mathbf{k} \\ \frac{\partial}{\partial x} & \frac{\partial}{\partial y} & \frac{\partial}{\partial z} \\ M & N & K \end{vmatrix} = \begin{vmatrix} \frac{\partial}{\partial y} & \frac{\partial}{\partial z} \\ N & K \end{vmatrix} \mathbf{i} - \begin{vmatrix} \frac{\partial}{\partial x} & \frac{\partial}{\partial z} \\ M & K \end{vmatrix} \mathbf{j} + \begin{vmatrix} \frac{\partial}{\partial x} & \frac{\partial}{\partial y} \\ M & N \end{vmatrix} \mathbf{k} \\
&= \left(\frac{\partial K}{\partial y} - \frac{\partial N}{\partial z} \right) \mathbf{i} + \left(\frac{\partial M}{\partial z} - \frac{\partial K}{\partial x} \right) \mathbf{j} + \left(\frac{\partial N}{\partial x} - \frac{\partial M}{\partial y} \right) \mathbf{k} \\
&= \left\langle \frac{\partial K}{\partial y} - \frac{\partial N}{\partial z}, \frac{\partial M}{\partial z} - \frac{\partial K}{\partial x}, \frac{\partial N}{\partial x} - \frac{\partial M}{\partial y} \right\rangle \qquad (14.1.8)
\end{aligned}
$$

The curl operator $\nabla \times$ is the most complicated of the differential operators that we will use on vector fields. We will discuss its geometric significance below. But first, let's look at the third important differential operator.

The Divergence Operator: If $\mathbf{F} = \langle M, N, K \rangle$ is a vector field on U, then the *divergence* of $\mathbf{F}$, denoted by $\nabla \cdot \mathbf{F}$, is the scalar field on U defined by

$$\nabla \cdot \mathbf{F} = \left\langle \frac{\partial}{\partial x}, \frac{\partial}{\partial y}, \frac{\partial}{\partial z} \right\rangle \cdot \langle M, N, K \rangle = \frac{\partial M}{\partial x} + \frac{\partial N}{\partial y} + \frac{\partial K}{\partial z} \qquad (14.1.9)$$

This is a very easy differential operator to apply to vector fields. Observe that the result of the operation is a scalar field.

NOTE: There is some alternative notation for the gradient, curl, and divergence operators:

$$\nabla = \text{grad} \qquad \nabla \times = \text{curl} \qquad \nabla \cdot = \text{div} \qquad (14.1.10)$$

The following box summarizes the discussion of the new curl and divergence operators introduced above.

The Curl and Divergence Operators

Suppose $\mathbf{F} : U \to \mathbb{R}^3$ *is a vector field on an open set U in $\mathbb{R}^3$ with component functions*

$$\mathbf{F} = \langle M, N, K \rangle$$

Then the curl and divergence operators applied to F give the vector and scalar fields

$$\text{curl } \mathbf{F} = \nabla \times \mathbf{F} = \left\langle \frac{\partial K}{\partial y} - \frac{\partial N}{\partial z}, \frac{\partial M}{\partial z} - \frac{\partial K}{\partial x}, \frac{\partial N}{\partial x} - \frac{\partial M}{\partial y} \right\rangle \qquad (14.1.11)$$

$$\text{div } \mathbf{F} = \nabla \cdot \mathbf{F} = \frac{\partial M}{\partial x} + \frac{\partial N}{\partial y} + \frac{\partial K}{\partial z} \qquad (14.1.12)$$

Example 14.1.1 (Computing the Curl and Divergence of Vector Fields)

Problem: Compute the curl and divergence of the following vector fields, which are defined on $U = \mathbb{R}^3$.

(a) $\mathbf{F} = \langle\, x^2yz^3,\, xy^2z^2,\, x^3yz \,\rangle$ (b) $\mathbf{F} = \langle\, \sin xy,\, \cos xz,\, \sin yz \,\rangle$

Solution Part(a): Applying the product and power rules easily gives

$$\nabla \times \mathbf{F} = \begin{vmatrix} \mathbf{i} & \mathbf{j} & \mathbf{k} \\ \frac{\partial}{\partial x} & \frac{\partial}{\partial y} & \frac{\partial}{\partial z} \\ x^2yz^3 & xy^2z^2 & x^3yz \end{vmatrix}$$

$$= \langle\, x^3z - 2xy^2z,\, 3x^2yz^2 - 3x^2yz,\, y^2z^2 - x^2z^3 \,\rangle$$

$$\nabla \cdot \mathbf{F} = \langle\, \tfrac{\partial}{\partial x},\, \tfrac{\partial}{\partial y},\, \tfrac{\partial}{\partial z} \,\rangle \cdot \langle\, x^2yz^3,\, xy^2z^2,\, x^3yz \,\rangle$$

$$= 2xyz^3 + 2xyz^2 + x^3y$$

Solution Part(b): Applying the chain rule easily gives

$$\operatorname{curl}\mathbf{F} = \begin{vmatrix} \mathbf{i} & \mathbf{j} & \mathbf{k} \\ \frac{\partial}{\partial x} & \frac{\partial}{\partial y} & \frac{\partial}{\partial z} \\ \sin xy & \cos xz & \sin yz \end{vmatrix}$$

$$= \langle\, z\cos yz + x\sin xz,\, 0,\, -z\sin xz - x\cos xy \,\rangle$$

$$\operatorname{div}\mathbf{F} = \langle\, \tfrac{\partial}{\partial x},\, \tfrac{\partial}{\partial y},\, \tfrac{\partial}{\partial z} \,\rangle \cdot \langle\, \sin xy,\, \cos xz,\, \sin yz \,\rangle$$

$$= y\cos xy + 0 + y\cos yz = y\cos xy + y\cos yz$$

There are important relationships among the differential operators discussed above. These are detailed in the following theorem.

THEOREM 14.1.1 (Important Operator Identities)

Suppose $\psi : U \to \mathbb{R}$ *is a scalar field and* $\mathbf{F} : U \to \mathbb{R}^3$ *a vector field on an open set* U *in* $\mathbb{R}^3$. *Then*

$$\nabla \times (\nabla\psi) = 0 \qquad \textit{and} \qquad \nabla \cdot (\nabla \times \mathbf{F}) = 0 \qquad (14.1.13\text{a,b})$$

In the alternative notation, these identities are

$$\operatorname{curl}(\operatorname{grad}\psi) = 0 \qquad \textit{and} \qquad \operatorname{div}(\operatorname{curl}\mathbf{F}) = 0 \qquad (14.1.14\text{a,b})$$

The proof of the theorem is left as an exercise.

In the second form of these identities, i.e., (14.1.14a,b) the content of the theorem is perhaps easier to understand. It says that if you apply two of these operators in succession (in the stated combinations and orders), then you get an identically zero vector field and identically zero scalar field, respectively.

Example 14.1.2 (Verifying the Identities in Theorem 14.1.1)

Problem: For the following scalar fields and vector fields on $U = \mathbb{R}^3$ verify the operator identities (14.1.14a,b)

Part (A) $\psi = x^2y^3z^4$

Solution Part(A): The gradient of ψ is

$$\operatorname{grad}\psi = \langle\, 2xy^3z^4,\, 3x^2y^2z^4,\, 4x^2y^3z^3 \,\rangle$$

and so

$$\text{curl}(\text{grad}\,\psi) = \begin{vmatrix} \mathbf{i} & \mathbf{j} & \mathbf{k} \\ \frac{\partial}{\partial x} & \frac{\partial}{\partial y} & \frac{\partial}{\partial z} \\ 2xy^3z^4 & 3x^2y^2z^4 & 4x^2y^3z^3 \end{vmatrix}$$

$$= \langle\, 12x^2y^2z^3 - 12x^2y^2z^3,\ 8xy^3z^3 - 8xy^3z^3,\ 6xy^2z^4 - 6xy^2z^4 \,\rangle$$

$$= \langle\, 0, 0, 0 \,\rangle$$

Part (B) $\psi = e^{xyz}$

Solution Part(B): Using the chain rule, the gradient of ψ is

$$\text{grad}\,\psi = \langle\, yze^{xyz},\ xze^{xyz},\ xye^{xyz} \,\rangle$$

and so

$$\text{curl}(\text{grad}\,\psi) = \begin{vmatrix} \mathbf{i} & \mathbf{j} & \mathbf{k} \\ \frac{\partial}{\partial x} & \frac{\partial}{\partial y} & \frac{\partial}{\partial z} \\ yze^{xyz} & xze^{xyz} & xye^{xyz} \end{vmatrix}$$

$$= \left\langle\, \begin{matrix} xe^{xyz} + x^2yze^{xyz} - xe^{xyz} - x^2yze^{xyz}, \\ ye^{xyz} + xy^2ze^{xyz} - ye^{xyz} - xy^2ze^{xyz}, \\ ze^{xyz} + xyz^2e^{xyz} - ze^{xyz} - xyz^2e^{xyz} \end{matrix} \,\right\rangle$$

$$= \langle\, 0, 0, 0 \,\rangle$$

Part (C) $\mathbf{F} = \langle\, xyz,\ x^2y^2z^2,\ x^3y^3z^3 \,\rangle$

Solution Part(C):

$$\text{curl}\,\mathbf{F} = \begin{vmatrix} \mathbf{i} & \mathbf{j} & \mathbf{k} \\ \frac{\partial}{\partial x} & \frac{\partial}{\partial y} & \frac{\partial}{\partial z} \\ xyz & x^2y^2z^2 & x^3y^3z^3 \end{vmatrix}$$

$$= \langle\, 3x^3y^2z^3 - 2x^2y^2z,\ xy - 3x^2y^3z^3,\ 2xy^2z^2 - xz \,\rangle$$

$$\text{div}(\text{curl}\,\mathbf{F}) = (9x^2y^2z^3 - 4xy^2z) + (x - 9x^2y^2z^3) + (4xy^2z - x) = 0$$

Part (D) $\mathbf{F} = \langle\, \sin xy,\ \sin xz,\ \sin yz \,\rangle$

Solution Part(D):

$$\text{curl}\,\mathbf{F} = \begin{vmatrix} \mathbf{i} & \mathbf{j} & \mathbf{k} \\ \frac{\partial}{\partial x} & \frac{\partial}{\partial y} & \frac{\partial}{\partial z} \\ \sin xy & \sin xz & \sin yz \end{vmatrix}$$

$$= \langle\, z\cos yz - x\cos xz,\ 0,\ z\cos xz - x\cos xy \,\rangle$$

$$\text{div}(\text{curl}\,\mathbf{F}) = (-\cos xz + xz\sin xz) + (0) + (\cos xz - xz\sin xz) = 0$$

Vector and Scalar Fields in the Plane

The differential operators grad, curl, and div can also be applied to vector and scalar fields in the plane $\mathbb{R}^2$. We usually identify $\mathbb{R}^2$ with the x-y plane in $\mathbb{R}^3$ and the identification of planar vector and scalar fields with spatial ones is done as follows.

Suppose $\mathbf{F} : U \to \mathbb{R}^2$ is a vector field on an open set U in $\mathbb{R}^2$ and in terms of components

$$\mathbf{F}(x, y) = \langle\, M(x, y),\, N(x, y) \,\rangle \qquad (4.1.15)$$

We identify U with the open set $\widetilde{U} = \{\, (x, y, z) \text{ in } \mathbb{R}^3 \,|\, (x, y) \text{ is in } U \,\}$. This is a solid generalized cylinder obtained by translating the boundary of U in the z-direction. Now we identify $\mathbf{F}$ with the vector field $\widetilde{\mathbf{F}}$ on $\widetilde{U}$ defined by

$$\widetilde{\mathbf{F}}(x, y, z) = \langle\, M(x, y),\, N(x, y),\, 0 \,\rangle \qquad (4.1.16)$$

Then since $\frac{\partial M}{\partial z} = 0$ and $\frac{\partial N}{\partial z} = 0$, it is easy to see that

$$\operatorname{curl} \widetilde{\mathbf{F}} \;=\; \begin{vmatrix} \mathbf{i} & \mathbf{j} & \mathbf{k} \\ \frac{\partial}{\partial x} & \frac{\partial}{\partial y} & \frac{\partial}{\partial z} \\ M & N & 0 \end{vmatrix}$$

$$= \; \langle\, 0,\, 0,\, \frac{\partial N}{\partial x} - \frac{\partial M}{\partial y} \,\rangle = \Big(\frac{\partial N}{\partial x} - \frac{\partial M}{\partial y} \Big)\, \mathbf{k} \qquad (4.1.17)$$

$$\operatorname{div} \widetilde{\mathbf{F}} \;=\; \frac{\partial M}{\partial x} + \frac{\partial N}{\partial y} \qquad (4.1.18)$$

CONVENTION: If $\mathbf{F}$ is a vector field in the plane, identified with the vector field $\widetilde{\mathbf{F}}$ in space, we will not distinguish between the two notationally: $\widetilde{\mathbf{F}} = \mathbf{F}$.

NOTE: The above calculation (and convention) show that the curl of a planar vector field $\mathbf{F}$ is vector field directed in the z-direction (vertical direction), i.e.,

$$\operatorname{curl} \mathbf{F} = \Big(\frac{\partial N}{\partial x} - \frac{\partial M}{\partial y} \Big)\, \mathbf{k} \qquad (14.1.19)$$

Also, the divergence of $\mathbf{F}$ is a scalar field on the plane (doesn't depend on z):

$$\operatorname{div} \mathbf{F} = \frac{\partial M}{\partial x} + \frac{\partial N}{\partial y} \qquad (14.1.20)$$

Finally, a scalar field $\psi : U \to \mathbb{R}^2$ on the plane has gradient $\nabla \psi$ which is a vector field on the plane. But, we can identify both with scalar and vector fields in space.

Exercises: 14.1 (Vector Fields and Differential Operators)

Calculating the Curl and the Divergence

In Exercises 1–20, calculate curl $\mathbf{F}$ and div$\mathbf{F}$ of the given vector fields $\mathbf{F}$.

1. $\mathbf{F} = \langle x^3yz^2, xy^2z, xy \rangle$ 2. $\mathbf{F} = \langle x^2yz^3, xyz^2, xz \rangle$

3. $\mathbf{F} = \langle ze^{xy}, xe^{yz}, ye^{xz} \rangle$ 4. $\mathbf{F} = \langle xe^{yz}, ze^{xy}, ye^{xz} \rangle$

5. $\mathbf{F} = \langle x\sin yz, y\sin xz, z\sin xy \rangle$

6. $\mathbf{F} = \langle y\sin xz, x\sin yz, z\sin xy \rangle$

7. $\mathbf{F} = \langle \sin x\cos z, \sin y\cos x, \sin z\cos y \rangle$

8. $\mathbf{F} = \langle \cos x\sin z, \cos y\sin x, \cos z\sin y \rangle$

9. $\mathbf{F} = \langle \sin y\cos x, \sin x\cos z, \sin z\cos y \rangle$

10. $\mathbf{F} = \langle \cos y\sin x, \cos x\sin z, \cos z\sin y \rangle$

11. $\mathbf{F} = \langle x^3y, xy^2, 0 \rangle$ 12. $\mathbf{F} = \langle x^2y, xy, 0 \rangle$

13. $\mathbf{F} = \langle xe^{2y}, ye^{3x}, 0 \rangle$ 14. $\mathbf{F} = \langle xe^{3y}, ye^{4x}, 0 \rangle$

15. $\mathbf{F} = \langle ye^{3x}, xe^{2y}, 0 \rangle$ 16. $\mathbf{F} = \langle ye^{4x}, xe^{3y}, 0 \rangle$

17. $\mathbf{F} = \langle x\sin y, y\sin x, 0 \rangle$ 18. $\mathbf{F} = \langle x\cos y, y\cos x, 0 \rangle$

19. $\mathbf{F} - \langle \sin x\cos y, \sin y\cos x, \sin z\cos y \rangle$

20. $\mathbf{F} = \langle \sin y\cos x, \sin x\cos y, \sin z\cos y \rangle$

Verifying Identities

In Exercises 21–30, verify that curl $\mathbf{F} = 0$ for the given vector field $\mathbf{F}$,

21. $\mathbf{F} = \langle 2xyz, x^2z, x^2y \rangle$ 22. $\mathbf{F} = \langle y^2z, 2xyz, xy^2 \rangle$

23. $\mathbf{F} = \langle y\sin z, x\sin z, xy\cos z \rangle$

24. $\mathbf{F} = \langle y\cos z, x\cos z, -xy\sin z \rangle$

25. $\mathbf{F} = \langle 2xe^{-yz}, -x^2ze^{-yz}, -x^2ye^{-yz} \rangle$

26. $\mathbf{F} = \langle 2ye^{-xz}, -y^2ze^{-xz}, -xy^2e^{-xz} \rangle$

27. $\mathbf{F} = \langle 3x^2y^2, 2x^3y, 0 \rangle$ 28. $\mathbf{F} = \langle 2xy^3, 3x^2y^2, 0 \rangle$

29. $\mathbf{F} = \langle y\cos xy, -x\cos xy, 0 \rangle$

30. $\mathbf{F} = \langle y\sin xy, x\sin xy, 0 \rangle$

In Exercises 31–38, verify that div $\mathbf{F} = 0$ for the given vector field $\mathbf{F}$,

31. $\mathbf{F} = \langle 2y - x, y, 0 \rangle$ 32. $\mathbf{F} = \langle 0, 2z - y, z \rangle$

33. $\mathbf{F} = \langle 4x^3y^3z^2 - xy^2, 3x^2yz^2 - 3x^2y^4z^2, y^2z - x^2z^3 \rangle$

34. $\mathbf{F} = \langle 3x^4y^2z^2 - x^2y, 3xy^2z^2 - 4x^3y^3z^2, 2xyz - 2xyz^3 \rangle$

35. $\mathbf{F} = \langle xe^{-z} - ye^{-x}, xe^{-y} - ye^{-z}, xze^{-y} - yze^{-x} \rangle$

36. $\mathbf{F} = \langle ze^{-x} - xe^{-y}, yze^{-x} - xye^{-z}, ze^{-y} - xe^{-z} \rangle$

37. $\mathbf{F} = \langle x\cos z - y\sin x, x\cos y - y\cos z,$
$$yz\cos x + xz\sin y \rangle$$

38. $\mathbf{F} = \langle xy\sin z - xz\sin y, y\sin x - z\cos y,$
$$y\cos z - z\cos x \rangle$$

Operator Identities

39. **(The Laplacian)** Show that for any scalar field ψ and any vector field $\mathbf{F}$, the following identities hold:

$$\mathrm{curl}(\nabla\psi) = 0$$

$$\mathrm{div}(\mathrm{curl}\mathbf{F}) = 0$$

$$\mathrm{div}(\nabla\psi) = \frac{\partial^2\psi}{\partial x^2} + \frac{\partial^2\psi}{\partial y^2} + \frac{\partial^2\psi}{\partial z^2}.$$

This last identity gives rise to an important operator, called the *Laplacian*, and denoted variously by ∇^2, since $\mathrm{div}(\nabla\psi) = \nabla \cdot (\nabla u)$, or also by Δ. Thus, the Laplacian of the scalar field ψ is the scalar field:

$$\nabla^2\psi \equiv \frac{\partial^2\psi}{\partial x^2} + \frac{\partial^2\psi}{\partial y^2} + \frac{\partial^2\psi}{\partial z^2} = \psi_{xx} + \psi_{yy} + \psi_{zz}$$

40. Another useful identity comes from a repeated application of the curl operator. Namely, show that for any vector field $\mathbf{F}$:

$$\mathrm{curl}\,(\mathrm{curl}\,\mathbf{F}) = \nabla(\mathrm{div}\mathbf{F}) - \nabla^2\mathbf{F}$$

Here $\nabla^2\mathbf{F} \equiv (\nabla^2 M, \nabla^2 N, \nabla^2 K)$.

In Exercises 41–45, prove the given operator identities. Here ψ, ϕ are scalar fields and $\mathbf{F}, \mathbf{G}$ are vector fields.

41. $\mathrm{div}(\psi\mathbf{F}) = \nabla\psi \cdot \mathbf{F} + \psi\,\mathrm{div}\mathbf{F}$.

42. $\mathrm{curl}\,(\psi\mathbf{F}) = \nabla\psi \times \mathbf{F} + \psi\,\mathrm{curl}\,\mathbf{F}$.

43. $\mathrm{div}(\mathbf{F} \times \mathbf{G}) = (\mathrm{curl}\,\mathbf{F}) \cdot \mathbf{G} - \mathbf{F} \cdot (\mathrm{curl}\,\mathbf{G})$.

44. $\dfrac{\partial}{\partial x}(\mathbf{F} \times \mathbf{G}) = \dfrac{\partial\mathbf{F}}{\partial x} \times \mathbf{G} + \mathbf{F} \times \dfrac{\partial\mathbf{G}}{\partial x}$.

45. $\mathrm{div}(\nabla\psi \times \nabla\phi) = 0$.

Calculus *Concepts & Computation*

14.2 Line Integrals

As we saw in the last section, many physical phenomena are best analyzed and studied using the concept of a *field*. While the concept of a scalar field, which is just a real-valued function, has long been familiar to you, the concept of a vector field introduced there was probably new.

The last section also introduced you to some aspects of the differential calculus for vector fields. Here, in this section, we begin the discussion of the appropriate integral calculus for vector fields and scalar fields. What is new about these integrals is that, rather than integrating over an interval $I = [a, b]$ or a region D in the plane, we want to be able to integrate along a curve C or over a surface S. These integrals over curves and surfaces will be defined in terms of single integrals over intervals I and double integrals over planar regions D. The integrands of these single and double integrals will come from combining (via dot products) a given vector field (the one you are studying) with vector fields geometrically related to the curve or surface.

We defer the discussion of surface integrals until Section 14.5 and start here with integrals along curves. INSTRUCTORS: See the note at the end of this section.

Line Integrals

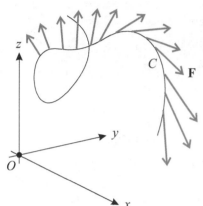

Figure 14.2.1: *A vector field on a curve C.*

Historically, integrals of vector fields along a curve C were called *line integrals* or *path integrals*. Figure 14.2.1 shows a vector field $\mathbf{F}$ on a curve C and you might guess that its line integral along C would involve its relation to the tangential vector field $\mathbf{r}'$ on C. The following definition shows the natural way of combining these vector fields to get an integral.

DEFINITION 14.2.1 (Line Integrals of Vector Fields)

Suppose C is a space curve parametrized by $\mathbf{r} : [a, b] \to \mathbb{R}^3$ *and* $\mathbf{F} : [a, b] \to \mathbb{R}^3$ *is a is a vector field on C. Then the line integral of* $\mathbf{F}$ *along C, denoted by* $\int_C \mathbf{F} \cdot d\mathbf{r}$, *is defined by*

$$\int_C \mathbf{F} \cdot d\mathbf{r} \equiv \int_a^b \mathbf{F}(t) \cdot \mathbf{r}'(t) dt \qquad (14.2.1)$$

Thus, the line integral $\int_C \mathbf{F} \cdot d\mathbf{r}$ (notation) is just the ordinary integral of the function $\mathbf{F} \cdot \mathbf{r}'$ over the interval $[a, b]$. The differential notation

$$d\mathbf{r} = \mathbf{r}' dt$$

is convenient to use for this new concept.

There are a number of topics in physics that serve to explain the geometric significance of the line integral. The notion of work done against(or with) a force when moving something from P to Q is one such topic. (See Section 5.7.)

Work Done in Moving Along a Path

The line integral (14.2.1) is best motivated by the example where the parametrization $\mathbf{r}$ gives a particle's position as it moves in space acted on by a force. At time t, the particle is at point $\mathbf{r}(t)$ and $\mathbf{F}(t)$ is the force acting on it at that time. The work done involves only the component of force $\mathbf{F}(t)$ in the direction of motion $\mathbf{r}'(t)$ at time t, i.e.,

$$\text{component of } \mathbf{F}(t) \text{ in the direction } \mathbf{r}'(t) = \frac{\mathbf{F}(t) \cdot \mathbf{r}'(t)}{\|\mathbf{r}'(t)\|},$$

(assuming $\mathbf{r}$ is a smooth parametrization). This component of force times the infinitesimal distance $ds = \|\mathbf{r}'(t)\|dt$ traveled gives the increment of work:

$$dW = \frac{\mathbf{F}(t) \cdot \mathbf{r}'(t)}{\|\mathbf{r}'(t)\|} \cdot \|\mathbf{r}'(t)\|dt = \mathbf{F}(t) \cdot \mathbf{r}'(t)\, dt$$

So, the total work done in moving from point $P = \mathbf{r}(a)$ to point $Q = \mathbf{r}(b)$ is

$$W = \int_a^b \mathbf{F}(t) \cdot \mathbf{r}'(t)\, dt \qquad \text{(Work Done)}$$

Example 14.2.1 (Calculating Work Done Along a Path)

Problem: Compute the work $W = \int_C \mathbf{F} \cdot d\mathbf{r}$ done as a particle moves along the given curve C, parametrized by $\mathbf{r}$, subject to the given force field $\mathbf{F}$ on C.

(a) $\mathbf{F} = \langle\, 1 + t^2, \frac{1}{2}t - \frac{1}{2}t^3, 4t \,\rangle$, $\mathbf{r} = \langle\, t, t^2, \frac{3}{4}t - \frac{1}{3}t^3 \,\rangle$, t in $[-2, 2]$.

(b) $\mathbf{F} = \langle\, \sin t, \cos t, \sin t \,\rangle$, $\mathbf{r} = \langle\, t - \sin t, 1 - \cos t, \frac{1}{2}t + \frac{1}{2}\sin t \,\rangle$, t in $[0, \pi]$.

Solution Part(a): First compute $\mathbf{r}' = \langle\, 1, 2t, \frac{3}{4} - t^2 \,\rangle$. Then

$$
\begin{aligned}
\mathbf{F} \cdot \mathbf{r}' &= \langle\, 1 + t^2, \tfrac{1}{2}t - \tfrac{1}{2}t^3, 4t \,\rangle \cdot \langle\, 1, 2t, \tfrac{3}{4} - t^2 \,\rangle \\
&= 1 + t^2 + t^2 - t^4 + 3t - 4t^3 = 1 + 3t + 2t^2 - 4t^3 - t^4
\end{aligned}
$$

Then the work is

$$
\begin{aligned}
\int_C \mathbf{F} \cdot d\mathbf{r} &= \int_a^b \mathbf{F}(t) \cdot \mathbf{r}'(t)dt = \int_{-2}^{2} \left(1 + 3t + 2t^2 - 4t^3 - t^4 \right)dt \\
&= \left(t + \tfrac{3}{2}t^2 + \tfrac{2}{3}t^3 - t^4 - \tfrac{1}{5}t^5 \right)\Big|_{-2}^{2} \\
&= (2 + 2) + \tfrac{3}{2}(0) + \tfrac{2}{3}(8 + 8) - (0) - \tfrac{1}{5}(32 + 32) \\
&= \frac{28}{15}
\end{aligned}
$$

Solution Part(b): First compute $\mathbf{r}' = \langle\, 1 - \cos t, \sin t, \frac{1}{2} + \frac{1}{2}\cos t \,\rangle$. Then

$$
\begin{aligned}
\mathbf{F} \cdot \mathbf{r}' &= \langle\, \sin t, \cos t, \sin t \,\rangle \cdot \langle\, 1 - \cos t, \sin t, \tfrac{1}{2} + \tfrac{1}{2}\cos t \,\rangle \\
&= \sin t - \sin t \cos t + \sin t \cos t + \tfrac{1}{2}\sin t + \tfrac{1}{2}\sin t \cos t \\
&= \tfrac{3}{2}\sin t + \tfrac{1}{2}\sin t \cos t = \tfrac{3}{2}\sin t + \tfrac{1}{4}\sin 2t
\end{aligned}
$$

Then the work is

$$
\begin{aligned}
\int_C \mathbf{F} \cdot d\mathbf{r} &= \int_a^b \mathbf{F}(t) \cdot \mathbf{r}'(t)dt = \int_{-2}^{2} \left(\tfrac{3}{2}\sin t + \tfrac{1}{4}\sin 2t \right)dt \\
&= \left(-\tfrac{3}{2}\cos t - \tfrac{1}{8}\cos 2t \right)\Big|_0^{\pi} = \tfrac{3}{2} - \tfrac{1}{8} + \tfrac{3}{2} + \tfrac{1}{8} = 3
\end{aligned}
$$

Line Integrals of Scalar Fields

Suppose C is a smooth curve parametrized by $\mathbf{r} : [a, b] \to \mathbb{R}^3$. Then since $\mathbf{r}'(t) \neq 0$ for any t, we can normalize the tangent vector field $\mathbf{r}'$ on C to get a *unit* tangent vector field on C:

$$\mathbf{T}(t) = \frac{\mathbf{r}'(t)}{\|\mathbf{r}'(t)\|} \qquad (14.2.2)$$

This was discussed in Section 13.3. and was useful in studying the geometry of the curve C. Here. let's consider the line integral of $\mathbf{T}$ along C

$$\int_C \mathbf{T} \cdot d\mathbf{r} = \int_a^b \mathbf{T}(t) \cdot \mathbf{r}'(t)\, dt = \int_a^b \frac{\mathbf{r}'(t)}{\|\mathbf{r}'(t)\|} \cdot \mathbf{r}'(t)\, dt$$

$$= \int_a^b \frac{\mathbf{r}'(t) \cdot \mathbf{r}'(t)}{\|\mathbf{r}'(t)\|} \, dt = \int_a^b \frac{\|\mathbf{r}'(t)\|^2}{\|\mathbf{r}'(t)\|} \, dt$$

$$= \int_a^b \|\mathbf{r}'(t)\| \, dt = L$$

This says that the line integral of the unit tangent vector field $\mathbf{T}$ along C is equal to the length L of C. The calculations for this show that $\mathbf{T} \cdot d\mathbf{r} = \|\mathbf{r}'(t)\| \, dt = ds$ (heuristically, with s the arc length function). Thus, if ψ is a scalar field along C, then

$$\psi \mathbf{T} \cdot d\mathbf{r} = \psi \|\mathbf{r}'(t)\| \, dt = \psi \, ds$$

Again, this is just heuristic pedagogy for the sake of symbolism. It does, however, suggest that integrating the vector field $\psi \mathbf{T}$ along C will be a good definition of the scalar integral of ψ along C. We make this definition as follows.

DEFINITION 14.2.2 (Line Integrals of Scalar Fields)

Suppose C is a space curve parametrized by $\mathbf{r}:[a,b] \to \mathbb{R}^3$ and $\psi:[a,b] \to \mathbb{R}$ is a is a scalar field on C. Then the line integral of ψ along C, denoted by $\int_C \psi \, ds$, is defined by

$$\int_C \psi \, ds \equiv \int_C \psi \mathbf{T} \cdot d\mathbf{r} = \int_a^b \psi(t) \|\mathbf{r}'(t)\| \, dt \qquad (14.2.3)$$

Total Mass of a Wire: A standard application of the scalar line integral is in the computation of the total mass of a wire which is bent in the shape of a curve C. Letting $\rho : [a, b] \to \mathbb{R}$ be the mass density function (mass per unit length), then the total mass of the wire is

$$M = \int_C \rho \, ds \qquad (14.2.4)$$

Example 14.2.2 (Calculating Total Masses of Wires)

Problem: For the following parametrized curves C, calculate the total mass of a wire bent in the shape C and having mass density ρ.

Part (a) $\mathbf{r} = \langle\, t^3, t^4, \frac{7}{24}t^3 - \frac{2}{5}t^5 \,\rangle$, $\rho = t^2$, for t in $[0, 1]$

Solution Part(a): First calculate $\mathbf{r}' = \langle\, 3t^2, 4t^3, \frac{7}{8}t^2 - 2t^4 \,\rangle$. Then

$$
\begin{aligned}
\|\mathbf{r}'\|^2 &= 9t^4 + 16t^6 + \left(\tfrac{7}{8}t^2 - 2t^4\right)^2 = 9t^4 + 16t^6 + \left(\tfrac{49}{64}t^4 - \tfrac{7}{2}t^6 + 4t^8\right) \\
&= 9t^4 + \tfrac{49}{64}t^4 + 16t^6 - \tfrac{7}{2}t^6 + 4t^8 = \tfrac{625}{64}t^4 + \tfrac{25}{2}t^6 + 4t^8 \\
&= \left(\tfrac{25}{8}t^2 + 2t^4\right)^2
\end{aligned}
$$

Thus, the mass of the wire is

$$
\begin{aligned}
M &= \int_C \rho \, ds = \int_a^b \rho(t) \|\mathbf{r}'(t)\| \, dt = \int_0^1 t^2 \left(\tfrac{25}{8}t^2 + 2t^4\right) dt \\
&= \int_0^1 \left(\tfrac{25}{8}t^4 + 2t^6\right) dt = \left(\tfrac{5}{8}t^5 + \tfrac{2}{7}t^7\right)\Big|_0^1 = \tfrac{5}{8} + \tfrac{2}{7} = \frac{51}{56}
\end{aligned}
$$

Part (b) An aluminum sculpture is made in a tubular shape that has for template the curve C with parametrization

$$\mathbf{r} = \langle\, \cos t, \sin t, \tfrac{1}{4}t^{4/3} - \tfrac{9}{8}t^{2/3} \,\rangle, \text{ for } t \text{ in } [1, 27].$$

Its base, corresponding to $t = 0$, is its thickest part (for stability) and the sculpture tapers, becoming thinner, as its height increases. Assuming the density function is $\rho = 12t^{-1/3}$ slugs/ft, find the total weight of the sculpture.

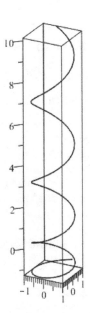

Figure 14.2.2:
A helical curve.

Solution Part(b): First calculate $\mathbf{r'} = \langle\ -\sin t,\ \cos t,\ \frac{1}{3}t^{1/3} - \frac{3}{4}t^{-1/3}\ \rangle$. Then

$$
\begin{aligned}
\|\mathbf{r'}\|^2 &=\ \sin^2 t + \cos^2 t + \left(\frac{1}{3}t^{1/3} - \frac{3}{4}t^{-1/3}\right)^2 = 1 + \left(\frac{1}{3}t^{1/3} - \frac{3}{4}t^{-1/3}\right)^2 \\
&=\ 1 + \frac{1}{9}t^{2/3} - \frac{1}{2} + \frac{9}{16}t^{-2/3} = \frac{1}{9}t^{2/3} + \frac{1}{2} + \frac{9}{16}t^{-2/3} \\
&=\ \left(\frac{1}{3}t^{1/3} + \frac{3}{4}t^{-1/3}\right)^2
\end{aligned}
$$

Thus, the mass of the sculpture is

$$
\begin{aligned}
M &=\ \int_C \rho\,ds = \int_a^b \rho(t)\|\mathbf{r'}(t)\|\,dt = \int_1^{27} 12t^{-1/3}\left(\frac{1}{3}t^{1/3} + \frac{3}{4}t^{-1/3}\right)dt \\
&=\ \int_1^{27}\left(4 + 9t^{-2/3}\right)dt = \left(4t + 27t^{1/3}\right)\Big|_1^{27} = 4(27) + +27(3) - 4 - 27 = 158
\end{aligned}
$$

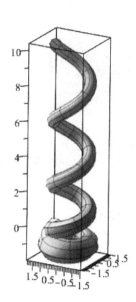

Figure 14.2.3:
A helical sculpture.

Line Integrals for Vector Fields in Space

A common situation for the use of line integrals is where there is a force field $\mathbf{F}$ in space (or the plane) and a particle is moving along a curve C in that space. This situation reduces to that which we have already discussed—just restrict $\mathbf{F}$ to C to a get a force field on C.

Specifically, suppose $\mathbf{F} : U \to \mathbb{R}^3$ is a vector field on an open set U in $\mathbb{R}^3$. If C is a curve which lies in U and has parametrization $\mathbf{r} : [a, b] \to \mathbb{R}^3$, then the composite function

$$\widetilde{\mathbf{F}} \equiv \mathbf{F} \circ \mathbf{r} : [a, b] \to \mathbb{R}^3$$

is a vector field on C, called the *restriction* of $\mathbf{F}$ to C. Thus, $\widetilde{\mathbf{F}}(t) = \mathbf{F}(\mathbf{r}(t))$ is the vector on the curve at the point $P(t) = \mathbf{r}(t)$. It will be convenient, notationally, to identify $\mathbf{F}$ with its restriction, i.e., $\mathbf{F} = \widetilde{\mathbf{F}}$. Then, the line integral $\int_C \mathbf{F} \cdot d\mathbf{r}$ looks the same even though its computation involves the extra step of computing the composite function $\mathbf{F} = \mathbf{F} \circ \mathbf{r}$. The following is a formal definition of this important concept.

DEFINITION 14.2.3 (Line Integrals of Vector Fields - Part 2)

Suppose $\mathbf{F} : U \to \mathbb{R}^3$ is a vector field on an open set U in $\mathbb{R}^3$ and C is a curve in U parametrized by $\mathbf{r} : [a,b] \to \mathbb{R}^3$. Then the line integral of $\mathbf{F}$ along C, denoted by $\int_C \mathbf{F} \cdot d\mathbf{r}$, is defined by

$$\int_C \mathbf{F} \cdot d\mathbf{r} \equiv \int_a^b \mathbf{F}(\mathbf{r}(t)) \cdot \mathbf{r'}(t)dt \qquad (14.2.5)$$

The definition in Equation (14.2.5) also applies to a planar vector field: $\mathbf{F} : U \to \mathbb{R}^2$ with $U \subseteq \mathbb{R}^2$.

Example 14.2.3 (Calculating Line Integrals for Vector Fields in Space)

Problem: For the following vector fields $\mathbf{F} : \mathbb{R}^3 \to \mathbb{R}^3$ and parametrized curves C, calculate the line integral $\int_C \mathbf{F} \cdot d\mathbf{r}$.

Part (a) $\mathbf{F} = \langle\ xz,\ x + y + z,\ y\ \rangle$, $\mathbf{r} = \langle\ t^2,\ t^3,\ t^4\ \rangle$, t in $[0, 1]$.

Solution Part(a): With $x = t^2$, $y = t^3$, and $z = t^4$, we first compute

$$\mathbf{F} \circ \mathbf{r} = \langle\ t^6,\ t^2 + t^3 + t^4,\ t^3\ \rangle,$$

Then

$$\mathbf{r}' = \langle\, 2t,\, 3t^2,\, 4t^3\, \rangle$$

So, that

$$
\begin{aligned}
(\mathbf{F}\circ\mathbf{r})\cdot\mathbf{r}' &= 2t^7 + (t^2+t^3+t^4)3t^2 + 4t^6 = 2t^7 + 3t^4 + 3t^5 + 3t^6 + 4t^6 \\
&= 2t^7 + 3t^4 + 3t^5 + 7t^6
\end{aligned}
$$

This gives the line integral

$$
\begin{aligned}
\int_C \mathbf{F}\cdot d\mathbf{r} &= \int_a^b \mathbf{F}(\mathbf{r}(t))\cdot\mathbf{r}'(t)\,dt = \int_0^1 \left(2t^7 + 3t^4 + 3t^5 + 7t^6\right)dt \\
&= \left(\tfrac14 t^8 + \tfrac35 t^5 + \tfrac12 t^6 + t^7\right)\Big|_0^1 = \tfrac14 + \tfrac35 + \tfrac12 + 1 = \frac{47}{20}
\end{aligned}
$$

Part (b) $\mathbf{F} = \langle\, e^{2x},\, \sin y,\, x^2 z\, \rangle$, $\quad \mathbf{r} = \langle\, \cos t,\, t^2,\, \sec t\, \rangle$, for t in $[0, \pi/4]$.

Solution Part(b): With $x = \cos t$, $y = t^2$, and $z = \sec t$, we first compute

$$\mathbf{F}\circ\mathbf{r} = \langle\, e^{2\cos t},\, \sin(t^2),\, \cos^2 t \sec t\, \rangle = \langle\, e^{2\cos t},\, \sin(t^2),\, \cos t\, \rangle,$$

Then

$$\mathbf{r}' = \langle\, -\sin t,\, 2t,\, \sec t \tan t\, \rangle$$

So, that

$$
\begin{aligned}
(\mathbf{F}\circ\mathbf{r})\cdot\mathbf{r}' &= -\sin t\, e^{2\cos t} + 2t \sin(t^2) + \cos t \sec t \tan t \\
&= -\sin t\, e^{2\cos t} + 2t \sin(t^2) + \tan t
\end{aligned}
$$

This then gives for the line integral

$$
\begin{aligned}
\int_C \mathbf{F}\cdot d\mathbf{r} &= \int_a^b \mathbf{F}(\mathbf{r}(t))\cdot\mathbf{r}'(t)\,dt = \int_0^{\pi/4}\left(-\sin t\, e^{2\cos t} + 2t \sin(t^2) + \tan t\right)dt \\
&= \left(\tfrac12 e^{2\cos t} - \cos(t^2) - \ln(\cos t)\right)\Big|_0^{\pi/4} \\
&= \tfrac12(e^{\sqrt2} - e^2) + 1 - \cos(\pi^2/16) + \tfrac12\ln 2
\end{aligned}
$$

In the above calculation of the integrals we used three u-substitutions

$$
\begin{aligned}
\int -\sin t\, e^{2\cos t}\,dt &= \int e^{2u}\,du = \tfrac12 e^{2u} \\
\int 2t \sin(t^2)\,dt &= \int \sin(u)\,du = -\cos(u) \\
\int \tan t\,dt &= \int \frac{\sin t}{\cos t}\,dt = -\int \frac1u\,du = -\ln u
\end{aligned}
$$

where $u = \cos t$, $u = t^2$, and $u = \cos t$, respectively. Also, note that $\ln(\cos(\frac\pi4)) = \ln(\frac{\sqrt2}{2}) = \ln(\sqrt2) - \ln 2 = \ln 2^{1/2} - \ln 2 = -\tfrac12\ln 2$.

Line Integrals for Scalar Fields in Space

Suppose $\psi : U \to \mathbb{R}^3$ is a scalar field on an open set U in $\mathbb{R}^3$. If C is a curve which lies in U and has parametrization $\mathbf{r} : [a, b] \to \mathbb{R}^3$, then the composite function

$$\widetilde{\psi} \equiv \psi \circ \mathbf{r} : [a, b] \to \mathbb{R}$$

is a scalar field on C, called the *restriction* of ψ to C. Thus, $\widetilde\psi(t) = \psi(\mathbf{r}(t))$ is number assigned to the point $P(t) = \mathbf{r}(t)$ on the curve. It will be convenient, notationally, to identify ψ with its restriction, i.e., $\psi = \widetilde\psi$. So, the line integral is

$$\int_C \psi\, ds \equiv \int_a^b \psi(\mathbf{r}(t))\|\mathbf{r}'(t)\|\,dt \qquad (14.2.6)$$

The notation on the left side of the equation is the same as before, but it is important to note that the computation on the right side involves the extra step of computing the composite function $\psi = \psi \circ \mathbf{r}$.

Example 14.2.4 (Calculating Line Integrals for Scalar Fields in Space)

Problem: For the following scalar field ψ and parametrized curve C, calculate the line integral $\int_C \psi \, ds$.

$$\psi = \frac{3x - y^2}{4zy}, \quad \mathbf{r} = \langle\, t, e^{2t}, \tfrac{3}{4}t - \tfrac{1}{4}e^{4t} \,\rangle, \text{ for } t \text{ in } [0, 1].$$

Solution: With $x = t$, $y = e^{2t}$, and $z = \tfrac{3}{4}t - \tfrac{1}{4}e^{4t}$, we first compute

$$\psi \circ \mathbf{r} = \frac{3t - (e^{2t})^2}{4\left(\tfrac{3}{4}t - \tfrac{1}{4}e^{4t}\right)e^{2t}} = \frac{3t - e^{4t}}{(3t - e^{4t})e^{2t}} = \frac{1}{e^{2t}} = e^{-2t}$$

Then

$$\mathbf{r}' = \langle\, 1, 2e^{2t}, \tfrac{3}{4} - e^{4t} \,\rangle$$

and so

$$\begin{aligned}
\|\mathbf{r}'\|^2 &= 1 + 4e^{4t} + \left(\tfrac{3}{4} - e^{4t}\right)^2 = 1 + 4e^{4t} + \tfrac{9}{16} - \tfrac{3}{2}e^{4t} + e^{8t} \\
&= 1 + \tfrac{9}{16} + (4 - \tfrac{3}{2})e^{4t} + e^{8t} = \tfrac{25}{16} + \tfrac{5}{2}e^{4t} + e^{8t} = \left(\tfrac{5}{4} + e^{4t}\right)^2
\end{aligned}$$

Thus, the line integral is

$$\begin{aligned}
\int_C \psi \, ds &\equiv \int_a^b \psi(\mathbf{r}(t))\|\mathbf{r}'(t)\| \, dt = \int_0^1 e^{-2t}\left(\tfrac{5}{4} + e^{4t}\right) dt = \int_0^1 \left(\tfrac{5}{4}e^{-2t} + e^{2t}\right) dt \\
&= \left(-\tfrac{5}{8}e^{-2t} + \tfrac{1}{2}e^{2t}\right)\Big|_0^1 = \tfrac{5}{8}(1 - e^{-2}) + \tfrac{1}{2}(e^2 - 1)
\end{aligned}$$

The Differential Form Notation for Line Integrals

Throughout the book we have used differentials, such as the dx in single integrals $\int f(x) \, dx$. This was done in a heuristic way to represent concepts and also as guides to certain techniques, such as u-substitutions and integration by parts.

For line integrals it will be convenient to use the *vector differential:*

$$d\mathbf{r} \equiv \langle\, dx, \, dy, \, dz \,\rangle$$

Then, for a vector field $\mathbf{F} = \langle\, M, \, N, \, K \,\rangle$, we can write

$$\mathbf{F} \cdot d\mathbf{r} = \langle\, M, \, N, \, K \,\rangle \cdot \langle\, dx, \, dy, \, dz \,\rangle = M\,dx + N\,dy + K\,dz \qquad (14.2.7)$$

The expression $M\,dx + N\,dy + K\,dz$ is what is known as a *differential form* (on the open set U that is the domain of $\mathbf{F}$). This gives an alternative, historically important, notation for the line integral:

$$\int_C \mathbf{F} \cdot d\mathbf{r} = \int_C M\,dx + N\,dy + K\,dz \qquad (14.2.8)$$

Similarly for a vector field $\mathbf{F} = \langle\, M, N \,\rangle$ in the plane, we use $d\mathbf{r} = \langle\, dx, dy \,\rangle$ for the vector differential and so $\int_C \mathbf{F} \cdot d\mathbf{r} = \int_C M\,dx + N\,dy$ is the differential for the line integral along a curve C in the plane.

In both cases we will often use the $\mathbf{i}, \mathbf{j}$ (and $\mathbf{k}$) notation. For example, if

$$\mathbf{F} = x^2y\,\mathbf{i} + xy^3\mathbf{j}, \text{ and } d\mathbf{r} - dx\,\mathbf{i} + dy\,\mathbf{j}$$

then

$$\int_C \mathbf{F} \cdot d\mathbf{r} = \int_C (x^2y\,\mathbf{i} + xy^3\mathbf{j}) \cdot (dx\,\mathbf{i} + dy\,\mathbf{j}) = \int_C x^2y\,dx + xy^3\,dy$$

We will use this notation from time to time in the reading material and the exercises. The topic of differential forms is an important part of differential geometry, but is too complicated to discuss fully here.

Example 14.2.5 (Line Integrals in The Differential Form Notation)

Problem: For the following vector fields $\mathbf{F} : \mathbb{R}^3 \to \mathbb{R}^3$ and parametrized curves C, calculate the line integral $\int_C \mathbf{F} \cdot d\mathbf{r}$.

Part (a) $\mathbf{F} = x^2 y\,\mathbf{i} + xy^2\mathbf{j}$, $\quad \mathbf{r} = t^3\,\mathbf{i} + t^2\mathbf{j}$, for t in $[0, 1]$.

Solution Part(a): With $x = t^3, y = t^2$ and $dx = 3t^2 dt$, $dy = 2t\,dt$, we have

$$
\begin{aligned}
\int_C M\,dx + N\,dy &= \int_C x^2 y\,dx + xy^2\,dy = \int_0^1 t^6 t^2 (3t^2 dt) + t^3 t^4 (2t\,dt) \\
&= \int_0^1 3t^{10} dt + 2t^8 dt = \left(\tfrac{3}{11} t^{11} + \tfrac{2}{9} t^9 \right)\Big|_0^1 = \tfrac{3}{11} + \tfrac{2}{9} = \tfrac{49}{99}
\end{aligned}
$$

Part (b) $\mathbf{F} = x\,\mathbf{i} + y\,\mathbf{j} + xz\mathbf{k}$, $\quad \mathbf{r} = (\cos t)\,\mathbf{i} + (\sin t)\mathbf{j} + t\,\mathbf{k}$, t for in $[0, \pi]$.

Solution Part(b): With $x = \cos t, y = \sin t, z = t$, we get $dx = -\sin t\,dt$ and $dy = \cos t\,dt, dz = dt$. So we have

$$
\begin{aligned}
\int_C M\,dx + N\,dy + P\,dz &= \int_C x\,dx + y\,dy + xz\,dz \\
&= \int_0^\pi \cos t(-\sin t\,dt) + \sin t(\cos t\,dt) + t\cos t(1\,dt) \\
&= \int_0^\pi t\cos t\,dt = \left(t\sin t + \cos t \right)\Big|_0^\pi = -1 - 1 = -2
\end{aligned}
$$

The Unit Tangent Vector Notation for Line Integrals

As mentioned in the discussion of work above, the quantity $\frac{\mathbf{F}\cdot\mathbf{r}'}{\|\mathbf{r}'\|} = \mathbf{F} \cdot \mathbf{T}$ is the component of force in the tangential direction. So we can write the line integral in terms of the unit tangent vector field $\mathbf{T}$:

$$
\begin{aligned}
\int_C \mathbf{F} \cdot d\mathbf{r} &= \int_a^b \mathbf{F}(t) \cdot \mathbf{r}'(t)\,dt = \int_a^b \mathbf{F}(t) \cdot \frac{\mathbf{r}'(t)}{\|\mathbf{r}'(t)\|} \|\mathbf{r}'(t)\|\,dt \\
&= \int_a^b \mathbf{F}(t) \cdot \mathbf{T}(t) \|\mathbf{r}'(t)\|\,dt = \int_C \mathbf{F} \cdot \mathbf{T}\,ds \qquad (14.2.9)
\end{aligned}
$$

NOTE: This form of the line integral using $\mathbf{T}$ is *not* one that you should use to compute the line integral. (Because $\mathbf{T}$ is usually a pretty complicated expression.) Rather, this form is merely for geometrical/physical interpretation of the line integral. For example it says that if $\mathbf{F}$ is everywhere perpendicular to C, i.e., if $\mathbf{F} \cdot \mathbf{T} = 0$, at all times, then there is no work done: $W = 0$.

NOTE TO INSTRUCTORS: The presentation here of line integrals is slightly different in approach than most calculus books. This is so because most, if not all, calculus books have a small notational error that has persisted in their presentations for decades. These books start with the definition of the line integral $\int_C f(x, y, z)\,ds$ of a scalar field $f : U \to \mathbb{R}$, on an open set U in $\mathbb{R}^3$. The definition is roughly:

$$
\int_C f(x, y, z)\,ds = \text{a certain limit}
$$

That's notationally OK. Then these books, for a vector field $\mathbf{F} : U \to \mathbb{R}^3$, on an open set U in $\mathbb{R}^3$, define the line integral of $\mathbf{F}$ in terms of the above definition of the line of a scalar field f:

$$
\int_C \mathbf{F} \cdot d\mathbf{r} = \int_C \mathbf{F} \cdot \mathbf{T}\,ds
$$

The problem with this is that $\mathbf{F} \cdot \mathbf{T}$ is not a scalar field on U because $\mathbf{T}$ not a vector field on U, but rather is only a vector field on C. (Theoretically, $\mathbf{T}$ can be extended to a vector field on a neighborhood of C, but that is too much theory for a calculus book.)

Exercises: 14.2 (Line Integals)

Calculating Work

In Exercises 1–6, calculate the work $W = \int_C \mathbf{F} \cdot d\mathbf{r}$ done along the path C, parametrized by $\mathbf{r}$, and subject to the force field $\mathbf{F}$ on C.

1. $\mathbf{F} = \langle t^2, t^3, t^4 \rangle$, $\mathbf{r} = \langle 1 + 2t, t^2, t^3 \rangle$, t in $[0, 1]$

2. $\mathbf{F} = \langle t^3, t^4, t^5 \rangle$, $\mathbf{r} = \langle 1 - t, t^3, t^4 \rangle$, t in $[0, 1]$

3. $\mathbf{F} = \langle \cos^2 t, \sin^5 t, t^2 \rangle$, $\mathbf{r} = \langle \cos t. \sin t, t \rangle$, t in $[0, \pi]$

4. $\mathbf{F} = \langle \sin^3 t, \cos^4 t, t^4 \rangle$, $\mathbf{r} = \langle \sin t. \cos t, t \rangle$, t in $[0, \pi]$

5. $\mathbf{F} = \langle e^{-2t}, e^{3t}, e^{4t} \rangle$, $\mathbf{r} = \langle e^{2t}, e^{-t}, e^{-3t} \rangle$, t in $[0, \ln 2]$

6. $\mathbf{F} = \langle e^{-3t}, e^{4t}, e^{5t} \rangle$, $\mathbf{r} = \langle e^{5t}, e^{-4t}, e^{-2t} \rangle$, t in $[0, \ln 2]$

Calculating Total Mass

In Exercises 7–12, calculate the total mass of the thin wire bent in the shape of the curve C with parametrization $\mathbf{r}$ and density function ρ.

7. $\mathbf{r} = \langle t, \frac{1}{2}t^2, \frac{15}{8}t - \frac{1}{24}t^3 \rangle$, $\rho = t^2$, t in $[0, 1]$

8. $\mathbf{r} = \langle t, \frac{1}{2}t^2, \frac{3}{4}t - \frac{1}{24}t^3 \rangle$, $\rho = t^2$, t in $[0, 1]$

9. $\mathbf{r} = \langle t^2, t^3, \frac{15}{8}t^2 - \frac{9}{64}t^4 \rangle$, $\rho = 1 - t$, t in $[0, 1]$

10. $\mathbf{r} = \langle t^2, t^3, \frac{3}{4}t^2 - \frac{9}{32}t^4 \rangle$, $\rho = 1 - t$, t in $[0, 1]$

11. $\mathbf{r} = \langle t, e^{2t}, \frac{3}{4}e^{2t} + \frac{1}{16}e^{-2t} \rangle$, $\rho = e^{-t}$, t in $[0, \ln 2]$

12. $\mathbf{r} = \langle t, e^t, \frac{3}{4}e^t + \frac{1}{4}e^{-t} \rangle$, $\rho = e^{-2t}$, t in $[0, \ln 2]$

Calculating Line Integrals of Vector Fields

In Exercises 13–18, calculate $\int_C \mathbf{F} \cdot d\mathbf{r}$ for the vector field $\mathbf{F}$ in space and the curve C parametrized by $\mathbf{r}$.

13. $\mathbf{F} = \langle x + y, xy, z^2 \rangle$, $\mathbf{r} = \langle t, t^2, t^3 \rangle$, t in $[0, 1]$

14. $\mathbf{F} = \langle x + y, y^2, xz \rangle$, $\mathbf{r} = \langle t^2, t, t^4 \rangle$, t in $[0, 1]$

15. $\mathbf{F} = \langle \sqrt{x + 1}, \sin y, yz \rangle$, $\mathbf{r} = \langle t^2, e^{2t} e^{4t} \rangle$, t in $[0, 1]$

16. $\mathbf{F} = \langle \sqrt{x + 1}, yz, \cos y \rangle$, $\mathbf{r} = \langle t^3, e^{4t} e^{3t} \rangle$, t in $[0, 1]$

17. $\mathbf{F} = \langle xy^3, x + y, z \rangle$, $\mathbf{r} = \langle \sin t, \cos t, t \rangle$, t in $[0, \pi]$

18. $\mathbf{F} = \langle x^3 y, x - y, z \rangle$, $\mathbf{r} = \langle \cos t, \sin t, t \rangle$, t in $[0, \pi]$

Calculating Line Integrals of Scalar Functions

In Exercises 19–24, calculate $\int_C \psi \, ds$ for the scalar field ψ in space and the curve C parametrized by $\mathbf{r}$.

19. $\psi = 16yz - 1$,
  $\mathbf{r} = \langle t, e^{2t}, \frac{3}{4}e^{2t} + \frac{1}{16}e^{-2t} \rangle$, t in $[0, \ln 2]$

20. $\psi = 4yz - 1$,
  $\mathbf{r} = \langle t, e^t, \frac{3}{4}e^t + \frac{1}{4}e^{-t} \rangle$, t in $[0, 1]$

21. $\psi = (x^2 + y^2)/z$,
  $\mathbf{r} = \langle \cos t, \sin t, e^{2t} + \frac{1}{16}e^{-2t} \rangle$, t in $[0, 2\pi]$

22. $\psi = (x^2 + y^2)/z$,
  $\mathbf{r} = \langle \cos t, \sin t, e^t + \frac{1}{4}e^{-t} \rangle$, t in $[0, 2\pi]$

23. $\psi = z^2$,
  $\mathbf{r} = \langle t + \sin t, 1 - \cos t, 3\sin\frac{t}{2} \rangle$, t in $[0, \pi]$

24. $\psi = z^2$,
  $\mathbf{r} = \langle t - \sin t, 1 - \cos t, 3\cos\frac{t}{2} \rangle$, t in $[0, \pi]$

Using the Differential Form Notation

In Exercises 25–28, use the differential form notation:
$$\int_C \mathbf{F} \cdot d\mathbf{r} = \int_C M\,dx + N\,dy$$
or
$$\int_C \mathbf{F} \cdot d\mathbf{r} = \int_C M\,dx + N\,dy + W\,dz$$
to calculate the line integrals of $\mathbf{F} = M\mathbf{i} + N\mathbf{j}$ or $\mathbf{F} = M\mathbf{i} + N\mathbf{j} + W\mathbf{k}$ and C is the curve parametrized by $\mathbf{r}$.

25. $\mathbf{F} = x^2 y \,\mathbf{i} + y^2 \,\mathbf{j}$, $\mathbf{r} = t^2 \mathbf{i} + t^3 \mathbf{j}$, t in $[0, 1]$

26. $\mathbf{F} = xy^2 \,\mathbf{i} + x^2 \,\mathbf{j}$, $\mathbf{r} = t^3 \mathbf{i} + t^2 \mathbf{j}$, t in $[0, 1]$

27. $\mathbf{F} = yz \,\mathbf{i} + xy \,\mathbf{j} + y^2 \mathbf{k}$, $\mathbf{r} = \sin t \,\mathbf{i} - \cos t \,\mathbf{j} + \sin t$,
  t in $[0, \pi]$

28. $\mathbf{F} = xy \,\mathbf{i} + yz \,\mathbf{j} + z^2 \mathbf{k}$, $\mathbf{r} = \cos t \,\mathbf{i} + \sin t \,\mathbf{j} + \cos t$,
  t in $[0, \pi]$

Calculus *Concepts & Computation*

14.3 The Fundamental Theorem of Line Integrals

In this section we discuss the first of several important theorems concerning line, surface, and volume integrals. This first theorem is sometimes called the Fundamental Theorem of Line Integrals (FTLI) or the Gradient Theorem. The other theorems, studied in later sections are Green's Theorem, Stokes' Theorem, and the Divergence Theorem (or Gauss' Divergence Theorem).

Recall the Fundamental Theorem of Calculus from Section 4.4 (Theorem 4.4.2), which we now use, almost automatically, to compute integrals $\int_a^b f(x)\,dx$. This theorem says that the computation can be done easily in terms of an antiderivative of f. Namely, if $f = F'$, then

$$\int_a^b f(x)\,dx = \int_a^b F'(x)\,dx = F(x)\Big|_a^b = F(b) - F(a)$$

Can we do something like this for line integrals $\int_C \mathbf{F} \cdot d\mathbf{r}$? Is there a corresponding antiderivative of a vector field $\mathbf{F}$? The answers to these questions are yes. Antiderivatives for vector fields are called *potential functions* and are defined naturally as follows.

DEFINITION 14.3.1 (Potential Functions)

Suppose $\mathbf{F}: U \to \mathbb{R}^3$ *is a vector field on an open set* U *in* $\mathbb{R}^3$. *A potential function for* $\mathbf{F}$ *is a scalar field* $\psi: U \to \mathbb{R}$ *on* U *such that*

$$\nabla\psi = \mathbf{F} \qquad (14.3.1)$$

on U.

NOTE 1: Not all vector fields $\mathbf{F} : U \to \mathbb{R}^3$ have potential functions on U. The existence of potential functions depends on (1) $\mathbf{F}$ satisfying certain "integrability conditions" and (2) the nature of the open set U. We will discuss this later.

NOTE 2: The definition also applies to vector fields $\mathbf{F} : U \to \mathbb{R}^2$ on the plane ($U \subseteq \mathbb{R}^2$). A potential for $\mathbf{F}$ is a scalar field ψ on the plane such that $\nabla\psi = \mathbf{F}$.

We assume, of course, that potential functions have partial derivatives which are continuous on U. As with antiderivatives, finding a potential function for $\mathbf{F}$ requires computing integrals (the hard part), which here amounts to three (or two) indefinite partial integrals. We will see how to do this below. But first let's look at an analog for the Fundamental Theorem of Calculus:

THEOREM 14.3.1 (The Fundamental Theorem of Line Integrals)

Suppose $\mathbf{F}: U \to \mathbb{R}^3$ *is a vector field on an open set* U *in* $\mathbb{R}^3$ *and* C *is a curve in* U *with parametrization* $\mathbf{r}: [a,b] \to \mathbb{R}^3$. *Let* $P = \mathbf{r}(a)$ *and* $Q = \mathbf{r}(b)$ *be the endpoints of the curve* C. *If* $\mathbf{F}$ *has a potential function,* $\nabla\psi = \mathbf{F}$, *on* U, *then*

$$\int_C \mathbf{F} \cdot d\mathbf{r} = \int_C \nabla\psi \cdot d\mathbf{r} = \psi\Big|_P^Q = \psi(Q) - \psi(P) \qquad (14.3.2)$$

Proof: The proof is easy. Using Equation (11.5.9), which is the vector version of a certain chain rule, we have

$$\frac{d}{dt}\big[\psi(\mathbf{r}(t))\big] = \nabla\psi(\mathbf{r}(t)) \cdot \mathbf{r}'(t)$$

From this and the ordinary Fundamental Theorem of Calculus we get

$$
\begin{aligned}
\int_C \mathbf{F} \cdot d\mathbf{r} &= \int_C \nabla\psi \cdot d\mathbf{r} = \int_a^b \nabla\psi(\mathbf{r}(t)) \cdot \mathbf{r}'(t)\, dt \\
&= \int_a^b \frac{d}{dt}\big[\psi(\mathbf{r}(t))\big]\, dt = \psi(\mathbf{r}(t))\Big|_a^b \\
&= \psi(\mathbf{r}(b)) - \psi(\mathbf{r}(a)) = \psi(Q) - \psi(P)
\end{aligned}
$$

NOTE 1: **(The Gradient Theorem)** The theorem is sometimes called the gradient theorem because vector fields of the form $\nabla\psi$ are known as *gradient vector fields*. So, without mention of $\mathbf{F}$ or potential functions, we can state the theorem as follows. For a gradient vector field $\nabla\psi$ on U and a curve C in U with endpoints P and Q:

$$\int_C \nabla\psi \cdot d\mathbf{r} = \psi\,\Big|_P^Q = \psi(Q) - \psi(P) \qquad (14.3.2)$$

NOTE 2: The theorem also applies to vector fields $\mathbf{F} : U \to \mathbb{R}^2$ on the plane ($U \subseteq \mathbb{R}^2$).

There are many consequences and uses of this theorem. Before discussing them, we look at several examples, where a potential function for a vector field is known in advance (so we do not have to calculate it).

Example 14.3.1 (Using the FTLI when the Potential Function is Known)
Problem: For the vector field $\mathbf{F}$, with the given potential ψ, use the FTLI to compute the line integral $\int_C \mathbf{F} \cdot d\mathbf{r}$ of $\mathbf{F}$ along the given curve C (parametrized by $\mathbf{r}$). Also check that $\nabla\psi = \mathbf{F}$.

(a) $\mathbf{F} = (3x^2y^2z + 2y^2z^2)\mathbf{i} + (2x^3yz + 6xy^2z^2)\mathbf{j} + (x^3y^2 + 4xy^3z)\mathbf{k}$,

  $\psi = x^3y^2z + 2xy^3z^2$, $\mathbf{r} = t\mathbf{i} + t^2\mathbf{j} + t^3\mathbf{k}$, for t in $[-1,1]$.

(b) $\mathbf{F} = \langle\, 2xe^{-y^2},\ -2x^2ye^{-y^2}\,\rangle$, $\psi = x^2e^{-y^2}$, $\mathbf{r} = \langle\, t,\ t^2\,\rangle$, for t in $[-1,1]$.

Solution Part(a): Here $P = \mathbf{r}(-1) = (-1,1,-1)$ and $Q = \mathbf{r}(1) = (1,1,1)$ and so

$$\int_C \mathbf{F} \cdot d\mathbf{r} = \psi\,\Big|_{(-1,1,-1)}^{(1,1,1)} = \big(x^3y^2z + 2xy^3z^2 \big)\,\Big|_{(-1,1,-1)}^{(1,1,1)} = (1+2) - (1-2) = 4$$

To check that ψ is actually a potential function, we compute the three partials:

$$
\begin{aligned}
\frac{\partial\psi}{\partial x} &= \frac{\partial}{\partial x}\left(x^3y^2z + 2xy^3z^2\right) = 3x^2y^2z + 2y^2z^2 \\
\frac{\partial\psi}{\partial y} &= \frac{\partial}{\partial y}\left(x^3y^2z + 2xy^3z^2\right) = 2x^3yz + 6xy^2z^2 \\
\frac{\partial\psi}{\partial z} &= \frac{\partial}{\partial z}\left(x^3y^2z + 2xy^3z^2\right) = x^3y^2 + 4xy^3z
\end{aligned}
$$

Solution Part(b): Here $P = \mathbf{r}(-1) = (-1,1)$ and $Q = \mathbf{r}(1) = (1,1)$ and so

$$\int_C \mathbf{F} \cdot d\mathbf{r} = \psi\,\Big|_{(-1,1)}^{(1,1)} = \big(x^2e^{-y^2} \big)\,\Big|_{(-1,1)}^{(1,1)} = e^{-1} - e^{-1} = 0$$

To check that ψ is actually a potential function, we compute the two partials:

$$\frac{\partial \psi}{\partial x} = \frac{\partial}{\partial x}\left(x^2 e^{-y^2}\right) = 2xe^{-y^2}$$

$$\frac{\partial \psi}{\partial y} = \frac{\partial}{\partial y}\left(x^2 e^{-y^2}\right) = -2x^2 y e^{-y^2}$$

If you wish, you can compute the line integrals in (a) and (b) directly (without using the FTLI) and you will see that this is more time-consuming. However using the FTLI is only quicker if you know a potential for $\mathbf{F}$. Computing a potential for $\mathbf{F}$, when one exists, generally takes longer than computing $\int_C \mathbf{F} d\mathbf{r}$ directly.

Conservative Vector Fields

When a vector field has a potential function it is called *conservative*. This terminology, as we shall see, comes from physics.

DEFINITION 14.3.2 (Conservative Vector Fields)

A vector field $\mathbf{F} : U \to \mathbb{R}^3$ *on an open set* U *in* $\mathbb{R}^3$ *is called* conservative *if it has a potential function* $\psi : U \to \mathbb{R}$ *on* U.

Two important examples of conservative vector fields come from gravitational force fields and electrostatic force fields. While being physically different in nature, these force fields are very similar in form. Consider the elementary case of fields generated by a body of mass m and a particle of charge q. The potential and field are

$$\psi = \frac{k}{(x^2 + y^2 + z^2)^{1/2}} \tag{14.3.4}$$

$$\mathbf{F} = \left\langle \frac{-kx}{(x^2 + y^2 + z^2)^{3/2}}, \frac{-ky}{(x^2 + y^2 + z^2)^{3/2}}, \frac{-kz}{(x^2 + y^2 + z^2)^{3/2}} \right\rangle$$

$$= -\frac{k}{\|\mathbf{X}\|^3}\mathbf{X} = -\frac{k}{\|\mathbf{X}\|^2}\frac{\mathbf{X}}{\|\mathbf{X}\|} \quad (\textit{inverse square law}), \tag{14.3.5}$$

where $\mathbf{X}$ is the vector field on $U = \mathbb{R}^3$ given by $\mathbf{X}(x, y, z) = \langle x, y, z \rangle$. Here $k = m > 0$ in the gravitational case and $k = \pm q$ in the electrostatic case.

The designation of $\mathbf{F}$ being a conservative force field comes from (1) the work done being independent of the path C and (2) the conservation of energy principle.

Work Done in Moving Along Different Paths

In Section 14.2 we calculated the work done in moving along a path (curve) C subject to a force $\mathbf{F}$ acting at each point of the path. If $\mathbf{F}$ is a vector field on an open set U in $\mathbb{R}^3$, then we can investigate the work done in moving along a number of different paths in U with the same starting point P and ending point Q.

Example 14.3.2 (Calculating Work Done Along a Two Paths)

Problem: For the force field $\mathbf{F} = \langle -y, x \rangle$ on the plane, compute the work $W = \int_C \mathbf{F} \cdot d\mathbf{r}$ done as a particle moves along the each of the curves C_1, C_2:

C_1: $\mathbf{r} = \langle \cos t, \sin t \rangle$, for t in $[0, \pi/2]$ (a quarter circle)

C_2: $\mathbf{r} = \langle (t-1)^2, t \rangle$, for t in $[0, 1]$ (a parabolic arc)

Solution: For C_1, we have

$$\mathbf{F} \circ \mathbf{r} = \langle -\sin t, \cos t \rangle \quad \text{and} \quad \mathbf{r}' = \langle -\sin t, \cos t \rangle$$

$$
\begin{aligned}
W_1 &= \int_{C_1} \mathbf{F} \cdot d\mathbf{r} = \int_0^{\pi/2} \langle -\sin t, \cos t \rangle \cdot \langle -\sin t, \cos t \rangle \, dt \\
&= \int_0^{\pi/2} \left(\sin^2 t + \cos^2 t \right) dt = \int_0^{\pi/2} 1 \, dt = \frac{\pi}{2}
\end{aligned}
$$

For C_2, we have

$$\mathbf{F} \circ \mathbf{r} = \langle -t, (t-1)^2 \rangle \quad \text{and} \quad \mathbf{r}' = \langle 2(t-1), 1 \rangle$$

$$
\begin{aligned}
W_2 &= \int_{C_2} \mathbf{F} \cdot d\mathbf{r} = \int_0^1 \langle -t, (t-1)^2 \rangle \cdot \langle (2t-2), 1 \rangle \, dt \\
&= \int_0^1 \left(-2t^2 + 2t + (t-1)^2 \right) dt = \int_0^1 \left(-2t^2 + 2t + t^2 - 2t + 1 \right) dt \\
&= \int_0^1 \left(1 - t^2 \right) dt = \left(t - \tfrac{1}{3}t^3 \right) \Big|_0^1 = 1 - \tfrac{1}{3} = \tfrac{2}{3}
\end{aligned}
$$

Figure 14.3.1 shows a plot of the vector field $\mathbf{F} = \langle -y, x \rangle$ and the two paths between P and Q that give different amounts of work.

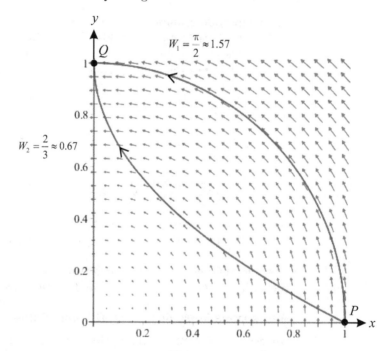

Figure 14.3.1: *Work done along two different paths.*

Since $W_1 \neq W_2$, we know that $\mathbf{F} = \langle -y, x \rangle$ is *not* a conservative force field. This is so because if it were, then it would have a potential function ψ. But since C_1, C_2 have the same endpoints $P = (1, 0)$, $Q = (0, 1)$, the FTLI would give

$$W_1 = \int_{C_1} \mathbf{F} \cdot d\mathbf{r} = \psi(Q) - \psi(P) = \int_{C_2} \mathbf{F} \cdot d\mathbf{r} = W_2 \qquad (14.3.6).$$

But this contradicts the calculations that $W_1 = \pi/2$ and $W_2 = 2/3$.

Equation (14.3.6) holds in general for any conservative vector field. This is one of the results is recorded in the following box.

Work and Conservative Force Fields

Suppose $\mathbf{F}: U \to \mathbb{R}^3$ is a conservative vector field on an open set U in $\mathbb{R}^3$.

(1) *For any two paths (i.e., curves) C_1 and C_2 in U with initial point P and terminal point Q, the work done in moving along either path from P to Q is the same:*

$$W_{PQ} = \int_{C_1} \mathbf{F} \cdot d\mathbf{r} = \int_{C_2} \mathbf{F} \cdot d\mathbf{r} \qquad (14.3.7)$$

(2) *For any closed curve C in U, the work done in moving around C is zero:*

$$W = \int_C \mathbf{F} \cdot d\mathbf{r} = 0 \qquad (14.3.8)$$

NOTE 1: The property of conservative vector fields stated in Equation (14.3.8) above follows from Equation (14.3.2) since, by definition, a *closed curve* is one whose endpoints P, Q are the same $P = Q$.

NOTE 2: It is common practice to use the notation $\oint_C \mathbf{F} \cdot d\mathbf{r}$ for the line integral when C is a closed curve. The small circle on the integral sign indicates that C is closed (like a circle).

NOTE 3: (**Path Independence**) The property that $\int_{C_1} \mathbf{F} \cdot d\mathbf{r} = \int_{C_2} \mathbf{F} \cdot d\mathbf{r}$ for any two curves C_1, C_2 with the same initial and terminal points is known as *path independence* or *independence of the path* for the line integral of $\mathbf{F}$.

Conservation of Energy

For a particle of mass m moving along a curve C, the position function $\mathbf{r}$ gives its location $\mathbf{r}(t)$ at each time t. The velocity vector field $\mathbf{v} = \mathbf{r}'$ and acceleration vector field $\mathbf{a} = \mathbf{v}' = \mathbf{r}''$, which are vector fields on C, play important roles in describing the particle's motion as well as the geometry of its trajectory C (Chapter 13).

For a *conservative* force field $\mathbf{F}: U \to \mathbb{R}^3$ on an open set U in $\mathbb{R}^3$, Newton's 2nd Law of motion: $\mathbf{F} = m\mathbf{a}$ leads to the principle that the trajectory of motion is one for which the total energy is conserved. Here are the definitions of the types of energies connected with the motion:

Kinetic Energy: $KE(t) \equiv \frac{1}{2} m \|\mathbf{v}(t)\|^2$ (14.3.9)

This quantity arises from a line integral of the vector field $m\mathbf{a}$ on C. To see this first note that by the product rule for dot products of vector-valued functions:

$$\frac{d}{dt}\left[\mathbf{r}'(t) \cdot \mathbf{r}'(t)\right] = \mathbf{r}''(t) \cdot \mathbf{r}'(t) + \mathbf{r}'(t) \cdot \mathbf{r}''(t) = 2\mathbf{r}''(t) \cdot \mathbf{r}'(t)$$

So, we get the identity:

$$\mathbf{r}''(t) \cdot \mathbf{r}'(t) = \frac{1}{2} \frac{d}{dt}\left[\mathbf{r}'(t) \cdot \mathbf{r}'(t)\right]$$

Next, let $C_{t_1 t_2}$ denote the portion of C described between times $t_1 < t_2$. Then

$$\int_{C_{t_1 t_2}} m\mathbf{a} \cdot d\mathbf{r} = \int_{C_{t_1 t_2}} m\mathbf{r}'' \cdot d\mathbf{r} = \int_{t_1}^{t_2} m\mathbf{r}''(t) \cdot \mathbf{r}'(t)\, dt$$

$$= \int_{t_1}^{t_2} \frac{1}{2} m \frac{d}{dt}\left[\mathbf{r}'(t) \cdot \mathbf{r}'(t)\right] dt = \int_{t_1}^{t_2} \frac{1}{2} m \frac{d}{dt}\left[\mathbf{v}(t) \cdot \mathbf{v}(t)\right] dt$$

$$= \int_{t_1}^{t_2} \frac{1}{2} m \frac{d}{dt}\left[\|\mathbf{v}(t)\|^2\right] dt = \frac{1}{2} m \|\mathbf{v}(t)\|^2 \Big|_{t_1}^{t_2} = KE(t) \Big|_{t_1}^{t_2}$$

$$= KE(t_2) - KE(t_1) \qquad (14.3.10)$$

Thus, the line integral $\int_{C_{t_1 t_2}} m\mathbf{a} \cdot d\mathbf{r} = KE(t_2) - KE(t_1)$ gives the difference in kinetic energies at times t_1 and t_2

Potential Energy: $\quad PE(t) \equiv \psi(\mathbf{r}(t)) \qquad (14.3.11)$

Here $-\psi$ is a potential function for the conservative force field $\mathbf{F} = -\nabla\psi$. NOTE: The minus sign in the last equation. This is the customary convention. Now, using the Fundamental Theorem of Line Integrals we get:

$$\int_{C_{t_1 t_2}} \mathbf{F} \cdot d\mathbf{r} = -\psi \Big|_{\mathbf{r}(t_1)}^{\mathbf{r}(t_2)} = \psi(\mathbf{r}(t_1)) - \psi(\mathbf{r}(t_2)) = PE(t_1) - PE(t_2) \qquad (14.3.12)$$

While, in general, the kinetic and potential energies continually change over time, it turns out that their sum remains constant over all time. The sum of the kinetic and potential energies is known as the total energy:

Total Energy: $\quad TE(t) \equiv KE(t) + PE(t) = \frac{1}{2} m\|\mathbf{v}(t)\|^2 + \psi(\mathbf{r}(t)) \qquad (14.3.13)$

The fact that this is a constant (conserved) quantity is due to Newton's 2nd Law. The position function is not just any vector-valued function, but rather one that satisfies Newton's law:

$$m\mathbf{a}(t) = \mathbf{F}(\mathbf{r}(t))$$

for all t in $[a, b]$ (where m and $\mathbf{F}$ are given). Taking dot products of both sides of this equation with $\mathbf{r}'(t)$ and integrating from t_1 to t_2, gives

$$\int_{C_{t_1 t_2}} m\mathbf{a} \cdot d\mathbf{r} = \int_{C_{t_1 t_2}} \mathbf{F} \cdot d\mathbf{r},$$

which, according to Equations (14.3.10) and (14.3.12), is the same as

$$KE(t_2) - KE(t_1) = PE(t_1) - PE(t_2)$$

Rearranging this gives

$$KE(t_2) + PE(t_2) = KE(t_1) + PE(t_1)$$

which says the total energy is the same at all times:

$$TE(t_2) = TE(t_1) \quad (\textit{Conservation of Energy}) \quad (14.3.14)$$

Constructing Potential Functions

As we mentioned above, not all vector fields in space $\mathbf{F} : U \to \mathbb{R}^3$ ($U \subseteq \mathbb{R}^3$) or vector fields in the plane $\mathbf{F} : U \to \mathbb{R}^2$ ($U \subseteq \mathbb{R}^2$) have potential functions ψ. But when they do you can try to find ψ by partial integration.

For a conservative vector field $\mathbf{F} = \langle M, N \rangle$ in the plane, a potential function ψ satisfies $\nabla\psi = \mathbf{F}$. This, in scalar form, is a pair of partial differential equations:

$$\psi_x = M, \quad \psi_y = N \qquad (14.3.15)$$

A naive method of solving this for ψ, which works in simple cases and where U is a suitable open set, is

Construction of a Potential Function – Two Variables:

$$\psi = \int M(x, y)\, dx + g(y), \quad \text{where } g \text{ is chosen so that: } \psi_y = N(x, y) \qquad (14.3.16)$$

The following example shows you specifically what is meant by this construction.

Example 14.3.3 (Constructing Potential Functions)

Problem: For the vector field

$$\mathbf{F} = \langle\, 2xy^2 + 2x,\, 2x^2y + 3y^2 \,\rangle,$$

try finding a potential function ψ for $\mathbf{F}$ using the method in (14.3.16).

Solution: Here $M(x,y) = 2xy^2 + 2x$ and $N(x,y) = 2x^2y + 3y^2$. So, first do a partial integral of M with respect to x and add on an arbitrary function of y

$$\psi = \int (2xy^2 + 2x)\, dx = x^2y^2 + x^2 + g(y)$$

Then compute ψ_y and set it equal to $N(x,y)$. This will determine $g(y)$.

$$\psi_y = \frac{\partial}{\partial y}\big[\, x^2y^2 + x^2 + g(y) \,\big] = 2x^2y + g'(y) \overset{need}{=} N(x,y) = 2x^2y + 3y^2$$

This gives $g'(y) = 3y^2$ and so $g(y) = y^3$. Putting this together with what we found for ψ, we get a potential function: $\psi = x^2y^2 + x^2 + y^3$.

Three Variable Case: Next, let's see if the method discussed above works for a conservative vector field $\mathbf{F} = \langle\, M,\, N,\, K \,\rangle$ in space. A potential function ψ satisfies $\nabla\psi = \mathbf{F}$. This, in scalar form is a set of three of partial differential equations:

$$\psi_x = M, \quad \psi_y = N, \quad \psi_z = K \qquad (14.3.17)$$

Construction of a Potential Function – Three Variables:

$$\psi = \int M(x,y)\, dx + g(y,z), \quad \text{where } g \text{ is chosen so that: } \quad \psi_y = N(x,y,z) \quad (14.3.18)$$

Now, since $g(y,z)$ depends on two variables, you will have to use one more partial integral and one ordinary integral to find g. The next example shows more details.

Example 14.3.4 (Constructing Potential Functions - Three Variables)

Problem: For the vector field

$$\mathbf{F} = (2xe^{yz})\mathbf{i} + (x^2ze^{yz} + 2ze^{2y})\mathbf{j} + (x^2ye^{yz} + e^{2y} - e^{-z})\mathbf{k},$$

try finding a potential function ψ for $\mathbf{F}$ using the Method in (14.3.17).

Solution: Here

$$M(x,y,z) = 2xe^{yz},$$
$$N(x,y,z) = x^2ze^{yz} + 2ze^{2y},$$
$$K(x,y,z) = x^2ye^{yz} + e^{2y} - e^{-z}.$$

So, first do a partial integral of M with respect to x and add on an arbitrary function of y and z:

$$\psi = \int 2xe^{yz}\, dx = x^2e^{yz} + g(y,z)$$

Then compute ψ_y and set it equal to $N(x,y,z)$. This determines $g_y(y,z)$.

$$\psi_y = \frac{\partial}{\partial y}\big[\, x^2e^{yz} + g(y,z) \,\big] = x^2ze^{yz} + g_y(y,z) \overset{need}{=} x^2ze^{yz} + 2ze^{2y}$$

This says $g_y(y,z) = 2ze^{2y}$ and so

$$g(y,z) = \int 2ze^{2y}\, dy = ze^{2y} + h(z)$$

where $h(z)$ is an arbitrary function of z. Putting this together with what we have found so far, we get

$$\psi = x^2e^{yz} + g(y,z) = x^2e^{yz} + ze^{2y} + h(z)$$

Finally, computing the partial of this with rest to z gives

$$\psi_z = \frac{\partial}{\partial z}\left[x^2 e^{yz} + ze^{2y} + h(z)\right] = x^2 ye^{yz} + e^{2y} + h'(z) \overset{need}{=} x^2 ye^{yz} + e^{2y} - e^{-z}$$

Hence, $h'(z) = -e^{-z}$ and so $h(z) = e^{-z}$. Thus, we have found the following potential for $\mathbf{F}$:

$$\psi = x^2 e^{yz} + ze^{2y} + e^{-z}$$

Integrability Conditions (Necessary Conditions)

If you apply the construction method in Examples 14.3.3–14.3.4 to non-conservative vector fields it will not work. For example, the vector field $\mathbf{F} = \langle -y, x \rangle$ was shown to be non-conservative in Example 14.3.2. The construction method in this case is to find a ψ that satisfies

$$\psi_x = -y, \quad \psi_y = x,$$

by doing a partial integral of the first equation with respect to x:

$$\psi = \int \psi_x\, dx = \int(-y)\, dx = -xy + g(y)$$

This is the general solution of $\psi_x = -y$. But, when we try to choose $g(y)$ so that the equation $\psi_y = x$ is satisfied, we get

$$\psi_y = \frac{\partial}{\partial y}\left[-xy + g(y)\right] = -x + g'(y) \overset{need}{=} x$$

Of course, there is no way to choose g so that $g'(y) = 2x$. Thus, the construction method for potentials shows us that $\mathbf{F} = \langle -y, x \rangle$ is not a conservative vector field. It also indicates that, in general, for $\mathbf{F} = \langle M, N \rangle$ there needs to be some condition for the equations

$$\psi_x = M, \quad \psi_y = N,$$

to be solvable. This condition comes from the observation that if there is a solution ψ, then necessarily

$$\psi_{xy} = \frac{\partial M}{\partial y} \quad \text{and} \quad \psi_{yx} = \frac{\partial N}{\partial x}.$$

But, since $\psi_{xy} = \psi_{yx}$ it is necessary that

$$\frac{\partial N}{\partial x} = \frac{\partial M}{\partial y}, \quad \text{or equivalently} \quad \frac{\partial N}{\partial x} - \frac{\partial M}{\partial y} = 0.$$

A more sophisticated way of deriving the same condition is to use Identity (14.1.14a). Namely, if $\mathbf{F} = \nabla\psi$, then

$$\text{curl}\,\mathbf{F} = \text{curl}(\nabla\psi) = 0$$

This is a condition that follows from $\mathbf{F}$ being conservative and is sometimes called an "integrability condition." We record this in the following box.

A Necessary Condition for the Existence of Potentials

If $\mathbf{F}$ is a conservative vector field, then necessarily

$$\text{curl}\,\mathbf{F} = 0 \qquad (14.3.19)$$

Recall that for a vector field $\mathbf{F} = \langle M, N, K \rangle$ in space

$$\text{curl}\,\mathbf{F} = \left\langle \frac{\partial K}{\partial y} - \frac{\partial N}{\partial z},\ \frac{\partial M}{\partial z} - \frac{\partial K}{\partial x},\ \frac{\partial N}{\partial x} - \frac{\partial M}{\partial y} \right\rangle$$

and so the necessary condition is that the following three equations hold when $\mathbf{F}$ is conservative:

$$\frac{\partial K}{\partial y} - \frac{\partial N}{\partial z} = 0, \quad \frac{\partial M}{\partial z} - \frac{\partial K}{\partial x} = 0, \quad \frac{\partial N}{\partial x} - \frac{\partial M}{\partial y} = 0 \qquad (14.3.20)$$

Properties of Conservative Vector Fields

Summarizing: If a vector field $\mathbf{F}$ is conservative, then it has three properties:

$$
\mathbf{F} \text{ conservative} \Longrightarrow
\begin{cases}
(1) \quad \displaystyle\int_{C_1} \mathbf{F} \cdot d\mathbf{r} = \int_{C_2} \mathbf{F} \cdot d\mathbf{r} & \text{\textit{for all curves having the same} } \atop \text{\textit{initial and terminal points}} & (14.3.21) \\[3mm]
(2) \quad W = \displaystyle\int_C \mathbf{F} \cdot d\mathbf{r} = 0 & \text{\textit{for every closed curve}} & (14.3.22) \\[3mm]
(3) \quad \operatorname{curl} \mathbf{F} = 0 & & (14.3.23)
\end{cases}
$$

It turns out that each of these three properties completely characterizes the class of conservative vector fields (assuming the open set U is *connected* or *simply connected*). This means that if a vector field $\mathbf{F}$ has the path independence property (1), then it must be conservative. If $\mathbf{F}$ has the closed path property (2), then it is conservative. If $\mathbf{F}$ has the curl free property (3), then it is conservative.

Thus, each of the three properties implies the existence of a potential function ψ for $\mathbf{F}$. Of course, it is impossible to use property (1) or property (2) to check that $\mathbf{F}$ is conservative because that would involve integrating along *all* pairs of coincident curves or integrating along *every* closed curve. Properties (1)–(2), their equivalence to each other, and each of them being equivalent to $\mathbf{F}$ being conservative, are things that are theoretical and very useful in higher-level geometry (algebraic topology)

On the other hand, property (3) is a practical, very easy condition to check.

NOTE: For a vector field $\mathbf{F} = \langle M, N \rangle \equiv \langle M, N, 0 \rangle$ in the plane, the curl is $\operatorname{curl} \mathbf{F} = \langle 0, 0, \frac{\partial N}{\partial x} - \frac{\partial M}{\partial y} \rangle$. So, $\operatorname{curl} \mathbf{F} = 0$ if and only if $\frac{\partial N}{\partial x} = \frac{\partial M}{\partial y}$

Example 14.3.5 (Use $\operatorname{curl} \mathbf{F} = 0$ to Check for Conservativeness)

Problem: Determine if the following vector fields are conservative or not.

Part (a): $\mathbf{F} = \langle y \cos xy + y^2 + 2x, \ x \cos xy + 2xy + 1 \rangle$

Solution Part(a): Here, $M = y \cos xy + y^2 + 2x$ and $N = x \cos xy + 2xy + 1$. So,

$$
\frac{\partial M}{\partial y} = \frac{\partial}{\partial y}\left(y \cos xy + y^2 + 2x \right) = \cos xy - xy \sin xy + 2y
$$

$$
\frac{\partial N}{\partial x} = \frac{\partial}{\partial x}\left(x \cos xy + 2xy + 1 \right) = \cos xy - xy \sin xy + 2y
$$

Since $\frac{\partial N}{\partial x} = \frac{\partial M}{\partial y}$, we can conclude that $\mathbf{F}$ is conservative.

Part (b): $\mathbf{F} = \langle yz + 2x, \ xz + 3y^2, \ xy + 4z^3 \rangle$

Solution Part(b): The curl of this vector field is

$$
\operatorname{curl} \mathbf{F} =
\begin{vmatrix}
\mathbf{i} & \mathbf{j} & \mathbf{k} \\
\frac{\partial}{\partial x} & \frac{\partial}{\partial y} & \frac{\partial}{\partial z} \\
yz + 2x & xz + 3y^2 & xy + 4z^3
\end{vmatrix}
= \langle x - x, \ y - y, \ z - z \rangle = \langle 0, 0, 0 \rangle
$$

Thus, $\mathbf{F}$ is a conservative vector field.

Part (c): $\mathbf{F} = \langle yz + 2x, \ x^2 z + 3y^2, \ xy^2 + 4z^3 \rangle$

Solution Part(c): The curl of this vector field is

$$
\operatorname{curl} \mathbf{F} =
\begin{vmatrix}
\mathbf{i} & \mathbf{j} & \mathbf{k} \\
\frac{\partial}{\partial x} & \frac{\partial}{\partial y} & \frac{\partial}{\partial z} \\
yz + 2x & x^2 z + 3y^2 & xy^2 + 4z^3
\end{vmatrix}
= \langle 2xy - x^2, \ y - y^2, \ 2xz - z \rangle
$$

Thus, $\mathbf{F}$ is *not* a conservative vector field.

Exercises: 14.3 (The Fundamental Theorem of Line Integrals)

Calculating Work

In Exercises 1–6, Use the FTLI and the given potential function ψ to compute the line integral $\int_C \mathbf{F} \cdot d\mathbf{r}$ along the curve C, parametrized by $\mathbf{r}$. Also verify that ψ is actually a potential for $\mathbf{F}$.

1. $\mathbf{F} = \langle 2xy + y^3,\ x^2 + 3xy^2 \rangle$, $\psi = x^2y + xy^3$
   $\mathbf{r} = \langle 1 + 2t,\ t^3 \rangle$, t in $[0, 1]$

2. $\mathbf{F} = \langle y^2 + 3x^2y,\ 2xy + x^3 \rangle$, $\psi = xy^2 + x^3y$
   $\mathbf{r} = \langle 1 + 2t,\ t^3 \rangle$, t in $[0, 1]$

3. $\mathbf{F} = \langle -2\sin 2x \sin 3y,\ 3\cos 2x \cos 3y \rangle$,
   $\psi = \cos 2x \sin 3y$, $\mathbf{r} = \langle \pi t^2,\ \frac{\pi}{6} + \frac{\pi}{3}t \rangle$, t in $[0, 1]$

4. $\mathbf{F} = \langle 2\cos 2x \cos 3y,\ -3\sin 2x \sin 3y \rangle$,
   $\psi = \sin 2x \cos 3y$, $\mathbf{r} = \langle \frac{\pi}{6} + \frac{\pi}{3}t,\ \pi t^2 \rangle$, t in $[0, 1]$

5. $\mathbf{F} = \langle y^2z^3 - 6xy^3z,\ 2xyz^3 - 9x^2y^2z,\ 3xy^2z^2 - 3x^2y^3 \rangle$
   $\psi = xy^2z^3 - 3x^2y^3z$, $\mathbf{r} = \langle t,\ t^2,\ t^3 \rangle$, t in $[-1, 1]$

6. $\mathbf{F} = \langle 2xyz^2 - 6x^2y^2z,\ x^2z^2 - 4x^3yz,\ 2x^2yz - 2x^3y^2 \rangle$
   $\psi = x^2yz^2 - 2x^3y^2z$, $\mathbf{r} = \langle t,\ t^2,\ t^3 \rangle$, t in $[-1, 1]$

Work Done Along Two Different Paths

In Exercises 7–10, calculate the work $W = \int_C \mathbf{F} \cdot d\mathbf{r}$ done along the two paths C_1, C_2 with parametrizations $\mathbf{r}_1, \mathbf{r}_2$. Also sketch the two paths and their directions.

7. $\mathbf{F} = \langle -y^3,\ x^2 \rangle$, $\mathbf{r}_1 = \langle t,\ t^2 \rangle$, $\mathbf{r}_2 = \langle t^3,\ t \rangle$,
   t in $[0, 1]$

8. $\mathbf{F} = \langle -y^2,\ x^3 \rangle$, $\mathbf{r}_1 = \langle t,\ t^4 \rangle$, $\mathbf{r}_2 = \langle t^4,\ t \rangle$,
   t in $[0, 1]$

9. $\mathbf{F} = \langle x - y,\ x \rangle$, $\mathbf{r}_1 = \langle \cos \frac{\pi t}{2},\ \sin \frac{\pi t}{2} \rangle$,
   $\mathbf{r}_2 = \langle 1 - t,\ t \rangle$, t in $[0, 1]$

10. $\mathbf{F} = \langle x - y,\ x \rangle$, $\mathbf{r}_1 = \langle \cos \frac{\pi t}{2},\ -\sin \frac{\pi t}{2} \rangle$,
    $\mathbf{r}_2 = \langle 1 - t,\ t \rangle$, t in $[0, 1]$

11. $\mathbf{F} = \langle x^2 + y^2,\ y,\ 3z^2 \rangle$, $\mathbf{r}_1 = \langle \cos t,\ \sin t,\ t \rangle$,
    $\mathbf{r}_2 = \langle 1,\ 0,\ t \rangle$, t in $[0, 2\pi]$

12. $\mathbf{F} = \langle x^2 + y^2,\ x,\ 3z^2 \rangle$, $\mathbf{r}_1 = \langle \sin t,\ \cos t,\ t \rangle$,
    $\mathbf{r}_2 = \langle 0,\ 1,\ t \rangle$, t in $[0, 2\pi]$

Finding Potentials for Conservative Vector Fields

In Exercises 13–22, find potential functions ψ for the following conservative vector fields $\mathbf{F}$.

13. $\mathbf{F} = \langle y^2 + 2x,\ 2xy + 3y^2 \rangle$

14. $\mathbf{F} = \langle y^3 + 3x^2,\ 3xy^2 + 4y^3 \rangle$

15. $\mathbf{F} = \langle y\cos xy + y^2 + 2x,\ x\cos xy + 2xy + 1 \rangle$

16. $\mathbf{F} = \langle y\sin xy + y^3 + 2x,\ x\sin xy + 3xy^2 + 1 \rangle$

17. $\mathbf{F} = \langle yz + 2x,\ xz + 3y^2,\ xy + 4z^3 \rangle$

18. $\mathbf{F} = \langle yz + 2x,\ xz + 3y^2,\ xy + 4z^3 \rangle$

19. $\mathbf{F} = \langle 2xy^2z^3 + z,\ 2x^2yz^3 + z^2,\ 3x^2y^2z^2 + x + 2yz \rangle$

20. $\mathbf{F} = \langle 2xy^2z^3 + z,\ 2x^2yz^3 + z^2,\ 3x^2y^2z^2 + x + 2yz, \rangle$

21. $\mathbf{F} = \langle y^2z - 4xy,\ 2xyz - 2x^2 + 6y,\ xy^2 + 6z \rangle$

22. $\mathbf{F} = \langle 2xyz - 2y^2 + 6x^2,\ x^2z - 4xy,\ x^2y + 9z^2 \rangle$

Testing for Conservativeness

In Exercises 23–28, use the condition curl $\mathbf{F} = 0$ to check whether $\mathbf{F}$ is conservative or not.

23. $\mathbf{F} = \langle x,\ y,\ 0 \rangle$ 24. $\mathbf{F} = \langle x^2,\ y^2,\ 0 \rangle$

25. $\mathbf{F} = \langle -y,\ x,\ 0 \rangle$ 26. $\mathbf{F} = \langle y^2,\ x^2,\ 0 \rangle$

27. $\mathbf{F} = \langle 2xy + y^3,\ x^2 + 3xy^2,\ 0 \rangle$

28. $\mathbf{F} = \langle y^2 + 3x^2y,\ 2xy + x^3,\ 0 \rangle$

29. $\mathbf{F} = \langle -2\sin 2x \sin 3y,\ 3\cos 2x \cos 3y,\ 0 \rangle$,

30. $\mathbf{F} = \langle 2\cos 2x \cos 3y,\ -3\sin 2x \sin 3y,\ 0 \rangle$,

31. $\mathbf{F} = \langle 2xy + z^3,\ x^2 + 3zy^2,\ xy \rangle$

32. $\mathbf{F} = \langle y^2 + 3z^2y,\ 2yz + x^3,\ xz \rangle$

Calculus *Concepts & Computation*

14.4 Surface Integrals

The line integral introduced in Section 14.2 has a direct analog in the surface integral discussed here. For vector fields and scalar fields (either on a surface S or on an open set U that contains S) the surface integral is an important tool in studying the properties of these fields as well as the equations from physics that involve these fields.

What is new about surface integrals is that, rather than integrating over a region D in the plane, we want to be able to integrate over a surface S in space. The surface integral will be defined in terms of a double integral over planar regions D. The integrand of the double integral, an ordinary function of two-variables, will come from combining (via dot products) a given vector field $\mathbf{F}$ with the standard normal vector field $\mathbf{n} = \mathbf{r}_u \times \mathbf{r}_v$ on S. Here $\mathbf{r} : D \to \mathbb{R}^3$ is the parametrization of S.

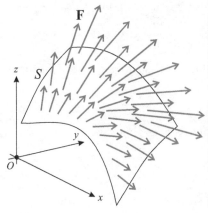

Figure 14.4.1: *A vector field on a surface S.*

Surface Integrals We first give the definition of the surface integral of a vector field $\mathbf{F}$ *on* S. Then we use this definition to define the surface integral of a scalar field ψ *on* S. Finally, for vector and scalar fields, $\mathbf{F}, \psi$ on opens sets in $\mathbb{R}^3$ containing S, we apply these prior definitions to the restrictions of $\mathbf{F}$ and ψ to S. This approach, which is slightly different from the customary one, is motivated by the same reasons for our approach to line integrals. (See the NOTE TO INSTRUCTORS at the end of Section 14.2.)

DEFINITION 14.4.1 (Surface Integrals of Vector Fields)

Suppose S is a surface parametrized by $\mathbf{r} : D \to \mathbb{R}^3$, *where D is a planar region in* $\mathbb{R}^2$

If $\mathbf{F} : D \to \mathbb{R}^3$ *is a vector field on S, then the surface integral of* $\mathbf{F}$ *over S, denoted by*

$\int_S \mathbf{F} \cdot d\mathbf{A}$, *is defined by*

$$\int_S \mathbf{F} \cdot d\mathbf{A} \equiv \iint_D \mathbf{F} \cdot (\mathbf{r}_u \times \mathbf{r}_v) dA \qquad (14.4.1)$$

Thus, the surface integral $\int_S \mathbf{F} \cdot d\mathbf{A}$ (notation) is just the double integral of the function $\mathbf{F} \cdot (\mathbf{r}_u \times \mathbf{r}_v)$ over the region D. The differential notation

$$d\mathbf{A} = (\mathbf{r}_u \times \mathbf{r}_v) \, dA$$

is convenient to use for this new concept. NOTE: Since $\mathbf{n} = \mathbf{r}_u \times \mathbf{r}_v$, we will often use $\mathbf{F} \cdot \mathbf{n}$ as the notation for the integrand of the double integral in Equation (14.4.1).

There are a number of topics in physics that serve to explain the geometric significance of the surface integral. The easiest one to visualize comes from fluid mechanics.

The Flux of Fluid Across a Surface

Suppose we consider a surface S, parametrized by $\mathbf{r} : D \to \mathbb{R}^3$, as a membrane immersed in a fluid that is in motion. Also Suppose $\mathbf{V} : D \to \mathbb{R}^3$ is a vector field on S, which generally is time dependent with $\mathbf{V}(t)(u, v)$ representing the velocity of the fluid motion at the point $P(u, v) = \mathbf{r}(u, v)$ on S at time t. Then surface integral

$$\int_S \mathbf{V} \cdot d\mathbf{A} = \text{flux of fluid across } S$$

A pedagogical argument for this is as follows.

At a point P on the surface during the increment of time from t to $t + dt$, consider the volume of fluid that flows across an infinitesimal "patch" $\mathcal{P}$ of S, which is the parallelogram with adjacent sides $\mathbf{r}_u du$ and $\mathbf{r}_v dv$ and area dA. The fluid is flowing in direction $\mathbf{V}$ and goes a distance $\mathbf{V}dt$. So, the volume of fluid flowing across $\mathcal{P}$ is the volume of the parallelepiped with adjacent sides $\mathbf{r}_u du$, $\mathbf{r}_v dv$, and $\mathbf{V}dt$. By the results in Section 10.3, this volume is the absolute value of

$$(\mathbf{V}dt) \cdot (\mathbf{r}_u du \times \mathbf{r}_v dv) = \mathbf{V} \cdot (\mathbf{r}_u \times \mathbf{r}_v) du\, dv\, dt$$

So over the increment dt of time, the volume of fluid $d\mathcal{V}$ that flows across $\mathcal{P}$ in the direction $\mathbf{V}$ is

$$d\mathcal{V} = \mathbf{V} \cdot (\mathbf{r}_u \times \mathbf{r}_v) du\, dv\, dt$$

This suggests that the total flux of fluid volume across S at time t is.

$$\frac{d\mathcal{V}}{dt} = \iint_D \mathbf{V} \cdot (\mathbf{r}_u \times \mathbf{r}_v)\, dA = \int_S \mathbf{V} \cdot d\mathbf{A}$$

In addition to fluid mechanics, there are other situations in physics where the surface integral $\int_S \mathbf{F} \cdot d\mathbf{A}$ of a vector field $\mathbf{F}$ is viewed as the flux of some quantity across S. So, we record this in the following box.

FLUX of a Vector Field Across a Surface

$$\mathcal{F} = \int_S \mathbf{F} \cdot d\mathbf{A} \qquad (14.4.2)$$

Example 14.4.1 (Calculating Flux Across Surfaces)

Problem: For the given vector field $\mathbf{F}$, compute the flux $\mathcal{F} = \int_S \mathbf{F} \cdot d\mathbf{A}$ of $\mathbf{F}$ across the given surface S, parametrized by $\mathbf{r}$.

Part (a): $\mathbf{F} = \langle u + v,\, v,\, u \rangle$, $\quad \mathbf{r} = \langle uv,\, u^2 + v^2,\, u^2 - v^2 \rangle$, (u, v) in $[0, 1] \times [0, 1]$.

Solution Part(a): First compute the partial derivatives of $\mathbf{r}$:

$$\mathbf{r}_u = \langle\, v,\, 2u,\, 2u\, \rangle, \quad \mathbf{r}_v = \langle\, u,\, 2v,\, -2v\, \rangle$$

and the normal vector is

$$\mathbf{n} = \mathbf{r}_u \times \mathbf{r}_v = \begin{vmatrix} \mathbf{i} & \mathbf{j} & \mathbf{k} \\ v & 2u & 2u \\ u & 2v & -2v \end{vmatrix} = \langle\, -8uv,\, 2u^2 + 2v^2,\, 2v^2 - 2u^2\, \rangle$$

Thus,

$$
\begin{aligned}
\mathbf{F} \cdot \mathbf{n} &= \langle\, u + v,\, v,\, u\, \rangle \cdot \langle\, -8uv,\, 2u^2 + 2v^2,\, 2v^2 - 2u^2\, \rangle \\
&= -8u^2 v - 8uv^2 + 2u^2 v + 2v^3 + 2uv^2 - 2u^3 \\
&= -6u^2 v - 6uv^2 + 2v^3 - 2u^3 \\
&= -2(3u^2 v + 3uv^2 - v^3 + u^3)
\end{aligned}
$$

Then the flux across S is

$$
\begin{aligned}
\mathcal{F} &= \int_S \mathbf{F} \cdot d\mathbf{A} = \iint_D \mathbf{F} \cdot \mathbf{n}\, dA = -2 \int_0^1 \int_0^1 \left(3u^2 v + 3uv^2 - v^3 + u^3 \right) du\, dv \\
&= -2 \int_0^1 \left(u^3 v + \tfrac{3}{2} u^2 v^2 - uv^3 + \tfrac{1}{4} u^4 \right) \Big|_{u=0}^{u=1} dv = -2 \int_0^1 \left(v + \tfrac{3}{2} v^2 - v^3 + \tfrac{1}{4} \right) dv \\
&= -2 \left(\tfrac{1}{2} v^2 + \tfrac{1}{2} v^3 - \tfrac{1}{4} v^4 + \tfrac{1}{4} v \right) \Big|_0^1 = -2 \left(\tfrac{1}{2} + \tfrac{1}{2} - \tfrac{1}{4} + \tfrac{1}{4} \right) = -2
\end{aligned}
$$

Part (b): $\mathbf{F} = \langle\, t^2,\, \cos^2 \theta,\, t^3\, \rangle$, $\quad \mathbf{r}(\theta, t) = \langle\, t \cos \theta,\, t \sin \theta,\, t\, \rangle$ (θ, t) in $[0, \pi] \times [0, 2]$.

Solution Part(b): The surface here is half of a half cone. First compute the partials of **r**

$$\mathbf{r}_\theta = \langle\, -t\sin\theta,\, t\cos\theta,\, 0\,\rangle, \quad \mathbf{r}_t = \langle\, \cos\theta,\, \sin\theta,\, 1\,\rangle$$

Then the normal vector is

$$\mathbf{n} = \mathbf{r}_\theta \times \mathbf{r}_t = \begin{vmatrix} \mathbf{i} & \mathbf{j} & \mathbf{k} \\ -t\sin\theta & t\cos\theta & 0 \\ \cos\theta & \sin\theta & 1 \end{vmatrix} = \langle\, t\cos\theta,\, t\sin\theta,\, -t\,\rangle$$

So, since $\mathbf{F} = \langle\, t^2,\, \cos^2\theta,\, t^3\,\rangle$, we get

$$
\begin{aligned}
\mathbf{F}\cdot\mathbf{n} &= \langle\, t^2,\, \cos^2\theta,\, t^3\,\rangle \cdot \langle\, t\cos\theta,\, t\sin\theta,\, -t\,\rangle \\
&= t^3\cos\theta + t\cos^2\theta\sin\theta - t^4
\end{aligned}
$$

Then the flux across S is

$$
\begin{aligned}
\mathcal{F} &= \int_S \mathbf{F}\cdot d\mathbf{A} = \iint_D \mathbf{F}\cdot\mathbf{n}\,dA = \int_0^1 \int_0^\pi \left(t^3\cos\theta + t\cos^2\theta\sin\theta - t^4 \right) d\theta\,dt \\
&= \int_0^1 \left(t^3\sin\theta - \tfrac{1}{3}t\cos^3\theta - t^4\theta \right)\Big|_{\theta=0}^{\theta=\pi} dt = \int_0^1 \left(\tfrac{2}{3}t - \pi t^4 \right) dt \\
&= \left(\tfrac{1}{3}t^2 - \tfrac{1}{5}\pi t^5 \right)\Big|_0^1 = \tfrac{1}{3} - \tfrac{1}{5}\pi = \frac{5 - 3\pi}{15}
\end{aligned}
$$

Surface Integrals of Scalar Fields

Suppose S is a smooth surface parametrized by $\mathbf{r} : D \to \mathbb{R}^3$. Then since the standard normal vector field $\mathbf{n}(u,v) = \mathbf{r}_u(u,v) \times \mathbf{r}_v(u,v) \neq 0$, for any (u,v) in D, we can normalize to get the standard *unit* normal vector field on S:

$$\mathbf{N} = \frac{\mathbf{n}}{\|\mathbf{n}\|} \quad \textit{(Standard Unit Normal Vector Field on }S\,)$$

This was discussed in Section 13.4. and was useful in studying the geometry of the surface S. Here, it is informative to consider the surface integral of $\mathbf{N}$ over S

$$
\begin{aligned}
\int_S \mathbf{N}\cdot d\mathbf{A} &= \iint_D \mathbf{N}\cdot\mathbf{n}\,dA = \iint_D \frac{\mathbf{n}}{\|\mathbf{n}\|}\cdot\mathbf{n}\,dA = \iint_D \frac{\mathbf{n}\cdot\mathbf{n}}{\|\mathbf{n}\|}\,dA \\
&= \iint_D \frac{\|\mathbf{n}\|^2}{\|\mathbf{n}\|}\,dA = \iint_D \|\mathbf{n}\|\,dA = \mathcal{A}
\end{aligned}
$$

This says that the surface integral of the standard unit normal vector field $\mathbf{N}$ over S is equal to the area $\mathcal{A}$ of S. The calculations for this show that $\mathbf{N}\cdot d\mathbf{A} = \|\mathbf{n}\|\,dA = d\mathcal{A}$ (heuristically). Thus, if ψ is a scalar field on S, then

$$\psi\mathbf{N}\cdot d\mathbf{A} = \psi\|\mathbf{n}\|\,dA = \psi\,d\mathcal{A}$$

Again, this is just heuristic pedagogy for the sake of symbolism. It does, however, suggest that integrating the vector field $\psi\mathbf{N}$ along C will be a good definition of the scalar integral of ψ over S. We make this definition as follows.

DEFINITION 14.4.2 (Surface Integrals of Scalar Fields)

Suppose S is a surface parametrized by $\mathbf{r}:D\to\mathbb{R}^3$ and $\psi:D\to\mathbb{R}$ is a scalar field on S. Then the surface integral of ψ over S, denoted by $\int_S \psi\,d\mathcal{A}$, is defined by

$$\int_S \psi\,d\mathcal{A} \equiv \int_S \psi\mathbf{N}\cdot d\mathbf{A} = \iint_D \psi(u,v)\|\mathbf{n}(u,v)\|\,dA \qquad (14.4.3)$$

Total Mass of a Thin Shell: A standard application of the scalar surface integral is in the computation of the total mass of a thin shell which is formed in the shape of a surface S. Letting $\rho : D \to \mathbb{R}$ be the mass density function (mass per unit area), then the total mass of the shell is

$$M = \int_S \rho \, d\mathcal{A} \qquad (14.4.4)$$

Example 14.4.2 (Calculating the Total Mass of a Shell)

Problem: For the following parametrized surfaces S, calculate the total mass of a thin shell formed in the shape S and having mass density ρ.

$$\mathbf{r} = \langle\, u^3 v^3,\, 3v - v^3,\, 3 - 3v^2\, \rangle, \quad \rho = 1 - v,$$

for (u, v) in $D = [0, 1] \times [0, 1]$

Solution: First compute the partial derivatives of $\mathbf{r}$:

$$\mathbf{r}_u = \langle\, 3u^2 v^3,\, 0,\, 0\, \rangle$$
$$\mathbf{r}_v = \langle\, 3u^3 v^2,\, 3 - 3v^2,\, -6v\, \rangle$$

Then the normal vector is

$$\mathbf{n} = \mathbf{r}_u \times \mathbf{r}_v = \begin{vmatrix} \mathbf{i} & \mathbf{j} & \mathbf{k} \\ 3u^2 v^3 & 0 & 0 \\ 3u^3 v^2 & 3 - 3v^2 & -6v \end{vmatrix} = \langle 0,\, 18u^2 v^4,\, 9u^2 v^3 (1 - v^2) \rangle$$

Then, the square of the length of $\mathbf{n}$ is

$$\begin{aligned} \|\mathbf{n}\|^2 &= \left(18u^2 v^4\right)^2 + \left[9u^2 v^3 (1 - v^2)\right]^2 = \left(9u^2 v^3\right)^2 (2v)^2 + \left[9u^2 v^3 (1 - v^2)\right]^2 \\ &= (9u^2 v^3)^2 \left[4v^2 + (1 - v^2)^2\right] = (9u^2 v^3)^2 \left[4v^2 + v^4 - 2v^2 + 1\right] \\ &= (9u^2 v^3)^2 \, (v^2 + 1)^2 \end{aligned}$$

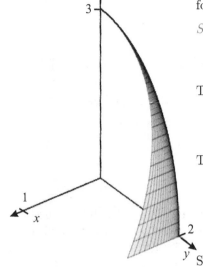

Figure 14.4.3: *An archway.*

So,

$$\|\mathbf{n}\| = 9u^2 v^3 (v^2 + 1)$$

Thus, the mass of the shell is

$$\begin{aligned} M &= \int_S \rho \, d\mathcal{A} = \int_D \rho(u, v) \|\mathbf{n}(u, v)\| \, dA = \int_0^1 \int_0^1 (1 - v)\, 9u^2 v^3 (v^2 + 1)\, du\, dv \\ &= \int_0^1 (1 - v) \left[3u^3\right]\Big|_0^1 v^3 (v^2 + 1)\, dv = \int_0^1 (1 - v) 3v^3 (v^2 + 1)\, dv \\ &= \int_0^1 3(1 - v)(v^5 + v^3)\, dv = 3 \int_0^1 (v^5 + v^3 - v^6 - v^4)\, dv \\ &= 3\left(\tfrac{1}{6} v^6 + \tfrac{1}{4} v^4 - \tfrac{1}{7} v^7 - \tfrac{1}{5} v^5\right)\Big|_0^1 = 3\left(\tfrac{1}{6} + \tfrac{1}{4} - \tfrac{1}{7} - \tfrac{1}{5}\right) \\ &= 3\left(\tfrac{5}{12} - \tfrac{12}{35}\right) = \frac{31}{140} \end{aligned}$$

Surface Integrals for Vector Fields in Space

A common situation for the use of surface integrals is where there is a force field $\mathbf{F}$ on an open set in space and you want to measure the flux across an number of different surfaces S in space. This situation reduces to that which we have already discussed — just restrict $\mathbf{F}$ to S to a get a force field on S.

Specifically, suppose $\mathbf{F} : U \to \mathbb{R}^3$ is a vector field on an open set U in $\mathbb{R}^3$. If S is a surface which lies in U and has parametrization $\mathbf{r} : D \to \mathbb{R}^3$, then the composite function

$$\widetilde{\mathbf{F}} \equiv \mathbf{F} \circ \mathbf{r} : D \to \mathbb{R}^3$$

is a vector field on S, called the *restriction* of $\mathbf{F}$ to S. Thus,

$$\widetilde{\mathbf{F}}(u,v) = \mathbf{F}(\mathbf{r}(u,v))) = \mathbf{F}(f(u,v), g(u,v), h(u,v))$$

is the vector on the surface at the point $P(u,v) = \mathbf{r}(u,v)$. It will be convenient, notationally, to identify $\mathbf{F}$ with its restriction, i.e., $\mathbf{F} = \widetilde{\mathbf{F}}$. Then, the surface integral $\int_D \mathbf{F} \cdot d\mathbf{A}$ looks the same even though its computation involves the extra step of computing the composite function $\mathbf{F} = \mathbf{F} \circ \mathbf{r}$. The following is a formal definition of this important concept.

DEFINITION 14.4.3 (Surface Integrals of Vector Fields - Part 2)

Suppose $\mathbf{F} : U \to \mathbb{R}^3$ is a vector field on an open set U in $\mathbb{R}^3$ and S is a surface in U parametrized by $\mathbf{r} : D \to \mathbb{R}^3$. Then the surface integral of $\mathbf{F}$ over S, denoted by $\int_S \mathbf{F} \cdot d\mathbf{A}$, is defined by

$$\int_S \mathbf{F} \cdot d\mathbf{A} \equiv \iint_D \mathbf{F}(\mathbf{r}(u,v)) \cdot \mathbf{n}(u,v) \, dA \qquad (14.4.5)$$

Example 14.4.3 (Flux for Vector Fields in Space)

Problem: For the following vector fields $\mathbf{F} : \mathbb{R}^3 \to \mathbb{R}^3$ and parametrized surfaces S, calculate the surface integral $\mathcal{F} = \int_S \mathbf{F} \cdot d\mathbf{A}$.

Part (a)

   $\mathbf{F} = \langle\, x, y, z \,\rangle$ (the standard radial field)

   $\mathbf{r} = \langle\, a\cos\theta, a\sin\theta, z \,\rangle$, (θ, z) in $D = [0, 2\pi] \times [0, h]$ (a cylinder)

Solution Part(a): First compute the partial derivatives of $\mathbf{r}$:

$$\mathbf{r}_\theta = \langle\, -a\sin\theta, a\cos\theta, 0 \,\rangle \qquad \mathbf{r}_z = \langle\, 0, 0, 1 \,\rangle$$

So, the normal vector is

$$\mathbf{n} = \mathbf{r}_\theta \times \mathbf{r}_\phi = \begin{vmatrix} \mathbf{i} & \mathbf{j} & \mathbf{k} \\ -a\sin\theta & a\cos\theta & 0 \\ 0 & 0 & 1 \end{vmatrix} = \langle\, a\cos\theta, a\sin\theta, 0 \,\rangle$$

The restriction of $\mathbf{F}$ to the cylinder is

$$\mathbf{F} \circ \mathbf{r} = \langle\, a\cos\theta, a\sin\theta, z \,\rangle,$$

So, that

$$\begin{aligned} (\mathbf{F} \circ \mathbf{r}) \cdot \mathbf{n} &= \langle\, a\cos\theta, a\sin\theta, z \,\rangle \cdot \langle\, a\cos\theta, a\sin\theta, 0 \,\rangle \\ &= a^2\cos^2\theta + a^2\sin^2\theta = a^2 \end{aligned}$$

This gives the surface integral

$$\int_S \mathbf{F} \cdot d\mathbf{A} = \iint_D \mathbf{F}(\mathbf{r}(\theta, z)) \cdot \mathbf{n}(\theta, z) \, dA = \int_0^h \int_0^{2\pi} a^2 \, d\theta \, dz = 2\pi a^2 h$$

Part (b) Consider the electric field generated by a point charge at the origin

$$\mathbf{F} = \frac{q}{(x^2 + y^2 + z^2)^{3/2}} \langle\, x, y, z \,\rangle$$

Calculate the electric flux of the field through the sphere S of radius a centered at the origin. Assume S is parametrized by

$$\mathbf{r} = \langle\, a\sin\phi\cos\theta, a\sin\phi\sin\theta, a\cos\phi \,\rangle,$$

for (θ, ϕ) in $D = [0, 2\pi] \times [0, \pi]$.

Solution Part(b): First compute the partial derivatives of $\mathbf{r}$:

$$\mathbf{r}_\theta = \langle\, -a\sin\phi\sin\theta, a\sin\phi\cos\theta, 0 \,\rangle$$

$$\mathbf{r}_\phi = \langle\, a\cos\phi\cos\theta,\ a\cos\phi\sin\theta,\ -a\sin\phi \,\rangle$$

So, the normal vector is

$$\mathbf{n} = \mathbf{r}_\theta \times \mathbf{r}_\phi \;=\; \begin{vmatrix} \mathbf{i} & \mathbf{j} & \mathbf{k} \\ -a\sin\phi\sin\theta & a\sin\phi\cos\theta & 0 \\ a\cos\phi\cos\theta & a\cos\phi\sin\theta & -a\sin\phi \end{vmatrix}$$

$$= \;\langle\, -a^2\sin^2\phi\cos\theta,\ -a^2\sin^2\phi\sin\theta,\ -a^2\sin\phi\cos\phi \,\rangle$$

$$= \;(-a\sin\phi)\,\mathbf{r}$$

The computation says that the standard normal $\mathbf{n}$ to the sphere (with this parametrization) is directed inward, radially, toward the origin. NOTE: $\|\mathbf{r}\| = a$.

To calculate the restriction of

$$\mathbf{F} = \frac{q}{(x^2+y^2+z^2)^{3/2}}\,\langle\, x,\, y,\, z \,\rangle$$

to the sphere, substitute $x = a\sin\phi\cos\theta$, $y = a\sin\phi\sin\theta$, $z = a\cos\phi\,\rangle$ in the expression for $\mathbf{F}$ and use the computation:

$$x^2 + y^2 + z^2 = a^2\sin^2\phi\cos^2\theta + a^2\sin^2\phi\sin^2\theta + a^2\cos^2\phi = a^2,$$

Thus, we get

$$\mathbf{F}\circ\mathbf{r} = \frac{q}{a^3}\,\langle\, a\sin\phi\cos\theta,\ a\sin\phi\sin\theta,\ a\cos\phi \,\rangle = \frac{q}{a^3}\,\mathbf{r}$$

These results give

$$(\mathbf{F}\circ\mathbf{r})\cdot\mathbf{n} = \frac{q}{a^3}\,\mathbf{r}\cdot(-a\sin\phi)\,\mathbf{r} = -(\frac{q}{a^2}\sin\phi)\,(\mathbf{r}\cdot\mathbf{r}) = -(\frac{q}{a^2}\sin\phi)\,(a^2) = -q\sin\phi$$

This gives the surface integral

$$\int_S \mathbf{F}\cdot d\mathbf{A} \;=\; \iint_D \mathbf{F}(\mathbf{r}(\theta,\phi))\cdot\mathbf{n}(\theta,\phi)\,dA = -\int_0^\pi\int_0^{2\pi} q\sin\phi\,d\theta\,d\phi$$

$$= \;-\int_0^\pi 2\pi q\sin\phi\,d\phi = 2\pi q\cos\phi\,\Big|_0^\pi = -4\pi q$$

Surface Integrals for Scalar Fields in Space

Suppose $\psi: U \to \mathbb{R}^3$ is a scalar field on an open set U in $\mathbb{R}^3$. If S is a surface which lies in U and has parametrization $\mathbf{r}: D \to \mathbb{R}^3$, then the composite function

$$\widetilde{\psi} \equiv \psi\circ\mathbf{r}: D \to \mathbb{R}$$

is a scalar field on S, called the *restriction* of ψ to S. Thus, $\widetilde{\psi}(u,v) = \psi(\mathbf{r}(u,v))$ is number assigned to the point $P(u,v) = \mathbf{r}(u,v)$ on the surface. It will be convenient, notationally, to identify ψ with its restriction, i.e., $\psi = \widetilde{\psi}$. So, the surface integral is

$$\int_S \psi\,d\mathcal{A} \equiv \iint_D \psi(\mathbf{r}(u,v))\|\mathbf{n}(u,v)\|\,dA \qquad (14.4.6)$$

The notation on the left side of the equation is the same as before, but it is important to note that the computation on the right side involves the extra step of computing the composite function $\psi = \psi\circ\mathbf{r}$.

Example 14.4.4 (Surface Integrals for Scalar Fields in Space)

Problem: For the following scalar field ψ and parametrized surface S, calculate the surface integral $\int_S \psi\,d\mathcal{A}$.

$$\psi = y^{1/3}, \quad \mathbf{r} = \langle\, u^3v^2,\ v^3,\ 9v^5 - \tfrac{1}{20}v \,\rangle, \text{ for } (u,v) \text{ in } [0,1]\times[0,1].$$

Solution: Clearly, $\psi \circ \mathbf{r} = (v^3)^{1/3} = v$. Next, compute the partial derivatives of $\mathbf{r}$:

$$\mathbf{r}_u = \langle\, 3u^2 v^2,\, 0,\, 0 \,\rangle$$

$$\mathbf{r}_v = \langle\, 2u^3 v,\, 3v^2,\, 45v^4 - \tfrac{1}{20} \,\rangle$$

and the normal vector is

$$\mathbf{n} = \mathbf{r}_u \times \mathbf{r}_v = \begin{vmatrix} \mathbf{i} & \mathbf{j} & \mathbf{k} \\ 3u^2 v^2 & 0 & 0 \\ 2u^3 v & 3v^2 & 45v^4 - \tfrac{1}{20} \end{vmatrix} = \langle\, 0,\, \tfrac{3}{20}u^2 v^2 - 135u^2 v^6,\, 9u^2 v^4 \,\rangle$$

Then, the square of the length of $\mathbf{n}$ is

$$\begin{aligned}
\|\mathbf{n}\|^2 &= \left[\, \tfrac{3}{20}u^2 v^2 - 135u^2 v^6 \,\right]^2 + 81u^4 v^8 \\
&= \left[\, \tfrac{9}{400}u^4 v^4 - \tfrac{81}{2}u^4 v^8 + (135)^2 u^4 v^{12} \,\right] + 81u^4 v^8 \\
&= \left[\, \tfrac{9}{400}u^4 v^4 + \tfrac{81}{2}u^4 v^8 + (135)^2 u^4 v^{12} \,\right] = \left[\, \tfrac{3}{20}u^2 v^2 + 135u^2 v^6 \,\right]^2
\end{aligned}$$

Thus, the surface integral of ψ over S is

$$\begin{aligned}
\int_S \psi \, d\mathcal{A} &= \int_D \psi \|\mathbf{n}\| \, dA = \int_0^1 \int_0^1 v\left[\, \tfrac{3}{20}u^2 v^2 + 135u^2 v^6 \,\right] du\, dv \\
&= \int_0^1 \int_0^1 u^2 \left[\, \tfrac{3}{20}v^3 + 135v^7 \,\right] du\, dv \\
&= \int_0^1 u^2 \, du \int_0^1 \left[\, \tfrac{3}{20}v^3 + 135v^7 \,\right] dv = \tfrac{1}{3}u^3 \Big|_0^1 \left[\, \tfrac{3}{80}v^4 + \tfrac{135}{8}v^8 \,\right]\Big|_0^1 \\
&= \tfrac{1}{3}\left[\, \tfrac{3}{80} + \tfrac{8}{135} \,\right] = \tfrac{1}{80} + \tfrac{45}{8} = \frac{451}{80}
\end{aligned}$$

The Unit Normal Vector Notation for Surface Integrals

As mentioned in the discussion of work above, the quantity $\frac{\mathbf{F}\cdot\mathbf{n}}{\|\mathbf{n}\|} = \mathbf{F} \cdot \mathbf{N}$ is the component of force in the tangential direction. So we can write the surface integral in terms of the unit normal vector field $\mathbf{N}$:

$$\begin{aligned}
\int_S \mathbf{F} \cdot d\mathbf{A} &= \iint_D \mathbf{F} \cdot \mathbf{n} \, dA = \iint_D \mathbf{F} \cdot \frac{\mathbf{n}}{\|\mathbf{n}\|} \, \|\mathbf{n}\| \, dA \\
&= \iint_D \mathbf{F} \cdot \mathbf{N} \, \|\mathbf{n}\| \, dA = \int_S \mathbf{F} \cdot \mathbf{N} \, d\mathcal{A}
\end{aligned} \tag{14.4.7}$$

NOTE: This form of the surface integral using $\mathbf{N}$ and $d\mathcal{A} = \|\mathbf{n}\| dA$ is *not* one that you should use to compute a surface integral. (Because $\mathbf{N}$ is usually a pretty complicated expression.) Rather, this form is merely for geometrical/physical interpretation of the surface integral. For example it says that if $\mathbf{F}$ is everywhere tangent to S, i.e., if $\mathbf{F} \cdot \mathbf{N} = 0$, at all points on S, then there is no flux, $\mathcal{F} = 0$, across S.

Exercises: 14.4 (Surface Integrals)

Computing the Flux Across a Surface

In Exercises 1–6, for the given vector field $\mathbf{F}$ and the surface S parametrized by $\mathbf{r} : D \to \mathbb{R}^3$, find the flux $\mathcal{F} = \int_S \mathbf{F} \cdot d\mathbf{A}$ of $\mathbf{F}$ across S.

1. $\mathbf{F} = \langle v, 2u, -uv^2 \rangle$, $\mathbf{r} = \langle uv, u^2, v^2 \rangle$, $[0,1] \times [0,1]$

2. $\mathbf{F} = \langle u^2, 2v, u^2v^2 \rangle$, $\mathbf{r} = \langle u^2v, v^2, u^2 \rangle$, $[0,1] \times [0,1]$

3. $\mathbf{F} = \langle -t, -t\sin^2\theta, t \rangle$, $\mathbf{r} = \langle t^2\sin\theta, t^2\cos\theta, t \rangle$,
for (θ, t) in $[0, \pi] \times [0,1]$

4. $\mathbf{F} = \langle t\sin^2\theta, t, t \rangle$, $\mathbf{r} = \langle t^3\cos\theta, t^3\sin\theta, t \rangle$,
for (θ, t) in $[0, \pi] \times [0,1]$

5. $\mathbf{F} = \langle ue^t, u^2, t \rangle$, $\mathbf{r} = \langle ue^{-t}, u^2e^t, t \rangle$,
for (u, t) in $[0, \ln 2] \times [0,1]$

6. $\mathbf{F} = \langle ue^{-2t}, u^2, t \rangle$, $\mathbf{r} = \langle ue^{2t}, u^2e^{-2t}, t \rangle$,
for (u, t) in $[0, \ln 2] \times [0,1]$

Total Mass of a Thin Shell

In Exercises 7–14, compute the total mass of the thin shell with mass density $\rho : D \to \mathbb{R}$ and shaped in the form of the surface S parametrized by $\mathbf{r} : D \to \mathbb{R}^3$, where $D = [a, b] \times [c, d]$.

7. $\mathbf{r} = \langle u^3v^2, v^3, v - \frac{9}{20}v^5 \rangle$, $\rho = uv$, $[0,1] \times [0,1]$

8. $\mathbf{r} = \langle u^3v^2, v^3, 9v^5 - \frac{1}{20}v \rangle$, $\rho = uv$, $[0,1] \times [0,1]$

9. $\mathbf{r} = \langle u^5 + uv^2, v^3, v - \frac{9}{20}v^5 \rangle$, $\rho = u$, $[0,1] \times [0,1]$

10. $\mathbf{r} = \langle u^5 + uv^2, v^2, v^3 - \frac{1}{3}v \rangle$, $\rho = u$, $[0,1] \times [0,1]$

11. $\mathbf{r} = \langle u^3 + ue^{-v}, e^{-2v}, e^{2v} + \frac{1}{12}e^{-6v} \rangle$,
$\rho = e^v$, $[0,1] \times [0, \ln 2]$

12. $\mathbf{r} = \langle u^3 + ue^{-v}, e^v, \frac{1}{12}e^{3v} + e^{-v} \rangle$,
$\rho = e^v$, $[0,1] \times [0, \ln 2]$

13. $\mathbf{r} = \langle u^3 + u\sin\frac{v}{2}, v + \sin v, 1 - \cos v \rangle$, $[0,2] \times [0, \pi]$
$\rho = \sin\frac{v}{2}$, $[0,2] \times [0, \pi]$

14. $\mathbf{r} = \langle u^3 + u\cos\frac{v}{2}, v - \sin v, 1 - \cos v \rangle$, $[0,2] \times [0, \pi]$
$\rho = \sin\frac{v}{2}$, $[0,2] \times [0, \pi]$

Computing the Flux Across a Surface

In Exercises 15–20, for the given vector field $\mathbf{F}$ in space and the surface S parametrized by $\mathbf{r} : D \to \mathbb{R}^3$, find the flux $\mathcal{F} = \int_S \mathbf{F} \cdot d\mathbf{A}$ of $\mathbf{F}$ across S.

NOTE: If you computed the normal $\mathbf{n}$ for these surfaces in Section 13.2, you may use that result here.

15. $\mathbf{F} = \langle -y, x, z^2 \rangle$, $\mathbf{r} = \langle t\cos\theta, t\sin\theta, \theta \rangle$,
for (θ, t) in $[0, 4\pi] \times [0, 2]$.   (Helicoid)

16. $\mathbf{F} = \langle -y, x, z^2 \rangle$, $\mathbf{r} = \langle 2t\cos\theta, 2t\sin\theta, \frac{1}{2}\theta \rangle$,
for (θ, t) in $[0, 4\pi] \times [0, 2]$.   (Helicoid)

17. $\mathbf{F} = \langle y, x, xz \rangle$,
$\mathbf{r} = \langle 4\cos\theta, 3\sin\theta\cos\phi, 2\sin\theta\sin\phi \rangle$,
for (θ, ϕ) in $[0, \pi/2] \times [0, \pi/2]$.   (Hyperboloid)

18. $\mathbf{F} = \langle y, x, xz \rangle$,
$\mathbf{r} = \langle 3\sin\theta\cos\phi,], 4\cos\theta, 2\sin\theta\sin\phi \rangle$,
for (θ, ϕ) in $[0, \pi/2] \times [0, \pi/2]$.   (Hyperboloid)

19. $\mathbf{F} = \langle y, x^2, z \rangle$, $\mathbf{r} = \langle \frac{1}{3}u^3v^3, v - \frac{1}{3}v^3, 1 - v^2 \rangle$,
for (u, v) in $[0,1] \times [0,1]$.

20. $\mathbf{F} = \langle y, x^2, 0 \rangle$, $\mathbf{r} = \langle \frac{1}{3}u^3v^3, 5v^3 = \frac{5}{2}v^7, 2v^5 \rangle$,
for (u, v) in $[0,1] \times [0,1]$.

Surface Integrals for Scalar Fieds

In Exercises 21-22, for the given scalar field ψ and parametrized surface S, compute $\int_S \psi \, d\mathcal{A}$.

21. $\mathbf{r} = \langle u + u^3v^2, 5v^4, 4v^3 - \frac{5}{3}v^5 \rangle$,
$\psi = y^{1/2}$, $[0,1] \times [0,1]$

22. $\mathbf{r} = \langle u + u^3v^2, v^4, v^6 - \frac{1}{3}v^2 \rangle$,
$\psi = y^{1/2}$, $[0,1] \times [0,1]$

Calculus Concepts & Computation

14.5 Stokes' Theorem - Green's Theorem

This section presents two theorems that are further analogs of the Fundamental Theorem of Calculus (FTC). Section 14.3 showed you one analog of the FTC, called the Fundamental Theorem of Line Integrals (FTLI). It says that the line integral of a gradient vector field $\nabla\psi : U \to \mathbb{R}^3$ along a curve C can be computed by evaluation of ψ at the endpoints of C:

$$\int_C \nabla\psi \cdot d\mathbf{r} = \psi\Big|_P^Q = \psi(Q) - \psi(P) \qquad \text{(FTLI)},$$

where P and Q are the initial and terminal points of C. What could be the analog of this for surface integrals? The answer to this is *Stokes' Theorem* along with the special case of Stokes' Theorem which is known as *Green's Theorem*.

To motivate Stokes' Theorem, consider again the ordinary Fundamental Theorem of Calculus, written in the form:

$$\int_a^b \frac{dF}{dx}\, dx = F(x)\Big|_a^b = F(b) - F(a) \qquad \text{(FTC)}$$

Here we have the standard derivative operator $\frac{d}{dx}$ applied to the function F. Integrating this over the interval $I = [a, b]$ results in just evaluating F at the boundary points a and b of I. So, heuristically, for surface integrals, involving a vector field $\mathbf{F}$ and a surface S, the form of Stokes' Theorem should be something like this:

$$\int_S (\textit{differential operator } \mathbf{F}) \cdot d\mathbf{A} = \mathbf{F} \textit{ evaluated along the boundary } C \textit{ of } S,$$

Here *evaluated along the boundary C of S* must mean the line integral along C. The *differential operator* could be either the curl operator or divergence operator. The best guess would be to choose the curl, since $\operatorname{curl}\mathbf{F}$ is a vector field, while $\operatorname{div}\mathbf{F}$ is a scalar field. Thus, with a little bit of guessing you might come up with the following:

$$\int_S \operatorname{curl}\mathbf{F} \cdot d\mathbf{A} = \int_C \mathbf{F} \cdot d\mathbf{r} \qquad \text{(Stokes' Theorem)}$$

This is indeed correct and is a wonderful way to relate surface integrals to line integrals. What makes it work is the use of $\operatorname{curl}\mathbf{F}$ and the "curve" C which is the boundary of the surface S.

Before stating Stokes' Theorem formally, we must consider the notion of the boundary of a surface and for this we first need some discussion about *piecewise differentiable* curves.

Piecewise Differentiable Curves

A set C in $\mathbb{R}^3$ is called a *piecewise differentiable curve* if it is the set-theoretic union

$$C \equiv C_1 \cup C_2 \cup \cdots \cup C_n \qquad (14.5.1)$$

of curves $C_1, C_2, \ldots, C_n$, with each C_i parametrized by a differentiable parameter map $\mathbf{r}_i : [a_i, b_i] \to \mathbb{R}^3$. There is similar definition of piecewise differentiable curves C in $\mathbb{R}^2$. NOTE: We do *not* require that a piecewise differentiable curve be parametrized.

Line Integrals for Piecewise Differentiable Curves

The definition of the line integral of a vector field $\mathbf{F}$ along a piecewise differentiable

curve C is

$$\int_C \mathbf{F} \cdot d\mathbf{r} \equiv \int_{C_1} \mathbf{F} \cdot d\mathbf{r} + \int_{C_2} \mathbf{F} \cdot d\mathbf{r} + \cdots + \int_{C_n} \mathbf{F} \cdot d\mathbf{r} \qquad (14.5.2)$$

As mentioned, the concept of piecewise differentiable curves is needed for the discussion of the *boundary* ∂S of a surface S. The simplest case of this is where the parameter domain for S is a rectangle $D = [a, b] \times [c, d]$.

Boundary Curves

Figure 14.5.1 shows a surface S with rectangular parameter domain $D = [a, b] \times [c, d]$ and parameter map $\mathbf{r} : D \to \mathbb{R}^3$. If we restrict $\mathbf{r}$ to the four bounding sides of the rectangle D, we get parametrizations of the four curves C_1, C_2, C_3, C_4 that form the boundary of the surface S. However: We need to change two if these restrictions so that the curves C_3, C_4 are directed as shown in the figure. This is necessary for the line integral in Stokes Theorem to give the correct value. More precisely, the following is the definition of the parameter maps for the curves C_1, C_2, C_3, C_4 which comprise the boundary of S.

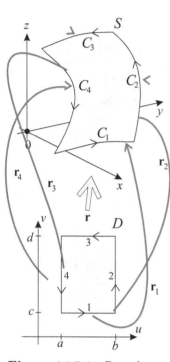

Figure 14.5.1: *Boundary curves* C_1, C_2, C_3, C_4.

DEFINITION 14.5.1 (The Boundary of a Surface S)

Suppose $\mathbf{r} : D = [a,b] \times [c,d] \to \mathbb{R}^3$ *is a (differentiable) parametrization of a surface S. Let* C_1, C_2, C_3, C_4 *be the curves with the following parametrizations.*

(1) $\mathbf{r}_1 : [a,b] \to \mathbb{R}^3$ *given by* $\mathbf{r}_1(u) = \mathbf{r}(u,c)$,   *for u in* $[a,b]$

(2) $\mathbf{r}_2 : [c,d] \to \mathbb{R}^3$ *given by* $\mathbf{r}_2(v) = \mathbf{r}(b,v)$,   *for v in* $[c,d]$

(3) $\mathbf{r}_3 : [a,b] \to \mathbb{R}^3$ *given by* $\mathbf{r}_3(u) = \mathbf{r}(a+b-u,d)$,   *for u in* $[a,b]$

(4) $\mathbf{r}_4 : [c,d] \to \mathbb{R}^3$ *given by* $\mathbf{r}_4(v) = \mathbf{r}(a,c+d-v)$,   *for v in* $[c,d]$

Then the boundary of *S is the piecewise differentiable curve*

$$C = \partial S = C_1 \cup C_2 \cup C_3 \cup C_4$$

NOTE 1: The boundary maps $\mathbf{r}_1, \mathbf{r}_2$ are just the restrictions of $\mathbf{r}$ to sides 1 and 2 of the rectangular parameter domain. However, the boundary maps $\mathbf{r}_3, \mathbf{r}_4$ are the "reversals" of the restrictions of $\mathbf{r}$ to sides 3 and 4. See Figure 14.5.1.

NOTE 2: To apply Stokes' theorem, in some examples below, you will have to write out explicitly the formulas for the boundary maps $\mathbf{r}_1, \mathbf{r}_1, \mathbf{r}_3, \mathbf{r}_4$. It is a common mistake to forget to do the "reversals" when doing $\mathbf{r}_3, \mathbf{r}_4$. The next example shows you how to do this (correctly).

Example 14.5.1 (Writing Out the Boundary Map Parametrizations)

Problem: For the given parametrization of a surface S, write out the parametrization formulas for the four boundary maps $\mathbf{r}_1, \mathbf{r}_2, \mathbf{r}_3, \mathbf{r}_4$ for ∂S.

Part(a): $\mathbf{r}(u, v) = \langle u, u^2 v, v^2 \rangle$, for (u, v) in $[1, 2] \times [1, 3]$

Solution Part(a): First write out the four restriction of $\mathbf{r}$ to the sides of the rectangular parameter domain. See Figure 14.5.2.

$$\mathbf{r}(u, 1) = \langle u, u^2, 1 \rangle, \text{ for } u \text{ in } [1, 2]$$
$$\mathbf{r}(2, v) = \langle 2, 4v, v^2 \rangle, \text{ for } v \text{ in } [1, 3]$$
$$\mathbf{r}(u, 3) = \langle u, 3u^2, 9 \rangle, \text{ for } u \text{ in } [1, 2]$$
$$\mathbf{r}(1, v) = \langle 1, v, v^2 \rangle, \text{ for } v \text{ in } [1, 3]$$

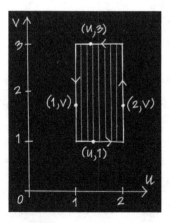

Figure 14.5.2:
A parameter domain.

Then, the formulas for $\mathbf{r}_1, \mathbf{r}_2$ come from the first two of the above:

$$\mathbf{r}_1(u) = \langle u, u^2, 1 \rangle, \text{ for } u \text{ in } [1, 2]$$
$$\mathbf{r}_2(v) = \langle 2, 4v, v^2 \rangle, \text{ for } v \text{ in } [1, 3]$$

and the formulas for $\mathbf{r}_3, \mathbf{r}_4$ come from "reversing" the second two of the above:

$$\mathbf{r}_3(u) = \langle 3 - u, 3(3 - u)^2, 9 \rangle, \text{ for } u \text{ in } [1, 2]$$
$$\mathbf{r}_4(v) = \langle 1, 4 - v, (4 - v)^2 \rangle, \text{ for } v \text{ in } [1, 3]$$

Part(b): $\mathbf{r}(\theta, z) = \langle \cos\theta, \sin\theta, z \rangle$, for (θ, z) in $[0, \pi] \times [1, 4]$ (*a half cylinder*)

Solution Part(b): First write out the four restriction of $\mathbf{r}$ to the sides of the rectangular parameter domain:

$$\mathbf{r}(\theta, 1) = \langle \cos\theta, \sin\theta, 1 \rangle, \text{ for } \theta \text{ in } [0, \pi]$$
$$\mathbf{r}(\pi, z) = \langle -1, 0, z \rangle, \text{ for } z \text{ in } [1, 4]$$
$$\mathbf{r}(\theta, 4) = \langle \cos\theta, \sin\theta, 4 \rangle, \text{ for } \theta \text{ in } [0, \pi]$$
$$\mathbf{r}(0, z) = \langle 1, 0, z \rangle, \text{ for } z \text{ in } [1, 4]$$

Then, the formulas for $\mathbf{r}_1, \mathbf{r}_2$ come from the first two of the above:

$$\mathbf{r}_1(\theta) = \langle \cos\theta, \sin\theta, 1 \rangle, \text{ for } \theta \text{ in } [0, \pi]$$
$$\mathbf{r}_2(z) = \langle -1, 0, z \rangle, \text{ for } z \text{ in } [1, 4]$$

and the formulas for $\mathbf{r}_3, \mathbf{r}_4$ come from "reversing" the second two of the above:

$$\mathbf{r}_3(\theta) = \langle \cos(\pi - \theta), \sin(\pi - \theta), 4 \rangle, \text{ for } \theta \text{ in } [0, \pi]$$
$$\mathbf{r}_4(z) = \langle 1, 0, 5 - z \rangle, \text{ for } z \text{ in } [1, 4]$$

A sketch of the boundary curves C_1, C_2, C_3, C_4 for this half cylinder is shown in Figure 14.5.3.

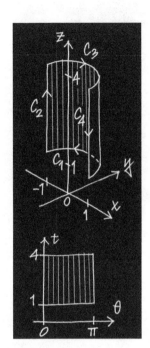

Figure 14.5.3:
*The boundary of
a half cylinder.*

We can now state a fairly general version of Stokes' Theorem. As you might expect, the concept of the boundary $C = \partial S$ of a surface S plays a big role in this theorem.

THEOREM 14.5.1 (Stokes' Theorem)

Suppose $\mathbf{F} : U \to \mathbb{R}^3$ *is a vector field on an open set U in $\mathbb{R}^3$ and S is a surface in U with parametrization* $\mathbf{r} : [a, b] \times [c, d] \to \mathbb{R}^3$. *Let* $C = \partial S$ *be the boundary of S. Then*

$$\int_S \operatorname{curl} \mathbf{F} \cdot d\mathbf{A} = \int_C \mathbf{F} \cdot d\mathbf{r} \qquad (14.5.3)$$

NOTE 1: The proof of this version of Stokes' Theorem is fairly easy and is given at the end of this section,

NOTE 2: The theorem also applies to vector fields $\mathbf{F}$ in the plane (i.e., the x-y-plane) and is known as *Green's Theorem*. We will discuss more about Green's Theorem shortly.

NOTE 3: The above version of Stokes' Theorem is for rectangular parameter domains $D = [a, b] \times [c, d]$. There are more general versions of Stokes' theorem (for example, allowing D to be a more general domain) and some of these will be discussed in the Exercises.

There are many consequences and uses of Stokes' Theorem (which are discussed in Section 14.7), but here we concentrate on understanding how and why it works. For this, we look at a number of examples, where we (1) verify the theorem works, (2) use the theorem to more simply compute line integrals, and (3) use the theorem to more simply compute surface integrals.

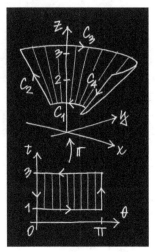

Figure 14.5.4:
A parametrization of half of a frustum of a cone.

Example 14.5.2 (Verifying Stokes' Theorem - CONE)

Problem: Verify that Stokes' Theorem holds for the vector field

$$\mathbf{F} = \langle\, -xy,\, xy,\, z^2\,\rangle \text{ on } U = \mathbb{R}^3$$

and the surface S parametrized by

$$\mathbf{r}(\theta, t) = \langle\, t\cos\theta,\, t\sin\theta,\, t\,\rangle, \qquad (\theta, t) \text{ in } [0, \pi] \times [1, 3]$$

NOTE: S is the surface bounding half of a frustum of a cone. See Figure 14.5.4.

Solution: First compute the curl of $\mathbf{F}$:

$$\operatorname{curl}\mathbf{F} = \begin{vmatrix} \mathbf{i} & \mathbf{j} & \mathbf{k} \\ \frac{\partial}{\partial x} & \frac{\partial}{\partial y} & \frac{\partial}{\partial z} \\ -xy & xy & z^2 \end{vmatrix} = \langle\, 0,\, 0,\, x + y\,\rangle$$

Then

$$\operatorname{curl}\mathbf{F} \circ \mathbf{r} = \langle\, 0,\, 0,\, t(\cos\theta + \sin\theta)\,\rangle$$

The partials of $\mathbf{r}$ are

$$\mathbf{r}_\theta = \langle\, -t\sin\theta,\, t\cos\theta,\, 0\,\rangle, \qquad \mathbf{r}_t = \langle\, \cos\theta,\, \sin\theta,\, 1\,\rangle$$

and so

$$\mathbf{n} = \mathbf{r}_\theta \times \mathbf{r}_t = \begin{vmatrix} \mathbf{i} & \mathbf{j} & \mathbf{k} \\ -t\sin\theta & t\cos\theta & 0 \\ \cos\theta & \sin\theta & 1 \end{vmatrix} = \langle\, t\cos\theta,\, t\sin\theta,\, -t\,\rangle$$

Consequently

$$\operatorname{curl}\mathbf{F} \cdot \mathbf{n} = \langle\, 0,\, 0,\, t(\cos\theta + \sin\theta)\,\rangle \cdot \langle\, t\cos\theta,\, t\sin\theta,\, -t\,\rangle = -t^2(\cos\theta + \sin\theta)$$

Thus, the surface integral of the curl is

$$\int_S \operatorname{curl}\mathbf{F} \cdot d\mathbf{A} = \int_0^\pi \int_1^3 -t^2(\cos\theta + \sin\theta)\, dt\, d\theta = \int_0^\pi (\cos\theta + \sin\theta)\, d\theta \int_1^3 -t^2\, dt$$

$$= \left(\, \sin\theta - \cos\theta\,\right)\Big|_0^\pi \left(\, -\tfrac{1}{3}t^3\,\right)\Big|_1^3 = 2\left(\, -\tfrac{26}{3}\,\right) = -\tfrac{52}{3}$$

Next we compute the four line integrals along the curves C_1, C_2, C_3, C_4. For this, it may help to view the movie created by `dboundaryplot` which shows the boundary of S being plotted dynamically. See Figure 14.5.5. For C_1, the parameter map is

$$\mathbf{r}_1(\theta) = \mathbf{r}(\theta, 1) = \langle\, \cos\theta,\, \sin\theta,\, 1\,\rangle,$$

for θ in $[0, \pi]$. So,

$$\mathbf{F} \circ \mathbf{r}_1 = \langle\, -\cos\theta\sin\theta,\, \cos\theta\sin\theta,\, 1\,\rangle \quad \text{and} \quad \mathbf{r}_1' = \langle\, -\sin\theta,\, \cos\theta,\, 0\,\rangle\,.$$

Thus, the line integral along C_1 is

$$\int_{C_1} \mathbf{F} \cdot d\mathbf{r} = \int_0^\pi (\mathbf{F} \circ \mathbf{r}_1) \cdot \mathbf{r}_1'\, d\theta = \int_0^\pi \left(\, \sin^2\theta\cos\theta + \cos^2\theta\sin\theta\,\right) d\theta$$

$$= \left(\, \tfrac{1}{3}\sin^3\theta - \tfrac{1}{3}\cos^3\theta\,\right)\Big|_0^\pi = \tfrac{2}{3}$$

For C_2, the parameter map is

$$\mathbf{r}_2(t) = \mathbf{r}(\pi, t) = \langle\, -t,\, 0,\, t\,\rangle,$$

for t in $[1, 3]$. So,

$$\mathbf{F} \circ \mathbf{r}_2 = \langle\, 0,\, 0,\, t^2\,\rangle \quad \text{and} \quad \mathbf{r}_2' = \langle\, -1,\, 0,\, 1\,\rangle.$$

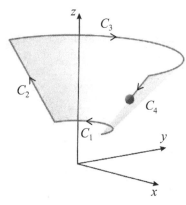

Figure 14.5.5: *The 18th frame in a dynamic plot of the boundary using* `dboundaryplot`.

Thus, the line integral along C_2 is

$$\int_{C_2} \mathbf{F} \cdot d\mathbf{r} = \int_1^3 (\mathbf{F} \circ \mathbf{r}_2) \cdot \mathbf{r}_2' \, d\theta = \int_1^3 t^2 \, dt = \tfrac{1}{3}t^3 \Big|_1^3 = \frac{26}{3}$$

For C_3, the parameter map is

$$\mathbf{r}_3(\theta) = \mathbf{r}(\pi - \theta, 3) = \langle\, 3\cos(\pi - \theta),\, 3\sin(\pi - \theta),\, 3\,\rangle = \langle\, -3\cos\theta,\, 3\sin\theta,\, 3\,\rangle,$$

for θ in $[0, \pi]$. Here we used the trig identities $\cos(a - b) = \cos a \cos b + \sin a \sin b$ and $\sin(a - b) = \sin a \cos b - \sin b \cos a$. Then

$$\mathbf{F} \circ \mathbf{r}_3 = \langle\, 9\cos\theta\sin\theta,\, -9\cos\theta\sin\theta,\, 9\,\rangle \quad \text{and} \quad \mathbf{r}_3' = \langle\, 3\sin\theta,\, 3\cos\theta,\, 0\,\rangle.$$

Thus, the line integral along C_3 is

$$\int_{C_3} \mathbf{F} \cdot d\mathbf{r} \;=\; \int_0^\pi (\mathbf{F} \circ \mathbf{r}_3) \cdot \mathbf{r}_3' \, d\theta = \int_0^\pi 27\big(\, \sin^2\theta\cos\theta - \cos^2\theta\sin\theta\,\big)d\theta$$

$$=\; 27\big(\tfrac{1}{3}\sin^3\theta + \tfrac{1}{3}\cos^3\theta\,\big)\Big|_0^\pi = -\frac{54}{3}$$

For C_4, the parameter map is

$$\mathbf{r}_4(t) = \mathbf{r}(0, 4 - t) = \langle\, 4 - t,\, 0,\, 4 - t\,\rangle,$$

for t in $[1, 3]$. So,

$$\mathbf{F} \circ \mathbf{r}_4 = \langle\, 0,\, 0,\, (4 - t)^2\,\rangle \quad \text{and} \quad \mathbf{r}_4' = \langle\, -1,\, 0,\, -1\,\rangle.$$

Thus, the line integral along C_4 is

$$\int_{C_4} \mathbf{F} \cdot d\mathbf{r} = \int_1^3 (\mathbf{F} \circ \mathbf{r}_4) \cdot \mathbf{r}_4' \, d\theta = \int_1^3 -(4 - t)^2 \, dt = \tfrac{1}{3}(4 - t)^3 \Big|_1^3 = -\frac{26}{3}$$

Putting together all these results gives

$$\int_S \operatorname{curl} \mathbf{F} \cdot d\mathbf{A} \;=\; -\tfrac{52}{3}$$

$$\int_C \mathbf{F} \cdot d\mathbf{r} \;\equiv\; \int_{C_1} \mathbf{F} \cdot d\mathbf{r} + \int_{C_2} \mathbf{F} \cdot d\mathbf{r} + \int_{C_3} \mathbf{F} \cdot d\mathbf{r} + \int_{C_4} \mathbf{F} \cdot d\mathbf{r}$$

$$=\; \tfrac{2}{3} + \tfrac{26}{3} - \tfrac{54}{3} - \tfrac{26}{3} = -\tfrac{52}{3}$$

Thus, $\int_S \operatorname{curl} \mathbf{F} \cdot d\mathbf{A} = \int_C \mathbf{F} \cdot d\mathbf{r}$ as predicted by Stokes' Theorem.

Example 14.5.3 (Verifying Stokes' Theorem - MÖBIUS STRIP)

Problem: Verify that Stokes' Theorem holds for the vector field

$$\mathbf{F} = \langle\, -y,\, x,\, 0\,\rangle \text{ on } U = \mathbb{R}^3$$

and the Möbius strip S parametrized by

$$\mathbf{r}(\theta, t) = \langle\, R\cos\theta,\, R\sin\theta,\, t\sin\tfrac{\theta}{2}\,\rangle,$$

where $R \equiv 2 + t\cos\tfrac{\theta}{2}$ and (θ, t) in $[0, 2\pi] \times [-1, 1]$.

NOTE: This is the parametrization of the Möbius strip used in Section 13.2. See Figure 14.5.6.

Solution: First compute the curl of $\mathbf{F}$:

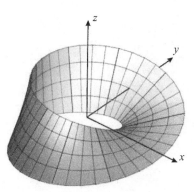

Figure 14.5.6: *A Möbius Strip.*

$$\operatorname{curl} \mathbf{F} = \begin{vmatrix} \mathbf{i} & \mathbf{j} & \mathbf{k} \\ \frac{\partial}{\partial x} & \frac{\partial}{\partial y} & \frac{\partial}{\partial z} \\ -y & x & 0 \end{vmatrix} = \langle\, 0,\, 0,\, 2\,\rangle$$

We can use the calculation of the standard normal $\mathbf{n}$ from Equation (13.2.21) in Section 13.2. It is:

$$\mathbf{n} = \langle\, -\tfrac{t}{2}\sin\theta + R\sin\tfrac{\theta}{2}\cos\theta,\ \tfrac{t}{2}\cos\theta + R\sin\tfrac{\theta}{2}\sin\theta,\ -R\cos\tfrac{\theta}{2}\,\rangle$$

From this and with $R = 2 + t\cos\tfrac{\theta}{2}$, we get

$$\operatorname{curl}\mathbf{F}\cdot\mathbf{n} = -2R\cos\tfrac{\theta}{2} = -2\big(2 + t\cos\tfrac{\theta}{2}\big)\cos\tfrac{\theta}{2} = -\big(4\cos\tfrac{\theta}{2} + 2t\cos^2\tfrac{\theta}{2}\big)$$

Thus, the surface integral of the curl is

$$
\begin{aligned}
\int_S \operatorname{curl}\mathbf{F}\cdot d\mathbf{A} &= -\int_0^{2\pi}\int_{-1}^{1}\big(4\cos\tfrac{\theta}{2} + 2t\cos^2\tfrac{\theta}{2}\big)\,dt\,d\theta \\
&= -\int_0^{2\pi}\big(4t\cos\tfrac{\theta}{2} + t^2\cos^2\tfrac{\theta}{2}\big)\Big|_{-1}^{1}\,d\theta = -\int_0^{2\pi} 8\cos\tfrac{\theta}{2}\,d\theta \\
&= -16\sin\tfrac{\theta}{2}\Big|_0^{2\pi} = 0
\end{aligned}
$$

Next we compute the four line integrals along the curves C_1, C_2, C_3, C_4.

For C_1, the parameter map is

$$\mathbf{r}_1(\theta) = \mathbf{r}(\theta, -1) = \langle\, A\cos\theta,\ A\sin\theta,\ -\sin\tfrac{\theta}{2}\,\rangle,$$

for θ in $[0, 2\pi]$ and $A \equiv 2 - \cos\tfrac{\theta}{2}$. So,

$$\mathbf{F}\circ\mathbf{r}_1 = \langle\, -A\sin\theta,\ A\cos\theta,\ 0\,\rangle$$

and

$$\mathbf{r}_1' = \langle\, A'\cos\theta - A\sin\theta,\ A'\sin\theta + A\cos\theta,\ -\tfrac{1}{2}\cos\tfrac{\theta}{2}\,\rangle$$

Then

$$
\begin{aligned}
(\mathbf{F}\circ\mathbf{r}_1)\cdot\mathbf{r}_1' &= -A\sin\theta\big(A'\cos\theta - A\sin\theta\big) + A\cos\theta\big(A'\sin\theta + A\cos\theta\big) \\
&= A^2 \qquad\qquad\qquad\qquad\qquad\qquad\qquad\qquad\qquad (14.5.4)\\
&= \big(2 - \cos\tfrac{\theta}{2}\big)^2 = 4 - 4\cos\tfrac{\theta}{2} + \cos^2\tfrac{\theta}{2} \\
&= 4 - 4\cos\tfrac{\theta}{2} + \tfrac{1}{2} + \tfrac{1}{2}\cos\theta \\
&= \tfrac{9}{2} - 4\cos\tfrac{\theta}{2} + \tfrac{1}{2}\cos\theta
\end{aligned}
$$

Thus, the line integral along C_1 is

$$\int_{C_1}\mathbf{F}\cdot d\mathbf{r} = \int_0^{2\pi}(\mathbf{F}\circ\mathbf{r}_1)\cdot\mathbf{r}_1'\,d\theta = \int_0^{2\pi} A^2\,d\theta \qquad\qquad (14.5.5)$$

$$= \int_0^{2\pi}\big(\tfrac{9}{2} - 4\cos\tfrac{\theta}{2} + \tfrac{1}{2}\cos\theta\big)d\theta = \big(\tfrac{9}{2}\theta - 8\sin\tfrac{\theta}{2} + \tfrac{1}{2}\sin\theta\big)\Big|_0^{2\pi} = 9\pi$$

For C_2, recall that $R = 2 + t\cos\tfrac{\theta}{2}$ and so the parameter map is

$$\mathbf{r}_2(t) = \mathbf{r}(2\pi, t) = \langle\, R(2\pi, t), 0, 0\,\rangle = \langle\, 2 - t, 0, 0\,\rangle,$$

for t in $[-1, 1]$. Then,

$$\mathbf{F}\circ\mathbf{r}_2 = \langle\, 0, 2 - t, 0\,\rangle \quad\text{and}\quad \mathbf{r}_2' = \langle\, -1, 0, 0\,\rangle.$$

Thus, the line integral along C_2 is zero

$$\int_{C_2}\mathbf{F}\cdot d\mathbf{r} = \int_{-1}^{1}(\mathbf{F}\circ\mathbf{r}_2)\cdot\mathbf{r}_2'\,d = \int_{-1}^{1} 0\,dt = 0$$

For C_3, the parameter map is $\mathbf{r}_3(\theta) = \mathbf{r}(2\pi - \theta, 1)$. To compute this we use the angle addition trig identities to get

$$\cos(2\pi - \theta) = \cos\theta \quad\text{and}\quad \sin(2\pi - \theta) = -\sin\theta$$

$$\sin \tfrac{2\pi-\theta}{2} = \sin(\pi - \tfrac{\theta}{2}) = \sin \tfrac{\theta}{2} \quad \text{and} \quad \cos \tfrac{2\pi-\theta}{2} = \cos(\pi - \tfrac{\theta}{2}) = -\cos \tfrac{\theta}{2}$$

Then since $R(\theta, 1) = 2 + \cos \tfrac{\theta}{2}$, we get $R(2\pi - \theta, 1) = 2 - \cos \tfrac{\theta}{2} = A$. Also, since

$$\mathbf{r}(\theta, 1) = \langle\, R \cos \theta,\ R \sin \theta,\ \sin \tfrac{\theta}{2} \,\rangle$$

we get

$$\mathbf{r}_3(\theta) = \mathbf{r}(2\pi - \theta, 1) = \langle\, A \cos \theta,\ -A \sin \theta,\ \sin \tfrac{\theta}{2} \,\rangle$$

Then

$$\mathbf{r}_3' = \langle\, A' \cos \theta - A \sin \theta,\ -A' \sin \theta - A \cos \theta,\ \tfrac{1}{2} \cos \tfrac{\theta}{2} \,\rangle$$

and

$$\mathbf{F} \circ \mathbf{r}_3 = \langle\, A \sin \theta,\ A \cos \theta,\ 0 \,\rangle$$

Then, similarly to the previous calculation in Equation (14.5.4), we have $(\mathbf{F} \circ \mathbf{r}_3) \cdot \mathbf{r}_3' = -A^2$. So we can use Equation (14.5.5), but now with a minus sign to get:

$$\int_{C_3} \mathbf{F} \cdot d\mathbf{r} = \int_0^{2\pi} (\mathbf{F} \circ \mathbf{r}_3) \cdot \mathbf{r}_3' \, d\theta = \int_0^{2\pi} -A^2 \, d\theta = -9\pi$$

For C_4, the parameter map is

$$\mathbf{r}_4(t) = \mathbf{r}(0, 0 - t) = \langle\, R(0, -t),\ 0,\ 0 \,\rangle = \langle\, 2 - t,\ 0,\ 0 \,\rangle = \mathbf{r}_2(t),$$

for t in $[-1, 1]$. Thus, since $\mathbf{r}_4 = \mathbf{r}_2$, the line integral for C_4 will be the same as that for C_2

$$\int_{C_4} \mathbf{F} \cdot d\mathbf{r} = \int_{C_2} \mathbf{F} \cdot d\mathbf{r} = 0$$

NOTE: Using `dboundaryplot` to dynamically plot the boundary curves C_1, C_2, C_3, C_4, will show you that $C_2 = C_4$ and they have the same direction. See Figure 14.5.7. Putting together all these results gives

$$\int_S \operatorname{curl} \mathbf{F} \cdot d\mathbf{A} = 0 \quad \text{and} \quad \int_C \mathbf{F} \cdot d\mathbf{r} = 0 + 9\pi - 9\pi + 0 = 0$$

Thus, $\int_S \operatorname{curl} \mathbf{F} \cdot d\mathbf{A} = \int_C \mathbf{F} \cdot d\mathbf{r}$ as predicted by Stokes' Theorem.

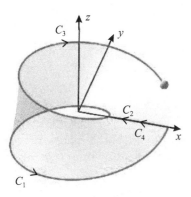

Figure 14.5.7: *The 30th frame in a dynamic plot of the boundary of a Möbius strip.*

Example 14.5.4 (Verifying Stokes' Theorem - SPHERE)

Problem: Verify that Stokes' Theorem holds for the vector field

$$\mathbf{F} = \langle\, yz^2,\ -xz^2,\ z^2 \,\rangle \quad \text{on } U = \mathbb{R}^3$$

and the sphere S parametrized by

$$\mathbf{r}(\theta, \phi) = \langle\, \sin \phi \cos \theta,\ \sin \phi \sin \theta,\ \cos \phi \,\rangle, \qquad (\theta, \phi) \text{ in } [0, 2\pi] \times [0, \pi]$$

Solution: First compute the curl of $\mathbf{F}$:

$$\operatorname{curl} \mathbf{F} = \begin{vmatrix} \mathbf{i} & \mathbf{j} & \mathbf{k} \\ \frac{\partial}{\partial x} & \frac{\partial}{\partial y} & \frac{\partial}{\partial z} \\ yz^2 & -xz^2 & z^2 \end{vmatrix} = \langle\, 2xz,\ 2yz,\ -2z^2 \,\rangle$$

Then

$$\operatorname{curl} \mathbf{F} \circ \mathbf{r} = \langle\, 2 \sin \phi \cos \phi \cos \theta,\ 2 \sin \phi \cos \phi \sin \theta,\ -2 \cos^2 \phi \,\rangle$$

The partials of $\mathbf{r} = \langle\, \sin \phi \cos \theta,\ \sin \phi \sin \theta,\ \cos \phi \,\rangle$ are

$$\mathbf{r}_\theta = \langle\, -\sin \phi \sin \theta,\ \sin \phi \cos \theta,\ 0 \,\rangle, \quad \mathbf{r}_\phi = \langle\, \cos \phi \cos \theta,\ \cos \phi \sin \theta,\ -\sin \phi \,\rangle$$

and so

$$\mathbf{n} = \mathbf{r}_\theta \times \mathbf{r}_\phi = \begin{vmatrix} \mathbf{i} & \mathbf{j} & \mathbf{k} \\ -\sin\phi\sin\theta & \sin\phi\cos\theta & 0 \\ \cos\phi\cos\theta & \cos\phi\sin\theta & -\sin\phi \end{vmatrix}$$

$$= \langle -\sin^2\phi\cos\theta, -\sin^2\phi\sin\theta, -\sin\phi\cos\phi \rangle$$

Consequently

$$(\text{curl } \mathbf{F} \circ \mathbf{r}) \cdot \mathbf{n} = -2\sin^3\phi\cos\phi\cos^2\theta - 2\sin^3\phi\cos\phi\sin^2\theta + 2\sin\phi\cos^3\phi$$
$$= -2\sin^3\phi\cos\phi + 2\sin\phi\cos^3\phi$$

Thus, the surface integral of the curl is

$$\int_S \text{curl } \mathbf{F} \cdot d\mathbf{A} = \int_0^{2\pi} \int_0^\pi \left(-2\sin^3\phi\cos\phi + 2\sin\phi\cos^3\phi \right) d\phi\, d\theta$$
$$= \int_0^{2\pi} 1\, d\theta \int_0^\pi \left(-2\sin^3\phi\cos\phi + 2\sin\phi\cos^3\phi \right) d\phi$$
$$= 2\pi\left(-\tfrac{1}{2}\sin^4\phi - \tfrac{1}{2}\cos^4\phi \right)\Big|_0^\pi = 0$$

Next we compute the four line integrals along the curves C_1, C_2, C_3, C_4.

For C_1 and C_3, the parameter maps are

$$\mathbf{r}_1(\theta) = \mathbf{r}(\theta, 0) = \langle 0, 0, 1 \rangle \quad \text{and} \quad \mathbf{r}_3(\theta) = \mathbf{r}(2\pi - \theta, \pi) = \langle 0, 0, -1 \rangle$$

for θ in $[0, 2\pi]$. These correspond to the north and south poles of the sphere. Since $\mathbf{r}'_1 = 0$ and $\mathbf{r}'_3 = 0$, this clearly gives $\int_{C_1} \mathbf{F} \cdot d\mathbf{r} = 0$ and $\int_{C_3} \mathbf{F} \cdot d\mathbf{r} = 0$

For C_2 and C_4, the parameter maps are

$$\mathbf{r}_2(\phi) = \mathbf{r}(2\pi, \phi) = \langle \sin\phi, 0, \cos\phi \rangle$$
$$\mathbf{r}_4(\phi) = \mathbf{r}(0, \pi - \phi) = \langle \sin(\pi - \phi), 0, \cos(\pi - \phi) \rangle$$

for ϕ in $[0, \pi]$. It is not too hard to see that these two boundary curves are semi-circles and in fact as sets: $C_2 = C_4$, but as paths are oppositely directed. You can also verify this by viewing the movie created by `dboundaryplot`. Figure 14.5.8 shows the last frame in this movie.

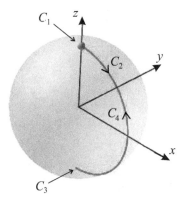

Figure 14.5.8: *The last frame in a dynamic plot of the boundary of a sphere.*

NOTE: One can show, in general, that if curves C_2, C_4 are the same as sets but oppositely directed as paths, then

$$\int_{C_4} \mathbf{F} \cdot d\mathbf{r} = -\int_{C_2} \mathbf{F} \cdot d\mathbf{r}, \quad \text{equivalently} \quad \int_{C_2} \mathbf{F} \cdot d\mathbf{r} + \int_{C_4} \mathbf{F} \cdot d\mathbf{r} = 0$$

See the Exercises.

In summary: $\int_{C_1} \mathbf{F} \cdot d\mathbf{r} = 0$, $\int_{C_3} \mathbf{F} \cdot d\mathbf{r} = 0$, and $\int_{C_2} \mathbf{F} \cdot d\mathbf{r} + \int_{C_4} \mathbf{F} \cdot d\mathbf{r} = 0$.

Thus, $\int_C \mathbf{F} \cdot d\mathbf{r} = 0$. This what we got for $\int_S \text{curl } \mathbf{F} \cdot d\mathbf{A}$, which we should have expected from Stokes' Theorem.

Closed Surfaces

In the colloquial sense, a closed surface is one which has no boundary. But, as the last example shows, our approach here is different. There, the sphere S has four "curves" forming its boundary $C = \partial S$. We saw that C_1, C_3 are just points (the north and south poles, respectively), while, as mentioned, C_2, C_4 are equal and oppositely directed semi-circles. You should view again in the movie, the last frame of which is shown in Figure 14.5.8.

If you examine the work we did computing the boundary integral $\int_C \mathbf{F} \cdot d\mathbf{r}$, in the sphere example, you will see that it did not depend on the specific $\mathbf{F}$ in the example.

Thus, for the sphere, $\int_C \mathbf{F} \cdot d\mathbf{r} = 0$, for *every* vector field $\mathbf{F}$. This discussion suggests the following definition.

DEFINITION 14.5.2 (Closed Surfaces)

A surface S is called closed *if* $\int_{\partial S} \mathbf{F} \cdot d\mathbf{r} = 0$, *for every vector field* $\mathbf{F}$ *on an open set U containing S.*

Next we turn to Green's Theorem, which has some interesting applications when studying phenomena that are essentially planar.

GREEN'S THEOREM (Parametric Version)

Green's Theorem results from applying Stokes' Theorem to a vector field $\mathbf{F}$ in the plane and a *parametrized region S* in the plane. In both cases, the "plane" is the x-y-plane in $\mathbb{R}^3$.

Vector Fields in the Plane: These are vector fields $\mathbf{F} : U \to \mathbb{R}^3$ of the form

$$\mathbf{F}(x, y, z) = \langle\, M(x,y),\, N(x,y),\, 0\,\rangle$$

where $U = O \times \mathbb{R}$, with O an open set in $\mathbb{R}^2$.

Parametrized Regions in the Plane: These are regions S in the plane parametrized by a parameter map $\mathbf{r} : [a,b] \times [c,d] \to \mathbb{R}^3$ of the form

$$\mathbf{r}(u, v) = \langle\, f(u,v),\, g(u,v),\, 0\,\rangle$$

We assume, as usual, that the component functions M, N, f, g have continuous partial derivatives.

NOTE: All the regions in the plane that we have studied so far can be parametrized (as we will see). These regions are (a) Type I and Type II regions from Chapters 4 and 5 and (b) polar regions from Chapter 9.

If we apply Stokes's Theorem in this situation (vector fields and parametrized regions in the plane), then the formula is the same, but the calculations are somewhat simpler:

THEOREM 14.5.2 (Green's Theorem - Parametric Version)

Suppose $\mathbf{F} : U \to \mathbb{R}^3$ *is a vector field in the plane and S is a parametrized region in the plane with parametrization* $\mathbf{r} : [a,b] \times [c,d] \to \mathbb{R}^3$. *Let* $C = \partial S$ *be the boundary of S. Then*

$$\int_S \operatorname{curl} \mathbf{F} \cdot d\mathbf{A} = \int_C \mathbf{F} \cdot d\mathbf{r} \qquad (14.5.6)$$

For the first example to illustrate this theorem, we need the following:

The Standard Parametrization of a Type I Region: Suppose S is the Type I region bounded by (1) the graphs of the functions $y = F(x)$ and $y = G(x)$ on $[a,b]$, where $G(x) \le F(x)$, and (2) by the vertical lines $x = a$ and $x = b$. The *standard parametrization* of S is given by $\mathbf{r} : [a,b] \times [0,1] \to \mathbb{R}^3$, where

$$\mathbf{r}(u, t) \equiv \langle\, u,\, G(u) + t\big[F(u) - G(u)\big],\, 0\,\rangle$$

for (u, t) in $[a,b] \times [0,1]$.

NOTE: The standard normal $\mathbf{n}$ to this type of region is calculated as follows.

$$
\begin{aligned}
\mathbf{r}_u &= \langle\, 1,\, G'(u) + t\big[\, F'(u) - G'(u)\,\big],\, 0 \,\rangle \\
\mathbf{r}_t &= \langle\, 0,\, F(u) - G(u),\, 0 \,\rangle \\
\mathbf{n} &= \langle\, 0,\, 0,\, F(u) - G(u) \,\rangle \qquad\qquad (14.5.7)
\end{aligned}
$$

Example 14.5.5 (Verifying Green's Theorem - Parametric Version)

Problem: Verify that Green's Theorem holds for the vector field

$$\mathbf{F} = \langle\, -y,\, x^2,\, 0 \,\rangle \ \text{on} \ U = \mathbb{R}^3$$

and the Type I region S in the plane bounded by the graphs of $y = x^3$, $y = 1 + x^2$ and the vertical lines $x = 0$, $x = 1$.

Solution: A plot of the region S is shown in Figure 14.5.9. You can rotate the corresponding Maple Figure to more clearly see that S is a planar region. The standard parametrization for this region is

$$\mathbf{r}(u,t) = \langle\, u,\, u^3 + t\big[\, 1 + u^2 - u^3 \,\big],\, 0 \,\rangle, \qquad (u,t) \ \text{in} \ [0,1] \times [0,1]$$

We calculate $\int_S \operatorname{curl}\mathbf{F} \cdot d\mathbf{A}$ and $\int_{\partial S} \mathbf{F} \cdot d\mathbf{r}$ as usual, starting with the computation:

$$\operatorname{curl}\mathbf{F} = \langle\, 0,\, 0,\, \frac{\partial N}{\partial x} - \frac{\partial M}{\partial y} \,\rangle = \langle\, 0,\, 0,\, 2x + 1 \,\rangle$$

Then

$$\operatorname{curl}\mathbf{F} \circ \mathbf{r} = \langle\, 0,\, 0,\, 2u + 1 \,\rangle$$

By Equation (14.4.7), the standard normal to this Type I parametrized region is

$$\mathbf{n} = \langle\, 0,\, 0,\, F(u) - G(u) \,\rangle = \langle\, 0, 0, 1 + u^2 - u^3 \,\rangle$$

Consequently

$$
\begin{aligned}
\operatorname{curl}\mathbf{F} \cdot \mathbf{n} &= (2u+1)(1 + u^2 - u^3) = 2u + 2u^3 - 2u^4 + 1 + u^2 - u^3 \\
&= 1 + 2u + u^2 + u^3 - 2u^4
\end{aligned}
$$

Thus, the parametrized-region integral is

$$
\begin{aligned}
\int_S \operatorname{curl}\mathbf{F} \cdot d\mathbf{A} &= \int_0^1 \int_0^1 \big[\, 1 + 2u + u^2 + u^3 - 2u^4 \,\big]\, dt\, du \\
&= \int_0^1 1\, dt \cdot \int_0^1 \big[\, 1 + 2u + u^2 + u^3 - 2u^4 \,\big]\, du \\
&= \Big[\, u + u^2 + \tfrac{1}{3}u^3 + \tfrac{1}{4}u^4 - \tfrac{2}{5}u^5 \,\Big]\Big|_0^1 \\
&= 1 + 1 + \tfrac{1}{3} + \tfrac{1}{4} - \tfrac{2}{5} = \frac{131}{60}
\end{aligned}
$$

Next we compute the four line integrals along the curves C_1, C_2, C_3, C_4. For C_1, the parameter map is

$$\mathbf{r}_1(u) = \mathbf{r}(u,0) = \langle\, u,\, u^3,\, 0 \,\rangle,$$

for u in $[0,1]$. So,

$$\mathbf{F} \circ \mathbf{r}_1 = \langle\, -u^3,\, u^2,\, 0 \,\rangle \quad \text{and} \quad \mathbf{r}_1' = \langle\, 1,\, 3u^2,\, 0 \,\rangle .$$

Thus, the line integral along C_1 is

$$
\begin{aligned}
\int_{C_1} \mathbf{F} \cdot d\mathbf{r} &= \int_0^1 (\mathbf{F} \circ \mathbf{r}_1) \cdot \mathbf{r}_1'\, du = \int_0^1 \big(\, -u^3 + 3u^4 \,\big)\, du \\
&= \Big(\, -\tfrac{1}{4}u^4 + \tfrac{3}{5}u^5 \,\Big)\Big|_0^1 = -\tfrac{1}{4} + \tfrac{3}{5} = \frac{7}{20}
\end{aligned}
$$

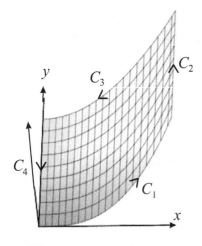

Figure 14.5.9: *A parametrized Type I region and its boundary curves.*

For C_2, the parameter map is

$$\mathbf{r}_2(t) = \mathbf{r}(1, t) = \langle\, 1,\, 1 + t,\, 0 \,\rangle,$$

for t in $[0, 1]$. So,

$$\mathbf{F} \circ \mathbf{r}_2 = \langle\, -(1 + t),\, 1,\, 0 \,\rangle \quad \text{and} \quad \mathbf{r}_2' = \langle\, 0,\, 1,\, 0 \,\rangle.$$

Thus, the line integral along C_2 is

$$\int_{C_2} \mathbf{F} \cdot d\mathbf{r} = \int_0^1 (\mathbf{F} \circ \mathbf{r}_2) \cdot \mathbf{r}_2'\, d\theta = \int_0^1 1\, dt = 1$$

For C_3, the parameter map is

$$\mathbf{r}_3(u) = \mathbf{r}(1 - u, 1) = \langle\, 1 - u,\, 1 + (1 - u)^2,\, 0 \,\rangle,$$

for u in $[0, 1]$. Then

$$\mathbf{F} \circ \mathbf{r}_3 = \langle\, -1 - (1 - u)^2,\, (1 - u)^2,\, 0 \,\rangle \quad \text{and} \quad \mathbf{r}_3' = \langle\, -1,\, -2(1 - u),\, 0 \,\rangle\,.$$

Thus, the line integral along C_3 is

$$
\begin{aligned}
\int_{C_3} \mathbf{F} \cdot d\mathbf{r} &= \int_0^1 (\mathbf{F} \circ \mathbf{r}_3) \cdot \mathbf{r}_3'\, d\theta = \int_0^1 \left[\, 1 + (1 - u)^2 - 2(1 - u)^3 \,\right] du \\
&= \int_1^0 \left[\, 1 + w^2 - 2w^3 \,\right](-dw) = \left[\, w + \tfrac{1}{3}w^3 - \tfrac{1}{2}w^4 \,\right]\Big|_0^1 \\
&= 1 + \tfrac{1}{3} - \tfrac{1}{2} = \frac{5}{6}
\end{aligned}
$$

For C_4, the parameter map is

$$\mathbf{r}_4(t) = \mathbf{r}(0, 1 - t) = \langle\, 0,\, 1 - t,\, 0 \,\rangle,$$

for t in $[0, 1]$. So,

$$\mathbf{F} \circ \mathbf{r}_4(t) = \langle\, t,\, 0,\, 0 \,\rangle \quad \text{and} \quad \mathbf{r}_4'(t) = \langle\, 0,\, -1,\, 0 \,\rangle.$$

Thus, the line integral along C_4 is

$$\int_{C_4} \mathbf{F} \cdot d\mathbf{r} = \int_0^0 (\mathbf{F} \circ \mathbf{r}_4) \cdot \mathbf{r}_4'\, d\theta = \int_0^1 0\, dt = 0$$

Putting together all these results gives

$$
\begin{aligned}
\int_S \operatorname{curl}\mathbf{F} \cdot d\mathbf{A} &= \tfrac{131}{60} \\
\int_C \mathbf{F} \cdot d\mathbf{r} &\equiv \int_{C_1} \mathbf{F} \cdot d\mathbf{r} + \int_{C_2} \mathbf{F} \cdot d\mathbf{r} + \int_{C_3} \mathbf{F} \cdot d\mathbf{r} + \int_{C_4} \mathbf{F} \cdot d\mathbf{r} \\
&= \tfrac{7}{20} + 1 + \tfrac{5}{6} + 0 = \tfrac{131}{60}
\end{aligned}
$$

Thus, $\int_S \operatorname{curl}\mathbf{F} \cdot d\mathbf{A} = \int_C \mathbf{F} \cdot d\mathbf{r}$ as predicted by Stokes'/Green's Theorem.

The Standard Parametrization of Special Polar Regions: Suppose S is a polar region bounded by (1) the polar curves $r = aR(\theta)$ and $r = bR(\theta)$, with $a < b$, and (2) by the radial lines with polar equations $\theta = \alpha$ and $\theta = \beta$, with $\alpha < \beta \le 2\pi$. Here R is a given function of θ. The standard parametrization of S is given by $\mathbf{r} : [\alpha, \beta] \times [a, b] \to \mathbb{R}^3$, where

$$\mathbf{r}(\theta, t) \equiv \langle\, tR\cos\theta,\, tR\sin\theta,\, 0 \,\rangle$$

for (θ, t) in $[\alpha, \beta] \times [a, b]$. See Figure 14.5.10.

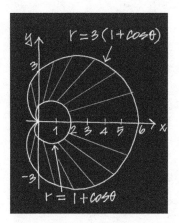

Figure 14.5.10:
An example of a special polar region.

NOTE 1: See the Exercises for how to parametrize the general type of polar region discussed in Chapter 9.

NOTE 2: The standard normal $\mathbf{n}$ to this type of region is calculated as follows.

$$\mathbf{r}_\theta = \langle\, tR'\cos\theta - tR\sin\theta,\ tR'\sin\theta + tR\cos\theta,\ 0\,\rangle$$
$$\mathbf{r}_t = \langle\, R\cos\theta,\ R\sin\theta,\ 0\,\rangle$$
$$\mathbf{n} = \langle\, 0,\ 0,\ -tR^2\,\rangle \tag{14.5.8}$$

Example 14.5.6 (Using Green's Theorem to Calculate Line Integrals)

Problem: Consider the polar region S bounded by

$$r = 2\sin 2\theta, \quad r = 5\sin 2\theta, \quad \theta = 0, \ \theta = \tfrac{\pi}{2}$$

Thus, S is the region between two petals of rose curves with four petals. See Figure 14.5.11. Use Green's Theorem to compute the line integral of

$$\mathbf{F} = \langle\, -y^3,\ x^3,\ 0\,\rangle$$

around the boundary $C = \partial S$ of S. See Figure 14.5.12 for a dynamic plot of the boundary.

Solution: The standard parametrization for this region is

$$\mathbf{r}(\theta, t) = \langle\, tR\cos\theta,\ tR\sin\theta,\ 0\,\rangle, \qquad (\theta, t) \text{ in } [0, \tfrac{\pi}{2}] \times [2, 5],$$

where $R = \sin 2\theta$. If we try to calculate $\int_{\partial S} \mathbf{F} \cdot d\mathbf{r}$ directly, we find some of the integrals are very difficult. So, we use the alternative afforded us by Green's Theorem, i.e., we calculate $\int_S \operatorname{curl} \mathbf{F} \cdot d\mathbf{A}$. We start with the computation:

$$\operatorname{curl}\mathbf{F} = \left\langle 0,\ 0,\ \frac{\partial N}{\partial x} - \frac{\partial M}{\partial y} \right\rangle = \langle\, 0,\ 0,\ 3(x^2 + y^2)\,\rangle$$

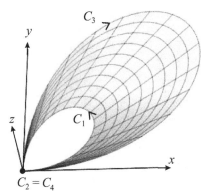

Figure 14.5.11:
A polar region and its boundary curves.

Then

$$\operatorname{curl}\mathbf{F} \circ \mathbf{r} = \langle\, 0,\ 0,\ 3t^2 R^2\,\rangle$$

By Equation (14.4.8), the standard normal to this type parametrized polar region is

$$\mathbf{n} = \langle\, 0,\ 0,\ -tR^2\,\rangle$$

Consequently

$$(\operatorname{curl}\mathbf{F} \circ \mathbf{r}) \cdot \mathbf{n} = -3t^3 R^4 = -3t^3 \sin^4 2\theta$$

Thus, the parametrized-region integral is

$$
\begin{aligned}
\int_S \operatorname{curl}\mathbf{F} \cdot d\mathbf{A} &= \int_2^5 \int_0^{\pi/2} -3t^3 \sin^4 2\theta\, d\theta\, dt = \int_2^5 -3t^3\, dt \int_0^{\pi/2} \sin^4 2\theta\, d\theta \\
&= -\tfrac{3}{4}t^4 \Big|_2^5 \cdot \int_0^{\pi/2} \sin^4 2\theta\, d\theta = -\tfrac{1827}{4} \int_0^{\pi/2} \sin^4 2\theta\, d\theta \\
&= -\tfrac{1827}{8} \int_0^{\pi/2} \sin^4 x\, dx \\
&= -\tfrac{1827}{8}\left[\tfrac{3}{4} \cdot \tfrac{1}{2} \cdot \tfrac{\pi}{2}\right] = -\tfrac{1827}{8}\left[\tfrac{3\pi}{16}\right] = \tfrac{5481}{128}\,\pi
\end{aligned}
$$

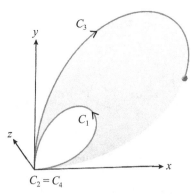

Figure 14.5.12: The 18th *frame in the dynamic plot of the boundary of the two rose petal region.*

In the above we used the substitution $x = 2\theta$, $dx = 2d\theta$ and then on the resulting integral we used a reduction formula:

$$\int_0^{\pi/2} \sin^n x\, dx = \tfrac{n-1}{n} \int_0^{\pi/2} \sin^{n-2} x\, dx,$$

which comes from reduction Formula (6.2.1) applied to definite integrals.

GREEN'S THEOREM (Double Integral Version)

To get the traditional form of Green's Theorem, which we will call the *double integral version*, we start with the parametric version that we have been using above.

The parametrized region S in the plane is $S = \mathbf{r}(D)$, where $\mathbf{r} : D \to \mathbb{R}^3$ is the parametrization and $D = [a,b] \times [c,d]$ is a rectangular parameter domain. We write out explicitly $\int_S \operatorname{curl} \mathbf{F} \cdot d\mathbf{A}$ in terms of what it is as a double integral over the parameter domain D.

Since $\mathbf{F} = \langle M(x,y), N(x,y), 0 \rangle$ and $\mathbf{r} = \langle f(u,v), g(u,v), 0 \rangle$, we have

$$
\begin{aligned}
\operatorname{curl}\mathbf{F} &= \langle 0, 0, \frac{\partial N}{\partial x} - \frac{\partial M}{\partial y} \rangle \\
\mathbf{r}_u &= \langle f_u, g_u, 0 \rangle \\
\mathbf{r}_v &= \langle f_v, g_v, 0 \rangle \\
\mathbf{n} &= \langle 0, 0, f_u g_v - f_v g_u \rangle
\end{aligned}
$$

Consequently,

$$
\begin{aligned}
(\operatorname{curl}\mathbf{F} \circ \mathbf{r}) \cdot \mathbf{n} &= \left[\left(\frac{\partial N}{\partial x} - \frac{\partial M}{\partial y} \right) \circ \mathbf{r} \right] \left[f_u g_v - f_v g_u \right] \\
&= \left[\left(\frac{\partial N}{\partial x} - \frac{\partial M}{\partial y} \right) \circ \mathbf{r} \right] \begin{vmatrix} f_u & g_u \\ f_v & g_v \end{vmatrix} \\
&= \left[\left(\frac{\partial N}{\partial x} - \frac{\partial M}{\partial y} \right) \circ \mathbf{r} \right] J(\mathbf{r})
\end{aligned}
$$

Here, we have used the notation for the *Jacobian* of the map $\mathbf{r}$:

$$
J(\mathbf{r}) \equiv \begin{vmatrix} f_u & g_u \\ f_v & g_v \end{vmatrix} = f_u g_v - f_v g_u
$$

viewed as having its range in $\mathbb{R}^2$, which we identify with the x-y-plane. See Chapter 12, where the *Change of Variables Theorem* is also discussed. We can apply this theorem to $\mathbf{r}$ if we place two additional restrictions on $\mathbf{r}$:

    (1) $\mathbf{r}$ is one-to-one on D° (2) $J(\mathbf{r}) \neq 0$ at any point in D°

Here $D^\circ \equiv (a,b) \times (c,d)$ is the "interior" of the rectangle D, i.e., D without its sides. Then the Change of Variables Theorem gives:

$$
\iint_D \left[\left(\frac{\partial N}{\partial x} - \frac{\partial M}{\partial y} \right) \circ \mathbf{r} \right] | J(\mathbf{r}) | \, dA = \iint_S \left(\frac{\partial N}{\partial x} - \frac{\partial M}{\partial y} \right) dA \qquad (14.5.9)
$$

Next note that since the Jacobian $J(\mathbf{r})$ is never zero in D° and is continuous on D°, then it is either positive, $J(\mathbf{r}) > 0$ at all points of D° or negative $J(\mathbf{r}) < 0$ at all point of D°. Thus,

$$
\frac{|J(\mathbf{r})|}{J(\mathbf{r})} = \pm 1
$$

on D°, with the sign being either $+$ at all points or $-$ at all points. Consequently, we can write the parametric version of Green's Theorem as follows

$$
\begin{aligned}
\int_C \mathbf{F} \cdot d\mathbf{r} &= \int_S \operatorname{curl}\mathbf{F} \cdot d\mathbf{A} = \iint_D \left[\left(\frac{\partial N}{\partial x} - \frac{\partial M}{\partial y} \right) \circ \mathbf{r} \right] J(\mathbf{r}) \, dA \\
&= \pm \iint_D \left\lfloor \left(\frac{\partial N}{\partial x} - \frac{\partial M}{\partial y} \right) \circ \mathbf{r} \right\rfloor J(\mathbf{r}) \, (\pm 1) \, dA \\
&= \pm \iint_D \left[\left(\frac{\partial N}{\partial x} - \frac{\partial M}{\partial y} \right) \circ \mathbf{r} \right] J(\mathbf{r}) \frac{|J(\mathbf{r})|}{J(\mathbf{r})} \, dA \\
&= \pm \iint_D \left[\left(\frac{\partial N}{\partial x} - \frac{\partial M}{\partial y} \right) \circ \mathbf{r} \right] | J(\mathbf{r}) | \, dA \\
&= \pm \iint_S \left(\frac{\partial N}{\partial x} - \frac{\partial M}{\partial y} \right) dA
\end{aligned}
$$

Finally note that $J(\mathbf{r})$ is the nonzero component of the normal $\mathbf{n}$ to S:

$$\mathbf{n} = \mathbf{r}_u \times \mathbf{r}_v = \langle\, 0,\, 0,\, J(\mathbf{r})\,\rangle$$

and so $\mathbf{n}$ points in the positive z-direction when $J(\mathbf{r}) > 0$. We can always make the latter happen by changing the order of the parameters in the parameter map. Namely, if $J(\mathbf{r}) < 0$, then change $\mathbf{r}(u,v)$ to $\mathbf{r}(v,u)$. With all of this background we can now state the following version of Green's Theorem.

THEOREM 14.5.3 (Green's Theorem - Double Integral Version)

Suppose $\mathbf{F} : O \times \mathbb{R} \to \mathbb{R}^3$ *is a vector field in the plane with component form*

$$\mathbf{F}(x,y,z) = \langle M(x,y), N(x,y), 0 \rangle$$

Further, suppose S is a parametrized region in the plane with parametrization $\mathbf{r} : D \to \mathbb{R}^3$, *where* $D = [a,b] \times [c,d]$, $\mathbf{r}(u,v) = \langle f(u,v), g(u,v), 0 \rangle$, *and* $\mathbf{r}(D)$ *is contained in O.*
Assume $\mathbf{r}$ *is one-to-one on the interior of D and* $\mathbf{n} \neq 0$ *at any point in the interior of D.*
If $\mathbf{r}$ *is chosen so that* $\mathbf{n}$ *points in the positive z-direction, then*

$$\int_C M\,dx + N\,dy = \iint_S \left(\frac{\partial N}{\partial x} - \frac{\partial M}{\partial y} \right) dA \qquad (14.5.10)$$

where $C = \partial S$ *is the boundary of S.*

Example 14.5.7 (Using Green's Theorem - Double Integral Version)

Problem: Consider again the polar region S from the last example. It is bounded by two petals of the rose curves:

$$r = 2\sin 2\theta, \quad r = 5\sin 2\theta, \quad \theta = 0,\ \theta = \tfrac{\pi}{2}$$

Use the *double integral version* of Green's Theorem to compute the line integral of

$$\mathbf{F} = \langle\, -y^3,\, x^3,\, 0\,\rangle$$

around the boundary $C = \partial S$ of S.

Solution: Again, instead of directly computing the line integral, we do the easier calculation of the double integral of the curl over the region S. We found that

$$\operatorname{curl}\mathbf{F} = \langle 0,\, 0,\, \frac{\partial N}{\partial x} - \frac{\partial M}{\partial y} \rangle = \langle 0,\, 0,\, 3(x^2 + y^2) \rangle$$

Consequently, we need to compute $\iint_S 3(x^2 + y^2)\,dA$. Since S is a polar region, we switch to polar coordinates:

$$
\begin{aligned}
\iint_S 3(x^2 + y^2)\,dA &= \int_0^{\pi/2} \int_{r=2\sin 2\theta}^{r=5\sin 2\theta} 3r^2\,r\,dr\,d\theta = \int_0^{\pi/2} \left[\tfrac{3}{4}r^4 \right]\Big|_{r=2\sin 2\theta}^{r=5\sin 2\theta} d\theta \\
&= \int_0^{\pi/2} \tfrac{3}{4}\left[5^4 - 2^2 \right] \sin^4 2\theta\,d\theta = \tfrac{1827}{4} \int_0^{\pi/2} \sin^4 2\theta\,d\theta
\end{aligned}
$$

The last integral here is the same as the integral that occurred in the last example. So, using the results from the last example, we get

$$\iint_S 3(x^2 + y^2)\,dA = \tfrac{5481}{128}\,\pi$$

In the last example we got $\int_S \operatorname{curl}\mathbf{F} \cdot d\mathbf{A} = -\tfrac{5481}{128}\pi$. Note that the minus sign resulted from the parametrization of S used there. That parametrization was

$$\mathbf{r}(\theta, t) = \langle\, tR\cos\theta,\, tR\sin\theta,\, 0\,\rangle,$$

where $R = \sin 2\theta$. This gave for the corresponding normal

$$\mathbf{n} = \mathbf{r}_\theta \times \mathbf{r}_t = \langle\, 0,\, 0,\, -tR^2\,\rangle,$$

which is a vector directed in the *negative* direction of the z-axis. If we change the order of the parameters to get a different parameter map $\bar{\mathbf{r}}(t, \theta) \equiv \mathbf{r}(\theta, t)$, then the expression for $\bar{\mathbf{r}}$ is the same:

$$\bar{\mathbf{r}}(t, \theta) = \langle\, tR\cos\theta,\, tR\sin\theta,\, 0\,\rangle,$$

but the corresponding normal is positively directed:

$$\bar{\mathbf{n}} = \bar{\mathbf{r}}_t \times \bar{\mathbf{r}}_\theta = \langle\, 0,\, 0,\, tR^2\,\rangle.$$

(Check this out!). Consequently, using $\bar{\mathbf{r}}$ gives a correctly oriented boundary: $\partial S = \overline{C}$ and by the double integral version of Green's Theorem we can say

$$\int_{\overline{C}} -y^3\,dx + x^3\,dy = \iint_S 3(x^2 + y^2)\,dA = \tfrac{5481}{128}\pi$$

NOTE: (LEFT SIDE RULE) If you do a dynamic plot of the boundary when the parametrization is $\bar{\mathbf{r}}(t, \theta)$, then the boundary is traced out differently than before. See Figure 14.5.13. Now $C_1 = C_3$ are the point at the origin and C_2, C_4 are the petal loops. It is also important to note that directions of these latter two curves coincide with the "left side rule." This rule says that *if you walk along the boundary curves with these direction, then the region S will alway be on your left side.*

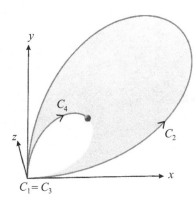

Figure 14.5.13: *The 22nd frame in the dynamic plot of the boundary of the two rose petal region with parameters in the order $\bar{\mathbf{r}}(t, \theta)$.*

GREEN'S THEOREM: Parametric Version vs Double Integral Version

If you use the Parametric Version of Green's Theorem (Theorem 14.5.2), then you do not have to worry about whether the parametrization $\mathbf{r}$ gives a positively directed normal $\mathbf{n}$. The equation

$$\int_S \operatorname{curl}\mathbf{F} \cdot d\mathbf{A} = \int_{\partial S} \mathbf{F} \cdot d\mathbf{r}$$

always holds. If you use the Double Integral Version of Green's Theorem (Theorem 14.5.3), then the equality of the double integral of $\operatorname{curl}\mathbf{F}$ and the line integral of $\mathbf{F}$ is only true up to a sign:

$$\iint_S \left(\frac{\partial N}{\partial y} - \frac{\partial M}{\partial x}\right) dA = \pm \int_{\partial S} M\,dx + N\,dy$$

The sign $\pm$ depends on the direction of $\mathbf{n}$ relative to the positive direction of the z-axis.

PROOF OF STOKES' THEOREM

Suppose in terms of components, $\mathbf{F} = \langle\, M,\, N,\, K\,\rangle$ and $\mathbf{r} = \langle\, f,\, g,\, h\,\rangle$. Then

$$\mathbf{n} = \langle\, g_u h_v - g_v h_u,\, f_v h_u - f_u h_v,\, f_u g_v - f_v g_u\,\rangle$$

and

$$\operatorname{curl}\mathbf{F} = \langle\, K_y - N_z,\, M_z - K_x,\, N_x - M_y\,\rangle$$

The surface integral in Stokes' theorem is

$$\int_S \operatorname{curl}\mathbf{F} \cdot d\mathbf{A} = \int_c^d \int_a^b \big[\operatorname{curl}\mathbf{F}\big](\mathbf{r}(u, v)) \cdot \mathbf{n}(u, v)\,du\,dv$$

The integrand in the iterated integral is a function of u, v and the key identity in the proof is to show that it is equal to

$$E \equiv \frac{\partial}{\partial u}\big[Mf_v + Ng_v + Kh_v\big] - \frac{\partial}{\partial v}\big[Mf_u + Ng_u + Kh_u\big]$$

In the above expression we have used abbreviations for the various functions of u, v that occur. For instance:

$$Mf_v \equiv M(f, g, h)f_v \equiv M(f(u, v), g(u, v), h(u, v))f_v(u, v)$$

With this understood, we can now use the chain rule to get

$$E = \frac{\partial}{\partial u}\left[Mf_v + Ng_v + Kh_v\right] - \frac{\partial}{\partial v}\left[Mf_u + Ng_u + Kh_u\right]$$

$$= \begin{cases} \left[M_x f_u + M_y g_u + M_z h_u\right]f_v + Mf_{uv} \\ +\left[N_x f_u + N_y g_u + N_z h_u\right]g_v + Ng_{uv} \\ +\left[K_x f_u + K_y g_u + K_z h_u\right]h_v + Kh_{uv} \\ -\left[M_x f_v + M_y g_v + M_z h_v\right]f_u - Mf_{uv} \\ -\left[N_x f_v + N_y g_v + N_z h_v\right]g_u - Ng_{uv} \\ -\left[K_x f_v + K_y g_v + K_z h_v\right]h_u - Kh_{uv} \end{cases}$$

$$= \begin{cases} K_y\left[g_u h_v - g_v h_u\right] - N_z\left[g_u h_v - g_v h_u\right] \\ +M_z\left[f_v h_u - f_u h_v\right] - K_x\left[f_v h_u - f_u h_v\right] \\ +N_x\left[f_u g_v - f_v g_u\right] - M_y\left[f_u g_v - f_v g_u\right] \end{cases}$$

$$= \begin{cases} \left(K_y - N_z\right)\left[g_u h_v - g_v h_u\right] \\ +\left(M_z - K_x\right)\left[f_v h_u - f_u h_v\right] \\ +\left(N_x - M_y\right)\left[f_u g_v - f_v g_u\right] \end{cases}$$

$$= \operatorname{curl}\mathbf{F}\cdot\mathbf{n}$$

Thus far we have,

$$\int_S \operatorname{curl}\mathbf{F}\cdot d\mathbf{A} = \int_c^d \int_a^b \operatorname{curl}\mathbf{F}\cdot\mathbf{n}\,du\,dv = \int_c^d \int_a^b E\,du\,dv$$

$$= \int_c^d \int_a^b \left[\frac{\partial}{\partial u}\left[Mf_v + Ng_v + Kh_v\right] - \frac{\partial}{\partial v}\left[Mf_u + Ng_u + Kh_u\right]\right]du\,dv$$

$$= \int_c^d \left[Mf_v + Ng_v + Kh_v\right]\Big|_a^b dv - \int_a^b \left[Mf_u + Ng_u + Kh_u\right]\Big|_c^d du \quad (14.5.11)$$

The first single integral in Equation (1451.11) above is just $\int_{C_2}\mathbf{F}\cdot d\mathbf{r} + \int_{C_4}\mathbf{F}\cdot d\mathbf{r}$. To see this, write everything out explicitly:

$$\int_c^d \left[Mf_v + Ng_v + Kh_v\right]\Big|_a^b dv$$

$$= \begin{cases} \int_c^d \left[M(\mathbf{r}(b,v))f_v(b,v) + N(\mathbf{r}(b,v))g_v(b,v) + K(\mathbf{r}(b,v))h_v(b,v)\right]dv \\ -\int_c^d \left[M(\mathbf{r}(a,v))f_v(a,v) + N(\mathbf{r}(a,v))g_v(a,v) + K(\mathbf{r}(a,v))h_v(a,v)\right]dv \end{cases}$$

$$= \int_c^d \mathbf{F}(\mathbf{r}(b,v))\cdot\mathbf{r}_v(b,v)\,dv - \int_c^d \mathbf{F}(\mathbf{r}(a,v))\cdot\mathbf{r}_v(a,v)\,dv \quad (14.5.12)$$

$$= \int_c^d \mathbf{F}(\mathbf{r}_2(v))\cdot\mathbf{r}_2'(v)\,dv + \int_c^d \mathbf{F}(\mathbf{r}_4(v))\cdot\mathbf{r}_4'(v)\,dv \quad (14.5.13)$$

To get the first integral in Equation (14.5.13), we used $\mathbf{r}_2(v) = \mathbf{r}(b,v)$ and $\mathbf{r}_2'(v) = \mathbf{r}_v(b,v))$ in the first integral in Equation (14.5.12). To get the second integral in Equation (14.5.13), we used the substitution $v = c+d-\bar{v}$ in the second integral in Equation (14.5.12). Then we used $\mathbf{r}_4(\bar{v}) = \mathbf{r}(a, c+d-\bar{v})$ and $\mathbf{r}_4'(\bar{v}) = -\mathbf{r}_v(a, c+d-\bar{v})$.

Similarly, one can show that the second single integral (with the minus sign included) in Equation (14.5.11) above is $\int_{C_1}\mathbf{F}\cdot d\mathbf{r} + \int_{C_3}\mathbf{F}\cdot d\mathbf{r}$. Just write everything out explicitly and use a substitution (change of variables).

Exercises: 14.5 (Stokes' Theorem - Green's Theorem)

NOTE: The reduction formulas (6.2.1)–(6.2.2) give the following ones for definite integrals:

$$\int_0^\pi \sin^n \theta \, d\theta = \frac{n-1}{n} \int_0^\pi \sin^{n-2} \theta \, d\theta$$

$$\int_0^\pi \cos^n \theta \, d\theta = \frac{n-1}{n} \int_0^\pi \cos^{n-2} \theta \, d\theta$$

These will be convenient to use in some of the exercises.

Verifying Stokes' Theorem

In Exercises 1–10, for the given vector field $\mathbf{F}$ and the surface S parametrized by $\mathbf{r} : D \to \mathbb{R}^3$, verify Stokes' Theorem:

$$\int_S \operatorname{curl} \mathbf{F} \cdot d\mathbf{A} = \int_C \mathbf{F} \cdot d\mathbf{r},$$

where $C = \partial S$ is the boundary of S. *Caution*: When setting up the parametrizations $\mathbf{r}_3, \mathbf{r}_4$, make sure you "reverse" the directions.

1. $\mathbf{F} = \langle xyz, x^2 z, 0 \rangle$, $\mathbf{r}(\theta, t) = \langle t, \cos\theta, \sin\theta \rangle$,
   for (θ, t) in $[0, \pi] \times [1, 3]$ (a half cylinder)

2. $\mathbf{F} = \langle y^2 z, xyz, 0 \rangle$, $\mathbf{r}(\theta, t) = \langle \cos\theta, t, \sin\theta \rangle$,
   for (θ, t) in $[0, \pi] \times [1, 2]$ (a half cylinder)

3. $\mathbf{F} = \langle x^2, -y^2 z, yz^2 \rangle$, $\mathbf{r}(\theta, t) = \langle t, t\cos\theta, t\sin\theta \rangle$,
   for (θ, t) in $[0, \pi] \times [1, 2]$ (a half frustum of a cone)

4. $\mathbf{F} = \langle x^2 z, y^2, -xz^2 \rangle$, $\mathbf{r}(\theta, t) = \langle t\cos\theta, t, t\sin\theta \rangle$,
   for (θ, t) in $[0, \pi] \times [1, 3]$ (a half frustum of a cone)

5. $\mathbf{F} = \langle yz^2, -xz^2, z^2 \rangle$,
   $\mathbf{r}(\theta, t) = \langle \sin\phi\cos\theta, \sin\phi\sin\theta, \cos\phi \rangle$,
   for (θ, ϕ) in $[0, 2\pi] \times [0, \frac{\pi}{4}]$ (a partial sphere)

6. $\mathbf{F} = \langle yz^2, -xz^2, z^2 \rangle$,
   $\mathbf{r}(\theta, t) = \langle \sin\phi\cos\theta, \sin\phi\sin\theta, \cos\phi \rangle$,
   for (θ, ϕ) in $[0, 2\pi] \times [0, \frac{3\pi}{4}]$ (a partial sphere)

7. $\mathbf{F} = \langle -y^2, x^2, 0 \rangle$, $\mathbf{r}(\theta, t) = \langle t\cos\theta, t\sin\theta, \theta \rangle$,
   for (θ, t) in $[0, \pi] \times [0, 2]$ (a helicoid)

8. $\mathbf{F} = \langle 0, -z^2, y^2 \rangle$, $\mathbf{r}(\theta, t) = \langle \theta, t\cos\theta, t\sin\theta \rangle$,
   for (θ, t) in $[0, \pi] \times [0, 3]$ (a helicoid)

9. $\mathbf{F} = \langle -y^3, x^3, 0 \rangle$, $\mathbf{r}(\theta, t) = \langle t\cos\theta, t\sin\theta, \theta \rangle$,
   for (θ, t) in $[0, \pi] \times [0, 2]$ (a helicoid)

10. $\mathbf{F} = \langle 0, -z^3, y^3 \rangle$, $\mathbf{r}(\theta, t) = \langle \theta, t\cos\theta, t\sin\theta \rangle$,
   for (θ, t) in $[0, \pi] \times [0, 3]$ (a helicoid)

Computing Line Integrals via Stokes' Theorem

In Exercises 11–16, for the given vector field $\mathbf{F}$, compute $\int_C \mathbf{F} \cdot d\mathbf{r}$, where $C = \partial S$. *Hint*: Use Stokes' Theorem to integrate curl $\mathbf{F}$ over S instead.

11. $\mathbf{F} = \langle x + 2yz, x^3 + y^3, xy + z \rangle$,
   $\mathbf{r}(\theta, t) = \langle \cos\theta, \sin\theta, t \rangle$, for (θ, t) in $[0, \pi] \times [1, 4]$

12. $\mathbf{F} = \langle x + yz, 2xz + y, y^3 + z^3 \rangle$,
   $\mathbf{r}(\theta, t) = \langle t, \cos\theta, \sin\theta \rangle$, for (θ, t) in $[0, \pi] \times [1, 2]$

13. $\mathbf{F} = \langle x + 2yz, x^2, xy + z \rangle$,
   $\mathbf{r}(\theta, t) = \langle t\cos\theta, t\sin\theta, t^2 \rangle$, for (θ, t) in $[0, \pi] \times [1, 2]$

14. $\mathbf{F} = \langle x + 2yz, x^2, xy + z \rangle$,
   $\mathbf{r}(\theta, t) = \langle 2t\cos\theta, 2t\sin\theta, 4t^2 \rangle$, for (θ, t)
   in $[0, \pi] \times [1, 2]$

15. $\mathbf{F} = \langle 2yz, y, xy \rangle$,
   $\mathbf{r}(\theta, t) = \langle R\cos\theta, R\sin\theta, t\sin\frac{\theta}{2} \rangle$, where
   $R = 2 + t\cos\frac{\theta}{2}$, for (θ, t) in $[0, 2\pi] \times [-1, 1]$

16. $\mathbf{F} = \langle 4yz, 2y, 2xy \rangle$,
   $\mathbf{r}(\theta, t) = \langle R\cos\theta, R\sin\theta, t\sin\frac{\theta}{2} \rangle$, where
   $R = 4 + t\cos\frac{\theta}{2}$, for (θ, t) in $[0, 2\pi] \times [-2, 2]$

Verifying Green's Theorem

In Exercises 17–22, for the given vector field $\mathbf{F}$ in the plane and the Type I region S, verify the parametric version of Green's Theorem:

$$\int_S \operatorname{curl} \mathbf{F} \cdot d\mathbf{A} = \int_C \mathbf{F} \cdot d\mathbf{r},$$

where $C = \partial S$ is the boundary of S. Use the standard parametrization for S and Equation (14.5.7) for $\mathbf{n}$. *Caution*: When setting up the parametrizations $\mathbf{r}_3, \mathbf{r}_4$ make sure you "reverse" the directions.

17. $y = 0$, $y = x^2$, $x = 0$, $x = 1$, $\mathbf{F} = \langle -y^2, x^2, 0 \rangle$

18. $y = 0$, $y = x^3$, $x = 0$, $x = 1$, $\mathbf{F} = \langle -y^2, x^2, 0 \rangle$

19. $y = 0$, $y = \sqrt{x}$, $x = 1$, $x = 4$, $\mathbf{F} = \langle -y^2, x^2, 0 \rangle$

20. $y = 0$, $y = \sqrt[3]{x}$, $x = 1$, $x = 27$, $\mathbf{F} = \langle -y^2, x^2, 0 \rangle$

21. $y = x^2$, $y = 2x$, $x = 0$, $x = 1$, $\mathbf{F} = \langle x - y^2, -\frac{2}{3}x^3, 0 \rangle$

22. $y = x^3$, $y = 2x$, $x = 0$, $x = 1$, $\mathbf{F} = \langle x - y^2, -\frac{1}{2}x^4, 0 \rangle$

Computing Line Integrals via Green's Theorem

In Exercises 23–34, the polar region S is bounded by the polar curves

$r = aR(\theta),\ r = bR(\theta),\ \theta = 0,\ \theta = \beta$

with $0 \le a < b$. For the given vector field $\mathbf{F}$, compute $\int_C \mathbf{F} \cdot d\mathbf{r}$, where $C = \partial S$. *Hint*: Use Green's Theorem, parametric version, to integrate over S instead. Also, use the standard parametrization for S and Equation (14.5.8) for $\mathbf{n}$.

23. $r = 1,\ r = 3,\ \theta = 0,\ \theta = 2\pi,\quad \mathbf{F} = \langle -y^3,\ x^3,\ 0 \rangle$
(an annulus)

24. $r = 2,\ r = 4,\ \theta = 0,\ \theta = 2\pi,\quad \mathbf{F} = \langle -y^3,\ x^3,\ 0 \rangle$
(an annulus)

25. $r = 0,\ r = \sin\theta,\ \theta = 0,\ \theta = \pi,\quad \mathbf{F} = \langle -y^3,\ x^3,\ 0 \rangle$,
(a disk tangent to the x-axis)

26. $r = 0,\ r = \cos\theta,\ \theta = 0,\ \theta = \pi,\quad \mathbf{F} = \langle -y^3,\ x^3,\ 0 \rangle$,
(a disk tangent to the y-axis)

27. $r = \cos\theta,\ r = 3\cos\theta,\ \theta = 0,\ \theta = \pi,\quad \mathbf{F} = \langle -y^3,\ x^3,\ 0 \rangle$
(an off-center annulus tangent to the y-axis)

28. $r = 3\sin\theta,\ r = \sin\theta,\ \theta = 0,\ \theta = \pi,\quad \mathbf{F} = \langle -y^3,\ x^3,\ 0 \rangle$
(an off-center annulus tangent to the x-axis)

29. $r = \theta,\ r = 3\theta,\ \theta = 0,\ \theta = \pi,\quad \mathbf{F} = \langle -y^3,\ x^3,\ 0 \rangle$,
(between two spirals)

30. $r = \sqrt{\theta},\ r = 2\sqrt{\theta},\ \theta = 0,\ \theta = \pi,\quad \mathbf{F} = \langle -y^3,\ x^3,\ 0 \rangle$
(between two spirals)

31. $r = e^{-\theta},\ r = 3e^{-\theta},\ \theta = 0,\ \theta = \pi,\quad \mathbf{F} = \langle -y^3,\ x^3,\ 0 \rangle$
(between two spirals)

32. $r = e^{-2\theta},\ r = 3e^{-2\theta},\ \theta = 0,\ \theta = \pi,\quad \mathbf{F} = \langle -y^3,\ x^3,\ 0 \rangle$
(between two spirals)

33. $r = 0,\ r = 1 + \cos\theta,\ \theta = 0,\ \theta = \pi,\quad \mathbf{F} = \langle -y^3,\ x^3,\ 0 \rangle$,
(a half cardioid) *Hint*: Use: $1 + \cos\theta = 2\cos^2\frac{\theta}{2}$.

34. $r = 0,\ r = 1 - \cos\theta,\ \theta = 0,\ \theta = \pi,\quad \mathbf{F} = \langle -y^3,\ x^3,\ 0 \rangle$,
(a half cardioid) *Hint*: Use: $1 + \cos\theta = 2\cos^2\frac{\theta}{2}$.

Calculus *Concepts & Computation*

14.6 The Divergence Theorem

The final analog of the Fundamental Theorem of Calculus is the *Divergence Theorem*, which is also known as *Gauss' Divergence Theorem*. This theorem involves a solid E in $\mathbb{R}^3$ and the boundary surface $S = \partial E$ of E.

It will be convenient to first state the *parametric version* of the Divergence Theorem. Then, using the Change of Variables Theorem, we get the traditional version of the Divergence Theorem. This is entirely similar to what we did with Green's Theorem in the last section. Here, we hope to make an even more compelling case for using the parametric version of the Divergence Theorem as opposed to using the traditional version.

The parametric version of the Divergence Theorem involves what is called a *solid integral*, which is analogous to the line and surface integrals we discussed in Sections 14.2 and 14.4. To define the notion of a solid integral of a scalar field ψ over a solid E, we need for E to be parametrized.

Parametrized Solids and Solid Integrals

A solid E in $\mathbb{R}^3$ is *parametrized* if there is a map $\mathbf{r}: B \to \mathbb{R}^3$, such that the image of the parameter domain B is E, i.e., $\mathbf{r}(B) = E$. We assume the parameter domain is a rectangular parallelepiped: $B = [a, b] \times [c, d] \times [p, q]$. This situation covers a great variety solids encountered in mathematics. In terms of components, the parameter map is:

$$\mathbf{r}(u, v, w) = \langle\, f(u, v, w)\, g(u, v, w),\, h(u, v, w)\, \rangle,$$

with parameters (u, v, w) in B. The component functions are assumed to have 1st order partials that are continuous on B. The *Jacobian* of the parameter map $\mathbf{r}$ is the determinant:

$$J(\mathbf{r}) \equiv \begin{vmatrix} f_u & g_u & h_u \\ f_v & g_v & h_v \\ f_w & g_w & h_w \end{vmatrix} = \begin{vmatrix} - \mathbf{r}_u - \\ - \mathbf{r}_v - \\ - \mathbf{r}_w - \end{vmatrix} = (\mathbf{r}_u \times \mathbf{r}_v) \cdot \mathbf{r}_w \qquad (14.6.1)$$

This Jacobian is the key element in the definition of the *solid integral*:

DEFINITION 14.6.1 (Solid Integrals)

Suppose E is a parametrized solid in $\mathbb{R}^3$ with parametrization $\mathbf{r}: B \to \mathbb{R}^3$. If ψ is a scalar field on an open set containing E, then the solid integral *of ψ over E is*

$$\int_E \psi\, d\mathcal{V} \equiv \iiint_B (\psi \circ \mathbf{r})\, J(\mathbf{r})\, dV \qquad (14.6.2)$$

Here the differential notation, $d\mathcal{V} = J(\mathbf{r})\, dV$, for the solid integral of a scalar function is entirely similar to that for the line integral: $ds = \|\mathbf{r}'\|\, dt$ and for the surface integral: $d\mathcal{A} = \|\mathbf{r}_u \times \mathbf{r}_v\|\, dA$.

To define the boundary of a parametrized solid, we need the following concept of piecewise-differentiable surfaces.

Piecewise Differentiable Surfaces

A set S in $\mathbb{R}^3$ is called a *piecewise differentiable surface* if it is the set-theoretic union

$$S \equiv S_1 \cup S_2 \cup \cdots \cup S_n \qquad (14.6.3)$$

of surfaces $S_1, S_2, \ldots, S_n$, with each S_i parametrized by a differentiable parameter map $\mathbf{r}_i : [a_i, b_i] \times [c_i, d_i] \to \mathbb{R}^3$. NOTE: We do *not* require that a piecewise differentiable surface be parametrized.

Surface Integrals for Piecewise Differentiable Surfaces

The definition of the surface integral of a vector field $\mathbf{F}$ along a piecewise differentiable surface S is

$$\int_S \mathbf{F} \cdot d\mathbf{A} \equiv \int_{S_1} \mathbf{F} \cdot d\mathbf{A} + \int_{S_2} \mathbf{F} \cdot d\mathbf{A} + \cdots + \int_{S_n} \mathbf{F} \cdot d\mathbf{A} \qquad (14.6.4)$$

With these concepts understood, we can now consider the definition of the *boundary* ∂E of a parametrized solid E.

Boundary Surfaces

Figure 14.6.1 shows a solid E with parameter map $\mathbf{r} : B \to \mathbb{R}^3$ and parameter domain $B = [a, b] \times [c, d] \times [p, q]$. If we restrict $\mathbf{r}$ to the six bounding sides (rectangles) of the box B, we get parametrizations of the six surfaces $S_1^+, S_1^-, S_2^+, S_2^-, S_3^+, S_3^-$ that form the boundary of the solid E. However: We need to change three of these restrictions so that the surface integrals over S_1^-, S_2^-, S_3^- give the correct sign in the Divergence Theorem. More precisely, we need to change the natural order of the parameters as the following definition indicates.

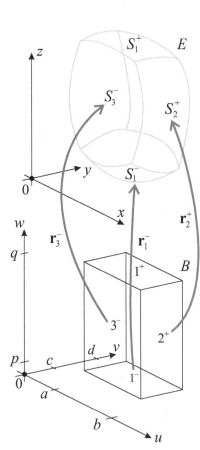

Figure 14.6.1: *Boundary surfaces $S_1^\pm, S_2^\pm, S_3^\pm$.*

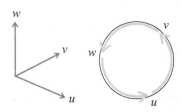

Figure 14.6.2: *The natural order of the parameters.*

> ## DEFINITION 14.6.2 (The Boundary of a Solid E)
>
> *Suppose* $\mathbf{r} : B \to \mathbb{R}^3$ *is a (differentiable) parametrization of a solid* E *with* $B = [a,b] \times [c,d] \times [p,q]$. *Let* $S_1^+, S_1^-, S_2^+, S_2^-, S_3^+, S_3^-$ *be the surfaces with parametrizations:*
>
> (1) $\mathbf{r}_1^+(u,v) = \mathbf{r}(u,v,q)$, *for* (u,v) *in* $[a,b] \times [c,d]$
>
> (2) $\mathbf{r}_1^-(v,u) = \mathbf{r}(u,v,p)$, *for* (u,v) *in* $[a,b] \times [c,d]$
>
> (3) $\mathbf{r}_2^+(v,w) = \mathbf{r}(b,v,w)$, *for* (v,w) *in* $[c,d] \times [p,q]$
>
> (4) $\mathbf{r}_2^-(w,v) = \mathbf{r}(a,v,w)$, *for* (v,w) *in* $[c,d] \times [p,q]$
>
> (5) $\mathbf{r}_3^+(w,u) = \mathbf{r}(u,d,w)$, *for* (u,w) *in* $[a,b] \times [p,q]$
>
> (6) $\mathbf{r}_3^-(u,w) = \mathbf{r}(u,c,w)$, *for* (u,w) *in* $[a,b] \times [p,q]$
>
> *Then the* boundary *of* E *is the piecewise differentiable surface*
>
> $$\partial E = S = S_1^+ \cup S_1^- \cup S_2^+ \cup S_2^- \cup S_3^+ \cup S_3^-$$

NOTE 1: The rectangular sides of the parameter domain are labeled with numbers $1^\pm, 2^\pm, 3^\pm$, *but* not all the numbers are shown in the figure because it is hard to do so clearly. The bottom of the box is labeled 1^- and the top of the box is labeled 1^+. The vertical sides of B are labeled $2^\pm, 3^\pm$.

NOTE 2: The boundary maps $\mathbf{r}_1^+, \mathbf{r}_2^+, \mathbf{r}_3^+$ are just the restrictions of $\mathbf{r}$ to sides $1^+, 2^+, 3^+$ of the parameter domain. The numbering corresponds to the three parameters u, v, w and their pairings are in the *natural order*: u, v and v, w, and w, u. See Figure 14.6.2. Note, however, that the boundary maps $\mathbf{r}_1^-, \mathbf{r}_2^-, \mathbf{r}_3^-$ have their parameters interchanged from the natural orders: v, u (instead of u, v) for $\mathbf{r}_1^-$, w, v (instead of v, w) for $\mathbf{r}_2^-$, and u, w (instead of w, u) for $\mathbf{r}_3^-$. The reason for this is explained below in the discussion of the *three standard normals*.

The examples below will give us practice in writing out the six parameter maps in specific situations. While this can be difficult at first, you will be successful if you approach it systematically and are persistent.

With these preliminaries out of the way, we can now state the Divergence Theorem.

THEOREM 14.6.1 (The Divergence Theorem)

Suppose $\mathbf{F}:U \to \mathbb{R}^3$ is a vector field on an open set U in $\mathbb{R}^3$ and E is a solid in U with parametrization $\mathbf{r}:[a,b]\times[c,d]\times[p,q]\to\mathbb{R}^3.$ Let $S=\partial E$ be the boundary of E. Then

$$\int_E \operatorname{div}\mathbf{F}\,dV = \int_S \mathbf{F}\cdot d\mathbf{A} \qquad (14.6.5)$$

NOTE 1: The proof of this version of the Divergence Theorem (which covers most of the solids that occur in mathematics and physics) is fairly easy and is given at the end of this section,

NOTE 2: The boundary surface $S = \partial E$ is piecewise differentiable with six differentiable pieces. So, the surface integral over S consists of six surface integrals:

$$\int_S \mathbf{F}\cdot d\mathbf{A} = \sum_{n=1}^{3}\Big[\int_{S_n^+}\mathbf{F}\cdot d\mathbf{A} + \int_{S_n^-}\mathbf{F}\cdot d\mathbf{A}\Big] \qquad (14.6.6)$$

As indicated in the notation, when computing these surface integrals you should do it in pairs: S_n^+ and S_n^-. The computation of the six *integrands* can take awhile, but in most cases this work can be shortened by using one, or both, of the following two techniques:

(1) The Three Standard Normals

The three *standard normals* for a solid E parametrized by $\mathbf{r}$ are

$$\mathbf{r}_u \times \mathbf{r}_v, \qquad \mathbf{r}_v \times \mathbf{r}_w \qquad \mathbf{r}_w \times \mathbf{r}_u \qquad (14.6.7)$$

These are vector fields on B and are plotted at the corresponding points in E. The reason that they are called normals is that they are normal (or perpendicular) to surfaces in E. For example, given a particular parameter value w_0 in $[p,q]$, consider the surface S^{w_0} with parameter map $\mathbf{r}^{w_0}(u,v) = \mathbf{r}(u,v,w_0)$. Then the vector field defined by $(u,v) \to \mathbf{r}_u(u,v,w_0) \times \mathbf{r}_v(u,v,w_0)$ is perpendicular to the surface S^{w_0} at each point $\mathbf{r}^{w_0}(u,v)$. See Figure 14.6.3.

In particular, note that when the standard normal $\mathbf{r}_u \times \mathbf{r}_v$ is restricted to the top of B (i.e., $w_0 = q$), then we get a normal to the boundary surface S_1^+. When restricted to the bottom (i.e., $w_0 = p$) then we get a normal to the boundary surface S_1^-, but we use the negative of it $-(\mathbf{r}_u \times \mathbf{r}_v)$. See Figure 14.6.4. Based on these observations, it is convenient to define the following three functions on B:

$$\begin{aligned}
I_1 &= (\mathbf{F}\circ\mathbf{r})\cdot(\mathbf{r}_u \times \mathbf{r}_v) & (14.6.8a)\\
I_2 &= (\mathbf{F}\circ\mathbf{r})\cdot(\mathbf{r}_v \times \mathbf{r}_w) & (14.6.8b)\\
I_3 &= (\mathbf{F}\circ\mathbf{r})\cdot(\mathbf{r}_w \times \mathbf{r}_u) & (14.6.8c)
\end{aligned}$$

Here, $\mathbf{F}$ is a vector field on an open set containing E. We can now use I_1, I_2, I_3 to form the integrands of the six surface integrals. For example, the first two are:

$$\int_{S_1^+}\mathbf{F}\cdot d\mathbf{A} = \int_c^d\int_a^b I_1(u,v,q)\,du\,dv, \qquad \int_{S_1^-}\mathbf{F}\cdot d\mathbf{A} = -\int_c^d\int_a^b I_1(u,v,p)\,du\,dv$$

NOTE: The minus sign in the second integral comes from the way we have ordered the parameters in $\mathbf{r}_1^-(v,u) = \mathbf{r}(u,v,p)$. Then the normal to S_1^- is

$$(\mathbf{r}_1^-)_v \times (\mathbf{r}_1^-)_u = \mathbf{r}_v \times \mathbf{r}_u = -\mathbf{r}_v \times \mathbf{r}_u$$

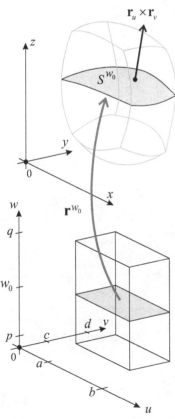

Figure 14.6.3: *A standard normal to a surface in E.*

$$\mathbf{r}_v \times \mathbf{r}_u = -(\mathbf{r}_u \times \mathbf{r}_v)$$

Figure 14.6.4: *Plus and minus the 1st standard normal give normals on $S_1^{\pm}$.*

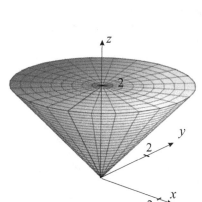

Figure 14.6.5: *A solid bounded by a cone and a disk.*

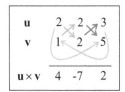

Figure 14.6.6: *Quick way to compute cross products of vectors.*

See Figure 14.6.4. Technically, the above equation should be written as

$$\left[(\mathbf{r}_1^-)_v \times (\mathbf{r}_1^-)_u\right]\big|_{(v,u)} = \left[\mathbf{r}_v \times \mathbf{r}_u\right]\big|_{(u,v,p)} = -\left[\mathbf{r}_u \times \mathbf{r}_v\right]\big|_{(u,v,p)}$$

But, for simplicity we have left off the more precise notation. In a similar fashion, S_2^- and S_3^- will have normals that involve the negatives of the 2nd and 3rd standard normals: $-(\mathbf{r}_v \times \mathbf{r}_w)$, $-(\mathbf{r}_w \times \mathbf{r}_u)$.

(2) Geometric Analysis

Also, as we found In Section 14.5, there are certain situations where the some of the boundary integrals are zero or cancel in pairs. If, looking at the geometry of the boundary surfaces, you can analyze in advance that these situations occur, then you do not need to compute some of the boundary integrals. The situations to look for are (a) the "surface" reduces to a point, (b) the "surface" reduces to a curve, and (c) the surfaces in one of the pairs are equal: $S_n^+ = S_n^-$, in which case $\int_{S_n^+} \mathbf{F} \cdot d\mathbf{A} + \int_{S_n^-} \mathbf{F} \cdot d\mathbf{A} = 0$

Example 14.6.1 (Verifying the Divergence Theorem)

Problem: Let E be the solid parametrized by

$$\mathbf{r}(\theta, t, w) = \langle\, wt\cos\theta,\ wt\sin\theta,\ t \,\rangle$$

where (θ, t, w) is in $[0, 2\pi] \times [0, 2] \times [0, 1]$. The solid E is bounded on its side by a cone and on its top by a circular disk. See Figure 14.6.5. Verify the Divergence Theorem for this solid E and the vector field

$$\mathbf{F} = \langle\, 0,\ 0,\ z^2 \,\rangle$$

Do this by computing the solid integral of div$\mathbf{F}$ over E and comparing it with the surface integral of $\mathbf{F}$ over the boundary $S = \partial E$.

Solution:

First we compute the partials of the parameter map $\mathbf{r}$:

$$\begin{aligned}
\mathbf{r}_\theta &= \langle\, -wt\sin\theta,\ wt\cos\theta,\ 0 \,\rangle \\
\mathbf{r}_t &= \langle\, w\cos\theta,\ w\sin\theta,\ 1 \,\rangle \\
\mathbf{r}_w &= \langle\, t\cos\theta,\ t\sin\theta,\ 0 \,\rangle
\end{aligned}$$

Then, the three standard normals are

$$\mathbf{r}_\theta \times \mathbf{r}_t = \begin{vmatrix} -wt\sin\theta & wt\cos\theta & 0 \\ w\cos\theta & w\sin\theta & 1 \end{vmatrix} = \langle\, wt\cos\theta,\ wt\sin\theta,\ -w^2 t \,\rangle$$

$$\mathbf{r}_t \times \mathbf{r}_w = \begin{vmatrix} w\cos\theta & w\sin\theta & 1 \\ t\cos\theta & t\sin\theta & 0 \end{vmatrix} = \langle\, -t\sin\theta,\ t\cos\theta,\ 0 \,\rangle$$

$$\mathbf{r}_w \times \mathbf{r}_\theta = \begin{vmatrix} t\cos\theta & t\sin\theta & 0 \\ -wt\sin\theta & wt\cos\theta & 0 \end{vmatrix} = \langle\, 0,\ 0,\ wt^2 \,\rangle$$

NOTE: In the above calculations we used the "short-cut' method of computing cross products. See Figure 14.6.6. We use the simplest one of these standard normals to compute the Jacobian:

$$J(\mathbf{r}) = (\mathbf{r}_w \times \mathbf{r}_\theta) \cdot \mathbf{r}_t = \langle\, 0,\ 0,\ wt^2 \,\rangle \cdot \langle\, w\cos\theta,\ w\sin\theta,\ 1 \,\rangle = wt^2$$

From $\mathbf{F} = \langle\, 0,\ 0,\ z^2 \,\rangle$ we get div$\mathbf{F} = \frac{\partial}{\partial x}(0) + \frac{\partial}{\partial y}(0) + \frac{\partial}{\partial z}(z^2) = 2z$. So,

$$\mathbf{F} \circ \mathbf{r} = \langle\, 0,\ 0,\ t^2 \,\rangle \quad \text{and} \quad \text{div}\mathbf{F} \circ \mathbf{r} = 2t$$

Thus, the integrand in the solid integral is

$$(\text{div}\mathbf{F} \circ \mathbf{r})\, J(\mathbf{r}) = (2t)rt^2 = 2wt^3,$$

while the integrands in the boundary-surface integrals involve:

$$
\begin{aligned}
I_1 &= (\mathbf{F} \circ \mathbf{r}) \cdot (\mathbf{r}_\theta \times \mathbf{r}_t) = \langle wt\cos\theta,\ wt\sin\theta,\ -w^2 t \rangle \cdot \langle 0,\ 0,\ t^2 \rangle = -w^2 t^3 \\
I_2 &= (\mathbf{F} \circ \mathbf{r}) \cdot (\mathbf{r}_t \times \mathbf{r}_w) = \langle -t\sin\theta,\ -t\cos\theta,\ 0 \rangle \cdot \langle 0,\ 0,\ t^2 \rangle = 0 \\
I_3 &= (\mathbf{F} \circ \mathbf{r}) \cdot (\mathbf{r}_w \times \mathbf{r}_\theta) = \langle 0,\ 0,\ t^2 \rangle \cdot \langle 0,\ 0,\ wt^2 \rangle = wt^4
\end{aligned}
$$

So, the solid integral of $\operatorname{div}\mathbf{F}$ over E is

$$
\begin{aligned}
\int_E \operatorname{div}\mathbf{F}\, d\mathcal{V} &= \iiint_B (\operatorname{div}\mathbf{F} \circ \mathbf{r})\, J(\mathbf{r})\, dV = \int_{w=0}^{w=1} \int_{\theta=0}^{\theta=2\pi} \int_{t=0}^{t=2} 2wt^3\, dt\, d\theta\, dw \\
&= = \int_{w=0}^{w=1} \int_{\theta=0}^{\theta=2\pi} 2w \left[\tfrac{1}{4} t^4 \right] \Big|_0^2 d\theta\, dw = \int_{w=0}^{w=1} \int_{\theta=0}^{\theta=2\pi} 8w\, d\theta\, dr \\
&= \int_{w=0}^{w=1} 16\pi\, w\, dw = 16\pi \left[\tfrac{1}{2} w^2 \right] \Big|_0^1 = 8\pi
\end{aligned}
$$

Next, we look at the surface integrals of $\mathbf{F}$ over each of the six boundary surfaces, doing the work in pairs.

For S_1^+, S_1^-, the integrals involve $I_1(\theta, t, w) = -w^2 t^3$ evaluated at $w = 1$ and $w = 0$:

$$
\begin{aligned}
\int_{S_1^+} \mathbf{F} \cdot d\mathbf{A} &= \int_0^2 \int_0^{2\pi} I_1(\theta, t, 1)\, d\theta\, dt = \int_0^2 \int_0^{2\pi} -t^3\, d\theta\, dt \\
&= \int_0^2 (2\pi)(-t^3)\, dt = -2\pi \left[\tfrac{1}{4} t^4 \right] \Big|_0^2 = -8\pi \\
\int_{S_1^-} \mathbf{F} \cdot d\mathbf{A} &= -\int_0^2 \int_0^{2\pi} I_1(\theta, t, 0)\, d\theta\, dr = \int_0^2 \int_0^{2\pi} 0\, d\theta\, dr = 0
\end{aligned}
$$

For S_2^+, S_2^-, the integrals involve $I_2(\theta, t, w) = 0$ and so both integrals are 0.

For S_3^+, S_3^-, the integrals involve $I_3(\theta, t, w) = wt^4$ evaluated at $t = 2$ and $t = 0$:

$$
\begin{aligned}
\int_{S_3^+} \mathbf{F} \cdot d\mathbf{A} &= \int_0^1 \int_0^{2\pi} I_3(\theta, 2, w)\, d\theta\, dw = \int_0^1 \int_0^{2\pi} 16w\, d\theta\, dw \\
&= \int_0^1 (2\pi)16w\, dw = 16\pi \left[w^2 \right] \Big|_0^1 = 16\pi \\
\int_{S_3^-} \mathbf{F} \cdot d\mathbf{A} &= -\int_0^1 \int_0^{2\pi} I_3(\theta, 0, w)\, d\theta\, dr = \int_0^1 \int_0^{2\pi} 0\, d\theta\, dw = 0
\end{aligned}
$$

In summary we have found:

$$
\begin{aligned}
\int_E \operatorname{div}\mathbf{F}\, d\mathcal{V} &= 8\pi \\
\int_S \mathbf{F} \cdot d\mathbf{A} &= \sum_{n=1}^{3} \left[\int_{S_n^+} \mathbf{F} \cdot d\mathbf{A} + \int_{S_n^-} \mathbf{F} \cdot d\mathbf{A} \right] \\
&= -8\pi + 0 + 0 + 0 + 16\pi + 0 = 8\pi
\end{aligned}
$$

This verifies the assertion of the Divergence Theorem.

Alternative Geometric Analysis

We can explain four of those zeros we got in the surface-integral calculation by looking at things geometrically, which also can, in some examples, provide a quicker way, since it eliminates the need to do the integrals.

We start with the parameter map for the solid:

$$\mathbf{r}(\theta, t, w) = \langle\, wt\cos\theta,\; wt\sin\theta,\; t\,\rangle$$

and look at the "bounding" surfaces in pairs:

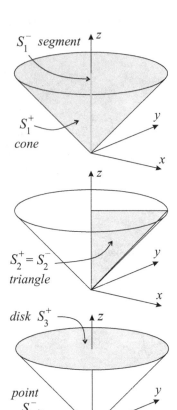

S_1^- segment

S_1^+ cone

S_1^+, S_1^-: For $w = 1$, we get

$$\mathbf{r}_1^+(\theta, t) = \mathbf{r}(\theta, t, 1) = \langle\, t\cos\theta,\; t\sin\theta,\; t\,\rangle,$$

which parametrizes a circular cone, with apex at the origin and base the disk at $z = 2$. For $w = 0$, we get

$$\mathbf{r}_1^-(t, \theta) = \mathbf{r}(\theta, t, 0) = \langle\, 0,\, 0,\, t\,\rangle,$$

which is a line segment along the z-axis (the axis of the cone). From this analysis, we see that we only need to do an integral of the conical surface S_1^+. See Figure 14.6.7.

$S_2^+ = S_2^-$ triangle

S_2^+, S_2^-: For $\theta = 2\pi$ and $\theta = 0$, we get the same parameter map

$$\mathbf{r}_2^+(t, w) = \mathbf{r}(2\pi, t, w) = \langle\, wt,\, 0,\, t\,\rangle = \mathbf{r}(0, t, w) = \mathbf{r}_2^-(w, t),$$

Thus, the surfaces are the same: $S_2^+ = S_2^-$, but their parameters in $\mathbf{r}_2^+, \mathbf{r}_2^-$ are in opposite orders. This means the normals for the surfaces are oppositely directed:

$$(\mathbf{r}_2^+)_t \times (\mathbf{r}_2^+)_w = \mathbf{r}_t \times \mathbf{r}_w, \quad \text{for } S_2^+,$$

$$(\mathbf{r}_2^-)_w \times (\mathbf{r}_2^-)_t = \mathbf{r}_w \times \mathbf{r}_t = -(\mathbf{r}_t \times \mathbf{r}_w), \quad \text{for } S_2^-$$

disk S_3^+

point S_3^-

Thus, the surface integrals are equal in magnitude but opposite in sign. So, $\int_{S_2^+} \mathbf{F} \cdot d\mathbf{A} + \int_{S_2^-} \mathbf{F} \cdot d\mathbf{A} = 0$. NOTE: The assertion here is for *any* vector field $\mathbf{F}$. It so happens, that for the $\mathbf{F}$ in this example, each of the surface integrals is zero.

S_3^+, S_3^-: For $t = 2$, we get

$$\mathbf{r}_3^+(w, \theta) = \mathbf{r}(\theta, 2, w) = \langle\, 2w\cos\theta,\; 2w\sin\theta,\; 2\,\rangle,$$

which parametrizes a circular disk with center $(0, 0, 2)$, and radius 2 in the plane $z = 2$. For $t = 0$, we get

$$\mathbf{r}_3^-(\theta, w) = \mathbf{r}(\theta, 0, w) = \langle\, 0,\, 0,\, 0\,\rangle,$$

Figure 14.6.7: *Analyzing the boundary surfaces* $S_1^{\pm}, S_2^{\pm}, S_3^{\pm}.$

which is a point (the origin. From this analysis, we see that we only need to do an integral of the surface S_3^+. See Figure 14.6.7.

Figure 14.6.8 shows the last frame in a dynamic plot of the four surfaces, single point, and line segment, that form the boundary of the solid in the example. Viewing the corresponding Maple Movie may help your understanding.

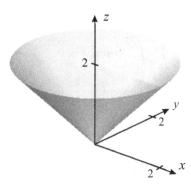

For the next example, we need the following formulas, which come from using the reduction formulas (6.2.1)–(6.2.2) in Chapter 6. *Assume* $n \geq 2$.

Trig-Integral Reduction Formulas:

$$\int_0^{2\pi} \sin^n x\, dx = \frac{n-1}{n} \int_0^{2\pi} \sin^{n-2} x\, dx \qquad (14.6.9a)$$

$$\int_0^{2\pi} \cos^n x\, dx = \frac{n-1}{n} \int_0^{2\pi} \cos^{n-2} x\, dx \qquad (14.6.9b)$$

Figure 14.6.8: *The last frame in a* `dboundaryplot`.

You can use these repeatedly to derive a formula involving only n and π (exercise), but here we only need these for low values of n. It is also clear that these definite integrals are 0 when n is odd.

Example 14.6.2 (Verifying the Divergence Theorem - SOLID TORUS)

Problem: Let E be the solid parametrized by

$$\mathbf{r}(\theta, \phi, w) = \langle\, X\cos\theta,\; X\sin\theta,\; w\sin\phi\,\rangle$$

where

$$X = 2 + w\cos\phi$$

and (θ, ϕ, w) is in $[0, 2\pi] \times [0, 2\pi] \times [0, 1]$. The solid E is a *solid torus* or *doughnut*. See Figure 14.6.9. Taking $w = 1$ in the solid parametrization gives a parametrization of the bounding surface of E, which is a torus. See Section 13.2. Verify the Divergence Theorem for this solid E and the vector field

$$\mathbf{F} = \langle\, \tfrac{1}{3}x^3,\ \tfrac{1}{3}y^3,\ 0 \,\rangle$$

Do this by computing the solid integral of $\operatorname{div}\mathbf{F}$ over E and comparing it with the surface integral of $\mathbf{F}$ over the boundary $S = \partial E$.

Solution: First we compute the partials of the parameter map $\mathbf{r}$:

$$
\begin{aligned}
\mathbf{r}_\theta &= \langle\, -X\sin\theta,\ X\cos\theta,\ 0 \,\rangle \\
\mathbf{r}_\phi &= \langle\, -w\sin\phi\cos\theta,\ -w\sin\phi\sin\theta,\ w\cos\phi \,\rangle \\
\mathbf{r}_w &= \langle\, \cos\phi\cos\theta,\ \cos\phi\sin\theta,\ \sin\phi \,\rangle
\end{aligned}
$$

Then, the three standard normals are

$$
\begin{aligned}
\mathbf{r}_\theta \times \mathbf{r}_\phi &= \begin{vmatrix} -X\sin\theta & X\cos\theta & 0 \\ -w\sin\phi\cos\theta & -w\sin\phi\sin\theta & w\cos\phi \end{vmatrix} \\
&= \langle\, wX\cos\theta\cos\phi,\ wX\sin\theta\cos\phi,\ wX\sin\phi \,\rangle \\[6pt]
\mathbf{r}_\phi \times \mathbf{r}_w &= \begin{vmatrix} -w\sin\phi\cos\theta & -w\sin\phi\sin\theta & w\cos\phi \\ \cos\phi\cos\theta & \cos\phi\sin\theta & \sin\phi \end{vmatrix} \\
&= \langle\, -w\sin\theta,\ w\cos\theta,\ 0 \,\rangle \\[6pt]
\mathbf{r}_w \times \mathbf{r}_\theta &= \begin{vmatrix} \cos\phi\cos\theta & \cos\phi\sin\theta & \sin\phi \\ -X\sin\theta & X\cos\theta & 0 \end{vmatrix} \\
&= \langle\, -X\cos\theta\sin\phi,\ -X\sin\theta\sin\phi,\ X\cos\phi \,\rangle
\end{aligned}
$$

We use the simplest one of these to compute the Jacobian:

$$J(\mathbf{r}) = (\mathbf{r}_\phi \times \mathbf{r}_w) \cdot \mathbf{r}_\theta = \langle\, -w\sin\theta,\ w\cos\theta,\ 0 \,\rangle \cdot \langle\, -X\sin\theta,\ X\cos\theta,\ 0 \,\rangle = wX$$

From $\mathbf{F} = \langle\, \tfrac{1}{3}x^3,\ \tfrac{1}{3}y^3,\ 0 \,\rangle$, we get $\operatorname{div}\mathbf{F} = x^2 + y^2$. So,

$$\mathbf{F} \circ \mathbf{r} = \langle\, \tfrac{1}{3}X^3\cos^3\theta,\ \tfrac{1}{3}X^3\sin^3\theta,\ 0 \,\rangle, \quad \operatorname{div}\mathbf{F} \circ \mathbf{r} = X^2$$

Thus, the integrand in the solid integral is

$$(\operatorname{div}\mathbf{F} \circ \mathbf{r})\, J(\mathbf{r}) = (X^2)wX = wX^3,$$

while the integrands in the boundary-surface integrals involve:

$$
\begin{aligned}
I_1 &= (\mathbf{F} \circ \mathbf{r}) \cdot (\mathbf{r}_\theta \times \mathbf{r}_\phi) = \tfrac{1}{3}wX^4 \big[\cos^4\theta + \sin^4\theta\big]\cos\phi \\
I_2 &= (\mathbf{F} \circ \mathbf{r}) \cdot (\mathbf{r}_\phi \times \mathbf{r}_w) = \tfrac{1}{3}wX^3 \big[\sin^3\theta\cos\theta - \cos^3\theta\sin\theta\big] \\
I_3 &= (\mathbf{F} \circ \mathbf{r}) \cdot (\mathbf{r}_w \times \mathbf{r}_\theta) = -\tfrac{1}{3}X^4 \big[\cos^4\theta + \sin^4\theta\big]\sin\phi
\end{aligned}
$$

So, the solid integral of $\operatorname{div}\mathbf{F}$ over E is

$$
\begin{aligned}
\int_E \operatorname{div}\mathbf{F}\, d\mathcal{V} &= \iiint_B (\operatorname{div}\mathbf{F} \circ \mathbf{r})\, J(\mathbf{r})\, dV = \int_{w=0}^{w=1} \int_{\phi=0}^{\phi=2\pi} \int_{\theta=0}^{\theta=2\pi} wX^3\, d\theta\, d\phi\, dw \\
&= \int_{w=0}^{w=1} \int_{\phi=0}^{\phi=2\pi} \int_{\theta=0}^{\theta=2\pi} w\big[2 + w\cos\phi\big]^3\, d\theta\, d\phi\, dw \\
&= \int_{w=0}^{w=1} \int_{\phi=0}^{\phi=2\pi} 2\pi w\big[2 + w\cos\phi\big]^3\, d\phi\, dw \\
&= \int_{w=0}^{w=1} \int_{\phi=0}^{\phi=2\pi} 2\pi w\big[8 + 12w\cos\phi + 6w^2\cos^2\phi + w^3\cos^3\phi\big]\, d\phi\, dw
\end{aligned}
$$

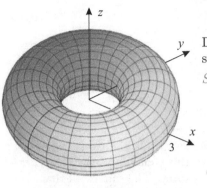

Figure 14.6.9:
A solid torus.

$$
\begin{aligned}
&= \int_{w=0}^{w=1} 2\pi w \left[8(2\pi) + 12w(0) + 6w^2(\tfrac{1}{2} \cdot 2\pi) + w^3(0) \right] dw \\
&= \int_{w=0}^{w=1} 2\pi w \left[16\pi + 6\pi w^2 \right] dw = \int_{w=0}^{w=1} \pi^2 \left[32w + 12w^3 \right] dw \\
&= \pi^2 \left[16w^2 + 3w^4 \right] \Big|_0^1 = 19\pi^2
\end{aligned}
$$

Next, we look at the surface integrals of **F** over each of the six boundary surfaces, doing the work in pairs.

For S_1^+, S_1^-, the integrals involve

$$
I_1(\theta, \phi, w) = \tfrac{1}{3} w X^4 \left[\cos^4 \theta + \sin^4 \theta \right] \cos \phi,
$$

evaluated at $w = 1$ and $w = 0$. For $w = 1$ the surface is the torus (bounding surface of the solid torus) and so the integral over this should give the value $19\pi^2$ that we found above for the integral over the solid torus. The sum of all the other five surface integrals should be zero. Here's the verification of this:

$$
\begin{aligned}
\int_{S_1^+} \mathbf{F} \cdot d\mathbf{A} &= \int_0^{2\pi} \int_0^{2\pi} I_1(\theta, \phi, 1) \, d\theta \, d\phi \\
&= \int_0^{2\pi} \int_0^{2\pi} \tfrac{1}{3} X^4 \left[\cos^4 \theta + \sin^4 \theta \right] \cos \phi \, d\theta \, d\phi \\
&= \int_0^{2\pi} \tfrac{1}{3} X^4 \cos \phi \, d\phi \cdot \int_0^{2\pi} \left[\cos^4 \theta + \sin^4 \theta \right] d\theta \\
&= \left[\int_0^{2\pi} \tfrac{1}{3} \left[2 + \cos \phi \right]^4 \cos \phi \, d\phi \right] \cdot \left[\tfrac{3}{4} \cdot \tfrac{1}{2}(2\pi) + \tfrac{3}{4} \cdot \tfrac{1}{2}(2\pi) \right] \\
&= \tfrac{1}{3} \cdot \tfrac{3\pi}{2} \int_0^{2\pi} \left[16 + 32 \cos \phi + 24 \cos^2 \phi + 8 \cos^3 \phi + \cos^4 \phi \right] \cos \phi \, d\phi \\
&= \tfrac{\pi}{2} \int_0^{2\pi} \left[16 \cos \phi + 32 \cos^2 \phi + 24 \cos^3 \phi + 8 \cos^4 \phi + \cos^5 \phi \right] d\phi \\
&= \tfrac{\pi}{2} \left[16(0) + 32(\tfrac{1}{2} \cdot 2\pi) + 24(0) + 8(\tfrac{3}{4} \cdot \tfrac{1}{2}(2\pi)) + 0 \right] \\
&= \tfrac{\pi}{2} \left[32\pi + 6\pi \right] = 19\pi^2
\end{aligned}
$$

The integral over S_1^- has integrand $-I_1(\theta, \phi, 0) = 0$, and so we get 0 for this integral.

For S_2^+, S_2^-, the integrals involve

$$
I_2(\theta, \phi, w) = \tfrac{1}{3} w X^3 \left[\sin^3 \theta \cos \theta - \cos^3 \theta \sin \theta \right]
$$

evaluated at $\theta = 2\pi$ and $\theta = 0$. But clearly

$$
I_2(2\pi, \phi, w) = 0, \qquad I_2(0, \phi, w) = 0,
$$

and so both the surface integrals are 0.

For S_3^+, S_3^-, the integrals involve

$$
I_3(\theta, \phi, w) = -\tfrac{1}{3} X^4 \left[\cos^4 \theta + \sin^4 \theta \right] \sin \phi
$$

evaluated at $\phi = 2\pi$ and $\phi = 0$. But clearly

$$
I_3(\theta, 2\pi, w) = 0, \qquad I_3(\theta, 0, w) = 0,
$$

and so both the surface integrals are 0.

In summary we have found:

$$
\int_E \mathrm{div} \mathbf{F} \, d\mathcal{V} = 19\pi^2
$$

$$
\int_S \mathbf{F} \cdot d\mathbf{A} = \sum_{i=1}^{3} \left[\int_{S_i^+} \mathbf{F} \cdot d\mathbf{A} + \int_{S_i^-} \mathbf{F} \cdot d\mathbf{A} \right]
$$

$$= 19\pi^2 + 0 + 0 + 0 + 0 + 0 = 19\pi^2$$

This verifies the assertion of the Divergence Theorem.

Alternative Geometric Analysis: As with the cone in the last example, we could here, as mentioned, only look at the one surface integral over S_1^+ to verify the theorem. This surface is the only "bounding surface of the solid torus. The other five surfaces are internal and are either degenerate or are a pair of surfaces which are the same but have oppositely directed normals. Here's the analysis:

The parametrization for the solid torus is

$$\mathbf{r}(\theta, \phi, w) = \langle X\cos\theta, \, X\sin\theta, \, w\sin\phi \rangle$$

where

$$X = 2 + w\cos\phi$$

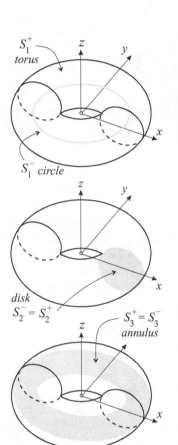

S_1^+: As mentioned above, for $w = 1$, the parameter map $\mathbf{r}_1^+(\theta, \phi) = \mathbf{r}(\theta, \phi, 1)$ parametrized a standard torus.

S_1^-: For $w = 0$, the parameter map is

$$\mathbf{r}_1^-(\phi, \theta) = \mathbf{r}(\theta, \phi, 0) = \langle 2\cos\theta, \, 2\sin\theta, \, 0 \rangle$$

This gives a circle of radius 2, centered at the origin, and in the x-y-plane. See Figure 14.6.10. So, S_1^- is a degenerate "surface" and the surface integral over it is 0.

S_2^+: For $\theta = 2\pi$, the parameter map is

$$\mathbf{r}_2^+(\phi, w) = \mathbf{r}(2\pi, \phi, w) = \langle X, \, 0, \, w\sin\phi \rangle = \langle 2 + w\cos\phi, \, 0, \, w\sin\phi \rangle$$

This is disk of radius 1, centered at $(2,0,0)$, and in the x-z-plane. In fact, the solid torus is generated by revolving this disk about the z-axis. See Figure 14.6.10. For a general vector field $\mathbf{F}$ (not the one we used above), its surface integral $\int_{S_2^+} \mathbf{F} \cdot d\mathbf{A}$ need not be zero. *However,* as seen in the next step, the surface S_2^+ is equal to S_2^- but has oppositely direct normal. So, $\int_{S_2^+} \mathbf{F} \cdot d\mathbf{A} = -\int_{S_2^-} \mathbf{F} \cdot d\mathbf{A}$.

S_2^-: For $\theta = 0$, the parameter map is

$$\mathbf{r}_2^-(w, \phi) = \mathbf{r}(0, \phi, w) = \langle X, \, 0, \, w\sin\phi \rangle = \langle 2 + w\cos\phi, \, 0, \, w\sin\phi \rangle$$

Thus, $\mathbf{r}_2^-(w, \phi) = \mathbf{r}_2^+(\phi, w)$ and so $S_2^- = S_2^+$. But, $\mathbf{r}_2^-$ and $\mathbf{r}_1^+$ have the parameters ϕ, w in opposite orders and so their normals are oppositely directed. Hence, as mentioned, $\int_{S_2^+} \mathbf{F} \cdot d\mathbf{A} = -\int_{S_2^-} \mathbf{F} \cdot d\mathbf{A}$.

S_3^+: For $\phi = 2\pi$, the parameter map is

$$\mathbf{r}_3^+(w, \theta) = \mathbf{r}(\theta, 2\pi, w) = \langle X\cos\theta, \, X\sin\theta, \, 0 \rangle = \langle (2+w)\cos\theta, \, (2+w)\sin\theta, \, 0 \rangle$$

This is an annulus formed by the two concentric circles in the x-y-plane with parametrizations

$$\mathbf{r}_3^+(1, \theta) = \langle 3\cos\theta, \, 3\sin\theta, \, 0 \rangle, \qquad \mathbf{r}_3^+(0, \theta) = \langle 2\cos\theta, \, 2\sin\theta, \, 0 \rangle$$

See Figure 14.6.10. For a general vector field $\mathbf{F}$ (not necessarily the one we used above), its surface integral $\int_{S_3^-} \mathbf{F} \cdot d\mathbf{A}$ need not be zero (as it was above). *However,* as seen in the next step, the surface S_3^+ is equal to S_3^- but has oppositely directed normal. So, $\int_{S_3^+} \mathbf{F} \cdot d\mathbf{A} = -\int_{S_3^-} \mathbf{F} \cdot d\mathbf{A}$.

S_3^-: For $\theta = 0$, the parameter map is

$$\mathbf{r}_3^-(\theta, w) = \mathbf{r}(\theta, 0, w) = \langle X\cos\theta, \, X\sin\theta, \, 0 \rangle = \langle (2+w)\cos\theta, \, (2+w)\sin\theta, \, 0 \rangle$$

Thus, $\mathbf{r}_3^-(\theta, w)$ and $\mathbf{r}_3^+(w, \theta)$ are the same expression and so $S_3^- = S_3^+$. But, $\mathbf{r}_3^-$ and $\mathbf{r}_3^+$ have the parameters w, θ in opposite orders and so their normals are oppositely directed. Hence, as mentioned, $\int_{S_3^+} \mathbf{F} \cdot d\mathbf{A} = -\int_{S_3^-} \mathbf{F} \cdot d\mathbf{A}$.

Figure 14.6.10: *Analyzing the boundary surfaces $S_1^{\pm}, S_2^{\pm}, S_3^{\pm}$.*

Figure 14.6.11 shows the last frame in a Maple Movie illustrating a dynamic plot of the six boundary "surfaces" of the solid torus.

SUMMARY: For the solid torus E and *any* vector field $\mathbf{F}$

$$\int_E \operatorname{div}\mathbf{F} \, d\mathcal{V} = \int_{S_1^+} \mathbf{F} \cdot d\mathbf{A},$$

where S_1^+ is the torus bounding E.

Example 14.6.3 (Computing a Flux - MÖBIUS SLAB)

Problem: Suppose E is the solid parametrized by

$$\mathbf{r}(\theta, t, w) = \langle\, T\cos\theta,\, T\sin\theta,\, P\,\rangle,$$

where

$$T = 2 + t\cos\tfrac{\theta}{2} - w\sin\tfrac{\theta}{2},$$
$$P = t\sin\tfrac{\theta}{2} + w\cos\tfrac{\theta}{2},$$

and (θ, t, w) is in $[0, 2\pi] \times [-1, 1] \times [-c, c]$. We call this solid a *Möbius slab* since it is gotten by giving a Möbius strip some thickness. Here $2c$ is the thickness. See Figure 14.6.12. For the vector field

$$\mathbf{F} = \langle\, 0,\, 0,\, z^2\,\rangle$$

use the Divergence Theorem to compute the flux of $\mathbf{F}$ through the boundary surface $S = \partial E$ of the Möbius slab.

Solution: As Figure 14.6.12. shows, the Möbius slab is bounded by four different surfaces — two are Möbius strips and two are ribbons connecting these strips. (View the Maple Movie to see these.) So we would have to compute four surface integrals to find the flux. In addition, these integrations would be very difficult to do. So, instead, we do a solid integral of $\operatorname{div}\mathbf{F}$. For this we first compute the partials of the parameter map $\mathbf{r}$:

$$\mathbf{r}_\theta = \langle\, T_\theta\cos\theta - T\sin\theta,\, T_\theta\sin\theta + T\cos\theta,\, P_\theta\,\rangle$$
$$\mathbf{r}_t = \langle\, \cos\tfrac{\theta}{2}\cos\theta,\, \cos\tfrac{\theta}{2}\sin\theta,\, \sin\tfrac{\theta}{2}\,\rangle$$
$$\mathbf{r}_w = \langle\, -\sin\tfrac{\theta}{2}\cos\theta,\, -\sin\tfrac{\theta}{2}\sin\theta,\, \cos\tfrac{\theta}{2}\,\rangle$$

Then, the Jacobian of $\mathbf{r}$ is

$$J(\mathbf{r}) = \begin{vmatrix} T_\theta\cos\theta - T\sin\theta & T_\theta\sin\theta + T\cos\theta & P_\theta \\ \cos\tfrac{\theta}{2}\cos\theta & \cos\tfrac{\theta}{2}\sin\theta & \sin\tfrac{\theta}{2} \\ -\sin\tfrac{\theta}{2}\cos\theta & -\sin\tfrac{\theta}{2}\sin\theta & \cos\tfrac{\theta}{2} \end{vmatrix}$$

$$= \left[T_\theta\cos\theta - T\sin\theta\right]\sin\theta - \left[T_\theta\sin\theta + T\cos\theta\right]\cos\theta + P_\theta(0)$$

$$= -T$$

Next, since $\mathbf{F} = \langle\, 0,\, 0,\, z^2\,\rangle$, we have $\operatorname{div}\mathbf{F} = 2z$, and so also $\operatorname{div}\mathbf{F} \circ \mathbf{r} = 2P$. Consequently, the flux calculation is

$$\mathcal{F} = \int_S \mathbf{F} \cdot d\mathbf{A} = \int_E \operatorname{div}\mathbf{F} \, d\mathcal{V} = \int_B (\operatorname{div}\mathbf{F} \circ \mathbf{r})\, J(\mathbf{r})\, dV$$

$$= \int_{-c}^{c}\int_{-1}^{1}\int_{0}^{2\pi} -2TP \, d\theta\, dt\, dw$$

$$= -2\int_{-c}^{c}\int_{-1}^{1}\int_{0}^{2\pi} \left[2 + t\cos\tfrac{\theta}{2} - w\sin\tfrac{\theta}{2}\right]\left[t\sin\tfrac{\theta}{2} + w\cos\tfrac{\theta}{2}\right] d\theta\, dt\, dw$$

$$= -2\int_{-c}^{c}\int_{-1}^{1}\int_{0}^{2\pi} \left[\begin{array}{l} 2t\sin\tfrac{\theta}{2} + 2w\cos\tfrac{\theta}{2} + (t^2 - w^2)\sin\tfrac{\theta}{2}\cos\tfrac{\theta}{2} \\ +tw\left[\cos^2\tfrac{\theta}{2} - \sin^2\tfrac{\theta}{2}\right] \end{array}\right] d\theta\, dt\, dw$$

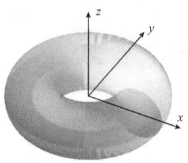

Figure 14.6.11: *The last frame in a* dboundaryplot.

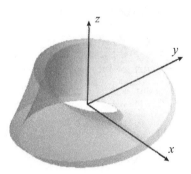

Figure 14.6.12:
A Möbius slab (the last frame in a movie created by dboundaryplot.

$$
= \begin{cases} -2\displaystyle\int_{-c}^{c}\int_{0}^{2\pi}\int_{-1}^{1} 2t\sin\tfrac{\theta}{2}\,dt\,d\theta\,dw - 2\displaystyle\int_{-1}^{1}\int_{0}^{2\pi}\int_{-c}^{c} 2w\cos\tfrac{\theta}{2}\,dw\,d\theta\,dt \\[2mm] -2\displaystyle\int_{-c}^{c}\int_{-1}^{1}\int_{0}^{2\pi}(t^2-w^2)\big[\sin\tfrac{\theta}{2}\cos\tfrac{\theta}{2}+tw\cos\theta\big]\,d\theta\,dt\,dw \end{cases}
$$

$$
= \begin{cases} -2\displaystyle\int_{-c}^{c}\int_{0}^{2\pi}\big[t^2\big]\Big|_{-1}^{1}\sin\tfrac{\theta}{2}\,d\theta\,dw - 2\displaystyle\int_{-1}^{1}\int_{0}^{2\pi}\big[w^2\big]\Big|_{-c}^{c}\cos\tfrac{\theta}{2}\,dw\,d\theta\,dt \\[2mm] -2\displaystyle\int_{-c}^{c}\int_{-1}^{1}(t^2-w^2)\big[\sin^2\tfrac{\theta}{2}+tw\sin\theta\big]\Big|_{0}^{2\pi}\,d\theta\,dt\,dw \end{cases}
$$

$$
= \left.\begin{cases} -2\displaystyle\int_{-c}^{c}\int_{0}^{2\pi}\big[0\big]\sin\tfrac{\theta}{2}\,d\theta\,dw - 2\displaystyle\int_{-1}^{1}\int_{0}^{2\pi}\big[0\big]\cos\tfrac{\theta}{2}\,dw\,d\theta\,dt \\[2mm] -2\displaystyle\int_{-c}^{c}\int_{-1}^{1}(t^2-w^2)\big[0\big]\,d\theta\,dt\,dw \end{cases}\right\} = 0
$$

Thus, the flux through the surface bounding the Möbius slab is zero.

NOTE 1: We used the trig identity $\cos^2 A - \sin^2 A = \cos 2A$ in the above calculation, with $A = \tfrac{\theta}{2}$.

NOTE 2: In the iterated integrals at the top of this page, we changed the orders of integration so that the first integral computed gives 0. For example, $\int_{-1}^{1} 2t\,dt = 0$. Consider doing this, where possible, to save yourself some work.

THE DIVERGENCE THEOREM (Traditional Version)

We can use the Change of Variables Theorem to get the traditional version of the Divergence Theorem from the parametrized version.. To apply the Change of Variables Theorem to $\mathbf{r}$ we must place two additional restrictions on $\mathbf{r}$:

$\quad$ (1) $\mathbf{r}$ is one-to-one on B° $\qquad$ (2) $J(\mathbf{r}) \neq 0$ at any point in B°

Here $B^\circ \equiv (a,b) \times (c,d) \times (p,q)$ is the "interior" of the box B, i.e., B without its sides. Then the Change of Variables Formula gives:

$$
\iiint_B (\operatorname{div}\mathbf{F} \circ \mathbf{r})\,|\,J(\mathbf{r})\,|\,dV = \iiint_E \operatorname{div}\mathbf{F}\,dV \qquad (14.6.10)
$$

Next note that since the Jacobian $J(\mathbf{r})$ is never zero in B° and is continuous on B°, then it is either positive, $J(\mathbf{r}) > 0$ at all points of B° or negative $J(\mathbf{r}) < 0$ at all point of B°. Thus, we can write the parametric version of the Divergence Theorem as follows

$$
\int_S \mathbf{F} \cdot d\mathbf{A} = \int_E \operatorname{div}\mathbf{F}\,dV = \iint_B (\operatorname{div}\mathbf{F} \circ \mathbf{r})\,J(\mathbf{r})\,dV = \pm\iiint_E \operatorname{div}\mathbf{F}\,dV
$$

Finally note that $J(\mathbf{r})$ is the determinant of the matrix whose columns are the standard normal vectors: $\mathbf{r}_u, \mathbf{r}_v, \mathbf{r}_w$. So, if $J(\mathbf{r}) < 0$ on B°, then we can reorder the parameters as v, u, w and get $J(\mathbf{r}) > 0$ on B^0. All of this discussion then gives us the following theorem.

THEOREM 14.6.2 (The Divergence Theorem - Traditional Version)

Suppose $\mathbf{F}: U \to \mathbb{R}^3$ *is a vector field on an open set* U *in* $\mathbb{R}^3$ *and* E *is a solid in* U *with parametrization* $\mathbf{r}: B = [a,b] \times [c,d] \times [p,q] \to \mathbb{R}^3$. *Assume* $\mathbf{r}$ *is one-to-one on the interior of* B *and* $J(\mathbf{r}) > 0$ *on the interior of* B *as well. If* $S = \partial E$ *is the boundary of* E, *then*

$$
\iiint_E \operatorname{div}\mathbf{F}\,dV = \int_S \mathbf{F} \cdot d\mathbf{A} \qquad (14.6.11)
$$

One could make the argument that this version of the Divergence Theorem is not as useful as the parametric version. To use it to compute the triple integral $\iiint_E \operatorname{div}\mathbf{F}\, dV$, one has to change variables, which essentially amounts to parametrizing E. The following example illustrates this.

Example 14.6.4 (The Traditional Version of the Divergence Theorem)

Problem: For each of the solids E and vector fields $\mathbf{F}$ in Examples 14.6.1–14.6.3 setup (or at least try to setup) the triple integral $\iiint_E \operatorname{div}\mathbf{F}\, dV$. If it is not too difficult, compute this integral.

Solution: In each of the three examples, we need to get Cartesian equations for the bounding surfaces of E and setup the triple integral as an iterated integral like we did in Chapter 12..

Example 14.6.1: The bounding surface for the side of E is a cone, which you might guess has Cartesian equation:

$$x^2 + y^2 = z^2$$

You can also get this equation by starting with the parametrization of the solid:

$$\mathbf{r} = \langle\, rt\cos\theta,\ rt\sin\theta,\ t\,\rangle$$

and taking $r = 1$ to get the parametrization of the cone. Writing this latter parametrization as

$$x = t\cos\theta,\quad y = t\sin\theta,\quad z = t$$

we see that

$$x^2 + y^2 = t^2\cos^2\theta + t^2\sin^2\theta = t^2\big(\cos^2\theta + \sin^2\theta\big) = t^2 = z^2$$

Either way, we get that E is bounded on the side (or bottom) by the cone, which we can view as the graph of

$$z = \sqrt{x^2 + y^2},\quad \text{for } (x,y) \text{ in the disk } x^2 + y^2 \le 4.$$

E is bounded on the top by the plane $z = 2$. Also, recall that in this example $\mathbf{F} = \langle 0,\, 0,\, z^2 \rangle$ and so $\operatorname{div}\mathbf{F} = 2z$. Consequently, the triple integral is

$$
\begin{aligned}
\iiint_E \operatorname{div}\mathbf{F}\, dV &= \int_{x=-2}^{x=2} \int_{y=-\sqrt{4-x^2}}^{y=\sqrt{4-x^2}} \int_{z=\sqrt{x^2+y^2}}^{z=2} 2z\, dz\, dy\, dx \\
&= \int_{\theta=0}^{\theta=2\pi} \int_{r=0}^{r=2} \int_{z=r}^{z=2} 2z\,r\, dz\, dr\, d\theta \\
&= \int_{\theta=0}^{\theta=2\pi} \int_{r=0}^{r=2} z^2 \Big|_{z=r}^{z=2} r\, dr\, d\theta \\
&= \int_{\theta=0}^{\theta=2\pi} \int_{r=0}^{r=2} (4 - r^2)\, r\, dr\, d\theta \\
&= \int_{\theta=0}^{\theta=2\pi} \left(2r^2 - \tfrac{1}{4}r^4\right)\Big|_{r=0}^{r=2} d\theta = \int_0^{2\pi} (8 - 4)\, d\theta = 8\pi
\end{aligned}
$$

This is the value we got for this integral in Example 14.6.1. NOTE: In the above we changed to cylindrical coordinates in order to compute the iterated integrals.

Example 14.6.2: The bounding surface for a solid torus E is, of course, a torus. You can get a Cartesian equation for it by starting with the parametrization of the solid torus:

$$\mathbf{r} = \langle\, (2 + w\cos\phi)\cos\theta,\ (2 + w\cos\phi)\sin\theta,\ w\sin\phi\,\rangle$$

and taking $w = 1$ to get the parametrization of the torus. We write this latter parametrization as

$$x = (2 + \cos\phi)\cos\theta,\quad y = (2 + \cos\phi)\sin\theta,\quad z = \sin\phi$$

To get Cartesian equation from this, we try eliminating the parameters θ and ϕ. From the form of the first two equations, we see that θ can be eliminated by taking the sum of the squares:

$$x^2 + y^2 = (2 + \cos\phi)^2, \quad \text{so } \sqrt{x^2+y^2} = 2 + \cos\phi, \quad \text{or } \sqrt{x^2+y^2} - 2 = \cos\phi$$

But then

$$\left[\sqrt{x^2+y^2} - 2\right]^2 + z^2 = \cos^2\phi + \sin^2\phi = 1$$

Thus,

A Cartesian Equation for a Torus: $\quad \left[\sqrt{x^2+y^2} - 2\right]^2 + z^2 = 1$

To setup the triple integral, we need to solve the above equation for z:

$$z = \pm\sqrt{1 - \left[\sqrt{x^2+y^2} - 2\right]^2}, \qquad (14.6.15)$$

where (x,y) is in the annulus: $D = \{(x,y) \text{ in } \mathbb{R}^2 \mid 1 \le x^2 + y^2 \le 3\}$. Equation (14.6.15) gives two functions: the one with the $+$ sign has graph which is the top part of the torus (the part above the x-y-plane), while the one with the $-$ sign has graph which is the bottom part of the torus.

Recall that $\mathbf{F} = \langle \frac{1}{3}x^3, \frac{1}{3}y^3, 0 \rangle$ and so $\operatorname{div}\mathbf{F} = x^2 + y^2$. So, the triple integral is

$$\iiint_E \operatorname{div}\mathbf{F}\, dV = \iint_D \int_{z=-\sqrt{1-\left[\sqrt{x^2+y^2}-2\right]^2}}^{z=\sqrt{1-\left[\sqrt{x^2+y^2}-2\right]^2}} (x^2+y^2)\, dz\, dA$$

$$= \int_{\theta=0}^{\theta=2\pi} \int_{r=1}^{r=3} \int_{z=-\sqrt{1-[r-2]^2}}^{z=\sqrt{1-[r-2]^2}} r^3\, dz\, dr\, d\theta$$

$$= \int_{\theta=0}^{\theta=2\pi} \int_{r=1}^{r=3} r^3\sqrt{1-[r-2]^2}\, dr\, d\theta$$

$$= 2\pi\int_1^3 r^3\sqrt{1-[r-2]^2}\, dr$$

As an exercise, you can complete the integration by using the substitution $r = 2 + \cos\phi$, which gives a complicated (but doable) trig integral. In all respects using the traditional version of the Divergence Theorem, seems more complicated.

Example 14.6.3: The parametric equations for the Möbius slab E are

$$x = T\cos\theta \quad y = T\sin\theta \quad z = P,$$

where

$$T = 2 + t\cos\tfrac{\theta}{2} - w\sin\tfrac{\theta}{2}, \quad P = t\sin\tfrac{\theta}{2} + w\cos\tfrac{\theta}{2},$$

The four bounding surfaces of E come from taking $w = \pm c$ and $t = \pm 1$ in this. It is far from clear how to eliminate the parameters in the resulting parametrizations and get Cartesian equations for these surfaces. It is also not clear if the triple integral $\iiint_E \operatorname{div}\mathbf{F}\, dV$ can be setup as an iterated integral in any of the three coordinate systems (Cartesian, cylindrical, spherical) we used in Chapter 12. So, the traditional version of the Divergence Theorem does not work here.

PROOF OF THE DIVERGENCE THEOREM

We need six key identities for the proof. The first comes from noting that the Jacobian $J(\mathbf{r})$ has rows $\nabla f, \nabla g$, and ∇h and so

$$J(\mathbf{r}) = \begin{vmatrix} f_u & f_v & f_w \\ g_u & g_v & g_w \\ h_u & h_v & h_w \end{vmatrix} = \begin{vmatrix} - \nabla f - \\ - \nabla g - \\ - \nabla h - \end{vmatrix}$$

$$= \nabla f \cdot (\nabla g \times \nabla h) = \nabla g \cdot (\nabla h \times \nabla f) = \nabla h \cdot (\nabla f \times \nabla g) \qquad \text{(I)}$$

Note the three different ways we can represent $J(\mathbf{r})$ in terms of a scalar triple product. Next, using the chain rule, one can show that if ψ is a scalar field defined on an open set containing E, then

$$\nabla(\psi \circ \mathbf{r}) = \psi_x \nabla f + \psi_y \nabla g + \psi_z \nabla h \tag{II}$$

To simplify the notation above (and below) we write, for example, ψ_x instead of the more correct notation $\psi_x \circ \mathbf{r}$.

Additionally, if ϕ, ψ are scalar fields and $\mathbf{G}$ a vector field on an open set in $\mathbb{R}^3$, then the following identities are easy to prove:

$$\operatorname{div}(\nabla\phi \times \nabla\psi) = 0 \tag{III}$$

$$\operatorname{div}(\psi\,\mathbf{G}) = \nabla\psi \cdot \mathbf{G} + \psi\operatorname{div}\mathbf{G} \tag{IV}$$

The next set of identities we need is

$$\nabla g \times \nabla h = \big\langle\, (\mathbf{r}_v \times \mathbf{r}_w)_1,\ (\mathbf{r}_w \times \mathbf{r}_u)_1,\ (\mathbf{r}_u \times \mathbf{r}_v)_1 \,\big\rangle \tag{Va}$$

$$\nabla h \times \nabla f = \big\langle\, (\mathbf{r}_v \times \mathbf{r}_w)_2,\ (\mathbf{r}_w \times \mathbf{r}_u)_2,\ (\mathbf{r}_u \times \mathbf{r}_v)_2 \,\big\rangle \tag{Vb}$$

$$\nabla f \times \nabla g = \big\langle\, (\mathbf{r}_v \times \mathbf{r}_w)_3,\ (\mathbf{r}_w \times \mathbf{r}_u)_3,\ (\mathbf{r}_u \times \mathbf{r}_v)_3 \,\big\rangle \tag{Vc}$$

In the above we used the subscript notation for the components of a vector field: $\mathbf{G}_1, \mathbf{G}_2, \mathbf{G}_3$ are the components of $\mathbf{G}$.

We now use these identities to get the following identity, which is instrumental in the proof.

FUNDAMENTAL IDENTITY:

$$(\operatorname{div}\mathbf{F} \circ \mathbf{r})\,J(\mathbf{r}) = \frac{\partial}{\partial u}(I_2) + \frac{\partial}{\partial v}(I_3) + \frac{\partial}{\partial w}(I_1) \tag{VI}$$

In the above I_1, I_2, I_3 are the scalar fields defined in Equations (14.6.8a)–(14.6.8c). To prove the Fundamental Identity (VI), we use Identities (1)–(V) in succession as follows.

$$
\begin{aligned}
&(\operatorname{div}\mathbf{F} \circ \mathbf{r})\,J(\mathbf{r}) \\
={}& (M_x + N_y + K_z)\,J(\mathbf{r}) = M_x J(\mathbf{r}) + N_y J(\mathbf{r}) + K_z J(\mathbf{r}) \\
={}& M_x\big[\nabla f \cdot (\nabla g \times \nabla h)\big] + N_y\big[\nabla g \cdot (\nabla h \times \nabla f)\big] + K_z\big[\nabla h \cdot (\nabla f \times \nabla g)\big] \\
={}& \begin{cases}
\big[M_x \nabla f + M_y \nabla g + M_z \nabla h\big] \cdot (\nabla g \times \nabla h) \\
\big[N_x \nabla f + N_y \nabla g + N_z \nabla h\big] \cdot (\nabla h \times \nabla f) \\
\big[K_x \nabla f + K_y \nabla g + K_z \nabla h\big] \cdot (\nabla f \times \nabla g)
\end{cases} \\
={}& \nabla(M \circ \mathbf{r}) \cdot (\nabla g \times \nabla h) + \nabla(N \circ \mathbf{r}) \cdot (\nabla h \times \nabla f) + \nabla(K \circ \mathbf{r}) \cdot (\nabla f \times \nabla g) \\
={}& \begin{cases}
\nabla(M \circ \mathbf{r}) \cdot (\nabla g \times \nabla h) + \nabla(N \circ \mathbf{r}) \cdot (\nabla h \times \nabla f) + \nabla(K \circ \mathbf{r}) \cdot (\nabla f \times \nabla g) \\
(M \circ \mathbf{r})\operatorname{div}(\nabla g \times \nabla h) + (N \circ \mathbf{r})\operatorname{div}(\nabla h \times \nabla f) + (K \circ \mathbf{r})\operatorname{div}(\nabla f \times \nabla g)
\end{cases} \\
={}& \operatorname{div}\big[(M \circ \mathbf{r})(\nabla g \times \nabla h)\big] + \operatorname{div}\big[(N \circ \mathbf{r})(\nabla h \times \nabla f)\big] + \operatorname{div}\big[(K \circ \mathbf{r})(\nabla f \times \nabla g)\big] \\
={}& \operatorname{div}\big[(M \circ \mathbf{r})(\nabla g \times \nabla h) + (N \circ \mathbf{r})(\nabla h \times \nabla f) + (K \circ \mathbf{r})(\nabla f \times \nabla g)\big] \\
={}& \operatorname{div}\begin{bmatrix}
(M \circ \mathbf{r})\big\langle (\mathbf{r}_v \times \mathbf{r}_w)_1,\ (\mathbf{r}_w \times \mathbf{r}_u)_1,\ (\mathbf{r}_u \times \mathbf{r}_v)_1 \big\rangle \\
+(N \circ \mathbf{r})\big\langle (\mathbf{r}_v \times \mathbf{r}_w)_2,\ (\mathbf{r}_w \times \mathbf{r}_u)_2,\ (\mathbf{r}_u \times \mathbf{r}_v)_2 \big\rangle \\
+(K \circ \mathbf{r})\big\langle (\mathbf{r}_v \times \mathbf{r}_w)_3,\ (\mathbf{r}_w \times \mathbf{r}_u)_3,\ (\mathbf{r}_u \times \mathbf{r}_v)_3 \big\rangle
\end{bmatrix} \\
={}& \operatorname{div}\Big[\big\langle (\mathbf{F} \circ \mathbf{r}) \cdot (\mathbf{r}_v \times \mathbf{r}_w),\ (\mathbf{F} \circ \mathbf{r}) \cdot (\mathbf{r}_u \times \mathbf{r}_u),\ (\mathbf{F} \circ \mathbf{r}) \cdot (\mathbf{r}_u \times \mathbf{r}_v) \big\rangle\Big] \\
={}& \operatorname{div}\big[\langle I_2,\ I_3,\ I_1 \rangle\big] \\
={}& \frac{\partial}{\partial u}(I_2) + \frac{\partial}{\partial v}(I_3) + \frac{\partial}{\partial w}(I_1)
\end{aligned}
$$

Using the Fundamental Identity, the proof of the Divergence Theorem is easy:

$$
\begin{aligned}
\int_E \operatorname{div}\mathbf{F}\, d\mathcal{V} \;&=\; \int_p^q \int_c^d \int_a^b (\operatorname{div}\mathbf{F}\circ\mathbf{r})\, J(\mathbf{r})\, du\, dv\, dw \\[2mm]
&=\; \int_p^q \int_c^d \int_a^b \Big[\, \tfrac{\partial}{\partial u}\big(I_2\big) + \tfrac{\partial}{\partial v}\big(I_3\big) + \tfrac{\partial}{\partial w}\big(I_1\big) \,\Big]\, du\, dv\, dw \\[2mm]
&=\; \left\{ \begin{aligned}
&\int_p^q \int_c^d I_2(u,v,w)\Big|_{u=a}^{u=b}\, dv\, dw + \int_p^q \int_a^b I_3(u,v,w)\Big|_{v=c}^{v=d}\, du\, dw \\[2mm]
&+ \int_c^d \int_a^b I_1(u,v,w)\Big|_{w=p}^{w=q}\, du\, dv
\end{aligned} \right. \\[3mm]
&=\; \left\{ \begin{aligned}
&\int_p^q \int_c^d \big[\, I_2(b,v,w) - I_2(a,v,w) \,\big]\, dv\, dw \\[2mm]
&+ \int_p^q \int_a^b \big[\, I_3(u,d,w) - I_3(u,c,w) \,\big]\, du\, dw \\[2mm]
&+ \int_c^d \int_a^b \big[\, I_1(u,v,q) - I_1(u,v,p) \,\big]\, du\, dv
\end{aligned} \right. \\[3mm]
&=\; \left\{ \begin{aligned}
&\int_{S_2^+} \mathbf{F}\cdot d\mathbf{A} + \int_{S_2^-} \mathbf{F}\cdot d\mathbf{A} \\[1mm]
&+ \int_{S_3^+} \mathbf{F}\cdot d\mathbf{A} + \int_{S_3^-} \mathbf{F}\cdot d\mathbf{A} \\[1mm]
&+ \int_{S_1^+} \mathbf{F}\cdot d\mathbf{A} + \int_{S_1^-} \mathbf{F}\cdot d\mathbf{A}
\end{aligned} \right\} \;=\; \int_S \mathbf{F}\cdot d\mathbf{A}
\end{aligned}
$$

Exercises: 14.6 (The Divergence Theorem)

NOTE: The reduction formulas (6.2.1)–(6.2.2) give the following ones for definite integrals:

$$\int_0^\pi \sin^n x\, dx = \frac{n-1}{n} \int_0^\pi \sin^{n-2} x\, dx$$

$$\int_0^\pi \cos^n x\, dx = \frac{n-1}{n} \int_0^\pi \cos^{n-2} x\, dx$$

These will be convenient to use in some of the exercises.

Verifying The Divergence Theorem

In Exercises 1–20, for the given solid E parametrized by $\mathbf{r}: B \to \mathbb{R}^3$ and given vector field $\mathbf{F}$, verify the Divergence Theorem:

$$\int_E \operatorname{div}\mathbf{F}\, d\mathcal{V} = \int_S \mathbf{F} \cdot d\mathbf{A},$$

where S is the boundary of E. HINT: For 1–18, see the discussion in Exercises 21 & 22 below which shows the solids here are bounded only by S_1^+ (a curved surface) and $S_3^\pm$ (top and bottom disks, either of which could degenerate to a point). These three surfaces are the only parts that contribute to the boundary integral.

1. $\mathbf{r}(\theta, t, w) = \langle\, wt\cos\theta,\, wt\sin\theta,\, t\,\rangle$,

for (θ, t, w) in $[0, 2\pi] \times [0, 2] \times [0, 1]$ (cone),

$\mathbf{F} = \langle\, \frac{1}{3}x^3,\, \frac{1}{3}y^3,\, 0\,\rangle$

2. $\mathbf{r}(\theta, t, w) = \langle\, t,\, wt\cos\theta,\, wt\sin\theta\,\rangle$,

for (θ, t, w) in $[0, 2\pi] \times [0, 3] \times [0, 1]$ (cone),

$\mathbf{F} = \langle\, 0,\, \frac{1}{3}y^3,\, \frac{1}{3}z^3\,\rangle$

3. $\mathbf{r}(\theta, t, w) = \langle\, w\cos\theta,\, w\sin\theta,\, t\,\rangle$,

for (θ, t, w) in $[0, 2\pi] \times [0, 3] \times [0, 1]$ (cylinder),

$\mathbf{F} = \langle\, 0,\, \frac{1}{3}y^3,\, \frac{1}{3}z^3\,\rangle$

4. $\mathbf{r}(\theta, t, w) = \langle\, 2w\cos\theta,\, 2w\sin\theta,\, t\,\rangle$,

for (θ, t, w) in $[0, 2\pi] \times [0, 4] \times [0, 1]$ (cylinder),

$\mathbf{F} = \langle\, \frac{1}{3}x^3,\, \frac{1}{3}y^3,\, 0\,\rangle$

5. $\mathbf{r}(\theta, t, w) = \langle\, wt\cos\theta,\, wt\sin\theta,\, t^2\,\rangle$,

for (θ, t, w) in $[0, 2\pi] \times [0, 2] \times [0, 1]$ (paraboloid),

$\mathbf{F} = \langle\, 0,\, 0,\, z^2\,\rangle$

6. $\mathbf{r}(\theta, t, w) = \langle\, wt\cos\theta,\, wt\sin\theta,\, t^3\,\rangle$

for (θ, t, w) in $[0, 2\pi] \times [0, 2] \times [0, 1]$ (paraboloidal),

$\mathbf{F} = \langle\, z^2,\, 0,\, 0\,\rangle$

7. $\mathbf{r}(\theta, t, w) = \langle\, w\sqrt{1 + t^2}\cos\theta,\, w\sqrt{1 + t^2}\sin\theta,\, t\,\rangle$,

for (θ, t, w) in $[0, 2\pi] \times [0, 2] \times [0, 1]$ (hyperboloid),

$\mathbf{F} = \langle\, 0,\, 0,\, 1 + z^2\,\rangle$

8. $\mathbf{r}(\theta, t, w) = \langle\, w\sqrt{4 + t^2}\cos\theta,\, w\sqrt{4 + t^2}\sin\theta,\, t\,\rangle$,

for (θ, t, w) in $[0, 2\pi] \times [0, 2] \times [0, 1]$ (hyperboloid),

$\mathbf{F} = \langle\, 1 + z^2,\, 0,\, 0\,\rangle$

9. $\mathbf{r}(\theta, t, w) = \langle\, w\sqrt{1 - t^2}\cos\theta,\, w\sqrt{1 - t^2}\sin\theta,\, t\,\rangle$,

for (θ, t, w) in $[0, 2\pi] \times [0, 1] \times [0, 1]$ (hemisphere),

$\mathbf{F} = \langle\, \frac{1}{3}x^3,\, \frac{1}{3}y^3,\, 0\,\rangle$

10. $\mathbf{r}(\theta, t, w) = \langle\, t,\, w\sqrt{4 - t^2}\cos\theta,\, w\sqrt{4 - t^2}\sin\theta\,\rangle$,

for (θ, t, w) in $[0, 2\pi] \times [0, 2] \times [0, 1]$ (hemisphere),

$\mathbf{F} = \langle\, \frac{1}{3}x^3,\, \frac{1}{3}y^3,\, 0\,\rangle$

11. $\mathbf{r}(\theta, t, w) = \langle\, wt\cos\theta,\, wt\sin\theta,\, e^t\,\rangle$,

for (θ, t, w) in $[0, 2\pi] \times [0, 1] \times [0, 1]$ (paraboloidal),

$\mathbf{F} = \langle\, 0,\, 0,\, z^2\,\rangle$

12. $\mathbf{r}(\theta, t, w) = \langle\, wt\cos\theta,\, wt\sin\theta,\, e^{2t}\,\rangle$,

for (θ, t, w) in $[0, 2\pi] \times [0, 1] \times [0, 1]$ (paraboloidal),

$\mathbf{F} = \langle\, 0,\, 0,\, z^2\,\rangle$

13. $\mathbf{r}(\theta, t, w) = \langle\, wt\cos\theta,\, wt\sin\theta,\, \sin t\,\rangle$,

for (θ, t, w) in $[0, 2\pi] \times [0, \pi] \times [0, 1]$ (bumpers),

$\mathbf{F} = \langle\, 0,\, 0,\, 1 + z^2\,\rangle$

14. $\mathbf{r}(\theta, t, w) = \langle\, wt\cos\theta,\, wt\sin\theta,\, \cos t\,\rangle$,

for (θ, t, w) in $[0, 2\pi] \times [0, \frac{\pi}{2}] \times [0, 1]$ (bumper),

$\mathbf{F} = \langle\, 0,\, 0,\, 1 + z^2\,\rangle$

15. $\mathbf{r}(\theta, t, w) = \langle\, w\sin t\cos\theta,\, w\sin t\sin\theta,\, t\,\rangle$,

for (θ, t, w) in $[0, 2\pi] \times [0, \pi] \times [0, 1]$ (spindle),

$\mathbf{F} = \langle\, 0,\, 0,\, z^2\,\rangle$

16. $\mathbf{r}(\theta, t, w) = \langle\, w\cos t\cos\theta,\, w\cos t\sin\theta,\, t\,\rangle$,

for (θ, t, w) in $[0, 2\pi] \times [0, \frac{\pi}{2}] \times [0, 1]$ (half spindle),

$\mathbf{F} = \langle\, 0,\, 0,\, z^2\,\rangle$

17. $\mathbf{r}(\theta, t, w) = \langle\, we^t\cos\theta,\, we^t\sin\theta,\, t\,\rangle$,

for (θ, t, w) in $[0, 2\pi] \times [0, 1] \times [0, 1]$ (fruit bowl),

$\mathbf{F} = \langle\, 0,\, 0,\, 1 + z^2\,\rangle$

18. $\mathbf{r}(\theta, t, w) = \langle\, 2we^t\cos\theta,\, 2we^t\sin\theta,\, t\,\rangle$,

for (θ, t, w) in $[0, 2\pi] \times [0, 1] \times [0, 1]$ (fruit bowl),

$\mathbf{F} = \langle\, 0,\, 0,\, 1 + z^2\,\rangle$

19. $\mathbf{r}(\theta, \phi, w)$

$= \langle\, (2 + w\cos\phi)\cos\theta,\, (2 + w\cos\phi)\sin\theta,\, w\sin\phi\,\rangle$,

for (θ, ϕ, w) in $[0, 2\pi] \times [0, 2\pi] \times [0, 1]$ (torus),

$\mathbf{F} = \langle\, 0,\, 0,\, z^3\,\rangle$

20. $\mathbf{r}(\theta, \phi, w)$

$= \langle\, (3 + w\cos\phi)\cos\theta,\, (3 + w\cos\phi)\sin\theta,\, w\sin\phi\,\rangle$, for (θ, ϕ, w) in $[0, 2\pi] \times [0, 2\pi] \times [0, 1]$ (torus),

$\mathbf{F} = \langle 0, 0, z^3 \rangle$

Parametrizing Solids of Revolution

Parametrizations of the solids in Exercises 1–18 were obtained by the following technique. In Section 13.2, we discussed how to parametrize a surface of revolution S_0 generated by revolving a curve C_0 in the x-z-plane about the z-axis. If $x = X(t), z = Z(t)$, for t in $[a, b]$, is a parametization of the curve, then

$$\mathbf{r}(\theta, t) = \langle X(t) \cos \theta, X(t) \sin \theta, Z(t) \rangle$$

is a parametrization of the surface of revolution. Assume that $Z'(t) \neq 0$ and $X(t) \geq 0$, for all t in (a, b). Then we get a ("Type II") region D in the x-z-plane, bounded on the left by the z-axis, on the right by the curve C_0 and above and below by the horizontal lines $z = Z(b), z = Z(a)$. See Figure 14.6.1x.

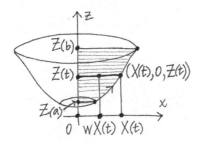

Figure 14.6.1x: *A solid of revolution.*

As shown in the figure, for a fixed t, the horizontal line segment through D at $Z(t)$ is parametrized by

$$x = wX(t), \ z = Z(t),$$

where the parameter w is in $[0, 1]$. Revolving each of these line segments about the z-axis creates a solid E of revolution with parametrization

$$\mathbf{r}(\theta, t, w) = \langle wX(t) \cos \theta, wX(t) \sin \theta, Z(t) \rangle,$$

where (θ, t, w) is in $[0, 2\pi] \times [a, b] \times [0, 1]$. Based on this, show the following:

21. The six boundary "surfaces" of E are:

$S_1^+ = S_0$,

$S_1^- = $ *the line segment* $(0, 0, Z(a))$ *to* $(0, 0, Z(b))$

$S_2^+ = S_2^- = D$

$S_3^+ = $ *the disk with center* $(0, 0, Z(b))$, *radius* $X(b)$

$S_3^- = $ *the disk with center* $(0, 0, Z(a))$, *radius* $X(a)$

22. $J(\mathbf{r}) = wX^2 Z'$.

Generalized Tori and Polar Solids of Revolution

Parametrizations of the solids in Exercises 23–50 below are obtained by the technique discussed above, before Exercises 21 & 22. Here polar solids of revolutions E are the special case of that where the curve C_0 is given by

a polar equation $r = R(\phi)$, with parameter ϕ in $[\alpha, \beta]$. As in Exercises 21 & 22 above, except with ϕ replacing t, slightly different notation for X, Z, and slightly different interpretation of the parameter w we get the following parametrization of the solid E:

$$\mathbf{r}(\theta, \phi, w) = \langle X(\phi, w) \cos \theta, X(\phi, w) \sin \theta, Z(\phi, w) \rangle,$$

where

$$X(\phi, w) = k + wR(\phi) \cos \phi, \quad Z(\phi, w) = wR(\phi) \sin \phi,$$

with (θ, ϕ, w) in $[0, 2\pi] \times [\alpha, \beta] \times [0, 1]$ and $k \geq 0$ is a constant. See See Figure 14.6.2x, which shows, for generality, the curve shifted out to the point $P = (k, 0, 0)$. This allows us to get generalized tori when $k > 0$ and polar solids of revolution when $k = 0$. NOTE: In Section 12.6, the angle ϕ is measured from vertical. Here it is measured from horizontal.

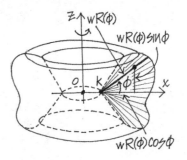

Figure 14.6.2x: *A polar solid of revolution.*

As shown in the figure, for a fixed ϕ, the radial line segment from the point $P = (k, 0, 0)$ out to the curve C_0 is parametrized by $x = wR(\phi) \cos \phi, z = wR(\phi) \sin \phi$, where the parameter w is in $[0, 1]$.

One can show that the Jacobian of $\mathbf{r}$ is

$$J(\mathbf{r}) = wR^2 X,$$

(Exercise).

In Exercises 23–50, use this and the Divergence Theorem to compute the flux $\mathcal{F} = \int_S \mathbf{F} \cdot d\mathbf{A}$ of the given vector field $\mathbf{F}$ across the boundary S of the given solid E.

NOTE 1: The reduction formulas (6.2.1)–(6.2.2) give the following ones for definite integrals:

$$\int_{-\pi/2}^{\pi/2} \sin^n x \, dx = \frac{n-1}{n} \int_{-\pi/2}^{\pi/2} \sin^{n-2} x \, dx$$

$$\int_{-\pi/2}^{\pi/2} \cos^n x \, dx = \frac{n-1}{n} \int_{-\pi/2}^{\pi/2} \cos^{n-2} x \, dx$$

These will be convenient to use in some of the exercises.

NOTE 2: In Exercises 23–44, take $k = 0$.
In Exercises 45–50, take $k = 2$.

23. $R - 2$, for ϕ in $[\frac{\pi}{4}, \frac{\pi}{2}]$, $\mathbf{F} = \langle \frac{1}{3}x^3, \frac{1}{3}y^3, 0 \rangle$,

24. $R = 3$, for ϕ in $[\frac{\pi}{2}, \frac{3\pi}{4}]$, $\mathbf{F} = \langle \frac{1}{3}x^3, \frac{1}{3}y^3, 0 \rangle$,

25. $R = 2 \cos \phi$, for ϕ in $[-\frac{\pi}{2}, \frac{\pi}{2}]$, $\mathbf{F} = \langle \frac{1}{3}x^3, \frac{1}{3}y^3, 0 \rangle$

26. $R = 3\cos\phi$, for ϕ in $[-\frac{\pi}{2}, \frac{\pi}{2}]$, $\mathbf{F} = \langle \frac{1}{3}x^3, \frac{1}{3}y^3, 0 \rangle$

27. $R = 1 + \sin\phi$, for ϕ in $[-\frac{\pi}{2}, \frac{\pi}{2}]$, $\mathbf{F} = \langle \frac{1}{3}x^3, \frac{1}{3}y^3, 0 \rangle$

28. $R = 1 - \sin\phi$, for ϕ in $[-\frac{\pi}{2}, \frac{\pi}{2}]$, $\mathbf{F} = \langle \frac{1}{3}x^3, \frac{1}{3}y^3, 0 \rangle$

29. $R = 1 - 2\sin\phi$, for ϕ in $[0, \frac{\pi}{6}]$, $\mathbf{F} = \langle \frac{1}{3}x^3, \frac{1}{3}y^3, 0 \rangle$

30. $R = 1 - 2\sin\phi$, for ϕ in $[\frac{5\pi}{6}, \pi]$, $\mathbf{F} = \langle \frac{1}{3}x^3, \frac{1}{3}y^3, 0 \rangle$

31. $R = \sin 2\phi$, for ϕ in $[0, \frac{\pi}{2}]$, $\mathbf{F} = \langle x^3, y^3, z^3 \rangle$

32. $R = 2\sin 2\phi$, for ϕ in $[\pi, \frac{3\pi}{2}]$, $\mathbf{F} = \langle x^3, y^3, z^3 \rangle$

33. $R = \sin 2\phi$, for ϕ in $[0, \frac{\pi}{2}]$, $\mathbf{F} = \langle 0, 0, z^2 \rangle$

34. $R = 2\sin 2\phi$, for ϕ in $[\pi, \frac{3\pi}{2}]$, $\mathbf{F} = \langle 0, 0, z^2 \rangle$

35. $R = 1 - \sin\phi$, for ϕ in $[-\frac{\pi}{2}, \frac{\pi}{2}]$, $\mathbf{F} = \langle x^3, y^3, z^3 \rangle$

36. $R = 1 + \sin\phi$, for ϕ in $[-\frac{\pi}{2}, \frac{\pi}{2}]$, $\mathbf{F} = \langle x^3, y^3, z^3 \rangle$

37. $R = \cos 2\phi$, for ϕ in $[0, \frac{\pi}{4}]$, $\mathbf{F} = \langle 0, 0, z^2 \rangle$

38. $R = 2\cos 2\phi$, for ϕ in $[-\frac{\pi}{4}, 0]$, $\mathbf{F} = \langle 0, 0, z^2 \rangle$

39. $R = 1 + \cos 2\phi$, for ϕ in $[0, \frac{\pi}{2}]$, $\mathbf{F} = \langle 0, 0, z^2 \rangle$

40. $R = 2 + \cos 2\phi$, for ϕ in $[0, \frac{\pi}{2}]$, $\mathbf{F} = \langle 0, 0, z^2 \rangle$

41. $R = 1 - 2\sin\phi$, for ϕ in $[0, \frac{\pi}{6}]$, $\mathbf{F} = \langle \frac{1}{3}x^3, \frac{1}{3}y^3, 0 \rangle$

42. $R = 1 - 2\sin\phi$, for ϕ in $[\frac{5\pi}{6}, \pi]$, $\mathbf{F} = \langle \frac{1}{3}x^3, \frac{1}{3}y^3, 0 \rangle$

43. $R = 2\sin\phi - 1$, for ϕ in $[\frac{\pi}{6}, \frac{\pi}{2}]$, $\mathbf{F} = \langle \frac{1}{3}x^3, \frac{1}{3}y^3, 0 \rangle$

44. $R = 2\sin\phi - 1$, for ϕ in $[\frac{\pi}{2}, \frac{5\pi}{6}]$, $\mathbf{F} = \langle \frac{1}{3}x^3, \frac{1}{3}y^3, 0 \rangle$

45. $R = 1$, for ϕ in $[\frac{\pi}{4}, \frac{3\pi}{4}]$, $\mathbf{F} = \langle \frac{1}{3}x^3, \frac{1}{3}y^3, 0 \rangle$

46. $R = 2$, for ϕ in $[\frac{\pi}{4}, \frac{3\pi}{4}]$, $\mathbf{F} = \langle \frac{1}{3}x^3, \frac{1}{3}y^3, 0 \rangle$

47. $R = 1 + \cos\phi$, for ϕ in $[0, \pi]$, $\mathbf{F} = \langle 0, 0, z^2 \rangle$

48. $R = 1 - \cos\phi$, for ϕ in $[0, \pi]$, $\mathbf{F} = \langle 0, 0, z^2 \rangle$

49. $R = 2\sin 2\phi$, for ϕ in $[0, \frac{\pi}{2}]$, $\mathbf{F} = \langle 0, 0, z^2 \rangle$

50. $R = \sin 2\phi$, for ϕ in $[0, \frac{\pi}{2}]$, $\mathbf{F} = \langle 0, 0, z^2 \rangle$

Flux Through a Möbius Slab

Consider the Möbius slab parametrized by

$$\mathbf{r}(\theta, t, w) = \langle T\cos\theta, T\sin\theta, P \rangle,$$

where

$$T = k + t\cos\tfrac{\theta}{2} - w\sin\tfrac{\theta}{2},$$
$$P = t\sin\tfrac{\theta}{2} + w\cos\tfrac{\theta}{2},$$

and (θ, t, w) is in $[0, 2\pi] \times [-b, b] \times [-c, c]$. We assume

$k > b + c$, so that $T > 0$.

For each of the following vector fields $\mathbf{F}$, use the Divergence Theorem to compute the flux $\mathcal{F} = \int_S \mathbf{F} \cdot d\mathbf{A}$ of $\mathbf{F}$ through the boundary S of the Möbius slab. As in Example 14.6.3, you may use the following facts to shorten the work:

(a) The iterated integral: $\int_{-c}^{c} \int_{-b}^{b} \int_{0}^{2\pi} H(\theta, t, w)\, d\theta\, dt\, dw$ can be computed in any order and some parts of the integrand H may have integral 0 for the 1st integral if the order is appropriately switched.

(b) $\int_{-b}^{b} t^n\, dt = 0$, if n is even and $\int_{-b}^{b} t^n\, dt = \frac{2}{n+1}b^{n+1}$, when n is odd. Similar results hold nonnegative integer powers of w.

(c) $\int_{0}^{2\pi} \sin\theta\, d\theta = 0 = \int_{0}^{2\pi} \cos\theta\, d\theta$

(d) $\int_{0}^{2\pi} \sin\frac{\theta}{2}\, d\theta = 4$, $\int_{0}^{2\pi} \cos\frac{\theta}{2}\, d\theta = 0$

(e) $\int_{0}^{2\pi} \sin^2\theta\, d\theta = \pi = \int_{0}^{2\pi} \cos^2\theta\, d\theta$

BIG HINT: Use the identities in Exercises 59–61 below.

51. $k = 2, b = 1, c \leq 0.1$, $\mathbf{F} = \langle \frac{1}{3}x, \frac{1}{3}y, \frac{1}{2}z \rangle$

52. $k = 3, b = 2, c \leq 0.1$, $\mathbf{F} = \langle \frac{1}{3}x, \frac{1}{3}y, \frac{1}{2}z \rangle$

53. $k = 2, b = 1, c \leq 0.1$, $\mathbf{F} = \langle 0, 0, z\sqrt{x^2 + y^2} \rangle$

54. $k = 3, b = 2, c \leq 0.1$, $\mathbf{F} = \langle 0, 0, z\sqrt{x^2 + y^2} \rangle$

55. $k = 2, b = 1, c \leq 0.1$, $\mathbf{F} = \langle x^2, 0, 0, \rangle$

56. $k = 2, b = 1, c \leq 0.1$, $\mathbf{F} = \langle 0, y^2, 0, \rangle$

57. $k = 2, b = 1, c \leq 0.1$, $\mathbf{F} = \langle \frac{1}{3}x^3, \frac{1}{3}y^3, \frac{1}{2}z^3 \rangle$

58. $k = 3, b = 2, c \leq 0.1$, $\mathbf{F} = \langle \frac{1}{3}x^3, \frac{1}{3}y^3, \frac{1}{2}z^3 \rangle$

Some Identities Connected with the Möbius Slab

For the functions T and P that occur in the parametrization of the Möbius slab, prove the following identities:

59. $(T - k)^2 + P^2 = t^2 + w^2$ and so $T^2 + P^2 = 2kT - k^2 + t^2 + w^2$.

60. $2T^2 = 2k^2 + t^2 + w^2 + 4kt\cos\frac{\theta}{2} + 4kw\sin\frac{\theta}{2}$ $+ (t^2 - w^2)\cos\theta - 2tw\sin\theta$

61. Compute the volume $V = \int_{-c}^{c} \int_{-b}^{b} \int_{0}^{2\pi} |J(\mathbf{r})|\, d\theta\, dt\, dw$ of the Möbius slab. Compare this with the volume of a washer with radii $r_1 = k - b, r_2 = k + b$ and thickness $2c$.

Calculus
Concepts & Computation

CHAPTER 1: Answers to Odd Exercises

Exercises: 1.2

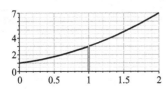

1. $\lim\limits_{x\to 1}\frac{x^3-1}{x-1}=3$

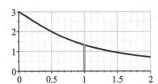

3. $\lim\limits_{x\to 1}\frac{x^2+2\,x-3}{x^3-1}=1.33$

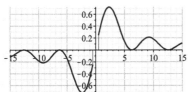

5. $\lim\limits_{x\to 0}\frac{1-\cos x}{x}=0$

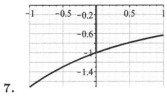

7. $\lim\limits_{x\to 0}\frac{e^{-x}-1}{x}=-1$

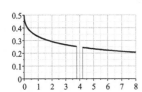

9. $\lim\limits_{x\to 4}\frac{\sqrt{x}-2}{x-4}=0.25$

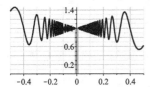

11. $\lim\limits_{x\to 0}1+x\sin(1/x^2)=1$

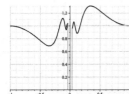

13. $\lim\limits_{x\to 0}[1+x\sin((\ln|x|)^2)]=1$

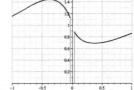

15. $\lim\limits_{x\to 0}\big|\sin x\big|^{\sin x}=1$

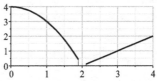

17. $\lim\limits_{x\to 2}f(x)=0$

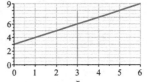

19. $\lim\limits_{x\to 3}\frac{x^2-9}{x-3}=6$

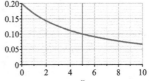

21. $\lim\limits_{x\to 5}\frac{x-5}{x^2-25}=0.1$

23. $\lim\limits_{x\to 0}\sin\left(\frac{x}{\sin x}\right)=0.84$

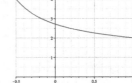

25. $\lim\limits_{x\to 0}(1+x)^{1/x}=2.72$

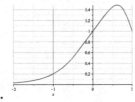

27. $\lim\limits_{x\to -1}\frac{1+x}{x^5+1}=0.2$

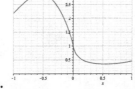

29. $\lim\limits_{x\to 0}(1-\cos x)^x=1$

31. 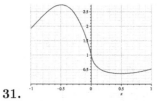 $\lim\limits_{x\to 0}(1-\cos x)^{\sin x}=1$

33. 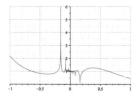 $\lim\limits_{x\to 0}(1-\cos x)^{1-\cos x}=1$

35. 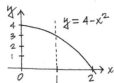 $\lim\limits_{x\to 0}(1-\cos(1/x))^x=1$

37. 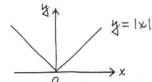 $\lim\limits_{x\to 1}\left(4-x^2\right)=3$

39. 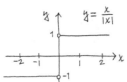 $\lim\limits_{x\to 0}|x|=0$

41. $\lim\limits_{x\to 0}\frac{x}{|x|}=\text{DNE}$

43. $\lim\limits_{x\to 0}\left[1+\frac{x^4}{|x|}\right]=1$

45. $\lim\limits_{x\to 0}x|x|=0$

47. 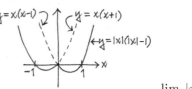 $\lim\limits_{x\to 0}|x|\,(|x|-1)=0$

49. 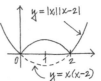 $\lim\limits_{x\to 0}|x||x-2|=0$

51. 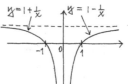 $\lim\limits_{x\to 0}\frac{|x|-1}{|x|}=\text{DNE}$

53. 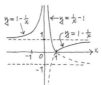 $\lim\limits_{x\to 1}\frac{|x-1|}{|x|}=0$

55. 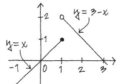 $\lim\limits_{x\to 1}f(x)=\text{DNE}$

57. $\lim\limits_{x\to 1}f(x)=2$

59. 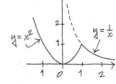 $\lim\limits_{x\to 1}f(x)=1$

61. 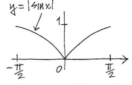 $\lim\limits_{x\to 0}|\sin x|=0$

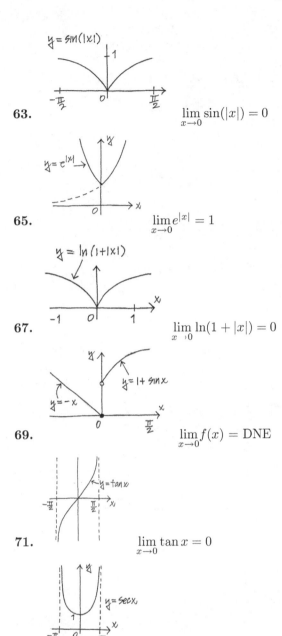

63. $\lim\limits_{x \to 0} \sin(|x|) = 0$

65. $\lim\limits_{x \to 0} e^{|x|} = 1$

67. $\lim\limits_{x \to 0} \ln(1 + |x|) = 0$

69. $\lim\limits_{x \to 0} f(x) = \text{DNE}$

71. $\lim\limits_{x \to 0} \tan x = 0$

73. $\lim\limits_{x \to 0} \sec x = 1$

75. (a) 3   (b) 0   (c) 6

77. (a) undetermined   (b) DNE   (c) 1

79. (a) 1   (b) 1   (c) 1

Exercises: 1.3

1. The estimated limit is 6 based on:

3.1, 6.100000000   2.9, 5.900000000
3.01, 6.010000000   2.99, 5.990000000
3.001, 6.001000000   2.999, 5.999000000
3.0001, 6.000100000   2.9999, 5.999000000

3. The estimated limit is 1 based on:

0.1, 1.051709180   -0.1, 0.9516258200
0.01, 1.005016700   -0.01, 0.9950166300

0.001, 1.000500000   -0.001, 0.9995002000
0.0001, 1.000050000   -0.0001, 0.9999500000

5. The estimated limit is 2.71 based on:

0.1, 2.593742460   -0.1, 2.867971991
0.01, 2.704813829   -0.01, 2.731999026
0.001, 2.716923932   -0.001, 2.719642216
0.0001, 2.718145927   -0.0001, 2.718417755

7. The estimated limit is 1 based on:

1.1, 0.9531017980   0.9, 1.053605157
1.01, 0.9950330853   0.99, 1.005033585
1.001, 0.9995003331   0.999, 1.000500334
1.0001, 0.9999500033 0.9999, 1.000050003

9. The estimated limit is 1 based on:

0.1, 1.003346721   -0.1, 1.003346721
0.01, 1.000033335   -0.01, 1.000033335
0.001, 1.000000333   -0.001, 1.000000333
0.0001, 1.000000003   -0.0001, 1.000000003

11. The estimated limit is DNE based on:

0.1, 10.03346721   -0.1, -10.03346721
0.01, 100.0033335   -0.01, -100.0033335
0.001, 1000.000333   -0.001, -1000.000333
0.0001, 10000.00003   -0.0001, -10000.00003

13. The estimated limit is 0.5 based on:

1.1, 0.4538579990   0.9, 0.5545290300
1.01, 0.4950413360   0.99, 0.5050420025
1.001, 0.4995004163   0.999, 0.5005004172
1.0001, 0.4999500041 0.9999, 0.5000500040

15. The estimated limit is 0 based on:

0.1, -0.05004170815   -0.1, 0.05004170815
0.01, -0.00500004333 -0.01, 0.005000043334
0.001, -0.0005000000   -0.001, 0.000500000083
0.0001, -0.000050000   -0.0001, 0.00005000000

17. The estimated limit is -4.5 based on:

0.1, -4.466351090   -0.1, -4.466351090
0.01, -4.499663000   -0.01, -4.499663000
0.001, -4.500000000   -0.001, -4.500000000
0.0001, -4.500000000 -0.0001, -4.500000000

19. The estimated limit is 1/3 based on:

0.1, 0.3333277778   -0.1, 0.3333277778
0.01, 0.3333333328   -0.01, 0.3333333328
0.001, 0.3333333333   -0.001, 0.3333333333
0.0001, 0.3333333333 -0.0001, 0.3333333333

21. The estimated limit is 0.3 based on:

0.1, 0.3346721000   -0.1, 0.3346721000
0.01, 0.3333500000   -0.01, 0.3333500000
0.001, 0.3330000000   -0.001, 0.3330000000
0.0001, 0.3000000000 -0.0001, 0.3000000000

23. The estimated limit is 0 based on:

0.1, -0.4605170186   -0.1, 0.4605170186
0.01, -0.09210340372   -0.01, 0.09210340372
0.001, -0.01381551056   -0.001, 0.01381551056
0.0001, -0.001842068074 -0.0001, 0.001842068074
0.00001, -0.0002302585093
0.000001, -0.00002763102112
0.0000001, -0.000003223619130

25. The estimated limit is 7.39 based on:

0.1, 6.191736422   -0.1, 9.313225746
0.01, 7.244646118   -0.01, 7.540366074
0.001, 7.374312390   -0.001, 7.403868772
0.0001, 7.387578632   -0.0001, 7.390534255

27. The estimated limit is 1 based on:

0.1, 0.6314415658   -0.1, 1.583677816
0.01, 0.9120122393   -0.01, 1.096476513
0.001, 0.9862794879   -0.001, 1.013911383
0.0001, 0.9981596275 -0.0001, 1.001843766

29. The estimated limit is 6 based on:
```
> f:=x->(x^2-9)/(x-3):
> for n from 1 to 4 do
> 3+(.1)^n, f(3+(.1)^n),
> 3-(.1)^n, f(3-(.1)^n);
> end do
```

3.1, 6.100000000,   2.9, 5.900000000
3.01, 6.010000000,   2.99, 5.990000000
3.001, 6.001000000,   2.999, 5.999000000
3.0001, 6.000100000, 2.9999, 5.999900000

31. The estimated limit is 1 based on:
```
> f:=x->(exp(x)-1)/x:
> for n from 1 to 4 do
> (.1)^n, f((.1)^n),
> -(.1)^n, f(-(.1)^n);
> end do
```

0.1, 1.051709180,   -0.1, 0.9516258200
0.01, 1.005016700,   -0.01, 0.9950166300
0.001, 1.000500000,   -0.001, 0.9995002000
0.0001, 1.000050000, -0.0001, 0.9999500000

33. The estimated limit is 2.71 based on:
```
> f:=x->(x+1)^(1/x):
> for n from 1 to 4 do
> (.1)^n, f((.1)^n),
> -(.1)^n, f(-(.1)^n);
> end do
```

0.1, 2.593742460,   -0.1, 2.867971991
0.01, 2.704813829,   -0.01, 2.731999026
0.001, 2.716923932,   -0.001, 2.719642216
0.0001, 2.718145927,   -0.0001, 2.718417755

35. The estimated limit is 1 based on:
```
> f:=x->ln(x)/(x-1):
> for n from 1 to 4 do
> 1+(.1)^n, f(1+(.1)^n),
> 1-(.1)^n, f(1-(.1)^n);
> end do
```

1.1, 0.9531017980,   0.9, 1.053605157
1.01, 0.9950330853,   0.99, 1.005033585
1.001, 0.9995003331,   0.999, 1.000500334
1.0001, 0.9999500033, 0.9999, 1.000050003

Exercises: 1.4

1. $\frac{1}{10}$ **3.** 27   **5.** $\frac{1}{3}$ **7.** $\frac{1}{2}$ **9.** 10   **11.** 12   **13.** $-\frac{1}{4}$
15. 2   **17.** $-1/2$ **19.** 12   **21.** -4 **23.** $\frac{4}{7}$ **25.** 0
27. 2   **29.** 2   **31.** -1 **33.** 0   **35.** 2   **37.** 2   **39.** 2
41. 1   **43.** -2 **45.** 2   **47.** 2   **49.** 1   **51.** $\frac{1}{8}$ **53.** 1

55. $\lim\limits_{x\to 2}\dfrac{x^2-4}{x-2}=4$ **57.** $\lim\limits_{x\to 2}\dfrac{x^3-8}{x-2}=12$

59. $\lim\limits_{x\to 2}\dfrac{x^4-16}{x-2}=32$ **61.** $\lim\limits_{x\to 4}\dfrac{\sqrt{x}-2}{x-4}=\dfrac{1}{4}$

63. $\lim\limits_{x\to 1}\dfrac{x^2-3x+2}{x-1}=-1$ **65.** $\lim\limits_{x\to 2}\dfrac{x^3+2x^2-16}{x-2}=20$

67. $\lim\limits_{x\to 2}\dfrac{x^3-4x}{x-2}=8$ **69.** $\lim\limits_{x\to 1}\dfrac{x^4-x}{x-1}=3$

71. $\lim\limits_{x\to 2}\dfrac{\frac{1}{x}-\frac{1}{2}}{x-2}=-\dfrac{1}{4}$ **73.** $\lim\limits_{x\to 2}\dfrac{\frac{1}{x^2}-\frac{1}{4}}{x-2}=-\dfrac{1}{4}$

75. $\lim\limits_{x\to 2}\dfrac{\frac{1}{x-1}-1}{x-2}=-1$ **77.** $\lim\limits_{x\to 1}\dfrac{\frac{x}{x+1}-\frac{1}{2}}{x-1}=\dfrac{1}{2}$

79. $\lim\limits_{x\to 1}\dfrac{\frac{x^2}{1+x^2}-\frac{1}{2}}{x-1}=\dfrac{1}{2}$ **81.** $\lim\limits_{x\to 1}\dfrac{\frac{1}{\sqrt{x}}-1}{x-1}=-\dfrac{1}{2}$

Exercises: 1.5

1. -7 **3.** -28 **5.** $\frac{3}{8}$ **7.** 81   **9.** $\frac{256}{3}$ **11.** -2
13. -12 **15.** 5   **17.** 7   **19.** $\frac{4}{5}$ **21.** $\frac{1}{4}$ **23.** $\frac{-1}{48}$
25. $\sqrt{109}$ **27.** DNE   **29.** 8   **31.** 4   **33.** 3   **35.** 4

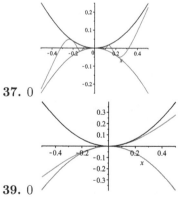

37. 0

39. 0

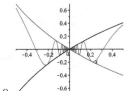

41. 0

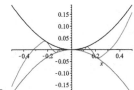

43. 0

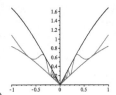

45. 0

47. (a) 3   (b) 2   (c) $\frac{1}{2}$ (d) 1

Exercises: 1.6

1. (a) 3   (b) 6   (c) DNE   (d) 5   (e) 4   (f) 4   (g) 8

3. $\lim\limits_{x \to 2^-} f(x) = 1, \ \lim\limits_{x \to 2^+} f(x) = 3, \ \lim\limits_{x \to 2} f(x) = \text{DNE}$

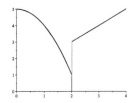

5. $\lim\limits_{x \to 1^-} f(x) = 1, \ \lim\limits_{x \to 1^+} f(x) = 1, \ \lim\limits_{x \to 1} f(x) = 1$

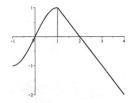

7. $\lim\limits_{x \to 1^-} f(x) = \text{DNE}, \ \lim\limits_{x \to 1^+} f(x) = 2, \ \lim\limits_{x \to 1} f(x) = \text{DNE}$

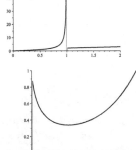

9. $\lim_{x \to 0^+} x^{3 \sin x} = 1$

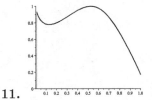

11. $\lim_{x \to 0^+} (\sin 3x)^{2 \sin x} = 1$

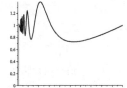

13. $\lim_{x \to 0^+} x^{x \sin(1/x)} = 1$

15. $\lim_{x \to 0^+} [x - x \cos(1/x)]^x = 1$

17. $\lim\limits_{x \to 1^-} f(x) = 1, \ \lim\limits_{x \to 1^+} f(x) = 1, \ \lim\limits_{x \to 1} f(x) = 1$

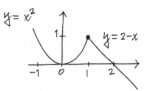

19. $\lim\limits_{x \to 1^-} f(x) = 1, \ \lim\limits_{x \to 1^+} f(x) = -1, \ \lim\limits_{x \to 1} f(x) = \text{DNE}$

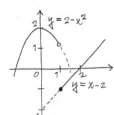

21. $\lim\limits_{x \to 0^-} f(x) = 2, \ \lim\limits_{x \to 0^+} f(x) = 4, \ \lim\limits_{x \to 1} f(x) = \text{DNE}$

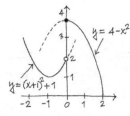

23. $\lim\limits_{x \to 1^-} f(x) = 2, \ \lim\limits_{x \to 1^+} f(x) = 2, \ \lim\limits_{x \to 1} f(x) = 2$

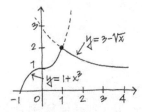

25. $\lim\limits_{x \to 1^-} f(x) = 2, \ \lim\limits_{x \to 1^+} f(x) = 1, \ \lim\limits_{x \to 1} f(x) = \text{DNE}$

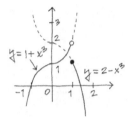

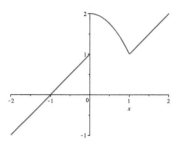

Exercises: 1.7

1. Discontinuous at $x = 4$, since $\lim_{x \to 4} f(x) =$ DNE (criterion (ii) fails).

3. Discontinuous at $x = 4$, since $\lim_{x \to 4} f(x) =$ DNE (criterion (ii) fails). Discontinuous at $x = 11$, since $f(11)$ is not defined (criterion (i) fails).

5. Discontinuous at $x = 1$, since $\lim_{x \to 1} f(x) =$ DNE (criterion (ii) fails). Discontinuous at $x = 5$, since $\lim_{x \to 5} f(x) =$ DNE (criterion (ii) fails).

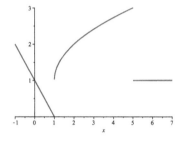

7. Discontinuous at $x = 0$, since $\lim_{x \to 0} f(x) =$ DNE (criterion (ii) fails).

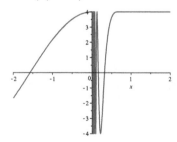

9. Discontinuous at $x = 0$, since $\lim_{x \to 0} f(x) =$ DNE (criterion (ii) fails). Discontinuous at $x = 2$, since $\lim_{x \to 2} f(x) =$ DNE (criterion (ii) fails).

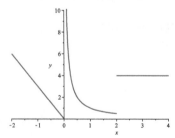

11. Discontinuous at $x = 0$, since $\lim_{x \to 0} f(x) =$ DNE (criterion (ii) fails).

13. The function is not continuous at $x = 0$, since $f(0)$ is not defined (criterion (i) fails). Also, $\lim_{x \to 0} f(x) =$ DNE (criterion (ii) fails).

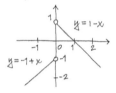

15. Continuous everywhere except at $x = 0$, where it is not defined (criterion (i) fails).

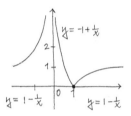

17. Discontinuous at $x = 1, 2$, because $\lim_{x \to 1} f(x) =$ DNE, and $\lim_{x \to 2} f(x) =$ DNE (criterion (ii) fails).

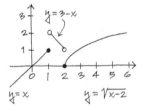

19. Discontinuous at $x = 3$, because $\lim_{x \to 3} f(x) =$ DNE (criterion (ii) fails).

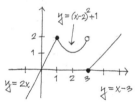

21. Discontinuous at $x = 1$, because, while

$\lim_{x \to 1^-} f(x) = 1 = \lim_{x \to 1^+} f(x)$, and so $\lim_{x \to 1} f(x) = 1$ exists, this is not the value of the function at $x = 1$ (criterion (iii) fails). Discontinuous at $x = 2$, because $\lim_{x \to 2} f(x) =$ DNE (criterion (ii) fails).

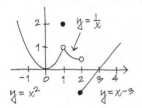

23. Discontinuous at $x = 0$, because $\lim\limits_{x\to 0} f(x) = \mathrm{DNE}$ (criterion (ii) fails).

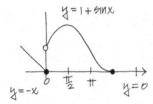

25. Discontinuous at $x = 2$ because $\lim\limits_{x\to 2} f(x) = \mathrm{DNE}$ (criterion (ii) fails). Discontinuous at $x = 4$, because, while $\lim\limits_{x\to 4^-} f(x) = 0 = \lim\limits_{x\to 4^+} f(x)$, and so $\lim\limits_{x\to 4} f(x) = 0$ exists, this is not the value of the function at $x = 4$ (criterion (iii) fails).

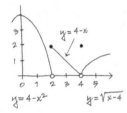

27. 0   **29.** 0   **31.** $-\pi^2$ **33.** 1   **35.** 0   **37.** $\sin(1)$
39. e^{-1} **41.** e **43.** -1
45. Approximate values $x \approx -3, -1.62, 0.62$

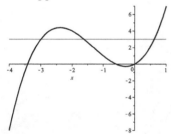

Exact values $x = -3, (-1 \pm \sqrt{5})/2$.
47. Approximate value $x \approx -2$

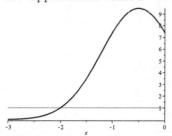

Exact value $x = -2$.
49. Approximate value $x \approx 1.315$

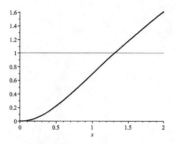

Exact value $x = \sqrt{e-1}$.

Exercises: 1.8

1. v.a.: $x = 3$. $\lim\limits_{x\to 3^+} \dfrac{x}{x-3} = \infty$, $\lim\limits_{x\to 3^-} \dfrac{x}{x-3} = -\infty$
3. v.a.: $x = -3, 2$.
$$\lim_{x\to -3^\pm} \frac{x+1}{(x+3)(x-2)} = \pm\infty$$
$$\lim_{x\to 2^\pm} \frac{x+1}{(x+3)(x-2)} = \pm\infty$$

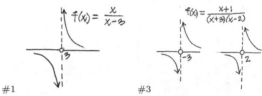

#1   #3

5. v.a.: $x = 1$.
$$\lim_{x\to 1^\pm} \frac{x+5}{x^2-2x+1} = \lim_{x\to 1^\pm} \frac{x+5}{(x-1)^2} = \frac{6}{+0} = \infty$$
7. v.a.: $x = -2, 0, 4$.
$$\lim_{x\to -2^\pm} \frac{x+6}{x(x+2)(x-4)} = \frac{4}{-2(\pm 0)(-6)} = \pm\infty$$
$$\lim_{x\to 0^\pm} \frac{x+6}{x(x+2)(x-4)} = \frac{6}{\pm 0(2)(-4)} = \mp\infty$$
$$\lim_{x\to 4^\pm} \frac{x+6}{x(x+2)(x-4)} = \frac{10}{4(6)(\pm 0)} = \pm\infty$$

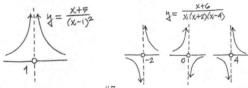

#5   #7

9. v.a.: $x = 0$.
$$\lim_{x\to 0^\pm} \frac{x+1}{\cos x - 1} = \frac{0+1}{-0} = -\infty$$

11. v.a.: $x = 0, \pi/2$.
$$\lim_{x\to 0^\pm} \frac{1}{\sin x \cos x} = \frac{1}{\pm 0(1)} = \pm\infty$$
$$\lim_{x\to \pi/2^\pm} \frac{1}{\sin x \cos x} = \frac{1}{1(\mp 0)} = \mp\infty$$
13. v.a.: $x = \pi/4, 5\pi/4$.

$$\lim_{x \to \pi/4^\pm} \frac{1}{\sin x - \cos x} = \frac{1}{\pm 0} = \pm\infty$$

$$\lim_{x \to 5\pi/4^\pm} \frac{1}{\sin x - \cos x} = \frac{1}{\mp 0} = \mp\infty$$

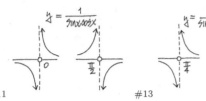

#11   #13

15. v.a.: $x = 0$. $\lim_{x \to 0^\pm} \ln|x| = -\infty$

17. v.a.: $x = 0$.

$$\lim_{x \to 0^\pm} \frac{e^x + e^{-x}}{e^x - e^{-x}} = \frac{1+1}{\pm 0} = \pm\infty$$

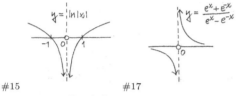

#15   #17

19. v.a.: $x = (\ln 2)/2$.

$$\lim_{x \to (\ln 2)/2^\pm} \frac{e^x + e^{-x}}{e^x - 2e^{-x}} = \frac{\sqrt{2} + \sqrt{2}}{\pm 0} = \frac{2\sqrt{2}}{\pm 0} = \pm\infty$$

#19

21. $\lim_{x \to \pm\infty} \frac{1}{x - 12} = \lim_{x \to \pm\infty} \frac{\frac{1}{x}}{1 - \frac{12}{x}} = 0$. h.a.: $y = 0$

23. $\lim_{x \to \pm\infty} \frac{1 - 2x}{x - 12} = \lim_{x \to \pm\infty} \frac{\frac{1}{x} - 2}{1 - \frac{12}{x}} = -2$. h.a.: $y = 2$

25. $\lim_{x \to \pm\infty} \frac{5x^2 + 7}{3x^2 - x} = \lim_{x \to \pm\infty} \frac{5 + \frac{7}{x^2}}{3 - \frac{1}{x}} = \frac{5}{3}$. h.a.: $y = \frac{5}{3}$

27. $\lim_{x \to \pm\infty} \frac{x - 2}{x^2 + 2x + 1} = \lim_{x \to \pm\infty} \frac{\frac{1}{x} - \frac{2}{x^2}}{1 + \frac{1}{x} + \frac{1}{x^2}} = \frac{0}{1} = 0$.
h.a.: $y = 0$

29. $\lim_{x \to \pm\infty} \frac{x^4 + 4x - 2}{x^2 + 2x + 1} = \lim_{x \to \pm\infty} \frac{x^2 + \frac{4}{x} - \frac{2}{x^2}}{1 + \frac{2}{x} + \frac{1}{x^2}} = \infty$. h.a.: none

31. $\lim_{x \to \infty} \frac{3x - 2}{\sqrt{x^2 + 1}} = \lim_{x \to \infty} \frac{3 - \frac{2}{x}}{\sqrt{1 + \frac{1}{x^2}}} = \frac{3}{1} = 3$

$$\lim_{x \to -\infty} \frac{3x - 2}{\sqrt{x^2 + 1}} = \lim_{x \to -\infty} \frac{3 - \frac{2}{x}}{-\sqrt{1 + \frac{1}{x^2}}} = \frac{3}{-1} = -3$$

h.a.: $x = \pm 3$

33. $\lim_{x \to \pm\infty} \frac{5\sqrt{x^4 - x^2 + 1}}{2x^2} = \lim_{x \to \pm\infty} \frac{5}{2}\sqrt{1 - \frac{1}{x^2} + \frac{1}{x^4}} = \frac{5}{2}$.
h.a.: $y = \frac{5}{2}$

35. $\lim_{x \to \infty} \sqrt{x + 2} = \infty$. h.a.: none

37. $\lim_{x \to \infty} \frac{\sqrt{x} + \frac{1}{\sqrt{x}}}{2\sqrt{x} + \frac{1}{x}} = \lim_{x \to \infty} \frac{1 + \frac{1}{x}}{2 + \frac{1}{x^{3/2}}} = \frac{1}{2}$. h.a.: $y = \frac{1}{2}$

39. $\lim_{x \to \infty} \frac{e^x - e^{-x}}{e^x + e^{-x}} = \lim_{x \to \infty} \frac{1 - e^{-2x}}{1 + e^{-2x}} = \frac{1}{1} = 1$.
h.a.: $y = 1$

41. $\lim_{x \to \infty} \tan^{-1} x = \frac{\pi}{2}$, $\lim_{x \to -\infty} \tan^{-1} x = -\frac{\pi}{2}$.
h.a.: $y = \pm\frac{\pi}{2}$

43. $\lim_{x \to \pm\infty} \tan^{-1}\left(1 + \frac{1}{x}\right) = \tan^{-1}(1) = \frac{\pi}{4}$. h.a.: $y = \frac{\pi}{4}$

45. $\lim_{x \to \pm\infty} \left(x^4 - 2x^3 + 5\right) = \lim_{x \to \pm\infty} x^4\left(1 - \frac{2}{x} + \frac{5}{x^4}\right) = \infty$
h.a.: none

47. $\lim_{x \to \pm\infty} \left(x^2 - x^4\right) = \lim_{x \to \pm\infty} x^4\left(\frac{1}{x^2} - 1\right) = -\infty$.
h.a.: none

49. $\lim_{x \to \infty} \left(3 - 5x - 2x^3\right) = \lim_{x \to \infty} x^3\left(\frac{2}{x^3} - \frac{5}{x^2} - 2\right) = -\infty$.
h.a.: none

$$\lim_{x \to -\infty} \left(3 - 5x - 2x^3\right) = \lim_{x \to -\infty} x^3\left(\frac{2}{x^3} - \frac{5}{x^2} - 2\right) = +\infty.$$
h.a.: none

51. $\lim_{x \to \infty} \ln x = \infty$. h.a.: none

53. $\lim_{x \to \infty} \frac{\ln x}{1 + 2\ln x} = \lim_{x \to \infty} \frac{1}{\frac{1}{\ln x} + 2} = \frac{1}{2}$. h.a.: $y = \frac{1}{2}$

55. v.a.: $x = 2$. h.a.: $y = 1$

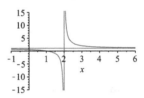

57. v.a.: $x = 1, 3$. h.a: $y = 1$

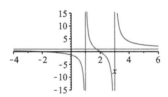

59. v.a.: $x = -1, 1, 2$. h.a.: $y = 0$

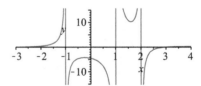

61. v.a.: none. h.a.: $y = 0$

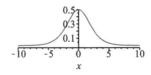

63. v.a.: $x = 0$. h.a.: $y = 0, 1$

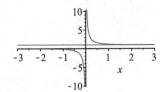

65. v.a.: $x = -\ln 3, \ln 2$. h.a.: $y = 0$

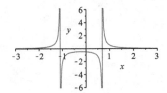

67. v.a.: $e^{-1/2}$. h.a.: $y = \frac{1}{2}$

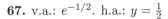

(69) v.a.: $x = 1$. asymptotic function: $h(x) = x + 2$

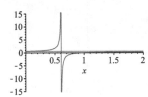

71. v.a.: $x = -2, 1$. asymptotic function:

$h(x) = x^2 - 2x + 1$

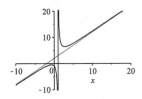

73. v.a.: $x = 1, 2$. asymptotic function: $h(x) = x$

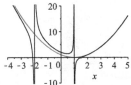

75. v.a.: $x = 2$. h.a.: $y = 0$

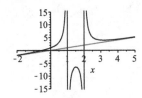

77. v.a.: $x = -1$. h.a. $y = 2$

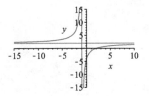

79. v.a.: $x = -3, 2$. h.a.: $y = 1$

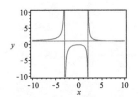

81. v.a.: $x = 0, \frac{1}{3}$. h.a.: $y = \frac{5}{3}$

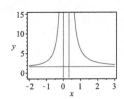

83. v.a.: $x = 0, \frac{\pi}{2}$, h.a.: $y = 0$

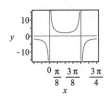

85. v.a.: $x = \frac{\pi}{4}, \frac{5\pi}{4}$. h.a.: $y = 0$

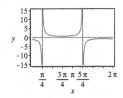

87. v.a.: $x = 0$. h.a.: $y = 1, -1$

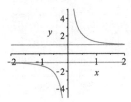

89. v.a.: $x = \frac{\ln 2}{2}$. h.a.: $y = 1, -\frac{1}{2}$

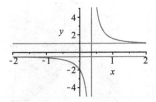

91. v.a.: none. h.a.: $y = \frac{\pi}{4}$

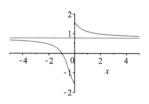

93. v.a.: none. h.a.: $y = e \approx 2.72$

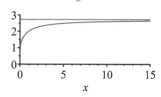

95. v.a.: $x = -1$. h.a.: $y = e \approx 2.72$

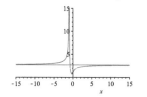

97. (a) $\lim\limits_{x \to -1^-} f(x) = \infty$ (b) $\lim\limits_{x \to -1^+} f(x) = -\infty$

(c) $\lim\limits_{x \to -1} f(x) = \text{DNE}$ (d) $\lim\limits_{x \to 3^-} f(x) = \infty$

(e) $\lim\limits_{x \to 3^+} f(x) = \infty$ (f) $\lim\limits_{x \to 3} f(x) = \infty$

(g) $\lim\limits_{x \to -\infty} f(x) = 1$ (h) $\lim\limits_{x \to \infty} f(x) = 3$

Exercises: 1.9

1. $\delta = 0.01$ **3.** $\delta = 0.04$ **5.** $\delta = 0.024$ **7.** $\delta = 0.16$

9. $\delta = \min\{1, 0.04\}$ **11.** $\delta = \min\{1, 0.672\}$ **13.** $\delta = \frac{\varepsilon}{2}$

15. $\delta = \frac{\varepsilon}{3}$ **17.** $\delta = \frac{\varepsilon}{3}$ **19.** $\delta = 2\varepsilon$ **21.** $\delta = \frac{\varepsilon}{6}$

23. $\delta < \min\{1, \frac{\varepsilon}{5}\}$ **25.** $\delta < \min\{1, \frac{\varepsilon}{7}\}$

27. $\delta = \min\{1, 56\varepsilon\}$ **29.** $\delta = \varepsilon$ **31.** $\delta = \min\{1, 3\varepsilon\}$

33. $\delta = \sqrt{\varepsilon}$ **35.** $\delta = \frac{\varepsilon}{2}$ **37.** $\delta = 0.34$

39. Choose $\delta = 0.02$ based on experiment:

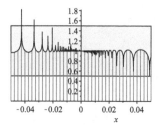 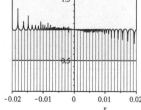

41. Choose $\delta = 0.01$ based on experiment:

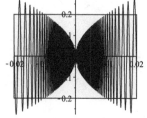 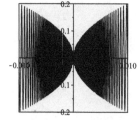

CHAPTER 2: Answers to Odd Exercises

Exercises: 2.1

1. $m \approx 4$

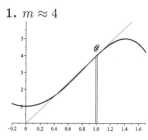

3. $m \approx 0.838$

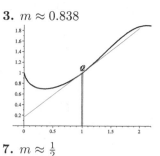

5. $m \approx 1$

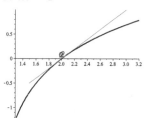

7. $m \approx \frac{1}{2}$

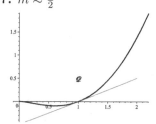

9. $m \approx 10$ and -10. "vertical tangent line"

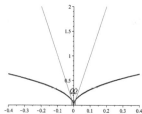

11. $m \approx 3.8$

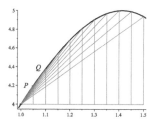

$f(x) = 4x^2 - x^4 + 1$

x_0	x_1	Δx	y_0	y_1	Δy	$\frac{\Delta y}{\Delta x}$
1	1.5	0.5	4	4.93	0.93	1.86
1	1.45	0.45	4	4.99	0.99	2.2
1	1.4	0.4	4	5.0	1	2.5
1	1.35	0.35	4	4.96	0.96	2.74
1	1.3	0.3	4	4.9	0.9	3
1	1.25	0.25	4	4.8	0.8	3.2
1	1.2	0.2	4	4.68	0.68	3.4
1	1.15	0.15	4	4.54	0.54	3.6
1	1.1	0.1	4	4.37	0.37	3.7
1	1.05	0.05	4	4.19	0.19	3.8

13. $m \approx 0.94$

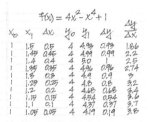

$f(x) = x^{\sin x}$

x_0	x_1	Δx	y_0	y_1	Δy	$\frac{\Delta y}{\Delta x}$
1	2.5	1.5	1	1.72	0.73	0.49
1	2.35	1.35	1	1.84	0.84	0.62
1	2.2	1.2	1	1.89	0.89	0.74
1	2.05	1.05	1	1.89	0.89	0.86
1	1.9	0.9	1	1.83	0.83	0.92
1	1.75	0.75	1	1.73	0.73	0.97
1	1.6	0.6	1	1.6	0.6	1.0
1	1.45	0.45	1	1.45	0.45	1.0
1	1.3	0.3	1	1.28	0.28	0.93
1	1.15	0.15	1	1.14	0.14	0.94

15. $m \approx 1$

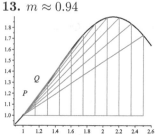

$f(x) = \ln(x-1)$

x_0	x_1	Δx	y_0	y_1	Δy	$\frac{\Delta y}{\Delta x}$
2	2.8	.8	0	.79	.59	.7375
2	2.72	.72	0	.54	.54	.75
2	2.64	.64	0	.50	.50	.7813
2	2.56	.56	0	.44	.44	.7857
2	2.48	.48	0	.39	.39	.8125
2	2.4	.4	0	.34	.34	.85
2	2.32	.32	0	.28	.28	.8750
2	2.24	.24	0	.21	.21	.8750
2	2.16	.16	0	.15	.15	.9375
2	2.08	.08	0	.08	.08	1

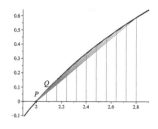

17. $m \approx 0.6$

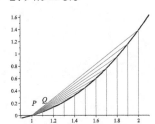 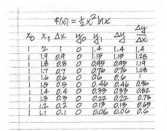

19. no tangent line

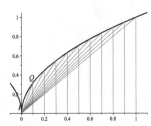 

21. $m_{sec}(x) = \dfrac{4x^2 - x^4 - 3}{x - 1}$, $m \approx 3.9$ based on:

1.5, 1.875000000　　1.45, 2.198875000
1.4, 2.496000000　　1.35, 2.767125000
1.3, 3.013000000　　1.25, 3.234375000
1.2, 3.432000000　　1.15, 3.606625000
1.1, 3.759000000　　1.05, 3.889875000

23. $m_{sec}(x) = \dfrac{x^{\sin x} - 1}{x - 1}$, $m \approx 0.9$ based on:

2.5, 0.4869585780　　2.35, 0.6196733689
2.2, 0.7430660633　　2.05, 0.8483521390
1.9, 0.9284750078　　1.75, 0.9791827453
1.6, 0.9994656317　　1.45, 0.9912873533
1.3, 0.9587663033　　1.15, 0.9070933667

25. $m_{sec}(x) = \dfrac{\ln(x - 1)}{x - 2}$, $m \approx 1$ based on:

2.8, 0.7347333311　　2.72, 0.7532281817
2.64, 0.7729628778　　2.56, 0.7940818238
2.48, 0.8167543496　　2.4, 0.8411805915
2.32, 0.8675991769　　2.24, 0.8962974150
2.16, 0.9276250319　　2.08, 0.9620130142

27. $m_{sec}(x) = \dfrac{x^2 \ln x}{2(x - 1)}$, $m \approx \frac{1}{2}$ based on:

2, 1.386294361　　1.9, 1.287273627
1.8, 1.190267996　　1.7, 1.095368319
1.6, 1.002674409　　1.5, 0.9122964932
1.4, 0.8243569796　　1.3, 0.7389926783
1.2, 0.6563576045　　1.1, 0.5766265880

29. $m_{sec}(x) = \dfrac{\sqrt{|x|}}{x}$, $m = $ DNE based on:

1, 1.000000000　　0.9, 1.054092553
0.8, 1.118033989　　0.7, 1.195228609

0.6, 1.290994449　　0.5, 1.414213562
0.4, 1.581138830　　0.3, 1.825741858
0.2, 2.236067978　　0.1, 3.162277660

31. $m_{sec}(x) = -(1 + x)$, $m = \lim\limits_{x \to 1} -(x + 1) = -2$,
$y - 3 = -2(x - 1)$, i.e., $y = -2x + 5$

33. $m_{sec}(x) = -(4 + 2x + x^2)$,
$m = \lim\limits_{x \to 2} -(4 + 2x + x^2) = -12$,
$y + 7 = -12(x - 2)$, i.e., $y = -12x + 17$

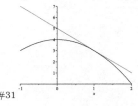 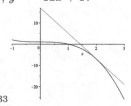

#31　　　　　　　　　#33

35. $m_{sec}(x) = \dfrac{-1}{2x}$, $m = \lim\limits_{x \to 2} \dfrac{-1}{2x} = \dfrac{-1}{4}$,
$y - \frac{1}{2} = -\frac{1}{4}(x - 2)$, i.e., $y = -\frac{1}{4}x + 1$

37. $m_{sec}(x) = \dfrac{-(3 + x)}{9x^2}$, $m = \lim\limits_{x \to 3} \dfrac{-(3 + x)}{9x^2} = \dfrac{-2}{27}$,
$y - \frac{1}{9} = -\frac{2}{27}(x - 3)$, i.e., $y = -\frac{2}{27}x + \frac{1}{3}$

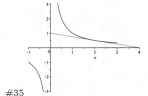 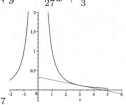

#35　　　　　　　　　#37

39. $m_{sec}(x) = \dfrac{-(4 + 2x + x^2)}{8x^3}$,
$m = \lim\limits_{x \to 2} \dfrac{-(4 + 2x + x^2)}{8x^3} = -\dfrac{3}{16}$,
$y - \frac{1}{8} = -\frac{3}{16}(x - 2)$, i.e., $y = -\frac{3}{16}x + \frac{1}{2}$

41. $m_{sec}(x) = \dfrac{-1}{2\sqrt{x}(2 + \sqrt{x})}$,
$m = \lim\limits_{x \to 4} \dfrac{-1}{2\sqrt{x}(2 + \sqrt{x})} = -\dfrac{1}{16}$,
$y - \frac{1}{2} = -\frac{1}{16}(x - 4)$, i.e., $y = -\frac{1}{16}x + \frac{3}{4}$

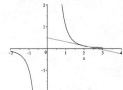 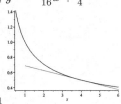

#39　　　　　　　　　#41

43. $m_{sec}(x) = \dfrac{-3}{2(x + 2)}$, $m = \lim\limits_{x \to 2} \dfrac{-3}{2(x + 2)} = \dfrac{-3}{8}$,
$y - \frac{3}{2} = -\frac{3}{8}(x - 2)$, i.e., $y = -\frac{3}{8}x + \frac{9}{4}$

45. $m_{sec}(x) = \dfrac{1}{3(1 + x)}$, $m = \lim\limits_{x \to 2} \dfrac{1}{3(1 + x)} = \dfrac{1}{9}$,

$y - \frac{2}{3} = \frac{1}{9}(x - 2)$, i.e., $y = \frac{1}{9}x + \frac{4}{9}$

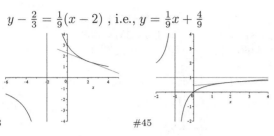

#43   #45

47. $m_{sec}(x) = \dfrac{2}{5(x+3)}$, $m = \lim\limits_{x \to 2} \dfrac{2}{5(x+3)} = \dfrac{2}{25}$,

$y - \frac{3}{5} = \frac{2}{25}(x-2)$, i.e., $y = \frac{2}{25}x + \frac{11}{25}$

49. $m_{sec}(x) = \dfrac{x+1}{\sqrt{5+x^2} + \sqrt{6}}$,

$m = \lim\limits_{x \to 1} \dfrac{x+1}{\sqrt{5+x^2} + \sqrt{6}} = \dfrac{1}{\sqrt{6}}$,

$y - \sqrt{6} = \frac{1}{\sqrt{6}}(x-1)$, i.e., $y = \frac{1}{\sqrt{6}}x + \frac{5}{\sqrt{6}}$

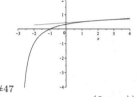 

#47   #49

51. $m_{sec}(x) = \dfrac{-(2+x))}{5(1+x^2)}$, $m = \lim\limits_{x \to 2} \dfrac{-(2+x)}{5(1+x^2)} = \dfrac{-4}{25}$,

$y - \frac{1}{5} = -\frac{4}{25}(x-2)$, i.e., $y = -\frac{4}{25}x + \frac{13}{25}$

53. $m_{sec}(x) = \dfrac{-(4+2x+x^2)}{9(1+x^3)}$,

$m = \lim\limits_{x \to 2} \dfrac{-(4+2x+x^2)}{9(1+x^3)} = -\dfrac{4}{27}$,

$y - \frac{1}{9} = -\frac{4}{27}(x-2)$, i.e., $y = -\frac{4}{27}x + \frac{11}{27}$

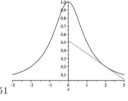 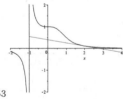

#51   #53

55. $m_{sec}(x) = \dfrac{x+2}{5(1+x^2)}$, $m = \lim\limits_{x \to 2} \dfrac{x+2}{5(1+x^2)} = \dfrac{4}{25}$,

$y - \frac{4}{5} = \frac{4}{25}(x-2)$, i.e., $y = \frac{4}{25}x + \frac{12}{25}$

57. $m_{sec}(x) = \dfrac{-(2x-1)}{5(1+x^2)}$, $m = \lim\limits_{x \to 2} \dfrac{-(2x-1)}{5(1+x^2)} = -\dfrac{3}{25}$,

$y - \frac{2}{5} = -\frac{3}{25}(x-2)$, i.e., $y = -\frac{3}{25}x + \frac{16}{25}$

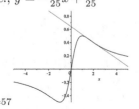

#55   #57

59. $m_{sec}(x) = \dfrac{x+4}{\sqrt{x^2+3x+2}}$,

$m = \lim\limits_{x \to 1} \dfrac{x+4}{\sqrt{x^2+3x+2}} = \dfrac{5}{4}$,

$y - 2 = \frac{5}{4}(x-1)$, i.e., $y = \frac{5}{4}x + \frac{3}{4}$

61. $m_{sec}(x) = \dfrac{x^2+x+1}{\sqrt{x^3+1} + \sqrt{2}}$,

$m = \lim\limits_{x \to 1} \dfrac{x^2+x+1}{\sqrt{x^3+1} + \sqrt{2}} = \dfrac{3\sqrt{2}}{4}$,

$y - \sqrt{2} = \frac{3\sqrt{2}}{4}(x-1)$, i.e., $y = \frac{3\sqrt{2}}{4}x + \frac{\sqrt{2}}{4}$

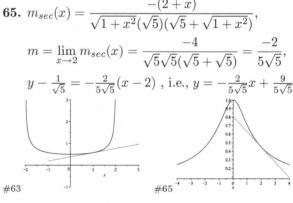

#59   #61

63. $m_{sec}(x) = \dfrac{x+1}{\sqrt{4-x^2}(\sqrt{3})(\sqrt{3} + \sqrt{4-x^2})}$,

$m = \lim\limits_{x \to 1} m_{sec}(x) = \dfrac{2}{\sqrt{3}\sqrt{3}(\sqrt{3} + \sqrt{3})} = \dfrac{1}{3\sqrt{3}}$,

$y - \frac{1}{\sqrt{3}} = \frac{1}{3\sqrt{3}}(x-1)$, i.e., $y = \frac{1}{3\sqrt{3}}x + \frac{2}{3\sqrt{3}}$

65. $m_{sec}(x) = \dfrac{-(2+x)}{\sqrt{1+x^2}(\sqrt{5})(\sqrt{5} + \sqrt{1+x^2})}$,

$m = \lim\limits_{x \to 2} m_{sec}(x) = \dfrac{-4}{\sqrt{5}\sqrt{5}(\sqrt{5} + \sqrt{5})} = \dfrac{-2}{5\sqrt{5}}$,

$y - \frac{1}{\sqrt{5}} = -\frac{2}{5\sqrt{5}}(x-2)$, i.e., $y = -\frac{2}{5\sqrt{5}}x + \frac{9}{5\sqrt{5}}$

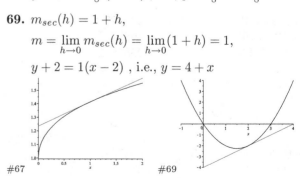

#63   #65

67. $m_{sec}(x) = \dfrac{1}{(\sqrt{1+\sqrt{x}} + \sqrt{2})(\sqrt{x} + 1)}$,

$m = \lim\limits_{x \to 1} m_{sec}(x) = \dfrac{1}{(\sqrt{2} + \sqrt{2})2} = \dfrac{1}{4\sqrt{2}} = \dfrac{\sqrt{2}}{8}$,

$y - \sqrt{2} = \frac{\sqrt{2}}{8}(x-1)$, i.e., $y = \frac{\sqrt{2}}{8}x + \frac{7\sqrt{2}}{8}$

69. $m_{sec}(h) = 1 + h$,

$m = \lim\limits_{h \to 0} m_{sec}(h) = \lim\limits_{h \to 0}(1+h) = 1$,

$y + 2 = 1(x-2)$, i.e., $y = 4 + x$

#67   #69

71. $m_{sec}(h) = -5 - h + h^2$,

$m = \lim\limits_{h \to 0} m_{sec}(h) = m = \lim\limits_{h \to 0}(-5 - h + h^2) = -5$,

$y - 9 = -5(x - 1)$, i.e., $y = 14 - 5x$

73. $m_{sec}(h) = \dfrac{1}{\sqrt{2 + h} + \sqrt{2}}$,

$m = \lim\limits_{h \to 0} m_{sec}(h) = \dfrac{1}{\sqrt{2} + \sqrt{2}} = \dfrac{1}{2\sqrt{2}} = \dfrac{\sqrt{2}}{4}$,

$y - \sqrt{2} = \dfrac{\sqrt{2}}{4}(x - 1)$, i.e., $y = \dfrac{\sqrt{2}}{4}x + \dfrac{3\sqrt{2}}{4}$

#71   #73

75. $m_{sec}(h) = \dfrac{-1}{2(2 + h)}$,

$m = \lim\limits_{h \to 0} m_{sec}(h) = \dfrac{-1}{2(2)} = -\dfrac{1}{4}$,

$y - \dfrac{1}{2} = -\dfrac{1}{4}(x - 2)$, i.e., $y = -\dfrac{1}{4}x + 1$

77. $m_{sec}(h) = \dfrac{-2}{5(5 + h)}$,

$m = \lim\limits_{h \to 0} m_{sec}(h) = \dfrac{-2}{5(5)} = -\dfrac{2}{25}$,

$y - \dfrac{2}{5} = -\dfrac{2}{25}(x - 2)$, i.e., $y = -\dfrac{2}{25}x + \dfrac{14}{25}$

#75   #77

79. $m_{sec}(h) = \dfrac{-4 - h}{4(2 + h)^2}$,

$m = \lim\limits_{h \to 0} m_{sec}(h) = \dfrac{-4}{4(4)} = -\dfrac{1}{4}$,

$y - \dfrac{1}{4} = -\dfrac{1}{4}(x - 2)$, i.e., $y = -\dfrac{1}{4}x + \dfrac{3}{4}$

81. $m_{sec}(h) = \dfrac{-12 - 6h - h^2}{8(2 + h)^3}$,

$m = \lim\limits_{h \to 0} m_{sec}(h) = \dfrac{-12}{8(8)} = -\dfrac{3}{16}$,

$y - \dfrac{1}{8} = -\dfrac{3}{16}(x - 2)$, i.e., $y = -\dfrac{3}{16}x + \dfrac{1}{2}$

#79   #81

83. $m_{sec}(h) = \dfrac{-1}{2\sqrt{4 + h}(2 + \sqrt{4 + h})}$,

$m = \lim\limits_{h \to 0} m_{sec}(h) = \dfrac{-1}{2(2)(2 + 2)} = -\dfrac{1}{16}$,

$y - \dfrac{1}{2} = -\dfrac{1}{16}(x - 4)$, i.e., $y = -\dfrac{1}{16}x + \dfrac{3}{4}$

85. $m_{sec}(h) = \dfrac{-3}{2(4 + h)}$,

$m = \lim\limits_{h \to 0} m_{sec}(h) = \dfrac{-3}{2(4)} = -\dfrac{3}{8}$,

$y - \dfrac{3}{2} = -\dfrac{3}{8}(x - 2)$, i.e., $y = -\dfrac{3}{8}x + \dfrac{9}{4}$

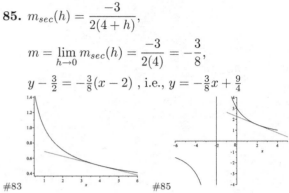

#83   #85

87. $m_{sec}(h) = \dfrac{1}{3(3 + h)}$,

$m = \lim\limits_{h \to 0} m_{sec}(h) = \dfrac{1}{3(3)} = -\dfrac{1}{9}$,

$y - \dfrac{2}{3} = \dfrac{1}{9}(x - 2)$, i.e., $y = \dfrac{1}{9}x + \dfrac{4}{9}$

89. $m_{sec}(h) = \dfrac{1}{4(4 + h)}$,

$m = \lim\limits_{h \to 0} m_{sec}(h) = \dfrac{1}{4(4)} = \dfrac{1}{16}$,

$y - \dfrac{3}{4} = \dfrac{1}{16}(x - 2)$, i.e., $y = \dfrac{1}{16}x + \dfrac{5}{8}$

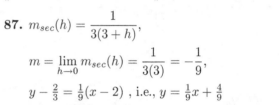

#87   #89

91. $m_{sec}(h) = \dfrac{-4 - h}{5[1 + (2 + h)^2]}$,

$m = \lim\limits_{h \to 0} m_{sec}(h) = \dfrac{-4}{5(5)} = -\dfrac{4}{25}$,

$y - \dfrac{1}{5} = -\dfrac{4}{25}(x - 2)$, i.e., $y = -\dfrac{4}{25}x + \dfrac{13}{25}$

93. $m_{sec}(h) = \dfrac{-12 - 6h - h^2}{9[1 + (2 + h)^3]}$,

$m = \lim\limits_{h \to 0} m_{sec}(h) = \dfrac{-12}{9(9)} = -\dfrac{4}{27}$,

$y - \dfrac{1}{9} = -\dfrac{4}{27}(x - 2)$, i.e., $y = -\dfrac{4}{27}x + \dfrac{11}{27}$

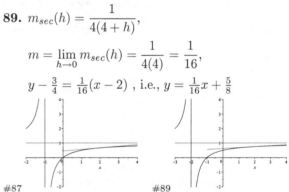
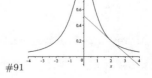
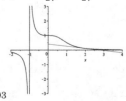

#91   #93

95. $m_{sec}(h) = \dfrac{4+h}{5[1+(2+h)^2]}$,

$m = \lim\limits_{h \to 0} m_{sec}(h) = \dfrac{4}{5(5)} = \dfrac{4}{25}$,

$y - \dfrac{4}{5} = \dfrac{4}{25}(x-2)$, i.e., $y = \dfrac{4}{25}x + \dfrac{12}{25}$

97. $m_{sec}(h) = \dfrac{-25}{(1+\sqrt{1+h})(5+5\sqrt{1+h})}$,

$m = \lim\limits_{h \to 0} m_{sec}(h) = \dfrac{-25}{2(5+5)} = -\dfrac{5}{4}$,

$y - 5 = -\dfrac{5}{4}(x-1)$, i.e., $y = -\dfrac{5}{4}x + \dfrac{25}{4}$

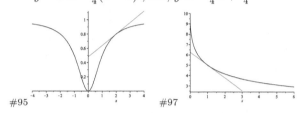

#95   #97

99. $m_{sec}(h) = \dfrac{1}{(\sqrt{1+\sqrt{1+h}}+\sqrt{2})(\sqrt{1+h}+1)}$,

$m = \lim\limits_{h \to 0} m_{sec}(h) = \dfrac{1}{(\sqrt{2}+\sqrt{2})2} = \dfrac{1}{4\sqrt{2}} = \dfrac{\sqrt{2}}{8}$,

$y - \sqrt{2} = \dfrac{\sqrt{2}}{8}(x-1)$, i.e., $y = \dfrac{\sqrt{2}}{8}x + \dfrac{7\sqrt{2}}{8}$

101. $m_{sec}(h) = 5\left(\dfrac{2\ln(2+h)-\ln(2)(2+h)}{h(2+h)}\right)$,

$m = \lim\limits_{h \to 0} m_{sec}(h) \approx 0.77$ (graphical method),

$y - 3.47 = 0.77(x-2)$, i.e., $y = 0.77x + 1.93$

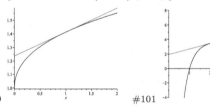

#99   #101

103. $m_{sec}(h) = \dfrac{(1+h)^2 e^{-(1+h)} - e^{-1}}{h}$,

$m = \lim\limits_{h \to 0} m_{sec}(h) \approx 0.37$ (graphical method),

$y - 0.37 = 0.37(x-1)$, i.e., $y = 0.37x$

105. $m_{sec}(h) = \begin{cases} 2-h & \text{if } h < 0 \\ -2+h & \text{if } h \geq 0 \end{cases}$,

$m = \lim\limits_{h \to 0^-} m_{sec}(h) = \lim\limits_{h \to 0^-} (2-h) = 2$ and

$m = \lim\limits_{h \to 0^+} m_{sec}(h) = \lim\limits_{h \to 0^+} (-2+h) = -2$

Thus, the two-sided limit $\lim\limits_{h \to 0} m_{sec}(h)$ does not exist

and so there is no tangent line at $a = -1$.

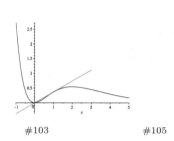

#103   #105

Exercises: 2.2

1. $f'(x) = 3$ **3.** $f'(x) = 2x - 3$ **5.** $f'(x) = 6x^2 - 4x^3$

7. $f'(x) = 2x + 6$ **9.** $f'(x) = -\dfrac{1}{x^2} = -x^{-2}$

11. $f'(x) = \dfrac{-3}{x^4} = -3x^{-4}$ **13.** $f'(x) = -\dfrac{1}{2}x^{-3/2}$

15. $f'(x) = \dfrac{-6}{(x+2)^2}$ **17.** $f'(x) = \dfrac{1}{(1+x)^2}$

19. $f'(x) = \dfrac{2}{(x+3)^2}$ **21.** $f'(x) = \dfrac{x}{\sqrt{5+x^2}}$

23. $f'(x) = \dfrac{-2x}{(1+x^2)^2}$ **25.** $f'(x) = \dfrac{-3x^2}{(1+x^3)^2}$

27. $f'(x) = \dfrac{2x}{(1+x^2)^2}$ **29.** $f'(x) = \dfrac{1-x^2}{(1+x^2)^2}$

31. $f'(x) = \dfrac{2x+3}{2\sqrt{x^2+3x}}$ **33.** $f'(x) = \dfrac{x}{\sqrt{x^2+1}}$

35. $f'(x) = \dfrac{x}{(4-x^2)^{3/2}}$ **37.** $f'(x) = \dfrac{-x}{(1+x^2)^{3/2}}$

39. $f'(x) = \dfrac{1}{4\sqrt{x}\sqrt{1+\sqrt{x}}}$

41. $f'(x) = \lim\limits_{h \to 0} 2^x \left(\dfrac{2^h - 1}{h}\right) \approx (0.69)2^x$

43. $f'(x) = \lim\limits_{h \to 0} e^{-2x}\left(\dfrac{e^{-2h}-1}{h}\right) = e^{2x}(-2) = -2e^{-2x}$

45. $f'(x) = 3x^2$, $f'(-1) = 3$; $f'(1) = 3$,
$y + 0 = 3(x+1)$, $y - 2 = 3(x-1)$.

47. $f'(x) = -2x$, $f'(-1) = 2$; $f'(1) = -2$,
$y - 3 = 2(x-1)$, $y - 3 = -2(x-1)$.

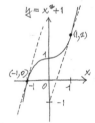   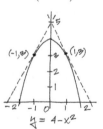

#45   #47

49. $f'(x) = 4 - 2x$, $f'(1) = 2$; $f'(2) = 0$,
$y - 3 = 3(x-1)$, $y - 4 = 0$.

51. $f'(x) = \dfrac{-x}{\sqrt{4-x^2}}$, $f'(-1) = \dfrac{\sqrt{3}}{3}$; $f'(1) = -\dfrac{\sqrt{3}}{3}$,
$y - \sqrt{3} = \dfrac{\sqrt{3}}{3}(x+1)$, $y - \sqrt{3} = -\dfrac{\sqrt{3}}{3}(x-1)$.

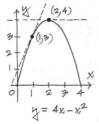

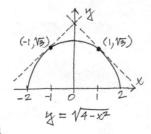

#49   #51

53. $f'(x) = \dfrac{-2x}{(1+x^2)^2}$, $f'(-1) = 1$, $f'(1) = -1$,

$y - \frac{1}{2} = x + 1$, $y - \frac{1}{2} = -(x-1)$.

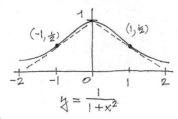

#53

55. $f'(x) = -2x$, $x = 0$. **57.** $f'(x) = 4 - 2x$, $x = 2$.

59. $f'(x) = 3 - 3x^2$, $x = -1, x = 1$

61. $f'(x) = 6x - 3x^2$, $x = 0, x = 2$.

63. $f'(x) = 2x - 4x^3$, $x = 0, x = -1, x = 1$.

65. $f'(x) = 1 - \dfrac{1}{x^2}$, $x = -1, x = 1$.

67. $f'(x) = 1 - \dfrac{2}{x^2}$, $x = 2^{1/3}$.

69. f is not differentiable at $x = 1$. For $x \neq 1$,

$$f'(x) = \begin{cases} 2x & \text{if } x < 1 \\ -\frac{1}{x^2} & \text{if } x > 1 \end{cases}$$

71. f is not differentiable at $x = 0$ and $x = 1$. It is discontinuous at $x = 1$. For $x \neq 0, 1$

$$f'(x) = \begin{cases} 0 & \text{if } x < 0 \\ \frac{1}{2\sqrt{x}} & \text{if } 0 < x < 1 \\ -1 & \text{if } x > 1 \end{cases}$$

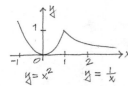

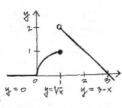

#69   #71

73. f is continuous and differentiable at everywhere.

$$f'(x) = \begin{cases} -2x & \text{if } x \leq 0 \\ 2x & \text{if } x > 0 \end{cases}$$

75. f is continuous everywhere. It is not differentiable at $x = 0$. For $x \neq 0$,

$$f'(x) = \begin{cases} 2x + 2 & \text{if } x < 0 \\ 2x - 2 & \text{if } x > 0 \end{cases}$$

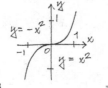

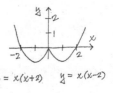

#73   #75

77. f is continuous and differentiable on each of the intervals $(-\infty, 0)$ and $(0, \infty)$. For $x \neq 0$,

$$f'(x) = \begin{cases} -1/x^2 & \text{if } x < 0 \\ 1/x^2 & \text{if } x > 0 \end{cases}$$

79. f is not differentiable at $x = 1$. It is continuous on $(-\infty, 0)$ and $(0, \infty)$.

$$f'(x) = \begin{cases} 1/x^2 & \text{if } x < 0 \\ -1/x^2 & \text{if } 0 < x < 1 \\ 1/x^2 & \text{if } x > 1 \end{cases}$$

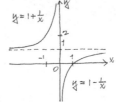

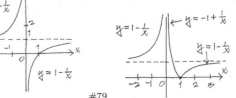

#77   #79

81. f is not continuous and not differentiable for $x = 0$. For $x \neq 0$,

$$f'(x) = \begin{cases} -1 & \text{if } x < 0 \\ 1 & \text{if } x > 0 \end{cases}$$

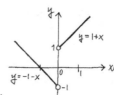

#81

Exercises: 2.3

1. $f'(x) = 16x^{3/5}$ **3.** $y' = -\frac{12}{5}x^{-8/5}$

5. $f'(x) = -15x^{-8/3}$ **7.** $y' = \frac{18}{17}x^{-23/17}$

9. $f'(x) = 28x^6 - 25x^4 + 6x^2$

11. $f'(x) = 4x^{1/3} - \frac{2}{3}x^{-1/3}$

13. $y' = \dfrac{1}{\sqrt{x}} - 7x^{-2}$ **15.** $y' = \frac{6}{5}x^{-2/5} - 28x^{-5}$

17. $y' = \frac{5}{3}x^{-2/3} + x^{-1/2} + \frac{15}{2}x^{-7/2}$ **19.** $R' = \frac{2}{3}x$

21. $y' = -\frac{10}{3}x^{-8/3} - 8x^{-3}$ **23.** $y' = -\frac{35}{6}x^{-13/6} - \frac{21}{2}x^{5/2}$

25. $f'(x) = \frac{25}{2}x^{3/2} - 30x^4 + 8x$ **27.** $f'(x) = 9x^2 + 7x^{1/6}$

29. $f'(x) = 4x^3 - 12x$ **31.** $f'(x) = 3x^2 + 12x + 12$

33. $f'(x) = 1 + \dfrac{5}{\sqrt{x}}$ **35.** $f'(x) = 2x - 2x^{-3}$

37. $f'(x) = 1 - x^{-2}$

39. $f'(x) = \frac{3}{2}x^{1/2} - \frac{3}{2}x^{-1/2} - \frac{3}{2}x^{-3/2} - \frac{3}{2}x^{-5/2}$

41. $f'(x) = -x^{-2} - 5x^{-6}$

43. $f'(x) = -4x^{-5} + 28x^{-8} - 40x^{-11}$

45. $f'(x) = 1 + \dfrac{1}{2\sqrt{x}}$ **47.** $f'(x) = 2x + 3x^{1/2} + 1$

49. $f'(x) = -\dfrac{5}{2}x^{-7/2} - \dfrac{7}{2}x^{-9/2}$

51. $f'(x) = -\dfrac{5}{3}x^{-8/3} - \dfrac{8}{3}x^{-11/3}$ **53.** $f(x) = -\dfrac{3}{2}x^{-5/2}$

55. $y = -\dfrac{3}{10}x + 1,\ y = \dfrac{17}{10}x - \dfrac{27}{5}$

57. $y = 2x + 1,\ y = 4$ **59.** $y = \dfrac{3}{4}x - 1,\ y = \dfrac{3}{4}x + 1$

61. $y = \dfrac{1}{\sqrt{2}}x - \dfrac{1}{\sqrt{2}},\ y = \dfrac{3}{4}x$

63. $y = 1.26x - 2.52,\ y = 0.337x + 0.404$

65. $x = -1, 2$ **67.** $x = \pm 1$ **69.** $x = \pm 2^{-1/4}$

71. $x = 1$ **73.** $x = 2$

75.

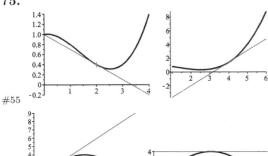

#55

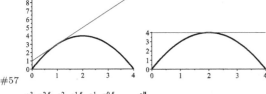

#57

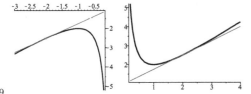

#59

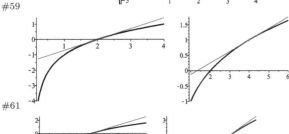

#61

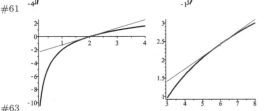

#63

Exercises: 2.4

1.

i	t_i	y_i	Δt_i	Δy_i	$\dfrac{\Delta y_i}{\Delta t_i}$
0	0	20	✳	✳	✳
1	.5	14.26	.5	-5.74	-11.48
2	1	12	.5	-2.26	-4.52
3	1.5	11.39	.5	-0.61	-1.22
4	2	12.01	.5	0.62	1.24
5	2.5	13.12	.5	1.11	2.22
6	3	14	.5	0.88	1.76
7	3.5	13.85	.5	-0.15	-0.30
8	4	12.01	.5	-1.84	-3.68
9	4.5	7.61	.5	-4.4	-8.8
10	5	0	.5	-7.61	-15.22

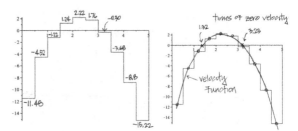

3.

i	t_i	y_i	Δt_i	Δy_i	$\dfrac{\Delta y_i}{\Delta t_i}$
0	0	10	✳	✳	✳
1	.5	8.1	.5	-1.9	-3.8
2	1	10.64	.5	2.54	5.08
3	1.5	14.24	.5	3.6	7.2
4	2	16.66	.5	2.42	4.84
5	2.5	16.77	.5	0.11	0.22
6	3	14.5	.5	-2.27	-4.54
7	3.5	10.97	.5	-3.53	-7.06
8	4	8.22	.5	-2.75	-5.5
9	4.5	9.55	.5	1.33	2.66
10	5	19.28	.5	9.73	19.46

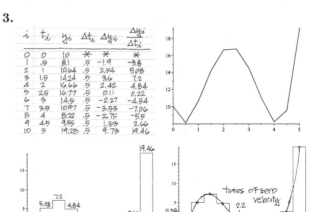

5. (a) $f(t) = -16t^2 + 48t$ (b) $v(t) = -32t + 48$
(c) 36 ft (d) $v(1) = 16$ ft/s , $v(2) = -16$ ft/s

7. (a) $f(t) = -16t^2 + 64t$ (b) $v(t) = -32t + 64$
(c) 64 ft (d) $v(1) = 32$ ft/s, $v(3) = -32$ ft/s

9. (a) $f(t) = -16t^2 + 80t$ (b) $v(t) = -32t + 80$
(c) 100 ft (d) $v(2) = 16$ ft/s, $v(3) = -16$ ft/s

11. (a) $f(t) = -16t^2 + 64$ (b) $v(t) = -32t$
(c) 2 s (d) 64 ft/s

13. (a) $f(t) = -16t^2 + 256$ (b) $v(t) = -32t$
(c) 4 s (d) 128 ft/s

15. (a) $f(t) = -16t^2 + 16t + 32$ (b) $v(t) = -32t + 16$
(c) 36 ft (d) t = 2 s (e) 48 ft/s

17. (a) $f(t) = -16t^2 - 16t + 192$ (b) $v(t) = -32t - 16$
(c) 192 ft (d) t = 3 s (e) 112 ft/s

19. (a) $f(t) = -16t^2 + 48t + 64$ (b) $v(t) = -32t + 48$
(c) 100 ft (d) 4 s (e) 80 ft/s

21. $v(t) = f'(t) = -3t^2 + 14t - 14$

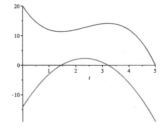

#21: position (in blue), velocity (in red)

Exercises: 2.5

1. $\dfrac{dy}{dx} = 12x^3 - 18x^2 + \dfrac{4}{3}x + 1,\ \dfrac{d^2y}{dx^2} = 36x^2 - 36x + \dfrac{4}{3}$

3. $\dfrac{dy}{dx} = \dfrac{15}{2}x^{3/2} - \dfrac{20}{3}x^{1/3} - x^{-3/2}$

$\dfrac{d^2y}{dx^2} = \dfrac{45}{4}x^{1/2} - \dfrac{20}{9}x^{-2/3} + 3/2x^{-5/2}$

5. $\dfrac{dy}{dx} = 1 + \dfrac{1}{2}x^{-1/2} - \dfrac{1}{2}x^{-3/2}, \quad \dfrac{d^2y}{dx^2} = -\dfrac{1}{4}x^{-3/2} + \dfrac{3}{4}x^{-5/2}$

7. $\dfrac{dy}{dx} = \dfrac{35}{2}x^{5/2} + 2, \quad \dfrac{d^2y}{dx^2} = \dfrac{175}{4}x^{3/2}$

9. $\dfrac{dy}{dx} = 6x^2 + \dfrac{1}{3}x^{-4/3}, \quad \dfrac{d^2y}{dx^2} = 12x - \dfrac{4}{9}x^{-7/3}$

11. $\dfrac{df}{dx}(x) = -3x^{-4} - 6x^{-3} - 4x^{-2}$

$\dfrac{d^2f}{dx^2}(x) = 12x^{-5} + 18x^{-4} + 8x^{-3}$

13. $\dfrac{df}{dx}(x) = 36x^3 + 24x, \dfrac{d^2f}{dx^2}(x) = 108x^2 + 24$

15. $\dfrac{dy}{dx} = 2x + 3\sqrt{x} + 1, \dfrac{d^2y}{dx^2} = 2 + \dfrac{3}{2\sqrt{x}}$

17. $\dfrac{dy}{dx} = 1 - x^{-2}, \dfrac{d^2y}{dx^2} = 2x^{-3} = \dfrac{2}{x^3}$

19. $\dfrac{df}{dx}(x) = -12 + 26x - 18x^2 + 4x^3$

$\dfrac{d^2f}{dx^2}(x) = 26 - 36x + 12x^2$

21. $\dfrac{dP}{dV}\Big|_{V=3} = -\dfrac{5}{9}\,\text{lb/ft}^3$

23. $\dfrac{dV}{dr} = 4\pi r^2, \dfrac{dV}{dr}\Big|_{r=3} = 400\pi, dV = 4\pi r^2 dr$

25. $\dfrac{dA}{dx} = 2x, dA = 2xdx$

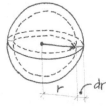

#23

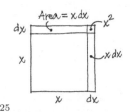

#25

27. (a)

t	y	Δy	$\dfrac{\Delta y}{\Delta t}$
0	0.800	*	*
40	0.775	-0.025	.000625
83	0.750	-0.025	.000981
129	0.725	-0.025	.000543
179	0.700	-0.025	.000500

(b) $\dfrac{dy}{dt} = f'(t) = \dfrac{-0.800k}{(kt+1)^2} = -\dfrac{k}{0.800}y^2$

29. $f'(x) = 3 - 10x + 12x^2, f''(x) = -10 + 24x$

$f'''(x) = 24, f^{(4)}(x) = 0$

31. $f'(x) = \dfrac{3}{2}x^{1/2} + 10x^{3/2}, f''(x) = \dfrac{3}{4}x^{-1/2} + 15x^{1/2}$

$f'''(x) = -\dfrac{3}{8}x^{-3/2} + \dfrac{15}{2}x^{-1/2}$

$f^{(4)}(x) = \dfrac{9}{16}x^{-5/2} - \dfrac{15}{4}x^{-3/2}$

33. $f'(x) = 3x^2 - x^{-2}, f''(x) = 6x + 2x^{-3}$

$f'''(x) = 6 - 6x^{-4}, f^{(4)}(x) = 24x^{-5}$

35. $f'(x) = \dfrac{1}{2}x^{-1/2}, f''(x) = -\dfrac{1}{4}x^{-3/2}$

$f'''(x) = \dfrac{3}{8}x^{-5/2}\ f^{(4)}(x) = -\dfrac{15}{16}x^{-7/2}$

37. $f'(x) = e^x, f''(x) = e^x, f'''(x) = e^x, f^{(4)}(x) = e^x$

39. $v = \dfrac{ds}{dt} = -3, a = \dfrac{dv}{dt} = 0.$

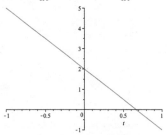

The particle is falling with a constant velocity of -3.

41. $v = \dfrac{ds}{dt} = 6 - 32t, a = \dfrac{dv}{dt} = -32.$

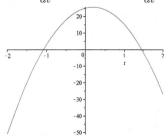

The particle is rising and slowing down until time $t = 3/16 = 0.1875$, where it comes to a stop and then begins to fall.

43. $v = \dfrac{ds}{dt} = 3t^2 - 3, a = \dfrac{ds}{dt} = 6t.$

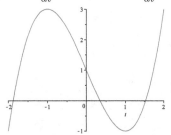

From the graph we see that the particle is rising and slowing down until time $t = -1$, after which it begins falling again until time $t = 1$. Then the particle begins to rise again.

45. $v = \dfrac{ds}{dt} = 1 - t^{-2}, a = \dfrac{dv}{dt} = 2t^{-3}.$

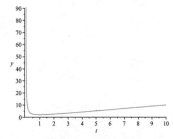

The particle is falling for positive values of t until time

$t = 1$, after which the particle begins to rise more an more slowly as time increases.

47. $v = \dfrac{ds}{dt} = 2t - 2t^{-3}$, $a = \dfrac{dv}{dt} = 2 + 6t^{-4}$.

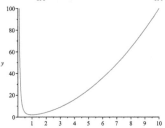

The particle is falling and slowing down until time $t = 1$, after which it begins to rise with increasing velocity.

Exercises: 2.6

1. $\dfrac{dx}{dy} = 2xe^x + (x^2 + 3)e^x = (x^2 + 2x + 3)e^x$

3. $y' = 42x^5 - 165x^4 - 320x^3 - 60x^2$

5. $\dfrac{dx}{dy} = (2x - x^2)e^{-x} = x(2 - x)e^{-x}$

7. $\dfrac{dx}{dy} = e^{-x}\sqrt{x} + e^{-x} \cdot \dfrac{1}{2\sqrt{x}} = e^{-x}\left(\dfrac{1 - 2x}{2\sqrt{x}}\right)$

9. $f'(x) = \frac{5}{6}x^{-1/6}$ **11.** $f'(x) = \frac{25}{2}x^{5/2} - \frac{15}{2}x^{1/2} + x^{-1/2}$

13. $\dfrac{df}{dx}(x) = \dfrac{x(15x - 16)}{2\sqrt{3x - 4}}$

15. $y' = 2e^{2x}$ **17.** $y' = e^x - e^{-x}$

19. $\dfrac{dy}{dx} = e^x + xe^x + 2xe^{-x} - x^2e^{-x}$

21. $y' = -\frac{1}{2}x^{-3/2}e^{2x} + 2x^{-1/2}e^{2x} + \frac{3}{2}x^{1/2}$

23. $y' = \dfrac{-15}{(2x - 5)^2}$ **25.** $y' = \dfrac{6x}{(2x^2 + 1)^2}$

27. $\dfrac{dy}{dx} = \dfrac{-2x^2 + 16x + 20}{(x^2 + 6x + 1)^2}$ **29.** $y' = \dfrac{-6x}{(1 + x^2)^2}$

31. $y' = -\dfrac{3 + 9x^2}{x^2(1 + x^2)^2}$ **33.** $y' = \dfrac{7x^2 + 4x - 5}{(x^2 + x + 1)^2}$

35. $\dfrac{dy}{dx} = \dfrac{1}{(x + 1)^2}$ **37.** $y' = \dfrac{3x^2}{x^3 + 1}$

39. $y' = \dfrac{3}{(2x + 1)^2}$ **41.** $\dfrac{dy}{dx} = \dfrac{1 + \frac{1}{2}\sqrt{x}}{(1 + \sqrt{x})^2}$

43. $f'(x) = \dfrac{1}{2\sqrt{x}(1 + \sqrt{x})^2}$ **45.** $f'(x) = \dfrac{-1}{\sqrt{x}(1 + \sqrt{x})^2}$

47. $f'(x) = \dfrac{1}{\sqrt{x}(1 + \sqrt{x})^2}$ **49.** $\dfrac{dy}{dx} = \dfrac{1 - \frac{1}{2}\sqrt{x} + \frac{1}{2\sqrt{x}}}{(\sqrt{x} + x)^2}$

51. $\dfrac{dy}{dx} = \dfrac{2}{(e^x + e^{-x})^2}$ **53.** $y' = \dfrac{-e^{-x}}{(e^x + 1)^2}$

55. $y' = \dfrac{-4}{(e^x + 2e^{-x})^2}$ **57.** $\dfrac{dy}{dx} = \dfrac{e^x + xe^x}{(2 + x)^2}$

59. $f'(x) = \dfrac{(2x^2 + x + 1)e^x}{(2x + 1)^2}$ **61.** $\dfrac{d^2y}{dx^2} = (2 - 4x + x^2)e^{-x}$

63. $\dfrac{d^2y}{dx^2} = \dfrac{6x^4 + 4x^2 - 2}{(1 + 2x^2 + x^4)^2}$ **65.** $\dfrac{d^2y}{dx^2} = \dfrac{2x^3 - 6x}{(1 + x^2)^3}$

67. $y - 3e^{-1} = 9e^{-1}(x - 1)$, i.e., $y = 9e^{-1}x - 6e^{-1}$

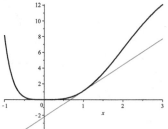

69. $y - 0.5 = (0)(x - 1$, i.e., $y = 0.5$

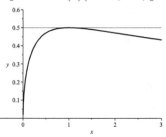

71. $y - \frac{3}{2} = -\frac{3}{2}(x - 1)$, or $y = -\frac{3}{2}x + 3$

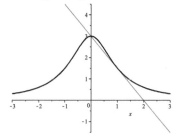

Exercises: 2.7

1. $f'(x) = 3\cos x + 6\sin x$

3. $\dfrac{df}{dx}(x) = 3x^2 \sin x + x^3 \cos x$

5. $\dfrac{dy}{dx} = \dfrac{\cos x}{2\sqrt{x}} - \sqrt{x}\sin x$

7. $f'(x) = e^x(\cos x - \sin x)$

9. $\dfrac{dy}{dx} = 2x\sec x + x^2 \sec x \tan x$

11. $\dfrac{dy}{dx} = 3x^2 \tan x + x^3 \sec^2 x$

13. $f'(x) = \dfrac{x\cos x - \sin x}{x^2}$

15. $y' = \dfrac{2x\cos x - \sin x}{2x^{3/2}}$ **17.** $y' = \dfrac{\cos x}{(1 + \sin x)^2}$

19. $f'(x) = \dfrac{\sin x - \cos x + 1}{(1 + \sin x)^2}$ **21.** $y' = \dfrac{2e^x \sin x}{(\sin x + \cos x)^2}$

23. $\dfrac{dy}{dx} = \dfrac{\cos x + e^x \cos x - e^x \sin x}{(1 + e^x)^2}$

25. $f'(x) = \dfrac{1 - \sin x - \cos x - x\sin x}{(x + 1)^2}$

27. $\dfrac{df}{dx}(x) = \dfrac{2x\cos x - 2\sin x - \sin x \cos x + x}{x^2(x + \cos x)^2}$

29. $f'(x) = \dfrac{\sec x \tan x - \sec x}{(1 + \tan x)^2}$

31. $y' = \dfrac{\sec^2 x + \sec^3 x - \sec x \tan^2 x}{(1 + \sec x)^2}$

33. $f'(x) = \sec x \tan^2 x + \sec^3 x$

35. $f'(x) = -\sin x$ **37.** $f'(x) = 2 \sin x \cos x$

39. $f'(x) = 2(\cos^2 x - \sin^2 x) = 2 \cos 2x$

41. $y - \pi = -(x - \pi)$, i.e., $y = -x + 2\pi$

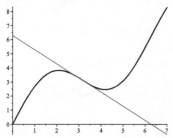

43. $y - \dfrac{\pi}{2} = -\left(x - \dfrac{\pi}{2}\right)$, i.e., $y = -x + \pi$

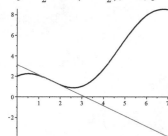

45. $y - \dfrac{\pi^3}{8} = \dfrac{3\pi^2}{4}\left(x - \dfrac{\pi}{2}\right)$, i.e., $y = \dfrac{3\pi^2}{4}x - \dfrac{\pi^3}{4}$

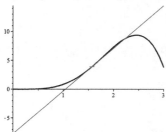

47. $y = \dfrac{\pi-1}{\pi+1} + \dfrac{2}{(\pi+1)^2}(x - \pi)$

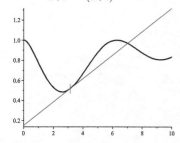

49. $y = -\dfrac{1}{3\pi} + \left(\dfrac{4+3\pi}{18\pi^2}\right)\left(x - \dfrac{3\pi}{2}\right)$

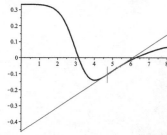

51. $y'' = -2 \sin x - x \cos x$ **53.** $\dfrac{d^2 y}{dx^2} = -2e^x \cos x$

55. $y'' = \sec x \tan^2 x + \sec^3 x$ **57.** $y'' = 2 \sec^2 x \tan x$

59. $\dfrac{d^2 y}{dx^2} = -4 \sin 2x$ **61.** $x = \pi, x = 3\pi$

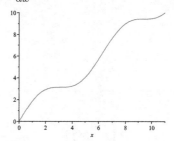

63. $x = \dfrac{\pi}{6}, x = \dfrac{5\pi}{6}$

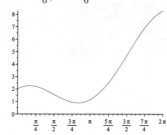

65. $x = \dfrac{2\pi}{3}, x = \dfrac{4\pi}{3}$

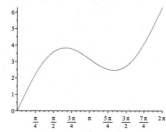

67. $x = \pi$

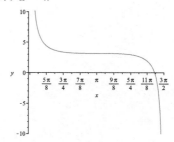

69. $x = \dfrac{\pi}{2}$

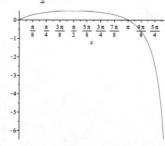

71. $x = 0$

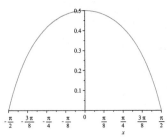

73. $\dfrac{d}{dx}(\cos x) = \lim\limits_{h\to 0}\dfrac{\cos(x+h) - \cos x}{h}$

$= \lim\limits_{h\to 0}\dfrac{\cos x\cos h - \sin x\sin h - \cos x}{h}$

$= \lim\limits_{h\to 0}\left[\cos x\left(\dfrac{\cos h - 1}{h}\right) - \sin x\left(\dfrac{\sin h}{h}\right)\right]$

$= \cos x\lim\limits_{h\to 0}\left(\dfrac{\cos h - 1}{h}\right) - \sin x\lim\limits_{h\to 0}\left(\dfrac{\sin h}{h}\right)$

$= \cos x(0) - \sin x(1) = -\sin x$

75. $\dfrac{d}{dx}(\sec x) = \dfrac{d}{dx}\left(\dfrac{1}{\cos x}\right) = \dfrac{(0)(\cos x) - 1(-\sin x)}{\cos^2 x}$

$= \dfrac{\sin x}{\cos^2 x} = \dfrac{1}{\cos x}\cdot\dfrac{\sin x}{\cos x} = \sec x\tan x$

Exercises: 2.8

1. $\dfrac{dy}{dx} = 17(x^3 + 2x + 3)^{16}(3x^2 + 2)$

3. $\dfrac{dy}{dx} = 8(x + \sin x)^7(1 + \cos x)$

5. $\dfrac{dy}{dx} = \frac{5}{2}(\cos x + x\sin x)^{3/2}(x\cos x)$

7. $\dfrac{dy}{dx} = \dfrac{6x - \sin x}{2\sqrt{3x^2 + \cos x}}$

9. $\dfrac{dy}{dx} = \dfrac{1}{3}\left(\dfrac{3x - 5}{2x + 7}\right)^{-2/3}\cdot\dfrac{31}{(2x + 7)^2}$

11. $\dfrac{dy}{dt} = \dfrac{5}{3}\left(\dfrac{t^2}{1 + t^2}\right)^{3/2}\cdot\dfrac{2t}{(1 + t^2)^2}$

13. $\dfrac{dy}{dx} = \dfrac{10\sin^9 x\cos x}{(1 + \sin x)^{11}}$

15. $\dfrac{dy}{dx} = \dfrac{\sec^2 x}{2\sqrt{\tan x}(1 + \tan x)^{3/2}}$

17. $\dfrac{dy}{dx} = \dfrac{8\sec^{8/5} x\tan x}{5(1 + \sec x)^{13/5}}$

19. $\dfrac{dy}{dx} = 10\sin 5x\cos^5 3x - 12\sin^3 5x\cos^3 3x\sin 3x$

21. $\dfrac{dy}{dx} = e^{\sin x}\cos x$ **23.** $\dfrac{dy}{dx} = \dfrac{e^{\sqrt{x}}}{2\sqrt{x}}$

25. $\dfrac{dy}{dx} = 2e^{\sin^2 x}\sin x\cos x$

27. $\dfrac{dy}{dx} = e^{x\sin 6x}(\sin 6x + 6x\cos 6x)$

29. $\dfrac{dy}{dx} = 2e^{\tan^2 x}\tan x\sec^2 x$ **31.** $\dfrac{dy}{dx} = \dfrac{e^{\sin x}\cos x}{(1 + e^{\sin x})^2}$

33. $\dfrac{dy}{dx} = \dfrac{e^x\cos(e^x)}{[1 + \sin(e^x)]^2}$

35. $\dfrac{dy}{dx} = (2x - 5)\cos(x^2 - 5x + 7)$

37. $\dfrac{dy}{dx} = 2\cos x + 6\sin x\cos x - 18\sin^2 x\cos x$

39. $\dfrac{dy}{dx} = -\dfrac{\sin(\sqrt{x})}{2\sqrt{x}}$ **41.** $\dfrac{dy}{dx} = -\dfrac{2}{x^3}\cos\left(\dfrac{1}{x^3}\right)$

43. $\dfrac{dy}{dx} = 2\sin x\cos^4 x - 3\sin^3 x\cos^2 x$

45. $\dfrac{dy}{dx} = 2\cos 2x\cos 3x - 3\sin 2x\sin 3x$

47. $\dfrac{dy}{dx} = 2\sec^2 x\tan^4 x + 3\sec^4 x\tan^2 x$

49. $\dfrac{dy}{dx} = 2\sec 2x\tan 2x\tan 3x + 3\sec 2x\sec^2 3x$

51. $\dfrac{dy}{dx} = 8\sin 4x\cos 4x$

53. $\dfrac{dy}{dx} =$
$10\sin 5x\cos 5x\cos^3 4x - 12\sin^2 5x\cos^3 3x\sin 3x$

55. $\dfrac{dy}{dx} =$
$10\sec^2 5x\tan 5x\tan^3 4x + 12\sec^2 5x\tan^4 4x\sec^2 4x$

57. $\dfrac{dy}{dx} = 3x^2\sin 5x + 5x^3\cos 5x$

59. $\dfrac{dy}{dx} = \cos\left(\dfrac{2x}{x + 2}\right)\cdot\left(\dfrac{8}{(x + 4)^2}\right)$

61. $\dfrac{dy}{dx} = -\sin x\cos(1 + \cos x)$

63. $\dfrac{dy}{dx} = \cos\left(\dfrac{e^{2x}}{1 + e^{3x}}\right)\cdot\left(\dfrac{2e^{2x} - e^{5x}}{(1 + e^{2x})^2}\right)$

65. $\dfrac{dy}{dx} = 14x\cos(7x^2)\cos^3 x - 3\sin(7x^2)\cos^2 x\sin x$

67. $\dfrac{dy}{dx} = \dfrac{1}{4\sqrt{x + x\sqrt{x}}}$

69. $\dfrac{dy}{dx} = \dfrac{1}{8\sqrt{1 + \sqrt{1 + \sqrt{x}}}\cdot\sqrt{x + x\sqrt{x}}}$

71. $v = \sin 4t + 4t\cos 4t$ (b) $y = 0.077t + 0.417$,
$y = 0.459t - 1.77$ (c). See graph below.

73. $v = \pi\cos\pi t\sin 8\pi t + 8\pi\sin\pi t\cos 8\pi t$ (b) $y = 8\pi t$,
$y = -8\pi t$ (c). See graph below.

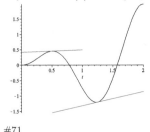

#71

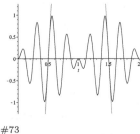

#73

Exercises: 2.9

1. $f'(x) = \dfrac{3x^2 + 4}{x^3 + 4x + 2}$

3. $\dfrac{df}{dx}(x) = \dfrac{\cos x}{\sin x} = \cot x$

5. $f'(x) = \dfrac{10x + 3}{(\ln 2)(5x^2 + 3x + 1)}$

7. $f'(x) = -5\ln(2)2^{-5x}$

9. $\dfrac{dy}{dx} = (5\cos 5x - \ln 10 \sin 5x)10^{-x}$

11. $\dfrac{dy}{dx} = e^{(x^2+3x)}(2x+3)$

13. $\dfrac{dy}{dx} = \dfrac{1}{x\ln x}$ **15.** $\dfrac{ds}{dt} = \dfrac{2\ln t}{t}$

17. $\dfrac{ds}{dt} = \dfrac{2\ln(\ln t)}{t\ln t}$ **19.** $f'(z) = \dfrac{1}{z(1+2\ln z)^2}$

21. $\dfrac{dV}{dx} = \dfrac{1-2x}{x(1-\ln x)^2}$ **23.** $\dfrac{dy}{dx} = \dfrac{\cos(\ln x)}{x}$

25. $\dfrac{dy}{dx} = \cos x \ln x + \dfrac{\sin x}{x}$

27. $\dfrac{dy}{dx} = e^{-x}\left(\dfrac{1-x}{x}\right)$ **29.** $f'(x) = \ln x$

31. $f'(x) = 2xe^{-x^2}\left[\dfrac{1-(1+x^2)\ln(1+x^2)}{1+x^2}\right]$

33. $f'(x) = e^{-x}(3\cos 3x - \sin 3x)$

35. $f'(x) = -6e^{\cos 6x}\sin 6x$ **37.** $\dfrac{dy}{dx} = x(2-x)e^{-x}$

39. $f'(x) = \dfrac{e^{2x}}{\sqrt{e^{2x}+1}}$

41. $f'(x) = 6e^{-x/2}(2e^{-x/2}+5)^{-7}$

43. $\dfrac{dy}{dx} = -e^{-x}\cos(e^{-x})$ **45.** $\dfrac{dy}{dx} = -\dfrac{e^{1/x}}{x^2}$

47. $\dfrac{dy}{dx} = \dfrac{x}{(x^2+1)\sqrt{x^2+1}}$ **49.** $f'(x) = x^2(3-2x)e^{-2x}$

51. $f'(x) = \dfrac{e^x(x\ln x - 1)}{x(\ln x)^2}$ **53.** $f'(x) = \dfrac{e^x}{(1+e^x)^2}$

55. $f'(x) = \dfrac{4}{(e^x+e^{-x})^2}$

57. Apply the chain rule with $y = f(u)$ where $u = g(x)$.
So $f'(x) = \dfrac{dy}{dx} = \dfrac{dy}{du}\dfrac{du}{dx} = \dfrac{1}{u}\cdot g'(x) = \dfrac{g'(x)}{g(x)}$.

59. $f'(x) = \dfrac{\sec^2(x)}{\tan x}$ **61.** $f'(x) = \dfrac{1}{x\ln x \ln(\ln x)}$

63. $f'(x) = \dfrac{10\sin 5x \cos 5x}{1+\sin^2 5x}$

65. $f'(x) = \dfrac{3}{2(3x+5)} - \dfrac{x}{x^2+1}$

67. $f'(x) = x^{\sin x}\left(\cos x \ln x + \dfrac{\sin x}{x}\right)$

69. $f'(x) = x^{x^2+3x}[(2x+3)\ln x + x + 3]$

71. e^{100} **73.** $e^{1/3}$

75. 140 days; $\dfrac{dN}{dt} = -(.00495N_0)2^{-t/140}$ atoms/day.
When $t = 140$, $dN/dt = -.002475N_0$ atoms/day.

77. (a) \$30,023.96 (b) \$30,206

Exercises: 2.10

1. $\dfrac{dy}{dx} = -\dfrac{x}{y}$ **3.** $y' = \dfrac{1-2xy-3y^2}{x^2+9xy^2}$

5. $y' = \dfrac{8x^3y^3 - 3x^2y^4 - 5y}{4x^3y^3 + 6x^4y^2 + 5x}$ **7.** $\dfrac{dy}{dx} = -\dfrac{y^2}{x^2}$

9. $\dfrac{dy}{dx} = -\dfrac{x^3}{y^3}$ **11.** $\dfrac{dy}{dx} = -\dfrac{x^2}{y^2}$

13. $\dfrac{dy}{dx} = -\dfrac{\sqrt{y}}{\sqrt{x}}$ **15.** $\dfrac{dy}{dx} = -\dfrac{(1+2\sqrt{x})\sqrt{y}}{\sqrt{x}}$

17. $y' = -\dfrac{y}{2\sqrt{xy}-x}$ **19.** $y' = -\dfrac{(\sqrt{y}(\sqrt{y}+1)}{\sqrt{x}(3y-\sqrt{x})}$

21. $y' = \dfrac{y^3 - x^2y}{xy^2 - x^3}$ **23.** $y' = \dfrac{1-18x(x^2+3y^2)^8}{54y(x^2+3y^2)^8}$

25. $\dfrac{dy}{dx} = \dfrac{\cos x}{\sin y}$ **27.** $\dfrac{dy}{dx} = \dfrac{\cos x \cos y - y}{\sin x \sin y + x}$

29. $y' = \dfrac{1-2xy\cos(x^2y^2)}{2x^2y\cos(x^2y^2)}$ **31.** $\dfrac{dy}{dx} = \dfrac{ye^{-xy}-20x}{20y - xe^{-xy}}$

33. $\dfrac{dy}{dx} = \dfrac{1-x^2}{xy}$

35. $y = \frac{1}{21}x + \frac{6}{7}$ **37.** $y = \frac{1}{2}x + \frac{1}{2}$ **39.** $y = \frac{-2}{11}x + \frac{24}{11}$

41. $y = \frac{e}{e-1}(x-1)$ **43.** $y = \frac{-1}{\pi+1}x + \frac{2\pi+1}{\pi+1}$ **45.** $y = x$

47. $y'' = \dfrac{2y^3}{x^3}$ **49.** $y'' = -\dfrac{3x^2}{y^7}$ **51.** $y'' = -\dfrac{2x}{y^5}$

53. $y'' = \dfrac{1}{2x^{3/2}}$ **55.** $y'' = \dfrac{-1}{4y^3}$ **57.** $y'' = \dfrac{-3}{(y-x)^3}$

59. $y = -\frac{4}{3}x + \frac{28}{3}$ and $y = \frac{4}{3}x - \frac{22}{3}$

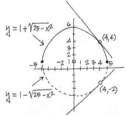

#59

61. $y = x$ and $y = -x$

63. $y = -2x+3$ and $y = -x$

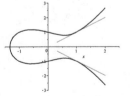

#61

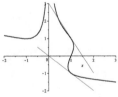

#63

65. $y = \sqrt{\dfrac{1+x^3}{x}}$ and $y = -\sqrt{\dfrac{1+x^3}{x}}$

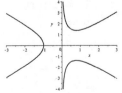

#65b

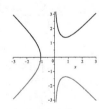

#65c

67. $y_1 = \sqrt{\dfrac{x+\sqrt{4-3x^2}}{2}}$, $y_2 = \sqrt{\dfrac{x-\sqrt{4-3x^2}}{2}}$

$y_3 = -\sqrt{\dfrac{x+\sqrt{4-3x^2}}{2}}$, $y_4 = -\sqrt{\dfrac{x-\sqrt{4-3x^2}}{2}}$

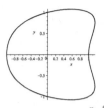

#67b   #67c

69. $y'' = -(p-1)a^p \dfrac{x^{p-2}}{y^{2p-1}}$

Exercises: 2.11

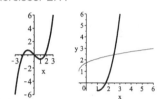

1.

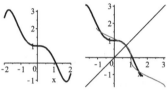

3.

5. $y = \frac{1}{3}x - 1$, $f^{-1}(x) = (x-1)^{1/3}$ **7.** $y = -\frac{1}{3}x$

9. $y = -\frac{1}{2}x + 4$, $f^{-1}(x) = \dfrac{x}{x-2}$

11. $y = -2x + 2$, $f_{\pm}^{-1}(x) = \pm\dfrac{\sqrt{1-x}}{\sqrt{x}}$

13. $y = \frac{4}{3}x - \frac{4}{3}$, $f_{\pm}^{-1}(x) = \dfrac{1}{2}(x \pm \sqrt{x^2-4})$

15. $y = \frac{1}{2}x + 1$ **17.** $y = -4x + 2$, $f^{-1}(x) = \ln\left(\dfrac{1-x}{x}\right)$

19. $\dfrac{dy}{dx} = \dfrac{10x}{\sqrt{1-25x^4}}$ **21.** $\dfrac{dy}{dx} = \dfrac{2x}{\sqrt{1-x^4}}$

23. $\dfrac{dy}{dx} = \dfrac{1}{2\sqrt{x}\sqrt{1-x}}$ **25.** $\dfrac{dy}{dx} = \dfrac{1}{x\sqrt{1-(\ln x)^2}}$

27. $\dfrac{dy}{dx} = \dfrac{-1}{x^2+1}$ **29.** $\dfrac{dy}{dx} = \dfrac{-2x}{x^4+1}$

31. $\dfrac{dy}{dx} = \dfrac{-1}{2\sqrt{x}\,(x+1)}$ **33.** $\dfrac{dy}{dx} = \dfrac{1}{2x\sqrt{x-1}}$

35. $\dfrac{dy}{dx} = \dfrac{-1}{2\sqrt{1=x}}$

37. $\dfrac{dy}{dx} = 2x \sin^{-1}(5x) + \dfrac{5x^2}{\sqrt{1-25x^2}}$

39. $\dfrac{dy}{dx} = -x^{-2}\tan^{-1}(2x) + \dfrac{2}{1+4x^2}$

41. $\dfrac{dy}{dx} = \dfrac{4\tan^{-1}(2x)}{1+4\,x^2}$

43. $\dfrac{dy}{dx} = \sqrt{1-x^2}$ **45.** $\dfrac{dy}{dx} = \dfrac{2e^{2x}}{1+e^{4x}}$

47. $\dfrac{dy}{dx} = \dfrac{10e^{5x}}{\sqrt{1-4\,e^{10x}}}$ **49.** $\dfrac{dy}{dx} = \dfrac{1}{\sqrt{16-x^2}}$

51. $\dfrac{dy}{dx} = \dfrac{1}{25+x^2}$ **53.** $\dfrac{dy}{dx} = \dfrac{1}{|x|\sqrt{x^2-49}}$

55. $\dfrac{dy}{dx} = \dfrac{-4}{|x|\sqrt{x^2-16}}$ **57.** $\dfrac{dy}{dx} = -\dfrac{25+x^2}{x^2}$

59. $\dfrac{dy}{dx} = \dfrac{-1}{7\sqrt{49-x^2}}$ **61.** $\dfrac{dy}{dx} = \dfrac{1}{\sqrt{a-x^2}}$

63. $\dfrac{dy}{dx} = \dfrac{1}{a^2+x^2}$ **65.** $\dfrac{dy}{dx} = \dfrac{1}{|x|\sqrt{x^2-a^2}}$

Exercises: 2.12

1. $f'(x) = \dfrac{\cosh(\sqrt{x})}{2\sqrt{x}}$

3. $f'(x) = 5\cosh 5x \cos 3x - 3\sinh 5x \sin 3x$

5. $f'(x) =$
   $\cosh x(2\sinh x \sin^3 5x + 15\cosh x \sin^2 5x \cos 5x)$

7. $f'(x) = e^x \sinh(e^{-x}) - \cosh(e^{-x})$

9. $f'(x) = 2\,\mathrm{sech}(e^{-2x})\left[e^{2x} + \tanh(e^{-2x})\right]$

11. $f'(x) = xe^{\sinh 5x}(2 + 5x\cosh 5x)$

13. $f'(x) = 2x\sinh 3x + 3x^2\cosh 3x$

15. $f'(x) = 2\,\mathrm{sech}\,2x \sec x(\tanh 2x - \tanh x)$

17. $f'(x) = -2\,\mathrm{sech}(\sec 2x)\tanh(\sec 2x)\sec 2x \tan 2x$

19. $f'(x) = 6x^2\tanh(x^3)\,\mathrm{sech}^2(x^3)$

21. $f'(x) = -2\,\mathrm{sech}^2\tanh^3 x + 2\,\mathrm{sech}^4 x \tanh x$

23. $f'(x) = \dfrac{\mathrm{sech}\,x(\mathrm{sech}\,x - \tanh x)}{\mathrm{sech}\,x + \tanh x}$

25. $f'(x) = \tanh x$

27. $f'(x) = \coth x$

29. $f'(x) = -\tanh x$

31. $f'(x) = -\coth x$

33. $f'(x) = \mathrm{sech}\,x\,\mathrm{csch}\,x$

35. $f'(x) = \dfrac{\cosh(\ln x)}{x}$

37. $f'(x) = \dfrac{\cosh x}{(\sinh x + 1)^2}$

39. $f'(x) = \dfrac{1}{\cosh x + 1}$

41. $f'(x) = \dfrac{1 - \tanh x}{\tanh x + 1}$

43. $f'(x) = \dfrac{\mathrm{sech}\,x \tanh x}{(\mathrm{sech}\,x + 1)^2}$

45. $f'(x) = \dfrac{1}{2\sqrt{x}\sqrt{x+1}}$

47. $f'(x) = \dfrac{1}{|x|\sqrt{1-x^2}}$

49. $f'(x) = \dfrac{1}{\sqrt{x^2 + 12x + 35}}$

51. $f'(x) = \dfrac{1}{2\sqrt{x}(1-x)}$

53. $f'(x) = \dfrac{-1}{x^2 - 1}$

55. $f'(x) = \dfrac{1}{-x^2 + 4x - 3}$

57. v.a.: none, h.a.: $y = 0$. even function.

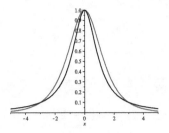

Graphs of sech x *(blue) and* $y = 1/(1+x^2)$ *(black)*

59. v.a.: $x = 0$, h.a.: $y = \pm 1$. odd function.

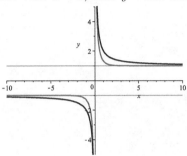

Graphs of coth x *(blue) and* $y = (|x|+1)/x$ *(black)*

61. $\sinh(-x) = \frac{1}{2}(e^{-x} - e^{-(-x)})$
$= \frac{1}{2}(e^{-x} - e^x) = -\sinh x$

63. Use $\sinh(x+y) = \sinh x \cosh y + \sinh y \cosh x$
with $y = x$, to get $\sinh 2x = \sinh(x+x)$
$= \sinh x \cosh x + \sinh x \cosh x = 2 \sinh x \cosh x$

65. Use $\cosh^2 x - \sinh^2 x = 1$, i.e., $\cosh^2 x = 1 + \sinh^2 x$
on the following identity
$\cosh 2x = \cosh^2 x + \sinh^2 x = 1 + \sinh^2 x + \sinh^2 x$
$= 1 + 2\sinh^2 x$. Solving for $\sinh^2 x$ gives the result.

67. Use $\tanh x = \frac{\sinh x}{\cosh x}$ and the identity
$\cosh^2 x - \sinh^2 x = 1$.

69. $\sinh(\ln x) = \frac{1}{2}\left(e^{\ln x} = e^{-\ln x}\right) = \frac{1}{2}(x - x^{-1}) = \frac{x^2-1}{2x}$

71. (a) 46.82 ft   (b) 16.82 ft   (c) 0.34

Exercises 2.13

1. $\frac{dr}{dt} = \frac{125}{12\pi} \approx 3.32$ cm/s.

3. $\frac{dx}{dt} = \frac{128}{15} = 8.5333$ in/s. In general, $\frac{dx}{dt} = \frac{256}{x}$, so
the side rate decreases over time. $x = 128$ inches.

5. $\frac{ds}{dt} = \frac{729}{16\sqrt{3}} \approx 26.31$ cm/s. In general, $\frac{ds}{dt} = \frac{3645}{\sqrt{3}\,s}$, so
side rate decreases over time. $s = \frac{3645}{2\sqrt{3}} \approx 1052$ cm.

7. $\frac{dx}{dt} = \sqrt{91} \approx 9.54$ ft/s. In general, $\frac{dx}{dt} = \frac{3y}{x}$, so the
rate goes to zero over time.

9. $\frac{dD}{dt} = \frac{-10}{\sqrt{850}} \approx -0.34$ ft/s.

11. $\frac{dh}{dt} = -\frac{27}{16\pi} \approx -0.537$ m/s. In general, $\frac{dh}{dt} = \frac{-243}{\pi h^2}$,
so the rate increases over time.

13. $\frac{dh}{dt} = \frac{50}{441} \approx 0.1134$ ft/min.

15. $\frac{d\theta}{dt} = \frac{15}{122} \approx 0.123$ rad/s.

17. $\frac{ds}{dt} = \frac{10,000}{\sqrt{634}} \approx 397.15$ mph.

19. $\frac{ds}{dt} = \frac{-795}{\sqrt{74}} \approx -92.4$ mph.

21. $\frac{dh}{dt} = \frac{1}{72} \approx 0.014$ m/s. **23.** $\frac{dh}{dt} = \frac{1}{48} \approx 0.02$ ft/s.

25. $\frac{dh}{dt} = \frac{1}{10(e-1)} \approx 0.058$ m/s.

CHAPTER 3: Answers to Odd Exercises

Exercises: 3.1

1. f decreases on the intervals $[-1, 0]$, $[1, 3]$ and increases
on the intervals $[0,1]$, $[3,4]$.

3. f increases on the interval $[-2, 3]$ and decreases on
$[3, 4.5]$.

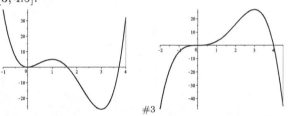

#1   #3

5. The function is increasing on the entire interval $[0, 20]$
even though at $x \approx 3.22, 9.64, 15.67$, the function levels
off.

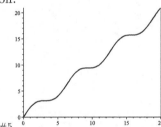

#5

7. $f'(x) = 4x(3-x)(3+x)$. critical numbers:
$x = -3, 0, 3$.

9. $f'(x) = 3(x^2 - 4x - 3)$. critical numbers:
$x = 2 \pm \sqrt{7} \approx 4.65, -0.65$

11. $f'(x) = 1 - 1/x^2$. critical numbers: $x = -1, 1$

13. $f'(x) = 2x - 32/x^3$. critical numbers: $x = -2, 2$

15. $f'(x) = \frac{2}{3}x^{-2/3}(1 - x^{1/3})$. critical numbers: $x = 0, 1$

17. $f'(x) = \frac{2}{5}x^{-4/5}(1 - 3x)$. critical numbers: $x = 0, 1/3$

19. $f'(x) = \frac{x^2(2x-3)}{(x-1)^2}$. critical numbers: $x = 0, 3/2$

21. $f'(x) = \frac{4(1-x^2)}{(x^2+1)^2}$. critical numbers: $x = -1, 1$

23. $f'(x) = \ln x$. critical number: $x = 1$

25. $f'(x) = x(2\ln x - 1)$. critical number: $\sqrt{e} \approx 1.65$

27. $f'(x) = 2x^3 e^{-2x}(2 - x)$. critical numbers: $x = 0, 2$

29. $f'(x) = \frac{1}{2\sqrt{x}}e^{-x/2}(1 - x)$. critical numbers: $x = 0, 1$

31. $f'(x) = 10e^{-x}(2 - x)$. critical number: $x = 2$.

33. $f'(x) = xe^{-x^2/2}(2 - x^2)$. critical numbers:

$x = 0, \pm\sqrt{2} \approx 0, \pm 1.414$.

35. $f'(x) = -2\sin x + 1$. critical numbers in $[0, 2\pi]$: $x = \pi/6, 5\pi/6$.

37. $f'(x) = \cos x - \sin x$. critical numbers in $[0, 2\pi]$: $x = \pi/4, 5\pi/4$

39. $f'(x) = -\sin x(2\cos x + 1)$. critical numbers in $[0, 2\pi]$: $x = 0, \pi, 2\pi, 2\pi/3, 4\pi/3$.

41. $f'(x) = \cos x(1 - 2\sin x)$. critical numbers in $[0, 2\pi]$ $x = \pi/2, 3\pi/2, \pi/6, 5\pi/6$.

43. $f'(x) = \sec^2 x - 4$. critical numbers in $[0, 2\pi]$: $x = \pi/3, 2\pi/3, 4\pi/3, 5\pi/3$

45. $f'(x) = \sec x - 2$. critical numbers in $[0, 2\pi]$: $x = \pi/3, 5\pi/3$

47. $f'(x) = 3x^2 - 3 = 3(x^2 - 1) = 3(x-1)(x+1)$. critical numbers: $x = -1, 1$.

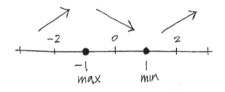

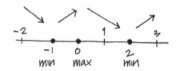

49. $f'(x) = 12x^3 - 12x^2 - 24x = 12x(x^2 - x - 2) = 12x(x-2)(x+1)$. critical numbers: $x = -1, 0, 2$

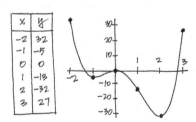

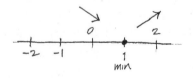

51. $f'(x) = 4x^3 - 4 = 4(x^3 - 1)$. critical number: $x = 1$

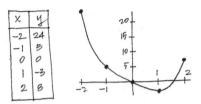

53. $f'(x) = 4x^3 - 4x = 4x(x^2 - 1) = 4x(x-1)(x+1)$. critical numbers: $x = -1, 0, 1$.

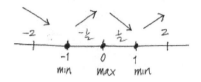

55. $f'(x) = x^4 - 9x^2 = x^2(x^2 - 9) = x^2(x-3)(x+3)$. critical numbers: $x = -3, 0, 3$

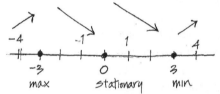

57. $f'(x) = 2(1 - x^2)e^{-1/2\,x^2}$. critical numbers: $x = -1, 1$.

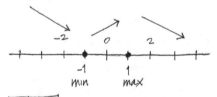

59. $f'(x) = -(x^2 - 2x - 1)e^{-x}$. critical numbers: $x = 1 \pm \sqrt{2} \approx -0.414, 2.414$

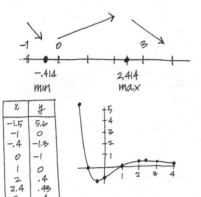

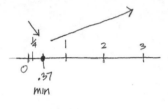

61. $f'(x) = \ln x + 1$. critical number: $x = e^{-1} \approx 0.37$.

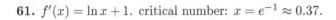

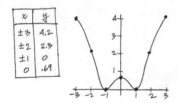

63. $f'(x) = \dfrac{4x(x^2-1)}{x^4 - 2\,x^2 + 2}$. critical numbers: $0, \pm 1$.

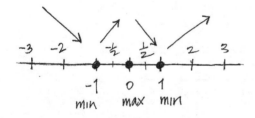

65. $f'(x) = 2x^{-3}(x^4 - 1)$. critical numbers: $x = \pm 1$.

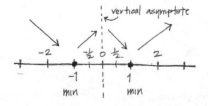

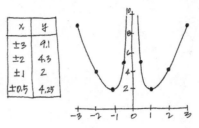

67. $f'(x) = \dfrac{-8x(x^3+2)}{(x^3-1)^2}$. critical numbers:

$0, -2^{1/3} \approx 0, -1.26$

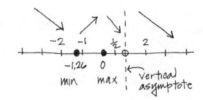

69. $f'(x) = \dfrac{3}{5} x^{-4/5}(1 - x^{2/5})$. critical numbers $x = 0, \pm 1$

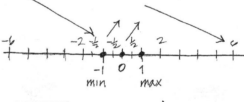

71. $f'(x) = \dfrac{\sin x}{(2 + \cos x)^2}$. critical numbers in

$[1, 12]$: $\pi, 2\pi, 3\pi$

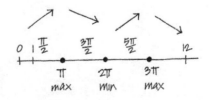

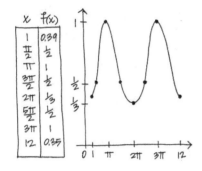

Exercises: 3.2

1. inflection point at $x \approx 2.38, 5.2$

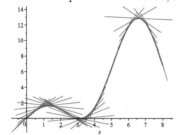

3. inflection point at $x \approx -1.17, 0, 1.17$

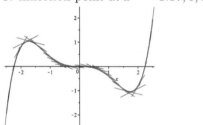

5. inflection point at $x \approx 0.28, 0.6, 0.91$

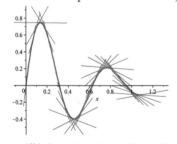

7. $f''(x) = 6x - 6 = 6(x - 1)$
inflection point $x = 1$

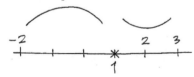

9. $f''(x) = 12x^2 - 24x = 12x(x - 2)$
inflection points: $x = 0, 2$.

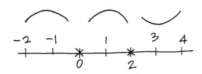

11. $f''(x) = 60x^3 - 120x^2 = 60x^2(x - 2)$

inflection point at $x = 2$.

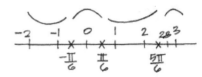

13. $f''(x) = 2 - 4\cos 2x = 2(1 - 2\cos 2x)$
inflection points in $[-2, 3]$: $x = -\pi/6, \pi/6, 5\pi/6$.

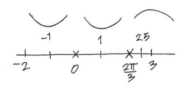

15. $f''(x) = -2\cos 2x + 2\cos x =$
$-2(2\cos^2 x - 1) + 2\cos x = -2(2\cos x + 1)(\cos x - 1)$.
inflection points in $[-2, 3]$: $x = 2\pi/3 \approx 2.09$.

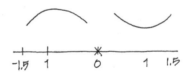

17. $f''(x) = 2\sec x(\sec x \tan x) = 2\sec^2 x \tan x$
inflection point in the interval $[-1.5, 1.5]$:
$x = 0$

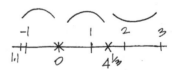

19. $f''(x) = 2x^2(x^3 - 4)e^{-x^3/3}$
inflection point: $4^{1/3} \approx 1.59$.

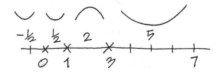

21. $f''(x) = 4x^2(x - 1)(x - 3)e^{-2x}$
inflection points: $x = 1, 3$

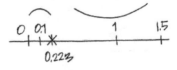

23. $f''(x) = 4\ln x + 6$
inflection point: $x = e^{-3/2} \approx 0.223$

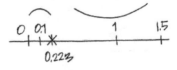

25. $f'(x) = 3x^2 - 6x = 3x(x - 2)$

critical numbers: $x = 0, 2$.

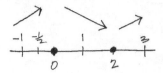

(b) $f''(x) = 6x - 6 = 6(x - 1)$. inflection point: $x = 1$

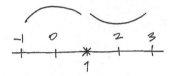

(c) Polynomials have no asymptotes

(d)

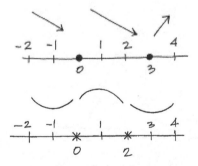

x	y
-1	-2
0	2
1	0
2	-2
3	2

27. (a)-(b) $f'(x) = 4x^3 - 12x^2 = 4x^2(x - 3)$

$f''(x) = 12x^2 - 24x = 12x(x - 2)$.

critical numbers: $x = 0, 3$, inflection points:

$x = 0, 2$.

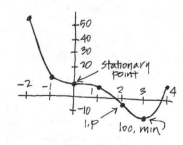

(c) Polynomials have no asymptotes.

(d)

x	y
-2	58
-1	15
0	10
1	7
2	-6
3	-17
4	10

29. (a) $f'(x) = 15x^4 - 75x^2 + 60$

$= 15(x - 1)(x + 1)(x - 2)(x + 2)$.

critical numbers: $x = \pm 1, \pm 2$

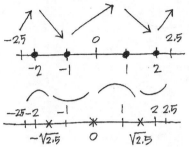

(b) $f''(x) = 60x^3 - 150x = 30x(2x^2 - 5)$.

inflection points: $x = 0, \pm\sqrt{2.5}$.

(c) Polynomials have no asymptotes.

(d)

x	y
-2.5	-52
-2	-16
-√2.5	-25.7
-1	-38
0	0
1	38
√2.5	25.7
2	16
2.5	52

31. $f'(x) = 1 - \dfrac{1}{\sqrt{x}}$. critical number: $x = 0$.

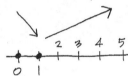

(b) $f''(x) = \dfrac{1}{2}x^{-3/2}$. inflection points: none

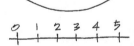

(c) This function has no asymptotes.

(d)

x	y
0	0
1	-1
2	-.83
3	-.46
4	0
5	.53

33. (a) $f'(x) = \dfrac{1 - 4x}{(2x^2 - x)^2}$.

critical number: $x = 1/4$

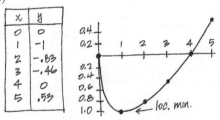

(b) $f''(x) = \dfrac{24x^2 - 12x + 2}{(2x^2 - x)^3}$

inflection points: none

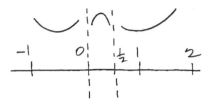

(c) v.a.: $x = 0, x = 1/2$, h.a.: $y = 0$

(d)

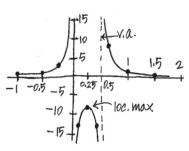

35. $f'(x) = \dfrac{4(1 - x^2)}{(x^2 + 1)^2}$

critical numbers: $x = \pm 1$.

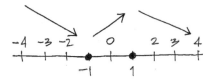

(b) $f''(x) = \dfrac{8x(x^2 - 3)}{(x^2 + 1)^3}$

inflection points: $x = 0, \pm\sqrt{3}$

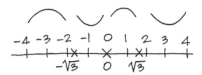

(c) v.a.: none, h.a.: $y = 0$

(d)

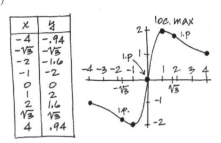

37. (a)-(b) $f'(x) = 10(2 - x)e^{-x}$, $f''(x) = 10(x - 3)e^{-x}$

critical number $x = 2$, inflection point: $x = 3$.

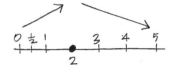

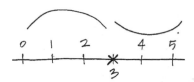

(c) v.a.: none, h.a.: $y = 0$

(d)

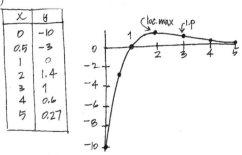

39. $f'(x) = -2xe^{-x^2/2}$, $f''(x) = 2(x^2 - 1)e^{-x^2/2}$

critical number: $x = 0$, inflection

points: $x = \pm 1$

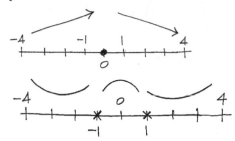

(c) v.a.: none, h.a.: $y = 0$

(d)

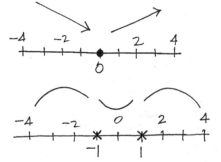

41. $f'(x) = \dfrac{2x}{x^2 + 1}$, $f''(x) = \dfrac{2 - 2x^2}{(x^2 + 1)^2}$

critical number: $x = 0$, inflection

points: $x = \pm 1$.

(c) The function has no asymptotes.

(d)

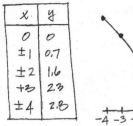 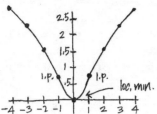

 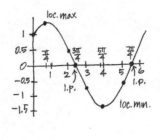

43. (a)-(b) $f'(x) = \ln x$, $f''(x) = \frac{1}{x}$

critical number: $x = 1$. inflection points: none

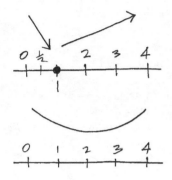

(c) This function has no asymptotes.

(d)

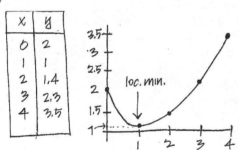

45. (a)-(b) $f'(x) = \cos x - \sin x$,

$f''(x) = -\sin x - \cos x$

critical numbers in $[0, 2\pi]$: $x = \pi/4, 5\pi/4$,

inflection points: $3\pi/4, 7\pi/4$

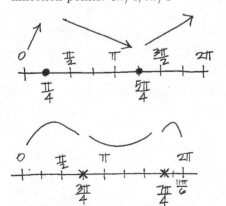

(c) This function has no asymptotes.

(d)

47. (a) $f'(x) = 2\sin x \cos x = \sin 2x$

$f''(x) = 2\cos 2x$.

critical number in $[0, \pi]$: $x = \pi/2$.

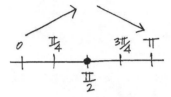

inflection points in $[0, \pi]$: $x = \pi/4, 3\pi/4$.

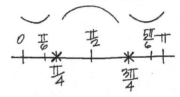

(c) This function has no asymptotes.

(d)

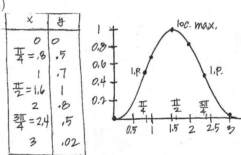

49. (a)-(b) $f'(x) = \dfrac{\cos x}{2 + \sin x}$. critical numbers in the

interval $[0, 2\pi]$: $x = \pi/2, 3\pi/2$.

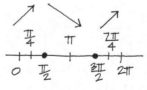

(b) $f''(x) = -\dfrac{2\sin x + 1}{(2 + \sin x)^2}$.

inflection points in $[0, 2\pi]$: $x = 7\pi/6, 11\pi/6$

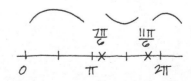

(c) This function has no asymptotes.

(d)

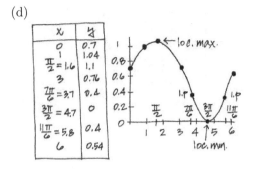

Exercises: 3.3

1.

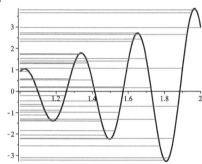

abs. max $y \approx 3.83$ at $x \approx 1.96$.
abs min $y \approx -3.34$ at $x \approx 1.82$.

3.

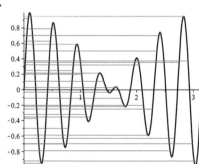

abs. max $y \approx 1$ at $x \approx 0.1$.
abs min $y \approx -1$ at $x \approx 3.04$.

5.

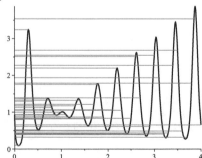

abs. max $y \approx 3.87$ at $x \approx 3.87$.
abs min $y \approx 0.1$ at $x \approx 0.08$.

7. $f'(x) = 3x^2 + 2x - 1 = (3x - 1)(x + 1)$
$f''(x) = 6x + 2$. c.n.: $x = 1/3, -1$
$f''(1/3) = 4 > 0 \implies$ local min at $x = 1/3$

$f''(-1) = -4 < 0 \implies$ local max at $x = -1$

9. $f'(x) = 4x - 4x^3 = 4x(1 - x^2)$
$f''(x) = 4 - 12x^2$. c.n.: $x = 0, \pm 1$
$f''(0) = 4 > 0 \implies$ local min at $x = 0$
$f''(\pm 1) = -8 < 0 \implies$ local max at $x = \pm 1$

11. $f'(x) = 6x^3(x^2 - 4)$
$f''(x) = 6x^2(5x^2 - 12)$. c.n.: $x = 0, \pm 2$
$f''(0) = 0 \implies$ test fails
$f''(\pm 2) = 192 > 0 \implies$ local min at $x = \pm 2$
1st derivative test for $x = 0$: test numbers $t = \pm 1$
$f'(-1) = 18 > 0 \implies$ incr. for $-2 < x < 0$
$f'(1) = -18 < 0 \implies$ decr. for $0 < x < 2$
local max at $x = 0$

13. $f'(x) = 15x^2(1 - x^2)$
$f''(x) = 30x(1 - 2x^2)$. c.n.: $x = 0, \pm 1$
$f''(0) = 0 \implies$ test fails
$f''(-1) = 30 > 0 \implies$ local min at $x = -1$
$f''(1) = -30 < 0 \implies$ local max at $x = 1$
1st derivative test for $x = 0$: test numbers $t = \pm 1/2$
$f'(-1/2) = 45/16 > 0 \implies$ incr. for $-1 < x < 0$
$f'(1/2) = 45/16 \implies$ incr. for $0 < x < 1$
stationary point at $x = 0$

15. $f'(x) = 5x^2(x - 1)(x - 3)$
$f''(x) = 10x(2x^2 - 6x + 3)$. c.n.: $x = 0, 1, 3$
$f''(0) = 0 \implies$ test fails
$f''(1) = -10 < 0 \implies$ local max at $x = 1$
$f''(3) = 90 > 0 \implies$ local min at $x = 3$
1st derivative test for $x = 0$: test numbers $t = -1, 1/2$
$f'(-1) = 40 > 0 \implies$ incr. for $x < 0$
$f'(1/2) = 25/16 > 0 \implies$ incr. for $0 < x < 1$
stationary point at $x = 0$

17. $f'(x) = (x + 1)(x - 3)e^{-x}$
$f''(x) = (-x^2 + 4x + 1)e^{-x}$. c.n.: $x = -1, 3$
$f''(-1) = -4e < 0 \implies$ local max at $x = -1$
$f''(3) = 4e^{-3} > 0 \implies$ local min at $x = 3$

19. $f'(x) = \frac{1}{2}x^{-3/2}(x - 1)$
$f''(x) = \frac{1}{4}x^{-5/2}(3 - x)$. c.n.: $x = 1$
$f''(1) = 1/2 > 0 \implies$ local min at $x = 1$

21. $f'(x) = 2x(2\ln x + 1)$
$f''(x) = 4\ln x + 6$. c.n.: $x = e^{-1/2}$
$f''(e^{-1/2}) = 4 > 0 \implies$ local min at $x = e^{-1/2}$

23. $f'(x) = \frac{1}{2\sqrt{x}}(\ln x + 2)$
$f''(x) = -\frac{1}{4}x^{-3/2}\ln x$. c.n.: $x = e^{-2}$
$f''(e^{-2}) = e^3/2 > 0 \implies$ local min at $x = e^{-2}$

25. $f'(x) = \frac{2x}{x^2 + 1}$
$f''(x) = \frac{2 - 2x^2}{(x^2 + 1)^2}$. c.n.: $x = 0$
$f''(0) = 2 > 0 \implies$ local min at $x = 0$

27. $f'(x) = -2xe^{-x^2}$
$f''(x) = (4x^2 - 2)e^{-x^2}$. c.n.: $x = 0$
$f''(0) = -2 < 0 \implies$ local max at $x = 0$

29. $f'(x) = 2(1 - x^3)e^{-x^3/3}$

$f''(x) = 2x^2(x^3 - 4)e^{-x^3/3}$. c.n.: $x = 1$

$f''(1) = -6e^{-1/3} < 0 \implies$ local max at $x = 1$

31. $f'(x) = 2x^3(2 - x)e^{-2x}$

$f''(x) = (4x^4 - 16x^3 + 12x^2)e^{-2x}$. c.n.: $x = 0, 2$

$f''(0) = 0 \implies$ test fails

$f''(2) = -16e^{-4} < 0 \implies$ local max at $x = 1$

1st derivative test for $x = 0$: test numbers $t = -1, 1$

$f'(-1) = -6e^2 < 0 \implies$ decr. for $-2 < x < 0$

$f'(1) = 2e^{-2} > 0 \implies$ incr. for $0 < x < 2$

local min at $x = 0$

33. $f'(x) = (\cos x - \sin x)e^{-x}$

$f''(x) = -2(\cos x)e^{-x}$. c.n.: $x = \pi/4, 5\pi/4$

$f''(\pi/4) = -\sqrt{2}e^{-\pi/4} < 0 \implies$ local max at $x = \pi/4$

$f''(5\pi/4) = \sqrt{2}e^{-5\pi/4} > 0 \implies$ local min at $x = 5\pi/4$

35. $f'(x) = 1 - 2\sin 2x$

$f''(x) = -4\cos 2x$. c.n.: $x = \pi/12, 5\pi/12$

$f''(\pi/12) = -2\sqrt{3} < 0 \implies$ local max at $x = \pi/12$

$f''(5\pi/12) = 2\sqrt{3} > 0 \implies$ local min at $x = 5\pi/12$

37. $f'(x) = 2\sin x(1 - \cos x)$

$f''(x) = -2\cos 2x + 2\cos x$. c.n.: $x = 0$

$f''(0) = 0 \implies$ test fails

1st derivative test for $x = 0$: test numbers $t = \pm\pi/2$

$f'(-\pi/2) = -2 < 0 \implies$ decr. for $-2 < x < 0$

$f'(\pi/2) = 2 > 0 \implies$ incr. for $0 < x < 2$

local min at $x = 0$

39. $f'(x) = \sec^2 x - 4$

$f''(x) = 2\sec^2 x \tan x$. c.n.: $x = \pm\pi/3$

$f''(-\pi/3) = -8\sqrt{3} < 0 \implies$ local max at $x = -\pi/3$

$f''(\pi/3) = 8\sqrt{3} > 0 \implies$ local min at $x = \pi/3$

41. $f'(x) = x^x(2\ln x + 1)$

$f''(x) = x^x[(\ln x + 1)^2 + 1/x]$. c.n.: $x = e^{-1}$

$f''(e^{-1}) = e^{1-e^{-1}} > 0 \implies$ local min at $x = e^{-1}$

43. $f'(x) = 36 - 2x$. c.n.: $x = 18$

$f(0) = 0, f(18) = 324, f(36) = 0$

abs max $= 324$, abs min $= 0$

45. $f'(x) = 2x^{-3}(x^4 - 16)$. c.n.: $x = 2$

$f(1) = 17, f(2) = 8, f(3) = 10\frac{7}{9}$

abs max $= 17$, abs min $= 8$

47. $f'(x) = 3(x^2 - 9)$. c.n.: $x = \pm 3$

$f(-4) = 44, f(-3) = 54, f(3) = -54, f(5) = -10$

abs max $= 54$, abs min $= -54$

49. $f'(x) = 5x^2(x^2 - 3)$. c.n.: $x = 0, \sqrt{3}$

$f(-1) = 4, f(0) = 0, f(\sqrt{3}) = -6\sqrt{3} \approx -10.39,$

$f(2) = -8$. abs max $= 4$, abs min $= -6\sqrt{3}$

51. $f'(x) = 4x(x^2 - 4)$. c.n.: $x = 0, 2$

$f(-1) = -7, f(0) = 0, f(2) = -16, f(3) = 9$

abs max $= 9$, abs min $= -16$

53. $f'(x) = 12x(x + 2)(x - 1)$. c.n.: $x = -2, 0, 1$

$f(-3) = 27, f(-2) = -32, f(0) = 0, f(2) = 32$

abs max $= 32$, abs min $= -32$

55. $f'(x) = 2x^3(2 - x)e^{-2x}$. c.n.: $x = 0, 2$

$f(0) = 0, f(2) = 16e^{-4} \approx 0.293, f(4) = 256e^{-8}$

≈ 0.086, abs max $= 16e^{-4}$, abs min $= 0$

57. $f'(x) = (1 - x)e^{-x/2}/\sqrt{x}$. c.n.: $x = 0, 1$

$f(0) = 0, f(1) = 2e^{-1/2} \approx 1.21306, f(4) = 4e^{-2}$

≈ 0.54134, abs max $= 2e^{-1/2}$, abs min $= 0$

59. $f'(x) = \cos x - \sin x$. c.n.: $x = \pi/4$

$f(0) = 1, f(\pi/4) = \sqrt{2}, f(\pi) = -1,$

abs max $= \sqrt{2}$, abs min $= -1$

61. $f'(x) = x(1 - 2\ln x)$. c.n.: $x = e^{1/2}$

$f(0.5) = \approx 0.423, f(e^{1/2}) \approx 1.359, f(3) \approx -0.888$

abs max $= e/2 \approx 1.359$, abs min $= \approx -0.888$

63. $f'(x) = e^{\sin x}\cos x$. c.n.: $x = \pi/2, 3\pi/2$

$f(0) = 1, f(\pi/2) = e \approx 2.72, f(3\pi/2) = e^{-1} \approx$

$0.36788, f(2\pi) = 1$. abs max $= e$, abs min $= e^{-1}$

65.

(a) abs. max $y \approx 1$ at $x \approx 1$.

abs min $y \approx 0$ at $x \approx 0$. i.p. at $x \approx 0.32, 1.6$

(b) Write $f(x) = x^{-\ln x} = e^{(-\ln x)\ln x} = e^{-(\ln x)^2}$

$f'(x) = e^{-(\ln x)^2}\left[-\dfrac{2\ln x}{x}\right]$

$f''(x) = 2e^{-(\ln x)^2}\left[\dfrac{2(\ln x)^2 + \ln x - 1}{x^2}\right]$

$f'(x) = 0 \implies \ln x = 0 \implies$ c.n.: $x = 1$.

$\lim\limits_{x \to 0^+} f(x) = \lim\limits_{x \to 0^+} e^{-(\ln x)^2} = e^{-\infty} = 0$

$f(1) = 1, f(4) \approx 01463$. So abs max is 1, abs min is 0.

$f''(x) = 0 \implies 2(\ln x)^2 + \ln x - 1 = 0 \implies$

$(2\ln x - 1)(\ln x + 1) = 0$. i.p. at: $x = e^{1/2}, e^{-1}$.

Exercises: 3.4

1. (a)

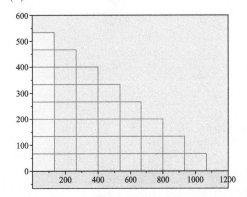

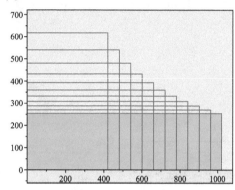

	b	h	b+2h	A=bh
1	1066.15	66.73	1199.61	71,144.19
2	932.09	134.27	1200.63	125,151.72
3	799.30	200.74	1200.78	160,451.40
4	666.51	267.22	1200.95	178,104.80
5	532.44	333.70	1199.84	177,675.23
6	399.65	400.17	1199.99	159,927.94
7	265.59	467.70	1200.99	124,216.44
8	132.80	534.18	1201.16	70,939.10

$b = 666$ yards, $h = 267$ yards, $A = 177,822$ sq. yards

(b) $A = (1200 - 2h) h = 1200h - 2h^2$ on $[0, 600]$.

$\dfrac{dA}{dh} = 1200 - 4h = 0$. c.n.: $h = 300$. $b = 600$ yards, $A = 180,000$ sq. yards

3. (a)

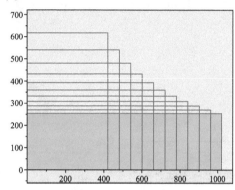

	b	h	A=bh	P=b+2h
1	419.46	618.09	259,634	1655.18
2	479.69	541.83	259,910	1563.35
3	539.93	481.30	259,868	1502.53
4	600.16	432.88	259,797	1465.92
5	660.40	394.14	260,290	1448.68
6	720.63	361.46	260,479	1443.55
7	780.87	333.61	260,506	1448.09
8	841.11	309.40	260,239	1459.91
9	901.34	288.82	260,325	1478.98
10	960.37	270.66	259,934	1501.69
11	1020.61	254.93	260,184	1530.47

$b = 720.63$ yards, $h = 361.46$ yards, $P = 1443.55$ yards

(b) $P = b + \dfrac{520000}{b}$, $\dfrac{dP}{db} = 1 - \dfrac{520,000}{b^2} = 0$

c.n.: $b = \sqrt{520,000} = 200\sqrt{13} \approx 721.11$ yards.

$h = 100\sqrt{13} \approx 360.56$ yards, $P = 400\sqrt{13} \approx 1442.22$ yards.

5. (a)

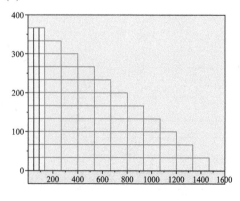

	b	h	P=b+4h	A=bh
1	1463.35	33.94	1599.11	49,666.01
2	1333.26	66.79	1600.42	89,048.44
3	1199.61	100.34	1600.97	120,368.87
4	1065.96	133.90	1601.56	142,732.04
5	934.10	166.75	1601.10	155,761.18
6	798.66	200.30	1599.86	159,971.60
7	665.01	233.86	1600.45	155,514.24
8	533.14	266.71	1599.98	142,193.77
9	399.44	300.26	1600.53	119,950.87
10	265.84	333.82	1601.12	88,742.71
11	132.19	366.67	1598.97	48,470.11

$b = 798.66$ yards, $h = 200.30$ yards, $A = 159,971.6$ sq. yards.

(b) $A = (1600 - 4h) h = 1600h - 4h^2$ on $[0, 400]$.

$\dfrac{dA}{dh} = 1600 - 8h = 0$. c.n.: $h = 200$ yards.

$b = 800$ yards $A = 160,000$ square yards

This confirms the approximate answer in Part (a).

7. $A = bh = b(800 - 3b/2) = 800b - 3b^2/2$ on $[0, 1600/3]$,

$\dfrac{dA}{db} = 800 - 3b = 0$. c.n.: $b = 800/3$. $h = 400$ yards.

$A = 106,667$ yads Note that the maximum area here is one-third of the maximum area in Example 3.4.1.

9. (a)

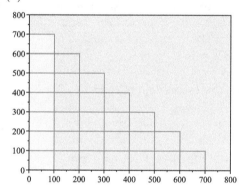

	b	h	P=2b+2h	A=bh
1	700	100	1600	70,000
2	600	200	1600	120,000
3	500	300	1600	150,000
4	400	400	1600	160,000
5	300	500	1600	150,000
6	200	600	1600	120,000
7	100	700	1600	70,000

$b = h = 400$ yards, $A = 160,000$ square yards

(b) $A = (800 - h) h = 800h - h^2$ on $[0, 800]$

$\dfrac{dA}{dh} = 800 - 2h = 0$. c.n.: $h = 400$ yards.

$b = 400$ yards. $A = 160,000$ square yards.

11. $A = \dfrac{1}{4} \cdot \dfrac{h - 2h^2}{1 - h}$ on $[0, 1/2]$

$\dfrac{dA}{dh} = \dfrac{1}{4} \cdot \dfrac{2h^2 - 4h + 1}{(1 - h)^2}$

c.n.: $h = (2 \pm \sqrt{2})/2$. Take $h = (2 - \sqrt{2})/2$.

Then $b = (2 - \sqrt{2})/2$. Thus, $b = h$ and the triangle is an *isosceles* right triangle.

13. (a)

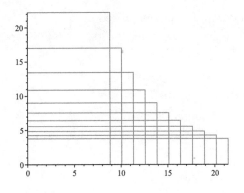

x	h	$V=x^2h$	$S=x(x+4h)$
8.8	22.24	1722.27	860.29
10.06	17.07	1727.55	788.10
11.34	13.47	1732.18	739.60
12.62	10.92	1739.17	710.51
13.87	9	1731.40	691.70
15.11	7.59	1732.89	687.05
16.39	6.46	1735.36	692.15
17.62	5.56	1726.18	702.33
18.88	4.89	1743.06	725.75
20.16	4.26	1731.37	749.95
21.41	3.76	1723.54	780.39

$S = 687.05\,\text{in}^2$. Dimensions: $x = 15.11$ inches, $h = 7.59$ inches

(b) $S = x^2 + 6912x^{-1}$,

$\dfrac{dS}{dx} = 2x - 6912x^{-2} = 2x^{-2}(x^3 - 3456)$

c.n.: $x = (3456)^{1/3} \approx 15.12$ inches.

$h = (3456)^{1/3}/2 \approx 7.56$ inches.

$S = 3(3456)^{2/3} \approx 685.76\,\text{in}^2$

15. (a)

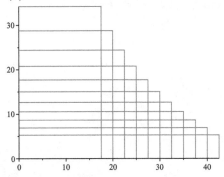

x	h	$S=x(x+4h)$	$V=x^2h$
17.74	33.68	2704.64	10,599.35
20.44	27.93	2701.35	11,668.98
23.15	23.36	2699.06	12,519.15
25.90	19.62	2703.44	13,161.29
28.60	16.42	2696.41	13,430.90
31.35	13.69	2699.55	13,454.84
32.46	12.7	2702.62	13,381.38
34.06	11.26	2694.15	13,062.54
36.81	9.19	2708.11	12,452.23
39.56	7.23	2709.07	11,314.90
42.26	5.45	2707.18	9,733.20

$V = 13,454.84.84\,\text{in}^3$. Dimensions: $x = 31.35$ inches, $h = 13.69$ inches

(b) $V = \tfrac{1}{4}(2700x - x^3)$, $\dfrac{dV}{dx} = \tfrac{1}{4}(2700 - 3x^2)$

c.n.: $x = 30$ inches. $h = 15$ inches. $V = 13,500\,\text{in}^2$

17. $V = \tfrac{1}{4}(Sx - 2x^3)$, $\dfrac{dV}{dx} = \tfrac{1}{4}(S - 6x^2)$

cn.: $x = \sqrt{S/6}$. $h = \sqrt{S/6} = x$,
$V = x^2h = x^2x = x^3 = (S/6)^{3/2}$

19. $V = 400r - \pi r^3$, $\dfrac{dV}{dr} = 400 - 3\pi r^2$

c.n.: $r = 20/\sqrt{3\pi} \approx 6.52$ m. $h = 40/\sqrt{3\pi} = 2r$
$V = \pi r^2 h = \pi r^2(2r) = 2\pi r^3 = \dfrac{1600\pi}{\sqrt{3\pi}} \approx 1737.25\,\text{in}^3$

21. $S = 2\pi r^2 + 452r^{-1}$, $\dfrac{dS}{dr} = 4\pi r - 452r^{-2}$

c.n.: $r = (113/\pi)^{1/3} \approx 3.3$ in. $h = 2(113/\pi)^{1/3} = 2r$
$S = 2\pi r^2 + 2\pi rh = 2\pi r^2 + 2\pi r(2r) =$
$6\pi r^2 = 6\pi(113/\pi)^{1/3}\,\text{in}^3 \approx 205.4\,\text{in}^3$

23. $V = (30 - 2x)(20 - 2x)x = 600x - 100x^2 + 4x^3$

$\dfrac{dV}{dx} = 600 - 200x + 12x^2$. c.n.: $x = (25 \pm 5\sqrt{7})/3$

Use $x = (25 - 5\sqrt{7})/3 \approx 3.924$ inches, since
$x = (25 + 5\sqrt{7})/3$ is not in $[0, 10]$. Then
$V = 1000(10 + 7\sqrt{7})/27 \approx 1056.31\,\text{in}^2$

25. (a) approximately 8.4 m

(b) $L = 3\sec\theta + 3\csc\theta$, $\dfrac{dL}{d\theta} = 3\sec\theta\tan\theta - 3\csc\theta\cot\theta$.

c.n. in $(0, \pi/2)$: $\theta = \pi/4$. $L + 6\sqrt{2} \approx 8.485$ m.

27. (a) approximately 9.25 m

(b) The following figure shows 3 ladders that get stuck.

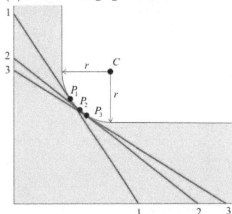

Use the following figure to find the length of a ladder that gets stuck.

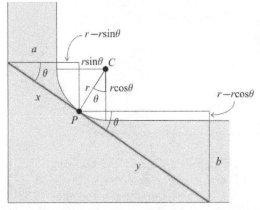

$L = \dfrac{4 - 2\sin\theta}{\cos\theta} + \dfrac{5.5 - 2\cos\theta}{\sin\theta} = \dfrac{4\sin\theta + 5.5\cos\theta - 2}{\sin\theta\cos\theta}$

$$\frac{dL}{d\theta} = \frac{4\sin^3\theta - 5.5\cos^3\theta + 2(\cos^2\theta - \sin^2\theta)}{\sin^2\theta\cos^2\theta}$$

Let $g(\theta) = 4\sin^3\theta - 5.5\cos^3\theta + 2(\cos^2\theta - \sin^2\theta)$. Then the c.n.s are the roots of $g(\theta) = 0$. Find these numerically on a graph of g, giving $\theta \approx 0.87$ rad, $L \approx 9.34$ m:

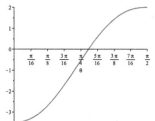

29. Output from the `paths` procedure:
Point, 0.5, Time, 1.814451221
Point, 1, Time, 1.798351633
Point, 1.5, Time, 1.790508592
Point, 2, Time, 1.791121722
Point, 2.5, Time, 1.800290574
The least of these times is $T = 1.79050$ hr for the run to the point $(1.5, -6)$.

$$T = \tfrac{1}{8}\left(\sqrt{x^2 + 64} + \sqrt{(3 - x)^2 + 36}\right)$$

$$\frac{dT}{dx} = \frac{1}{8}\left(\frac{x}{\sqrt{x^2 + 64}} - \frac{3 - x}{\sqrt{(3 - x)^2 + 36}}\right)$$

c.n.: $x = 12/7 \approx 1.714$ miles. Least time: $T = \sqrt{205}/8 \approx 1.789$ hr.

31. (a) Output from the `paths` procedure:
Point, 0.5, Time, 0.4763270491
Point, 1, Time, 0.4562851924
Point, 1.5, Time, 0.4506939096
Point, 2, Time, 0.4562851924
Point, 2.5, Time, 0.4763270491
The least of these times is $T = 0.45069$ hr for the run to the point $(1.5, 1)$.

$$T = \tfrac{1}{8}\left(\sqrt{x^2 + 1} + \sqrt{(3 - x)^2 + 1}\right)$$

$$\frac{dT}{dx} = \frac{1}{8}\left(\frac{x}{\sqrt{x^2 + 1}} - \frac{3 - x}{\sqrt{(3 - x)^2 + 1}}\right)$$

c.n.: $x = 1.5$ miles. Least time: $T = \sqrt{13}/8 \approx 0.4506939094$ hr. To prove that PSQ is a straight line, use the following diagram:

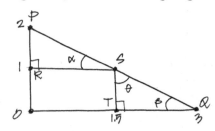

The right triangles PRS and STQ are congruent, so the pair of corresponding angles α, β are equal. So $\alpha + \theta = \beta + \theta$. By construction the angle RST is a right angle. Thus, the angles at the point S add up to 180. This makes PSQ a straight line.

(b) Output from the `paths` procedure:
Point, 0.5, Time, 0.5885179826
Point, 1, Time, 0.5494546915
Point, 1.5, Time, 0.5258095611
Point, 2, Time, 0.5152107575
Point, 2.5, Time, 0.5229117987
The least of these times is $T = 0.5152$ hr for the run to the point $(1.5, 2)$.

$$T = \frac{\sqrt{x^2 + 1}}{8} + \frac{\sqrt{(3 - x)^2 + 1}}{6}$$

$$\frac{dT}{dx} = \frac{x}{8\sqrt{x^2 + 1}} - \frac{3 - x}{6\sqrt{(3 - x)^2 + 1}}$$

c.n.: roots of
$$g(x) = 7x^4 - 42x^3 + 70x^2 - 96x + 144 = 0$$
Graphical solution gives $x \approx 2.09, T \approx 0.515$:

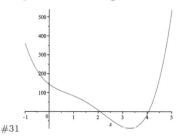

#31

33. (a) Output from the `paths` procedure:
Point, 0.5, Time, 0.4660274349
Point, 1, Time, 0.4461751639
Point, 1.5, Time, 0.4375000000
Point, 2, Time, 0.4368867239
Point, 2.5, Time, 0.4418619316
The least of these times is $T = 0.4369$ hr for the run to the point (2.0).

$$T = \frac{\sqrt{x^2 + 4}}{8} + \frac{3 - x}{12}, \quad \frac{dT}{dx} = \frac{x}{8\sqrt{x^2 + 4}} - \frac{1}{12}$$

c.n.: $x = 4/\sqrt{5} \approx 1.7889$ miles

Exercises: 3.5

1. (a) $c \approx 0.5$

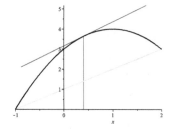

(b) $f'(c) = 2 - 2c$, $\dfrac{f(2) - f(1)}{2 - 1} = 1$

$2 - 2c = 1$, $c = 1/2$

3. (a) $c \approx 1.38$

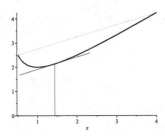

(b) $f'(c) = 1 - \dfrac{1}{c^2}, \quad \dfrac{f(4) - f(1/2)}{4 - 1/2} = \dfrac{1}{2}$

$1 - \dfrac{1}{c^2} = \dfrac{1}{2}, \quad c = \sqrt{2}$

5. (a) $c \approx 0$

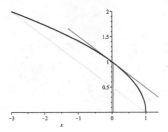

(b) $f'(c) = \dfrac{-1}{2\sqrt{1-c}}, \quad \dfrac{f(1) - f(-3)}{1 - (-3)} = -\dfrac{1}{2}$

$\dfrac{-1}{2\sqrt{1-c}} = -\dfrac{1}{2}, \quad c = 0$

7. (a) $c \approx 0$

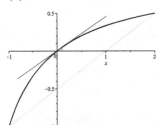

(b) $f'(c) = \dfrac{2}{(c+2)^2}, \quad \dfrac{f(2) - f(1)}{2 - (-1)} = \dfrac{1}{2}$

$\dfrac{2}{(c+2)^2} = \dfrac{1}{2}, \quad c = 0$

9. (a) $c \approx 1$

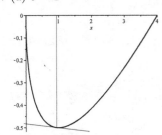

(b) $f'(c) = \dfrac{1}{2} - \dfrac{1}{2\sqrt{c}}, \quad \dfrac{f(4) - f(0)}{4 - 0} = 0$

$\dfrac{1}{2} - \dfrac{1}{2\sqrt{c}} = 0, \quad c = 1$

11. (a) $c \approx 0.85$

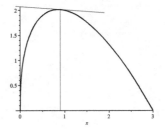

(b) $f'(c) = \dfrac{1}{5} x^{-3/5}(6 - 7c), \quad \dfrac{f(3) - f(0)}{3 - 0} = 0$

$\dfrac{1}{5} x^{-3/5}(6 - 7c) = 0, \quad c = 6/7 \approx 0.857$

13. (a) $c \approx 1.5$

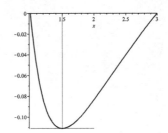

(b) $f'(c) = c^{-3}\left(\dfrac{4}{3}c - 2\right), \quad \dfrac{f(3) - f(1)}{3 - 1} = 0$

$c^{-3}\left(\dfrac{4}{3}c - 2\right) = 0, \quad c = 3/2 = 1.5$

15. (a) $c \approx 1.5 - 1.5$

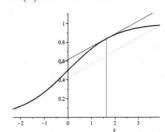

(b) $f'(c) = \dfrac{e^c}{(e^c + 1)^2}, \quad \dfrac{f(\ln 50) - f(\ln 0.1)}{\ln 50 - \ln 0.1} = m$

$\dfrac{e^c}{(e^c + 1)^2} = m, \quad c = \ln[(1 - 2m \pm \sqrt{1 - 4m})/(2m)]$

$\approx \pm 1.56$

17. (a) $c \approx \pi/2, 3\pi/2, 5\pi/2, 7\pi/2$

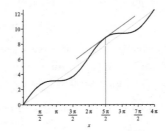

(b) $f'(c) = 1 + \cos(c), \quad \dfrac{f(4\pi) - f(0)}{4\pi - 0} = 1$

$1 + \cos(c) = 1, \quad c = \pi/2, 3\pi/2, 5\pi/2, 7\pi/2$

19. (a) $c \approx \pm 0.8$

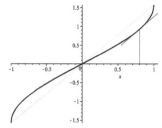

(b) $f'(c) = \dfrac{1}{\sqrt{1-c^2}}$, $\dfrac{f(1)-f(-1)}{1-(-1)} = \pi/2$

$\dfrac{1}{\sqrt{1-c^2}} = \pi/2$, $c = \pm\sqrt{1-4/\pi^2} \approx \pm 0.771$

21. (a) $c \approx 4.9$

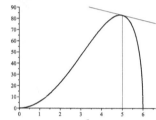

(b) $f'(c) = \dfrac{3c(24-c^2)}{\sqrt{36-c^2}}$, $\dfrac{f(6)-f(0)}{6-0} = 0$

$\dfrac{3c(24-c^2)}{\sqrt{36-c^2}} = 0$, $c = 2\sqrt{6} \approx 4.9$

23. Since $f(-1) = -1 < 3 = f(1)$ the IVT gives one root in the interval $(-1,1)$. Since $f'(x) = 7x^6 + 1 \neq 0$ for any x, Rolle's Theorem shows this is the only root.

25. Since $f(2) = 2\ln 2 - 3 < 4\ln 4 - 3 = f(4)$ the IVT gives one root in the interval $(2,4)$. Since $f'(x) = \ln x + 1 = 0$ for only $x = e^{-1} \approx 0.37$, which is not in $[2,4]$, Rolle's Theorem shows this is the only root.

27. Since $f(-1) = -2.8 < 4.8 = f(1)$ the IVT gives one root in the interval $(-1,1)$. Since $f'(x) = \cos x + 3 > 0$ for any x, Rolle's Theorem shows this is the only root.

29. Let $f(x) = \ln(x^r)$, $g(x) = r\ln x$. Then

$f'(x) = \dfrac{1}{x^r} \cdot rx^{r-1} = \dfrac{r}{x} = g'(x)$. Since f and g have the same derivative, there is a constant C so that $\ln(x^r) = r\ln x + C$, for all $x > 0$. Take $x = 1$ in this equation to get $0 = 0 + C$.

31. Let $f(x) = \tan^{-1}(x^{-1})$, $g(x) = \cot^{-1} x$. Then

$f'(x) = \dfrac{1}{1+(x^{-1})^2} \cdot (-x^{-2}) = \dfrac{-1}{x^2+1} = g'(x)$. Since f and g have the same derivative, there is a constant C so that $\tan^{-1}(x^{-1}) = \cot^{-1} x + C$, for all $x > 0$. Take $x = 1$ in this equation to get $\pi/4 = \pi/4 + C$.

33. Let $g(x) = -\tan^{-1}\left(\dfrac{\sqrt{1-x^2}}{x}\right)$, $f(x) = \sin^{-1} x$. Then

$g'(x) = \dfrac{1}{1+\left(\frac{\sqrt{1-x^2}}{x}\right)^2} \cdot \dfrac{\frac{-x^2}{\sqrt{1-x^2}}-\sqrt{1-x^2}}{x^2} = \dfrac{1}{\sqrt{1-x^2}}$

$= f'(x)$. Since f and g have the same derivative, there is a constant C so that $\sin^{-1} x = -\tan^{-1}\left(\dfrac{\sqrt{1-x^2}}{x}\right) + C$,

for all $0 < x < 1$. Take $x = 1$ in this equation to get $\pi/2 = 0 + C$.

35. Let $g(x) = \tan^{-1}\left(\sqrt{x^2-1}\right)$, $f(x) = \sec^{-1} x$. Then

$g'(x) = \dfrac{1}{1+\left(\sqrt{x^2-1}\right)^2} \cdot \dfrac{x}{\sqrt{x^2-1}} = \dfrac{1}{x\sqrt{x^2-1}}$

$= f'(x)$. Since f and g have the same derivative, there is a constant C so that $\sec^{-1} x = \tan^{-1}\left(\sqrt{x^2-1}\right) + C$, for all $x \geq 1$.

Exercises: 3.6

1. $\frac{3}{13}$ **3.** 3   **5.** 0   **7.** 8   **9.** $\frac{1}{27}$ **11.** $\frac{1}{2}$ **13.** $\frac{1}{2\pi}$

15. $\frac{1}{3}$ **17.** 2   **19.** $-\frac{9}{2}$ **21.** 0   **23.** $\frac{1}{2}$ **25.** 1   **27.** $\frac{1}{3}$

29. $\lim\limits_{x\to 0} \dfrac{\sin ax}{x} = \lim\limits_{x\to 0} \dfrac{a\cos ax}{1} = a$

31. 3   **33.** 0   **35.** $-\frac{5}{2}$ **37.** $\frac{\ln 2}{\ln 3}$ **39.** $\frac{2}{3}$ **41.** 0   **43.** 0

45. ∞ **47.** $-\frac{5}{3}$ **49.** 0   **51.** 0   **53.** 1   **55.** 0   **57.** 0

59. $e^0 = 1$ **61.** $e^0 = 1$ **63.** $e^{-5/3}$ **65.** 1   **67.** e^4 **69.** 1

71. ∞ **73.** $e^0 = 1$ **75.** 0   **77.** $\frac{9}{2}$ **79.** 0   **81.** $\frac{1}{2}$

Exercises: 3.7

1. $2x^5 - 2x^3 + 2x^2 - 5x + C$

3. $-\frac{10}{3}x^{-3} + 6x^{-1} + 4\ln x - \frac{1}{5}x + C$

5. $\frac{3}{4}x^{\frac{8}{3}} - \frac{5}{8}x^{\frac{2}{5}} + C$ **7.** $\frac{6}{13}x^{\frac{13}{6}} - \frac{2}{5}x^{\frac{5}{2}} + C$

9. $\frac{1}{4}x^4 + \frac{6}{7}x^{\frac{7}{2}} + x^3 + \frac{2}{5}x^{\frac{5}{2}} + C$

11. $-\frac{1}{3}x^{-3} - \frac{4}{7}x^{-\frac{7}{2}} - \frac{1}{4}x^{-4} + C$

13. $\ln x + 2x^{-1} - \frac{1}{2}x^{-2} + C$ **15.** $x + \ln x + C$

17. $4\ln x - 20x + \frac{25}{2}x^2 + C$ **19.** $x - e^{-x} + C$

21. $e^x + x + c$ **23.** $\frac{1}{\ln 4} \cdot 4^x + \frac{2}{\ln 2} \cdot 2^x + x + C$

25. $-\cos x + 2\sin x + C$ **27.** $-\frac{1}{4}(\cos^2 x - \sin^2 x) + C$

29. $\tan x + C$ **31.** $\tan x + \sec x + C$

33. $\sin x - \cos x + C$ **35.** $\tan x + C$ **37.** $\tan x + C$

39. $\sin x + C$ **41.** $x + \cos x + C$ **43.** $\tan x + C$

45. $\sec x + C$ **47.** $-\cos(x-2) + C$

49. $\frac{1}{2} \cdot \frac{1}{\ln 4} \cdot 4^x + C$

51. $f(x) = x^3 - 3x^2 + 1$, $y = -3x + 2$, $y = 9x + 6$

53. $f(x) = x - \ln x - 2$, $y = -1$, $y = \frac{1}{2}x - \ln 2 - 1$

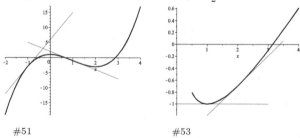

#51   #53

55. $f(x) = x - e^{-x} + 1$, $y = 2x$, $y = (1+e)x + 1$

57. $f(x) = x - 2\cos x + 1$, $y = x - 1$, $y = 3x - \pi + 1$

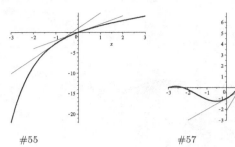

#55   #57

59. $e^x - 2x - e^{-x} + 2, y = 2, y = (e - 2 + e^{-1})x + (2 - 2e^{-1})$

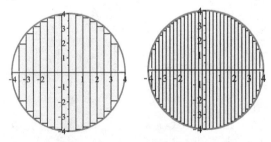

#59

CHAPTER 4: Answers to Odd Exercises

Exercises: 4.1

1. $\Delta x = 1$. Heights: $y_1 = 1.6, y_2 = 2, y_3 = 3.4, y_4 = 6.4$
$A = 1.6(1) + 2(1) + 3.4(1) + 6.4(1) = 13.4$

3. $\Delta x = 5/6 \approx 0.83$. Heights: $y_1 = 70, y_2 = 68,$
$y_3 = 41, y_4 = 17, y_5 = 10, y_6 = 25$
$A = (70 + 68 + 41 + 17 + 10 + 25)0.83 = 191.73$

5. $\Delta x = 1$. Heights: $y_1 = 10, y_2 = 73,$
$y_3 = 58, y_4 = 25, y_5 = 10, y_6 = 25, y_7 = 58, A =$
$\frac{1}{2}(10 + 2(73) + 2(58) + 2(25) + 2(10) + 2(25) + 58)(1)$
$= 225$

7.

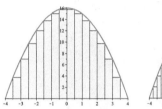

(a) ($n = 16$) $\Delta x = 0.5$. Heights in 1st quadrant:
$3.984, 3.852, 3.703, 3.472, 3.109, 2.646, 1.92, 0$
$A = 4 \left[\begin{array}{l} 3.984 + 3.852 + 3.703 + 3.472 \\ +3.109 + 2.646 + 1.92 + 0 \end{array} \right] 0.5 = 44.832$
(b) ($n = 32$) $\Delta x = 0.25$. Heights in 1st quadrant:
$3.985, 3.955, 3.94, 3.85, 3.776, 3.716, 3.626, 3.432$
$3.297, 3.117, 2.893, 2.623, 2.324, 1.92, 1.381, 0$
$A = 4 \left[\begin{array}{l} 3.985 + 3.955 + 3.94 + 3.85 \\ +3.776 + 3.716 + 3.626 + 3.432 \\ +3.297 + 3.117 + 2.893 + 2.623 \\ +2.324 + 1.92 + 1.381 + 0 \end{array} \right] 0.25$
$= 47.85$

9.

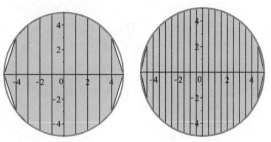

(a) ($n = 10$) $\Delta x = 1$. Bases in 1st quadrant:
$5, 4.876, 4.582, 4, 3, 0$
$A =$
$4 \cdot \frac{1}{2} [5 + 2(4.876) + 2(4.582) + 2(4) + 2(3)+)] \cdot 1$
$= 75.796$
(b) ($n = 20$) $\Delta = 0.5$. Bases in 1st quadrant:
$5, 4.959, 4.877, 4.57, 4.325, 3.936, 3.568, 3, 2.178, 0$
$A = 4 \cdot \frac{1}{2} \left[\begin{array}{l} 5 + 2(4.959 + 2(4.877) + 2(4.775) \\ +2(4.57) + 2(4.325) + 2(3.936) \\ +2(3.568) + 2(3) + 2(2.178) + 0 \end{array} \right] 0.25$
$= 77.376$

11.

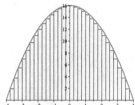

(a) ($n = 16$) $\Delta x = 0.5$. Heights in 1st quadrant:
$15.8, 15, 13.7, 12, 9.8, 7, 3.8, 0$
$A = 2 \left[\begin{array}{l} 15.8 + 15 + 13.7 + 12 \\ +9.8 + 7 + 3.8 + 0 \end{array} \right] 0.5 = 77.1$
(b) ($n = 32$) $\Delta x = 0.25$. Heights in 1st quadrant:
$15.9, 15.7, 15.4, 15, 14.4, 13.7, 13, 12$
$11, 9.7, 8.4, 7, 5.4, 3.8, 2, 0$
$A = 2 \left[\begin{array}{l} 15.9 + 15.7 + 15.4 + 15 \\ 14.4 + 13.7 + 13 + 12 \\ 11 + 9.7 + 8.4 + 7 \\ 5.4 + 3.8 + 2 + 0 \end{array} \right] 0.25 = 81.2$

13. 1780 **15.** 27,110 **17.** 388,520 **19.** 35,000

21. $\frac{4}{n^2} \left[\frac{n(n+1)}{2} \right] + \frac{14}{n^2} \left[\frac{n(n+1)}{2} \right]^2$ **23.** 9,840

25. 108.0346831

Exercises: 4.2

1. $\Delta x = 0.5$. Heights: $y_1 = 2.4, y_2 = 2, y_3 = 1.7,$
$y_4 = 1.4, y_5 = 1.5, y_6 = 2, y_7 = 3.2, y_8 = 5$
$R_8 = \left[\begin{array}{l} 2.4 + 2 + 1.7 + 1.4 \\ +1.5 + 2 + 3.2 + 5 \end{array} \right] (0.5) = 9.6$

3. $\Delta x = 0.5$. Heights: $y_1 = 4.33, y_2 = 4.33, y_3 = 3.57,$
$y_4 = 2.8, y_5 = 2.5, y_6 = 2.8, y_7 = 3.57, y_8 = 4.33,$
$y_9 = 4.33, y_{10} = 2.5$
$R_{10} = \left[\begin{array}{l} 4.33 + 4.33 + 3.57 + 2.8 + 2.5 \\ +2.8 + 3.57 + 4.33 + 4.33 + 2.5 \end{array} \right] (0.5)$

$= 17.53$

5. $\Delta x = 0.4$. Heights: $y_1 = 1.13, y_2 = 0.86, y_3 = 0.71$, $y_4 = 0.71, y_5 = 0.87, y_6 = 1.33, y_7 = 2.11$, $y_8 = 2.74, y_9 = 1.76, y_{10} = 0.4$

$$R_{10} = \left[\begin{array}{l} 1.13 + 0.86 + 0.71 + 0.71 + 0.87 \\ +1.33 + 2.11 + 2.74 + 1.76 + 0.40 \end{array} \right] (0.4)$$
$$= 5.048$$

7.

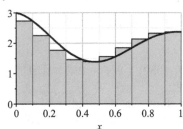

$\Delta x = 0.1$. Heights: $y_1 = 2.75, y_2 = 2.25, y_3 = 1.8$, $y_4 = 1.5, y_5 = 1.4, y_6 = 1.6, y_7 = 1.8$, $y_8 = 2.15, y_9 = 2.3, y_{10} = 2.35$

$$R_{10} = \left[\begin{array}{l} 2.75 + 2.25 + 1.8 + 1.5 + 1.4 \\ +1.6 + 1.8 + 2.15 + 2.3 + 2.35 \end{array} \right] (0.1)$$
$$= 1.99$$

9.

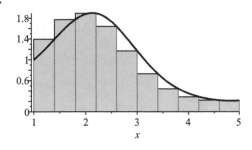

$\Delta x = 0.4$. Heights: $y_1 = 1.39, y_2 = 1.77, y_3 = 1.88$, $y_4 = 1.64, y_5 = 1.17, y_6 = 0.73, y_7 = 0.44$, $y_8 = 0.29, y_9 = 0.22, y_{10} = 0.21$

$$R_{10} = \left[\begin{array}{l} 1.39 + 1.77 + 1.88 + 1.64 + 1.17 \\ +0.73 + 0.44 + 0.29 + 0.22 + 0.21 \end{array} \right] (0.4)$$
$$= 3.896$$

11.

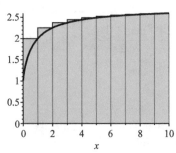

$\Delta x = 1$. Heights: $y_1 = 2, y_2 = 2.25, y_3 = 2.37$, $y_4 = 2.44, y_5 = 2.49, y_6 = 2.52, y_7 = 2.54$, $y_8 = 2.56, y_9 = 2.58, y_{10} = 2.59$

$$R_{10} = \left[\begin{array}{l} 2 + 2.25 + 2.37 + 2.44 + 2.49 \\ +2.52 + 2.54 + 2.56 + 2.58 + 2.59 \end{array} \right] (1)$$
$$= 24.34$$

13.

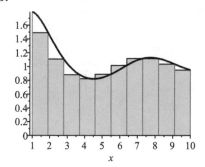

$\Delta x = 0.9$. Heights: $y_1 = 1.48, y_2 = 1.11, y_3 = 0.88$, $y_4 = 0.82, y_5 = 0.89, y_6 = 1.02, y_7 = 1.11$, $y_8 = 1.11, y_9 = 1.03, y_{10} = 0.95$

$$R_{10} = \left[\begin{array}{l} 1.48 + 1.11 + 0.88 + 0.82 + 0.89 \\ +1.02 + 1.11 + 1.11 + 1.03 + 0.95 \end{array} \right] (0.9)$$
$$= 9.369$$

15. $\Delta x = 0.5, x_i = -2 + 0.5i$

$$\left[\begin{array}{ccccccccc} i & 1 & 2 & 3 & 4 & 5 & 6 & 7 & 8 \\ x_i & -1.5 & -1 & -0.5 & 0 & 0.5 & 1 & 1.5 & 2 \\ f(x_i) & 1.75 & 3 & 3.75 & 4 & 3.75 & 3 & 1.75 & 0 \end{array} \right]$$

$R_8 = (1.75 + 3 + 3.75 + 4 + 3.75 + 3 + 1.75 + 0)(0.5) = 10.5$

17. $\Delta x = 0.5, x_i = 0.5i$

$$\left[\begin{array}{ccccccccc} i & 1 & 2 & 3 & 4 & 5 & 6 & 7 & 8 \\ x_i & 0.5 & 1 & 1.5 & 2 & 2.5 & 3 & 3.5 & 4 \\ f(x_i) & 1.75 & 3 & 3.75 & 4 & 3.75 & 3 & 1.75 & 0 \end{array} \right]$$

$R_8 = (1.75 + 3 + 3.75 + 4 + 3.75 + 3 + 1.75 + 0)(0.5) = 10.5$

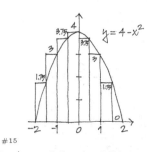

#15

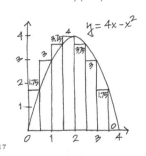

#17

19. $\Delta x = 0.5, x_i = 0.5i$

$$\left[\begin{array}{ccccccccccc} i & 1 & 2 & 3 & 4 & 5 & 6 & 7 & 8 & 9 & 10 \\ x_i & 0.5 & 1 & 1.5 & 2 & 2.5 & 3 & 3.5 & 4 & 4.5 & 5 \\ f(x_i) & 6.75 & 8 & 8.75 & 9 & 8.75 & 8 & 6.75 & 5 & 2.75 & 0 \end{array} \right]$$

$R_{10} =$
$(6.75 + 8 + 8.75 + 9 + 8.75 + 8 + 6.75 + 5 + 2.75 + 0)(0.5)$
$= 31.875$

21. $\Delta x = 0.5, x_i = 0.5i$

$$\left[\begin{array}{ccccccccc} i & 1 & 2 & 3 & 4 & 5 & 6 & 7 & 8 \\ x_i & 0.5 & 1 & 1.5 & 2 & 2.5 & 3 & 3.5 & 4 \\ f(x_i) & \sqrt{0.5} & 1 & \sqrt{1.5} & \sqrt{2} & \sqrt{2.5} & \sqrt{3} & \sqrt{3.5} & 2 \end{array} \right]$$

$R_8 =$
$(\sqrt{0.5} + 1 + \sqrt{1.5} + \sqrt{2} + \sqrt{2.5} + \sqrt{3} + \sqrt{3.5} + 2)(0.5)$
$= 5.76$

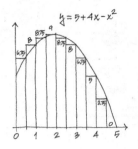

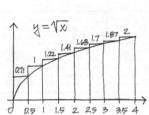

#19   #21

23. $\Delta x = 0.5, x_i = 0.5i$

$$\begin{bmatrix} i & 1 & 2 & 3 & 4 & 5 & 6 & 7 & 8 \\ x_i & 0.5 & 1 & 1.5 & 2 & 2.5 & 3 & 3.5 & 4 \\ f(x_i) & 3.97 & 3.87 & 3.7 & 3.46 & 3.12 & 2.64 & 1.94 & 0 \end{bmatrix}$$

$R_8 =$
$(3.97 + 3.87 + 3.7 + 3.46 + 3.12 + 2.64 + 1.94 + 0)(0.5)$
$= 11.35$

25. $\Delta x = 0.25, x_i = -1 + 0.25i$

$$\begin{bmatrix} i & 1 & 2 & 3 & 4 & 5 & 6 & 7 & 8 \\ x_i & -0.75 & -0.5 & -0.25 & 0 & 0.25 & 0.5 & 0.75 & 1 \\ f(x_i) & 24.2 & 21.3 & 20.2 & 20 & 19.8 & 18.8 & 15.8 & 10 \end{bmatrix}$$

$R_8 =$
$(24.2 + 21.3 + 20.2 + 20 + 19.8 + 18.8 + 15.8 + 10)(0.25)$
$= 37.525$

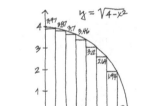

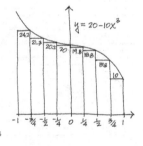

#23   #25

27. $\Delta x = 0.5, x_i = -1 + 0.5i$

$$\begin{bmatrix} i & 1 & 2 & 3 & 4 & 5 & 6 & 7 & 8 & 9 & 10 \\ x_i & -0.5 & 0 & 0.5 & 1 & 1.5 & 2 & 2.5 & 3 & 3.5 & 4 \\ f(x_i) & 2.75 & 5 & 6.75 & 8 & 8.75 & 9 & 8.75 & 8 & 6.75 & 5 \end{bmatrix}$$

$R_{10} =$
$(2.75 + 5 + 6.75 + 8 + 8.75 + 9 + 8.75 + 8 + 6.75 + 5)(0.5)$
$= 34.375$

29. $\Delta x = 0.125, x_i = 0.125i$

$$\begin{bmatrix} i & 1 & 2 & 3 & 4 & 5 & 6 & 7 \\ x_i & 0.125 & 0.25 & 0.375 & 0.5 & 0.625 & 0.75 & 0.875 \\ f(x_i) & 1.09 & 1.19 & 1.30 & 1.41 & 1.54 & 1.68 & 1.83 \end{bmatrix}$$

$$\begin{bmatrix} i & 8 \\ x_i & 1 \\ f(x_i) & 2 \end{bmatrix}$$

$R_8 =$
$(1.09 + 1.19 + 1.30 + 1.41 + 1.54 + 1.68 + 1.83 + 2)(0.125)$
$= 1.505$

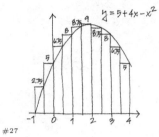

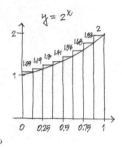

#27   #29

31. $\Delta x = 0.125, x_i = 1 + 0.125i$

$$\begin{bmatrix} i & 1 & 2 & 3 & 4 & 5 & 6 & 7 \\ x_i & 1.125 & 1.25 & 1.375 & 1.5 & 1.625 & 1.75 & 1.875 \\ f(x_i) & 3.08 & 3.49 & 3.96 & 4.48 & 5.08 & 5.75 & 6.52 \end{bmatrix}$$

$$\begin{bmatrix} i & 8 \\ x_i & 2 \\ f(x_i) & 7.39 \end{bmatrix}$$

$R_8 =$
$(3.08 + 3.49 + 3.96 + 4.48 + 5.08 + 5.75 + 6.52 + 7.39)(0.125)$
$= 4.97$

33. $\Delta x - 0.125, x_i = 0.125i$

$$\begin{bmatrix} i & 1 & 2 & 3 & 4 & 5 & 6 & 7 \\ x_i & 0.125 & 0.25 & 0.375 & 0.5 & 0.625 & 0.75 & 0.875 \\ f(x_i) & 0.882 & 0.779 & 0.687 & 0.607 & 0.535 & 0.472 & 0.417 \end{bmatrix}$$

$$\begin{bmatrix} i & 8 \\ x_i & 1 \\ f(x_i) & 0.368 \end{bmatrix}$$

$$R_8 = \begin{bmatrix} 0.882 + 0.779 + 0.687 + 0.607 \\ +0.535 + 0.472 + 0.417 + 0.368 \end{bmatrix} (0.125)$$
$= 0.593$

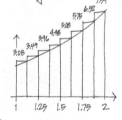

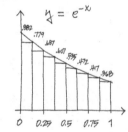

#31   #33

35. $\Delta x = 0.125, x_i = 0.125i$

$$\begin{bmatrix} i & 1 & 2 & 3 & 4 & 5 & 6 & 7 \\ x_i & 0.125 & 0.25 & 0.375 & 0.5 & 0.625 & 0.75 & 0.875 \\ f(x_i) & 0.917 & 0.841 & 0.771 & 0.707 & 0.648 & 0.594 & 0.545 \end{bmatrix}$$

$$\begin{bmatrix} i & 8 \\ x_i & 1 \\ f(x_i) & 0.5 \end{bmatrix}$$

$$R_8 = \begin{bmatrix} 0.917 + 0.841 + 0.771 + 0.707 \\ +0.648 + 0.594 + 0.545 + 0.5 \end{bmatrix} (0.125)$$
$= 0.6903$

37. $\Delta x = 0.25, x_i = 0.25i$

$$\begin{bmatrix} i & 1 & 2 & 3 & 4 & 5 & 6 & 7 & 8 \\ x_i & 0.25 & 0.5 & 0.75 & 1 & 1.25 & 1.5 & 1.75 & 2 \\ f(x_i) & 6.72 & 6.35 & 5.88 & 5.28 & 4.51 & 3.52 & 2.25 & 0.61 \end{bmatrix}$$

$$R_8 = \begin{bmatrix} 6.72 + 6.35 + 5.88 + 5.28 \\ +4.51 + 3.52 + 2.25 + 0.61 \end{bmatrix} (0.25)$$

$= 8.78$

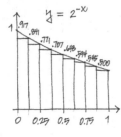

#35

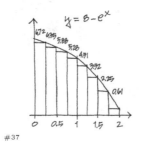

#37

39. $\Delta x = 0.1, x_i = 0.1i$

$$\begin{bmatrix} i & 1 & 2 & 3 & 4 & 5 & 6 & 7 \\ x_i & 0.1 & 0.2 & 0.3 & 0.4 & 0.5 & 0.6 & 0.7 \\ f(x_i) & 0.309 & 0.588 & 0.81 & 0.951 & 1 & 0.951 & 0.81 \end{bmatrix}$$

$$\begin{bmatrix} i & 8 & 9 & 10 \\ x_i & 0.8 & 0.9 & 1 \\ f(x_i) & 0.588 & 0.309 & 0 \end{bmatrix}$$

$$R_{10} = \begin{bmatrix} 0.309 + 0.588 + 0.81 + 0.951 + 1 \\ +0.951 + 0.81 + 0.588 + 0.309 + 0 \end{bmatrix} (0.1)$$

$= 0.6316$

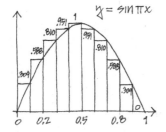

#39

41. $R_n = 2 + \dfrac{8}{n^3}\left(\dfrac{n(n+1)(2n+1)}{6}\right)$

43. $R_n = 60 - \dfrac{120}{n^2}\left(\dfrac{n(n+1)}{2}\right)$

$\quad + \dfrac{240}{n^3}\left(\dfrac{n(n+1)(2n+1)}{6}\right) - \dfrac{160}{n^4}\left(\dfrac{n(n+1)}{2}\right)^2$

45. $R_n = \dfrac{150}{n^2}\left(\dfrac{n(n+1)}{2}\right) - \dfrac{125}{n^3}\left(\dfrac{n(n+1)(2n+1)}{6}\right)$

47. $R_n = \dfrac{2^{1/n}}{n(2^{1/n}-1)}$ **49.** $R_n = \dfrac{e^{1/n}e(e-1)}{n(e^{1/n}-1)}$

51. $R_n = \dfrac{(e-1)}{ne(e^{1/n}-1)}$ **53.** $R_n = \dfrac{1}{2n(2^{1/n}-1)}$

55.

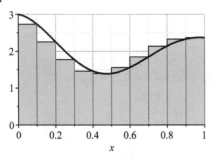

$$R_{10} = \begin{bmatrix} 2.75 + 2.25 + 1.8 + 1.5 + 1.4 \\ +1.6 + 1.8 + 2.15 + 2.3 + 2.35 \end{bmatrix} (0.1)$$

$= 1.99$

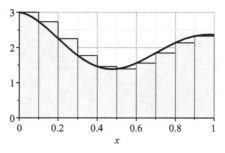

$$L_{10} = \begin{bmatrix} 3 + 2.73 + 2.25 + 1.77 + 1.46 \\ +1.4 + 1.56 + 1.85 + 2.14 + 2.33 \end{bmatrix} (0.1)$$

$= 2.049$

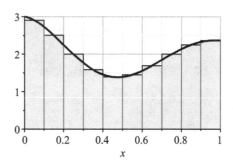

$$M_{10} = \begin{bmatrix} 2.9 + 2.5 + 2 + 1.59 + 1.4 \\ +1.45 + 1.7 + 2 + 2.25 + 2.37 \end{bmatrix} (0.1)$$

$= 2.016$

57.

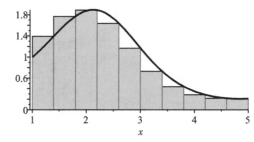

$$R_{10} = \begin{bmatrix} 1.39 + 1.77 + 1.89 + 1.64 + 1.17 \\ +0.74 + 0.44 + 0.29 + 0.22 + 0.21 \end{bmatrix} (0.4)$$

$= 3.904$

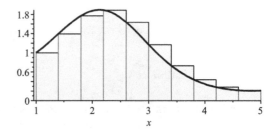

$$L_{10} = \begin{bmatrix} 1 + 1.4 + 1.77 + 1.89 + 1.64 \\ +1.16 + 0.73 + 0.44 + 0.29 + 0.22 \end{bmatrix} (0.4)$$

$= 4.216$

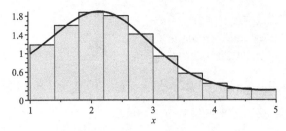

$$M_{10} = \left[\begin{array}{c} 1.19 + 1.6 + 1.88 + 1.8 + 1.4 \\ +0.94 + 0.57 + 0.35 + 0.24 + 0.2 \end{array} \right] (0.4)$$
$$= 4.068$$

59. $\Delta x = 0.5, x_i = 0.5i, m_i = (x_i + x_{i-1})/2 = 0.5i - 0.25$

$$\left[\begin{array}{ccccccccc} i & 0 & 1 & 2 & 3 & 4 & 5 & 6 & 7 & 8 \\ x_i & 0 & 0.5 & 1 & 1.5 & 2 & 2.5 & 3 & 3.5 & 4 \\ f(x_i) & 0 & 0.7 & 1 & 1.2 & 1.4 & 1.58 & 1.7 & 1.9 & 2 \\ f(m_i) & \star & 0.5 & 0.9 & 1.1 & 1.3 & 1.5 & 1.7 & 1.8 & 1.9 \end{array} \right]$$

$$R_8 = \left[\begin{array}{c} 0.7 + 1 + 1.2 + 1.4 \\ +1.58 + 1.7 + 1.9 + 2 \end{array} \right] (0.5) = 5.74$$

$$L_8 = \left[\begin{array}{c} 0 + 0.7 + 1 + 1.2 \\ +1.4 + 1.58 + 1.7 + 1.9 \end{array} \right] (0.5) = 4.74$$

$$M_8 = \left[\begin{array}{c} 0.5 + 0.9 + 1.1 + 1.3 \\ +1.5 + 1.7 + 1.8 + 1.9 \end{array} \right] (0.5) = 5.35$$

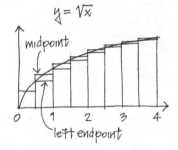

See Exercise 21 above for the sketch of R_8.

61. $\Delta x = 0.25, x_i = -1 + 0.25i, m_i = (x_i + x_{i-1})/2 = $
$-1.125 + 0.25i$

$$\left[\begin{array}{cccccccc} i & 0 & 1 & 2 & 3 & 4 & 5 & 6 \\ x_i & -1 & -0.75 & -0.5 & -0.25 & 0 & 0.25 & 0.5 \\ f(x_i) & 30 & 24.2 & 21.3 & 20.2 & 20 & 19.8 & 18.8 \\ f(m_i) & \star & 26.7 & 22.4 & 20.5 & 20.1 & 20 & 19.5 \end{array} \right]$$

$$\left[\begin{array}{ccc} i & 7 & 8 \\ x_i & 0.75 & 1 \\ f(x_i) & 15.8 & 10 \\ f(m_i) & 17.6 & 13.3 \end{array} \right]$$

$$R_8 = \left[\begin{array}{c} 24.2 + 21.3 + 20.2 + 20 \\ +19.8 + 18.8 + 15.8 + 10 \end{array} \right] (0.25) = 37.525$$

$$L_8 = \left[\begin{array}{c} 30 + 24.2 + 21.3 + 20.2 \\ +20 + 19.8 + 18.8 + 15.8 \end{array} \right] (0.25) = 42.525$$

$$M_8 = \left[\begin{array}{c} 26.7 + 22.4 + 20.5 + 20.1 \\ +20 + 19.5 + 17.6 + 13.3 \end{array} \right] (0.25) = 20.025$$

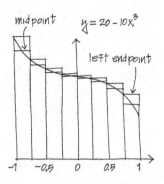

See Exercise 25 above for the sketch of R_8.

63. $\Delta x = 0.5, x_i = -1 + 0.5i, m_i = (x_i + x_{i-1})/2 = $
$-1.25 + 0.5i$

$$\left[\begin{array}{cccccccc} i & 0 & 1 & 2 & 3 & 4 & 5 & 6 & 7 \\ x_i & -1 & -0.5 & 0 & 0.5 & 1 & 1.5 & 2 & 2.5 \\ f(x_i) & 0 & 2.75 & 5 & 6.75 & 8 & 8.75 & 9 & 8.75 \\ f(m_i) & \star & 1.44 & 3.94 & 5.94 & 7.44 & 8.44 & 8.94 & 8.94 \end{array} \right]$$

$$\left[\begin{array}{cccc} i & 8 & 9 & 10 \\ x_i & 3 & 3.5 & 4 \\ f(x_i) & 8 & 6.75 & 5 \\ f(m_i) & 8.44 & 7.44 & 5.94 \end{array} \right]$$

$$R_{10} = \left[\begin{array}{c} 2.75 + 5 + 6.75 + 8 + 8.75 \\ +9 + 8.75 + 8 + 6.75 + 5 \end{array} \right] (0.5) = 34.375$$

$$L_{10} = \left[\begin{array}{c} 0 + 2.75 + 5 + 6.75 + 8 \\ +8.75 + 9 + 8.75 + 8 + 6.75 \end{array} \right] (0.5) = 31.875$$

$$M_{10} = \left[\begin{array}{c} 1.44 + 3.94 + 5.94 + 7.44 + 8.44 \\ +8.94 + 8.94 + 8.44 + 7.44 + 5.94 \end{array} \right] (0.5)$$
$$= 33.45$$

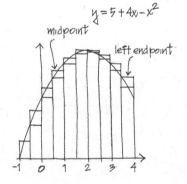

See Exercise 27 above for the sketch of R_8.

Exercises: 4.3

1. $\lim\limits_{n \to \infty} \left[\frac{8}{n^3} \left(\frac{n(n+1)(2n+1)}{6} \right) - 2 \right] = \frac{2}{3}$

3. $\lim\limits_{n \to \infty} \left[\frac{36}{n^2} \left(\frac{n(n+1)}{2} \right) - \frac{81}{n^4} \left(\frac{n(n+1)}{2} \right)^2 \right] = -\frac{9}{4}$

5. $\lim\limits_{n \to \infty} \left[12 - \frac{64}{n^2} \left(\frac{n(n+1)}{2} \right) + \frac{64}{n^3} \left(\frac{n(n+1)(2n+1)}{6} \right) \right] = \frac{4}{3}$

7. $\lim\limits_{n \to \infty} \left[9 - \frac{63}{n^2} \left(\frac{n(n+1)}{2} \right) + \frac{135}{n^3} \left(\frac{n(n+1)(2n+1)}{6} \right) \right.$
$\left. - \frac{81}{n^4} \left(\frac{n(n+1)}{2} \right)^2 \right] = \frac{9}{4}$

9. $\lim\limits_{n\to\infty} \dfrac{2^{1/n}}{n(2^{1/n}-1)} = \dfrac{1}{\ln 2}$

11. $\lim\limits_{n\to\infty} \dfrac{e^{1/n}e(e-1)}{n(e^{1/n}-1)} = e(e-1)$

13. $\lim\limits_{n\to\infty} \dfrac{e-1}{n(e^{1/n}-1)} = 1-e^{-1}$

15. $\lim\limits_{n\to\infty} \dfrac{e-1}{e^2 n(e^{1/n}-1)} = e^{-1}-e^{-2}$

17. $A = \frac{3}{2}$ **19.** $A_1 + A_2 = \frac{1}{2} + 2 = \frac{5}{2}$

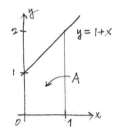
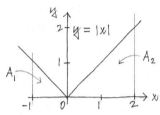

#17   #19

21. $-A_1 + A_2 = -\frac{1}{2} + 2 = \frac{3}{2}$

23. $A_{above} - A_{below} = \frac{3}{2} - \frac{1}{2} = 1$

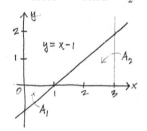
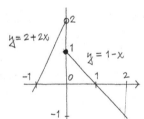

#21   #23

25. $A = 2\pi$ **27.** $-A_{below} + A_{above} = -\pi - 2 + \frac{1}{2} = -\pi - \frac{3}{2}$

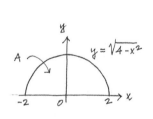
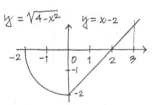

#25   #27

29. $A_1 + A_2 = \frac{3}{2} + 2 = \frac{7}{2}$ **31.** $A_1 + A_2 + A_3 = (\pi + 10)/4$

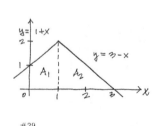
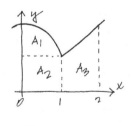

#29   #31

33. The first formula is

$$\lim\limits_{n\to\infty} \tfrac{1}{n^2}\left[\tfrac{n(n+1)}{2}\right] = \lim\limits_{n\to\infty} \tfrac{1}{2}\left[\tfrac{n(n+1)}{n\cdot n}\right] = \lim\limits_{n\to\infty} \tfrac{1}{2}\cdot\tfrac{n+1}{n}$$

$$= \lim\limits_{n\to\infty} \tfrac{1}{2}\left(1 + \tfrac{1}{n}\right) = \tfrac{1}{2}$$

The second formula is

$$\lim\limits_{n\to\infty} \tfrac{1}{n^3}\left[\tfrac{n(n+1)(2n+1)}{6}\right] = \lim\limits_{n\to\infty} \tfrac{1}{6}\left[\tfrac{n(n+1)(2n+1)}{n\cdot n\cdot n}\right]$$

$$= \lim\limits_{n\to\infty} \tfrac{1}{6}\left(1 + \tfrac{1}{n}\right)\left(2 + \tfrac{1}{n}\right) = \tfrac{1}{6}(1+0)(2+0) = \tfrac{1}{3}$$

The third formula is

$$\lim\limits_{n\to\infty} \tfrac{1}{n^4}\left[\tfrac{n(n+1)}{2}\right]^2 = \lim\limits_{n\to\infty}\left[\tfrac{1}{n^2}\cdot\tfrac{n(n+1)}{2}\right]^2$$

$$= \left[\lim\limits_{n\to\infty} \tfrac{1}{n^2}\cdot\tfrac{n(n+1)}{2}\right]^2 = \left[\tfrac{1}{2}\right]^2 = \tfrac{1}{4}$$

35. $\int_0^1 4(x - x^2)\,dx = 4\int_0^1 x\,dx - 4\int_0^1 x^2\,dx = \frac{2}{3}$

37. $\int_0^1 (x^2 - 1)\,dx = \int_0^1 x^2\,dx - \int_0^1 1\,dx = -\frac{2}{3}$

39. $\int_0^1 (4x - x^3)\,dx = 4\int_0^1 x\,dx - \int_0^1 x^3\,dx = \frac{7}{4}$

41. $\int_1^2 (x^2 - 1)\,dx = \int_0^2 (x^2 - 1)\,dx - \int_0^1 (x^2 - 1)\,dx$

$$= \tfrac{2}{3} - \left(-\tfrac{2}{3}\right) = \tfrac{4}{3}$$

43. $\int_1^3 (4x - x^3)\,dx = \int_0^3 (4x - x^3)\,dx - \int_0^1 (4x - x^3)\,dx$

$$= -\tfrac{9}{4} - \tfrac{7}{4} = -4$$

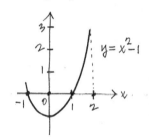
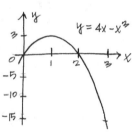

#41   #43

45. $\int_0^2 e^x\,dx = \int_0^1 e^x\,dx + \int_1^2 e^x\,dx$

$$= e - 1 + e^2 - e = e^2 - 1$$

47. $\int_0^2 e^{-x}\,dx = \int_0^1 e^{-x}\,dx + \int_1^2 e^{-x}\,dx$

$$= 1 - e^{-1} + e^{-1} - e^{-2} = 1 - e^{-2}$$

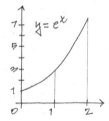
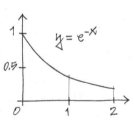

#45   #47

Exercises: 4.4

1. $55/6$ **3.** -6 **5.** $-1/15$ **7.** $\ln 2 + \frac{1}{2}$ **9.** $3 - 4\ln 2$

11. $184/105$ **13.** $1/6$ **15.** $2 - e^{-1}$ **17.** $e - 2$

19. $\frac{39}{8\ln 2} + 2$ **21.** $\frac{5}{\ln 6} - \frac{9}{\ln 10}$ **23.** $\frac{242}{9\ln 243}$ **25.** 2

27. 6π **29.** $1 - \sqrt{2} + \sqrt{3}$ **31.** 2 **33.** $\sqrt{2} - 1$

35. 1 **37.** 2 **39.** $\frac{\sqrt{3}}{2}$ **41.** $\frac{\pi}{6} + \frac{1-\sqrt{3}}{2}$ **43.** $\frac{2}{\sqrt{3}}$

45. $A_1 = \frac{4}{3}$, $A_2 = \frac{4}{3}$, $A_{net} = -A_1 + A_2 = 0$

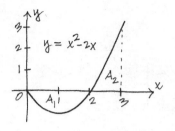

47. $A_1 = \frac{229}{20}$, $A_2 = \frac{21}{20}$, $A_3 = \frac{117}{20}$

$A_{net} = A_1 - A_2 + A_3 = \frac{65}{4}$

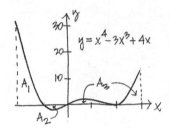

49. $A_1 = \ln 2 - \frac{1}{2}$, $A_2 = 1 - \ln 2$, $A_{net} = -A_1 + A_2$

$= \frac{3}{2} - 2\ln 2$

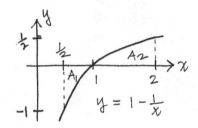

51. $A_1 = \frac{1}{3}$, $A_2 = \frac{5}{3}$, $A_{net} = A_1 - A_2 = -\frac{4}{3}$

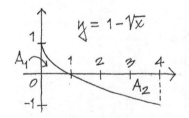

53. $A_1 = e - 2$, $A_2 = e^{-2} + 1$, $A_{net} = A_1 - A_2 = e - e^{-2} - 3$

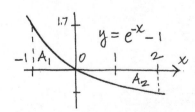

55. $A_1 = 2\ln 2 + e - 4$, $A_2 = e^{-2} + 2 + 2\ln 2$,

$A_{net} = A_1 - A_2 = e - e^{-2} - 6$

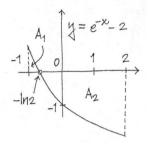

57. $A_1 = \frac{\pi}{3} + \frac{\sqrt{3}}{2}$, $A_2 = -\frac{\pi}{6} + \frac{\sqrt{3}}{2}$, $A_{net} = A_1 - A_2 = \frac{\pi}{2}$

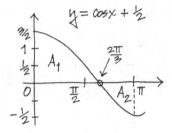

59. $A_1 = 2\sqrt{2}$, $A_2 = 2\sqrt{2}$, $A_{net} = A_1 - A_2 = 0$

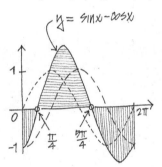

61. $A_1 = \frac{\sqrt{3}}{4} - \frac{\pi}{12}$, $A_2 = \frac{\pi}{6} + \frac{\sqrt{3}}{4}$, $A_{net} = -A_1 + A_2 = \frac{\pi}{4}$

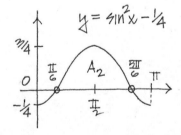

63. $A_1 = \ln\sqrt{2} + \frac{7\pi}{12}$, $A_2 = \ln\sqrt{2} - \frac{\pi}{12}$,

$A_{net} = -A_1 + A_2 = -\frac{2\pi}{3}$

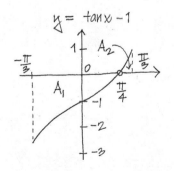

65. $A_{above} = 2\ln(2 + \sqrt{3}) + \frac{2\pi}{3\sqrt{3}} - \ln 3$, $A_{below} = -\ln 3 - \frac{2\pi}{3\sqrt{3}}$, $A_{net} = -A_1 + A_2 = 2\ln(2 + \sqrt{3}) + \frac{4\pi}{3\sqrt{3}}$

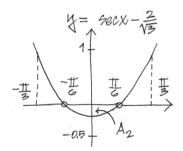

67. See Exercise 93 below for the computer plot.

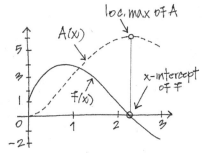

69. See Exercise 93 below for the computer plot.

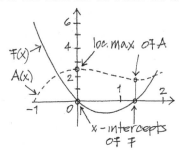

71. See Exercise 93 below for the computer plot.

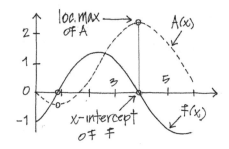

73. $A(x) = \frac{1}{3}x^3 - x^2$ **75.** $A(x) = \frac{1}{5}x^5 - \frac{3}{4}x^4 + 2x^2 + \frac{52}{5}$

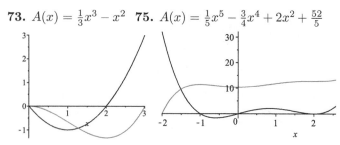

77. $A(x) = x - \ln x - \frac{1}{2} - \ln 2$ **79.** $A(x) = x - \frac{2}{3}x^{3/2}$

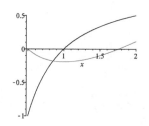 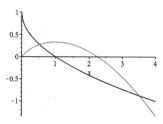

81. $A(x) = -e^{-x} - x + e - 1$ **83.** $A(x) = -e^{-x} - 2x + e - 2$

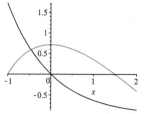 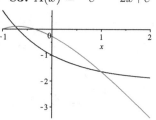

85. $A(x) = \frac{1}{2}x + \sin x$ **87.** $A(x) = \frac{1}{4}x + \frac{1}{4}\sin 2x$

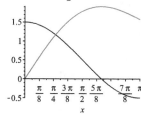 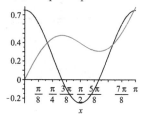

89. $A(x) = \ln|\sec x| - x - \ln 2 - \frac{\pi}{3}$ **91.** $A(x) = -\frac{2}{\sqrt{3}}x + \ln|\sec x + \tan x| - \ln(2 - \sqrt{3}) - \frac{2\pi}{3\sqrt{3}}$

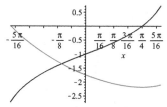 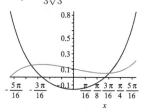

93.

   #67 $A(x) = \frac{1}{4}x^4 - 2x^3 + 4x^2 + x$ **#69.** $A(x) = e^x - 4e^{-x} - 5x - e^{-1} + 4e - 5$

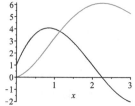 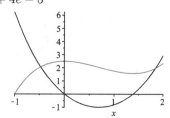

   #71 $A(x) = -\cos x - \sin x + 1$

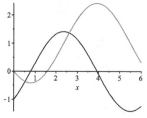

Exercises: 4.5

1. $u = 1 + x^4$, $I = \frac{1}{6}(1 + x^4)^{3/2} + C$

3. $u = 1 + x^{3/2}$, $I = \frac{2}{3}\ln|1 + x^{3/2}| + C$

5. $u = t^2$, $I = \frac{1}{2}\sin(t^2) + C$ **7.** $u = -y^3$, $I = -\frac{1}{3}e^{-y^3} + C$

9. $u = 1 - x^2$, $I = -\sqrt{4 - x^2} + C$

11. $u = x - 1$
$I = \frac{3}{11}(x-1)^{11/3} + \frac{3}{4}(x-1)^{8/3} + \frac{3}{5}(x-1)^{5/3} + C$

13. $u = x - 2$
$I = \ln|x - 2| - 4(x-2)^{-1} - 2(x-2)^{-2} + C$

15. $u = \ln x$, $I = -\cos(\ln x) + C$

17. $u = \ln x$, $I = \ln|\ln x| + C$

19. $u = 1 + \sqrt{x}$, $I = -4(1 + \sqrt{x})^{-1/2} + C$

21. $u = \sqrt{x}$, $I = 2\sin(\sqrt{x}) + C$

23. $u = x^{-1}$, $I = -\tan(x^{-1}) + C$

25. $u = x^{-1}$, $I = -\tan(x^{-1}) + x^{-1} + C$

27. $u = x^3 + 1$, $I = \frac{1}{3}\ln|x^3 + 1| + C$

29. $u = x^2$, $I = \frac{1}{2}\tan^{-1}(x^2) + C$

31. $u = \sqrt{x}$, $I = \tan^{-1}(\sqrt{x}) + C$

33. $u = \sqrt{x}$, $I = \sin^{-1}(\sqrt{x}) + C$

35. $u = x^3$, $I = \frac{1}{3}\sin^{-1}(x^3) + C$

37. $u = \sin x$, $I = \frac{1}{4}\sin^4 x + C$

39. $u = \tan x$, $I = \frac{1}{3}\tan^3 x + C$

41. $u = \sec x$, $I = \frac{1}{3}\sec^3 x - \sec x + C$

43. $u = 1 + \cos x$, $I = -\frac{2}{3}\sqrt{1 + \cos 3x} + C$

45. $u = 3x$, $I = \frac{1}{3}\sin^{-1} 3x + C$

47. $u = e^x$, $I = \sin^{-1}(e^x) + C$

49. $u = \sin x$, $I = \tan^{-1}(\sin x) + C$

51. $A = A_{net} = \ln(1 + e^{10}) - \ln 2$

53. $A_1 = \frac{64}{21}$, $A_2 = \frac{10}{21}$, $A_{net} = -A_1 + A_2 = -\frac{18}{7}$

55. $A_1 = \frac{\pi}{4}$, $A_2 = -\tan^{-1}(\frac{\sqrt{2}}{2}) + \frac{\pi}{4}$, $A_{net} =$
$A_1 - A_2 = \tan^{-1}(\frac{\sqrt{2}}{2})$

57. $A = A_{net} = \frac{135}{56}$ **59.** $-\frac{1}{8}\cos 8x + C$

61. $-\frac{5}{4}e^{-4x/5} + C$ **63.** $\frac{1}{3}(x + 3)^3 + C$

65. $\ln|x + 7| + C$ **67.** $\frac{1}{2}\sin(2x + 3) + C$

69. $\frac{1}{3}\ln|3x + 1| + C$ **71.** $\frac{1}{44}(2x + 5)^{22} + C$

73. $\frac{1}{3}\tan^{-1}(3x) + C$ **75.** $\frac{1}{2}\tan^{-1}(2x + 5) + C$

77. $-\frac{6}{5}e^{-5x/6 + 1} + C$

CHAPTER 5: Answers to Odd Exercises

Exercises: 5.1

1. $a = -2$, $b = 6$, $\Delta x = 1$

x_i	$f(x_i)$	$g(x_i)$	h	$h\Delta x$
-1	8	1	7	7
0	12	0	12	12
1	16	1	15	15
2	20	4	16	16
3	24	9	15	15
4	28	16	12	12
5	32	25	7	7
6	36	36	0	0
			Total	84

The approximations using, 8, rectangles is, 84

The approximations using, 32, rectangles is, 85.25

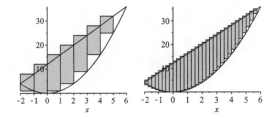

3. $c = -4$, $d = 4$, $\Delta y = 1$

y_i	$v(y_i)$	$k(y_i)$	w	$w\Delta y$
-3	21	-28	49	49
-2	24	-48	72	72
-1	15	-60	75	75
0	0	-64	64	64
1	-15	-60	45	45
2	-24	-48	24	24
3	-21	-28	7	7
4	0	0	0	0
			Total	336

The approximations using, 8, rectangles is, 336

The approximations using, 32, rectangles is, 341

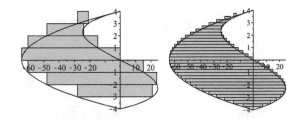

5. $A = \int_{-1}^{2}(x + 2 - x^2)\,dx = \frac{9}{2}$

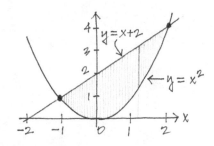

7. $A = \int_{-1}^{2}(-2x^2 - 2x + 4)\,dx = 9$

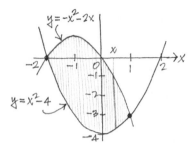

9. $A = \int_{-1}^{1} (1 + x - x^2 - x^3)\, dx = \frac{4}{3}$

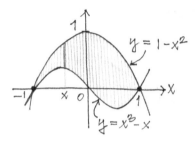

11. $A = \int_{0}^{1} \left(\frac{2}{x+1} - \sqrt{x} \right) dx = 2\ln 2 - \frac{2}{3}$

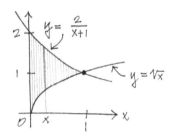

13. $A = \int_{0}^{\ln 2} (2 - e^x)\, dx = \ln 4 - 1$

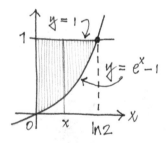

15. $A = \int_{0}^{\pi/6} (\cos x - \sin 2x)\, dx + \int_{\pi/6}^{\pi/2} (\sin 2x - \cos x)\, dx =$
$\frac{1}{4} + \frac{1}{4} = \frac{1}{2}$

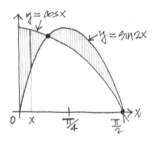

17. $A = \int_{-\pi/3}^{\pi/3} (2 - \sec x)\, dx = \frac{4\pi}{3} + 2\ln(2 - \sqrt{3})$

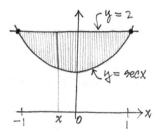

19. $A = \int_{-4}^{4} (x^3 - 4x^2 - 16x + 64)\, dx = \frac{1024}{3}$

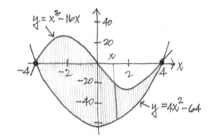

21. $A = \int_{0}^{3} x\, dx + \int_{1}^{2} \frac{1}{x}\, dx = \frac{1}{2} + \ln 3$

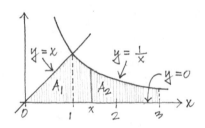

23. $A = \int_{0}^{1} 2x\, dx + \int_{1}^{3} (3 - x)\, dx = 1 + 2 = 3$

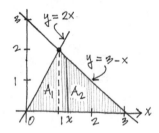

25. $A = \int_{1}^{2} \frac{18}{5}(x-1)\, dx + \int_{2}^{6} -\frac{9}{10}(x-6)\, dx = \frac{9}{5} + \frac{36}{5} = 9$

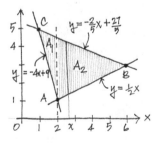

27. $A = \int_{1}^{4} \left[\left(\frac{1}{2}x + 3 \right) - \left(\frac{1}{2}x + 1 \right) \right] dx = \int_{1}^{4} 2\, dx = 6$

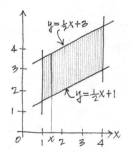

29. $A = \int_0^1 (x+1)\,dx + \int_1^2 2(2-x)\,dx = \frac{3}{2} + 1 = \frac{5}{2}$

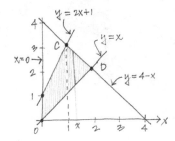

31. $A = \int_{-2}^1 2(x+2)\,dx + \int_1^3 (x+6-x^2)\,dx = 9 + \frac{22}{3} = \frac{49}{3}$

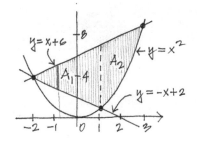

33. $A = \int_0^1 (2-y-y^2)\,dy = \frac{7}{6}$

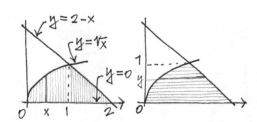

35. $A = \int_1^2 \left[\frac{4}{y^2} - \frac{1}{2}y\right] dy = \frac{5}{4}$

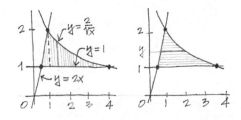

37. $A = \int_0^1 (e^y - \sqrt{y})\,dy = e - \frac{5}{3}$

39. $A = \int_{-1}^1 (y+1-y^{1/3})\,dy = 2$

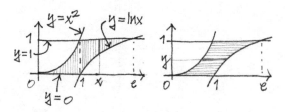

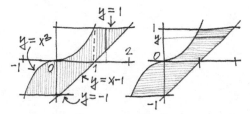

41. $A = \int_1^2 (2+y^{1/2} - y^{1/3})\,dy = \frac{4\sqrt{2}}{3} + \frac{3\sqrt[3]{2}}{2} + \frac{23}{12}$

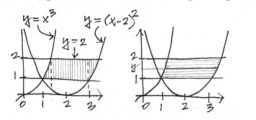

43. $A = \int_0^{\pi/2} (1 - \sin y)\,dy = \frac{\pi}{2} - 1$

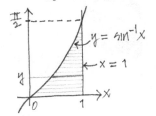

45. $A = \int_0^{\ln 3} (3 - e^y)\,dy = \ln 9 - 2$

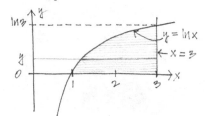

47. $A = \int_0^{\ln 2} (2e^y - e^{2y})\,dy = \frac{1}{2}$

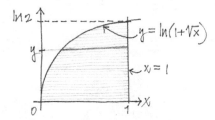

Exercises: 5.2

1. $\frac{320\pi}{3}$ in^3 **3.** 144π m^3

5. $V = \int_0^{40} 20(3 + \frac{1}{8}x)\,dx = 4800\,\text{ft}^3$

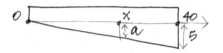

7. $V = \int_0^{10} \frac{1}{50}x^2\,dx = \frac{20}{3}\,\text{ft}^3$

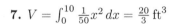

9. $V_1 = \int_0^{500}(34 + \frac{21}{500}x)^2\,dx = 1,008,500\,\text{ft}^3$

$V_2 = \int_0^{55}(\frac{34}{55})^2 x^2\,dx = 21,193\,\text{ft}^3,\ V = V_1 + V_2$

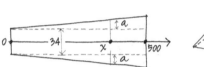

11. $V = \int_0^1 4(1-x^2)^2\,dx = \int_0^1 4(1-2x^2+x^4)\,dx = \frac{32}{15}$

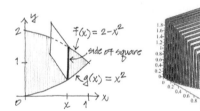

13. $V = \int_0^1 \frac{\sqrt{3}}{4}(1-x^3)^2\,dx = \int_0^1 \frac{\sqrt{3}}{4}(1-2x^3+x^6)\,dx$

$= \frac{9\sqrt{3}}{56}$

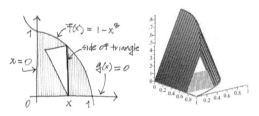

15. $V = \int_0^{\pi/4} \frac{\pi}{8}(1 - 2\sin x \cos x)\,dx = \frac{\pi}{32}(\pi - 2)$

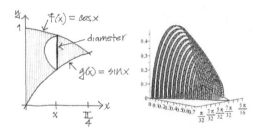

17. $V = \int_0^{\pi/2} \frac{\pi}{8}(\frac{3}{2} - 2\sin x - \frac{1}{2}\cos 2x)\,dx = \frac{3\pi}{4} - 2$

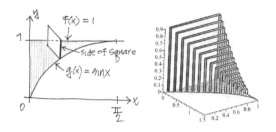

19. $V = \int_0^1 \frac{1}{2}(e^{2x} - 2 + e^{-2x})\,dx = \frac{1}{8}(e^2 - e^{-2}) - \frac{1}{2}$

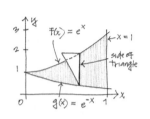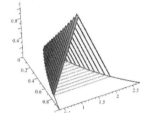

21. $V = \int_0^1 \frac{1}{3}(\sqrt{x} + x)^3\,dx$

$= \int_0^1 \frac{1}{3}(x^{3/2} + 3x^2 + 3x^{5/2} + x^3)\,dx = \frac{117}{140}$

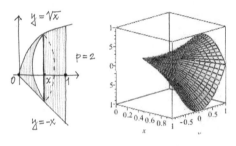

23. $V = \int_0^\pi \frac{8}{3}\sin^3 x\,dx = \frac{32}{9}$

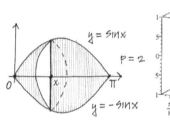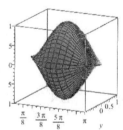

25. $V = \int_0^1 \frac{16}{5}x^{5/2}\,dx = \frac{32}{35}$

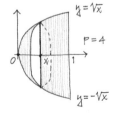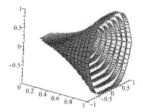

27. $V = \int_0^1 \frac{16}{5}(1-x)^5\,dx = \frac{8}{15}$

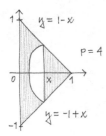
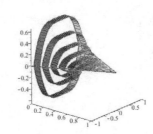

29. $V = \int_0^1 \frac{4}{3} x^{3/2}\, dx = \frac{8}{15}$

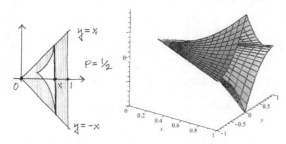

31. $V = \frac{1}{5}(\text{Area of Base})(\text{Height}) = \frac{800}{3}\,\text{ft}^3$

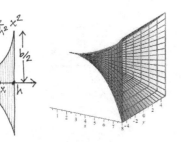

33. $V = \frac{1}{2}(\text{Area of Base})(\text{Height}) = 400\,\text{ft}^3$

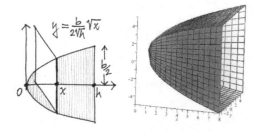

35. $V = 400\,\text{ft}^3$

37. $V = \frac{2}{5}(\text{Area of Base})(\text{Height}) = \frac{3200}{3}\,\text{ft}^3$

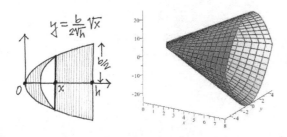

39. $V = \int_0^1 (4x^2 - 4x^4)\, dx = \frac{8}{15}$

41. $V = \int_0^1 \left[2\cos(\pi x/2) - \frac{1}{2} - \frac{1}{2}\cos \pi x\right] dx = \frac{4}{\pi} - \frac{1}{2}$

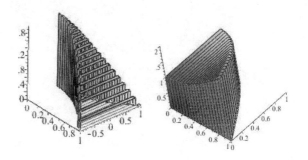

#39   #41

43. $V = \int_0^1 (1 - x)\, dx = \frac{1}{2}$

45. $V = \int_0^1 (1 - e^{-4x})\, dx = \frac{3}{4} + \frac{1}{4}e^{-4}$

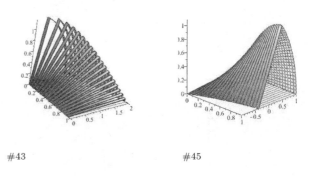

#43   #45

Exercises: 5.3

1. $V = \int_0^1 \pi(1 - 2\sqrt{x} + x)\, dx = \frac{\pi}{6}$

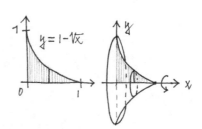

3. $V = \int_0^3 \pi(16x^2 - 8x^3 + x^4)\, dx = \frac{153\pi}{5}$

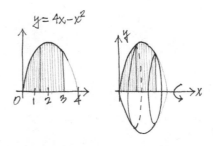

5. $V = \int_{-1}^1 \pi(x^6 + 2x^3 + 1)\, dx = \frac{16\pi}{7}$

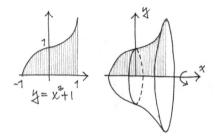

7. $V = \int_{1/2}^{4} \pi (\frac{1}{16}x^2 + \frac{1}{2} + x^{-2}) \, dx = \frac{1855\pi}{384}$

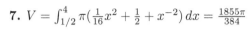

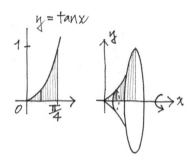

17. $V = \int_{0}^{\pi} \pi \sin^2 x \, dx = \frac{\pi^2}{2}$

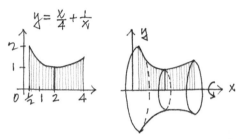

9. $V = \int_{1/2}^{2} \pi (\frac{1}{9}x^6 + \frac{1}{6}x^2 + \frac{1}{16}x^{-2}) \, dx = \frac{6889\pi}{2688}$

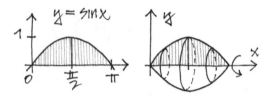

19. $V = \int_{0}^{\pi} \pi (4 + 4\sin x + \sin^2 x) \, dx = 9\pi^2$

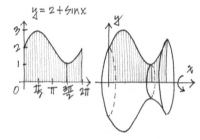

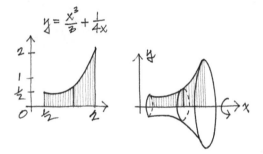

11. $V = \int_{-1}^{1} \pi (e^{2x} + 2 + e^{-2x}) \, dx = \pi(e^2 + 4 - e^{-2})$

21. (a) $V = \int_{0}^{h} \pi r^2 \, dx = \pi r^2 h$

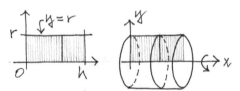

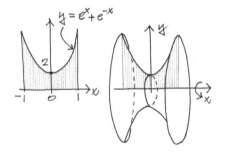

(b) $V = \int_{0}^{h} \frac{\pi r^2}{h^2} x^2 \, dx = \frac{1}{3}\pi r^2 h$

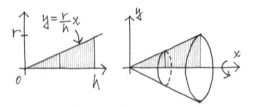

13. $V = \int_{-\pi/3}^{\pi/3} \pi \sec^2 x \, dx = 2\pi\sqrt{3}$

(c) $V = \int_{-r}^{r} \pi (r^2 - x^2) \, dx = \frac{4}{3}\pi r^3$

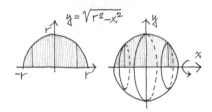

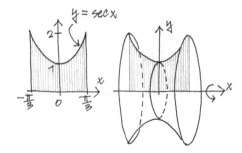

15. $V = \int_{0}^{\pi/4} \pi \tan^2 x \, dx = \pi(1 - \frac{\pi}{4})$

23. $V_{exact} = \frac{\pi}{6} \approx 0.5236$ (From Exercise 1)

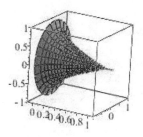

$$V_5 = 0.3158 \qquad V_{10} = 0.4052$$

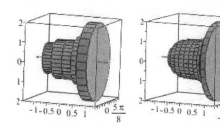

29. $V_{exact} = \frac{1855\pi}{384} \approx 15.176$ (From Exercise 7)

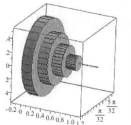 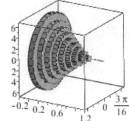

25. $V_{exact} = \frac{153\pi}{5} \approx 96.133$ (From Exercise 3)

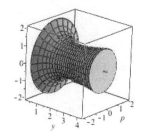

$$V_5 = 13.61792884 \qquad V_{10} = 14.03976265$$

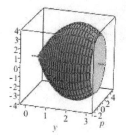

$$V_5 = 103.44347 \qquad V_{10} = 100.0885873$$

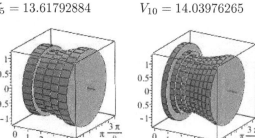

31. $V_{exact} = \frac{6889\pi}{2688} \approx 8.05$ (From Exercise 9)

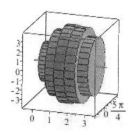 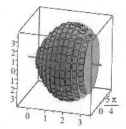

27. $V_{exact} = \frac{16\pi}{7} \approx 7.18$ (From Exercise 5)

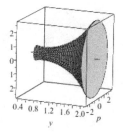

$$V_5 = 12.11783954 \qquad V_{10} = 9.952598843$$

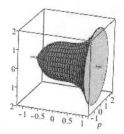

$$V_5 = 10.17051666 \qquad V_{10} = 8.561418036$$

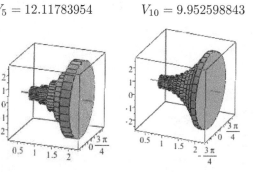

33. $V_{exact} = \pi(e^2 - e^{-2} + 4) \approx 35.36$ (From Exercise 11)

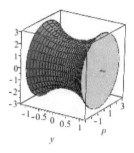

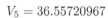

$V_5 = 36.55720967$ $V_{10} = 35.65764260$

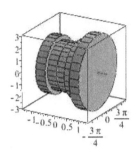   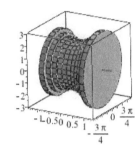

35. $V_{exact} = 2\pi\sqrt{3} \approx 10.88$ (From Exercise 13)

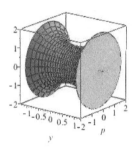

$V_5 = 12.03577027$ $V_{10} = 11.19178015$

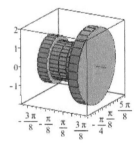   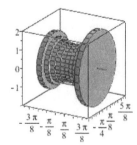

37. $V_{exact} = \pi(1 - \frac{\pi}{4}) \approx 0.6742$ (From Exercise 15)

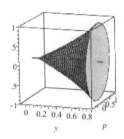

$V_5 = 0.9465634926$ $V_{10} = 0.8040080616$

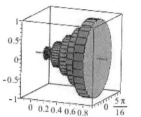   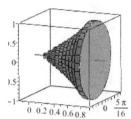

39. $V_{exact} = \pi^2/2 \approx 4.935$ (From Exercise 17)

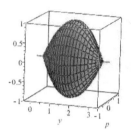

$V_5 = 4.934802203$ $V_{10} = 4.934802201$

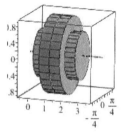   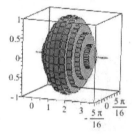

41. $V_{exact} = 9\pi^2 \approx 88.82$ (From Exercise 19)

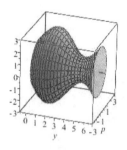

$V_5 = 88.82643965$ $V_{10} = 88.82643960$

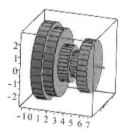   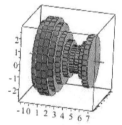

Exercises: 5.4

1. $V = \int_0^4 \pi(x - \frac{1}{16}x^2)\,dx = \frac{20\pi}{3}$

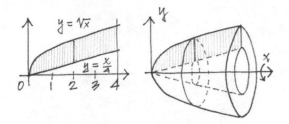

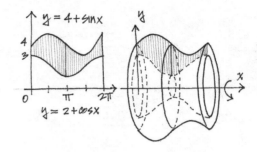

3. $V = \int_0^1 \pi(4 + 4x^2 + x^4 - e^{-2x})\,dx = (\frac{83}{15} + \frac{1}{2}e^{-2})\pi$

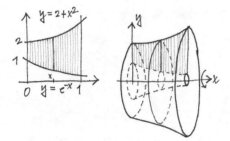

13. $V = \int_0^{\pi/4} \pi(2 + \sec^2 x)\,dx = \pi(\frac{\pi}{2} + 1)$

5. $V = \int_{-2}^1 \pi(16 - 6x - 11x^2 + x^4)\,dx = \frac{153\pi}{5}$

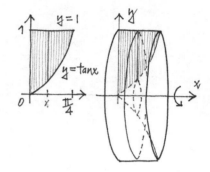

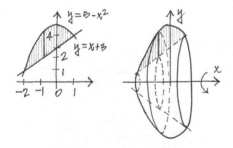

15. $V = \int_0^1 \pi(3 - 4x + x^2 + 2e^{-x} - e^{-2x})\,dx$

$= \pi(\frac{17}{6} - 2e^{-1} + \frac{1}{2}e^{-2})$

7. $V = \int_{-2}^2 \pi(64 - 16x^2)\,dx = \frac{512\pi}{3}$

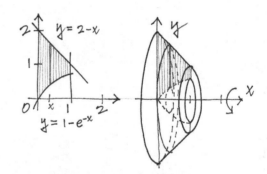

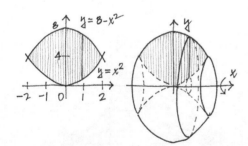

17. $V = \int_0^{\pi/3} \pi(\sec^2 x - \frac{1}{2} - \frac{1}{2}\cos 2x)\,dx$

$= \pi(\frac{7\sqrt{3}}{8} - \frac{\pi}{6})$

9. $V = \int_0^1 \pi(\frac{3}{2} + 2\sin \pi x - \frac{1}{2}\cos 2\pi x - x^2)\,dx = (\frac{7}{6} + \frac{4}{\pi})\pi$

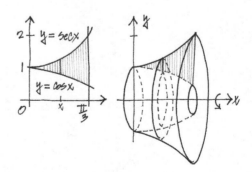

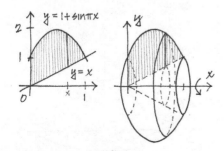

19. $V = \int_1^2 \pi(1 + 2\sqrt{y} + y + y^{2/3})\,dy$

$= \pi[\frac{17}{30} + \frac{8\sqrt{2}}{3} + \frac{6(2^{2/3})}{5}]$

11. $V = \int_0^\pi \pi(12 + 8\sin x - 4\cos x - \cos 2x)\,dx$

$= \pi(12\pi + 16)$

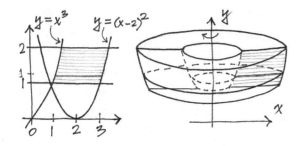

21. $V = \int_0^1 \pi(e^{2y} - y)\, dy = \pi(\frac{e^2}{2} - 1)$

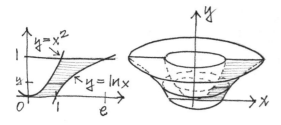

23. $V = \int_0^{\pi/2} \pi(\frac{1}{2} + \frac{1}{2}\cos 2y)\, dy = \frac{\pi^2}{4}$

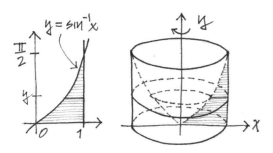

25. $V = \int_0^{\ln 2} \pi(2 - e^y)\, dy = \pi(\ln 4 - 1)$

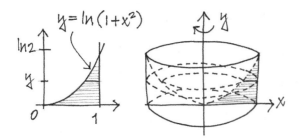

27. $V = \int_0^1 2\pi(2x - x^4 - x^{3/2})\, dx = \frac{4\pi}{5}$

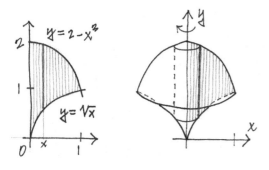

29. $V = \int_0^1 2\pi(2x - x^3 - x^4)\, dx = \frac{11\pi}{10}$

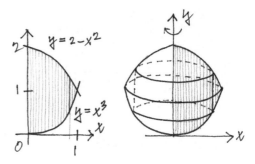

31. $V = \int_0^4 2\pi(4x^3 - x^3)\, dx = \frac{128\pi}{3}$

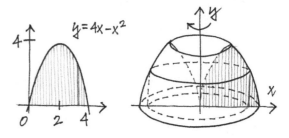

33. $V = \int_0^4 2\pi(x^4 - 5x^3 + 6x^2 + x)\, dx = \frac{117\pi}{10}$

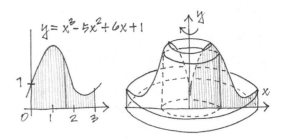

35. $V = \int_0^2 \frac{4\pi x}{1 + x^2}\, dx = 2\pi \ln 5$

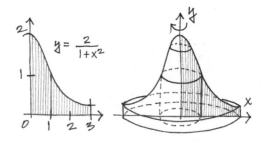

37. $V = \int_0^2 2\pi x e^{-x^2}\, dx = \pi(1 - e^{-4})$

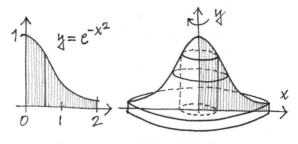

39. $V = \int_1^2 \frac{2\pi x}{3 - x}\, dx = 2\pi(1 + \ln 8)$

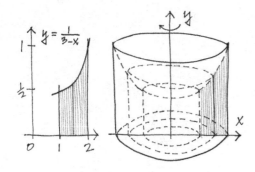

41. $V = \int_1^2 2\pi(x + x^2 + x^3)\, dx = \frac{13\pi}{6}$

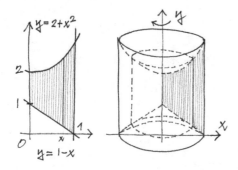

43. $V = \int_0^4 2\pi(6x - x^2 - x^{3/2})\, dx = \frac{416\pi}{15}$

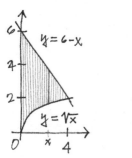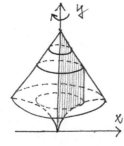

45. $V = \int_0^{3/4} \dfrac{2\pi x}{\sqrt{1 - x^2}}\, dx = 2\pi\left(1 - \frac{\sqrt{7}}{4}\right)$

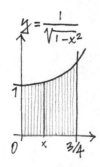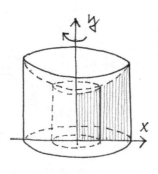

47. $V = \int_0^{\sqrt{\pi}} 2\pi x \sin(x^2)\, dx = 2\pi$

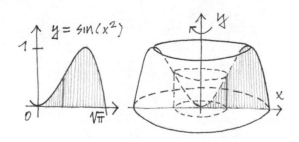

49. $V = \int_0^{\pi/3} \pi \sec^2 x \tan^2 x\, dx = \pi\sqrt{3}$

51. $V = \int_0^{\pi/3} \pi \sin^2 x \cos x\, dx = \frac{\pi\sqrt{3}}{2}$

53. $V = \int_0^1 \pi x^2 (1 + x^2)^{1/2}\, dx = \frac{2\pi}{9}(2\sqrt{2} - 1)$

55. $V = \int_0^2 \dfrac{6\pi x^2}{1 + x^3}\, dx = 2\pi \ln 9$

57. $V = \int_1^2 2\pi x^{-2} e^{x^{-1}}\, dx = 2\pi(e - e^{1/2})$

59. $V = \int_{0.4}^1 2\pi x^{-2} \sin^2(x^{-1})\, dx = \pi(\frac{1}{2}\sin 2 - \frac{1}{2}\sin 5 + \frac{3}{2})$

61. $V = \int_1^4 2\pi[x + x^{-1/2}\sin(10 + 10\sqrt{x})]\, dx$
$= \pi(15 + \frac{2}{5}\cos 20 - \frac{2}{5}\sin 30)$

63. washer: $V = \int_0^1 \pi(1 - y^{2/3})\, dy = \frac{2\pi}{5}$

shell: $\int_0^1 2\pi x^4\, dx = \frac{2\pi}{5}$

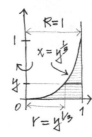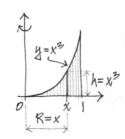
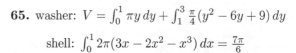

65. washer: $V = \int_0^1 \pi y\, dy + \int_1^3 \frac{\pi}{4}(y^2 - 6y + 9)\, dy$

shell: $\int_0^1 2\pi(3x - 2x^2 - x^3)\, dx = \frac{7\pi}{6}$

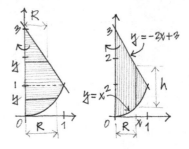

67. washer: $V = \int_0^{1/2} 9\pi\, dy + \int_{1/2}^1 \pi(y^{-4} - 2y^{-2} + 1)\, dy$

shell: $\int_0^3 \dfrac{2\pi x}{\sqrt{x + 1}}\, dx = \frac{16\pi}{3}$

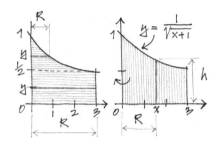

69. washer: $V = \int_0^1 \pi(y^2 + 2y + 1 - y^{2/3})\,dy$

shell: $\displaystyle\int_0^1 2\pi x^4\,dx + \int_1^2 2\pi(2x - x^2)\,dx = \frac{26\pi}{15}$

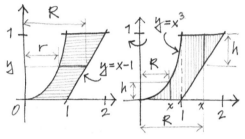

71. washer: $V = \int_0^{1/2} \pi(4 - y^2)\,dy + \int_{1/2}^1 \pi(y^{-2} - y^2)\,dy$

shell: $\displaystyle\int_0^1 2\pi x^2\,dx + \int_1^2 2\pi\,dx = \frac{8\pi}{3}$

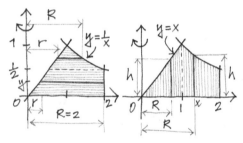

75. $\int_0^4 \pi(8 - 6\sqrt{x} + x)\,dx = 8\pi$

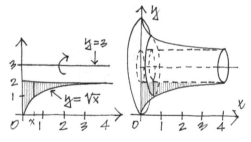

77. $\int_0^1 \pi(2 - 3x - \sqrt{x} + x^2 + x^{3/2})\,dx = \frac{17\pi}{15}$

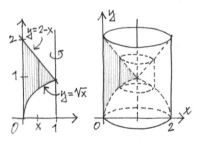

79. $\int_0^1 2\pi(3 + 4x^2 + x^4 - e^{-2x} + 2e^{-x})\,dx$

$= (\frac{61}{30} + \frac{1}{2}e^{-2} + 2e^{-1})\pi$

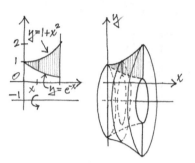

81. $\int_0^1 \pi(4 - 4x + x^2 - x^4)\,dx = \frac{32\pi}{15}$

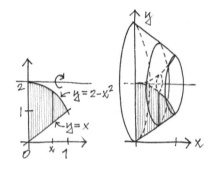

83. $\int_0^1 \pi(5 - 2x + 6x^2 - 2x^3 + x^4)\,dx = \frac{57\pi}{10}$

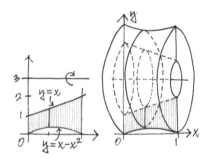

85. $\int_0^1 2\pi(3x - x^2)\,dx + \int_1^2 2\pi(3x^{-1} - 1)\,dx$

$= (\ln 64 + \frac{1}{3})\pi$

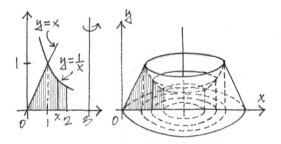

87. $\int_0^1 \pi(\frac{9}{2} - 4\sin(\pi x/2) - \frac{1}{2}\cos \pi x - x^2)\,dx$

$= \frac{25\pi}{6} - 8$

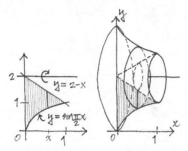

89. $\int_0^{\pi/4} \pi(-2\sin x + 2\cos x - \cos 2x)\,dx$
$= \left(2\sqrt{2} - \frac{5}{2}\right)\pi$

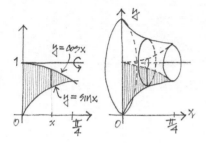

91. $\int_0^1 \pi(-4\tan x + 4\sec x - 1)\,dx$
$= 4\pi \ln(1 + \sqrt{2}/2) - \pi^2/4$

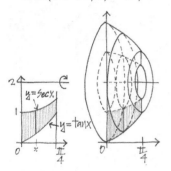

93. $\int_{-1}^1 2\pi(1 - 2x^2 + x^4)\,dx = \frac{32\pi}{15}$

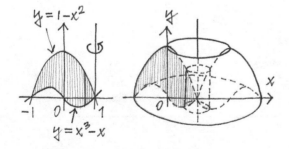

95. $\int_0^\pi 2\pi x^2 \sin x\,dx$

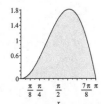

$V_8 = 36.08335116,\ V_{20} = 36.75231535$

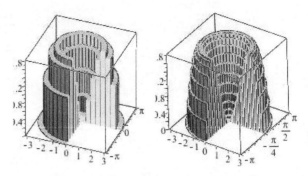

$V_{100} = 36.87471183,\ V_{200} = 36.87853702,$
$V_{800} = 36.87973249$

97. $\int_0^2 6\pi x^2 e^{-x}\,dx$

$V_8 = 13.46387863,\ V_{20} = 12.69919754$

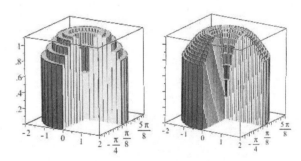

$V_{100} = 12.29105233,\ V_{200} = 12.24003212,$
$V_{800} = 12.20176702$

Exercises: 5.5

1. $L = \int_0^{\pi/3} \sec x\,dx = \ln(2 + \sqrt{3})$

3. $L = \int_{-2}^2 \cosh x\,dx = 2\sinh 2$

5. $L = \int_1^2 \frac{x}{\sqrt{x^2 - 1}}\,dx = \sqrt{3}$

7. $L = \int_0^{\ln 2} \frac{e^x}{\sqrt{e^{2x} - 1}}\,dx = \ln(2 + \sqrt{3})$

9. $L = \int_1^3 \left(x^2 + \frac{1}{4x^2}\right)dx = \frac{53}{6}$

11. $L = \int_1^2 \left(x^3 + \frac{1}{4x^3}\right)dx = \frac{123}{32}$

13. $L = \int_1^3 \left(x^4 + \frac{1}{4x^4}\right)dx = \frac{3011}{480}$

15. $L = \int_1^4 (x^{3/2} + \frac{1}{4}x^{-3/2})\,dx = \frac{253}{20}$

17. $L = \int_1^4 \left(\frac{1}{x} + \frac{1}{4}x\right)dx = \ln 4 + \frac{15}{8}$

19. $L = \int_0^{\pi/4} \left(\dfrac{\sec^2 x}{\tan x} + \dfrac{1}{4} \sin x \cos x \right) dx = \dfrac{1}{16}$

21. $L = \int_0^{\pi/4} \left(\cos x + \dfrac{1}{4} \sec x \right) dx = \dfrac{\sqrt{2}}{2} + \dfrac{1}{4} \ln(\sqrt{2} + 1)$

23. $L = \int_0^1 \left(1 + x^2 + \dfrac{1}{4} \cdot \dfrac{1}{1+x^2} \right) dx = \dfrac{4}{3} + \dfrac{\pi}{16}$

25. $L = \int_1^4 \left(\dfrac{1}{1+\sqrt{x}} \cdot \dfrac{1}{2\sqrt{x}} + \dfrac{1}{2} x^{1/2} + \dfrac{1}{2} x \right) dx$
$= \ln(3/2) + \dfrac{73}{12}$

27. $L = \int_1^2 \left(4y^3 - \dfrac{1}{16} y^{-2} \right) dy = \dfrac{1923}{128}$

29. $L = \int_1^2 \left(\dfrac{1}{2} e^{y/2} + \dfrac{1}{2} e^{-y/2} \right) dy = e^{1/2} - e^{-1/2}$

31. $L = \int_0^2 \left(\dfrac{1}{(y+1)^2} + \dfrac{1}{4}(y+1)^2 \right) dy = \dfrac{5}{4}$

33. $s(x) = -\ln|\csc x + \cot x| = \ln\left(\dfrac{\sin x}{1+\cos x} \right)$
$s(3\pi/4) = \ln\left(\dfrac{\sqrt{2}}{2-\sqrt{2}} \right) \approx 0.8814$

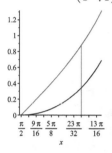

35. $s(x) = \sinh x$
$s(1) = \sinh(1) \approx 1.175$

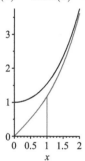

37. $s(x) = \arcsin x.$ $s(0.4) = \arcsin(0.4) \approx 0.412$

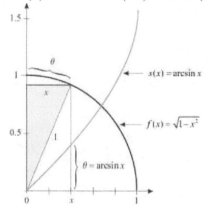

39. $L = \int_0^1 \sqrt{1 + 9x^4}\, dx = 1.547865654 \cdots$
$L_{10} = 1.546816956$

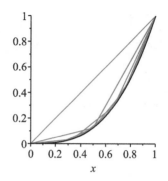

$L_{50} = 1.547823663, L_{100} = 1.547855156$

41. $L = \int_0^\pi \sqrt{1 + \cos^2 x}\, dx = 3.820197788 \cdots$
$L_{10} = 3.815282727$

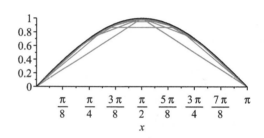

$L_{50} = 3.820000724, L_{100} = 3.820148519$

43. $L = \int_0^1 \sqrt{1 + x^{2\sin x} \left[\cos x \ln x + \dfrac{\sin x}{x} \right]^2}\, dx$
$= 4.965332812 \cdots, L_{10} = 4.940733719$

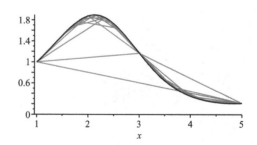

$L_{50} = 4.964317450, L_{100} = 4.965078822$

45. $f'(x) = g'(x) + h'(x) = g'(x) - \dfrac{1}{4g'(x)}$. So,
$1 + [f'(x)]^2 = 1 + [g'(x) - \dfrac{1}{4g'(x)}]^2 = [g'(x) + \dfrac{1}{4g'(x)}]^2$
$= [g'(x) - h'(x)]^2$. Then,
$s(x) = g(x) - h(x) - g(a) + h(a)$.

47. A sketch of a hypothetical f and f^{-1}:

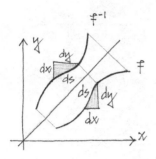

Use the inverse function derivative formula to get
$$\sqrt{1+[(f^{-1})'(z)]^2} = \sqrt{1+1/[f'(f^{-1}(z))]^2}$$
$$= \sqrt{\frac{1+[f'(f^{-1}(z))]^2}{[f'(f^{-1}(z))]^2}} = \frac{\sqrt{1+[f'(f^{-1}(z))]^2}}{f'(f^{-1}(z))}$$

In the integral use a substitution: $u = f^{-1}(z)$ to get the result.

Exercises: 5.6

1. $S = \int_0^1 2\pi x^3 \sqrt{1+9x^4}\, dx = \dfrac{\pi}{27}(10\sqrt{10}-1)$

3. $S = \int_1^4 \pi\sqrt{4x+1}\, dx = \dfrac{\pi}{6}(17\sqrt{17}-5\sqrt{5})$

5. $S = \int_1^2 \pi\big(\frac{1}{2}x^7 + \frac{3}{8}x + \frac{1}{16}x^{-5}\big)\, dx = \dfrac{16,911\pi}{1024}$

7. $S = \int_1^2 2\pi\big(e^{2x} + \frac{1}{2} + \frac{1}{16}e^{-2x}\big)\, dx = \pi\big(e^2 - \frac{1}{16}e^{-2} + \frac{1}{16}\big)$

9. $S = \int_1^4 \pi\big(1 + \frac{2}{3}x - \frac{1}{3}x^2\big)\, dx = \pi$

11. $S = \int_1^2 2\pi\big(\frac{2}{5}x^4 + \frac{3}{5}x + \frac{1}{8}x^{-2}\big)\, dx = \dfrac{1377\pi}{200}$

13. $b = \pi/30 \approx 0.105$ cm, $a = 30/\pi \approx 9.55$ cm, $ab = 1$
$$S = \int_0^{\pi/b} 2\pi a \sin bx \sqrt{1+\cos^2 bx}\, dx$$
$$= 2\pi a^2\big[\sqrt{2} + \ln(\sqrt{2}+1)\big] \approx 1315.3 \text{ cm}^2$$

15. $a = 2$ m, $b = 4$ m
$$S = \int_0^4 \pi\sqrt{17-4x}\, dx = \dfrac{\pi}{6}(17\sqrt{17}-1) \approx 36.177 \text{ m}^2$$

17. A sketch of a hypothetical f and f^{-1}:

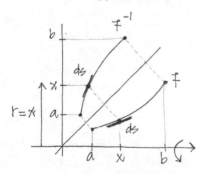

Use the inverse function derivative formula to get

$$\sqrt{1+[(f^{-1})'(z)]^2} = \sqrt{1+1/[f'(f^{-1}(z))]^2}$$
$$= \sqrt{\frac{1+[f'(f^{-1}(z))]^2}{[f'(f^{-1}(z))]^2}} = \frac{\sqrt{1+[f'(f^{-1}(z))]^2}}{f'(f^{-1}(z))}$$

In the integral use a substitution: $u = f^{-1}(z)$ to get the result.

19. $S_{inv} = \int_1^4 2\pi\big(x^3 + \frac{1}{4x}\big)\, dx = \big(\dfrac{255}{2} + \ln 2\big)\pi$

21. $S_{inv} = \int_1^2 \pi\big(2x^4 + \frac{1}{2x^2}\big)\, dx = \dfrac{253\pi}{20}$

23. $S_{inv} = \int_1^4 \pi\big(\sqrt{x} + x^{3/2}\big)\, dx = \dfrac{256\pi}{15}$

25. $S_{inv} = \int_1^8 \pi\big(2x^{7/3} + \frac{1}{2}x^{-1/3}\big)\, dx = \dfrac{12,351\pi}{20}$

27. $S_{inv} = \int_1^4 \pi\big(4x^2 + \frac{1}{4}\big)\, dx = \dfrac{1017\pi}{12}$

29. $S = \int_0^1 2\pi x^4 \sqrt{1+16x^6}\, dx = 3.436526697\cdots$

$S_{25} = 3.437928102$. The 25 frusta approximation:

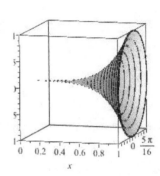

$S_{50} = 3.436877081$, $S_{100} = 3.436614297$

31. $S = \int_0^\pi 2\pi \sin^2 x \sqrt{1+\sin^2 2x}\, dx = 12.00150531\cdots$

$S_{25} = 11.99161425$. The 25 frusta approximation:

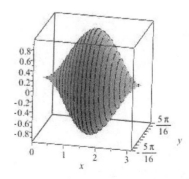

$S_{50} = 11.99902963$, $S_{100} = 12.00088621$
$S_{150} = 12.00123014$, $S_{200} = 12.00135056$

33. $f'(x) = g'(x) + h'(x) = g'(x) - \frac{1}{4g'(x)}$. So,
$$1 + [f'(x)]^2 = 1 + \big[g'(x) - \tfrac{1}{4g'(x)}\big]^2 = \big[g'(x) + \tfrac{1}{4g'(x)}\big]^2$$

$= [g'(x) - h'(x)]^2$. Then,

$$S = \int_a^b 2\pi \big[g(x) + h(x) \big] \big[g'(x) - h'(x) \big] \, dx$$

$$= \pi \big[(g(x))^2 - (h(x))^2 + 2g(x)h(x) + k(x) \big] \Big|_a^b$$

35. A sketch of a hypothetical C and C^{-1}:

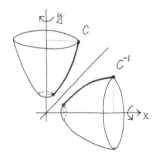

(a) Take $C = f$. Then $C^{-1} = f^{-1}$. The surface areas are the same and by Exercise 17 these are

$$S_{inv} = \int_a^b 2\pi x \sqrt{1 + [f'(x)]^2} \, dx$$

(b) Take $C = f^{-1}$. Then $C^{-1} = f$. The surface areas are the same and by the reading material these are

$$S = \int_a^b 2\pi f(x) \sqrt{1 + [f'(x)]^2} \, dx$$

Exercises: 5.7

1. 140 ft-lb **3.** $W = \sum_{i=1}^{12} 25\left(\frac{4i}{12}\right) = 650$ ft-lb

5. $W = \sum_{i=1}^{12} 7.2\left(\frac{4+3i}{12}\right) = 169.2$ ft-lb   **7.** $25/8$ ft-lb

9. 79.5 N-m **11.** 71,568 ft-lb. Not leaking: 72,000 ft-lb

13. 1000 ft-lb   **15.** $W = \int_0^{10}(10 - x)9200\pi\left(\frac{4}{25}x^2\right) dx$

$= \frac{3,680,000\pi}{3}$ N-m   **17.** $W = \int_0^{15}(30 - x)60\pi(144) \, dx$

$= 291,600\pi$ ft-lb   **19.** $W = \int_0^{16}(16 - x)42\pi(4x) \, dx$

$= 114,688\pi$ ft-lb   **21.** $W = \int_0^4(4-x)9200\pi\left(\frac{1}{64}x^4\right) dx$

$= 58,880\pi$ N-m   **23.** $F = \int_0^2 512(8 - x) \, dx = 6144$ lb

25. $F = \int_0^2 63(4x - x^2) \, dx = 1024/3 \approx 341.33$ lb

27. $F = \int_0^2 64(8 - 6x + x^2) \, dx = 1280/3 \approx 426.67$ lb

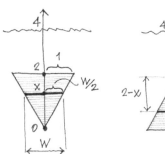
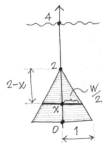

#25   #27

29. $F = \int_0^2 128(8 - 6x + x^2) \, dx = 2560/3 \approx 853.33$ lb

31. $F = \int_0^2 64(10x^2 - x^3) \, dx = 4352/3 \approx 1450.67$ lb

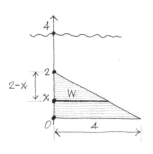
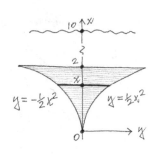

#29   #31

33. $F = \int_0^1 128(10x^{1/2} - x^{3/2}) \, dx = 12032/15 \approx 802.33$

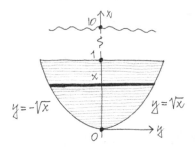

#33

35. $F = \int_0^2 64(24 - 4x - 6x^2 + x^3) \, dx = 1792$ lb

37. $F = \int_0^4 128(20 - 10x^{1/2} - 2x + x^{3/2}) \, dx = 352/15$

≈ 23.47 lb

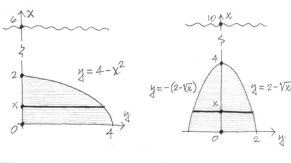

#35   #37

39. $F = \int_0^{400} 62(640000 - 2200x + \frac{3}{2}x^2) \, dx = 6944 \cdot 10^6$

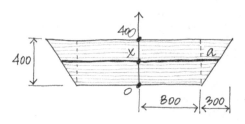

#39

Exercises: 5.8

1. 7.5 ft from the smaller child **3.** $M_2 = 74$, clockwise.

$M_6 = -30$, counterclockwise. $x^\star = 64/13$.

5. $x^\star = 4.5$, $y^\star = 3.8$ **7.** $X = 3.8$

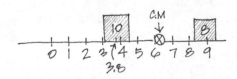

$x' = 55/9 = x^\star$ **9.** $X = 28/11, Y = 41/11$

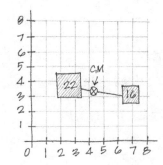

$x' = 84/19 = x^\star,\ y' = 65/19 = y^\star.$

11. $X = \dfrac{m_1 x_1 + m_2 x_2}{m_1 + m_2}$, $Y = \dfrac{m_1 y_1 + m_2 y_2}{m_1 + m_2}$. Let $M = m_1 + m_2$.

$x' = \dfrac{MX + m_3 x_3}{M + m_3} = \dfrac{(m_1 + m_2)\left(\frac{m_1 x_1 + m_2 x_2}{m_1 + m_2}\right) + m_3 x_3}{m_1 + m_2 + m_3} = x^\star$

$y' = \dfrac{MY + m_3 y_3}{M + m_3} = \dfrac{(m_1 + m_2)\left(\frac{m_1 y_1 + m_2 y_2}{m_1 + m_2}\right) + m_3 y_3}{m_1 + m_2 + m_3} = y^\star$

13. Let $m_1 = 12\rho$, $(x_1, y_1) = (1.5, 2)$ and

$m_2 = 6\rho$, $(x_2, y_2) = (4.5, 1)$. Then $x^\star = 2.5, y^\star = 1.67$.

15. Let $m_1 = 18.75\rho$, $(x_1, y_1) = (6.25, 7.75)$ and

$m_2 = 7\rho$, $(x_2, y_2) = (12, 3.5)$. Then $x^\star = 7.8, y^\star = 6.6$.

17. Rectangle: $m_1 = 12\rho, (x_1, y_1) = (1, 3)$.

Triangle: $m_2 = 9\rho, (x_2, y_2) = (4, 1)$.

Then $x^\star = 16/7 \approx 2.3, y^\star = 15/7 \approx 2.1$.

19. Rectangle: $m_1 = 24\rho, (x_1, y_1) = (2, 3)$

Circle: $m_2 = 4\pi\rho, (x_2, y_2) = (6, 4)$.

Then $x^\star = \dfrac{12 + 6\pi}{6 + \pi} \approx 3.4, y^\star = \dfrac{18 + 4\pi}{6 + \pi} \approx 3.3$.

21. $x^\star = 1.5, y^\star = 1.2$ **23.** $x^\star = 2.4, y^\star = 0.75$

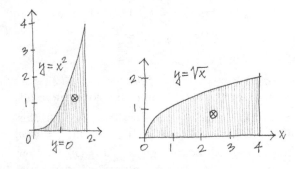

#21   #23

25. $x^\star = 2, y^\star = 1.6$ **27.** $x^\star = 1.2, y^\star = 0.5$

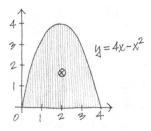   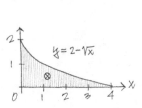

#25   #27

29. $x^\star = \dfrac{98}{33} \approx 3,\ y^\star = \dfrac{21 - \ln 4}{11} \approx 1.8$

31. $x^\star = \dfrac{8}{9 - 3\ln 4} \approx 1.65,\ y^\star = \dfrac{11}{6(3 - \ln 4)} \approx 1.14$

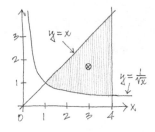   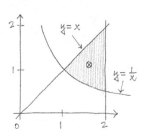

#29   #31

33. $x^\star = 0.56, y^\star = 1$ **35.** $x^\star = 0.55, y^\star = 0.9$

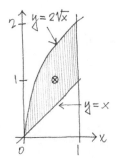   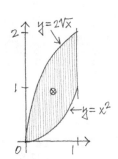

#33   #35

37. $x^\star = 1, y^\star = -0.6$ **39.** $x^\star = 2.9, y^\star = \dfrac{45 - 6\ln 4}{32}$

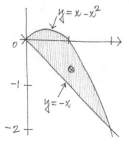   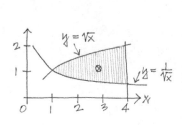

#37   #39

41. $x^\star = \dfrac{1}{2(4 - e)} \approx 0.4,\ y^\star = \dfrac{29 - 12e + e^2}{4(4 - e)} \approx 0.74$

43. $x^\star = \pi/2, y^\star = \pi/8 \approx 0.39$

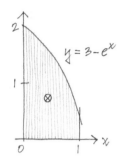

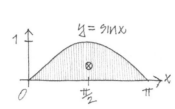

#41   #43

45. $x^\star = \frac{\pi}{2} \approx 1.57$, $y^\star = \frac{8+3\pi}{8+2\pi} \approx 1.22$

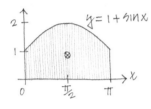

#45

CHAPTER 6: Answers to Odd Exercises

Exercises: 6.1

1. $u = x$, $I = -\frac{1}{2}x\cos 2x + \frac{1}{4}\sin 2x$

3. $u = x$, $I = \frac{1}{3}xe^{3x} - \frac{1}{9}e^{2x}$

5. $u = x$, $I = x\tan x - \ln|\sec x|$

7. $u = x$, $I = x\sec x - \ln|\sec x + \tan x|$

9. $u = x$, $I = -\dfrac{xe^x}{1+e^x} - \ln(1+e^x)$

11. $u = \ln(\sec x)$, $I = \ln(\sec x)\tan x - \tan x + x$

13. $u = \ln x$, $I = \frac{1}{4}x^4\ln x - \frac{1}{16}x^4$

15. $u = (\ln x)^2$, $I = \frac{1}{3}x^3(\ln x)^2 - \frac{2}{9}x^3\ln x + \frac{2}{27}x^3$

17. $u = (\ln x)^3$, $I = \frac{1}{3}x^3(\ln x)^3 - \frac{1}{3}x^3(\ln x)^2 - \frac{2}{27}x^3$

19. For $n \neq 1$, let $u = (\ln x)^p$. Then
$$I = \frac{1}{n+1}x^{n+1}(\ln x)^p - \frac{p}{n+1}\int x^n(\ln x)^{p-1}\,dx$$

21. $u = \ln(1+e^x)$, $I = -e^{-x}\ln(1+e^x) - \ln(1+e^x)$

23. $u = \ln x$, $I = \ln x\,\sin(\ln x) + \cos(\ln x)$

25. $u = \ln x$, $I = \ln x\,\tan(\ln x) - \ln|\sec(\ln x)|$

27. $u = \ln(\cos x)$, $I = \ln(\cos x)\tan x - x + \tan x$

29. $u = \ln(\cos x)$, $I = \ln(\cos x)\sec x + \sec x$

31. $u = \ln(\cos x)$
$I = \sin x\ln(\cos x) + \ln|\sec x + \tan x| - \sin x$

33. $u = \ln(1+\cos x)$
$I = \sin x\ln(1+\cos x) + x - \sin x$

35. $u = \tan^{-1}(x^{-1/2})$, $I = 2x^{1/2}\tan^{-1}(x^{-1/2}) + \ln|x+1|$

37. $u = \tan^{-1}x$, $I = \frac{1}{3}x^3\tan^{-1}x - \frac{1}{6}x^2 + \frac{1}{6}\ln(x^2+1)$

39. $u = \tan^{-1}x$, $I = \frac{1}{4}x^4\tan^{-1}x - \frac{1}{12}x^3 + \frac{1}{4}x - \frac{1}{4}\tan^{-1}x$

41. $u = \tan^{-1}x$, $I = \frac{1}{n+1}x^{n+1}\tan^{-1} - \frac{1}{n+1}\int \frac{x^{n+1}}{x^2+1}\,dx$
Next divide $x^2 + 1$ into x^{n+1} and integrate the resulting terms.

43. $u = \ln(x^2+1)$
$I = \frac{1}{3}x^3\ln(x^2+1) - \frac{2}{9}x^3 + \frac{2}{3}x - \frac{2}{3}\tan^{-1}x$

45. $u = \tan^{-1}x$, $I = x\tan^{-1} - \frac{1}{2}\ln(x^2+1)$

47. $u = \sin^{-1}x$, $I = x\sin^{-1} + \sqrt{1-x^2}$

49. $u = \ln(x^2+1)$, $I = x\ln(x^2+1) - 2x + 2\tan^{-1}x$

51. $u = \ln(\sqrt{x}+1)$
$I = x\ln(\sqrt{x}+1) - \frac{1}{2}(\sqrt{x}-1)^2 - \ln(\sqrt{x}+1)$

53. $u = \sin(\ln x)$, $I = \frac{1}{2}x\sin(\ln x) - \frac{1}{2}x\cos(\ln x)$

55. $u = \tan^{-1}(\sqrt{x})$
$I = x\tan^{-1}(\sqrt{x}) - \sqrt{x} + \tan^{-1}(\sqrt{x})$

57. $u = e^{\sqrt{x}}$, $I = 2\sqrt{x}\,e^{\sqrt{x}} - 2e^{\sqrt{x}}$

59. $u = x^2$, $I = -\frac{1}{3}x^2e^{-3x} - \frac{2}{9}xe^{-3x} - \frac{2}{27}e^{-3x}$

61. $u = x^2$, $I = -\frac{1}{5}x^2\cos 5x + \frac{2}{25}x\sin 5x + \frac{2}{125}\cos 5x$

63. $u = x^2$, $I = \frac{1}{2}x^2\tan^2 x - x\tan x - \frac{1}{2}x^2 + \ln|\sec x|$

65. $u = x^3$, $I = \frac{1}{2}x^3e^{2x} - \frac{3}{4}x^2e^{2x} + \frac{3}{4}xe^{2x} - \frac{3}{8}e^{2x}$

67. $u = x^n$, $I = \frac{1}{a}x^ne^{ax} - \frac{n}{a}\int x^{n-1}e^{ax}\,dx$

69. $I = \frac{1}{2}x^4e^{2x} - x^3e^{2x} + \frac{3}{2}x^2e^{2x} - \frac{3}{2}xe^{2x} + \frac{3}{4}e^{2x}$

71. $u = e^x$, $I = \frac{1}{2}e^x\sin x + \frac{1}{2}e^x\cos x$

73. $u = e^{-x}$, $I = -\frac{1}{2}e^x\cos x - \frac{1}{2}e^{-x}\sin x$

75. $u = e^{4x}$, $I = \frac{3}{25}e^{4x}\sin 3x + \frac{4}{25}e^{4x}\cos 3x$

77. $u = e^{ax}$, $I = -\frac{b}{a^2+b^2}\,e^{ax}\cos bx + \frac{a}{a^2+b^2}\,e^{ax}\sin bx$

79. $w = x^{1/3}$, $I = x\tan^{-1}(x^{1/3}) - \frac{1}{2}x^{2/3} + \frac{1}{2}\ln(1+x^{2/3})$

81. $w = x^{1/4}$
$I = x\tan^{-1}(x^{1/4}) - \frac{1}{3}x^{3/4} - x^{1/4} + \tan^{-1}(x^{1/4})$

83. $w = x^{1/3}$, $I = 3x^{2/3}e^{(x^{1/3})} - 6x^{1/3}e^{(x^{1/3})} + 6e^{(x^{1/3})}$

85. $w = x^{1/4}$, $I =$
$4x^{3/4}e^{(x^{1/4})} - 12x^{1/2}e^{(x^{1/4})} + 24x^{1/4}e^{(x^{1/4})} - 24e^{(x^{1/4})}$

87. $V = \int_0^2 2\pi xe^{-x}\,dx = 2\pi(1 - 4e^{-3})$

89. $V = \int_0^3 2\pi x^2e^{-x}\,dx = 2\pi(1 - 17e^{-3})$

91. $V = \int_0^{\pi/3} 2\pi x^2\sin 3x\,dx = \frac{2\pi^3}{27}$

93. $V = \int_0^e 2\pi x^4\ln x\,dx = \frac{2\pi}{25}(4e^5 + 1)$

95. $V = \int_0^\pi 2\pi x(1+\cos x)\,dx = \pi^3 - 4\pi$

97. $V = \int_0^1 2\pi x\tan^{-1}x\,dx = \pi\left(\frac{\pi}{2} - 1\right)$

99. Since $\int f(x)g(x)\,dx = f(x)G(x) - \int f'(x)G(x)\,dx$, evaluating both sides from a to b gives the result.

101. In the integral on the left side of Eq. (6.1.4ex) use the substitution $x = f^{-1}(y)$, so that $y = f(x)$ and $dy = f'(x)dx$. This gives $\int_a^b x^2 f'(x)\,dx$. Now integrate by parts to get the result. A geometric interpretation (and verification) of the validity of Formula (6.1.1ex) is based on the following sketch.

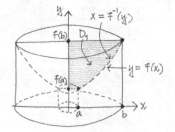

103. $A = \int_1^2 \sec^{-1} y \, dy = \frac{2\pi}{3} - \ln(2 + \sqrt{3})$

105. $A = \int_0^1 \tan^{-1} y \, dy = \frac{\pi}{4} - \frac{1}{2} \ln 2$

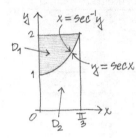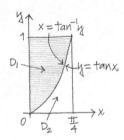

#103   #105

107. $A = \int_1^3 f^{-1}(y) \, dy$

$= 1f(1) - 0f(0) - \int_0^1 (x^3 + x + 1) \, dx = \frac{5}{4}$

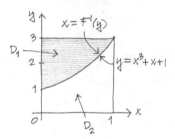

109. $V = \int_0^1 \pi \left[f^{-1}(y) \right]^2 dy$

$= \pi \left[\left(\frac{\pi}{2} \right)^2 \cdot 1 - 0^2 \cdot 0 \right] - \pi \int_0^{\pi/2} 2x \sin x \, dx = \frac{\pi^3}{4} - 2\pi$

111. $V = \int_1^e \pi \left[f^{-1}(y) \right]^2 dy$

$= \pi \left[1^2 \cdot e - 0^2 \cdot 1 \right] - \pi \int_1^e 2x e^x \, dx = (e - 2)\pi$

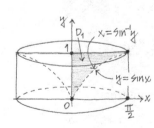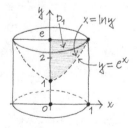

#109   #111

113. $V = \int_1^3 \pi \left[f^{-1}(y) \right]^2 dy$

$= \pi \left[(1)^2 \cdot 3 - 0^2 \cdot 1 \right] - \pi \int_0^1 2x(x^3 + x + 1) \, dx = \frac{14\pi}{15}$

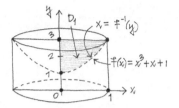

115. $x^\star = \int_0^{\pi/2} x \cos x \, dx = \frac{\pi}{2} - 1 \approx 0.57$

$y^\star = \int_0^{\pi/2} \frac{1}{2} \cos^2 x \, dx = \frac{\pi}{8} \approx 0.39$

117. $x^\star = 2 \int_0^{\ln 2} x e^{-x} \, dx = 1 - \ln 2 \approx 0.31$

$y^\star = \int_0^{\ln 2} e^{-2x} x \, dx = \frac{3}{8} \approx 0.38$

119. $x^\star = \int_0^e x \ln x \, dx = \frac{1}{4}(e^2 + 1) \approx 2.1$

$y^\star = \int_0^e \frac{1}{2}(\ln x)^2 \, dx = \frac{1}{2}(e - 2) \approx 0.36$

121. $x^\star = \frac{e}{e-2} \int_0^1 x^2 e^{-x} \, dx = \frac{2e-5}{e-2} \approx 0.61$

$y^\star = \frac{e}{2(e-2)} \int_0^1 x^2 e^{-2x} x \, dx = \frac{e^2-5}{8e(e-2)} \approx 0.15$

123. $x^\star = \frac{4}{e^2+1} \int_1^e x^2 \ln x \, dx = \frac{4(2e^3+1)}{9(e^2+1)} \approx 2.18$

$y^\star = \frac{2}{e^2+1} \int_1^e x^2 (\ln x)^2 \, dx = \frac{2(5e^3-2)}{27(e^2+1)} \approx 0.87$

125. $x^\star = \frac{4e^2}{e^2-3} \int_1^e x^{-2} \ln x \, dx = \frac{4(e-2)}{e^2-3} \approx 1.78$

$y^\star = \frac{2e^2}{e^2-3} \int_1^e x^{-6} (\ln x)^2 \, dx = \frac{4e^5-74}{125(e^2-3)} \approx 0.47$

127. $x^\star = \int_0^{\pi/2} x^2 \sin x \, dx = \pi - 2 \approx 1.14$

$y^\star = \int_0^{\pi/2} \frac{1}{2} x^2 \sin^2 x \, dx = \frac{\pi^3}{96} + \frac{\pi}{16} \approx 0.52$

129. $V = 4\pi \int_1^{2e} x \ln x \, dx = 4\pi(2e^2 \ln 2 + e^2 + \frac{1}{4})$

$\approx 224.72 \, \text{in}^3 \approx 224.72/231 \approx 0.973$ gallons

131. For $k = 1, 2, \ldots$, let $g_{k+1}(x) = \int g_k(x) \, dx$. Use IP to get Eq. (6.1.6x). Use IP on the integral in Eq. (6.1.6x) to get $\int x^n g(x) \, dx = x^n g_1(x) - nx^{n-1} g_2(x) + \int n(n-1)x^{n-2} g_2(x) \, dx$. Continuing in this fashion, you see that, when n is a positive integer, the power of x in the integrand will eventually be 0. We can arrange the work in a table as follows:

Differentiate	Integrate
x^n	$g(x)$
nx^{n-1}	$g_1(x)$
$n(n-1)x^{n-2}$	$g_2(x)$
.	.
.	.
$n!$	$g_n(x)$
0	$g_{n+1}(x)$

Note that when you combine entries from the table to get an answer, multiply one from the 1st column into the one in the second column but down one row. Combine the products using alternating signs.

133. $I = \left(-\frac{1}{3}x^2 - \frac{2}{9}x - \frac{2}{27} \right) e^{-3x}$

Differentiate	Integrate
x^2	e^{-3x}
$2x$	$-\frac{1}{3}e^{-3x}$
2	$\frac{1}{9}e^{-3x}$
0	$-\frac{1}{27}e^{-3x}$

135. $I = \left(\frac{1}{2}x^3 - \frac{3}{4}x^2 + \frac{3}{4}x - \frac{3}{8}\right)e^{2x}$

Differentiate	Integrate
x^3	e^{2x}
$3x^2$	$\frac{1}{2}e^{2x}$
$6x$	$\frac{1}{4}e^{2x}$
6	$\frac{1}{8}e^{2x}$
0	$\frac{1}{16}e^{2x}$

137. $I = \left(-\frac{1}{2}x^4 - x^3 - \frac{3}{2}x^2 - \frac{3}{2}x - \frac{3}{4}\right)e^{-2x}$

Differentiate	Integrate
x^4	e^{2x}
$4x^3$	$-\frac{1}{2}e^{-2x}$
$12x^2$	$\frac{1}{4}e^{-2x}$
$24x$	$-\frac{1}{8}e^{-2x}$
24	$\frac{1}{16}e^{-2x}$
0	$-\frac{1}{32}e^{-2x}$

139.
$$I = \left(-\frac{1}{2}x^6 - \frac{3}{2}x^5 - \frac{15}{4}x^4 - \frac{15}{2}x^3 - \frac{45}{4}x^2 - \frac{45}{4}x - \frac{45}{8}\right)e^{-2x}$$

Differentiate	Integrate
x^6	e^{-2x}
$6x^5$	$-\frac{1}{2}e^{-2x}$
$30x^4$	$\frac{1}{4}e^{2x}$
$120x^3$	$-\frac{1}{8}e^{-2x}$
$360x^2$	$\frac{1}{16}e^{-2x}$
$720x$	$-\frac{1}{32}e^{-2x}$
720	$\frac{1}{64}e^{-2x}$
0	$-\frac{1}{128}e^{-2x}$

141. $I = -\frac{1}{3}x^2\cos 3x + \frac{2}{9}x\sin 3x + \frac{2}{27}\cos 3x$

Differentiate	Integrate
x^2	$\sin 3x$
$2x$	$-\frac{1}{3}\cos 3x$
2	$-\frac{1}{9}\sin 3x$
0	$\frac{1}{27}\cos 3x$

143. $I = -\frac{1}{2}x^4\cos 2x + x^3\sin 2x$
$$+\frac{3}{2}x^2\cos 2x - \frac{3}{2}x\sin 2x - \frac{3}{4}\cos 2x$$

Differentiate	Integrate
x^4	$\sin 2x$
$4x^3$	$-\frac{1}{2}\cos 2x$
$12x^2$	$-\frac{1}{4}\sin 2x$
$24x$	$\frac{1}{8}\cos 2$
24	$\frac{1}{16}\sin 2x$
0	$-\frac{1}{32}\cos 2x$

145. $I = -x^6\cos x + 6x^5\sin x + 30x^4\cos x$
$$- 120x^3\sin x - 360x^2\cos x + 720x\sin x + 720\cos x$$

Differentiate	Integrate
x^6	$\sin x$
$6x^5$	$-\cos x$
$30x^4$	$-\sin x$
$120x^3$	$\cos x$
$360x^2$	$\sin x$
$720x$	$-\cos x$
720	$-\sin x$
0	$\cos x$

147. $\int e^{(x^{1/n})}dx = n\int u^{n-1}e^u\,du$

149. $\int \tan^{-1}(x^{1/n})dx = n\int u^{n-1}\tan^{-1}u\,du$

Exercises: 6.2

1. $\frac{1}{5}\cos^5 x - \frac{1}{3}\cos^3 x$ **3.** $-\frac{1}{5}\cos^5 x + \frac{2}{7}\cos^7 x - \frac{1}{9}\cos^9 x$

5. $\frac{1}{3}\cos^3 x - \cos x$ **7.** $\frac{1}{10}\sin^{10}x - \frac{1}{12}\sin^{12}x$

9. $\frac{1}{6}\sin^5 x\cos x - \frac{1}{24}\sin^3 x\cos x - \frac{1}{16}\sin x\cos x + \frac{1}{16}x$

11. $\frac{1}{3}\sec^3 x - \sec x$ **13.** $\frac{1}{5}\sec^5 x - \frac{2}{3}\sec^3 x + \sec x$

15. $\frac{1}{5}\sec^5 x - \frac{1}{3}\sec^3 x$ **17.** $\frac{1}{3}\tan^3 x + \frac{1}{5}\tan^5 x$

19. $\frac{1}{10}\sec^{10}x - \frac{1}{8}\sec^8 x$

21. $\frac{1}{2}\sec x\tan x + \frac{1}{2}\ln|\sec x + \tan x|$

23. $\frac{1}{4}\sec^3 x\tan x - \frac{1}{8}\sec x\tan x - \frac{1}{8}\ln|\sec x + \tan x|$

25. $\cos x + \sec x$ **27.** $\tan x - x$

29. $\tan x - \frac{3}{2}x + \frac{1}{4}\sin 2x$ **31.** $-\frac{1}{3}\csc^3 x + 2\csc x + \sin x$

33. $\frac{2}{5}\cos^{5/2}x + 2\cos^{1/2}x$ **35.** $-\frac{1}{3}\csc^3 x$

37. $-\frac{1}{3}\cot^3 x - \cot x$ **39.** $\frac{1}{3}\cos^3 x - \cos x$

41. $\frac{1}{3}\sec^3 x - 2\sec x - \cos x$ **43.** $\frac{1}{5}\sin^5 x$

45. $\frac{1}{3}\sin^3 x - \frac{1}{5}\sin^5 x$ **47.** $-\csc x - \sin x$

49. Assume n, k are positive integers.

CASE 1: $\int \sin^n x\cos^k x\,dx$. See the book.

CASE 2: $\int \frac{\sin^n x}{\cos^k x}\,dx$. If n is odd, let $u = \cos x$.

If $n = 2p$ is even, write $\sin^{2p}x = (1 - \cos^2 x)^p$,
multiply out, and then divide by $\cos^k x$. Use reduc-

tion formulas on the resulting powers of $\cos x, \sec x$.

CASE 3: $\int \dfrac{\cos^k x}{\sin^n x}\, dx$. If k is odd, let $u = \sin x$.

If $k = 2p$ is even, write $\cos^{2p} x = (1 - \sin^2 x)^p$, multiply out, and then divide by $\sin^n x$. Use reduction formulas on the resulting powers of $\sin x, \csc x$.

CASE 4: $\int \dfrac{1}{\sin^n x \cos^k x}\, dx = \int \csc^n x \sec^k x\, dx$

Use a reduction formula from Exercise 51 below.

51.

CSRF 1: $\int \csc^n x \sec^k x\, dx = \int \csc^n x \sec^{k-2} x \sec^2 x\, dx$.
Use IP with $dv = \sec^2 x\, dx$

CSRF 2: $\int \csc^n x \sec x\, dx = \int \csc^{n-2} x \sec x \csc^2 x\, dx$.
Use IP with $dv = \csc^2 x\, dx$

CSRF 3: $\int \csc^n x\, dx = \int \csc^{n-2} x \csc^2 x\, dx$.
Use IP with $dv = \csc^2 x\, dx$

53. $V = \int_0^{\pi/3} \pi \sec^4 x\, dx = 2\pi\sqrt{3}$

55. $V = \int_0^{\pi} \pi \sin^4 x\, dx = \dfrac{3\pi^2}{8}$

57. $V = \int_0^{\pi/4} \pi \tan^4 x\, dx = \pi\left(\dfrac{\pi}{4} - \dfrac{2}{3}\right)$

59. $V = \int_0^{\pi/2} \pi \sin^4 x \cos^2 x\, dx = \pi\left(\dfrac{\pi}{64} - \dfrac{1}{48}\right)$

Exercises: 6.3

1. $-\dfrac{4}{3}(4 - x^2)^{3/2} + \dfrac{1}{5}(4 - x^2)^{5/2}$

3. $\dfrac{1}{3}(4 + x^2)^{3/2} - 4(4 + x^2)^{1/2}$

5. $\dfrac{1}{5}(x^2 - 1)^{5/2} - \dfrac{1}{7}(x^2 - 1)^{7/2}$ **7.** $\dfrac{x}{25\sqrt{25 - x^2}}$

9. $\dfrac{(x^2 - 9)^{3/2}}{27x^3}$ **11.** $-\dfrac{x^3}{27(x^2 - 9)^{3/2}}$

13. $\dfrac{1}{4}x^3(9 - x^2)^{1/2} - \dfrac{9}{8}x(9 - x^2)^{1/2} + \dfrac{81}{8}\sin^{-1}\left(\dfrac{x}{3}\right)$

15. $\dfrac{-(1 + 2x^2)}{x\sqrt{1 + x^2}}$ **17.** $\dfrac{-(4 + x^2)^{5/2}}{20x^5}$ **19.** $\dfrac{-(6 + x^2)}{(9 + x^2)^{3/2}}$

21. $\dfrac{1}{3}(4 + x^2)^{3/2} - 8(4 + x^2)^{1/2} - 16(4 + x^2)^{-1/2}$

23. $\dfrac{x}{\sqrt{16 - x^2}} - \sin^{-1}\left(\dfrac{x}{4}\right)$

25. $\dfrac{-(1 + x^2)^{1/2}}{5x^5} + \dfrac{(1 + x^2)^{3/2}}{3x^3}$

27. $\dfrac{-(1 + x^2)^{7/2}}{7x^7} + \dfrac{2(1 + x^2)^{5/2}}{5x^5} - \dfrac{(1 + x^2)^{3/2}}{3x^3}$

29. $\dfrac{1}{4}x(25 + x^2)^{3/2} - \dfrac{175}{8}x(25 + x^2)^{1/2}$
$\quad + \dfrac{4375}{8}\ln\left|\sqrt{25 + x^2} + x\right|$

31. $\dfrac{1}{2}x\sqrt{x^2 - 4} + 2\ln\left|x + \sqrt{x^2 - 4}\right|$

33. $-\dfrac{1}{625}\left[\dfrac{x}{\sqrt{x^2 - 25}} + \dfrac{\sqrt{x^2 - 25}}{x}\right]$

35. $\dfrac{1}{3x(1 - x^2)^{3/2}} + \dfrac{4}{3x(1 - x^2)^{1/2}} - \dfrac{8(1 - x^2)^{1/2}}{3x}$

37. $\dfrac{-1}{64\sqrt{x^2 - 4}} + \dfrac{3}{128}\ln\left|\dfrac{2 + x}{\sqrt{x^2 - 4}}\right| + \dfrac{3}{128}\sec^{-1}\left(\dfrac{x}{2}\right) - \dfrac{1}{64x}$

39. $\dfrac{1}{50}\ln|x^2 - 25| + \dfrac{1}{25}\ln|x|$

41. $\dfrac{1}{729}\left[\dfrac{-x^3}{3(x^2 - 9)^{3/2}} + \dfrac{2x}{(x^2 - 9)^{1/2}} + \dfrac{(x^2 - 9)^{1/2}}{x}\right]$

43. $\dfrac{4}{3}(x^2 - 4)^{3/2} + \dfrac{1}{5}(x^2 - 4)^{5/2}$

45. $-\dfrac{\sqrt{4 - x^2}}{x} - \sin^{-1}\left(\dfrac{x}{2}\right)$ **47.** $\dfrac{(x^2 - 1)^{5/2}}{5x^5}$

49. $\dfrac{(x^2 - 1)^{3/2}}{3x^3} - \dfrac{(x^2 - 1)^{5/2}}{5x^5}$

51. $\dfrac{1}{2}\sin^{-1} x + \dfrac{1}{2}x\sqrt{1 - x^2}$

53. $\dfrac{1}{2}x\sqrt{1 + x^2} + \dfrac{1}{2}\ln\left|x + \sqrt{1 + x^2}\right|$

55. $\dfrac{1}{2}x\sqrt{x^2 - 1} - \dfrac{1}{2}\ln\left|x + \sqrt{x^2 - 1}\right|$ **57.** $\sin^{-1} x$

59. $\ln\left|\sqrt{1 + x^2} + x\right|$ **61.** $\ln\left|x + \sqrt{x^2 - 1}\right|$

63. $-\ln\left|\dfrac{1 + \sqrt{1 - x^2}}{x}\right|$ **65.** $\ln\left|\dfrac{\sqrt{1 + x^2} + 1}{x}\right|$

67. $\sec^{-1} x$ **69.** $-\ln\left|\dfrac{1 + \sqrt{1 - x^2}}{x}\right| + \sqrt{1 - x^2}$

71. $\dfrac{\sqrt{1 + x^2}}{x^2} - \ln\left|\dfrac{\sqrt{1 + x^2} + 1}{x}\right|$

73. $\sqrt{x^2 - 1} + \sec^{-1} x$

75. $A = 2\int_0^1 \sqrt{1 + x^2}\, dx = \sqrt{2} + 2\ln(1 + \sqrt{2})$

77. $V = 2\pi\int_0^1 x^2 \sin^{-1} x\, dx = 2\pi\left(\dfrac{\pi}{6} - \dfrac{2}{9}\right)$

79. $x^\star = \dfrac{1}{2\sqrt{2} - 1}\int_0^1 \dfrac{x^2}{\sqrt{x^2 + 1}}\, dx$
$\quad = \dfrac{1}{2\sqrt{2} - 1}\left[\dfrac{\sqrt{2}}{2} - \dfrac{1}{2}\ln(1 + \sqrt{2})\right] \approx 0.437$

$\quad y^\star = \dfrac{1}{4\sqrt{2} - 2}\int_0^1 \dfrac{x^2}{x^2 + 1}\, dx = \dfrac{1}{4\sqrt{2} - 2}\left(1 - \dfrac{\pi}{4}\right) \approx 0.138$

81. In the IP formula use w instead of u:
$\int w\, dv = wv - \int v\, dw$. To derive (1) write
$\int \dfrac{u^s}{(1 + u^2)^p}\, du = \int u^{s-1} \cdot \dfrac{u}{(1 + u^2)^p}\, du$
Then let $w = u^{s-1}$, $dv = \dfrac{u}{(1 + u^2)^p}\, du$. The
proofs of (2) and (3) are similar.

83. $\dfrac{1}{9}(4 - x^2)^{9/2} - \dfrac{4}{7}(4 - x^2)^{7/2}$

85. $\dfrac{1}{9}(x^2 - 9)^{9/2} + \dfrac{18}{7}(x^2 - 9)^{7/2} + \dfrac{81}{5}(x^2 - 9)^{5/2}$

87. $\dfrac{-1}{(9 + x^2)^{1/2}} - \dfrac{3}{(9 + x^2)^{3/2}}$ **89.** $\dfrac{x^3}{75(25 - x^2)^{3/2}}$

91. $\dfrac{x^2 - 2}{8x(4 - x^2)^{1/2}}$

93. $\dfrac{1}{4096}\left[\dfrac{-(16 + x^2)^{3/2}}{3x^3} + \dfrac{2(16 + x^2)^{1/2}}{x} + \dfrac{x}{(16 + x^2)^{1/2}}\right]$

95. $\dfrac{-(4 + x^2)^{5/2}}{20x^5}$ **97.** $\dfrac{-1}{\sqrt{x^2 - 1}} - \tan^{-1}\left(\sqrt{x^2 - 1}\right)$

99. $\dfrac{-1}{2x(x^2 - 1)^{3/2}} - \dfrac{1}{2(x^2 - 1)^{3/2}} + \dfrac{3}{2(x^2 - 1)^{1/2}}$
$\quad + \dfrac{3}{2}\tan^{-1}\left(\sqrt{x^2 - 1}\right)$

101. $\dfrac{1}{4\sqrt{4-x^2}} + \dfrac{1}{16}\ln\left|\dfrac{2+\sqrt{4-x^2}}{2-\sqrt{4-x^2}}\right|$

103. $\ln|x+\sqrt{x^2+1}|$　**105.** $\tan^{-1}(\sqrt{x^2-1})$

Exercises: 6.4

1. $\frac{1}{4}x^4 + \frac{2}{3}x^3 + 2x + 4\ln|x-2|$

3. $\frac{1}{2}x^4 + x^2 + \ln|x^2-1|$

5. $-\ln|x-3| + 2\ln|x+1|$　**7.** $-3\ln|x+5| + 5\ln|x+4|$

9. $\ln|x| - \ln|x+2|$

11. $x^2 + x + 2\ln|x-2| + 3\ln|x+2|$

13. $4\ln|2x-3| - 2\ln|x-1|$　**15.** $\ln|x-1| - \dfrac{2}{x-1}$

17. $2\ln|x| + \ln|x+5| + \dfrac{1}{x+5}$

19. $\ln|x| + x^{-2} + \ln|x-2|$

21. $\frac{1}{3}x^3 - x^2 + 3x + \frac{1}{2}\ln(x^2+1) + \tan^{-1}x$

23. $\frac{1}{2}\ln(x^2+4x+13) - \frac{4}{3}\tan^{-1}\left(\frac{x+2}{3}\right)$

25. $\ln|x| + \frac{1}{2}\ln(x^2+1) - 2\tan^{-1}x$

27. $-2\ln|x+3| + \ln(x^2+1)$

29. $2\ln|x| + \frac{1}{2}\ln|x+3| - 8\tan^{-1}(x+3)$

31. $\frac{1}{2}\ln(x^2+1) + \frac{1}{2}\ln(x^2+4) - \tan^{-1}\left(\frac{x}{2}\right)$

33. $2\ln|x-3| - \dfrac{1}{2(x^2+1)}$

35. $\frac{1}{2}\tan^{-1}x + \dfrac{x}{2(x^2+1)}$

37. $ax^2 + bx + c = a\left[\left(x - \dfrac{b}{2a}\right)^2 + \dfrac{4ac-b^2}{4a^2}\right]$

So let $r = \frac{\sqrt{4ac-b^2}}{2a}$ and $u = x - \frac{b}{2a}$. Also
$Ax + B = A\left(u + \frac{b}{2a}\right) + B = Cu + D$

39. $\tan^{-1}x + \dfrac{2x-3}{2(x^2+1)}$

41. $\dfrac{x}{4(x^2+1)^2} + \dfrac{3x}{8(x^2+1)} + \frac{3}{8}\tan^{-1}x$

43. $-\dfrac{x+5}{2(x^2+4x+8)} - \frac{1}{4}\tan^{-1}\left(\frac{x+2}{2}\right)$

Exercises: 6.5

NOTE: BB stands for Back of the Book.

1. (Compare with Exercise 7 in 6.1)
```
f:=x->x*sec(x)*tan(x); int(f(x),x);
```
$\dfrac{x}{\cos(x)} - \ln(\sec(x) + \tan(x))$

Use $\sec x = \frac{1}{\cos x}$ to get the answer in the BB.

3. (Compare with Exercise 9 in 6.1)
```
f:=x->x*exp(x)/(1+exp(x))^2; int(f(x),x);
```
$-\ln(1+e^x) + \dfrac{xe^x}{1+e^x}$

5. (Compare with Exercise 11 in 6.1)
```
f:=x->ln(sec(x))*(sec(x))^2; int(f(x),x);
```
Maple's answer not comparable. Uses complex analysis.

7. (Compare with Exercise 14 in 6.1)
```
f:=x->x^n*ln(x); int(f(x),x);
```
$\dfrac{x\ln(x)e^{n\ln(n)}}{n+1} - \dfrac{xe^{n\ln(n)}}{2n+n^2+1}$

Since $xe^{n\ln(x)} = xe^{\ln(x^n)} = x\cdot x^n = x^{n+1}$,
Maple's answer can be written as
$$\int x^n \ln x\, dx = \dfrac{x^{n+1}\ln x}{n+1} - \dfrac{x^{n+1}}{(n+1)^2}$$

9. (Compare with Exercise 15 in 6.1)
```
f:=x->x^2*(ln(x))^2; int(f(x),x);
```
$\frac{1}{3}x^3\ln(x)^2 - \frac{2}{9}x^3\ln(x) + \frac{2}{27}x^3$
Maple's answer same as BB.

11. (Compare with Exercise 17 in 6.1)
```
f:=x->x^2*(ln(x))^3; int(f(x),x);
```
$\frac{1}{3}x^3\ln(x)^3 - \frac{1}{3}x^2\ln(x)^2 + \frac{2}{9}x^3\ln(x) + \frac{2}{27}x^3$
Maple's answer same as BB.

13. (Compare with Exercise 21 in 6.1)
```
f:=x->exp(-x)*ln(1+exp(x)); int(f(x),x);
```
$\dfrac{xe^x - \ln(1+e^x)e^x - \ln(1+e^x)}{e^x}$

Rewrite Maple's answer as
$x - \ln(1+e^x) - e^{-x}\ln(1+e^x)$
But $x - \ln(1+e^x) = -\left[\ln(1+e^x) - x\right]$
$= -\left[\ln(1+e^x) - \ln(e^x)\right] = \ln((1+e^x)/e^x)$
$= \ln(e^{-x} + 1)$

15. (Compare with Exercise 23 in 6.1)
```
f:=x->ln(x)*cos(ln(x))/x; int(f(x),x);
```
$\cos(\ln(x)) + \ln(x)\sin(\ln(x))$
Maple's answer same as BB.

17. (Compare with Exercise 27 in 6.1).
```
f:=x->(sec(x))^2*ln(cos(x)); int(f(x),x);
```
Maple's answer not comparable. Uses complex analysis.

19. (Compare with Exercise 29 in 6.1)
```
f:=x->sec(x)*tan(x)*ln(cos(x));
int(f(x),x);
```
Maple's answer not comparable. Uses complex analysis.

21. (Compare with Exercise 31 in 6.1)
```
f:=x->cos(x)*ln(cos(x)); int(f(x),x);
```
Maple's answer not comparable. Uses complex analysis.

23. (Compare with Exercise 33 in 6.1)
```
f:=x->cos(x)*ln(1+cos(x)); int(f(x),x);
```
Maple's answer not comparable. Uses complex analysis.

25. (Compare with Exercise 35 in 6.1)

```
f:=x->x^(-1/2)*arctan(x^(-1/2));
  int(f(x),x);
```

$$2\sqrt{x}\arctan\left(\tfrac{1}{\sqrt{x}}\right) + \ln\left(1 + \tfrac{1}{x}\right) + \ln(x)$$

Note that the last two terms above are
$\ln\left(1 + \tfrac{1}{x}\right) + \ln x = \ln\left(\tfrac{x+1}{x}\right) + \ln x$
$= \ln(x+1) - \ln x + \ln x = \ln(x+1)$
Maple's answer is essentially that in the BB.

27. (Compare with Exercise 63 in 6.1)

```
f:=x->x^2*tan(x)*(sec(x))^2; int(f(x),x);
```

$$\frac{1}{2}\frac{x^2}{\cos(x)^2} - x\tan(x) - \ln(\cos(x))$$

To convert this to the answer in the BB, note that
$\dfrac{1}{2}\dfrac{x^2}{\cos^2 x} = \dfrac{1}{2}x^2\sec^2 x = \dfrac{1}{2}x^2(\tan^2 x + 1)$, and also
$-\ln(\cos x) = \ln(\cos x)^{-1} = \ln\left(\tfrac{1}{\cos x}\right) = \ln(\sec x)$

29. (Compare with Exercise 67 in 6.1)

```
f:=x->x^n*exp(a*x); int(f(x),x);
```

$$-\frac{(\ a)^{-n}\left[x^n(\ a)^n n\Gamma(n)(\ ax)^{-n} \quad x^n(\ a)^n e^{ax}\right]}{a}$$

$$-\frac{(-a)^{-n}\left[x^n(-a)^n n(-ax)^{-n}\Gamma(n,-ax)\right]}{a}$$

Two obvious simplifications are
$x^n(-a)^n n\Gamma(n)(-ax)^{-n} = n\Gamma(n)$ and
$x^n(-a)^n n(-ax)^{-n}\Gamma(n,-ax) = n\Gamma(n,-ax)$
Using these and other obvious simplifications, one can show that Maple's version of the reduction formula is
$\int x^n e^{ax}\,dx = \tfrac{1}{a}x^n e^{ax} + \tfrac{(-1)^n}{a^{n+1}}\,n\left[\Gamma(n,-ax) - \Gamma(n)\right]$
Here, Γ stands for either the Gamma function or the incomplete Gamma function. See Maple's documentation. Also see Exercise 60 in Section 6.6. The preferred answer is the reduction formula:
$\int x^n e^{ax}\,dx = \tfrac{1}{a}x^n e^{ax} - \tfrac{n}{a}\int x^{n-1}e^{ax}\,dx$

31. (Compare with Exercise 1 in 6.2)

```
f:=x->(sin(x))^3*(cos(x))^2; int(f(x),x);
```

$$-\tfrac{1}{5}\sin(x)^2\cos(x)^3 - \tfrac{2}{15}\cos(x)^3$$

To get the BB answer use $\sin^2 x = 1 - \cos^2 x$ in the first term.

33. (Compare with Exercise 3 in 6.2)

```
f:=x->(sin(x))^5*(cos(x))^4; int(f(x),x);
```

$$-\tfrac{1}{9}\sin(x)^4\cos(x)^5 - \tfrac{4}{63}\sin(x)^2\cos(x)^5 - \tfrac{8}{315}\cos(x)^5$$

To get the BB answer use $\sin^2 x = 1 - \cos^2 x$ in the first term.

35. (Compare with Exercise 5 in 6.2)

```
f:=x->(sin(x))^3; int(f(x),x);
```

$$-\tfrac{1}{3}\sin(x)^2\cos(x) - \tfrac{2}{3}\cos(x)$$

To get the BB answer use $\sin^2 x = 1 - \cos^2 x$ in the first term.

37. (Compare with Exercise 7 in 6.2)

```
f:=x->(sin(x))^9*(cos(x))^3; int(f(x),x);
```

$$-\tfrac{1}{12}\sin(x)^8\cos(x)^4 - \tfrac{1}{15}\sin(x)^6\cos(x)^4$$
$$-\tfrac{1}{20}\sin(x)^4\cos(x)^4 - \tfrac{1}{30}\sin(x)^2\cos(x)^4 - \tfrac{1}{60}\cos(x)^4$$

To get the BB answer factor $-\tfrac{1}{60}\cos^4 x$ out of all the terms. Then substitute $\cos^4 x = (1 - \sin^2 x)^2$ and multiply everything out.

39. (Compare with Exercise 9 in 6.2)

```
f:=x->(sin(x))^4*(cos(x))^2; int(f(x),x);
```

$$-\tfrac{1}{6}\sin(x)^3\cos(x)^3 - \tfrac{1}{8}\sin(x)\cos(x)^3 + \tfrac{1}{16}\cos(x)\sin(x)$$
$$+\tfrac{1}{16}x$$

To get the BB answer, factor $\cos x$ out of the first two terms and use the trig identity: $\cos^2 x = 1 - \sin^2 x$ in the first term.

41. (Compare with Exercise 11 in 6.2)

```
f:=x->(tan(x))^3*sec(x); int(f(x),x);
```

$$\frac{1}{3}\frac{\sin(x)^4}{\cos(x)^3} - \frac{1}{3}\frac{\sin(x)^4}{\cos(x)} - \tfrac{1}{3}\sin(x)^2\cos(x) - \tfrac{2}{3}\cos(x)$$

To get the BB answer, use the trig identity $\sin^2 x = 1 - \cos^2 x$ in the first three terms.

43. (Compare with Exercise 13 in 6.2)

```
f:=x->(tan(x))^5*sec(x); int(f(x),x);
```

$$\frac{1}{5}\frac{\sin(x)^6}{\cos(x)^5} - \frac{1}{15}\frac{\sin(x)^6}{\cos(x)^3} + \frac{1}{5}\frac{\sin(x)^6}{\cos(x)}$$
$$+\tfrac{1}{5}\sin(x)^4\cos(x) + \tfrac{4}{15}\sin(x)^2\cos(x) + \tfrac{8}{15}\cos(x)$$

To get the BB answer, factor
$\sin^6 x = (1 - \cos^2 x)^3 = 1 - 3\cos^2 x + 3\cos^4 x - \cos^6 x$
out of the first three terms and multiply out the result. Then use $\sin^2 x = 1 - \cos^2 x$ and
$\sin^4 x = (1 - \cos^2 x)^2 = 1 - 2\cos^2 x + \cos^4 x$ on the last three terms.

45. (Compare with Exercise 15 in 6.2)

```
f:=x->(tan(x))^3*(sec(x))^3; int(f(x),x);
```

$$\frac{1}{5}\frac{\sin(x)^4}{\cos(x)^5} + \frac{1}{15}\frac{\sin(x)^4}{\cos(x)^3} - \frac{1}{15}\frac{\sin(x)^4}{\cos(x)}$$
$$-\tfrac{1}{15}\sin(x)^2\cos(x) - \tfrac{2}{15}\cos(x)$$

To get the BB answer, factor
$\sin^4 x = (1 - \cos^2 x)^4 = 1 - 2\cos^2 x + \cos^4 x$
out of the first three terms and multiply out the result. Then use $\sin^2 x = 1 - \cos^2 x$ on the last two terms.

47. (Compare with Exercise 1 in 6.3)

```
f:=x->x^3*sqrt(4-x^2); int(f(x),x);
```

$$\tfrac{1}{15}(x-2)(x+2)(8+3x^2)\sqrt{4-x^2}$$

To get the BB answer note that
$(x-2)(x+2)\sqrt{4-x^2} = -(4-x^2)(4-x^2)^{1/2}$
$= (4-x^2)^{3/2}$

49. (Compare with Exercise 3 in 6.3)

```
f:=x->x^3/sqrt(4+x^2); int(f(x),x);
```

$$\tfrac{1}{3}\sqrt{4+x^2}(-8+x^2)$$

To get this factor the BB answer.

51. (Compare with Exercise 5 in 6.3)

```
f:=x->x^3*(x^2-1)^(3/2); int(f(x),x);
```

$\frac{1}{35}(-1+x)(x+1)(2+5x^2)(-1+x^2)^{3/2}$

To get the BB answer note that

$(-1+x)(x+1)(-1+x^2)^{3/2} = (x^2-1)(x^2-1)^{3/2}$
$= (x^2-1)^{5/2}$

Now factor the BB answer and compare.

53. (Compare with Exercise 13 in 6.3)

`f:=x->x^2*sqrt(9-x^2); int(f(x),x);`
$$-\frac{1}{4}x(9-x^2)^{3/2} + \frac{9}{8}x\sqrt{9-x^2} + \frac{81}{8}\arcsin\left(\frac{1}{3}x\right)$$

To get the BB answer write the first two terms as

$-\frac{1}{4}x(9-x^2)(9-x^2)^{1/2} + \frac{9}{8}x\sqrt{9-x^2}$
$= -\frac{9}{4}x(9-x^2)^{1/2} + \frac{1}{4}x^3(9-x^2)^{1/2} + \frac{9}{8}x(9-x^2)^{1/2}$
$= -\frac{9}{8}x(9-x^2)^{1/2} + \frac{1}{4}x^3(9-x^2)^{1/2}$

55. (Compare with Exercise 21 in 6.3)

`f:=x->x^5/(4+x^2)^(3/2); int(f(x),x);`
$$\frac{1}{3}\frac{-128-16x^2+x^4}{\sqrt{4+x^2}}$$

Factor the answer in the BB as

$\frac{1}{3}(4+x^2)^{3/2} - 8(4+x^2)^{1/2} - \frac{16}{(4+x^2)^{1/2}}$
$= \frac{1}{3}\frac{1}{(4+x^2)^{1/2}}\left[(4+x^2)^2 - 24(4+x^2) - 48\right]$

Now simplify the expression in the square brackets to get Maple's answer.

57. (Compare with Exercise 25 in 6.3)

`f:=x->(1+x^2)^(1/2)/x^6; int(f(x),x);`
$$\frac{1}{15}\frac{(x^2+1)^{3/2}(-3+2x^2)}{x^5}$$

Factor the answer in the BB:

$\frac{-(1+x^2)^{5/2}}{5x^5} + \frac{(1+x^2)^{3/2}}{3x^3}$
$= \frac{(1+x^2)^{3/2}}{15x^5}\left[-3(1+x^2) + 5x^2\right]$
$= \frac{(x^2+1)^{3/2}(-3+2x^2)}{15x^5}$

which is Maple's answer above.

59. (Compare with Exercise 27 in 6.3)

`f:=x->(1+x^2)^(1/2)/x^8; int(f(x),x);`
$$-\frac{1}{105}\frac{(x^2+1)^{3/2}(15-12x^2+8x^4)}{x^7}$$

Factor the answer in the BB:

$\frac{-(1+x^2)^{7/2}}{7x^7} + \frac{2(1+x^2)^{5/2}}{5x^5} - \frac{(1+x^2)^{3/2}}{3x^3}$
$= \frac{(1+x^2)^{3/2}}{105x^7}\left[-15(1+x^2)^2 + 42x^2(1+x^2) - 35x^4\right]$
$= \frac{(1+x^2)^{3/2}}{105x^7}\left[-15 + 12x^2 - 8x^4\right]$

which is Maple's answer above.

61. (Compare with Exercise 7 in 6.4)

`f:=x->(2*x+13)/(x^2+9*x+20); int(f(x),x);`
$$-3\ln(x+5) + 5\ln(x+4)$$

which is the same as the BB's answer.

63. (Compare with Exercise 41 in 6.4)

`f:=x->1/(x^2+1)^3; int(f(x),x);`
$$\frac{1}{4}\frac{x}{(x^2+1)^2} + \frac{3}{8}\frac{x}{x^2+1} + \frac{3}{8}\arctan(x)$$

which is the same as the BB's answer.

65. `f:=x->sqrt(x)*cos(x);`
`A:=int(f(x),x=0..Pi/2); eval(A):`
$A := \frac{1}{2}\sqrt{2}\sqrt{\pi} - \frac{1}{2}\sqrt{2}\sqrt{\pi}\text{FresnelS}(1)$ 0.7040377520
`V:=int(Pi*(f(x))^2,x=0..Pi/2); eval(V):`
$V := \frac{1}{2}\pi + \frac{1}{16}\pi^3$ 1.152494130
```
plot(f(x),x=0..Pi/2,color=black,
     filled=[color="Gold"]);
with(code_ch5sec3and4):
revolve1X(f,0,0,Pi/2);
```

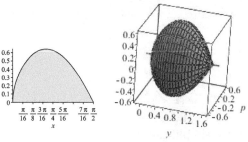

67. `f:=x->sqrt(1+(sin(x))^2);`
`A:=int(f(x),x=0..Pi); eval(A):`
$A := 2\sqrt{2}\text{EllipticE}\left(\frac{1}{2}\sqrt{2}\right)$ 3.820197788
`V:=int(Pi*(f(x))^2,x=0..Pi); eval(V):`
$V := \frac{3}{2}\pi^2$ 14.80440661
```
plot(f(x),x=0..Pi,color=black,
     filled=[color="Gold"]);
with(code_ch5sec3and4): revolve1X(f,0,0,Pi);
```

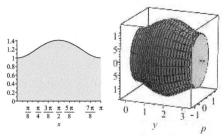

69. `f:=x->x^(3/2)/(1+x^{2});`
`A:=int(f(x),x=0..5); eval(A):`
$A := -\frac{1}{4}\sqrt{2}\left(-4\sqrt{2}\sqrt{5} - \ln\left(\frac{6}{5} - \frac{1}{5}\sqrt{2}\sqrt{5}\right)\right.$
$\left. -2\arctan\left(\frac{1}{9}\sqrt{2}\sqrt{5} + \frac{1}{9}\right) + \ln\left(\frac{6}{5} + \frac{1}{5}\sqrt{2}\sqrt{5}\right)\right.$
$\left. -2\arctan\left(\frac{1}{9}\sqrt{2}\sqrt{5} - \frac{1}{9}\right)\right)$ 2.309326040
`V:=int(Pi*(f(x))^2,x=0..5); eval(V):`
$V := -\frac{25}{52}\pi + \frac{1}{2}\pi\ln(2) + \frac{1}{2}\pi\ln(13)$ 3.607424991
```
plot(f(x),x=0..5,color=black,
     filled=[color="Gold"]);
with(code_ch5sec3and4): revolve1X(f,0,0,5);
```

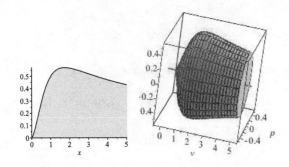

Exercises: 6.6

1. $\frac{5}{2}$ **3.** ∞ **5.** ∞ **7.** 6   **9.** 1   **11.** ∞ **13.** $3 + 3^{4/3}$

15. ∞ **17.** $\frac{1}{2}$ **19.** DNE   **21.** $\ln 2$ **23.** $\frac{\pi}{4}$

25. $\sin^{-1}(e^{-1})$ **27.** $\ln 2$ **29.** $2e^{-1}$ **31.** $2 - 2e^{-1}$

33. $\ln\left(\frac{5+\sqrt{21}}{2}\right)$ **35.** $\frac{\pi}{2}$ **37.** $1/\ln 2$ **39.** ∞ **41.** DNE

43. $2e^{-1}$ **45.** $\frac{1}{9}$ **47.** ∞ **49.** 2

51. L' Hospital's Rule gives

$$\lim_{x\to\infty}\frac{(\ln x)^c}{x^p} = \lim_{x\to\infty}\frac{c(\ln x)^{c-1}\cdot\frac{1}{x}}{px^{p-1}} = \frac{c}{p}\lim_{x\to\infty}\frac{(\ln x)^{c-1}}{x^p}$$

If $c - 1 \le 0$, then the limit clearly is $\frac{c}{p}\cdot\frac{1}{\infty} = 0$. Otherwise keep applying L' Hospital's Rule until $\ln x$ has a power less than or equal to 0.

53. 2   **55.** $\frac{1}{9}$ **57.** $\frac{6}{a^4}$ **59.** $\frac{n!}{a^{n+1}}$

61. ∞ **63.** $\frac{\pi}{4} - \frac{1}{2}\ln 2$ **65.** $\frac{1}{2}$ **67.** $\frac{1}{2}$ **69.** $\frac{3}{10}$ **71.** $\frac{5}{29}$

CHAPTER 7: Answers to Odd Exercises

Exercises: 7.1

1. $y' = 2x - 2Cx^{-3}$. Substituting in the left side of the DE gives $4x^2$.

3. $y' = \sec x + (x + C)\sec x \tan x$. Substituting in the left side of the DE gives $\sec x$.

5. For $y = e^{-2t}$: $y' = -2e^{-2t}$, $y'' = 4e^{-2t}$
Substituting in the left side of the DE gives 0.
For $y = e^{-3t}$: $y' = -3e^{-3t}$, $y'' = 9e^{-3t}$
Substituting in the left side of the DE gives 0.

7. For $y = e^{-t}$: $y' = -e^{-t}$, $y'' = e^{-t}$
Substituting in the left side of the DE gives 0.
For $y = te^{-t}$: $y' = e^{-t} - te^{-t}$, $y'' = -2e^{-t} + te^{-t}$
Substituting in the left side of the DE gives 0.

9. For $y = \sin 2t$: $y' = 2\cos 2t$, $y'' = -4\sin 2t$
Substituting in the left side of the DE gives 0.
For $y = \cos 2t$: $y' = -2\sin 2t$, $y'' = -4\cos 2t$
Substituting in the left side of the DE gives 0.

11. The derivatives of $y = e^{-t}\sin 2t$ are:
$y' = -e^{-t}\sin 2t + 2e^{-t}\cos 2t$
$y'' = -3e^{-t}\sin 2t - 4e^{-t}\cos 2t$

Substituting in the left side of the DE gives 0.

13. For $y = x^{-1}$: $y' = -x^{-2}$, $y'' = 2x^{-3}$
Substituting in the left side of the DE gives 0.
For $y = x^3$: $y' = 3x^2$, $y'' = 6x$
Substituting in the left side of the DE gives 0.

15. For $y = 1$: $y' = 0$, $y'' = 0$
Substituting in the left side of the DE gives 0.
For $y = x^{-2}$: $y' = -2x^{-3}$, $y'' = 6x^{-4}$
Substituting in the left side of the DE gives 0.

17. For $y = x^{1/2}$: $y' = \frac{1}{2}x^{-1/2}$, $y'' = -\frac{1}{4}x^{-3/2}$
Substituting in the left side of the DE gives 0.
For $y = x^{-1/2}$: $y' = -\frac{1}{2}x^{-3/2}$, $y'' = \frac{3}{4}x^{-5/2}$
Substituting in the left side of the DE gives 0.

19. $r = -3$ **21.** $r = -3, 0$ **23.** $r = -2, 1$

25. $r = -2, 2$ **27.** $r = -2, 2$ **29.** $r = -3, 3$

31. $r = 1, 2$ **33.** $r = 1 \pm \frac{\sqrt{3}}{2}$

35. $y = Ce^{-0.002t}$. $y = 2e^{-0.002t}$ (in red):

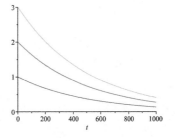

37. $y = \dfrac{1}{(0.006t + C)^{1/4}}$. $y = \dfrac{1}{(0.006t + 0.0625)^{1/4}}$ (in red):

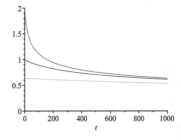

39. $v = -4e^{-32t} - 1$, $\lim\limits_{t\to\infty} v = -1$ ft/s

41. $v = 97e^{-4t} - 8$. $v = 0$ at $t = \frac{1}{4}\ln\left(\frac{97}{8}\right) \approx 0.264$

43. $y = x^3 + x\ln x - x + C_1 x + C_2$

45. $y = -x\sin x - 2\cos x + C_1 x + C_2$

47. $y = -\frac{1}{8}C_1 e^{-8x} + C_2$ **49.** $y = -\frac{1}{8}C_1 e^{-4x} - \frac{1}{2}x + C_2$

51. $y = -\ln|x + C_1| + C_2$ **53.** $y = \frac{1}{4}(3x + C_1)^{4/3} + C_2$

55. $y = \ln|\sec(x + C_1)| + C_2$

Exercises: 7.2

1. $y = ae^{-4t}$, $y = 2e^{-4t}$

3. $y = 3 + ae^{-4t}$, $y = 3 - e^{-4t}$

5. $y = \dfrac{1}{1 - re^{-12t}}$, $y = 0$, $y = 3$, $y = \dfrac{6}{2 + e^{-12t}}$

7. $y = \dfrac{y(y-4)}{y-2} = ae^{-t}$, $y = 0, 2, 4$, $y = \dfrac{y(y-4)}{y-2} = 3e^{-t}$

9. $y = \dfrac{y^3(y-5)^2}{(y-2)^5} = ae^{-t}$, $y = 0, 2, 5$,

$y = \dfrac{y^3(y-5)^2}{(y-2)^5} = 108e^{-t}$

11. $\ln|y-1| - \dfrac{1}{y-1} = -t + C$, $y = 1$,

$\ln|y-1| - \dfrac{1}{y-1} = -t + 1$

13. $y = \dfrac{x}{1 - Cx}$, $y = 0$, $y = x$

15. $y = \dfrac{|x|}{\pm\sqrt{1 - Cx^2}}$, $y = 0$, $y = \dfrac{2x}{\sqrt{4 - 3x^2}}$

17. $y = \dfrac{1 + rx}{1 - rx}$, $y = -1, 1$, $y = 1$

19. $y = \dfrac{rx}{1 + rx}$, $y = 0, 1$, $y = 1$

21. $y = \dfrac{rx}{1 + (r-1)x}$, $y = 0, 1$, $y = 1$

23. $y = r(1 + e^x) - 1$, $y = -1$, $y = \dfrac{2}{1+e^2}(1 + e^x) - 1$

25. $y = \tan(x + x^2 + C)$, $y = \tan(x + x^2 + \frac{\pi}{4})$

27. $y = \tan(\tan^{-1} x + C)$, $y = \tan(\tan^{-1} x + \frac{\pi}{4})$

29. $y = \tan^{-1}(x^3 + C)$, $y = \dfrac{(2n+1)\pi}{2}$, $y = \tan^{-1}(x^3 + \sqrt{3})$

31. $y = \cos^{-1}(-(\sin x + C))$, $y = \cos^{-1}(-\sin x + \frac{1}{2})$

33. $y = \sec^{-1}(re^{\tan x})$, $y = \dfrac{(2n+1)\pi}{2}$, $y = \sec^{-1}(2e^{\tan x})$

35. $y = C_1 \ln|x| + C_2$ **37.** $y = C_1(x + \frac{1}{3}x^3) + C_2$

39. $y = C_1(\frac{1}{2}x^2 - \frac{1}{2}x^4) + C_2$ **41.** $y = C_1(3 - x)e^x + C_2$

43. $y = \frac{1}{2}C_1 \ln(1 + x^2) + C_2$ **45.** $y = C_1 \ln(e^x + 1) + C_2$

47. $y = C_1 \ln|\sec x + \tan x| + C_2$

49. $y = -C_1(\cos x + \sin x) + C_2$

Exercises: 7.3

1. $y = -e^{-5x} + Ce^{-2x}$ **3.** $y = -\frac{1}{3}x - \frac{1}{9} + Ce^{3x}$

5. $y = \frac{1}{2}x^2 e^{3x} + Ce^{3x}$ **7.** $y = -\cos x + \dfrac{\sin x}{x} + \dfrac{C}{x}$

9. $y = \frac{1}{2}\ln x - \frac{1}{4}x^2 + \dfrac{C}{x^2}$ **11.** $y = -x^3 \cos x + Cx^3$

13. $y = \dfrac{\ln|1 + x^2|}{x^2} + \dfrac{C}{x^2}$

15. $y = -\dfrac{1}{x} + \dfrac{1}{2x^2}\ln\left|\dfrac{1+x}{1-x}\right| + \dfrac{C}{x^2}$

17. $y = -(x^{-2} + 2x^{-1} + 1)e^{-x} + Cx^{-2}$

19. $y = \dfrac{1}{2}\ln x - \dfrac{1}{4} + \dfrac{C}{x^2}$

21. $y = \frac{1}{3}x + \frac{4}{7}x^{3/2} + \frac{1}{4}x^2 + \dfrac{C}{x^2}$

23. $y = \frac{1}{2}\sec x + \frac{1}{2}\sin x + C\sec x$

25. $y = \frac{1}{2}x^2 \sec x + C \sec x$

27. $y = \dfrac{1}{1 + \sin x}\left[\frac{1}{2}x^2 - x\cos x + \sin x + C\right]$

29. $y = \dfrac{1}{2 + \tan x}\left[2\sin x - \cos x + C\right]$

31. $y = \dfrac{1}{x + \sin x}\left[\frac{1}{3}x^3 - x\cos x + \sin x + C\right]$

33. $y = \dfrac{1}{1 + \ln x}\left[\frac{1}{9}x^3 + \frac{1}{3}x^3 \ln x + C\right]$

35. $Q = \frac{2}{5}(100 + 2t) + \dfrac{C}{(100 + 2t)^{2/2}}$

$Q = \frac{2}{5}(100 + 2t) - \dfrac{25000}{(100 + 2t)^{2/2}}$

$t = 450$ min, $Q(450)/1000 \approx 0.3992$ lb/gal

$\displaystyle\lim_{t\to\infty}\dfrac{Q(t)}{V(t)} = 0.4$ lb/gal

37. $Q = 3(500 - t) - \dfrac{29(500 - t)^3}{2500000}$, $t = 500$ min

39. $Q = 1500 + Ce^{-t/250}$, $\displaystyle\lim_{t\to\infty} Q(t) = 1500$ lb

41. $y = \dfrac{e^x}{e^x + C}$ **43.** $y = \dfrac{x^{1/3}}{(x + C)^{1/3}}$

45. $y = \dfrac{1}{x(C - x^2)}$ **47.** $y = \dfrac{1}{x^{3/2}(C - 3x)^{1/2}}$

49. $y = \dfrac{2e^x}{2C - e^{2x}}$ **51.** $y = \dfrac{1}{(2 - x)e^x + Ce^{x/2}}$

53. $y = \dfrac{e^{3x/2}}{[3(x-1)e^x + C]^{1/2}}$ **55.** $y = \dfrac{1}{(C - x)\cos x}$

CHAPTER 8: Answers to Odd Exercises

Exercises: 8.1

1. 1   **3.** $\frac{1}{9}$ **5.** $\frac{4}{25}$ **7.** $-\frac{1}{3}$ **9.** e^{-1} **11.** $\frac{\pi}{4}$ **13.** $\frac{1}{2}$

15. 0   **17.** $\frac{2}{3}$ **19.** 1   **21.** 0   **23.** 1   **25.** 0   **27.** 1

29. 1   **31.** 0   **33.** 1   **35.** ∞ **37.** $\frac{1}{2}$ **39.** 0   **41.** 0

43. 0   **45.** 0   **47.** 0   **49.** 1   **51.** e^2 **53.** $\frac{1}{243}$ **55.** e^{-5}

57. e^2 **59.** $\frac{1}{2}$ **61.** $e^{-2/\pi}$ **63.** 1   **65.** 1

67. $a_n = \dfrac{n+1}{n} = 1 + \dfrac{1}{n} > 1 + \dfrac{1}{n+1} = a_{n+1}$, decreasing,

$\displaystyle\lim_{n\to\infty} a_n = \lim_{n\to\infty}\left(1 + \dfrac{1}{n}\right) = 1$

69. $f(x) = \dfrac{x}{x+1}$, $f'(x) = \dfrac{1}{(x+1)^2} > 0$, increasing,

$\displaystyle\lim_{n\to\infty} a_n = \lim_{n\to\infty}\dfrac{n}{n+1} \overset{L'Hosp}{=} \lim_{n\to\infty}\dfrac{1}{1} = 1$

71. $f(x) = \dfrac{x^2 + 1}{x+1}$, $f'(x) = \dfrac{x^2 + 2x - 1}{(x+1)^2} > 0$, increasing,

$\displaystyle\lim_{n\to\infty} a_n = \lim_{n\to\infty}\dfrac{n^2 + 1}{n+1} \overset{L'Hosp}{=} \lim_{n\to\infty}\dfrac{2n}{1} = \infty$

73. $f(x) = \dfrac{x}{x^2 - 1}$, $f'(x) = \dfrac{-1 - x^2}{(x^2 - 1)^2} < 0$, decreasing,

$$\lim_{n \to \infty} a_n = \lim_{n \to \infty} \frac{n}{n^2 - 1} \overset{L'Hosp}{=} \lim_{n \to \infty} \frac{1}{2n} = 0$$

75. $f(x) = \dfrac{\sqrt{x}}{\sqrt{x} + 1}$, $f'(x) = \dfrac{1/(2\sqrt{x})}{(\sqrt{x} + 1)^2} > 0$, increasing,

$$\lim_{n \to \infty} a_n = \lim_{n \to \infty} \frac{\sqrt{n}}{\sqrt{n} + 1} \overset{Algebra}{=} \lim_{n \to \infty} \frac{1}{1 + 1/\sqrt{n}} = 1$$

77. $f(x) = \tan^{-1}\left(\dfrac{x}{x + 1}\right)$, $f'(x) = \dfrac{1}{(x + 1)^2 + x^2} > 0$,

increasing,

$$\lim_{n \to \infty} a_n = \lim_{n \to \infty} \tan^{-1}\left(\frac{n}{n + 1}\right) = \tan^{-1}(1) = \frac{\pi}{4}$$

79. $\dfrac{a_{n+1}}{a_n} = \dfrac{n + 1}{2^{n+1}} \cdot \dfrac{2^n}{n} = \dfrac{1}{2} \cdot \dfrac{n + 1}{n} < 1$, for $n \geq 2$,

decreasing,

$$\lim_{n \to \infty} a_n = \lim_{n \to \infty} \frac{n}{2^n} \overset{L'Hosp}{=} \lim_{n \to \infty} \frac{1}{(\ln 2)2^n} = 0$$

81. $\dfrac{a_{n+1}}{a_n} = \dfrac{3^{n+1}}{(n + 2)!} \cdot \dfrac{(n + 1)!}{3^n} = \dfrac{3}{n + 2} < 1$, for

$n \geq 2$, decreasing,

$$\lim_{n \to \infty} a_n = \lim_{n \to \infty} \frac{3^n}{(n + 1)!} = 0 \text{ (Squeeze Theorem)}$$

83. $\dfrac{a_{n+1}}{a_n} = \dfrac{n!}{(n + 1)^n} \cdot \dfrac{n^n}{n!} = \left(\dfrac{n}{n + 1}\right)^n < 1$,

decreasing, $\lim_{n \to \infty} a_n = 0$ (See Example 8.1.5 (a))

Exercises: 8.2

1. $\dfrac{10}{9}$ **3.** 15 **5.** $-\dfrac{7}{3}$ **7.** $\dfrac{15}{8}$ **9.** $\dfrac{1}{240}$ **11.** $\dfrac{8}{5}$ **13.** $\dfrac{41}{11}$

15. $\dfrac{175}{72}$ **17.** $\dfrac{20}{3}$ **19.** 3 **21.** 2 **23.** $\dfrac{3}{2}$ **25.** $\dfrac{3}{2}$ **27.** $\dfrac{1}{3}$

29. $\dfrac{13}{12}$ **31.** $\dfrac{7}{12}$ **33.** $1 + \dfrac{1}{\sqrt{2}}$ **35.** $\dfrac{1}{\ln 2} + \dfrac{1}{\ln 3}$ **37.** 1

39. $-\dfrac{1}{2}$ **41.** 0 **43.** 0 **45.** $-\dfrac{\pi}{4}$ **47.** $\sin(1) - 1$

49. $2^{1/2}$ **51.** $\dfrac{7}{9}$ **53.** 1 **55.** $\dfrac{23}{99}$ **57.** $\dfrac{61}{165}$ **59.** $\dfrac{349}{660}$

61. $\dfrac{64293}{9990}$ **63.** $\dfrac{1}{10}$

Exercises: 8.3

1. diverges **3.** fails. diverges to ∞ **5.** diverges

7. fails. diverges to ∞ **9.** fails **11.** diverges

13. diverges **15.** fails **17.** diverges **19.** diverges

21. diverges **23.** diverges **25.** converges

27. converges **29.** converges **31.** converges

33. $p = 5/2$ series, converges

35. $p = 3/2$ series, converges **37.** converges

39. converges **41.** diverges **43.** converges

45. converges **47.** converges **49.** converges

51. converges **53.** diverges **55.** converges

57. converges **59.** converges

61. converges **63.** $p = 2$ series, converges

65. Integral test is not possible because of the factorials. However, show that

$$\frac{n!}{(2n)!} < \frac{1}{2^n}, \text{ for all } n, \sum_{n=1}^{\infty} \frac{n!}{(2n)!} < \sum_{n=1}^{\infty} \frac{1}{2^n} < \infty$$

Exercises: 8.4

1. $\dfrac{n^2}{n^5 + 6} < \dfrac{1}{n^3}$, converges

3. $\dfrac{1}{n^2 + 3n + 7} < \dfrac{1}{n^2}$, converges

5. $\dfrac{n}{\sqrt{n^5 + 1}} < \dfrac{n}{\sqrt{n^5}} = \dfrac{1}{n^{3/2}}$, converges

7. $\dfrac{3^n}{(5^n + 1)^2} < \dfrac{3^n}{(5^n)^2} < \left(\dfrac{3}{25}\right)^n$, converges

9. $\dfrac{2^{-n}}{1 + 2^{-n}} = \dfrac{1}{2^n + 1} < \dfrac{1}{2^n}$, converges

11. $\dfrac{2^n + 3^n}{6^n + 1} < \left(\dfrac{1}{3}\right)^n + \left(\dfrac{1}{2}\right)^n$, converges

13. $\dfrac{\sqrt{9^n + 1}}{2^n - 1} > \left(\dfrac{3}{2}\right)^n$, diverges

15. $\dfrac{\sqrt{2^n + 3^n}}{4^n + 5^n} < \sqrt{2}\left(\dfrac{\sqrt{3}}{4}\right)^n$, converges

17. $\dfrac{n - 1}{n(n + 1)(n + 2)} < \dfrac{1}{n^2}$, converges

19. $\dfrac{\tan^{-1} n}{n^2} < \dfrac{\pi/2}{n^2}$, converges

21. $\dfrac{\tan^{-1} n}{\sqrt{n}} \geq \dfrac{\pi/4}{\sqrt{n}}$, diverges

23. $\dfrac{e^n}{e^{2n} + 1} < \left(\dfrac{1}{e}\right)^n$, converges

25. $\dfrac{(n!)^2}{[(n + 1)!]^2} = \dfrac{1}{(n + 1)^2} < \dfrac{1}{n^2}$, converges

27. $\dfrac{n!}{(2n)!} = \dfrac{1}{2^n(2n - 1)(2n - 3)\cdots 3 \cdot 1} < \dfrac{1}{2^n}$, converges

29. $\left(\dfrac{1}{n^4}\right) / \left(\dfrac{n^3}{n^7 - 1}\right) = 1 - \dfrac{1}{n^7} \to 1$, converges

31. $\left(\dfrac{n - 1}{n^2 + 1}\right) / \left(\dfrac{1}{n}\right) = 1 - \dfrac{1}{2n} \to 1$, diverges

33. $\left(\dfrac{1}{n^{3/2}}\right) / \left(\dfrac{n^{1/2}}{n^2 - 1}\right) = 1 - \dfrac{1}{n^2} \to 1$, converges

35. $\left(\dfrac{1}{n}\right) / \left(\dfrac{2n - 1}{(n + 2)(n + 3)}\right)$

$= (1 + 2/n)\left(\dfrac{1 + 3/n}{2 - 1/n}\right) \to \dfrac{1}{2}$, diverges

37. $\left(\dfrac{4^n}{5^n}\right) / \left(\dfrac{4^n}{2\sqrt{25^n - 1}}\right) = 2\sqrt{1 - \dfrac{1}{25^n}} \to 2$,

converges

39. $\left(\dfrac{3(n+1)^2}{n^6}\right) / \left(\dfrac{1}{n^4}\right) = \left(1 - \dfrac{1}{4^n}\right) \to 1$, converges

41. $\left(\dfrac{1}{2^n}\right) / \left(\dfrac{2^n}{4^n - 1}\right) = 3\left(1 + \dfrac{1}{n}\right) \to 3$, converges

43. DCT: $\dfrac{2^n}{5^n + 1} < \left(\dfrac{2}{5}\right)^n$, converges

45. DCT: $\dfrac{\sqrt{n^3}}{\sqrt[3]{n^{20}} + 1} < \dfrac{1}{n^{31/6}}$, converges

47. DCT: $\dfrac{2^{n!}}{3^{n!}} = \left(\dfrac{2}{3}\right)^{n!} < \left(\dfrac{2}{3}\right)^n$, converges

49. NTT: $\lim\limits_{n \to \infty} \dfrac{e^n}{e^n - 1} = 1 \neq 0$, diverges

51. IT: $\displaystyle\int_1^\infty x^2 e^{-x^3}\, dx = \dfrac{1}{3}$, converges

53. DCT: $\dfrac{\sin^2 n}{n^{5/4}} \leq \dfrac{1}{n^{5/4}}$, converges

55. IT: $\displaystyle\int_2^\infty \dfrac{1}{x(\ln x)^7}\, dx = \dfrac{1}{6(\ln 2)^6}$, converges

57. NTT: $\lim\limits_{n \to \infty} \dfrac{1}{n^{1/n}} = 1 \neq 0$, diverges

59. DCT: $\dfrac{(n-1)!}{n!} > \dfrac{1}{n}$, diverges

61. $\left(\dfrac{1}{n^2}\right) / \left(\dfrac{n^{1/n}}{n^2 + 1}\right) = \dfrac{1}{n^{1/n}}\left(1 + \dfrac{1}{n^2}\right) \to 1$,
      converges

63. $\sqrt{\dfrac{25^{-n}}{4^n}} = \left(\dfrac{1}{10}\right)^n$, convergent geometric series

65. DCT: $\dfrac{3^n + 1}{2^n - 1} > \left(\dfrac{3}{2}\right)^n$, diverges

Exercises: 8.5

1. $\dfrac{a_{n+1}}{a_n} = \dfrac{2}{n+1} \to 0 < 1$, converges

3. $\dfrac{a_{n+1}}{a_n} = \dfrac{(n+1)^2}{3(3n+2)(3n+1)} \to \dfrac{1}{27} < 1$, converges

5. $\dfrac{a_{n+1}}{a_n} = \dfrac{1}{(1 + 1/n)^n} \to \dfrac{1}{e} < 1$, converges

7. $\dfrac{a_{n+1}}{a_n} = \dfrac{1}{3}\left(1 + \dfrac{1}{n}\right)^5 \to \dfrac{1}{3} < 1$, converges

9. $\dfrac{a_{n+1}}{a_n} = \dfrac{1}{2}\left(1 + \dfrac{1}{n}\right) \to \dfrac{1}{2} < 1$, converges

11. $\dfrac{a_{n+1}}{a_n} = \dfrac{1}{2(2n+3)} \to 0 < 1$, converges

13. $\dfrac{a_{n+1}}{a_n} = \dfrac{n+1}{2(n+2)(2n+1)} \to 0 < 1$, converges

15. $\dfrac{a_{n+1}}{a_n} = \dfrac{2(4^n - 1)}{4^{n+1} - 1} \to \dfrac{1}{2} < 1$, converges

17. $\dfrac{a_{n+1}}{a_n} = \dfrac{n+1}{(2^{n!})^n} < \dfrac{n+1}{2^n} \to 0 < 1$, converges

19. $\dfrac{a_{n+1}}{a_n} = \dfrac{(2n+3)(2n+2)}{5(n+1)^2} \to \dfrac{4}{5} < 1$, converges

21. $\dfrac{a_{n+1}}{a_n} = \dfrac{(2n+2)(2n+1)}{9(n+1)^2} \to \dfrac{4}{9} < 1$, converges

23. $\dfrac{a_{n+1}}{a_n} = \dfrac{n+1}{(2n+4)(2n+5)} \to 0 < 1$, converges

25. $(a_n)^{1/n} = \dfrac{2n+1}{3n+2} \to \dfrac{2}{3} < 1$, converges

27. $(a_n)^{1/n} = \dfrac{n^2 + 1}{5n^2 + 2} \to \dfrac{1}{5} < 1$, converges

29. $(a_n)^{1/n} = \dfrac{(n^{1/n})^3}{4} \to \dfrac{1}{4} < 1$, converges

31. $(a_n)^{1/n} = \dfrac{1}{2}e^{(\ln n)/n^2} \to \dfrac{1}{2} < 1$, converges

33. $(a_n)^{1/n} = \dfrac{\ln n}{n} \to 0 < 1$, converges

35. $(a_n)^{1/n} = \dfrac{\sqrt{n}}{n+1} \to 0 < 1$, converges

37. $(a_n)^{1/n} = \dfrac{\sqrt{n}}{\sqrt{n} - 1} \to 1$, inconclusive.
    diverges by the NTT.

39. $(a_n)^{1/n} = \dfrac{n^{1/n}}{(1 + 2/n)^n} \to \dfrac{1}{e^2} < 1$, converges

41. $(a_n)^{1/n} = \dfrac{e^{(\ln(\ln n)/n}}{(n^{1/n})^2} \to 1$, inconclusive
    converges by the IT.

43. DCT: $\dfrac{1}{(\sqrt{n} + 2)^3} < \dfrac{1}{(\sqrt{n})^3} = \dfrac{1}{n^{3/2}}$, convrges

45. $(a_n)^{1/n} = \dfrac{1 + e^{-n}}{2 + e^{-n}} \to \dfrac{1}{2} < 1$, converges

47. LCT: $\left(\dfrac{1}{(\sqrt{n})^3}\right) / \left(\dfrac{1}{(\sqrt{n} - 2)^3}\right) = (1 - 2/\sqrt{n})^3 \to 1$,
    converges

49. $\dfrac{a_{n+1}}{a_n} = \dfrac{1}{2} \cdot \left[\dfrac{1}{(1 + 1/n)^n}\right]^2 \to \dfrac{1}{2e^2} < 1$, converges

51. NTT: $\lim\limits_{n \to \infty} \dfrac{1}{\tan^{-1}(n)} = \dfrac{1}{\pi/2} \neq 0$, diverges

53. $\dfrac{a_{n+1}}{a_n} = \dfrac{1}{2(2n+1)} \to 0 < 1$, converges

55. LCT: $\left(\dfrac{n^2}{\sqrt{n^5}}\right) / \left(\dfrac{n^2}{(\sqrt{n^5 + 1})}\right) = \sqrt{1 + 1/n^5} \to 1$,
    converges

57. DCT: $\dfrac{\tan^{-1}(n)}{n} \geq \dfrac{\pi}{4} \cdot \dfrac{1}{n}$, diverges.

59. DCT: $\left[\dfrac{\tan^{-1}(n)}{n}\right]^2 \leq \left[\dfrac{\pi}{2}\right]^2 \cdot \dfrac{1}{n^2}$, converges.

61. LCT: $\left(\dfrac{2^n}{(3^n)^2}\right) \Big/ \left(\dfrac{2^n+1}{(3^n-1)^2}\right)$

$= \left(1 - \dfrac{1}{3^n}\right)^2 \cdot \dfrac{1}{1+2^{-n}} \to 1$, converges

63. DCT: $\dfrac{1}{\sqrt{n}(n+1)} \leq \dfrac{1}{\sqrt{n}(n)} = \dfrac{1}{n^{3/2}}$, converges.

65. $(a_n)^{1/n} = \left(\dfrac{\ln n}{n}\right)^2 \to 0 < 1$, converges

Exercises: 8.6

1. $c_n = \dfrac{1}{1+\sqrt{n}} > \dfrac{1}{1+\sqrt{n+1}} = c_{n+1}$,

$\lim\limits_{n\to\infty} \dfrac{1}{1+\sqrt{n}} = 0$. Series converges

3. $f(x) = \dfrac{x}{x^2-1}$, $f'(x) = \dfrac{-1-x^2}{(x^2-1)^2} < 0$, $x \geq 2$,

so $\left\{\dfrac{n}{n^2-1}\right\}$ decreases. $\lim\limits_{n\to\infty}\dfrac{n}{n^2-1} = 0$. Series converges

5. $f(x) = \dfrac{x^3+x}{x^4-1}$, $f'(x) = \dfrac{-x^6-3x^4-3x^2-1}{(x^4-1)^2} < 0$

$x \geq 2$, so $\left\{\dfrac{n^3+n}{n^4-1}\right\}$ decreases. $\lim\limits_{n\to\infty}\dfrac{n^3+n}{n^4-1} = 0$.
Series converges

7. $f(x) = \dfrac{x}{x-1}$, $f'(x) = \dfrac{-1}{(x-1)^2} < 0$, $x \geq 2$,

so $\left\{\dfrac{n}{n-1}\right\}$ decreases. $\lim\limits_{n\to\infty}\dfrac{n}{n-1} = 1$. AST fails.
Series diverges by the NTT.

9. $f(x) = xe^{-x}$, $f'(x) = (1-x)e^{-x} < 0$, $x \geq 2$,
so $\left\{ne^{-n}\right\}$ decreases. $\lim\limits_{n\to\infty} ne^{-n} = 0$. Series converges

11. $f(x) = \tan^{-1}(1+x^{-1})$,

$f'(x) = \dfrac{1}{(1+(1+x^{-1})^2)} \cdot (-x^{-2}) < 0$, $x \geq 1$,

so $\left\{\tan^{-1}(1+n^{-1})\right\}$ decreases. $\lim\limits_{n\to\infty} \tan^{-1}(1+n^{-1})$

$= \frac{\pi}{4} \neq 0$. Series diverges by NTT.

13. $f(x) = \dfrac{x^{3/2}}{x^2-1}$, $f'(x) = \dfrac{\frac{1}{2}x^{1/2}(-3-x^2)}{(x^2-1)^2} < 0$, $x \geq 2$,

so $\left\{\dfrac{n^{3/2}}{n^2-1}\right\}$ decreases. $\lim\limits_{n\to\infty}\dfrac{n^{3/2}}{n^2-1} = 0$. Series
converges

15. $f(x) = \dfrac{1}{e^x+e^{-x}}$, $f'(x) = \dfrac{-(e^x-e^{-x})}{(e^x+e^{-x})^2} < 0$, $x \geq 1$,

so $\left\{\dfrac{1}{e^n+e^{-n}}\right\}$ decreases. $\lim\limits_{n\to\infty}\dfrac{1}{e^n+e^{-n}} = 0$. Series
converges

17. $f(x) = \dfrac{e^x+e^{-x}}{e^x-e^{-x}} = \dfrac{e^{2x}+1}{e^{2x}-1}$,

$f'(x) = \dfrac{2e^{2x}(-2)}{(e^{2x}-1)^2} < 0$, $x \geq 1$, so $\left\{\dfrac{e^{2n}+1}{e^{2n}-1}\right\}$

decreases. $\lim\limits_{n\to\infty}\dfrac{e^{2n}+1}{e^{2n}-1} = 1$. Series diverges by NTT.

19. $f(x) = \dfrac{\ln x}{x^2}$, $f'(x) = \dfrac{x(1-2\ln x)}{x^4} < 0$, $x \geq e^{1/2}$,

so $\left\{\dfrac{\ln n}{n^2}\right\}$ decreases. $\lim\limits_{n\to\infty}\dfrac{\ln n}{n^2} = 0$. Series
converges

21. $f(x) = \dfrac{(\ln x)^2}{\sqrt{x}}$, $f'(x) = \dfrac{\ln x(4-\ln x)}{2x\sqrt{x}} < 0$, $x \geq e^4$,

so $\left\{\dfrac{(\ln n)^2}{\sqrt{n}}\right\}$ decreases. $\lim\limits_{n\to\infty}\dfrac{(\ln n)^2}{\sqrt{n}} = 0$. Series
converges

23. $f(x) = \dfrac{\tan^{-1}(x^{-1})}{x^2}$

$f'(x) = \dfrac{\frac{-1}{1+x^{-2}} - \tan^{-1}(x^{-1})2x}{x^2} < 0$, $x \geq 1$,

so $\left\{\dfrac{\tan^{-1}(n^{-1})}{n^2}\right\}$ decreases. $\lim\limits_{n\to\infty}\dfrac{(\ln n)^2}{\sqrt{n}} = 0$.
Series converges

25. $f(x) = \sin^{-1}(x^{-1})$, $f'(x) = \cos(x^{-1})(-x^{-2}) < 0$,
$x \geq 1$, so $\left\{\sin^{-1}(n^{-1})\right\}$ decreases.
$\lim\limits_{n\to\infty} \sin^{-1}(n^{-1}) = 0$. Series converges

NOTE: AC = Absolutely Convergent,
CC = Conditionally Convergent, D = Divergent
27. CC **29.** AC **31.** CC **33.** D **35.** AC **37.** CC
39. CC **41.** AC **43.** AC **45.** CC **47.** AC
49. CC **51.** D **53.** CC **55.** CC

57. Let $\{s_n\}$ denote the sequence of partial sums.
First show that the odd terms form a decreasing
sequence $s_1 \geq s_3 \geq s_5 \geq \cdots$, with each ≥ 0. Next show
that the even terms form a increasing sequence
$s_2 \leq s_4 \leq s_6 \leq \cdots$, with each $\leq c_1$. Then use
Theorem 8.1.5 to get that the sequences of odd and
even terms have limits, which are the same.

Exercises: 8.7

1. 5, $[-5,5)$ **3.** 1, $[-1,1)$ **5.** $\frac{1}{2}$, $[-\frac{1}{2},\frac{1}{2}]$
7. 2, $[-1,3]$ **9.** 1, $(-1,1)$ **11.** 3, $(-3,3)$
13. 2, $(-2,2)$ **15.** 2, $[1,3]$ **17.** 2, $(-2,2)$
19. 1, $[-1,1)$ **21.** 3, $[-3,3]$ **23.** 1, $[2.4]$
25. $\frac{1}{2}$, $[-\frac{1}{2},\frac{1}{2})$ **27.** 2, $(-1,3)$ **29.** $\frac{1}{3}$, $[-\frac{1}{3},\frac{1}{3}]$
31. ∞, $(-\infty,\infty)$ **33.** 0, $\{0\}$ **35.** $\frac{2}{3}$, $(-\frac{2}{3},\frac{3}{3})$
37. 3, $(-1,5)$ **39.** 5, $(-5,5)$ **41.** 0, $\{3\}$
43. 2, $[-2,2)$ **45.** 3, $(-3,3)$ **47.** 1, $(-1,1)$
49. ∞, $(-\infty,\infty)$ **51.** ∞, $(-\infty,\infty)$ **53.** ∞, $(-\infty,\infty)$
55. First show that

$(2n)! = 2^n n!(2n-1)(2n-3)(2n-5)\cdots 3\cdot 1$
Then
$$b_n = \frac{2^n n!}{(2n-1)(2n-3)(2n-5)\cdots 3\cdot 1}$$
$$= \frac{2n}{2n-1}\cdot\frac{2n-2}{2n-3}\cdot\frac{2n-4}{2n-5}\cdots\frac{4}{3}\cdot\frac{2}{1} > 1$$

Exercises: 8.8

1. $e^x = \sum_{n=0}^{\infty}\frac{x^n}{n!},\ R=\infty$

3. $\cos x = \sum_{k=0}^{\infty}\frac{(-1)^k x^{2k}}{(2k)!},\ R=\infty$

5. $\ln(1+x) = \sum_{n=1}^{\infty}(-1)^{n+1}\frac{x^n}{n},\ R=1$

7. $\sinh x = \sum_{k=0}^{\infty}\frac{x^{2k+1}}{(2k+1)!},\ R=\infty$

9. $\cosh x = \sum_{k=0}^{\infty}\frac{x^{2k}}{(2k)!},\ R=\infty$

11. $2^x = \sum_{n=0}^{\infty}\frac{(\ln 2)^n}{n!}x^n,\ R=\infty$

13. $e^{-x} = \sum_{n=0}^{\infty}\frac{(-1)^n}{n!}x^n,\ R=\infty$

15. $e^{2x} = \sum_{n=0}^{\infty}\frac{2^n}{n!}x^n,\ R=\infty$

17. $\sin 2x = \sum_{k=0}^{\infty}\frac{(-1)^k 2^{2k+1}}{(2k+1)!}x^{2k+1},\ R=\infty$

19. $f(x) = 1 + 3x - 5x^2 + 2x^3,\ R=\infty$

21. $\sin(x+\pi) = \sum_{k=0}^{\infty}\frac{(-1)^{k+1}}{(2k+1)!}x^{2k+1} = -\sin x,\ R=\infty$

23. $\cos(x+1) = \sum_{n=0}^{\infty}\frac{(-1)^n c_n}{n!}x^n$, where $c_{2k}=\cos(1)$, $c_{2k+1}=\sin(1)$, $k=0,1,2,\ldots,\ R=\infty$

25. $e^{x+1} = \sum_{n=0}^{\infty}\frac{e}{n!}x^n,\ R=\infty$

27. $2^x - 2^{-x} = \sum_{k=0}^{\infty}\frac{2(\ln 2)^{2k+1}}{(2k+1)!}x^{2k+1},\ R=\infty$

29. $2^x + 2^{-x} \sum_{k=0}^{\infty}\frac{2(\ln 2)^{2k}}{(2k)!}x^{2k},\ R=\infty$

31. $xe^x = \sum_{n=1}^{\infty}\frac{x^n}{(n-1)!},\ R=\infty$

33. $\ln x = \ln 2 + \sum_{n=1}^{\infty}\frac{(-1)^{n+1}}{n2^n}(x-2)^n,\ R=2$

35. $\sin x = \sum_{k=0}^{\infty}\frac{(-1)^k\sqrt{3}}{2(2k)!}(x-\tfrac{\pi}{3})^{2k}$
$\quad + \sum_{k=0}^{\infty}\frac{(-1)^k}{2(2k+1)!}(x-\tfrac{\pi}{3})^{2k+1},\ R=\infty$

37. $\sin x = \sum_{k=0}^{\infty}\frac{(-1)^k\sqrt{2}}{2(2k)!}(x-\tfrac{\pi}{4})^{2k}$
$\quad + \sum_{k=0}^{\infty}\frac{(-1)^k\sqrt{2}}{2(2k+1)!}(x-\tfrac{\pi}{4})^{2k+1},\ R=\infty$

39. $e^x = \sum_{n=0}^{\infty}\frac{e}{n!}(x-1)^n,\ R=\infty$

41. $2^x = \sum_{n=0}^{\infty}\frac{4(\ln 2)^n}{n!}(x-2)^n,\ R=\infty$

43. $\sqrt[3]{x} =$
$1 + \sum_{n=1}^{\infty}(-1)^n\frac{-1\cdot 2\cdot 5\cdot 8\cdots(3n-4)}{3^n n!}(x-1)^n,\ R=1$

45. $\frac{1}{\sqrt{x}} =$
$1 + \sum_{n=1}^{\infty}(-1)^n\frac{1\cdot 3\cdot 5\cdot 7\cdots(2n-1)}{2^n n!}(x-1)^n,\ R=1$

47. $\frac{1}{x} = \sum_{n=0}^{\infty}(-1)^n(x-1)^n,\ R=1$

49. $\frac{1}{x^2} = \sum_{n=0}^{\infty}(-1)^n(n+1)(x-1)^n,\ R=1$

51. $f(x) = 1 - (x-1) + (x-1)^2 + 2(x-1)^3$

53. $P_1(x) = x,\ P_3(x) = x - \frac{1}{6}x^3,\ P_5(x) - x - \frac{1}{6}x^3 + \frac{1}{120}x^5$
$P_7(x) = x - \frac{1}{6}x^3 + \frac{1}{120}x^5 - \frac{1}{5040}x^7$
$P_1(1) = 1,\ P_3(1) = \frac{5}{6},\ P_5(1) = \frac{101}{120},\ P_7(1) = \frac{4241}{5040}$

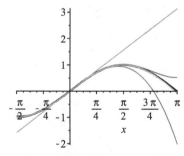

55. $P_1(x) = x,\ P_3(x) = x - \frac{1}{6}x^3,\ P_5(x) = x - \frac{1}{6}x^3 + \frac{1}{120}x^5$
$P_7(x) = x - \frac{1}{6}x^3 + \frac{1}{120}x^5 - \frac{1}{5040}x^7$
$P_1\left(\frac{\pi}{8}\right) \approx 0.3926991,\ P_3\left(\frac{\pi}{8}\right) \approx 0.3826059,$
$P_5\left(\frac{\pi}{8}\right) \approx 0.3826837,\ P_7\left(\frac{\pi}{8}\right) \approx 0.3826834$

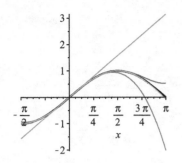

57. $P_0(x) = 1$, $P_1(x) = 1 + \frac{1}{3}(x-1)$

$P_2(x) = 1 + \frac{1}{3}(x-1) - \frac{1}{9}(x-1)^2$

$P_3(x) = 1 + \frac{1}{3}(x-1) - \frac{1}{9}(x-1)^2 + \frac{5}{81}(x-1)^3$

$P_4(x) = 1 + \frac{1}{3}(x-1) - \frac{1}{9}(x-1)^2 + \frac{5}{81}(x-1)^3$

$\qquad - \frac{10}{243}(x-1)^4$

$P_0(1) = 1$, $P_1(1) = \frac{4}{3}$, $P_2(1) = \frac{11}{9}$, $P_3(1) = \frac{104}{81}$

$P_4(1) = \frac{302}{243}$

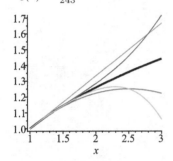

59. $P_0(x) = 0$, $P_1(x) = x - 1$

$P_2(x) = (x-1) - \frac{1}{2}(x-1)^2$

$P_3(x) = (x-1) - \frac{1}{2}(x-1)^2 + \frac{1}{3}(x-1)^3$

$P_4(x) = (x-1) - \frac{1}{2}(x-1)^2 + \frac{1}{3}(x-1)^3 - \frac{1}{4}(x-1)^4$

$P_0(2) = 0$, $P_1(2) = 1$, $P_2(2) = \frac{1}{2}$, $P_3(2) = \frac{5}{6}$

$P_4(2) = \frac{7}{12}$

61. $P_0(x) - 1$, $P_1(x) = 1$, $P_2(x) = 1 + \frac{1}{2}x^2$

$P_3(x) 1 + \frac{1}{2}x^2$, $P_4(x) = 1 + \frac{1}{2}x^2 + \frac{5}{24}x^4$

$P_0\left(\frac{\pi}{3}\right) = P_1\left(\frac{\pi}{3}\right) = 1$, $P_2\left(\frac{\pi}{3}\right) = P_3\left(\frac{\pi}{3}\right) \approx 1.519$,

$P_4\left(\frac{\pi}{3}\right) \approx 1.77$

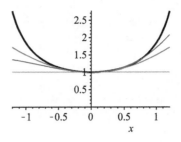

63. $(1+x)^{-3/2} = \sum_{n=0}^{\infty} (-1)^n \frac{(2n+1)!}{4^n (n!)^2} x^n$

65. $(1+x)^{1/3} = 1 + \sum_{n=1}^{\infty} (-1)^{n-1} \frac{\prod_{i=1}^{n}(3i-4)}{3^n n!} x^n$

67. $(1+x)^{3/2} =$

$1 + \frac{3}{2}x + \frac{3}{4}x^2 + \sum_{n=3}^{\infty} (-1)^{n-2} \frac{\prod_{i=1}^{n}(2i-5)}{2^n n!} x^n$

69. $(a+b)^{1/2} =$

$1 + \frac{1}{2}x + \sum_{n=2}^{\infty} (-1)^{n-1} \frac{(2n)!}{4^n (n!)^2 (2n-1)} a^{1/2-n} b^n$

71. $(1-x)^{-3/2} = \sum_{n=0}^{\infty} \frac{(2n+1)!}{4^n (n!)^2} x^n$

73. $(1+x^2)^{1/3} = 1 + \sum_{n=1}^{\infty} (-1)^{n-1} \frac{\prod_{i=1}^{n}(3i-4)}{3^n n!} x^{2n}$

75. $(1+2x)^{3/2} =$

$1 + 3x + 3x^2 + \sum_{n=3}^{\infty} (-1)^{n-2} \frac{\prod_{i=1}^{n}(2i-5)}{n!} x^n$

77. $(a-b)^{1/2} =$

$1 + \frac{1}{2}x - \sum_{n=2}^{\infty} \frac{(2n)!}{4^n (n!)^2 (2n-1)} a^{1/2-n} b^n$

Exercises: 8.9

1. $\frac{1}{1+x^4} = \sum_{n=0}^{\infty} (-1)^n x^{4n}$, $(-1, 1)$

3. $\frac{1}{2-x} = \sum_{n=0}^{\infty} \frac{x^n}{2^{n+1}}$, $(-2, 2)$

5. $\frac{1}{e^{5x}} = e^{-5x} = \sum_{n=0}^{\infty} (-1)^n \frac{5^n}{n!} x^n$, $(-\infty, \infty)$

7. $e^{x^2} + \frac{1}{1-x^2} = \sum_{n=0}^{\infty} \left(\frac{1}{n!} + 1\right) x^{2n}$, $(-1, 1)$

9. $e^{2x} + e^{-3x} = \sum_{n=0}^{\infty} \frac{2^n + (-1)^n 3^n}{n!} x^n$, $(-\infty, \infty)$

11. $e^x + e^{-x} = \sum_{k=0}^{\infty} \frac{2}{(2k)!} x^{2k}$, $(-\infty, \infty)$

13. $x \ln(1+x) = \sum\limits_{n=1}^{\infty} \dfrac{(-1)^{n+1}}{n} \, x^{n+1}, \ (-1,1]$

15. $x^2 \cos x = \sum\limits_{n=0}^{\infty} \dfrac{(-1)^n}{(2n)!} \, x^{2n+2}, \ (-\infty, \infty)$

17. $x \sin(2x^3) = \sum\limits_{n=0}^{\infty} (-1)^n \dfrac{2^{2n+1}}{(2n+1)!} \, x^{6n+4}, \ (-\infty, \infty)$

19. $x^2 e^{-5x} = \sum\limits_{n=0}^{\infty} (-1)^n \dfrac{5^n}{n!} \, x^{n+3}, \ (-\infty, \infty)$

21. $(1+x)e^x = \sum\limits_{n=0}^{\infty} \dfrac{1+n}{n!} \, x^n, \ (-\infty, \infty)$

23. $\ln(1+x^2) = \sum\limits_{n=1}^{\infty} \dfrac{(-1)^{n+1}}{n} \, x^{2n}, \ (-1,1]$

25. $\ln(1+2x) = \sum\limits_{n=0}^{\infty} \dfrac{(-1)^{n+1}2^n}{n} \, x^n, \ (-\frac{1}{2}, \frac{1}{2}]$

27. $\ln(2+x^4) = \ln 2 + \sum\limits_{n=1}^{\infty} \dfrac{(-1)^{n+1}}{2^n n} \, x^{4n}, \ [-2^{1/4}, 2^{1/4}]$

29. $(x+x^3)\tan^{-1}(2x)$
$= 2x^2 + \sum\limits_{n=1}^{\infty} \dfrac{(-1)^{n-1}2^{2n-1}(5-6n)}{4n^2-1} \, x^{2n+2}, \ [-\frac{1}{2}, \frac{1}{2}]$

31. $(1+x^2)\sin^{-1}(3x) = 3x$
$+ \sum\limits_{n=1}^{\infty} \dfrac{(2n-2)!3^{2n-1}}{4^{n-1}[(n-1)!]^2}\left[\dfrac{40n^2-34n+9}{2n(4n^2-1)}\right]x^{2n+1}, \ [-\frac{1}{3}, \frac{1}{3}]$

33. $\cos(\sqrt{x}) = \sum\limits_{n=0}^{\infty} \dfrac{(-1)^n}{(2n)!} \, x^{2n}, \ [0, \infty)$

35. $\dfrac{\sin x}{x} = \sum\limits_{n=0}^{\infty} (-1)^n \dfrac{x^{2n}}{(2n+1)!}, \ (-\infty, \infty)$

37. $\dfrac{e^x - 1}{x} = \sum\limits_{k=0}^{\infty} \dfrac{x^k}{(k+1)!}, \ (-\infty, \infty)$

39. $\dfrac{1}{2^x} = e^{-x \ln 2} = \sum\limits_{n=0}^{\infty} (-1)^n \dfrac{(\ln 2)^n}{(n)!} \, x^n, \ (-\infty, \infty)$

41. $e^{-x} \ln(1+x) = x - \frac{3}{2}x^2 + \frac{4}{3}x^3 - x^4 + \cdots, \ (-1, 1)$

43. $e^{-x} \sin x =$
$x - x^2 + \frac{1}{3}x^3 - \frac{3}{40}x^5 + \frac{7}{360}x^6 + \frac{1}{240}x^7 + \cdots, \ (-\infty, \infty)$

45. $\tan x = x + \frac{1}{3}x^3 + \frac{2}{5}x^5 + \frac{17}{315}x^7 + \cdots$

47. $\dfrac{\ln(1+x)}{\sqrt{1+x}} = x - x^2 + \frac{23}{24}x^3 - \frac{11}{12}x^4 + \cdots$

49. $\displaystyle\int \dfrac{2}{1-x^2} \, dx = \sum\limits_{n=0}^{\infty} \dfrac{2}{2n+1} \, x^{2n+1} = \ln\left|\dfrac{1+x}{1-x}\right|$

51. $\displaystyle\int \dfrac{1}{\sqrt{1+x^2}} \, dx = \sum\limits_{n=0}^{\infty} (-1)^n \dfrac{(2n)!}{4^n(n!)^2(2n+1)} \, x^{2n+1}$
$= \ln\left|x + \sqrt{1+x^2}\right|$

53. $\displaystyle\int \dfrac{1}{\sqrt{1-x^2}} \, dx = \sum\limits_{n=0}^{\infty} \dfrac{(2n)!}{4^n(n!)^2(2n+1)} \, x^{2n+1}$
$= \sin^{-1} x$

55. $\displaystyle\int \dfrac{1}{1+x^3} \, dx = C + \sum\limits_{n=0}^{\infty} (-1)^n \dfrac{x^{3n+1}}{3n+1}$

57. $\displaystyle\int e^{-x^2} \, dx = C + \sum\limits_{n=0}^{\infty} (-1)^n \dfrac{x^{2n+1}}{n!(2n+1)}$

59. $\displaystyle\int \cos(-x^2) \, dx = C + \sum\limits_{n=0}^{\infty} (-1)^n \dfrac{x^{4n+1}}{(2n)!(4n+1)}$

61. $y' = \sum\limits_{n=1}^{\infty} \dfrac{(-1)^n}{(3n-1)!} \, x^{3n-1}, \ y'' = \sum\limits_{n=1}^{\infty} \dfrac{(-1)^n}{(3n-2)!} \, x^{3n-2}$
$y''' = \sum\limits_{n=1}^{\infty} \dfrac{(-1)^n}{(3n-3)!} \, x^{3n-3}, \ \text{change index } n = k+1,$
to get $-y$

63. $y' = 1 + \sum\limits_{n=0}^{\infty} \dfrac{1}{(3n+3)!} \, x^{3n+3},$
$y'' = \sum\limits_{n=0}^{\infty} \dfrac{1}{(3n+2)!} \, x^{3n+2}$
$y''' = \sum\limits_{n=0}^{\infty} \dfrac{1}{(3n+1)!} \, x^{3n+1} = x + \sum\limits_{n=1}^{\infty} \dfrac{1}{(3n+1)!} \, x^{3n+1},$
change index $n = k+1$, to get y

65. $y' = 1 + \sum\limits_{n=0}^{\infty} \dfrac{(-1)^{n+1}}{(4n+4)!} \, x^{4n+4},$
$y'' = \sum\limits_{n=0}^{\infty} \dfrac{(-1)^{n+1}}{(4n+3)!} \, x^{4n+3}$
$y''' = \sum\limits_{n=0}^{\infty} \dfrac{(-1)^{n+1}}{(4n+2)!} \, x^{4n+2}$
$y^{(4)} = \sum\limits_{n=0}^{\infty} \dfrac{(-1)^{n+1}}{(4n+1)!} \, x^{4n+1}$
$= -x + \sum\limits_{n=1}^{\infty} \dfrac{(-1)^{n+1}}{(4n+1)!} \, x^{4n+1},$
change index $n = k+1$, to get $-y$

67. $y = \sum\limits_{k=0}^{\infty} \dfrac{(-1)^k}{2^k k!} \, x^{2k}, \ (n = k)$
$y' = \sum\limits_{k=0}^{\infty} \dfrac{(-1)^k}{2^k k!} (2k) x^{2k-1}, \ (n = k)$
$y'' = -\sum\limits_{k=0}^{\infty} \dfrac{(-1)^k}{2^k k!} (2k+1) x^{2k}, \ (n = k+1)$
Substitute these in $y'' + xy' + y$ to get 0.

CHAPTER 9: Answers to Odd Exercises

Exercises: 9.1

1. Graph of $x = t^2$, $y = 1 + t$ for t in $[-3, 3]$

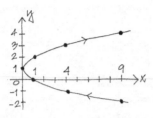

t	t^2	$1+t$
-3	9	-2
-2	4	-1
-1	1	0
0	0	1
1	1	2
2	4	3
3	9	4

3. Graph of $x = \frac{1}{2}t + 1$, $y = t + 2$ for t in $[-3, 3]$

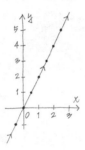

t	$\frac{1}{2}t+1$	$t+2$
-3	-0.5	-1
-2	0	0
1	0.5	1
0	1	2
1	1.5	3
2	2	4
3	2.5	5

5. Graph of $x = 2(t^2 - 1)$, $y = t(t^2 - 4)$ for t in $[-3, 3]$

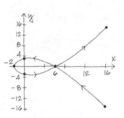

t	$2(t^2-1)$	$t(t^2-4)$
-3	16	-15
-2	6	0
-1	0	3
0	-2	0
1	0	-3
2	6	0
3	16	15

7. Graph of $x = -t^2$, $y = (t-1)(t-2)(t-3)$, for t in $[-3, 3]$

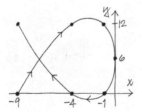

t	$-t^2$	$(t-1)(t-2)(t+3)$
-3	-9	0
-2	-4	12
-1	-1	12
0	0	6
1	-1	0
2	-4	0
3	-9	12

9. Graph of $x = \cos t$, $y = \cos t + \sin t$ for t in $[0, 2\pi]$

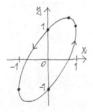

t	$\cos t$	$\cos t + \sin t$
0	1	1
$\frac{\pi}{4}$	$\sqrt{2}/2$	$\sqrt{2}$
$\frac{\pi}{2}$	0	1
π	-1	-1
$\frac{3\pi}{2}$	0	-1
2π	1	1

11. Graph of $x = \sin t$, $y = \cos t + \sin 2t$ for t in $[0, 2\pi]$

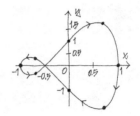

t	$\sin t$	$\cos t + \sin 2t$
0	0	1
$\frac{\pi}{4}$	0.7	1.7
$\frac{\pi}{2}$	1	0
$\frac{3\pi}{4}$	0.7	-1.7
π	0	-1
$\frac{5\pi}{4}$	-0.7	0.3
$\frac{3\pi}{2}$	-1	0
$\frac{7\pi}{4}$	-0.7	-0.3
2π	0	1

13. Graph of $x = \cos t$, $\cos t + \sin 2t$ for t in $[0, 2\pi]$

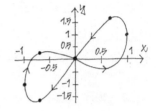

t	$\cos t$	$\cos t + \sin 2t$
0	1	1
$\frac{\pi}{4}$	-0.7	1.7
$\frac{\pi}{2}$	0	0
$\frac{3\pi}{4}$	-0.7	-1.7
π	-1	-1
$\frac{5\pi}{4}$	-0.7	0.3
$\frac{3\pi}{2}$	0	0
$\frac{7\pi}{4}$	0.7	-0.3
2π	1	1

15. $y = 2x + 1$. line with slope 2 and y-intercept $(1, 0)$.

17. $x + 1 = (y - 2)^2$. parabola with vertex $(-1, 2)$, axis: $y = 2$.

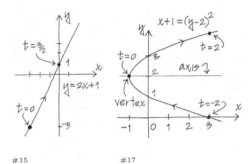

#15   #17

19. $y = x^2 - 1$. parabola with vertex $(0, -1)$, $x \geq 0$, axis: $x = 0$.

21. $x - 2 = (y - 1)^2$. parabola with vertex $(2, 1)$, axis: $y = 1$.

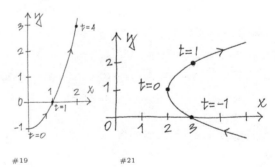

#19   #21

23. $x^2 + y^2 = 1$. circle with center $(0, 0)$ and radius 1. The particle cycles clockwise around the circle starting at $(-1, 0)$ at $t = 0$, completing the first revolution at $t = 2\pi$.

25. $x^2 + y^2 = 1$. circle with center $(0, 0)$ and radius 1. The particle cycles counterclockwise around the circle starting at $(1, 0)$ at $t = 0$, completing the first revolution at $t = 2\pi/3$.

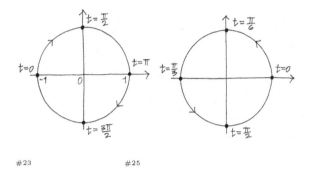

#23   #25

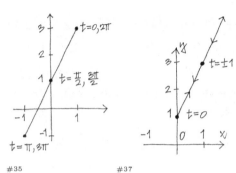

#35   #37

27. $(x-1)^2 + (y-2)^2 = 9$. circle with center $(1,2)$ and radius 3. The particle cycles counterclockwise around the circle starting at $(4,2)$ at $t=0$, completing the first revolution at $t=2\pi$.

29. $y - 1 = (x-2)^2$. parabola with vertex $(2,1)$, axis: $x=2$. The particle moves back and forth along the curve between the points $(3,2)$ and $(1,2)$.

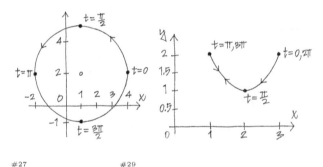

#27   #29

31. $y - 2 = (x-1)^2$. parabola with vertex $(1,2)$, axis: $x=1$. The particle moves back and forth along the curve between the points $(2,3)$ and $(0,3)$.

33. $x^2 + y^2 = 1$. circle with center $(0,0)$ and radius 1. At $t = -\infty$ the particle is at the point $(0,-1)$ and moves along the right semicircle to $(0,1)$ at $t = \infty$.

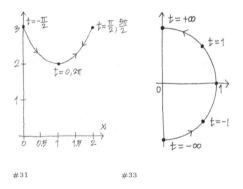

#31   #33

35. $y = 2x + 1$. line with slope 2 and y-intercept $(0,2)$. The particle moves back and forth along the line between the points $(1,3)$ and $(-1,0)$.

37. $y = 2x + 1$. line with slope 2 and intercept $(0,2)$. The particle starts at $(0,1)$ at $t=0$ and moves along the ray in the direction of the point $(1,3)$.

39. (a) $-16t^2 + 32t + 24 = 0 \implies t = 1 + \frac{1}{2}\sqrt{10} \approx 2.68$
(b) $y = -\frac{1}{25}(x-20)^2 + 40$, $a = \frac{-1}{25}$, $h = 20$, $k = 40$
hits ground at $x = 20 + 10\sqrt{10} \approx 53.6$ ft
(c) max height $= 40$ ft
(d)

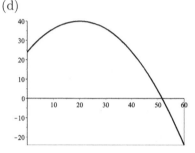

41. (a) $-16t^2 + 64t = 0 \implies t = 4$
(b) $y = -\frac{1}{16}(x-32)^2 + 64$, $a = \frac{-1}{16}$, $h = 32$, $k = 64$
hits ground at $x = 16(4) = 64$ ft
(c) max height $= 64$ ft
(d)

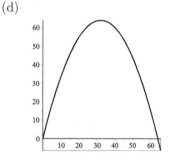

43. (a) $-16t^2 + 20 = 0 \implies t = \frac{1}{2}\sqrt{5} \approx 1.12$
(b) $y = -\frac{1}{16}x^2 + 20$, $a = \frac{-1}{16}$, $h = 0$, $k = 20$
hits ground at $x = 8\sqrt{5} \approx 17.8$ ft
(c) max height $= 20$ ft
(d)

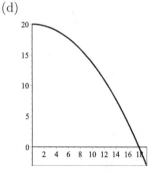

Exercises: 9.2

1. (a) $x' = 2t$, $y' = 3t^2 - 5$ $\implies$ $\frac{dy}{dx} = \frac{3t^2-5}{2t}$.
$\frac{dy}{dx}\big|_{t=1} = \frac{-2}{2} = -1$; $x(1) = 1$, $y(1) = -4$,
tangent line: $y = -x - 3$. (b) horiz tangents:
$t = \pm\sqrt{5/3}$, vert tangent: $t = 0$.
(c) $t = \pm\sqrt{5} \implies (x(t), y(t)) = (5, 0)$.
$\frac{dy}{dx}\big|_{t=\pm\sqrt{5}} = \pm\sqrt{5}$. tangent lines: $y = \pm\sqrt{5}x - 5\sqrt{5}$.

3. (a) $x' = 2t$, $y' = 3t^2 - 2t - 4$ $\implies$ $\frac{dy}{dx} = \frac{3t^2-2t-4}{2t}$.
$\frac{dy}{dx}\big|_{t=-1} = \frac{1}{-2} = -\frac{1}{2}$; $x(-1) = 1$, $y(-1) = 6$,
tangent line: $y = -\frac{1}{2}x + \frac{13}{2}$. (b) horiz tangents:
$t = (1 \pm \sqrt{13})/3$, vert tangent: $t = 0$.
(c) $t = \pm 2 \implies (x(t), y(t)) = (4, 0)$.
$\frac{dy}{dx}\big|_{t=\pm 2} = 1, -3$. tangent lines: $y = x - 4$, $y = -3x + 12$.

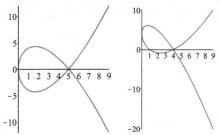

#1 Part (d)   #3 Part (d)

5. (a) $x' = 2t$ $y' = 5t^4 - 15t^2 + 6$ $\implies$ $\frac{dy}{dx} = \frac{5t^4-15t^2+6}{2t}$.
$\frac{dy}{dx}\big|_{t=1} = -2$, $x(1) = 1$, $y(1) = 2$. tangent line:
$y = -2x + 4$. (b) horiz. tangents: $t^2 = \frac{3\pm\sqrt{3}}{2} \approx 2.37, 0.63$
so $t \approx \pm\sqrt{2.37}, \pm\sqrt{0.63}$ vert. tangent: $t = 0$.
(c) $t = \pm\sqrt{2} \implies (x(t), y(t)) = (2, 0)$.
$\frac{dy}{dx}\big|_{t=\pm\sqrt{2}} = \mp\sqrt{2}$.
tangent lines: $y = -\sqrt{2}x + 2\sqrt{2}$, $y = \sqrt{2}x - 2\sqrt{2}$.

7. (a) $x' = -\sin t$, $y' = \cos t + \sin t$ $\implies$ $\frac{dy}{dx} = \frac{\cos t+\sin t}{-\sin t}$.
$\frac{dy}{dx}\big|_{t=\pi/2} = -1$, $x(\pi/2) = 0$, $y(\pi/2) = 1$. tangent line:
$y = -x + 1$ (b) horiz. tangents: $t = 3\pi/4, 7\pi/4$ vert.
tangents: $t = 0, \pi$.

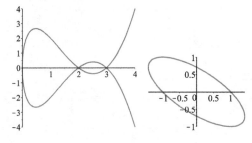

#5 Part (d)   #7 Part (d)

9. (a) $x' = \cos t - \sin t$, $y' = \cos t + \sin t$ $\implies$ $\frac{dy}{dx} = \frac{\cos t+\sin t}{\cos t-\sin t}$. $\frac{dy}{dx}\big|_{t=\pi/2} = -1$, $x(\pi/2) = 1$, $y(\pi/2) = 1$. tangent line: $y = -x + 2$ (b) horiz. tangents: $t = 3\pi/4, 7\pi/4$ vert. tangents: $t = \pi/4, 5\pi/4$.

11. (a) $x' = 2\cos 2t$, $y' = \cos t - \sin t$, $\frac{dy}{dx} = \frac{\cos t-\sin t}{2\cos 2t} = \frac{\cos t-\sin t}{2(\cos^2 t-\sin^2 t)} = \frac{1}{2(\cos t+\sin t)}$. $\frac{dy}{dx}\big|_{t=\pi/4} = \frac{1}{2\sqrt{2}}$, $x(\pi/4) =$

1, $y(\pi/2) = \sqrt{2}$. tangent line: $y = \frac{1}{2\sqrt{2}}x + \frac{3}{2\sqrt{2}}$. (b) horiz.
tangents: none; vert.tangents: $t = 3\pi/4, 7\pi/4$.

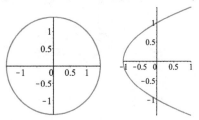

#9 Part (d)   #11 Part (d)

13. (a) $x' = 2\cos 2t$, $y' = -\frac{1}{2}\sin 2t + \cos t$, $\frac{dy}{dx} = \frac{-\frac{1}{2}\sin 2t+\cos t}{2\cos 2t}$; $\frac{dy}{dx}\big|_{t=0} = \frac{1}{2}$, $x(0) = 0, y(0) = \frac{1}{4}$. tangent
line: $y = \frac{1}{2}x + \frac{1}{4}$. (b) horiz. tangents: $t = \pi/2, 3\pi/2$; vert.tangents: $t = \pi/4, 3\pi/4, 5\pi/4, 7\pi/4$.

15. (a) $x' = -\sin t$, $y' = \cos t - 2\sin 2t$, $\frac{dy}{dx} = \frac{2\sin 2t-\cos t}{\sin t}$; $\frac{dy}{dx}\big|_{t=\pi/4} = 2\sqrt{2} - 1$, $x(\pi/4) = 1/\sqrt{2}, y(\pi/4) = 1/\sqrt{2}$. tangent line: $y = (2\sqrt{2}-1)x - 2 + \sqrt{2}$. (b) horiz. tangents: $t = \pi/2, 3\pi/2, 0.25, 2.89$; vert.tangents: $t = \pi, 2\pi$.

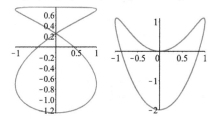

#13 Part (d)   #15 Part (d)

17. (a) $x' = -\sin t$, $y' = -\sin t + 2\cos 2t$, $\frac{dy}{dx} = \frac{\sin t-2\cos 2t}{\sin t}$; $\frac{dy}{dx}\big|_{t=\pi/4} = 1$, $x(\pi/4) = 1/\sqrt{2}, y(\pi/4) = 1/\sqrt{2} + 1$. tangent line: $y = x - 1$. (b) horiz. tangents: $t = .64, 2.5, 3.8, 5.64$; vert.tangents: $t = 0, \pi, 2\pi$.

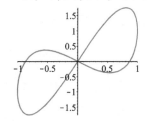

#17 Part (d)

19. $\frac{dy}{dx} = \frac{3t^2-5}{2t}$
horiz: $t = \pm\sqrt{5/3} \approx \pm 1.3$, vert: $t = 0$

t	-2	-1	1	2
$\frac{dy}{dx}$	-1.75	1	-1	1.75
$\pm$	$-$	$+$	$-$	$+$

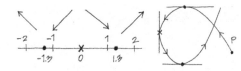

Cartesian eq. $y = \pm\sqrt{x}\,(x - 5)$

21. $\frac{dy}{dx} = \frac{3t^2-2t-4}{2t}$

horiz: $t = (1 \pm \sqrt{13})/3 \approx 1.5, -0.9$, vert: $t = 0$

t	-1.5	-0.5	1	2
$\frac{dy}{dx}$	-1.36	0.25	-1.5	1
$\pm$	$-$	$+$	$-$	$+$

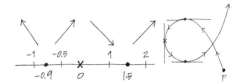

Cartesian eq.: $y = (\pm\sqrt{x} - 1)(x - 4)$

23. $\frac{dy}{dx} = \frac{5t^4 - 15t^2 + 6}{2t}$

horiz: $t = \pm 1.6, \pm 0.7$, vert: $t = 0$

t	-2	-1	-0.5	0.5	1	2
$\frac{dy}{dx}$	-6.5	1	-2.56	2.56	-2	2
$\pm$	$-$	$+$	$-$	$+$	$-$	$+$

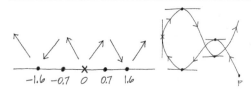

Cartesian eq.: $y = \pm\sqrt{x}(x - 2)(x - 3)$

25. $\frac{dy}{dx} = \frac{\cos t + \sin t}{-\sin t}$

horiz: $t = \pm 3\pi/4, 7\pi/4$, vert: $t = 0, \pi, 2\pi$

t	$\pi/2$	$7\pi/8$	$3\pi/2$	$15\pi/8$
$\frac{dy}{dx}$	-1	-1.4	-1	1.4
$\pm$	$-$	$+$	$-$	$+$

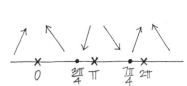

27. $\frac{dy}{dx} = \frac{\cos t + \sin t}{\cos t - \sin t}$

horiz: $t = \pm 3\pi/4, 7\pi/4$, vert: $t = \pi/4, 5\pi/4$

t	$\pi/8$	$\pi/2$	π	$3\pi/2$	$15\pi/8$
$\frac{dy}{dx}$	2.4	-11	1	-1	0.41
$\pm$	$+$	$-$	$+$	$-$	$+$

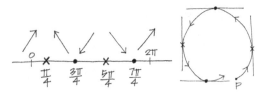

Cartesian eq.: $x^2 + y^2 = 2$

29. $\frac{dy}{dx} = \frac{1}{2(\cos t + \sin t)}$

horiz: none, vert: $t = 3\pi/4, 7\pi/4$

t	$\pi/2$	π	$15\pi/8$
$\frac{dy}{dx}$	0.5	-0.5	0.9
$\pm$	$+$	$-$	$+$

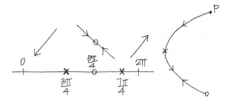

Cartesian eq.: $y^2 = 1 + x$

31. $\frac{dy}{dx} = \frac{-\frac{1}{2}\sin 2t + \cos t}{2\cos 2t}$

horiz: $t = \pi/2, 3\pi/2$, vert: $t = \pi/4, 3\pi/4, 5\pi/4, 7\pi/4$

t	$\pi/6$	$\pi/3$	$2\pi/3$	π	$4\pi/3$	$5\pi/3$	$11\pi/6$
$\frac{dy}{dx}$	1.3	-0.13	0.02	-0.5	0.12	-0.23	1.3
$\pm$	$+$	$-$	$+$	$-$	$+$	$-$	$+$

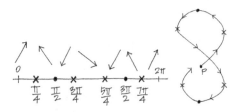

33. $\frac{dy}{dx} = \frac{2\sin 2t - \cos t}{\sin t}$

horiz: $t = \pi/2, 3\pi/2, 0.25, 2.89$, vert: $t = 0, \pi, 2\pi$

t	0.1	1	2	3	4	5
$\frac{dy}{dx}$	-6	1.5	-1.2	3.06	-3.5	0.6
$\pm$	$-$	$+$	$-$	$+$	$-$	$+$

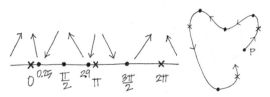

35. $\frac{dy}{dx} = \frac{\sin t - 2\cos 2t}{\sin t}$

horiz: $t = .64, 2.5, 3.8, 5.64$, vert: $t = 0, \pi, 2\pi$

t	0.5	$\pi/2$	2.9	3.4	4.7	6
$\frac{dy}{dx}$	-1.25	3	-6.4	7.8	-1	7
$\pm$	$-$	$+$	$-$	$+$	$-$	$+$

37. $\frac{d^2y}{dx^2} = \frac{3t^2 + 5}{4t^3}$.

$$= \tfrac{2\sqrt{3}+1}{4} + \tfrac{1}{4}\ln(2+\sqrt{3})$$

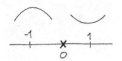

39. $\frac{d^2y}{dx^2} = \frac{3t^2+4}{4t^3}$.

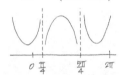

41. $\frac{d^2y}{dx^2} = \frac{15t^4-15t^2-6}{4t^3}$.

43. $\frac{d^2y}{dx^2} = \frac{-1}{\sin^3 t}$.

45. $\frac{d^2y}{dx^2} = \frac{2}{(\cos t - \sin t)^3}$.

Exercises: 9.3

1. $A = -2\int_{-\sqrt{3}}^{0} (t^3 - 5t)\, 2t\, dt = \frac{264\sqrt{3}}{15}$

3. $A = 2\int_{0}^{\sqrt{2}} (t^5 - 5t^3 + 6t)\, 2t\, dt = \frac{32\sqrt{2}}{7}$

5. $A = \int_{-3}^{0} (t^3 - 7t + 6)\, 3t^2\, dt = \frac{891}{4}$

7. $A = 2\int_{-\pi/6}^{\pi/2} (\cos t + \sin 2t)\, \cos t\, dt = \frac{8\pi+3\sqrt{3}}{12}$

9. $A = 2\int_{0}^{\pi/2} \sin 2t(-\tfrac{1}{2}\sin 2t + \cos t)\, dt = \frac{16-3\pi}{12}$

11. $A = A_1 - A_2 + A_3 = \frac{956}{60}$, where

$A_1 = -\int_{-2}^{0}(t^4 - t^3 - 4t^2 + 4t)\, 2\, dt = \frac{248}{15}$

$A_2 = \int_{0}^{1}(t^4 - t^3 - 4t^2 + 4t)\, 2\, dt = \frac{74}{60}$

$A_3 = -\int_{1}^{2}(t^4 - t^3 - 4t^2 + 4t)\, 2\, dt = \frac{48}{60}$

13. $L = \int_{0}^{2}(1 + t^2)\, dt = \frac{14}{3}$

15. $L = \int_{0}^{3/2}(2t + 2t^5)\, dt = \frac{387}{192}$

17. $L = \int_{0}^{3/2}(1 + \tfrac{9}{4}t^4)\, dt = \frac{3147}{640}$

19. $L = \int_{1}^{2}(1 + \tfrac{1}{4}t^{-2})\, dt = \frac{3}{8}$

21. $L = \int_{1}^{4} \tfrac{1}{2}(t^{-1/2} + t^{-3/2})\, dt = \frac{3}{2}$

23. $L = \int_{0}^{1}(e^{-t} + \tfrac{1}{4}e^{3t})\, dt = \frac{1}{2}e^3 - e^{-1} + \frac{11}{12}$

25. $L = \int_{0}^{1}\left[\frac{e^t}{1+e^t} + \tfrac{1}{4}e^t(1+e^t)\right] dt = \ln 2 + \tfrac{1}{8}(1+e)^2 - \tfrac{1}{2}$

27. $L = \int_{0}^{2\pi} 2\sin\tfrac{t}{2}\, dt = 8$

29. $L = \int_{0}^{2\pi}(1 + \tfrac{1}{4}\sin^2 t)\, dt = \frac{5\pi}{4}$

31. $L = \int_{0}^{2\pi}\left(1 + \tfrac{1}{4}[1+\sin 2t\,]\right) dt = \frac{5\pi}{2}$

33. $L = \int_{0}^{\pi/3}\left(\cos t + \tfrac{1}{4}[\sec t + 2\sin t\,]\right) dt$

Exercises: 9.4

1. (a) $x = \sqrt{3},\ y = 1$ (b) $x = \sqrt{3},\ y = 1$
   (c) $x = \sqrt{3},\ y = 1$

3. (a) $r = 2,\ \theta = \frac{\pi}{4}$ (b) $r = 2,\ \theta = \frac{5\pi}{3}$
   (c) $r = 2,\ \theta = \pi$

5. 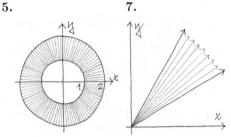   **7.**

9. 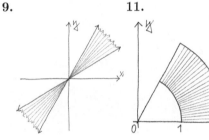   **11.**

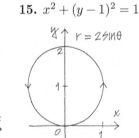

13. $y = 3$ **15.** $x^2 + (y-1)^2 = 1$

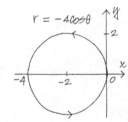 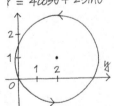

17. $(x+2)^2 + y^2 = 4$ **19.** $(x-2)^2 + (y-1)^2 = 5$

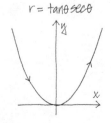 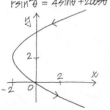

21. $y = x^2$ **23.** $(y-2)^2 = 2(x+2)$

25. $x^2y = 1$

27. $r \sin \theta = 1$ **29.** $r = 2$ **31.** $r = 4 \cos \theta$

33. $r \cos^2 \theta - 2 \cos \theta \sin \theta$

35.   **37.**

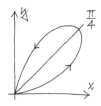 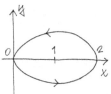

39.

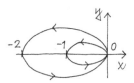

41.

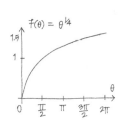 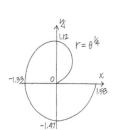

43.

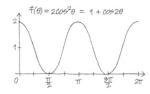 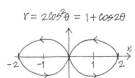

45.

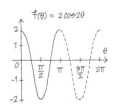 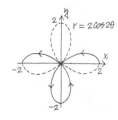

47.

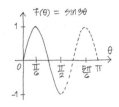 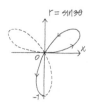

49.

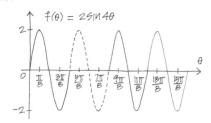

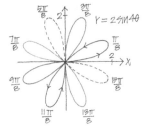

51.

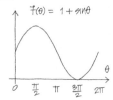 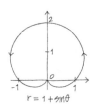

53.

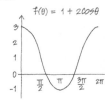 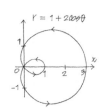

55.

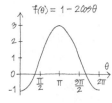 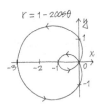

57

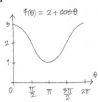 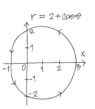

Exercises: 9.5

1. $x = \cos^2 \theta$, $y = \cos \theta \sin \theta = \frac{1}{2} \sin 2\theta$.
$x' = -2 \cos \theta \sin \theta$, $y' = \cos 2\theta$
$\frac{dy}{dx}\big|_{t=\frac{\pi}{3}} = -\frac{\cos 2\theta}{2 \cos \theta \sin \theta}\big|_{t=\frac{\pi}{3}} = \frac{\sqrt{3}}{3}$, $x(\frac{\pi}{3}) = \frac{1}{4}$,
$y(\frac{\pi}{3}) = \frac{\sqrt{3}}{4}$, tangent line: $y = \frac{\sqrt{3}}{4}x + \frac{\sqrt{3}}{6}$.

3. $x = (1 - \cos \theta) \cos \theta$, $y = (1 - \cos \theta) \sin \theta$.
$x' = \sin \theta \cos \theta - (1 - \cos \theta) \sin \theta$,
$y' = \sin^2 \theta + (1 - \cos \theta) \cos \theta$

$\frac{dy}{dx}\big|_{t=\frac{\pi}{2}} = \frac{1}{-1} = -1$, $x(\frac{\pi}{2}) = 0$,

$y(\frac{\pi}{2}) = 1$, tangent line: $y = -x + 1$.

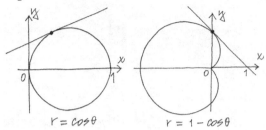

#1   #3

5. $x = (1 + 2\cos\theta)\cos\theta$, $y = (1 + 2\cos\theta)\sin\theta$.

$x' = -2\sin\theta\cos\theta - (1 + 2\cos\theta)\sin\theta$,

$y' = -2\sin^2\theta + (1 + 2\cos\theta)\cos\theta$

$\frac{dy}{dx}\big|_{t=\frac{\pi}{2}} = \frac{-2}{-1} = 2$, $x(\frac{\pi}{2}) = 0$,

$y(\frac{\pi}{2}) = 1$, tangent line: $y = 2x + 1$.

7. $x = \sin 3\theta \cos\theta$, $y = \sin 3\theta \sin\theta$.

$x' = 3\cos 3\theta \cos\theta - \sin 3\theta \sin\theta$,

$y' = 3\cos 3\theta \sin\theta + \sin 3\theta \cos\theta$

$\frac{dy}{dx}\big|_{t=\frac{\pi}{6}} = \frac{\sqrt{3}/2}{-1/2} = -\sqrt{3}$, $x(\frac{\pi}{6}) = \frac{\sqrt{3}}{2}$,

$y(\frac{\pi}{6}) = \frac{1}{2}$, tangent line: $y = -\sqrt{3}x + 2$.

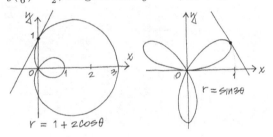

#5   #7

9. $x = \sin 3\theta \cos\theta$, $y = \sin 3\theta \sin\theta$.

$x' = 3\cos 3\theta \cos\theta - \sin 3\theta \sin\theta$,

$y' = 3\cos 3\theta \sin\theta + \sin 3\theta \cos\theta$

Use $\theta = \frac{\pi}{3}$ as an angle with $r = 0$.

$\frac{dy}{dx}\big|_{t=\frac{\pi}{3}} = \frac{-3\sin\frac{\pi}{3}}{-3\cos\frac{\pi}{3}} = \tan\frac{\pi}{3} = \sqrt{3}$, $x(\frac{\pi}{3}) = 0$,

$y(\frac{\pi}{3}) = 0$, tangent line: $y = (\tan\frac{\pi}{3})x = \sqrt{3}\,x$.

11. $x = (1 - 2\cos\theta)\cos\theta$, $y = (1 - 2\cos\theta)\sin\theta$.

$x' = 2\sin\theta\cos\theta - (1 - 2\cos\theta)\sin\theta$,

$y' = 2\sin^2\theta + (1 - 2\cos\theta)\cos\theta$

Use $\theta = \frac{\pi}{3}$ as an angle with $r = 0$.

$\frac{dy}{dx}\big|_{t=\frac{\pi}{3}} = \frac{2\sin^2\frac{\pi}{3}}{2\sin\frac{\pi}{3}\cos\frac{\pi}{3}} = \tan\frac{\pi}{3} = \sqrt{3}$, $x(\frac{\pi}{3}) = 0$,

$y(\frac{\pi}{3}) = 0$, tangent line: $y = (\tan\frac{\pi}{3})x = \sqrt{3}\,x$.

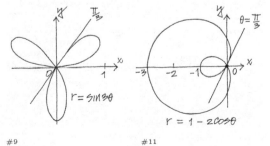

#9   #11

13. $x = \cos 2\theta \cos\theta$, $y = \cos 2\theta \sin\theta$

$x' = -\sin 2\theta \cos\theta - \cos 2\theta \sin\theta$

$y' = -2\sin 2\theta \sin\theta + \cos 2\theta \cos\theta$

$\frac{dy}{dx}\big|_{\theta=\frac{\pi}{6}} = \frac{-\frac{1}{2}}{-\sqrt{3}} = \frac{\sqrt{3}}{6}$, $x(\frac{\pi}{6}) = \frac{\sqrt{3}}{4}$,

$y(\frac{\pi}{6}) = \frac{1}{4}$, tangent line: $y = \frac{\sqrt{3}}{6}x + \frac{1}{8}$.

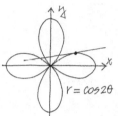

#13

15. By #1, $\frac{dy}{dx} = -\frac{\cos 2\theta}{2\cos\theta\sin\theta}$.

horiz. tangent: $\cos 2\theta = 0 \implies \theta = \frac{\pi}{4}, \frac{3\pi}{4}$

vert. tangent: $\cos\theta\sin\theta = 0 \implies \theta = 0, \frac{\pi}{2}$

17. By #3, $x' = \sin\theta\cos\theta - (1 - \cos\theta)\sin\theta$

$= 2\sin\theta\cos\theta - \sin\theta = \sin\theta(2\cos\theta - 1) = 0$.

$\implies$ vert. tangents: $\theta = \frac{\pi}{3}, \frac{5\pi}{3}, \pi$

$y' = \sin^2\theta + (1 - \cos\theta)\cos\theta = 1 + \cos\theta - 2\cos^2\theta$

$= -(2\cos\theta + 1)(\cos\theta - 1) = 0$

$\implies$ horiz. tangents: $\theta = \frac{2\pi}{3}, \frac{4\pi}{3}, 0$

Note: $x'(0) = 0$, $y'(0) = 0$, but by L' Hospital:

$\lim_{\theta\to 0} \frac{y'(\theta)}{x'(\theta)} = 0$. So a horiz. tangent at $\theta = 0$.

19. By #13 $x' = -2\sin 2\theta \cos\theta - \cos 2\theta \sin\theta$

$= -4\sin\theta\cos^2\theta - (\cos^2\theta - \sin^2\theta)\sin\theta$

$= -4\sin\theta(1 - \sin^2\theta) - ((1 - \sin^2\theta) - \sin^2\theta)\sin\theta$

$= \sin\theta(6\sin^2\theta - 5) = 0$.

$\implies$ vert. tangents: $\theta = 0, \pi, \pm\sin^{-1}(\sqrt{5/6})$,

$\pm\sin^{-1}(\sqrt{5/6}) + \pi \approx 0°, 180°, \pm 66°, 114°, 246°$

$y' = -2\sin 2\theta \sin\theta + \cos 2\theta \cos\theta$

$= -4\sin^2\theta\cos\theta + (\cos^2\theta - \sin^2\theta)\cos\theta$

$= -4(1 - \cos^2\theta)\cos\theta + (\cos^2\theta - (1 - \cos^2\theta))\cos\theta$

$= \cos\theta(6\cos^2\theta - 5) = 0$

$\implies$ horiz. tangents: $\theta = \frac{\pi}{2}, \frac{3\pi}{2}, \pi, \pm\cos^{-1}(\sqrt{5/6})$

$\pm\cos^{-1}(\sqrt{5/6}) + \pi \approx 90°, 270°, \pm 24°, 156°, 204°$

21. $A = \frac{1}{2}\int_0^{\pi/2} 36\cos^2\theta\,d\theta - \frac{9\pi}{2}$

23. $A = \frac{1}{2}\int_0^\pi 9(1 - \cos\theta)^2 d\theta = \frac{27\pi}{4}$

25. $A = \frac{1}{2}\int_0^\pi 36\cos^6\frac{\theta}{3}\,d\theta = \frac{81\pi}{16} + 3\pi$

27. $A = \frac{1}{2}\int_0^\pi 100\theta\,e^{-\theta^2/2}\,d\theta = 50(1 - e^{-\pi^2/2})$

29. $A = \frac{1}{2}\int_0^\pi 100\cos\frac{\theta}{2}\sin^4\frac{\theta}{2}\,d\theta = 20$

31. $A = \frac{1}{2}\int_0^\pi (1 + \cos\theta)^2 d\theta = \frac{3\pi}{4}$

33. $A = \frac{1}{2}\int_{2\pi/3}^{4\pi/3} (1 + 2\cos\theta)^2 d\theta = \pi - \frac{3\sqrt{3}}{2}$

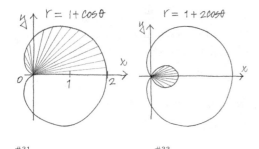

#31   #33

35. $A = 6 \cdot \frac{1}{2} \int_0^{\pi/6} 4 \cos^2 3\theta \, d\theta = \pi$

37. $A = \frac{1}{2} \int_0^{\pi/4} \left[4(1 + \cos \theta)^2 - (1 + \cos \theta)^2 \right] d\theta$

$= \frac{9}{2} \left(\frac{3\pi}{8} + \sqrt{2} + \frac{1}{4} \right)$

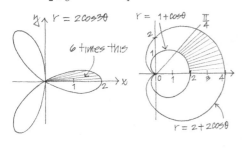

#35   #37

39. $A = \frac{1}{2} \int_0^{\pi/2} \left[4(1 + \cos \theta)^2 - 4 \sin^2 2\theta \right] d\theta = \pi + 4$

41. $A = \frac{1}{2} \int_{\pi/6}^{5\pi/6} \left(16 \sin^2 \theta - 4 \right) d\theta = \frac{2\pi}{3} + 2\sqrt{3}$

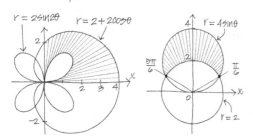

#39   #41

43. $A = \frac{1}{2} \int_0^{\pi/3} \left[4(1 + \cos \theta)^2 - 9 \right] d\theta = \frac{9\sqrt{3}}{4} - \frac{\pi}{6}$

45. $A = \frac{1}{2} \int_{\pi/12}^{5\pi/12} \left(4 \sin^2 3\theta - 1 \right) d\theta = \frac{\pi}{6}$

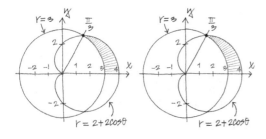

#43   #45

47. $A_1 = \frac{1}{2} \int_{\pi/2}^{5\pi/6} \left(1 - \cos^2 3\theta \right) d\theta = \frac{\pi}{12}$

$A_2 = \frac{1}{2} \int_{5\pi/6}^{\pi} 1 \, d\theta = \frac{\pi}{12}, \; A = A_1 + A_2 = \frac{\pi}{6}$

49. $A = \frac{1}{2} \int_0^{\pi} \left(4 \sin^2 2\theta - \sin^2 2\theta \right) d\theta = \frac{3\pi}{4}$

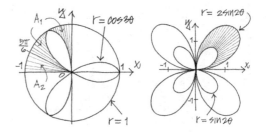

#47   #49

51. $A = 2 \cdot \frac{1}{2} \int_0^{\pi/4} \left(1 - \cos^2 2\theta \right) d\theta = \frac{\pi}{8}$

53. $A_1 = \frac{1}{2} \int_0^{\pi/3} \left(1 - \sin^2 3\theta \right) d\theta = \frac{\pi}{12}$

$A_2 = \frac{1}{2} \int_{\pi/3}^{\pi/2} 1 \, d\theta = \frac{\pi}{12}, \; A = A_1 + A_2 = \frac{\pi}{6}$

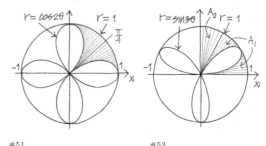

#51   #53

55. $L = \int_0^{\pi} 2 \cos \frac{\theta}{2} \, d\theta = 4$

57. $L = \int_0^{\pi} \theta \sqrt{\theta^2 + 4} \, d\theta = \frac{1}{3} (\pi^2 + 4)^{3/2} - \frac{8}{3}$

59. $L = \int_0^{\pi} \theta \sqrt{\theta^3 + 16} \, d\theta$

$= \frac{1}{5} (\pi^2 + 16)^{5/2} - \frac{16}{3} (\pi^2 + 16)^{3/2} + \frac{544}{15}$

61. $L = \int_0^{\pi} \sqrt{\theta^2 + 1} \, d\theta = \frac{1}{2} \pi \sqrt{\pi^2 + 1} + \frac{1}{2} \ln(\pi + \sqrt{\pi^2 + 1})$

63. $L = \int_0^{\pi} (2\theta + \frac{1}{8} \theta^3) e^{-\theta^2/16} \, d\theta = 32 - 132 e^{-25/4}$

65. $L = 10 \int_0^{2\pi} (\frac{1}{4} \cos^5 \frac{\theta}{4} + \sin^2 \frac{\theta}{4} \cos^3 \frac{\theta}{4}) \, d\theta = \frac{32}{3}$

67. $L = 100 \int_0^{16\pi} (\frac{1}{4} \cos \frac{\theta}{8} \sin^9 \frac{\theta}{8} + \cos^3 \frac{\theta}{8} \sin^7 \frac{\theta}{8}) \, d\theta = 40$

69. $L = 10 \int_0^{\pi} (\frac{1}{4} \cos^{-1/2} \frac{\theta}{2} \sin^3 \frac{\theta}{2} + \cos^{3/2} \frac{\theta}{2} \sin \frac{\theta}{2}) \, d\theta = 16$

71. $L = 10 \int_0^{3\pi} (\frac{1}{4} \cos^{1/2} \frac{\theta}{6} \sin^7 \frac{\theta}{6} + \cos^{5/2} \frac{\theta}{6} \sin^5 \frac{\theta}{6}) \, d\theta$

$= \frac{384}{221}$

73. $L = \int_0^{\pi} 6 \sin^2 \frac{\theta}{3} \, d\theta = 3\pi - \frac{9\sqrt{3}}{2}$

75. $L = \int_0^{\pi} 6 \sin^3 \frac{\theta}{4} \, d\theta = 16 - 10\sqrt{2}$

77. $L = \int_0^{\pi/4} \sec^2 \theta \, d\theta = 1$

79. $L = \int_0^{\pi/3} \sec^3 \frac{\theta}{2} \, d\theta = 2\sqrt{3} + \ln(2 + \sqrt{3})$

Exercises: 9.6

1. $a = 10, b = 6, c = 8$ **3.** $a = 8, b = 6, c = 10$

$\frac{x^2}{100} + \frac{y^2}{36} = 1$ $\frac{x^2}{64} - \frac{y^2}{36} = 1$

5. $a = 3, b = 4, c = 5$ **7.** $p = 1$

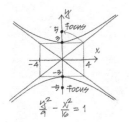

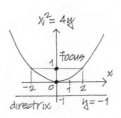

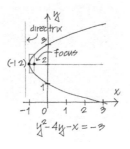

9. $p = 1$ **11.** $a = 3$, $b = 6$, $c = 3\sqrt{5}$

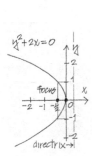

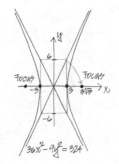

29. $\frac{(x-1)^2}{16} + \frac{(y-2)^2}{9} = 1$ **31.** $\frac{(x-1)^2}{9} + \frac{(y-2)^2}{25} = 1$

33. $\frac{(x-1)^2}{9} - \frac{(y-1)^2}{16} = 1$ **35.** $\frac{(y-2)^2}{16} - \frac{(x-1)^2}{25} = 1$

37. $\frac{(x-4)^2}{16} - \frac{(y-2)^2}{16} = 1$ **39.** $x - 1 = 2(y-2)^2$

41. $4(x-2) = (y-3)^2$ **43.** $x = -2(y-1)^2$

CHAPTER 10: Answers to Odd Exercises

Exercises: 10.1

13. $a = 5$, $b = 2$, $c = \sqrt{21}$ **15.** $a = 5$, $b = 3$, $c = 4$

1. $|PQ| = 3$, $|P'Q'| = \sqrt{5}$

3. $|PQ| = \sqrt{17}$, $|P'Q'| = \sqrt{13}$

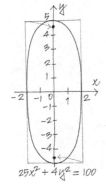

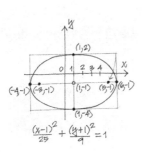

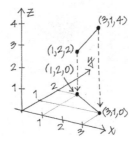

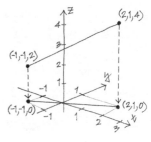

5. $|PQ| = 2\sqrt{2}$, $|P'Q'| = 2\sqrt{2}$

7. $|PQ| = 2$, $|P'Q'| = 2$

17. $p = -\frac{1}{2}$ **19.** $a = 2$, $b = 2$, $c = 2\sqrt{2}$

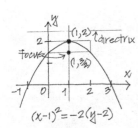

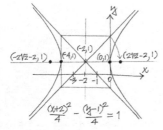

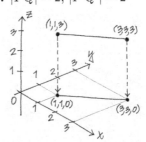

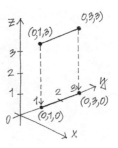

21. $a = 4$, $b = 3$, $c = \sqrt{7}$ **23.** $a = 4$, $b = 3$, $c = 5$

9. $|PQ| = 3$, $|P'Q'| = \sqrt{5}$

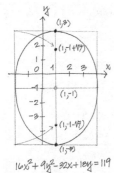

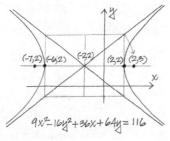

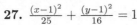

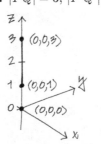

25. $p = \frac{1}{4}$ **27.** $\frac{(x-1)^2}{25} + \frac{(y-1)^2}{16} = 1$

#9

11. $|PQ|^2 = 49$, $|PR|^2 = 196$, $|QR|^2 = 245$.

right triangle

13. $|PQ|^2 = 14$, $|PR|^2 = 14$, $|QR|^2 = 14$.

equilateral triangle

15. center $= (2, -1, 3)$, radius $= 2$

17. center $= (0, 0, 2)$, radius $= 3$

19. center $= (3, -2, 1)$, radius $= 4$

21. center $= (2, 1, 4)$, radius $= \sqrt{21}$

23. center $= (1, -2, 2)$, radius $= 3$

25. center $= (3, 2, 1)$, radius $= 3$

27. Intercepts $x = 6$, $y = 15$, $z = 10$

29. Intercepts $x = 3$, $y = 5$, $z = 2$

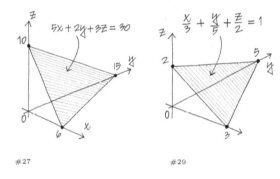

#27   #29

31. Intercepts $x = 2$, $y = 4$

33. Intercepts $x = 2$

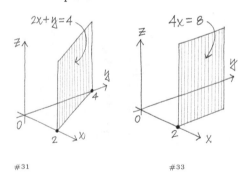

#31   #33

35. $6x + 3y + 2z = 6$ **37.** $2x + z = 2$

39. $x = 3 + 2t$, $y = -1 + 4t$, $z = t$

41. $x = 6 + 6t$, $y = 2 + 6t$, $z = t$

43. $x = 4$, $y = 2$, $z = t$

Exercises: 10.2

1.

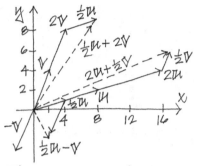

3. $\overrightarrow{PQ} = \langle 4, -1 \rangle$ **5.** $\overrightarrow{PQ} = \langle 3, -5, -5 \rangle$

7. $X = (1, 4, -1)$, $\overrightarrow{PX} = \langle -1, -1, 0 \rangle$

9. $X = (3, 5)$, $\overrightarrow{PX} = \langle 2, 3 \rangle$ **11.** $\mathbf{v} = \langle 6, 4 \rangle$

13. $\mathbf{w} = \langle -6, 4, -2 \rangle$, $\|\mathbf{w}\| = \sqrt{56} \approx 7.5$

15. $\mathbf{w} = \langle -1, 14, -23 \rangle$, $\|\mathbf{w}\| = \sqrt{7266} \approx 26.9$

17. $\mathbf{w} = \langle 18, -20, 19 \rangle$, $\|\mathbf{w}\| = \sqrt{1085} \approx 32.9$

19. $\mathbf{w} = \langle 2, 4, -8 \rangle$, $\|\mathbf{w}\| = \sqrt{84} \approx 9.2$

21. $\frac{\mathbf{v}}{\|\mathbf{v}\|} = \langle \frac{3}{\sqrt{10}}, \frac{1}{\sqrt{10}} \rangle$ **23.** $\frac{\mathbf{v}}{\|\mathbf{v}\|} = \langle \frac{2}{\sqrt{21}}, \frac{-1}{\sqrt{21}}, \frac{4}{\sqrt{21}} \rangle$

25. $\frac{\mathbf{v}}{\|\mathbf{v}\|} = \langle \frac{3}{\sqrt{29}}, \frac{-2}{\sqrt{29}}, \frac{4}{\sqrt{29}} \rangle$ **27.** $\mathbf{x} = \langle 1, 2 \rangle$

29. $\mathbf{x} = \langle 3, 4 \rangle$, $\mathbf{y} = \langle -1, -1 \rangle$

31. $\mathbf{x} = \langle 2, 1, 3 \rangle$, $\mathbf{y} = \langle 1, 4, 3 \rangle$, $\mathbf{z} = \langle -2, -1, -4 \rangle$

33. $F_1 = \frac{\sqrt{3}}{\sqrt{2}} \left(\frac{200}{1+\sqrt{3}} \right) \approx 89.6$ lb, $F_2 = \frac{200}{1+\sqrt{3}} \approx 73.2$ lb

Exercises: 10.3

1. $\mathbf{u} \cdot \mathbf{v} = 2$ **3.** $\mathbf{u} \cdot \mathbf{v} = 0$ **5.** $\mathbf{u} \cdot \mathbf{v} = 16$

7. $\mathbf{u} \cdot \mathbf{v} = -15$ **9.** $\mathbf{u} \cdot \mathbf{v} = -13$ **11.** $\mathbf{u} \cdot \mathbf{v} = 0$

13. $\theta = \cos^{-1}\left(\frac{2}{\sqrt{200}} \right) \approx 81.87° \approx 1.43$ rad

15. $\theta = \cos^{-1}(0) = 90° = \pi/2$ rad

17. $\theta = \cos^{-1}\left(\frac{16}{\sqrt{13}\sqrt{29}} \right) \approx 34.51° \approx 0.60$ rad

19. $\theta = \cos^{-1}\left(\frac{-15}{\sqrt{30}\sqrt{29}} \right) \approx 120.57° \approx 2.10$ rad

21. $\theta = \cos^{-1}\left(\frac{-13}{\sqrt{21}\sqrt{38}} \right) \approx 117.4° \approx 2.05$ rad

23. $\theta = \cos^{-1}(0) = \pi/2$ rad

25. $\angle QPR = \cos^{-1}\left(\frac{8}{\sqrt{10}\sqrt{26}} \right) \approx 60.26° \approx 1.05$ rad

$\angle RQP = \cos^{-1}\left(\frac{2}{\sqrt{20}\sqrt{26}} \right) \approx 84.97° \approx 1.48$ rad

$\angle PRQ \approx 180° - (60.26° + 84.97°) \approx 34.7° \approx .61$ rad

27. $\angle QPR = \cos^{-1}\left(\frac{11}{\sqrt{15}\sqrt{34}} \right) \approx 60.85° \approx 1.06$ rad

$\angle RQP = \cos^{-1}\left(\frac{3}{\sqrt{26}\sqrt{14}} \right) \approx 80.95° \approx 1.41$ rad

$\angle PRQ \approx 180° - (60.85° + 80.95°) \approx 38.2° \approx .67$ rad

29. $\angle QPR = \cos^{-1}\left(\frac{4}{\sqrt{41}(3)} \right) \approx 77.98° \approx 1.36$ rad

$\angle RQP = \cos^{-1}\left(\frac{37}{\sqrt{42}\sqrt{41}} \right) \approx 26.92° \approx .47$ rad

$\angle PRQ \approx 180° - (77.98° + 26.92°) \approx 75.1° \approx 1.31$ rad

31. $\mathbf{u} \cdot \mathbf{v} = 0$ so $\mathbf{u}$ is perpendicular to $\mathbf{v}$

33. $\mathbf{u} = 2\mathbf{v}$ so $\mathbf{u}$ is parallel to $\mathbf{v}$

35. $\mathbf{u} = \frac{1}{2}\mathbf{v}$ so $\mathbf{u}$ is parallel to $\mathbf{v}$

37. $\mathbf{u} \cdot \mathbf{v} = 0$ so $\mathbf{u}$ is perpendicular to $\mathbf{v}$

39. $\text{proj}_{\mathbf{v}}\mathbf{u} = \frac{7}{10}\mathbf{v} = \langle \frac{21}{10}, \frac{7}{10} \rangle$

$\mathbf{w} = \langle 1, 4 \rangle - \langle \frac{21}{10}, \frac{7}{10} \rangle = \langle \frac{-11}{10}, \frac{33}{10} \rangle$

41. $\text{proj}_{\mathbf{v}}\mathbf{u} = \frac{12}{6}\mathbf{v} = \langle 2, 2, 4 \rangle$, $\mathbf{w} = \langle 0, 2, -1 \rangle$

43. $\text{proj}_{\mathbf{v}}\mathbf{u} = \frac{9}{9}\mathbf{v} = \langle 2, -2, 1 \rangle$, $\mathbf{w} = \langle 1, 4, 6 \rangle$

45. $\text{proj}_{\mathbf{v}}\mathbf{u} = \frac{3}{14}\mathbf{v} = \langle \frac{3}{7}, \frac{-3}{14}, \frac{9}{14} \rangle$, $\mathbf{w} = \langle \frac{4}{7}, \frac{73}{14}, \frac{19}{14} \rangle$

47. $\text{proj}_{\mathbf{v}}\mathbf{u} = 0\mathbf{v} = \langle 0, 0, 0 \rangle$, $\mathbf{w} = \langle 1, -1, -1 \rangle$

Exercises: 10.4

1. -41　　**3.** 95　　**5.** 48　　**7.** $\langle 0, 0, 14 \rangle$

9. $\langle 0, 0, 29 \rangle$　　**11.** $\langle 0, 0, -11 \rangle$　　**13.** $\langle -16, 17, 10 \rangle$

15. $18\mathbf{i} - 17\mathbf{j} - 4\mathbf{k}$　　**17.** $\langle 16, 11 - 10 \rangle$

19. $\langle 0, 0, 14 \rangle$　　**21.** $\langle 0, 0, -11 \rangle$　　**23.** $\langle -16, 17, 10 \rangle$

25. $18\mathbf{i} - 17\mathbf{j} - 4\mathbf{k}$　　**27.** (a) $A = 10$ (b) $h = \sqrt{20}$

29. $A = \sqrt{355}$ (b) $h = \frac{2\sqrt{355}}{\sqrt{14}}$　　**31.** (a) $A = \sqrt{353}$

(b) $h = \frac{2\sqrt{353}}{\sqrt{41}}$　　**33.** 15　　**35.** -2　　**37.** (a) $S = 4$

(b) $A_1 = \sqrt{21}, A_2 = \sqrt{21}, A_3 = \sqrt{101}$ (c) $h_1 = \frac{4}{\sqrt{21}}$

39. (a) $S = 8$ (b) $A_1 = \sqrt{12}, A_2 = \sqrt{35}, A_3 = \sqrt{11}$

(c) $h_1 = \frac{8}{\sqrt{12}}$　　**41.** (a)$S = 2$ (b) $A_1 = \sqrt{3}$,

$A_2 = \sqrt{3}, A_3 = \sqrt{3}$ (c) $h_1 = \frac{2}{\sqrt{3}}$

Exercises: 10.5

1. $x = 4 + t, y = 1 + 3t, z = 2 + 6t$

3. $x = 5 - 4t, y = 2 + 2t, z = 1 + 4t$

5. $x = 4 + 3t, y = -1 + t, z = 2 - 4t$

7. $x = 2 + 2t, y = -1 + 3t, z = 4 + 7t$

9. $2x - 4y + 3z = 11$　　**11.** $7x + 5y - 3z = 14$

13. $2x - 5y + 2z = 26$　　**15.** $6x - 3y - z = 14 = -18$

17. $3x + 1y - 4z = 9$

19. $x = t, y = -6 + 3t, z = -10 + 5t$

21. $P = (1, 2, 1)$　　**23.** $3x + 7y - 19z = 148$

25. $180° - \cos^{-1}(\frac{1}{6}) \approx 80.4°$　　**27.** $\cos^{-1}(\frac{11}{\sqrt{6}\sqrt{30}}) \approx 35°$

29. $P = (1, -3, 2)$, $\mathbf{u} = \langle 3, 1, -4 \rangle$, $\overrightarrow{PS} = \langle 3, 2, 0 \rangle$

$d = \|\mathbf{u} \times \overrightarrow{PS}\|/\|\mathbf{u}\| = \sqrt{217}/\sqrt{26}$

31. Choose $P = x\text{-intercept} = (3, 0, 0)$, $\mathbf{n} = \langle 2, 1, -3 \rangle$,

$\overrightarrow{PS} = \langle -1, -1, 1 \rangle$,

$d = |\mathbf{n} \cdot \overrightarrow{PS}|/\|\mathbf{n}\| = 6/\sqrt{14}$

33. Choose $P = x\text{-intercept of 1st plane} = (5, 0, 0)$,

Choose $S = x\text{-intercept of 2nd plane} = (3, 0, 0)$

$\mathbf{n} = \langle 2, 1, -3 \rangle, \overrightarrow{PS} = \langle -2, 0, 0 \rangle$,

$d = |\mathbf{n} \cdot \overrightarrow{PS}|/\|\mathbf{n}\| = 4/\sqrt{14}$

35. $\mathbf{u}_1 = \langle 3, 1, 2 \rangle, \langle 1, 1, 3 \rangle, \mathbf{n} = \langle 1, -10, 3 \rangle$,

$P_1 = (5, 3, 1) = P, P_2 = (-1, -8, = 3) = S$,

$\overrightarrow{PS} = \langle -6, -11, -5 \rangle$,

$d = |\mathbf{n} \cdot \overrightarrow{PS}|/\|\mathbf{n}\| = 89/\sqrt{110}$

Exercises: 10.6

1. G　　**2.** D　　**3.** H　　**4.** C

5. E　　**6.** B　　**7.** F　　**8.** A

9.

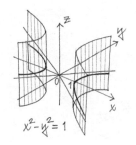

$x^2 - y^2 = 1$

11.

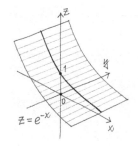

$z = e^{-x}$

13.

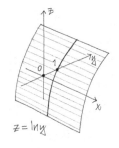

$z = \ln y$

15.

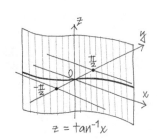

$z = \tan^{-1} x$

17.

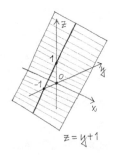

$z = y + 1$

19.

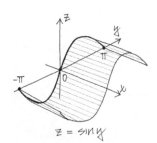

$z = \sin y$

21.

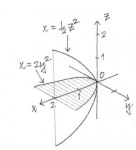

$x = \frac{1}{2}z^2$

$x = 2y^2$

23.

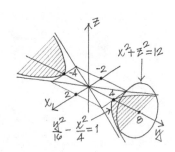

$x^2 + z^2 = 12$

$\frac{y^2}{16} - \frac{x^2}{4} = 1$

25.

27.

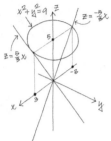

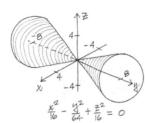

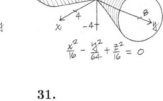

$$\frac{x^2}{16} - \frac{y^2}{64} + \frac{z^2}{16} = 0$$

29.

31.

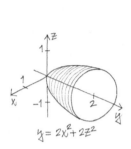

$$y = 2x^2 + 2z^2$$

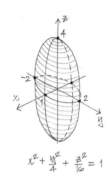

$$x^2 + \frac{y^2}{4} + \frac{z^2}{16} = 1$$

33.

35.

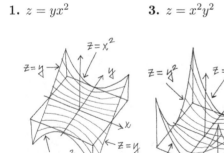

$$\frac{x^2}{16} - \frac{y^2}{4} - \frac{z^2}{4} = 1$$

$$z = y^2 - x^2$$

CHAPTER 11: Answers to Odd Exercises

Exercises: 11.1

1. $z = yx^2$ **3.** $z = x^2 y^2$

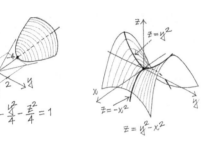

5. $z = xy^3$ **7.** $z = y^2 e^{-x}$

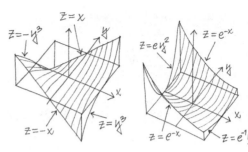

9. $z = y^3 e^{-x}$ **11.** $z = y^2 \cos \pi x$

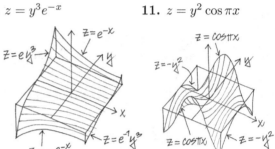

13. $z = (1 - x^3) y^2$ **15.** $z = (1 - x^2) y^2$

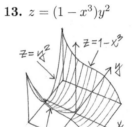

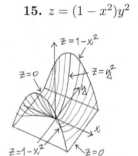

17. $z = (1 - x^2) y^3$ **19.** $z = (1 - x^3) y^3$

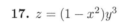

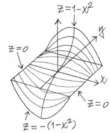

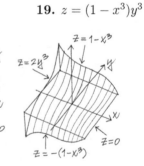

21. $z = x^2 \sqrt{|y|}$ **23.** $z = (1 - x)\sqrt{|y|}$

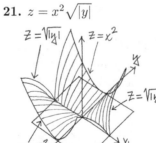

25. $z = x^2 + y$ **27.** $z = x^2 + y^2$

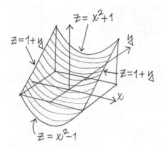

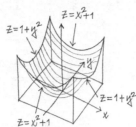

29. $z = x^2 - y^2$ **31.** $z = x^3 + y^3$

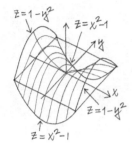

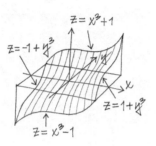

33. $z = y^3 - x^3$ **35.** $z = y^3 - x^2 + 1$

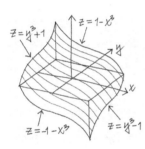

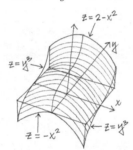

37. $z = x^3 + y^2$ **39.** $z = 2x + 3y$

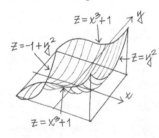

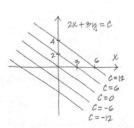

41. $z = y + x^2$ **43.** $z = y/(1 + x^2)$

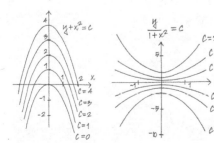

45. $z = yx^2$ **47.** $z = xy^{-2}$

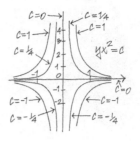

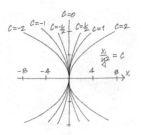

49. $z = y^2 e^x$ **51.** $z = x^3 e^y$

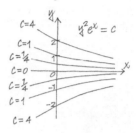

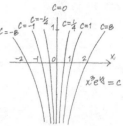

53. $z = x^2 + y^2$ **55.** $z = x^2 - y^2$

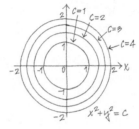

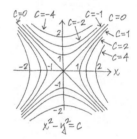

57. $z = y^3 - x^2 + 1$ **59.** $z = y^3 - x^3$

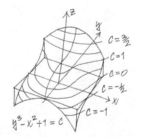

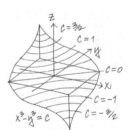

61. 1 peaks, 1 valley

63. 2 peaks, 1 valley, 3 saddle points

65. 2 peaks, 1 valley, 3 saddle points

67. I-B, II-D, III-A, IV-E, V-C

Exercises: 11.2

1. 12   **3.** -2 **5.** 4   **7.** $-2e^{-2}$ **9.** 1   **11.** 4

13. 4   **15.** $\frac{1}{6}$ **17.** $\frac{1}{4}$ **19.** $\frac{1}{2}$ **21.** 3   **23.** $\frac{1}{4}$ **25.** 9

27. $f(t, mt) = \frac{1+m+m^2}{1+m^2}$. When $m = 0$, $f(t, 0) = 1$ and when $m = 1$, $f(t, t) = \frac{3}{2}$, for all $t \neq 0$.

29. $f(t, mt) = \frac{m}{1+m^4}$. When $m = 0$, $f(t, 0) = 0$ and when $m = 1$, $f(t, t) = \frac{1}{2}$, for all $t \neq 0$.

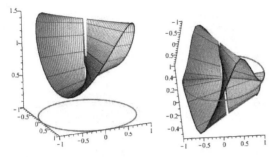

31. $f(t, mt^2) = \frac{2m}{1+m^2}$. When $m = 0$, $f(t, 0) = 0$ and when $m = 1$, $f(t, t) = 1$, for all $t \neq 0$.

33. $f(t, mt^3) = \frac{1-m^2}{1+m^2}$. When $m = 0$, $f(t, 0) = 1$ and when $m = 1$, $f(t, t) = 0$, for all $t \neq 0$.

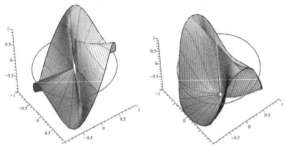

35. $f(t, mt) = \frac{1}{\sqrt{1+m^4}}$. When $m = 0$, $f(t, 0) = 1$ and when $m = 1$, $f(t, t) = \frac{1}{\sqrt{2}}$, for all $t \neq 0$.

37. $f(t, mt) = \frac{m}{|m|}$. When $m = 1$, $f(t, t) = 1$ and when $m = -1$, $f(t, -t) = -1$, for all $t \neq 0$.

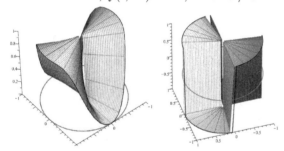

39. None   **41.** points on $x^2 + y^2 = 2n\pi$, $n = 0, 1, 2, \ldots$

43. points on $y = x$ **45.** points on $y = x^2$

47. points satisfying $x^2 < y$ **49.** points on $y = x$

51. points on $y = x^2$

Exercises: 11.3

1. $f_x = 3x^2y^4 + 30x^4$, $f_y = 4x^3y^3 - 9y^2$

3. $f_x = 8x^2y^{1/2} - 15x^{3/2}y^3$
$f_y = 2x^2y^{-1/2} - 18x^{5/2}y^2$

5. $f_x = \frac{\sqrt{y}}{2\sqrt{x}}$, $f_y = \frac{\sqrt{x}}{2\sqrt{y}}$

7. $f_x = \frac{x}{\sqrt{x^2 + y^2}}$, $f_y = \frac{y}{\sqrt{x^2 + y^2}}$

9. $f_x = \frac{-x}{(x^2+y^2)^{3/2}}$, $f_y = \frac{-y}{(x^2+y^2)^{3/2}}$

11. $f_x = \frac{-x}{(x^2+y^2)^2}$, $f_y = \frac{-y}{(x^2+y^2)^2}$

13. $f_x = \frac{6x^2 + 4xy + 3y^2}{\sqrt{x^2+y^2}}$, $f_y = \frac{4x^2 + 3xy + 8y^2}{\sqrt{x^2+y^2}}$

15. $f_x = \frac{8x^4 - xy^2 + 6x^2y^3}{\sqrt{x^2+y^2}}$, $f_y = \frac{2x^3y - 2x^2y - 3y^3}{\sqrt{x^2+y^2}}$

17. $f_x = \frac{-y}{(3x+7y)^2}$, $f_y = \frac{x}{(3x+7y)^2}$

19. $f_x = \frac{x^3y^3(x^3 + 4y^2)}{(x^3+y^2)^2}$, $f_y = \frac{x^4y^2(3x^3 + y^2)}{(x^3+y^2)^2}$

21. $f_x = \frac{-x^4 - 3x^2y^3 + 2xy^2}{(x^3+y^2)^2}$, $f_y = \frac{3x^3y^2 - 2x^2y + y^4}{(x^3+y^2)^2}$

23. $f_x = \frac{\sqrt{y}}{2\sqrt{x}(\sqrt{x} + \sqrt{y})^2}$, $f_y = \frac{\sqrt{y}}{2\sqrt{x}(\sqrt{x} + \sqrt{y})^2}$

25. $f_x = \frac{-2e^xe^y}{(e^x - e^y)^2}$, $f_y = \frac{2e^xe^y}{(e^x - e^y)^2}$

27. $f_x = \frac{2 + e^xe^y - e^{-x}e^{-y}}{(e^{-x} + e^y)^2}$, $f_y = \frac{2 + e^{-x}e^{-y} - e^xe^y}{(e^{-x} + e^y)^2}$

29. $f_x = \frac{\sin x \sin y - \sin x \cos y}{(\cos x + \cos y)^2}$
$f_y = \frac{1 + \cos x \cos y + \cos x \sin y}{(\cos x + \cos y)^2}$

31. $f_x = \frac{-\cos y - \sin x \sin y \cos y}{(\sin x + \sin y)^2}$,
$f_y = \frac{-\cos x - \sin x \cos x \sin y}{(\sin x + \sin y)^2}$

33. $f_x = \frac{y \cos xy}{(1 + \sin xy)^2}$, $f_y = \frac{x \cos xy}{(1 + \sin xy)^2}$

35. $f_x = 2xy^2 \sec(x^2y^3)$, $f_y = 3x^2y^2 \sec(x^2y^3)$

37. $f_x = 2xy^3 \sec(x^2y^3) \tan(x^2y^3)$
$f_y = 3x^2y^2 \sec(x^2y^3) \tan(x^2y^3)$

39. $f_x = -y^2e^{-xy^2} \cos e^{-xy^2}$, $f_y = -2xye^{-xy^2} \cos e^{-xy^2}$

41. $f_x = y^2 \cos xy^2 e^{\sin xy^2}$, $f_y = 2xy \cos xy^2 e^{\sin xy^2}$

43. $f_x = y^2e^{xy^2}(\cos xy^2 - \sin xy^2)$
$f_y = 2xye^{xy^2}(\sin xy^2 + \cos xy^2)$

45. $f_x = 2xy^2e^{-(x^2+y^2)}$, $f_y = 2ye^{-(x^2+y^2)}(1 + y^2)$

47. $f_x = \frac{2x}{x^2+y^2}$, $f_y = \frac{2y}{x^2+y^2}$ **49.** $f_x = \frac{2}{x}$, $f_y = \frac{2}{y}$

51. $f_x = \frac{2}{x}$, $f_y = \frac{1}{y \ln y}$

53. $f_x = 1 + y + \ln x + \frac{1}{x} \ln y$, $f_y = 1 + x + \ln y + \frac{1}{y} \ln y$

55. $f_x = \frac{y + \ln x - 1 - \frac{1}{x} \ln y}{(y + \ln x)^2}$,
$f_y = \frac{1 + \frac{1}{y} \ln x - x - \ln y}{(y + \ln x)^2}$

57. $f_x = \frac{y}{2\sqrt{xy}(1 + xy)}$, $f_y = \frac{x}{2\sqrt{xy}(1 + xy)}$

59. $f_x = \frac{\sqrt{y}}{2y\sqrt{x} + x\sqrt{x}}$, $f_y = \frac{-\sqrt{x}}{2y\sqrt{y} + 2x\sqrt{y}}$

61. $f_x = \frac{x}{(1 + x^2 + y^2)\sqrt{x^2 + y^2}}$,

$$f_y = \frac{y}{(1 + x^2 + y^2)\sqrt{x^2 + y^2}}$$

63. $f_x = 3x^2y^2z^5 - 8xyz^3$, $f_y = 2x^3yz^5 - 4x^2z^3$,
$f_z = 5x^3y^2z^4 - 12x^2yz^2$

65. $f_x = \dfrac{x}{\sqrt{x^2 + y^2 + z^2}}$, $f_y = \dfrac{y}{\sqrt{x^2 + y^2 + z^2}}$,
$f_z = \dfrac{z}{\sqrt{x^2 + y^2 + z^2}}$

67. $f_x = \dfrac{7x^4y^3z^4 + 4xy^6z^4 + 4xy^3z^7}{2\sqrt{x^3 + y^3 + z^3}}$,
$f_y = \dfrac{9x^2y^5z^4 + 6x^5y^2z^4 + 6x^2y^2z^7}{2\sqrt{x^3 + y^3 + z^3}}$,
$f_z = \dfrac{11x^2y^3z^6 + 8x^5y^3z^3 + 8x^3y^3z^6}{2\sqrt{x^3 + y^3 + z^3}}$

69. $f_x = y^2z^3 \sin xyz + xy^3z^4 \cos xyz$,
$f_y = 2xyz^3 \sin xyz + x^2y^2z^4 \cos xyz$
$f_z = 3xy^2z^2 \sin xyz + x^2y^2z^3 \cos xyz$

71. $f_x = \dfrac{1}{y + z}$, $f_y = \dfrac{z - x}{(y + z)^2}$, $f_z = \dfrac{-(x + y)}{(y + z)^2}$

73. $f_x = \dfrac{y^3z - x^2yz + yz^3}{(x^2 + y^2 + z^2)^2}$, $f_y = \dfrac{x^3z - xy^2z + xz^3}{(x^2 + y^2 + z^2)^2}$,
$f_z = \dfrac{x^3y - xyz^2 + xy^3}{(x^2 + y^2 + z^2)^2}$

75. $f_x = \dfrac{y^4z^3 + y^2z^6}{(x + y^2 + z^3)^2}$, $f_y = \dfrac{2x^2yz^3 + 2xyz^6}{(x + y^2 + z^3)^2}$
$f_z = \dfrac{3x^2y^2z^2 + 3xy^4z^2}{(x + y^2 + z^3)^2}$

77. $f_x = ye^{-2yz^3}$, $f_y = xe^{-2yz^3}(1 - 2yz^3)$,
$f_z = -6xy^2z^2e^{-2yz^3}$

79. $f_{xx} = 36x^2y - 10y^3$, $f_{yy} = -30x^2y$,
$f_{xy} = 12x^3 - 30xy^2$, $f_{yx} = 12x^3 - 30xy^2$

81. $f_{xx} = 6xy^4 \cos x^3y^4 - 9x^4y^8 \sin x^3y^4$
$f_{yy} = 12x^3y^2 \cos x^3y^4 - 16x^6y^6 \sin x^3y^4$
$f_{xy} = f_{yx} = 12x^2y^3 \cos x^3y^4 - 12x^5y^7 \sin x^3y^4$

83. $f_{xx} = \dfrac{2y^2 - 2x^2}{(x^2 + y^2)^2}$, $f_{yy} = \dfrac{2x^2 - 2y^2}{(x^2 + y^2)^2}$
$f_{xy} = f_{yx} = \dfrac{-4xy}{(x^2 + y^2)^2}$

85. $f_{xx} = \dfrac{6x^2 - 2y^2}{(x^2 + y^2)^3}$, $f_{yy} = \dfrac{6y^2 - 2x^2}{(x^2 + y^2)^3}$
$f_{xy} = f_{yx} = \dfrac{8xy}{(x^2 + y^2)^3}$

87. $f_{xx} = 2y^3 e^{-x^2y^3}(2x^2y^3 - 1)$,
$f_{yy} = 3x^2ye^{-x^2y^3}(3x^2y^3 - 2)$
$f_{xy} = f_{yx} = 6xy^2e^{-x^2y^3}(x^2y^3 - 1)$

89. $f_{xx} = \dfrac{-2xy^3}{(1 + x^2y^2)^2}$, $f_{yy} = \dfrac{-2x^3y}{(1 + x^2y^2)^2}$
$f_{xy} = f_{yx} = \dfrac{1 - x^2y^2}{(1 + x^2y^2)^2}$

91. $f_{xx} = \dfrac{-(4x^2 + y^2 + z^2)}{(x^2 + y^2 + z^2)^{5/2}}$, $f_{yy} = \dfrac{-(x^2 + 4y^2 + z^2)}{(x^2 + y^2 + z^2)^{5/2}}$
$f_{zz} = \dfrac{-(x^2 + y^2 + 4z^2)}{(x^2 + y^2 + z^2)^{5/2}}$
$f_{xy} = f_{yx} = \dfrac{3xy}{(x^2 + y^2 + z^2)^{5/2}}$
$f_{yz} = f_{zy} = \dfrac{3yz}{(x^2 + y^2 + z^2)^{5/2}}$
$f_{xz} = f_{zx} = \dfrac{3xz}{(x^2 + y^2 + z^2)^{5/2}}$

93. $f_{xx} = -2(x^2 + y^2 + z^2 + w^2)^{-3}(y^2 + z^2 + w^2 - 3x^2)$
$f_{yy} = -2(x^2 + y^2 + z^2 + w^2)^{-3}(x^2 + z^2 + w^2 - 3y^2)$
$f_{zz} = -2(x^2 + y^2 + z^2 + w^2)^{-3}(x^2 + y^2 + w^2 - 3z^2)$
$f_{ww} = -2(x^2 + y^2 + z^2 + w^2)^{-3}(x^2 + y^2 + z^2 - 3w^2)$
$f_{xy} = f_{yx} = 8xy(x^2 + y^2 + z^2 + w^2)^{-3}$
$f_{xz} = f_{zx} = 8xz(x^2 + y^2 + z^2 + w^2)^{-3}$
$f_{zy} = f_{yz} = 8zy(x^2 + y^2 + z^2 + w^2)^{-3}$
$f_{xw} = f_{wx} = 8xw(x^2 + y^2 + z^2 + w^2)^{-3}$
$f_{yw} = f_{wy} = 8yw(x^2 + y^2 + z^2 + w^2)^{-3}$
$f_{zw} = f_{wz} = 8zw(x^2 + y^2 + z^2 + w^2)^{-3}$

95. $f_{xxxx} = 16y^4e^{-2xy}$, $f_{xxy} = 8ye^{-2xy}(1 - xy)$

97. $f_{xxxx} = y^4 \sin xy$
$f_{xxyy} = (x^2y^2 - 2) \sin xy - 4xy \cos xy$

99. $w_{sstt} = 0$, $w_{tss} = e^{-s^2}(-14s^3 + 4s^5 + 6s)$

101. $\dfrac{\partial^3 P}{\partial V^3} = -6TV^{-4}$, $\dfrac{\partial^3 P}{\partial T \partial V^2} = 2V^{-3}$

103. $\dfrac{\partial^3 w}{\partial u \partial v^2} = -6u^{-2}v^{-4}$, $\dfrac{\partial^3 w}{\partial u^2 \partial v} = -4u^{-3}v^{-3}$

Exercises: 11.4

1. $\dfrac{dw}{dt} = (6xy^3 - 20x^3x^2)\dfrac{dx}{dt} + (9x^2y^2 - 10x^4y)\dfrac{dy}{dt}$

3. $\dfrac{dw}{dt} = \dfrac{3x^3 + 2xy^2}{\sqrt{x^2 + y^2}}\dfrac{dx}{dt} + \dfrac{x^2y}{\sqrt{x^2 + y^2}}\dfrac{dy}{dt}$

5. $\dfrac{dw}{dt} = e^{-x}(3x^2y^2 - x^3y^2)\dfrac{dx}{dt} + 2x^3ye^{-x}\dfrac{dy}{dt}$

7. $\dfrac{dw}{dt} = \left(\ln(x^2 + y^4) + \dfrac{2x^2}{x^2 + y^4}\right)\dfrac{dx}{dt} + \dfrac{4xy^3}{x^2 + y^4}\dfrac{dy}{dt}$

9. $\dfrac{dw}{dt} = [2x \cos(x^2) \cos(x + y) - \sin(x^2) \sin(x + y)]\dfrac{dx}{dt}$
$\qquad - \sin x^2 \sin(x + y)\dfrac{dy}{dt}$

11. $\dfrac{dw}{dt} = f_x\dfrac{dx}{dt} + f_y\dfrac{dy}{dt} = 5x^4y^6\dfrac{dx}{dt} + 6x^5y^5\dfrac{dy}{dt}$
(i) $\dfrac{dw}{dt} = 5t^4t^{12}(1) + 6t^5t^{10}(2t) = 17t^{16}$
(ii) $\dfrac{dw}{dt} = 5\cos^4 t \sin^6 t(-\sin t) + 6\cos^5 t \sin^5 t(\cos t)$
$\qquad = -5\cos^4 t \sin^7 t + 6\cos^6 t \sin^5 t$

13. $\dfrac{dw}{dt} = f_x\dfrac{dx}{dt} + f_y\dfrac{dy}{dt} = \sqrt{1 + y}\dfrac{dx}{dt} + \dfrac{x}{2\sqrt{1 + y}}\dfrac{dx}{dt}$
(i) $\dfrac{dw}{dt} = \sqrt{1 + t^2}(1) + \dfrac{t}{2\sqrt{1 + t^2}}(2t) = \dfrac{1 + 2t^2}{\sqrt{1 + t^2}}$

(ii) $\dfrac{dw}{dt} = \sqrt{1+\sin t}(-\sin t) + \dfrac{1}{2\sqrt{1+\sin t}}(\cos t)$

$\qquad = \dfrac{-2\sin t - 2\sin^2 t + \cos^2 t}{2\sqrt{1+\sin t}}$

15. $\dfrac{dw}{dt} = (2xe^{-xy} - x^2ye^{-xy})\dfrac{dx}{dt} - x^3 e^{-xy}\dfrac{dy}{dt}$

(i) $\dfrac{dw}{dt} = (2te^{-t^3} - t^4 e^{-t^3})(1) - t^3 e^{-t^3}(2t)$

$\qquad = 2te^{-t^3} - 3t^4 e^{-t^3}$

(ii) $\dfrac{dw}{dt} = e^{-\cos t \sin t}(2\cos t - \cos^2 t \sin t)(-\sin t)$
$\qquad\quad - \cos^3 t\, e^{-\cos t \sin t}(\cos t)$

$\qquad = e^{-\cos t \sin t}(-2\cos t \sin t + \cos^2 t \sin^2 t - \cos^4 t)$

17. $\dfrac{dw}{dt} = \dfrac{2xy^3}{1+x^2 y}\dfrac{dx}{dt} + \dfrac{3x^2 y^2}{1+x^2 y}\dfrac{dy}{dt}$

(i) $\dfrac{dw}{dt} = \dfrac{2t^7}{1+t^4}(1) + \dfrac{3t^6}{1+t^4}(2t) = \dfrac{8t^7}{1+t^4}$

(ii) $\dfrac{dw}{dt} = \dfrac{2\cos t \sin^3 t}{1+\cos^2 t \sin t}(-\sin t)$

$\qquad\quad + \dfrac{3\cos^2 t \sin^2 t}{1+\cos^2 t \sin t}(\cos t)$

$\qquad = \dfrac{-2\cos t \sin^4 t + 3\cos^3 t \sin^2 t}{1+\cos^2 t \sin t}$

19. $\dfrac{dw}{dt} = \dfrac{1}{(x+y^2)^2}\dfrac{dx}{dt} + \dfrac{2y}{(x+y^2)^2}\dfrac{dy}{dt}$

(i) $\dfrac{dw}{dt} = \dfrac{1}{(t+t^4)^2}(1) + \dfrac{2t^2}{(t+t^4)^2}(2t)$

$\qquad = \dfrac{1+4t^4}{(t+t^4)^2}$

(ii) $\dfrac{dw}{dt} = \dfrac{1}{(\cos t + \sin^2 t)^2}(-\sin t)$

$\qquad\quad + \dfrac{2\sin t}{(\cos t + \sin^2 t)^2}(\cos t)$

$\qquad = \dfrac{-\sin t + 2\sin t \cos t}{(\cos t + \sin^2 t)^2}$

21. $\dfrac{dw}{dt} = \dfrac{2x}{(x+y)^2}\dfrac{dx}{dt} - \dfrac{2y}{(x+y)^2}\dfrac{dy}{dt}$

(i) $\dfrac{dw}{dt} = \dfrac{2t}{(t+t^2)^2}(1) - \dfrac{2t^2}{(t+t^2)^2}(2t) = \dfrac{2t - 4t^2}{(t+t^2)^2}$

(ii) $\dfrac{dw}{dt} = \dfrac{2\cos t}{(\cos t + \sin t)^2}(-\sin t)$

$\qquad\quad - \dfrac{2\sin t}{(\cos t + \sin t)^2}(\cos t)$

$\qquad = \dfrac{-4\sin t \cos t}{(\cos t + \sin t)^2}$

23. $\dfrac{dw}{dt} = \dfrac{y^2}{(1+xy^2)}\dfrac{dx}{dt} + \dfrac{2xy}{(1+xy^2)}\dfrac{dy}{dt}$

(i) $\dfrac{dw}{dt} = \dfrac{t^4}{(1+t^5)^2}(1) + \dfrac{2t^3}{(1+t^5)^2}(2t) = \dfrac{3t^4}{(1+t^5)^2}$

25. $\dfrac{\partial w}{\partial s} = \dfrac{y^2 - x^2}{(x^2+y^2)^2}\dfrac{\partial x}{\partial s} + \dfrac{-2xy}{(x^2+y^2)^2}\dfrac{\partial y}{\partial s}$

$\qquad = \dfrac{s^4 t^4 - s^2 t^2}{(s^4 t^4 + s^2 t^2)^2}(t) + \dfrac{-2s^3 t^3}{(s^4 t^4 + s^2 t^2)^2}(2st^2)$

$\qquad = \dfrac{-(t + 3s^2 t^3)}{(s^3 t^3 + st)^2}$

$\dfrac{\partial w}{\partial t} = \dfrac{y^2 - x^2}{(x^2+y^2)^2}\dfrac{\partial x}{\partial t} + \dfrac{-2xy}{(x^2+y^2)^2}\dfrac{\partial y}{\partial t}$

$\qquad = \dfrac{s^4 t^4 - s^2 t^2}{(s^4 t^4 + s^2 t^2)^2}(s) + \dfrac{-2s^3 t^3}{(s^4 t^4 + s^2 t^2)^2}(2s^2 t)$

$\qquad = \dfrac{-(s + 3s^3 t^2)}{(s^3 t^3 + st)^2}$

27. $\dfrac{\partial w}{\partial u} = \dfrac{y^2}{(x+y)^2}\dfrac{\partial x}{\partial u} + \dfrac{x^2}{(x+y)^2}\dfrac{\partial y}{\partial u}$

$\qquad = \dfrac{(u^2+v^2)^2 v + 2u^3 v^2}{(uv + u^2 + v^2)^2}$

$\dfrac{\partial w}{\partial v} = \dfrac{y^2}{(x+y)^2}\dfrac{\partial x}{\partial v} + \dfrac{x^2}{(x+y)^2}\dfrac{\partial y}{\partial v}$

$\qquad = \dfrac{(u^2+v^2)^2 u + 2u^3 v^3}{(uv + u^2 + v^2)^2}$

29. $\dfrac{\partial w}{\partial s} = \left(2x\sqrt{x+y} + \dfrac{x^2}{2\sqrt{x+y}}\right)\dfrac{\partial x}{\partial s} + \dfrac{x^2}{2\sqrt{x+y}}\dfrac{\partial y}{\partial s}$

$\qquad = \dfrac{(4st^2(st^2 + s^2 t) + s^2 t^4)(t^2) + (st^2)^2(2st)}{2\sqrt{st^2 + s^2 t}}$

$\qquad = \dfrac{5s^2 t^6 + 6s^3 t^5}{2\sqrt{st^2 + s^2 t}}$

$\dfrac{\partial w}{\partial t} = \left(2x\sqrt{x+y} + \dfrac{x^2}{2\sqrt{x+y}}\right)\dfrac{\partial x}{\partial t} + \dfrac{x^2}{2\sqrt{x+y}}\dfrac{\partial y}{\partial t}$

$\qquad = \dfrac{(5s^2 t^4 + 4s^3 t^3)(2st) + (s^2 t^4)(s^2)}{2\sqrt{st^2 + s^2 t}}$

$\qquad = \dfrac{5s^3 t^5 + 4s^4 t^4}{\sqrt{st^2 + s^2 t}}$

31. $\dfrac{\partial w}{\partial u} = 3e^{3x}\sin 2y\dfrac{\partial x}{\partial u} + 2e^{3x}\cos 2y\dfrac{\partial y}{\partial u}$

$\qquad = 3ve^{3uv}\sin(2u^2 + 2v^2) + 4ue^{3uv}\cos(2u^2 + 2v^2)$

$\dfrac{\partial w}{\partial v} = 3e^{3x}\sin 2y\dfrac{\partial x}{\partial v} + 2e^{3x}\cos 2y\dfrac{\partial y}{\partial v}$

$\qquad = 3ue^{3uv}\sin(2u^2 + 2v^2) + 4ve^{3uv}\cos(2u^2 + 2v^2)$

33. $\dfrac{\partial w}{\partial t} = \dfrac{\partial w}{\partial x}\dfrac{\partial x}{\partial t} + \dfrac{\partial w}{\partial y}\dfrac{\partial y}{\partial t} + \dfrac{\partial w}{\partial z}\dfrac{\partial z}{\partial t}$

$\qquad = y^2 z^3(1) + 2xyz^3(2t) + 3xy^2 z^2(3t^2)$

$\qquad = t^{13} + 4t^{13} + 9t^{13} = 14t^{13}$

35. $\dfrac{\partial w}{\partial t} = \dfrac{\partial w}{\partial x}\dfrac{\partial x}{\partial t} + \dfrac{\partial w}{\partial y}\dfrac{\partial y}{\partial t} + \dfrac{\partial w}{\partial z}\dfrac{\partial z}{\partial t}$

$\qquad = \dfrac{2x}{y^2 + z^2}(1) - \dfrac{2x^2 y}{(y^2 + z^2)^2}(2t) - \dfrac{2x^2 z}{(y^2 + z^2)^2}(3t^2)$

$\qquad = \dfrac{2t(t^4 + t^6) - 4t^5 - 6t^7}{(t^4 + t^6)^2} = \dfrac{-2t - 4t^3}{(t^2 + t^4)^2}$

37. $\dfrac{\partial w}{\partial u} = \dfrac{\partial w}{\partial x}\dfrac{\partial x}{\partial u} + \dfrac{\partial w}{\partial y}\dfrac{\partial y}{\partial u} + \dfrac{\partial w}{\partial z}\dfrac{\partial z}{\partial u}$

$\qquad = \dfrac{1}{yz}(v) + \dfrac{-x}{y^2 z}(1) + \dfrac{-x}{yz^2}(1)$

$$= \frac{v}{(u+v)(u-v)} - \frac{uv}{(u+v)^2(u-v)} - \frac{uv}{(u+v)(u-v)^2}$$

$$= \frac{v^3 - u^2 v}{(u+v)^2(u-v)^2}$$

$$\frac{\partial w}{\partial v} = \frac{\partial w}{\partial x}\frac{\partial x}{\partial v} + \frac{\partial w}{\partial y}\frac{\partial y}{\partial v} + \frac{\partial w}{\partial z}\frac{\partial z}{\partial v}$$

$$= \frac{1}{yz}(u) + \frac{-x}{y^2 z}(1) + \frac{-x}{yz^2}(-1)$$

$$= \frac{u}{(u+v)(u-v)} - \frac{uv}{(u+v)^2(u-v)} + \frac{uv}{(u+v)(u-v)^2}$$

$$= \frac{u^3 + uv^2}{(u+v)^2(u-v)^2}$$

39. $\dfrac{\partial w}{\partial u} = \dfrac{\partial w}{\partial x}\dfrac{\partial x}{\partial u} + \dfrac{\partial w}{\partial y}\dfrac{\partial y}{\partial u} + \dfrac{\partial w}{\partial z}\dfrac{\partial z}{\partial u}$

$$= \frac{-(y+z)}{(x+y)^2}(v) + \frac{x-z}{(x+y)^2}(1) + \frac{1}{x+y}(1)$$

$$= \frac{-2uv}{(uv+u+v)^2} + \frac{uv-u+v}{(uv+u+v)^2} + \frac{1}{uv+u+v}$$

$$= \frac{2v}{(uv+u+v)^2}$$

$$\frac{\partial w}{\partial v} = \frac{-(y+z)}{(x+y)^2}(u) + \frac{x-z}{(x+y)^2}(1) + \frac{1}{x+y}(-1)$$

$$= \frac{-2u^2}{(uv+u+v)^2} + \frac{uv-u+v}{(uv+u+v)^2} - \frac{1}{uv+u+v}$$

$$= \frac{-2u^2 - 2u}{(uv+u+v)^2}$$

41. $\dfrac{\partial w}{\partial u} = \dfrac{1}{y}(v) + \left(\dfrac{-x}{y^2} + \dfrac{1}{z}\right)(1) + \left(\dfrac{-y}{z^2}\right)(1)$

$$= \frac{v}{u+v} - \frac{uv}{(u+v)^2} + \frac{1}{u-v} - \frac{u+v}{(u-v)^2}$$

$$\frac{\partial w}{\partial v} = \frac{1}{y}(u) + \left(\frac{-x}{y^2} + \frac{1}{z}\right)(1) + \left(\frac{-y}{z^2}\right)(-1)$$

$$= \frac{u}{u+v} - \frac{uv}{(u+v)^2} + \frac{1}{u-v} + \frac{u+v}{(u-v)^2}$$

Exercises: 11.5

1. $\nabla f = \langle 2xy^3 + 4y^2, 3x^2y^2 + 8xy \rangle$, $\nabla f(2,-1) = \langle 0, -4 \rangle$

3. $\nabla f = \langle \dfrac{xy^2}{\sqrt{1+x^2y^2}}, \dfrac{x^2y}{\sqrt{1+x^2y^2}} \rangle$,

$\nabla f(2,-3) = \langle \dfrac{18}{\sqrt{37}}, \dfrac{-12}{\sqrt{37}} \rangle$

5. $\nabla f = \langle \dfrac{3xy+2y^2}{2\sqrt{x+y}}, \dfrac{3xy+2x^2}{2\sqrt{x+y}} \rangle$,

$\nabla f(4,5) = \langle \dfrac{55}{9}, \dfrac{46}{9} \rangle$

7. $\nabla f = \langle \dfrac{2y}{(x+y)^2}, \dfrac{-2x}{(x+y)^2} \rangle$,

$\nabla f(1,1) = \langle \dfrac{1}{2}, -\dfrac{1}{2} \rangle$

9. $\nabla f = \langle \dfrac{y}{(1+xy)^2}, \dfrac{x}{(1+xy)^2} \rangle$,

$\nabla f(1,1) = \langle \dfrac{1}{4}, \dfrac{1}{4} \rangle$

11. $\nabla f = \langle \dfrac{ye^{xy}}{(1+e^{xy})^2}, \dfrac{xe^{xy}}{(1+e^{xy})^2} \rangle$,

$\nabla f(0,0) = \langle 0, 0 \rangle$

13. $\nabla f = \langle yx^{y-1}, x^y \ln x \rangle$,

$\nabla f(2,1) = \langle 1, \ln 4 \rangle$

15. $\nabla f = \langle \pi \cos \pi x \sin \pi y, \pi \sin \pi x \cos \pi y \rangle$,

$\nabla f(1, 1/4) = \langle \dfrac{\pi\sqrt{2}}{2}, -\dfrac{1}{2} \rangle$

17. $\nabla f = \langle 6x^2 y^2 z^2, 4x^3 yz^2, 4x^3 y^2 z \rangle$,

$\nabla f(1,1,1) = \langle 6, -4, 4 \rangle$

19. $\nabla f = \langle \dfrac{xy^2 z^2}{\sqrt{1+x^2y^2z^2}}, \dfrac{x^2 yz^2}{\sqrt{1+x^2y^2z^2}}, \dfrac{x^2 y^2 z}{\sqrt{1+x^2y^2z^2}} \rangle$,

$\nabla f(2,-3,1) = \langle \dfrac{18}{\sqrt{37}}, \dfrac{-12}{\sqrt{37}}, \dfrac{36}{\sqrt{37}} \rangle$

21. $\nabla f = \langle \dfrac{3xyz + 2y^2 z + 2yz^2}{2\sqrt{x+y+z}}, \dfrac{3xyz + 2x^2 z + 2xz^2}{2\sqrt{x+y+z}},$

$\dfrac{3xyz + 2x^2 y + 2xy^2}{\sqrt{x+y+z}} \rangle$,

$\nabla f(1,1,2) = \langle 9, 9, 5 \rangle$

23. $\nabla f = \langle \dfrac{2(y+z)}{(x+y+z)^2}, \dfrac{-2(x+z)}{(x+y+z)^2}, \dfrac{-2(x+z)}{(x+y+z)^2} \rangle$,

$\nabla f(1,1,2) = \langle \dfrac{3}{8}, -\dfrac{3}{8}, -\dfrac{3}{8} \rangle$

25. $\nabla f = \langle \dfrac{yz}{(1+xyz)^2}, \dfrac{xz}{(1+xyz)^2}, \dfrac{xy}{(1+xyz)^2} \rangle$,

$\nabla f(1,-1,-1) = \langle \dfrac{1}{4}, -\dfrac{1}{4}, -\dfrac{1}{4} \rangle$

27. $\nabla f = \langle \dfrac{yze^{xyz}}{(1+e^{xyz})^2}, \dfrac{xze^{xyz}}{(1+e^{xyz})^2}, \dfrac{xye^{xyz}}{(1+e^{xyz})^2} \rangle$,

$\nabla f(0,0,0) = \langle 0, 0, 0 \rangle$

29. $\nabla f = \langle yzx^{yz-1}, zx^{yz} \ln x, yx^{yz} \ln x \rangle$,

$\nabla f(2,1,1) = \langle 1, \ln 4, \ln 4 \rangle$

31. $\nabla f = \langle \pi \cos \pi x \sin \pi y \sin \pi z, \pi \sin \pi x \cos \pi y \sin \pi z,$

$\pi \sin \pi x \sin \pi y \cos \pi z \rangle$,

$\nabla f(\tfrac{1}{2}, \tfrac{1}{4}, \tfrac{1}{2}) = \langle 0, \dfrac{\pi\sqrt{2}}{2}, 0 \rangle$

33. $\nabla f = \langle 2xy - 9x^2 y^4, x^2 - 12x^3 y^3 \rangle$,

$\nabla f(1,1) = \langle -7, -11 \rangle$, $\mathbf{u} = \langle \dfrac{1}{\sqrt{2}}, -\dfrac{1}{\sqrt{2}} \rangle$,

$D_{\mathbf{u}}f(1,1) = \dfrac{4}{\sqrt{2}}$

35. $\nabla f = \dfrac{3x^2 + 2xy}{2\sqrt{x+y}}\mathbf{i} + \dfrac{3y^2 + 2xy}{2\sqrt{x+y}}\mathbf{j}$,

$\nabla f(3,1) = \dfrac{33}{4}\mathbf{i} + \dfrac{9}{4}\mathbf{j}$, $\mathbf{u} = \dfrac{3}{5}\mathbf{i} + \dfrac{4}{5}\mathbf{j}$, $D_{\mathbf{u}}f(3,1) = 27$

37. $\nabla f = \langle \dfrac{2x^2 + y^2}{\sqrt{x^2 + y^2}}, \dfrac{xy}{\sqrt{x^2 + y^2}} \rangle$,,

$\nabla f(3,4) = \langle \dfrac{34}{5}, \dfrac{12}{5} \rangle$ $\mathbf{u} = \langle \dfrac{1}{\sqrt{10}}, -\dfrac{3}{\sqrt{10}} \rangle$,

$D_{\mathbf{u}}f(3,4) = \dfrac{14}{\sqrt{10}}$

39. $\nabla f = \dfrac{y}{1+xy}\mathbf{i} + \dfrac{x}{1+xy}\mathbf{j}$, $\nabla f(1,2) = \dfrac{2}{3}\mathbf{i} + \dfrac{1}{3}\mathbf{j}$

$\mathbf{u} = -\dfrac{1}{\sqrt{5}}\mathbf{i} + \dfrac{2}{\sqrt{5}}\mathbf{j}$, $D_{\mathbf{u}}f(3,1) = 0$

41. $\nabla f = \langle \dfrac{2x^2 + y^2 + z^2}{\sqrt{x^2 + y^2 + z^2}}, \dfrac{xz}{\sqrt{x^2 + y^2 + z^2}},$

$\dfrac{xy}{\sqrt{x^2 + y^2 + z^2}} \rangle$,

$\nabla f(1,1,1) = \langle \dfrac{4}{\sqrt{3}}, \dfrac{1}{\sqrt{3}}, \dfrac{1}{\sqrt{3}} \rangle$, $\mathbf{u} = \langle \dfrac{-1}{\sqrt{11}}, \dfrac{3}{\sqrt{11}}, \dfrac{1}{\sqrt{11}} \rangle$,

$$D_{\mathbf{u}}f(1,1,1) = 0$$

43. $\nabla f = \dfrac{yz}{1+xyz}\mathbf{i} + \dfrac{xz}{1+xyz}\mathbf{j} + \dfrac{xy}{1+xyz}\mathbf{k}$,

$\nabla f(1,2,1) = \frac{2}{3}\mathbf{i} + \frac{1}{3}\mathbf{j} + \frac{2}{3}\mathbf{k}$, $\mathbf{u} = -\frac{3}{\sqrt{13}}\mathbf{i} - \frac{2}{\sqrt{13}}\mathbf{k}$,

$D_{\mathbf{u}}f(1,2,1) = \frac{2}{3\sqrt{13}}$

45. $\nabla f = \langle y^2 - 6xy, 2xy - 3x^2 \rangle$, $\nabla f(1,-1) = \langle 7,-5 \rangle$

max/min: $\pm\sqrt{74}$, directions: $\pm\langle \frac{7}{\sqrt{74}}, -\frac{5}{\sqrt{74}} \rangle$

47. $\nabla f = \langle \dfrac{2y}{(x+y)^2}, \dfrac{-2x}{(x+y)^2} \rangle$, $\nabla f(1,1) = \langle \frac{1}{4}, -\frac{1}{4} \rangle$

max/min: $\pm\frac{\sqrt{2}}{4}$, directions: $\pm\langle \frac{1}{\sqrt{2}}, -\frac{1}{\sqrt{2}} \rangle$

49. $\nabla f = \langle \dfrac{y^2 - x^2}{(x^2+y^2)^2}, \dfrac{-2xy}{(x^2+y^2)^2} \rangle$,

$\nabla f(1,2) = \langle \frac{3}{25}, -\frac{4}{25} \rangle$

max/min: $\pm\frac{1}{5}$, directions: $\pm\langle \frac{3}{5}, -\frac{4}{5} \rangle$

51. $\nabla f = \langle \dfrac{y^2}{(x+y)^2}, \dfrac{x^2}{(x+y)^2} \rangle$, $\nabla f(2,1) = \langle \frac{1}{9}, \frac{4}{9} \rangle$

max/min: $\pm\frac{\sqrt{17}}{9}$, directions: $\pm\langle \frac{1}{\sqrt{17}}, \frac{4}{\sqrt{17}} \rangle$

53. $\nabla f = \langle \dfrac{3x+2y}{2\sqrt{x+y}}, \dfrac{x}{2\sqrt{x+y}} \rangle$, $\nabla f(2,2) = \langle \frac{5}{2}, \frac{1}{2} \rangle$

max/min: $\pm\frac{\sqrt{26}}{2}$, directions: $\pm\langle \frac{5}{\sqrt{26}}, \frac{1}{\sqrt{26}} \rangle$

55. $\nabla f = \langle 6x^2y^3z^2, 6x^3y^2z^2, 4x^3y^3z \rangle$,

$\nabla f(1,-1,1) = \langle -6, 6, -4 \rangle$, max/min: $\pm 2\sqrt{22}$,

directions: $\pm\langle -\frac{3}{\sqrt{22}}, \frac{3}{\sqrt{22}}, -\frac{3}{\sqrt{22}} \rangle$

57. $\nabla f = \langle \dfrac{y^2z + yz^2}{(x+y+z)^2}, \dfrac{x^2z + xz^2}{(x+y+z)^2}, \dfrac{x^2y + xy^2}{(x+y+z)^2} \rangle$,

$\nabla f(2,-1,3) = \langle -\frac{3}{8}, \frac{15}{8}, -\frac{1}{8} \rangle$, max/min: $\pm\frac{\sqrt{235}}{8}$,

directions: $\pm\langle -\frac{3}{\sqrt{235}}, \frac{15}{\sqrt{235}}, -\frac{1}{\sqrt{235}} \rangle$

59. $\nabla f = \langle 2x, 1 \rangle$, $\nabla f(1,1) = \langle 2,1 \rangle$

level curve: $y + x^2 = 2$, tangent: $y = -2x + 3$

61. $\nabla f = \langle \dfrac{-2xy}{(1+x^2)^2}, \dfrac{1}{1+x^2} \rangle$, $\nabla f(1,2) = \langle -1, \frac{1}{2} \rangle$

level curve: $\dfrac{y}{1+x^2} = 1$, tangent: $y = -2x$

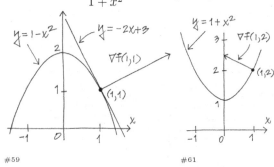

#59 #61

63. $\nabla f = \langle y^2 e^x, 2ye^x \rangle$, $\nabla f(0,-1) = \langle 1,-2 \rangle$

level curve: $y = -e^{-x/2}$, tangent: $y = \frac{1}{2}x - 1$

65. $\nabla f = \langle 2x, 4y \rangle$, $\nabla f(2,\sqrt{3}) = \langle 4, 4\sqrt{3} \rangle$

level curve: $x^2 + 4y^2 = 16$, tangent: $y = -\frac{1}{\sqrt{3}}x + \frac{5}{\sqrt{3}}$

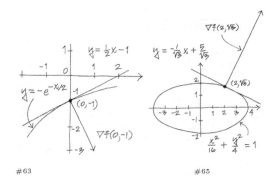

#63 #65

67. $\nabla f = \langle -\dfrac{y^3}{4x^3}, \dfrac{3y^2}{8x^2} \rangle$, $\nabla f(1,2) = \langle -2, \frac{3}{2} \rangle$

level curve: $y = 2x^{2/3}$, tangent: $y = \frac{4}{3}x + \frac{2}{3}$

69. $\nabla f = \langle \dfrac{2xy^2}{(1-x^2)^2}, \dfrac{2y}{1-x^2} \rangle$, $\nabla f(\frac{1}{2}, \sqrt{3}) = \langle \frac{16}{3}, \frac{8\sqrt{3}}{3} \rangle$

level curve: $x^2 + \frac{1}{4}y^2 = 1$, tangent: $y = -\frac{2}{\sqrt{3}}x + \frac{4}{\sqrt{3}}$

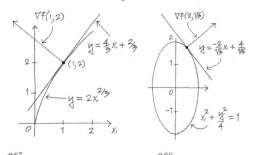

#67 #69

71. $\nabla f = \langle 2(x-1), 2(y-1) \rangle$, $\nabla f(1,1) = \langle 0,0 \rangle$

73. $\nabla f = \langle \dfrac{\ln y}{x}, \dfrac{\ln x}{y} \rangle$, $\nabla f(1,1) = \langle 0,0 \rangle$

75. $\nabla f = \langle -\pi \sin\pi x \cos\pi y - \pi \cos\pi x \sin\pi y \rangle$,

$\nabla f(1,1) = \langle 0,0 \rangle$

77. $\nabla f = \langle \dfrac{-\pi \sin\pi x}{\cos\pi y}, \dfrac{\pi \cos\pi x \sin\pi y}{\cos^2 \pi y} \rangle$,

$\nabla f(1,1) = \langle 0,0 \rangle$

Exercises: 11.6

1. $\nabla f = \langle 4x^3 - 2x, 3y^2 - 4 \rangle$, $\nabla f(1,1) = \langle 2,-1 \rangle$

$f(1,1,) = -3$, $\mathbf{n} = \langle -2, 1, 1 \rangle$

$-2x + y + z + 4 = 0$

3. $\nabla f = \langle 2x(y^3 - 2y), (x^2-1)(3y^2-2) \rangle$

$\nabla f(2,1) = \langle -4, 3 \rangle$, $f(2,1) = -3$, $\mathbf{n} = \langle 4, 3, 1 \rangle$

$4x - 3y + z = 2$

5. $\nabla f = \langle 2xy^3 + 4y^2, 3x^2y^2 + 8xy \rangle$

$\nabla f(1,-1) = \langle -2, 5 \rangle$, $f(1,-1) = 3$, $\mathbf{n} = \langle -2, 5, 1 \rangle$

$-2x + 5y + z = 4$

7. $\nabla f = \langle \dfrac{y}{2\sqrt{1+xy}}, \dfrac{x}{2\sqrt{1+xy}} \rangle$

$\nabla f(3,1) = \langle \frac{1}{4}, \frac{3}{4} \rangle$, $f(3,1) = 2$, $\mathbf{n} = \langle -\frac{1}{4}, -\frac{3}{4}, 1 \rangle$

$x + 3y - 4z + 2 = 0$

9. $\nabla f = \langle \dfrac{3x+2y}{2\sqrt{x+y}}, \dfrac{x}{2\sqrt{x+y}} \rangle$

$\nabla f(1,3) = \langle \frac{9}{4}, \frac{1}{4} \rangle, f(1,3) = 2, \mathbf{n} = \langle -\frac{9}{4}, -\frac{1}{4}, 1 \rangle$
$9x + y - 4z = 4$

11. $\nabla f = \langle \frac{\ln y}{x}, \frac{\ln x}{y} \rangle,$

$\nabla f(e,e) = \langle e^{-1}, e^{-1} \rangle, f(e,e) = 1, \mathbf{n} = \langle e^{-1}, e^{-1}, 1 \rangle$
$x + y - ez = e$

13. $\nabla f = \langle -(2+3x)(1+y)e^{-3x-4y},$
$\qquad -(1+x)(3+4y)e^{-3x-4y} \rangle$
$\nabla f(0,0) = \langle -2, -3 \rangle, f(0,0) = 1, \mathbf{n} = \langle 2, 3, 1 \rangle$
$2x + 3y - z + 1 = 0$

15. $\nabla f = \langle (x+1)^{y-1}y, (x+1)^y \ln(x+1) \rangle$
$\nabla f(1,2) = \langle 4, 4\ln 2 \rangle, f(1,2) = 4,$
$\mathbf{n} = \langle -4, -4\ln 2, 1 \rangle, \; -4x - (4\ln 2)y + z = 8\ln 2$

17. $\nabla f = \langle -\pi \sin \pi x \sin \pi y, \pi \cos \pi x \cos \pi y \rangle$
$\nabla f(\frac{1}{4}, \frac{1}{4}) = \langle -\frac{\pi}{2}, \frac{\pi}{2} \rangle, f(\frac{1}{4}, \frac{1}{4}) = \frac{1}{2}, \mathbf{n} = \langle \frac{\pi}{2}, -\frac{\pi}{2}, 1 \rangle$
$\pi x + \pi y + 2z = 1$

19. $\nabla H = \langle y^2, 2xy + z^3, 3yz^2 \rangle$
$\qquad \mathbf{n} = \nabla H(2,-2,1) = \langle -4, -7, -6 \rangle$
$\qquad 4x - 7y - 6z = 16$

21. $\nabla H = \langle \dfrac{2x}{1+x^2+y^2+z^2}, \dfrac{2y}{1+x^2+y^2+z^2}$
$\qquad\qquad \dfrac{2z}{1+x^2+y^2+z^2} \rangle$
$\qquad \mathbf{n} = \nabla H(-1,2,1) = \langle -\frac{1}{3}, \frac{2}{3}, \frac{1}{3} \rangle$
$\qquad -x + 2y + z = 2$

23. $\nabla H = \langle (1-2x^2)yze^{-x^2-y^3-z^4},$
$\qquad x(1-3y^3)ze^{-x^2-y^3-z^4}, xy(1-4z^4)e^{-x^2-y^3-z^4} \rangle$
$\qquad \mathbf{n} = \nabla H(1,1,1) = \langle -e^{-3}, -2e^{-3}, -3e^{-3} \rangle$
$\qquad x + 2y + 3z = 6$

25. $\nabla H = \langle (x+1)^{yz-1}yz, (x+1)^{yz}z\ln(x+1),$
$\qquad (x+1)^{yz}y\ln(x+1) \rangle$
$\qquad \mathbf{n} = \nabla H(1,2,1) = \langle 4, 4\ln 2, 8\ln 2 \rangle$
$\qquad x + (\ln 2)y + (2\ln 2)z = 1 - 4\ln 2$

27. $H = (4 - x^2)^2 - y^2 - z^2$
$\qquad \nabla H = \langle -4x(4-x^2), -2y, -2z \rangle$
$\qquad \mathbf{n} = \nabla H(1,2,\sqrt{5}) = \langle -12, -4, -2\sqrt{5} \rangle$
$\qquad 12x + 4y + 2\sqrt{5}\,z = 30$

29. $H = x^4(4-x^2)^2 - y^2 - z^2$
$\qquad \nabla H = \langle 8x(2-x^2), -2y, -2z \rangle$
$\qquad \mathbf{n} = \nabla H(1,1,2\sqrt{2}) = \langle 8, -2, -4\sqrt{2} \rangle$
$\qquad 8x - 2y - 4\sqrt{2}\,z + 10 = 0$

31. $H = e^{-2x} - y^2 - z^2$
$\qquad \nabla H = \langle -2e^{-2x}, -2y, -2z \rangle$
$\qquad \mathbf{n} = \nabla H(0, \frac{\sqrt{3}}{2}, \frac{1}{2}) = \langle -2, -\sqrt{3}, -1 \rangle$
$\qquad x + \sqrt{3}\,y + z = 2$

33. $H = \sin^2 x - y^2 - z^2$
$\qquad \nabla H = \langle 2\sin x \cos x, -2y, -2z \rangle$
$\qquad \mathbf{n} = \nabla H(\frac{3\pi}{4}, \frac{\sqrt{2}}{4}, \frac{\sqrt{6}}{4}) = \langle -1, -\frac{\sqrt{2}}{2}, -\frac{\sqrt{6}}{2} \rangle$

$x + \frac{\sqrt{2}}{2}y + \frac{\sqrt{6}}{2}z = 1 + \frac{3\pi}{4}$

35. $H = x^2 + y^2, G = y^2 + z^2$
$\qquad \nabla H = \langle 2x, 2y, 0 \rangle, \nabla G = \langle 0, 2y, 2z \rangle$
$\qquad \mathbf{n}_1 = \langle 2, 2, 0 \rangle, \mathbf{n}_2 = \langle 0, 2, 2 \rangle$
$\qquad \mathbf{v} = \mathbf{n}_1 \times \mathbf{n}_2 = \langle 4, -4, 4 \rangle$
$\qquad x = 1 + 4t, y = 1 - 4t, z = 1 + 4t$
$\qquad x = t, y = \pm\sqrt{2 - t^2}, z = \pm\sqrt{2 - t^2}$

36. $H = y^2 + z^2, G = x^2 + y^2 - z^2$
$\qquad \nabla H = \langle 0, 2y, 2z \rangle, \nabla G = \langle 2x, 2y, -2z \rangle$
$\qquad \mathbf{n}_1 = \langle 0, \sqrt{2}, \sqrt{2} \rangle, \mathbf{n}_2 = \langle 2, \sqrt{2}, -\sqrt{2} \rangle$
$\qquad \mathbf{v} = \mathbf{n}_1 \times \mathbf{n}_2 = \langle -4, 2\sqrt{2}, -2\sqrt{2} \rangle$
$\qquad x = 1 - 4t, y = \frac{\sqrt{2}}{2} + 2\sqrt{2}t, z = \frac{\sqrt{2}}{2} - 2\sqrt{2}t$
$\qquad x = t, y = \pm\sqrt{2 - t^2}/\sqrt{2}, z = \pm\frac{\sqrt{2}}{2}t$

37. $H = x^2 + y^2 - z^2, G = y^2 + z^2 - x^2$
$\qquad \nabla H = \langle 2x, 2y, -2z \rangle, \nabla G = \langle -2x, 2y, 2z \rangle$
$\qquad \mathbf{n}_1 = \langle 2, 2, -2 \rangle, \mathbf{n}_2 = \langle -2, 2, 2 \rangle$
$\qquad \mathbf{v} = \mathbf{n}_1 \times \mathbf{n}_2 = \langle 8, 0, 8 \rangle$
$\qquad x = 1 + 8t, y = 1, z = 1 + 8t$
$\qquad x = t, y = \pm 1, z = \pm t$

38. $H = x^2 + y^2 - z^2, G = -x^2 + y^2 + z^2$
$\qquad \nabla H = \langle 2x, 2y, -2z \rangle, \nabla G = \langle -2x, 2y, 2z \rangle$
$\qquad \mathbf{n}_1 = \langle 2, \sqrt{6}, -\sqrt{2} \rangle, \mathbf{n}_2 = \langle -2, \sqrt{6}, \sqrt{2} \rangle$
$\qquad \mathbf{v} = \mathbf{n}_1 \times \mathbf{n}_2 = \langle 4\sqrt{3}, 0, 4\sqrt{6} \rangle$
$\qquad x = 1 + 4\sqrt{3}t, y = \frac{\sqrt{6}}{2}, z = \frac{\sqrt{2}}{2} + 4\sqrt{6}t$
$\qquad x = t, y = \pm\sqrt{3}/\sqrt{2}, z = \pm\sqrt{2t^2 - 1}/\sqrt{2}$

39. $H = x^2 + y^2 - z^2, G = \frac{x^2}{16} + \frac{y^2}{4} + \frac{z^2}{4}$
$\qquad \nabla H = \langle 2x, 2y, -2z \rangle, \nabla G = \langle \frac{1}{8}x, \frac{1}{2}y, \frac{1}{2}z \rangle$
$\qquad \mathbf{n}_1 = \langle 2, \frac{\sqrt{15}}{\sqrt{2}}, -\frac{\sqrt{15}}{\sqrt{2}} \rangle, \mathbf{n}_2 = \langle \frac{1}{8}, \frac{\sqrt{15}}{4\sqrt{2}}, \frac{\sqrt{15}}{4\sqrt{2}} \rangle$
$\qquad \mathbf{v} = \mathbf{n}_1 \times \mathbf{n}_2 = \langle \frac{15}{4}, -\frac{5\sqrt{15}}{8}, \frac{3\sqrt{15}}{8} \rangle$
$\qquad x = 1 + \frac{15}{4}t, y = \frac{\sqrt{15}}{2\sqrt{2}} - \frac{5\sqrt{15}}{8}t, z = \frac{\sqrt{15}}{2\sqrt{2}} + \frac{3\sqrt{15}}{8}t$
$\qquad x = t, y = \pm\frac{\sqrt{5}}{2\sqrt{2}}\sqrt{4 - t^2}, z = \pm\frac{\sqrt{3}}{2\sqrt{2}}\sqrt{4 + t^2}$

40. $H = x^2 + y^2, G = z - x^2 + y^2$
$\qquad \nabla H = \langle 2x, 2y, 0 \rangle, \nabla G = \langle -2x, 2y, 1 \rangle$
$\qquad \mathbf{n}_1 = \langle 1, \sqrt{3}, 0 \rangle, \mathbf{n}_2 = \langle -1, \sqrt{3}, 1 \rangle$
$\qquad \mathbf{v} = \mathbf{n}_1 \times \mathbf{n}_2 = \langle \sqrt{3}, -1, 2\sqrt{3} \rangle$
$\qquad x = \frac{1}{2} + \sqrt{3}t, y = \frac{\sqrt{3}}{2} - t, z = -\frac{1}{2} + 2\sqrt{3}t$
$\qquad x = t, y = \pm\sqrt{1 - t^2}, z = 2t^2 - 1$

41. $H = -x^2 + y^2 + z, G = z - x^2 - y^2 + 2$
$\qquad \nabla H = \langle -2x, 2y, 1 \rangle, \nabla G = \langle -2x, 2y, 1 \rangle$
$\qquad \mathbf{n}_1 = \langle -4, 2, 1 \rangle, \mathbf{n}_2 = \langle -4, -2, 1 \rangle$
$\qquad \mathbf{v} = \mathbf{n}_1 \times \mathbf{n}_2 = \langle 4, 0, 16 \rangle$
$\qquad x = 2 + 4t, y = 1, z = 3 + 16t$
$\qquad x = t, y = \pm 1, z = t^2 - 1$

42. $H = x^2 + y^2 - z^2, G = y^2 + z^2$
$\qquad \nabla H = \langle 2x, 2y, -2z \rangle, \nabla G = \langle 0, 2y, 2z \rangle$
$\qquad \mathbf{n}_1 = \langle 1, \frac{\sqrt{6}}{2}, -\frac{\sqrt{10}}{2} \rangle, \mathbf{n}_2 = \langle 0, \frac{\sqrt{6}}{2}, \frac{\sqrt{10}}{2} \rangle$

$$\mathbf{v} = \mathbf{n}_1 \times \mathbf{n}_2 = \langle \sqrt{15}, -\tfrac{\sqrt{10}}{2}, \tfrac{\sqrt{6}}{2} \rangle$$
$$x = \tfrac{1}{2} + \sqrt{15}\,t, \; y = \tfrac{\sqrt{6}}{4} - \tfrac{\sqrt{10}}{2}t, \; z = \tfrac{\sqrt{10}}{4} + \tfrac{\sqrt{6}}{2}t$$
$$x = t, \; y = \pm\tfrac{1}{\sqrt{2}}\sqrt{1 - t^2}, \; z = \pm\tfrac{1}{\sqrt{2}}\sqrt{1 + t^2}$$

Exercises: 11.7

1. $f = x^2y^3 + 4xy^2$, $\nabla f = \langle 2xy^3 + 4y^2, 3x^2y^2 + 8xy \rangle$

$$H = \begin{vmatrix} 2y^3 & 6xy^2 \\ 6xy^2 & 6x^2y + 8x \end{vmatrix}$$

$$H(-2, -1) = \begin{vmatrix} -2 & 12 \\ 12 & -8 \end{vmatrix} = -128$$

3. $f = (x \ln x)(y \ln y)$,
$\nabla f = \langle (\ln x + 1)y \ln y, x \ln x(\ln y + 1) \rangle$

$$H = \begin{vmatrix} \frac{y \ln y}{x} & (\ln x + 1)(\ln y + 1) \\ (\ln x + 1)(\ln y + 1) & \frac{x \ln x}{y} \end{vmatrix}$$

$$H(e, e) = \begin{vmatrix} 1 & 4 \\ 4 & 1 \end{vmatrix} = -15$$

5. $f = \cos x \sin y$, $\nabla f = \langle -\sin x \sin y, \cos x \cos y \rangle$

$$H = \begin{vmatrix} -\cos x \sin y & -\sin x \cos y \\ -\sin x \cos y & -\cos x \sin y \end{vmatrix}$$

$$H(\tfrac{\pi}{6}, \tfrac{\pi}{3}) = \begin{vmatrix} -\frac{3}{4} & -\frac{1}{4} \\ -\frac{1}{4} & -\frac{3}{4} \end{vmatrix} = \tfrac{1}{2}$$

7. $f = xye^{-(x^2+y^2)/2}$,
$\nabla f = \langle (1 - x^2)ye^{-(x^2+y^2)/2}, x(1 - y^2)e^{-(x^2+y^2)/2} \rangle$

$$H =$$
$$\begin{vmatrix} (x^3 - 3x)ye^{-\frac{(x^2+y^2)}{2}} & (1 - x^2)(1 - y^2)e^{-\frac{(x^2+y^2)}{2}} \\ (1 - x^2)(1 - y^2)e^{-\frac{(x^2+y^2)}{2}} & x(y^3 - 3y)e^{-\frac{(x^2+y^2)}{2}} \end{vmatrix}$$

$$H(1, 1) = \begin{vmatrix} -2e^{-1} & 0 \\ 0 & -2e^{-1} \end{vmatrix} = 4e^{-2}$$

9. $f = x^2 + ye^{-y}$, $\nabla f = \langle 2x, (1 - y)e^{-y} \rangle$
$2x = 0, \; (1 - y)e^{-y} = 0 \implies (x, y) = (0, 1)$

$$H = \begin{vmatrix} 2 & 0 \\ 0 & (y - 2)e^{-y} \end{vmatrix}$$

$$H(0, 1) = \begin{vmatrix} 2 & 0 \\ 0 & -e^{-1} \end{vmatrix} = -2e^{-1}, \text{ saddle}$$

11. $f = x \ln x + y^2$, $\nabla f = \langle \ln x + 1, 2y \rangle$
$\ln x + 1 = 0, \; 2y = 0 \implies (x, y) = (e^{-1}, 0)$

$$H = \begin{vmatrix} \frac{1}{x} & 0 \\ 0 & 2 \end{vmatrix}, \; H(e^{-1}, 0) = \begin{vmatrix} e & 0 \\ 0 & 2 \end{vmatrix} = 2e, \text{ local min.}$$

13. $f = xe^{-x} + ye^{-y}$, $\nabla f = \langle (1 - x)e^{-x}, (1 - y)e^{-y} \rangle$
$(1 - x)e^{-x} = 0, \; (1 - y)e^{-y} = 0 \implies (x, y) = (1, 1)$

$$H = \begin{vmatrix} (x - 2)e^{-x} & 0 \\ 0 & (y - 2)e^{-y} \end{vmatrix}$$

$$H(1, 1) = \begin{vmatrix} -e^{-1} & 0 \\ 0 & -e^{-1} \end{vmatrix} = e^{-2}, \text{ local max.}$$

15. $f = xe^{-x^3/3} + ye^{-x^3/3}$,
$\nabla f = \langle (1 - x^3)e^{-x^3/3}, (1 - y^3)e^{-x^3/3} \rangle$
$(1 - x^3)e^{-x^3/3} = 0, \; (1 - y^3)e^{-x^3/3} = 0$

$$\implies (x, y) = (1, 1)$$

$$H = \begin{vmatrix} x^2(x^3 - 4)e^{-x^3/3} & 0 \\ 0 & y^2(y^3 - 4)e^{-x^3/3} \end{vmatrix}$$

$$H(1, 1) = \begin{vmatrix} -3e^{-1/3} & 0 \\ 0 & -e^{-1/3} \end{vmatrix} = 9e^{-2/3}, \text{ local max.}$$

17. $f = x^2 + \ln(1 + y^2)$, $\nabla f = \langle 2x, \frac{2y}{1+y^2} \rangle$
$2x = 0, \; 2y/(1 + y^2) = 0 \implies (x, y) = (0, 0)$

$$H = \begin{vmatrix} 2 & 0 \\ 0 & \frac{2(1 - y^2)}{(1 + y^2)^2} \end{vmatrix}$$

$$H(0, 0) = \begin{vmatrix} 2 & 0 \\ 0 & 2 \end{vmatrix} = 4, \text{ local min.}$$

19. $f = (e^x + e^{-x})(y^2 - 1)$,
$\nabla f = \langle (e^x - e^{-x})(y^2 - 1), (e^x + e^{-x})2y \rangle$
$(e^x - e^{-x})(y^2 - 1) = 0, \; (e^x + e^{-x})2y = 0$
$\implies (x, y) = (0, 0)$

$$H = \begin{vmatrix} (e^x + e^{-x})(y^2 - 1) & 2(e^x - e^{-x})y \\ 2(e^x - e^{-x})y & 2(e^x + e^{-x}) \end{vmatrix}$$

$$H(0, 0) = \begin{vmatrix} -2 & 0 \\ 0 & 2 \end{vmatrix} = -4, \text{ saddle}$$

21. $f = \ln(\ln x)\ln(\ln y)$, $\nabla f = \langle \frac{\ln(\ln y)}{x \ln x}, \frac{\ln(\ln x)}{y \ln y} \rangle$
$\frac{\ln(\ln y)}{x \ln x} = 0, \; \frac{\ln(\ln x)}{y \ln y} = 0 \implies (x, y) = (e, e)$

$$H = \begin{vmatrix} \ln(\ln y)\left[\frac{-(\ln x + 1)}{x^2(\ln x)^2}\right] & \frac{1}{xy \ln x \ln y} \\ \frac{1}{xy \ln x \ln y} & \ln(\ln x)\left[\frac{-(\ln y + 1)}{y^2(\ln y)^2}\right] \end{vmatrix}$$

$$H(e, e) = \begin{vmatrix} 0 & \frac{1}{e^2} \\ \frac{1}{e^2} & 0 \end{vmatrix} = -\frac{1}{e^4}, \text{ saddle}$$

23. $f = x^2 + 3y - y^3$, $\nabla f = \langle 2x, 3(1 - y^2) \rangle$
c.p.'s: $(0, 1), (0, -1)$

$$H = \begin{vmatrix} 2 & 0 \\ 0 & -6y \end{vmatrix}$$

$$H(0, 1) = \begin{vmatrix} 2 & 0 \\ 0 & -6 \end{vmatrix} = -12, \text{ saddle}$$

$$H(0, -1) = \begin{vmatrix} 2 & 0 \\ 0 & 6 \end{vmatrix} = 12, \text{ local min.}$$

25. $f = x \ln x + 3y - y^3$, $\nabla f = \langle \ln x + 1, 3(1 - y^2) \rangle$
c.p.'s: $(e^{-1}, 1), (e^{-1}, -1)$

$$H = \begin{vmatrix} \frac{1}{x} & 0 \\ 0 & -6y \end{vmatrix}$$

$$H(e^{-1}, 1) = \begin{vmatrix} e & 0 \\ 0 & -6 \end{vmatrix} = -6e, \text{ saddle}$$

$$H(e^{-1}, -1) = \begin{vmatrix} e & 0 \\ 0 & 6 \end{vmatrix} = 6e, \text{ local min.}$$

27. $f = xye^{-(x+y)}$,
$\nabla f = \langle (1 - x)ye^{-(x+y)}, x(1 - y)e^{-(x+y)} \rangle$
c.p.'s: $(1, 1), (0, 0)$

$$H = \begin{vmatrix} (x-2)ye^{-(x+y)} & (1-x)(1-y)e^{-(x+y)} \\ (1-x)(1-y)e^{-(x+y)} & x(y-2)e^{-(x+y)} \end{vmatrix}$$

$$H(0,0) = \begin{vmatrix} 0 & 1 \\ 1 & 0 \end{vmatrix} = -1, \text{ saddle}$$

$$H(1,1) = \begin{vmatrix} -e^{-2} & 0 \\ 0 & -e^{-2} \end{vmatrix} = e^{-4}, \text{ local max.}$$

29. $f = (1+x^2)(y^3 - 3y)$,
$\nabla f = \langle 2x(y^3 - 3y), (1+x^2)3(y^2-1) \rangle$

c.p.'s: $(0,1), (0,-1)$

$$H = \begin{vmatrix} 2(y^3 - 3y) & 6x(y^2-1) \\ 6x(y^2-1) & (1+x^2)6y \end{vmatrix}$$

$$H(0,1) = \begin{vmatrix} -4 & 0 \\ 0 & 6 \end{vmatrix} = -24, \text{ saddle}$$

$$H(0,-1) = \begin{vmatrix} 4 & 0 \\ 0 & -6 \end{vmatrix} = -24, \text{ saddle}$$

31. $f = e^x + e^{-x} + y^3 - 3y$,
$\nabla f = \langle e^x - e^{-x}, 3(y^2-1) \rangle$

c.p.'s: $(0,1), (0,-1)$

$$H = \begin{vmatrix} e^x + e^{-x} & 0 \\ 0 & 6y \end{vmatrix}$$

$$H(0,1) = \begin{vmatrix} 2 & 0 \\ 0 & 6 \end{vmatrix} = 12, \text{ local min.}$$

$$H(0,-1) = \begin{vmatrix} 2 & 0 \\ 0 & -6 \end{vmatrix} = -12, \text{ saddle}$$

33. $f = \ln(1+x^2) + y^3 - 27y$,
$\nabla f = \langle \frac{2x}{1+x^2}, 3(y^2-9) \rangle$

c.p.'s: $(0,3), (0,-3)$

$$H = \begin{vmatrix} \frac{2(1-x^2)}{(1+x^2)^2} & 0 \\ 0 & 6y \end{vmatrix}$$

$$H(0,3) = \begin{vmatrix} \frac{1}{2} & 0 \\ 0 & 18 \end{vmatrix} = 9, \text{ local min.}$$

$$H(0,-3) = \begin{vmatrix} \frac{1}{2} & 0 \\ 0 & -18 \end{vmatrix} = -12, \text{ saddle}$$

35. $f = x^2 + y^4 - 2y^2$, $\nabla f = \langle 2x, 4y(y^2-1) \rangle$

c.p.'s: $(0,0), (0,1), (0,-1)$

$$H = \begin{vmatrix} 2 & 0 \\ 0 & 12y^2 - 4 \end{vmatrix}$$

$$H(0,0) = \begin{vmatrix} 2 & 0 \\ 0 & -4 \end{vmatrix} = -8, \text{ saddle}$$

$$H(0,1) = \begin{vmatrix} 2 & 0 \\ 0 & 8 \end{vmatrix} = 16, \text{ local min.}$$

$$H(0,-1) = \begin{vmatrix} 2 & 0 \\ 0 & 8 \end{vmatrix} = 16, \text{ local min.}$$

37. $f = (x^2 - 1)ye^{-y}$,
$\nabla f = \langle 2xye^{-y}, (x^2-1)(1-y)e^{-y} \rangle$,

c.p.'s: $(0,1), (1,0), (-1,0)$

$$H = \begin{vmatrix} 2ye^{-y} & 2x(1-y)e^{-y} \\ 2x(1-y)e^{-y} & (x^2-1)(y-2)e^{-y} \end{vmatrix}$$

$$H(0,1) = \begin{vmatrix} 2e^{-1} & 0 \\ 0 & e^{-1} \end{vmatrix} = 2e^{-2}, \text{ local min}$$

$$H(1,0) = \begin{vmatrix} 0 & 2 \\ 2 & 0 \end{vmatrix} = -4, \text{ saddle}$$

$$H(-1,0) = \begin{vmatrix} 0 & -2 \\ -2 & 0 \end{vmatrix} = -4, \text{ saddle}$$

39. $f = e^x + e^{-x} + 8y^2 - y^4$,
$\nabla f = \langle e^x - e^{-x}, 16y - 4y^3 \rangle$,

c.p.'s: $(0,0), (0,2), (0,-2)$

$$H = \begin{vmatrix} e^x + e^{-x} & 0 \\ 0 & 16 - 12y^2 \end{vmatrix}$$

$$H(0,0) = \begin{vmatrix} 2 & 0 \\ 0 & 16 \end{vmatrix} = 32, \text{ local min.}$$

$$H(0,2) = \begin{vmatrix} 2 & 0 \\ 0 & -32 \end{vmatrix} = -64, \text{ saddle}$$

$$H(0,-2) = \begin{vmatrix} 2 & 0 \\ 0 & -32 \end{vmatrix} = -64, \text{ saddle}$$

41. $f = 3x - x^3 + y^3 - 27y$, $\nabla f = \langle 3(1-x^2), 3(y^2-9) \rangle$,

c.p.'s: $(1,3), (1,-3), (-1,3), (-1,-3)$

$$H = \begin{vmatrix} -6x & 0 \\ 0 & 6y \end{vmatrix}$$

$$H(1,3) = \begin{vmatrix} -6 & 0 \\ 0 & 18 \end{vmatrix} = -108, \text{ saddle}$$

$$H(1,-3) = \begin{vmatrix} -6 & 0 \\ 0 & -18 \end{vmatrix} = 108, \text{ local max.}$$

$$H(-1,3) = \begin{vmatrix} 6 & 0 \\ 0 & 18 \end{vmatrix} = 108, \text{ local min.}$$

$$H(-1,-3) = \begin{vmatrix} 6 & 0 \\ 0 & -18 \end{vmatrix} = -108, \text{ saddle}$$

43. $f = x^2 e^{-x} + y^2 e^{-y}$,
$\nabla f = \langle (2x - x^2)e^{-x}, (2y - y^2)e^{-y} \rangle$,

c.p.'s: $(0,0), (0,2), (2,0), (2,2)$

$$H = \begin{vmatrix} (2 - 4x + x^2)e^{-x} & 0 \\ 0 & (2 - 4y + y^2)e^{-y} \end{vmatrix}$$

$$H(0,0) = \begin{vmatrix} 2 & 0 \\ 0 & 2 \end{vmatrix} = 4, \text{ local min.}$$

$$H(0,2) = \begin{vmatrix} 2 & 0 \\ 0 & -2e^{-2} \end{vmatrix} = -4e^{-2}, \text{ saddle}$$

$$H(2,0) = \begin{vmatrix} -2e^{-2} & 0 \\ 0 & 2 \end{vmatrix} = -4e^{-2}, \text{ saddle}$$

$$H(2,2) = \begin{vmatrix} -2e^{-2} & 0 \\ 0 & -2e^{-2} \end{vmatrix} = 4e^{-4}, \text{ local max.}$$

45. $f = 3x^5 - 25x^3 + 60x + y^2 - 2y$,
$\nabla f = \langle 15x^4 - 75x^2 + 60, 2(y-1) \rangle$,

c.p.'s: $(1,1), (-1,1), (2,1), (-2,1)$

$H = \begin{vmatrix} 60x^3 - 150x & 0 \\ 0 & 2 \end{vmatrix}$

$H(1,1) = \begin{vmatrix} -90 & 0 \\ 0 & 2 \end{vmatrix} = -180$, saddle

$H(-1,1) = \begin{vmatrix} 90 & 0 \\ 0 & 2 \end{vmatrix} = 180$, local min.

$H(2,1) = \begin{vmatrix} 180 & 0 \\ 0 & 2 \end{vmatrix} = 360$, local min.

$H(-2,1) = \begin{vmatrix} -180 & 0 \\ 0 & 2 \end{vmatrix} = -360$, saddle

47. $f = (x^3 - 3x + 18)(y^2 - 1)$,

$\nabla f = \langle 3(x^2-1)(y^2-1), (x^3-3x+18)(2y) \rangle$,

c.p.'s: $(1,0), (-1,0), (-3,1), (-3,-1)$

$H = \begin{vmatrix} 6x(y^2-1) & 6(x^2-1)y \\ 6(x^2-1)y & 2(x^3-3x+18) \end{vmatrix}$

$H(1,0) = \begin{vmatrix} -6 & 0 \\ 0 & 32 \end{vmatrix} = -192$, saddle

$H(-1,0) = \begin{vmatrix} 6 & 0 \\ 0 & 40 \end{vmatrix} = 240$, local min.

$H(-3,1) = \begin{vmatrix} 0 & 48 \\ 48 & 0 \end{vmatrix} = -2304$, saddle

$H(-3,-1) = \begin{vmatrix} 0 & -48 \\ -48 & 0 \end{vmatrix} = -2304$, saddle

49. $f = (x^2-1)(y^2-1)$,

$\nabla f = \langle (2x(y^2-1), 2(x^2-1)y \rangle$,

c.p.'s: $(0,0), (1,1), (1,-1), (-1,1), (-1,-1)$

$H = \begin{vmatrix} (2(y^2-1) & 4xy \\ 4xy & 2(x^2-1) \end{vmatrix}$

$H(0,0) = \begin{vmatrix} -2 & 0 \\ 0 & -2 \end{vmatrix} = 4$, local max.

$H(\pm 1, \pm 1) = \begin{vmatrix} 0 & 4 \\ 4 & 0 \end{vmatrix} = -16$, saddles

51. $f = (x^3 - 3x + 18)(y^3 - 3x + 18))$,

$\nabla f = \langle (3x^2-3)(y^3-3y+18)), (x^3-3x+18)(3y^2-3) \rangle$,

c.p.'s: $(1,1), (1,-1), (-1,1), (-1,-1), (-3,-3)$

$H = \begin{vmatrix} 6x(y^3-3y+18) & (3x^2-3)(3y^2-3) \\ (3x^2-3)(3y^2-3) & 6y(x^3-3x+18) \end{vmatrix}$

$H(1,1) = \begin{vmatrix} 96 & 0 \\ 0 & 96 \end{vmatrix} = 9216$, local min.

$H(-1,-1) = \begin{vmatrix} -120 & 0 \\ 0 & -120 \end{vmatrix} = 14400$, local max.

$H(1,-1) = \begin{vmatrix} 120 & 0 \\ 0 & -96 \end{vmatrix} = -11520$, saddle

$H(-1,1) = \begin{vmatrix} -96 & 0 \\ 0 & 120 \end{vmatrix} = -11520$, saddle

$H(-3,-3) = \begin{vmatrix} 0 & 576 \\ 576 & 0 \end{vmatrix} = -331776$, saddle

53. $f = \ln\left(\frac{1+x^2}{2}\right)(y^2-1)$,

$\nabla f = \langle \frac{2x(y^2-1)}{1+x^2}, 2y\ln\left(\frac{1+x^2}{2}\right) \rangle$,

c.p.'s: $(0,0), (1,1), (1,-1), (-1,1), (-1,-1)$

$H = \begin{vmatrix} \frac{2(1-x^2)(y^2-1)}{(1+x^2)^2} & \frac{4xy}{1+x^2} \\ \frac{4xy}{1+x^2} & 2\ln\left(\frac{1+x^2}{2}\right) \end{vmatrix}$

$H(0,0) = \begin{vmatrix} -2 & 0 \\ 0 & -2\ln 2 \end{vmatrix} = 4\ln 2$, local max.

$H(\pm 1, \pm 1) = \begin{vmatrix} 0 & 2 \\ 2 & 0 \end{vmatrix} = -4$, saddles

55. $f = xye^{-(x^2+y^2)/2}$,

$\nabla f = \langle y(1-x^2)e^{-(x^2+y^2)/2}, x(1-y^2)e^{-(x^2+y^2)/2} \rangle$,

c.p.'s: $(0,0), (1,1), (1,-1), (-1,1), (-1,-1)$

$H = $

$\begin{vmatrix} x(x^2-3)ye^{-(x^2+y^2)/2} & (1-x^2)(1-y^2)e^{-(x^2+y^2)/2} \\ (1-x^2)(1-y^2)e^{-(x^2+y^2)/2} & xy(y^2-3)e^{-(x^2+y^2)/2} \end{vmatrix}$

$H(0,0) = \begin{vmatrix} 0 & 1 \\ 1 & 0 \end{vmatrix} = -1$, saddle

$H(1,1) = H(-1,-1) = \begin{vmatrix} -2e^{-1} & 0 \\ 0 & -2e^{-1} \end{vmatrix} = 4e^2$, local max's.

$H(1,-1) = H(-1,1) = \begin{vmatrix} 2e^{-1} & 0 \\ 0 & 2e^{-1} \end{vmatrix} = 4e^2$, local min's.

57. $f = 3x - x^3 + y^4 - 2y^2$, $\nabla f = \langle 3 - 3x^2, 4y^3 - 4y \rangle$,

c.p.'s: $(1,0), (-1,0), (1,1), (1,-1), (-1,1), (-1,-1)$

$H = \begin{vmatrix} -6x & 0 \\ 0 & 12y^2 - 4 \end{vmatrix}$

$H(1,0) = \begin{vmatrix} -6 & 0 \\ 0 & -4 \end{vmatrix} = 24$, local max.

$H(-1,0) = \begin{vmatrix} 6 & 0 \\ 0 & -4 \end{vmatrix} = -24$, saddle

$H(1,\pm 1) = \begin{vmatrix} -6 & 0 \\ 0 & 8 \end{vmatrix} = -48$, saddles

$H(-1,\pm 1) = \begin{vmatrix} 6 & 0 \\ 0 & 8 \end{vmatrix} = 48$, local mins.

59. $f = (x^2-1)(y^3-3y)$,

$\nabla f = \langle 2x(y^3-3y), (x^2-1)(3y^2-3) \rangle$,

c.p.'s: $(0,\pm 1), (\pm 1, 0), (\pm 1, \pm\sqrt{3})$

$H = \begin{vmatrix} 2y(y^2-3) & 6x(y^2-1) \\ 6x(y^2-1) & (x^2-1)6y \end{vmatrix}$

$H(0,1) = \begin{vmatrix} -4 & 0 \\ 0 & -6 \end{vmatrix} = 24$, local max.

$H(0,-1) = \begin{vmatrix} 4 & 0 \\ 0 & 6 \end{vmatrix} = 24$, local min.

$H(\pm 1, 0) = \begin{vmatrix} 0 & \mp 6 \\ \mp 6 & 0 \end{vmatrix} = -36$, two saddles

$H(-1, \pm 1) = \begin{vmatrix} 0 & \pm 12 \\ \pm 12 & 0 \end{vmatrix} = -144$, 4 saddles

CHAPTER 12: Answers to Odd Exercises

Exercises: 12.1

1. $\displaystyle\sum_{j=1}^{m}\sum_{i=1}^{n}\left[2 + 12 \cdot \frac{2i}{n} \cdot \frac{5j}{m}\right]\frac{10}{nm}$

$= 10\left[2 + \frac{120}{n^2} \cdot \frac{n(n+1)}{2} \cdot \frac{1}{m^2} \cdot \frac{m(m+1)}{2}\right]$

limit $= 10\left[2 + 120 \cdot \frac{1}{2} \cdot \frac{1}{2}\right] = 320$

3. $\displaystyle\sum_{j=1}^{m}\sum_{i=1}^{n}\left[3 \cdot \frac{2i}{n} + 4 \cdot \frac{5j}{m}\right]\frac{10}{nm}$

$= 10\left[\frac{6}{n^2} \cdot \frac{n(n+1)}{2} + \frac{20}{m^2} \cdot \frac{m(m+1)}{2}\right]$

limit $= 10\left[6 \cdot \frac{1}{2} + 20 \cdot \frac{1}{2}\right] = 130$

5. $\displaystyle\sum_{j=1}^{m}\sum_{i=1}^{n}\left[\frac{4i^2}{n^2} \cdot \frac{5j}{m} - \frac{25j^2}{m^2}\right]\frac{10}{nm}$

$= 10\left[\frac{20}{n^3} \cdot \frac{n(n+1)(2n+1)}{6} \cdot \frac{1}{m^2} \cdot \frac{m(m+1)}{2}\right.$

$\left. - \frac{25}{m^3} \cdot \frac{m(m+1)(2m+1)}{6}\right]$

limit $= 10\left[20 \cdot \frac{1}{3} \cdot \frac{1}{2} - 25 \cdot \frac{1}{3}\right] = -50$

7. $\displaystyle\sum_{j=1}^{m}\sum_{i=1}^{n}\left[\frac{2i}{n} \cdot \frac{25j^2}{m^2} + \frac{8i^3}{n^3} \cdot \frac{5j}{m}\right]\frac{10}{nm}$

$= 10\left[\frac{2}{n^2} \cdot \frac{n(n+1)}{2} \cdot \frac{25}{m^3} \cdot \frac{m(m+1)(2m+1)}{6}\right.$

$\left. + \frac{8}{n^4} \cdot \left[\frac{n(n+1)}{2}\right]^2 \cdot \frac{5}{m^2} \cdot \frac{m(m+1)}{2}\right]$

limit $= 10\left[2 \cdot \frac{1}{2} \cdot 25 \cdot \frac{1}{3} + 8 \cdot \frac{1}{4} \cdot 5 \cdot \frac{1}{2}\right] = \frac{400}{3}$

9. $\displaystyle\sum_{j=1}^{m}\sum_{i=1}^{n}e^{\frac{2i}{n}}e^{\frac{5j}{m}}\frac{10}{nm} = 10 \cdot \frac{e^{2/n}(e-1)}{n(e^{2/n}-1)} \cdot \frac{e^{5/m}(e-1)}{m(e^{5/m}-1)}$

limit $= 10 \cdot \frac{e^2-1}{\ln(e^2)} \cdot \frac{e^5-1}{\ln(e^5)}] = (e^2-1)(e^5-1)$

11. $2x^4y^2 + 3x^3y^5$ **13.** $x^3y - 2xy^3$ **15.** $\tan x \tan y$

17. $\frac{1}{2}e^{x^2y}$ **19.** $\sqrt{x^2+y^2}$ **21.** $x\ln|\sec(xy)|$

23. $2x^2e^{x\sqrt{y}}$ **25.** $-\cos(y\ln x)$ **27.** $y\tan^{-1}(xy)$

29. $\sin^{-1}(e^{xy})$ **31.** $\frac{y(3-xy)}{(xy-2)^2}$ **33.** -21 **35.** 76

37. 68 **39.** $\frac{1}{3}e^3 - \frac{1}{2}e^2 + \frac{1}{6}$ **41.** $\frac{2}{\pi}$ **43.** $\frac{2}{3}(7-3\sqrt{3})$

45. $\frac{\pi}{3}$ **47.** $(\ln 2)^2$ **49.** $\cos(1)-\cos(2)$ **51.** 12

53. $\frac{3}{16}$ **55.** $1-\cos(e)$ **57.** $\ln(\frac{4}{3})$ **59.** $2\ln 2 - 1$

61. $\frac{4}{5}(2^{5/2}-2)$ **63.** $e-2e^{1/2}+1$

Exercises: 12.2

1. $\frac{2}{3}$ **3.** 3 **5.** $\frac{4}{3}$ **7.** 4 **9.** $\ln 2 - \frac{1}{4}$ **11.** $21 - 8\ln 2$

13. $\frac{1}{5}(e^5-1)$ **15.** 1 **17.** $\frac{1}{2}(e-2)$ **19.** $1-\cos(1)$

21. $1-\frac{\pi}{4}$ **23.** $\frac{\pi}{2}-1$ **25.** 1 **27.** 2

29. $2^{3/2}-3\sqrt{2}+2$ **31.** 8 **33.** $\ln(\frac{16}{9})$ **35.** $4+6\ln(\frac{2}{9})$

37. $\frac{\pi}{4}+\ln(\frac{9}{8})$ **39.** $\frac{5}{12}$ **41.** $\frac{2}{15}(\sqrt{2}+1)$ **43.** $\frac{\pi}{2}-1$

45. $\frac{8}{3}\ln 2 - \frac{7}{9}$ **47.** $\frac{\pi}{4}-\frac{1}{2}\ln 2$ **49.** $e-\tan^{-1}(e)-1+\frac{\pi}{4}$

51. $1-\cos(e^2)$ **53.** $\int_0^2 \int_0^{x^2} f(x,y)\,dy\,dx$

55. $\int_0^4 \int_{\sqrt{x}}^2 f(x,y)\,dy\,dx$ **57.** $\int_0^{\pi/2} \int_0^{\sin x} f(x,y)\,dy\,dx$

59. $\int_0^{\ln 2} \int_0^{2-e^x} f(x,y)\,dy\,dx$ **61.** 1 **63.** 336

65. $2e^3 - \frac{7}{2}$ **67.** $2\ln 2 - 1$ **69.** $e-2$ **71.** $\frac{1}{2}-\frac{\pi}{8}$

73. 2 **75.** $\int_0^4 \int_{\sqrt{y}}^2 f(x,y)\,dx\,dy$ **77.** $\int_0^2 \int_{\sqrt{x}}^2 f(x,y)\,dx\,dy$

79. $\int_0^1 \int_{\sin^{-1} x}^{\pi/2} f(x,y)\,dx\,dy$ **81.** $\int_0^1 \int_0^{\ln(2-x)} f(x,y)\,dx\,dy$

83. $\tan(8)-6$ **85.** $16\sqrt{2}-8$ **87.** $8-\tan^{-1}(8)$

89. $16-\sin(16)$ **91.** $\frac{2}{15}$ **93.** $\frac{8}{15}$ **95.** $\ln(\frac{5}{3})-\frac{1}{2}$

Exercises: 12.3

1. $\frac{1}{6}$ **3.** $\frac{7}{5}$ **5.** 6 **7.** $\frac{256}{7}$ **9.** $\frac{5\pi}{4}+\frac{11}{3}$ **11.** π^4

13. $\frac{\pi}{4}+\frac{1}{2}\ln 2 - \frac{\pi^2}{32}$ **15.** $12-3\pi^2$ **17.** $2-\frac{\pi}{2}$ **19.** $\frac{1}{2}$

21. $2\pi^{7/2}$ **23.** $(1+\pi)\ln(1+\pi)-\pi$ **25.** $\frac{\pi}{2}-1$

27. $\frac{63\pi^4}{64}$ **29.** $\frac{4}{3}$ **31.** $\frac{16}{15}$ **33.** $\frac{1}{5}$ **35.** $\frac{16}{15}$

37. $\int_0^{\pi/2} \int_0^1 15r^4 \cos\theta \sin^2\theta \, dr\,d\theta = 1$

39. $\int_0^\pi \int_0^1 14r^6 \cos^2\theta \sin^3\theta \, dr\,d\theta = \frac{8}{15}$

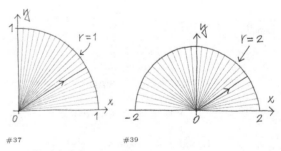

#37   #39

41. $\int_0^{\pi/2} \int_0^{\sin\theta} r^5 \cos^3\theta \sin\theta \, dr\,d\theta = \frac{1}{240}$

43. $\int_0^{\pi/4} \int_2^{2\sec\theta} 3r^2 \cos\theta \, dr\,d\theta = 8-4\sqrt{2}$

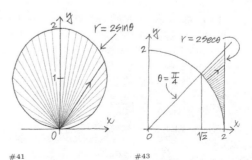

#41   #43

45. $\frac{500\pi}{3}$ **47.** $\frac{16\pi}{3}$ **49.** 8π **51.** 81π **53.** $\frac{122\pi}{3}$

55. $\frac{128\pi}{3}$ **57.** $\frac{8\pi(2-\sqrt{2})}{3}$

Exercises: 12.4

1. $\frac{845}{96}$ **3.** $\frac{85}{6}$ **5.** $\frac{9615}{128}$ **7.** $\frac{153}{32}$ **9.** $\frac{10}{3} + \frac{5\pi}{32}$

11. $\frac{17}{16}(e^2 - e^{-2})(\sqrt{5} + \frac{1}{2}\ln(\sqrt{5} + 2)$ **13.** $\frac{13}{12}$

15. $\frac{1}{54}(11^{3/2} - 2^{3/2})$ **17.** $\frac{52\sqrt{2}}{105}$ **19.** $\frac{\pi}{6}(17^{3/2} - 1)$

21. 8π **23.** 8π **25.** 20π **27.** 30π **29.** π

31. $4\pi - 8$ **33.** $\frac{2\pi}{3}(2\sqrt{2} - 1)$ **35.** $\frac{\pi}{6}[(1 + 4a^2)^{3/2} - 1]$

37. $\pi a^2(1 + m^2)$ **39.** $4\pi a^2$ **41.** $2\pi a(a - b)$

43. $m = \frac{1}{24}, (\frac{8}{9}, \frac{3}{5})$ **45.** $m = \frac{1}{2}, (\frac{3}{4}, \frac{5}{12})$

47. $m = \frac{44}{105}, (\frac{25}{33}, \frac{175}{352})$ **49.** $m = \frac{1}{15}, (\frac{8}{15}, \frac{8}{15})$

51. $m = \frac{3}{16}, (\frac{1}{2} - \frac{\ln 2}{3}, \frac{14}{27})$

53. $m = \frac{1}{4}(e^2 + 1), (\frac{4(2e^3+1)}{9(e^2+1)}, \frac{e^2-1}{2(e^2+1)})$

55. $m = 3, (\frac{\pi}{4}, \frac{1}{3})$ **57.** $m = \frac{\ln 2}{2}, (\frac{4-\pi}{2\ln 2}, \frac{4-\pi}{4\ln 2})$

59. Figure A (# 33), Figure B (# 21, 22, 37)

Figure C (# 31, 32), Figure D (# 27, 28, 42)

Figure E (# 29, 30), Figure F (# 25, 26, 41, 42)

Figure G (# 19, 20, 35)

Exercises: 12.5

1. 3   **3.** 2   **5.** $e - \frac{1}{2}$ **7.** $\cos(1) - \frac{1}{2}$ **9.** $\frac{\pi}{20} + \frac{1}{15}$

11. 4   **13.** 4   **15.** 3   **17.** $2\ln 2 - 1$ **19.** $\frac{4}{15}$

21. $\frac{1}{4}$ **23.** $\frac{2}{15}$ **25.** 89   **27.** $1 + \ln(\frac{2}{3}) - \frac{1}{2}\ln 2$

29. $\ln(\frac{5}{2}) - \tan^{-1}(3)$ **31.** $4\ln(\frac{6}{5}) - \ln(\frac{3}{2})$ **33.** $\frac{\pi}{2}$

35. $1 - \ln 2$

37. $\int_{x=0}^{x=2} \int_{y=0}^{y=x/2} \int_{z=0}^{z=3y} f(x, y, z)\, dzdydx$

39. $\int_{x=0}^{x=1} \int_{y=x^2}^{y=1} \int_{z=0}^{z=y^2} f(x, y, z)\, dzdydx$

41. $\int_{x=1}^{x=e} \int_{y=0}^{y=\ln x} \int_{z=0}^{z=\sqrt{y}} f(x, y, z)\, dzdydx$

43. $\int_{x=0}^{x=1} \int_{y=0}^{y=x} \int_{z=0}^{z=\sqrt{y}} 90x^8 y^2 z^5 e^{x^2 z^6}\, dzdydx = e - \frac{1}{2}$

45. $\int_{x=0}^{x=1} \int_{y=0}^{y=\sqrt{x}} \int_{z=0}^{z=\sqrt{y}} 48x^{15} yz^3 \sin(x^5 z^4)\, dzdydx$
$= \cos(1) - \frac{1}{2}$

47. $\int_{x=0}^{x=\pi/4} \int_{y=0}^{y=\tan x} \int_{z=0}^{z=\sqrt{y}} 8y^2 z \sec^4 x\, dzdydx = \frac{12}{35}$

49. $\int_{x=0}^{x=1} \int_{y=0}^{y=x} \int_{z=0}^{z=y} \frac{18x^5 z}{(1+x^3 y^3)^2}\, dzdydx = 1 - \frac{\pi}{4}$

51. $\int_{x=0}^{x=1} \int_{y=0}^{y=x^2} \int_{z=0}^{z=y^2} \frac{24x^9 y}{(1+x^2 z)^2}\, dzdydx = 3 - 4\ln 2$

53. $\int_{y=0}^{y=1} \int_{x=2y}^{x=2} \int_{z=0}^{z=3y} f(x, y, z)\, dzdxdy$
$\int_{y=0}^{y=1} \int_{z=0}^{z=3y} \int_{x=2y}^{x=2} f(x, y, z)\, dxdzdy$
$\int_{z=0}^{z=3} \int_{y=z/3}^{y=1} \int_{x=2y}^{x=2} f(x, y, z)\, dxdydz$
$\int_{x=0}^{x=2} \int_{z=0}^{z=3x/2} \int_{y=z/3}^{y=1} f(x, y, z)\, dydzdx$

$\int_{z=0}^{z=3} \int_{x=2z/3}^{x=2} \int_{y=z/3}^{y=1} f(x, y, z)\, dydxdz$

55. $\int_{y=0}^{y=1} \int_{x=0}^{x=\sqrt{y}} \int_{z=0}^{z=y^2} f(x, y, z)\, dzdxdy$
$\int_{y=0}^{y=1} \int_{z=0}^{z=y^2} \int_{x=0}^{x=\sqrt{y}} f(x, y, z)\, dxdzdy$
$\int_{z=0}^{z=1} \int_{y=\sqrt{z}}^{y=1} \int_{x=0}^{x=\sqrt{y}} f(x, y, z)\, dxdydz$
$\int_{x=0}^{x=1} \int_{z=0}^{z=x^4} \int_{y=x^2}^{y=1} f(x, y, z)\, dydzdx$
$\int_{z=0}^{z=1} \int_{x=z^{1/4}}^{x=1} \int_{y=x^2}^{y=1} f(x, y, z)\, dydxdz$

57. $\int_{y=0}^{y=1} \int_{x=e^y}^{x=e} \int_{z=0}^{z=\sqrt{y}} f(x, y, z)\, dzdxdy$
$\int_{y=0}^{y=1} \int_{z=0}^{z=\sqrt{y}} \int_{x=e^y}^{x=e} f(x, y, z)\, dxdzdy$
$\int_{z=0}^{z=1} \int_{y=z^2}^{y=1} \int_{x=e^y}^{x=e} f(x, y, z)\, dxdydz$
$\int_{x=1}^{x=e} \int_{z=0}^{z=\sqrt{\ln x}} \int_{y=z^2}^{y=1} f(x, y, z)\, dydzdx$
$\int_{z=0}^{z=1} \int_{x=1}^{x=e} \int_{y=z^2}^{y=1} f(x, y, z)\, dydxdz$

59. $\int_{x=0}^{x=1} \int_{y=0}^{y=x^2} \int_{z=0}^{z=y} 24x^9 yze^{x^2 z^2}\, dzdydx = e - 2$
$\int_{y=0}^{y=1} \int_{x=\sqrt{y}}^{x=1} \int_{z=0}^{z=y} 24x^9 yze^{x^2 z^2}\, dzdxdy$
$\int_{y=0}^{y=1} \int_{z=0}^{z=y} \int_{x=\sqrt{y}}^{x=1} 24x^9 yze^{x^2 z^2}\, dxdzdy$
$\int_{x=0}^{x=1} \int_{z=0}^{z=x^2} \int_{y=z}^{y=1} 24x^9 yze^{x^2 z^2}\, dydzdx$
$\int_{z=0}^{z=1} \int_{x=\sqrt{z}}^{x=1} \int_{y=z}^{y=1} 24x^9 yze^{x^2 z^2}\, dydxdz$

61. $\int_{x=0}^{x=1} \int_{y=0}^{y=x^2} \int_{z=0}^{z=y^2} \frac{20x^{14} y^5 z}{(1+x^4 yz^2)^3}\, dzdydx = \frac{\pi}{28} + \frac{1}{21}$
$\int_{y=0}^{y=1} \int_{x=\sqrt{y}}^{x=1} \int_{z=0}^{z=y^2} \frac{20x^{14} y^5 z}{(1+x^4 yz^2)^3}\, dzdxdy$
$\int_{z=0}^{z=1} \int_{y=\sqrt{z}}^{y=1} \int_{x=\sqrt{y}}^{x=1} \frac{20x^{14} y^5 z}{(1+x^4 yz^2)^3}\, dxdydz$
$\int_{x=0}^{x=1} \int_{z=0}^{z=x^4} \int_{y=\sqrt{z}}^{y=1} \frac{20x^{14} y^5 z}{(1+x^4 yz^2)^3}\, dydzdx$
$\int_{z=0}^{z=1} \int_{x=z^{1/4}}^{x=1} \int_{y=\sqrt{z}}^{y=1} \frac{20x^{14} y^5 z}{(1+x^4 yz^2)^3}\, dydxdz$

63. $\int_{x=0}^{x=\pi/2} \int_{y=0}^{y=\cos x} \int_{z=0}^{z=\sqrt{y}} 6yz \sin^8 x\, dzdydx = \frac{2}{99}$
$\int_{y=0}^{y=1} \int_{x=0}^{x=\cos^{-1} y} \int_{z=0}^{z=\sqrt{y}} 6yz \sin^8 x\, dzdxdy$
$\int_{z=0}^{z=1} \int_{y=z^2}^{y=1} \int_{x=0}^{x=\cos^{-1} y} 6yz \sin^8 x\, dxdydz$
$\int_{x=0}^{x=\pi/2} \int_{z=0}^{z=\sqrt{\cos x}} \int_{y=0}^{y=\cos x} 6yz \sin^8 x\, dydzdx$
$\int_{z=0}^{z=1} \int_0^{x=\cos^{-1}(z^2)} \int_{y=0}^{y=\cos x} 6yz \sin^8 x\, dydxdz$

Exercises: 12.6

1. $\frac{8}{15}$ **3.** $\frac{8}{3}$ **5.** $\frac{\pi}{13}$ **7.** $2\pi(5\ln 5 + 1)$ **9.** 4π

11. $\frac{1024}{225}$ **13.** $\frac{8}{15}$ **15.** $\frac{\pi^4}{5}$ **17.** $\frac{64\pi}{5}$ **19.** $\frac{62\pi}{5}$

21. $\frac{\pi}{3}$ **23.** $\frac{9\pi}{28}$ **25.** $\frac{256\pi}{1287}$ **27.** $3\ln 3 - \frac{4}{3}$

29. $2\pi[1 - \tan^{-1}(2) - \frac{1}{4}\ln 5]$ **31.** $\frac{16}{105}$ **33.** $\frac{\pi}{3}$

35. $2e^{-1} - \frac{1}{2}(e^{-2} + 1)$ **37.** $\frac{4\pi}{3}$ **39.** 2π **41.** $\frac{2\pi^2}{3}$

43. $\frac{4\pi}{3}$ **45.** $\frac{8\pi^3}{3}$ **47.** $\frac{56\pi}{3}$ **49.** $\frac{56\pi}{3}$ **51.** $\frac{64}{9}$

53. $\frac{512}{9}$ **55.** $\frac{448}{9}$ **57.** $\frac{4(9-\pi)}{9}$

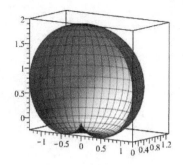

#37

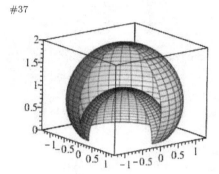

#39

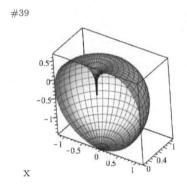

X

#41

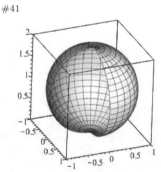

#43

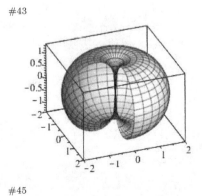

#45

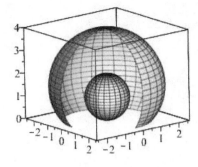

#47

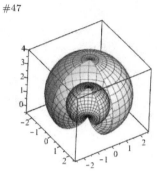

#49

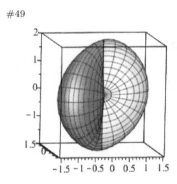

#51

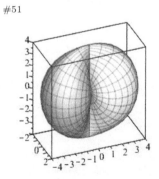

#53

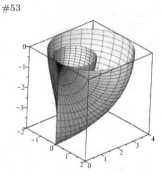

#55 Cut in half for clarity of viewing.

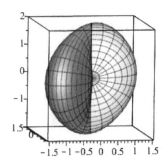

#51

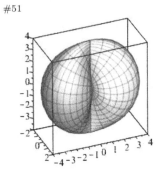

#53

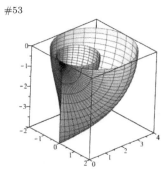

#55 Cut in half for clarity of viewing.

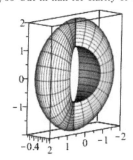

#57

59. E: bounded by the coordinate surfaces $\rho = 2$ (on top) and $\phi = \frac{\pi}{6}$ (on bottom). so

$$\iiint_E 1\, dV = \int_{\theta=0}^{\theta=2\pi} \int_{\phi=0}^{\phi=\pi/6} \int_{\rho=0}^{\rho=2} 1 \cdot \rho^2 \sin\phi\, d\rho d\phi d\theta =$$

$$\int_{\theta=0}^{\theta=2\pi} 1\, d\theta \cdot \int_{\phi=0}^{\phi=\pi/6} \sin\phi\, d\phi \cdot \int_{\rho=0}^{\rho=2} \rho^2 d\rho = \frac{8(2-\sqrt{3})\pi}{3}$$

Exercises: 13.1

1. $\mathbf{r} = \langle\, t, t^2, t^3\,\rangle$, $\mathbf{v} = \mathbf{r}' = \langle\, 1, 2t, 3t^2\,\rangle$,
  $\mathbf{v}(1) = \langle\, 1, 2, 3\,\rangle$, $\|\mathbf{v}(1)\| = \sqrt{14}$

3. $\mathbf{r} = \langle\, t^{1/2}, t^{3/2}, t^{5/2}\,\rangle$,
  $\mathbf{v} = \mathbf{r}' = \langle\, \frac{1}{2}t^{-1/2}, \frac{3}{2}t^{1/2}, \frac{5}{2}t^{3/2}\,\rangle$,
  $\mathbf{v}(4) = \langle\, \frac{1}{4}, 3, 20\,\rangle$, $\|\mathbf{v}(4)\| = \frac{\sqrt{6545}}{4}$

5. $\mathbf{r} = \langle\, e^t, e^{2t}, e^{3t}\,\rangle$, $\mathbf{v} = \mathbf{r}' = \langle\, e^t, 2e^{2t}, 3e^{3t}\,\rangle$,
  $\mathbf{v}(\ln 2) = \langle 2, 8, 24\rangle$, $\|\mathbf{v}(\ln 2)\| = 2\sqrt{161}$

7. $\mathbf{r} = \langle\, t^2, t\ln t, t^2\ln t\,\rangle$, $\mathbf{v} = \mathbf{r}' = \langle\, 2t, \ln t + 1, 2t\ln t + t\,\rangle$,
  $\mathbf{v}(1) = \langle\, 2, 1, 1\,\rangle$, $\|\mathbf{v}(1)\| = \sqrt{6}$

9. $\mathbf{r} = \langle\, \cos(t^2), \sin(t^2), t^2\,\rangle$,
  $\mathbf{v} = \mathbf{r}' = \langle\, -2t\sin(t^2), 2t\cos(t^2), 2t\,\rangle$,
  $\mathbf{v}(\sqrt{\pi}) = \langle\, 0, -2\sqrt{\pi}, 2\sqrt{\pi}\,\rangle$, $\|\mathbf{v}(\sqrt{\pi})\| = 2\sqrt{2\pi}$

11. $\mathbf{r} = \langle\, t\cos t, t^2\sin t, t^3\,\rangle$,
  $\mathbf{v} = \mathbf{r}' = \langle\, \cos t - t\sin t, 2t\sin t + t^2\cos t, 3t^2\,\rangle$,
  $\mathbf{v}(\pi) = \langle\, -1, -\pi^2, 3\pi^2\,\rangle$, $\|\mathbf{v}(\pi)\| = \sqrt{1 + 10\pi^4}$

13. $\mathbf{r} = \langle\, \ln(\cos t), \ln(\sin t), \sqrt{2}\,t\,\rangle$,
  $\mathbf{v} = \mathbf{r}' = \langle\, -\tan t, \cot t, \sqrt{2}\,\rangle$,
  $\mathbf{v}(\frac{\pi}{4}) = \langle\, -1, 1, \sqrt{2}\,\rangle$, $\|\mathbf{v}(\frac{\pi}{4})\| = 2$

15. $\mathbf{r} = \langle te^{2t}, te^t, te^{-t}\,\rangle$,
  $\mathbf{v} = \mathbf{r}' = \langle e^{2t} + 2te^{2t}, e^t + te^t, e^{-t} - te^{-t}\,\rangle$,
  $\mathbf{v}(0) = \langle\, 1, 1, 1\,\rangle$, $\|\mathbf{v}(0)\| = \sqrt{3}$

17. $\mathbf{r} = \langle e^{2t} + e^{-2t}, e^{2t} - e^{-2t}, e^{2t}\,\rangle$,
  $\mathbf{v} = \mathbf{r}' = \langle 2e^{2t} - 2e^{-2t}, 2e^{2t} + 2e^{-2t}, 2e^{2t}\,\rangle$,
  $\mathbf{v}(0) = \langle\, 0, 4, 2\,\rangle$, $\|\mathbf{v}(0)\| = 2\sqrt{5}$

19. $\mathbf{r} = \langle\, \dfrac{t}{1+t^2}, \dfrac{t^2}{1+t^2}, \dfrac{t^3}{1+t^2}\,\rangle$,
  $\mathbf{v} = \mathbf{r}' = \langle\, \dfrac{1-t^2}{(1+t^2)^2}, \dfrac{2t}{(1+t^2)^2}, \dfrac{3t^2 + t^4}{(1+t^2)^2}\,\rangle$,
  $\mathbf{v}(1) = \langle\, 0, \frac{1}{2}, 1\,\rangle$, $\|\mathbf{v}(1)\| = \frac{\sqrt{5}}{2}$

21. $\mathbf{r} = \langle\, \dfrac{\sin t}{1+\cos t}, \dfrac{\cos t}{1+\sin t}, \cos t - \sin t\,\rangle$,
  $\mathbf{v} = \mathbf{r}' = \langle\, \dfrac{1}{1+\cos t}, \dfrac{-1}{1+\sin t}, -\sin t - \cos t\,\rangle$,
  $\mathbf{v}(0) = \langle\, \frac{1}{2}, -1, -1\,\rangle$, $\|\mathbf{v}(0)\| = \frac{3}{2}$

23. $L = \int_0^1 \left(\frac{5}{4} + \frac{1}{4}t^2\right) dt = \frac{4}{3}$

25. $L = \int_0^1 \left(\frac{5}{2}t + \frac{9}{8}t^3\right) dt = \frac{49}{32}$

27. $L = \int_0^1 \left(\frac{15}{4}t^2 + \frac{4}{3}t^4\right) dt = \frac{91}{60}$

29. $L = \int_1^2 \left(\frac{5}{2}t + \frac{1}{4t}\right) dt = \frac{1}{4}\left(20 + \ln 2\right)$

31. $L = \int_0^1 \frac{1}{4}\left(5e^t + e^{-t}\right) dt = \frac{1}{4}\left(5e - e^{-1}\right) - 1$

33. $L = \int_0^1 \left(\frac{15}{4}e^{6t} + \frac{1}{12}e^{-6t}\right) dt = \frac{5}{8}e^6 - \frac{1}{72}e^{-6} - \frac{11}{18}$

35. $L = \int_0^1 \left(\frac{5}{4} - \frac{1}{4}e^{2t}\right) dt = \frac{1}{8}\left(11 - e^2\right)$

37. $L = \int_0^{2\pi} \sqrt{\frac{5}{4}}\, dt = 2\pi\sqrt{\frac{5}{4}}$

39. $L = \int_0^9 \left(\frac{1}{2}t^{1/2} + \frac{1}{2}t^{-1/2}\right) dt = 12$

41. $L = \int_0^1 \left(e^t + \frac{1}{4}e^{-t}\right) dt = e - \frac{1}{4}e^{-1} - \frac{3}{4}$

43. $L = \int_0^{2\pi} \frac{5}{2}\sin\frac{t}{2}\, dt = 10$

45. $L = \int_0^{2\pi} \left(\frac{3}{2} + \frac{1}{2}\cos t\right) dt = 3\pi$

47. $L = \int_0^{2\pi} \left(\frac{3}{2} + \frac{1}{2}\cos t\right) dt = 3\pi$

49. $L = \int_0^{2\pi} \left(\frac{21}{8} + \frac{1}{2}\cos t\right) dt = \frac{21\pi}{4}$

51. $L = \int_0^{\pi} \frac{5}{2}\cos\frac{t}{2}\, dt = 5$

53. $L = \int_0^{2\pi} \sqrt{2}\left(1 + \sin\frac{t}{2}\cos\frac{t}{2}\right) dt = 2\pi\sqrt{2}$

55. $L = \int_0^{\pi} \left(\frac{5}{4} + \frac{1}{4}t^2\right) dt = \frac{5}{4}\pi + \frac{1}{12}\pi^3$

57. $L = \int_0^{1} \left(\frac{1}{4}e^{3t} + e^{-t}\right) dt = \frac{1}{12}e^3 - e^{-1} + \frac{11}{12}$

59. $L = \int_0^{1} \left(\frac{1}{4}e^{4t} + 2e^{-2t}\right) dt = \frac{1}{16}e^4 - e^{-2} + \frac{15}{16}$

61. $L = \int_0^{\pi/2} \frac{25}{8}\sin 2t\, dt = \frac{25}{8}$

63. $L = \int_0^{2\pi} \left(\frac{11}{2} - \frac{1}{2}\cos 4t\right) dt = 11\pi$

65. $L = \int_0^{2\pi} 2\, dt = 4\pi$

67. $L = \int_0^{2\pi} 3\, dt = 6\pi$

69. $L = \int_0^{2\pi} 2\, dt = 4\pi$

Exercises: 13.2

1. $\mathbf{r}_u = \langle\, v, 1, 2uv^2 \,\rangle, \quad \mathbf{r}_v = \langle\, u, 1, 2u^2 v \,\rangle,$

$\mathbf{n} = \langle\, 2u^2 v - 2uv^2, 0, v - u \,\rangle$

3. $\mathbf{r}_u = \langle\, \dfrac{1}{v}, -\dfrac{v}{u^2}, v \,\rangle, \quad \mathbf{r}_v = \langle\, -\dfrac{u}{v^2}, \dfrac{1}{u}, u \,\rangle,$

$\mathbf{n} = \langle\, -\dfrac{2v}{u}, -\dfrac{2u}{v}, 0 \,\rangle$

5. $\mathbf{r}_u = \langle\, \dfrac{1}{2u^{1/2}v^{1/2}}, -\dfrac{v^{1/2}}{2u^{3/2}}, \dfrac{v^{1/2}}{2u^{1/2}} \,\rangle,$

$\mathbf{r}_v = \langle\, -\dfrac{u^{1/2}}{2v^{3/2}}, \dfrac{1}{2u^{1/2}v^{1/2}}, \dfrac{u^{1/2}}{2v^{1/2}} \,\rangle,$

$\mathbf{n} = \langle\, -\dfrac{1}{2u}, -\dfrac{1}{2v}, 0 \,\rangle$

7. $\mathbf{r}_s = \langle\, \dfrac{2s}{s^2+t^2}, -\dfrac{t}{1+s^2 t^2}, 2st^2 \,\rangle,$

$\mathbf{r}_t = \langle\, \dfrac{2t}{s^2+t^2}, -\dfrac{s}{1+s^2 t^2}, 2s^2 t \,\rangle,$

$\mathbf{n} = \langle\, 0, -\dfrac{4st^3 - 4s^3 t}{s^2+t^2}, \dfrac{-2s^2 + 2t^2}{(s^2+t^2)(1+s^2 t^2)} \,\rangle$

9. $\mathbf{r}_u = \langle\, 2ue^{u^2+v^2}, -2ue^{-u^2-v^2}, v \,\rangle,$

$\mathbf{r}_v = \langle\, 2ve^{u^2+v^2}, -2ve^{-u^2-v^2}, u \,\rangle,$

$\mathbf{n} = \langle\, 2(v^2 - u^2)e^{-u^2-v^2}, 2(v^2 - u^2)e^{u^2+v^2}, 0 \,\rangle$

11. $\mathbf{r}_s = \langle\, ve^{st}, -te^{-st}, 1 \,\rangle, \quad \mathbf{r}_t = \langle\, se^{st}, -se^{-st}, 1 \,\rangle,$

$\mathbf{n} = \langle\, (s-t)e^{-st}, (s-t)e^{st}, 0 \,\rangle$

13. $\mathbf{r}_\theta = \langle\, -t\sin\theta, t\cos\theta, 1 \,\rangle, \quad \mathbf{r}_t = \langle\, \cos\theta, \sin\theta, 0 \,\rangle,$

$\mathbf{n} = \langle\, -\sin\theta, \cos\theta, -t \,\rangle$

15. $\mathbf{r}_\theta = \langle\, -4\sin\theta, 3\cos\theta\cos\phi, 2\cos\theta\sin\phi \,\rangle,$

$\mathbf{r}_\phi = \langle\, 0, -3\sin\theta\sin\phi, 2\sin\theta\cos\phi \,\rangle,$

$\mathbf{n} = \langle\, 6\sin\theta\cos\theta, 8\sin^2\theta\cos\phi, 12\sin^2\theta\sin\phi \,\rangle$

17. $\mathbf{r}_\phi = \langle\, -4\cosh t\sin\phi, 3\cosh t\cos\phi, 0 \,\rangle,$

$\mathbf{r}_t = \langle\, 4\sinh t\cos\phi, 3\sinh t\sin\phi, \cosh t \,\rangle,$

$\mathbf{n} = \langle\, 3\cosh^2 t\cos\phi, 4\cosh^2 t\sin\phi, -12\sinh\phi\cosh\phi \,\rangle$

19. $\mathbf{r}_x = \langle\, 1, 0, \frac{1}{2}x \,\rangle, \quad \mathbf{r}_y = \langle\, 0, 1, \frac{2}{9}y \,\rangle,$

$\mathbf{n} = \langle\, -\frac{1}{2}x, \frac{2}{9}y, 1 \,\rangle$

21. $\mathbf{r}_u = \langle\, 3\cosh v, 3\sinh v, 2u \,\rangle,$

$\mathbf{r}_v = \langle\, 3u\sinh v, 3u\cosh v, 0 \,\rangle,$

$\mathbf{n} = \langle\, -6u^2\cosh v, 6u^2\sinh v, 9u \,\rangle$

23. $\mathcal{A} = \int_{-1}^{1}\int_{-1}^{1} 3u^2 v^2\left(1 + \frac{9}{4}v^4\right) du\, dv = \frac{55}{21}$

25. $\mathcal{A} = \int_{-1}^{1}\int_{-1}^{1} u^2 |v^3|\left(1 + v^2\right) du\, dv = \frac{5}{9}$

27. $\mathcal{A} = \int_{0}^{1}\int_{0}^{2} 2uv\left(6v^5 + \frac{2}{3}v\right) du\, dv = \frac{272}{63}$

29. $\mathcal{A} = \int_{-1}^{1}\int_{-1}^{1} \left(5u^4 + v^2\right)\left(3v^2 + \frac{1}{3}v\right) du\, dv = \frac{368}{45}$

31. $\mathcal{A} = \int_{-1}^{1}\int_{-1}^{1} \left(1 + u^2 v^2\right)\left(3 + 3v^4\right) du\, dv = \frac{1712}{105}$

33. $\mathcal{A} = \int_{0}^{1}\int_{0}^{1} \left(u^2 + v^2\right)\left(200v^7 + 2v\right) du\, dv = \frac{175}{6}$

35. $\mathcal{A} = \int_{0}^{1}\int_{0}^{1} \left(3u^2 + e^{-v}\right)\left(\frac{1}{4}e^{3v} + e^{-v}\right) du\, dv$

$= \frac{1}{6}\left(e^3 - e^{-3}\right) + \frac{5}{4}\left(e^2 - e^{-2}\right) + 2\left(e - e^{-1}\right)$

37. $\mathcal{A} = \int_{0}^{\pi}\int_{0}^{2} 2\left(3u^2 + \sin\frac{v}{2}\right)\cos\frac{v}{2}\, du\, dv = 36$

39. $\mathcal{A} = \int_{1}^{8}\int_{-1}^{1} \left(5u^4 + v^2\right)\left(\frac{1}{3}v^{-2/3} + \frac{3}{4}v^{-4/3}\right) du\, dv$

$= \frac{9581}{140}$

41. $\mathcal{A} = \int_{0}^{1}\int_{0}^{1} u^2 v\left(\frac{1}{1+v^2} + \frac{1}{4}v\right) du\, dv = \frac{1}{6}\ln 2 + \frac{1}{36}$

43. $\mathcal{A}_1 = 2\pi \int_{0}^{\sqrt{3}/2} \left(t - \frac{4}{3}t^3\right)\left(1 + 4t^2\right) dt = \frac{3\pi}{4}$

$\mathcal{A}_2 = 2\pi \int_{\sqrt{3}/2}^{1} -\left(t - \frac{4}{3}t^3\right)\left(1 + 4t^2\right) dt = \frac{3\pi}{4} - \frac{5\pi}{9} = \frac{7\pi}{36}$

$\mathcal{A} = \mathcal{A}_1 + \mathcal{A}_2 = \frac{17\pi}{18}$

45. $\mathcal{A}_1 = 2\pi \int_{0}^{2/\sqrt{3}} \left(2t - \frac{3}{2}t^3\right)\left(2 + \frac{9}{2}t^2\right) dt = \frac{16\pi}{3}$

$\mathcal{A}_2 = 2\pi \int_{2/\sqrt{3}}^{2} -\left(2t - \frac{3}{2}t^3\right)\left(2 + \frac{9}{2}t^2\right) dt = \frac{256\pi}{3}$

$\mathcal{A} = \mathcal{A}_1 + \mathcal{A}_2 = \frac{272\pi}{3}$

47. $\mathcal{A} = 2\pi \int_{0}^{1} 2t^3\left(9 + t^2\right) dt = \frac{19\pi}{2}$

49. $\mathcal{A} = 2\pi \int_{0}^{1} t^4\left(3t^2 + \frac{4}{3}t^4\right) dt = \frac{218\pi}{189}$

51. $\mathcal{A} = 2\pi \int_{0}^{1} 4t^5\left(20t^3 + 5t^5\right) dt = \frac{2120\pi}{99}$

53. $\mathcal{A} = 2\pi \int_{0}^{1} t^5\left(3t^2 + \frac{25}{12}t^6\right) dt = \frac{79\pi}{72}$

55. $\mathcal{A} = 2\pi \int_{0}^{1} t^4\left(1 + 4t^6\right) dt = \frac{62\pi}{55}$

57. $\mathcal{A}_1 = 2\pi \int_{-1}^{1} \left(e^{-t} + \frac{1}{12}e^{3t}\right)\left(e^{-t} + \frac{1}{4}e^{3t}\right) dt$

$= 2\pi\left[\frac{2}{3}\left(e^2 - e^{-2}\right) + \frac{1}{288}\left(e^6 - e^{-6}\right)\right]$

59. $\mathcal{A}_1 = 2\pi \int_{-1}^{1} e^{-2t}\left(e^{-t} + e^{-3t}\right) dt$

$\quad = 2\pi\left[\frac{1}{3}\left(e^3 - e^{-3}\right) + \frac{1}{20}\left(e^5 - e^{-5}\right)\right]$

61. $\mathcal{A} = 2\pi \int_{1}^{2} \frac{1}{2}t^2\left(4t^3 + \frac{1}{16t}\right) dt = \frac{1347}{32}\pi$

63. $\mathcal{A} = 2\pi \int_{1}^{2} \left(t + \frac{1}{4}t^{-1}\right)\left(1 + \frac{1}{4}t^{-2}\right) dt = \left[\frac{195}{64} + \ln 2\right]\pi$

65. $\mathcal{A} = 2\pi \int_{1}^{4} \left(\sqrt{t} + \frac{1}{\sqrt{t}}\right)\left(\frac{1}{2\sqrt{t}} + \frac{1}{2t^{3/2}}\right) dt = \left[\frac{15}{4} + \ln 16\right]\pi$

67. $\mathcal{A} = 2\pi \int_{1}^{4} \sqrt{1 + t^2}\left(2t + \frac{1}{8}\frac{t}{1+t^2}\right) dt = \frac{\pi}{12}\left(35\sqrt{2} - 19\right)$

69. $\mathcal{A} = 2\pi \int_{0}^{2\pi} \left(\frac{7}{8}t + \frac{1}{16}\sin 2t\right)\left(\frac{9}{8} - \frac{1}{8}\cos 2t\right) dt = \frac{63}{16}\pi^3$

Exercises: 14.1

1. $\operatorname{curl}\mathbf{F} = \langle\, x + -xy^2,\ 2x^3yz - y,\ y^2z - x^3z^2 \,\rangle$,
$\operatorname{div}F = 3x^2yz^2 + 2xyz$

3. $\operatorname{curl}\mathbf{F} = \langle\, e^{xz} - xye^{yz},\ e^{xy} - yze^{xz},\ e^{yz} - xze^{xy} \,\rangle$,
$\operatorname{div}F = yze^{xy} + xze^{yz} + xye^{xz}$

5. $\operatorname{curl}\mathbf{F} = \langle\, xz\cos xy - xy\cos xz,$
$\qquad\qquad xy\cos yz - yz\cos xy,\ yz\cos xz - xz\cos yz \,\rangle$
$\operatorname{div}F = \sin yz + \sin xz + \sin xy$

7. $\operatorname{curl}\mathbf{F} = \langle\, -\sin y\sin z,\ -\sin x\sin z,\ -\sin x\sin y \,\rangle$,
$\operatorname{div}F = \cos x\cos z + \cos y\cos x + \cos z\cos y$

9. $\operatorname{curl}\mathbf{F} = \langle\, -\sin z\sin y + \sin x\sin z,\ 0,$
$\qquad\qquad \cos x\cos z - \cos y\cos x \,\rangle$,
$\operatorname{div}F = -\sin y\sin x + \cos z\cos y$

11. $\operatorname{curl}\mathbf{F} = \langle 0,\ 0,\ y^2 - x^3 \rangle$, $\operatorname{div}F = 3x^2y + 2xy$

13. $\operatorname{curl}\mathbf{F} = \langle 0,\ 0\ 3ye^{3x} - 2e^{2y} \rangle$, $\operatorname{div}F = e^{2y} + e^{3x}$

15. $\operatorname{curl}\mathbf{F} = \langle 0,\ 0\ e^{2y} - e^{3x} \rangle$, $\operatorname{div}F = 3ye^{3x} + 2xe^{2y}$

17. $\operatorname{curl}\mathbf{F} = \langle 0,\ 0\ y\cos x - x\cos y \rangle$,
$\operatorname{div}F = \sin y + \sin x$

19. $\operatorname{curl}\mathbf{F} = \langle\, -\sin z\sin y,\ 0,\ 0 \,\rangle$,
$\operatorname{div}F = 2\cos y\cos x + \cos z\cos y$

39. $\operatorname{curl}(\nabla\psi) = \begin{vmatrix} \mathbf{i} & \mathbf{j} & \mathbf{k} \\ \frac{\partial}{\partial x} & \frac{\partial}{\partial y} & \frac{\partial}{\partial z} \\ \psi_x & \psi_y & \psi_z \end{vmatrix}$

$\quad = \langle \psi_{zy} - \psi_{yz},\ \psi_{xz} - \psi_{zx},\ \psi_{yx} - \psi_{xy} \rangle = \langle 0,\ 0,\ 0 \rangle$

$\operatorname{div}(\operatorname{curl}(\mathbf{F})) = \operatorname{div}\begin{vmatrix} \mathbf{i} & \mathbf{j} & \mathbf{k} \\ \frac{\partial}{\partial x} & \frac{\partial}{\partial y} & \frac{\partial}{\partial z} \\ M & N & K \end{vmatrix}$

$\quad = \operatorname{div}\langle K_y - N_z,\ M_z - K_x,\ N_x - M_y \rangle$
$\quad = K_{yx} - N_{zx} + M_{zy} - K_{xy} + N_{xz} - M_{yz} = 0$

$\operatorname{div}(\nabla\psi) = \operatorname{div}(\langle \psi_x,\ \psi_y,\ \psi_z \rangle) = \psi_{xx} + \psi_{yy} + \psi_{zz}$

41. $\operatorname{div}(\psi\mathbf{F}) = \operatorname{div}(\psi\langle M,\ N,\ K \rangle)$
$\quad = \operatorname{div}(\langle \psi M,\ \psi N,\ \psi K \rangle)$
$\quad = \frac{\partial}{\partial x}(\psi M) + \frac{\partial}{\partial y}(\psi N) + \frac{\partial}{\partial z}(\psi K)$
$\quad = \psi_x M + \psi M_x + \psi_y N + \psi N_y + \psi_z K + \psi K_z$
$\quad = (\psi_x M + \psi_y N + \psi_z K) + (\psi M_x + \psi N_y + \psi K_z)$

$\quad = \nabla\psi\cdot\mathbf{F} + \psi\operatorname{div}\mathbf{F}$

43. $\operatorname{div}(\mathbf{F}\times\mathbf{G}) = \operatorname{div}\begin{vmatrix} \mathbf{i} & \mathbf{j} & \mathbf{k} \\ M & N & K \\ P & Q & R \end{vmatrix}$

$\quad = \operatorname{div}\langle NR - QK,\ PK - MR,\ MQ - PN \rangle$
$\quad = \frac{\partial}{\partial x}(NR - QK) + \frac{\partial}{\partial y}(PK - MR) + \frac{\partial}{\partial z}(MQ - PN)$
$\quad = \begin{cases} N_xR + NR_x - Q_xK - QK_x \\ +P_yK + PK_y - M_yR - MR_y \\ +M_zQ + MQ_z - P_zN - PN_z \end{cases}$

Next compute

$(\operatorname{curl}\mathbf{F})\cdot\mathbf{G} = \begin{vmatrix} \mathbf{i} & \mathbf{j} & \mathbf{k} \\ \frac{\partial}{\partial x} & \frac{\partial}{\partial y} & \frac{\partial}{\partial z} \\ M & N & K \end{vmatrix}\cdot\langle P,\ Q,\ R \rangle$

$\quad = \langle K_y - N_z,\ M_z - K_x,\ N_x - M_y \rangle\cdot\langle P,\ Q,\ R \rangle$
$\quad = PK_y - PN_z + QM_z - QK_x + RN_x - RM_y$

$\mathbf{F}\cdot(\operatorname{curl}\mathbf{G}) = \langle M,\ N,\ K \rangle\cdot\begin{vmatrix} \mathbf{i} & \mathbf{j} & \mathbf{k} \\ \frac{\partial}{\partial x} & \frac{\partial}{\partial y} & \frac{\partial}{\partial z} \\ P & Q & R \end{vmatrix}$

$\quad = \langle M,\ N,\ K \rangle\cdot\langle R_y - Q_z,\ P_z - R_x,\ Q_x - P_y \rangle$
$\quad = MR_y - MQ_z + NP_z - NR_x + KQ_x - KP_y$

Thus, $\operatorname{div}(\mathbf{F}\times\mathbf{G}) = (\operatorname{curl}F)\cdot\mathbf{G} - \mathbf{F}\cdot(\operatorname{curl}\mathbf{G})$.

45. Use the identity in Exercise 43 with $\mathbf{F} = \nabla\psi$,
$\mathbf{G} = \nabla\phi$ and Identity (14.1.14a) to get
$\operatorname{div}(\nabla\psi\times\nabla\phi) = \operatorname{curl}(\nabla\psi)\cdot\nabla\phi - \nabla\psi\cdot\operatorname{curl}(\nabla\phi)$
$\quad = 0\cdot\nabla\phi - \nabla\psi\cdot 0 = 0$

Exercises: 14.2

1. $W = \int_0^1 \left(2t^2 + 2t^4 + 3t^6\right) dt = \frac{157}{105}$

3. $W = \int_0^\pi \left(-\cos^3 t\sin t + \sin^5 t\cos t + t^2\right) dt = \frac{1}{3}\pi^3 - \frac{2}{3}$

5. $W = \int_0^{\ln 2} \left(22 - e^{2t} - 3e^t\right) dt = \ln 4 - \frac{9}{2}$

7. $M = \int_0^1 t^2\left(\frac{17}{8} + \frac{1}{8}t^2\right) dt = \frac{11}{15}$

9. $M = \int_0^1 \left(1 - t\right)\left(\frac{17}{4}t + \frac{9}{16}t^3\right) dt = \frac{707}{960}$

11. $M = \int_0^{\ln 2} e^{-t}\left(\frac{5}{2}e^{2t} + \frac{1}{8}e^{-2t}\right) dt = \frac{487}{192}$

13. $W = \int_0^1 \left(t + t^2 + 2t^4 + 3t^8\right) dt = \frac{47}{30}$

15. $W = \int_0^1 \left(2t\sqrt{t^2 + 1} + 2\sin(e^{2t})e^{2t} + 4e^{10t}\right) dt$
$\quad = \cos(1) - \cos(e^2) + \frac{4}{3}\sqrt{2} + \frac{2}{5}e^{10} - \frac{16}{15}$

17. $W = \int_0^\pi \left(\cos^4 t\sin t - \cos t\sin t - \sin^2 t + t\right) dt$
$\quad = \frac{2}{5} + \frac{1}{2}\pi(\pi - 1)$

19. $M = \int_0^{\ln 2} 12e^{4t}\left(\frac{5}{2}e^{2t} + \frac{1}{8}e^{-2t}\right) dt = \frac{1269}{4}$

21. $M = \int_0^{2\pi} \frac{2(e^{2t} + \frac{1}{16}e^{-2t})}{e^{2t} + \frac{1}{16}e^{-2t}} dt = \int_0^{2\pi} 2\, dt = 4\pi$

23. $M = \int_0^\pi \left(9\sin^2 \frac{t}{2}\right)\cdot\left(\frac{9}{4}\cos \frac{t}{2}\right) dt = \frac{27}{2}$

25. With $x = t^2, y = t^3, dx = 2t\, dt, dy = 3t^2\, dt$ and so

$\int_C x^2 y \, dx + y^2 \, dy = \int_0^1 \left(2t^7 + 3t^8 \right) dt = \frac{7}{12}$

27. With $x = \sin t, y = -\cos t, z = \sin t,$
$dx = \cos t \, dt, dy = \sin t \, dt, dz = \cos t$
and so
$\int_C yz \, dx + xy \, dy + y^2 \, dz$
$= \int_0^\pi \left(= \cos^2 t \sin t - \sin^2 t \cos t + \cos^3 t \right) dt = -\frac{2}{3}$

Exercises: 14.3

1. $W = \int_C \mathbf{F} \cdot d\mathbf{r} = \left(x^2 y + xy^2 \right)\Big|_{(0,0)}^{(3,1)} = 12$

3. $W = \int_C \mathbf{F} \cdot d\mathbf{r} = \left(\cos 2c \sin 2y \right)\Big|_{(0,\pi/6)}^{(\pi,\pi/2)} = -2$

5. $W = \int_C \mathbf{F} \cdot d\mathbf{r} = \left(xy^2 z^3 - 3 * x^2 y^3 z \right)\Big|_{(-1,1,-1)}^{(1,1,1)} = -6$

7. $W_1 = \int_0^1 \left(-t^6 + 2t^3 \right) dt = \frac{15}{4}$
$W_2 = \int_0^1 \left(t^6 - 2t^3 \right) dt = -\frac{15}{4}$

9. $W_1 = \int_0^1 \frac{\pi}{2}\left(1 - \frac{1}{2}\sin \pi t \right) dt = \frac{1}{2}(\pi - 1)$
$W_2 = \int_0^1 1 \, dt = 1$

11. $W_1 = \int_0^{2\pi} \left(-\sin t + \sin t \cos t + 3t^2 \right) dt = 8\pi^3$
$W_2 = \int_0^{2\pi} 3t^2 \, dt = 8\pi^3$

13. $\psi = xy^2 + x^2 + 3y^2$

15. $\psi = \sin xy + xy^2 + x^2 + y$

17. $\psi = xyz + x^2 + y^3 + z^4$

19. $\psi = x^2 y^2 z^3 + xz + yz^2$

21. $\psi = xy^2 z - 2x^2 y + y^2 + 3z^2$

23. Yes **25.** No **27.** Yes **27.** Yes
29. Yes **31.** No

Exercises: 14.4

1. $\int_S \mathbf{F} \cdot d\mathbf{A} = \int_0^1 \int_0^1 2u^3 v^2 \, du \, dv = \frac{1}{6}$

3. $\int_S \mathbf{F} \cdot d\mathbf{A}$
$= \int_0^\pi \int_0^1 \left(t^3 \sin \theta + t^3 \sin^2 \theta \cos \theta + 2t^4 \right) dt \, d\theta = \frac{1}{6}$

5. $\int_S \mathbf{F} \cdot d\mathbf{A}$
$= \int_0^{\ln 2} \int_0^1 \left(2u^2 e^{2t} - u^2 e^{-t} + 3u^2 t \right) du \, dt = \frac{5}{6} + \frac{1}{2}(\ln 2)^2$

7. $M = \int_0^1 \int_0^1 3u^3 v^3 (1 + \frac{9}{4}v^4) \, du \, dv = \frac{51}{128}$

9. $M = \int_0^1 \int_0^1 (5u^5 + uv^2)(1 + \frac{9}{4}v^4) \, du \, dv = \frac{235}{112}$

11. $M = \int_0^1 \int_0^1 e^v (2u^2 + e^{-v})(2e^{2v} + \frac{1}{2}e^{-6v}) \, du \, dv$
$= \frac{4}{9}(e^3 - 1) - \frac{1}{15}(e^{-5} - 1) + (e^2 - 1) - \frac{1}{12}(e^{-6} - 1)$

13. $M = \int_0^\pi \int_0^1 (3u^2 + \sin \frac{v}{2}) 2 \sin \frac{v}{2} \cos \frac{v}{2} \, du \, dv = \frac{5}{3}$

15. $\mathcal{F} = \int_0^\pi \int_0^1 t(1 - \theta) \, dt \, d\theta = (2\pi - \pi^2)/4$

17. $\mathcal{F} = \int_0^{\pi/2} \int_0^{\pi/2} 50 \sin^2 \theta \cos \theta \cos \phi \, d\phi \, d\theta = \frac{50}{3}$

19. $\mathcal{F} = \int_0^1 \int_0^1 50u^2 v^3 (1 - v^2)^2 \, du \, dv = \frac{25}{36}$

21. $\mathcal{F} = \int_0^1 \int_0^1 \sqrt{5}v^2 (1 + 3u^2 v)(\frac{25}{3}v^4 + 12v^2) \, du \, dv$
$= \frac{1857}{280}\sqrt{5}$

Exercises: 14.5

1. $\int_S \operatorname{curl}\mathbf{F} \cdot d\mathbf{A} = \int_0^\pi \int_1^3 t \, dt \, d\theta = 4\pi$
$\int_{C_1} \mathbf{F} \cdot d\mathbf{r} = \int_0^\pi -\sin^2 \theta \, d\theta = -\frac{\pi}{2}$
$\int_{C_3} \mathbf{F} \cdot d\mathbf{r} = \int_0^\pi 9 \sin^2 \theta \, d\theta = \frac{9\pi}{2}$
$\int_{C_2} \mathbf{F} \cdot d\mathbf{r} = 0 = \int_{C_4} \mathbf{F} \cdot d\mathbf{r}$

3. $\int_S \operatorname{curl}\mathbf{F} \cdot d\mathbf{A} = \int_0^\pi \int_1^2 -t^2 \, dt \, d\theta = -\frac{15\pi}{4}$
$\int_{C_1} \mathbf{F} \cdot d\mathbf{r} = \int_0^\pi \frac{1}{2}\sin^2 2\theta \, d\theta = \frac{\pi}{4}$
$\int_{C_2} \mathbf{F} \cdot d\mathbf{r} = \int_1^2 t^2 \, dt = \frac{7}{3}$
$\int_{C_3} \mathbf{F} \cdot d\mathbf{r} = -32 \int_0^\pi \cos^2 \theta \sin^2 \theta \, d\theta = -4\pi$
$\int_{C_4} \mathbf{F} \cdot d\mathbf{r} = -\int_1^2 (3 - t)^2 \, dt = -\frac{7}{3}$

5. $\int_S \operatorname{curl}\mathbf{F} \cdot d\mathbf{A} =$
$\int_0^{2\pi} \int_0^{\pi/4} 2\left(\cos^3 \phi \sin \phi - \sin^3 \phi \right) d\phi \, d\theta = \frac{\pi}{2}$
$\int_{C_1} \mathbf{F} \cdot d\mathbf{r} = 0$
$\int_{C_2} \mathbf{F} \cdot d\mathbf{r} = \int_0^{\pi/4} -\cos^2 \phi \sin \phi \, d\phi = \frac{\sqrt{2}}{12} - \frac{1}{3}$
$\int_{C_3} \mathbf{F} \cdot d\mathbf{r} = \int_0^{2\pi} \frac{1}{4} \, d\theta = \frac{\pi}{2}$
$\int_{C_4} \mathbf{F} \cdot d\mathbf{r} = \int_0^{\pi/4} \cos^2(\frac{\pi}{4} - \phi) \sin(\frac{\pi}{4} - \phi) \, d\phi = \frac{1}{3} - \frac{\sqrt{2}}{12}$

7. $\int_S \operatorname{curl}\mathbf{F} \cdot d\mathbf{A} = -\int_0^\pi \int_0^2 2t^2 (\cos \theta + \sin \theta) \, dt \, d\theta = -\frac{32}{3}$
$\int_{C_3} \mathbf{F} \cdot d\mathbf{r} = -8 \int_0^\pi (\sin^3 \theta + \cos^3 \theta) \, d\theta = -\frac{32}{3}$
$\int_{C_1} \mathbf{F} \cdot d\mathbf{r} = \int_{C_2} \mathbf{F} \cdot d\mathbf{r} = \int_{C_4} \mathbf{F} \cdot d\mathbf{r} = 0$

9. $\int_S \operatorname{curl}\mathbf{F} \cdot d\mathbf{A} = \int_0^\pi \int_0^2 -3t^3 \, dt \, d\theta = -12\pi$
$\int_{C_3} \mathbf{F} \cdot d\mathbf{r} = -16 \int_0^\pi (\sin^4 \theta + \cos^4 \theta) \, d\theta = -12\pi$
$\int_{C_1} \mathbf{F} \cdot d\mathbf{r} = \int_{C_2} \mathbf{F} \cdot d\mathbf{r} = \int_{C_4} \mathbf{F} \cdot d\mathbf{r} = 0$

11. $\int_S \operatorname{curl}\mathbf{F} \cdot d\mathbf{A} = \int_1^4 \int_0^\pi 1 \, d\theta \, dt = 3\pi$

13. $\int_S \operatorname{curl}\mathbf{F} \cdot d\mathbf{A} = \int_1^2 \int_0^\pi (4t^3 - 2t^2 \cos \theta) \, d\theta \, dt = 15\pi$

15. $\int_S \operatorname{curl}\mathbf{F} \cdot d\mathbf{A} =$
$\int_0^{2\pi} \int_{-1}^1 \left[4 + 8t \cos \frac{\theta}{2} + 3t^2 \cos^2 \frac{\theta}{2} \right] dt \, d\theta = \frac{104}{3}$

17. $\int_S \operatorname{curl}\mathbf{F} \cdot d\mathbf{A} = \int_0^1 \int_0^1 \left(2u^3 + 2tu^4 \right) dt \, du = \frac{7}{10}$
$\int_{C_2} \mathbf{F} \cdot d\mathbf{r} = \int_0^1 1 \, dt = 1$
$\int_{C_3} \mathbf{F} \cdot d\mathbf{r} = \int_0^1 \left[(1 - u)^4 - 2(1 - u)^3 \right] = -\frac{3}{10}$
$\int_{C_1} \mathbf{F} \cdot d\mathbf{r} = 0 = \int_{C_4} \mathbf{F} \cdot d\mathbf{r}$

19. $\int_S \operatorname{curl}\mathbf{F} \cdot d\mathbf{A} = \int_1^4 \int_0^1 \left(2u^{3/2} + 2tu \right) dt \, du = \frac{323}{10}$
$\int_{C_1} \mathbf{F} \cdot d\mathbf{r} = 0$
$\int_{C_2} \mathbf{F} \cdot d\mathbf{r} = \int_0^1 32 \, dt = 32$

$\int_{C_3} \mathbf{F} \cdot d\mathbf{r} = \int_1^4 \left[5 - u - \frac{1}{2}(5-u)^{3/2} \right] du = \frac{13}{10}$

$\int_{C_4} \mathbf{F} \cdot d\mathbf{r} = \int_0^1 -1 \, dt = -1$

21. $\int_S \text{curl} \, \mathbf{F} \cdot d\mathbf{A} = \int_0^1 \int_0^1 2t(2u - u^2)^2 \, dt \, du = \frac{8}{15}$

$\int_{C_1} \mathbf{F} \cdot d\mathbf{r} = \int_0^1 \left(u - \frac{7}{3}u^4 \right) du = \frac{1}{30}$

$\int_{C_2} \mathbf{F} \cdot d\mathbf{r} = \int_0^1 -\frac{2}{3} \, dt = -\frac{2}{3}$

$\int_{C_3} \mathbf{F} \cdot d\mathbf{r} = \int_0^1 \left[u - 1 + 4(1-u)^2 + \frac{4}{3}(1-u)^3 \right] = \frac{7}{6}$

$\int_{C_4} \mathbf{F} \cdot d\mathbf{r} = 0$

23. $\int_S \text{curl} \, \mathbf{F} \cdot d\mathbf{A} = \int_0^{2\pi} \int_1^3 -3t^3 \, dt \, d\theta = -120\pi$

25. $\int_S \text{curl} \, \mathbf{F} \cdot d\mathbf{A} = \int_0^\pi \int_0^1 -3t^3 \sin^4 \theta \, dt \, d\theta = -\frac{9\pi}{32}$

27. $\int_S \text{curl} \, \mathbf{F} \cdot d\mathbf{A} = \int_0^\pi \int_1^3 -3t^3 \cos^4 \theta \, dt \, d\theta = -\frac{9\pi}{32}$

29. $\int_S \text{curl} \, \mathbf{F} \cdot d\mathbf{A} = \int_0^\pi \int_1^3 -3t^3 \theta^4 \, dt \, d\theta = -12\pi^5$

31. $\int_S \text{curl} \, \mathbf{F} \cdot d\mathbf{A} = \int_0^\pi \int_1^3 -3t^3 e^{-4\theta} \, dt \, d\theta = 15(1 - e^{-4\pi})$

33. $\int_S \text{curl} \, \mathbf{F} \cdot d\mathbf{A} = \int_0^\pi \int_0^1 -3t^3 \left(2\cos^2 \frac{\theta}{2} \right)^4 dt \, d\theta = -\frac{9\pi}{4}$

Exercises: 14.6

1. $\int_E \text{div} \mathbf{F} \, d\mathcal{V} = \int_{w=0}^{w=1} \int_{\theta=0}^{\theta=2\pi} \int_{t=0}^{t=2} w^3 t^4 \, dt \, d\theta \, dw = \frac{16\pi}{5}$

$\int_{S_1^+} \mathbf{F} \cdot d\mathbf{A} = \int_0^2 \int_0^{2\pi} \frac{1}{3} t^4 \left[\cos^4 \theta + \sin^4 \theta \right] d\theta \, dt = \frac{16\pi}{5}$

$\int_{S_3^+} \mathbf{F} \cdot d\mathbf{A} = 0 = \int_{S_3^-} \mathbf{F} \cdot d\mathbf{A}$

3. $\int_E \text{div} \mathbf{F} \, d\mathcal{V} = \int_{w=0}^{w=1} \int_{\theta=0}^{\theta=2\pi} \int_{t=0}^{t=3} w^3 \, dt \, d\theta \, dw = \frac{3\pi}{2}$

$\int_{S_1^+} \mathbf{F} \cdot d\mathbf{A} = \int_0^3 \int_0^{2\pi} \frac{1}{3} \left[\cos^4 \theta + \sin^4 \theta \right] d\theta \, dt = \frac{3\pi}{2}$

$\int_{S_3^+} \mathbf{F} \cdot d\mathbf{A} = 0 = \int_{S_3^-} \mathbf{F} \cdot d\mathbf{A}$

5. $\int_E \text{div} \mathbf{F} \, d\mathcal{V} = \int_{w=0}^{w=1} \int_{\theta=0}^{\theta=2\pi} \int_{t=0}^{t=2} 4wt^5 \, dt \, d\theta \, dw = \frac{128\pi}{3}$

$\int_{S_1^+} \mathbf{F} \cdot d\mathbf{A} = \int_0^2 \int_0^{2\pi} -t^5 \, d\theta \, dt = -\frac{64\pi}{3}$

$\int_{S_3^+} \mathbf{F} \cdot d\mathbf{A} = \int_0^1 \int_0^{2\pi} 64w \, d\theta \, dw = 64\pi$

$\int_{S_3^-} \mathbf{F} \cdot d\mathbf{A} = 0$

7. $\int_E \text{div} \mathbf{F} \, d\mathcal{V} = \int_{w=0}^{w=1} \int_{\theta=0}^{\theta=2\pi} \int_{t=0}^{t=2} 2wt(1 + t^2) \, dt \, d\theta \, dw$
$= 12\pi$

$\int_{S_1^+} \mathbf{F} \cdot d\mathbf{A} = \int_0^2 \int_0^{2\pi} -t(1+t^2) \, d\theta \, dt = -12\pi$

$\int_{S_3^+} \mathbf{F} \cdot d\mathbf{A} = \int_0^1 \int_0^{2\pi} 25w \, d\theta \, dw = 25\pi$

9. $\int_E \text{div} \mathbf{F} \, d\mathcal{V} = \int_{w=0}^{w=1} \int_{\theta=0}^{\theta=2\pi} \int_{t=0}^{t=1} w^3(1 - t^2)^2 \, dt \, d\theta \, dw$
$= \frac{4\pi}{15}$

$\int_{S_1^+} \mathbf{F} \cdot d\mathbf{A} = \int_0^2 \int_0^{2\pi} \frac{1}{3}(1-t^2)^2 \left[\cos^4 \theta + \sin^4 \theta \right] d\theta \, dt$
$= \frac{4\pi}{15}$

$\int_{S_3^+} \mathbf{F} \cdot d\mathbf{A} = 0 = \int_{S_3^-} \mathbf{F} \cdot d\mathbf{A}$

11. $\int_E \text{div} \mathbf{F} \, d\mathcal{V} = \int_{w=0}^{w=1} \int_{\theta=0}^{\theta=2\pi} \int_{t=0}^{t=1} w^3(1 - t^2)^2 \, dt \, d\theta \, dw$

$= \frac{4\pi}{15}$

$\int_{S_1^+} \mathbf{F} \cdot d\mathbf{A} = \int_0^2 \int_0^{2\pi} \frac{1}{3}(1-t^2)^2 \left[\cos^4 \theta + \sin^4 \theta \right] d\theta \, dt$
$= \frac{4\pi}{15}$

$\int_{S_3^+} \mathbf{F} \cdot d\mathbf{A} = 0 = \int_{S_3^-} \mathbf{F} \cdot d\mathbf{A}$

13. $\int_E \text{div} \mathbf{F} \, d\mathcal{V}$
$= \int_{w=0}^{w=1} \int_{\theta=0}^{\theta=2\pi} \int_{t=0}^{t=\pi} 2wt^2 \sin t \cos t \, dt \, d\theta \, dw = -\frac{\pi^3}{2}$

$\int_{S_1^+} \mathbf{F} \cdot d\mathbf{A} = \int_0^\pi \int_0^{2\pi} -\left[t + t\sin^2 t \right] d\theta \, dt = -\frac{3\pi^3}{2}$

$\int_{S_3^+} \mathbf{F} \cdot d\mathbf{A} = 0 = \int_{S_3^-} \mathbf{F} \cdot d\mathbf{A}$

15. $\int_E \text{div} \mathbf{F} \, d\mathcal{V} = \int_{\theta=0}^{\theta=2\pi} \int_{t=0}^{t=\pi} \int_{w=0}^{w=1} 2wt \sin^2 t \, dw \, dt \, d\theta$
$= \frac{\pi^3}{2}$

$\int_{S_1^+} \mathbf{F} \cdot d\mathbf{A} = \int_0^\pi \int_0^{2\pi} -\left[t + t\sin^2 t \right] d\theta \, dt$

$= -\frac{3\pi^3}{2}$

$\int_{S_3^+} \mathbf{F} \cdot d\mathbf{A} = 0 = \int_{S_3^-} \mathbf{F} \cdot d\mathbf{A}$

17. $\int_E \text{div} \mathbf{F} \, d\mathcal{V} = \int_{t=0}^{t=1} \int_{\theta=0}^{\theta=2\pi} \int_{w=0}^{w=1} 2wte^{2t} \, dw \, d\theta \, dw$
$= \frac{\pi}{2} \left[e^2 + 1 \right]$

$\int_{S_1^+} \mathbf{F} \cdot d\mathbf{A} = \int_0^{2\pi} \int_0^1 \left[t^2 e^{2t} + e^{2t} \right] dt \, d\theta = \frac{3\pi}{2} \left[1 - e^2 \right]$

$\int_{S_3^+} \mathbf{F} \cdot d\mathbf{A} = \int_0^{2\pi} \int_0^1 2we^2 \, dw \, d\theta = 2\pi e^2$

$\int_{S_3^-} \mathbf{F} \cdot d\mathbf{A} = \int_0^{2\pi} \int_0^1 w \, dw \, d\theta = -\pi$

19. $\int_E \text{div} \mathbf{F} \, d\mathcal{V}$
$= \int_{w=0}^{w=1} \int_{\theta=0}^{\theta=2\pi} \int_{t=0}^{\phi=2\pi} 3w^3(2 + w\cos\phi)\sin^2\phi \, d\phi \, d\theta \, dw$
$= 3\pi^2$

$\int_{S_1^+} \mathbf{F} \cdot d\mathbf{A} = \int_0^\pi \int_0^{2\pi} \left(2 + \cos\phi \right) \sin^4\phi \, d\theta \, d\phi = 3\pi^2$

21. $\mathbf{r}_1^+(\theta, t) = \mathbf{r}(\theta, t, 1) = \langle X(t)\cos\theta, \, X(t)\sin\theta, \, Z(t) \rangle$
$\mathbf{r}_1^-(\theta, t) = \mathbf{r}(\theta, t, 0) = \langle 0, \, 0, \, Z(t) \rangle$
$\mathbf{r}_2^+(t, w) = \mathbf{r}(2\pi, t, w) = \langle wX(t), \, 0 \, wZ(t) \rangle = \mathbf{r}_2^-$
$\mathbf{r}_3^+(w, \theta) = \mathbf{r}(\theta, 1, w)$
$\qquad = \langle wX(1)\cos\theta, \, wX(1)\sin\theta, \, wZ(1) \rangle$
$\mathbf{r}_3^-(w, \theta) = \mathbf{r}(\theta, 0, w)$
$\qquad = \langle wX(0)\cos\theta, \, wX(0)\sin\theta, \, wZ(0) \rangle$

23. $\mathcal{F} = \int_{\phi=\pi/4}^{\phi=\pi/2} \int_{\theta=0}^{\theta=2\pi} \int_{w=0}^{w=1} 16w^4 \cos^3\phi \, dw \, d\theta \, d\phi$
$= \frac{32\pi}{5} \left[\frac{2}{3} - \frac{5\sqrt{2}}{12} \right]$

25. $\mathcal{F} = \int_{-\phi=\pi/2}^{\phi=\pi/2} \int_{\theta=0}^{\theta=2\pi} \int_{w=0}^{w=2} 8w^4 \cos^8\phi \, dw \, d\theta \, d\phi = \frac{7\pi}{8}$

27. $\mathcal{F} =$
$\int_{\phi=-\pi/2}^{\phi=\pi/2} \int_{\theta=0}^{\theta=2\pi} \int_{w=0}^{w=1} w^4(1 + \sin\phi)^5 \cos^3\phi \, dw \, d\theta \, d\phi$
$= \frac{64\pi}{49}$

29. $\mathcal{F} =$
$\int_{\phi=0}^{\phi=\pi/6} \int_{\theta=0}^{\theta=2\pi} \int_{w=0}^{w=1} w^4(1 - 2\sin\phi)^5 \cos^3\phi \, dw \, d\theta \, d\phi$

$$= \frac{32\pi}{49}$$

31. $\mathcal{F} =$

$$\int_{\phi=0}^{\phi=\pi/2} \int_{\theta=0}^{\theta=2\pi} \int_{w=0}^{w=1} 3w^4 \sin^5 2\phi \cos \phi \, dw \, d\theta \, d\phi = \frac{512\pi}{1155}$$

33. $\mathcal{F} =$

$$\int_{\phi=0}^{\phi=\pi/2} \int_{\theta=0}^{\theta=2\pi} \int_{w=0}^{w=1} 2w^3 \sin^4 2\phi \cos \phi \sin \phi \, dw \, d\theta \, d\phi$$
$$= \frac{2\pi}{5}$$

35. $\mathcal{F} =$

$$\int_{\phi=0}^{\phi=\pi/2} \int_{\theta=-\pi/2}^{\theta=\pi/2} \int_{w=0}^{w=1} 3w^4 (1-\sin\phi)^5 \cos \phi \, dw \, d\theta \, d\phi$$
$$= \frac{\pi}{6}$$

37. $\mathcal{F} =$

$$\int_{\phi=0}^{\phi=\pi/2} \int_{\theta=0}^{\theta=2\pi} \int_{w=0}^{w=1} 2w^3 \cos^4 2\phi \cos \phi \sin \phi \, dw \, d\theta \, d\phi$$
$$= \frac{\pi}{20}$$

39. $\mathcal{F} =$

$$\int_{\phi=0}^{\phi=\pi/2} \int_{\theta=0}^{\theta=2\pi} \int_{w=0}^{w=1} 2w^3 (1+\cos\phi)^4 \cos \phi \sin \phi \, dw \, d\theta \, d\phi$$
$$= \frac{33\pi}{20}$$

41. $\mathcal{F} =$

$$\int_{\phi=0}^{\phi=\pi/6} \int_{\theta=0}^{\theta=2\pi} \int_{w=0}^{w=1} w^4 (1-2\sin\phi)^5 \cos^3 \phi \, dw \, d\theta \, d\phi$$
$$= \frac{37\pi}{1120}$$

43. $\mathcal{F} =$

$$\int_{\phi=\pi/6}^{\phi=\pi/2} \int_{\theta=0}^{\theta=2\pi} \int_{w=0}^{w=1} w^4 (2\sin\phi - 1)^5 \cos^3 \phi \, dw \, d\theta \, d\phi$$
$$= \frac{\pi}{224}$$

45. $\mathcal{F} =$

$$\int_{\phi=\pi/4}^{\phi=3\pi/4} \int_{\theta=0}^{\theta=2\pi} \int_{w=0}^{w=1} \left[\begin{array}{c} 8w + 12w^2 \cos \phi \\ 6w^3 \cos^2 \phi + w^4 \cos^3 \phi \end{array} \right] dw \, d\theta \, d\phi$$
$$= \frac{19}{4}\pi^2 - \frac{3}{2}\pi$$

47. $\mathcal{F} =$

$$\int_{\phi=0}^{\phi=\pi} \int_{\theta=0}^{\theta=2\pi} \int_{w=0}^{w=1} \left[\begin{array}{c} 2w^2(1+\cos\phi)^3 \sin\phi + \\ 2w^3(1+\cos\phi)^4 \cos \phi \sin \phi \end{array} \right] dw \, d\theta \, d\phi$$
$$= \frac{48\pi}{5}$$

49. $\mathcal{F} =$

$$\int_{\phi=0}^{\phi=\pi/2} \int_{\theta=0}^{\theta=2\pi} \int_{w=0}^{w=1} \left[\begin{array}{c} 16w^2 \sin^3 2\phi \sin\phi + \\ 32w^3 \sin^4 2\phi \cos \phi \sin \phi \end{array} \right] dw \, d\theta \, d\phi$$
$$= \frac{64\pi}{7}$$

51. $\mathcal{F} = \int_{w=-c}^{w=c} \int_{t=-1}^{t=1} \int_{\theta=0}^{\theta=2\pi} \left[2 + t\cos\frac{\theta}{2} - w\sin\frac{\theta}{2} \right] d\theta \, dt \, dw$
$$= 16\pi c$$

53. $\mathcal{F} = -\int_{w=-c}^{w=c} \int_{t=-1}^{t=1} \int_{\theta=0}^{\theta=2\pi} 2 \left[2 + t\cos\frac{\theta}{2} - w\sin\frac{\theta}{2} \right]^2 d\theta \, dt \, dw$
$$= -8\pi \left[\frac{25}{3}c + \frac{1}{3}c^3 \right]$$

55. $\mathcal{F} =$

$$-\int_{w=-c}^{w=c} \int_{t=-1}^{t=1} \int_{\theta=0}^{\theta=2\pi} 2 \left[2 + t\cos\frac{\theta}{2} - w\sin\frac{\theta}{2} \right]^2 \cos\theta \, d\theta \, dt \, dw$$
$$= \frac{4\pi}{3}c(c^2 - 1)$$

57. $\mathcal{F} =$

$$\int_{w=-c}^{w=c} \int_{t=-1}^{t=1} \int_{\theta=0}^{\theta=2\pi} \left[T^2 + P^2 \right] T \, d\theta \, dt \, dw$$
$$= \int_{w=-c}^{w=c} \int_{t=-1}^{t=1} \int_{\theta=0}^{\theta=2\pi} 2kT^2 \, d\theta \, dt \, dw$$
$$= \frac{4\pi}{3}c(c^2 + 50\pi)$$

59. $T^2 - 2kT + k^2 + P^2 = [T - k]^2 + P^2$

$$\left[t\cos\frac{\theta}{2} - w\sin\frac{\theta}{2} \right]^2 + \left[t\sin\frac{\theta}{2} + w\cos\frac{\theta}{2} \right]^2 = t^2 + w^2$$

Rearranging gives $T^2 + P^2 = 2kT - k^2 + t^2 + w^2$

61. Since $J(\mathbf{r}) = -T$, with $T > 0$, the volume of the Möbius slab is

$$\mathcal{V} = \int_E 1 \, d\mathcal{V} = \int_{w=-c}^{w=c} \int_{t=-b}^{t=b} \int_{\theta=0}^{\theta=2\pi} T \, d\theta \, dt \, dw$$
$$= \int_{w=-c}^{w=c} \int_{t=-b}^{t=b} \int_{\theta=0}^{\theta=2\pi} \left[2 + t\cos\frac{\theta}{2} - w\sin\frac{\theta}{2} \right] d\theta \, dt \, dw$$
$$= 2\pi k(2b)(2c) = \text{volume of a washer with radii}$$

$r_1 = k - b, r_2 = k + b$ and thickness $2c$.

Index

BASIC DERIVATIVES

Power Rule

1. $\dfrac{d}{dx}\left(x^n\right) = nx^{n-1}$　　　　Special Case: $\dfrac{d}{dx}(\sqrt{x}) = \dfrac{1}{2\sqrt{x}}$

Trig Derivatives

2. $\dfrac{d}{dx}\left(\sin x\right) = \cos x$　　　　　　3. $\dfrac{d}{dx}\left(\cos x\right) = -\sin x$

4. $\dfrac{d}{dx}\left(\tan x\right) = \sec^2 x$　　　　　5. $\dfrac{d}{dx}\left(\cot x\right) = -\csc^2 x$

6. $\dfrac{d}{dx}\left(\sec x\right) = \sec x \tan x$　　　7. $\dfrac{d}{dx}\left(\csc x\right) = -\csc x \cot x$

Exponential and Log Derivatives

8. $\dfrac{d}{dx}\left(e^x\right) = e^x$　　　　　　　9. $\dfrac{d}{dx}\left(a^x\right) = (\ln a)a^x$

10. $\dfrac{d}{dx}\left(\ln x\right) = \dfrac{1}{x}$　　　　　11. $\dfrac{d}{dx}\left(\log_a x\right) = \dfrac{1}{(\ln a)\,x}$

Inverse Trig Derivatives

12. $\dfrac{d}{dx}\left(\sin^{-1} x\right) = \dfrac{1}{\sqrt{1-x^2}}$　　13. $\dfrac{d}{dx}\left(\cos^{-1} x\right) = \dfrac{-1}{\sqrt{1-x^2}}$

14. $\dfrac{d}{dx}\left(\tan^{-1} x\right) = \dfrac{1}{1+x^2}$　　15. $\dfrac{d}{dx}\left(\cot^{-1} x\right) = \dfrac{-1}{1+x^2}$

16. $\dfrac{d}{dx}\left(\sec^{-1} x\right) = \dfrac{1}{|x|\sqrt{x^2-1}}$　17. $\dfrac{d}{dx}\left(\csc^{-1} x\right) = \dfrac{-1}{|x|\sqrt{x^2-1}}$

BASIC DERIVATIVES WITH THE CHAIN RULE

Power Rule

1. $\dfrac{d}{dx}\left(u^n\right) = nu^{n-1} \cdot \dfrac{du}{dx}$

Trig Derivatives

2. $\dfrac{d}{dx}\left(\sin u\right) = \cos u \cdot \dfrac{du}{dx}$　　　3. $\dfrac{d}{dx}\left(\cos u\right) = -\sin u \cdot \dfrac{du}{dx}$

4. $\dfrac{d}{dx}\left(\tan u\right) = \sec^2 u \cdot \dfrac{du}{dx}$　　5. $\dfrac{d}{dx}\left(\cot u\right) = -\csc^2 u \cdot \dfrac{du}{dx}$

6. $\dfrac{d}{dx}\left(\sec u\right) = \sec u \tan u \cdot \dfrac{du}{dx}$　7. $\dfrac{d}{dx}\left(\csc u\right) = -\csc u \cot u \cdot \dfrac{du}{dx}$

Exponential and Log Derivatives

8. $\dfrac{d}{dx}\left(e^u\right) = e^u \cdot \dfrac{du}{dx}$　　　　9. $\dfrac{d}{dx}\left(a^u\right) = (\ln a)a^u \cdot \dfrac{du}{dx}$

10. $\dfrac{d}{dx}\left(\ln u\right) = \dfrac{1}{u} \cdot \dfrac{du}{dx}$　　　11. $\dfrac{d}{dx}\left(\log_a u\right) = \dfrac{1}{(\ln a)\,u} \cdot \dfrac{du}{dx}$

Inverse Trig Derivatives

12. $\dfrac{d}{dx}\left(\sin^{-1} u\right) = \dfrac{1}{\sqrt{1-u^2}} \cdot \dfrac{du}{dx}$　13. $\dfrac{d}{dx}\left(\cos^{-1} u\right) = \dfrac{-1}{\sqrt{1-u^2}} \cdot \dfrac{du}{dx}$

14. $\dfrac{d}{dx}\left(\tan^{-1} u\right) = \dfrac{1}{1+u^2} \cdot \dfrac{du}{dx}$　15. $\dfrac{d}{dx}\left(\cot^{-1} u\right) = \dfrac{-1}{1+u^2} \cdot \dfrac{du}{dx}$

16. $\dfrac{d}{dx}\left(\sec^{-1} u\right) = \dfrac{1}{|u|\sqrt{u^2-1}} \cdot \dfrac{du}{dx}$　17. $\dfrac{d}{dx}\left(\csc^{-1} u\right) = \dfrac{-1}{|u|\sqrt{u^2-1}} \cdot \dfrac{du}{dx}$